ENCYCLOPEDIA OF
BIOINFORMATICS AND COMPUTATIONAL BIOLOGY

ENCYCLOPEDIA OF
BIOINFORMATICS AND
COMPUTATIONAL BIOLOGY

EDITORS IN CHIEF

Shoba Ranganathan

Macquarie University, Sydney, NSW, Australia

Michael Gribskov

Purdue University, West Lafayette, IN, United States

Kenta Nakai

The University of Tokyo, Tokyo, Japan

Christian Schönbach

*Nazarbayev University, School of Science and Technology, Department of Biology,
Astana, Kazakhstan*

VOLUME 3
Applications

Mohammad Asif Khan

Centre for Bioinformatics, Perdana University, Selangor, Malaysia

ELSEVIER

AMSTERDAM • BOSTON • HEIDELBERG • LONDON • NEW YORK • OXFORD
PARIS • SAN DIEGO • SAN FRANCISCO • SINGAPORE • SYDNEY • TOKYO

Elsevier
Radarweg 29, PO Box 211, 1000 AE Amsterdam, Netherlands
The Boulevard, Langford Lane, Kidlington, Oxford OX5 1GB, United Kingdom
50 Hampshire Street, 5th Floor, Cambridge MA 02139, United States

Notices
Knowledge and best practice in this field are constantly changing. As new research and experience broaden our understanding, changes in research methods, professional practices, or medical treatment may become necessary.

Practitioners and researchers may always rely on their own experience and knowledge in evaluating and using any information, methods, compounds, or experiments described herein. In using such information or methods they should be mindful of their own safety and the safety of others, including parties for whom they have a professional responsibility.

To the fullest extent of the law, neither the Publisher nor the authors, contributors, or editors, assume any liability for any injury and/or damage to persons or property as a matter of products liability, negligence or otherwise, or from any use or operation of any methods, products, instructions, or ideas contained in the material herein.

Library of Congress Cataloging-in-Publication Data
A catalog record for this book is available from the Library of Congress

British Library Cataloguing-in-Publication Data
A catalogue record for this book is available from the British Library

ISBN 978-0-12-811414-8

For information on all publications visit our
website at http://store.elsevier.com

Working together
to grow libraries in
developing countries

www.elsevier.com • www.bookaid.org

Publisher: Oliver Walter
Acquisition Editor: Sam Crowe
Content Project Manager: Paula Davies
Associate Content Project Manager: Ebin Clinton Rozario
Designer: Greg Harris

EDITORS IN CHIEF

Shoba Ranganathan holds a Chair in Bioinformatics at Macquarie University since 2004. She has held research and academic positions in India, USA, Singapore and Australia as well as a consultancy in industry. She hosted the Macquarie Node of the ARC Centre of Excellence in Bioinformatics (2008–2013). She was elected the first Australian Board Director of the International Society for Computational Biology (ISCB; 2003–2005); President of Asia-Pacific Bioinformatics Network (2005–2016) and Steering Committee Member (2007–2012) of Bioinformatics Australia. She initiated the Workshops on Education in Bioinformatics (WEB) as an ISMB2001 Special Interest Group meeting and also served as Chair of ICSB's Educaton Committee. Shoba currently serves as Co-Chair of the Computational Mass Spectrometry (CompMS) initiative of the Human Proteome Organization (HuPO), ISCB and Metabolomics Society and as Board Director, APBioNet Ltd.

Shoba's research addresses several key areas of bioinformatics to understand biological systems using computational approaches. Her group has achieved both experience and expertise in different aspects of computational biology, ranging from metabolites and small molecules to biochemical networks, pathway analysis and computational systems biology. She has authored as well as edited several books as well as articles for the 2013 Encyclopedia of Systems Biology. She is currently an Editor-in-Chief of the Encyclopedia of Bioinformatics and Computational Biology and the Bioinformatics Section Editor of the Reference Module in Life Science as well as an editorial board member of several bioinformatics journals.

Dr. Gribskov graduated from Oregon State University in 1979 with a Bachelors of Science degree (with Honors) in Biochemistry and Biophysics. He then moved to the University of Wisconsin-Madison for graduate studies focused on the structure and function of the sigma subunit of *E. coli* RNA polymerase, receiving his Ph.D. in 1985. Dr. Gribskov studied X-ray crystallography as an American Cancer Society post-doctoral fellow at UCLA in the laboratory of David Eisenberg, and followed this with both crystallographic and computational studies at the National Cancer Institute. In 1992, Dr. Gribskov moved to the San Diego Supercomputer Center at the University of California, San Diego where he was lead scientist in the area of computational biology and an adjunct associate professor in the department of Biology. From 2003 to 2007, Dr. Gribskov was the president of the International Society for Computational Biology, the largest professional society devoted to bioinformatics and computational biology. In 2004, Dr. Gribskov moved to Purdue University where he holds an appointment as a full professor in the Biological Sciences and Computer Science departments (by courtesy). Dr. Gribskov's interests include genomic and transcriptomic analysis of model and non-model organisms, the application of pattern recognition and machine learning techniques to biomolecules, the design and implementation of biological databases to support molecular and systems biology, development of methods to study RNA structural patterns, and systems biology studies of human disease.

Kenta Nakai received the PhD degree on the prediction of subcellular localization sites of proteins from Kyoto University in 1992. From 1989, he has worked at Kyoto University, National Institute of Basic Biology, and Osaka University. From 1999 to 2003, he was an Associate Professor at the Human Genome Center, the Institute of Medical Science, the University of Tokyo, Japan. Since 2003, he has been a full Professor at the same institute. His main research interest is to develop computational ways for interpreting biological information, especially that of transcriptional regulation, from genome sequence data. He has published more than 150 papers, some of which have been cited more than 1,000 times.

Christian Schönbach is currently Department Chair and Professor at Department of Biology, School of Science and Technology, Nazarbayev University, Kazakhstan and Visiting Professor at International Research Center for Medical Sciences at Kumamoto University, Japan. He is a bioinformatics practitioner interfacing genetics, immunology and informatics conducting research on major histocompatibility complex, immune responses following virus infection, biomedical knowledge discovery, peroxisomal diseases, and autism spectrum disorder that resulted in more than 80 publications. His previous academic appointments included Professor at Kumamoto University (2016–2017), Nazarbayev University (2013–2016), Kazakhstan, Kyushu Institute of Technology (2009–2013) Japan, Associate Professor at Nanyang Technological University (2006–2009), Singapore, and Team Leader at RIKEN Genomic Sciences Center (2002–2006), Japan. Other prior positions included Principal Investigator at Kent Ridge Digital Labs, Singapore and Research Scientist at Chugai Institute for Molecular Medicine, Inc., Japan. In 2018 he became a member of International Society for Computational Biology (ISCB) Board of Directors. Since 2010 he is serving Asia-Pacific Bioinformatics Network (APBioNet) as Vice-President (Conferences 2010–2016) and President (2016–2018).

VOLUME EDITORS

Mario Cannataro is a Full Professor of Computer Engineering and Bioinformatics at University "Magna Graecia" of Catanzaro, Italy. He is the director of the Data Analytics research center and the chair of the Bioinformatics Laboratory at University "Magna Graecia" of Catanzaro. His current research interests include bioinformatics, medical informatics, data analytics, parallel and distributed computing. He is a Member of the editorial boards of Briefings in Bioinformatics, High-Throughput, Encyclopedia of Bioinformatics and Computational Biology, Encyclopedia of Systems Biology. He was guest editor of several special issues on bioinformatics and he is serving as a program committee member of several conferences. He published three books and more than 200 papers in international journals and conference proceedings. Prof. Cannataro is a Senior Member of IEEE, ACM and BITS, and a member of the Board of Directors for ACM SIGBIO.

Bruno Gaeta is Senior Lecturer and Director of Studies in Bioinformatics in the School of Computer Science and Engineering at UNSW Australia. His research interests cover multiple areas of bioinformatics including gene regulation and protein structure, currently with a focus on the immune system, antibody genes and the generation of antibody diversity. He is a pioneer of bioinformatics education and has trained thousands of biologists and trainee bioinformaticians in the use of computational tools for biological research through courses, workshops as well as a book series. He has worked both in academia and in the bioinformatics industry, and currently coordinates the largest bioinformatics undergraduate program in Australia.

Mohammad Asif Khan, PhD, is an associate professor and the Dean of the School of Data Sciences, as well as the Director of the Centre for Bioinformatics at Perdana University, Malaysia. He is also a visiting scientist at the Department of Pharmacology and Molecular Sciences, Johns Hopkins University School of Medicine (JHUSOM), USA. His research interests are in the area of biological data warehousing and applications of bioinformatics to the study of immune responses, vaccines, inhibitory drugs, venom toxins, and disease biomarkers. He has published in these areas, been involved in the development of several novel bioinformatics methodologies, tools, and specialized databases, and currently has three patent applications granted. He has also led the curriculum development of a Postgraduate Diploma in Bioinformatics programme and an MSc (Bioinformatics) programme at Perdana University. He is an elected ExCo member of the Asia-Pacific Bioinformatics Network (APBioNET) since 2010 and is currently the President of Association for Medical and Bio-Informatics, Singapore (AMBIS). He has donned various important roles in the organization of many local and international bioinformatics conferences, meetings and workshops.

CONTENTS OF VOLUME 3

LIST OF CONTRIBUTORS FOR VOLUME 3

Dalia A. Abdel-Haleem
National Research Centre, Cairo, Egypt

Abdelaziz E. Abdelnaiem
Zagazig University, Zagazig, Egypt

Jiri Adamec
University of Nebraska-Lincoln, Lincoln, NE, United States

Subash Adhikari
Macquarie University, Sydney, NSW, Australia

Shandar Ahmad
Jawaharlal Nehru University, New Delhi, India

Rubbiya A. Ali
University of Queensland, Brisbane, QLD, Australia

Sarah Ali
Hamdard Institute of Engineering and Technology, Islamabad, Pakistan

Md. Altaf-Ul-Amin
Nara Institute of Science and Technology, Ikoma, Japan

Nanyonga Aziida
University of Malaya, Kuala Lumpur, Malaysia

Nani Azman
PAPRSB Institute of Health Sciences, Universiti Brunei Darussalam, Bandar Seri Begawan, Brunei Darussalam

Mohammad H. Baig
Yeungnam University Gyeongsan, Gyeongbuk, South Korea

Manju Bansal
Indian Institute of Science, Bangalore, India

Ankush Bansal
Jaypee University of Information Technology, Solan, India

Matteo Barberis
University of Amsterdam, Amsterdam, The Netherlands

Jyotsna Batra
Institute of Health and Biomedical Innovation and School of Biomedical Sciences, Queensland University of Technology, Brisbane, QLD, Australia; and Australian Prostate Cancer Research Centre – Queensland, Translational Research Institute, Woolloongabba, QLD, Australia

Saharuddin Bin Mohamad
University of Malaya, Kuala Lumpur, Malaysia

David I. Cantor
Macquarie University, Sydney, NSW, Australia

Ramesh Chandra
University of Delhi, Delhi, India

Pragya Chaturvedi
Birla Institute of Scientific Research, Jaipur, India

Song Cheen
University of Malaya, Kuala Lumpur, Malaysia

Lie Chen
PAPRSB Institute of Health Sciences, Universiti Brunei Darussalam, Bandar Seri Begawan, Brunei Darussalam

Yi-An Chen
National Institutes of Biomedical Innovation, Health and Nutrition, Osaka, Japan

Jieming Chen
Genentech Inc., South San Francisco, CA, United States

Yi-An Chen
National Institutes of Biomedical Innovation, Health and Nutrition, Osaka, Japan

Harish R. Cheruku
Preston, VIC, Australia

Lou Chitkushev
Boston University, Boston, MA, United States

Sy-Bing Choi
Universiti Sains Malaysia, Pulau Pinang, Malaysia

Sy Bing Choi
Universiti Sains Malaysia, Pulau Pinang, Malaysia

Li C. Chong
Universiti Putra Malaysia, Serdang, Malaysia

Yee Siew Choong
Universiti Sains Malaysia, Pulau Pinang, Malaysia

Vincent T.K. Chow
National University of Singapore, Singapore

Alan Christoffels
University of the Western Cape, Cape Town, South Africa

Charles W. Christoffer
Purdue University, West Lafayette, IN, United States

Xuefeng Cui
Tsinghua University, Beijing, China

M.I. Dessouky
Menoufia University, Menouf, Egypt

Jaspreet Kaur Dhanjal
DBT-AIST International Laboratory for Advanced Biomedicine (DAILAB), Indian Institute of Technology Delhi, New Delhi, India

Petros Drineas
Purdue University, West Lafayette, IN, United States

Mahmoud ElHefnawi
Nile University, Giza, Egypt and National Research Centre, Cairo, Egypt.

Tsuyoshi Esaki
National Institutes of Biomedical Innovation, Health and Nutrition, Osaka, Japan

Mashal Fatima
Bahauddin Zakariya University, Multan, Pakistan

Antonino Fiannaca
Universiti Brunei Darussalam, Bandar Seri Begawan, Brunei Darussalam

Mohd Firdaus-Raih
Universiti Kebangsaan Malaysia, Bangi, Malaysia

Joshy George
The Jackson Laboratory, CT, United States

Nur Syatila Abdul Ghani
Universiti Kebangsaan Malaysia, Bangi, Malaysia

Samik Ghosh
The Systems Biology Institute, Tokyo, Japan

Arpita Ghosh
Eurofins Genomics India Pvt. Ltd., Bangalore, India; and Centre for Bioinformatics, Perdana University, Selangor, Malaysia

Michael Gribskov
Purdue University, West Lafayette, IN, United States

Massimo Guarascio
Universiti Brunei Darussalam, Bandar Seri Begawan, Brunei Darussalam

Sonal Gupta
Birla Institute of Scientific Research, Jaipur, India; and Amity University, Jaipur, India

Swagata Halder
Indian Institute of Science, Bangalore, India

Hazrina Y. Hamdani
Universiti Sains Malaysia, Kepala Batas, Malaysia

Russell S. Hamilton
University of Cambridge, Cambridge, United Kingdom

Xusi Han
Purdue University, West Lafayette, IN, United States

Aimi Hanafi
University of Malaya, Kuala Lumpur, Malaysia

Ari Hardianto
Macquarie University, Sydney, NSW, Australia; and Universitas Padjadjaran, Jatinangor, West Java, Indonesia

Ranjeev Hari
Perdana University, Selangor, Malaysia

Maywan Hariono
Sanata Dharma University, Sleman, Indonesia

Akdes S. Harmanci
The University of Texas Health Science Center at Houston, Houston, TX, United States

Marwa S. Hassan
National Research Centre, Cairo, Egypt

Masahira Hattori
RIKEN Center for Integrative Medical Sciences, Yokohama City, Japan; and Waseda University, Tokyo, Japan

Huey Ying Heng
Sime Darby Plantation R&D Centre, Selangor, Malaysia

Petter Holland
Chalmers University of Technology, Gothenburg, Sweden

Cham Hui
University of Malaya, Kuala Lumpur, Malaysia

Xiaojing Huo
National University of Singapore, Singapore

Zalikha Ibrahim
International Islamic University Malaysia, Kuantan, Malaysia

Musarat Ishaq
St. Vincent's Institute of Medical Research, Melbourne, VIC, Australia

Mari N. Itoh
National Institutes of Biomedical Innovation, Health and Nutrition, Osaka, Japan

Fransiskus Xaverius Ivan
Nanyang Technological University, Singapore

Amara Jabeen
Macquarie University, Sydney, NSW, Australia

Sudhir Jadhao
Institute of Health and Biomedical Innovation, School of Biomedical Sciences, Queensland University of Technology, Brisbane, QLD, Australia

Narong Jaturas
Naresuan University, Phitsanulok, Thailand

Yongshuai Jiang
Harbin Medical University, Harbin, China

Ezatul E. Kamarulzaman
Universiti Sains Malaysia, Minden, Pulau Pinang, Malaysia

Piotr J. Kamola
RIKEN Center for Integrative Medical Sciences, Yokohama, Kanagawa, Japan; and Japan Science and Technology Agency, Tokyo, Japan

Shigehiko Kanaya
Nara Institute of Science and Technology, Ikoma, Japan

Radha K.M. Karuturi
The Jackson Laboratory, CT, United States

Sandeep Kaushik
European Institute of Excellence on Tissue Engineering and Regenerative Medicine, Guimaraes, Portugal

Derin B. Keskin
Harvard Medical School, Boston, MA, United States; and Broad Institute, Boston, MA, United States

Asif M. Khan
Perdana University, Selangor, Malaysia; and John Hopkins University, Baltimore, MD, United States

Asif M. Khan
Perdana University, Selangor, Malaysia

Daisuke Kihara
Purdue University, West Lafayette, IN, United States

Anton I. Korobeynikov
St. Petersburg State University, St Petersburg, Russia

Shanker L. Kothari
Amity University, Jaipur, India

Anuj Kumar
Uttarakhand Council for Biotechnology, Dehradun, India

Prasun Kumar
University of Bristol, Bristol, United Kingdom

Ammu P. Kumar
Khalifa University of Science and Technology, Abu Dhabi, United Arab Emirates

Anjani Kumari
DBT-AIST International Laboratory for Advanced Biomedicine (DAILAB), Indian Institute of Technology Delhi, New Delhi, India

Chee Keong Kwoh
Nanyang Technological University, Singapore

Chee-Keong Kwoh
Nanyang Technological University, Singapore

Qi Bin Kwong
Sime Darby Plantation R&D Centre, Selangor, Malaysia

Massimo La Rosa
Universiti Brunei Darussalam, Bandar Seri Begawan, Brunei Darussalam

Yosvany LÃ³pez
Genesis Healthcare Co., Tokyo, Japan

Vijay Lakhujani
Xcelris Labs Ltd., Ahmedabad, Gujarat, India

Alla L. Lapidus
St. Petersburg State University, St Petersburg, Russia

Chong-Yew Lee
Universiti Sains Malaysia, Minden, Pulau Pinang, Malaysia

Bryan T. Li
Temasek Polytechnic, Singapore

Jin X. Lim
Temasek Polytechnic, Singapore

Maurice H.T. Ling
Colossus Technologies, LLP, Singapore

Maurice H.T. Ling
Colossus Technologies, LLP, Singapore; and University of Melbourne, Melbourne, VIC, Australia

Fei Liu
Macquarie University, Sydney, NSW, Australia

Mun Fai Loke
University of Malaya, Kuala Lumpur, Malaysia

Wai Yee Low
Davies Research Centre, University of Adelaide, Roseworthy, SA, Australia

Zen H. Lu
Universiti Brunei Darussalam, Bandar Seri Begawan, Brunei Darussalam

Suryani Lukman
Khalifa University of Science and Technology, Abu Dhabi, United Arab Emirates

Haslina Makmur
Universiti Kebangsaan Malaysia, Bangi, Selangor, Malaysia

Sorayya Malek
University of Malaya, Kuala Lumpur, Malaysia

Babita Malik
Manipal University, Jaipur, India

Vidhi Malik
DBT-AIST International Laboratory for Advanced Biomedicine (DAILAB), Indian Institute of Technology Delhi, New Delhi, India

Adeel Malik
Chungnam National University, Daejeon, South Korea

Balachandran Manavalan
Ajou University School of Medicine, Suwon, Republic of Korea

Giuseppe Manco
Universiti Brunei Darussalam, Bandar Seri Begawan, Brunei Darussalam

Srikanth Manda
Institute of Bioinformatics, Bangalore, India

Toral Manvar
Xcelris Labs Ltd., Ahmedabad, Gujarat, India

Sandeep K. Mathur
SMS Medical College, Jaipur, India

Shuhaila Mat-Sharani
Universiti Kebangsaan Malaysia, Selangor, Malaysia

Venkata S.K. Mattaparthi
Tezpur University, Tezpur, Assam, India

Mohit Mazumder
Jawaharlal Nehru University, Delhi, India; and University of Saskatchewan, Saskatoon, Canada

Krishna M. Medicherla
Birla Institute of Scientific Research, Jaipur, India

Ahmed M. Mehdi
University of Queensland, Brisbane, QLD, Australia

Biswa R. Meher
Berhampur University, Berhampur, India

Aditya Mehta
Eurofins Genomics India Pvt. Ltd., Bangalore, India

Amir Feisal. Merican
University of Malaya, Kuala Lumpur, Malaysia

Daliah Michael
Indian Institute of Science, Bangalore, India

Pozi Milow
University of Malaya, Kuala Lumpur, Malaysia

Yaosen Min
Tsinghua University, Beijing, China

Hoda Mirsafian
University of Malaya, Kuala Lumpur, Malaysia; and University of Southern California, Los Angeles, CA, United States

Kenji Mizuguchi
National Institutes of Biomedical Innovation, Health and Nutrition, Osaka, Japan

Abidali Mohamedali
Macquarie University, Sydney, NSW, Australia

Zeti-Azura Mohamed-Hussein
Universiti Kebangsaan Malaysia, Bangi, Selangor, Malaysia

Thierry D.G.A. Mondeel
University of Amsterdam, Amsterdam, Netherlands

Lyman Monroe
Purdue University, West Lafayette, IN, United States

Eiji Morita
Hirosaki University, Hirosaki, Japan

Ahmed Moussa
École Nationale Des Sciences Appliquées de Tanger, Tangier, Morocco

Ng S. Mun
Universiti Kebangsaan Malaysia, Bangi, Selangor, Malaysia

Yoichi Murakami
Tokyo University of Information Sciences, Wakaba-ku, Chiba, Japan

Shivashankar H Nagaraj
Nanyang Technological University, Singapore

Shivashankar H. Nagaraj
Perdana University, Selangor, Malaysia

Kenta Nakai
The University of Tokyo, Tokyo, Japan

Ali Naqi
Queensland University of Technology, Brisbane, QLD, Australia

Siuk M. Ng
Universiti Kebangsaan Malaysia, Bangi, Selangor, Malaysia

Jeremy Ng
National University of Singapore, Singapore

Chyan L. Ng
Universiti Kebangsaan Malaysia, Selangor, Malaysia

Minh N. Nguyen
Agency for Science, Technology and Research, Singapore

Jens Nielsen
Chalmers University of Technology, Gothenburg, Sweden

Zainab Noor
Macquarie University, Sydney, NSW, Australia

Nor A. Nor Muhammad
Universiti Kebangsaan Malaysia (UKM), Bangi, Selangor, Malaysia

ChuangKee Ong
European Bioinformatics Institute (EMBL-EBI), Hinxton, United Kingdom

Ai Ling Ong
Sime Darby Plantation R&D Centre, Selangor, Malaysia

Hui San Ong
Perdana University, Selangor, Malaysia

Munyati Othman
Universiti Kebangsaan Malaysia, Bangi, Selangor, Malaysia

Sucheendra K. Palaniappan
The Systems Biology Institute, Tokyo, Japan

Nicolas Palopoli
Universidad Nacional de Quilmes & CONICET, Bernal, Buenos Aires, Argentina

Sung-J. Park
The University of Tokyo, Tokyo, Japan

Suhanya Parthasarathy
Perdana University, Selangor, Malaysia

Suhanya Parthasarathy
Monash University Malaysia, Segamat, Malaysia

Peristera Paschou
Purdue University, West Lafayette, IN, United States

Seema Patel
San Diego State University, San Diego, CA, United States

William R. Pearson
University of Virginia School of Medicine, Charlottesville, VA, United States

Camila Pereira Braga
University of Nebraska-Lincoln, Lincoln, NE, United States

Mark I.R. Petalcorin
PAPRSB Institute of Health Sciences, Universiti Brunei Darussalam, Bandar Seri Begawan, Brunei Darussalam

Marwenie F. Petalcorin
Queen Mary University of London, London, United Kingdom

Mark I.R. Petalcorin
Universiti Brunei Darussalam, Bandar Seri Begawan, Brunei Darussalam

Mukta Poojary
Institute of Bioinformatics, Bangalore, India

Sushmita Pradhan
Tezpur University, Tezpur, Assam, India

Malwina Prater
University of Cambridge, Cambridge, United Kingdom

Andrey D. Prjibelski
St. Petersburg State University, St Petersburg, Russia

Dwi A. Pujianto
Universitas Indonesia, Jakarta, Indonesia

Doris H.X. Quay
Universiti Kebangsaan Malaysia, Selangor, Malaysia

Navaneethan Radhakrishnan
DBT-AIST International Laboratory for Advanced Biomedicine (DAILAB), Indian Institute of Technology Delhi, New Delhi, India

Upadhyayula S. Raghavender
Birla Institute of Scientific Research (BISR), Jaipur, India

Mohd Basyaruddin Abd Rahman
Universiti Putra Malaysia, Serdang, Selangor, Malaysia

Effirul I. Ramlan
Malaysia Genome Institute (MGI-NIBM), Kajang, Selangor, Malaysia; and University of Malaya, Kuala Lumpur, Malaysia

Shoba Ranganathan
Macquarie University, Sydney, NSW, Australia

Ravindranath S. Rathore
Central University of South Bihar, Patna, India

Valentina Ravì
Universiti Brunei Darussalam, Bandar Seri Begawan, Brunei Darussalam

Raimi M. Redwan
Faculty of Agro-based Industry, University of Malaysia, Kelantan, Malaysia

Adiratna Mat Ripen
Institute of Medical Research, Kuala Lumpur, Malaysia

Raul Rodriguez-Esteban
F. Hoffmann-La Roche Ltd., Basel, Switzerland

Yutaka Saito
National Institute of Advanced Industrial Science and Technology (AIST), Koto-ku, Japan; and National Institute of Advanced Industrial Science and Technology (AIST), Shinjuku-ku, Japan

Meena K. Sakharkar
University of Saskatchewan, Saskatoon, SK, Canada

Himakshi Sarma
Tezpur University, Tezpur, India

Anita Sathyanarayanan
Institute of Health and Biomedical Innovation and School of Biomedical Sciences, Queensland University of Technology, Brisbane, QLD, Australia.

A.A. Shaalan
Zagazig University, Zagazig, Egypt

Naeem Shafqat
Universiti Brunei Darussalam, Bandar Seri Begawan, Brunei Darussalam

Mansi Sharma
Uttarakhand Council for Biotechnology, Dehradun, India

Ronesh Sharma
University of the South Pacific, Suva, Fiji; and Fiji National University, Suva, Fiji

Alok Sharma
RIKEN Center for Integrative Medical Sciences, Yokohama, Japan, University of the South Pacific, Suva, Fiji; and Griffith University, Brisbane, QLD, Australia

Daichi Shigemizu
RIKEN Center for Integrative Medical Sciences, Yokohama, Japan; Japan Science and Technology Agency, Tokyo, Japan; RIKEN Cluster for Science and Technology Hub, Yokohama, Japan; National Center for Geriatrics and Gerontology, Obu, Japan; and Tokyo Medical and Dental University, Tokyo, Japan

Woong-Hee Shin
Purdue University, West Lafayette, IN, United States

Shweta Shrotriya
Birla Institute of Scientific Research, Jaipur, India

Ankita Shukla
Jaypee University of Information Technology, Solan, India

Moolchand Sigar
DBT-AIST International Laboratory for Advanced Biomedicine (DAILAB), Indian Institute of Technology Delhi, New Delhi, India

Kong-Wah Sing
Kunming Institute of Zoology, Chinese Academy of Sciences, Yunnan, P.R. China

Tiratha R. Singh
Jaypee University of Information Technology, Solan, India

Monisha Singhal
Birla Institute of Scientific Research, Jaipur, India

Dean Southwood
Macquarie University, Sydney, NSW, Australia

Srilakshmi Srinivasan
Institute of Health and Biomedical Innovation and School of Biomedical Sciences, Queensland University of Technology, Brisbane, QLD,, Australia

Anuj Srivastava
The Jackson Laboratory, CT, United States

Wataru Suda
RIKEN Center for Integrative Medical Sciences, Yokohama City, Japan

Suhaila Sulaiman
Universiti Kebangsaan Malaysia, Bangi, Selangor, Malaysia

Durai Sundar
DBT-AIST International Laboratory for Advanced Biomedicine (DAILAB), Indian Institute of Technology Delhi, New Delhi, India

Vijayaraghava S. Sundararajan
Ministry of Environmental Agency, Singapore; and Bioclues.org, Hyderabad, India

Prashanth Suravajhala
Birla Institute of Scientific Research, Jaipur, India

Y.-h. Taguchi
Chuo University, Tokyo, Japan

Lena Takayasu
RIKEN Center for Integrative Medical Sciences, Yokohama City, Japan

Mingchen Tan
National University of Singapore, Singapore

Bensellak Taoufik
École Nationale Des Sciences Appliquées de Tanger, Tangier, Morocco

Bimo A. Tejo
UCSI University, Cheras, Kuala Lumpur, Malaysia

Genki Terashi
Purdue University, West Lafayette, IN, United States

Pradeep Tiwari
Manipal University, Jaipur, India; Birla Institute of Scientific Research, Jaipur, India; and SMS Medical College, Jaipur, India

Sooh Toh
University of Malaya, Kuala Lumpur, Malaysia

Vartika Tomar
University of Delhi, Delhi, India

Lokesh P. Tripathi
National Institutes of Biomedical Innovation, Health and Nutrition, Osaka, Japan

Fotis Tsetsos
Democritus University of Thrace, Alexandroupolis, Greece

Tatsuhiko Tsunoda
RIKEN Center for Integrative Medical Sciences, Yokohama, Japan; Japan Science and Technology Agency, Tokyo, Japan; and Tokyo Medical and Dental University, Tokyo, Japan

Greg Tucker-Kellogg
National University of Singapore, Singapore

Alfonso Urso
Universiti Brunei Darussalam, Bandar Seri Begawan, Brunei Darussalam

Megha Vaishnavi
Central University of Jharkhand, Ranchi, India

Peter van Heusden
University of the Western Cape, Cape Town, South Africa

Brigitte Vannier
University of Poitiers, Poitiers France

Habibah Wahab
Universiti Sains Malaysia, Pulau Pinang, Malaysia

Habibah A. Wahab
Universiti Sains Malaysia, Pulau Pinang, Malaysia

John-James Wilson
University of South Wales, Pontypridd, United Kingdom; and Naresuan University, Phitsanulok, Thailand

Adison Wong
Singapore Institute of Technology, Singapore

Jin Xing Lim
Temasek Polytechnic, Singapore

Jing Xu
Harbin Medical University, Harbin, China

Ayako Yachie-Kinoshita
The Systems Biology Institute, Tokyo, Japan

Zatil H. Yahaya
Universiti Kebangsaan Malaysia, Bangi, Malaysia

Jian Yang
University of Saskatchewan, Saskatoon, SK, Canada

Beow Keat Yap
Universiti Sains Malaysia, Pulau Pinang, Malaysia

Ragothaman M. Yennamalli
Jaypee University of Information Technology, Waknaghat, Himachal Pradesh, India

Rui Yin
Nanyang Technological University, Singapore

Teo Chian Ying
International Medical University, Bukit Jalil, Kuala Lumpur, Malaysia

Nur S. Yusoff
Universiti Kebangsaan Malaysia, Bangi, Malaysia

Muhammad Yusuf
Universitas Padjadjaran, Jatinangor, Indonesia

Guang Lan Zhang
Boston University, Boston, MA, United States and Harvard Medical School, Boston, MA, United States

Jie Zheng
Nanyang Technological University, Singapore, Singapore

PREFACE

Bioinformatics and Computational Biology (BCB) combine elements of computer science, information technology, mathematics, statistics, and biotechnology, providing the methodology and *in silico* solutions to mine biological data and processes, for knowledge discovery. In the era of molecular diagnostics, targeted drug design and Big Data for personalized or even precision medicine, computational methods for data analysis are essential for biochemistry, biology, biotechnology, pharmacology, biomedical science, and mathematics and statistics. Bioinformatics and Computational Biology are essential for making sense of the molecular data from many modern high-throughput studies of mice and men, as well as key model organisms and pathogens. This Encyclopedia spans basics to cutting-edge methodologies, authored by leaders in the field, providing an invaluable resource to students as well as scientists, in academia and research institutes as well as biotechnology, biomedical and pharmaceutical industries.

Navigating the maze of confusing and often contradictory jargon combined with a plethora of software tools is often confusing for students and researchers alike. This comprehensive and unique resource provides up-to-date theory and application content to address molecular data analysis requirements, with precise definition of terminology, and lucid explanations by experts.

No single authoritative entity exists in this area, providing a comprehensive definition of the myriad of computer science, information technology, mathematics, statistics, and biotechnology terms used by scientists working in bioinformatics and computational biology. Current books available in this area as well as existing publications address parts of a problem or provide chapters on the topic, essentially addressing practicing bioinformaticists or computational biologists. Newcomers to this area depend on Google searches leading to published literature as well as several textbooks, to collect the relevant information.

Although curricula have been developed for Bioinformatics education for two decades now (Altman, 1998), offering education in bioinformatics continues to remain challenging from the multidisciplinary perspective, and is perhaps an NP-hard problem (Ranganathan, 2005). A minimum Bioinformatics skill set for university graduates has been suggested (Tan *et al.*, 2009). The Bioinformatics section of the Reference Module in Life Sciences (Ranganathan, 2017) commenced by addressing the paucity of a comprehensive reference book, leading to the development of this Encyclopedia. This compilation aims to fill the "gap" for readers with succinct and authoritative descriptions of current and cutting-edge bioinformatics areas, supplemented with the theoretical concepts underpinning these topics.

This Encyclopedia comprises three sections, covering Methods, Topics and Applications. The theoretical methodology underpinning BCB are described in the Methods section, with Topics covering traditional areas such as phylogeny, as well as more recent areas such as translational bioinformatics, cheminformatics and computational systems biology. Additionally, Applications will provide guidance for commonly asked "how to" questions on scientific areas described in the Topics section, using the methodology set out in the Methods section. Throughout this Encyclopedia, we have endeavored to keep the content as lucid as possible, making the text "… as simple as possible, but not simpler," attributed to Albert Einstein. Comprehensive chapters provide overviews while details are provided by shorter, encyclopedic chapters.

During the planning phase of this Encyclopedia, the encouragement of Elsevier's Priscilla Braglia and the constructive comments from no less than ten reviewers lead our small preliminary editorial team (Christian Schönbach, Kenta Nakai and myself) to embark on this massive project. We then welcomed one more Editor-in-Chief, Michael Gribskov and three section editors, Mario Cannataro, Bruno Gaeta and Asif Khan, whose toils have results in gathering most of the current content, with all editors reviewing the submissions. Throughout the production phase, we have received invaluable support and guidance as well as milestone reminders from Paula Davies, for which we remain extremely grateful.

Finally we would like to acknowledge all our authors, from around the world, who dedicated their valuable time to share their knowledge and expertise to provide educational guidance for our readers, as well as leave a lasting legacy of their work.

We hope the readers will enjoy this Encyclopedia as much as the editorial team have, in compiling this as an ABC of bioinformatics, suitable for naïve as well as experienced scientists and as an essential reference and invaluable teaching guide for students, post-doctoral scientists, senior scientists, academics in universities and research institutes as well as pharmaceutical, biomedical and biotechnological industries. Nobel laureate Walter Gilbert predicted in 1990 that "In the year 2020 you will be able to go into the drug store, have your DNA sequence read in an hour or so, and given back to you on a compact disk so you can analyze it." While technology may have already arrived at this milestone, we are confident one of the readers of this Encyclopedia will be ready to extract valuable biological data by computational analysis, resulting in biomedical and therapeutic solutions, using bioinformatics to "measure" health for early diagnosis of "disease."

References

Altman, R.B., 1998. A curriculum for bioinformatics: the time is ripe. Bioinformatics. 14 (7), 549–550.

Ranganathan, S., 2005. Bioinformatics education–perspectives and challenges. PLoS Comput Biol 1 (6), e52.

Tan, T.W., Lim, S.J., Khan, A.M., Ranganathan, S., 2009. A proposed minimum skill set for university graduates to meet the informatics needs and challenges of the "-omics" era. BMC Genomics. 10 (Suppl 3), S36.

Ranganathan, S., 2017. Bioinformatics. Reference Module in Life Sciences. Oxford: Elsevier.

Shoba Ranganathan

Ecosystem Monitoring Through Predictive Modeling

Sorayya Malek, Cham Hui, Nanyonga Aziida, Song Cheen, Sooh Toh, and Pozi Milow, University of Malaya, Kuala Lumpur, Malaysia

Introduction

Water bodies represent significant accumulations of water on the earth's surface. These accumulations of water can include oceans, seas, lakes, ponds and wetlands. They can be still (or contained) or mobile. Rivers, streams, and canals are some examples of natural water. There are also manmade artificial water bodies such as reservoirs and wetlands. In order to maintain aqueous systems capable of sustaining life forms, preserving water quality is very important. However, water bodies all over the world are facing a few common problems, namely eutrophication, sedimentation, and weed infestation. Eutrophication is the result of water bodies' enrichment, increased growth of microscopic floating plants, algae, and the formation of dense mats of floating plants. Algae have long been used to assess environmental conditions in aquatic habitats throughout the world. Algae respond to a wide range of pollutants. They provide an early caution signal of worsening ecological conditions. They are highly sensitive to changes in their environment and therefore a good indicator. Shifts in abundance of algal species can be used to detect environmental changes, and to indicate trophic status and nutrient problems in the lake. Nutrient stimulation of algal growth made algae part of the problem in the eutrophication of lakes, and trophic status of lakes can be monitored by algal taxa found in them (Mogeeb *et al.*, 2012). Chlorophyll-a has been used to estimate algal biomass in aquatic ecosystems as it is common in most algae. Algal biomass indicates the trophic status of a water body. Chlorophyll- a therefore is an effective indicator for monitoring eutrophication, which is a common problem of lakes and reservoirs all over the world (Malek *et al.*, 2011a,b).

Eutrophication can bring the effects of anoxia, which kills fish and invertebrates and results in release of unpleasant and injurious gases. Algae will bloom and other aquatic plants' growth will be uncontrolled. Species and diversity of plants and animals has decreased in number. Polluted water resources can cause severe effects on human as well as aquatic life. Hence, water quality monitoring is essential in exploitation of aquatic resources conservation. Water quality can be defined as a complex of chemical, physical, microbiological, and radiological properties with respect to its suitability for particular purposes (Kambourova, 2006; Boyd, 2015) or simply the physical, chemical, and biological characteristics of water (Orouji *et al.*, 2013). A water quality variable refers to any physical, chemical, or biological property that influences the suitability of water for natural ecological systems or use by humans (Boyd, 2015).

The quality of water helps in regulating the biotic diversity and biomass, energy, and rate of succession. Various factors can affect water quality parameters that are essential in preserving water quality. Quality of water is divided into three main categories, which are physical, chemical, and biological. Physical measurement involves turbidity, color, odor, and taste. Chemical parameters include the organic and inorganic forms of metals and nutrients. Measurement of ammonia nitrogen and iron are used for organic parameters. Meanwhile, inorganic parameters were measured by pH, iron, sulfate, and chloride. The biological parameters include total and fecal coliform, heterotrophic plate count, chlorophyll concentration, and *Escherichia coli* counts (Ngadiman *et al.*, 2016).

Various factors affect water quality parameters. Surface water temperature for example is affected by urbanization and industrial waste that effects fluctuation in dissolved oxygen (DO) concentration in water. DO is important for living organisms in water. The amount of DO in water bodies is dependent on water temperature, sedimentation, amount of oxygen used by respiring and decaying organisms, and amount of oxygen produced from photosynthesizing plants. Water high in organic matter and nutrients can lead to decrease in DO level as a result of increased microbial activity occurring during the degradation of organic matter. Oxygen is an important parameter as it is essential in the metabolism of all aerobic aquatic organisms. Two other important factors are chemical oxygen demand (COD) and biochemical oxygen demand (BOD). COD and BOD are measurements of the susceptibility to oxidation of the organic and inorganic materials and amount of biodegradable organic matter present in water sample. Water pH can be affected by waste or pollutant from human activities. Salinization process leads to reduction on pure drinking water. Turbidity is defined as clarity of water; the clearer the water the higher the water quality. During the raining season turbidity values of water reservoirs are higher due to the sedimentation process. Nutrients such as nitrates, phosphorus, and ammonia are also important for maintaining water quality and aquatic life.

Databases for water bodies contain a vast amount of information that is not possible to be analyzed using conventional statistical methods. Predictive water quality modeling can help to capture relationships among various factors for water quality monitoring. Predictive modeling can be defined as a process by which a model is created or chosen to try to best predict the probability of an outcome (Geisser, 1993). Kuhn and Johnson (2013) modified this definition "to the process of developing a mathematical tool or model that generates an accurate prediction." Studies to develop predictive models for environmental monitoring began by the use statistical approach. A cursory literature search indicates that computational approach to predictive modeling for environmental models is culminated in a volume that was edited by Racknaegel (2003). The computational approach and procedure involve machine learning (ML), a term that literally means learning how to predict from data. ML can be defined as the capability to acquire knowledge by computers without being explicitly programmed. ML algorithms serve as a common tool for data analysis tasks including data imputation, clustering, classification, and regression. However with the emergence of visualization using Google Earth for water quality monitoring, the investigation and monitoring of water quality has improved. Application of Google Earth gives intuitive visualization and can reflect the relationship between water quality and geographical position. Google Earth Engine enables water resource scientists to overcome tasks involved with remote sensing data analysis such as locating and downloading the data from various providers, data processing, model applications, results interpretation, and accessing current or updated data.

This article presents an overview of ML approaches, followed by application of these methods to water quality modeling, using three representative case studies. Visualization of the results of water quality monitoring is discussed in the final section.

Introduction to Machine Learning Methods in Water Quality Modeling

ML methods are categorized into supervised and unsupervised learning, and optimization techniques. Supervised learning is where a mapping function is used to learn from input variables to an output variable. It is done using a training dataset where the output variable value is already known. The aim of the mapping functions is to adjust the parameters of a particular model such that the outputs of the system approximate the outputs as closely as possible. Supervised learning can be further categorized into classification and regression. Common methods for supervised learning are artificial neural networks (ANN), random forest (RF), and support vector machine (SVM). In unsupervised learning the output variable is not presented during the learning process. The algorithm discovers on its own structures or patterns in data. Unsupervised learning can be categorized into clustering and association. An example for unsupervised learning is Kohonen self organizing feature maps (SOM). Optimization based methods identify the best set of variables that will minimize a predefined cost function. An example includes genetic algorithms (GAs).

Artificial Neural Network

ANNs gather their knowledge by detecting the patterns and relationships in data and learns (or is trained) through experience. An ANN consists of an input layer of neurons (nodes), one or two or even three hidden layers of neurons, and a final layer of output neurons. Each connection is associated with a numeric number called weight (Wang *et al.*, 2003). Liu *et al.* (2015) applied decision tree, back propagation neural networks, radial basis neural network, and logistic regression for water quality modeling. The RBF neural network outperformed all three supervised models for water quality prediction with the highest accuracy. Palani *et al.* (2008) applied an ANN to predict and forecast quantitative characteristics of water bodies such as salinity, temperature, DO, and chlorophyll-alpha. The ANN model was provided with unseen data and was able to simulate values with high accuracy for the desired locations at which measured data are unavailable yet required for water quality models hence making the ANN algorithm a good model when it comes to monitoring of water quality.

Random Forest

Breiman *et al.* (2001) defined RF, which add an additional layer of randomness to bagging. In addition to constructing each tree using a different bootstrap sample of the data, RFs change how the classification or regression trees are constructed. In standard trees, each node is split using the best split among all variables and is usually not very sensitive to their values (Liaw and Wiener, 2002). The efficiency, accuracy, and association between trees in the forest improve with increasing number of selected variables. RF model advantages have a high accuracy of classification and variable importance function. The RF model is also nonparametric, does not require data transformation, and is able to handle a large number of predictors (Cutler *et al.*, 2007). Hollister *et al.* (2015) applied RF for regression and RF for classification to determine chlorophyll-a concentration and lake trophic status. Both regression and classification models were developed using a combination of in situ and universally available GIS data and only universally available GIS data. RF for classification and regression using a combination of both in situ and universally available GIS data resulted in higher performance and better accuracy. This indicates that RF can work well for both regression and classification problem. In another study thirteen ML models such as ANN, SVM, RF, K-nearest neighbors, generalized boosted models were compared for the prediction of groundwater dissolved organic nitrogen by Wang *et al.* (2016). RF was selected as one of the tree based models with optimal model performance illustrating high generalization ability to different data conditions as well as high interpretability. The study identified factors that affect dissolved organic nitrogen using a limited dataset, which can be cost saving in groundwater monitoring. Yajima and Derot (2017) applied a RF model with a sliding window strategy using multivariate historical water quality records of over 10 years to forecast the concentration of chlorophyll-a in fresh and saline water bodies in Japan. The RF model was able to predict trends of the chlorophyll-a in the water bodies with high accuracy and the study concluded that the most dominant parameters for water quality assessment for chlorophyll-a was BOD, COD, pH, and TN/TP.

Support Vector Machine

SVM is a supervised training algorithm that can be useful for the purpose of classification and regression (Vapnik, 1998). SVM can be used to analyze data for classification and regression using algorithms and kernels in SVM (Cortes and Vapnik, 1995). Support vector classification (SVC) also is an algorithm that searches for the optimal separating surface. SVC is outlined first for the linearly separable case (Burbidge and Buxton, 2001). SVM kernel methods are used when complete separations of the two classes are not possible. Some widely used kernels in SVM are polynomial, quadratic, and radial basis function.

Applied SVC and regression (SVR), which was used in monitoring of surface water quality data by predicting biochemical oxygen demand (BOD) of water. The SVR model predicted water BOD values with high correlation value of 0.952, and RMSE of 1.53, hence providing a tool for the prediction of BOD of surface water quality using set of a few measurable variables. Proposed a smooth support vector machine (SSVM) to predict water quality. SSVM is an algorithm that is used for solving nonlinear function estimation problems. The RMSE reported for aquaculture water quality prediction was very low with a value of 0.0275. This value shows that SSVM is proven to be an effective approach to predict aquaculture water quality.

Fuzzy Logic

Fuzzy logic (FL) is an approach to computing based on "degrees of truth" rather than the usual "true or false" (1 or 0) Boolean logic on which the modern computer is based. Fuzzy reasoning is the process in which fuzzy rules are used to transform input into output and consists of four steps: (1) the input variables are fuzzified, (2) the firing strength of each rule is determined, (3) the consequence of each rule is resolved, and (4) the consequences are aggregated. FL rules consist of a premise and consequence and are believed to be able to capture the reasoning of a human working in an environment with uncertainty and imprecision (Shrestha *et al.*, 1996). Used FL to make their complex reservoir optimization models more appealing to operators, who are reluctant to use procedures they do not fully understand. They use optimization techniques, such as deterministic and stochastic dynamic programming. Water quality index (WQI) is determined using a statistical approach and it is used to communicate information on river water quality. Raman *et al.* (2009) used FL method to calculate WQI value and compared the findings with conventional WQI value. The FL base WQI model generated almost similar results with the conventional method. FL is developed using natural language and it is more understandable for river water classification compared to conventional methods and is tolerant towards imprecise data.

Self-Organizing Feature Maps

SOM, also called Kohonen map, is a popular neural network method based on unsupervised learning (Kohonen, 2013). U-matrix is a visualization technique used in SOM. U-matrix visualizes the distances between the neighboring map units and thus portrays the cluster structure of the map. Darker color with the high values denotes the cluster separator while uniform areas of low values indicate clusters (Stefanovic and Kurasova, 2011). In order to extract the most important parameter in assessing high and low flow period variations in terms of river water quality, Sengorur *et al.* (2015) used SOM and ANN to investigate the nonlinear relationship between the input and output variables in complex data for river and water quality management. Chang *et al.* (2008) applied SOM and K-Means arithmetic model on water quality evaluation. An *et al.* (2016) used a combination of principal component analysis (PCA) for dimension reduction and SOM for pattern identification. The author considered that both PCA and SOM are efficient tools to evaluate and analyze the behavior of multivariable, complex, and nonlinear related surface water quality data to unravel patterns, relationship, and the behaviors of water quality parameters used in the study.

Genetic Algorithm

GAs are a type of optimization algorithm, used to find the optimal solution(s) to a given computational problem that maximizes or minimizes a particular function. GAs represent one branch of the field of study called evolutionary computation (Kinnear, 1994) in that they imitate the biological processes of reproduction and natural selection to solve for the "fittest" solutions. GA was applied to determine plant efficiency to reduce wastewater treatment cost in a river basin to improve water quality with high accuracy (Aras *et al.*, 2007). Lee *et al.* (2016) combined GA algorithm with ANN, called a neurogenetic algorithm (NGA). The NGA was designed to determine the effective number of nodes and the optimal activated functions for the ANN structure. NGA and correlation analysis was used to identify input parameters for chlorophyll-a concentrations prediction in lakes used as drinking water sources. The best NGA model architecture was using double hidden layers and logistic sigmoid function that resulted in a high accuracy in training and testing data in comparison to single hidden layer and linear and hyperbolic tangent function.

Case Study: Application of ML Methods in Water Quality Prediction

Common steps in involved in water quality analysis are data preprocessing, data splitting model training and testing, and results evaluation. These are the common steps involved in development in almost all ML methods. Finlay (2014) provided steps for building predictive models, which are outlined as follows:

(1) Exploring the data landscape
(2) Sampling and shaping the development sample
(3) Data preparation (data cleaning)
(4) Creating derived data

(5) Understanding the data
(6) Preliminary variable selection (data reduction)
(7) Preprocessing (data transformation)
(8) Model construction (modeling)
(9) Validation

The steps illustrated by Finlay (2014) and Chapman *et al.* (2000) are illustrated in the following case studies for water quality modeling using ML methods.

Case Study 1: Supervised and Unsupervised Method in Water Quality Modeling

Malek *et al.* (2012) applied supervised and unsupervised learning method to identify the relationship between algal abundance with water quality parameters in a tropical lake. The diatom is an algae type that can be used to distinguish water quality status. Two types of ML methods have been applied in this study: Supervised method (Recurrent artificial neural network (RANN)) and unsupervised method (Kohonen self organizing feature maps (SOM)).

RANN is suitable for water quality model prediction involving dynamic time series data. Applied RANN to determine total nitrogen, phosphorus, and DO at Lake Taihu during water diversion. Shim & Tollner applied RANN and sensitivity analysis to predict and identify significant water quality variables at a composting pond. Sensitivity analysis, an analytical approach, was used to select model inputs for RANN. Malek *et al.* (2012) also applied sensitivity analysis where input variables having greater sensitivity value are deemed important and those with smaller values are discarded. Variable selection or dimension reduction is an important step in water quality modeling. This enables effective water quality management by effectively managing limited resources for water quality management. **Fig. 1** below illustrates results obtained from sensitivity analysis against output variable, that is, diatom abundance. It can be seen that input variables such as water temperature, pH, DO, and turbidity play an important role in diatom abundance in a lake. RANN model performance in this study was measured using root mean square error (RMSE) and *r* value, which are standard performance evaluators for regression models.

Unsupervised method SOM was applied in this study to classify and cluster diatom abundance using significant variables identified from sensitivity analysis. The SOM generated in this study was confirmed against the sensitivity curve produced from RANN as illustrated in **Fig. 2**. SOM cluster map and component plane in **Fig. 2** illustrates that diatom is highly abundant at lower temperature less than 30° C; this was conformed with results from sensitivity analysis graph.

SOM has also been used for pattern discovery to extract rules governing alga abundance in terms of propositional IF...else rules (Malek *et al.*, 2009, 2010a,b, 2011a,b, 2012). SOM component planes together with SOM cluster map can be used to extract rules to generate a rule-based system prediction.

Case Study 2: Assessment of Predictive Models for Chlorophyll-a Concentration of a Tropical Lake

Malek *et al.* (2011a,b) assesses four predictive water quality models: FL, RANN, hybrid evolutionary algorithm (HEA) and multiple linear regressions (MLR). RANN, FL, and HEA models are suitable for data that represents a nonlinear relationship such as in water quality data. The application of MLR model in water quality modeling in this study was deemed oversimplified as water pollution or eutrophication process represents complex nonlinear relationships between various water quality variables that are not possible to be explained using simplified models.

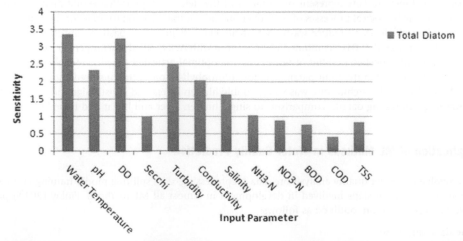

Fig. 1 Sensitivity analysis graph. Reproduced from Malek, S., Salleh, A., Milow, P., Baba, M.S., Sharifah, S., 2012. Applying artificial neural network theory to exploring diatom abundance at tropical Putrajaya Lake, Malaysia. Journal of Freshwater Ecology 27 (2), 211–227. doi:10.1080/02705060.2011.635883.

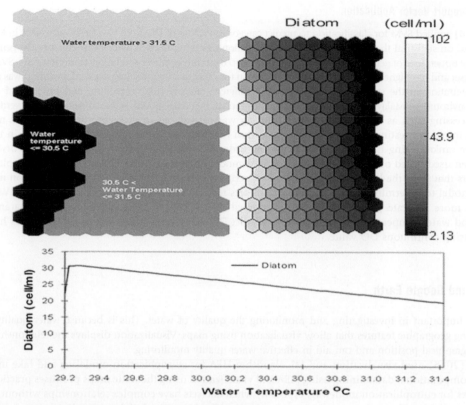

Fig. 2 SOM showing relationship between diatom density and water temperature.

FL based models on the other hand could provide insight into their own operation because the fuzzy rules provide an easily understood and common sense description of the action of the FL system. FL models have been noted to outperformed feed forward ANN in determining algal concentration and RANN in determining chlorophyll-a concentration (Malek *et al.*, 2010b, 2011a,b).

The study by Malek *et al.* (2011a,b) also uses genetic programming to generate the structure of the rule set and GA for parameter optimization for an HEA based model. The HEA model outperformed FL, RANN, and MLR. In raw datasets, some variables have large variation or spread. Normalization of the raw datasets for predictive modeling approach is an important step to ensure all the variables are within the same range. Variable selection is another important step as presenting a large number of variables to ML algorithms may compromise processing speed. Hence reducing dimension of variables used in model development reduces the size of the ML model architecture, which reduces the processing time, decreases the cost of data collection, and improves accuracy of ML models. Reduction in variable dimension for FL based models provides a simpler formulation of inference rules. In formulating FL membership and inference rules the SOM based approach has been applied by the author. SOM is deemed as an effective approach in formulating FL rules. The preferred method of variable selection should comprise prior knowledge and analytical approaches such as sensitivity analysis, backward elimination, stepwise selection, and genetic algorithm based feature selection.

Model performance evaluation adopted in the study was RMSE, r for regression type of ML models and AUROC for binary classification. RMSE is a measure of the average level of prediction error. It indicates the absolute fit of the model to the data or how close the observed data points are to the model's predicted values. The r value is a measure of correlation between the predicted and observed values of the independent variable. The r value indicates agreement between predicted and observed values but it does not indicate the performance of the models. Models are considered reliable when their predicted values correlate with observed values at r value of 0.5 or above. AUROC curve is a graphical plot of sensitivity or true positive rate versus false positive rate. It is based on binary classification task.

The higher performance of FL model reported by the author over RANN and HEA in this study is due to categorizing continuous response (chlorophyll-a concentration) into two classes. AUROC is a better measure for model evaluation than accuracy, which is measured using RMSE and is suitable for characterizing responses that are dichotomous such as lake eutrophication.

ANN models are "black-box" in nature unlike explanatory methods such as FL and HEA. An FL approach according to the author proves to be a practical and successful technique when dealing with semiqualitative knowledge and semiqualitative data. Generation of membership function and inference rules associated with FL model is dependent on knowledge and expertise of a domain expert, which can be overcome by using the HEA approach, which allows discovery of predictive rule set in complex data. The author noted that there are however drawbacks and advantages associated with each model.

Case Study 3: Support Vector Application

Malek *et al.* (2014) applied SVM for classification to predict categorized values of DO from two freshwater lakes in Malaysia. SVM is a ML method based on statistical theory and derived from instruction risk minimization, which can enhance the generalization ability and minimize the upper limit of generalization error. SVM is able to deal with complex and highly nonlinear data. SVM also works well on a limited dataset and has higher accuracy with better prediction for water quality modeling if a kernel method was used compared to ANN. DO concentration in the study was classified into 3 different category (high, medium, and low) based on guidelines by Department of Environment Malaysia. Classification of output for ML methods should be based on valid and verified categories.

Data preprocessing such as normalization and splitting was carried out to increase efficiency of the model. Data was divided into training and testing datasets. Variable selection method was based on linear SVM kernel in this study. Input parameters were ranked using linear kernel in ascending order based on the cross validation errors. Forward elimination method was then used based on ranked variables for SVM model developed using RBF, ANOVA, and Laplace kernel. Optimum parameters that yield the lowest errors, and highest accuracy were determined. Forward elimination method was used for each SVM model to determine most optimum parameters for water quality modeling. In this study SVM using ANOVA kernel resulted more accurate predication results compared with RBF and Laplacian kernels. The parameters were pH, conductivity, and water temperature. SVM models to predict DO using categorized values of DO yields higher prediction accuracy than using continuous DO value.

Visualization and Google Earth

Visualization is important in investigating and monitoring the quality of water. This is because water quality data collection involves capturing geographic features that allow visualization using maps. Visualization displays the relationship between water quality and geographical position and can aid in effective water quality monitoring.

Malek *et al.* (2015) used visualization and ML algorithm HEA for eutrophication modeling and lake management. The integration of computational data mining using HEA and visualization using thematic maps promises practical solutions and better techniques for eutrophication modeling, especially when datasets have complex relationships without clear distinction between various variables. Thematic maps are considered as an effective method of data visualization and are widely used for coastal management, and detection of the toxic algae and eutrophication. The data visualization approach in this study combines thematic cartography with volume visualization. Volume visualization is a set of techniques that present and show an object without mathematical representation. The study uses a choropleth map, which is a type of thematic map. Chloropleth maps represent quantitative data such as percentage, density, and average value of an event in a geographical area using color. The rules generated using HEA are integrated with thematic map visualization over time as depicted in **Fig. 3**. The

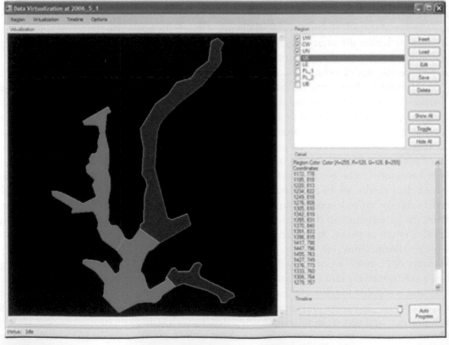

Fig. 3 Illustrates integration thematic map and HEA rules set. Reproduced from Malek, S., Hui, C., Fong, L.C., *et al.*, 2015. Ecological data prediction and visualization system. Frontiers in Life Science 8 (4), 387–398. doi:10.1080/21553769.2015.1041167.

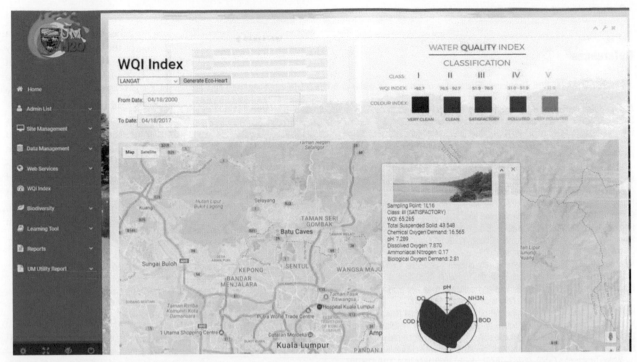

Fig. 4 Google Earth for visualization of WQI index. *Source*: http://umlivinglabsystem.com.

visualization system was evaluated by its capability in representing the output data on a map, and by predicting the abundance of chlorophyte based on other water quality parameters. Rules for predicting chlorophyte abundance had a success rate of almost 90%.

The emergence of Google Earth has added a visualization element for water quality monitoring. Google Earth was used for water quality monitoring using climate and hydrology data in South Africa (Silberbauer and Geldenhuys, 2009). Remote sensing via Google Earth is used to evaluate river ecosystem service, which is applicable to any ecoregion and any river size based on the degree of modification and nature (Large and Gilvear, 2014). Assessing water quality on a large scale using remote sensing models can be costly. Applied Google Earth Engine, a petabyte-scale data archive and remote sensing inquiry atmosphere in order to solve the main problems in designing and implementing water quality models on a large scale. Problems related to large amount of data visualization on Google Earth using the heat map was solved using Hadoop, an open source software, to store and process water quality data set effectively for visualization on Google Earth (Huang *et al.*, 2017). In an unpublished study Google Earth application was used to visualize WQI. Visualization of WQI using varying color and shape allows effective communication to the general public regarding water quality status at a particular location. This can assist in decision making for recreational activities as well as water quality monitoring. The WQI index was represented using series of varying color and shapes to indicate water quality status at a particular site as depicted in **Fig. 4**.

Conclusion

Water quality forecast and management comprises a substantial amount of uncertainty. There are uncertainties involved in water quality measurement methods as well as models used to predict the water quality and actions required to maintain the water quality status. These models however are necessary to assist water quality personnel involved in monitoring and managing water quality as deteriorating quality of natural water resources such as lakes, streams, and estuaries is a problem faced by mankind. Therefore, monitoring and effectively managing water resources is vital in order to optimize the quality of water. The problems associated with water contamination can be handled if water quality is predicted early using predictive models. This concern has been addressed in many prior studies, however, extensive work is still required in terms of applicability, efficiency, and reliability of existing water quality modeling. The methods presented here can be applied to other ecosystems, in order to sustain a healthy environment.

Acknowledgment

The authors would like to thank university of Malaya research grant LL023–16SUS for allowing to use unpublished materials from "see Relevant Website section".

See also: Natural Language Processing Approaches in Bioinformatics

References

An, Y., Zou, Z., Li, R., 2016. Descriptive characteristics of surface water quality in Hong Kong by a self-organising map. International Journal of Environmental Research and Public Health 13 (1), 115. doi:10.3390/ijerph13010115.

Aras, E., Toğan, V., Berkun, B., 2007. River water quality management model using genetic algorithm. Environmental Fluid Mechanics 7, 439–450. doi:10.1007/s10652-007-9037-4.

Boyd, C.E., 2015. Water Quality: An Introduction, second ed. Heidelberg, New York, Dordrecht, London: Springer Cham.

Breiman, L., Last, M., Rice, J., 2001. Random forests: Finding quasars. Statistical Challenges in Astronomy. 243–254. doi:10.1007/0-387-21529-8_16.

Burbidge, R., Buxton, B., 2001. An introduction to support vector machines for data mining. Keynote Papers, Young OR 12, pp. 3–15.

Chang, K., Gao, J., Yuan, Y., Li, N., 2008. Research on water quality comprehensive evaluation index for water supply network using SOM. In: Proceedng of the International Symposium on Information Science and Engineering. doi:10.1109/isise.2008.103.

Cortes, C., Vapnik, V., 1995. Support-vector networks. Machine Learning 20 (3), 273–297.

Cutler, D.R., Edwards Jr, T.C., Beard, K.H., et al., 2007. Random forests for classification in ecology. Ecology 88, 2783–2792.

Finlay, S., 2014. Predictive Analytics, Data Mining and Big Data: Myths, Misconceptions and Methods. Basingstoke: Palgrave Macmillan.

Geisser, S., 1993. Predictive inference, vol. 55.

Hollister, J.W., Milstead, W.B., Kreakie, B.J., 2015. Modelling lake trophic state: A random forest approach. doi:10.7287/peerj.preprints.1319.

Huang, W., Zhao, X., Han, Y., Du, W., Cheng, Y., 2017. Characterizing water quality monitoring visualization with Hadoop and Google Maps. Water Practice and Technology 12 (4), 882–893. doi:10.2166/wpt.2017.093.

KambourovaV., 2006. Potential water quality problems posed by intentional/accidental interventions. NATO Security Through Science Series Management of Intentional and Accidental Water Pollution, pp. 1–10. doi:10.1007/1-4020-4800-9_1.

Kinnear, K.E., 1994. Fitness landscapes and difficulty in genetic programming. In: Proceedings of the First IEEE Conference on Evolutionary Computation, 1994. IEEE World Congress on Computational Intelligence, pp. 142–147. IEEE.

Kohonen, T., 2013. Essentials of the self-organizing map. Neural Networks 3, 52–65.

Kuhn, M., Johnson, K., 2013. A summary of grant application models. Applied Predictive Modeling. 415–418. doi:10.1007/978-1-4614-6849-3_15.

Large, A.R., Gilvear, D.J., 2014. Using google earth, a virtual-globe imaging platform, for ecosystem services-based river assessment. River Research and Applications 31 (4), 406–421. doi:10.1002/rra.2798.

Lee, G., Bae, J., Lee, S., Jang, M., Park, H., 2016. Monthly chlorophyll-a prediction using neuro-genetic algorithm for water quality management in Lakes. Desalination and Water Treatment 57 (55), 26783–26791. doi:10.1080/19443994.2016.1190107.

Liaw, A., Wiener, M., 2002. Classification and regression by randomForest. R News 2 (3), 18–22.

Liu, B., Wan, X., Wu, X., Li, Y., Zhu, H., 2015. Application of decision tree and neural network algorithm in water quality assessment forecast. In: Proceedings of the 2015 International Conference on Material Science and Applications. doi:10.2991/icmsa-15.2015.137.

Malek, S., Ahmad, S.S., Singh, S.K., Milow, P., Salleh, A., 2011b. Assessment of predictive models for chlorophyll-a concentration of a tropical lake. BMC Bioinformatics 12 (Suppl. 13), doi:10.1186/1471-2105-12-s13-s12.

Malek, S., Hui, C., Fong, L.C., et al., 2015. Ecological data prediction and visualization system. Frontiers in Life Science 8 (4), 387–398. doi:10.1080/21553769.2015.1041167.

Malek, S., Mogeeb, M., Ahmad, S.M., 2014. Dissolved oxygen prediction using support vector machine. International Journal of Bioengineering and Life Sciences 8, 1.

Malek, S., Salleh, A., Ahmad, S.M., 2009. Analysis of algal growth using Kohonen self organizing feature map (SOM) and its prediction using rule based expert system. In: Proceeding of the 2009 International Conference on Information Management and Engineering. doi:10.1109/icime.2009.63.

Malek, S., Salleh, A., Baba, M.S., 2010a. Analysis of selected algal growth (Pyrrophyta) in tropical lake using Kohonen self organizing feature map (SOM) and its prediction using rule based system. In: Proceedings of the International Conference and Workshop on Emerging Trends in Technology – ICWET 10. doi:10.1145/1741906.1742083.

Malek, S., Salleh, A., Baba, M.S., 2010b. A comparison between neural network based and fuzzy logic models for chlorophll-a estimation. In: Proceedings of the 2010s International Conference on Computer Engineering and Applications. doi:10.1109/iccea.2010.217.

Malek, S., Salleh, A., Baba, M.S., Ahmad, S.M., 2011a. A self organizing map (SOM) guided rule based system for freshwater tropical algal analysis and prediction. Scientific Research and Essays 6 (25), 5279–5284. doi:10.5897/SRE10.866. Available online at. http://www.academicjournals.org/SRE.

Malek, S., Salleh, A., Milow, P., Baba, M.S., Sharifah, S., 2012. Applying artificial neural network theory to exploring diatom abundance at tropical Putrajaya Lake, Malaysia. Journal of Freshwater Ecology 27 (2), 211–227. doi:10.1080/02705060.2011.635883.

Mogeeb, A.A., Hayat, Sorayya, Pozi, Aishah, 2012. A preliminary study on automated freshwater algae recognition and classification system. BMC Bioinformatics 2012–13 (Suppl. 17), S25.

Ngadiman, N., Bahari, N.I., Kaamin, M., et al., 2016. Water quality of hills water, supply water and RO water machine at Ulu Yam Selangor. IOP Conference Series: Materials Science and Engineering, vol. 136. IOP Publishing. p. 012081. No. 1.

Orouji, H., Bozorg Haddad, O., Fallah-Mehdipour, E., Mariño, M.A., 2013. Modeling of water quality parameters using data-driven models. Journal of Environmental Engineering 139, 947–957.

Palani, S., Liong, S., Tkalich, P., 2008. An ANN application for water quality forecasting. Marine Pollution Bulletin 56 (9), 1586–1597. doi:10.1016/j.marpolbul.2008.05.021.

Raman, B.V., Bouwmeester, R., Mohan, S., 2009. Fuzzy logic water quality index and importance of water quality parameters. Air, Soil and Water Research 2. doi:10.4137/aswr.s215.

Sengorur, B., Koklu, R., Ates, A., 2015. Water quality assessment using artificial intelligence techniques: SOM and ANN – A case study of Melen River Turkey. Water Quality, Exposure and Health 7 (4), 469–490. doi:10.1007/s12403-015-0163-9.

Shrestha, B.P., Duckstein, L., Stakhiv, E.Z., 1996. Fuzzy rule-based modeling of reservoir operation. Journal of Water Resources Planning and Management 122 (4), 262–269. doi:10.1061/(asce)0733-9496(1996)122:4(262).

SilberbauerM., Geldenhuys, W., 2009. Google Earth-a spatial interface for SA water resource data. PositionIT, pp. 42–47.

Stefanovic, P., Kurasova, O., 2011. Visual analysis of self-organizing maps. Nonlinear Analysis: Modelling and Control 16 (4), 488–504.

Vapnik, V., 1998. Statistical Learning Theory. New York: Wiley, p. 1998.

Wang, H., Fan, W., Yu, P.S., Han, J., 2003. Mining concept-drifting data streams using ensemble classifiers. In: Proceedings of the Ninth ACM SIGKDD International Conference on Knowledge discovery and data mining, pp. 226–235. ACM.

Wang, B., Oldham, C., Hipsey, M.R., 2016. Comparison of machine learning techniques and variables for groundwater dissolved organic nitrogen prediction in an Urban Area. Procedia Engineering 154, 1176–1184. doi:10.1016/j.proeng.2016.07.527.

Yajima, H., Derot, J., 2017. Application of the Random Forest model for chlorophyll-a forecasts in fresh and brackish water bodies in Japan, using multivariate long-term databases. Journal of Hydroinformatics 20 (1), 206–220. doi:10.2166/hydro.2017.010.

Relevant Website

http://umlivinglabsystem.com
    LivingLab.

Large Scale Ecological Modeling With Viruses: A Review

Vijayaraghava S Sundararajan, Ministry of Environmental Agency, Singapore; Bioclues.org, Hyderabad, India

Introduction

Ecology is the study of organisms and their environments. Viruses are not usually categorized as free living organisms and merely treated as part of the environment. From late 1980s, several researchers started validating through molecular, experimental, micrographic, and model-based research on how viruses should be considered as ecological actors, and it was established that viruses are regulators of planetary biogeochemistry. A study by OMalley (2016) suggests that viruses should be considered as ecological actors that are comparably equal to organismal actors (OMalley, 2016).

In this review article, we will describe previous research studies in modeling large scale data with Dengue virus, in and around Singapore. These research methodologies, statistical analysis, and steps will give researchers an idea in how to deal with the large scale virus data and create models on virus locally and internationally to take appropriate steps to prevent the diseases spread.

1. Dengue viruses (DENV) cause 500,000 infections (dengue hemorrhagic fever, DHF, shock syndrome, and DSS) (WHO, 2009). DENV is a single stranded positive sense RNA virus with an 11.8 kb genome flanked by two untranslated regions, a single coding region, the precursor of membrane (prM), and seven nonstructural proteins (Chambers et al., 1990). Being a RNA virus, DENV undergoes a rapid evolutionary process (Holmes and Burch, 2000; Holmes and Twiddy, 2003) and selects strains with enhanced adaptation, resulting in mutant variants that differ in their ability to spread and cause disease (Holmes and Burch, 2000; Twiddy et al., 2002) and all four DENV serotypes are capable of causing severe dengue clinically (Whitehorn and Simmons, 2011). Previous studies implicated host genetics (Coffey et al., 2009; Khor et al., 2011) immune response (Green and Rothman, 2006), infection status, and viremia levels (Wang et al., 2006; Vaughn et al., 2000) as predisposing factors for severe dengue. Mild to severe dengue outbreaks subsequent to emergence of a DENV-2 genotype of Asian origin in Latin and Central America (Rico-Hesse et al., 1997a) were seen and disease severity could be even strain-dependent (Holmes and Burch, 2000). Viral genetic differences correlate with clinical severity (Pandey and Igarashi, 2000; Tuiskunen et al., 2011; Chen et al., 2008; Leitmeyer et al., 1999; Guzman et al., 1995) and virus attenuation (Whitehead et al., 2003) to support the strain-dependent concept of virulence.

2. Dengue reemergence is increasingly associated with a shift in epidemiology to older cohorts with different clinical manifestations and severity compared with very young children (Chen and Vasilakis, 2011). The dengue serotypes circulating all year round in Singapore are DENV-1, DENV-2, and DENV-3 with sporadic reports of DENV-4 (Lee et al., 2010). There were major outbreaks in 2005 by DENV-1 and by DENV-2 in 2007 (Ler et al., 2011). DENV-1 and DENV-2 are the main circulating serotypes out of 4 types (Ministry of Health, 2012). Infections with different serotypes may cause nearly identical clinical syndrome (Halstead, 2008), but some differences in clinical manifestations have been reported, although conclusions are usually based on limited serotype comparisons and small sample sizes (Chan et al., 2009; Kumaria, 2009). The exception is a recent large cross-sectional study from the Americas comprising 1716 children and adults (Halsey et al., 2012). Multiple factors have been suggested to contribute to severe dengue (SD) such as secondary infections, age, viral load, as well infecting serotype and genotype (Burke et al., 1988; Guzman and Kouri, 2003; Rico-Hesse et al., 1997b; Sangkawibha et al., 1984). Infection with secondary DENV-2 is more likely to result in severe disease compared with other serotypes (Balmaseda et al., 2006; Fried et al., 2010; Nisalak et al., 2003; Vaughn et al., 2000). Primary DENV-1 cases were more overt whereas primary DENV-2 and DENV-3 cases were usually silent (Guzman et al., 2012, 2000). DENV-2 genotype in is the Asian genotype rather than the Cosmopolitan genotype circulating in Singapore (Rabaa et al., 2010; Zhang et al., 2006) and extensive diversity resulting in epidemic potential (Rico-Hesse, 2003).

3. The "United in Tackling Epidemic Dengue (UNITEDengue)" portal was launched on August 28, 2012, to initiate cross-border dengue case and virus surveillance (Ng, 2011). In Singapore, the economic impact of dengue during 2000–2009 was estimated about US$1.15 billion (Carrasco et al., 2011) and in Klang Valley, Malaysia during 2005–2009 is about US$56 million (Shepard et al., 2012; Suaya et al., 2009). In 2013, Malaysia reported a total of 43,348 cases (peak in 2008 with 49,335) and Singapore reported a historical high of 22,170 cases (Anon, 2013; Anon, 2014a), which was almost 50% more than the worst dengue epidemic in 2005 with 14,209 cases, over previous years (2008–2012).

4. In the Western Pacific Region (such as, …), dengue is the main viral infection that occurs yearly in multiple countries due to complex interplay of virus, vector, and host biology, as well as climatic and socioeconomic factors (Arima et al., 2015; Bhatt et al., 2013; Lee et al., 2012; Ritchie, 2014; Banu et al., 2011; Wilder-Smith and Gubler, 2008). A 2014 study showed that DENV-serotype switches from previous years (Governments of Malaysia and Singapore, 2014; Anon, 2014b) and secondary heterotypic infection is believed because larger numbers equal severe dengue cases (Guzman et al., 2013). External quality assessment (EQA) is used to compare laboratory performance and reveal potential problems associated with diagnostic kits or procedures (Anon, 2011a). The WHO Regional Office for the Western Pacific launched an EQA for dengue diagnostics testing in 2013, under the Asia Pacific Strategy for Emerging Diseases (APSED) 2010 (Anon, 2012a).

5. *Aedes aegypti* vectors acquire the dengue virus when they feed on viremia hosts (the dengue infected human patient) (Kramer and Ebel, 2003) and the role of mosquito vector in the transmission of dengue fever was first recognized by Bancroft (1906). In 1906, feeding

mosquitoes on dengue patients was further studied by Cleland et al., (1919, 1918). Comprehensive human to mosquito transmission studies were conducted in the Philippines (Siler et al., 1926; Simmons et al., 1931), and several epidemiologically important observations (Nguyet et al., 2013) in Vietnam involve feeding mosquitoes with vertebrate blood spiked with cell cultured virus, using a device, such as a "double-jacketed" glass cylinder (Rutledge et al., 1964) or a Hemotek membrane feeding system (Diehlmann, 1999). Earlier studies may not accurately mimic that of the natural setting (Rodhain and Rosen, 1997) and infection rates were lower in mosquitoes (Jupp, 1976; Meyer et al., 1983), and use of virus stock that had been frozen and thawed, or phenotypic virus adaptation due to numerous passages in cell culture (Richards et al., 2007; Chen et al., 2003; Miller, 1987).

6. In the Western Pacific Region during the 2014 outbreaks, there were 1513 dengue cases in the Solomon Islands (Anon, 2014c) 45,171 cases in China, and 108,698 cases in Malaysia (Anon, 2015), and Japan reported its first autochthonous outbreak in over 70 years (Arima et al., 2014; Kutsuna et al., 2015). DENV-serotype 3 was found to be circulating in the Pacific after an absence of 18 years (Cao-Lormeau et al., 2014). CHIKV has probably had an unappreciated circulation in the region due to its cocirculation with DENV (Weaver and Lecuit, 2015; Horwood et al., 2013). Zika virus , a flavivirus that was detected in Asia in the 1960s but has recently emerged in the Pacific and the Americas (Kindhauser et al., 2016), is linked to clusters of micro-cephaly and other neurological disorders that WHO declared on 1-Feb-2016 as of international concern (Anon, 2016). A. aegypti and A. albopictus mosquito vectors require different control strategies (Yap et al., 2010) and clinicians require specialized training to treat severe dengue cases (Anon, 2012b). Genotype data is useful for tracking the movement of viruses and for risk assessment (Hapuarachchi et al., 2016), and point-of-care tests for dengue diagnosis (Prat et al., 2014) was introduced. EQA in the WHO Western Pacific Region (Pok et al., 2015b) was studied and APSED (Anon, 2011b) was initiated.

Research Studies

Clinical Outcome and Genetic Differences Within a Monophyletic Dengue Virus Type 2 Population (Hapuarachchi et al., 2015)

The new findings showed that primary and secondary infections that progressed to DHF and DSS were likely due to host rather than virus factors.

Data: DENV-2 with 89 whole genomes were obtained from patients diagnosed with dengue fever (DF, $n=58$), dengue hemorrhagic fever (DHF, $n=30$) and dengue shock syndrome (DSS, $n=1$) during July 2010 to January 2013 in Singapore. 70% of DENV-2 serotyped cases in Singapore (2007–2011) (Han et al., 2012) were noted. Primary and secondary infection cases (Gan et al., 2014) were based on serum IgM and IgG in patient sera, by using Panbio Dengue Capture IgM ELISA and Dengue Capture IgG, and Indirect IgG ELISA kits.

Method: Viral RNA was extracted from patient sera/plasma by using the QIAamp Viral RNA Mini Kit and crossing point values from the real-time PCR assay results were used as a surrogate indicator of virus titers (Lai et al., 2007). DENV was isolated from sera/plasma using the Ae. albopictus clone C6/36 mosquito cell line (ATCC CRL-1660). The presence of DENV in cell supernatants was confirmed by an immunofluorescent assay (IFA) using DENV group-specific and serotype-specific monoclonal antibodies derived from hybridoma cultures (ATCC: HB112, HB114, HB47, HB46, HB49, and HB48).

Packages: Contiguous sequences were assembled using the Lasergene package version 8.0 and were aligned in the BioEdit Sequence Alignment Editor version 7.0.9.0 (Hall, 1999). The phylogeny of study sequences was inferred by the maximum likelihood (ML) method based on the general time reversible substitution model and gamma distributed rates with invariant sites in MEGA 6.06 (Tamura et al., 2013). The median joining network was constructed using the whole genome sequences in Network version 4.6.1.2 (Bandelt et al., 1999). Genome-wide dN/dS ratios were computed using Hyphy package (Pond et al., 2005). The single likelihood ancestor counting , fixed effects likelihood , internal fixed effects likelihood, and the mixed effect model of evolution methods (Murrell et al., 2012) were used to detect the molecular signatures of selection within an alignment of 272 complete coding sequences (Asian, American Asian, and American genotypes of DENV-2) consisting of all study isolates ($n=89$) and those obtained from the GenBank database. Significance levels were set at $p<0.05$ and the secondary structures of the variable region of 3′ UTR and complete 5′ UTR of wild type (NS2A-V83) and mutant (NS2A-V83I) variants of DENV-2 cosmopolitan clade III were predicted using the mfold web server under standard conditions (37°C) (Zuker, 2003). The statistical significance, using R software (RCoreTeam, 2013) on association of primary and secondary infections within the DHF and DSS categories was cal-culated using the exact binomial test. Probability values less than 0.05 were considered statistically significant.

Conclusions: 89 patients were modeled as DF=58 and DHF=30, DSS=1. 45 patients had secondary dengue infections and 27 patients had primary infections and the primary/secondary status of 17 patients could not be classified. Findings indicated that subtle genetic differences in a highly homogenous, monotypic DENV-2 population potentially modified the clinical outcome of study subjects, regardless of primary and secondary infection status.

Dengue Serotype-Specific Differences in Clinical Manifestation, Laboratory Parameters, and Risk of Severe Disease in Adults, Singapore (Yung et al., 2015)

Serotype-specific features and disease severity on patients from April 2005 to December 2011 were studied on dengue hemorrhagic fever (DHF) and severe dengue (SD). 469 dengue-confirmed patients comprising 22.0% dengue virus serotype 1 (DENV-1), 57.1% DENV-2, 17.1% DENV-3, and 3.8% DENV-4 were studied.

Patients: The study included dengue cohorts recruited from two service settings: Primary care clinics and Singapore's Communicable Disease Centre, an infectious disease center that provides an outpatient walk-in service supporting Tan Tock Seng Hospital, a university teaching hospital with 1500 beds.

Methods: Phylogenetic analysis on DENV sequences was conducted by using the maximum-likelihood method as implemented in PAUP* software and compared with sequence data obtained from GenBank. Serology testing was carried out using: Platelia™ NS1 ELISA, Panbio® Dengue IgG Indirect, IgG Capture, and IgM Capture ELISAs.

Data: Headache, drowsiness, eye pain, muscle pain, joint pain, rash, bleeding, anorexia, nausea, vomiting, red eyes (conjunctival injection), and abdominal pain are used as clinical manifestations in the analysis. The WHO (2009) warning signs of lethargy/drowsiness, severe abdominal pain, and mucosal bleeding were assessed as one variable defined as patients who fulfilled any of the three warning signs (WS). Plasma viral RNA level, temperature, systolic blood pressure, pulse rate, hematocrit, platelet, and leukocyte count at the first day of presentation were analyzed. Between April 2005 and December 2011, a total of 3468 patients were enrolled into study cohorts.

Analysis: For descriptive analyses, number and percentage were used for categorical variables; median and range were used for continuous variables. The χ^2 test was used to compare univariate categorical data whereas Fisher's exact test was used if expected cell sizes <5. Adjustment was done for clinically relevant potential confounders: Age, gender, year of infection, recruitment site, fever day, and primary/secondary infection status unless stated otherwise. All analysis was done using R and in-house SAS software.

Results: Dengue was confirmed in 617 (18.2%) patients. Serotype information was available for 469 (76%) of dengue-confirmed patients comprising 103 (22.0%) DENV-1, 268 (57.1%) DENV-2, 80 (17.1%) DENV-3, and 18 (3.8%) DENV-4.

Conclusion: DENV-1 infection may be more severe compared with DENV-2 infection. A findings model that included a prospective adult dengue cohort found that DENV-1 cases were more likely to present with red eyes whereas absence of red eyes but presence of joint pain and lower platelet count was associated with DENV-2 cases. The differences in severity may be attributable to variations in plasma viral RNA levels between serotypes. At a molecular level, our findings may be associated with DENV-1 genotype 1 and DENV-2 cosmopolitan genotype.

Dengue Outbreaks in Singapore and Malaysia Caused by Different Viral Strains (Ng *et al.*, 2013)

A consortium of ASEAN countries formulated UNITEDengue with 14,079 circulating DENV in a cross-border surveillance program revealed that in the 2013 outbreaks in Singapore and Malaysia, the predominant virus in Singapore switched from DENV2 to DENV1, with DENV2 becoming predominant in neighboring Malaysia. Dominance of DENV2 was most evident in the southern states where higher fatality rates were observed. A shared secured web-portal UNITEDengue (see "Relevant Website section") features weekly incidence, monthly Dengue virus (DENV), serotype distribution, and sequences of the envelope (*E*) gene of viruses.

DENV serotype surveillance revealed that outbreaks in both countries were associated with a switch in predominant serotypes. In Malaysia, DENV2 overtook a preexisting DENV3 and DENV4 dominance pattern in 2013 (**Fig. 1(A) and (B)**). DENV2 was most dominant in the southernmost states of Johor and Malacca (**Fig. 1(C)**), where the proportion of DENV2 rose to 70%–90% after August 2013. Incidentally, the fatality rates of 0.5% in those two states were unusually high when compared with those of the whole of Malaysia and Selangor (0.18% and 0.08%, respectively), where surveillance protocols were the same. The association of DENV2 dominance with high fatality is of concern although the reasons remain unclear. Hypothetically, it could be because of the inherent virulence of DENV2 strain or the antibody-dependent enhancement, which causes sequential infection of DENV1 (or DENV3) followed by DENV2 to be more severe.

Envelope gene-based virus surveillance: DENV1 strains circulating in Singapore during the 2013 epidemic were first detected in November 2012 and belonged to genotype III. From April 2013 onward, more than 50% of all viruses sampled in Singapore clustered in this clade. Interestingly, only 42 (12%) of 349 DENV1 samples sequenced in Malaysia belonged to this clade. The predominant DENV2 strain found in Johor and Malacca belonged to the cosmopolitan genotype (named as cladeIb;) and was distinct from those that were predominant in the northern part of Malaysia. Though closely related to the cosmopolitan virus that caused Singapore's outbreak in 2007, and to strains that continue to circulate in Singapore, DENV-2 cladeIb in Johor and Malacca clustered distinctively (supported by a bootstrap value of 98%) from DENV-2 strains in Singapore. Out of five dengue-related death cases in Johor, four were due to cladeIb viruses. Close monitoring in Singapore initially detected sporadic cases (40 (11%) out of 363 DENV2 sequenced) due to cladeIb, and seven of those 40 sequences were identical to the cladeIb strains in Johor. Incidentally, the first death case in Singapore in early 2014 was due to a virus from the same clade.

First Round of External Quality Assessment of Dengue Diagnostics in the World Health Organization Western Pacific Region, 2013 (Pok *et al.*, 2015a)

Nineteen national-level public health laboratories from 18 countries and areas (two in Vietnam) in the WHO Western Pacific Region where dengue is endemic or where imported cases have been detected were invited to participate in the EQA. All 19 agreed and the EQA panel was dispatched to these laboratories between May and July 2013, and the labs performed routine dengue diagnostic assays on a proficiency testing panel consisting of two modules.

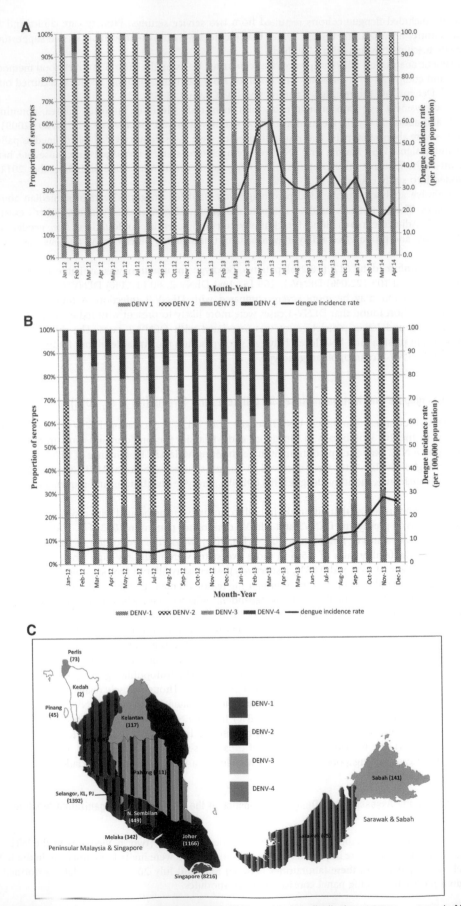

Fig. 1 (A) Monthly distribution of DENV serotypes in Singapore 2012–2014. (B) Monthly distribution of DENV serotypes in Malaysia 2012–2013. Predominant serotype switched from DENV2 to DENV1 in Singapore, while it switched from DENV3/4 to DENV2 in Malaysia. (C) Spatial distribution of predominant DENV serotypes in Malaysia and Singapore (2013). Reproduced from Ng, L.-C., Chem, Y.-K., , Koo, C., *et al.*, 2013. Dengue outbreaks in Singapore and Malaysia caused by different viral strains. American Journal of Tropical Medicine and Hygiene 92, 1150–1155.

Module A: Samples A2013-V01 and A2013-V03 contained at least 10^6 RNA copies/mL of in vitro-cultured DENV of different serotypes: DENV-1 genotype III and DENV-2 cosmopolitan clade II, deposited in Genbank with accession numbers KP685233 and KP685236, respectively.

Module B: Samples B2013-S01 and B2013-S02 were split serum samples from a convalescent dengue patient included to assess reproducibility of testing by the participating laboratories. These samples were confirmed by PRNT to contain neutralizing antibodies against DENV 1–4 ($> 1:1000$) and confirmed DENV-negative.

Analysis: In Module A, two points each were awarded for the correct detection of DENV by RT–PCR or NS1 assay and accurate serotyping of DENV. In Module B, two points each were awarded for the correct detection of anti-DENV IgG and IgM antibodies. The final score was the proportion of points earned out of the possible awardable points. Accuracy for each assay (e.g., serotyping) was defined as the proportion of laboratories scoring 100% for that assay. Quantitative data (RT–PCR cycle threshold values and ELISA values) submitted were used for reference and for assessing reproducibility of laboratory results. For ELISA assays, the percentage coefficient of variation was calculated from values recorded in triplicate runs to evaluate the reproducibility of results.

Module A: (Viral RNA and NS1 antigen): For laboratories using RT–PCR in Module A, the majority (11/16) used the QIAmp Viral RNA Mini Kit for extraction and purification of DENV RNA and commercial kits to perform RT–PCR. More than half (56.3%) used real-time RT–PCR, while the remainder used conventional RT–PCR methods The laboratory reporting equivocal results for the negative sample in Module A used the real-time methodology.

Module B: (Serology): All 18 laboratories that requested Module B chose the ELISA methodology to detect anti-DENV IgM. Half used the Panbio Dengue IgM Capture ELISA with two also using a rapid diagnostic test. The two laboratories detecting anti-DENV IgM in only one of the split samples used an in-house IgM MAC-ELISA protocol and a commercial Dengue IgM ELISA kit, respectively. This first round of EQA in the Western Pacific Region strengthens the regional public health laboratory system for detecting emerging infectious diseases, in line with APSED (2010).

Results: Module A was performed by 16 laboratories with reverse transcriptase polymerase chain reaction (RT-PCR) for both RNA and serotype detection. Of these, 15 had correct results for RNA detection and all 16 correctly serotyped the viruses. All nine laboratories performing NS1 antigen detection obtained the correct results. Sixteen of the 18 laboratories using IgM assays in Module B obtained the correct results as did the 13 laboratories that performed IgG assays.

Membrane Feeding of Dengue Patient's Blood as a Substitute for Direct Skin Feeding in Studying Aedes-Dengue Virus Interaction (Tan *et al.*, 2016)

Understanding the interaction between Aedes vectors and DENV has significant implications in determining the transmission dynamics of dengue. The absence of an animal model and ethical concerns regarding direct feeding of mosquitoes on patients has resulted in most infection studies using blood meals spiked with laboratory-cultured DENV.

Patients: The patient criteria were: (1) Adult, ≥ 21 years of age, (2) ≤ 5 days of fever, and (3) positive for DENV by point-of-care dengue NS1 Ag rapid test kit (Standard Diagnostic Inc., Korea) and written consent was obtained. A total of 26 dengue patients, 20 (80%) were found to be infected with DENV-1, three (12%) were infected with DENV-3, and two (8%) with DENV-2. The viremia level (DENV Log10 RNA copies/ml) of patients ranged from 4.75 to 9.41 (DENV-1), 3.73 to 5.6 (DENV-2), and 3.69 to 8.69 (DENV-3).

Methods: The number of RNA copies in patient's serum was measured using a TaqMan® one-step qRT-PCR assay targeting a highly conserved 3'UTR region of DENVs. Oligonucleotide sequences used were DENVF2: 5'- AAACAGCATATTGACGCTGGGA-3' and DENVR3: 5'-GGCGYTCTGTGCCTGGAWTGATG-3', with a probe sequence of 5'-FAM- AGACCAGAGATCCTGCTGTCTC-MGB-3'. PCR reactions were carried out using the TaqMan® Fast Virus 1-step Master Mix. Larvae were reared in 25 cm × 30 cm × 9 cm enamel pans containing 800 mL of water and fed with Plecomin® fish food (Tetra, Germany). Pupae were placed in 30 cm × 30 cm × 30 cm (H × W × L) cages. 17–34 mosquitoes (4–6 days old) were transferred into paper cups covered with net and were starved for at least 24 h before exposure to dengue patients. After the EDTA blood was collected, the cup was placed on patient's forearm and the mosquitoes were exposed to feed through the net for 15 min. Total RNA was amplified from mosquito midguts using the QIAamp Viral Mini. The number of RNA copies in mosquito midguts was estimated using the same TaqMan® one-step qRT-PCR assay.

Feeding rates: Overall, DSFA consistently resulted in higher mosquito feeding rates when compared to membrane feeding. In 11 out of 25 feeding events, a significantly higher number of mosquitoes were found to be fully engorged when they fed directly on a patient's arm as compared to those fed on the EDTA blood through a membrane ($P \leq 0.05$). Direct skin feeding consistently achieved more than 90% feeding rates, while the rates for membrane feeding were between 48.2% and 98.2%.

Results: Direct skin feeding assay (DSFA) consistently showed higher mosquito feeding rates (93.3%–100%) when compared with the membrane feeding assay (MFA) (48%–98.2%). Pair-wise comparison between methods showed no significant difference in midgut infection rates between mosquitoes exposed via each method and a strong correlation was observed in midgut infection rates for both feeding methods ($r = 0.89$, $P < 0.0001$). A strong correlation between salivary gland infection and patient serum viremia were observed for both DSFA ($r = 0.80$, $P < 0.0001$) and MFA ($r = 0.79$, $P < 0.0001$) methods. Unlike midgut infection, salivary gland infection was only observed in mosquitoes that fed on patients with viremia of more than 5.5 Log_{10}copies/ml.

External Quality Assessment of Dengue and Chikungunya Diagnostics in the Asia Pacific Region, 2015 (Soh *et al.*, 2016)

Twenty-four national-level public health laboratories performed routine diagnostic assays on a proficiency testing panel consisting of two modules. Module A contained serum samples spiked with cultured DENV or chikungunya virus for the detection of nucleic acid and DENV nonstructural protein 1 (NS1) antigen. Module B contained human serum samples for the detection of anti-DENV antibodies.

Analysis: The appropriate dengue diagnostic tools must be used at the correct time for the correct diagnosis of dengue. While 19/24 (79.2%) laboratories employed assays for both acute (RT–PCR) and recent (anti-DENV IgM) DENV infection, four performed antibody testing for dengue but lacked assays for early detection (preantibody immunological response) of dengue such as RT–PCR or NS1 kits and one could perform RT–PCR but had no serology capacity. With an incomplete set of diagnostics, these laboratories may be unable to diagnose a proportion of DENV infections and should consider quickly strengthening their capacity through the use of commercial ELISA assays for the detection of NS1 antigen or anti-DENV IgM antibodies. Accuracy was high ($\geq$ 85%) for DENV and CHIKV detection and DENV serotyping by RT–PCR. The few errors in DENV detection (false negatives) appeared to be clustered in samples A2015-V01 and V02, which were identical, high-titer DENV-1 samples. Most of the inaccuracies in Module A were in NS1 testing. Specifically, 87.5% of NS1 testing errors were derived from a single DENV-positive sample, A2015-V03, being reported as negative or equivocal (7/8 laboratories), particularly when using the Platelia Dengue NS1 Ag kit. This suggests that the NS1 levels in the sample may have been at the threshold of detection for the kit, making complementary assays for virus detection, such as RT–PCR, highly relevant.

RESULTS: Among 20 laboratories testing Module A, 17 (85%) correctly detected DENV RNA by reverse transcription polymerase chain reaction (RT-PCR), 18 (90%) correctly determined serotype, and 19 (95%) correctly identified CHIKV by RT-PCR. Ten of 15 (66.7%) laboratories performing NS1 antigen assays obtained the correct results. In Module B, 18/23 (78.3%) and 20/20 (100%) of laboratories, correctly detected anti-DENV IgM and IgG, respectively. Detection of acute/recent DENV infection by both molecular (RT-PCR) and serological methods (IgM) was available in 19/24 (79.2%) participating laboratories.

Acknowledgments

We thank Elsevier for giving us an opportunity to write this article. We sincerely thank Dr. Asif Khan for the invitation to write a book article.

See also: Ecosystem Monitoring Through Predictive Modeling. Natural Language Processing Approaches in Bioinformatics

References

Anon, 2011a. Laboratory Quality Management System. Geneva: World Health Organization.

Anon, 2011b. Asia Pacific Strategy for Emerging Diseases (2010). Manila: World Health Organization Regional Office for the Western Pacific.

Anon, 2012a. WHO External Quality Assessment Project for the detection of influenza Virus Type A by PCR. Manila: World Health Organization Regional Office for the Western Pacific.

Anon, 2012b. World Health Organization and Special Programme for Research and Training in Tropical Diseases: Handbook for clinical management of dengue. Geneva: World Health Organization.

Anon, 2013. Dengue Situation Update – 25 December 2013. Manila: World Health Organization Regional Office for the Western Pacific.

Anon, 2014a. Communicable Disease Surveillance in Singapore 2013. Singapore: Ministry of Health.

Anon, 2014b. Dengue Situation Update – 22 April 2014. Manila: World Health Organization Regional Office for the Western Pacific.

Anon, 2014c. Dengue Situation Update – 3 June 2014. Manila: World Health Organization Regional Office for the Western Pacific.

Anon, 2015. Dengue Situation Update – 13 January 2015. Manila: World Health Organization Regional Office for the Western Pacific.

Anon, 2016. WHO Director-General summarizes the Outcome of the Emergency Committee Regarding Clusters of Microcephaly and Guillain-Barré Syndrome. Geneva: World Health Organization.

Arima, Y., et al., 2014. Ongoing local transmission of dengue in Japan, August to September 2014. Western Pacific Surveillance and Response Journal 5 (4), 27–29. 10.5365/wpsar.2014.5.3.007.

Arima, Y., et al., 2015. Epidemiologic update on the dengue situation in the Western Pacific Region, 2012. Western Pacific Surveillance and Response Journal 6 (2), doi:10.5365/wpsar.2014.5.4.002.

Balmaseda, A., Hammond, S.N., Perez, L., et al., 2006. Serotype-specific differences in clinical manifestations of dengue. The American Journal of Tropical Medicine and Hygiene 74, 449–456.

Bancroft, T.L., 1906. On the etiology of dengue fever. The Australasian Medical Gazette 25, 17.

Bandelt, H.J., Forster, P., Rohl, A., 1999. Median-joining networks for inferring intraspecific phylogenies. Molecular Biology and Evolution 16 (1), 37–48. pmid:10331250.

Banu, S., et al., 2011. Dengue transmission in the Asia-Pacific region: Impact of climate change and socio-environmental factors. Tropical Medicine & International Health 16, 598–607.

Bhatt, S., et al., 2013. The global distribution and burden of dengue. Nature 496, 504–507. doi:10.1038/nature12060.

Burke, D.S., Nisalak, A., Johnson, D.E., Scott, R.M., 1988. A prospective study of dengue infections in Bangkok. The American Journal of Tropical Medicine and Hygiene 38, 172–180.

Cao-Lormeau, V.M., Roche, C., Musso, D., et al., 2014. Dengue virus type 3, South Pacific Islands, 2013. Emerging Infectious Diseases 20 (6), 1034–1036.

Carrasco, L.R., Lee, L.K., Lee, V.J., et al., 2011. Economic impact of dengue illness and the cost-effectiveness of future vaccination programs in Singapore. PLOS Neglected Tropical Diseases 5, e1426.

Chambers, T.J., Hahn, C.S., Galler, R., Rice, C.M., 1990. Flavivirus genome organization, expression, and replication. Annual Review of Microbiology 44, 649–688. Pmid: 2174669.

Chan, K.S., Chang, J.S., Chang, K., et al., 2009. Effect of serotypes on clinical manifestations of dengue fever in adults. Journal of Microbiology, Immunology and Infection 42, 471–478.

Chen, H.L., Lin, S.R., Liu, H.F., et al., 2008. Evolution of dengue virus type 2 during two consecutive outbreaks with an increase in severity in southern Taiwan in 2001–2002. The American Journal of Tropical Medicine and Hygiene 79 (4), 495–505. pmid:18840735.

Chen, R., Vasilakis, N., 2011. Dengue – Quo tu et quo vadis? Viruses 3, 1562–1608.

Chen, W.J., Wu, H.R., Chiou, S.S., 2003. E/NS1 modifications of dengue 2 virus after serial passages in mammalian and/or mosquito cells. Intervirology 46 (5), 289–295.

Cleland, J.B., Bradley, B., McDonald, W., 1918. Dengue fever in Australia. The Journal of Hygiene 16 (4), 319–418.

Cleland, J.B., Bradley, B., McDonald, W., 1919. Further experiments in the etiology of dengue fever. The Journal of Hygiene 18 (3), 217–254.

Coffey, L.L., Mertens, E., Brehin, A.C., et al., 2009. Human genetic determinants of dengue virus susceptibility. Microbes and Infection 11 (2), 143–156. pmid:19121645.

Diehlmann, H., 1999. Laboratory Rearing Of Mosquitoes Using a Hemotek Feeding System. Hronov: Czech Republic Grafické závody.

Fried, J.R., Gibbons, R.V., Kalayanarooj, S., et al., 2010. Serotype-specific differences in the risk of dengue hemorrhagic fever: An analysis of data collected in Bangkok, Thailand from 1994 to 2006. PLOS Neglected Tropical Diseases 4, e617.

Gan, V.C., Tan, L.K., Lye, D.C., et al., 2014. Diagnosing dengue at the point-of-care: Utility of a rapid combined diagnostic kit in Singapore. PLOS ONE. 9 (3), e90037. pmid:24646519.

Governments of Malaysia and Singapore, 2014. Joint Media Release: UNITEDengue Cross-Border Data Sharing Provides Countries With Timely Risk Alerts. Singapore: National Environment Agency.

Green, S., Rothman, A., 2006. Immunopathological mechanisms in dengue and dengue hemorrhagic fever. Current Opinion in Infectious Diseases 19 (5), 429–436. pmid:16940865.

Guzman, M.G., Alvarez, M., Halstead, S.B., 2013. Secondary infection as a risk factor for dengue hemorrhagic fever/dengue shock syndrome: An historical perspective and role of antibody-dependent enhancement of infection. Archives of Virology 158, 1445–1459.

Guzman, M.G., Alvarez, A., Vazquez, S., et al., 2012. Epidemiological studies on dengue virus type 3 in Playa municipality, Havana, Cuba, 2001–2002. International Journal of Infectious Diseases 16, e198–e203.

Guzman, M.G., Deubel, V., Pelegrino, J.L., et al., 1995. Partial nucleotide and amino acid sequences of the envelope and the envelope/non-structural protein-1 gene junction of four dengue-2 virus strains isolated during the 1981 Cuban epidemic. The American Journal of Tropical Medicine and Hygiene 52 (3), 241–246. pmid:7694966.

Guzman, M.G., Kouri, G., 2003. Dengue and dengue hemorrhagic fever in the Americas: Lessons and challenges. Journal of Clinical Virology 27, 1–13.

Guzman, M.G., Kouri, G., Valdes, L., et al., 2000. Epidemiologic studies on dengue in Santiago de Cuba, 1997. American Journal of Epidemiology 152, 793–799. discussion 804.

Hall, T.A., 1999. BioEdit: A user-friendly biological sequence alignment editor and analysis program for Windows 95/98/NT. Nucleic Acids Symposium Series 41, 95–98.

Halsey, E.S., Marks, M.A., Gotuzzo, E., et al., 2012. Correlation of serotype-specific dengue virus infection with clinical manifestations. PLOS Neglected Tropical Diseases 6, e1638.

Halstead, S.B., 2008. Dengue virus-mosquito interactions. Annual Review of Entomology 53, 273–291.

Han, H.K., Ang, L.W., Tay, J., 2012. Review of Dengue Serotype Surveillance Programme in Singapore. Epidemiological News Bulletin.

Hapuarachchi, H.C., Chua, R.C.R., Shi, Y., et al., 2015. Clinical outcome and genetic differences within a monophyletic Dengue virus type 2 populations. PLOS ONE 10 (3), e0121696.

Hapuarachchi, H.C., Koo, C., Kek, R., et al., 2016. Intra-epidemic evolutionary dynamics of a Dengue virus type 1 population reveal mutant spectra that correlate with disease transmission. Scientific Reports 6, 22592.

Holmes, E.C., Burch, S.S., 2000. The causes and consequences of genetic variation in dengue virus. Trends in Microbiology 8 (2), 74–77. pmid:10664600.

Holmes, E.C., Twiddy, S.S., 2003. The origin, emergence and evolutionary genetics of dengue virus. Infection, Genetics and Evolution 3 (1), 19–28. pmid:12797969.

Horwood, P., Bande, G., Dagina, R., et al., 2013. The threat of chikungunya in Oceania. Western Pacific Surveillance and Response 4 (2), 8–10.

Jupp, P.G., 1976. The susceptibility of four South African species of Culex to West Nile and Sindbis viruses by two different infecting methods. Mosquito News 36, 166–173.

Khor, C.C., Chau, T.N., Pang, J., et al., 2011. Genome-wide association study identifies susceptibility loci for dengue shock syndrome at MICB and PLCE1. Nature Genetics 43 (11), 1139–1141. pmid:22001756.

Kindhauser, M.K., Allen, T., Frank, V., Santhana, R.S., Dye, C., 2016. Zika: The origin and spread of a mosquito-borne virus. Bull World Health Organization. (submitted) 10.2471/BLT.16.171082.

Kramer, L.D., Ebel, G.D., 2003. Dynamics of flavivirus infection in mosquitoes. Advances in Virus Research 60, 187–232.

Kumaria, R., 2009. Correlation of disease spectrum among four dengue serotypes: A five years hospital based study from India. Brazilian Journal of Infectious Diseases 14, 141–146.

Kutsuna, S., Kato, Y., Moi, M.L., et al., 2015. Autochthonous dengue fever, Tokyo, Japan, 2014. Emerging Infectious Diseases 21 (3), 517–520.

Lai, Y.L., Chung, Y.K., Tan, H.C., et al., 2007. Cost-effective real-time reverse transcriptase PCR (RT-PCR) to screen for Dengue virus followed by rapid single-tube multiplex RT-PCR for serotyping of the virus. Journal of Clinical Microbiology 45 (3), 935–941. pmid:17215345.

Lee, K.S., et al., 2012. Dengue virus surveillance in Singapore reveals high viral diversity through multiple introductions and in situ evolution. Infection, Genetics and Evolution 12, 77–85.

Lee, K.S., Lai, Y.L., Lo, S., et al., 2010. Dengue virus surveillance for early warning, Singapore. Emerging Infectious Diseases 16, 847–849.

Leitmeyer, K.C., Vaughn, D.W., Watts, D.M., et al., 1999. Dengue virus structural differences that correlate with pathogenesis. Journal of Virology 73 (6), 4738–4747. pmid:10233934.

Ler, T.S., Ang, L.W., Yap, G.S.L., et al., 2011. Epidemiological characteristics of the 2005 and 2007 dengue epidemics in Singapore – similarities and distinctions. Western Pacific Surveillance and Response J2, 24–29.

Meyer, R.P., Hardy, J.L., Presser, S.B., 1983. Comparative vector competence of Culex tarsalis and Culex quinquefasciatus from the Coachella, Imperial, and San Joaquin Valleys of California for St. Louis encephalitis virus. The American Journal of Tropical Medicine and Hygiene 32 (2), 305–311.

Miller, B.R., 1987. Increased yellow fever virus infection and dissemination rates in Aedes aegypti mosquitoes orally exposed to freshly grown virus. Transactions of the Royal Society of Tropical Medicine and Hygiene 81 (6), 1011–1012.

Ministry of Health, 2012. Communicable Disease Surveillance in Singapore 2011. Singapore: Ministry of Health.

Murrell, B., Wertheim, J.O., Moola, S., et al., 2012. Detecting individual sites subject to episodic diversifying selection. PLOS Genetics 8 (7), e1002764.

Ng, L.-C., Y-k, C., Koo, C., et al., 2013. dengue outbreaks in Singapore and Malaysia caused by different viral strains. The American Journal of Tropical Medicine and Hygiene 2015 (92), 1150–1155.

Ng, L.C., 2011. Challenges in dengue surveillance and control (Editorial). Western Pacific Surveillance and Response Journal 2, 1–3.

Nguyet, M.N., Duong, T.H., Trung, V.T., et al., 2013. Host and viral features of human dengue cases shape the population of infected and infectious Aedes aegypti mosquitoes. Proceedings of the National Academy of Sciences of the United States of America 110 (22), 9072–9077.

Nisalak, A., Endy, T.P., Nimmannitya, S., et al., 2003. Serotype-specific dengue virus circulation and dengue disease in Bangkok, Thailand from 1973 to 1999. The American Journal of Tropical Medicine and Hygiene 68, 191–202.

OMalley, M.A., 2016. The ecological virus. Studies in History and Philosophy of Biological and Biomedical. Sciences 59, 71–79.

Pandey, B.D., Igarashi, A., 2000. Severity-related molecular differences among nineteen strains of dengue type 2 viruses. Medical Microbiology and Immunology 44 (3), 179–188. pmid:10789505.

Pok, K.Y., Squires, R.C., Tan, L.K., et al., 2015a. First round of external quality assessment of dengue diagnostics in the WHO Western Pacific Region, 2013. Western Pacific Surveillance and Response Journal 6 (2), 73–81.

Pok, K.Y., Squires, R.C., Tan, L.K., et al., 2015b. First round of external quality assessment of dengue diagnostics in the WHO Western Pacific Region, 2013. Western Pacific Surveillance and Response. 6 (2), 73–81. doi:10.5365/wpsar.2015.6.1.017.

Pond, S.L., Frost, S.D., Muse, S.V., 2005. HyPhy: Hypothesis testing using phylogenies. Bioinformatics 21 (5), 676–679. pmid:15509596.

Prat, C.M., Flusin, O., Panella, A., et al., 2014. Evaluation of commercially available serologic diagnostic tests for chikungunya virus. Emerging Infectious Diseases 20 (12), 2129–2132. doi:10.3201/eid2012.141269.

Rabaa, M.A., Ty Hang, V.T., Wills, B., et al., 2010. Phylogeography of recently emerged DENV-2 in southern Vietnam. PLOS Neglected Tropical Diseases 4, e766.

RCoreTeam, 2013. R: A Language and Environment for Statistical Computing. R Foundation for Statistical Computing. Austria: Vienna, Available at: http://www.R-project.org/.

Richards, S.L., Pesko, K., Alto, B.W., Mores, C.N., 2007. Reduced infection in mosquitoes exposed to blood meals containing previously frozen flaviviruses. Virus Research 129, 224–227.

Rico-Hesse, R., Harrison, L.M., Salas, R.A., *et al.*, 1997a. Origins of dengue type 2 viruses associated with increased pathogenicity in the Americas. Virology 230 (2), 244–251. pmid:9143280.

Rico-Hesse, R., Harrison, L.M., Salas, R.A., *et al.*, 1997b. Origins of dengue type 2 viruses associated with increased pathogenicity in the Americas. Virology 230, 244–251.

Rico-Hesse, R., 2003. Microevolution and virulence of dengue viruses. Advances in Virus Research 59, 315–341.

Ritchie, S.A., 2014. Dengue vector bionomics: Why Aedes aegypti is such a good vector. In: Gubler, D.J., Ooi, E.E., Vasudevan, S., Farrar, J. (Eds.), Dengue and Dengue Hemorrhagic Fever. Oxfordshire: CABI, pp. 455–480.

Rodhain, F., Rosen, L., 1997. Mosquito vectors and dengue virus-vector relationships. In: Gubler, D.J., Kuno, G. (Eds.), Dengue and Dengue Hemorrhagic Fever. Cambridge, MA: CABI Publishing, pp. 47–60.

Rutledge, L.C., Ward, R.A., Gould, D.J., 1964. Studies on the feeding response of mosquitoes to nutritive solutions in a new membrane feeder. Mosquito News 24, 407–419.

Sangkawibha, N., Rojanasuphot, S., Ahandrik, S., *et al.*, 1984. Risk factors in dengue shock syndrome: A prospective epidemiologic study in Rayong, Thailand. I. The 1980 outbreak. American Journal of Epidemiology 120, 653–669.

Shepard, D.S., Undurraga, E.A., Lees, R.S., *et al.*, 2012. Use of multiple data sources to estimate the economic cost of dengue illness in Malaysia. The American Journal of Tropical Medicine and Hygiene 87, 796–805.

Siler, J.E., Hall, M.W., Hitchens, A.P., 1926. Dengue: Its history, epidemiology, mechanism of transmission, etiology, clinical manifestations, immunity and prevention. Philippine Journal of Science 29, 1–302.

Simmons, J.S., St John, J.H., Reynolds, F.H.K., 1931. Experimental studies of dengue. Philippine Journal of Science 44, 1–247.

Soh, L.T., Squires, R.C., Tan, L.K., *et al.*, 2016. External quality assessment of dengue and chikungunya diagnostics in the Asia Pacific region, 2015. Western Pacific Surveillance and Response Journal: WPSAR 7 (2), 26–34.

Suaya, J.A., Shepard, D.S., Siqueira, J.B., *et al.*, 2009. Cost of dengue cases in eight countries in the Americas and Asia: A prospective study. The American Journal of Tropical Medicine and Hygiene 80, 846–855.

Tamura, K., Stecher, G., Peterson, D., Filipski, A., Kumar, S., 2013. MEGA6: Molecular Evolutionary Genetics Analysis version 6.0. Molecular Biology and Evolution 30 (12), 2725–2729. Pmid:24132122.

Tan, C.H., Wong, P.S., Li, M.Z., *et al.*, 2016. Membrane feeding of dengue patient's blood as a substitute for direct skin feeding in studying Aedes-dengue virus interaction. Parasites & Vectors 9, 211.

Tuiskunen, A., Monteil, V., Plumet, S., *et al.*, 2011. Phenotypic and genotypic characterization of dengue virus isolates differentiates dengue fever and dengue hemorrhagic fever from dengue shock syndrome. Archives of Virology 156 (11), 2023–2032.

Twiddy, S.S., Woelk, C.H., Holmes, E.C., 2002. Phylogenetic evidence for adaptive evolution of dengue viruses in nature. Journal of General Virology 83 (Pt 7), 1679–1689. pmid:12075087.

Vaughn, D.W., Green, S., Kalayanarooj, S., *et al.*, 2000. Dengue viremia titer, antibody response pattern, and virus serotype correlate with disease severity. The Journal of Infectious Diseases 181 (1), 2–9. pmid:10608744.

Vaughn, D.W., Green, S., Kalayanarooj, S., *et al.*, 2000. Dengue viremia titer, antibody response pattern, and virus serotype correlate with disease severity. The Journal of Infectious Diseases 181, 2–9.

Wang, W.K., Chen, H.L., Yang, C.F., *et al.*, 2006. Slower rates of clearance of viral load and virus-containing immune complexes in patients with dengue hemorrhagic fever. Clinical Infectious Diseases 43 (8), 1023–1030. pmid:16983615.

Weaver, S.C., Lecuit, M., 2015. Chikungunya virus and the global spread of a mosquito-borne disease. The New England Journal of Medicine 372 (13), 1231–1239. 10.1056/NEJMra1406035.

Whitehead, S.S., Hanley, K.A., Blaney Jr, J.E., *et al.*, 2003. Substitution of the structural genes of dengue virus type 4 with those of type 2 results in chimeric vaccine candidates which are attenuated for mosquitoes, mice, and rhesus monkeys. Vaccine 21 (27–30), 4307–4316. pmid:14575763.

Whitehorn, J., Simmons, C.P., 2011. The pathogenesis of dengue. Vaccine 29 (42), 7221–7228. pmid:21781999.

WHO, 2009. Dengue: Guidelines for Diagnosis, Treatment, Prevention and Control, New ed. Geneva: World Health Organization.

Wilder-Smith, A., Gubler, D.J., 2008. Geographic expansion of dengue: The impact of international travel. The Medical Clinics of North America 92, 1377–1390.

Yap, G., Pok, K.Y., Lai, Y.L., *et al.*, 2010. Evaluation of Chikungunya diagnostic assays: Differences in sensitivity of serology assays in two independent outbreaks. PLOS Neglected Tropical Diseases 4 (7), e753. doi:10.1371/journal.pntd.0000753.

Yung, C.F., Lee, K.S., Thein, T.L., *et al.*, 2015. Dengue serotype-specific differences in clinical manifestation, laboratory parameters and risk of severe disease in adults, Singapore. The American Journal of Tropical Medicine and Hygiene. https://www.ncbi.nlm.nih.gov/pubmed/25825386.

Zhang, C., Mammen Jr, M.P., Chinnawirotpisan, P., *et al.*, 2006. Structure and age of genetic diversity of dengue virus type 2 in Thailand. Journal of General Virology 87, 873–883.

Zuker, M., 2003. Mfold web server for nucleic acid folding and hybridization prediction. Nucleic Acids Research 31 (13), 3406–3415. pmid:12824337.

Relevant Website

www.unitedengue.org
UniteDengue.

Biographical Sketch

Dr. Vijayaraghava Seshadri Sundararajan has been an advisor to Bioclues.org, and has organized international conferences/workshops.

Mapping the Environmental Microbiome

Lena Takayasu and **Wataru Suda,** RIKEN Center for Integrative Medical Sciences, Yokohama City, Japan
Masahira Hattori, RIKEN Center for Integrative Medical Sciences, Yokohama City, Japan and Waseda University, Tokyo, Japan

Introduction

On the earth, highly diverse bacteria adaptively reside in various environments from animal and plant body sites to extreme environments such as the deep ocean and hot springs. The total number of bacterial cells on the earth are estimated to be $4\text{--}6*10^{30}$, suggesting that the total amount of cellular carbon from bacteria exceeds that of plants and animals (Whitman et al., 1998). Bacteria inhabiting natural environments such as oceans, fresh water, and soil play important roles in global resource renewal cycles such as the carbon cycle and nitrogen cycle by making organics and inorganics available to other living things. On the other hand, animal- and plant-related microbiomes are highly dense compared with environmental microbiomes (Whitman et al., 1998), although total cell numbers are less than those of environmental microbiomes (**Table 1**). Among them, human-associated microbiomes are attracting attention in the medical field, as current studies strongly suggest the profound relationship between the human gut microbiome and host health and disease.

The human microbiomes such as the gut, oral, and skin microbiome are known to be highly body-site-specific and highly variable between individuals (The Human Microbiome Project Consortium, 2012). These characteristic features of human microbiomes are associated with various internal and external factors such as host genetic background, dietary intake, antibiotic use, pregnancy, age, and geography (Benson et al., 2010; Wu et al., 2011; Manichanh et al., 2010; DiGiulio et al., 2015; Yatsunenko et al., 2012; Goodrich et al., 2014). In addition, microbial imbalance, called dysbiosis, was also observed in patients with various diseases such as inflammatory bowel disease (IBD), type 2 diabetes, and obesity (Frank et al., 2007; Qin et al., 2012; Karlsson et al., 2013; Turnbaugh et al., 2009), demonstrating that the structural change in normal microbiomes is linked with diseases and the host homeostasis. Furthermore, in 2013, fecal microbiota transplantation (FMT), in which feces from healthy donors are transplanted to disease-afflicted patients, was first reported to be an effective therapy for chronic colitis caused by *Clostridium difficile*, and since then FMT has been tried for various diseases (Van Nood et al., 2013; Moayyedi et al., 2015). These studies implied that the human gut microbiome is involved in both disease onset and health maintenance. In fact, it was reported that some human gut species regulate differentiation and proliferation of pro- and antiinflammatory T cells (Treg and Th17) in the gut (Atarashi et al., 2013, 2015). However, since the microbial community is composed of numerous species that interact with each other and with host cells with complex mechanisms, elucidating the feature of bacterial community through time and space is required to exactly and deeply understand how the microbial ecosystem is shaped and how it maintains our health by controlling the microbiomes.

Background/Fundamentals

In the 1800s, knowledge on bacterial fermentation and infectious diseases accumulated for the agricultural and medical fields by development of methods for isolating and culturing the bacterial species from the natural environments and host animals/humans. Today, the technologies for DNA analysis have revolutionarily advanced, enabling us to comprehensively evaluate ecological and functional features of the microbial communities and ecosystems, which is represented by a culture-independent metagenomic sequencing of the microbial community using next-generation sequencing (NGS) technologies. We herein present the development and improvement of analytical methods in microbiome research.

Table 1   Order of bacterial cell number on the earth

	Location	Order of Bacterial cell number
Environment	Soil	$10^{29}\text{--}10^{30}$
	Fresh water	10^{26}
	Sea water	10^{29}
Host-related	Human	10^{23}
	Animal	10^{24}
	Plant	10^{26}

Source: Reproduced from Morris, C. E., Kinkel, L.L., 2002. Fifty years of phylosphere microbiology: Significant contributions to research in related fields. In: Lindow, S.E., Hecht-Poinar, E.I., Elliott, V. (Eds.), Phyllosphere Microbiology. St. Paul, Minn: APS Press, pp. 365–375. Phyllosphere microbiology.
Source: Reproduced from Whitman, W.B., Coleman, D.C., Wiebe, W.J., 1998. Prokaryotes: The unseen majority. Proceedings of the National Academy of Sciences of the United States of America 95, 6578–6583. PNAS.

Culture-Based Approach

Pure culture technology by which the specific microbial species are isolated and cultured on agar was established in the 1800s by Pasteur and Koch and others, and since then, microbiologists have intensively performed culture-based studies of pathogenic bacteria causative for human infectious diseases, and microorganisms useful for fermentation such as wine production in agriculture. In 1885, the commensal bacterium *Escherichia coli* was isolated from human feces by Theodor Escherich, and the early anaerobic culturing method succeeded in the pure culture of *Bifidobacterium* in 1899. In the mid-1980s, culture-independent DNA-based technologies such as bacterial 16S ribosomal RNA (rRNA) gene analysis were developed, and revealed that many more bacteria existed in environments including the human gut than those isolated by the conventional cultural methods. For example, only about 0.1% of bacteria in the ocean and 0.3% in the soil could be cultivated (Amann *et al.*, 1995). Thus, naturally occurring microbes include many species difficult to culture in the laboratory (Staley and Konopka, 1985).

DNA-Based Approach

In 1978, Carl Woese proposed three domains of life (bacteria, archaea, and eukaryotes) based on ribosomal RNA genes of which the gene products RNA molecules are essential components of ribosome in the cell. In the microbial ecological study, the 16S rRNA gene sequence has been extensively used to be a molecular marker in the taxonomy of prokaryotes (Woese and Fox, 1977; Woese, 1987). The first culture-independent 16S rRNA gene analysis of the environmental microbiome was reported in 1990 (Giovannoni *et al.*, 1990). The paper showed that the bacterial diversity estimated by the 16S gene data far exceeded that by the culture-dependent approach.

Another incredible advance in the culture-independent approach is use of the NGS technologies in place of the traditional Sanger method-based sequencing coupled with the recombinant DNA technology, which began around 2005, leading to the high-throughput analysis of 16S rRNA gene sequences from community samples with low cost. The NGS technologies have also determined numerous 16S rRNA gene and genome sequences of tens of thousands of microbes isolated individually, of which the databases are useful for precise assignment of the observed 16S sequences to known bacterial taxa by sequence similarity search, establishing a solid way to elucidate the overall microbial community structure.

However, it is difficult for the 16S rRNA gene analysis to obtain or infer the community's functional features such as metabolism of various biological compounds. To uncover the functionality of the microbial community, the metagenomic analysis based on whole genome shotgun sequencing was developed as the third method, in which many of the microbial gene sequences in the community can be randomly and comprehensively determined (Venter *et al.*, 2004; Tyson *et al.*, 2004). For the human gut microbiome, metagenomic sequencing was performed by the traditional Sanger method in the early days (Gill *et al.*, 2006; Kurokawa *et al.*, 2007), and thereafter by NGS technologies in 2009 and 2010 (Turnbaugh *et al.*, 2009; Qin *et al.*, 2010). Gene sequences can be assigned to the function by similarity search to public databases such as KEGG (Kyoto Encyclopedia of Genes and Genomes) and COG (Clusters of Orthologous Groups) (Kanehisa *et al.*, 2002; Tatusov *et al.*, 1997). In addition, the NCBI genome database composed of numbers of the individual microbial genome sequences has also been developed (see "Relevant Website section"). Particularly, the genome database of human-derived cultured microbes allowed us to analyze not only the gene composition but also the taxonomic composition in human microbiomes by directly mapping metagenomic sequences to the microbial genomes.

Application

We herein showed two popular methods using 16S rRNA gene and metagenomic sequences produced by NGS for human microbiome research.

16S rRNA Gene Analysis

The 16S rRNA gene (16S) analysis may be used most frequently for investigating the microbial diversity and composition in microbial communities coupled with the subsequent computational analysis of 16S sequences. The 16S rRNA gene is about 1500 bp long and contains conserved regions (functionally important) and nine alternatively located variable regions (V1–V9; functionally less important) among bacterial species (Andersson *et al.*, 2008; **Fig. 1**). The sequence similarity or diversity in variable regions can be used to discriminate taxonomically different species and to identify the particular species. In the 16S analysis, DNA fragments containing variable regions of almost all bacterial species in the community are simultaneously amplified by universal PCR primer sets annealed to the conserved regions.

The overall process of typical 16S analysis using the MiSeq sequencing system was shown in **Fig. 1**. MiSeq is the NGS that produces reads of ~350-bp covering at least two variable regions (e.g., V1–V2 in **Fig. 1**) by paired-end sequencing. Since MiSeq and other NGS sequencers generate tens of millions of 16S reads with one sequencing run, it is possible to sequence 16S amplicons from multiple different samples simultaneously in one sequencing run by using different sets of barcoded universal primers for the samples. The 16S reads of several thousands to ten thousands per sample are then subjected to quality check to remove low-quality reads including ones less than threshold of the average quality value (QV < 20) of base-calling, lacking PCR

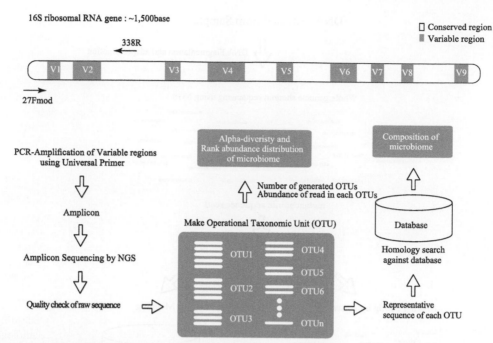

Fig. 1 Outline flowchart of 16S rRNA gene analysis.

primer sequences, and possible chimerisms. After trimming PCR primer sequences from the filter-passed reads, high-quality reads are clustered with a 97% sequence identity to obtain taxonomically different groups called operational taxonomic units (OTUs), which correspond to the bacterial "species." The number of observed OTUs represents the community's species richness (called α diversity), the number of 16S reads in an OTU approximates the abundance of the OTU, and their ratio represents the relative composition of all the OTUs. It is noted that overestimation of the OTU number is generally observed in the clustering of NGS reads with the sequencing error rate as high as ∼0.5%. Therefore, clustering of more 16S reads with the high error rate generates OTUs greater than the actual species number (Kim *et al.*, 2013). The bacterial taxa are assigned for the OTUs by similarity search of the OTU-representative 16S reads to the public 16S databases (Ribosomal Database Project (Cole *et al.*, 2008) and Green genes (DeSantis *et al.*, 2006)) and the NCBI genome database (also see below). Several software programs such as QIIME are useful for 16S analysis (Caporaso *et al.*, 2010). Direct mapping of all the 16S reads to the 16S and genome databases without making OTUs can also be used to analyze the species diversity and richness in the microbial community (Miyake *et al.*, 2015).

For evaluation of the overall structural similarity between two or more bacterial communities (called β diversity), the UniFrac distance analysis was developed for the 16S data (Lozupone and Knight, 2005). In this analysis, the similarity of phylogenetic trees constructed from the OTU sequences between the communities is calculated as UniFrac distance based on the common branch length between the samples. The UniFrac distance ranging from 0 to 1 represents 100% and 0% similarity between the communities. Furthermore, principle coordinate analysis (PCoA) based on UniFrac distance is also a useful tool to visualize the overall structural similarity between the samples (also see below). Multivariate analysis such as permutational multivariate analysis of variance (PERMANOVA) is used to test the statistical significance of the similarity and dissimilarity between different communities.

Metagenomic Analysis

As described above, the 16S analysis provides the microbial profiles in the communities, but it is not suitable to obtain functional features of the communities. On the other hand, metagenomic sequencing can collect many gene sequences representing the function of microbial communities.

The process of metagenomic analysis is shown in **Fig. 2**. Microbial DNA prepared from the community is subjected to whole-genome shotgun sequencing by NGS. Tens of millions of metagenomic reads of ∼300 bp accounting for a total of several gigabases per sample are obtained and filtered with the quality check to remove low-quality reads similar to the 16S analysis. There are two processes for microbial and functional profiling in the metagenomic analysis. For the functional analysis, metagenomic reads are assembled with appropriate assemblers such as Newbler to obtain nonredundant microbial sequences/contigs, from which protein-coding genes can be predicted by several prediction software programs such as MetaGeneAnnotator (Noguchi *et al.*, 2008). The predicted genes are then subjected to similarity search to functional databases of genes and metabolic pathways such as COG and KEGG to assign and classify the genes into functions. The quantification of the identified genes is performed by mapping metagenomic reads to the genes. For the microbial analysis, taxonomic assignment and quantification of the microbial abundance

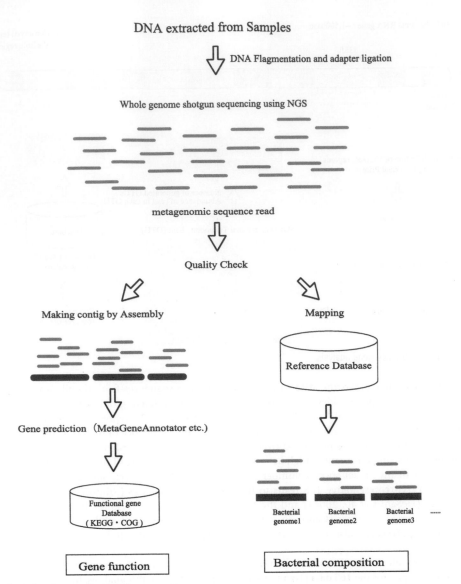

Fig. 2 Outline flowchart of metagenomic analysis.

can be conducted by mapping metagenomic reads to the NCBI genome databases compiled with more than 20,000 individual genomes including ~3000 human microbes. Metagenomic analysis usually requires a high-spec computation system to handle larger datasets than the 16S analysis. For the high-performance computational analysis, cloud server systems such as MG-RAST have been developed, in which the quality check and calculation of the community's structures regarding microbial and functional profiles can be carried out automatically (Meyer et al., 2008).

Most of metagenomic sequencing analyses have used NGS sequencers such as Illumina HiSeq and MiSeq because those rapidly collect large amounts of sequence data with low cost. However, since these sequencers produce short reads of ~300 bp, and the assembly of them generates relatively short contigs possibly containing misassembled contigs mainly due to the presence of high-similarity sequences such as 16S rRNA genes and horizontally transferred genes within and between microbial genomes in the community. Therefore, short-read assembly includes some ambiguity in reconstruction of individual genomes and contigs. To improve these problems encountered in standard short-read sequencing, several computational tools have been developed for reconstruction of the high-quality genomes by binning short contigs based on coabundance across samples (Nielsen et al., 2014; Alneberg et al., 2014; Kang et al., 2015; Cleary et al., 2015), and by incorporating independently preassembled synthetic reads of ~10 kb in assembly of short reads, which improved the assembly accuracy and the contig length (Sharon et al., 2015; Kuleshov et al., 2016). Use of long-read NGS sequencers such as PacBio and MinION that produce longer reads (>10 kb) than the short-read sequencers is also an alternative approach to improve the outcomes in metagenomic analysis (Leonard et al., 2014; Tsai et al., 2016). Actually, long-read sequencing facilitated accurately assembled long contigs for a wide range of individual microbial and eukaryotic genomes (Rasko et al., 2011; Chin et al., 2013; Chaisson et al., 2015).

Illustrative Example(s) or Case Studies

Diversity Index

There are several indices to evaluate ecological profiles of the microbial community structure. The simplest diversity index is the number of distinct OTUs/species detected in 16S analysis and the number of genomes mapped by metagenomic reads in metagenomic analysis (see section "Application"). In 16S analysis, unseen novel species can be included as unassigned OTUs that have <70% identity with known species, while only known species/genomes having high similarity to metagenomic reads are identified but original genomes/species of unmapped reads are still unknown in metagenomic analysis. Also, estimation of the microbial abundance may be more or less influenced by the PCR bias at the amplification step of the target 16S rRNA gene using universal primers in 16S analysis, while metagenomic analysis includes no PCR step at all. These differences may cause some discrepancy in the outcomes between these two methods. Other diversity indices, Chao1 and ACE, are also used for estimating the maximum OTU/species number by extrapolation of the observed OTU number, respectively (Chao, 1987; Chazdon et al., 1998).

The Shannon index is also a popular metric for evaluation of the community structure, in which both the species richness and the abundance evenness are considered. The Shannon index is calculated based on Shannon's information entropy, that is, the more equally distributed the microbial abundance, the higher the score of the index when the species richness is the same.

We compared the OTU (see section "16S rRNA Gene Analysis") number, the Shannon index, and the number of phyla based on our in-house 16S datasets among 39 microbiomes including 23 gut microbiomes of orangutans (domestic zoos), humans (Japanese healthy adults), pigs (domestic farms), experimental mice (conventional), and experimental rats (conventional); foliar microbiomes of *Cerasus* and *Ginkgo*, and four soil microbiomes from a potato field; and five samples from river fresh water (Saitama, Japan) and five samples from oceanic water (Saga, Japan) (**Fig. 3**). The soil communities showed the highest diversity in the three indices followed by the sea and river communities. The diversity in the sea communities was slightly higher than that of river in all three indices. The three indices also revealed the tendency of the diversity to be relatively lower in the host-related microbiomes than the environmental microbiomes, suggesting less complex community structure of the host-related microbiomes than the environmental ones. These differences also suggest that the host-related microbiomes have selective pressures on the colonization by host physiology including immunity compared with the environmental microbiomes.

Cumulative Relative Abundance Distribution

We observed the cumulative relative abundance distribution (CRAD) shared among various types of human gut microbiomes from healthy adults, infants, and disease-afflicted patients where the taxonomic composition was significantly varied (Takayasu et al., 2017b). The CRADs showed linear relationship between the population size of bacterial species (X) and the existing bacterial species number holding more than X in a log-log plot, which can be approximated by power law function.

CRADs of the 39 microbiomes described above also indicated the linearity in a log-log plot (**Fig. 4**), suggesting that all of the microbial communities from environments, animal guts, and plants also follow the power law. However, the slopes of the CRADs corresponding to the power exponent of power law function were distinct ranging from 0.6 and 1.5 among the microbiomes, in which the soil community was characterized by the highest power exponent, and the human microbiome by the smallest power exponent. These data suggested that the exponent of CRAD has the tendency of correlation with the α diversity indices represented by the species richness and the Shannon index.

Taxonomic Assignment

We showed the average phylum-level microbial composition of 10 communities from the different hosts and environments described in 4.1 based on 16S data in **Fig. 5**, respectively. The species assignment of the 16S OTUs was performed with similarity search with a 70% identity to the databases. The soil community was dominated by higher number of phyla than the others, as

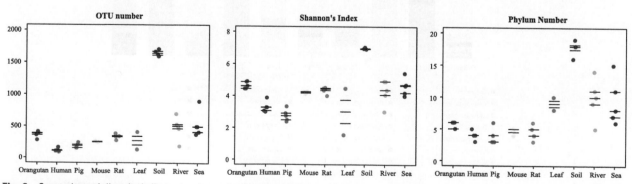

Fig. 3 Comparison of diversity indices of various microbiomes.

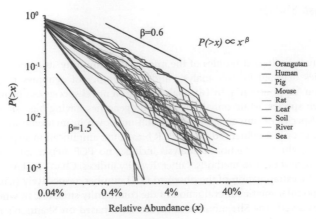

Fig. 4 Cumulative relative abundance distributions of various microbiomes.

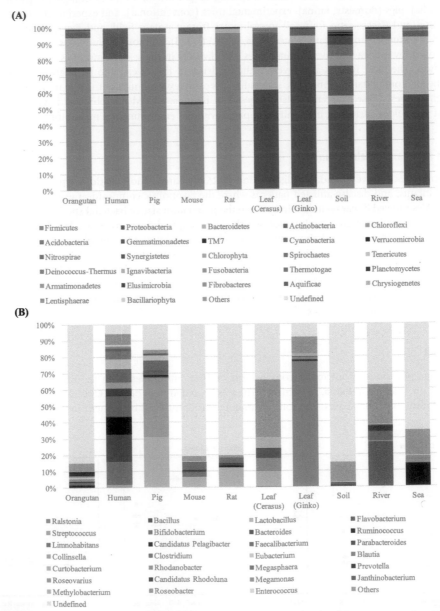

Fig. 5 The average bacterial composition of nine microbiomes based on 16S data. (A) Nine microbiomes at the phylum level. (B) Nine microbiomes at the genus level.

shown in **Fig. 3**. The environmental microbiomes were prominently dominated by the species belonging to the phylum Proteobacteria, while the host-related microbiomes were dominated by the species in Firmicutes. Four major phyla, Proteobacteria, Bacteroidetes, Actinobacteria, and Firmicutes occupied up to ~92% of the total abundance in all microbiomes except for soil, for which the combined abundance of the top four phyla (Proteobacteria, Actinobacteria, Chloroflexi, and Acidobacteria) was around ~76% of the total abundance. Several phyla such as Gemmatimonadetes and Nitrospirae were characteristically detected in the soil microbiomes. The hydrosphere microbiomes (river and sea) were abundant in two phyla, Proteobacteria and Bacteroidetes, different from the leaf and soil microbiomes. On the other hand, the animal gut microbiomes were dominated by the four phyla, Firmicutes, Bacteroidetes, Actinobacteria, and Proteobacteria up to 99% or more with the strong selective pressure on the colonization as described above.

However, at the genus-level species assignment, many of the microbiomes were composed of many of the unidentified species distinct from known genera, particularly for orangutans, mice, rats, soil, and sea (**Fig. 5(B)**). This poor genus-level assignment may be largely due to an insufficient number of bacterial strains isolated from these environments and the high abundance of phylogenetically distant species from known species in these communities. Thus, taxonomic analysis based on the 16S and metagenomic data largely depends on the quality of the databases, although the overall structural or functional features can be evaluated from these data. In contrast, the database of human microbes has been systematically constructed by an effort of the Human Microbiome Project for the current 10 years, in which genomes of ~3000 human microbes were determined. Similarity search of human microbiome 16S data to the public 16S and genome databases was performed with the range from 97% to 70% identities. Almost all of the OTUs can be assigned to known phyla with a $\geq 70\%$ identity, 60% of them to genera with a $\geq 94\%$ identity, and 30% of them to species with a $\geq 97\%$ identity, while less than 20% of murine gut OTUs can be assigned to known genera and species (**Fig. 6(A)**). The combined abundance of the assigned OTUs in the human gut microbiome accounted for over 80% of the total abundance at the genus and species levels, indicating that the majority of dominant species in the human gut microbiome were uncovered and the species yet-unidentified might be minor members (**Fig. 6(B)**). The sufficient taxonomic assignment of pig microbiomes may be because the highly abundant species were coincidentally shared between human and pig microbiomes. Again, poor species assignment of mouse, rat, and orangutan microbiomes at the genus level may be due to insufficient 16S and genome databases and phylogenetic differences in the constituted taxa between gut microbiomes of these animals and humans, similar to the environmental microbiomes mentioned above. For taxonomic assignment in metagenome analysis, metagenomic reads are directly mapped to known genomes in the genome databases with a $\geq 95\%$ identity and a $\geq 90\%$ length coverage. The reads mapped to known genomes account for ~70% of the total reads in human gut microbiomes (Nishijima *et al.*, 2016).

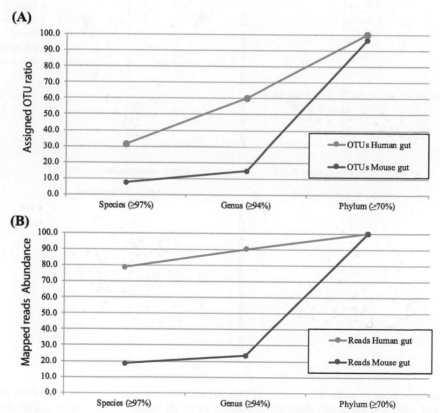

Fig. 6 Taxonomic assignment of 16S data of human and mouse gut microbiomes. (A) Ratios of OTUs taxonomically assigned at the species, genus, and phylum levels. (B) Ratios of 16S reads taxonomically assigned at the species, genus, and phylum levels.

Multivariate Analysis Based on Unifrac Distance

We herein show three examples of multivariate analysis based on the Unifrac distance calculated from 16S data. The UniFrac distance-based PCoA of the nine microbiome samples is shown in **Fig. 7(A)**. The results revealed that the gut samples from the same hosts tended to aggregate to make independent clusters both in the weighted and unweighted UniFrac distance analyses, respectively, in which clusters of the human, orangutan, and pig gut samples were close to each other, but distant from those of the rodent (mouse and rat) gut samples, which were close to each other in the unweighted UniFrac analysis. All of the four environmental samples clearly form a cluster distinct from the gut samples both in the weighted and unweighted UniFrac analyses. The unweighted UniFrac distance analysis considers the presence or absence of the phylogenetically close OTUs/species between the samples, while the weighted UniFrac distance considers differences in the abundance of commonly existing OTUs/species between the samples (Lozupone and Knight, 2005). The present data suggested that the human, orangutan, and pig gut microbiomes were relatively similar to each other in the species members compared with the rodent gut microbiomes, both of which had similar species members. The human and orangutan

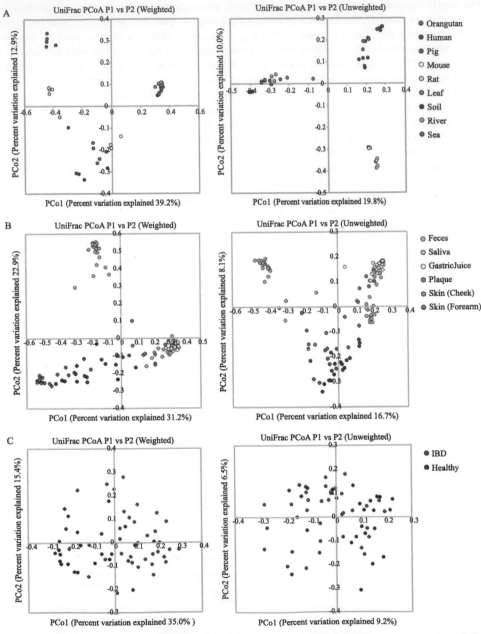

Fig. 7 UniFrac distance-based PCoA of various microbiomes. (A) Weighted and unweighted UniFrac distance-based PCoA of nine microbiomes (orangutans, humans, pigs, mice, rats, leaves, soil, river water, and oceanic water). (B) Weighted and unweighted UniFrac distance-based PCoA of human microbiomes from feces, saliva, gastric juice, plaque, skin (cheek), and skin (forearm). (C) Weighted and unweighted UniFrac distance-based PCoA of human salivary microbiomes from IBD patients and healthy subjects.

gut microbiomes also had relatively similar species abundance, but differed from the pig gut microbiomes in the species abundance. Similarly, although the mouse and rat gut microbiomes had relatively similar species members, the species abundance was different between them. The four environmental microbiomes had relatively similar species members and abundance compared with the different gut microbiomes. In addition, the high similarity between the human and orangutan microbiome structures suggested that the host's genetics more or less contributed to shaping of the gut microbiomes (Goodrich *et al.*, 2014).

We also showed an example for the UniFrac-based PCoA of human microbiomes from different body sites including gut, saliva, plaque, gastric juice, and two skins (cheek and forearm) in **Fig. 7(B)**. The results revealed that the gut samples formed a distinct cluster from the other samples both in the weighted and unweighted UniFrac distance. The saliva, plaque, and gastric juice samples tended to form clusters relatively similar to each other, suggesting that the two oral microbiomes had relatively close community structure with the gastric microbiomes (Tsuda *et al.*, 2015). The two skin samples also formed a distinct cluster from each other though the inter-individual diversities were relatively high comparing to non-skin samples.

Fig. 7(C) further shows an example for the UniFrac-based PCoA analysis of the salivary microbiomes between healthy individuals and patients with IBD. The results found that both samples were segregated from each other both in the weighted and unweighted UniFrac analyses, indicating the typical dysbiosis of the IBD salivary microbiomes (Said *et al.*, 2013). The differences between the two sample sets showed the statistical significance with P-values <0.01 by Student's t-test.

Periodic Analysis

Several studies have reported the long and short-term periodic changes in the microbial composition of host-related and environmental microbiomes (Kuipers *et al.*, 2000; Thaiss *et al.*, 2014; Takayasu *et al.*, 2017a). A few computational tools have been developed to determine the diurnal periodicity of the microbial abundance in the gut and salivary microbiomes across samples longitudinally collected at time intervals (Hughes *et al.*, 2010; Takayasu *et al.*, 2017a). We herein introduce a method called the periodicity discrimination method (PDM), which uses the Fisher exact test, and can be effective even for small datasets often containing the "zero read" abundance across the samples (Takayasu *et al.*, 2017a). In the PDM, the time series abundance data of each day were first subjected to the min-max normalization, respectively, and the average normalized abundance of each time zone was calculated. Next, the time zones of a day were divided into two groups, and the Fisher exact test p-value was calculated for every combination of the two groups for every possible relative abundance threshold.

We showed diurnal changes in the human salivary microbiome as an example using the PDM. We obtained 16S data from the salivary samples collected from six healthy adults with 4-h intervals for three consecutive days. The periodicity of species abundance in longitudinally collected samples for each individual was evaluated by the PDM. The results revealed that the higher abundant genera tended to have the stronger circadian periodicity, and the genera accounting for 68.4%–89.6% of the total abundance significantly oscillated (**Fig. 8(A)**). The two major phyla, Bacteroidetes and Firmicutes, were found to have the periodicity of ~ 24 h by autocorrelation coefficient analysis (**Fig. 8(B)**). The analysis also revealed that the two highly abundant genera *Prevotella* and *Streptococcus* had the opposite oscillation patterns in which the abundance of *Prevotella* increased exclusively in the morning, while that of *Streptococcus* increased exclusively in the evening in the all six subjects, respectively (**Fig. 8(C)**). We further showed the oscillated patterns in the gene functions of the salivary microbiomes by metagenomic analysis (**Fig. 8(D)**). The functions of salivary microbiomes were categorized by assigning the metagenomic genes to functions in the KEGG database. The results showed that the circadian oscillation appeared to enrich the functions of environmental responses such as various transporters and two-component regulatory systems in the evening, and those of metabolisms such as the biosynthesis of vitamins and fatty acids in the morning.

Discussion

We presented several analytical methods and tools useful for evaluation of the 16S and metagenomic data of various types of microbiomes. The analysis of a community's diversity suggested the strong selective pressure of host physiologies on the colonization of host-related microbiomes compared with the environmental microbiomes. The taxonomic analysis revealed differences in the dominant species between host-related and environmental microbiomes at the phylum level, and poor species assignment at the genus level for many of the environmental microbiomes. Multivariate analysis based on the UniFrac distance showed that the microbiomes were highly variable according to their habitats in the host-related and the environmental microbiomes. Significant differences in the overall community structure of the salivary microbiome between the IBD patients and healthy individuals suggested the profound association between the salivary microbiome and the host's physiological state. The response of the salivary microbiome to the host's signals may also be the case for the circadian oscillation of the human salivary microbiome, implying the concerted regulation of the human microbiome with the host's homeostasis.

As described above, various microbiomes exhibited similar CRADs, which follow the power-law-like long-tail distribution, and the power exponents are likely to be characteristic to the animal and environmental microbiomes, respectively. The power-law-like long-tailed cumulative distribution is distinct from the Gaussian distribution generally observed in stature and manufacturing quality distributions. In the economic sciences, it has been reported that the richest, accounting for 20% of the world's population, contribute to $\sim 80\%$ of the world's total income (United Nations Development Program, 1992; Table 3.1). Interestingly, this distribution in human society structure is analogous to the CRADs representing the microbial community structure where a small numbers of species predominate the abundance in the community over a vast number of other members. For example, $\sim 20\%$ of the species contribute to 80%–90% of the total abundance in the adult human gut microbiomes as shown in **Figs. 3–5**. It is of

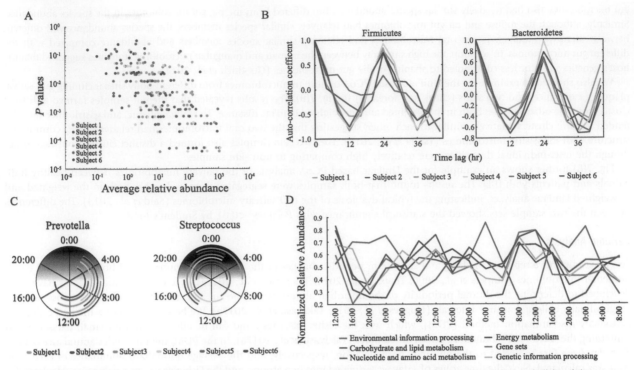

Fig. 8 Circadian rhythm in human salivary microbiomes. (A) Correlations between the relative abundance and circadian periodicity of the genera. (B) Autocorrelation coefficients of the relative abundance of the two major phyla Firmicutes and Bacteroidetes in all the subjects. (C) Circadian proliferation time zones of the two genera *Prevotella* and *Streptococcus*. (D) Diurnal oscillation patterns of the normalized relative gene abundance of several KEGG modules. Reproduced from Takayasu, L., Suda, W., Takanashi, K., *et al.* (2017a). Circadian oscillations of microbial and functional composition in the human salivary microbiome. DNA Research 24(3), 261–270.

interest to explore whether there is a similar mechanism for development and establishment of the community structure between human society and gut microbial community.

We also proposed a mathematical model for the power-law-like CRADs in the microbial communities, in which the observed CRADs were reproduced by incorporation of a parameter of spatial competition for the nutrient source between bacterial species (Takayasu *et al.*, 2017b). When the bacteria in the compact assemblage like biofilm or particulate organic matters compete with each other for common nutrient sources, the species with higher proliferation rate could access more resources than other groups with lower rates, resulting in a long-tail structure with large differences in the abundance between these species after repeating the spatial competition. This simple mathematical mechanism could produce power law CRADs similar to those observed in many of the gut microbiomes.

Future Directions

In the environmental microbiomes, it is anticipated to manipulate and improve the environment by controlling bacterial community, which is deeply associated with resource renewal cycles, while the host-related microbiomes are expected to be keys for developing therapies for diseases. Practically, FMT showed the feasibility of medical treatments for several diseases such as *Clostridium difficile* associated diarrhea, irritable bowel syndrome, and acute graft-versus-host disease (Van Nood *et al.*, 2013; Mizuno *et al.*, 2017; Kakihana *et al.*, 2016). However, since mechanisms for successful FMT have been largely unknown, it will be required to explore how donor microbiomes change and shape the alternative form contributing to healing in the patient gut. Our mathematical model for proliferation and restoration of the human gut microbiome will be useful for these FMT studies.

In addition, microbiomes may also be potential biomarkers that respond to changes in host physiologies. This is because the human salivary microbiome is sensitive to systemic changes in a host's physiological states such as circadian rhythms and lesions in the IBD gut as shown here, but likely to show little sensitivity to external stimuli such as dietary intake and administration of medicines including antibiotics (Cabral *et al.*, 2017). The human salivary microbiome was also reported to be a potential marker for pancreatic cancer, which is difficult to diagnose in the early stage (Farrell *et al.*, 2011).

Closing Remarks

OTU number, the Shannon index, and the observed phylum number are shown for five gut microbiomes from orangutans (domestic zoos), humans (Japanese healthy adults), pigs (domestic farms), experimental mice (conventional), and experimental rats (conventional), foliar microbiomes of *Cerasus* and *Ginkgo*, and three natural environmental microbiomes from soil (a potato field), river fresh water (Saitama, Japan), and oceanic water (Saga, Japan). The data are obtained from 16S data.

CRADs of nine microbiomes indicated in **Fig. 3** are shown. The sample numbers are five for orangutans, five for humans, five for pigs, three for mice, five for rats, one for leaf *Cerasus*, one for leaf *Ginkgo*, four for soil, five for river fresh water, and five for oceanic water, respectively. The exponents (βs) of CRADs calculated from the given equation are shown.

Nine microbiomes are from feces of orangutans, humans, pigs, mice, and rats, and from leaves, soil, river water, and oceanic water, respectively.

See also: Ecosystem Monitoring Through Predictive Modeling. Large Scale Ecological Modeling With Viruses: A Review. Natural Language Processing Approaches in Bioinformatics

---

References

Alneberg, J., Bjarnason, B.S., De Bruijn, I., *et al.*, 2014. Binning metagenomic contigs by coverage and composition. Nature Methods 11, 1144–1146.

Amann, R.I., Ludwig, W., Schleifer, K.-H., 1995. Phylogenetic identification and in situ detection of individual microbial cells without cultivation. Microbiological Reviews 59, 143–169.

Andersson, A.F., Lindberg, M., Jakobsson, H., *et al.*, 2008. Comparative analysis of human gut microbiota by barcoded pyrosequencing. PLOS ONE 3, e2836.

Atarashi, K., Tanoue, T., Ando, M., *et al.*, 2015. Th17 cell induction by adhesion of microbes to intestinal epithelial cells. Cell 163, 367–380.

Atarashi, K., Tanoue, T., Oshima, K., *et al.*, 2013. T reg induction by a rationally selected mixture of Clostridia strains from the human microbiota. Nature 500, 232–236.

Benson, A.K., Kelly, S.A., Legge, R., *et al.*, 2010. Individuality in gut microbiota composition is a complex polygenic trait shaped by multiple environmental and host genetic factors. Proceedings of the National Academy of Sciences of the United States of America 107, 18933–18938.

Cabral, D.J., Wurster, J.I., Flokas, M.E., *et al.*, 2017. The salivary microbiome is consistent between subjects and resistant to impacts of short-term hospitalization. Scientific Reports 7, 11040.

Caporaso, J.G., Kuczynski, J., Stombaugh, J., *et al.*, 2010. QIIME allows analysis of high-throughput community sequencing data. Nature Methods 7, 335–336.

Chaisson, M.J., Huddleston, J., Dennis, M.Y., *et al.*, 2015. Resolving the complexity of the human genome using single-molecule sequencing. Nature 517, 608–611.

Chao, A., 1987. Estimating the population size for capture-recapture data with unequal catchability. Biometrics. 783–791.

Chazdon, R.L., Colwell, R.K., Denslow, J.S., *et al.*, 1998. Statistical methods for estimating species richness of woody regeneration in primary and secondary rain forests of northeastern Costa Rica. Man and the Biosphere Series No. vol. 20. In: Dallmeier, F., Comiskey, J.A. (Eds.), Forest Biodiversity Research, Monitoring and Modeling: Conceptual Background and Old World Case Studies., pp. 285–309.

Chin, C.-S., Alexander, D.H., Marks, P., *et al.*, 2013. Nonhybrid, finished microbial genome assemblies from long-read SMRT sequencing data. Nature Methods 10, 563–569.

Cleary, B., Brito, I.L., Huang, K., *et al.*, 2015. Detection of low-abundance bacterial strains in metagenomic datasets by eigengenome partitioning. Nature Biotechnology 33, 1053–1060.

Cole, J.R., Wang, Q., Cardenas, E., *et al.*, 2008. The Ribosomal Database Project: Improved alignments and new tools for rRNA analysis. Nucleic Acids Research 37, D141–D145.

DeSantis, T.Z., Hugenholtz, P., Larsen, N., *et al.*, 2006. Greengenes, a chimera-checked 16S rRNA gene database and workbench compatible with ARB. Applied and Environmental Microbiology 72, 5069–5072.

DiGiulio, D.B., Callahan, B.J., McMurdie, P.J., *et al.*, 2015. Temporal and spatial variation of the human microbiota during pregnancy. Proceedings of the National Academy of Sciences of the United States of America 112, 11060–11065.

Farrell, J.J., Zhang, L., Zhou, H., *et al.*, 2011. Variations of oral microbiota are associated with pancreatic diseases including pancreatic cancer. Gut 61 (4), 582–588. doi:10.1136/gutjnl-2011-300784.

Frank, D.N., Amand, A.L.S., Feldman, R.A., *et al.*, 2007. Molecular-phylogenetic characterization of microbial community imbalances in human inflammatory bowel diseases. Proceedings of the National Academy of Sciences of the United States of America 104, 13780–13785.

Gill, S.R., Pop, M., DeBoy, R.T., *et al.*, 2006. Metagenomic analysis of the human distal gut microbiome. Science 312, 1355–1359.

Giovannoni, S.J., Britschgi, T.B., Moyer, C.L., *et al.*, 1990. Genetic diversity in Sargasso Sea bacterioplankton. Nature 345, 60–63.

Goodrich, J.K., Waters, J.L., Poole, A.C., *et al.*, 2014. Human genetics shape the gut microbiome. Cell 159, 789–799.

Hughes, M.E., Hogenesch, J.B., Kornacker, K., 2010. JTK_CYCLE: An efficient nonparametric algorithm for detecting rhythmic components in genome-scale data sets. Journal of Biological Rhythms 25, 372–380.

Kakihana, K., Fujioka, Y., Suda, W., *et al.*, 2016. Fecal microbiota transplantation for patients with steroid-resistant acute graft-versus-host disease of the gut. Blood 128, 2083–2088.

Kanehisa, M., Goto, S., Kawashima, S., *et al.*, 2002. The KEGG databases at GenomeNet. Nucleic Acids Research 30, 42–46.

Kang, D.D., Froula, J., Egan, R., *et al.*, 2015. MetaBAT, an efficient tool for accurately reconstructing single genomes from complex microbial communities. PeerJ 3, e1165.

Karlsson, F.H., Tremaroli, V., Nookaew, I., *et al.*, 2013. Gut metagenome in European women with normal, impaired and diabetic glucose control. Nature 498, 99–103.

Kim, S.-W., Suda, W., Kim, S., *et al.*, 2013. Robustness of gut microbiota of healthy adults in response to probiotic intervention revealed by high-throughput pyrosequencing. DNA Research 20, 241–253.

Kuipers, B., van Noort, G.J., Vosjan, J., *et al.*, 2000. Diel periodicity of bacterioplankton in the euphotic zone of the subtropical Atlantic Ocean. Marine Ecology Progress Series 201, 13–25.

Kuleshov, V., Jiang, C., Zhou, W., *et al.*, 2016. Synthetic long-read sequencing reveals intraspecies diversity in the human microbiome. Nature Biotechnology 34, 64–69.

Kurokawa, K., Itoh, T., Kuwahara, T., *et al.*, 2007. Comparative metagenomics revealed commonly enriched gene sets in human gut microbiomes. DNA Research 14, 169–181.

Leonard, M.T., Davis-Richardson, A.G., Ardissone, A.N., *et al.*, 2014. The methylome of the gut microbiome: Disparate Dam methylation patterns in intestinal Bacteroides dorei. Frontiers in Microbiology 5, 361.

Lozupone, C., Knight, R., 2005. UniFrac: A new phylogenetic method for comparing microbial communities. Applied and Environmental Microbiology 71, 8228–8235.

Manichanh, C., Reeder, J., Gibert, P., *et al.*, 2010. Reshaping the gut microbiome with bacterial transplantation and antibiotic intake. Genome Research 20, 1411–1419.

Meyer, F., Paarmann, D., D'Souza, M., *et al.*, 2008. The metagenomics RAST server – A public resource for the automatic phylogenetic and functional analysis of metagenomes. BMC Bioinformatics 9, 386.

Miyake, S., Kim, S., Suda, W., *et al.*, 2015. Dysbiosis in the gut microbiota of patients with multiple sclerosis, with a striking depletion of species belonging to clostridia XIVa and IV clusters. PLOS ONE 10, e0137429.

Mizuno, S., Masaoka, T., Naganuma, M., et al., 2017. Bifidobacterium-rich fecal donor may be a positive predictor for successful fecal microbiota transplantation in patients with irritable bowel syndrome. Digestion 96, 29–38.

Moayyedi, P., Surette, M.G., Kim, P.T., et al., 2015. Fecal microbiota transplantation induces remission in patients with active ulcerative colitis in a randomized controlled trial. Gastroenterology 149, 102–109. e106.

Nielsen, H.B., Almeida, M., Juncker, A.S., et al., 2014. Identification and assembly of genomes and genetic elements in complex metagenomic samples without using reference genomes. Nature Biotechnology 32, 822–828.

Nishijima, S., Suda, W., Oshima, K., et al., 2016. The gut microbiome of healthy Japanese and its microbial and functional uniqueness. DNA Research 23, 125–133.

Noguchi, H., Taniguchi, T., Itoh, T., 2008. MetaGeneAnnotator: Detecting species-specific patterns of ribosomal binding site for precise gene prediction in anonymous prokaryotic and phage genomes. DNA Research 15, 387–396.

Qin, J., Li, R., Raes, J., et al., 2010. A human gut microbial gene catalogue established by metagenomic sequencing. Nature 464, 59–65.

Qin, J., Li, Y., Cai, Z., et al., 2012. A metagenome-wide association study of gut microbiota in type 2 diabetes. Nature 490, 55–60.

Rasko, D.A., Webster, D.R., Sahl, J.W., et al., 2011. Origins of the E. coli strain causing an outbreak of hemolytic–uremic syndrome in Germany. The New England Journal of Medicine 365, 709–717.

Said, H.S., Suda, W., Nakagome, S., et al., 2013. Dysbiosis of salivary microbiota in inflammatory bowel disease and its association with oral immunological biomarkers. DNA Research 21, 15–25.

Sharon, I., Kertesz, M., Hug, L.A., et al., 2015. Accurate, multi-kb reads resolve complex populations and detect rare microorganisms. Genome Research 25, 534–543.

Staley, J.T., Konopka, A., 1985. Measurement of in situ activities of nonphotosynthetic microorganisms in aquatic and terrestrial habitats. Annual Review of Microbiology. 39, 321–346.

Takayasu, L., Suda, W., Takanashi, K., et al., 2017a. Circadian oscillations of microbial and functional composition in the human salivary microbiome. DNA Research 24 (3), 261–270.

Takayasu, L., Suda, W., Watanabe, E., et al., 2017b. A 3-dimensional mathematical model of microbial proliferation that generates the characteristic cumulative relative abundance distributions in gut microbiomes. PLOS ONE 12, e0180863.

Tatusov, R.L., Koonin, E.V., Lipman, D.J., 1997. A genomic perspective on protein families. Science 278, 631–637.

Thaiss, C.A., Zeevi, D., Levy, M., et al., 2014. Transkingdom control of microbiota diurnal oscillations promotes metabolic homeostasis. Cell 159, 514–529.

The Human Microbiome Project Consortium, 2012. Structure, function and diversity of the healthy human microbiome. Nature 486, 207–214.

Tsai, Y.-C., Conlan, S., Deming, C., et al., 2016. Resolving the complexity of human skin metagenomes using single-molecule sequencing. mBio 7, e01948–01915.

Tsuda, A., Suda, W., Morita, H., et al., 2015. Influence of proton-pump inhibitors on the luminal microbiota in the gastrointestinal tract. Clinical and Translational Gastroenterology 6, e89.

Turnbaugh, P.J., Hamady, M., Yatsunenko, T., et al., 2009. A core gut microbiome in obese and lean twins. Nature 457, 480–484.

Tyson, G.W., Chapman, J., Hugenholtz, P., et al., 2004. Community structure and metabolism through reconstruction of microbial genomes from the environment. Nature 428, 37–43.

United Nations Development Program, 1992. Human Development Report. New York: Oxford University Press.

Van Nood, E., Vrieze, A., Nieuwdorp, M., et al., 2013. Duodenal infusion of donor feces for recurrent Clostridium difficile. The New England Journal of Medicine. 368, 407–415.

Venter, J.C., Remington, K., Heidelberg, J.F., et al., 2004. Environmental genome shotgun sequencing of the Sargasso Sea. Science 304, 66–74.

Whitman, W.B., Coleman, D.C., Wiebe, W.J., 1998. Prokaryotes: The unseen majority. Proceedings of the National Academy of Sciences of the United States of America 95, 6578–6583.

Woese, C.R., 1987. Bacterial evolution. Microbiological Reviews. 51, 221–271.

Woese, C.R., Fox, G.E., 1977. Phylogenetic structure of the prokaryotic domain: The primary kingdoms. Proceedings of the National Academy of Sciences of the United States of America 74, 5088–5090.

Wu, G.D., Chen, J., Hoffmann, C., et al., 2011. Linking long-term dietary patterns with gut microbial enterotypes. Science 334, 105–108.

Yatsunenko, T., Rey, F.E., Manary, M.J., et al., 2012. Human gut microbiome viewed across age and geography. Nature 486, 222–227.

Relevant Website

https://www.ncbi.nlm.nih.gov/
    NCBI.

Biological Database Searching

Nor A Nor Muhammad, Universiti Kebangsaan Malaysia (UKM), Bangi, Selangor, Malaysia

Introduction

Biological databases are databases which store information from biological experiments, especially high throughput molecular experiments. There are many types of biological databases, including sequence databases, protein domain databases, protein structure databases, and non-coding RNA databases, among others. These databases house biological information that can be used for annotation and characterization of new biological data. New inferences may also be obtained from processing data from these databases using bioinformatics.

A simple analysis pipeline that uses biological databases would consist of four main steps (**Fig. 1**). First would be the data collection step. This can either be from data mining or from generating your own data from sequencing or other omics experiments. Once collected, things to note regarding the data includes the data type, what is known regarding the data and what do you want to know about the data. Hypotheses and objectives of the bioinformatic analysis can then be constructed. These will determine the bioinformatic pipeline that needs to be used. The second stage of the analysis is the selection of relevant databases that needs to be incorporated. For example, annotation of protein sequences would require the UniProt database while the annotation of gene sequences would require the GenBank database. Next, we do the homology searching. The tools used for this step depends on the data collected and the database chosen. For sequence-based data, NCBI BLAST would be the go to choice (Madden, 2013). HMM profile data on the other hand can be processed using the HMMER package (Mistry *et al.*, 2013). Often, these tools are embedded in the databases. Finally, manual curation might be necessary when interpreting the results. The use of multiple databases may either verify results or may produce contradicting results. Results from gene annotation can be mapped onto reference pathways to identify pathways that might be in the data collected.

Biological Databases and Types of Data Stored

Sequence Databases

The largest and main databases for biological data are sequence databases. They house digital versions of nucleotide or amino acid sequences. The nucleotide sequences may correspond to whole genomes, genes, expressed sequence tags (ESTs) or ribonucleic acids (RNAs), while amino acid sequences correspond to protein sequences.

The National Center for Biotechnology Information (NCBI) (Acland *et al.*, 2014) houses one of the biggest nucleotide sequence database named GenBank. GenBank is a collection of annotated nucleotide sequences that are publicly available. It supports bibliographic and biological annotation of each nucleotide sequence. NCBI builds GenBank mainly from data submitted by authors, whole-genome shotgun (WGS) and other data from high-throughput sequencing centers. Over 370,000 formerly

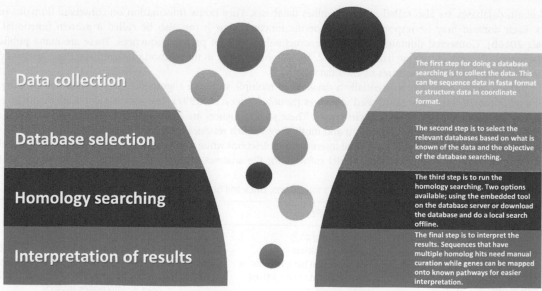

Fig. 1 Overview of analysis pipeline that uses biological databases.

described species are being covered by the GenBank database (Benson *et al.*, 2017). Thus, this makes GenBank one of the main reference for nucleotide sequence analyses.

The European Nucleotide Archive (ENA) is a nucleotide sequence repository developed by The European Bioinformatics Institute (EMBL-EBI) (Leinonen *et al.*, 2010). Compared with GenBank, ENA is broader in the types of nucleotide sequences being stored from raw reads to annotated sequences. Data came from both small-scale research laboratories and large-scale sequencing centers. As of 2016, ENA had collected data from 192,000 studies, with 770 million sequence records linked to 200,000 literature publications. ENA are friendly to both users that look for single sequences as well as bioinformaticians that intend to incorporate the ENA database in their analyses pipeline. Both simple and advanced search tools are provided for users at ENA's website. For bioinformaticians that need programmatic access to ENA, the search and download function are being provided by RESTful services (Toribio *et al.*, 2017).

The National Institute of Genetics (NIG) established the DNA Data Bank of Japan (DDBJ) database. Like GenBank and ENA, DDBJ stores nucleotide sequences that were submitted from laboratories and sequencing centers. Submission of next-generation sequencing data is handled by DDBJ Sequence Read Archive (DRA). There is also BioProject to handle the sequencing project metadata and BioSample for handling sample information. In 2013, DDBJ with their partner, the National Bioscience Database Center (NBDC) launched the Japanese Genotype-phenotype Archive (JGA). This database stores the genotype and phenotype data of individuals. Data from JGA is restricted to certain research based on the individuals consent. The DDBJ center is primarily a supercomputing center that provide services to the research community. Their services include web services, submission systems, data retrieval systems, WebApi and DDBJ Read Annotation Pipeline (Mashima *et al.*, 2016). The latest release of DDBJ was on June 2017, Release 109.0 with 874,923,909 entries.

Together with GenBank and ENA, they form the International Nucleotide Sequence Database Collaboration (INSDC; see "Relevant Websites section"). These three databases shares data submitted to them with each other. They all contribute to one pool of nucleotide sequences under the INSDC initiative. They also work together in the development of the database platform and tools. INSDC champions the work of establishing standards, formats and protocols for nucleotide data and metadata. They have become the model for data sharing in the field of life sciences (Cochrane *et al.*, 2016).

UniProt Knowledgebase or UniProtKB is the main protein sequence resource, which is developed and maintained by EMBL-EBI. It consists of two main components, Swiss-Prot and TrEMBL. Swiss-Prot houses over 500 thousand manually annotated and reviewed protein sequences while TrEMBL has over 60 million computationally annotated protein sequences (Consortium, 2017). The annotation of proteins in Swiss-Prot depends on experimental characterization of proteins, thus each entry has a publication attached to it. UniProtKB also houses a non-redundant database of all known protein sequences called UniParc. It currently has over 120 million sequences (Consortium, 2017). UniProtKB is linked to over 150 databases, thus acting as a central hub for organizing protein information. Its accession number plays a key role as a fixed reference for protein sequences, allowing tagging of proteins in informatics applications (Consortium, 2014).

These sequence databases are used as point of reference for either finding your gene or protein sequence of interest. They can also be used for annotating sequences of interest using sequence alignment tools such as NCBI BLAST (Basic Local Alignment Search Tool) (Camacho *et al.*, 2009). In any characterization of sequence, this will be the first method in finding annotation for your sequence of interest. The web links for all mentioned and other sequence databases is in **Table 1**.

Protein Domain Databases

Protein domain databases are also called protein families databases. They house information on conserved domains in protein sequences. Each domain may be responsible for a specific function, thus it can also be called a protein functional domain (Finn *et al.*, 2016b). Conserved domains may also be structural features of protein sequences. There are many public protein domain databases, of which eleven are listed in **Table 2**. The databases differ in the method of identifying the conserved domains. We will be exploring some of the features of each database.

Pfam, a protein family database, is essentially a database of multiple sequence alignments. Each protein family entry in Pfam consists of a set of protein sequences called seed sequences (Sonnhammer *et al.*, 1997). The seed sequences are manually curated to make sure they are true members of the protein family. These seed sequences are then aligned to produce the motif logo of the family/domain. The multiple sequence alignment and motif shows which residues are more conserved than others in the domain. Some regions of the domain will be able to tolerate insertions and deletions while some might not. The multiple sequence alignment is profiled using HMMER, a Hidden Markov Model software for the analyses of biological sequences (Finn *et al.*, 2011). A full

Table 1   List of publicly available sequence database with their names, URLs and hosts/maintainers.

Database name	Database URL	Database host
DNA Data Bank of Japan (DDBJ)	www.ddbj.nig.ac.jp	National Institute of Genetics (NIG)
European Nucleotide Archive (ENA)	www.ebi.ac.uk/ena	European Bioinformatics Institute (EMBL-EBI)
GenBank	www.ncbi.nlm.nih.gov/genbank	National Center for Biotechnology Information (NCBI)
Reference Sequence (RefSeq)	www.ncbi.nlm.nih.gov/refseq	National Center for Biotechnology Information (NCBI)
Universal Protein Resource (UniProt)	www.uniprot.org	European Bioinformatics Institute

Table 2 List of public protein domain/family database with their names, URLs and hosts/maintainers.

Database name	Database URL	Database host
CDD (Conserved Domain Database)	www.ncbi.nlm.nih.gov/Structure/cdd/cdd.shtml	National Center for Biotechnology Information (NCBI)
Gene3d	gene3d.biochem.ucl.ac.uk	University College London
HAMAP (High-Quality Automated and Manual Annotation of Proteins)	hamap.expasy.org	Swiss Institute of Bioinformatics
Panther (Protein Analysis Through Evolutionary Relationship)	www.pantherdb.org	University of Southern California
Pfam	pfam.xfam.org	European Bioinformatics Institute
PIRSF (Protein Information Resource Super Family)	pir.georgetown.edu/pirwww/dbinfo/pirsf.shtml	Georgetown University Medical Center
PRINTS	130.88.97.239/PRINTS/index.php	The University of Manchester
PROSITE (Database of protein domains, families and functional sites)	prosite.expasy.org	Swiss Institute of Bioinformatics
ProDom	prodom.prabi.fr/prodom/current/html/home.php	French National Institute for Agricultural Research (INRA)
SMAT (Simple Modular Architecture Research Tool)	smart.embl-heidelberg.de	European Molecular Biology Laboratory
SUPERFAMILY (HMM library and genome assignments server)	supfam.org/SUPERFAMILY	MRC Laboratory of Molecular Biology
TIGRFAM	www.jcvi.org/cgi-bin/tigrfams/index.cgi	J. Craig Venter Institute (JCVI)

alignment of the protein family is built by aligning all members with the HMM profile (Eddy, 1998). This full alignment is useful for identifying features of the protein family such as the distribution of the protein family in living species, the size of the protein family, the level of conservation of the domain of interest as well as identifying homologs of the protein sequence being analyzed. The relationship between the protein family and taxonomic hierarchy can also be studied by generating the taxonomic tree of all the members of the protein family. Each Pfam entry is also cross referenced with literatures and UniProtKB in order to access annotations of the protein family (Finn et al., 2016b). Current version of Pfam is version 31.0, released in March 2017 with 16,712 entries.

New publications that describe protein characterization usually provide one or two proven homologs of the protein. No rules or definitions are provided for the identification of protein homologs from all other organisms. Furthermore, the grouping of protein into functional groups differ from case to case and no fixed heuristics are available that work in most cases. Thus, TIGRFAM was developed to facilitate automated annotations of proteins by providing a library of protein family definitions. Like Pfam, TIGRFAM is a manually curated database. However, TIGRFAM has additional features which make it suitable for automated genome annotation. The annotation of a protein family is always traced back to its original source that is not linked to any computational annotation pipeline. Stringent rules are applied in the selection of seed sequences. Multiple sequence alignment of the seed sequences is checked for misalignments, inconsistent domain architecture and altered active or binding sites. Hidden Markov Models of high quality are then produced from the alignments. The aim is that each HMM produced by TIGRFAM pipeline can be the representative of an expert curator who operates with BLAST-like speeds (Haft et al., 2012). The current release version is 15.0 with 4488 families.

Biologist turn to protein family databases, such as Pfam and TIGRFAM to annotate protein sequences that do not have any matched homologs from protein sequence databases. Both Pfam and TIGRFAM uses HMM profiles, but they differ in their intended use cases. Pfam tries to be as broad as possible to allow for detection of distant homologs to a protein family in the Pfam database. Thus, each protein family in Pfam encodes a small part of the functional domain, with a conservation profile indicative of high sensitivity. The small conserved domain allows the generated HMM to match distant homologs. TIGRFAM on the other hand was developed based on the concept of equivalogs, which are genes or encoded proteins that have a common conserved function since their last common ancestor. This contrasts with the definition of orthologs where only the evolutionary history is concerned (Haft et al., 2003); as such equivalogs may include more than orthologs (i.e., xenologs) and orthologs may not be equivalogs (because of neofunctionalization).

The Conserved Domain Database (CDD) was developed to accelerate the annotation of new protein sequences. Due to the exponential increase in the size of public sequence data, it is impractical to keep aligning new sequences to each sequence in the database for characterization purposes. The strategy took by the developers of CDD was to identify representative sequences for conserved domains. This representative set is unlikely to grow at the same exponential rate as new protein sequences (Marchler-Bauer et al., 2014). CDD collects its protein and protein domain models from Pfam (Sonnhammer et al., 1997), SMART (Letunic et al., 2014), COG Database (Tatusov et al., 2003), TIGRFAM (Haft et al., 2012), NCBI Protein Cluster Database (Klimke et al., 2008) and in house curations efforts (Marchler-Bauer et al., 2003). Each CDD entry is crosslinked to other databases for annotation and search purposes. They include NCBI Entrez Search, Entrez/protein, Entrez/gene, molecular modelling database (MMDB), NCBI Biosystems, PubMed and PubChem (Marchler-Bauer et al., 2014). Current live version of CDD is v3.16 with 56,066 entries, where 12,805 entries are by CDD curation efforts. The entries are grouped into 5697 multi-model superfamilies.

PROSITE is the first database created for identification of protein families or domains. Each entry in the database is a motif descriptor dedicated for identification of protein families. The description can be of two types, patterns or profiles (Sigrist *et al.*, 2002). Patterns are regular expression of short sequence motif that often relate to functionally or structurally important residues. Profiles on the other hand are weight matrices that describe the protein family or domain (Sigrist *et al.*, 2013). Annotation rules in PROSITE are called ProRules. ProRules define annotations relating to protein sequence such as the active site, ligand binding residues and the conditions relating to the annotations (Sigrist *et al.*, 2005). To search protein sequence of interest against PROSITE, the ScanProsite tool can be used. ScanProsite can also search for matches in UniProtKB and Protein Data Bank (PDB) structure database (De Castro *et al.*, 2006). The latest PROSITE release was on 5th July 2017 with 1309 patterns, 1189 profiles and 1208 ProRules.

ProDom is a protein domain database that uses automation instead of relying on manual curation like in Pfam (Finn *et al.*, 2016b) and SMART (Letunic *et al.*, 2014). ProDom algorithm applies automated clustering towards a database of non-redundant sequences from Swiss-Prot, TrEMBL, complete proteomes on the ExPASy server and on the Proteome Analysis pages. The clustering program used is MKDOM2. It uses PSI-BLAST to look for homologous domains amongst the sequences in the database. Sequences that belong to a cluster become a ProDom family and are removed from the database. This is iterated until all the sequences in the database have been exhausted (Servant *et al.*, 2002). In the latest version of ProDom, 3D structure information is used during the generation of ProDom families. 3D structure information is obtained from the Structural Classification of Proteins (SCOP) database (Andreeva *et al.*, 2004). ProDom-CG is a subset of the ProDom database; members of ProDom-CG are restricted to protein sequences from completely sequenced genomes. ProDom also hosts the ProDom-SG, a server for structural genomics. This server identifies protein candidates suitable for crystallization that have potential in having new folds that are yet to be seen in proteins (Bru *et al.*, 2005). The live version of ProDom currently has 1,718,157 domain families (that have at least two members); 426,997 families have links to PDB, 128,882 families have links to PROSITE and 823,801 families have links to Pfam.

PRINTS is a protein 'fingerprint' database. Where other domain databases have entries of single motif representing a conserved domain, 'fingerprint' consist of multiple short motifs that represent a protein family or structural features (Attwood and Beck, 1994). Thus, 'fingerprint' can be more powerful compared to single motif approaches as it depends on multiple motifs. 'Fingerprint' can also annotate the relationships between protein families (domains) as matches to a 'fingerprint' will have multiple domains. Given this, the hierarchical or evolutionary relationship between matches of a 'fingerprint' may also be inferred (Attwood *et al.*, 2012). PRINTS database is currently at version 39.0 with 1950 entries and 11,625 motifs.

SUPERFAMILY is a library of Hidden Markov Models (HMMs) representing protein of known structure. The structural information is obtained from the SCOP database, where proteins are grouped together at several levels; one such level is 'superfamily'. Proteins in a superfamily group shares a common ancestor, thus having functional, structural and sequence similarity. The SUPERFAMILY database was derived from this level because this is the level with most distantly related domains. The framework behind SUPERFAMILY database is HMMs, similar to Pfam (Sonnhammer *et al.*, 1997), SMART (Letunic *et al.*, 2014) and TIGRFAM (Haft *et al.*, 2012) databases. The difference is that SUPERFAMILY only covers proteins with known structure where else the other databases covers all protein sequences (Gough and Chothia, 2002). The SUPERFAMILY database has also been integrated with InterPro (Finn *et al.*, 2016a) and Gene Ontology terms. Abstract from InterPro entries have been imported into SUPERFAMILY. SUPERFAMILY database also provides the users with taxonomic visualization of the families in the database. Users can also search for domain architectures with similar function to find related domains to domains of interest (Wilson *et al.*, 2009). Current SUPERFAMILY database has 1962 entries based on SCOP 1.75 superfamilies.

The Protein Analysis Through Evolutionary Relationships or PANTHER is a database resource of protein families, subfamilies, phylogenetic trees and functions. PANTHER aims to practically infer functions of genes and proteins in large sequence databases. It uses phylogenetic tree approach to extrapolate experimental information from model organisms onto other sequences. Trees generated in PANTHER describes the evolutionary events in gene family histories. One tree is generated for each family. Nodes on the tree are annotated with gene attributes. There are three types of gene attributes annotated in PANTHER. They are 'subfamily membership', 'protein class' and 'gene function'. The trees also include information on speciation and gene duplication events (Mi *et al.*, 2013). Current live version of the database is PANTHER12.0, with 103 genomes, 1,378,820 genes, 14,710 families, and 76,032 subfamilies.

Gene3D derives its domain entries from the CATH (class, architecture, topology & homology) database. CATH is a protein domain structure database. Structures from the Protein Data Bank (PDB) are broken down into smaller domain structures. These domains are then grouped into superfamilies if evidences of common ancestry were found (Sillitoe *et al.*, 2015). From these superfamilies, profile HMMs are generated and put into the Gene3D library.

Protein Structure Databases

Protein structure databases stores coordinate data from protein and other biomolecules structures. The main source for the data are X-ray crystallography experiments. These databases also provide tools for searching proteins that have their structure solved, tools for comparing input proteins with protein structures in the database, visualization tools for generating 3D images of the protein structures in the databases and annotations for each protein structure entry. Advance users may also download raw coordinate data for custom computational biology works. Main databases in this field include the Protein Data Bank, CATH database and SCOP2 database.

The Protein Data Bank (PDB) was founded in 1971 for archiving biomolecular macromolecular crystal structures (Berman *et al.*, 2014). The emergence of new structural biology technologies has forced PDB to evolve into what it is today. Today, after over 46 years, PDB is the largest public database that hosts structural data of biomolecules. PDB employs the best of current data science technologies and practices. Everything is centralized and various checkpoints are implemented in the PDB pipeline to maintain data integrity and consistency. In 2013, more than 400 million coordinate sets have been downloaded from PDB partner sites. The well-developed data structure and data processing practices has enabled the development of resources for small molecules and ligands such as ChEMBL (Bento *et al.*, 2014), DrugBank (Law *et al.*, 2013), BindingDB (Gilson *et al.*, 2016), BindingMOAD (Ahmed *et al.*, 2014) and PDBBind (Liu *et al.*, 2014a). There are also resources developed for protein structure classification and annotation such as CATH (Cuff *et al.*, 2008), SCOP2 (Andreeva *et al.*, 2013) and PDBsum (De Beer *et al.*, 2013). Last but not least, there are specialty annotation resources developed from PDB data such as Protein Data Bank of Transmembrane Proteins (PDBTM) (Kozma *et al.*, 2012), ArchDB (Bonet *et al.*, 2013) and 3did (Mosca *et al.*, 2013).

The CATH (class, architecture, topology & homology) database is a hierarchical database of domains. The lowest level of the hierarchy is the H-level or the homologous superfamily. At this level, the domains share significant sequence similarity, structural similarity and/or functional similarity. The next level up is the T-level or the fold or topology groups. Domains in a group at this level share only structure similarity. Topology groups that have similarities in the arrangement of their secondary structures are then put into the same architecture group. This is also called the A-level. The top level of the hierarchy is the C-level or class level. The groupings at this level depends on the percentage composition of α-helices and β-strands in the domains (Pearl *et al.*, 2003).

SCOP2 database organizes protein structures based on their structure and evolutionary relationships. The main feature of SCOP2 compared to other protein structure database is its focus on protein evolution. The relationship between proteins are represented as a complex network of nodes. There are four major categories of relationships in SCOP2, protein types, evolutionary events, structural classes and protein relationships which have three subtypes: structural, evolutionary and other. SCOP2 uses five levels of evolutionary classification: species, protein, family, superfamily and hyperfamily. At the species level, each gene product is considered as one entity and is represented by its full sequence length. At the protein level, orthologous proteins are grouped together. Conserved residues between proteins forms the next level, which is the family level. Sharing of common structural regions then forms the fourth level, i.e., the superfamily level. The highest level is the hyperfamily level. A domain at this level are shared between superfamilies. These can be smaller than structural domains and was introduced to cater highly populated superfamilies (Andreeva *et al.*, 2013). There are also other protein/biomolecule structure related databases as listed in **Table 3**.

Non-Coding RNA Databases

Non-coding RNAs or ncRNA are RNAs that do not code for proteins. They are abundant and have important roles in cellular processes. There are several known types of ncRNA including snoRNAs, scaRNAs, miRNAs, siRNAs, snRNAs, exRNAs, piRNAs and long ncRNAs. Small nucleolar RNAs (snoRNAs) are a class of small RNA that assist in chemical modifications of other RNAs such as ribosomal RNAs. A subset of snoRNAs are located in Cajal bodies, thus sometimes called scaRNAs. Micro RNA (miRNA) is a class of small non-coding RNA that can be found in plants, animals and viruses. They are responsible for RNA silencing and post transcriptional regulation of gene expression. Small interfering RNAs (siRNAs) also called short interfering RNAs or silencing RNAs, are nucleotides up to 21 residues long that can interfere with protein translation. They do this by binding to and promoting the degradation of messenger RNAs (mRNAs). Small nuclear RNAs (snRNAs) are confined to the nucleus. They are involved in splicing and other RNA processing (Mattick and Makunin, 2006). Extracellular RNA (exRNA) is a class of RNA found extra-cellularly. In humans, it has been found in bodily fluids such as blood and saliva. They have many roles depending on types but generally involved in cell-to-cell communication. When the RNA reaches the target cell, it initiates certain biological process

Table 3   List of public protein/biomolecules structure databases as well as related resources.

Database name	Database URL	Database host
3did (Three-Dimensional Interacting Domains)	3did.irbbarcelona.org	Institute for Research in Biomedicine
ArchDB	sbi.imim.es/archdb	Structural Bioinformatics Lab
BindingDB	www.bindingdb.org	University of California
BindingMOAD	bindingmoad.org	University of Michigan
CATH	www.cathdb.info	University College London
ChEMBL	www.ebi.ac.uk/chembl	European Molecular Biology Laboratory
DrugBank	www.drugbank.ca	University of Alberta
ModBase: Database of Comparative Protein Structure Models	modbase.compbio.ucsf.edu	University of California
PDB (The Protein Data Bank)	www.rcsb.org	San Diego Supercomputer Center
PDBe (Protein Data Bank in Europe)	www.ebi.ac.uk/pdbe	European Bioinformatics Institute
PDBBind	www.pdbbind.org	University of Michigan
PDBBind-CN	www.pdbbind.org.cn	Shanghai Institute of Organic Chemistry
PDBj (Protein Data Bank Japan)	pdbj.org	Osaka University
PDBsum	www.ebi.ac.uk/pdbsum	European Bioinformatics Institute
PDBTM: Protein Data Bank of Transmembrane Proteins	pdbtm.enzim.hu	Institute of Enzymology
SCOP2 (Structural Classification of Proteins 2)	scop2.mrc-lmb.cam.ac.uk	MRC Laboratory of Molecular Biology
SWISS-MODEL Repository	swissmodel.expasy.org/repository	Swiss Institute of Bioinformatics
Protein Model Portal	www.proteinmodelportal.org	Swiss Institute of Bioinformatics

(Benner, 1988). Piwi-interacting RNA (piRNA) is a class of non-coding RNA abundant in animal cells. They form RNA-protein complexes by binding to piwi proteins and are associated with silencing of genetic elements (Seto *et al.*, 2007). LncRNA or long non-coding RNA are nucleotides with over 200 residues but do not encode proteins. They form majority of the human transcriptome but their function remain largely unknown (Mattick and Rinn, 2015).

Generally, ncRNA databases and resources can be grouped into two types, an integrated type which houses annotations of ncRNAs regardless of the subtype and another group which focuses on a specific type of ncRNA. Examples of centralized ncRNA databases are RNAcentral and NONCODE. They provide annotations of the different types of ncRNA by doing data mining and merging of information from other databases. RNAcentral for example, combined information from 42 external databases providing a one stop solution for annotation of ncRNA sequences. There are three main tools in RNAcentral that can be used for finding ncRNA of interest. The tools are text-based searching, sequences-based searching and genome browser. In the text-based searching, one can search based on gene, species, publication and author. The sequence-based searching accepts RNA sequence in FASTA format or an RNAcentral ID. This is similar to searching with web NCBI BLAST (see "Relevant Websites section"). Lastly is the genome browser tool. Currently, there are 12 genomes available in the genome browser. They are *Arabidopsis thaliana*, *Bos taurus*, *Bombyx mori*, *Caenorhabditis elegans*, *Canis familiaris*, *Danio rerio*, *Drosophila melanogaster*, *Homo sapiens*, *Mus musculus*, *Pan troglodytes*, *Rattus norvegicus* and *Schizosaccharomyces pombe*. With the genome browser, one can go to the chromosome of interest to see the genes, transcripts and RNAcentral entries at that location in the genome. The current 8th release has over 13.1 million sequences.

NONCODE is another ncRNA knowledgebase, like the RNAcentral. However, NONCODE has 17 genomes in its genome browser and also does a lot of literature mining to gather ncRNA data. It houses most ncRNA types but focuses on lncRNA (long non-coding RNA). Apart from BLAST and genome browser, NONCODE also provides an ID conversion tool and a pipeline for identification of lncRNA. Other sources of ncRNA can be seen in **Table 4**.

Applications/Use Cases

The mass amount of biological data housed in various databases is an invaluable resource for fields related to biology: biotechnology, systems biology, bioinformatics, genomics, transcriptomics, proteomics and metabolomics to name a few. In the **Fig. 2** below are examples of the databases described in the previous section grouped into their respective types.

Characterization of an Unknown Sequence

Due to the wealth of databases and tools, characterization of unknown sequences, both nucleotides and amino acid sequences can be done relatively quickly. The limitation is the information in the databases itself. If the unknown sequence is truly novel and has

Table 4   List of non-coding RNA databases and resources with their corresponding URLs and hosts.

Database name	Database URL	Database host
5SrRNAdb	combio.pl/rrna	Adam Mickiewicz University
ATtRACT (A Database of RNA Binding Proteins and Associated Motifs)	https://attract.cnic.es/	The Centro Nacional de Investigaciones Cardiovasculares Carlos III (CNIC)
CRW (Comparative RNA Web Site and Project)	www.rna.ccbb.utexas.edu	The University of Texas at Austin
lncRNAdb	www.lncrnadb.org	Garvan Institute of Medical Research
LncBase	http://carolina.imis.athena-innovation.gr/diana_tools/web/index.php?r=lncbasev2%2Findex	University of Thessaly
LNCipedia 4.1	lncipedia.org	
miRBase	www.mirbase.org	University of Manchester
NONCODE	www.noncode.org	Chinese Academy of Sciences
RBPBD (The database of RNA-binding protein specificities)	http://rbpdb.ccbr.utoronto.ca/	University of Toronto
Rfam	rfam.xfam.org	European Bioinformatics Institute
RNAcentral	rnacentral.org	European Bioinformatics Institute
RNApathwaysDB	www.genesilico.pl/rnapathwaysdb	International Institute of Molecular and Cell Biology in Warsaw
SILVA (High Quality Ribosomal RNA Databases)	www.arb-silva.de	Max Plank Institute for Marine Microbiology and Jacobs University
snOPY (snoRNA Orthological Gene Database)	snoopy.med.miyazaki-u.ac.jp	University of Miyazaki
sRNAMap	srnamap.mbc.nctu.edu.tw	National Chiao-Tung University
Tarbase	http://andrea.imis.athena-innovation.gr/diana_tools/web/index.php?r=tarbasev8%2Findex	University of Thessaly

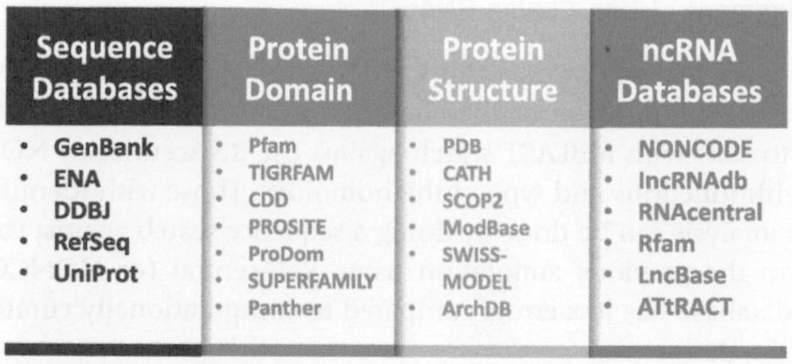

Sequence Databases	Protein Domain	Protein Structure	ncRNA Databases
• GenBank	• Pfam	• PDB	• NONCODE
• ENA	• TIGRFAM	• CATH	• lncRNAdb
• DDBJ	• CDD	• SCOP2	• RNAcentral
• RefSeq	• PROSITE	• ModBase	• Rfam
• UniProt	• ProDom	• SWISS-MODEL	• LncBase
	• SUPERFAMILY	• ArchDB	• ATtRACT
	• Panther		

Fig. 2 Example databases for different types of biological data.

not be seen before, *in silico* characterization might then be limited. Given an unknown sequence, the first instinct would be to figure out whether there are similar sequences to the sequence in the databases. Using tools based on homology searching such as BLAST (Camacho, 2015), homologs of the unknown sequence can be identified from the databases. If the homologs are well known, their annotations can be ascribed as putative annotations of the unknown sequence.

Exploring Sequence Patterns and Profiles

Now biologist and researchers in general can explore vast number of domain databases with ease. Each database is equipped with search function and various filters for finding domains of interest. Once the domain of interest is found, users can explore the features and annotations of the domain. Most domain databases provide the motif logo, the multiple sequence alignment and the description of the domain. We can infer a lot from the motif logo; we can observe which residues at which position in the domain are conserved. We can also see alternative residues for positions that are not absolutely conserved in the members of the domain. Databases such as Pfam and TIGRFAM also allows the download of the HMM profile of the domain. With the HMM profile, users can search for sequences that contain the domain or align sequences of interest with the domain. Generating our own HMM profile is also easily done using HMMER. Firstly, we generate a multiple sequence alignment containing the domain of interest. Then using HMMER (hmmbuild), a HMM profile can be generated. This profile can then be searched against sequence databases to find members having the same domain (Mistry *et al.*, 2013).

Mining for Immune Epitopes

There are now databases and resources that provides information on immune epitopes that have been found. From these resources, tools that can predict the existence of immune epitopes in new data have been generated. The main resource for analyzing immune epitopes is the Immune Epitope Database and Analysis Resource (IEDB) (Peters *et al.*, 2005). This resource provides both simple search engine for finding immune epitopes that have been deposited in the database and analysis tools and scripts for prediction of immune epitopes in sequence data. The analysis tools can be found at the website provided in "Relevant Websites section". There are four categories of analysis tools being provided at IEDB. They are T Cell Epitope Prediction Tools, B Cell Epitope Prediction Tools, Analysis Tools and IEDB Analysis Resource Labs. In the T Cell Epitope Prediction Tools category, there are six tools provided. The use of these tools allows for the identification of peptides that may bind to MHC molecules, peptides that may be T-cell epitopes and the ability of peptides to induce an immune response. In the B Cell Prediction Tools category, there are five tools provided. They allow the prediction of linear B cell epitopes from amino acid sequences, prediction of B cell epitopes from protein structures and structure prediction of antibodies. Tools for analysis of known epitopes have also been developed. The tools can do population coverage analysis, epitope conservation analysis, epitope cluster analysis and mapping of mimotope (Kim *et al.*, 2012).

Global Identification of Protein Post-Translational Modifications

The development of protein sequence databases has accelerated the field of global post-translational modifications identification. There are many types of protein post-translational modifications including phosphorylation, glycosylation, amidation, hydroxylation, methylation and others. Due to the wealth of post-translational modification types, many resources and tools have been developed for the identification of post-translational modifications. As an example, there are 17 or more databases that are related to protein phosphorylation. Choosing appropriate database or resource will depend on the analysis intended or biological question to be answered. For prediction or annotation purposes, there are also databases and tools that can predict multiple post-translational modifications. Some of them include DbPTM 3.0 (Lu *et al.*, 2012), PhosphoSitePlus (PSP) (Hornbeck *et al.*, 2014), PTMcode v2 (Minguez *et al.*, 2014), Compendium of Protein Lysine Modifications (CPLM) (Liu *et al.*, 2014b) and ProteomeScout (Matlock *et al.*, 2014). For doing custom advance bioinformatics, one can download data from post-translational modifications databases and use as training data for machine learning algorithms. Once trained, the machine learning (e.g., neural network or support vector machine) algorithm can identify putative post-translational modifications when input with a new protein sequence data (Gnad *et al.*, 2010).

Characterizing and Functional Assignment of Non-Coding RNAs

Non-coding RNAs from sequencing experiments or data mining efforts can be characterized via several methods depending on what is known about the dataset and the objective of the characterization. If none is known regarding the ncRNA sequences dataset, a good strategy would be to start with a BLAST search against the RNAcentral or NONCODE database. Sequences with identified homologs are ascribed with functions and type of the homologs. Those with identified homologs can be grouped into their putative ncRNA types. Further analysis can be done by doing a sequence search against curated database of a specific ncRNA type. The search will either confirm the previous annotation using RNAcentral (or NONCODE) database or give a different annotation. Assuming the curated database has less errors compared to computationally curated databases, the new function can be assigned to those sequences in the dataset.

Additionally, it may be worthwhile to characterize the ncRNA dataset with all available ncRNA databases. This can be done through at least two strategies. The first strategy is to download all the sequences from the databases. Once downloaded, the sequences can be appended into a single flat file. This flat file can then be converted into a BLAST database using makeblastdb, which is part of the NCBI BLAST software package. Details on generating a BLAST database can be found in the official BLAST guide (see "Relevant Websites section"). The ncRNA sequence dataset can then be searched using the local install of the NCBI BLAST against the custom BLAST database created. The best homologs for each query sequence across all ncRNA databases (source of the custom database) can then be found.

The second strategy is to search each database separately then download all the results. For easier processing, the results can be input into database applications such as mysql or MS Access. With the pooled results, one can now proceed to reduce the results into a non-redundant list. This can be done easily using remove redundant tools in those applications. Some sequences might have different annotations from different database. Manual curation is best at this stage where the investigator can select the best annotation based on what is known regarding the sequences. Once ncRNA sequence databases have been exhaustively searched, sequences that are yet to be annotated can be searched against the Rfam RNA domain database (Daub *et al.*, 2015) or any other RNA motif databases including ATtRACT (Giudice *et al.*, 2016) and RBPBD (Cook *et al.*, 2011).

Future Directions

There are many classes of biological databases today and in each class, there is often more than one database. The protein domain database class for example, twelve databases have been listed in this article. The challenge in having so many public databases of the same class is how to control for overlap of information; this is from the perspective of the database developers. On the other hand, from the user's perspective, how can one integrate the results from so many databases into his or her analysis pipeline. Each database often has its own ID and set of annotations making the removal of redundant results between databases a not trivial task. Thus, the effort of building a centralized database must continue. In the case of domain databases, InterProScan is one of the efforts for doing search against multiple domain databases (Jones *et al.*, 2014).

Another area of gap in the field of biological databases is the integration of different database class. An integrated database would consist of DNA sequences, RNA sequences, protein sequences, protein structures, protein domains, RNA domains etc. The reason this has yet to be seen is due to the challenges that comes with integration of biological data. The biggest challenge is figuring out the relationships between the different molecular entities. Biological data is big and after integration, it will be even bigger. Thus, there is also the challenge of navigating through the data and data visualization. Finally, is the issue of storage and management due to the sheer size of these integrated databases.

Closing Remarks

Biological databases have been and will always be an essential part of any molecular biology research. The wealth of information gathered since the start of the genomic era is priceless and have led to many new discoveries since then. Developments in biological databases must continue in line with the generation of new biological data.

See also: Information Retrieval in Life Sciences. Integrative Bioinformatics. Integrative Bioinformatics of Transcriptome: Databases, Tools and Pipelines. Natural Language Processing Approaches in Bioinformatics

---

References

Acland, A., Agarwala, R., Barrett, T., *et al.*, 2014. Database resources of the national center for biotechnology information. Nucleic Acids Research 42 (Database issue), D7.

Ahmed, A., Smith, R.D., Clark, J.J., Dunbar Jr, J.B., Carlson, H.A., 2014. Recent improvements to Binding MOAD: A resource for protein – Ligand binding affinities and structures. Nucleic Acids Research 43 (D1), D465–D469.

Andreeva, A., Howorth, D., Brenner, S.E., *et al.*, 2004. SCOP database in 2004: Refinements integrate structure and sequence family data. Nucleic Acids Research 32 (Suppl. 1), D226–D229.

Andreeva, A., Howorth, D., Chothia, C., Kulesha, E., Murzin, A.G., 2013. SCOP2 prototype: A new approach to protein structure mining. Nucleic Acids Research 42 (D1), D310–D314.

Attwood, T., Beck, M., 1994. PRINTS – A protein motif fingerprint database. Protein Engineering, Design and Selection 7 (7), 841–848.

Attwood, T.K., Coletta, A., Muirhead, G., et al., 2012. The PRINTS database: A fine-grained protein sequence annotation and analysis resource – Its status in 2012. Database 2012, bas019.

Benner, S.A., 1988. Extracellular 'communicator RNA'. FEBS Letters 233 (2), 225–228.

Benson, D.A., Cavanaugh, M., Clark, K., et al., 2017. GenBank. Nucleic Acids Research 45 (Database issue), D37–D42.

Bento, A.P., Gaulton, A., Hersey, A., et al., 2014. The ChEMBL bioactivity database: An update. Nucleic Acids Research 42 (D1), D1083–D1090.

Berman, H.M., Kleywegt, G.J., Nakamura, H., Markley, J.L., 2014. The Protein Data Bank archive as an open data resource. Journal of Computer-Aided Molecular Design 28 (10), 1009–1014.

Bonet, J., Planas-Iglesias, J., Garcia-Garcia, J., et al., 2013. ArchDB 2014: Structural classification of loops in proteins. Nucleic Acids Research 42 (D1), D315–D319.

Bru, C., Courcelle, E., Carrère, S., et al., 2005. The ProDom database of protein domain families: More emphasis on 3D. Nucleic Acids Research 33 (Suppl. 1), D212–D215.

Camacho, C., 2015. BLAST+ Release Notes.

Camacho, C., Coulouris, G., Avagyan, V., et al., 2009. BLAST+: Architecture and applications. BMC Bioinformatics 10, 421.

Cochrane, G., Karsch-Mizrachi, I., Takagi, T., 2016. The International nucleotide sequence database collaboration. Nucleic Acids Research 44 (D1), D48–D50.

Consortium, U., 2014. UniProt: A hub for protein information. Nucleic Acids Research. gku989.

Consortium, U., 2017. UniProt: The universal protein knowledgebase. Nucleic Acids Research 45 (D1), D158–D169.

Cook, K.B., Kazan, H., Zuberi, K., Morris, Q., Hughes, T.R., 2011. RBPDB: A database of RNA-binding specificities. Nucleic Acids Research 39 (Suppl. 1), D301–D308.

Cuff, A.L., Sillitoe, I., Lewis, T., et al., 2008. The CATH classification revisited – Architectures reviewed and new ways to characterize structural divergence in superfamilies. Nucleic Acids Research 37 (Suppl. 1), D310–D314.

Daub, J., Eberhardt, R.Y., Tate, J.G., Burge, S.W., 2015. Rfam: Annotating families of non-coding RNA sequences. RNA Bioinformatics. 349–363.

De Beer, T.A., Berka, K., Thornton, J.M., Laskowski, R.A., 2013. PDBsum additions. Nucleic Acids Research 42 (D1), D292–D296.

De Castro, E., Sigrist, C.J., Gattiker, A., et al., 2006. ScanProsite: Detection of PROSITE signature matches and ProRule-associated functional and structural residues in proteins. Nucleic Acids Research 34 (Suppl. 2), W362–W365.

Eddy, S.R., 1998. Profile hidden Markov models. Bioinformatics (Oxford) 14 (9), 755–763.

Finn, R.D., Attwood, T.K., Babbitt, P.C., et al., 2016a. InterPro in 2017 – Beyond protein family and domain annotations. Nucleic Acids Research 45 (D1), D190–D199.

Finn, R.D., Clements, J., Eddy, S.R., 2011. HMMER web server: Interactive sequence similarity searching. Nucleic Acids Research. gkr367.

Finn, R.D., Coggill, P., Eberhardt, R.Y., et al., 2016b. The Pfam protein families database: Towards a more sustainable future. Nucleic Acids Research 44 (D1), D279–D285.

Gilson, M.K., Liu, T., Baitaluk, M., et al., 2016. BindingDB in 2015: A public database for medicinal chemistry, computational chemistry and systems pharmacology. Nucleic Acids Research 44 (D1), D1045–D1053.

Giudice, G., Sánchez-Cabo, F., Torroja, C., Lara-Pezzi, E., 2016. ATtRACT – A database of RNA-binding proteins and associated motifs. Database: The Journal of Biological Databases and Curation 2016, baw035.

Gnad, F., Ren, S., Choudhary, C., Cox, J., Mann, M., 2010. Predicting post-translational lysine acetylation using support vector machines. Bioinformatics 26 (13), 1666–1668.

Gough, J., Chothia, C., 2002. SUPERFAMILY: HMMs representing all proteins of known structure. SCOP sequence searches, alignments and genome assignments. Nucleic Acids Research 30 (1), 268–272.

Haft, D.H., Selengut, J.D., Richter, R.A., et al., 2012. TIGRFAMs and genome properties in 2013. Nucleic Acids Research 41 (D1), D387–D395.

Haft, D.H., Selengut, J.D., White, O., 2003. The TIGRFAMs database of protein families. Nucleic Acids Research 31 (1), 371–373.

Hornbeck, P.V., Zhang, B., Murray, B., et al., 2014. PhosphoSitePlus, 2014: Mutations, PTMs and recalibrations. Nucleic Acids Research 43 (D1), D512–D520.

Jones, P., Binns, D., Chang, H.-Y., et al., 2014. InterProScan 5: Genome-scale protein function classification. Bioinformatics 30 (9), 1236–1240.

Kim, Y., Ponomarenko, J., Zhu, Z., et al., 2012. Immune epitope database analysis resource. Nucleic Acids Research 40 (W1), W525–W530.

Klimke, W., Agarwala, R., Badretdin, A., et al., 2008. The national center for biotechnology information's protein clusters database. Nucleic Acids Research 37 (Suppl. 1), D216–D223.

Kozma, D., Simon, I., Tusnády, G.E., 2012. PDBTM: Protein Data Bank of Transmembrane Proteins after 8 years. Nucleic Acids Research 41 (D1), D524–D529.

Law, V., Knox, C., Djoumbou, Y., et al., 2013. DrugBank 4.0: Shedding new light on drug metabolism. Nucleic Acids Research 42 (D1), D1091–D1097.

Leinonen, R., Akhtar, R., Birney, E., et al., 2010. The European nucleotide archive. Nucleic Acids Research 39 (Suppl. 1), D28–D31.

Letunic, I., Doerks, T., Bork, P., 2014. SMART: Recent updates, new developments and status in 2015. Nucleic Acids Research 43 (D1), D257–D260.

Liu, Z., Li, Y., Han, L., et al., 2014a. PDB-wide collection of binding data: Current status of the PDBbind database. Bioinformatics 31 (3), 405–412.

Liu, Z., Wang, Y., Gao, T., et al., 2014b. CPLM: A database of protein lysine modifications. Nucleic Acids Research 42 (D1), D531–D536.

Lu, C.-T., Huang, K.-Y., Su, M.-G., et al., 2012. DbPTM 3.0: An informative resource for investigating substrate site specificity and functional association of protein post-translational modifications. Nucleic Acids Research 41 (D1), D295–D305.

Madden, T., 2013. The BLAST Sequence Analysis Tool.

Marchler-Bauer, A., Anderson, J.B., DeWeese-Scott, C., et al., 2003. CDD: A curated Entrez database of conserved domain alignments. Nucleic Acids Research 31 (1), 383–387.

Marchler-Bauer, A., Derbyshire, M.K., Gonzales, N.R., et al., 2014. CDD: NCBI's conserved domain database. Nucleic Acids Research 43 (D1), D222–D226.

Mashima, J., Kodama, Y., Kosuge, T., et al., 2016. DNA data bank of Japan (DDBJ) progress report. Nucleic Acids Research 44 (D1), D51–D57.

Matlock, M.K., Holehouse, A.S., Naegle, K.M., 2014. ProteomeScout: A repository and analysis resource for post-translational modifications and proteins. Nucleic Acids Research 43 (D1), D521–D530.

Mattick, J.S., Makunin, I.V., 2006. Non-coding RNA. Human Molecular Genetics 15 (Suppl. 1), R17–R29.

Mattick, J.S., Rinn, J.L., 2015. Discovery and annotation of long noncoding RNAs. Nature Structural & Molecular Biology 22 (1), 5–7.

Mi, H., Muruganujan, A., Thomas, P.D., 2013. PANTHER in 2013: Modeling the evolution of gene function, and other gene attributes, in the context of phylogenetic trees. Nucleic Acids Res 41 (Database issue), D377–D386.

Minguez, P., Letunic, I., Parca, L., et al., 2014. PTMcode v2: A resource for functional associations of post-translational modifications within and between proteins. Nucleic Acids Research 43 (D1), D494–D502.

Mistry, J., Finn, R.D., Eddy, S.R., Bateman, A., Punta, M., 2013. Challenges in homology search: HMMER3 and convergent evolution of coiled-coil regions. Nucleic Acids Research 41 (12), e121.

Mosca, R., Céol, A., Stein, A., Olivella, R., Aloy, P., 2013. 3did: A catalog of domain-based interactions of known three-dimensional structure. Nucleic Acids Research 42 (D1), D374–D379.

Pearl, F.M.G., Bennett, C., Bray, J.E., et al., 2003. The CATH database: An extended protein family resource for structural and functional genomics. Nucleic Acids Research 31 (1), 452–455.

Peters, B., Sidney, J., Bourne, P., et al., 2005. The immune epitope database and analysis resource: From vision to blueprint. PLOS Biology 3 (3), e91.

Servant, F., Bru, C., Carrère, S., et al., 2002. ProDom: Automated clustering of homologous domains. Briefings in Bioinformatics 3 (3), 246–251.

Seto, A.G., Kingston, R.E., Lau, N.C., 2007. The coming of age for Piwi proteins. Molecular Cell 26 (5), 603–609.

Sigrist, C.J., Cerutti, L., Hulo, N., et al., 2002. PROSITE: A documented database using patterns and profiles as motif descriptors. Briefings in Bioinformatics 3 (3), 265–274.

Sigrist, C.J., de Castro, E., Cerutti, L., *et al.*, 2013. New and continuing developments at PROSITE. Nucleic Acids Research 41 (Database issue), D344–D347.

Sigrist, C.J., De Castro, E., Langendijk-Genevaux, P.S., *et al.*, 2005. ProRule: A new database containing functional and structural information on PROSITE profiles. Bioinformatics 21 (21), 4060–4066.

Sillitoe, I., Lewis, T., Orengo, C., *et al.*, 2015. Using CATH-Gene3D to Analyze the Sequence, Structure, and Function of Proteins. Current protocols in bioinformatics. 1.28. 1–1.28. 21.

Sonnhammer, E.L., Eddy, S.R., Durbin, R., 1997. Pfam: A comprehensive database of protein domain families based on seed alignments. Proteins: Structure, Function and Genetics 28 (3), 405–420.

Tatusov, R.L., Fedorova, N.D., Jackson, J.D., *et al.*, 2003. The COG database: An updated version includes eukaryotes. BMC Bioinformatics 4 (1), 41.

Toribio, A.L., Alako, B., Amid, C., *et al.*, 2017. European Nucleotide Archive in 2016. Nucleic Acids Research 45 (D1), D32–D36.

Wilson, D., Pethica, R., Zhou, Y., *et al.*, 2009. SUPERFAMILY – Sophisticated comparative genomics, data mining, visualization and phylogeny. Nucleic Acids Research 37 (Suppl. 1), D380–D386.

Relevant Websites

http://tools.iedb.org/main
   IEDB Analysis Resource.
http://www.insdc.org
   INSDC: International Nucleotide Sequence Database Collaboration.
https://www.ncbi.nlm.nih.gov/books/NBK279688/
   NCBI BLAST User Manual.
https://blast.ncbi.nlm.nih.gov/Blast.cgi
   NCBI BLAST Web Server.

Extraction of Immune Epitope Information

Guang Lan Zhang, Boston University, Boston, MA, United States and Harvard Medical School, Boston, MA, United States
Derin B Keskin, Harvard Medical School, Boston, MA, United States and Broad Institute, Boston, MA, United States
Lou Chitkushev, Boston University, Boston, MA, United States

Introduction

The adaptive immune system is composed of highly specialized cells and processes that recognize "non-self" antigens, mount immune responses to eliminate the antigens or antigen-infected cells, and develop immunological memory through memory B cells and memory T cells that leads to an enhanced response to subsequent encounters with the same antigens. Two arms of adaptive immunity, the humoral immunity mediated by B cells and the cell-mediated immunity mediated by T cells, work closely to combat infection and malignancy in an antigen specific manner. Major histocompatibility complex (MHC) proteins play a vital role in the regulation of cell-mediated immune responses. MHC class I molecules are found on every nucleated cell of the body, while MCH class II molecules are expressed on specialized cells, including professional APCs such as B cells, macrophages and dendritic cells (Janeway, 2005). They bind short peptides derived from protein antigens through proteolytic mechanisms and subsequently present MHC-peptide complexes on the cell surface for recognition by T cells. T cells identify foreign antigens through their T-cell receptors (TCRs), which interacts with MHC-peptide complexes in conjunction with CD4 or CD8 co-receptors (Meuer et al., 1982; Wang and Reinherz, 2002). MHC class I antigen processing pathway steps include proteasome cleavage of proteins into shorter peptides, translocation of peptides into the endoplasmic reticulum (ER) by TAP (the transporter associated with antigen processing), optional ER trimming by aminopeptidases, insertion of peptides, typically 8–11 amino acid residues in length, into the binding groove of MHC molecules, and transport of peptide-MHC complexes to the cell surface for presentation to CD8 + T cells (Purcell and Gorman, 2004; Strehl et al., 2005). In humoral immunity, B cells produce antibodies to eliminate extracellular microorganisms and prevent the spread of infection. T lymphocytes expressing the CD4 co-receptor recognize MHC class II molecules complexed to peptides generated from endogenous cellular proteins that are typically 8–30 amino acids in length and are often nested sets of peptides with a core sequence shared among them (Rudensky et al., 1991; Engelhard, 1994; Bozzacco et al., 2011). The recognition of peptide-MHC class II complexes by CD4 + T cells, stimulating them to make proteins that stimulate the B cells to differentiate into antibody secreting cells. Thus the activation of B cells is triggered by antigens and usually requires helper T cells (Janeway, 2005). B cells identify antigens through B-cell receptors, which recognize discrete sites on the surface of target antigens called B-cell epitopes (Van Regenmortel, 2009). Peptides that are presented by MHC and recognized by T-cells are termed T cell epitopes. They are important targets of adaptive immune responses and rational vaccine design. This article focuses on the MHC binding peptides and T cell epitopes.

Identification of T cell epitopes in essential in the development of epitope-based vaccines. One of the key steps in T-cell epitope prediction is the prediction of MHC binding, as it is considered the most selective step in T cell recognition. The challenge in the identification of broadly protective vaccine targets stems from two principal sources – the diversity of pathogens and the diversity of human immune system. HLA (Human Leukocyte Antigen, human MHC) are among the most polymorphic human proteins, with more than 12,000 known HLA Class I alleles and 4700 HLA class II variants as of Dec 2017 (Robinson et al., 2015). To handle HLA polymorphism, the concept of HLA supertypes was proposed to group HLA alleles showing similar peptide binding specificity into supertypes (Sidney et al., 1996; Sette and Sidney, 1999). The ideal vaccine targets are conserved immune epitopes that are broadly cross-reactive to viral subtypes and protective of a large human population (Zhang et al., 2014). In this article we reviewed in silico and in vitro methods for immune epitope discovery.

In Vitro Methods for Identification of MHC Ligands and T Cell Epitopes

In Vitro Discovery of MHC Ligands

MHC binding to a potential peptide can be tested in vitro using binding assays or Mass spectrometry (MS) based methods. Note that MHC binding does not guarantee T cell reactivity. In binding assays, purified MHC proteins or TAP deficient cells lines are used to test peptide binding to specific MHC molecules. These assays are only useful in testing MHC/peptide binding, a prerequisite for T-cell activation. It does not guarantee T cells will recognize the binding peptide as antigen. For example, TAP-deficient T2 cell HLA stabilization assay was used to confirm 10 HPV (human papillomavirus) E6 and E7 peptides that bind to HLA-A*0201 (Riemer et al., 2010).

MHC-peptide complexes may be immunoprecipitated from target cells. Peptides may be released from MHC using fractionation (e.g., using HPLC, the physical separation capabilities of liquid chromatography). These peptides can be analyzed by MS analysis that produces detailed information of the MHC ligandome. MS based ligand discovery physically detect the peptides that are naturally processed and presented on the cell surface. We refer to these peptides as "eluted peptides". The immunogenicity of these peptides needs further in vivo and in vitro testing. MS based assays require extensive optimization for pure MHC-Peptide complex isolation. MS analysis also requires rare expertise, which are not directly applicable to all laboratories (Bozzacco et al., 2011; Abelin et al., 2017).

In Vitro Discovery of T Cell Epitopes

T cell epitope discovery without the help of bioinformatics prediction algorithms applies T cell immunogenicity assays on overlapping peptides. These synthesized peptides are typically 15–16 amino acids (aa) in length with 10aa overlap and cover the protein sequence of the whole pathogen. They are pooled together to be tested. T cells can be tested *ex-vivo* from previously infected, immune donors or after a few rounds of stimulation in cell culture from naïve donors. Generation of an antigen specific T cell line may take up to four weekly antigen stimulations. Cloning of a T cell may require further culture for up to two months of hands-on work.

In T cell reactivity testing, multiple experimental assays including intra-cellular cytokine staining, proliferation assays and Elispot assays are available to test peptide epitope reactivity. In intra-cellular cytokine staining, T cells produce cytokines such as IFNγ, TNFα and IL-2 after epitope recognition and activation. After a brief *ex-vivo* culture with possible reactive peptides or peptide pools, T cells are stained for these cytokines *in vitro* using specific antibodies linked to fluorochromes. Cell membranes need to be permeabilized for antibody access using detergents, which makes the assay less sensitive than other available assays. Golgi blocking agents can be used briefly in culture for cytokine deposition in the cytoplasm. After antibody staining the cells are analyzed using a flow-cytometer (Ott *et al.*, 2017).

In proliferation assays, T cells start proliferating 2–3 days after antigen recognition. T cell proliferation can be measured using tritiated Thymidine incorporation or dilution of cell permeable marker dyes such as CFSE (Carboxyfluorescein succinimidyl ester) by flow cytometry. These assays are sensitive however require long term cell culture (Mellor *et al.*, 2002).

Elispot assays utilize cytokine capture antibody coated plates. T cells produce cytokines such as IFNγ, TNFα and IL-2 after epitope recognition and activation. T cells can be stimulated in this cytokine capture antibody coated plates up to 48 h. After removal of T cells, the captured cytokines on plates are detected by a sandwich assay utilizing a biotinylated secondary cytokine specific antibody and streptavidin enzyme conjugate. These assays produce spots, which represents each cytokine producing T cells. Spot forming cells can be calculated from each assay and will give accurate antigen specific T cell frequency in a sample (Keskin *et al.*, 2015).

In Silico Methods for Epitope Identification

The advancement in high throughput methods such as whole-genome sequencing and in bioinformatics led to the identification of potential vaccine targets without the need for growing the pathogen. The concept of reverse vaccinology supports identification of vaccine targets by large-scale bioinformatics screening of entire pathogenic genomes followed by experimental validation (Rappuoli, 2000; Mora *et al.*, 2003; Rappuoli *et al.*, 2016).

Publicly available bioinformatics resources include biological databases that organize and catalog immune epitopes and their related information as well as computational systems that model the biological processes involved in antigen processing and presentation, i.e., proteasome cleavage, TAP transportation, and MHC binding.

Databases Hosting Immune Epitopes

Table 1 summarizes immune epitopes databases that are publically available. Some are general-purpose databases, including SYFPEITHI, the Immune Epitope Database and Analysis Resource (IEDB), MCHBN, and Dana-Farber Repository for Machine Learning in immunology (DFRMLI), hosting MHC binding peptides and immune epitopes from various types of antigens. Some host immune epitopes from tumor antigens, such as the Cancer Immunome database and Tantigen. Some host immune epitopes from specific viruses, such as EBVdb (Epstein-Barr virus T cell antigen database), FLAVIdB (Flaviviruses database), FluKB (Influenza virus knowledge-base), HPVdb (Human Papillomavirus T cell Antigen Database), Los Alamos hepatitis C immunology database, and Los Alamos HIV Molecular Immunology Database.

DFRMLI hosts standardized data sets of HLA-binding peptides with all binding affinities mapped onto a common scale and a list of experimentally validated naturally processed eluted peptides and non-binding peptides derived from tumor or virus antigens (Zhang *et al.*, 2011). Some of the data in DFRMLI were aggregated from publicly available databases such as MHCPEP (Brusic *et al.*, 1994), IEDB, CBS (Center for Biological Sequence Analysis). Some data are our in-house data and the validation data sets were made of carefully selected independent data. These data sets were used to support the 1st and 2nd machine learning competitions in immunology in 2011 and 2012 (Zhang *et al.*, 2011). IEDB established in 2004 catalogs experimentally characterized B and T cell epitopes, MHC binding peptides, and data on corresponding experimental assays. It also hosts computational tools for immune epitope prediction and analysis (Vita *et al.*, 2015; Fleri *et al.*, 2017). Domain experts manually curated the data in IEDB to ensure quality and data completeness. The IEDB intentionally does not contain HIV (human immunodeficiency virus) epitopes as they are archived in the Los Alamos HIV Molecular Immunology Database (Altman and Safrit, 1998). MHCBN is a database hosting experimentally validated T cell epitopes, binding peptides to MHC and TAP, and non-binding peptides to MHC and TAP. MHCBN also provides bioinformatics tools for the analysis and retrieval of information like mapping of antigenic regions, creation of allele specific dataset, BLAST search, various diseases associated with MHC alleles etc (Lata *et al.*, 2009). SYFPEITHI is among the earliest online database that host immune epitopes (Rammensee *et al.*, 1999; Schuler *et al.*, 2007). It

Table 1   Online databases hosting immune epitopes listed in alphabetical order. The information is up to date as of Dec 2017

Database	Description of content	URL
Cancer Immunome Database	Four data tables containing over 400 T cell epitopes identified in tumor antigens	www.cancerresearch.org/scientists/events-and-resources/peptide-database
Dana-Farber Repository for Machine Learning in Immunology (DFRMLI)	MHC class I and II binding peptides, eluted peptides, non-binding peptides	projects.met-hilab.org/DFRMLI/
EBVdb, Epstein-Barr virus (EBV) T cell antigen database	610 T cell epitopes and 26 HLA ligands from EBV antigens	projects.met-hilab.org/ebv
FLAVIdb, Flaviviruses database	184 verified T-cell epitopes, 201 verified B-cell epitopes	cvc.dfci.harvard.edu/flavi/
FluKB, a knowledge-base for influenza viruses	357 T-cell epitopes, 685 HLA binding peptides, 16 naturally processed MHC ligands, and 28 influenza antibodies and their structurally defined B-cell epitopes	research4.dfci.harvard.edu/cvc/flukb/
HPVdb, Human Papillomavirus (HPV) T cell Antigen Database	191 T cell epitopes and 45 HLA ligands from HPV antigens	projects.met-hilab.org/hpv
IEDB	422,219 peptide epitopes, 2553 non-peptidic epitopes, T cell and B cell assays, MHC binding assays etc.	www.iedb.org/
Los Alamos hepatitis C immunology database	383 CD8 + T cell epitopes, 222 CD4 + T cell epitopes, and 60 antibody binding sites from HCV proteins for human, mouse, chimpanzee, and rat	hcv.lanl.gov/content/immuno/immuno-main.html
Los Alamos HIV Molecular Immunology Database	9821 CD8 + T cell epitopes, 1578 CD4 + T cell epitopes, and 3306 antibody binding sites from HIV proteins for human, macaque, chimpanzee, mouse etc.	www.hiv.lanl.gov/content/immunology/
MHCBN	6722 T cell epitopes, 4022 non-binding peptides, 1022 TAP binding peptides	crdd.osdd.net/raghava/mhcbn/
SYFPEITHI	>7000 MHC class I and II binding peptides	www.syfpeithi.de/
Tantigen	>1000 HLA class I and II binding peptides, eluted peptides, and T cell epitopes from tumor antigens	projects.met-hilab.org/tadb or cvc.dfci.harvard.edu/tantigen/

allows users to search for MHC ligands, peptide binding motifs, natural ligands, and T cell epitopes by specifying MHC alleles, source proteins/organisms, etc., It also supports MHC binding prediction.

The identification of tumor antigens is a high priority in cancer research and is an essential component in developing immune-based strategies to combat cancer. The following databases introduced are useful resources for the study of immune responses against tumors. The Cancer Immunome database is a continuation of the SEREX database, maintained by the Ludwig Institute for Cancer Research since 1997, in a more organized form. The database contains T cell epitopes in tumor antigens that are classified based on their tumor specificity into four data tables (Jongeneel, 2001; Vigneron *et al.*, 2013). All immune epitopes in the database have been documented to elicit immune responses in cancer patients. Tantigen is a database of human tumor T cell antigens that catalogued more than 1000 tumor peptides. The peptides are labelled as one of four categories: (1) peptides measured *in vitro* to bind the HLA, (2) peptides found to bind the HLA and to elicit an *in vitro* T cell response, (3) peptides shown to elicit *in vivo* tumor rejection, and (4) peptides processed and naturally presented as defined by physical detection. The Tumor T Cell Antigen Database (TANTIGEN) is a data source and analysis platform for cancer vaccine target discovery focusing on human tumor-derived HLA ligands and T cell epitopes. It contains 4006 curated antigen entries representing 251 unique proteins, information on experimentally validated T cell epitopes and HLA ligands, antigen isoforms, antigen sequence mutations, and tumor antigen classification. TANTIGEN provides a rich data resource and tailored analysis tools for tumor associated epitope and neoepitope discovery studies (Olsen *et al.*, 2017).

Some viruses such as Epstein-Barr virus (EBV) and human papillomaviruses (HPVs) are the causes of many cancers, which some such as influenza viruses, flaviviruses, and HIV cause various infectious disease. To facilitate diagnosis, prognosis and characterization of these diseases, it is necessary to make full use of the immunological data on the viruses. Epstein-Barr virus (EBV) T cell antigen database is a data source and analysis platform for EBV immune target discovery by focusing on EBV antigens that contain T cell epitopes (Zhang *et al.*, 2015). It hosts 2622 curated EBV antigen sequences, 610 T cell epitopes and 26 HLA ligands. FLAVIdb combines antigenic data of flaviviruses, specialized analysis tools, and workflows for automated complex analyses focusing on applications in immunology and vaccinology (Olsen *et al.*, 2011). It contains 12,858 entries of flavivirus antigen sequences, 184 T-cell epitopes, 201 B-cell epitopes, and four representative molecular structures of the dengue virus envelope protein. FluKB provides access to more than 400,000 curated influenza protein sequences, known epitope data (357 verified T-cell epitopes, 685 HLA binders, and 16 naturally processed MHC ligands), and a collection of 28 influenza antibodies and their structurally defined B-cell epitopes (Simon *et al.*, 2015). HPVdb is a data mining system for knowledge discovery in HPV with applications in T cell immunology and vaccinology. It contains 2781 curated antigenic proteins derived from 18 genotypes of high-risk HPV and 18 genotypes of low-risk HPV, 191 T cell epitopes and 45 HLA ligands (Zhang *et al.*, 2014). Los Alamos hepatitis C immunology database contains T-cell epitopes and antibody binding sites in hepatitis C virus (HCV) for human and multiple animal models, as well as relevant retrieval and analysis tools (Yusim *et al.*, 2005). The HIV Molecular Immunology Database provides an annotated collection of HIV-1 cytotoxic and helper T-cell epitopes and antibody binding sites (Immunology, 2016).

Prediction Systems for Proteasome Cleavage, TAP Binding, and MHC Binding

Computational tools that model the proteolytic activities of the proteasome and TAP binding can be integrated with prediction systems for MHC class I binding peptides to improve the performance of *in silico* prediction of T-cell epitopes. NetChop predicts cleavage sites of the human proteasome using artificial neural network (ANN) models trained on data from *in vitro* digestion experiments with constitutive proteasomes and MHC Class I ligand data that reflect immunoproteasome specificity (Kesmir *et al.*, 2002; Nielsen *et al.*, 2005). NetChop team maintains the tool and updated it periodically. The latest version is NetChop v3.1. MAPPP models two essential steps in endogenous antigen processing pathway, the proteasome cleavage and MHC binding. FRAGPREDICT that predicts the proteasome cleavage sites using motifs encoding cleavage-enhancing and -inhibiting amino acids is the part that models proteasome cleavage in MAPPP (Holzhutter *et al.*, 1999). PAProC (Prediction Algorithm for Proteasomal Cleavages) is an online prediction system for cleavages by constitutive proteasomes of human and yeast based on experimental cleavage data (Nussbaum *et al.*, 2001). Pcleavage is a prediction system for constitutive as well as immunoproteasome cleavage sites using a support vector machine (SVM) based method (Bhasin and Raghava, 2005). Saxova and co-authors evaluated the performance of PAProC, FRAGPREDICT and two versions of NetChop, v1.0 and v2.0 and found that NetChop v2.0 performed the best (Saxova *et al.*, 2003) (**Tables 2**).

TAP is a transmembrane protein that transports antigenic peptides into the ER. It has been shown that the efficiency of TAP-mediated translocation of a peptide correlates positively to its TAP binding affinity (Brusic *et al.*, 1999). Peptides of 8–16 amino acids and have sufficient TAP binding affinity are efficiently translocated by TAP into the ER, while longer peptides may be transported but with lower efficiency (Saveanu *et al.*, 2005). SVMTAP employs a matrix-based method and support vector regression to predict peptides transported by TAP (Donnes and Kohlbacher, 2005). TAPPred is based on cascade SVM using sequence and properties of the amino acids (Bhasin and Raghava, 2004) (**Table 3**).

MHC binding is the most selective step in the antigen presentation pathway. Quite a few online prediction systems have been developed for the prediction of peptide binding to MHC molecules based on algorithms including binding motifs, quantitative matrices, and machine learning methods such as ANN models and support vector machines. In addition there has been effort to develop a prediction algorithm based on naturally processed and presented MHC eluted peptide epitopes detected by MS together with gene expression and protein processing (Abelin *et al.*, 2017). While the prediction systems listed in **Table 4** were designed for different purposes with various methods, all of them have peptide binding predictions implemented as specific modules. MAPPP, ProPred-I, and RANKPEP predict proteasomal cleavage sites and MHC binding, MULTIPRED2 predicts peptide binding to HLA supertypes, and BIMAS predicts peptide binding as half-time dissociation (off-rate).

BIMAS is one of the first online tools that predicts 8-mer, 9-mer, or 10-mer binding peptides using class I mouse and human MHC binding motifs (Parker *et al.*, 1994). SYFPEITHI predicts MHC class I and class II binding peptides in human, mouse and rat based on allele-specific peptide motifs (Schuler *et al.*, 2007). The MHC binding prediction part of MAPPP identifies potential 8-mer, 9-mer and 10mer peptides that bind human, mouse and bovine MHC class I alleles with the option to use either BIMAS matrix or SYFPEITHI matrix for prediction (Hakenberg *et al.*, 2003). Note that MAPPP (BIMAS) and MAPPP (SYFPEITHI) showed identical predictions to BIMAS and SYFPEITHI, respectively (Lin *et al.*, 2008). RANKPEP predicts binding peptides of 88 MHC class I and 50 MHC class II alleles in human and mouse using position specific scoring matrices (PSSMs) (Reche *et al.*, 2002, 2004). There is option to add in the proteasome cleavage step in the prediction.

Table 2   Online prediction tools for proteasome cleavage listed in alphabetical order. The information is up to date as of Dec 2017

Online tool	URL
FRAGPREDICT	www.mpiib-berlin.mpg.de/MAPPP/cleavage.html
NetChop	www.cbs.dtu.dk/services/NetChop/
PAProC	www.paproc.de/
Pcleavage	crdd.osdd.net/raghava/pcleavage/

Table 3   Online prediction tools for TAP binding listed in alphabetical order. The information is up to date as of Dec 2017

Online tool	URL
SVMTAP	abi.inf.uni-tuebingen.de/Services/SVMTAP
TAPPred	crdd.osdd.net/raghava/tappred/

Table 4   Online tools for predicting MHC binding peptides listed in alphabetical order. The information is up to date as of Dec 2017

Online tool	Description	URL
BIMAS	Predicts MHC class I binding peptides in human and mouse	www-bimas.cit.nih.gov/molbio/hla_bind/
IEDB MCH class I tool	Predicts MHC class I binding peptides in human and multiple animal models	tools.immuneepitope.org/mhci/
IEDB MCH class II tool	Predicts MHC class II binding peptides in human and mouse	tools.iedb.org/mhcii/
MAPPP	Predicts MHC class I binding peptides in human and mouse	www.mpiib-berlin.mpg.de/MAPPP/binding.html
Multipred2	Predicts binding peptides of multiple alleles in HLA class I and class II supertypes and of alleles belonging to an individual's genotype	projects.met-hilab.org/multipred2/
NetMHC	Predicts MHC class I binding peptides in human, monkey, cattle, pig, and mouse	www.cbs.dtu.dk/services/NetMHC/
NetMHCcons	Predicts MHC class I binding peptides in human, chimpanzee, monkey, gorilla, pig, and mouse	www.cbs.dtu.dk/services/NetMHCcons/
NetMHCpan	Predicts binding peptides of any MHC class I molecule of known sequence	www.cbs.dtu.dk/services/NetMHCpan/
NetMHCII	Predicts MHC class II binding peptides in human and mouse	www.cbs.dtu.dk/services/NetMHCII/
NetMHCIIpan	Predicts binding peptides of HLA-DR, -DP, -DQ molecules and H2 class II molecules	www.cbs.dtu.dk/services/NetMHCIIpan/
PickPocket	Predicts MHC class II binding peptides in human and mouse	www.cbs.dtu.dk/services/PickPocket/
ProPred	Predicts binding peptides of HLA class II alleles	crdd.osdd.net/raghava/propred/
ProPred-I	Predicts peptides that bind human, mouse and bovine MHC class I alleles	crdd.osdd.net/raghava/propred1/
RANKPEP	Predicts MHC class I and class II binding peptides in human and mouse	imed.med.ucm.es/Tools/rankpep.html
SVMHC	Predicts binding peptides of MHC class I and class II alleles in human and mouse	abi.inf.uni-tuebingen.de/Services/SVMHC
SYFPEITHI	Predicts MHC class I and Class II binding peptides in human, mouse, and rat	www.syfpeithi.de/bin/MHCServer.dll/EpitopePrediction.htm
TEPITOPEpan	Predicts binding peptides to HLA-DR alleles	datamining-iip.fudan.edu.cn/service/TEPITOPEpan/TEPITOPEpan.html

NetMHC v4.0 predicts peptides that bind 81 different HLA-A, -B, -C and -E alleles as well as 41 MHC class I alleles of monkey, cattle, pig, and mouse. It employs a sequence alignment method based on ANN that allows insertions and deletions in the alignment (Nielsen *et al.*, 2003; Andreatta and Nielsen, 2016). NetMHCpan v4.0 predicts peptides that bind any MHC class I molecule of known sequence based on an ANN model trained using pseudo-sequences representing peptide/MHC interactions (Nielsen *et al.*, 2007a,b; Jurtz *et al.*, 2017). The pseudo-sequences that capture the specific HLA–peptide interaction by combining each amino acid of the peptide with the variable amino acids of its positional environment was first proposed in Brusic *et al.* (2002). NetMHCpan v4.0 was trained on a combination of quantitative MHC binding data and MS derived MHC eluted ligands (Hoof *et al.*, 2009; Jurtz *et al.*, 2017). PickPocket v1.1 predicts binding peptides of any known MHC class I molecule using position specific weight matrices that capture receptor-pocket similarities between MHC molecules. Predictions can be made for HLA-A, -B, -C, -E and -G alleles as well as MHC class I alleles in mouse, cattle and pig (Zhang *et al.*, 2009). NetMHCcons a consensus method for MHC class I binding predictions integrating three methods, NetMHC, NetMHCpan and PickPocket (Karosiene *et al.*, 2012). NetMHCII v2.2 predicts binding peptides for 14 HLA-DR alleles, six HLA-DQ, six HLA-DP, and two mouse H2 class II alleles. It employs an ANN-based alignment method, NN-align, trained using an algorithm that incorporates information on the residues flanking the peptide-binding core (Nielsen *et al.*, 2007a,b; Nielsen and Lund, 2009). NetMHCIIpan v3.1 predicts binding peptides of MHC class II molecules in human (HLA-DR, HLA-DP and HLA-DQ) and mouse (H2) (Karosiene *et al.*, 2013; Andreatta *et al.*, 2015).

IEDB MCH class I tool predicts binding peptides of MHC class I alleles in human and multiple animals. It allows users to choose from a number of prediction methods including Stabilized matrix method (SMM) (Peters and Sette, 2005), NetMCHpan, NetMHC, NetMHCcons, PickPocket and so on. IEDB MCH class II tool predicts binding peptides of MHC class I alleles in human and multiple animals. It allows users to choose from a number of prediction methods including the consensus method (Wang *et al.*, 2008), NetMHCII, NetMCHIIpan and so on. MULTIPRED2 screens for peptide binding to multiple alleles belonging to HLA class I and class II supertypes as well as to alleles belonging to an individual's genotype. The prediction engines used are NetMHCpan and NetMH-CIIpan. In total MULTIPRED2 performs binding predictions on 1077 alleles belonging to 26 HLA supertypes (Zhang *et al.*, 2011).

ProPred-I predicts binding peptides of 47 MHC class-I alleles in human, mouse and cow using quantitative matrices. ProPred-I provides the option to filter out the peptides with predicted proteasomal cleavage sites (Singh and Raghava, 2003). The ProPred1 predictions were found highly correlated with BIMAS predictions for five HLA-I alleles (HLA-A*02:01, -A*03:01, -A*11:01, -A*24:01, and -B*08:01,) as some of the BIMAS matrices were adopted by ProPred1 (Lin *et al.*, 2008). ProPred predicts binding peptides of 51 HLA-DRB1 and -DRB5 alleles using quantitative matrices (Singh and Raghava, 2001). SVMHC predicts of 9-mer and 10-mer peptides that bind multiple MHC class I alleles in human and mouse using SVM based methods. It also predicts binding peptides to HLA-DRB1 alleles using PSSMs from TEPITOPE, a widely used method containing PSSMs that cover 51 different HLA-DR alleles (Sturniolo *et al.*, 1999; Donnes and Kohlbacher, 2006). TEPITOPEpan was built by extrapolating from the

HLA-DR alleles with known binding specificities in TEPITOPE to the HLA-DR molecules with unknown binding specificities based on pocket similarity (Zhang et al., 2012). TEPITOPEpan is able to predict binding peptides of more than 700 HLA-DR alleles.

With many MHC binding prediction systems available, the next question is how to choose the most suitable one for predicting binding to a given MHC molecule. Several groups have reported their effort in assessing performance of computational methods that predict peptide binding to several common MHC class I (Peters et al., 2006; Lin et al., 2008; Gowthaman et al., 2010; Zhang et al., 2011; Trolle et al., 2015) and II alleles (Lin et al., 2008). Machine learning competition in immunology organized by Dana-Farber Cancer Institute evaluated the performance of 20 computational methods in predicting 9-mer and 10-mer peptides binding to HLA-A*01:01, A*02:01, and B*07:02. The evaluation data sets used in the competition are available at DFRMLI. It was found that NetMHC, NetMHCpan, and NetMHCcons demonstrated the best performance overall (Zhang et al., 2011). Lin et al. (2008) compare the performance of 30 computational methods in predicting peptides binding to seven HLA class I alleles, A*0201, 0301, 1101, 2402, B*0702, 0801, and 1501. In general they found the prediction methods for A*0201, 0301, 1101, B*0702, 0801, and 1501 have excellent, and for A*2402 moderate classification accuracy (Lin et al., 2008). Gowthaman et al. evaluated eight prediction systems in predicting peptides binding to seven HLA class I alleles, A*0101, 0201, 0301, 1101, 2402, B*0702, and 0801. It was found that NetMHC, NetMHCpan, and IEDB showed better overall efficiency (Gowthaman et al., 2010). In Lin et al. (2008), 21 HLA class II prediction methods were evaluated for their performance in predicting binding peptides of seven common HLA-DR allele, DRB1*0101, 0301, 0401, 0701, 1101, 1301, and 1501. It was found that the HLA class II predictors do not match prediction capabilities of HLA class I ones. It is more difficult to predict MHC class II binding as, unlike MHC class I molecules, binding grooves of a MHC class II molecules have open ends allowing them to accommodate the 9-mer binding core of the peptides inside while peptide termini protrude outside of the grooves (Stern et al., 1994). Not a single method is consistently the best for all the alleles and users have to select the suitable predictors by referring to the detailed findings in the papers. A framework that supports automated benchmarking of MHC binding prediction tools was developed. It runs weekly benchmarks on data that are newly entered into IEDB to provide up-to-date performance evaluations available at the website provided in "Relevant Website section" (Trolle et al., 2015; Andreatta et al., 2017).

Discussion

Immune epitopes are the targets of adaptive immune responses and rational vaccine design. We reviewed in silico and in vitro methods for immune epitope discovery. In silico methods include databases of immune epitopes, prediction systems for proteasome cleavage, TAP binding, and MHC binding. These in silico tools support downstream in vitro and in vivo studies. Publically available immune epitope databases allow both scientists and clinicians to utilize target genome information to support rational vaccine design and development. The availability of curated MHC binding data and T cell epitopes in turn improves target selection. These technologies are finding real life applications, for example the vaccines against HIV, the causative agent of AIDS (Stephenson et al., 2016). The vast genetic diversity of HIV type 1 (HIV-1) envelope glycoprotein poses challenges in developing a global vaccine. Currently a mosaic HIV virus vaccine that contains mosaic HIV virus components designed utilizing Los Alamos HIV database to provide global virus coverage is in clinical trial (Ad26-env mosaic vaccine) (Nkolola et al., 2014). Similar efforts are underway to develop universal Influenza vaccines utilizing FluKB and vaccines against cancer causing viruses such as HPV utilizing HPVdb (Riemer et al., 2010; Keskin et al., 2011; Keskin et al., 2015). Computational tools and databases also play a role in support of developing personalized neo-antigen based cancer vaccines. Neo-antigens arise from tumor specific mutations, these epitopes are exclusively tumor specific and they circumvent T cell tolerance against self-epitopes (Fritsch et al., 2013). Next generation sequencing and utilization of T cell epitope prediction algorithms provide tools to design cancer vaccines against an individual's own tumor from the Tumor gene sequencing data, one patient at a time (Melief, 2017; Ott et al., 2017; Sahin et al., 2017). These personalized cancer vaccines provide a leap in cancer treatment in the direction of personalized immunotherapy.

Future Directions

Identification of peptide presentation and processing rules through MS analysis of HLA binding peptides is currently perfecting epitope prediction algorithms (Abelin et al., 2017). Next-generation sequencing (NGS) enables rapid and accurate deduction of the genomics of viruses, bacteria and cancers, in which we can identify mutated new epitopes (neoepitopes) (Ott et al., 2017). Many existing prediction systems predict MHC binding peptides and MS analysis of these peptides detect the presentation of them on cell surface, however not all of these presented peptides are seen by T cells as antigens. Those silent, stealth epitopes complicate reverse vaccinology. There are efforts to improve the prediction of antigenicity of epitopes, however it requires large amount of validated antigen data. "T cell receptor (TCR) sequences are very diverse, with many more possible sequence combinations than T cells in any one individual" (Davis and Bjorkman, 1988; Shortman et al., 1990; Qi et al., 2014) Technologies to rapidly detect T cell epitopes are currently in development (Gee et al., 2018). The next advancement in rapid vaccine design would be algorithms that can predict the immunogenicity of HLA binding peptides. Combinations of all three of these technologies, (i) rapid NGS sequencing to deduce protein coding sequences, (ii) HLA allele specific, predictive epitope processing and presentation algorithms and (iii) development of TCR specific antigenicity prediction would finally enable rapid vaccine design through reverse vaccinology.

Conflict of Interest

The authors declare that they have no conflict of interest.

See also: Biological Database Searching. Information Retrieval in Life Sciences. Natural Language Processing Approaches in Bioinformatics

References

Abelin, J.G., Keskin, D.B., Sarkizova, S., *et al.*, 2017. Mass Spectrometry Profiling of HLA-Associated Peptidomes in Mono-allelic Cells Enables More Accurate Epitope Prediction. Immunity 46 (2), 315–326.

Altman, J.D., Safrit, J.T., 1998. MHC tetramer analyses of CD8+ T-cell responses to HIV and SIV. HIV Molecular Immunology. Database 1998.

Andreatta, M., Karosiene, E., Rasmussen, M., *et al.*, 2015. Accurate pan-specific prediction of peptide-MHC class II binding affinity with improved binding core identification. Immunogenetics 67, 641–650.

Andreatta, M., Nielsen, M., 2016. Gapped sequence alignment using artificial neural networks: Application to the MHC class I system. Bioinformatics 32, 511–517.

Andreatta, M., Trolle, T., Yan, Z., *et al.*, 2017. An automated benchmarking platform for MHC class II binding prediction methods. Bioinformatics.

Bhasin, M., Raghava, G.P., 2004. Analysis and prediction of affinity of TAP binding peptides using cascade SVM. Protein Science 13, 596–607.

Bhasin, M., Raghava, G.P., 2005. Pcleavage: An SVM based method for prediction of constitutive proteasome and immunoproteasome cleavage sites in antigenic sequences. Nucleic Acids Research 33 (Web Server issue), W202–W207.

Bozzacco, L., Yu, H., Zebroski, H.A., *et al.*, 2011. Mass spectrometry analysis and quantitation of peptides presented on the MHC II molecules of mouse spleen dendritic cells. Journal of Proteome Research 10, 5016–5030.

Brusic, V., Petrovsky, N., Zhang, G., Bajic, V.B., 2002. Prediction of promiscuous peptides that bind HLA class I molecules. Immunology and Cell Biology 80, 280–285.

Brusic, V., Rudy, G., Harrison, L.C., 1994. MHCPEP: A database of MHC-binding peptides. Nucleic Acids Research 22, 3663–3665.

Brusic, V., van Endert, P., Zeleznikow, J., *et al.*, 1999. A neural network model approach to the study of human TAP transporter. In Silico Biology 1, 109–121.

Davis, M.M., Bjorkman, P.J., 1988. T-cell antigen receptor genes and T-cell recognition. Nature 334 (6181), 395–402.

Donnes, P., Kohlbacher, O., 2005. Integrated modeling of the major events in the MHC class I antigen processing pathway. Protein Science 14, 2132–2140.

Donnes, P., Kohlbacher, O., 2006. SVMHC: A server for prediction of MHC-binding peptides. Nucleic Acids Research 34 (Web Server issue), W194–W197.

Engelhard, V.H., 1994. Structure of peptides associated with class I and class II MHC molecules. Annual Review of Immunology 12, 181–207.

Fleri, W., Paul, S., Dhanda, S.K., *et al.*, 2017. The immune epitope database and analysis resource in epitope discovery and synthetic vaccine design. Frontiers in Immunology 8, 278.

Gee, M.H., Han, A., Lofgren, S.M., *et al.*, 2018. Antigen Identification for Orphan T Cell Receptors Expressed on Tumor-Infiltrating Lymphocytes. Cell 172 (3), 549–563. e516.

Gowthaman, U., Chodisetti, S.B., Parihar, P., Agrewala, J.N., 2010. Evaluation of different generic in silico methods for predicting HLA class I binding peptide vaccine candidates using a reverse approach. Amino Acids 39, 1333–1342.

Hacohen, N., Fritsch, E.F., Carter, T.A., Lander, E.S., Wu, C.J., 2013. Getting personal with neoantigen-based therapeutic cancer vaccines. Cancer Immunology Research 1, 11–15.

Hakenberg, J., Nussbaum, A.K., Schild, H., *et al.*, 2003. MAPPP: MHC class I antigenic peptide processing prediction. Applied Bioinformatics 2, 155–158.

Holzhutter, H.G., Frommel, C., Kloetzel, P.M., 1999. A theoretical approach towards the identification of cleavage-determining amino acid motifs of the 20 S proteasome. Journal of Molecular Biology 286, 1251–1265.

Hoof, I., Peters, B., Sidney, J., *et al.*, 2009. NetMHCpan, a method for MHC class I binding prediction beyond humans. Immunogenetics 61, 1–13.

Immunology, H.M., 2016. HIV Molecular Immunology 2016. Los Alamos, New Mexico: Los Alamos National Laboratory, Theoretical Biology and Biophysics.

Janeway, C., 2005. Immunobiology: The Immune System in Health and Disease. New York, NY, USA: Garland Science.

Jongeneel, V., 2001. Towards a cancer immunome database. Cancer Immunology 1, 3.

Jurtz, V., Paul, S., Andreatta, M., *et al.*, 2017. NetMHCpan-4.0: Improved peptide-MHC class I interaction predictions integrating eluted ligand and peptide binding affinity data. Journal of Immunology 199, 3360–3368.

Karosiene, E., Lundegaard, C., Lund, O., Nielsen, M., 2012. NetMHCcons: A consensus method for the major histocompatibility complex class I predictions. Immunogenetics 64, 177–186.

Karosiene, E., Rasmussen, M., Blicher, T., *et al.*, 2013. NetMHCIIpan-3.0, a common pan-specific MHC class II prediction method including all three human MHC class II isotypes, HLA-DR, HLA-DP and HLA-DQ. Immunogenetics 65, 711–724.

Keskin, D.B., Reinhold, B., Lee, S.Y., *et al.*, 2011. Direct identification of an HPV-16 tumor antigen from cervical cancer biopsy specimens. Frontiers in Immunology 2, 75.

Keskin, D.B., Reinhold, B.B., Zhang, G.L., *et al.*, 2015. Physical detection of influenza A epitopes identifies a stealth subset on human lung epithelium evading natural CD8 immunity. Proceedings of the National Academy of Sciences of the United States of America 112, 2151–2156.

Kesmir, C., Nussbaum, A.K., Schild, H., Detours, V., Brunak, S., 2002. Prediction of proteasome cleavage motifs by neural networks. Protein Engineering 15, 287–296.

Lata, S., Bhasin, M., Raghava, G.P., 2009. MHCBN 4.0: A database of MHC/TAP binding peptides and T-cell epitopes. BMC Research Notes 2, 61.

Lin, H.H., Zhang, G.L., Tongchusak, S., Reinherz, E.L., Brusic, V., 2008. Evaluation of MHC-II peptide binding prediction servers: Applications for vaccine research. BMC Bioinformatics 9, S22.

Lin, H.H., Ray, S., Tongchusak, S., Reinherz, E.L., Brusic, V., 2008. Evaluation of MHC class I peptide binding prediction servers: Applications for vaccine research. BMC Immunology 9, 8.

Melief, C.J.M., 2017. Cancer: Precision T-cell therapy targets tumours. Nature 547, 165–167.

Mellor, A.L., Keskin, D.B., Johnson, T., Chandler, P., Munn, D.H., 2002. Cells expressing indoleamine 2,3-dioxygenase inhibit T cell responses. Journal of Immunology 168, 3771–3776.

Meuer, S.C., Schlossman, S.F., Reinherz, E.L., 1982. Clonal analysis of human cytotoxic T lymphocytes: T4+ and T8+ effector T cells recognize products of different major histocompatibility complex regions. Proceedings of the National Academy of Sciences 79, 4395–4399.

Mora, M., Veggi, D., Santini, L., Pizza, M., Rappuoli, R., 2003. Reverse vaccinology. Drug Discovery Today 8, 459–464.

Nielsen, M., Lundegaard, C., Blicher, T., *et al.*, 2007a. NetMHCpan, a method for quantitative predictions of peptide binding to any HLA-A and -B locus protein of known sequence. PLOS ONE 2, e796.

Nielsen, M., Lundegaard, C., Lund, O., 2007b. Prediction of MHC class II binding affinity using SMM-align, a novel stabilization matrix alignment method. BMC Bioinformatics 8, 238.

Nielsen, M., Lundegaard, C., Lund, O., Kesmir, C., 2005. The role of the proteasome in generating cytotoxic T-cell epitopes: Insights obtained from improved predictions of proteasomal cleavage. Immunogenetics 57, 33–41.

Nielsen, M., Lundegaard, C., Worning, P., *et al.*, 2003. Reliable prediction of T-cell epitopes using neural networks with novel sequence representations. Protein Science 12, 1007–1017.

Nielsen, M., Lund, O., 2009. NN-align. An artificial neural network-based alignment algorithm for MHC class II peptide binding prediction. BMC Bioinformatics 10, 296.

Nkolola, J.P., Bricault, C.A., Cheung, A., *et al.*, 2014. Characterization and immunogenicity of a novel mosaic M HIV-1 gp140 trimer. Journal of Virology 88, 9538–9552.

Nussbaum, A.K., Kuttler, K.P., Rammensee, H.G., Schild, H., 2001. PAProC: A prediction algorithm for proteasomal cleavages available on the WWW. Immunogenetics 53, 87–94.

Olsen, L.R., Tongchusak, S., Lin, H., Reinherz, E.L., Brusic, V., Zhang, G.L., 2017. TANTIGEN: A comprehensive database of tumor T cell antigens. Cancer Immunology, Immunotherapy 66, 731–735.

Olsen, L.R., Zhang, G.L., Reinherz, E.L., Brusic, V., 2011. FLAVIdB: A data mining system for knowledge discovery in flaviviruses with direct applications in immunology and vaccinology. Immunome Research 7 (3).

Ott, P.A., Hu, Z., Keskin, D.B., et al., 2017. An immunogenic personal neoantigen vaccine for patients with melanoma. Nature 547 (7662), 217–221.

Parker, K.C., Bednarek, M.A., Coligan, J.E., 1994. Scheme for ranking potential HLA-A2 binding peptides based on independent binding of individual peptide side-chains. Journal of Immunology 152, 163–175.

Peters, B., Sette, A., 2005. Generating quantitative models describing the sequence specificity of biological processes with the stabilized matrix method. BMC Bioinformatics 6, 132.

Peters, B., Bui, H.H., Frankild, S., et al., 2006. A community resource benchmarking predictions of peptide binding to MHC-I molecules. PLOS Computational Biology 2, e65.

Purcell, A.W., Gorman, J.J., 2004. Immunoproteomics: Mass spectrometry-based methods to study the targets of the immune response. Molecular & Cellular Proteomics 3, 193–208.

Qi, Q., Liu, Y., Cheng, Y., et al., 2014. Diversity and clonal selection in the human T-cell repertoire. Proc. Natl. Acad. Sci. USA 111 (36), 13139–13144.

Rammensee, H., Bachmann, J., Emmerich, N.P., Bachor, O.A., Stevanovic, S., 1999. SYFPEITHI: Database for MHC ligands and peptide motifs. Immunogenetics 50, 213–219.

Rappuoli, R., 2000. Reverse vaccinology. Current Opinion in Microbiology 3, 445–450.

Rappuoli, R., Bottomley, M.J., D'Oro, U., Finco, O., De Gregorio, E., 2016. Reverse vaccinology 2.0: Human immunology instructs vaccine antigen design. Journal of Experimental Medicine 213, 469–481.

Reche, P.A., Glutting, J.P., Reinherz, E.L., 2002. Prediction of MHC class I binding peptides using profile motifs. Human Immunology 63, 701–709.

Reche, P.A., Glutting, J.P., Zhang, H., Reinherz, E.L., 2004. Enhancement to the RANKPEP resource for the prediction of peptide binding to MHC molecules using profiles. Immunogenetics 56, 405–419.

Riemer, A.B., Keskin, D.B., Zhang, G., et al., 2010. A conserved E7-derived cytotoxic T lymphocyte epitope expressed on human papillomavirus 16-transformed HLA-A2 + epithelial cancers. Journal of Biological Chemistry 285, 29608–29622.

Robinson, J., Halliwell, J.A., Hayhurst, J.D., et al., 2015. The IPD and IMGT/HLA database: Allele variant databases. Nucleic Acids Research 43 (Database issue), D423–D431.

Rudensky, A., Preston-Hurlburt, P., Hong, S.C., Barlow, A., Janeway Jr., C.A., 1991. Sequence analysis of peptides bound to MHC class II molecules. Nature 353, 622–627.

Sahin, U., Derhovanessian, E., Miller, M., et al., 2017. Personalized RNA mutanome vaccines mobilize poly-specific therapeutic immunity against cancer. Nature 547, 222–226.

Saveanu, L., Carroll, O., Hassainya, Y., van Endert, P., 2005. Complexity, contradictions, and conundrums: Studying post-proteasomal proteolysis in HLA class I antigen presentation. Immunological Reviews 207, 42–59.

Saxova, P., Buus, S., Brunak, S., Kesmir, C., 2003. Predicting proteasomal cleavage sites: A comparison of available methods. International Immunology 15, 781–787.

Schuler, M.M., Nastke, M.D., Stevanovikc, Ş., 2007. SYFPEITHI: Database for searching and T-cell epitope prediction. Methods in Molecular Biology 409, 75–93.

Sette, A., Sidney, J., 1999. Nine major HLA class I supertypes account for the vast preponderance of HLA-A and -B polymorphism. Immunogenetics 50, 201–212.

Shortman, K., Egerton, M., Spangrude, G.J., Scollay, R., 1990. The generation and fate of thymocytes. Semin Immunol 2 (1), 3–12.

Sidney, J., Grey, H.M., Kubo, R.T., Sette, A., 1996. Practical, biochemical and evolutionary implications of the discovery of HLA class I supermotifs. Immunology Today 17, 261–266.

Simon, C., Kudahl, U.J., Sun, J., et al., 2015. FluKB: A knowledge-based system for influenza vaccine target discovery and analysis of the immunological properties of influenza viruses. Journal of Immunology Research 2015, 380975.

Singh, H., Raghava, G.P., 2001. ProPred: Prediction of HLA-DR binding sites. Bioinformatics 17, 1236–1237.

Singh, H., Raghava, G.P., 2003. ProPred1: Prediction of promiscuous MHC Class-I binding sites. Bioinformatics 19, 1009–1014.

Stephenson, K.E., D'Couto, H.T., Barouch, D.H., 2016. New concepts in HIV-1 vaccine development. Current Opinion in Immunology 41, 39–46.

Stern, L.J., Brown, J.H., Jardetzky, T.S., et al., 1994. Crystal structure of the human class II MHC protein HLA-DR1 complexed with an influenza virus peptide. Nature 368, 215–221.

Strehl, B., Seifert, U., Kruger, E., et al., 2005. Interferon-gamma, the functional plasticity of the ubiquitin-proteasome system, and MHC class I antigen processing. Immunological Reviews 207, 19–30.

Sturniolo, T., Bono, E., Ding, J., et al., 1999. Generation of tissue-specific and promiscuous HLA ligand databases using DNA microarrays and virtual HLA class II matrices. Nature Biotechnology 17, 555–561.

Trolle, T., Metushi, I.G., Greenbaum, J.A., et al., 2015. Automated benchmarking of peptide-MHC class I binding predictions. Bioinformatics 31, 2174–2181.

Van Regenmortel, M.H., 2009. What is a B-cell epitope? Methods in Molecular Biology 524, 3–20.

Vigneron, N., Stroobant, V., Van den Eynde, B.J., van der Bruggen, P., 2013. Database of T cell-defined human tumor antigens: The 2013 update. Cancer immunology 13, 15.

Vita, R., Overton, J.A., Greenbaum, J.A., et al., 2015. The immune epitope database (IEDB) 3.0. Nucleic Acids Research 43 (Database issue), D405–D412.

Wang, J.H., Reinherz, E.L., 2002. Structural basis of T cell recognition of peptides bound to MHC molecules. Molecular immunology 38, 039–1049.

Wang, P., Sidney, J., Dow, C., et al., 2008. A systematic assessment of MHC class II peptide binding predictions and evaluation of a consensus approach. PLOS Computational Biology 4, e1000048.

Yusim, K., Richardson, R., Tao, N., et al., 2005. Los alamos hepatitis C immunology database. Applied Bioinformatics 4, 217–225.

Zhang, G.L., Ansari, H.R., Bradley, P., et al., 2011. Machine learning competition in immunology – Prediction of HLA class I binding peptides. The Journal of Immunological Methods 374, 1–4.

Zhang, G.L., DeLuca, D.S., Keskin, D.B., et al., 2011. MULTIPRED2: A computational system for large-scale identification of peptides predicted to bind to HLA supertypes and alleles. The Journal of Immunological Methods 374, 53–61.

Zhang, G.L., Keskin D.B., Chitkushev L., Reinherz E.L., Brusic V., 2015. EBVdb: A data repository and analysis platform for knowledge discovery in Epstein-Barr virus with applications in T cell immunotherapy. In: Proceedings of the International Conference on Swarm Intelligence (ICSI3). Taomina, Italy.

Zhang, G.L., Lin, H.H., Keskin, D.B., Reinherz, E.L., Brusic, V., 2011. Dana-Farber repository for machine learning in immunology. The Journal of Immunological Methods 374, 18–25.

Zhang, G.L., Riemer, A.B., Keskin, D.B., et al., 2014. HPVdb: A data mining system for knowledge discovery in human papillomavirus with applications in T cell immunology and vaccinology. Database (Oxford) 2014, bau031.

Zhang, G.L., Sun, J., Chitkushev, L., Brusic, V., 2014. Big data analytics in immunology: A knowledge-based approach. BioMed Research International 2014, 437987.

Zhang, H., Lund, O., Nielsen, M., 2009. The PickPocket method for predicting binding specificities for receptors based on receptor pocket similarities: Application to MHC-peptide binding. Bioinformatics 25, 1293–1299.

Zhang, L., Chen, Y., Wong, H.S., Zhou, S., Mamitsuka, H., Zhu, S., 2012. TEPITOPEpan: Extending TEPITOPE for peptide binding prediction covering over 700 HLA-DR molecules. PLoS One 7, e30483.

Relevant Website

http://tools.iedb.org/auto_bench/mhcii/weekly/
MHC II Automated Server Benchmarks – IEDB Analysis Resource.

Characterizing and Functional Assignment of Noncoding RNAs

Pradeep Tiwari, Manipal University, Jaipur, India; Birla Institute of Scientific Research, Jaipur, India; and SMS Medical College, Jaipur, India
Sonal Gupta, Birla Institute of Scientific Research, Jaipur, India and Amity University, Jaipur, India
Anuj Kumar and Mansi Sharma, Uttarakhand Council for Biotechnology, Dehradun, India
Vijayaraghava S Sundararajan, Ministry of Environmental Agency, Singapore and Bioclues.org, Hyderabad, India
Shanker L Kothari, Amity University, Jaipur, India
Sandeep K Mathur, SMS Medical College, Jaipur, India
Krishna M Medicherla and Prashanth Suravajhala, Birla Institute of Scientific Research, Jaipur, India
Babita Malik, Manipal University, Jaipur, India

Introduction

Noncoding RNAs (ncRNAs) are a family of RNA molecules that do not code for proteins. A large number of studies on cell proliferation, metabolism, epigenetic, and physiological processes (Gao *et al.*, 2017) have shown their role specific to regulation leading to a number of molecular mechanisms (Wang and Chang, 2011). Essentially ncRNAs are classified into small ncRNAs, which include microRNAs (miRNAs) and circular RNAs (CiRNAs); and long intergenic noncoding RNAs (lincRNAs) and long noncoding RNAs (lncRNAs) (Shah *et al.*, 2016). Recent human whole transcriptomic data have revealed that less than 2% of the genome encodes protein-coding transcripts, even though the majority of the genome is actively transcribed into ncRNAs under multiple physiological conditions (Liz and Esteller, 2016). Diseases that are associated with an altered transcriptome are not only restricted to the abnormal production of protein-coding RNAs, but also in the expression of many noncoding RNAs. Although there has been an increase in evidence for the link between ncRNAs and diverse human diseases, studies on ncRNA–protein association studies have caught an immense interest and have opened a new possibility in identifying cause for diseases (Wapinski and Chang, 2011). This has allowed us to improve next generation sequencing (NGS) tools for identifying functional moieties, for example, pseudogenes in making novel proteins (Shidhi *et al.*, 2015).

Background

With transcriptome and high-throughput sequencing (HITS) analysis revealing a large number of ncRNAs in various organisms, studies on their functional characterization have resulted in data on interactions with their RNA peers, DNA, or proteins (Novikova *et al.*, 2013). While the ncRNAs are believed to be associated with a wide number of human diseases including development, imprinting, mental and psychiatric disorders, and tumor growth (Liu *et al.*, 2012), they are also associated with plant growth, environmental stress, biological processes and development, besides capacity to encode small peptides (Lv *et al.*, 2016). The miRNAs play an important role in posttranscriptional gene regulation by either translation repression or directing the degradation of complementary mRNA targets. The miRNA molecules are derived from the primary miRNAs (pri-miRNAs) and negatively regulate the gene expression in various plants and animals. It was also known that the plant pri-miRNAs containing small open reading frames (ORFs) have the capacity to encode regulatory peptides (Lauressergues *et al.*, 2015). It has been reported that primary transcripts of plant miRNAs encode peptides (miPEPs) and increases the transcription of other associated miRNAs (Couzigou *et al.*, 2015). Unlike miRNAs, which are short and ca. 22–23 bp, lncRNAs are more than 200 nucleotides without ORFs. Most of these transcripts are coded by RNA polymerase II, either spliced or poly-adenylated. Whereas the ncRNAs play a role as key regulators in life cycle of the organism, this concept of regulation driven by ncRNAs has begun to be understood in mitochondria and chloroplasts as well (Lung *et al.*, 2006). For example, nuclear-encoded miRNAs were found to be associated with mito-chondrial transcription and translation in eukaryotes (Rackham *et al.*, 2011). In addition, ncRNAs of various sizes are thought to play a role in RNA interference or antisense pathways (Kaczmarek *et al.*, 2017). Like the traditional proteins piggy-backing from nucleus/cytoplasm to mitochondria, the ncRNAs also operate in the nucleus or cytoplasm while targeting the mitochondria. With regards to numerous ncRNAs identified in chloroplasts, they have been known to map to the plastid genome (Dietrich *et al.*, 2015) and play a role in various functions of the plant cell. A broad classification of ncRNAs based on their mode of function is presented in **Fig. 1**.

While transcription of ncRNAs is done by RNA polymerase II, the transcripts are capped and polyadenylated (Kim, 2005). Classes of small RNAs such as short interfering RNAs (siRNAs), piwi-interacting RNAs (piRNAs), and miRNAs found in eukaryotes regulate endogenous genes and defend the genome from invasive nucleic acids. For example, in 1993, the first miRNA, *lin-4* from *Caenorhabditis elegans* was discovered by Ambros, which is known to control developmental timing (Bartel, 2004). In addition, their role in genome defense is documented (Mello and Conte, 2004).

The pri-miRNA transcribed from DNA is excised by Drosha, to produce the pre-miRNA (**Fig. 2**). The pre-miRNA is exported to the cytoplasm by exportin-5 and spliced by Dicer to generate a miRNA duplex, which is then assembled into the RNA-induced silencing complex (Bartel, 2004). The miRNAs modulate target mRNA translation by complementary

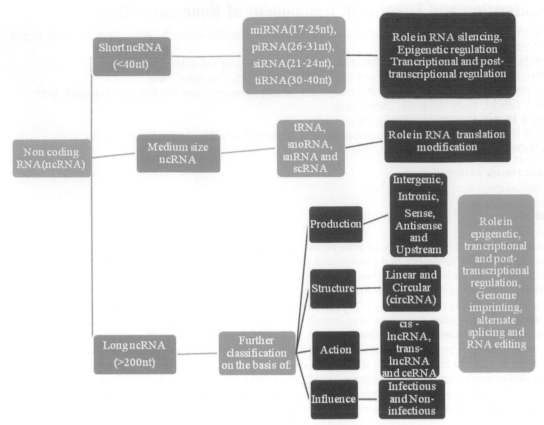

Fig. 1 Classification of ncRNAs based on different modes of action and function. Conceptualized from Katsarou *et al.* (2015), Hou and Bonkovsky, 2013. Non-coding RNAs in hepatitis C-induced hepatocellular carcinoma: Dysregulation and implications for early detection, diagnosis and therapy. World Journal of Gastroenterology 19(44), 7836–7845. Dey *et al.*, 2012. Non-micro-short RNAs: The new kids on the block. Molecular Biology of the Cell 23(24), 4664–4667. Abbreviations: ncRNA: noncoding RNA, miRNA: micro RNA, piRNA: piwi RNA, siRNA: small interfering RNA, tiRNA: transcription initiation RNA, tRNA: transfer RNA, snoRNA: small nucleolar RNA, snRNA: small nuclear RNA, scRNA: small cytoplasmic RNA, *cis*-lncRNA: *cis*-acting long noncoding RNA, *trans*-lncRNA: *trans*-acting long noncoding RNA, ceRNA: competing endogenous RNA.

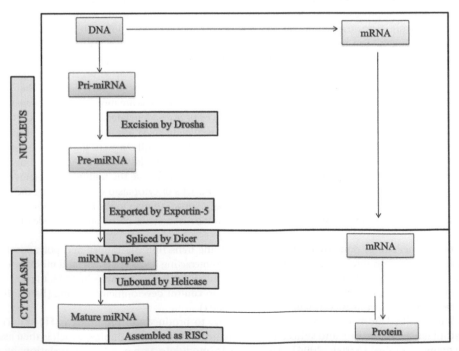

Fig. 2 Illustrative representation of formation of mature miRNAs. The primary miRNAs synthesized in nucleus are exported to cytoplasm by exportin later spliced by Dicer before assembly.

binding, within the 3′ UTR, 5′ UTR, or coding regions. The miRNAs also function by binding to DNA promoters, acting as RNA decoys or through direct binding of target mRNAs. Small RNAs bounded with effector proteins target the nucleic acids and sets of macromolecules, such as Dicer, Argonaute protein and ∼21–23 nucleotide duplex-derived RNAs are recognized as main components in RNA silencing (Meister and Tuschl, 2004). While Dicer plays a role in RNA gene silencing, Dicer-1 is required for miRNA biogenesis and Dicer-2 in the siRNA pathway (Tomari and Zamore, 2005). The second core component of the effector machinery is a member of the Argonaute protein superfamily that functions in eukaryotic gene silencing, which is also present in bacterial and archaeal species. The argonaute protein superfamily can be divided into three subgroups: The Piwi clade that binds to piRNAs, the Ago that clade binds to miRNAs and siRNAs, and a third clade described only in nematodes thus far (Yigit et al., 2006). While it is known that the eukaryotic genes are regulated by ncRNAs, validating miRNAs from their progenitor mRNAs is needed for assigning putative function (Singh et al., 2013). However, it is not so clear how RNA regulatory networks have existed with the emergence of rRNAs, tRNA, and other progenitors. Theories on their presence in earlier stages of life in archea and bacteria have been documented (Daly et al., 2013) as well as questions on how classes of ncRNAs play a role in human diseases (Esteller, 2011). The ncRNAs in bacteria serve as one of the functional elements and play an important role in gene regulation, predominantly at the post-transcription level. Primarily, they can be divided into cis-encoded and trans-encoded ncRNAs, RNA thermometers, and riboswitches, small noncoding RNAs that influence the translation and stability of mRNAs by binding to the base-pairing sites in their target transcripts. In pathogenic bacteria, numerous ncRNAs are involved in the coordinated expression of virulence determinants to facilitate the pathogenicity (Han et al., 2013). With recent reports revealing that there are around 15,000 lincRNAs encoded by the human genome (Deniz and Erman, 2017), the lncRNAs in eukaryotes have also been studied in establishing genotype–phenotype associations, which has led to advancements in prognosis, diagnosis, and treatment of human disorders.

In all living organisms, molecular machinery is activated by long double-stranded RNAs to transcribe the RNAs into short miRNAs. The miRNAs are generated from long double-stranded RNAs where they are produced by their own genes or specific part of sequences of the protein-coding genes (Yao, 2016). The biogenesis of these miRNA molecules starts with the synthesis of pri-miRNAs (Bartel, 2004; Ha and Kim, 2014; Yao, 2016). While pri-miRNAs are transcribed in the form of polycistronic transcripts, they also arise from individual transcripts constituting exonic, intergenic, or intronic sequences (Kim and Nam, 2006). Based on the location of the miRNA generation, miRNAs can be classified into two classes (Wang et al., 2009): (1) intergenic miRNAs generated from transcripts of miRNA genes located inside protein-coding genes; (2) intragenic miRNAs generated from transcripts of intronic or exonic sequences of the protein-coding genes. Whereas features of ncRNAs, such as TATA box, CpG islands, TBIIF recognition, histone modifications, and initiator elements are much similar to protein-coding genes (Ozsolak et al., 2008; Corcoran et al., 2009), it is believed that the same regulation mechanisms of gene expression are applicable to miRNA molecules as well. RNA polymerases II and III facilitate a wide range of regulatory options and the miRNAs encoded as clusters are transcribed in the form of long polycistronic primary transcripts (Melo and Melo, 2014) or regulated autonomously (Diederichs and Haber, 2006; Yanaihara et al., 2006). For example, the tumor-suppressor p53 is responsible to activate the entire miR-34 family, which plays a critical role in transactivation or repression in cell cycle mediated apoptosis (He et al., 2005; Chang et al., 2008). The transcription activation found in response to various growth factors such as transforming growth factor-β, platelet-derived growth factor, and bone-derived neurotrophic factor have been well studied in lieu of miRNA regulation (Corcoran et al., 2009; Chan et al., 2010). Further studies on epigenetics significant to miRNA gene regulation for understanding the methylation of CpG islands have shown to contribute to silence their transcription (Lujambio et al., 2007, 2008; Davalos et al., 2012). Specific promoters of miRNA genes are also regulated by the histone modifications process during various developmental stages and disease (Scott et al., 2006).

Similarly, the three forms of lncRNAs, such as antisense lncRNAs, intronic lncRNAs and long intergenic noncoding RNAs (lincRNAs), which are the classes of lncRNAs, are spliced from multiexonic precursors (Ma et al., 2013). Their role on regulation and evolutionary conservation and predicting secondary structures have been well documented (Johnsson et al., 2014; Yan et al., 2016). With the advent of NGS technologies, several novel lncRNAs have been identified using various approaches. How the lncRNA-–protein interactions play a role in immunomodulation further taking part in the gene regulatory networks has been shown (Suravajhala et al., 2015; Weikard et al., 2013; Kung et al., 2013). Furthermore, as lncRNAs are identified from whole transcriptome or RNA-Seq methods, interestingly a few lncRNAs have also been reported from whole exome sequencing as well (Pan et al., 2016a,b). The nuclear lncRNAs in particular are known to play a major role in regulation especially serving as both cis- and trans-regulators. For example, HOTAIR, a class of lncRNAs, is well transcribed from regulatory regions and further plays a role in regulatory networks. A myriad of other ncRNAs in the form of enhancer RNAs (eRNAs) and complementary enhancer RNAs (ceRNAs) play a role in such processes. On the other hand, cytoplasmic lncRNAs are known to serve as endogenous "sponges" for miRNAs, which in turn repress miRNA repression on targeting genes (Rashid et al., 2016; Thomson and Dinger, 2016). Many lncRNA–protein interactions have been shown to be associated with coactivation, repression, sequestration and organelle formation (Ferre et al., 2016) while showing expression at multiple levels in the cell cycle (Paralkar and Weiss, 2013). In addition, the transposable elements (TE) have contributed widely to genome evolution and are known to play a role in maturity of noncoding transcripts (Hadjiargyrou and Delihas, 2013). Conversely, the TEs playing a role in formation of ncRNAs especially lncRNA transcripts have accounted for about 30% portion of total sequences in human. While these are rarely found in protein-coding transcripts (Kapusta et al., 2013), they are known to help cause signals essential for the biogenesis of many lncRNAs such as transcription initiation, splicing, or polyadenylation in human. Their role, however, in development of biomarkers has recently begun to be understood (Xi et al., 2017).

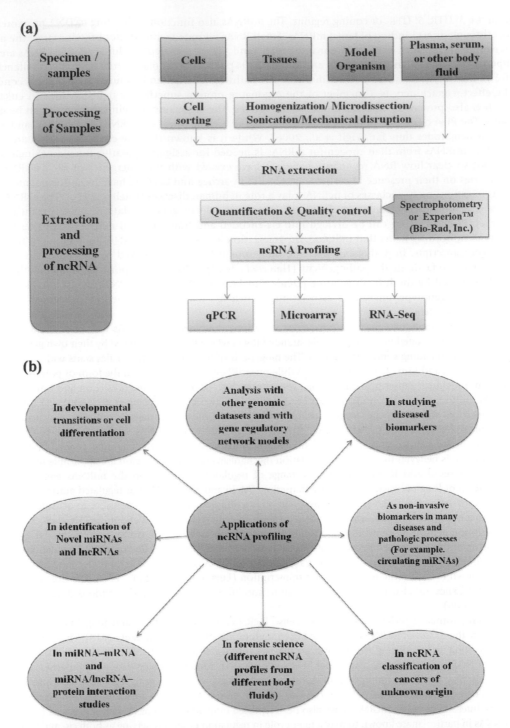

Fig. 3 (a) The ncRNAs can be extracted from various specimen types such as cultured cells, model organisms, tissue and body fluids such as plasma and serum. Homogenization, laser capture microdissection (LCM), and cell sorting can be used to purify specific cell types. The ncRNA populations can be purified by gel electrophoresis and AGO2 immunoprecipitation (AGO2-IP) along with or without ultraviolet crosslinking and immunoprecipitation (CLIP). The ncRNA isolation can be done using commercially available extraction kits. miRNA quality can be assessed after using various methods that includes spectrophotometry, automated capillary electrophoresis with Bioanalyzer or Experion. (b) Applications of ncRNA profiling. Abbreviations: qPCR, quantitative PCR; RNA-Seq, RNA sequencing. Image conceptualized from Pritchard *et al.*, 2012. MicroRNA profiling: approaches and considerations. Nature Reviews Genetics 13, 358–369.

Comparing the ncRNA profiles between different stages of development has facilitated in developmental transitions or cellular differentiation. Whole transcriptome or RNA sequencing (RNA-Seq) is an important approach for both identifying and profiling of novel ncRNAs. The miRNAs linked with mRNA or with RNA-binding protein can be analyzed using crosslinking immunoprecipitation (CLIP) using ultraviolet rays to create covalent bonds between RNA-binding proteins and RNA (**Fig. 3**).

Table 1 A gist of ncRNA databases and tools along with their association with other small molecules

Type	Database name	Function	Strengths	Weaknesses, if any	Reference	URL
Micro RNA databases	miRBASE	Database of published miRNA sequences and annotation	User-friendly with good number of options for analyzing the miRNA. A new option to identify the novel miRNAs	miRNA–mRNA interactions cannot be ascertained completely	Griffiths-Jones et al. (2006)	http://www.mirbase.org/
	miRwalk	Database on predicted and validated microRNA targets	A whole set of miRNA targets including pathway information is made accessible through this. A comprehensive list of targets including other ncRNAs is detailed	Targeted regions are many. A careful double check is required to analyze them, Not so user-friendly	Dweep et al. (2011)	http://zmf.umm.uni-heidelberg.de/apps/zmf/mirwalk/
	miRDB	MicroRNA target prediction and functional study database	Users have the flexibility to study any custom miRNAs or target genes of interest, related to functional miRNA annotations	—	Wong and Wang (2015)	http://www.mirdb.org/.
	miRTarBase	Experimentally validated microRNA–target interactions database	Comprehensively annotated, experimentally validated miRNA–target interactions database		Hsu et al. (2011)	http://mirtarbase.mbc.nctu.edu.tw/
	VirMIRDB	Predicts viral microRNA candidate hairpins	Beneficial for viral miRNAs and host-gene interaction studies	Not so user-friendly, Execution of the entire bioinformatics' pipeline is tough to scan for putative miRNA hairpins	Li et al. (2008)	http://alk.ibms.sinica.edu.tw/cgi-bin/miRNA/miRNA.cgi
LncRNA–protein interaction databases	NONCODE	An integrated knowledge database dedicated to ncRNAs, especially lncRNAs	Provides both basic and advance information about LncRNA such expression profile, conservation info, predicted function and disease relation	Does not give information about tRNAs and rRNAs	Zhao et al. (2016)	http://www.noncode.org/
	LncRNAwiki	Community-curated lncRNA knowledgebase	Integrates information on human lncRNAs from multiple different resources	Relies on community intelligence to curate a wide range of lncRNA-related topic, improvement is needed to link with other existing relevant databases	Ma et al. (2015)	http://lncrna.big.ac.cn/index.php/Main_Page
	LncRNAdb	The reference database for functional long noncoding RNAs	User-friendly and thoroughly compiled and updated information of lncRNAs in a variety of systems	Limited to the location of lncRNA only	Amaral et al. (2011)	http://www.lncrnadb.org/
LncRNA–protein interaction prediction databases	Interaction Pattern (IP) Miner	Predicts ncRNA–protein interactions from protein sequences	Good performance for mining the ncRNA–protein interactions	Bash/command line tools and applicable for commandline user interface (CUI). Uses Python scripts	Pan et al. (2016a, b)	http://www.csbio.sjtu.edu.cn/bioinf/IPMiner/IPMiner.tar.gz

(Continued)

Table 1 Continued

Type	Database name	Function	Strengths	Weaknesses, if any	Reference	URL
	lncPro	Predicts the interaction between long noncoding RNAs and proteins	Computational friendly	Interaction data is still considered unsatisfactory because of the large number of proteins. *Bona fidelity* is at risk	Lu *et al.* (2013)	http://bioinfo.bjmu.edu.cn/lncpro/
	ncRNAs and protein related bio macromolecules interaction database	Integrates experimentally verified functional interactions between noncoding RNAs and other biomolecules (proteins, RNAs and genomic DNAs)	Novel integrated functional interactions between ncRNAs and protein related macromolecules (PRM) into a single, easily accessible database	Interactions are manually collected from publication, however, they are curated	Wu *et al.* (2006)	http://www.bioinfo.org/NPInter
	RNA–protein Association and Interaction Networks	A database of ncRNA–RNA and ncRNA–protein interactions	Integrated with the STRING database	Does not give information about RNA–protein binding site integration	Junge *et al.* (2017)	https://rth.dk/resources/rain/
	Protein–RNA interaction prediction	Predicts structural fragments information of given protein and RNA	User-friendly with support-vector machine-based method. Predicts protein–RNA interaction pairs, based on both the sequences and structures	Does not give information and determines the binding partners for other types of proteins which are able to interact with both DNA and RNA	Suresh *et al.* (2015)	http://ctsb.is.wfubmc.edu/projects/rpi-pred
	RNA-associated interaction database	Predicts RNA-associated (RNA–Protein/RNA–RNA) interactions	Users can query, browse, analyze, and manipulate RNA-associated (RNA–RNA/RNA–protein) interaction		Zhang *et al.* (2014)	http://www.rna-society.org/raid/
Binding site databases	Protein–RNA Interface Database (PRIDB)	Database of RNA–Protein interfaces	It displays interfacial amino acids and ribonucleotides within the primary sequences of the interacting protein and RNA chains. PRIDB also identifies ProSite motifs in protein chains and FR3D motifs in RNA chains and provides links to external databases	Highly reliant on Java. Interfaces in the RNA–protein complexes can be visualized using an integrated JMol applet or downloaded in a machine-readable format	Lewis *et al.* (2011)	http://bindr.gdcb.iastate.edu/PRIDB
	RNA-Binding Protein Database (RBPDB)	Repository of experimental observation of RNA-binding sites	Freely accessible by a web interface. Can also use to scan sequences for RBP-binding sites	Currently populated only with data from metazoans	Cook *et al.* (2011)	http://rbpdb.ccbr.utoronto.ca
	RsiteDB	Describes, classifies and predicts the interactions between RNA and protein binding pockets	Provides information about the protein binding pockets that interact with single-stranded RNA nucleotide bases	Uses Java to visualize the results through Java applets	Shulman-Peleg *et al.* (2009)	http://bioinfo3d.cs.tau.ac.il/RsiteDB
Bacteria	NOCO RNAc	A Java based tool for the prediction and characterization of ncRNA transcripts in bacteria	Characterizes noncoding RNAs in prokaryotes. Gives genome-wide prediction of ncRNA transcripts in bacteria	Does not predict, for example, 23S ribosomal RNA	Herbig and Nieselt (2011)	http://www.swmath.org/software/17423

RNA sequences bound by a protein of interest are then detected by high-throughput sequencing in combination with HITS--CLIP or photoactivatable ribonucleoside-enhanced CLIP (PAR-CLIP) using photoreactive analogs. Integrative analyses of miRNAs and lncRNAs are done in *silico* using MAGIA95 and mirConnX96, Cytoscape, a network visualization tool, as well as with other databases such as miRbase, lncRNAdb, and NONCODE (see **Table 1**). Such profiling has enabled study of miRNAs as biomarkers for a wide variety of diseases such as cancer, autoimmune, psychiatric, and neurological disorders. While it has been applied successfully for the cancer classification of unknown origin, various clinical diagnostic assays those including specific cancer-derived miRNAs and different body fluids have been characterized (Pritchard *et al.*, 2012). In profiling lncRNAs, they can be functionally impaired by blocking their molecular interactions by applying small molecule inhibitors that mask the binding sites and further help in diagnosis of diseases (Sanchez and Huarte, 2013). For example, preventing the interaction of HOTAIR with the PRC2 or LSD1 complexes using small molecular inhibitors may limit the metastatic potential of breast cancers (Tsai *et al.*, 2011). In this process, oligonucleotides have also been used to target a specific ncRNA region and block its correct folding (Colley and Leedman, 2009).

Illustrative Example

The role of ncRNAs in various diseases, especially cancers, has been well documented (Esteller, 2011) with less focus on stem cells. The cancer stem cells (CSC) are a small subset of cancer cells that are associated with normal stem cells and are responsible for drug/treatment resistance, tumor recurrence, and metastasis (Garg, 2015). While they were recognized few years ago, their identification and characterization have already been done continuously for 15 years in some malignancies, such as leukemia and other tumors (Bonnet and Dick, 1997). Due to self-renewal and tumor generation capacity, CSCs have become potential targets for various cancer treatments including prostate, breast, colon, head and neck, colorectal, and brain (Huang and Rofstad, 2017). It has been reported that miRNAs play a vital role in the regulation of CSCs in various types of malignant tumors at the posttranscriptional level (Ali *et al.*, 2013) while it is widely accepted that CSCs play a significant role in cell biology of cancers. Further, they are known to work via signaling pathways that mediate the expression through self-renewal, such as Notch and Wnt (Prokopi *et al.*, 2015). In several studies many miRNAs showed different expression profiles in the various types of cancer (Ma *et al.*, 2015) and their role as potential targets for cancer therapy is widely known (**Fig. 4**) (Bimonte *et al.*, 2016). Based on their important roles in progression of human cancer and expression profile miRNAs are classified into two groups: (1) oncogenic miRNAs, which are reported to upregulate in tumor cells (Bao *et al.*, 2011; Albulescu *et al.*, 2011); (2) tumor suppressor miRNAs, which are reported to be downregulated in pancreatic cancer (Ji *et al.*, 2009; Haselmann *et al.*, 2014). Reports on downregulation of brain specific neuromiR-124 in glioblastoma has shown to improve the number of CSCs and oncogenic capacity (Bian and Sun, 2011) and let-7 downregulation in lung cancer linked with poor survival (Calin and Croce, 2006). Likewise, pneumomiR-29, a lung specific miRNA, is shown to suppress the tumorigenicity in non-small cell lung cancer cells while two other, such as miR-143 and miR-145, have been reported to be downregulated in

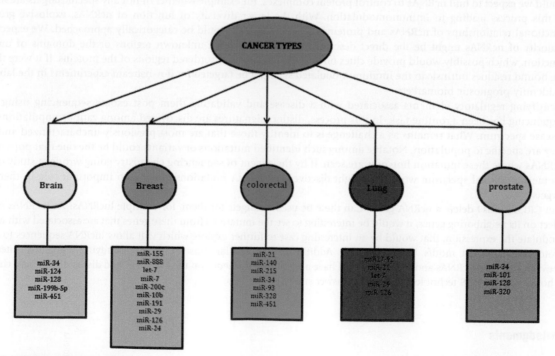

Fig. 4 The miRNAs targeted to various major cancer types.

various cancers including breast, cervical, and colorectal (Prokopi *et al.*, 2015). Despite these results, more studies on the function of ncRNAs in biology of CSCs will be needed in the future in order to discover novel oncology therapeutics (Parasramka *et al.*, 2016).

Technological developments enabled us to get volumes of data using the high-throughput NGS technologies. Evidence suggests that large amount of transcripts especially miRNAs have been modeled (Friedlander *et al.*, 2008; Lu *et al.*, 2009). The first reports on analyzing the RNA data to search new ncRNA gene sequences and predicting their targets came in the year 2003 (Lim *et al.*, 2003). While computational modeling was employed to use precursors as input and functional end products as ncRNAs, previous approaches used finding new miRNAs based on sequence data (Mendes *et al.*, 2009). Xie *et al.* (2005) reported artificial intelligence using learning algorithms used with sets of test known data and targets are predicted. Since then, many new ncRNA annotations were reported and put in use for the public domain. With high-throughput deep sequencing creating much more roadmaps for the ncRNA discovery (Lu *et al.*, 2005), hairpin structures are used to mimic miRNA byproducts (Friedlander *et al.*, 2008) and least-square classification algorithm for miRNAs (Lu *et al.*, 2009). While earlier methods were used to predict ncRNAs understanding ncRNA biogenesis and target specificity, HITS approaches involving bioinformatics simulations/predictions are needed. Even though constraints in using sequence data would be hard to predict ncRNA computationally, complex diseases affected by a number of ncRNAs rather than a single ncRNAs have been documented (Kargul and Laurent, 2011). Characterizing transcript structures and understanding expression profiles mediating regulatory roles are in agreement with good number of databases and repositories documented for ncRNAs (**Table 1**). Nevertheless, with big data revolution enabling us to handle huge exponential volume of ncRNA data, developing robust mathematical models for prediction of ncRNAs would be beneficial to the research community.

Future Directions

The list of ncRNAs in the genomes has consistently grown without worthy annotation with many of them associated with diseases. Although the role of ncRNAs towards their regulation in important diseases, such as cancer, obesity, immunomodulatory diseases etc. are well reported, the larger diversity of their function, explosive growth in the known functional relationships between ncRNAs and diseases such as cancer can be categorically approached. These can be characterized based on in silico predictions carried out in the laboratory keeping in view of the following documentation:

(1) While finding ncRNAs linked to immunomodulatory disease types, finding the various interaction partners of ncRNAs especially those that can affect protein function and localization needs to be attempted. As far as computational methods to the problem are concerned, this focus could not only allow us to process such data but also ensure we build a healthy community annotated wiki catalog of ncRNAs. This resource can serve for wet-lab validation or develop a machine learning intensive web server in predicting the interactions among the unknown ncRNA–protein pairs.

(2) Could we expect to find ncRNAs to control protein complexes, for example whether or not any specific targets are involved in this process leading to immunomodulation. With the larger diversity of function of ncRNAs, explosive growth in functional relationships of ncRNAs and proteins causal to diseases would be categorically approached. We expect that a majority of ncRNAs might be the direct descendants from the known unknown regions or the domains of unknown function, which possibly would provide clues on ncRNAs binding to disordered regions of the proteins. If it were the case, the bound residues intrinsic to the immunomodulated state can be targeted for downstream experiments in the laboratory to identify prognostic biomarkers.

(3) Identifying regulatory elements associated with a disease and validating them post exome sequencing using Sanger sequencing has been a routine task. In this process, distinct signatures are discovered among various populations across disease spectrum. What remains as a challenge is to identify those that are most previously uncharacterized and find if they are specific to population. Notable among such identified mutations or variants could be the one that pops up from ncRNAs where these mutation hotspots are seen. If by the advent of sequencing chemistry going wrong, a study defining exome mutational spectrum would highlight discovery of ncRNA mutations playing an important role in therapeutic targets.

(4) Can CRISPR/Cas9 delete a ncRNA gene? Can these be used as targets for them, for example lncRNAs? As lncRNAs make an effect on its neighboring genes, it would be interesting to see the mutations from these genes that are associated with it. If they modulate the expression, that would be an interesting case to further explore which will allow lncRNA sequences to serve as protospacer adjacent motifs in the genome. Additionally, molecular causes especially studying regulatory interactions between classes of ncRNAs and proteins would have a significant influence on the organism and diseases remains a challenge. A hope that the NGS technologies have an answer subtly proves this.

Acknowledgments

PS thanks Asif Khan and Shobha Ranganathan for inviting us to write a book article.

Authors' contributions

PT, SG, and PS wrote the entire initial draft with AK and MS focusing on miRNAs and diseases. SM, SLK, BM, and KM wrote the parts on regulation and biogenesis of ncRNAs, and VSS on big data challenges. PS proofread the manuscript. All authors read and approved the book article.

See also: Natural Language Processing Approaches in Bioinformatics

References

Albulescu, R., Neagu, M., Albulescu, L., Tanase, C., 2011. Tissular and soluble miRNAs for diagnostic and therapy improvement in digestive tract cancers. Expert Review of Molecular Diagnostics 11, 101–120.

Ali, A.S., Ahmed, A., Ali, S., et al., 2013. The role of cancer stem cells and miRNAs in defining the complexities of brain metastasis. Journal of Cellular Physiology 228, 36–42.

Amaral, P.P., Clark, M.B., Gascoigne, D.K., Dinger, M.E., Mattick, J.S., 2011. lncRNAdb: A reference database for long noncoding RNAs. Nucleic Acids Research 39, D146–D151.

Bao, B., Wang, Z., Ali, S., et al., 2011. Notch-1 induces epithelial-mesenchymal transition consistent with cancer stem cell phenotype in pancreatic cancer cells. Cancer Letters 307, 26–36.

Bartel, D.P., 2004. MicroRNAs: Genomics, biogenesis, mechanism, and function. Cell 116, 281–297.

Bian, S., Sun, T., 2011. Functions of noncoding RNAs in neural development and neurological diseases. Molecular Neurobiology 44, 359–373.

Bimonte, S., Barbieri, A., Leongito, M., et al., 2016. The role of miRNAs in the regulation of pancreatic cancer stem cells. Stem Cells International 2016, 8352684.

Bonnet, D., Dick, J.E., 1997. Human acute myeloid leukemia is organized as a hierarchy that originates from a primitive hematopoietic cell. Nature Medicine 3, 730–737.

Calin, G.A., Croce, C.M., 2006. MicroRNA signatures in human cancers. Nature Reviews Cancer 6, 857–866.

Chan, M.C., Wu, C., Davis, B.N., et al., 2010. Molecular basis for antagonism between PDGF and the TGF beta family of signalling pathways by control of miR-24 expression. EMBO Journal 29, 559–573.

Chang, T.C., Chang, T.C., Yu, D., et al., 2008. Widespread microRNA repression by Myc contributes to tumorigenesis. Nature Genetics 40, 43–50.

Colley, S.M., Leedman, P.J., 2009. SRA and its binding partners: An expanding role for RNA-binding coregulators in nuclear receptor-mediated gene regulation. Critical Reviews in Biochemistry and Molecular Biology 44, 25–33.

Cook, K.B., Kazan, H., Zuberi, K., et al., 2011. RBPDB: A database of RNA-binding specificities. Nucleic Acids Research 39, D301–D308.

Corcoran, D.L., Pandit, K.V., Gordon, B., et al., 2009. Features of mammalian microRNA promoters emerge from polymerase II chromatin immunoprecipitation data. PLOS ONE 4, e5279.

Couzigou, J.M., Lauressergues, D., Becard, G., Combier, J.P., 2015. miRNA-encoded peptides (miPEPs): A new tool to analyze the roles of miRNAs in plant biology. RNA Biology 12, 1178–1180.

Daly T., Chen S.X., Penny D., 2013. How old are RNA networks? Available at: https://www.ncbi.nlm.nih.gov/books/NBK53775/.

Davalos, V., Moutinho, C., Villanueva, A., et al., 2012. Dynamic epigenetic regulation of the microRNA-200 family mediates epithelial and mesenchymal transitions in human tumorigenesis. Oncogene 31, 2062–2074.

Deniz, E., Erman, B., 2017. Long noncoding RNA (lincRNA), a new paradigm in gene expression control. Functional & Integrative Genomics 17, 135–143.

Dey, B.K., Mueller, A.C., Dutta, A., 2012. Non-micro-short RNAs: The new kids on the block. Molecular Biology of the Cell 23, 4664–4667.

Diederichs, S., Haber, D.A., 2006. Sequence variations of microRNAs in human cancer: Alterations in predicted secondary structure do not affect processing. Cancer Research 66, 6097–6104.

Dietrich, A., Wallet, C., Iqbal, R.K., Gualberto, J.M., Lotfi, F., 2015. Organellar non-coding RNAs: Emerging regulation mechanisms. Biochimie 117, 48–62.

Dweep, H., Sticht, C., Pandey, P., Gretz, N., 2011. miRWalk–database: Prediction of possible miRNA binding sites by "walking" the genes of three genomes. Journal of Biomedical Informatics 44, 839–847.

Esteller, M., 2011. Non-coding RNAs in human disease. Nature Reviews Genetics 12, 861.

Ferre, F., Colantoni, A., Helmer-Citterich, M., 2016. Revealing protein–lncRNA interaction. Briefings in Bioinformatics 17, 106–116.

Friedlander, M.R., Chen, W., Adamidi, C., et al., 2008. Discovering microRNAs from deep sequencing data using miRDeep. Nature Biotechnology 26, 407–415.

Gao, J., Xu, W., Wang, J., Wang, K., Li, P., 2017. The role and molecular mechanism of non-coding RNAs in pathological cardiac remodeling. International Journal of Molecular Sciences 18, 608.

Garg, M., 2015. Emerging role of microRNAs in cancer stem cells: Implications in cancer therapy. World Journal of Stem Cells 7, 1078–1089.

Griffiths-Jones, S., Grocock, R.J., Dongen, S., Alex Bateman, A., Enright, A.J., 2006. miRBase: MicroRNA sequences, targets and gene nomenclature. Nucleic Acids Research 34, D140–D144.

Ha, M., Kim, V.N., 2014. Regulation of microRNA biogenesis. Nature Reviews Molecular Cell Biology 15, 509–524.

Hadjiargyrou, M.1., Delihas, N., 2013. The intertwining of transposable elements and non-coding RNAs. International Journal of Molecular Sciences 14, 13307–13328. 26.

Han, Y., Liu, L., Fang, N., Yang, R., Zhou, D., 2013. Regulation of pathogenicity by noncoding RNAs in bacteria. Future Microbiology 8, 579–591.

Haselmann, V., Kurz, A., Bertsch, U., et al., 2014. Nuclear death receptor TRAIL-R2 inhibits maturation of let-7 and promotes proliferation of pancreatic and other tumor cells. Gastroenterology 146, 278–290.

He, L., Thomson, J.M., Hernann, M.T., et al., 2005. A microRNA polycistron as a potential human oncogene. Nature 435, 828–833.

Herbig, A., Nieselt, K., 2011. nocoRNAc: Characterization of non-coding RNAs in prokaryotes. BMC Bioinformatics 12, 40.

Hsu, S.D., Lin, F.M., Wu, W.Y., et al., 2011. miRTarBase: A database curates experimentally validated microRNA-target interactions. Nucleic Acids Research 39, D163–D169.

Huang, R., Rofstad, E.K., 2017. Cancer stem cells (CSCs), cervical CSCs and targeted therapies. Oncotarget. 8, 35351–35367.

Ji, Q., Hao, X., Zhang, M., et al., 2009. MicroRNA miR-34 inhibits human pancreatic cancer tumor-initiating cells. PLOS ONE. 4, e6816.

Johnsson, P., Lipovich, L., Grandér, D., Morris, K.V., 2014. Evolutionary conservation of long noncoding RNAs; sequence, structure, function. Biochimica et Biophysica Acta. 1840, 1063–1071.

Junge, A., Refsgaard, J.C., Garde, C., et al., 2017. RAIN: RNA–protein association and interaction networks. Database (Oxford), 2017. p. baw167.

Kaczmarek, J.C., Kowalski, P.S., Anderson, D.G., 2017. Advances in the delivery of RNA therapeutics: From concept to clinical reality. Genome Medicine 27 (1). 60. 9.

Kapusta, A., Kronenberg, Z., Lynch, V.J., et al., 2013. Transposable elements are major contributors to the origin, diversification, and regulation of vertebrate long noncoding RNAs. PLoS Genetics 9 (4).

Kargul, J., Laurent, G.J., 2011. Liver growth, development, and disease – New research revealing new horizons. The International Journal of Biochemistry & Cell Biology 43, 171.

Kim, V.N., 2005. MicroRNA biogenesis: Coordinated cropping and dicing. Nature Reviews Molecular Cell Biology 6, 376–385.

Kim, V.N., Nam, J.W., 2006. Genomics of microRNA. Trends in Genetics 22, 165–173.

Kung, J.T.Y., Colognori, D., Lee, J.T., 2013. Long noncoding RNAs: Past, present, and future. Genetics 193, 651–669.

Lauressergues, D., Couzigou, J.M., Clemente, H.S., et al., 2015. Primary transcripts of microRNAs encode regulatory peptides. Nature 520, 90–93.

Lewis, B.A., Walia, R.R., Terribilini, M., et al., 2011. PRIDB: A potein-RNA interface database. Nucleic Acids Research 39, D277–D282.

Li, S.C., Shiau, C.K., Lin, W.C., 2008. Vir-Mir db: Prediction of viral microRNA candidate hairpins. Nucleic Acids Research 36, D184–D189.

Lim, L.P., Glasner, M.E., Yekta, S., Burge, C.B., Bartel, D.P., 2003. Vertebrate microRNA genes. Science 299, 1540.

Liu, C.H., Wu, D., Pollock, J.D., 2012. Bioinformatic challenges of big data in non-coding RNA research. Frontiers in Genetics 3, 178.

Liz, J., Esteller, M., 2016. lncRNAs and microRNAs with a role in cancer development. Biochimica et Biophysica Acta 1859, 169–176.

Lu, C., Tej, S.S., Luo, S., et al., 2005. Elucidation of the small RNA component of the transcriptome. Science 309, 1567–1569.

Lu, Q., Ren, S., Lu, M., et al., 2013. Computational prediction of associations between long non-coding RNAs and proteins. BMC Genomics. 14, 651.

Lu, Y.C., Smielewska, M., Palakodeti, D., et al., 2009. Deep sequencing identifies new and regulated microRNAs in Schmidtea mediterranea. RNA 15, 1483–1491.

Lujambio, A., Calin, G.A., Villanueva, A., et al., 2008. A microRNA DNA methylation signature for human cancer metastasis. Proceedings of the National Academy of Sciences of the United States of America 105, 13556–13561.

Lujambio, A., Ropero, S., Ballestar, E., Fraga, M.F., et al., 2007. Genetic unmasking of an epigenetically silenced microRNA in human cancer cells. Cancer Research 67, 1424–1429.

Lung, B., Zemann, A., Madej, M.J., et al., 2006. Identification of small non-coding RNAs from mitochondria and chloroplasts. Nucleic Acids Research 34, 3842–3852.

Lv, S., Pan, L., Wang, G., 2016. Commentary: Primary transcripts of microRNAs encode regulatory peptides. Frontiers in Plant Science 7, 1436.

Ma, C., Huang, T., Ding, Y.C., et al., 2015. MicroRNA-200c overexpression inhibits chemoresistance, invasion and colony formation of human pancreatic cancer stem cells. International Journal of Clinical and Experimental Pathology 8, 6533–6539.

Ma, L., Bajic, V.B., Zhang, Z., et al., 2013. On the classification of long non-coding RNAs. RNA Biol. 1 10 (6). 924–933.

Ma, L., Li, A., Zou, D., Xu, X., et al., 2015. LncRNAWiki: Harnessing community knowledge in collaborative curation of human long non-coding RNAs. Nucleic Acids Research 43, D187–D192.

Meister, G., Tuschl, T., 2004. Mechanisms of gene silencing by double-stranded RNA. Nature 431, 343–349.

Mello, C.C., Conte, D., 2004. Revealing the world of RNA interference. Nature 431, 338–342.

Melo, C.A., Melo, S.A., 2014. MicroRNA biogenesis: Dicing assay RNA mapping. Methods in Molecular Biology 1182, 219–226.

Mendes, N.D., Freitas, A.T., Sagot, M.F., 2009. Current tools for the identification of miRNA genes and their targets. Nucleic Acids Research 37, 2419–2433.

Novikova, I.V., Hennelly, S.P., Tung, C.S., Sanbonmatsu, K.Y., 2013. Rise of the RNA machines: Exploring the structure of long non-coding RNAs. Journal of Molecular Biology 425, 3731–3746.

Ozsolak, F., Poling, L.L., Wang, Z., et al., 2008. Chromatin structure analyses identify miRNA promoters. Genes & Development 22, 3172–3183.

Pan, W., Zhou, L., Ge, M., et al., 2016a. Whole exome sequencing identifies lncRNA GAS8-AS1 and LPAR4 as novel papillary thyroid carcinoma driver alternations. Human Molecular Genetics 25, 1875–1884.

Pan, X., Fan, Y.X., Yan, J., Shen, H.B., 2016b. IPMiner: Hidden ncRNA-protein interaction sequential pattern mining with stacked autoencoder for accurate computational prediction. BMC Genomics 17, 582.

Paralkar, V.R., Weiss, M.J., 2013. Long noncoding RNAs in biology and hematopoiesis. Blood 121, 4842–4846.

Parasramka, M.A., Maji, S., Matsuda, A., Yan, I.K., Patel, T., 2016. Long non-coding RNAs as novel targets for therapy in hepatocellular carcinoma. Pharmacology & Therapeutics 161, 67–78.

Pritchard, C.C, Cheng, H.H., Tewari, M., 2012. MicroRNA profiling: Approaches and considerations. Nature Reviews Genetics 13.358:369.

Prokopi, M., Kousparou, C.A., Epenetos, A.A., 2015. The secret role of microRNAs in cancer stem cell development and potential therapy: A notch-pathway approach. Frontiers in Oncology 4, 389.

Rackham, O., Shearwood, A.M., Mercer, T.R., et al., 2011. Long noncoding RNAs are generated from the mitochondrial genome and regulated by nuclear-encoded proteins. RNA. 12, 2085–2093.

Rashid, F., Shah, A., Shan, G., 2016. Long non-coding RNAs in the cytoplasm. Genomics Proteomics Bioinformatics 14, 73–80.

Sanchez, Y., Huarte, M., 2013. Long non-coding RNAs: Challenges for diagnosis and therapies. Nucleic Acid Therapeutics 23, 15–20.

Scott, G.K., Berger, C.E., Benz, S.C., Benz, C.C., 2006. Rapid alteration of microRNA levels by histone deacetylase inhibition. Cancer Research 66, 1277–1281.

Shah, M.Y., Ferrajoli, A., Sood, A.K., Lopez-Berestein, G., Calin, G.A., 2016. MicroRNA therapeutics in cancer – An emerging concept. EBioMedicine. 12, 34–42.

Shidhi, P.R., Suravajhala, P., Nayeema, A., et al., 2015. Making novel proteins from pseudogenes. Bioinformatics 31 (1). 33–39.

Shulman-Peleg, A., Nussinov, R., Wolfson, H.J., 2009. RsiteDB: A database of protein binding pockets that interact with RNA nucleotide bases. Nucleic Acids Research 37, D369–D373.

Singh, T.R., Gupta, A., Suravajhala, P., 2013. Challenges in the miRNA research. International Journal of Bioinformatics Research and Applications 9, 576–583.

Suravajhala, P., Kogelman, L.J.A., Mazzoni, G., Kadarmideen, H.N., 2015. Potential role of lncRNA cyp2c91–protein interactions on diseases of the immune system. Frontiers in Genetics 6, 255.

Suresh, V., Liu, L., Adjeroh, D., Zhou, X., 2015. RPI-Pred: Predicting ncRNA-protein interaction using sequence and structural information. Nucleic Acids Research 43, 1370–1379.

Thomson, D.W., Dinger, M.E., 2016. Endogenous microRNA sponges: Evidence and controversy. Nature Reviews Genetics 17, 272–283.

Tomari, Y., Zamore, P.D., 2005. Perspective: Machines for RNAi. Genes & Development 19, 517–529.

Tsai, M.C., Spitale, R.C., Chang, H.Y., 2011. Long intergenic noncoding RNAs: New links in cancer progression. Cancer Research 71, 3–7.

Wang, K.C., Chang, H.Y., 2011. Molecular mechanisms of long noncoding RNAs. Molecular Cell 43, 904–914.

Wang, X., Xuan, Z., Zhao, X., Li, Y., Zhang, M.Q., 2009. High-resolution human core-promoter prediction with CoreBoost_HM. Genome Research 19, 266–275.

Wapinski, O., Chang, H.Y., 2011. Long noncoding RNAs and human disease. Trends Cell in Biology 21, 354–361.

Weikard, R., Hadlich, F., Kuehn, C., 2013. Identification of novel transcripts and noncoding RNAs in bovine skin by deep next generation sequencing. BMC Genomics 14, 789.

Wong, N., Wang, X., 2015. miRDB: An online resource for microRNA target prediction and functional annotations. Nucleic Acids Research 43, D146–D152.

Wu, T., Jie Wang, J., Liu, C., et al., 2006. NPInter: The noncoding RNAs and protein related biomacromolecules interaction database. Nucleic Acids Research 34, D150–D152.

Xi, X., Li, T., Huang, Y., et al., 2017. RNA biomarkers: Frontier of precision medicine for cancer. Non-Coding RNA 3, 9.

Xie, X., Lu, J., Kulbokas, E.J., et al., 2005. Systematic discovery of regulatory motifs in human promoters and 3′ UTRs by comparison of several mammals. Nature 434, 338–345.

Yan, K., Arfat, Y., Li, D., et al., 2016. Structure prediction: New insights into decrypting long noncoding RNAs. International Journal of Molecular Sciences 17, 132.

Yanaihara, N., Caplen, N., Bowman, E., et al., 2006. Unique microRNA molecular profiles in lung cancer diagnosis and prognosis. Cancer Cell 9, 189–198.

Yao, S., 2016. MicroRNA biogenesis and their functions in regulating stem cell potency and differentiation. Biological Procedures Online 18, 8.

Yigit, E., Batista, P.J., Bei, Y., *et al.*, 2006. Analysis of the *C. elegans* Argonaute family reveals that distinct Argonautes act sequentially during RNAi. Cell 127, 747–757.

Zhang, X., Wu, D., Chen, L., *et al.*, 2014. RAID: A comprehensive resource for human RNA-associated (RNA–RNA/RNA–protein) interaction. RNA 20, 989–993.

Zhao, Y., Li, H., Fang, S., *et al.*, 2016. NONCODE 2016: An informative and valuable data source of long non-coding RNAs. Nucleic Acids Research 44, D203–D208.

Biographical Sketch

Pradeep Tiwari is a PhD fellow in the Department of Chemistry at School of Basic Sciences, Manipal University Jaipur. He is working for his PhD on Systems Genomics Approach for understanding noncoding RNAs in Asian Indian Type 2 Diabetes Mellitus (AITDM).

Sonal Gupta is a PhD fellow in Department of Biotechnology at Amity University, Jaipur. She is working for her PhD on long noncoding RNAs (lncRNA) and proteins specific to congenital pouch colon.

Anuj Kumar is a Bioinformatician at Advance Center for Computational and Applied Biotechnology, Uttarakhand Council for Biotechnology (UCB), Silk Park, Prem Nagar, Dehradun.

Mansi Sharma is a Senior Research fellow at Uttarakhand Council for Biotechnology (UCB), Silk Park, Prem Nagar, Dehradun.

Dr. Vijayaraghava Seshadri Sundararajan is a Scientist at Environmental Health Institute, National Environment Agency, Singapore.

Professor S.L. Kothari is the Director, Amity Institute of Biotechnology, Amity University Rajasthan, Jaipur.

Dr. Sandeep Kumar Mathur is a Senior Medical Professor and Head, Department of Endocrinology, S.M.S. Medical college and hospital, Jaipur.

Dr. Krishna Mohan Medicherla is the head of Research and Development at Birla Institute of Scientific Research, Jaipur.

Dr. Babita Malik is the Professor and Head, Department of Chemistry, School of Basic Sciences, Manipal University, Jaipur.

Dr. Prashanth Suravajhala is a Research Scientist in Systems Biology at Department of Biotechnology and Bioinformatics, Birla Institute of Scientific Research, Jaipur.

Identification and Extraction of Biomarker Information

Vijayaraghava S Sundararajan, Ministry of Environmental Agency, Singapore and Bioclues.org, Hyderabad, India
Shweta Shrotriya, Monisha Singhal, Pragya Chaturvedi, and **Prashanth Suravajhala,** Birla Institute of Scientific Research, Jaipur, India

Introduction

The development of biomarker discovery has revolutionized the field of disease diagnosis and prognosis. Bioinformatics based approaches for biomarker identification are growing with the advances in genome sequencing resulting in a huge amount of sequences. Various bioinformatics based techniques, such as machine learning, network-based approach, and text-mining for identification and characterization of biomarkers are widely in use (Cohen and Hersh, 2005). As per the World Health Organization, biomarkers reflect an interaction between a biological system and a potential hazard, which may be chemical, physical, or biological (WHO International Programme on Chemical Safety Biomarkers and Risk Assessment: Concepts and Principles, 1993). While biomarkers can help in the care of patients with disease or no disease, on the basis of this clinical perspective, biomarkers are classified into prognostic, diagnostic, predictive and therapeutic (Carlomagno *et al.*, 2017). Prediction of disease is not the only application of biomarkers but it helps in monitoring toxicity for the development and discovery of new drugs. With bioinformatics applications important in filling this gap between bioanalytics and initial discovery phase, semantic searches and biomedical literature by and large have allowed us to efficiently identify and characterize biomarkers (Bundschus *et al.*, 2008). The main focus of this review is to provide information on extraction and identification of biomarker information.

Exploring Contextual Genes

A complex cellular system of higher organisms consists of huge number of processes running simultaneously. Maintaining a particular cellular state is one of the major tasks regulated synchronously in a cell. Transition of cellular state from one state to another requires the alterations in regulatory pathways as well, which consists of a large number of genes functioning to get a particular state. Such genes with functional relatedness are called contextual genes (Ferrer *et al.*, 2010). Genome context methods were used to predict this functional relatedness between genes using the patterns of existence and relative locations of the homologs. While annotating functional and structural information of genes in newly sequenced genomes, homology is used a reliable tool; we also explore contextual genes in targeted genomes to find out their functional relatedness. Widely used context methods in literature are phylogenetic profiles, gene neighbor, gene cluster, and gene fusion (**Fig. 1**) (Ferrer *et al.*, 2010). The important criteria for these methods are presence of homologous sequences for the genes in the target genome where in this case the degree of sequence similarity is checked. The contextual gene methods are classified by and large into (1) full coverage and (2) restricted coverage with the former generating scores for all possible gene pairs from a genome, while the other essentially generates scores only for some pairs. One widely employed full coverage method is the phylogenetic profile (**Fig. 1**) and gene neighbor methods (**Fig. 1**), which are used to compare sequences based on the degree of full coverage, whereas the gene cluster and the gene fusion are a part of restricted coverage methods (**Fig. 1**). However, the contexts used to infer functional relationships between genes with or without sequence similarity based on evolutionary relationships can be biased in some cases (Krawczuk and Łukaszuk, 2016). To check this, crude statistics and normalization are done to enhance the performance and genome dependence (Lehmann and Romano, 2005). In addition, combining scores from two different methods, machine learning and classification with parameter selection and tuning, would help achieve better results. Among these methods, the gene neighbor methods are known to outperform the phylogenetic profile method by as much as 40% in sensitivity when compared with the gene cluster method at low sensitivities.

Methods Used for Biomarker Identification

Identifying biomarkers is one of the greatest challenges as different genotype–phenotype correlation from large-scale biological data is assessed. There are a good number of text mining, knowledge-based and network-based methods to discover biomarkers from literature (Hall and Holmes, 2003). These can be better made by constructing a resource based on indexed text or dictionary used from a finite state machine. One of the key components of identifying contextual genes is condition-specific interactions in biological networks. Valuable mechanistic insights can be derived from functional analyses of genomic data. A list of commonly used data mining methods is given below.

- Unpaired null hypothesis testing: This is a univariate filter method where the calculated probability (*P*-value) serves as the evaluation measure to rate variables on their discriminatory ability (Lehmann and Romano, 2005).
- Principal component analysis: This technique is an unsupervised projection method, which employs linear combinations of variables based on the variance of the original data (Ringnér, 2008).

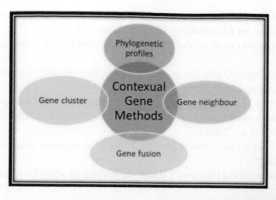

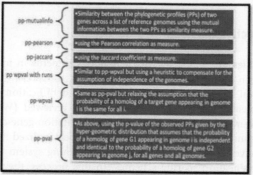

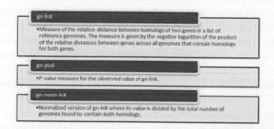

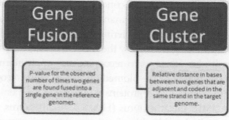

Fig. 1 Widely used context methods. (a) Contextual gene methods and their classification, (b) an overview of phylogenetic profiles methods, (c) gene neighbor methods and (d) gene fusion and cluster methods.

- Information gain: Is another univariate filter method, which evaluates entropy reduction of data due to feature separation (Hall and Holmes, 2003).
- ReliefF (RF): This is a multivariate filtration method, in which the RF score relies on the concept that values of a significant feature are correlated with the feature values of an instance of the same class and uncorrelated with the feature values of an instance of the other class (Robnik-Sikonja, 2016).
- Associative voting: This is another multivariate filter method and uses a rule-based evaluation criterion by a special form of association rules; considers interaction among features (Osl et al., 2008).
- Unpaired biomarker identifier: Is a univariate filter method, in which a statistical score can be determined by combining a discriminant measure with a biological effect term appropriate for binary classifications alone (Baumgartner et al., 2010).
- Support vector machine recursive feature elimination is an embedded selection method that optimizes the weights of SVM classifiers to rank features (Guyon et al., 2002).

- Random forest models is an embedded selection method, using bagging and random subspace methods to construct a collection of decision trees to identify a complete set of significant features (Enot *et al.*, 2006).
- Aggregating feature selection is an ensemble selection method that aggregates multiple feature selection results to a consensus ranking (Saeys *et al.*, 2008).
- Stacked feature ranking is an ensemble selection method that has stacked learning architecture to construct a consensus feature ranking by combining multiple feature selection methods (Netzer *et al.*, 2009).
- Wrapper approach evaluates the merit of a feature subset by accuracy estimates using a classifier and produces a subset of very few features that are dominated by stronger and uncorrelated attributes (Hall and Holmes, 2003). There are a few guilt-by-association studies to check these features (Shin *et al.*, 2008).
- Paired null hypothesis testing is a univariate filter method where *P*-value serves as evaluation measure for the discriminatory ability of variables (Lehmann and Romano, 2005).
- Paired biomarker identifier is an univariate filter method that uses a statistical evaluation score by combining biological effects (Baumgartner *et al.*, 2010) (**Fig. 2**).

Other Feature Selection Methods

Next-generation sequencing has given us tremendous impetus in identifying the biomarkers and with the help of feature selection/classification methods, there arose an interest to discern them using deep learning approaches (Lee *et al.*, 2018). Several combinatorial based methods are known for identification of biomarkers, for example heuristic searches, hybrid methods, and exhaustive methods, which have been reviewed (Wang *et al.*, 2016). There is still apaucity of resources employing these features. For example, a database of mutation-gene-drug relations for such classification features could prove to be a valuable resource for researchers interested in personalized medicine and genealogy (Wu *et al.*, 2014). For example, Wu *et al.* (2014) have developed a large-scale text-mining system to generate molecular profiles of thyroid cancer using literature based classification scoring schemes. In this process, they are able to identify key genes and pathways for easy prioritizing diagnostic biomarkers for therapeutic use. Similarly, Li *et al.* (2014) prioritized cancer-related miRNAs using network-based approaches by employing the random-walk algorithm to elucidate miRNA-disease networks. In the recent past knowledge-driven text-mining approaches have shown tremendous applications for extracting biomarker information covering all therapeutic areas (Bravo *et al.*, 2014). These are preferentially used by taking Medline publications containing the MeSH terms and other bibliometric analysis. Automated extraction of biomarkers using semantic graphs has also been attempted recently (Vlietstra *et al.*, 2017). Within the last few years, systems biology approaches clubbed with NGS became more amenable in extracting the useful information (Mayer *et al.*, 2012), biomarker identification and computationally expensive and challenging task methods such as knowledge graphs prove to be very useful in bringing exponential growth of biomedical literature and databases (Bravo *et al.*, 2014).

Structured knowledge is better represented in the form of a knowledge graph where unique relationships are defined using the Unified Medical Language System (UMLS), which integrates relationships extracted from Medline abstracts (Bodenreider, 2004). The knowledge graph runs on a 1.8.3 Neo4j graph database, the 3,527,423 biomedical concepts are represented as vertices, with 68,413,238 relationships between them. The individual concepts represent units of thought, which are atomic and unique. Two concepts can be connected to each other with one or more semantic relationships (also referred to as predicates), such as "causes" or "inhibits," thereby forming a triple. In addition, ranking and filtering methods are applied by checking recall, precision, and cumulative gains. The list of potential biomarker compounds generated by the method could be retrieved by the aforementioned processes and later assigned to the error categories. This will also allow us to recognize and apply normalization methods for the disease and biomarker entities in biomedical publications by means of the biomedical named entity recognition system. A gene dictionary constituting a huge collection of terms referring to human genes and proteins is integrated with data from three biological databases. This is complemented by a disease dictionary with UMLS metathesaurus (UMLS Methathesaurus, 2018), a large, multipurpose, and multilingual thesaurus that contains millions of biomedical and health-related concepts, their synonymous names, and their known relationships. Both dictionaries are curated and extended semiautomatically using different rules to facilitate the matching task.

Methodology focused on the extraction of disease–biomarker associations reported in the literature is not just limited to the methods as mentioned above but a knowledge-driven approach takes advantage of the annotation of MEDLINE publications pertaining to biomarkers with MeSH terms, narrowing the search for specific publications and therefore minimizing the false positive ratio. The application of this methodology is shown using a neural network-based biomarker association extraction approach for cancer classification (Bravo *et al.*, 2014; Kim *et al.*, 2007). These are complemented by a linear biomarker association network (LN), a fully connected neural network algorithm that assumes that the expression level of a biomarker is associated with some other biomarkers and can be estimated using a linear combination. This is briefly described below.

Consider a set of p biomarkers. The input of the LN represents the observed levels of the p biomarkers, denoted as $x = [x1, x2, ..., xp]T$, and the output represents the corresponding estimated results, denoted as $y = [y1, y2, ..., yp]T$. Let $A = \{aij \in R, aii = 0 ; i,j = 1,2, ..., p\}$ denotes the connection matrix of the network, the operation of the LN can be represented as follows:

$$y = Ax + B, \ B = [b1, \ b2, \ ..., \ bp]T$$

where $bi, i = 1,2,...,p$, represents the expression baseline of the *i*th biomarker.

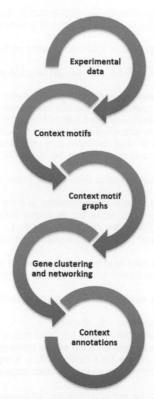

Fig. 2 An overview of context mining process flow. The experimental data is measured from contextual information, before annotations are drawn from various methods.

The classification features using conventional methods include Fisher discriminant analysis, k-nearest neighborhood, Bayesian network classifier (BN), and support vector machines with both linear kernels (linear-SVM) and radial basis function kernels (rbf-SVM). Among these conventional methods, the BN classifier, linear-SVM, and RBF-SVM require their parameters to be tuned for best performance. Wang *et al.* (2018) have developed a new cancer classification approach based on the concept of a biomarker association network (BAN) and a neural network structure to model the biomarker association patterns responsible for cancer. Using publicly available datasets it has been shown that the BAN-based classification approaches, in particular, the NLN classifier, achieve excellent classification performances on the four datasets (Wang *et al.*, 2018). On the other hand, extracting semantic biomedical relations with a sequence labeling approach based on conditional random fields is studied with general free text searchers containing concise phrases. However, these are bound by limitations because an effective search using gene cards and other secondary repositive database searchers are necessitated to study them (Wang *et al.*, 2009).

Conclusions

We have presented an overview of extraction and identification of biomarker information using different methods, primarily based on feature selection, knowledge-derived methods, and graphs. Identification of biomarkers not only serves as a distinct identity for understanding molecular, physiological, and structural variations but also helps disseminate a contextual flow for future methods in accurately classifying the biomarkers. An integrated embedded approach to identify biomarkers through graph theories, biological networking, and modeled through learning algorithms would be of much use to the research community. There is a vivid hope that classification feature selection methods through machine learning approaches would bring identification of the biomarkers more accurately.

See also: Biological Database Searching. Natural Language Processing Approaches in Bioinformatics

References

Baumgartner, C., Lewis, G.D., Netzer, M., Pfeifer, B., Gerszten, R.E., 2010. A new data mining approach for profiling and categorizing kinetic patterns of metabolic biomarkers after myocardial injury. Bioinformatics 26, 1745–1751.

Bodenreider, O., 2004. The Unified Medical Language System (UMLS): Integrating biomedical terminology. Nucleic Acids Research 32, 267D–270D.

Bravo, À., Cases, M., Queralt-Rosinach, N., Sanz, F., Furlong, A., 2014. Knowledge-driven approach to extract disease-related biomarkers from the literature. BioMed Research International vol. Article ID 253128.

Bundschus, M., Dejori, M., Stetter, M., Tresp, V., Kriegel, H.P., 2008. Extraction of semantic biomedical relations from text using conditional random fields. BMC Bioinformatics. 9.207-10.1186/1471-2105-9-207.

Carlomagno, N., Incollingo, P., Tammaro, V., et al., 2017. Diagnostic, predictive, prognostic, and therapeutic molecular biomarkers in third millennium: A breakthrough in gastric cancer. BioMed Research International 2017, 7869802.

Cohen, A.M., Hersh, W.R., 2005. A survey of current work in biomedical text mining. Briefings in Bioinformatics 6 (1), 57–71.

Enot, D.P., Beckmann, M., Overy, D., Draper, J., 2006. Predicting interpretability of metabolome models based on behavior, putative identity, and biological relevance of explanatory signals. Proceedings of the National Academy of Sciences of the United States of America 103, 14865–14870.

Ferrer, L., Dale, J.M., Karp, P.D., 2010. A systematic study of genome context methods: Calibration, normalization and combination. BMC Bioinformatics. 11, 493.

Guyon, I., Weston, J., Barnhill, S., Vapnik, V., 2002. Gene selection for cancer classification using support vector machines. Machine Learning 46, 389–422.

Hall, M.A., Holmes, G., 2003. Benchmarking attribute selection techniques for discrete class data mining. IEEE Transactions on Knowledge and Data Engineering 15, 1437–1447.

Kim, S., Sen, I., Bittner, M., 2007. Mining molecular contexts of cancer via in-silico conditioning. In: Proceedings of the IEEE Computational Systems Bioinformatics Conference, vol. 6, pp. 169–179.

Krawczuk, J., Łukaszuk, T., 2016. The feature selection bias problem in relation to high-dimensional gene data. Artificial Intelligence in Medicine 66, 63–71.

Lee, K., Kim, B., Choi, Y., et al., 2018. Deep learning of mutation-gene-drug relations from the literature. BMC Bioinformatics. 19 (1), 21.

Lehmann, E.L., Romano, J.P., 2005. Testing Statistical Hypotheses, third ed. New York, NY: Springer Verlag.

Li, L., Hu, X., Yang, Z., et al., 2014. Establishing reliable miRNA-cancer association network based on text-mining method. Computational and Mathematical Methods in Medicine. 746979.

Mayer, P., Mayer, B., Mayer, G., 2012. Systems biology: Building a useful model from multiple markers and profiles. Nephrology Dialysis Transplantation 27 (11), 3995–4002.

Netzer, M., Millonig, G., Osl, M., et al., 2009. A new ensemble-based algorithm for identifying breath gas marker candidates in liver disease using ion molecule reaction mass spectrometry. Bioinformatics 25, 941–947.

Osl, M., Dreiseitl, S., Pfeifer, B., et al., 2008. A new rule-based data mining algorithm for identifying metabolic markers in prostate cancer using tandem mass spectrometry. Bioinformatics 24, 2908–2914.

Ringnér, M., 2008. What is principal component analysis? Nature Biotechnology 26, 303–304.

Robnik-Sikonja, M., 2016. Data generators for learning systems based on RBF networks. IEEE Transactions on Neural Networks and Learning Systems 27 (5), 926–938.

Saeys Y., Abeel T., Van de Peer Y., 2008. Robust feature selection using ensemble feature selection techniques. In: Proceedings of the European Conference on Machine Learning and Knowledge Discovery in Databases, vol. 5212, pp. 313–325. Part II Berlin, Heidelberg: Springer-Verlag. (Lecture Notes in Artificial Intelligence).

Shin, H., Sheu, B., Joseph, M., Markey, M.K., 2008. Guilt-by-association feature selection: Identifying biomarkers from proteomic profiles. Journal of Biomedical Informatics 41, 124–136.

UMLS Methathesareus: https://www.nlm.nih.gov/research/umls/knowledge_sources/metathesaurus/ last accessed: April 28, 2018.

Vlietstra, W.J., Zielman, R., van Dongen, R.M., et al., 2017. Automated extraction of potential migraine biomarkers using a semantic graph. Journal of Biomedical Informatics 71, 178–189.

Wang, L., Wang, Y., Chang, Q., 2016. Feature selection methods for big data bioinformatics: A survey from the search perspective. Methods 111, 21–31.

Wang, H.Q., Wong, H.S., Zhu, H., Yip, T.T., 2009. A neural network-based biomarker association information extraction approach for cancer classification. Journal of Biomedical Informatics 42, 654–666.

Wang, X., Yang, C., Guan, R., 2018. A comparative study for biomedical named entity recognition. International Journal of Machine Learning and Cybernetics 9 (3), 373–382.

WHO International Programme on Chemical Safety Biomarkers and Risk Assessment: Concepts and Principles. 1993. Retrieved from: http://www.inchem.org/documents/ehc/ehc/ehc155.htm. (accessed: 04.28.2018).

Wu, C., Schwartz, J.M., Brabant, G., Nenadic, G., 2014. Molecular profiling of thyroid cancer subtypes using large-scale text mining. BMC Medical Genomics 7 (Suppl. 3), S3.

Biographical Sketch

Dr. Vijayaraghava Seshadri Sundararajan is on the board of advisers for Bioclues, a not-for-profit virtual organization in India.

Shweta Shrotriya is a Research fellow at Department of Biotechnology and Bioinformatics, Birla Institute of Scientific Research, Jaipur.

Monisha Singhal is a Research fellow at Department of Biotechnology and Bioinformatics, Birla Institute of Scientific Research, Jaipur.

Pragya Chaturvedi is pursuing a doctorate and working as Research fellow at Department of Biotechnology and Bioinformatics, Birla Institute of Scientific Research, Jaipur.

Dr. Prashanth Suravajhala is a Research Scientist in Systems Biology at Department of Biotechnology and Bioinformatics, Birla Institute of Scientific Research, Jaipur.

Computational Systems Biology Applications

Ayako Yachie-Kinoshita, Sucheendra K Palaniappan, and Samik Ghosh, The Systems Biology Institute, Tokyo, Japan

Introduction

Since its emergence in the mid-1990s, Systems Biology has laid the foundations for developing systems level understanding of living systems beyond the paradigms of single gene/protein/molecular view of biology (Kitano, 2002a,b; Ideker *et al.*, 2001). With the rapid development of large scale omics experimental systems in tandem with computational tools for molecular pathway visualization, modeling, data management and analysis, the field has contributed to deeper understanding of fundamental mechanisms of biological processes as well as their applications in various branches of medicine and biotechnology (Tyson *et al.*, 2001; Novak and Tyson, 1993; Chen *et al.*, 2004; Aoki *et al.*, 2011; Schoeberl *et al.*, 2010, 2009).

Particularly, modeling and simulation efforts have been applied in early approaches to study cell cycle dynamics (Tyson *et al.*, 2001; Novak and Tyson, 1993; Chen *et al.*, 2004) and in analysis of signaling pathways implicated in cancer, for example, the mitogen-activated protein kinase (MAPK) dynamics (Aoki *et al.*, 2011). Such modeling efforts have also found application in drug discovery and clinical trial designs as demonstrated by the development of MM-121 an ErbB3 antibody as an investigational drug candidate for various cancer sub-types (e.g., heregulin positive Non-small cell lung cancer) (Schoeberl *et al.*, 2010, 2009).

Further, approaches from systems biology have been integrated with traditional pharmacodynamics/pharmacokinetic (PKPD) and ADME-Tox (drug administration, distribution, metabolism and excretion and toxicology) modeling techniques to develop novel analysis pipelines in systems toxicology as reviewed in (Ghosh *et al.*, 2013b). Particularly, multiple spatio-temporal modeling efforts have been developed as part of the High Definition (HD) Physiology project in Japan and the Virtual Physiological Human (VPH) project in Europe (Ghosh *et al.*, 2013b). In recent years, systems approach to the study of chemical toxicology have gained increasing attention with the restriction on animal testing for toxicity studies in various industries like cosmetics and food. Concurrently, new analytical constructs, like the Adverse Outcome Pathways (AOP) have been mandated by the OECD which "*...describe sequential chain of causally linked events at different levels of biological organization that lead to an adverse health or ecotoxicological effect*" (see "Relevant Websites section"). Various *in silico* pipelines are been developed for multiscale modeling of safety assessments based on *in vitro* studies as well as toxicogenomics data on chemical compound screens (Bois *et al.*, 2017; Vinken, 2015).

While hypothesis-driven modeling approaches have yielded practical applications of systems biology as noted above, data-driven techniques are gaining traction in recent years (Webb, 2018). Wide-ranging applications of deep learning models have been developed in cheminformatics, translational biomarker and drug discovery and clinical applications (comprehensive reference available at (Webb, 2018)). Particularly, success of such deep architecture models has been demonstrated in genomics field including the DeepVariant model for variant calling, enhancer predictions, and population genomics (Poplin *et al.*, 2017). With the ability to generate omics scale data at various biological layers (transcriptomics, proteomics, metabolomics), novel analytics and data management are being developed for obtaining systems level insights from multi-omics data (Yi *et al.*, 2014; Shehzad *et al.*, 2014; Imam *et al.*, 2015; Schulz *et al.*, 2014; Yugi *et al.*, 2016). Specifically, *Trans-Omics* approach has been proposed such as in (Yugi *et al.*, 2016) to reconstruct biochemical and regulatory networks across multiple layers of data.

Such methods which bridge multiple dimensions of data and analysis/modeling approaches herald a new direction for systems biology. Specifically, with the advent of *big data* in biology together with the rapid pace of development of machine learning (ML)/artificial intelligence (AI), it is increasing evident that new horizons need to be explored to leverage systems level approaches on a broader scale spanning basic biology, drug discovery to translational and clinical applications and moving to patient reported phenotypic data, as shown schematically in **Fig. 1**.

In this article, to overview the new horizons in systems biology-guided approaches in biology and medicine, we identify the digital drivers shaping the current landscape and explore the need for next generation platforms to connect the drivers. Some case studies of connecting multi-dimensional data and analysis for different workflows are also discussed. We then conclude with perspectives on the vision driving next-generation research in biology and healthcare.

Digital Drivers at the Intersection of Technology and Medicine

This section outlines some of the digital drivers which are playing a pivotal role in the changing landscape of systems biology and its applications in biology and medicine. Highlighting the key areas as identified in (Hird *et al.*, 2016), the section captures impact of the digital drivers before presenting the role of potential new approaches in the next section.

Role of Data

With increasing volumes of data been generated in multiple dimensions, the role of data is becoming center stage in biology and medicine. High-throughput biotechnologies including DNA sequencing, transcriptomics, proteomics and metabolomics comprise

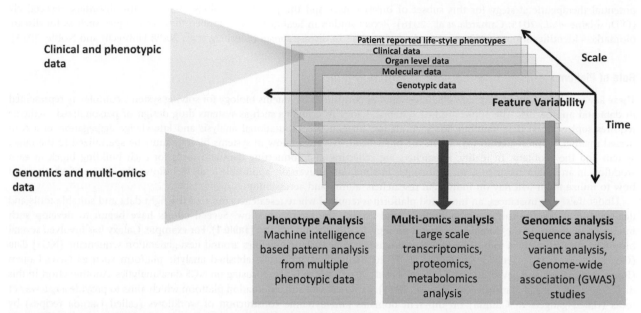

Fig. 1 New Horizons of data and analytics in biology and medicine. Multiple dimensions of data are being generated in the new era of medicine having distinct features- from genomics and molecular data to clinical and life-style phenotypes); such high dimensional (HD) data needs connection to novel HD analytics with different analytics techniques to obtain insights at different scales. Reproduced from Hird, N., Ghosh, S., Kitano, H., 2016. Digital health revolution: Perfect storm or perfect opportunity for pharmaceutical R&D? Drug Discovery Today. Available at: http://doi.org/10.1016/j.drudis.2016.01.010.

"Big data", characterized by the 4 'V's – data having high Volume, Variety, Velocity and Variability, are been generated in next generation experimental systems at the levels of single cells, tissues, organs to individuals. The most prevalent data at individual level is genotype, and genotype-phenotype correlations. A number of systems biology approaches have emerged to fill the gap between genotype and phenotype with the use of molecular big data such as protein-protein interaction network (Ben-Hamo and Efroni, 2013). On the other hand, a variety of "Small data" for each individual is being collected by multiple digital sources in hospital (Hood and Stephen, 2011) as well as home settings, such as personalized and time or event-dependent physiological parameters, social network and patterns in behavior and its geographical areas.

The integration of the multi-level, multi-scope and multi-scale data has given rise to the concepts of "extended phenotype" (Jain *et al.*, 2015). Such a paradigm shift in data in systems biology will enable to assess the open question how the phenotype is generated from the genotype, bringing the most important 'V' of Value to data.

Role of Devices

Another key driver in digital technologies is the rapid evolution in computers, sensors, and robotics, both in power and performance. Wearable devices with embedded sensors for measuring vital signs, to telemedicine devices and robotic automation of large scale laboratory experiments are now been developed. Moreover, together with the progress in Information and Communication Technologies (ICT) like the internet ubiquity, high network intensity and substantial data security, these hardware devices can be connected with smart devices such as wearable monitors, smart watches, cell phones or even household electrical appliances, generally defined under the umbrella term of Internet of Things (IoT). In the sense of extended phenotype, these "off the shelf" technologies bring about a transition from the world of a collection of scattered small data to a new future of integrated big data – enabling specialists from diverse domains, such as biologists and data analysts to access and analyze the data from different perspectives.

Role of Advanced Analytics and Machine Intelligence

The flood of data coming from multiple device source far exceeds the cognitive threshold of researchers. The development of advanced analytics techniques for such High-dimension (HD) data is ranging from inference techniques (Schadt *et al.*, 2005) to so-called Machine Intelligence (Chouard and Venema, 2015) including the methodologies of machine learning and artificial intelligence (AI). These techniques provide powerful predictions to identify patterns in the data and insights for deep phenotyping of the target systems. For example, the community challenges of applying machine learning techniques in inference of gene regulatory network (GRN) have established community-based methodologies as a powerful approach to predict GRN from accumulative transcriptome data (Marbach *et al.*, 2012). Genome-wide association studies (GWAS)-guided or targeted metabolomics technology-driven weighted co-expression network analysis (WGCNA) of HD transcriptome data have provided insights on potential therapeutic strategy for this subset of breast cancer and the potential etiology of psychiatric disorders, respectively (O'Dushlaine *et al.*, 2015; Camarda *et al.*, 2016). Recent studies in healthcare have applied these techniques such as for disease biomarkers identification, drug discovery and trend analysis in disease spread (Ginsberg *et al.*, 2009; Libbrecht and Noble, 2015).

Role of Platforms

These key trends are opening up new challenges and opportunities in systems biology for solving systems complexity represented in data and approaches. The application of systems biology in domains such as systems drug design or personalized medicine requires sophisticated data-handling tools, modeling, integrated computational analysis and knowledge aggregation in a connected manner, as presented in **Fig. 2**. On the other hand, every workflow in systems biology must be specialized to the target system and the problem. In reality, researchers are collecting and connecting data and tools for each building block in each workflow in an ad-hoc manner. Also, as no single method/data universally applicable to all workflows, the choice of whether and how to utilize them will rely on individual researchers' ability and accessibility.

Under these circumstances, an integrated platform is required where researchers can find the right data and suitable tools and devices, build the problem-specific workflow, and execute the entire workflow. Several efforts have begun to develop such integrated platforms in the domain of systems biology, healthcare and beyond (**Table 1**). For example, Galaxy has involved several bioinformatics researchers to build a robust and reusable data analytic pipelines around next-generation sequencing (NGS) data (Goecks *et al.*, 2010). Genome-space (Qu *et al.*, 2016) involves another established analytic platform such as Gene Pattern (Reich *et al.*, 2006) and geWorkBench5 (Floratos *et al.*, 2010), which is also focusing on NGS data analytics. Another effort in this direction is the Garuda Platform (Ghosh *et al.*, 2011), a connectivity and automation platform which aims to provide a gateway of tools (called gadgets in Garuda) on different domains and dynamic construction of workflows (called Garuda recipes) by discovering and connecting different gadgets in a system agnostic manner (web -based applications and standalone software). Garuda is built as a light-weight programming language independent framework which allows seamless connection of software, devices in a social community network (called gadget graphs).

Role of Community – Human in the Loop Research

Finally, we identify and discuss on the critical role of as a key driver in digital technologies-driven systems biology and its applications. It is becoming increasingly apparent that for large-scale projects which involve massive amounts of data, diverse ICT needs and analytics techniques, cross and inter-disciplinary skills are the need of the future – it is impossible for a single researcher or even a single laboratory to harness all the different dimensions of a research project.

Community-driven data collection through data repositories has grown in its popularity and necessity, especially for the omics data (Perez-Riverol *et al.*, 2017), while the application of mass spectrometry analysis such as metabolomics and proteomics have certain difficulties to standardize the needs and usability with regards to the type of data and analysis (Kind *et al.*, 2009, Wang *et al.*, 2016). Apart from the data, notably, the concept of Wisdom of Crowd, where the collective knowledge of a community is greater than the knowledge of any individual, has become proven in both network inference of living organisms (Marbach *et al.*, 2012). Under these circumstances, consistency and the interoperability of various algorithms, tools and devices are the first step towards the goal.

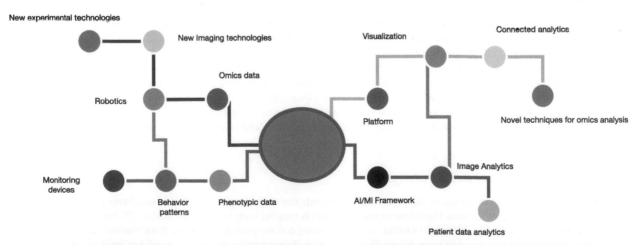

Fig. 2 Digital drivers at the intersection of technology and medicine. Various dimensions of big data, novel high-throughput experimental technologies, smart devices coupled with rapid development in ML/AI is driving the frontiers of computational systems biology and its application; such digital drivers highlight the need of next generation connected platforms to leverage the multi-dimensional drivers.R eproduced from Hird, N., Ghosh, S., Kitano, H., 2016. Digital health revolution: Perfect storm or perfect opportunity for pharmaceutical R&D? Drug Discovery Today. Available at: http://doi.org/10.1016/j.drudis.2016.01.010.

Table 1   Integrated platforms applicable in systems biology and beyond

Platform	Focused domain	Environment		Automation	Device connectivity	Availability	Development community	Web link
		Local	Cloud					
Galaxy	NGS analytics	○	○	○	×	Free	Open	https://galaxyproject.org/
Garuda	Data analytics	○	Δ[v2.0 or later]	Δ[v2.0 or later]	○	Free/ Commercial	Open	https://www.garuda-aliance.org/
Genomespace	NGS analytics	×	○	×	×	Free	Open	http://www.genomespace.org/
Knime	Workfrow builder	○	○	○	×	Free	Open	https://www.knime.org/
Pipeline Pilot	Workfrow builder	○	×	○	×	Commercial	Developer	http://accelrys.com/products/collaborative-science/biovia-pipeline-pilot/
Synapse	Data management	×	○	×	×	Free/ Commercial	Developer	https://www.synapse.org/
Taverna	Data analytics	Δ	○	○	×	Free	Open	http://www.taverna.org.uk/

Note: Adapted from Yachie, A., Matsuoka, Y., 2016. Systems drug and therapy design. Igaku No Ayumi 259 (8), 853–858 (in Japanese).

The standardization of the software, i.e., a common language for inter-operability, is the key to store and share information in a seamless and unambiguous fashion. One successful case is The Systems Biology Markup Language (SBML: see "Relevant Websites section"), which is set of standardization for mathematical modeling and simulation executable through various modeling and simulation software in systems biology. Importantly, the SBML community was evolved to structure themselves and keeps growing themselves to engage, reach out and educate the scientific community. Over 200 modeling and simulation software in biology domain comply with SBML enabling the community to share and reuse the models across them (Klipp et al., 2007). Further, open source, open development software and environments have significantly moved the field forward, which is mostly based on specific programming language including R: Bioconductor (Huber et al., 2015) and python (such as PySB; Systems biology modeling in Python (Lopez et al., 2013)).

On the other hand, data, tools and platforms may not be enough to frame and motivate open-ended collaboration to solve the big problems in science. Bringing humans in the loop, empowered by advanced devices, data and analytics are important to drive new horizons of research in computational systems biology. For example, as a community organization level, the study group at NIH on quantitative systems pharmacology (QSP) proposed the establishment of inter-disciplinary programs for research and training at various levels, ranging from individual teams to multi-investigator, multi-center programs (Ghosh et al., 2013a). Similarly, Kitano et al. (2011) have suggested the needs of virtual big science (Kitano et al., 2011), and the community of mathematical modeling and simulation has started identification of the required tools and concepts and possible approaches of integration of existing ones towards whole cell modeling (Goldberg et al., 2018; Karr et al., 2015).

While digital drivers, as identified in this section, do indeed play an important role for the next generation of computational systems biology, social engineering efforts for community engagement will be equally vital to the success of systems biology.

Case Studies in Multi-Dimensional Data Analysis in Systems Biology and Healthcare

Data and computational methodologies in systems biology have become horizontally and vertically extended and no single analytics can handle all of them. When models and tools are independently developed without an explicit strategy on how they can be integrated, they are likely to be inconsistent in their use of data formats as well as operating procedures. Researchers spend a lot of time and frequently face problems of converting data formats, learning tool operations, and even adjusting operating environments. This hinders productivity, counteracts the flexibility in individual workflows and are liable to errors.

How can we ensure the connectivity among multiple tools in one workflow while securing reusability? As discussed in the former section, several integrated platforms have been developed aiming to have a high-level interoperability between tools in a language-agnostic manner. These platforms strive to offer a consistent user experiences and a broader access to a large plethora of tools and resources. The intention of such platform is to host substantial numbers of analytic tools, data resources or knowledge bases such as domain-specific omics database or molecular database.

There are a wide variety of research motivations to participate in various roles to move the Systems Biology field forward (**Fig. 3**). In this section, we illustrate a case study of multi-dimensional data analysis based on the Garuda platform (Ghosh et al., 2011). We will begin with a brief introduction of the Garuda platform and its features before moving to specific research workflows.

As discussed before, the Garuda platform is a connectivity, discoverability and automation platform striving to seamlessly and intuitively build analytics workflows. One of the key components of the Garuda Platform is the Garuda Protocol which are a series of messages encoded in JSON format that facilitate applications (gadgets) to exchange information. Comprehensive Application

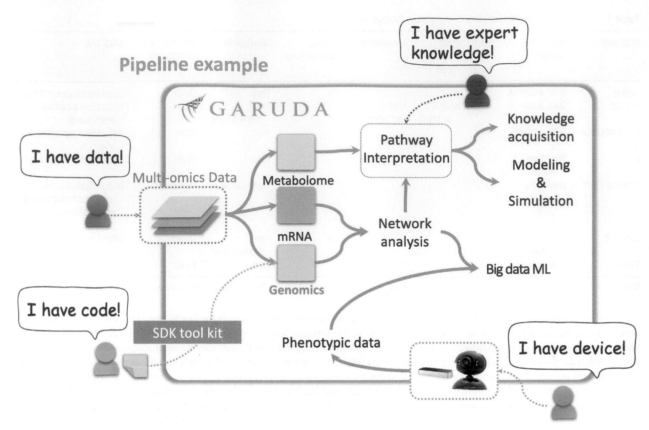

Fig. 3 A wide variety of research motivations for integrated platform-based workflow.

Programming Interfaces (APIs) power connectivity in Garuda. Any application that has been configured to understand these core messages and communicate using them to other tools is said to be "Garudified". Garudified tools communicate with each other using messages which are coordinated by the Garuda Core. APIs implement the Garuda Protocol in language specific bindings and provide the hooks to communicate with the core. The Garuda core also maintains a gadget graph which depicts the global connectivity of all gadgets in the platform. In addition to connecting existing software tools, one of the attractive feature of the Garuda ecosystem is the ease with which even scripts written in languages like R, python or Perl can be effortlessly wrapped and made into standalone Garudified tools. This facilitates easy sharing and reuse of scripts developed by researchers by making it more visible and available to the community.

Gadgets are distributed using the Garuda Gateway (gateway.garuda-alliance.org). Developers who have garudified their software can list their tools on the gateway with an appropriate license term for the usage of their software. This points to another interesting aspect of the Garuda Platform, the BYOL (bring your own license) model where by while the platform itself is open by design, gadget providers can enforce their own license terms for gadget usage.

There are many interesting use cases of Garuda. For instance, assume that computational analysis was performed on some gene expression data in Garuda, Many times, domain-expert knowledge is required to interpret these analytics results to first gain an understanding of the underlying mechanism as well to point to any gaps . For such cases, deep curated molecular pathway maps (Oda *et al.*, 2005; Oda and Kitano, 2006; Kaizu *et al.*, 2010; Matsuoka *et al.*, 2013) have been made available as a part of Garuda Platform. The results of analytics (which can be a set of gene symbols) can now be mapped onto these maps seamlessly using the Garuda protocol. Practical use cases for Garuda platform are found in a diverse set of applications including clustering, network-based analysis, visualization, machine-learning and mathematical modeling of gene regulatory networks (Hu *et al.*, 2016; Caron *et al.*, 2017; Yachie-Kinoshita *et al.*, 2018). Even for non-specialists, Garuda-compliant software tools offer fast adoptability owing to uniform user-interface guidelines. Garuda platform also provides access to a wide panel of software tools from unrestricted domains without the need for additional learning.

In an example research workflow of oncogenic signaling pathway, researchers may first try to find the mutations associated with a focused cancer subgroup by accessing the sequences of genes encoding the pathway members. They may next predict how the mutations affect the protein structures by searching a three-dimensional protein structure database. Virtual docking simulations can be used to explore possible candidate of kinase inhibitors for the cancer specific signaling. Taking the name of the top-rated inhibitor candidate, they could search for articles of experimental or clinical research reporting the potential effects of the compound or similar compounds on the cell line of interest.

In another scenario, researchers may be eager to know the molecular mechanism of action (MOA), based on the output from the docking simulation. They might want to predict the impact of the kinase inhibitor candidate. In this scenario, they first explore the curated molecular map of the pathway and find the possible influential path from focusing molecule to the molecular end-phenotype such as apoptosis. Next they explore how the candidate inhibitor changes the static path whether a bypass exist. The search for a molecular MOA needs understanding of the dynamics of cell behavior. The researcher may develop or modify existing dynamic simulation model of the pathway to incorporate the mutation-driven changes in the network to predict the cellular dynamics in cancer upon the compounds.

Currently, these entire workflows require a series of separate software tools without information transfer among the tools. A platform successfully integrate these software tools would make such workflows executable with fewer actions, so that researchers can focus on their science rather than on tool operations.

Another key advantage of Garuda is that it can also provide device connectivity and subsequent analytics. Any measurement devices including mass-spectrometers, or any physical devices such as motion sensors and cameras can also be a part of workflow which enables one-stop analysis by connecting the hardware seamlessly with downstream analytics tools (see "Relevant Websites section"). This way experts of various domain other than systems biology, including machine operators, chemist, biologists, data analysts can share the existing and frequently-used workflow in systems biology.

Another interesting use case is when a web-camera takes a picture and using the Garuda protocol automatically sends the data to the next tool where mood detection algorithm is implemented. Such a workflow can be used in clinical settings to monitor patients. Assuming yet another tool downstream of these tools that analyzes the correlation and dynamics between the patient mode and lab results such as blood test and genotype, now the user can have an insight by the integration of phenotypic-level, molecular-level and genetic-level.

Notably, this device connectivity works not only when the device is used as a data source, but also when used as an output. This is realized in the scenario when data analytic tool detects unusual behavior, and can send the alert to doctor's or patient's cell phone in real-time if it is implemented in the platform. Similarly, the connectivity with the device of motion detection, data analytics tools, one can assume the possibility of game-therapy supported by multi-level integrative data such as in diagnosis or monitoring of dementia.

As a whole, the discoverability, navigability and connectivity of multi-dimensional data and analysis are key ingredients that will drive the digital era in biology and medicine (**Fig. 4**).

Perspectives

Computational systems biology is poised for a paradigm shift standing the cusp of rapidly advancing technologies in experimental systems, data analytics and visualization, machine learning and artificial intelligence (AI) and device technologies.

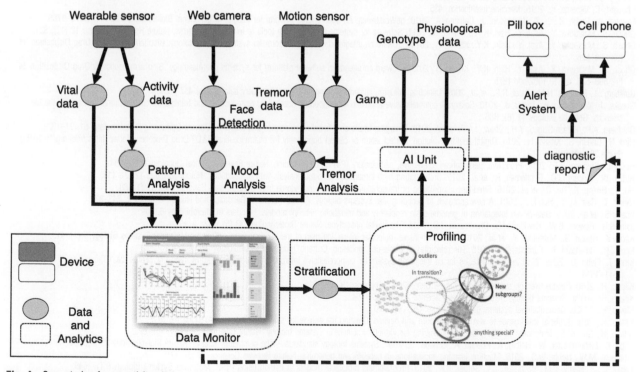

Fig. 4 Case study of connectivity platform for the integration of phenotypic data and data analytics. Adapted from Yachie, A., Matsuoka, Y., 2016. Systems drug and therapy design. Igaku No Ayumi 259 (8), 853–858 (in Japanese).

As outlined in this article, these developments underscore the importance of combining the digital drivers of research and technologies in multi-disciplinary, community-driven approaches to research in biology and medicine.

Novel experimental techniques to study biological processes at multiple levels in exquisite details are been developed. Similarly, advanced in computing and machine learning are allowing researchers to extract hitherto unknown patterns in the data and generate novel hypotheses. In order to connect these diverse tools and methodologies, as highlighted in this article, computational systems biology needs to move towards platforms – large-scale, cloud-enabled frameworks which allows flexible connectivity of these tools to build, execute and re-use research pipelines.

At the same time, the inherent complexity of biological systems, particularly, as manifested in multi-omics scale projects, push the cognitive boundaries of the human mind. As outlined in (Kitano, 2016), several issues emerge in large-scale systems level study of biological processes – information horizon problem, information gap, phenotyping inaccuracy, cognitive bias, and minority report problem. Developments in machine learning, text analytics and robotic automation technologies hold the promise of alleviating some of the problems. It is pertinent to note that unlike other fields where advanced in AI have shown unprecedented success, their application in biology and medicine needs to be predicated on explainability and interpretability – the ability to trace the model-based decision-making criteria and interpret the results in the context of the biology.

Intelligent platforms, with humans in the loop and powered by high-precision robotic systems, big data management, analysis and highly explainable and interpretable models will usher in new horizons in computational systems biology towards deeper understanding of biology and its applications in medicine and healthcare.

See also: Cloud-Based Molecular Modeling Systems. Natural Language Processing Approaches in Bioinformatics

---

References

Aoki, K., Yamada, M., Kunida, K., Yasuda, S., Matsuda, M., 2011. Processive phosphorylation of ERK MAP kinase in mammalian cells. Proceedings of the National Academy of Sciences of the United States of America 108, 12675–12680.

Ben-Hamo, R., Efroni, S., 2013. Network as biomarker: Quantifying transcriptional co-expression to stratify cancer clinical phenotypes. Systems Biomedicine 1 (1), 35–41.

Bois, F.Y., et al., 2017. Multiscale modelling approaches for assessing cosmetic ingredients safety. Toxicology 392, 130–139. doi:10.1016/j.tox.2016.05.026. Epub 2016 Jun 4.

Camarda, R., Alicia, Y.Z., Kohnz, R.A., et al., 2016. Inhibition of fatty acid oxidation as a therapy for MYC-overexpressing triple-negative breast cancer. Nature Medicine 22 (4), 427.

Caron, E., Roncagalli, R., Hase, T., et al., 2017. Precise temporal profiling of signaling complexes in primary cells using SWATH mass spectrometry. Cell Report 18 (13), 3219–3226.

Chen, K.C., et al., 2004. Integrative analysis of cell cycle control in budding yeast. Molecular Biology of the Cell 15, 3841–3862.

Chouard, T., Venema, L., 2015. Machine Intelligence. 435.

Floratos, A., Smith, K., Ji, Z., Watkinson, J., Califano, A., 2010. geWorkbench: An open source platform for integrative genomics. Bioinformatics 26 (14), 1779–1780.

Ghosh, S., Matsuoka, Y., Asai, Y., Hsin, K.-Y., Kitano, H., 2011. Software for systems biology: From tools to integrated platforms. Nature Reviews Genetics 12 (12), 821.

Ghosh, S., Matsuoka, Y., Asai, Y., Hsin, K.Y., Kitano, H., 2013a. Toward an integrated software platform for systems pharmacology. Biopharmaceutics & Drug Disposition 34 (9), 508–526.

Ghosh, S., Matsuoka, Y., Asai, Y., Hsin, K.Y., Kitano, H., 2013b. Toward an integrated software platform for systems pharmacology. Biopharmaceutics & Drug Disposition 34 (9), 508–526. doi:10.1002/bdd.1875.

Ginsberg, J., Matthew, H.M., Patel, R.S., et al., 2009. Detecting influenza epidemics using search engine query data. Nature 457 (7232), 1012.

Goecks, J., Nekrutenko, A., Taylor, J., 2010. Galaxy: A comprehensive approach for supporting accessible, reproducible, and transparent computational research in the life sciences. Genome Biology 11 (8), R86.

Goldberg, A.P., Balázs Szigeti, Y.H., Chew, J.A.P., et al., 2018. Emerging whole-cell modeling principles and methods. Current Opinion in Biotechnology 51, 97–102.

Hird, N., Ghosh, S., Kitano, H., 2016. Digital health revolution: Perfect storm or perfect opportunity for pharmaceutical R&D? Drug Discovery Today. https://doi.org/10.1016/j.drudis.2016.01.010.

Hood, L., Stephen, H.F., 2011. Predictive, personalized, preventive, participatory (P4) cancer medicine. Nature Reviews Clinical Oncology 8 (3), 184.

Huber, W., Vincent, J.C., Gentleman, R., et al., 2015. Orchestrating high-throughput genomic analysis with bioconductor. Nature Methods 12 (2), 115.

Hu, Y., Huang, K., An, Q., et al., 2016. Simultaneous profiling of transcriptome and DNA methylome from a single cell. Genome Biol. 17 (1), 88.

Ideker, T., Galitski, T., Hood, L., 2001. A new approach to decoding life: Systems biology. Annual Review of Genomics and Human Genetics 2, 343–372.

Imam, S., et al., 2015. Data-driven integration of genome-scale regulatory and metabolic network models. Frontiers in Microbiology 6, 409.

Jain, S.H., Powers, B.W., Hawkins, J.B., Brownstein, J.S., 2015. The digital phenotype. Nature Biotechnology 33 (5), 462.

Kaizu, K., Ghosh, S., Matsuoka, Y., et al., 2010. A comprehensive molecular interaction map of the budding yeast cell cycle. Molecular Systems Biology 6 (1), 415.

Karr, J.R., Takahashi, K., Funahashi, A., 2015. The principles of whole-cell modeling. Current Opinion in Microbiology 27, 18–24.

Kind, T., Fiehn, O., 2009. What are the obstacles for an integrated system for comprehensive interpretation of cross-platform metabolic profile data? Bioanalysis 1 (9), 1511–1514.

Kitano, H., 2000. Perspectives on systems biology. New Generation Computing 18, 199–216.

Kitano, H., 2002a. Systems biology: A brief overview. Science 295, 1662–1664.

Kitano, H., 2002b. Computational systems biology. Nature 420, 206–210.

Kitano, H., 2016. Artificial intelligence to win the nobel prize and beyond: Creating the engine for scientific discovery. AI Magazine 37.

Kitano, H., Ghosh, S., Matsuoka, Y., 2011. Social engineering for virtual'big science'in systems biology. Nature Chemical Biology 7 (6), 323.

Klipp, E., Liebermeister, W., Helbig, A., Kowald, A., Schaber, J., 2007. Systems biology standards – The community speaks. Nature Biotechnology 25 (4), 390.

Libbrecht, M.W., Noble, W.S., 2015. Machine learning applications in genetics and genomics. Nature Reviews Genetics 16 (6), 321.

Lopez, C.F., Jeremy, L.M., Bachman, J.A., Sorger, P.K., 2013. Programming biological models in Python using PySB. Molecular Systems Biology 9 (1), 646.

Marbach, D., Costello, J.C., Küffner, R., et al., 2012. Wisdom of crowds for robust gene network inference. Nature Methods 9 (8), 796.

Matsuoka, Y., Matsumae, H., Katoh, M., et al., 2013. A comprehensive map of the influenza A virus replication cycle. BMC Systems Biology 7 (1), 97.

Novak, B., Tyson, J.J., 1993. Numerical analysis of a comprehensive model of M-phase control in Xenopus oocyte extracts and intact embryos. Journal of Cell Science 106, 1153–1168.

Oda, K., Kitano, H., 2006. A comprehensive map of the toll-like receptor signaling network. Molecular Systems Biology 2 (1).

Oda, K., Matsuoka, Y., Funahashi, A., Kitano, H., 2005. A comprehensive pathway map of epidermal growth factor receptor signaling. Molecular Systems Biology 1 (1).

O'Dushlaine, C., Rossin, L., Lee, P.H., et al., 2015. Psychiatric genome-wide association study analyses implicate neuronal, immune and histone pathways. Nature Neuroscience 18 (2), 199.

Perez-Riverol, Y., Bai, M., da Veiga Leprevost, F., et al., 2017. Discovering and linking public omics data sets using the Omics Discovery Index. Nature Biotechnology 35 (5), 406.

Poplin, R., Newburger, D., Dijamco, J., et al., 2017. Creating a universal SNP and small indel variant caller with deep neural networks. BioRxiv. 092890.

Qu, K., Zheng, Y., Dai, S., Qiao, S.Z., 2016. Graphene oxide-polydopamine derived N, S-codoped carbon nanosheets as superior bifunctional electrocatalysts for oxygen reduction and evolution. Nano Energy 19, 373–381.

Reich, M., Liefeld, T., Gould, J., et al., 2006. GenePattern 2.0. Nature Genetics 38 (5), 500.

Schadt, E.E., et al., 2005. An integrative genomics approach to infer causal associations between gene expression and disease. Nature Genetics 37 (7), 710.

Schoeberl, B., et al., 2009. Therapeutically targeting ErbB3: A key node in ligand-induced activation of the ErbB receptor-PI3K axis. Science Signaling 2, ra31.

Schoeberl, B., et al., 2010. An ErbB3 antibody, MM-121, is active in cancers with ligand-dependent activation. Cancer Research 70, 2485–2494.

Schulz, J.C., et al., 2014. Large-scale functional analysis of the roles of phosphorylation in yeast metabolic pathways. Science Signaling 7, rs6.

Shehzad, Z., et al., 2014. A multivariate distance-based analytic framework for connectome-wide association studies. Neuroimage 93, 74–94.

Tyson, J.J., Chen, K., Novak, B., 2001. Network dynamics and cell physiology. Nature Reviews Molecular Cell Biology 2, 908–916.

Vinken, M., 2015. Adverse outcome pathways and drug-induced liver injury testing. Chemical Research in Toxicology 28 (7), 1391–1397.

Wang, M., et al., 2016. Sharing and community curation of mass spectrometry data with GNPS. Nature Biotechnology 34, 828–837.

Webb, S., 2018. Deep Learning for Biology. 555.

Yachie-Kinoshita, A., Onishi, K., Ostblom, J., et al., 2018. Modeling signaling-dependent pluripotency with Boolean logic to predict cell fate transitions. Molecular Systems Biology 14 (1), e7952.

Yi, T., et al., 2014. Quantitative phosphoproteomic analysis reveals system-wide signaling pathways downstream of SDF-1/CXCR4 in breast cancer stem cells. Proceedings of the National Academy of Sciences of the United States of America 111, E2182–E2190.

Yugi, K., 2016. Trans-Omics: How to reconstruct biochemical networks across multiple 'Omic' layers. Trends in Biotechnology 34 (4), 276–290.

Relevant Websites

http://www.oecd.org/chemicalsafety/testing/adverse-outcome-pathways-molecular-screening-and-toxicogenomics.htm
   OECD.org.

www.sbml.org
   SBML.caltech.edu.

http://www.garuda-alliance.org/gadgetpack/shimadzu
   The Garuda Alliance.

Coupling Cell Division to Metabolic Pathways Through Transcription

Petter Holland[1] and Jens Nielsen, Chalmers University of Technology, Gothenburg, Sweden
Thierry DGA Mondeel[1] and Matteo Barberis, University of Amsterdam, Amsterdam, The Netherlands

Introduction: The Right Timing of Cell Division

Living organisms have the ability to survive in (un)favourable environmental conditions due to the capacity of their individual cells to grow and divide. The regulation of cell growth and division is realized by the cell cycle, which is set in motion by molecules that regulate and coordinate these events at the right timing.

The cell cycle is defined by four different phases, which are accompanied by strictly ordered and irreversible biochemical reactions. In the G1 phase, the cell grows to a critical cell size that allows it to duplicate its genetic material (DNA) in the S phase, before to continue growing in the G2 phase and, finally, dividing into two daughter cells in the M phase. Because of its crucial role in cell survival, the cell cycle and its component have been conserved across evolution.

In the budding yeast *Saccharomyces cerevisiae*, the maintenance of strictly alternating cycles of DNA duplication and cell division requires a regulator. Dimeric complexes formed by an enzyme, called cyclin-dependent kinase (Cdk1), and a differential pool of phase-specific, regulatory subunits (cyclins) represent the driving force behind cell cycle progression. Cyclin/Cdk1 kinase complexes must be active for entry into S phase and passage through metaphase, and must be inactivated to allow cytokinesis (cell division) in M phase and licensing (activation) in G1 phase of DNA sequences at which new rounds of DNA duplication are initiated. This regulator ensures that each cell cycle phase is completed before the next one initiates, thus guaranteeing alternation between DNA duplication and cell division with a specific temporal delay.

In order to complete these events, periodic waves of cyclin/Cdk1 activities regulate, and are regulated by DNA-binding proteins, called transcription factors (TFs). These proteins stimulate four waves of gene expression (i) at the transition from G1 phase to S phase (G1/S transcription), (ii) in S phase (S phase transcription), (iii) at the transition from G2 phase to M phase (G2/M transcription), and (iv) at the transition from M phase to G1 phase (M/G1 transcription) (Cho *et al.*, 1998; Spellman *et al.*, 1998; Orlando *et al.*, 2008). TFs are activated by cyclin/Cdk activity through biochemical modifications, i.e., phosphorylation, and regulate expression of phase-specific genes throughout the cell cycle. In turn, a transcriptional network drives Cdk activity by stimulating a timely expression of specific cyclin genes. Thus, Cdk activity and the transcription network are interlocked to tightly control the timing of cell cycle progression (Bähler, 2005; Wittenberg and Reed, 2005; McInerny, 2011; Haase and Wittenberg, 2014).

The coupling between these cellular layers of regulation has consequences at the system-level. That is, cyclin/Cdk1-mediated waves of gene expression do not just modulate the transcription of cyclin genes at the right timing, but also of a large number of genes involved in the cell's wellbeing. In this context, identification of TFs that may convert a cell cycle response to metabolic switches, and/or that may initiate metabolic reactions whose end products fuel cell cycle reactions, is pivotal to understand how the precise timing of a cell's response is achieved. Ideally, TFs may bridge multiple spatial, temporal and functional scales within various cellular layers of regulation. Thus, they may be hubs (nodes in a network characterized by a high connectivity) at the interface of cellular networks in multi-scale models, which aim to understand how a function emerges from a network of interactions (Castiglione *et al.*, 2014).

By using a Systems Biology strategy, which integrates predictive computer models with biochemical experimentation, we have recently discovered a dynamic coupling of cyclin/Cdk1 complexes to the Forkhead (Fkh) TFs Fkh1 and Fkh2 to guarantee a timely cell cycle progression. Specifically, we have demonstrated that the waves of cyclin/Cdk1 complexes active from S through M phases are synchronized by Fkh2 (and, perhaps, to a lesser extent by Fkh1): S and M phase-specific cyclin/Cdk complexes phosphorylate Fkh2, which in turn promotes expression of S and M phase cyclins (Linke *et al.*, 2017).

The discovery that DNA duplication and cell division are temporally coordinated by Fkh, leads us to ask what is their specific role in the different cell cycle phases. In this study, we aim to understand whether or not Fkh may act as hubs to bridge regulatory processes spanning cell cycle/division, DNA replication, signal transduction and metabolic networks. To this end, we identify targets of Fkh1 and Fkh2 across the budding yeast genome, and indicate whether, and to which extent, a Fkh-mediated transcriptional program leading to the activation of cellular pathways may contribute to the timely cell's cycling. Specifically, we show (i) how definite metabolic pathways may be possibly activated by Fkh, and (ii) their relevance in the synchronization of the cyclin/Cdk1 kinase activities that guarantee alternation of DNA duplication and cell division.

Background: The Interplay Between DNA and Proteins

For the DNA to serve its role as carrier of information in designing proteins in the cell, it is essential to retrieve this information timely and accurately. While protein designs are carried within the DNA sequence, regulation of when and how much of a given protein is produced is achieved by an interplay between the DNA and associated proteins, such as TFs, within the nucleus of eukaryotic cells.

---

[1]Petter Holland and Thierry DGA Mondeel contributed equally to this work.
Corresponding Author: Matteo Barberis, E-mail: matteo@barberislab.com.

Encyclopedia of Bioinformatics and Computational Biology, Volume 3   doi:10.1016/B978-0-12-809633-8.20081-2

One of the most abundant proteins in the cell are histones, which were first discovered as structural components that DNA wraps around. Chemical modifications of histones were later found to regulate DNA functions, affecting how tightly the DNA-histone complexes are packed and interacting with other proteins to modulate gene expression (Tessarz and Kouzarides, 2014).

The signals that regulate gene expression are integrated at the Transcription Start Site (TSS) of genes by a complex of proteins that includes the RNA polymerase. How different signals can lead to various levels of transcription is not well understood; however, a wide range of cellular components and reactions have been demonstrated to influence this process. In addition to the aforementioned histone modifications, the relative position of a gene in the nucleus has been shown to influence gene expression, introducing the concept of transcriptional factories whereby the expression level of a gene may be influenced by the proximity to an active factory (Papantonis and Cook, 2013).

Another group of proteins influencing transcription through a direct interaction with the DNA sequence is represented by TFs. TFs are defined as proteins that bind to a specific 'motif', i.e., a well-defined DNA sequence, with a typical length of 5–12 base pairs. In budding yeast, TFs are thought to influence transcription, first, by binding relatively close to the TSS, and then by interacting with histones and other TFs on the DNA, thereby influencing the assembly of a productive TSS protein complex. In multicellular eukaryotes, enhancer elements exist that can influence transcription at a long distance from the TSS.

Fundamentals: Methodologies to Investigate DNA–TF Interaction

Understanding how, when and why TFs to DNA has become a major undertaking to understand transcriptional regulation. The first genome-wide method realized to experimentally map TF binding across the genome in living cells was Chromatin Immunoprecipitation (ChIP) with microarray detection of bound DNA (ChIP-chip) (Solomon et al., 1988). This technique relies on: (i) Using formaldehyde to chemically link proteins and DNA together, (ii) sonicating the DNA to fragment it, (iii) purifying a selected protein by antibody, and (iv) detecting the DNA fragments that are bound to the purified protein. Studies that have mapped the DNA binding sites of many TFs provided the first integrated view of the proteins and regulatory mechanisms that control eukaryotic gene expression (Harbison et al., 2004).

With the emergence of next generation sequencing, further development of the ChIP methodology led to ChIP-seq (Robertson et al., 2007), which could achieve higher resolution as compared to ChIP-chip because of not being limited by the amount of probes on the chip. Multiplexing with barcoded adaptors and increased availability of commercial sequencing services have lowered the costs of ChIP-seq experiments, to a point where it has now replaced ChIP-chip as the dominant method of genome-wide determination of TF binding to the DNA (Park, 2009). Importantly, ChIP-seq was used as the method of choice for the ENCODE consortia to map a large number of human TFs with a consistent set of experimental and data processing protocols (Landt et al., 2012).

The latest development of the ChIP methodology is called ChIP-exo, which further ameliorate ChIP-seq by using an exonuclease to degrade one strand of the isolated DNA (Rhee and Pugh, 2011). The exonuclease cleaves one DNA strand until the TF – DNA crosslink, and adaptors are then ligated to the cleaved ends, leading to a high resolution information of the TF – DNA contact surface. The general ChIP protocol and differences among the three ChIP methods are illustrated in **Fig. 1**, whereas the main advantages between ChIP-seq and ChIP-exo are listed in **Table 1**. An impressive demonstration of the increased resolution of ChIP-exo was the mapping of components of the pre-initiation complex in budding yeast. In this study, the area of DNA that was protected by the exonuclease was a good match for how a specific protein was predicted to cross-link to the DNA from a model of DNA and protein structures (Rhee and Pugh, 2012).

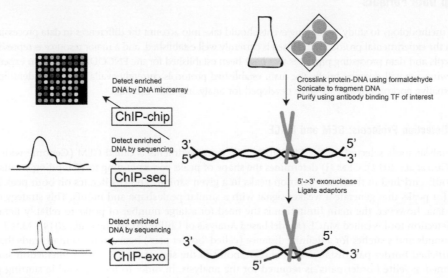

Fig. 1 Summary of the ChIP experimental protocol and overview of the main differences between three ChIP methods: ChIP-chip, ChIP-seq and ChIP-exo (see text for details).

Table 1   Advantages of ChIP-seq and ChIP-exo when compared to each other

ChIP-seq	ChIP-exo
– Easier and quicker experimental protocol	– Higher resolution mapping of TF–DNA binding
– Fewer costly reagents	– Footprinting several TFs can provide structural insights of protein complexes
– More developed tools for data analysis	– Less background binding to the DNA due to exonuclease treatment
– Immunoprecipitation control allows for the analysis of unspecific antibody binding	

The choice of which ChIP methodology to use when investigating a given TF is not obvious, and several factors should be considered. Although ChIP-exo is the most recent development and seems to be the most attractive choice if the resources are available, new challenges are introduced when using this ChIP methodology as compared to ChIP-seq. Notably, a treatment with the exonuclease makes it impossible to have an immunoprecipitation (IP) control, as typically used in ChIP-seq experiments. Recently, an interesting solution to this problem, called protein attached chromatin capture (PAtCh-Cap) (Terooatea *et al.*, 2016), was proposed. PAtCh-Cap seems to increase the confidence in peak identification; however, it remains untested at a large scale to exclude any introduction of bias. The lack of an IP control means that the most common ChIP peak quantification metric, i.e., ChIP peak signal/IP control signal, is no longer possible and other metrics have to be used. While the lack of an IP control complicates the measurement of a ChIP peak signal, ChIP-exo seems to have a reduced level of background binding as compared to ChIP-seq (Rhee and Pugh, 2011), resulting in a potentially more accurate quantitative measurement of TF binding to the DNA. In addition, an increased resolution given by the exact position of the TF binding event can potentially be used in a system-level analysis to describe gene regulation in detail.

The network of cellular signals that regulate expression of a gene or of a group of genes is often referred to as Transcriptional Regulatory Network (TRN). While a variety of signals affects gene transcript levels, much of the current studies focus on TFs. Importantly, in recent years, the power of system-level analyses that integrate TF binding information with transcriptome analysis has been demonstrated, for example to understand the bacterial TRN of gene expression (Arrieta-Ortiz *et al.*, 2015; Fang *et al.*, 2017). Although many details are known about eukaryotic gene regulation, a TRN with demonstrated predictive power is lacking. This is partially due to the fact that the eukaryotes genome comprehends more genes and TFs, and that additional complexity exists that is introduced by histone occupancy and modifications, TF subcellular localization and a variety of post-translational modifications. These additional levels of regulation mean that more information needs to be taken into account in a system-level analysis to understand how eukaryotic TRNs regulate gene expression.

ChIP data provide a list of targets of TFs that may be subsequently analyzed for their specific function within cellular networks. Given the wealth of data that is available about genes and the proteins they encode, ChIP data can predict novel functions of TFs. When retrieving these data, a number of challenges are faced: (i) False-positives binding events have to be excluded, and (ii) a comprehensive picture of the TF functions from the wealth of data generated shall be drawn. In this study, we present and discuss our approach to dealing with these challenges when investigating the Fkh-mediated transcriptional program. A picture of Fkh's functions within the multi-scale network of the budding yeast cell demonstrates the power of the ChIP methodology to generate hypotheses and suggest definite experiments that may shed light on novel regulatory events underlying timely cellular responses upon stimulation.

Application: Chip Data Formats

Choosing the ChIP methodology to study TF binding events should take into account the differences in data processing between these, in addition to those in the experimental protocols. ChIP-seq is currently well established, and a major resource is represented by the detailed experimental protocols and data processing pipelines that have been established for the ENCODE consortium experiments (Landt *et al.*, 2012). In the following, we will describe briefly the main established protocols currently available for the identification of a ChIP-seq signal, and the alternative approaches that we have developed for analyzing ChIP-exo data.

Established Peak Detection Protocols: GEM and MACE

One of the data analysis tools selected for the ENCODE ChIP-seq experiments is called GEM (Genome wide Event finding and Motif discovery) (Guo *et al.*, 2012). GEM (i) determines the shape of peaks corresponding to TF binding events on the DNA (peak detection), and motifs enriched in the most common peaks in a given sample, and (ii) iterates on both peak shape and motif to enrich the dataset for peaks that generate a weaker signal with a similar peak shape and motifs. This strategy can also be used to analyze ChIP-exo data; however, the main limitation is the need for a large number of peaks to reliably iterate the procedure.

Another peak detection tool is called MACE (Model based Analysis of ChIP-Exo) (Wang *et al.*, 2014). MACE separates the reads of different DNA strands and searches for a definite distance (called 'border pair') between the start of reads that is enriched across the sample. The enriched border pair distance should correspond to the size of the TF – DNA interaction surface. A set of clear (strong) peaks defined as 'elite border pairs' is required for the analysis, in order to have a reliable starting point to define the remaining weaker peaks. Thus, the limitations of MACE are similar to GEM, with a requirement for a relatively large amount of strong peaks.

Alternative Approaches: *maxPeak* and *loessPeak*

While studies of human TFs binding to DNA typically provide a sufficient number of peaks to be analyzed by iteration-based peak detection methods, our experience with budding yeast indicates that not all TFs will have enough targets to achieve a reliable iteration procedure when using GEM or MACE. This led us to develop alternative tools to define peaks that are not dependent on iteration, thus that can process data containing fewer peaks. To define what a peak is, relative to an uneven background signal, is not a trivial task when only relatively few peaks are detected.

According to the principle of ChIP-exo, the positions inside the TF – DNA binding surface should be highly enriched for overlapping reads from each DNA strand, while unspecific reads from experimental background or technical noise may be on only one DNA strand. One approach that we have developed is to reduce the background signal by using the strand-specific information and counting up reads only where there were reads overlapping on each DNA strand; we will denote this approach by OL, for overlapping DNA strand, as opposed to AD, for additive DNA strand approach. The term 'overlap' is here to be interpreted as having, at a minimum, one read on each DNA strand covering the same single nucleotide position. Hence, these two reads overlap on that nucleotide, albeit on different DNA strands.

To further reduce the background noise, we determine a read length to be used where a TF binding site is covered by reads on each strand, but not extending out on each side. Reads coming from our experimental setup have a length of 75 base pairs, and choosing a read length of 10 would correspond to taking the left-most 10 base pairs into account. The exact read length to be used is tested by quantifying the highest point of overlapping reads per gene for read lengths from 1 to 75 base pairs, and by selecting the read length where the increase in highest peak counts is most increased over the previous three read lengths. For the Fkh TFs investigated in this study, this read length was determined to be equal to seven. Given the read length, each read is shortened to correspond to the read length (starting to count at the left-most base pair). Given the read length, either through the optimisation procedure indicated above or by choosing it manually, and the approach for dealing with the strands, OL or AD, we will hereafter denote the combination of these two as e.g., OL7 or AD10, for read lengths of 7 or 10 base pairs, respectively.

When investigating TF binding events, a choice has to be made with respect to the part of the genome to be explored. Two options may be considered: (i) Use of the known TSS for the subset of genes for which this information is available, and search 1000 base pairs upstream of TSS, or (ii) use the known locations of the ORF (Open Reading Frame) for each gene, and search 1000 base pairs upstream of the start codon. The choice of a region of 1000 base pairs is somewhat arbitrary, but is limited by the fact that a too large region might end up in the ORF of an upstream gene. The advantage of the former approach is that transcription starts from the TSS so it defines a more accurate region as the promoter of a gene, whereas the advantage of the latter is that information can be retrieved from a higher number of genes even if the TSS location is unknown. In practice, the difference of using the two approaches is minimal for the majority of genes that have a defined TSS, which have a distance from the TSS to the start codon of about 20–80 base pairs. In a parallel study, we have considered TSS from the study of Iyer and colleagues (Park *et al.*, 2014) as well as 166 manually added approximate TSSs based on RNAseq data, for a total of 5373 TSSs (unpublished). Here, we instead search upstream of the start codon of the ORF for each gene.

At this point, the ChIP-exo dataset consists of short reads, overlapping on one (AD) or both (OL) DNA strands, which we can count at each base pair. Consequently, a series of peaks of different heights may be retrieved along the genome. In this work, we present two novel approaches to determine TF binding locations on the DNA, which we refer to as 'maxPeak' and 'loessPeak'.

In the maxPeak approach, we locate the base pair with the highest count of reads for each gene's promoter region. This means that only one TF binding location for any given gene may be found. As previously mentioned, a challenge with ChIP-exo as compared to ChIP-seq is the lack of an antibody immunoprecipitation (IP) control that can be used to measure quantitatively a specific TF – DNA enrichment relative to an unspecific antibody – DNA enrichment. In order to have a relative measurement of the peak strength (signal/noise) and to remove the background signal, we detect peaks by using peak quantiles. Quantiles are calculated from the maximum signal per gene promoter of all promoters that have any signal. Our experience from ChIP-exo analysis of other budding yeast TFs is that the 65% quantile (the 65th percentile) is a threshold that results in a good representation of peaks as well as removal of the majority of the background and noisy signal (unpublished observations). In contrast, the signal/noise for GEM is calculated by dividing the IP signal of the peak by the 'expected binding strength' that calculates the background signal in the local context around the detected peak. In MACE, peak significance is reported as a p-value. A subtlety to take into account when considering the 65th percentile threshold is that a similar background noise may be assumed across experiments based on different conditions (e.g., different growth) for the same TF. In these cases, it may be useful to average the threshold for the conditions and use the new value as the normalizing factor. We will return to this specific point in the section of the ChIP data analysis.

After applying the maxPeak approach, and before applying the loessPeak approach, TF binding sites may be ordered by the height of their signal. In the maxPeak approach, this corresponds to the number of reads at the peak binding position (i.e., zero or one location per gene). For the loessPeak approach, this corresponds to potentially many peaks per gene. For either approach, TF binding locations may first be sorted in ascending order and then reduced by applying the threshold of the 65th percentile, which is chosen as the quantile threshold to consider a binding position non-random. For the maxPeak approach, the signal of each identified peak is then normalized (divided) by this quantile, yielding a Signal-to-Noise Ratio (SNR) below 1 if the location has a lower signal than the threshold and a SNR > 1 if its signal is above the threshold. For the loessPeak approach, any signal in the promoter that is below the 65th percentile is set to that value.

In the loessPeak approach, after leveling any signal below the 65th percentile, the signal at the promoter is smoothed with a loess function using a span of 0.05. This is only a mild amount of smoothing where the main goal is to get an accurate position of the highest point of the peak while also having a small differential effect on strong and weak peaks. The smoothing causes weak peaks that are, for example, very narrow to be relatively reduced as compared to wider and stronger peaks. Subsequently, peaks are identified by searching for a pattern signal change in the smoothed signal containing minimum 7 consecutive increasing signal values and then minimum 7 consecutive decreasing signal values. For a gene, all identified peaks are listed by order of signal strength and, if a lower peak signal is within 100 base pairs of a stronger peak, the weaker one is discarded. All peaks are then normalized by the 65th percentile. Generally, peaks with a remaining, smoothed and normalized, SNR< 1 are discarded.

Biological duplicates are explicitly averaged in the maxPeak and loessPeak approaches when the number of reads for each nucleotide is quantified. GEM and MACE internally deal with the biological duplicates.

The workflow of our experimental protocol, starting from ChIP-exo sequencing reads, is summarized in **Fig. 2**, whereas a visualization of the maxPeak and loessPeak approaches in shown in **Fig. 3**.

Case Study: ChIP-exo Data Analysis of Fkh1 and Fkh2 TFs

The Forkhead (Fkh) TFs Fkh1 and Fkh2 modulate a timely cell's cycling in budding yeast, by coordinating DNA duplication with cell division. Fkh2 is expressed from the G1 phase until the M phase, with Fkh1 overlapping during S and G2 phases (Lee *et al.*, 2002).

In the G1 phase of the cell cycle, Fkh guarantee the right spatial organization of chromatin within the nucleus of yeast cells. Specific DNA binding sites, called origins of replication or replication origins, timely cluster prior DNA duplication and are subsequently recognized by enzymes (DNA polymerases) that initiate this process. Fkh1 and Fkh2 were shown to be involved in this mechanism by binding to, and regulating the transcription timing of a number of replication origins (Knott *et al.*, 2012; Ostrow *et al.*, 2014) by acting as rate-limiting activators (Peace *et al.*, 2016). We have also demonstrated that Fkh proteins are responsible for the clustering of replication origins in the S phase, thereby of the timing of DNA duplication, through a structural motif that allows dimerization to bring distal DNA binding sites into close proximity (Ostrow *et al.*, 2017).

Fkh-dependent activity also drives transcriptional regulation of genes at the G2/M transition, in particular of the *CLB2* cyclin gene promoting cell division (Koranda *et al.*, 2000; Kumar *et al.*, 2000). Although Fkh1 and Fkh2 have overlapping functions, only Fkh2 can form a complex, together with the scaffold protein Mcm1 and the co-activator Ndd1, that binds to and modulate the activity of both *CLB2* and *CLB3* promoters (Koranda *et al.*, 2000; Kumar *et al.*, 2000; Pic *et al.*, 2000; Reynolds *et al.*, 2003; Linke *et al.*, 2017). Conversely, Fkh1 binds less efficiently to the *CLB2* promoter and represses *CLB2* transcription (Hollenhorst *et al.*, 2000, 2001; Sherriff *et al.*, 2007).

Fkh expression and function throughout cell cycle progression suggests that these TFs may have the potential to establish regulatory interactions with cellular networks beside the cell cycle. Therefore, in this study, we have explored the capability of Fkh1 and Fkh2 to bind promoters of genes across the budding yeast genome through ChIP-exo. ChIP data have been gathered under two different experimental conditions (cells grown exponentially, or logarithmic phase, and in stationary phase) to compare the data analysis tools described above, and their challenges and advantages will be highlighted in the following. Fkh1 and Fkh2 have an intermediate amount of peaks as compared to other budding yeast TFs (unpublished observations), thus may serve as good case studies to test the workflow and challenges in working with ChIP-exo in this organism. The workflow shown in **Fig. 2** has been implemented in this study for the Fkh1 and Fkh2 data analysis.

Challenges With GEM and MACE

GEM did reliably iterate on Fkh1 data (two different experimental conditions, two biological replicates of each condition), but not on Fkh2 data. Considering that Fkh1 and Fkh2 are proposed to have similar binding motifs (de Boer and Hughes, 2012), we ran Fkh1 and Fkh2 data together in the GEM analysis, treating them as different conditions of the same TF. As a result, a reliable iteration was possible for both data. Similarly, MACE also presented challenges when analyzing Fkh2 data; the detected amount of elite border pairs was only 25, and the MACE python script by default fails with less than 30 elite border pairs. Therefore, the script was modified to reduce the existing threshold, thus allowing us to analyze the data for Fkh2 as well.

Determination of the Read Length

As described above, the OL and AD approaches applied to the maxPeak and loessPeak methods of peak detection do not require iteration or minimal numbers of peaks of a certain quality. Data analysis was performed four times: the optimal read length was determined to be 7 base pairs for both Fkh1 and Fkh2; however, in order to test the sensitivity to the read length setting, we have also performed the analysis for a manually determined read length of 10 base pairs. For both read lengths we performed the analysis by using the overlapping DNA strand approach (OL) and the additive DNA strand approach (AD). In **Fig. 4** the raw reads and peak detection results are visualized for the four data analysis methods (maxPeak, loessPeak, GEM and MACE,) for the genes *PES4* (coding for a poly(A) binding protein) and *CLB2* (coding for a mitotic cyclin that promotes the transition from the G2 to M phase), which have the highest SNR for Fkh1 and Fkh2, respectively.

In **Fig. 5** the signal of the peaks against the percentiles of raw data for both Fkh1 and Fkh2 is plotted. As previously mentioned, based on prior experience, the 65th percentile represents a good threshold, and it also seems to be a good choice to analyze Fkh1 and Fkh2 data. In fact, this value sits in a relatively flat area of the curves where the difference between both TFs is not too large.

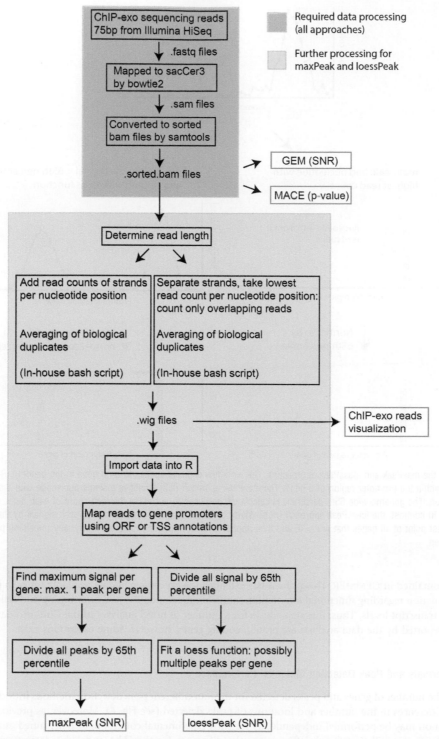

Fig. 2 Overview of the ChIP-exo data analysis workflow. To map reads to the budding yeast genome, raw reads were mapped to the SacCer3 genome (S288C_reference_sequence_R64-2-1_20150113.fsa, downloaded from the Saccharomyces Genome Database (SGD) website (see "Relevant Websites Section") with Bowtie 2. (Langmead and Salzberg, 2012). SAM files were converted to BAM files, sorted and indexed using SAMtools (Li *et al.*, 2009). Output indicated as blue rectangles is shown in **Fig. 5**.

Data Integration and Annotation

After ChIP data processing was completed, we have integrated and annotated the data to retrieve biological information. We have recently developed GEMMER (see "Relevant Websites section"), a web-based visualization tool of multi-scale interaction networks that integrates information from various databases for budding yeast (Mondeel *et al.*, 2018). The ChIP data were merged with the

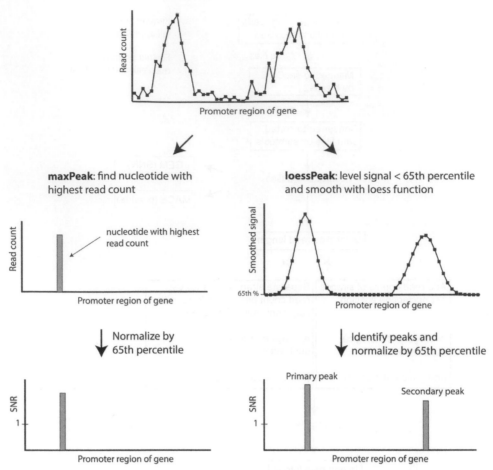

Fig. 3 Illustration of the maxPeak and loessPeak approaches. The workflow depicted applies to each gene in the genome. Reads are counted across all base pairs within the promoter region of a gene. The maxPeak approach (left) identifies a single nucleotide with the highest read count in each promoter region. The genome-wide 65th percentile is calculated, and used to normalize the read count of each peak, generating a Signal-to-Noise Ratio (SNR). In contrast, the loessPeak approach (right) starts by calculating and normalizing the peak signals by the genome-wide 65th percentile of the highest point of all genes that are > 0, and then applies a loess smoothing function; finally, any remaining peaks with a $SNR > = 1$ are identified.

gene annotations contained in GEMMER. This process has extended the experimental data available for each protein-coding gene in SGD, with information regarding functional annotation, localization, abundance, and both timing and cell cycle phase of peak occurrence of RNA transcript levels. Thus, this step allows for a number of novel analyses of the ChIP-exo data. Of note, the vast majority of genes reported by the data analysis are protein-coding genes; however, some exceptions exist.

Comparing Data Formats and Peak Detection Methods' Performance

We have explored the number of genes and peaks detected for the four different peak detection methods introduced above, and we found significant differences in the number and locations of peaks detected (see **Fig. 4**). Moreover, as previously mentioned, the quantile determination may be performed independently for each experimental condition, or determined as average for multiple conditions for each TF. We will therefore briefly explore the difference for the Fkh1 and Fkh2 datasets with respect to these different determinations.

Table 2 reports the number of TF binding locations above threshold in unique genes and the (equal or larger) number of distinct peaks for GEM ($SNR > = 1$), MACE (p-value $< = 0.01$), maxPeak (OL7 and AD10 with $SNR > = 1$) and loessPeak (OL7 and AD10 with $SNR > = 1$) when determining the average quantile for both experimental conditions (growth of cells in logarithmic phase or in stationary phase) for each TF. Similarly, **Table 3** reports the number of peaks and genes retrieved when the quantiles are determined independently for each experimental condition. Of note, only the maxPeak and loessPeak approaches are affected by the choice of the quantiles (see workflow in **Fig. 2**). In **Table 2** a significant increase in genes/peaks may be observed in stationary phase for both Fkh1 and Fkh2 as compared to the logarithmic phase, when using maxPeak and loessPeak. This evidence suggests that the assumption of an equal background noise across these conditions may be not realistic. In **Table 3** a reduced ratio of genes/

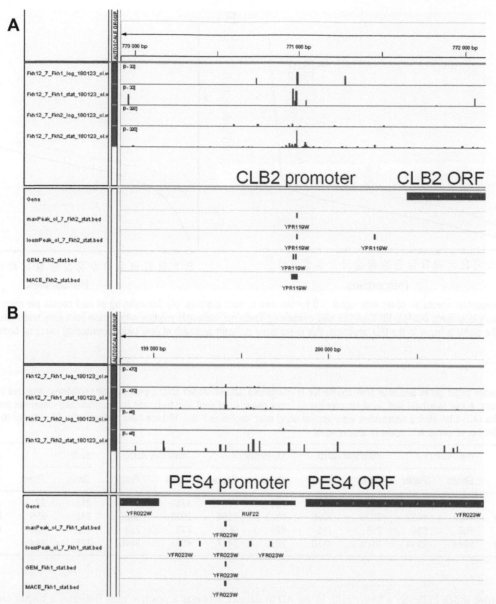

Fig. 4 Analysis of ChIP-exo reads (top part of panels) by different peak detection methods for two genes. (A) *CLB2*, selected for having the highest peak for Fkh2. (B) *PES4*, selected for having the highest peak for Fkh1. The maxPeak (OL7) approach returns a single peak for in the promoter region of both genes. GEM and loessPeak may return multiple peaks, whereas MACE returns a region of several consecutive nucleotides as the peak.

peaks across experimental conditions may be observed, although a large increase in the signal above threshold still occurs in stationary phase experiments. For example, the ratio of target genes identified by maxPeak OL7 between the two conditions for Fkh1 changes from $747/1422 = 0.525$, to $816/1363 = 0.599$. We have proceeded to analyze ChIP data based on quantiles determined independently for each experimental condition.

Investigating the Discrepancy Between OL7 and AD10

So far we have been considering the AD10 dataset as a simultaneous illustration of the additive approach to counting reads on both DNA strands, and of the change of the read length. **Tables 2** and **3** clearly point out that large differences exist in the analysis between the OL7 and AD10 datasets, even within one approach, e.g., maxPeak. In **Fig. 6(A)** the fold-change in the SNR among three sets of genes is shown when using the maxPeak OL7 and AD10 datasets for Fkh1 in logarithmic phase: (i) The 100 genes with the highest signal in OL7, (ii) all genes in OL7 with a SNR$> = 1$, and (iii) all genes in OL7 with a SNR> 0. Large fold changes are observed in all three groups. This difference is more apparent in **Fig. 6(B)**, where the difference in rank for genes in each of the three groups is plotted. The term 'rank' here indicates the index of a given gene when the dataset is sorted on the SNR in descending

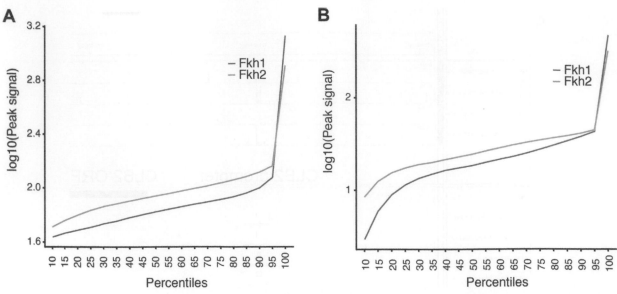

Fig. 5 Peak percentiles across all genes with signal >0 for two data formats explored. (A) Summing up all read counts per nucleotide position with 10 base pairs long reads (AD10). (B) Counting only overlapping reads per nucleotide position with 7 base pairs long reads (OL7). It can be observed that the signal is lower in the OL7 approach, due to the more stringent approach of only taking overlapping reads on both DNA strands.

Table 2   Unique target genes and total peak counts for TF normalized data (averaged across experimental conditions) analyzed by four peak detection methods. A low threshold was used for considering target genes significant (see text), and for maxPeak and loessPeak both overlapping (OL) and additive (AD) DNA strand approaches were applied using read lengths of 7 and 10 base pairs, respectively. Of note, for the maxPeak approach the number of genes and peaks is always equal

	maxPeak OL7		maxPeak AD10		loessPeak OL7		loessPeak AD10		GEM		MACE	
	Genes	Peaks	Genes	Peaks	Genes	Peaks	Genes	Peaks	Genes	Peaks	Genes	Peaks
Fkh1 mid-log	747	747	1880	1880	726	779	1786	2116	215	221	439	451
Fkh1 stationary	1422	1422	3029	3029	1372	1564	2923	3937	248	259	814	841
Fkh2 mid-log	686	686	755	755	628	655	713	783	132	139	691	699
Fkh2 stationary	2944	2944	4170	4170	2800	3497	4055	5940	170	184	1142	1196

order. A negative index indicates a lower rank in the AD10 dataset, whereas a positive rank indicates a higher rank in the OL7 dataset. Strikingly, there are large shifts in rank that correspond with the fold changes; even among the top 100 OL7 targets there are genes that shift down hundreds of places in AD10.

What is the reason for the observed difference? In **Fig. 6(C)** and **(D)** the same fold change and rank displacement analysis is reported when comparing OL7 and OL10. Here, the differences are almost insignificant, especially among the genes with a higher signal. It appears that changing the read length from 7 to 10 base pairs has only a little consequence to the data analysis. To drive the point home, in **Fig. 6(E)** and **(F)** the same analysis is performed among OL7 and AD7 datasets. The similarity with **Fig. 6(A)** is remarkable. Therefore, we conclude that the maxPeak and loessPeak (the latter not shown) approaches are relatively insensitive to the read length setting, but very sensitive to the choice of how to deal with reads on different DNA strands. Given that the OL approach reduces the background noise – as it is intuitively apparent and reflected in the number of genes/peaks reported in **Tables 2** and **3** –, we hereafter proceed considering only the OL approach with a read length of 7.

Increasing the Stringency for TF Binding Significance

Analyzing in more detail **Table 3**, it can be observed that GEM is the most stringent among the peak detection methods by far in terms of the number of genes and peak locations it returns as being significant. Following the results shown in **Fig. 6**, we have realized that especially the maxPeak and loessPeak approaches may overestimate the number of significant TF binding events when using a threshold of SNR$> =1$. Therefore, we have repeated the data analysis for more stringent thresholds with the aim of uncovering the more reliable Fkh target genes (see **Table 4**).

Table 3 Unique target genes and total peak counts for condition-normalized data analyzed by four peak detection methods. A low threshold was used for considering target genes significant (see text), and for maxPeak and loessPeak both OL and AD DNA strand approaches were applied using read lengths of 7 and 10 base pairs, respectively. Of note, for the maxPeak approach the number of genes and peaks is always equal

	maxPeak OL7		maxPeak AD10		loessPeak OL7		loessPeak AD10		GEM		MACE	
	Genes	Peaks	Genes	Peaks	Genes	Peaks	Genes	Peaks	Genes	Peaks	Genes	Peaks
Fkh1 mid-log	816	816	2460	2460	796	858	2349	2910	215	221	439	451
Fkh1 stationary	1363	1363	2473	2473	1319	1499	2365	3062	248	259	814	841
Fkh2 mid-log	1292	1292	2463	2463	1182	1283	2362	2911	132	139	691	699
Fkh2 stationary	2361	2361	2470	2470	2239	2672	2367	2919	170	184	1142	1196

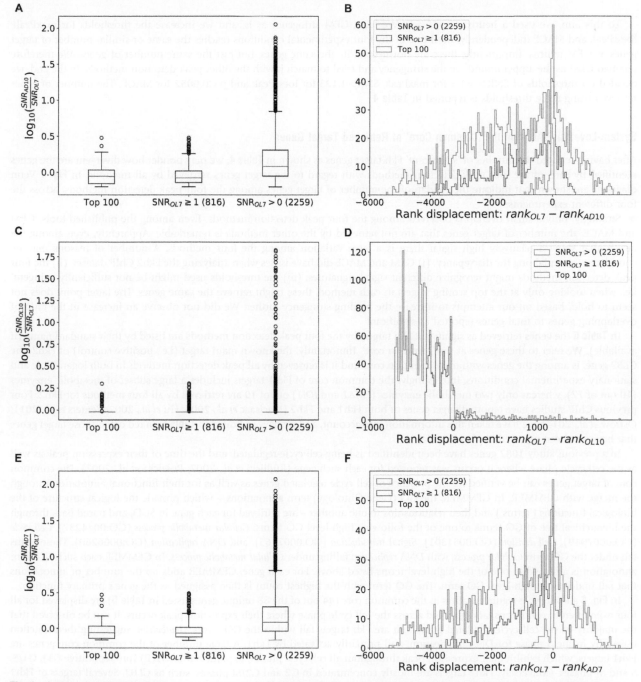

Fig. 6 Comparison of the rank displacement and SNR log10 fold-change between the maxPeak OL7 and AD10 datasets for Fkh1 in logarithmic phase.

Table 4   Unique target genes and total peak counts for condition-normalized data analyzed by four peak detection methods. A higher threshold was used for considering target genes significant (see text), and for maxPeak and loessPeak only the OL DNA strand approach was applied using a read lengths of 7 base pairs. Numbers highlighted in red color indicate the condition for a particular dataset that approximately reaches the number of genes retrieved by GEM for definite stringency settings

	maxPeak OL7		loessPeak OL7		GEM		MACE	
	Genes	Peaks	Genes	Peaks	Genes	Peaks	Genes	Peaks
Fkh1 mid-log	348	348	287	301	215	221	219	223
Fkh1 stationary	530	530	467	496	248	259	403	408
Fkh2 mid-log	452	452	360	370	132	139	191	193
Fkh2 stationary	167	167	169	169	170	184	281	282

To this aim, we used a heuristic approach: We leave GEM stringency as is, and we increase the thresholds for maxPeak, loessPeak and MACE independently, until one of the four experimental conditions reaches the same or similar number of target genes as GEM returns. Importantly, these are not necessarily the same genes, but just the same number of genes. We therefore retained GEM as the 'upper bound' on the stringency and tried to match it with the other peak detection methods. In the end, we decided on thresholds of $SNR > = 1.5$ for maxPeak, $SNR > 1.123$ for loessPeak and $p < 0.0052$ for MACE. The number of genes retrieved using these thresholds is reported in **Table 4**.

System-Level Insight From the 'Common Core' of Retrieved Target Genes

After having reduced the number of 'significant' Fkh target genes as shown in **Table 4**, we may ponder how divergent are the genes identified by each of the four peak detection methods with regard to the target genes retrieved by all methods. In **Fig. 7** Venn diagrams are shown that indicate the overlap of the number of target genes among the four peak detection methods, across the four different experiments.

Strikingly, only a small overlap is observed among the four peak detection methods. Even among the published tools, GEM and MACE, the number of target genes that are not retrieved by the other methods is remarkable. Apparently, even among the targets that show a relatively high signal there is a large variation among the four methods. A number of reasons may be considered for explaining the discrepancy: (i) GEM and MACE did have issues when analyzing the Fkh2 ChIP dataset; (ii) the four peak detection methods might recognize different signal signatures; (iii) the thresholds used might be not sufficiently stringent, i.e., when looking only at the top scoring targets in each method, these might retrieve the same genes. The latter point does not seem to hold, based on our attempts to increase the binding stringency further: We did not observe an increase in the ratio of overlapping genes to total genes reported as significant.

In **Table 5** the genes retrieved as significant Fkh targets by the four peak detection methods are listed by their standard name (if available). We refer to these genes as the 'common core'. Importantly, the known main target (i.e., positive control) of Fkh2, the *CLB2* gene, is among the genes within the common core, and it is retrieved by all peak detection methods in both logarithmic and stationary experimental conditions. Interestingly, the common core of Fkh1 targets includes a large subset of metabolic enzymes (10 out of 77), whereas only two metabolic enzymes (*PMA1* and *IDI1*) out of 19 are retrieved by all four methods for Fkh2. Four previous ChIP studies have reported target genes of both Fkh1 and Fkh2 (MacIsaac *et al.*, 2006; Hu *et al.*, 2007; Venters *et al.*, 2011; Ostrow *et al.*, 2014); we have taken this information into account, and we have indicated in **Table 5**, in red color, those target genes that have not been reported by these studies.

In a previous study 1082 genes have been identified as being cell cycle-regulated, and the time of their expression peak as well as the cell cycle phase where it occurs was reported for each such gene (Kudlicki *et al.*, 2007; Rowicka *et al.*, 2007). The common core of target genes can be verified for the presence of cell cycle regulated genes as well as for their functional annotation through the merge with GEMMER. In GEMMER, the GO (Gene Ontology) term annotations – which provide the logical structure of the biological functions ('terms') and their relationships to one another – are retrieved for each gene in SGD, and traced back through the hierarchical tree of GO terms to one of the following high-level GO terms: *Cellular metabolic process* (GO:0044237), *Cell cycle* (GO:0007049), *Cell division* (GO:0051301), *Signal transduction* (GO:0007165), and *DNA replication* (GO:0006260). These terms fall under the GO term *Cellular process*, with *DNA replication* falling under *Cellular metabolic process*. In GEMMER each such GO term annotation is assigned to one of the high-level terms listed above. For each gene, GEMMER adds up the number of annotations that fall under each high-level GO term. The GO term with the highest count is then assigned as the gene's primary function.

In **Fig. 8** all cell cycle-regulated genes in the common core (44 out of the 88 unique genes listed in **Table 5**) are displayed for all four experimental conditions, and grouped across the cell cycle phase where their expression peak occurs. It can be observed that the majority of the cell cycle-regulated genes that are Fkh targets fall within the GO terms *Metabolism*, suggesting their function especially in the S phase for DNA duplication, and primarily activated by Fkh1. A large number of the common core genes are Fkh1 targets, which exhibit their expression peak throughout all cell cycle phases, in particular in G1(P) (pre-replicative G1), G1/S, S and M phases. Conversely, Fkh2 targets are mostly concentrated in G2 and G2/M phases, such as *CLB2*. Several targets of Fkh1

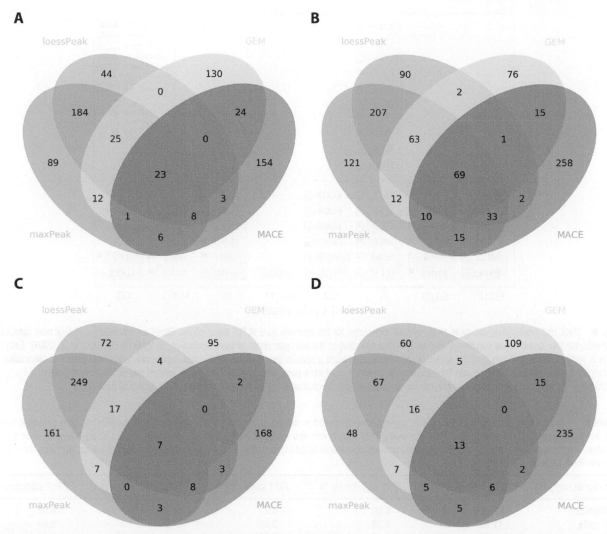

Fig. 7 4-way Venn diagrams of the overlap of the number of target genes among the four peak detection methods: maxPeak, loessPeak, GEM and MACE. (A) Fkh1 logarithmic phase. (B) Fkh1 stationary phase. (C) Fkh2 logarithmic phase. (D) Fkh2 stationary phase.

Table 5   Target genes in the 'common core', i.e., target genes retrieved by each of the four peak detection methods discussed in this work. Genes encoding a metabolic enzyme are indicated in bold. Genes that have not previously been observed as Fkh targets in previous ChIP studies are indicated in red color

Experiment	Target genes retrieved by maxPeak, loessPeak, GEM and MACE
Fkh1 logarithmic	ALG5, BRN1, DIN7, EGO2, **ERS1**, ESP1, **EXG1**, FLR1, FRK1, HOS3, **IDI1**, KIP2, NEW1, OSH7, PES4, **RNR1**, RPS1B, SUN4, TEL2, TEM1, VIK1, YLR299C-A, YPL251W
Fkh1 stationary	ABP140, **ADH4**, AIM46, ALG5, ARK1, BRN1, BUD3, BUD8, CIK1, **CIT2**, CSI1, CSN9, DCC1, **DIT1**, **DIT2**, DSE2, ECM10, EDC3, FHL1, FIN1, FIR1, FLR1, FRK1, GAS3, HOS3, **HXT5**, **IDI1**, KIP2, MKK2, MNT2, MUM3, NBL1, NEW1, NPP2, NUP2, NVJ3, OSH7, PDS5, PES4, **PMA1**, **RNR1**, RPL39, RPL8A, RPN10, RPN11, RPS1B, RPS22A, SAS3, SFG1, SGO1, SPC24, TDA7, TEM1, TIM18, TMN2, TRS85, VIK1, VTI1, WTM1, YCS4, YGL007C-A, YGR111W, YLR334C, YMC2, YNL174W, YOR314W-A, YPI1, YPL251W, YPT31
Fkh2 logarithmic	CIS3, CLB2, ENV9, **PMA1**, SRL1, YGL007C-A, YOR248W
Fkh2 stationary	ASE1, BUD4, CLB2, CLN1, HOS3, **IDI1**, JSN1, KIP2, MTC6, OSH7, SFG1, SPO12, YOR314W-A

and Fkh2 have their primary function in the cell cycle, e.g., *KIP2*, *CIK1*, *ESP1*, *VIK1* (Fkh1 targets) and *CLN1*, *CLB2* (Fkh2 targets). Noteworthy, a non-cell cycle target for Fkh1 is *RNR1*, the large subunit of the ribonucleoside-diphosphate reductase (RNR) that catalyzes the rate-limiting step in dNTP synthesis.

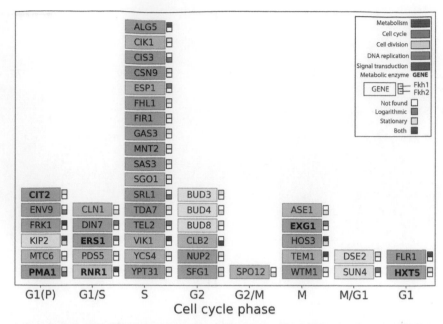

Fig. 8 Stack plot representing cell cycle phase of peak expression for the common core of Fkh target genes. Genes are retrieved by all four peak detection methods, for four experimental conditions, and are grouped according to the cell cycle phase of peak expression, as reported (Rowicka *et al.*, 2007). Each gene is indicated as a rectangle, and the colors of each rectangle indicate a specific gene function. The colors (white, red, yellow and green) of the smaller rectangles on the side of a gene indicate the experimental condition in which a gene was found as Fkh1 target (upper) and/or Fkh2 target (lower), respectively. Genes encoding a metabolic enzyme are indicated in bold. Vertical ordering is based on alphabet of the standard gene name.

Table 6   Enrichment of global function of Fkh target genes compared to the set of all protein-coding genes (genome-wide %). The percentages in the last four columns (Fkh1 logarithmic, Fkh1 stationary, Fkh2 logarithmic and Fkh2 stationary) are calculated with respect to the "Genome-wide %" column. The genes considered for the last four columns are considered to be significant at least by *one* of the four peak detection methods for the chosen thresholds (see text)

Functional category	Genome-wide %	Fkh1 logarithmic %	Fkh1 stationary %	Fkh2 logarithmic %	Fkh2 stationary %
Metabolism	75.65	− 6.90	− 6.21	− 6.74	− 6.93
Cell cycle	11.99	1.33	0.85	0.71	2.69
Signal transduction	6.85	− 0.66	− 0.57	− 1.14	− 1.58
Cell division	4.54	0.66	− 0.38	1.22	1.22
DNA replication	0.96	− 0.4	0.26	− 0.34	− 0.13

Exploration of Unique Sets of Fkh Targets Unravels Regulatory Links With Metabolism

The relatively small number of common core target genes retrieved by all four peak detection methods provides an insufficiently large dataset to systematically compare enrichment in function and timing. Therefore, we have considered the larger set of genes that, for each independent experiment and experimental condition, is retrieved as a Fkh target using the stringent thresholds by at least *one* method. In other words, this set of genes is the set of unique genes indicated in **Fig. 7**, for each Fkh and for each experimental condition: 703 (Fkh1 logarithmic), 974 (Fkh1 stationary), 796 (Fkh2 logarithmic) and 593 (Fkh2 stationary). Subsequently, we calculated the enrichment of functions of target genes relative to the whole genome (see **Table 6**).

From the analysis, we have observed that both Fkh1 and Fkh2 show an increased percentage of target genes that fall within the GO terms *Cell cycle* and *Cell division*, both in logarithmic and stationary phases, with the exception of Fkh1 in stationary phase. This result supports the earlier finding that Fkh targets are primarily cell cycle genes (Spellman *et al.*, 1998). Interestingly, we observed that a fraction of genes with a metabolic function is present among the targets. Specifically, we identified 73 and 101 metabolic enzymes targets of Fkh1 and Fkh2, respectively, in logarithmic phase, and 101 and 71 metabolic enzymes, respectively, in stationary phase. This provides a clear indication of the potential role of Fkh as hubs connecting cell cycle and metabolism.

Similarly to the calculated functional enrichment shown in **Table 6**, we calculated the enrichment of cell cycle-regulated target genes that peak in specific cell cycle phases (**Fig. 9**). When comparing the distributions of the identified target genes in our four ChIP-exo experiments to the genome-wide distribution (Kudlicki *et al.*, 2007; Rowicka *et al.*, 2007), we observed that Fkh1 targets are shifted mainly towards S, G2 and M/G1, and away from G1/P, G1/S and M, in both logarithmic and stationary phases. There are instead mixed results for G1 and G2/M. Fkh2 targets are shifted mainly towards G2, G2/M and M/G1, and away from G1, G1(P), G1/S and M, in both logarithmic and stationary phases. There are instead mixed results for S phase. Between G2 and M/G1, Fkh2 has an

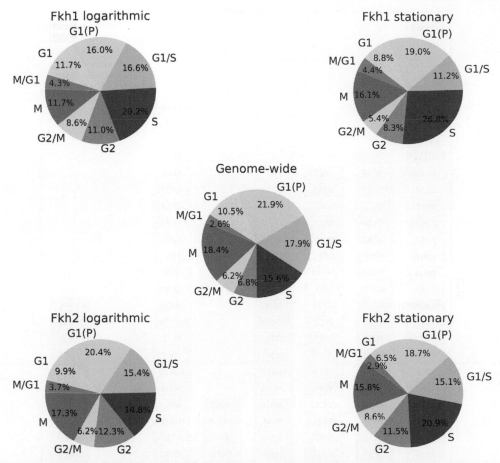

Fig. 9 Distribution of the expression peak for cell cycle-regulated genes. A genome-wide dataset was compared to the ChIP-exo Fkh dataset to identify target genes that are cell cycle-regulated. The distribution of the cell cycle-regulated genes (Rowicka *et al.*, 2007) is shown in the center, whereas the other four pies show the distribution of Fkh1 and Fkh2 targets, in both logarithmic and stationary phases. The set of genes considered for the latter four pies is the subset of cell cycle-regulated genes that are retrieved as being significant at least by *one* of the four peak detection methods.

enrichment of 5.5% and 4.8% in target genes, in logarithmic and stationary phase, respectively, whereas Fkh1 of 1.6% and 0.2%, respectively, consistent with data showing that Fkh are mainly expressed during late cell cycle phases (Lee *et al.*, 2002).

In order to visualize the cell cycle-regulated target genes of Fkh1 and Fkh2 with transcription peaks across different cell cycle phases, stack plots were generated for the larger sets of retrieved significant genes, similarly to the information presented in **Fig. 8**. As an example, we show here the result for Fkh2 in logarithmic phase (**Fig. 10**). It becomes apparent that the majority of target genes, for this experimental condition, falls primarily within the GO terms *Metabolism*, followed by *Cell cycle* and *Cell division*. This evidence further supports that the Fkh-dependent transcriptional program may be also activate metabolic pathways to guarantee a timely cell cycle progression.

To investigate the network effects of the Fkh targets, these have been annotated to include the list of KEGG Pathways each gene is mapped on. As an example, we visualize the target genes of both Fkh1 and Fkh2 in central carbon metabolism, which enzymes are retrieved as significant by each of the four peak detection methods (**Fig. 11**). Alternatively, by using the Pathview library for R (Luo and Brouwer, 2013), the target genes may be superimposed on KEGG maps in an automated way. Strikingly, identified reliable target genes of Fkh1 in central carbon metabolism are *HXT5*, *ADH4* and *CIT2*; conversely, Fkh2 generally lacks potential reliable targets, based on our data.

Discussion

As compared to previous ChIP-based methodologies, which have been conducted in logarithmic phase, our ChIP-exo analyses were performed in two experimental conditions, logarithmic and stationary phases. In either or both conditions we observed that targets of Fkh1, but not Fkh2, are mainly found in metabolic processes (see **Fig. 11**), with a substantial number of metabolic enzymes (see **Table 5** and **Fig. 8**). Therefore, we were interested to identify which specific KEGG Pathways are populated by the common core genes, which are retrieved as significant by each of the four peak detection methods used in this study.

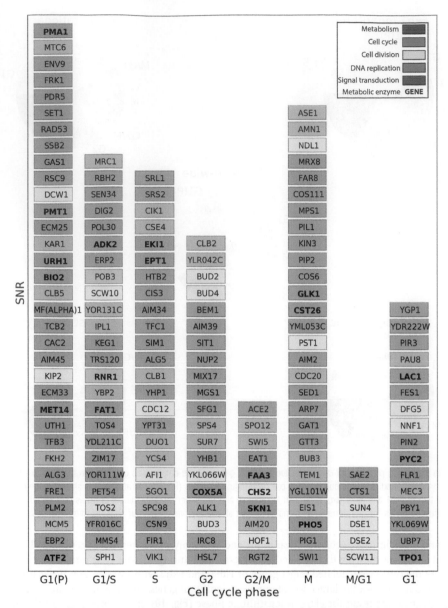

Fig. 10 Stack plot representing the Fkh2 target genes in logarithmic phase retrieved by any of the four peak detection methods. Genes are grouped according to their cell cycle phase of peak expression (Rowicka *et al.*, 2007). Vertical ordering is based on the SNR of target genes in the maxPeak dataset. Each gene is colored according to its specific function. Genes encoding a metabolic enzyme are indicated in bold.

In **Table 7** the Fkh target genes retrieved by all methods for each experimental condition were categorized according to the KEGG Pathways they occur in. A large difference between the target genes of Fkh1 and Fkh2 may be observed, due to the larger number of Fkh1 targets considered as significant. Fkh1 appears to target many different cellular processes including fatty acid metabolism, purine and pyrimidine metabolism, and central carbon metabolism. Strikingly, four Fkh1 target genes relate to the ribosome (*RPL39, RPL8A, RPS1B, RPS22A*). *EXG1*, a novel Fkh1 target never reported before in the literature, is a metabolic enzyme, i.e. exo-1,3-beta-glucanase, involved in cell wall beta-glucan assembly.

In the smaller set of target genes retrieved for Fkh2, only one connection with metabolism is observed. This regards the metabolic enzyme *PMA1*, plasma membrane ATPase which pumps protons out of the cell, and major regulator of cytoplasmic pH and plasma membrane potential. This gene has been previously reported as a Fkh target by a ChIP-chip study (Ostrow *et al.*, 2014). However, the other Fkh2 target genes are functional to cell cycle and signaling (*CLN1, CLB2, SPO12*), consistently with the current view of the Fkh2 role in cell cycle progression. This evidence indicates that Fkh1 and Fkh2 appear to have divergent functions, and that these TFs may serve as hubs that integrate multi-scale regulatory networks to achieve proper timing of cell division.

The latter aspect is particularly relevant, as a number of biochemical reactions requires to be completed for a timely cell division. Coordination of these reactions requires cyclin/Cdk1 kinase complexes, which are activated upon sequential transcription of cyclin genes with a characteristic staggered behavior known as waves of cyclins (Nasmyth, 1993; Futcher, 1996). Progressive

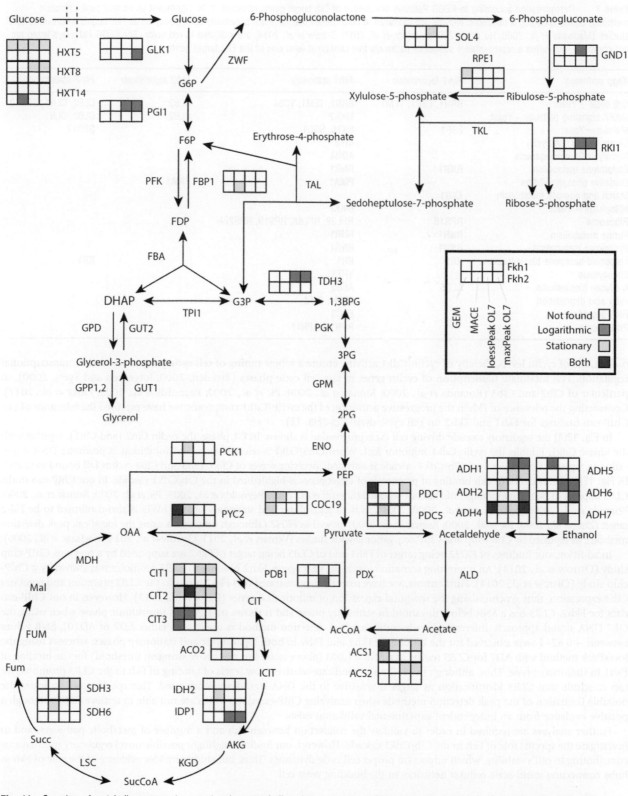

Fig. 11 Overview of metabolic enzymes in central carbon metabolism that are targets of Fkh1 and Fkh2. Each enzyme is associated with eight squares divided in two rows (Fkh1, top row; Fkh2, bottom row) representing data analysis with four peak detection methods. Empty squares indicate that the gene was not retrieved as a significant target, whereas colored squares indicated positive evidence. A distinction between the results in logarithmic and stationary phases is visualized through the color of the squares (see the figure insert). Isoenzymes that have no available evidence in any of the four studies were neglected. In some cases, metabolic enzymes may have no associated squares when no isoenzyme is available with an experimental validation. In this latter case, we sometimes referred to a generic name of the isoenzyme, e.g., *GPM* as opposed to *GPM1*.

Table 7   Categorization according to KEGG Pathway occurrence of Fkh target genes retrieved to be significant by all four peak detection methods. Genes encoding a metabolic enzyme are indicated in bold. Genes that have not previously been observed as Fkh targets in previous ChIP studies (MacIsaac et al., 2006; Hu et al., 2007; Venters et al., 2011; Ostrow et al., 2014) are indicated in red color. The KEGG Pathways listed are not complete, but rather a representative subset of pathways that contain at least one of the Fkh target genes

Kegg pathways	Fkh1 logarithmic	Fkh1 stationary	Fkh2 logarithmic	Fkh2 stationary
Cell cycle – Yeast	BRN1, ESP1, TEM1	BRN1, TEM1, YCS4	CLB2	CLB2, CLN1, SPO12
MAPK signaling pathway – Yeast		MKK2	CLB2	CLB2, CLN1
Meiosis – Yeast	ESP1	**HXT5**, SGO1		SPO12
Citrate cycle (TCA cycle)		**CIT2**		
Glycolysis/Gluconeogenesis		**ADH4**		
Glutathione metabolism	**RNR1**	**RNR1**		
Oxidative phosphorylation		**PMA1**	**PMA1**	
Starch and sucrose metabolism	EXG1			
Mitophagy – Yeast		MKK2		
Ribosome	RPS1B	RPL39, RPL8A, RPS1B, RPS22A		
Purine metabolism	**RNR1**	**RNR1**		
Pyrimidine metabolism	**RNR1**	**RNR1**		
Terpenoid backbone biosynthesis	**IDI1**	**IDI1**		**IDI1**
Endocytosis		YPT31		
N-Glycan biosynthesis	ALG5	ALG5		
Fatty acid degradation		**ADH4, DIT2**		
RNA degradation		EDC3		
Proteasome		RPN10, RPN11		

oscillations of cyclin levels, thereby of cyclin/Cdk1 activity, ensure a robust timing of cell cycle progression and of transcriptional regulation. Fkh modulate transcription of cyclin genes in late cell cycle phases (Breeden, 2000; Jorgensen and Tyers, 2000), in particular of Clb2 and Clb3 (Koranda et al., 2000; Kumar et al., 2000; Pic et al., 2000; Reynolds et al., 2003; Linke et al., 2017). Considering the relevance of Fkh in the progressive activation of the cyclin/Cdk1 complexes, we have explored the relevance of our ChIP-exo findings for Fkh1 and Fkh2 on cell cycle dynamics (**Fig. 12**).

In **Fig. 12(A)** the regulatory cascade driving cell cycle progression is shown: In G1 phase, the cyclin Cln2 (and Cln1), together with the kinase Cdk1, inhibits the cyclin/Cdk1 inhibitor Sic1. When Clb5/Cdk1 is released from Sic1 inhibition, it promotes DNA duplication in S phase. Consequently, a Clb/Cdk1 cascade is activated, involving waves of Clb5, Clb3 and Clb2 cyclins (all bound to Cdk1). In **Fig. 12(B)** the evidence of Fkh binding at promoters of target genes is highlighted in the Clb/Cdk1 cascade. In our ChIP-exo study, *CLB2* appears to be the major target of Fkh2, as reported (Sherriff et al., 2007; Reynolds et al., 2003; Pic et al., 2000; Kumar et al., 2000; Koranda et al., 2000; Hollenhorst et al., 2000, 2001), in both logarithmic and stationary phases. *SWI5* is also confirmed to be Fkh2 target (Zhu et al., 2000; Pic et al., 2000; Kumar et al., 2000) as well as *FKH2* (although only when using the loessPeak peak detection method), as reported by ChIP-chip and ChIP-seq, genome-wide studies (Venters et al., 2011; Ostrow et al., 2014; MacIsaac et al., 2006).

In addition, our findings of *FKH2* being target of Fkh1 and of *CLB5* being target of Fkh2 are supported by a previous ChIP-chip study (Ostrow et al., 2014). An interesting scenario regards the *CLB3* gene. Fkh2 binding to *CLB3* promoter was shown by a ChIP-chip study (Ostrow et al., 2014). Furthermore, we have recently demonstrated that Fkh2 binds to the *CLB3* promoter and regulates Clb3 expression, thus synchronizing the temporal expression of mitotic *CLB* genes (Linke et al., 2017). However, in our ChIP-exo data for Fkh2, *CLB3* has a SNR below threshold in stationary phase and it shows no signal in logarithmic phase when using the OL7 DNA strand approach. Interestingly, when the maxPeak detection method is used (with either AD7 or AD10), SNR values between ~0.62–1 were observed for the binding of Fkh1 and Fkh2 in both logarithmic and stationary phases, whereas using the loessPeak method with AD7 for *CLB3* results in a SNR = 1.003 (above noise but not above stringent threshold) for the binding of Fkh1 in stationary phase. Thus, although the SNR values indicate relatively low levels of binding of Fkh to the *CLB3* promoter, we can conclude that *CLB3* identification as target is sensitive to the DNA strand approach used. This specific case indicates the possible limitation of the peak detection methods when analyzing ChIP-exo data, which are not able to retrieve *CLB3* although a positive evidence from an independent experimental validation exists.

Further analyses are required in order to validate the connection between Fkh and a number of metabolic pathways, and to investigate the specific role of Fkh in the Clb/Cdk1 cascade. However, our findings highlight possible novel regulatory mechanisms contributing to cell's viability, which impact on proper cell cycle dynamics. Thus, our study provides evidence of the role of Fkh as hubs connecting multi-scale cellular networks in the budding yeast cell.

Future Directions

The study that we have presented highlights the divergence in retrieving ChIP data by using a number of data analysis methods, and stimulates further research to (i) identify the more stable method(s), (ii) investigate in depth the advantages and shortcomings of each method, and (iii) measure the accuracy of the data analysis methods with regard to identifying functional targets.

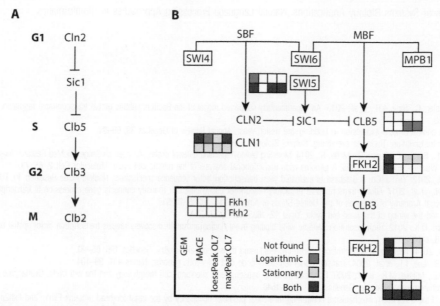

Fig. 12 Fkh1 and Fkh2 target genes in the molecular cascade regulating dynamics of cell cycle progression. (A) Molecular players driving cell cycle progression (see text for details). (B) Overview of cell cycle regulators that are Fkh targets. The transcription factors *SWI4*, *SWI6*, *MPB1*, *SWI5* and *FKH2* are shown within rectangles. Genes without associated rectangles were not identified as significant Fkh targets in the various dataset.

Closing Remarks

Various ChIP-based methodologies exist, with ChIP-exo being the newest instantiation. In this study, we have presented the main differences between ChIP-exo and currently in-use ChIP techniques, and discussed two existing (GEM and MACE) and two novel (maxPeak and loessPeak) methods for analyzing ChIP-exo data. We have described a pipeline to be followed when analyzing the data, and applied it to two Forkhead (Fkh) transcription factors (Fkh1 and Fkh2) that regulate cell division in budding yeast. The result of our analysis indicates a large diversity of the target genes retrieved by the four methods. This may be explained, in part, by failure of the existing algorithms (GEM and MACE) to properly analyze the data considered here, and may point to the fact that these approaches might be less reliable when the number of high-quality peaks is relatively low. However, importantly, a small common set of retrieved target genes exists, pointing to an accurate, reliable output that is insensitive to the method used.

In this study, we have also highlighted how to integrate ChIP data with existing literature data from a number of databases containing information of genes in budding yeast, such as functional annotation, localization, abundance, and both timing and cell cycle phase of peak occurrence of RNA transcript levels. This integration has been made possible through GEMMER, a web/based visualization tool that we have recently developed.

Altogether, we have shown that our pipeline of analyzing ChIP data and integrating these with literature information allows for predicting and understanding the function of transcription factors in a multi-scale, networked, cellular system.

Author Contributions

M.B. conceived and designed the study. P.H., T.D.G.A.M., J.N. and M.B. designed the experimental analysis, which was performed by P.H.. M.B. and T.D.G.A.M. designed the computational analysis, which was performed by T.D.G.A.M.. T.D.G.A.M. and M.B. analyzed the data. M.B. provided the biological interpretation of data. P.H., T.D.G.A.M. and M.B. wrote the paper, with contribution from J.N.. M.B. provided scientific leadership and supervised the study. Petter Holland and Thierry DGA Mondeel contributed equally to this work.

Acknowledgement

This work was supported by the Swammerdam Institute for Life Science Starting Grant of the University of Amsterdam to M.B., and by the Novo Nordisk Foundation, Vetenskapsrådet, and Knut and Alice Wallenberg Foundation to J.N.

See also: Computational Systems Biology Applications. Natural Language Processing Approaches in Bioinformatics

References

Arrieta-Ortiz, M.L., Hafemeister, C., Bate, A.R., et al., 2015. An experimentally supported model of the Bacillus subtilis global transcriptional regulatory network. Molecular Systems Biology 11, 839.

Bähler, J., 2005. Cell-cycle control of gene expression in budding and fission yeast. Annual Review of Genetics 39, 69–94.

Breeden, L.L., 2000. Cyclin transcription: Timing is everything. Current Biology 10, R586–R588.

Castiglione, F., Pappalardo, F., Bianca, C., Russo, G., Motta, S., 2014. Modeling biology spanning different scales: An open challenge. BioMed Research International 2014, 902545.

Cho, R.J., Campbell, M.J., Winzeler, E.A., et al., 1998. A genome-wide transcriptional analysis of the mitotic cell cycle. Molecular Cell 2, 65–73.

de Boer, C.G., Hughes, T.R., 2012. YeTFaSCo: A database of evaluated yeast transcription factor sequence specificities. Nucleic Acids Research 40, D169–D179.

Fang, X., Sastry, A., Mih, N., et al., 2017. Global transcriptional regulatory network for Escherichia coli robustly connects gene expression to transcription factor activities. Proceedings of the National Academy of Sciences of the United States of America 114, 10286–10291.

Futcher, B., 1996. Cyclins and the wiring of the yeast cell cycle. Yeast 12, 1635–1646.

Guo, Y., Mahony, S., Gifford, D.K., 2012. High resolution genome wide binding event finding and motif discovery reveals transcription factor spatial binding constraints. PLOS Computational Biology 8, e1002638.

Haase, S.B., Wittenberg, C., 2014. Topology and control of the cell-cycle-regulated transcriptional circuitry. Genetics 196, 65–90.

Harbison, C.T., Gordon, D.B., Lee, T.I., et al., 2004. Transcriptional regulatory code of a eukaryotic genome. Nature 431, 99–104.

Hollenhorst, P.C., Bose, M.E., Mielke, M.R., et al., 2000. Forkhead genes in transcriptional silencing, cell morphology and the cell cycle. Overlapping and distinct functions for FKH1 and FKH2 in Saccharomyces cerevisiae. Genetics 154, 1533–1548.

Hollenhorst, P.C., Pietz, G., Fox, C.A., 2001. Mechanisms controlling differential promoter-occupancy by the yeast forkhead proteins Fkh1p and Fkh2p: Implications for regulating the cell cycle and differentiation. Genes and Development 15, 2445–2456.

Hu, Z., Killion, P.J., Iyer, V.R., 2007. Genetic reconstruction of a functional transcriptional regulatory network. Nature Genetics 39, 683–687.

Jorgensen, P., Tyers, M., 2000. The fork'ed path to mitosis. Genome Biology 1, 1022.1–1022.4.

Knott, S.R., Peace, J.M., Ostrow, A.Z., et al., 2012. Forkhead transcription factors establish origin timing and long-range clustering in S. cerevisiae. Cell 148, 99–111.

Koranda, M., Schleiffer, A., Endler, L., Ammerer, G., 2000. Forkhead-like transcription factors recruit Ndd1 to the chromatin of G2/M-specific promoters. Nature 406, 94–98.

Kudlicki, A., Rowicka, M., Otwinowski, Z., et al., 2007. SCEPTRANS: An online tool for analyzing periodic transcription in yeast. Bioinformatics 23, 1559–1561.

Kumar, R., Reynolds, D.M., Shevchenko, A., Goldstone, S.D., Dalton, S., 2000. Forkhead transcription factors, Fkh1p and Fkh2p, collaborate with Mcm1p to control transcription required for M-phase. Current Biology 10, 896–906.

Landt, S.G., Marinov, G.K., Kundaje, A., et al., 2012. ChIP-seq guidelines and practices of the ENCODE and modENCODE consortia. Genome Research 22, 1813–1831.

Langmead, B., Salzberg, S.L., 2012. Fast gapped-read alignment with Bowtie 2. Nature Methods 9, 357–359.

Lee, T.I., Rinaldi, N.J., Robert, F., et al., 2002. Transcriptional regulatory networks in Saccharomyces cerevisiae. Science 298, 799–804.

Li, H., Handsaker, B., Wysoker, A., et al., 2009. The Sequence Alignment/Map format and SAMtools. Bioinformatics 25, 2078–2079.

Linke, C., Chasapi, A., González-Novo, A., et al., 2017. A Clb/Cdk1-mediated regulation of Fkh2 synchronizes CLB expression in the budding yeast cell cycle. Nature Partner Journals Systems Biology and Applications 3, 7.

Luo, W., Brouwer, C., 2013. Pathview: An R/Bioconductor package for pathway-based data integration and visualization. Bioinformatics 29, 1830–1831.

MacIsaac, K.D., Wang, T., Gordon, D.B., et al., 2006. An improved map of conserved regulatory sites for Saccharomyces cerevisiae. BMC Bioinformatics 7, 113.

McInerny, C.J., 2011. Cell cycle regulated gene expression in yeasts. Advances in Genetics 73, 51–85.

Mondeel, T.D.G.A., Crémazy, F., Barberis, M., 2018. GEMMER: GEnome-wide tool for Multi-scale Modeling data Extraction and Representation for Saccharomyces cerevisiae. Bioinformatics bty052, https://doi.org/10.1093/bioinformatics/bty052.

Nasmyth, K., 1993. Control of the yeast cell cycle by the Cdc28 protein kinase. Current Opinion in Cell Biology 5, 166–179.

Orlando, D.A., Lin, C.Y., Bernard, A., et al., 2008. Global control of cell-cycle transcription by coupled CDK and network oscillators. Nature 453, 944–947.

Ostrow, A.Z., Kalhor, R., Gan, Y., et al., 2017. Conserved forkhead dimerization motif controls DNA replication timing and spatial organization of chromosomes in S. cerevisiae. Proceedings of the National Academy of Sciences of the United States of America 114, E2411–E2419.

Ostrow, A.Z., Nellimoottil, T., Knott, S.R., et al., 2014 Fkh1 and Fkh2 bind multiple chromosomal elements in the S. cerevisiae genome with distinct specificities and cell cycle dynamics. PLOS ONE 9, e87647.

Papantonis, A., Cook, P.R., 2013. Transcription factories: Genome organization and gene regulation. Chemical Reviews 113, 8683–8705.

Park, D., Morris, A.R., Battenhouse, A., Iyer, V.R., 2014. Simultaneous mapping of transcript ends at single-nucleotide resolution and identification of widespread promoter-associated non-coding RNA governed by TATA elements. Nucleic Acids Research 42, 3736–3749.

Park, P.J., 2009. ChIP–seq: Advantages and challenges of a maturing technology. Nature Reviews Genetics 10, 669–680.

Peace, J.M., Villwock, S.K., Zeytounian, J.L., Gan, Y., Aparicio, O.M., 2016. Quantitative BrdU immunoprecipitation method demonstrates that Fkh1 and Fkh2 are rate-limiting activators of replication origins that reprogram replication timing in G1 phase. Genome Research 26, 365–375.

Pic, A., Lim, F.L., Ross, S.J., et al., 2000. The forkhead protein Fkh2 is a component of the yeast cell cycle transcription factor SFF. EMBO Journal 19, 3750–3761.

Reynolds, D., Shi, B.J., McLean, C., et al., 2003. Recruitment of Thr319-phosphorylated Ndd1p to the FHA domain of Fkh2p requires Clb kinase activity: A mechanism for CLB cluster gene activation. Genes and Development 17, 1789–1802.

Rhee, H.S., Pugh, B.F., 2011. Comprehensive genome-wide protein-DNA interactions detected at single-nucleotide resolution. Cell 147, 1408–1419.

Rhee, H.S., Pugh, B.F., 2012. Genome-wide structure and organization of eukaryotic pre-initiation complexes. Nature 483, 295–301.

Robertson, G., Hirst, M., Bainbridge, M., et al., 2007. Genome-wide profiles of STAT1 DNA association using chromatin immunoprecipitation and massively parallel sequencing. Nature Methods 4, 651–657.

Rowicka, M., Kudlicki, A., Tu, B.P., Otwinowski, Z., 2007. High-resolution timing of cell cycle-regulated gene expression. Proceedings of the National Academy of Sciences of the United States of America 104, 16892–16897.

Sherriff, J.A., Kent, N.A., Mellor, J., et al., 2007. The Isw2 chromatin-remodeling ATPase cooperates with the Fkh2 transcription factor to repress transcription of the B-type cyclin gene CLB2. Molecular and Cellular Biology 27, 2848–2860.

Solomon, M.J., Larsen, P.L., Varshavsky, A., 1988. Mapping protein-DNA interactions in vivo with formaldehyde: Evidence that histone H4 is retained on a highly transcribed gene. Cell 53, 937–947.

Spellman, P.T., Sherlock, G., Zhang, M.Q., et al., 1998. Comprehensive identification of cell cycle-regulated genes of the yeast Saccharomyces cerevisiae by microarray hybridization. Molecular Biology of the Cell 9, 3273–3297.

Terooatea, T.W., Pozner, A., Buck-Koehntop, B.A., 2016. PAtCh-Cap: Input strategy for improving analysis of ChIP-exo data sets and beyond. Nucleic Acids Research 44, e159.

Tessarz, P., Kouzarides, T., 2014. Histone core modifications regulating nucleosome structure and dynamics. Nature Reviews Molecular Cell Biology 15, 703–708.

Venters, B.J., Wachi, S., Mavrich, T.N., *et al.*, 2011. A comprehensive genomic binding map of gene and chromatin regulatory proteins in Saccharomyces. Molecular Cell 41, 480–492.

Wang, L., Chen, J., Wang, C., *et al.*, 2014. MACE: Model based analysis of ChIP-exo. Nucleic Acids Research 42, e156.

Wittenberg, C., Reed, S.I., 2005. Cell cycle-dependent transcription in yeast: Promoters, transcription factors, and transcriptomes. Oncogene 24, 2746–2755.

Zhu, G., Spellman, P.T., Volpe, T., *et al.*, 2000. Two yeast forkhead genes regulate the cell cycle and pseudohyphal growth. Nature 406, 90–94.

Relevant Websites

http://gemmer.barberislab.com/
    GEMMER.

https://downloads.yeastgenome.org/sequence/S288C_reference/genome_releases/
    Reference genome sequence R.64.1.1.

Studies of Body Systems

Amir Feisal Merican, University of Malaya, Kuala Lumpur, Malaysia
Hoda Mirsafian, University of Malaya, Kuala Lumpur, Malaysia and University of Southern California, Los Angeles, CA, United States
Adiratna Mat Ripen, Institute of Medical Research, Kuala Lumpur, Malaysia
Saharuddin Bin Mohamad, University of Malaya, Kuala Lumpur, Malaysia

Introduction

The human body is made up of a combination of specialized biological systems with specific functions. These body systems represent groups of organs, tissues, and cells that act together to perform various tasks for growth, reproduction, and survival of the body. Some organs may be part of more than one body system, if they serve more than one function. The systems work and interact with each other to form a functioning human body. The human body system comprises the skeletal system (bones, cartilage, ligaments), muscular system (cardiac or heart muscle, skeletal muscle, smooth muscle, tendons), nervous system (brain, spinal cord, nerves), respiratory system (trachea, larynx, pharynx, lungs), lymphatic system (lymph nodes, lymph vessels), immune system (bone marrow, spleen, white blood cells), endocrine system (pituitary gland, hypothalamus, adrenal glands, thyroid, parathyroids, pancreas, ovaries, testes), cardiovascular or circulatory system (heart, blood vessels, blood), digestive or excretory system (esophagus, stomach, small intestine, large intestine), urinary or renal system (kidneys, urinary bladder), integumentary or exocrine system (skin, hair, nails), and reproductive system (female: uterus, vagina, fallopian tubes, ovaries; male: penis, testes, seminal vesicles) (McDowell, 2010; Taylor, 2017). Although these body systems are all very different, they do have one thing in common, of which all of them begin with cells. During the process of cellular differentiation, a cell changes from one cell type to another with specialized function forming tissues and organs. Different cell types express characteristic sets of proteins that are encoded by respective genes within a cell's DNA (Slack, 2013).

Cells can dynamically access and translate specific information through gene expression by selectively switching on and off particular genes. In the selected genes, the information encoded is transcribed into RNA molecules, which consequently can be translated into proteins or can be directly used to control gene expression (Finotello and Di Camillo, 2015). The investigation and analysis of any individual dysregulations occurring within the genomic, transcriptomic, proteomic, and metabolomic levels could utilize advanced high-throughput technologies (Likić et al., 2010; Ayers and Day 2015; Krauss et al., 2017).

The transcriptome is a set of all RNA transcripts existing in a cell or tissue at a certain point of time under specific conditions (Sirri et al., 2008). The transcriptome encompasses multiple types of coding and noncoding RNA species. Thus, transcriptomic study is essential to identify the current state of the cells and fundamental pathogenic mechanisms of diseases. In addition, differential gene expression study facilitates the comparison of gene expression profiles from different cells and conditions to characterize genes that are responsible in the determination of phenotypes. For example, the comparison of healthy versus diseased cells can present new insights on genetic aspects involved in pathology (Finotello and Di Camillo, 2015). Previously, microarray has been the most important and commonly used method for transcriptome analysis (Baldi and Hatfield, 2002), however in recent years, high-throughput RNA sequencing (RNA-Seq) has become a powerful alternative approach for transcriptome profiling studies. RNA-Seq is able to qualitatively and quantitatively investigate any RNA molecules including messenger RNAs (mRNAs), long noncoding RNAs (lncRNAs), microRNAs (miRNAs), and small interfering RNAs (siRNA) (Dong and Chen, 2013, Kukurba and Montgomery, 2015).

The immune system is one of the most complex body systems that the human has. The immune system comprises the innate and the adaptive systems. Monocytes, a type of leukocyte or white blood cells, are key elements of the innate immune-mediated processes that become the first line of defense response against pathogens (Janeway, 2001). They can differentiate into macrophages and myeloid lineage dendritic cells. They are mononuclear cells and play a central role in the clearance of microbial infections and cellular debris, secretion of immunoregulatory bioactive factors including interleukins, interferons, chemokines, and growth factors, and control of cancer progression (Kraft-Terry and Gendelman, 2011).

Recent studies have applied RNA-Seq technology for transcriptome profiling of several tissues and cell types such as endometrium (Zieba et al., 2015), spleen (Dang et al., 2016), T cells (Mitchell et al., 2015), B cells (Toung et al., 2011), and macrophages (Beyer et al., 2012). In addition, by using the RNA-Seq approach, the global gene transcription changes that occur during the differentiation of monocyte to macrophage have been reported (Ancuta et al., 2009; Dong et al., 2013; Ziegler-Heitbrock et al., 2010). Furthermore, the RNA-Seq data are valuable for postgenomic study leading to the development of diagnostic and therapeutic applications for precision medicine. Recently, Fuchs et al. (2016) established an integrative tool for postgenomic data analysis utilizing next-generation sequencing, RNA-Seq, and microarray data. However, there is limited or no data exist on the genome-wide transcriptome expression profile of human primary monocytes under healthy and disease states.

We have used bioinformatics approaches to catalogue the entire transcriptome of primary monocytes from healthy subjects using deep polyadenylated (Poly(A) +) paired-end RNA sequencing (RNA-Seq) technique. Firstly, we integrated this dataset with other publicly available RNA-Seq datasets for human monocytes to provide a comprehensive gene reference catalogue of human primary monocytes (Mirsafian et al., 2016b). The reference gene catalogue of immune cells based on their transcriptome expression profiles would be useful for immune-related research, particularly for understanding disease states, pathogenesis, and developing therapeutic biomarkers. As a second step, we characterized long noncoding RNAs (lncRNAs) in human monocytes and

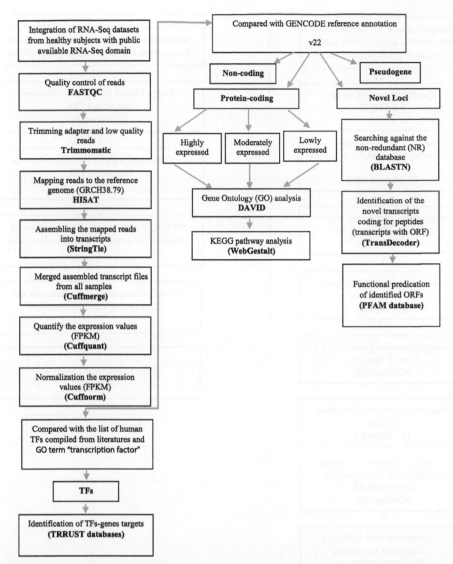

Fig. 1 Schematic representation of workflow to generate the gene catalogue of primary monocytes from healthy subjects.

identified unannotated lncRNAs that were not yet annotated in the public databases, of which this could facilitate future experimental studies to understand the functions of these molecules in the innate immune system (Mirsafian et al, 2016a).

As an example, we present the analysis of deep RNA-Seq datasets of primary monocytes of patients with X-linked agamma-globulinemia (XLA), which is a rare X-linked genetic disorder that affects the male (Mirsafian et al., 2017). XLA is caused by mutations in gene coding for *BTK* (Bruton's tyrosine kinase) located in the Xq21.3-q22 region, which is essential for B cell development and function (Vetrie et al., 1993). XLA disorder is characterized by few or absent of peripheral B cells leading to a decrease in all serum immunoglobulin levels and recurrent infections with encapsulated bacteria and enteroviruses (Ochs and Smith, 1996). The expression of *BTK* is not limited to B cells. It is also expressed in other immune cells such as NK cells (Bao et al., 2012), neutrophils (Honda et al., 2012), and monocytes/macrophages (Koprulu and Ellmeier, 2009). It is well known that *BTK* mutations affected B cell development and functions in XLA patients (Lee et al., 2010; Mohamed et al., 2009; Ochs and Smith, 1996). However, the effect of *BTK* deficiency in primary monocytes of XLA patients is not fully understood and there is no or limited data available on transcriptome profiles of primary monocytes from XLA patients. Moreover, despite the evidence for a role of lncRNAs in the immune system regulation (Derrien et al., 2012; Karapetyan et al., 2013; Guttman et al., 2009), the functions of lncRNAs in primary monocytes of XLA have not been studied yet. Through this study, a comparative gene expression analysis of primary monocytes was conducted between RNA-Seq datasets of XLA patients and healthy male subjects to look into the possible differences in expression patterns of protein-coding genes and lncRNAs in XLA patients compared to healthy individuals, which may affect the function of primary monocytes in these patients. The high-resolution genome-wide transcriptome expression profile of primary monocytes based on the RNA-Seq approach would provide a better understanding of monocytes' characterization and function in healthy and XLA states. It also assists the detailed analyses of innate immune system abnormalities and novel pathomechanisms concerning XLA.

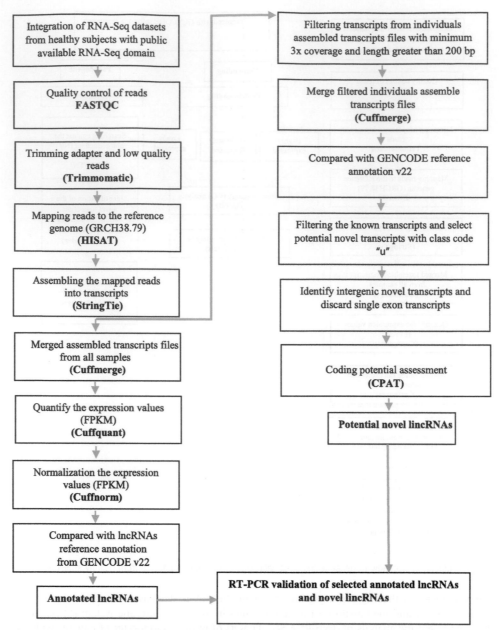

Fig. 2 Schematic representation of workflow to profile the lncRNAs expression landscape of primary monocytes from healthy subjects.

Step 1: Techniques for Cell Preparation and Transcriptome Profiling

The techniques used for monocyte isolation and transcriptome profiling have been described in Mirsafian *et al.* (2016a,b, 2017). Briefly, the peripheral blood samples from 6 healthy individuals (3 male and 3 female) and 3 male patients with XLA were collected. The classical monocytes (CD14 + +CD16 −) were isolated from peripheral blood mononuclear cells, which are a mixed population of different cell types including lymphocytes, monocytes, and macrophages) using a negative selection technique. Using this method, the nonmonocyte cells including T cells, B cells, dendritic cells, NK cells, and basophils were indirectly magnetically labeled and the untouched monocytes were then isolated by depletion of the magnetically labeled cells. The purity of isolated monocytes from all samples were checked separately by flow cytometry analysis and were found to be >90% for all samples. The total RNA was extracted from monocytes and the quality, quantity, and integrity of the extracted RNA from all samples were checked separately. The purified RNA was used to perform deep poly(A) + paired-end RNA sequencing. All the reads were mapped to the reference genome (Ensembl GRCH38.79) and assembled into a transcriptome. The transcripts were reconstructed for all aligned reads separately and then merged together to form a single nonredundant set of transcripts. The abundance of assembled transcripts was estimated using fragments per kilobase of exon per million fragments mapped value. Detailed information on the bioinformatics analysis workflows and pipeline is described in **Figs. 1–3**.

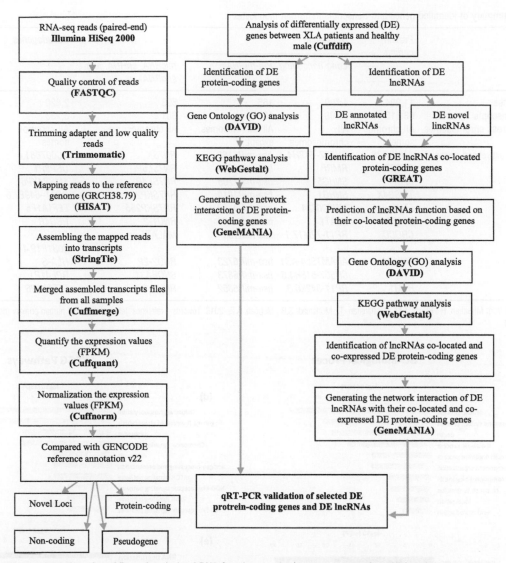

Fig. 3 Schematic representation of workflow of analysis of RNA-Seq dataset of primary monocytes from XLA patients.

Step 2: Establishment of a Reference Gene Catalog of Human Primary Monocytes

RNA-Seq datasets from 6 healthy individuals were integrated with other publicly available RNA-Seq datasets for monocytes. Based on these datasets, we were able to capture most of the genes transcribed in human monocytes including; 11,994 protein-coding genes, 5558 noncoding genes, 2820 pseudogenes, and 7034 putative novel transcripts. The summary of identified genes and transcripts with regard to their biotype is presented in **Table 1**.

The functional analysis of identified protein-coding genes expressed in monocytes revealed that highly expressed genes were mainly involved in several processes belonging to the immune system while the moderately expressed genes and lowly expressed genes were mainly involved in metabolic processes and biological regulations (**Fig. 4**). These results showed that genes within a particular process are expressed at similar levels, which is in agreement with a previous study (Toung *et al.*, 2011). It has been reported that in B cells, the high-expressing genes were involved in translation, RNA processing, and splicing transcription, and the medium- and low-expressing genes were related to cell adhesion and ion transport and transcription, respectively (Toung *et al.*, 2011)

Using these datasets, the expression pattern of 1155 transcription factors (TFs) in human primary monocytes were also profiled. TFs are key molecules that control gene transcriptions (Vaquerizas *et al.*, 2009). Over the past 30 years, several TFs involved in the immune system have been discovered and their mechanisms of action were studied (Smale, 2014). The interaction network between the top 20 highly expressed identified TFs with their targeted genes is presented in **Fig. 5**.

Addition of publicly available RNA-Seq datasets for monocytes to our RNA-Seq dataset from healthy individuals also allowed us to provide a landscape of lncRNAs in human primary monocytes. Several recent studies have shown the role of lncRNAs in relation to immune regulation and their role in several autoimmune diseases like SLE (Shi *et al.*, 2014) and rheumatoid arthritis (Müller *et al.*, 2014). Recent studies have also indicated the possible role of lncRNA expression and its correlation to immune cells' differentiation and

Table 1   Summary of identified genes and transcripts in human monocytes

Gene biotype	Protein-coding	Noncoding			Pseudogenes	Novel
		Long noncoding	Pre-miRNAs	micRNA, snRNA, and snoRNA)		
Number of genes	11,994	4,799	165	593	2,820	N/A
Number of transcripts	63,515	5,608	186	601	3,233	7,034
Distribution across chromosomes	All chromosomes	All chromosomes	All chromosomes, except: Y	All chromosomes	All chromosomes	All chromosomes
Top 10 highly expressed genes (FPKM > 20)	ANKRD28	CH507–513H4.4	hsa-miR5188	RN7SK	AC007881.4	XLOC_038138
	PTPRD	RMRP	hsa-miR6805	RN7SL5P	USP8P1	XLOC_029167
	B2M	SNHG5	hsa-miR7705	RN7SL4P	TMSB4XP6	XLOC_019828
	TMSB4X	SNHG1	hsa-miR181b	RN7SKP203	RP11–649E7.8	XLOC_029358
	FTH1	LINC00824	hsa-miR4709	RN7SKP255	EEF1A1P5	XLOC_047644
	S100A9	NEAT1	hsa-miR–129	RNU1-2	HCG4B	XLOC_011102
	CROCC	RP11-72M17.1	hsa-miR155	MALAT1	CTD-2031P19.4	XLOC_067917
	EEF1A1	ADAMTSL4-AS1	hsa-miR6723	RNU2-2P	HLA-S	XLOC_020955
	LYZ,	CH507-513H4.6	hsa-miR6873	SNORA31	RPL41P1	XLOC_069963
	HFM1	RP11-342K6.3	hsa-miR6852	RNU1-1	EEF1A1P6	XLOC_006796

Note: Reproduced from Mirsafian, H., Ripen, A.M., Manaharan, T., Mohamad, S.B., Merican, A.F., 2016. Towards a reference gene catalogue of human primary monocytes. OMICS, 20 (11), 627–634.

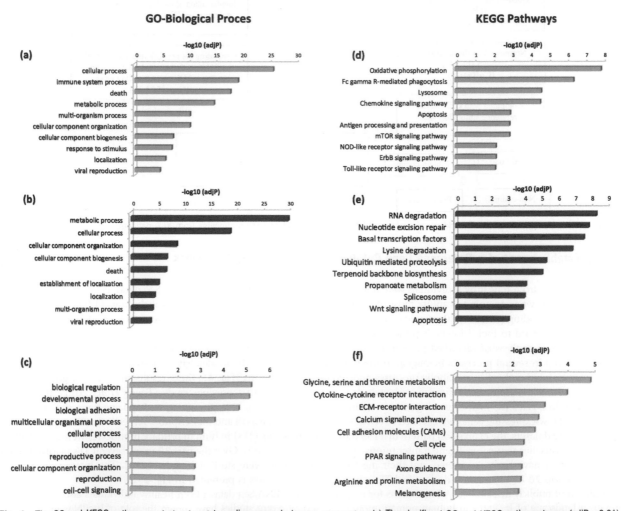

Fig. 4   The GO and KEGG pathway analysis of protein-coding genes in human monocytes. (a) The significant GO and KEGG pathway terms (adjP < 0.01) of highly expressed protein-coding genes. (b) The significant GO and KEGG pathway terms (adjP < 0.01) of moderately expressed protein-coding genes. (c) The significant GO and KEGG pathway terms (adjP < 0.01) of low expressed protein-coding genes. Reproduced from Mirsafian, H., Ripen, A.M., Manaharan, T., Mohamad, S.B., Merican, A.F., 2016. Towards a reference gene catalogue of human primary monocytes. OMICS, 20 (11), 627–634.

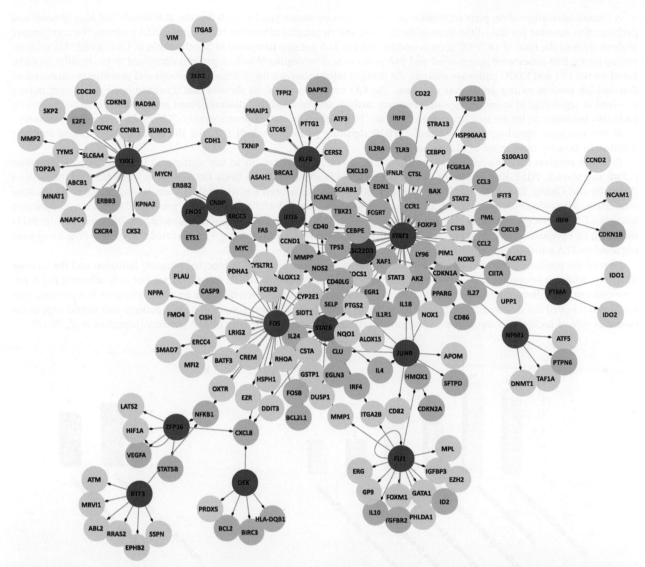

Fig. 5 Interaction network analysis of the top 20 highly expressed TFs with their target in human monocytes. The network contains 226 interactions between 20 TFs and 146 targeted genes. The pink circles represented TFs, while the blue and green circles represented TF-target genes. The green circles represent the genes that are involved in immune system process and death. Reproduced from Mirsafian, H., Ripen, A.M., Manaharan, T., Mohamad, S.B., Merican, A.F., 2016a. Towards a reference gene catalogue of human primary monocytes. OMICS, 20 (11), 627–634.

maturation (Stachurska *et al.*, 2014). However, most of the lncRNAs transcribed in the innate immune system remain unknown. From this study, the expression of 6382 lncRNAs (40% of the known lncRNAs reported in GENCODE database (version 22)) were characterized in human primary monocytes. Using a computational pipeline developed in-house, a total of 1032 unannotated lincRNAs in monocytes were identified that have not been annotated in the public databases (Mirsafian *et al.*, 2016a).

The study described above resulted in a comprehensive reference gene catalog of human primary monocytes under healthy states, which could be used as an important resource for postgenomics and system biology research on human monocytes under healthy and diseased states (Mirsafian *et al.*, 2016b).

Step 3: Comparative Analysis of Transcriptome Profile of Healthy Individuals and XLA Patients

Deep RNA-Seq approach on primary monocytes from 3 XLA patients generated approximately 477 million reads of 100 bp read length. This led to the profiles of 17,510 genes (including 11,788 protein-coding genes, 3681 noncoding genes, 2041 pseudogenes) and 62,367 transcripts (including 58,136 annotated and 4231 novel transcripts) in the primary monocytes of XLA patients. In addition, the lncRNAs expression patterns in primary monocytes of XLA patients were analyzed and a total of 3363 annotated lncRNAs were identified. By using multistep mapping and filtering criteria, the expression of 430 potential novel lincRNAs in the patients were also identified.

A comparative analysis on gene expression profiles of primary monocytes between healthy individuals and XLA patients was performed to examine possible differences in the gene expression patterns of primary monocytes in XLA patients. The comparative analysis showed the total of 1827 DE protein-coding genes in XLA patients compared to healthy subjects. Out of 1827 DE protein-coding genes, 859 genes were upregulated and 968 genes were downregulated in XLA patients compared to the healthy subjects. Based on the GO and KEGG pathways analysis, the detailed information on the biological functions and potential mechanisms of detected DE protein-coding genes were obtained. The GO enrichment analysis showed that downregulated genes were mainly involved in regulation of immune response. Pathway analysis also revealed that downregulated genes mainly enriched in several pathways belonged to innate immune system such as "Fc gamma R-mediated phagocytosis," "Chemokine signaling pathways," "Toll like receptors signaling pathway," and "MTOR signaling pathway," which reflected the deficiencies of innate immune function in primary monocytes of XLA patients (**Fig. 6**).

Evidence suggests that in addition to protein-coding genes, lncRNAs can act as key regulators of various biologic processes (Clark and Mattick, 2011; Kim and Sung, 2012). The lncRNAs function via DNA–DNA, DNA–RNA, or other kinds of interactions (Satpathy and Chang, 2015). The lncRNAs dysregulated expression has been has reported in many human diseases (Hrdlickova *et al.*, 2014; Wapinski and Chang, 2011). However, little is known about lncRNAs' role in XLA patients. Through the comparative analysis of lncRNA expressions in primary monocytes between XLA patients and healthy subjects, 95 DE annotated lncRNAs including 56 upregulated and 39 downregulated and 20 DE novel lincRNAs including 5 upregulated and 15 downregulated were obtained in XLA patients compared to healthy subjects.

Overall the results as presented above indicated the inclusive dysregulation of monocytes' immune functions and the increase of susceptibility to apoptosis in monocytes of XLA patients. This suggests that BTK mutations are not only affecting the B cell development and differentiation, they would be also contributing to dysregulation of innate immune system in XLA patients. This study also revealed the differentially expression patterns of lncRNAs in primary monocytes of XLA patients that would suggest the potential role of lncRNAs in regulation of immune functions in primary monocytes of XLA patients (Mirsafian *et al.*, 2017).

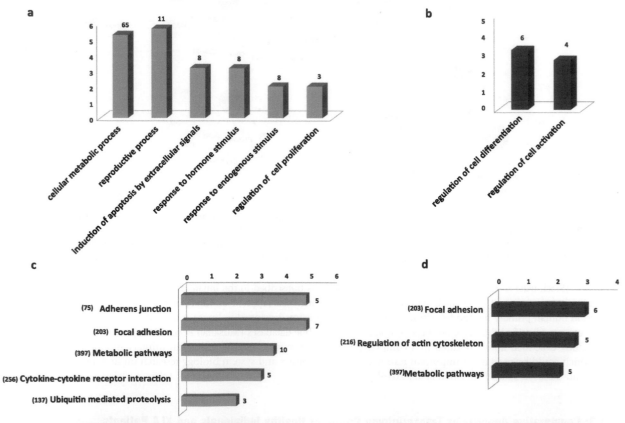

Fig. 6   The GO and KEGG pathway analysis of DE lncRNAs colocated genes in primary monocytes of XLA patients compared to healthy subjects. The significant GO biological process terms enriched for (a) DE annotated lncRNAs colocated genes, and (b) DE novel lincRNAs colocated genes. The number of DE lncRNAs colocated genes enriched in each GO terms is depicted above the bars in the figure. The significant KEGG pathway terms enriched for (c) DE annotated lncRNAs colocated genes, and (b) DE novel lincRNAs colocated genes. The numbers in the brackets indicated the total numbers of genes available in the KEGG database for each pathway terms. The number of identified DE lncRNAs colocated genes enriched in each KEGG pathways is depicted above the bars in the figure. Reproduced from Mirsafian, H., Ripen, A.M., Leong, W.M., *et al.*, 2017. Transcriptome profiling of monocytes from XLA patients revealed the innate immune function dysregulation due to the BTK gene expression deficiency. Scientific Reports 7 (1), 6836.

Conclusions

Transcriptomic data based on deep RNA-Seq approach can provide valuable information on differential gene and transcript expression patterns in specific cell types. Herein, we described the analysis of transcriptomic datasets from monocytes of the innate immune system, which resulted in a comprehensive expression profile of human primary monocytes under healthy and XLA disease states. This also includes the establishment of a reference gene catalog of human primary monocytes. A set of differentially expressed (DE) protein-coding genes and DE lncRNAs identified in XLA patients compared to the healthy individuals opens exciting and several potential avenues of research that will help us to better understand the complex pathophysiology in XLA disease. We believe that transcriptomic profiling based on the RNA-Seq approach offers significant promise towards precision medicine, systems diagnostics, immunogenomics, and the development of genomic markers as well as innovative therapeutic monitoring strategies.

Closing Remarks

The availability of high coverage and greater resolution transcriptomic datasets generated from high-throughput RNA-Seq approaches have made possible the applications of systems bioinformatics to further elucidate the functional complexity and provide better understanding of the human body systems towards advancement in healthcare and biomedical research. One of the big challenges that lie ahead is to integrate different types of "omics" datasets (i.e., multiomics datasets comprising, for example, genomics, transcriptomics, proteomics, and metabolomics data from similar or identical biological background) generated from multiomics measurement platforms in order to provide meaningful insights and in-depth understanding on how a given genotype affects the phenotypic features of a given individual through various molecular mediators as well as interaction between a genotype and the environment. We believe that as technologies mature and computational data analysis pipelines and methodologies become more robust and sophisticated, such challenges will be overcome in the very near future.

Acknowledgements

The authors acknowledged the financial support for the research on the transcriptome profiling of the monocytes using RNA-Seq approach from the UM-MOHE High Impact Research (HIR) Grant Scheme: UM.S/P/HIR/MOHE/30; Ministry of Higher Education Malaysia Fundamental Research Grant Scheme (FRGS): FP050–2016; University of Malaya Research Grant (UMRG): RP004C: 13AFR and University of Malaya PPP Postgraduate Grant: PG086–2013B. The authors would also like to thank the Director General of Health, Malaysia for supporting the work carried out by the authors on this subject.

See also: Computational Systems Biology Applications. Coupling Cell Division to Metabolic Pathways Through Transcription. Natural Language Processing Approaches in Bioinformatics

References

Ancuta, P., Liu, K.-Y., Misra, V., *et al.*, 2009. Transcriptional profiling reveals developmental relationship and distinct biological functions of CD16 + and CD16- monocyte subsets. BMC Genomics 10 (1), 403.

Ayers, D., Day, P.J., 2015. Systems medicine: The application of systems biology approaches for modern medical research and drug development. Molecular Biology International 2015, 698169.

Baldi, P., Hatfield, G.W., 2002. DNA microarrays and Gene Expression: From Experiments To Data Analysis And Modeling. Cambridge: Cambridge University Press, Paperback reissue.

Bao, Y., Zheng, J., Han, C., *et al.*, 2012. Tyrosine kinase Btk is required for NK cell activation. Journal of Biological Chemistry 287 (28), 23769–23778.

Beyer, M., Mallmann, M.R., Xue, J., *et al.*, 2012. High-resolution transcriptome of human macrophages. PLOS ONE 7 (9), e45466.

Clark, M.B., Mattick, J.S., 2011. Long noncoding RNAs in cell biology. Seminars in Cell & Developmental Biology 22 (4), 366–376.

Dang, Y., Xu, X., Shen, Y., *et al.*, 2016. Transcriptome analysis of the innate immunity-related complement system in spleen tissue of ctenopharyngodon idella infected with aeromonas hydrophila. PLOS ONE 11 (7), e0157413.

Derrien, T., Johnson, R., Bussotti, G., *et al.*, 2012. The GENCODE v7 catalog of human long noncoding RNAs: Analysis of their gene structure, evolution, and expression. Genome Research 22 (9), 1775–1789.

Dong, C., Zhao, G., Zhong, M., *et al.*, 2013. RNA sequencing and transcriptomal analysis of human monocyte to macrophage differentiation. Gene 519 (2), 279–287.

Dong, Z., Chen, Y., 2013. Transcriptomics: Advances and approaches. Science China. Life Sciences 56 (10), 960–967.

Finotello, F., Di Camillo, B., 2015. Measuring differential gene expression with RNA-seq: Challenges and strategies for data analysis. Briefings in Functional Genomics 14 (2), 130–142.

Fuchs, S.B.A., Lieder, I., Stelzer, G., *et al.*, 2016. GeneAnalytics: An integrative gene set analysis tool for next generation sequencing, RNAseq and microarray data. OMICS 20, 139–151.

Guttman, M., Amit, I., Garber, M., *et al.*, 2009. Chromatin signature reveals over a thousand highly conserved large non-coding RNAs in mammals. Nature 458 (7235), 223–227.

Honda, F., Kano, H., Kanegane, H., *et al.*, 2012. The kinase Btk negatively regulates the production of reactive oxygen species and stimulation-induced apoptosis in human neutrophils. Nature Immunology 13 (4), 369–378.

Hrdlickova, B., Kumar, V., Kanduri, K., et al., 2014. Expression profiles of long non-coding RNAs located in autoimmune disease-associated regions reveal immune cell-type specificity. Genome Medicine 6 (10),

Immunobiology: The Immune System in Health and Disease ; [Animated CD-ROM Inside]. Janeway, C.A. (Ed.), New York, NY: Garland Publications. [u.a.].

Karapetyan, A., Buiting, C., Kuiper, R., Coolen, M., 2013. Regulatory roles for long ncRNA and mRNA. Cancers 5 (2), 462–490.

Kim, E.-D., Sung, S., 2012. Long noncoding RNA: Unveiling hidden layer of gene regulatory networks. Trends in Plant Science 17 (1), 16–21.

Koprulu, A.D., Ellmeier, W., 2009. The role of Tec family kinases in mononuclear phagocytes. Critical Reviews in Immunology 29 (4), 317–333.

Kraft-Terry, S.D., Gendelman, H.E., 2011. Proteomic biosignatures for monocyte–macrophage differentiation. Cellular Immunology 271 (2), 239–255.

Krauss, M., Hofmann, U., Schafmayer, C., et al., 2017. Translational learning from clinical studies predicts drug pharmacokinetics across patient populations. NPJ Systems Biology and Applications 3, 11.

Kukurba, K.R., Montgomery, S.B., 2015. RNA sequencing and analysis. Cold Spring Harbor Protocols 2015 (11), 951–969.

Lee, P.P.W., Chen, T.-X., Jiang, L.-P., et al., 2010. Clinical Characteristics and Genotype-phenotype Correlation in 62 Patients with X-linked Agammaglobulinemia. Journal of Clinical Immunology 30 (1), 121–131.

Likić, V.A., McConville, M.J., Lithgow, T., Bacic, A., 2010. Systems Biology: The Next Frontier for Bioinformatics. Advances in Bioinformatics 2010, 268925.

McDowell, J., ed. 2010. Encyclopedia of Human Body Systems. vol. 1 Santa Barbara, California: Greenwood.

Mirsafian, H., Manda, S.S., Mitchell, C.J., et al., 2016a. Long non-coding RNA expression in primary human monocytes. Genomics 108 (1), 37–45.

Mirsafian, H., Ripen, A.M., Leong, W.M., et al., 2017. Transcriptome profiling of monocytes from XLA patients revealed the innate immune function dysregulation due to the BTK gene expression deficiency. Scientific Reports 7 (1), 6836.

Mirsafian, H., Ripen, A.M., Manaharan, T., Mohamad, S.B., Merican, A.F., 2016b. Towards a reference gene catalogue of human primary monocytes. OMICS 20 (11), 627–634.

Mitchell, C.J., Getnet, D., Kim, M.-S., et al., 2015. A multi-omic analysis of human naïve CD4 + T cells. BMC Systems Biology 9 (1),

Mohamed, A.J., Yu, L., Bäckesjö, C.-M., et al., 2009. Bruton's tyrosine kinase (Btk): Function, regulation, and transformation with special emphasis on the PH domain. Immunological Reviews 228 (1), 58–73.

Müller, N., Döring, F., Klapper, M., et al., 2014. Interleukin-6 and tumour necrosis factor-α differentially regulate lincRNA transcripts in cells of the innate immune system in vivo in human subjects with rheumatoid arthritis. Cytokine 68 (1), 65–68.

Ochs, H.D., Smith, C.I., 1996. X-linked agammaglobulinemia. A clinical and molecular analysis. Medicine 75 (6), 287–299.

Satpathy, A.T., Chang, H.Y., 2015. Long noncoding RNA in hematopoiesis and immunity. Immunity 42 (5), 792–804.

Shi, L., Zhang, Z., Yu, A.M., et al., 2014. The SLE transcriptome exhibits evidence of chronic endotoxin exposure and has widespread dysregulation of non-coding and coding RNAs. PLOS ONE 9 (5), e93846.

Sirri, V., Urcuqui-Inchima, S., Roussel, P., Hernandez-Verdun, D., 2008. Nucleolus: The fascinating nuclear body. Histochemistry and Cell Biology 129 (1), 13–31.

Slack, J.M.W., 2013. Essential Developmental Biology. Oxford: Wiley-Blackwell.

Smale, S.T., 2014. Transcriptional regulation in the immune system: A status report. Trends in Immunology 35 (5), 190–194.

Stachurska, A., Zorro, M.M., van der Sijde, M.R., Withoff, S., 2014. Small and long regulatory RNAs in the immune system and immune diseases. Frontiers in Immunology 5.

Taylor, C., 2017. The Kingfisher Science Encyclopedia, fourth ed. London, England: Kingfisher Publications Plc.

Toung, J.M., Morley, M., Li, M., Cheung, V.G., 2011. RNA-sequence analysis of human B-cells. Genome Research 21 (6), 991–998.

Vaquerizas, J.M., Kummerfeld, S.K., Teichmann, S.A., Luscombe, N.M., 2009. A census of human transcription factors: Function, expression and evolution. Nature Reviews Genetics 10 (4), 252–263.

Vetrie, D., Vořechovský, I., Sideras, P., et al., 1993. The gene involved in X-linked agammaglobulinaemia is a member of the src family of protein-tyrosine kinases. Nature 361 (6409), 226–233.

Wapinski, O., Chang, H.Y., 2011. Long noncoding RNAs and human disease. Trends in Cell Biology 21 (6), 354–361.

Zieba, A., Sjöstedt, E., Olovsson, M., et al., 2015. The human endometrium-specific proteome defined by transcriptomics and antibody-based profiling. OMICS: A Journal of Integrative Biology 19 (11), 659–668.

Ziegler-Heitbrock, L., Ancuta, P., Crowe, S., et al., 2010. Nomenclature of monocytes and dendritic cells in blood. Blood 116 (16), e74–e80.

Host-Pathogen Interactions

Dean Southwood and Shoba Ranganathan, Macquarie University, Sydney, NSW, Australia

Introduction

"You must not fight too often with one enemy, or you will teach him all your art of war."
– Plutarch

Humanity's war against infectious disease is an epic and gruelling conflict, one which has not yet been won. In the last two centuries, advances in science and technology have turned the tide on many fronts, through the development of treatments to help the body subdue, eradicate, or prevent infections. This is a war where espionage and intelligence go a long way – the more knowledge we have about pathogens and their interactions with their respective host systems, the easier it is to find new ways of defeating them; or at the very least, subduing them. Substantial improvements made in recent decades in genomic and proteomic technology have allowed for vast amounts of data to be created. The challenge now is to find elegant and efficient methods of analysing this data to work out the fine details of host-pathogen interactions – how pathogens invade, evade, and proliferate, and the damage they do to their hosts in the process. Such information is key to the development of new therapeutics, treatment strategies, methods of diagnosis, and vaccines to prevent and mediate infection.

The field of bioinformatics has been essential in keeping up with the flood of new data in this area. Strategies for storing, handling, and analysing such data have been developed, and are continuing to be improved on. The post-genomic era has seen an explosion of databases and methodologies for investigating the different aspects of host-pathogen interactions. Each omics field has developed its own approaches to tackling the problem, through processing, analysis, and prediction. There are also current efforts to synthesise the information obtained from a variety of different omics fields to create a global approach to host-pathogen interaction determination.

This article is divided into four main sections. The first section sets up the fundamentals of host-pathogen interactions and current methods to investigate them. This includes a discussion of the terminology of pathogenesis, and the contention around how it is defined, as well as discussion of infection, and current bioinformatics tools to probe it. The second section focusses on how these fundamentals have been applied in the design of drugs and vaccines. The third section discusses the current issues and unresolved contentions surrounding host-pathogen interactions, and the role of bioinformatics in solving them. The last section deals with possible outlooks to the future, with an emphasis on open questions and areas requiring a synthesis of ideas.

Fundamentals

Defining Pathogens

Before we can begin to discuss current approaches to elucidating the details of host-pathogen interactions, we need to clarify what it is we mean by pathogens, what kinds of hosts they invade, and the nature of possible interactions between the two. Historically, as our understanding of disease and its causative agents has increased, the emphasis has shifted from an invader-centric view to a more holistic, host-invader view, where factors such as the type of host and its immune defences, as well as the interaction between the invader and the host are important to defining what a pathogen is. In the last two decades, there has been significant discussion on redefining terms; such as, pathogen, pathogenicity, and virulence; to match this equal emphasis (Casadevall and Pirofski, 1999, 2000, 2001; Methot and Alizon, 2014). These are summarised in **Table 1**, where the common thread concerns the ability to cause damage in a particular host, and the possible extent of this damage. Such an idea makes host-pathogen interactions the centrepiece in investigating disease as they form the crucial connection between the intricate details of a pathogen and the intricate details of the host, which taken individually do not give us a good picture of disease itself.

If we take a pathogen as being something which causes damage in a host, the next questions to ask are: what kind of pathogens do we know about already, and what hosts do they infect? At present, it is useful to categorise pathogens into six types: viruses, bacteria, fungi, protozoa, parasites, and prions. Most work concerning host-pathogen interactions has been done with respect to the first four categories. The fifth category, parasites, is essentially a catch-all for infective organisms which do not fit well into any of the other categories, helminths being prominent examples. The final category, prions, is unique in that the pathogen is (in some cases hypothesised to be) a misfolded protein, rather than an organism. Key representatives of each category (with humans as hosts) are given in **Table 2**, along with the diseases they cause.

Not every possible invasive species is pathogenic in humans – how pathogenic a particular organism is depends strongly on the host it is trying to invade. The defences that must be evaded and the conditions that must be adapted to vary widely in their details from host to host, and will often require a unique set of machinery. Therefore, most pathogens evolve to target a particular host almost exclusively. It is important to recognise that interactions pathogens may have with non-human hosts are hints rather than concrete answers as to their interactions with humans. However, there are several good reasons to investigate pathogens in organisms aside from humans. Firstly, the study of pathogenesis in model organisms is often more achievable than in humans, due to well-established methods and comprehensive databases. Organisms; such as, the nematode *Caenorhabditis elegans* (Kurz and

Table 1   Definitions of common terms associated with host-pathogen interactions, emphasising the dual sources of pathogenicity – pathogen and host

Term	Definition (as per Casadevall and Pirofski, 1999)
Pathogen	A microbe capable of causing host damage; host damage can result from either direct microbial action or the host immune response
Pathogenicity	The capacity of a microbe to cause damage in a host
Virulence	The relative capacity of a microbe to cause damage in a host
Virulence factor	A component of a pathogen that damages the host; this can include components essential for viability

Casadevall, A., Pirofski, L.A., 1999. Host-pathogen interactions: Redefining the basic concepts of virulence and pathogenicity. Infection and Immunity 67(8), 3703–3713.

Table 2   Common examples of each type of pathogen in humans, including the corresponding diseases they cause

Pathogen Type	Pathogens	Diseases
Viruses	Hepatitis (A-E) virus	Hepatitis (A-E)
	Herpes simplex virus (1–2)	Herpes
	Human immunodeficiency virus	HIV/AIDS
	Influenza virus A	Influenza
	Measles virus	Measles
	Dengue virus	Dengue fever
	Varicella zoster virus	Chicken pox
	Zika virus	Zika fever
Bacteria	*Clostridium tetani*	Tetanus
	Vibrio cholerae	Cholera
	Mycobacterium tuberculosis	Tuberculosis
	Streptococcus pneumoniae	Pneumonia
	Salmonella Typhi	Typhoid
	Salmonella Typhimurium	Gastroenteritis
	Borrelia burgdorferi	Lyme disease
	Treponema pallidum	Syphilis
	Yersinia pestis	Plague
Fungi	*Aspergillus fumigatus*	Aspergillosis
	Candida albicans	Candidiasis (thrush)
	Trichophyton rubrum	Ringworm
	Histoplasma capsulatum	Histoplasmosis
	Cryptococcus neoformans	Cryptococcus and fungal meningitis
Protozoa	*Plasmodium falciparum*	Malaria
	Entamoeba histolytica	Amoebic dysentery
	Trypanosoma brucei	African sleeping sickness
	Giardia lamblia	Giardiasis (Beaver fever)
Parasites	*Ancylostoma duodenale*	Hookworm
	Schistosoma mansoni	Schistosomiasis (Swamp fever)
	Taenia solium	Tapeworm infection
Prions	CJD prion	Creutzfeldt-Jakob disease
	vCJD prion	Variant Creutzfeldt-Jakob disease
	Kuru prion	Kuru

Ewbank, 2000), the fruit fly *Drosophila melanogaster* (Vodovar *et al.*, 2004), and the zebrafish *Danio rerio* (Meijer and Spaink, 2011; Tobin *et al.*, 2012); are significant non-human hosts in the study of host-pathogen interactions. Secondly, by analysing data obtained from other host organisms, we can investigate tools that pathogens have to invade, evade, and proliferate, which provide leads to finding key interactions with humans. Thirdly, animal and plant diseases are economically and ecologically significant due to their role in food production and conservation. Lastly, the possibility of diseases undergoing a zoonotic jump from animals to humans means the study of animal diseases is of preventative significance (Baigent and McCauley, 2003).

Due to the current directions of the field, as well as pressing medical relevance, the primary focus of the current chapter will be on human hosts and their interactions with pathogens, with only secondary mentions of non-human hosts.

Stages of Infection

In broad terms, there are four stages of host-pathogen interactions: the pathogen invading the host system, the pathogen evading the host system's defences, the pathogen proliferating in the host system, and the host system's immune response to the invader.

Different pathogens will possibly have different machinery at each stage, with some mechanisms developing in response to very specific host system defences. The four stages are not disjoint; there is some overlap between them, with some stages being more infectious for certain pathogens than others. An overview of our current knowledge of host-pathogen interactions at each stage is provided below; state-of-the-art methods used to gain knowledge in these areas are discussed in more detail in the next section.

Invading the host system

Initial infection can occur *via* a number of pathways – the pathogen may enter the body through the mouth or nose, the bloodstream (possibly through a contaminated needle), or through mucosal membranes, as well as other more specialised means. However, once the pathogen has entered, it must interact with the host cells in order to remain within the host and continue its invasion. The form this interaction takes depends on the type of pathogen. Viral pathogens invade host cells by merging their envelope with the membrane of either a cell or an endosome. For other pathogens, including Gram-negative bacteria, specialised protein secretion systems are used to release so-called effector proteins into host cells which trigger a particular response mechanism in the host, allowing the invader to migrate to a preferable environment. Such secretion and injection machinery is not always required, especially in fungal pathogens. Instead, effector proteins are expressed on the surface of the invader, and interact with host cell receptors. The host's response to these proteins typically allows the pathogen to invade deeper into the host system.

In most cases, viral pathogens invade by merging with the host cell membrane itself. This is aided through the use of fusion proteins provided by the virus, promoting attachment and fusing of the host and pathogen membranes. In general, the fusion proteins used by each type of virus are distinct, meaning that vaccines and drug therapies must be designed specifically for each type (Cohen, 2016).

So far, six distinct secretion systems have been discovered in Gram-negative bacteria: Type I (Welch *et al.*, 1981), Type II (d'Enfert *et al.*, 1987), Type III (Galán and Curtiss, 1989), Type IV (Kuldau *et al.*, 1990), Type V (Pohlner et al., 1987), and Type VI (Pukatzki *et al.*, 2006; Mougous *et al.*, 2006). In mycobacteria, there is the Type VII secretory system, also known as the ESX system (Stanley *et al.*, 2003). In general, these systems act as injectors, transporting effector proteins from the invading pathogen to the host cell. The particular proteins secreted by each type of system are still being determined; recent methods for such investigations are discussed in Section "Bioinformatic Methods of Discovery". The details of the delivery mechanisms are also still being discovered; for an in-depth discussion of our current knowledge of secretion system machinery itself, see Further Reading 1 (**Costa** *et al.*, 2015).

Fungal invasion mechanisms in many ways lie between those of viruses and bacteria. Instead of effector proteins being injected into the host cell, they are only located on the hyphal surface of the pathogen. These are then presented to host cell receptors, which induce a change that the pathogen can exploit. In the case of *Candida albicans*, the changes can lead to induced endocytosis or cellular uptake of the pathogen, as well as active penetration, where the pathogen exploits the interaction to penetrate the epithelial lining (Yang *et al.*, 2014).

As most known invasion mechanisms proceed *via* protein-protein interactions on the surface of cells, glycosylation plays a significant role in determining pathogenicity (Hooper and Gordon, 2001). If the glycosylation of surface proteins in one part of the body is not compatible with the pathogen, the interaction is weakened and invasion is also significantly reduced. Either the presence or the absence of glycosylation can be essential to pathogenicity depending on the type of invader, as some effector proteins selectively bind to certain glycoproteins (Hooper and Gordon, 2001).

Evading the host system

Once the pathogen has successfully gained a foothold inside the host system, it will in most cases attempt to evade the host's defences in order to survive. There are a number of mechanisms through which pathogens try to evade defence systems, including affecting essential pathways in the host to increase or decrease defence activity, inhibiting macrophage activity, and sabotaging crosstalk in pathways using miRNA and short linear motifs (SLiMs).

Immune responses are triggered through a variety of essential pathways, resulting in the activation of both intra- and extra-cellular mechanisms to tackle the invader. In order to evade these mechanisms, pathogens have adapted to target specific pathways in order to optimise their survival chances. One such target is the NF-κB pathway, which plays a role in the regulation of apoptosis (Tato and Hunter, 2002). A variety of bacterial, viral and parasitic pathogens have all been found to attack the NF-κB pathway, either through activation or inhibition (Rahman and McFadden, 2011), and it is therefore crucial to early infection. Other possible targets for pathogens are so-called 'hub' proteins, which connect with a variety of signal pathways (Dyer *et al.*, 2008), in particular in the case of the Epstein-Barr virus (Calderwood *et al.*, 2007).

Upon activating the immune defences of the host, the invader is in most cases hunted down and consumed by the macrophage. Therefore, many pathogens attempt to avoid detection by the macrophage, or inhibit its activity. In the case of *Mycobacterium tuberculosis*, this is possibly achieved by inhibiting interleukin-12 production, in turn inhibiting macrophage activation (Nau *et al.*, 2002). In the case of viruses, between 26 and 37 HIV-1 proteins have been associated with monocyte-derived macrophages (Chertova *et al.*, 2006), indicating this is a significant target of the host defence system.

Invaders also attempt to sabotage the molecular crosstalk of the host *via* microRNA regulation (Scaria *et al.*, 2007). This is particularly the case for viral pathogens, where the invading microRNA can modulate the expression of viral and antiviral genes, therefore playing an essential role in staying undetected in the host (Ghosh *et al.*, 2009). Fungal pathogens have also been shown to suppress immunity in plants by hijacking RNA interference pathways using sRNAs (Weiberg *et al.*, 2013).

Another possible avenue for sabotage is through protein-protein interaction, by use of short linear motifs (SLiMs). By mimicking the protein interactions of the host, the pathogen can regulate essential pathways to its benefit (Via *et al.*, 2015). There have been recent attempts to predict such mimicry in the HIV-1-human interaction using disorder prediction algorithms (Becerra *et al.*, 2017).

Proliferating in the host system

It is not normally sufficient for a pathogen to invade and evade a host; there must be some benefit to the pathogen once it has taken root in the host system. This is largely due to adaptations by pathogens to more easily proliferate in the host system, rather than on their own. In many pathogens, there is a substantial difference in the number of genes required to survive inside the host as opposed to outside, with the mechanisms for proliferating inside the host requiring significantly less genes (Raghunathan *et al.*, 2009). The methods through which the pathogen co-opts the host machinery also depend on the type of pathogen. Host factors, or proteins produced by the host which end up playing a significant role in the proliferation of the pathogen, also tend to be significant players in establishing pathogen replication.

The hijacking of host cells by viruses (Davey *et al.*, 2011) and bacteria (Bhavsar *et al.*, 2007) is a key part of the pathogen not only surviving, but thriving in the host. How a particular pathogen has adapted to exploit the inherent machinery of the host is often a significant difference between pathogen types. This is particularly essential in the case of viruses, where the extremely compact nature of their genome requires the host cell machinery for replication. Indeed, the relationship between viruses and their host is so intimate that the host can act as vehicle for gene transfer between viruses (Rappoport and Linial, 2012).

The host can also unknowingly provide essential components for the replication and survival of pathogens. Such host factors are the subject of intense study as possible drug targets which do not depend as heavily on the specific genetic details of the invading pathogen. As many as 295 human host factors have been identified as necessary in the replication of the influenza virus (König *et al.*, 2010), while 213 host factors have been associated with HIV-1 replication (Brass *et al.*, 2008).

Immune control of invader

An invader is unlikely to escape the immune response of the host indefinitely; therefore, at some point the host will seek to control the threat. What methods does a host have at its disposal to control the pathogen? At the fundamental level, the host can trigger gene pathways to create an immune response to destroy the invader. Within a cell, autophagy can be used to remove the threat. Extracellularly, the use of dendritic cells, especially in the intestine, is important in suppressing pathogens. In many immune processes, iron regulation is essential and must be carefully controlled. Therefore, all of the above processes are potential targets for pathogens to prevent immune control and subsequent destruction.

The initial response of a host to the detection of invaders is the activation of immune signalling cascades. Depending on the type of pathogen, particular genes may also be highly expressed; these genes are significant both as targets for pathogens, as well as targets for possible drug therapies in activating the immune system to combat invaders. In the particular case of *Mycobacterium tuberculosis* infection in a mouse host, 67 genes were identified as being highly expressed in immune-competent mice, but not in immune-compromised mice (Talaat *et al.*, 2004). This suggests that these 67 genes are significant in combatting tuberculosis infection in mice, and give potential leads to similar genes in humans.

Autophagy is an intracellular lysosomal degradation process which is usually used to break down damaged organelles and other hazardous cellular products. It is also essential to the degradation of *Mycobacterium tuberculosis* during infection (Vergne *et al.*, 2006). However, the precise mechanisms by which *Mycobacterium tuberculosis* does or does not avoid autophagy in the macrophage is still under discussion, with strong indications that microRNA plays a role (Kim *et al.*, 2017).

Dendritic cells are antigen-presenting cells which act as regulators of both the innate and adaptive immune systems (Kelsall *et al.*, 2002). While they are essential in generating an appropriate immune response from the host, they are not immune to manipulation by invaders. In particular, dendritic cells are able to migrate from sites of infection to the lymph nodes, in turn activating T cells. However, this also allows for the possible migration of pathogens around the body; in the event of build-up of migratory dendritic cells, this also creates persistent inflammatory responses (Worbs *et al.*, 2017). For a thorough discussion of the role of dendritic cells in health and disease, see Worbs *et al.* (2017).

Iron is an essential part of both the responses of hosts to invaders, as well as pathogen survival. During infection, host responses tend to withdraw iron from pathogen sites; however, pathogens have developed methods of harvesting iron from other sources, such as heme, transferrin, ferritin and lactoferrin (Doherty, 2007). Therefore, in iron-deficient patients presenting infections such as tuberculosis, the decision to supplement iron must be weighed against aiding the pathogen (Doherty, 2007).

Bioinformatic Methods of Discovery

Bioinformatics has played, and will continue to play, an extremely large role in determining host-pathogen interactions. In the post-genomic scientific landscape, the emphasis on 'big data' is extremely high; methods which can fully utilise the wealth of data available have an edge on traditional, small-sample methods. Therefore, there has been more recent emphasis on machine learning and network methods in predicting and analysing the connections between hosts and pathogens. However, there is also still a strong contribution from more biochemistry-based approaches which utilise homology and structure to predict novel host-pathogen interactions.

The analysis of current methods in bioinformatics is divided into two broad, and by no means strictly exclusive, categories: biological methods, which arise from traditional biologically-inspired methodologies informed by structure and homology; and computational methods, which arise from more computationally-inspired methodologies such as network analysis and machine learning.

Biological methods

Computational methods of predicting host-pathogen interactions can make significant use of the structural information of proteins, as well as previously known interactions with other proteins, in order to narrow results. This can be done by searching for homologous proteins in the pathogen or host which may also interact with known proteins (so-called interologues). Alternatively, it can be done by comparing structural features such as domains or motifs to those present in known interactions. There is also the possibility of using the 3D structural information of proteins, such as those with known crystal structures, to inform analysis methods. A more detailed recent review of structure-based methods can be found in Further Reading 2 (**Mariano** and **Wuchty, 2017**), but highlights are presented in this section to capture the prevailing methods.

Homology-based prediction methods only work well in situations where there is a large degree of similarity or evolutionary conservation between the organisms or proteins under discussion. However, this is often the case in related pathogens, for example between different bacterial serotypes. Such an approach has been taken in analysing malaria in the *Homo sapiens-Plasmodium falciparum* host-pathogen pairing (Krishnadev and Srinivasan, 2008). The method analyses the genomic data of both organisms, and identifies homologous proteins with known protein-protein interactions. These are then compared between the two organisms to determine the likelihood of any protein-protein host-pathogen interactions occurring. A significant problem with homology-based methods is the high false positive rate (**Mariano** and **Wuchty, 2017**) – protein pairs identified may not be expressed at the same time, in the same location, and may not ever come into contact, let alone interact. Therefore, successful homology approaches require filters that account for these criteria, such as the use of random forest classifiers in again analysing the *Homo sapiens-Plasmodium falciparum* pairing (Dyer *et al.*, 2007; Wuchty, 2011). There has also been prediction of protein-protein interactions through comparative modelling (Davis *et al.*, 2007), which was applied across 10 pathogens, including species of *Mycobacterium*.

The analysis of smaller sections of candidate proteins from either the host or the pathogen can also provide good indications of host-pathogen interactions. By determining the domains of these proteins, and comparing to databases of known domain-domain interactions, lists of possible candidates can be narrowed down (König *et al.*, 2008). There is also the potential for domain-motif and motif-motif interactions through smaller sections of the protein. Such short linear motifs or SLiMs have also been used to improve the accuracy of predictive methods (Becerra *et al.*, 2017), and in HIV-1 (Via *et al.*, 2015). Conserved peptide motifs in human proteins have been used to predict possible human-HIV-1 protein-protein interactions (Evans *et al.*, 2009).

Computational methods

In order to find new host-pathogen interactions, a vast pool of data must be processed, sorting good predictors in the data from bad predictors, and weighing up their contributions to give an overall predictive strategy. This is precisely the domain in which machine learning and network analysis excel. There are two possible approaches within machine learning to solve such problems concerning host-pathogen interactions. Supervised learning is the most prevalent set of methods in analysing host-pathogen interactions, wherein possible predictors are identified beforehand, leaving their weights and relative importance to be determined by a training set of data. This is because in many cases we think we know what features we want to analyse through, and like to rely on curated datasets. For example, some common chosen features include gene expression profiles, gene ontology annotations, topological properties of known proteins, functional motifs and post-translational modifications. However, semi-supervised learning methods are also gaining traction through the prevalence of partially-labelled datasets, allowing other features to be identified throughout the model construction process that may not have been identified as inputs beforehand. Due to the highly interdependent nature of intracellular interactions, network analysis methods have also seen significant use, utilising the vast connections and possible interactions between proteins to identify possible intersections and new host-pathogen interactions.

Classifier-based methods have been a popular choice in identifying host-pathogen interactions, including random forest methods (Tastan *et al.*, 2009; Wuchty, 2011). In these cases, the interactions between *Homo sapiens* and HIV-1, and *Homo sapiens* and *P. falciparum*, respectively, were analysed, using appropriate feature choices in each case to encompass the most reliable known information about the pairing, such as known feature motifs, gene expression profiles, and amino acid profiles. These methods have had some success in predicting known (and recently experimentally verified) interactions, as well as previously unknown ones, with varying accuracy. Other methods, such as Naïve Bayes (Arnold *et al.*, 2009), Support Vector Machines (SVMs) (Wang *et al.*, 2011) and group lasso methods (Kshirsagar *et al.*, 2012) have also had varying levels of success in identifying known host-pathogen interactions and predicting new host-pathogen interactions from big data sets. Many of the features used across models include the amino acid profile of proteins, relative positions of residues in the structures, as well as overarching secondary features that can be identified from the primary sequence. Other methods take information such as known protein-protein interactions to predict new ones using structural similarities. Often, these models require regularizers in order to minimise the bias introduced from the biological assumption that similar proteins will interact in similar ways, which would otherwise limit the power to predict novel interactions.

Multi-task learning and semi-supervised auxiliary tasks, including multi-layer perceptron methods (supervised) and perceptron methods with partial label reference (semi-supervised), are also being used to predict novel host-pathogen interactions from current data

Table 3   Databases for analysing host-pathogen interactions; links current as of September 2017

Name	ID	URL	References
PATRIC	1	http://www.patricbrc.org/	Wattam *et al.* (2014), Driscoll *et al.* (2009)
ViPR	2	https://www.viprbrc.org/brc/home.spg?decorator=vipr/	Pickett *et al.* (2012)
EuPathDB	3	http://eupathdb.org/	Aurrecoechea *et al.* (2017), Aurrecoechea *et al.* (2013)
VectorBase	4	http://www.vectorbase.org/	Giraldo-Calderón *et al.* (2015)
IRD	5	https://www.fludb.org/brc/home.spg?decorator=influenza/	Zhang *et al.* (2017)
VirHostNet 2.0	6	http://virhostnet.prabi.fr/	Guirimand *et al.* (2015), Navratil *et al.* (2009)
VirusMentha	7	http://virusmentha.uniroma2.it/	Calderone *et al.* (2015)
ViralZone	8	http://viralzone.expasy.org/	Hulo *et al.* (2011)
ViTa	9	http://vita.mbc.nctu.edu.tw/index.php	Hsu *et al.* (2007)
HPIDB 2.0	10	http://hpidb.igbb.msstate.edu/	Ammari *et al.* (2016), Kumar and Naduri (2010a, b)
GPS-Prot	11	http://gpsprot.org/	Fahey *et al.* (2011)
PHI-base	12	http://phi-base.org/	Urban *et al.* (2017), Winnenberg *et al.* (2006)
PID	13	http://www.ndexbio.org/#/user/301a91c6-a37b-11e4-bda0–000c29202374	Schaefer *et al.* (2009)
HIV-1, Human Protein Interaction Database	14	http://www.ncbi.nlm.nih.gov/genome/viruses/retroviruses/hiv-1/interactions/	Fu *et al.* (2009)
HIV Database Tools LANL	15	https://www.hiv.lanl.gov/content/index/	N/A
HCV Database Tools LANL	16	https://hcv.lanl.gov/content/index/	N/A
HFV Database Tools LANL	17	https://hfv.lanl.gov/content/index/	N/A
hpvPDB	18	http://www.bicjbtdrc-mgims.in/hpvPDB/index.html	Kumar *et al.* (2013)
PHIDIAS	19	http://www.phidias.us/	Xiang *et al.* (2007)
PHISTO	20	http://www.phisto.org/	Durmuş Tekir *et al.* (2013)
HoPaCI-DB	21	http://mips.helmholtz-muenchen.de/HoPaCI	Bleves *et al.* (2014)
VFDB	22	http://www.mgc.ac.cn/VFs/main.htm	Chen *et al.* (2016), Chen *et al.* (2005)
IntAct	23	http://www.ebi.ac.uk/intact/	Aranda *et al.* (2010)
BioGRID	24	http://thebiogrid.org/	Chatr-aryamontri *et al.* (2017)
Mentha	25	http://mentha.uniroma2.it/	Calderone *et al.* (2013)

(Qi *et al.*, 2010; Kshirsagar *et al.*, 2013). In this case, fully labelled reference data has been used to train a (supervised) perceptron model, while partially labelled reference data has been used afterwards to improve the feature determination and weighting (semi-supervised) in the case of the *Homo sapiens*-HIV-1 host-pathogen system. Indeed, there has been significant recent emphasis on HIV-1 analysis due to the development of the HIV-1, Human protein interaction database (Fu *et al.*, 2009). Previous machine learning methods have been well-characterized and summarised (Pinney *et al.*, 2009), while more recent *in silico* approaches to *Homo sapiens*-HIV-1 protein-protein interactions have also been thoroughly reviewed (Bandyopadhyay *et al.*, 2015). Network analysis-based methods have also seen use in this area, with interactome-based network analysis of interaction between HIV-1 proteins and signal transduction pathways identifying possible alternatives around the proteins targeted by HIV-1 (Balakrishnan *et al.*, 2009).

For further details and methods of machine learning approaches, Further Reading 3 (**Carvalho Leite** *et al.*, 2017) has a substantial recent review of methods in this area. For a more thorough recent review of network methods, see Further Reading 4 (**Pan** *et al.*, 2016), as well as a review of computational systems biology methods in Further Reading 5 (**Durmuş** *et al.*, 2015).

Databases for Host-Pathogen Interaction

The need for comprehensive, well-curated data sources is a persistent problem in the field of bioinformatics. In some areas this has been solved through large-scale collaborative efforts, such as with the RCSB Protein Data Bank for structural data of proteins (Berman *et al.*, 2000). However, in the field of host-pathogen interactions, there is still a lot of discussion and contention over good data sources, and several curated databases to choose from, varying in the type of data, the quality, and the level of detail in the curation. This section in conjunction with **Table 3**, aims to provide a survey of currently available sources of large datasets related to host-pathogen interactions. The IDs provided in brackets correspond to those in the ID column of **Table 3**.

The PATRIC (1), ViPR (2), EuPathDB (3), VectorBase (4), and IRD (5) databases are currently funded by the National Institute of Allergy and Infectious Diseases (NIAID). PATRIC is a bacterial pathogen database which is extremely comprehensive, and has available a number of tools such as genome annotation and comparative pathway analysis. ViPR is a viral pathogen database which is also quite comprehensive in terms of its scope. EuPathDB is a eukaryotic pathogen database, including fungal pathogens, protozoal pathogens, and other parasitic pathogens. VectorBase is a database of interactions between pathogens and invertebrate vectors, such as mosquitos. The Influenza Research Database (IRD) is a database focussed on interactions between influenza viruses and various hosts. While very specific, it is very comprehensive. VirHostNet 2.0 (6) is a virus-virus, virus-host, and host-host interaction network database. Other virus databases include VirusMentha (7), ViralZone (8), and ViTa (9). Specific databases for particular viruses also exist, such as the HIV-1, Human Protein

Interaction Database (14) and HIV Database Tools LANL (15) (for human immunodeficiency virus), HCV Database Tools LANL (16) (for hepatitis C virus), HFV Database Tools LANL (17) (for haemorrhagic fever virus or Ebola), and hpvPDB (18) (for human papilloma virus). Protein-protein interaction databases such as HPIDB 2.0 (10), PHI-base (12), PID (13), PHIDIAS (19), and PHISTO (20) all provide differing levels of detail, as well as a variety of search tools. More specific databases are available for certain uses, such as HoPaCI-DB (21) for investigations into *Pseodomonas aeruginosa* and *Coxiella*, and the VFDB (22) for virulence factors. Databases such as IntAct (23), BioGRID (24), and Mentha (25) are primarily useful for molecular interactions, and often have more protein-focussed or organism-specific equivalents, such as VirusMentha (7).

Applications

The successful design of drugs and therapeutics to treat infection relies heavily on the knowledge of how the host and pathogen interact. In times where antibiotic resistance is increasing, new strategies are required to treat and prevent infection. There are two main possible strategies for using host-pathogen interactions in drug design: targeting machinery used by the pathogen disable or reduce its virulence, and targeting machinery used by the host to bolster immune response. Vaccine design typically proceeds *via* the identification of target proteins from the pathogen which can be used as antigens by the immune system. By streamlining the process required to identify new protein targets and immune system mechanisms, drug and vaccine design can be sped up. Therefore, the prediction of key host-pathogen interactions is highly significant to clinical outcomes.

Recent trends in pharmacological design have focussed on both virulence factor disabling and host system boosting (Munguia and Nizet, 2017). The identification of key virulence factors allows for the design of potential inhibitors to neutralize their activity, and possibly render them vulnerable to attack by the immune system, reducing and possibly preventing serious infection. On the other side, therapies can be designed against host mechanisms that are implicated in infection. Strategies such as boosting phagocyte activity as well as reducing immune suppression by pathogens require significant knowledge of how the host and pathogen interact, but present promising leads that allow for the development of non-traditional antibiotics and other therapeutics. Host-pathogen interactions have been used recently in the design of antimalaria drugs *in silico* (Samant *et al.*, 2016), where protein targets were identified through the analysis of protein-protein interaction networks, and the targets subsequently tested for potential inhibitors.

Vaccine design proceeds by targeting the particular features of organisms that interact with the host. This requires knowledge of effector proteins and mechanisms, available through machine learning approaches as well as more traditional structural approaches, followed by experimental validation. Successful prediction of key effector proteins is essential for streamlining the vaccine design process (Zagursky *et al.*, 2003). In the case of viruses, there has been significant progress in recent years towards designing new and more successful vaccines. However, there is still much work to be done, such as in the case of HIV-1 (Haynes *et al.*, 2016). In the case of bacteria, there has also been significant work done in assembling methods to predict protein vaccine candidates (Jaiswal *et al.*, 2013). The study of host-pathogen interactions presents a promising avenue to continue to make progress in this area. Further perspectives can be found in Further Reading 6 (**Marston** *et al.*, 2014).

Discussion and Future Directions

While much progress has been made in recent years in the investigation of host-pathogen interactions, there are still a number of pressing issues that must be addressed. In broad terms, the main issues can be classed as a lack of detailed understanding of the relationship between pathogens, a lack of variety of different host-pathogen pairs under analysis, and the quality, type, and curation of data available to the community.

There is still uncertainty in how different or similar mechanisms of virulence are across pathogens of related strains, or even related types. As related strains may target different hosts, there can be significant differences between them in terms of how they invade, proliferate, and damage their hosts. However, in the case of *Mycobacteria*, there are distinct similarities between key mechanisms of virulence (Converse and Cox, 2005). More investigation is required into how similar such key pieces of machinery are across strains, species and types, and how possible similarities can be exploited to improve prediction of host-pathogen interactions in newly identified pathogens.

Previous studies from both biological and computational perspectives have focussed on a few key host-pathogen pairs. However, with the variety of infectious diseases already identified, broader and more numerous studies are required to fill in important gaps. Therefore, as the field progresses, it is important that more novel host-pathogen pairs are investigated in the detail that more prominent examples (such as HIV-1, *Mycobacterium tuberculosis*, *Yersinia pestis* and *Plasmodium falciparum*) are.

Computational models are only as good as the data on which they are built. Therefore, it is imperative that the data available for analysing host-pathogen interactions is of the highest possible quality, collected with detailed documentation, labelled and stored in easily accessible ways, and indexed or collated with other data to enable broad analysis across studies and organisms. With a wide variety of different databases available of varying quality which do not contain all current host-pathogen interaction data (as discussed in Section "Databases for Host-Pathogen Interaction" above), there are significant advances to be made in this area. Improvements in text mining methods are a promising avenue for filling in gaps in knowledge; however, they are still lacking in the accuracy required (Thieu *et al.*, 2012). There is also a lack of indexing, maintenance, and reviewing of current host-pathogen interaction databases, making efforts to find and use already-collected data more laborious than should be required. Therefore, future efforts to curate and review currently available databases, as well as identify areas which are not adequately serviced by current databases, would be extremely valuable.

Closing Remarks

Host-pathogen interactions are vital to our understanding of infectious disease, as well as its treatment and prevention. Through the investigation and analysis of the different stages of infection, the mechanisms by which pathogens invade and proliferate in their hosts can be elucidated. Bioinformatics has and will continue to play a large role in expanding our knowledge in this field, especially in the post-genomic era with the advent of extremely large datasets. Traditional alignment methods, structural analysis, and machine learning methods are all essential to furthering our understanding of host-pathogen interactions, and how such interactions can be exploited to treat disease. The development of novel drugs, vaccines and other therapeutics going into the future will be highly dependent on the knowledge gained from investigating host-pathogen interactions. There is still work to be done in collating and curating data in the field despite significant recent efforts, and this presents an ongoing challenge which must be addressed.

See also: Computational Systems Biology Applications. Extraction of Immune Epitope Information. Large Scale Ecological Modeling With Viruses: A Review. Mapping the Environmental Microbiome. Natural Language Processing Approaches in Bioinformatics

References

Ammari, M.G., Gresham, C.R., McCarthy, F.M., Naduri, B., 2016. HPIDB 2.0: A curated database for host-pathogen interactions. Database. 1–9. baw103.
Aranda, B., Achuthan, P., Alam-Faruque, Y., et al., 2010. The IntAct molecular interaction database in 2010. Nucleic Acids Res. 38, D525–D531.
Arnold, R., Brandmaier, S., Kleine, F., et al., 2009. Sequence-based prediction of type III secreted proteins. PLOS Pathog. 5 (4).
Aurrecoechea, C., Barreto, A., Basenko, E.Y., et al., 2017. EuPathDB: The eukaryotic pathogen genomics database resource. Nucleic Acids Res. 45, D581–D591.
Aurrecoechea, C., Barreto, A., Brestelli, J., et al., 2013. EuPathDB: The eukaryotic pathogen database. Nucleic Acids Res. 41, D684–D691.
Baigent, S.J., McCauley, J.W., 2003. Influenza type A in humans, mammals and birds: Determinants of virus virulence, host-range and interspecies transmission. Bioessays 25 (7). 657–671.
Balakrishnan, S., Tastan, O., Carbonell, J., Klein-Seetharaman, J., 2009. Alternative paths in HIV-1 targeted human signal transduction pathways. BMC Genom. 10 (Suppl. 3). S30.
Bandyopadhyay, S., Ray, S., Mukhopadhyay, A., et al., 2015. A review of in silico approaches for analysis and prediction of HIV-1-human protein-protein interactions. Brief. Bioinform. 16 (5). 830–851.
Becerra, A., Bucheli, V.A., Moreno, P.A., 2017. Prediction of virus-host protein-protein interactions mediated by short linear motifs. BMC Bioinform. 163 (18). 1–11.
Berman, H.M., Westbrook, J., Feng, Z., et al., 2000. The protein data bank. Nucleic Acids Res. 28 (1). 235–242.
Bhavsar, A.P., Guttman, J.A., Finlay, B.B., 2007. Manipulation of host-cell pathways by bacterial pathogens. Nature 449 (7164). 827–834.
Bleves, S., Dunger, I., Walter, M.C., et al., 2014. HoPaCI-DB: Host-*Pseudomonas* and *Coxiella* interaction database. Nucleic Acids Res. 42, D671–D676.
Brass, A.L., Dykxhoorn, D.M., Benita, Y., et al., 2008. Identification of host proteins required for HIV infection through a functional genomic screen. Science 319 (5865). 921–926.
Calderone, A., Castagnoli, L., Cesareni, G., 2013. Mentha: A resource for browsing integrated protein-interaction networks. Nat. Methods 10 (8). 690–691.
Calderone, A., Licata, L., Cesareni, G., 2015. VirusMentha: A new resource for virus-host protein interactions. Nucleic Acids Res. 43, D588–D592.
Calderwood, M.A., Venkatesan, K., Xing, L., et al., 2007. Epstein-Barr virus and virus human protein interaction maps. Proc. Natl. Acad. Sci. USA 104 (18). 7606–7611.
Casadevall, A., Pirofski, L.A., 1999. Host-pathogen interactions: Redefining the basic concepts of virulence and pathogenicity. Infect. Immun. 67 (8). 3703–3713.
Casadevall, A., Pirofski, L.A., 2000. Host-pathogen interactions: Basic concepts of microbial commensalism, colonization, infection, and disease. Infect. Immun. 68 (12). 6511–6518.
Casadevall, A., Pirofski, L.A., 2001. Host-pathogen interactions: The attributes of virulence. J. Infect. Dis. 184, 337–344.
Chatr-aryamontri, A., Oughtred, R., Boucher, L., et al., 2017. The BioGRID interaction database: 2017 update. Nucleic Acids Res. 45, D369–D379.
Chen, L., Yang, J., Yu, J., et al., 2005. VFDB: A reference database for bacterial virulence factors. Nucleic Acids Res. 33, D325–D328.
Chen, L., Zheng, D., Liu, B., Yang, J., Jin, Q., 2016. VFDB 2016: Hierarchical and refined dataset for big data analysis – 10 years on. Nucleic Acids Res. 44, D694–D697.
Chertova, E., Chertov, O., Coren, L.V., et al., 2006. Proteomic and biochemical analysis of purified human immunodeficiency virus type 1 produced from infected monocyte-derived macrophages. J. Virol. 80 (18). 9039–9052.
Cohen, F.S., 2016. How viruses invade cells. Biophys. J. 110 (5). 1028–1032.
Converse, S.E., Cox, J.S., 2005. A protein secretion pathway critical for *Mycobacterium tuberculosis* virulence is conserved and functional in *Mycobacterium smegmatis*. J. Bacteriol. 187 (4). 1238–1245.
Davey, N.E., Travé, G., Gibson, T.J., 2011. How viruses hijack cell regulation. Trends Biochem. Sci. 36 (3). 159–169.
Davis, F.P., Barkan, D.T., Eswar, N., McKerrow, J.H., Sali, A., 2007. Host-pathogen protein interactions predicted by comparative modelling. Protein Sci. 16, 2585–2596.
Doherty, C.P., 2007. Host-pathogen interactions: The role of iron. J. Nutr. 137 (5). 1341–1344.
Driscoll, T., Dyer, M.D., Murali, T.M., Sobral, B.W., 2009. PIG – The pathogen interaction gateway. Nucleic Acids Res. 37, 647–650.
Durmuş Tekir, S., Çakir, T., Ardiçs, E., et al., 2013. PHISTO: Pathogen-host interaction search tool. Bioinformatics 29 (10). 1357–1358.
Dyer, M.D., Murali, T.M., Sobral, B.W., 2007. Computational prediction of host-pathogen protein-protein interactions. Bioinformatics 23, i159–i166.
Dyer, M.D., Murali, T.M., Sobral, B.W., 2008. The landscape of human proteins interacting with viruses and other pathogens. PLOS Pathog. 4 (2).
d'Enfert, C., Ryter, A., Pugsley, A.P., 1987. Cloning and expression in *Escherichia coli* of the *Klebsiella pneumoniae* genes for production, surface localization and secretion of the lipoprotein pullulanase. EMBO J. 6 (12). 3531–3538.
Evans, P., Dampier, W., Ungar, L., Tozeren, A., 2009. Prediction of HIV-1 virus-host protein interactions using virus and host sequence motifs. BMC Med. Genom. 2 (27).
Fahey, M.E., Bennett, M.J., Mahon, C., et al., 2011. GPS-Prot: A web-based visualization platform for integrating host-pathogen interaction data. BMC Bioinform. 298 (12).
Fu, W., Sanders-Beer, B.E., Katz, K.S., et al., 2009. Human immunodeficiency virus type 1, human protein interaction database at NCBI. Nucleic Acids Res. 37, D417–D422.

Galán, J.E., Curtiss, R., 1989. Cloning and molecular characterization of genes whose products allow *Salmonella typhimurium* to penetrate tissue culture cells. Proc. Natl. Acad. Sci. USA 86, 6383–6387.

Ghosh, Z., Mallick, B., Chakrabarti, J., 2009. Cellular versus viral microRNAs in host-virus interaction. Nucleic Acids Res. 37 (4). 1035–1048.

Giraldo-Calderón, G.I., Emrich, S.J., MacCallum, R.M., et al., 2015. VectorBase: An updated bioinformatics resource for invertebrate vectors and other organisms related with human diseases. Nucleic Acids Res. 43, D707–D713.

Guirimand, T., Delmotte, S., Navratil, V., 2015. VirHostNet 2.0: Surfing on the web of virus/host molecular interactions data. Nucleic Acids Res. 43, D583–D587.

Haynes, B.F., Shaw, G.M., Korber, B., et al., 2016. HIV-host interactions: Implications for vaccine design. Cell Host Microbe 19 (3). 292–303.

Hooper, L.V., Gordon, J.I., 2001. Glycans as legislators of host-microbial interactions: Spanning the spectrum from symbiosis to pathogenicity. Glycobiology 11 (2). 1R–10R.

Hsu, P.W., Lin, L., Hsu, S., Hsu, J.B., Huang, H., 2007. ViTa: Prediction of host microRNAs targets on viruses. Nucleic Acids Res. 35, D381–D385.

Hulo, C., de Castro, E., Masson, P., et al., 2011. ViralZone: A knowledge resource to understand virus diversity. Nucleic Acids Res. 39, D576–D582.

Jaiswal, V., Chanumolu, S.K., Gupta, A., Chauhan, R.S., Rout, C., 2013. Jenner-predict server: Prediction of protein vaccine candidates (PVCs) in bacteria based on host-pathogen interactions. BMC Bioinform. 211 (14).

Kelsall, B.L., Biron, C.A., Sharma, O., Kaye, P.M., 2002. Dendritic cells at the host-pathogen interface. Nat. Immunol. 3, 699–702.

Kim, J.K., Kim, T.S., Basu, J., Jo, E.K., 2017. MicroRNA in innate immunity and autophagy during mycobacterium infection. Cell. Microbiol. 19, e12687.

König, R., Stertz, S., Zhou, Y., et al., 2010. Human host factors required for influenza virus replication. Nature 463 (7282). 813–817.

König, R., Zhou, Y., Elleder, D., et al., 2008. Global analysis of host-pathogen interactions that regulate early-stage HIV-1 replication. Cell 135, 49–60.

Krishnadev, O., Srinivasan, N., 2008. A data integration approach to predict host-pathogen protein-protein interactions: Application to recognize protein interactions between human and a malarial parasite. In Silico Biol. 8 (3). 235–250.

Kshirsagar, M., Carbonell, J., Klein-Seetharaman, J., 2012. Techniques to cope with missing data in host-pathogen protein interaction prediction. Bioinformatics 28 (18). i466–i472.

Kshirsagar, M., Carbonell, J., Klein-Seetharaman, J., 2013. Multi-task learning for host-pathogen protein interactions. Bioinformatics 29 (13). i217–i226.

Kuldau, G.A., De Vos, G., Owen, J., McCaffrey, G., Zambryski, P., 1990. The *virB* operon of *Agrobacterium tumefaciens* pTiC58 encodes 11 open reading frames. Mol. Gen. Genet. 221, 256–266.

Kumar, S., Jena, L., Daf, S., et al., 2013. hpvPDB: An online proteome reserve for human papillomavirus. Genom. Inform. 11 (4). 289–291.

Kumar, R., Naduri, B., 2010a. HPIDB – A unified resource for host-pathogen interactions. BMC Bioinform. 11, 1–6.

Kumar, R., Nanduri, B., 2010b. HPIDB – A unified resource for host-pathogen interactions. BMC Bioinform. 11 (Su). S16.

Kurz, C.L., Ewbank, J.J., 2000. *Caenorhabditis elegans* for the study of host-pathogen interactions. Trends Microbiol. 8 (3). 142–144.

Meijer, A.H., Spaink, H.P., 2011. Host-pathogen interactions made transparent with the zebrafish model. Curr. Drug Targets 12, 1000–1017.

Methot, P.O., Alizon, S., 2014. What is a pathogen? Toward a process view of host-parasite interactions. Virulence 8 (5). 775–785.

Mougous, J.D., Cuff, M.E., Raunser, S., et al., 2006. A virulence locus of *Pseudomonas aeruginosa* encodes a protein secretion apparatus. Science 312 (5779). 1526–1530.

Munguia, J., Nizet, V., 2017. Pharmacological targeting of the host-pathogen interaction: Alternatives to classical antibiotics to combat drug-resistant superbugs. Trends Pharmacol. Sci. 38 (5). 473–488.

Nau, G.J., Richmond, J.F.L., Schlesinger, A., et al., 2002. Human macrophage activation programs induced by bacterial pathogens. Proc. Natl. Acad. Sci. USA 99 (3). 1503–1508.

Navratil, V., de Chassey, B., Meyniel, L., et al., 2009. VirHostNet: A knowledge base for the management and the analysis of proteome-wide virus-host interaction networks. Nucleic Acids Res. 37, D661–D668.

Pickett, B.E., Sadat, E.L., Zhang, Y., et al., 2012. ViPR: An open bioinformatics database and analysis resource for virology research. Nucleic Acids Res. 40, D593–D598.

Pinney, J.W., Dickerson, J.E., Fu, W., et al., 2009. HIV-host interactions: a map of viral perturbation of the host system. AIDS 23 (5). 549–554.

Pohlner, J., Halter, R., Beyreuther, K., Meyer, T.F., 1987. Gene structure and extracellular secretion of *Neisseria gonorrhoeae* IgA protease. Nature 325, 458–462.

Pukatzki, S., Ma, A.T., Sturtevant, D., et al., 2006. Identification of a conserved bacterial protein secretion system in *Vibrio cholerae* using the *Dictyostelium* host model system. Proc. Natl. Acad. Sci. 103 (5). 1528–1533.

Qi, Y., Tastan, O., Carbonell, J.G., et al., 2010. Semi-supervised multi-task learning for prediction interactions between HIV-1 and human proteins. Bioinform. 26, i645–i652.

Raghunathan, A., Reed, J., Shin, S., Palsson, B., Daefler, S., 2009. Constraint-based analysis of metabolic capacity of *Salmonella typhimurium* during host-pathogen interaction. BMC Syst. Biol. 3 (1).

Rahman, M.M., McFadden, G., 2011. Modulation of NF-κB signalling by microbial pathogens. Nat. Rev. Microbiol. 9 (4). 291–306.

Rappoport, N., Linial, M., 2012. Viral proteins acquired from a host converge to simplified domain architectures. PLOS Comput. Biol. 8 (2).

Samant, M., Chadha, N., Tiwari, A.K., et al., 2016. In silico designing and analysis of inhibitors against target protein identified through host-pathogen interactions in malaria. Int. J. Med. Chem. 2016, 2741038.

Scaria, V., Hariharan, M., Pillai, B., Maiti, S., Brahmachari, S.K., 2007. Host-virus genome interactions: Macro roles for microRNAs. Cell. Microbiol. 9 (12). 2784–2794.

Schaefer, C.F., Anthony, K., Krupa, S., et al., 2009. PID: The pathway interaction database. Nucleic Acids Res. 37, D674–D679.

Stanley, S.A., Raghavan, S., Hwang, W.W., et al., 2003. Acute infection and macrophage subversion by Mycobacterium tuberculosis require a specialized secretion system. Proc. Natl. Acad. Sci. USA. 100 (22). 13001–13006.

Talaat, A.M., Lyons, R., Howard, S.T., Johnston, S.A., 2004. The temporal expression profile of *Mycobacterium tuberculosis* infection in mice. Proc. Natl. Acad. Sci. USA 101 (13). 4602–4607.

Tastan, O., Qi, Y., Carbonell, J.G., Klein-Seetharaman, J., 2009. Prediction of interactions between HIV-1 and human proteins by information integration. Pac. Symp. Biocomput. 2009, 516–527.

Tato, C.M., Hunter, C.A., 2002. Host-pathogen interactions: Subversion and utilization of the NF-κB pathway during infection. Infect. Immun. 70 (7). 3311–3317.

Thieu, T., Joshi, S., Warren, S., Korkin, D., 2012. Literature mining of host-pathogen interactions: Comparing feature-based supervised learning and language-based approaches. Bioinformatics 28 (6). 1357–1358.

Tobin, D.M., May, R.C., Wheeler, R.T., 2012. Zebrafish: A see-through host and fluorescent toolbox to probe host-pathogen interaction. PLOS Pathog. 8 (1).

Urban, M., Cuzick, A., Rutherford, K., et al., 2017. PHI-base: A new interface and further additions for the multi-species pathogen-host interactions database. Nucleic Acids Res. 45, D604–D610.

Vergne, I., Singh, S., Roberts, E., et al., 2006. Autophagy in immune defense against *Mycobacterium tuberculosis*. Autophagy 2 (3). 175–178.

Via, A., Uyar, B., Brun, C., Zanzoni, A., 2015. How pathogens use linear motifs to perturb host cell networks. Trends Biochem. Sci. 40 (1). 36–48.

Vodovar, N., Acosta, C., Lemaitre, B., Boccard, F., 2004. *Drosophila*: A polyvalent model to decipher host-pathogen interactions. Trends Microbiol. 12 (5). 235–242.

Wang, Y., Zhang, Q., Sun, M., Guo, D., 2011. High-accuracy prediction of bacterial type III secreted effectors based on position-specific amino acid composition profiles. Bioinformatics 27 (6). 777–784.

Wattam, A.R., Abraham, D., Dalay, O., et al., 2014. PATRIC, the bacterial bioinformatics database and analysis resource. Nucleic Acids Res. 42, 581–591.

Weiberg, A., Wang, M., Lin, F., et al., 2013. Fungal small RNAs suppress plant immunity by hijacking host RNA interference pathways. Science 342 (6154). 118–123.

Welch, R.A., Dellinger, E.P., Minshew, B., Falkow, S., 1981. Haemolysin contributes to virulence of extra-intestinal *E. coli* infections. Nature 294, 665–667.

Winnenberg, R., Baldwin, T.K., Urban, M., et al., 2006. PHI-base: A new database for pathogen-host interactions. Nucleic Acids Res. 34, D459–D464.

Worbs, T., Hammerschmidt, S.I., Förster, R., 2017. Dendritic cell migration in health and disease. Nat. Rev. Immunol. 17, 30–48.

Wuchty, S., 2011. Computational prediction of host-parasite protein interactions between *P. falciparum* and *H. sapiens*. PLOS ONE 6 (11).

Xiang, Z., Tian, Y., He, Y., 2007. PHIDIAS: A pathogen-host interaction data integration and analysis system. Genome Biol. 8 (7). R150.

Yang, W., Yan, L., Wu, C., Zhao, X., Tang, J., 2014. Fungal invasion of epithelial cells. Microbiol. Res. 169, 803–810.

Zagursky, R.J., Olmsted, S.B., Russell, D.P., Wooters, J.L., 2003. Bioinformatics: How it is being used to identify bacterial vaccine candidates. Expert Rev. Vaccines 2 (3). 417–436.

Zhang, Y., Aevermann, B.D., Anderson, T.K., et al., 2017. Influenza Research Database: An integrated bioinformatics resource for influenza virus research. Nucleic Acids Res. 45, D466–D474.

Further Reading

Carvalho Leite, D.M., Brochet, X., Resch, G., et al., 2017. Computational prediction of host-pathogen interactions through omics data analysis and machine learning. In: Rojas, I., Ortuño, F. (Eds.), Bioinformatics and Biomedical Engineering. IWBBIO 2017. Lecture Notes in Computer Science 10209. Springer.

Costa, T.R.D., Felisberto-Rodrigues, C., Meir, A., et al., 2015. Secretion systems in Gram-negative bacteria: Structural and mechanistic insights. Nat. Rev. Microbiol. 13, 343–359.

Durmuş, S., Çakir, T., Özgür, A., Guthke, R., 2015. A review on computational systems biology of pathogen-host interactions. Front. Microbiol. 6, 235.

Mariano, R., Wuchty, S., 2017. Structure-based prediction of host-pathogen protein interactions. Curr. Opin. Struct. Biol. 44, 119–124.

Marston, H.D., Folkers, G.K., Morens, D.M., Fauci, A.S., 2014. Emerging viral diseases: Confronting threats with new technologies. Sci. Transl. Med. 6 (253). 253ps10.

Pan, A., Lahiri, C., Rajendiran, A., Shanmugham, B., 2016. Computational analysis of protein interaction networks for infectious diseases. Brief. Bioinform. 17 (3). 517–526.

Biographical Sketch

Dean Southwood is a PhD student in the Department of Molecular Sciences at Macquarie University. His background is in theoretical quantum physics, quantum computation, and bioinformatics. His current research interests involve determining novel biomarkers for cancer and disease using machine learning methods.

Shoba Ranganathan holds a Chair in Bioinformatics at Macquarie University since 2004. She has held research and academic positions in India, USA, Singapore and Australia as well as a consultancy in industry. Shoba's research addresses several key areas of bioinformatics to understand biological systems using computational approaches. Her group has achieved both experience and expertise in different aspects of computational biology, ranging from metabolites and small molecules to biochemical networks, pathway analysis and computational systems biology. She has authored as well as edited several books in as well as contributed several articles to Springer's Encyclopedia of Systems Biology. She is currently the Editor-in-Chief of Elsevier's Encyclopedia of Bioinformatics and Computational Biology as well as the Bioinformatics Section Editor for Elsevier's Reference Module in Life Sciences.

Computational Pipelines and Workflows in Bioinformatics

Yosvany López, Genesis Healthcare Co., Tokyo, Japan
Piotr J Kamola, RIKEN Center for Integrative Medical Sciences, Yokohama, Japan and Japan Science and Technology Agency, Tokyo, Japan
Ronesh Sharma, University of the South Pacific, Suva, Fiji and Fiji National University, Suva, Fiji
Daichi Shigemizu, RIKEN Center for Integrative Medical Sciences, Yokohama, Japan; Japan Science and Technology Agency, Tokyo, Japan; RIKEN Cluster for Science and Technology Hub, Yokohama, Japan; National Center for Geriatrics and Gerontology, Obu, Japan; and Tokyo Medical and Dental University, Tokyo, Japan
Tatsuhiko Tsunoda, RIKEN Center for Integrative Medical Sciences, Yokohama, Japan; Japan Science and Technology Agency, Tokyo, Japan; and Tokyo Medical and Dental University, Tokyo, Japan
Alok Sharma, RIKEN Center for Integrative Medical Sciences, Yokohama, Japan; University of the South Pacific, Suva, Fiji; and Griffith University, Brisbane, QLD, Australia

Introduction

The research field of bioinformatics is gaining momentum due to its role in the examination of huge volumes of biological data. Nowadays, technological advancements in sequencer and microscope technology have opened many novel and interesting avenues to study organisms at the molecular level. These advances should be accompanied by efficient computational tools and pipelines, geared towards processing and analysis of the data. This combination will allow for more accurate quantification of molecular interaction, and lead to better understanding of the underlying mechanisms. In the field of molecular biology, next-generation sequencing (NGS) technology is playing a key role already. For instance, studies aimed at assessing DNA–protein interactions often make use of chromatin immunoprecipitation-sequencing (ChIP-seq) data, whereas those focused on trying to understand the genetics behind rare diseases or cancers take advantage of whole genome (WGS) or whole exome sequencing (WES) data. Studies that focus on profiling coding and noncoding RNA on a larger scale have the choice of DNA-chip and RNA-sequencing (RNA-seq) technologies. Complex cellular structures can be studied with microscopes that are capable of generating high-quality images. Given the above circumstances, computational algorithms and methodologies are necessary to face such challenges (Roy *et al.*, 2016, 2018; Metzker, 2010). Bioinformatics pipelines combine a set of software tools, each designed to deal with a specific task, to take full advantage of the biological information.

In this article, we discuss the computational pipelines and workflows used for analyzing a wide range of sequencing and biomedical image information. Accordingly, it is hereafter divided into five sections. Section "Genome Analysis" covers genome analysis pipelines, especially tools for dealing with ChIP-seq and genomic variation. Section "Transcriptome Analysis" describes transcriptome strategies, including differential expression analysis, pathway and network approaches, and machine learning (ML) methods for sample subclassification and biomarker discovery. Section "Workflows in Proteomics" focuses on proteomics, specifically on molecular recognition of features in intrinsically disordered proteins (IDPs). Section "Bioimage Analysis Pipelines" briefly introduces the standard workflow for processing bioimages from cellular structures, while Section "Conclusions" highlights the challenges and future directions.

Genome Analysis

The function of molecular structures is ultimately encoded in the genome sequence, thereby bioinformatics pipelines designed for its analysis are of utmost importance. In this section, we present the workflow and tools available for effectively analyzing ChIP-seq and genomic variation data.

ChIP-Seq Pipeline

A great number of studies have been currently focusing on deciphering the molecular consequences of DNA–protein interactions. In this case, NGS data has played a key role because it allows us to sequence the DNA sequence around binding sites. Subsection "ChIP-Seq Pipeline" introduces the standard workflow (**Fig. 1**) used by many laboratories for such analyses.

Alignment

Because read quality is often affected by artifacts such as adapter contamination and base calling errors, the quality check of reads is sometimes the first procedure before mapping the raw reads to a reference genome. It is here where biases or sequencing errors are identified and low-quality reads are filtered out. Given its flexibility and applicability to many sequencing platforms, the software FastQC (Babraham-Bioinformatics, 2018) is frequently utilized. A more detailed explanation and additional tools can be found in Pabinger *et al.* (2014).

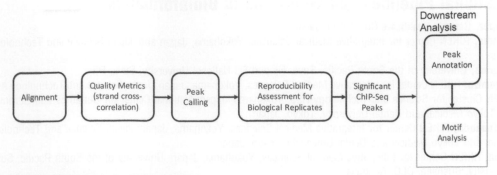

Fig. 1   Standard workflow for the analysis of ChIP-seq data.

After conducting the above filtering, high-quality reads are aligned to the corresponding reference genome using aligners such as Bowtie2 (Langmead and Salzberg, 2012), SOAP (Li et al., 2009b), BWA (Li and Durbin, 2009) and MAQ (Li et al., 2008). It is worth noting that unlike transcriptome analysis pipelines, aligners capable of detecting splice sites are not required whatsoever. The alignment results (the number of uniquely mapped reads) should be carefully checked to validate the success of the mapping procedure.

Quality metrics
When processing ChIP-seq data, the assessment of immunoprecipitation enrichment, sequencing depth or fragment-size selection is a must. This is often referred to as the signal-to-noise ratio and assessed with metrics like strand cross-correlation (Landt et al., 2012) or immunoprecipitation enrichment estimation (Landt et al., 2012). Although the package CHANCE (Diaz et al., 2012) is widely utilized, current peak callers such as MACS (Zhang et al., 2008) already include strand cross-correlation analysis.

Peak calling
Peak calling is one of the most important steps in a ChIP-seq analysis pipeline. It is here where bound DNA regions are detected. Of note, if the improvement of specificity is prioritized, duplicate reads should be removed before peak calling. Moreover, the success of this step will depend on the peak caller and the type of protein being analyzed. For the purpose of analysis, DNA-binding proteins (DBPs) are divided into three groups depending on their binding signals: point-source DBPs, broadly enriched DBPs, and DBPs with mixed characteristics.

Point-source DBPs
These proteins are the most common and therefore many peak callers have been designed to deal with their signals. For instance, peak callers like MACS (Zhang et al., 2008) and SPP (Kharchenko et al., 2008) are able to accurately detect the size of the genomic gap between reads aligned to plus and minus strands. Other software such as BEADS (Cheung et al., 2011) use background models from control samples or GC content for reducing noise. To assess enriched peaks, software such as MACS (Zhang et al., 2008) and CisGenome (Jiang et al., 2010), which rely on statistical distributions, or BayesPeak (Spyrou et al., 2009) and HPeak (Qin et al., 2010), which implement hidden Markov models, are often utilized.

Broadly enriched DBPs
These proteins are usually involved in epigenetic regulation. For their analysis, peak callers such as SICER (Xu et al., 2014) and ZINBA (Rashid et al., 2011) can be utilized to detect broad regions, whereas others such as MACS (Zhang et al., 2008), PeakRanger (Feng et al., 2011), and SPP (Kharchenko et al., 2008) can be used as long as their bandwidth is increased and their peak cut-off decreased.

DBPs with mixed signals
For analyzing molecules with mixed characteristics, for example the RNA Polymerase II, peak callers such as MACS (Zhang et al., 2008), ZINBA (Rashid et al., 2011), and PeakRanger (Feng et al., 2011) can be employed.

Assessment of reproducibility
Because the quality of detected peaks could be affected by the peak caller, sequencing depth, or the number of binding sites, pipelines should always include an assessment of reproducibility. This procedure is intended to check whether the peaks are really reproducible, and should comprise at least two replicates of the same experiment. To do this, it is advisable to filter out those regions with high ChIP signals and then compute the Pearson correlation coefficient of mapped reads at genomic positions. The consistency of peak sets detected in biological replicates is evaluated with the irreproducible discovery rate, and those peaks passing a specific cut-off are finally retrieved. This assessment is often conducted as described in Li et al. (2011).

Differential binding analysis

A typical ChIP-seq experiment aims to detect binding differences between biological conditions. Current studies follow two strategies: quantitative and qualitative. The quantitative approach takes into consideration the differential binding between conditions by using the number of reads or the density of reads in peaks. For this, tools such as DBChIP (Liang and Keleş, 2012), which relies on read counts or MAnorm (Shao *et al.*, 2012), which uses read densities, can be utilized. The qualitative approach considers overlapping peaks and should only be regarded for exploration purposes. It is important to point out that reproducible peaks should be computed per condition before regarding one of the above strategies.

Downstream analysis

This step comprises important tasks such as peak annotation and motif analysis. The detection of peaks is often not the ultimate goal, but it is followed by the discovery of functional genomic regions. To do this, the peaks should be first formatted in BED or GFF files so that they can be easily analyzed with a genome browser, or annotated with in-house scripts. Current packages such as BEDTools (Quinlan and Hall, 2010) include functions for annotation purposes and calculate the genomic distance of each peak to relevant genomic features. Other libraries like ChIPpeakAnno (Zhu *et al.*, 2010) can be further used for associating binding sites with gene expression activity. On the other hand, motif analysis could also help to identify those genomic sites bound by a specific regulatory protein, thereby facilitating the validation of the ChIP experiment. To detect motif sequences, the genomic regions of the detected peaks are analyzed with motif-discovery software. These algorithms complement each other so that it is advisable to consider different methods. For instance, algorithms such as MEME-ChIP (Machanick and Bailey, 2011) and peak-motifs (Thomas-Chollier *et al.*, 2012) are often employed. Detailed information on motif analysis can be found in Zambelli *et al.* (2013).

Mutation and Genomic Variation

The low cost of NGS technology has made possible international collaborations such as the 1000 Genomes (Genomes Project *et al.*, 2015) and HapMap (International Hapmap Consortium, 2005) Projects. These efforts have provided detailed catalogs of human genetic variation, which are of vital importance to identify disease-associated variants. Consequently, recent studies have aimed at pinpointing genetic risk factors for common diseases, including rheumatoid arthritis and type 2 diabetes, cancers, and Mendelian diseases such as long QT syndrome and Huntington's disease. Because the accurate detection of variants proves critical for clinical treatments and novel drugs, the main challenges are no longer in the sequencing technology but in the development of suitable bioinformatics pipelines. This section addresses two impacted areas: genome-wide association studies (GWAS), and whole genome and exome analysis.

Genome-wide association studies

The genetics behind complex diseases has been long studied by focusing on disease-related genes. However, the massive amounts of genotype data have paved the way for broader approaches like GWAS, which regard linkage disequilibrium at the population level. GWAS has proven absolutely necessary for identifying the genetic risk factors for common diseases (Ozaki *et al.*, 2002; Newton-Cheh *et al.*, 2009), and investigating associations between single nucleotide polymorphisms (SNPs) from case/control studies. The most common tool for GWAS analysis is PLINK (Purcell *et al.*, 2007). PLINK is an open-source and freely available software, which also provides quality controls of the data. It requires two standard formats: PED and MAP files, though binary files such as BED, BIM, and FAM are acceptable as well. The PED file is a space or tab delimited file, composed of a family identifier, individual identifier, father and mother identifiers, gender, phenotype, and genotypes. Of note, when creating a PED file, strand orientation should be checked for allele calls (i.e., forward or reverse complement). The TOP/BOT strand and A/B allele coding, developed by Illumina, along with the database of genetic variation dbSNP (Sherry *et al.*, 2001) are widely used for uniformly designating SNP entries. The MAP file consists of a chromosome, identifier, genetic distance, and physical position for each marker. As for the experimental dataset, it should pass different quality checks in which the samples and markers are carefully examined. The samples should be checked for (1) sex inconsistencies (–check-sex[a]), (2) inbreeding coefficient (–het[a] 0.1), (3) genotype missingness (–missing[a] 0.05), (4) kinship coefficient (–genome[a] 0.2), and (5) population stratification. Similarly, the markers should be checked for (1) genotyping efficiency or call rate (–geno[a] 0.99), (2) minor allele frequency (–freq[a] 0.01), and (3) Hardy–Weinberg equilibrium (–hwe[a] 0.001). The remaining dataset can now be used for association analysis (–assoc[a]) whose significance cut-off should be set at $p < 5 \times 10^{-8}$. These association results can be further visualized with Q-Q and Manhattan plots included in the R package *qqman*.

Often, the number of markers in an experimental dataset is not enough for accurate analysis, limiting the power and resolution of the GWAS strategy. To overcome this limitation, genotype imputation at ungenotyped loci is strongly recommended. The most common imputation software include IMPUTE2 (Marchini *et al.*, 2007), BEAGLE (Browning and Browning, 2009), and minimac (Neumann *et al.*, 2010). Of note, reference panels from the HapMap (International Hapmap Consortium, 2005) or 1000 Genomes (Genomes Project *et al.*, 2015) Projects should be used.

Thus far, we have described a typical SNP-based association analysis. However, gene-based association approaches can sometimes turn out effective. These statistical methods are classified into three categories: (1) the burden test (Li and Leal, 2008; Madsen and Browning, 2009; Morgenthaler and Thilly, 2007; Price *et al.*, 2010), (2) the variance component test (Wu *et al.*, 2011),

---

[a]PLINK parameter

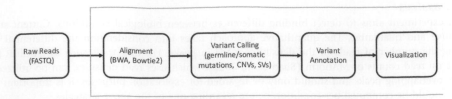

Fig. 2 Standard workflow for whole genome/exome sequencing data analysis.

and (3) the combination methods (Lee *et al.*, 2012). Recently, a method called SMR, which integrates summary-level data of GWAS and expression quantitative trait locus, was developed (Zhu *et al.*, 2016). Additional examples of risk prediction models for several diseases, which regarded disease-associated genes, can be found in Imamura *et al.* (2013); Shigemizu *et al.* (2014).

Genome and exome analysis pipelines

For rare Mendelian diseases, NGS technology (Metzker, 2010; Rusk and Kiermer, 2008) has made WGS and WES possible at an individual level. Extensive studies have revised the pipelines aimed to detect genetic variations by analyzing NGS data (Hwang *et al.*, 2015; Pabinger *et al.*, 2014). A standard pipeline consists of five main steps: quality check of raw reads, alignment to a reference genome, variant identification, variant annotation, and visualization (**Fig. 2**). The first two steps are discussed in Section "Alignment" so that we will focus on the remaining steps.

Variant identification

The identification of genomic variants is the main step of a variant detection pipeline. This step is intended to detect genomic variations between biological samples. Most of the available software require the aligned reads in BAM format and sorted by genomic coordinates. Both requirements can be easily achieved with SAMtools (Li *et al.*, 2009a).

The current variant identification tools can be used for detecting (1) germline mutations, (2) somatic mutations, (3) copy number variations (CNVs), and (4) structural variations (SVs). Among the variant callers for discovering germline mutations are the Genome Analysis Tool Kit (GATK) HaplotypeCaller (McKenna *et al.*, 2010), SAMtools (Li *et al.*, 2009a) and VarScan 2 (Koboldt *et al.*, 2012). The GATK includes a statistical model based on Bayesian genotype likelihood for computing genotypes and allele frequencies. Nevertheless, one disadvantage is that it produces many false positives which have to be filtered for downstream analysis (McKenna *et al.*, 2010). SAMtools can be easily integrated into one single pipeline because of its additional functions for aligning reads, as well as sorting and indexing alignment results (Li *et al.*, 2009a). VarScan 2 implements heuristic and statistical approaches for detecting single nucleotide variants, indels, somatic mutations, and copy number alterations between cancer and control samples (Koboldt *et al.*, 2012). SAMtools and VarScan 2, along with SomaticSniper (Larson *et al.*, 2012) can be also employed for identifying somatic mutations. SomaticSniper statistically compares the genotype likelihoods of cancer and control samples, which could turn out useful for cancer-related studies (Larson *et al.*, 2012). Tools such as CNVnator (Abyzov *et al.*, 2011) and ExomeCNV (Sathirapongsasuti *et al.*, 2011) were mainly developed for identifying CNVs. CNVnator combines the mean-shift approach with multiple-bandwidth partitioning and GC correction for detecting atypical CNVs like *de novo* and multiallelic events. However, it often misses CNVs generated by retrotransposable elements (Abyzov *et al.*, 2011). On the other hand, ExomeCNV was specifically created for identifying loss of heterozygosity in addition to CNVs. This software is able to correctly discover small indels due to the inclusion of B-allele frequencies and depth-of-coverage (Sathirapongsasuti *et al.*, 2011). For detecting SVs such as inversions, translocations, or large indels, the software CLEVER is still widely utilized because of its efficient use of internal segment sizes (Marschall *et al.*, 2012).

According to one study that revised several pipelines for whole exome analysis, the combined use of the aligner BWA and SAMtools, or of any aligner with Freebayes, turns out suitable for SNP calling. This study also claims the software GATK (HaplotypeCaller) as the best variant caller for indels, and Freebayes as the most convenient tool when low-quality variants are previously filtered out (Hwang *et al.*, 2015).

Variant annotation

After identifying variants, the detected variants are annotated to understand their biological implications. This step aims to filter out irrelevant variants and retrieve those disease-related ones. Although the current tools are able to annotate SNPs and indels, the annotation of CNVs has not been fully implemented. The available software includes ANNOVAR (Wang *et al.*, 2010), Vcfanno (Pedersen *et al.*, 2016), and VarMatch (Sun and Medvedev, 2017). ANNOVAR can be utilized for annotating SNVs and indels. It analyzes the function of those genes harboring variants, detects variants in conserved genomic stretches, and predicts cytogenetic bands (Wang *et al.*, 2010). Vcfanno includes a "chromosome sweeping" approach, making possible the annotation of a large number of variants (Pedersen *et al.*, 2016). VarMatch can be used when dealing with dense areas of variants or low complexity genomic regions. It implements an optimization strategy known as edit distance, which contributes to improving robustness (Sun and Medvedev, 2017). Furthermore, the detected variants should be matched against those in mutation databases such as dbSNP (Sherry *et al.*, 2001) or COSMIC (Forbes *et al.*, 2008). Consequently, the variants could be classified as deleterious or accepted variants.

Visualization

Variant visualization is also an essential step because it offers better interpretations of the experiment. There are many genome browsers that facilitate the visualization of genomic regions. Some are useful for visualization and annotation, for example, ABrowse (Kong *et al.*, 2012), Apollo (Lee *et al.*, 2013), Ensembl (Ruffier *et al.*, 2017), and GenomeView (Abeel *et al.*, 2012). Others are specifically designed for visualization, including BamView (Carver *et al.*, 2013), JBrowse (Buels *et al.*, 2016), and MapView (Bao *et al.*, 2009). An extensive review of visualization tools can be found in Pabinger *et al.* (2014).

Transcriptome Analysis

Alterations at the genome level, which can be detected using DNA-sequencing approaches such as WGS, are responsible for a wide range of adverse health phenotypes. Such diseases can often be linked to a single mutation within a crucial gene or accumulation of changes that, when combined, can lead to cancer or age-related illnesses (Podolskiy *et al.*, 2016). However, most complex biological mechanisms arise through the interplay of hundreds of interactome elements, with the disease often being a result of perturbation to those systems and networks (Vidal *et al.*, 2011). The most accessible genomic layer, in terms of easiness of profiling and basic examination, is the transcriptome. A global view of gene activity, which takes place at the RNA level, provides means to perform a wide variety of studies. This includes analysis of cellular functions, identification of predictive biomarkers and diseases subtypes, or pathway and network-oriented studies that can more comprehensively explain changes in the state of biological systems (Brodie *et al.*, 2014). Here we will present several computational approaches to study the transcriptome, and avenues to explore when linking such profiles to actionable results. Emphasis will be placed on popular, open-source tools and libraries and on the fundamentals, which can be easily built upon and extended.

Profiling Platforms

The two most widespread platforms for studying global gene changes are NGS and DNA microarrays. The former, a high-throughput approach that superseded Sanger sequencing, relies on "reading" millions of small RNA fragments in parallel. As each RNA transcript is represented by multiple overlapping fragments, it is possible to combine the sequence pieces together by mapping them to a specie-specific reference (Behjati and Tarpey, 2013). DNA microarray (or DNA-chip) technology, on the other hand, uses a collection of DNA probes attached to a solid surface, with each oligonucleotide probe cluster designed to match a specific short region from a gene of interest. Binding a complementary sequence produces a signal (generated by a fluorophore-labeled antibody), whose strength is used to quantify the abundance of the corresponding target gene (Shalon *et al.*, 1996). While the choice between platforms is often based on personal preference and technical capabilities available within a given group, there are several factors that should be considered when making the decision. Microarrays contain a set of predefined target genes, which makes the data processing simple and straightforward. The methodology has matured to a point where the process can be accomplished using a single package – an overview using a representative tool is provided in Section "DNA-Chip Data Processing." While convenient, the technology does not offer as much flexibility as NGS alternatives (Hurd and Nelson, 2009). If a project would benefit from detecting novel or rare transcripts, fusion genes, or splice variant analysis, or requires higher confidence in the findings (which can be achieved by increasing the sequencing depth of coverage), NGS methods offer an advantage. The analysis of RNA-seq data does, however, require some understanding of the process on the molecular level, as well as familiarity with additional software tools. Each step of the process is described in Section "RNA-Seq Data Processing," and a graphical overview of the whole transcriptome section is shown in **Fig. 3**.

DNA-Chip Data Processing

In this section, we will provide a basic overview of initial DNA microarray data processing using limma package (Ritchie *et al.*, 2015) within R software environment. While these steps can be accomplished using manufacturer provided software solutions, limma offers more built-in functionalities and can be easily integrated with other bioinformatics tools. Furthermore, a similar methodology can be utilized for other types of arrays, such as those profiling protein expression levels. R is a statistical computing environment that is widely used for exploratory data analytics and visualization. It can be installed on any operating systems by following the instructions found on the project's website (see "Relevant Websites" section). Subsequently, a wide range of genomic packages can be downloaded from Bioconductor, a repository for high-throughput genomic analysis tools (see "Relevant Websites" section).

The initial chip processing step is automatically performed by the image analysis software, where the TIFF scan of the array is translated into a list of intensities for each of the small "spots" (i.e., areas with multiple copies of a unique DNA probe). limma provides a read function that loads and converts data (together with sample annotation) from a wide range of microarray formats. Probe annotation, usually stored in GenePix Array List (GAL) format, should be provided separately, in case it is not included in the output files.

Issues with the sample quality can be introduced at any stage of preparation, from low-quality biological material to problems during scanning. It is thus important to detect such problems early during analysis. There are two common quality control

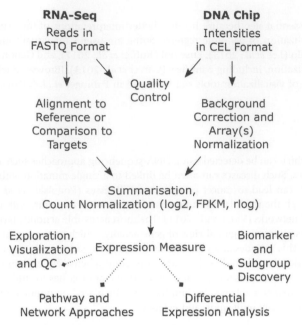

Fig. 3　Graphical overview of the standard pipeline for transcriptome data analysis.

strategies that are applicable to both individual spots within arrays (much higher complexity) and to cross-array comparison – assigning quality weights that are used in a downstream analysis or removing problematic cases (Kauffmann and Huber, 2010). limma has built-in functions to cover the former, which calculate spot weight quality as well as array variance (Ritchie *et al.*, 2006). Lower scores are assigned to spots with quality issues and to arrays that are less reproducible, ensuring that results are not affected by bad samples. Alternatively, arrayQualityMetrics package (Kauffmann, 2009) can be used to calculate and visualize the distance between arrays and exclude those that are significantly different from the rest.

When measuring the fluorescence intensities there are several factors that affect the scan, by introducing ambient noise, both within and between the arrays (Silver *et al.*, 2009). Such signals are adjusted with background correction algorithms, which estimate and remove nonspecific binding or spatial heterogeneity effects (Ritchie *et al.*, 2007). Plotting the foreground against the background intensities can guide the choice of optimal correction algorithm. Lastly, the samples should be normalized to ensure that the biological signal is not "diluted" by technical variation or biases. Depending on the type (single- or two-color) and technology of the array, limma provides several approaches to normalize (i.e., remove some of the variations) within and between the arrays. This ensures that all samples are on the same measuring scale and that technical differences are not influencing the results. The choice of algorithms for background correction and normalization is the only challenging step in the processing of DNA microarrays, and both should be guided by the assessment of the data. As the subsequent steps in the analysis are common between sequencing and DNA-chip platforms, they will be described together in Section "Differentially Expressed Genes and Visualization."

RNA-Sequencing Data Processing

The field of NGS profiling encompasses a wide range of protocols, though from the analysis standpoint the main difference lies in the type of sequence that is enriched during library preparation. These can include small regulatory RNA such as miRNA, total or coding RNA, degraded RNA (German *et al.*, 2008), or RNA amplified from a single cell rather than a population of cells (Eberwine *et al.*, 2014). While there are differences in how each of the types is analyzed, the initial data processing steps and general principles are similar. The section below will focus on processing data from total or polyA selected RNAs, though with small changes to the reference the methodology can be applied to other types of protocols. For the purpose of this section, we will presume that the sequencing was performed on Illumina's HiSeq or MiSeq machine, and that demultiplexing (the process of separating individual libraries that were sequenced on the same lane) was performed during data export to FASTQ files. FASTX-Toolkit (Hannon, 2010) and EMBOSS seqret (Cock *et al.*, 2010) are two useful tools for checking, manipulating, and converting FASTQs to match the input format requirements of other programs.

The quality of reads, or short sequences obtained at the end of NGS protocols, depends on the integrity of the initial sample, proficiency in library construction, and handling during final sequencing stage. FastQC (Babraham-Bioinformatics, 2018) is a quality control tool that generates comprehensive graphical reports on several important characteristics of any sequence data. It should be noted that modern alignment algorithms can deal with cases such as adapter (short DNA sequences used in library preparation and sequencing) contamination or when part of the reads are of lower quality. However, in more severe cases, trimming the sequences or removing the adapters can increase the quality and number of aligned reads. This can be achieved using tools such as Cutadapt (Martin, 2012), FASTX (Hannon, 2010) or Trimmomatic (Bolger *et al.*, 2014). It is important to repeat the quality control step after each manipulation to ensure that the overall quality of the library has improved. If the entire length of the reads is of very low quality (below the score of 20 for Illumina's version 1.3 or later encoding), adapters make up most of the reads, or there is a significant overexpression of few "background" genes (such as ribosomal RNAs), it is usually advisable to repeat the sample and/or library preparation. The aims of the project and type of data will naturally influence the software stack and parameters used in the data processing. Differential splicing and metatranscriptomics assembly require a more complex setup, though the principles are the same once the fundamentals are understood. For the purpose of this and the next three subsections, we will focus on transcriptome profile comparison between two phenotypes or conditions.

The RNA-Seq reads are small sections of the transcriptome, hence the traditional way of processing them was to align the reads to a reference genome or transcriptome. From there, the reads were "stitched" together, and the overlap with regions of interest was used for abundance estimation. Abundance can be calculated for exons, transcripts, or genes, though gene-level analysis is generally recommended when transcript information is not required. Transcript quantification is more challenging due to a combination of short sequencing length and lack of unique sequences in many splice variants. Increasing the read length through gradual improvements in the technology will solve this problem in the near future. A prime example of the "traditional" approach is STAR aligner (Dobin *et al.*, 2013), where the genome index created prior to mapping is used during alignment. STAR gained widespread adaptation due to high-performance relative to other methods available at its launch. After the alignment is completed, programs such as featureCounts (Liao *et al.*, 2014) are run to count the mapped reads to genomic features, and provide a summary of the alignment. The postalignment report contains information on the percentage of mapped, unique, and duplicated reads, and serves as a final quality check before downstream analysis. A more detailed overview of the alignment can be generated using RNA-SeQC (DeLuca *et al.*, 2012). A recently developed alternative to this software stack is the so-called "pseudoaligners," which instead of aligning to the reference, determine read compatibility with defined targets (Bray *et al.*, 2016). kallisto is an example of such approach, and the algorithm has not only been shown to be very fast but also accurate and more robust to errors (Bray *et al.*, 2016). The transcript level abundance estimates produced by kallisto can be converted to counts using the R package tximport (Soneson *et al.*, 2015), after which they can be analyzed in the same fashion as any other alignment result. Lastly, and similarly to DNA-chip data, the reads should be normalized so that a comparison can be made between samples from different lanes or sequencing runs. Fragments per kilobase of transcript per million mapped reads (FPKM) is a popular expression unit that normalizes for sequencing depth and corresponding gene length. A similar type of normalization can be achieved in tximport using the lengthScaledTPM parameter, which is the final step in the processing of raw sequencing reads.

Differentially Expressed Genes and Visualization

The downstream analysis of normalized counts varies greatly depending on the experimental design, type of data and sample characteristics. While biological replicates and appropriate controls are crucial in many studies, in settings such as clinical bioinformatics, the lack of controls or a low number of samples is still common. Whenever paired samples are available (e.g., control and treated, or normal and diseased tissue from the same patient), differential expression analysis is usually performed first. It is a quantitative measure of expression change that can be used to rank genes based on a degree of under- or overexpression. It is a good practice to remove lowly expressed genes beforehand, which can be accomplished either using sophisticated software models or more simply by removing genes with a count ≤10.

Fold change, or the magnitude of change between conditions, is a preferred method for quantification of differential expression. It can be calculated using a variety of packages such as limma, DESeq2 (Love *et al.*, 2014), or sleuth (Pimentel *et al.*, 2017), all of which offer technically advanced though slightly different implementations. For a simpler manual calculation, the genes should first be transformed to account for the presence of extreme values and mean-variance dependency. This is most commonly achieved using log2 transformation, though alternatives such as rlog or VST are also used (Lin *et al.*, 2008). Subsequently, the log2(mean) of all replicates from a healthy control/untreated samples are subtracted from the log2(mean) of all replicates from a disease phenotype/treated samples. For datasets with no paired samples, a comparison can be made between groups with and without a certain condition or phenotype.

Visualization is an important component in bioinformatics as it is challenging to identify patterns in tens of thousands of genes based on text data alone. The most common graphics libraries used for high-quality plotting are ggplot2 in R (Ginestet, 2011) and matplotlib in Python 3 (Hunter, 2007). The built-in statistics and graphics capabilities in R are usually sufficient for initial data exploration purposes. Bioinformatics investigation is often initiated with a thorough check on how closely the samples match the experimental design. This is performed to identify population structures in the data that are previously unknown, or subgroups of samples with different characteristics. Furthermore, outliers, or samples with abnormally low or high values (which could represent technical issues), can be identified and removed. Principal component analysis (PCA) helps to find such characteristics by obtaining a combination of variables, in this case, gene expression values, that best differentiate the samples (Abraham and Inouye, 2014; Sharma and Paliwal, 2007). Any aberrant samples should be removed at this stage so that they do not influence the results. Subsequently, two-group expression comparison can be visualized using MA plots, which show the relationship between logged fold change and mean expression. Such plots are equally suited for diagnosing data-related issues as well as checking the number, magnitude, and pattern of differentially expressed genes. Another way of exploring global changes in gene expression is the Kolmogorov-Smirnov nonparametric test. It compares the distribution of each gene between two defined groups and is a good approach to visualize changes in mean expression and variability. The above-mentioned plots show general patterns of expression and should be supplemented with more direct visualizations. A very popular and information-rich example is heatmaps, which are two-dimensional grids where a range of values is represented by colors. They are often paired with hierarchical clustering, which sorts rows (which represent gene expression) and columns (which represent samples) in a way that most clearly shows patterns in the data. The combination can reveal commonly regulated genes or sets of samples with distinct expression profiles and characteristics (such as disease subtypes). Another way of using heatmaps is correlation matrices, which show a correlation of expression between multiple genes. More advanced plotting methods often contain a higher density of information within a single figure, utilizing colors, shapes, and opacity in a third-dimensional space.

Functional, Pathway, and Network Analysis

While global profiling of gene (or protein) expression provides a significant amount of information, it is often challenging to link such results to tangible biological insights. Employing annotation regarding a gene's (or its product's) involvement in a certain biological process, signaling pathway, or molecular function is one of the most effective approaches to study RNA-Seq data. Gene set enrichment analysis is one of the most widely used solutions, which verifies if the differentially expressed gene results show an enrichment or depletion of genes associated with a certain biological aspect (Subramanian *et al.*, 2005). This can include genes connected with cancer development, drug response, a wide range of signaling pathways, and more (Curtis *et al.*, 2005). There are numerous approaches for performing gene set analysis (e.g., overrepresentation analysis, pathway topology), most of which are implemented in R or are available as online tools (Tarca *et al.*, 2013). Pathway information can be easily retrieved from online databases such as KEGG (Kanehisa *et al.*, 2016), Reactome (Fabregat *et al.*, 2016), or WikiPathways (Slenter *et al.*, 2018), either manually or using the associated application programming interfaces. A different approach makes use of topological properties of genes within molecular interaction networks. Based on the direct interaction partners, or close proximity neighbors, it is possible to infer novel insights such as biological function (Sharan *et al.*, 2007) or prioritize candidate disease genes (Yu *et al.*, 2013). Cytoscape is the most popular environment for network studies (Shannon *et al.*, 2003), though it is also possible to perform a wide variety of network analyses using igraph in R (Csardi and Nepusz, 2006) or networkx in Python 3 (Hagberg *et al.*, 2008). Weighted gene coexpression network analysis is a great example of a network-based exploratory tool that provides additional data reduction and feature selection capabilities (Langfelder and Horvath, 2008). It is based on correlation patterns between gene expression, which forms the basis for finding clusters of potentially associated genes. It also identifies relationships between multiple such modules. Network approaches are also very useful for integrating different types of data, such as multiomics profiles (e.g., mutation, expression, or methylation datasets) or electronic medical records. Similarity network fusion is a popular example – it constructs a network of samples for each data layer and fuses them into a combined structure (Wang *et al.*, 2014). This approach strengthens strong signals (i.e., similarities between layers) and allows the samples to be grouped into distinctive subtypes.

Machine Learning Approaches in Genomics

The unprecedented growth in volume and complexity of biomedical datasets and literature has made bioinformatics analyses more challenging than ever. The very high ratio of features (e.g., mutation or expression) to the number of samples, and the considerable time investment needed to achieve expert-level knowledge on a particular biological phenomenon translate into the additional level of complexity. This has led to growing popularity of ML approaches, algorithms designed to automatically learn from data without an explicit set of rules to follow. While genomic datasets pose many unique challenges that need to be considered, ML algorithms can be extremely useful, particularly when combined with standard bioinformatics tools and databases. There are three main types of algorithms that are of direct use to genomic studies – unsupervised, supervised, and semisupervised. They are all easily accessible through Python, R, or Java libraries, although it requires familiarity with statistical analysis and programming.

Unsupervised learning is geared towards inferring "hidden structures" in unlabeled data – labels being the output values that in biological context can mean disease subtypes, months of patient survival or type of response to a treatment. Given the previously mentioned high number of features, dimensionality reduction is the first area of interest. PCA has traditionally been used to reduce the dimensionality of the data by geometrically projecting them onto lower dimensions (Lever *et al.*, 2017). This transformation allows for noise removal and easier classification, though recently developed t-distributed stochastic neighbor embedding was shown to outperform it in some biological applications (Fonville *et al.*, 2013). Such methods can be combined with pathway annotation to better explain variations in the phenotype (Ma and Kosorok, 2009). One of the primary aims of personalized medicine efforts is finding subgroups of patients with distinct phenotypes, which would allow for a more tailored prognosis, care, and treatment. To this end, a plethora of clustering approaches are routinely used on genomic data, mainly in hopes of finding novel disease subtypes (Van Rooden *et al.*, 2010). Hierarchical clustering, k-means, and spectral clustering are popular algorithms, though many specialized methods have been created specifically for biomedical application (Sharma *et al.*, 2017a,b,c, 2016a).

When label data is available, supervised learning approaches can be used to identify significant features or build models to predict categorical classes (classification) or continuous values (regression). While the identification of biomarkers for detecting and monitoring diseases has long been a focus in medicine, in many cases more complex models are needed to make an accurate diagnosis (Kidd *et al.*, 2015). Overfitting is a common challenge when building prediction models – given the high number of features in genomic datasets, it is relatively easy to find a combination of genes that will correlate with outcome labels by pure chance. Such results will not generalize well when tested with an independent dataset. It is thus important to separate the data into training and testing datasets (a popular split is 70%–30%), and only use the latter for sporadic validation of the model. Models with fewer features and lower complexity are always preferred, especially if the features are already known to be predictive of the outcome of interest, or are connected to a biologically relevant mechanism or pathway. The baseline prediction performance can be established using simple annotation (patient information, sample characteristics) or using biomarkers already reported in the literature. Such model can be further expanded or replaced entirely depending on its performance and complexity. Subsequently, feature selection approaches (Sharma *et al.*, 2012a,b,c,d, 2014, 2011; Sharma and Paliwal, 2011) can be applied to find biological components that best explain the phenotype of interest. Simple univariate methods such as t-test or Pearson's correlation were shown to be the optimal methods for feature selection in genomic data (Haury *et al.*, 2011). Alternatively, tree-based algorithms or recursive feature elimination paired with an estimator are popular choices as they allow to rank features based on their importance to the model. Once a subset of features is selected, a model can be constructed using a variety of algorithms – LASSO, ElasticNet, and random forest regressor are popular choices for predicting quantity while support vector machine (SVM), random forest classifier, or k-nearest neighbors (kNN) are popular for predicting categories. More advanced strategies such as boosting, bagging, or stacking can be used to decrease variance or increase accuracy – xgboost, being a representative example, usually provides satisfactory out-of-the-box (i.e., using default parameters) results (Chen and Guestrin, 2016). Neural networks, while popular in many fields such as medical image recognition, are used more sporadically in biomedical applications where decision-making transparency is often crucial. An iterative process of constructing, tuning (i.e., tweaking parameters), and testing the model is usually performed on the training data, using a 10-fold cross-validation (CV) technique. The process partitions the data into 10 equal parts and uses nine parts for training and one for evaluation. This is repeated 10 times, each time using different parts of the data for training and testing, and the final result is calculated as an average from all the runs. The performance metric depends on the type of the label, with accuracy, precision, and recall being popular for classification and root mean squared error and coefficient of determination (R^2) for regression. Once satisfactory results are achieved, the model should be trained on the entire training data (70% in our example) and tested on the remaining test data (the leftover 30%). The performance of a good model should show comparable or better results relative to the 10-fold CV evaluation. While some improvements can be achieved using different ML algorithms or by tweaking the parameters, poor performance usually means that the selected features are not enough to predict the outcome. Feature engineering, or creation of novel features using domain knowledge, is often the best approach to improve the model (Ang *et al.*, 2016). A more recent development in the ML field is semisupervised algorithms, which take advantage of the information contained within unlabeled data in classification problems (Scholkopf and Zien, 2006). Mixing unlabeled and labeled data has been shown to improve the supervised learning accuracy and is of particular interest to biology, where unlabeled data is abundant but labeled data is difficult to obtain.

Workflows in Proteomics

Proteomics is an extensive field of research where a plethora of studies are being conducted. These studies cover the following areas: protein fold recognition, structural class prediction, function analysis, posttranslational modification, and molecular recognition of features (Dehzangi *et al.*, 2018, 2017; López *et al.*, 2018, 2017; Chou, 2017). Various bioinformatics tools and packages have thus been developed for advancing the above research areas. The implementation of modern pipeline frameworks requires detailed guidelines and often offers a command line or workbench interface. In this section, we survey on the pipeline frameworks for identifying molecular recognition features (MoRFs) in IDPs. Specifically, we emphasize the design strategy of MoRF prediction systems and provide practical recommendations based on the requirements of high-throughput bioinformatics analyses.

The Necessity of Molecular Recognition Feature Prediction

In the traditional view of protein structure–function paradigm, proteins fold into a stable three-dimensional structure that ultimately determines their function. However, recent progress in computational and experimental methods has revealed a lack of this stable tertiary structure in certain protein regions (Dyson and Wright, 2005, 2015; Lee *et al.*, 2014; Uversky, 2014). Proteins comprising such regions are called IDPs and reportedly have important biological functions related to signal transduction and cell regulation (Wright and Dyson, 2015; Lee *et al.*, 2014). IDPs often achieve their functions through the loosely structured MoRF region. This region binds to a structured partner and consequently undergoes a disorder-to-order transition to adopt a well-defined conformation (Lee *et al.*, 2014). MoRF length varies up to 70 amino acids. Although there are many documented experimental techniques for identification and analysis of MoRF regions, they are still expensive and time-consuming. To overcome this challenge, computational approaches have become absolutely necessary for predicting these MoRFs in disordered protein sequences (Sharma *et al.*, 2018a,b, 2016b; Malhis *et al.*, 2016; Disfani *et al.*, 2012; Dosztányi *et al.*, 2009).

State-of-the-Art Molecular Recognition Feature Predictors

An abundance of computational methods and predictors have been already developed to predict MoRFs. These include ANCHOR (Dosztányi *et al.*, 2009), MoRFpred (Disfani *et al.*, 2012), MoRFchibi (Malhis and Gsponer, 2015), MoRFpred-plus (Sharma *et al.*, 2018a), MoRFchibi-web (Malhis *et al.*, 2016), PROMIS, and OPAL (Sharma *et al.*, 2018b). OPAL, the latest proposed predictor, has also proven the most accurate predictor in the literature. The above-mentioned predictors are currently available as online web servers and downloadable software packages. The subsequent sections illustrate the guidelines of MoRFs prediction and how to evaluate the pipeline of MoRF prediction.

Fundamentals of Protein Sequence Analysis

Sequence

The protein sequence is retrieved from an experimental setup where all the amino acids of the protein or peptide are determined. For computational analyses, a large number of protein sequences are at present available in different databanks, which were generated and annotated through high-throughput technologies.

Feature source and feature extraction technique

The features of protein sequences can be captured from different sources of information. These can be chemical, physical and physicochemical properties of amino acids, evolutionary and structural information of protein sequences, functional domains, and gene ontology information of protein sequences.

Some of the existing feature extraction techniques have been used to create feature vectors from protein attributes such as occurrence, composition, transition and distribution, pairwise frequencies, amino acid composition, autocorrelation, and bigram (Sharma *et al.*, 2013, 2015; Liu *et al.*, 2015; Dehzangi *et al.*, 2015; Du *et al.*, 2014). Early studies used to focus on sequential, syntactical, and physicochemical features. However, more recent studies have considered evolutionary-based features because they tend to provide good prediction accuracy for protein-related problems (Sharma *et al.*, 2018a; Yang *et al.*, 2017; Lyons *et al.*, 2016; Dehzangi *et al.*, 2015).

Classifiers

For classification purposes, several classifiers have been widely explored, including SVMs, artificial neural networks, kNN, as well as ensembles of classifiers. Amongst the aforementioned classifiers, SVMs is a well-known classifier that has delivered promising results in recent studies (Sharma *et al.*, 2018b; Malhis and Gsponer, 2015).

Design of a Molecular Recognition Feature Predictor

This section will cover the benchmark dataset and the framework of MoRF prediction.

Benchmark dataset

A wide collection of benchmark databases has been introduced, assembled, and used for developing MoRF predictors. These repositories include MoRFpred, MoRFchibi, MoRFpred-plus, MoRFchibi-web, and OPAL (**Table 1**).

The sequences in TRAIN and TEST464 sets were obtained from Protein Data Bank and filtered to retain protein-peptide regions of 5 to 25 residues in size (Disfani *et al.*, 2012). The sequences in TEST464 share a less than 30% sequence identity with sequences in TRAIN (Disfani *et al.*, 2012). MoRF predictors are always trained using the sequences in TRAIN set and assessed using the sequences of TEST464 set (Sharma *et al.*, 2018a,b; Malhis and Gsponer, 2015; Malhis *et al.*, 2016). According to the principles used to assemble TRAIN and TEST464 sequences, it is not verified whether identified protein-peptides are disordered in isolation and also TEST464 is not free of redundancy as its sequences share more than 30% sequence identity to each other (Disfani *et al.*, 2012). In order to address the above and validate a MoRF predictor, the EXP53 set is often used. The EXP53 set contains 53 nonredundant protein sequences with MoRFs which have been experimentally verified to be disordered in isolation (Malhis *et al.*, 2016; Sharma *et al.*, 2018b).

Table 1   Description of OPAL benchmark dataset

Datasets		No. of sequences	Total residues	No. of molecular recognition features (MoRF) residues	No. of non-MoRF residues
Training set	TRAIN	421	245,984	5396	240,588
Test sets	TEST464	464	296,362	5779	290,583
	EXP53	53	25,186	2432	22,754

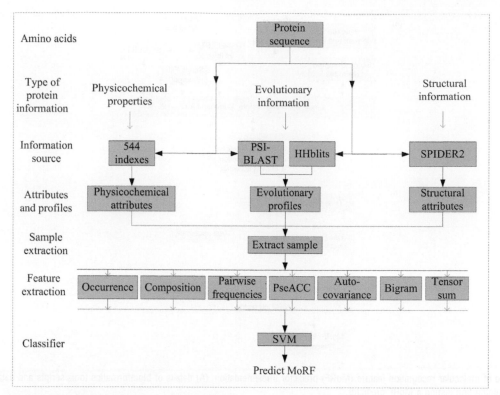

Fig. 4 Framework of molecular recognition feature (MoRF) prediction.

Framework of Molecular Recognition Feature Prediction

Fig. 4 shows the framework of MoRF prediction, whose input is the protein sequence. For prediction purposes, protein sequences are commonly represented using different features. These characteristics comprise physicochemical properties of amino acids such as 544 common physicochemical indexes (Kawashima *et al.*, 2008), evolutionary profiles such as position specific scoring matrix generated with PSI-BLAST (Altschul *et al.*, 1997) and hidden Markov model profiles generated with HHblits (Remmert *et al.*, 2011), as well as structural attributes such as secondary structure, accessible surface area and dihedral torsion angles predicted by tools as SPIDER2 (Yang *et al.*, 2017). To predict each residue in the protein as MoRF and non-MoRF, a sample is first extracted, described as a feature vector, and finally predicted with a suitable classifier.

Fig. 5(A) outlines the bioinformatics tools/scripts and the data format required for implementing a framework of MoRF prediction. These tools are generally run on a Linux operating system and protein sequences are organized in a FASTA format file. Tools such as PSI-BLAST, HHblits, and SPIDER2 can be installed and run via command line. On the other hand, scripts are written with software tools such as MATLAB, OCTAVE, and C-code. Finally, **Fig. 5(B)** shows the procedure of training and scoring a MoRF predictor.

Implementation Steps of a Molecular Recognition Feature Predictor

To identify MoRFs in a protein sequence, each residue should be initially scored. This score will help predict the residues as MoRF or non-MoRF. Two of the methods often used in a MoRF classification scheme are ResidueMoRF and RegionMoRF. These methods are used to extract samples from protein sequences during the training and test steps. The following subsections will discuss the training and test steps, which are of utmost importance to construct a MoRF predictor.

Training step

In this step, features are extracted from MoRFs and non-MoRFs and grouped in a training set. Let us assume the segment *F*, which represents a MoRF with flanks, and the segment *G*, which describes a non-MoRF with flanks. Both segments *F* and *G* are from a protein sequence in the training set. Let us also suppose that a protein sequence P_i is given as

$$P_i = A_1 A_2 ... A_j ... A_{n_i} (i = 1, 2, ..., T) \tag{1}$$

where A_j is the *j*th amino acid in the sequence, T is the total number of protein sequences in the training set, and n_i is the length of the protein sequence P_i. For instance, let us consider a protein sequence P_1 whose length $n_1 = 150$ and which contains one MoRF located between A_{30} and A_{40}. The segments *F* and *G* for this protein P_1 are illustrated in **Fig. 6**. For illustration purposes, a flank size of 20 amino acids has been considered. Of note, the flank size should be selected during training and evaluation.

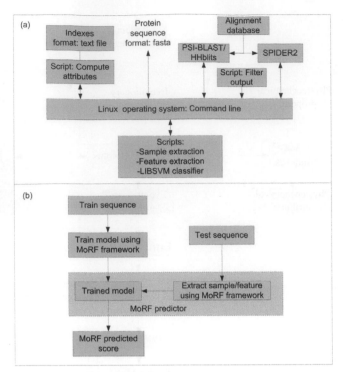

Fig. 5 Pipeline of molecular recognition feature (MoRF) predictor implementation. (A) details of bioinformatics tools/scripts and data formats, (B) procedure of training and testing a MoRF predictor.

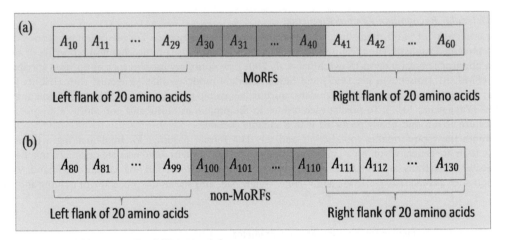

Fig. 6 Schematic illustration of (a) segment F and (b) segment G.

MoRFs can have a variable length of 5 to 25 amino acids. Additionally, zeros are padded to create flanks of 20 amino acids if the MoRF is present at the beginning or end of the protein sequence. Positive and negative samples representing MoRFs and non-MoRFs are extracted from segments F and G, respectively.

For sample extraction, two methods named ResidueMoRF and RegionMoRF, which are detailed below, are commonly used.

ResidueMoRF method
With this method, a window size of 41 ((flank size $\times$ 2) + 1) amino acids is regarded for extracting samples from a segment. For extracting positive samples, the center of the window is placed on the MoRF residue of segment F, with amino acids upstream and downstream of the MoRF residue. For example, the sample S_α for a MoRF residue is defined as

$$S_\alpha = \{A_{\alpha-20}, \cdots\cdots A_{\alpha-2}, A_{\alpha-1}, A_\alpha, A_{\alpha+1}, A_{\alpha+2} \cdots\cdots, A_{\alpha+20}\} \tag{2}$$

where A_α is the MoRF residue (i.e., in **Fig. 7(A)**, $\alpha = 30$). Positive samples extracted from a segment F using Eq. (2) are interpreted as

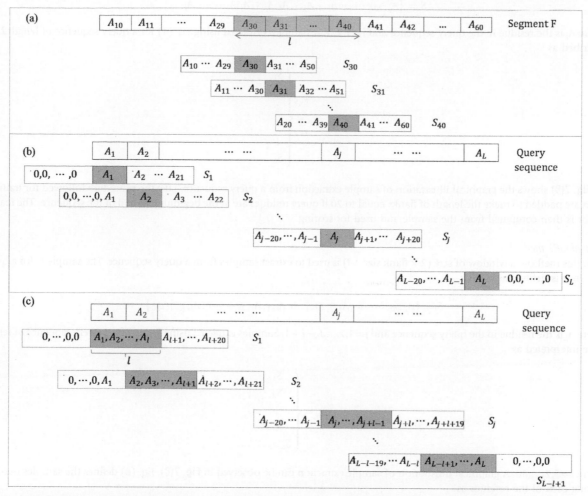

Fig. 7 Graphical illustration of (a) sample extraction from segment F, (b) sample extraction for scoring a query protein sequence of length L (A_j is the jth amino acid in the sequence), and (c) sample extraction from a query sequence of length L.

$$\gamma_{tr} = \begin{cases} S_\alpha \\ S_{\alpha+1} \\ \vdots \\ \vdots \\ S_{\alpha+l-1} \end{cases} \text{for } 5 \leq l \leq 25 \tag{3}$$

where l is the MoRF length (i.e., in **Fig. 7(A)**, $l=11$). **Fig. 7(A)** shows the graphical illustration of sample extraction from the segment F. In a similar way, negative samples are extracted from segment G.

After applying either of the above models, the feature vector is finally computed from the sample and used for model training.

RegionMoRF method

With this method, the entire segment F with a MoRF region of length l (as depicted in **Fig. 7(A)**) is taken as a positive sample. Likewise, the entire segment G is taken as a negative sample.

Test step

The scoring of each residue in a query protein sequence also requires the extraction of samples. In this case, the sample extraction procedure makes use of the above methods ResidueMoRF and RegionMoRF as well.

ResidueMoRF method

Like the procedure described in the above section, a window size of 41 ((flank size × 2) + 1) amino acids is used to extract a sample for each query residue. The sample S_j represents a query residue defined as

$$S_j = \left\{A_{j-20}, \cdots\cdots A_{j-2}, A_{j-1}, A_j, A_{j+1}, A_{j+2} \cdots\cdots, A_{j+20}\right\} \tag{4}$$

where A_j is the residue in the query sequence and $j=1,2,\ldots,L$. Samples extracted using Eq. (4) for a query sequence of length L are described as

$$\gamma_{ts} = \begin{cases} S_1 \\ S_2 \\ \vdots \\ \vdots \\ \vdots \\ S_L \end{cases} \tag{5}$$

Fig. 7(B) shows the graphical illustration of sample extraction from a query sequence. Like the procedure followed for training, zeros are padded to make the length of flanks equal to 20 if query residues are at the beginning or end of the sequence. The feature vector is then computed from the sample and used for scoring.

RegionMoRF method
With this method, a window of size $(2 \times \text{flank size} + l)$ is used to extract samples from a query sequence. The sample S_j for a query sequence is defined as

$$S_j = \left\{A_{j-20}, \cdots\cdots, A_{j-2}, A_{j-1}, A_j, A_{j+1}, A_{j+2}, \cdots\cdots, A_{j+(l-1)+20}\right\} \tag{6}$$

where A_j is the residue in the query sequence and $j=1,2,\ldots,L-l+1$. Samples extracted using Eq. (6) for a query sequence of length L are interpreted as

$$\gamma_{ts} = \begin{cases} S_1 \\ S_2 \\ \vdots \\ \vdots \\ S_{L-l+1} \end{cases} \tag{7}$$

where $l=6,7,\ldots,30$. A graphical illustration of sample extraction can be observed in **Fig. 7(C)**. Eq. (8) defines the samples used for scoring each of the residues as

$$A_i \rightarrow \begin{cases} \{S_1, S_2, \cdots, S_i\}, 1 \leq i < l \\ \{S_{i-l+1}, S_{i-l+2}, \cdots, S_i\}, l \leq i \leq L-l+1 \\ \{S_{i-l+1}, S_{i-l+2}, \cdots, S_{L-l+1}\}, i > L-l+1 \end{cases} \tag{8}$$

where $i=1,2,\ldots,L$. By varying l from 6 to 30, 450 $(6+7+\cdots+29+30)$ samples are obtained for each residue, except for the residues at the beginning and end of the query sequence. The feature vector is computed from the sample and used for scoring. For each residue, the maximum score of the samples defined in Eq. (8) is set as final propensity score.

Summary of Molecular Recognition Feature Prediction

For the prediction of MoRFs in protein sequences, state-of-the-art predictors such as ANCHOR, MoRFpred, MoRchibi, MoRFchibi-web, and OPAL are currently available as web servers. Thus, end users or scientists can easily use a graphical web interface to predict MoRF and non-MoRF residues in a protein sequence. Except for MoRFpred, the other predictors can be further installed and configured locally (in personal computers). The performance of the above-mentioned predictors is shown in **Table 2**. As it clearly shows, the OPAL predictor outperforms the other approaches, achieving a significant accuracy and confirming its practical use in real scenarios.

To select a target protein for further experimental analysis, the sequences of large databases need to be scored. To do this, the end user can write SQL query scripts to obtain such scores from the MoRF predictor (**Fig. 8(A)**).

As **Table 2** clearly indicates, the prediction accuracies are still limited when it comes to selecting a target protein for further experimental analysis for drug design. However, these limitations can be further improved by considering certain strategies. There is a need for high-performance workbenches, which could be accessible via the web to obtain protein sequence alignments. In the current MoRF web servers, the alignment tools are locally installed and run instead of using available alignment web servers. This is partly because alignment tools require a huge amount of time to provide alignment results. In addition, future MoRF pipelines similar to the one in **Fig. 8(B)** are expected. In other words, a core database server should store the experimental annotation from research labs whereas the computational annotation should be guaranteed by high-throughput bioinformatics analyses.

Table 2 Performance of state-of-the-art MoRF predictors. The results are reported for the TEST464 and EXP53 datasets using the area under the curve (AUC) as the performance metric

Predictor/method	TEST464	EXP53
ANCHOR	0.605	0.615
MoRFpred	0.675	0.620
MoRFchibi	0.743	0.712
PROMIS	0.790	0.818
MoRFchibi-web	0.805	0.797
OPAL	0.816	0.836

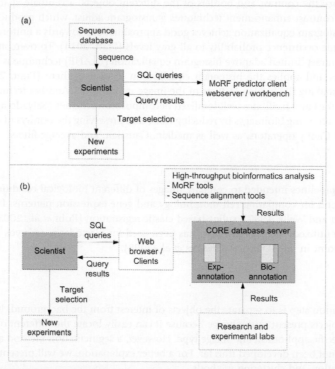

Fig. 8 Requirements for an improvement to molecular recognition feature (MoRF) prediction. (a) procedure of target protein selection for further experimentation, and (b) future pipeline for MoRF analysis.

Bioimage Analysis Pipelines

One of the areas in bioinformatics which is experiencing an enormous transformation is related to bioimage analysis. This is because a great number of bioinformatics applications are relying on image data for assessing different cellular and molecular mechanisms and thus validating the biological hypothesis. More and more images of biological mechanisms are generated by microscopes every single day, making necessary the design of accurate computational approaches.

In this direction, distinct imaging techniques such as PALM (Betzig et al., 2006), STORM (Rust et al., 2006), and STED (Hell, 2003) are currently able to detect individual proteins separated a few nanometers. Moreover, images related to biological mechanisms like RNA interference and chemical compounds (Echeverri and Perrimon, 2006; Moffat et al., 2006; Sepp et al., 2008) are absolutely necessary to shed light on scientific problems such as the differentiation of cancer cell phenotypes (Long et al., 2007a).

However, the complexity of bioimages makes it extremely difficult to apply conventional medical image analysis workflows because the objects of interest sometimes possess different morphologies and intensities. Therefore, it is necessary to start paying attention to this emerging subfield of bioinformatics, which is not widely covered in the scientific literature.

The development of bioimage analysis pipelines often consists of the following steps (**Fig. 9**): preprocessing in which noise is reduced, image registration (Qu et al., 2015) where images are aligned for pixel-by-pixel comparisons, image segmentation (Meijering, 2012) in which the objects of interest are separated from the background, feature extraction where object descriptors such as shape (Pincus and Theriot, 2007) and texture (Depeursinge et al., 2014) are computed, classification where objects are detected by ML techniques (Shamir et al., 2010), and visualization (Walter et al., 2010).

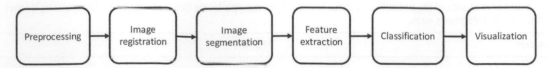

Fig. 9 Bioimage analysis workflow.

In this section, we will go through each of the above steps and explain the different methods.

Preprocessing

Preprocessing should be the first step of any pipeline. Its main objective is to improve the appearance of a bioimage or highlight additional information about the objects of interest, which might not be clearly observable. Many enhancement techniques and filters are often used to enhance the contrast and borders of the different objects, accentuate space frequencies, and remove or attenuate noise. One of these contrast enhancement techniques is histogram adjust, which produces a histogram with a specific form for the output image. Histogram equalization achieves good approximations towards a uniform distribution of the values of gray scale levels, giving the same occurrence probability to all gray levels (Pratt, 2014). To overcome the limitations of standard histogram equalization, the contrast-limited adaptive histogram equalization (CLAHE) technique is sometimes used. It divides the images into contextual regions and applies the histogram equalization to each of them (Pratt, 2014). This evens out the distribution of used gray values, making the hidden features of the image more visible. Another technique is the wavelet transform, which increases the image contrast and facilitates well-localized decomposition schemes (Salvado and Roque, 2005). In addition, digital filters are also used for enhancing bioimages by reducing noise and preserving the borders of those objects of interest. Some of these filters are Prewitt and Canny operators, as well as median, Gaussian, and average filters.

Image Registration

This step is often included in pipelines intended to compare images of different biological conditions such as those for building brain atlas (Ng *et al.*, 2007), and for comparing cell morphology and gene expression patterns. Here, methods such as mutual information registration (Viola and Wells, 1997), spline-based elastic registration (Rohr *et al.*, 2003), and congealing registration (Learned-Miller, 2006) can be utilized. Image registration has been used for blastoderm embryos in *D. Melanogaster* where each nucleus is described using a point in the 3D space (Fowlkes *et al.*, 2008).

Image Segmentation

The main aim of the segmentation step is to separate the objects of interest from the background. It is sometimes considered as a classification process of the objects present in the image because it can easily locate the different objects. Segmentation methods can vary depending on the specific application and image type. However, a segmentation method able to reach acceptable results for all types of bioimages has not been developed thus far. For a better explanation, we will present the segmentation methods in two groups: classical segmentation and clustering methods.

Classical segmentation methods

Thresholding is a method that segments scalar images, creating a binary partition of the image intensities. Once thresholding determines an intensity value, segmentation is achieved by grouping all the pixels based on intensity into two different classes. Its main limitation is that it only considers the intensity instead of other relationships between the pixels. One of the most reported methods is the Otsu's method, which selects the optimal threshold by maximizing the between-class variance with an exhaustive search. Although there are different methods to find a threshold, most of them are not satisfactory when analyzing real images, such as bioimages, due to the presence of noise, plain histograms, or an inadequate illumination.

Another classical method is deformable models, which are based on physical motivations, and used to delineate the borders of regions using curves or closed parametric surfaces deformed under the influence of external and internal forces. Two important deformable models are snakes (Kass *et al.*, 1988) which segments objects whose morphology is variable, and intelligent scissors (Liang *et al.*, 2006) which allows us to segment with minimal user interaction.

Clustering methods

Clustering techniques are also important in biomedical analysis pipelines because they achieve a correct separation of the regions of interest from the image background. Two of the frequently used clustering techniques are fuzzy *C*-means (Dulyakarn and Rangsanseri, 2001; Yang *et al.*, 2004) and hierarchical clustering, including single-linkage, complete-linkage, and average-linkage.

The segmentation of bioimages depends on which features are needed. For instance, texture features can be extracted for chromatin compositions whereas concavity features could be employed for nuclear morphology. When the images are of cell-based assays where nuclear compartments are colored, methods such as globular template segmentation, watershed segmentation, or active contour/snake methods are recommended.

Nevertheless, when the images contain nonglobular objects such as neurons, the neuroanatomical analysis software Neuro-lucida (Glaser and Glaser, 1990) is often used. Alternatively, directional kernels are also considered for searching neuronal structures in confocal images (Al-Kofahi *et al.*, 2003). Finally, the tool ImageJ plugin NeuronJ (Meijering *et al.*, 2004) is advisable as well.

Feature extraction/selection

The feature extraction/selection step is of vital importance when we aim to classify objects in bioimages. In this step, representative feature vectors are usually obtained. To do this, dimensionality reduction techniques like PCA are necessary. In addition, in-depth knowledge of the research domain is needed because it will allow us to select those features that can help discriminate between objects of interest. For example, if the aim is to analyze dynamic fluorescent images, texture features should be used (Dorn *et al.*, 2008). For clustering gene expression patterns, global decomposition by eigen-embryo analysis is recommended (Peng *et al.*, 2006) whereas wavelet features able to detect global and local properties are advisable to recognize and annotate gene expression patterns (Zhou and Peng, 2007). When a collection of image characteristics is extracted, we would then recommend the use of minimum-redundant maximum-relevant feature selection algorithms (Ding and Peng, 2005; Peng *et al.*, 2005b) so that redundant features can be eliminated.

Classification

The classification step is also of vital importance in bioimage analysis pipelines because it is here where the features of the object of interest will be used for classification. Standard ML techniques are often employed to achieve this goal. Some of these classifiers are the following:

- Bayesian classifiers, which rely on the Bayes' theorem, can be used in binary classification problems. The naïve Bayes classifier is often employed for classifying objects of interest because it requires a small amount of training data for parameter estimation.
- The kNN rule (Kuncheva, 2014) does not require knowledge of a priori probabilities whereas it assigns an unknown object to the class of its nearest neighbor in the measurement space. Moreover, it does not require patterns to be represented in a suitable vector space but only a similarity measure or distance function.
- Decision trees (Kuncheva, 2014) do not use comparison functions to infer general properties of the training matrix. Nor do they use all the features for object classification but each class can be inferred using its own feature set.
- SVMs (Hastie *et al.*, 2001b) search the hyperplane that separates a set of training objects while maximizing the margin between their classes. This method aims to minimize the bound on the generalization error rather than minimize the mean squared error over the dataset.

When the training set consists of few bioimages, an ensemble of machines is advisable. This strategy builds several basic classifiers and combines their outputs for improving classification. In such cases, a diverse ensemble in which the classifiers have adequately different decision boundaries is needed. To achieve this diversity, strategies such as bagging, boosting, AdaBoost, stacked generalization, and a mixture of experts are often considered (Kuncheva, 2014; Polikar, 2006). Bagging (Kuncheva, 2014; Polikar, 2006) draws different training subsets with replacement and is particularly recommended when the number of images is limited. Boosting (Kuncheva, 2014; Polikar, 2006) makes new machines pay more attention to those examples in which previous machines produced errors. AdaBoost (Kuncheva, 2014; Polikar, 2006) generates a set of hypotheses by training weak machines and making sure that the cases misclassified by previous classifiers are included in the training data of the next classifier.

One of the methods used for clustering mRNA expression patterns of coexpressed genes was the minimum spanning tree cut (Peng *et al.*, 2006) whereas for determining cell identities, the absolute three-dimensional location of the cell along with its location patterns was employed (Long *et al.*, 2008). However, for assigning bioimage patterns to different annotation terms, parallel classifiers are highly recommended (Zhou and Peng, 2007).

Visualization

As in other bioinformatics pipelines, visualization is vital for result verification. Among the techniques often used in bioimage analyses are surface and flow visualization. Tools for the visualization of images of protein surfaces and gene expression can be utilized in addition to immersive visualization systems such as NCMIR's ATLAS and ImmersaDeskTM (Ai *et al.*, 2005).

Conclusions

The spectrum of bioinformatics tools and methods is currently too wide for an exhaustive review. The computational approaches grow in sophistication alongside technological improvements in the corresponding experimental protocols. New requirements, which become more evident with increase in volume and complexity of biological data, will further push the development of efficient and comprehensive solutions. This article covers four main research areas: genomics, transcriptomics, proteomics, and bioimage analysis.

Within the genomics area, we presented current efforts that focus on accurate mapping of sequences to the reference and identifying regions that show variation. As the number of quantifiable changes will continue to rise, new frameworks geared towards integrating this information and linking them to phenotypic changes will be required.

In the transcriptome section, we examined several computational data processing approaches and covered linking expression profiles to actionable results. We summarized popular tools and libraries that can be easily built upon and extended. As our understanding of pathways, networks and omics interaction grows, so will the scope of the analyses. Future solutions will look at RNA changes more in the context of global interaction network, rather than few genes with higher or lower expression.

For proteomics, we have provided a detailed guideline for MoRF prediction, including data description, examples of state-of-the-art tools, MoRF classification schemes, and pipelines of MoRF downstream analysis. Any reader can easily follow the steps to develop a new MoRF predictor, and thus analyze MoRFs in protein sequences using the presented methodology.

Finally, within the bioimage analysis area, we described the standard workflow for analyzing digital images, which includes preprocessing, image registration and segmentation, feature extraction, classification, and visualization. With the capture of high-resolution images of different cellular mechanisms, future bioinformatics approaches will definitely be necessary to keep up with the technological advances.

Author Contributions

AS and PJK defined the structure of the article. YL, AS and PJK wrote the abstract, introduction, and conclusions. YL and DS covered Section "Genome Analysis" (Genome). PJK covered Section "Transcriptome Analysis" (Transcriptome). RS and AS covered Section "Workflows in Proteomics" (Proteome). YL covered Section "Bioimage Analysis Pipelines" (Bioimages). AS and TT oversaw and managed article creation.

See also: Computing for Bioinformatics. Natural Language Processing Approaches in Bioinformatics

References

Abeel, T., Parys, T.V., Saeys, Y., Galagan, J., Peer, Y.V.D., 2012. GenomeView: A next-generation genome browser. Nucleic Acids Research 40, e12.

Abraham, G., Inouye, M., 2014. Fast principal component analysis of large-scale genome-wide data. PLoS ONE 9. e93766.

Abyzov, A., Urban, A.E., Snyder, M., Gerstein, M., 2011. CNVnator: An approach to discover, genotype, and characterize typical and atypical CNVs from family and population genome sequencing. Genome Research 21, 974–984.

Ai, Z., Chen, X., Rasmussen, M., Folberg, R., 2005. Reconstruction and exploration of three-dimensional confocal microscopy data in an immersive virtual environment. Computerized Medical Imaging and Graphics 29, 313–318.

Al-Kofahi, K.A., Can, A., Lasek, S., et al., 2003. Median-based robust algorithms for tracing neurons from noisy confocal microscope images. IEEE Transactions on Information Technology in Biomedicine 7, 302–317.

Altschul, S.F., Madden, T.L., Schaffer, A.A., et al., 1997. Gapped blast and psi-blast: A new generation of protein database search programs. Nucleic Acids Research 17, 3389–3402.

Ang, J.C., Mirzal, A., Haron, H., Hamed, H.N.A., 2016. Supervised, unsupervised, and semi-supervised feature selection: A review on gene selection. IEEE/ACM Transactions on Computational Biology and Bioinformatics 13, 971–989.

Babraham-Bioinformatics, 2018. A quality control tool for high throughput sequence data. Available at: http://www.bioinformatics.bbsrc.ac.uk/projects/fastqc.

Bao, H., Guo, H., Wang, J., et al., 2009. MapView: Visualization of short reads alignment on a desktop computer. Bioinformatics 25, 1554–1555.

Behjati, S., Tarpey, P.S., 2013. What is next-generation sequencing? Archives of Disease in Childhood - Education and Practice 98, 236–238.

Betzig, E., Patterson, G.H., Sougrat, R., et al., 2006. Imaging intracellular fluorescent proteins at nanometer resolution. Science 313, 1642–1645.

Bolger, A.M., Lohse, M., Usadel, B., 2014. Trimmomatic: A flexible trimmer for Illumina sequence data. Bioinformatics 30, 2114–2120.

Bray, N.L., Pimentel, H., Melsted, P., Pachter, L., 2016. Near-optimal probabilistic RNA-seq quantification. Nature Biotechnology 34, 525–527.

Brodie, A., Tovia-Brodie, O., Ofran, Y., 2014. Large scale analysis of phenotype-pathway relationships based on GWAS results. PLoS ONE. e100887.

Browning, B.L., Browning, S.R., 2009. A unified approach to genotype imputation and haplotype-phase inference for large data sets of trios and unrelated individuals. American Journal of Human Genetics 84, 210–223.

Buels, R., Yao, E., Diesh, C.M., et al., 2016. JBrowse: A dynamic web platform for genome visualization and analysis. Genome Biology, 17. p. 66.

Carver, T., Harris, S.R., Otto, T.D., et al., 2013. BamView: Visualizing and interpretation of next-generation sequencing read alignments. Briefings in Bioinformatics 14, 203–212.

Chen, T., Guestrin, C., 2016. XGBoost: A scalable tree boosting system. In: KDD'16 Proceedings of the 22nd ACM SIGKDD International Conference on Knowledge Discovery and Data Mining. San Francisco, California pp. 785–794.

Cheung, M.-S., Down, T.A., Latorre, I., Ahringer, J., 2011. Systematic bias in high-throughput sequencing data and its correction by BEADS. Nucleic Acids Research 39, e103.

Chou, K.C., 2017. An unprecedented revolution in medicinal chemistry driven by the progress of biological science. Current Topics in Medicinal Chemistry 17, 2337–2358.

Cock, P.J.A., Fields, C.J., Goto, N., Heuer, M.L., Rice, P.M., 2010. The Sanger FASTQ file format for sequences with quality scores, and the Solexa/Illumina FASTQ variants. Nucleic Acids Research 38, 1767–1771.

Csardi, G., Nepusz, T., 2006. The igraph software package for complex network research. Inter Journal Complex Systems. 1695.

Curtis, R.K., Oresic, M., Vidal-Puig, A., 2005. Pathways to the analysis of microarray data. Trends in Biotechnology 23, 429–435.

Dehzangi, A., Heffernan, R., Sharma, A., et al., 2015. Gram-positive and Gram-negative protein subcellular localization by incorporating evolutionary-based descriptors into Chou's general PseAAC. Journal of Theoretical Biology 364, 284–294.

Dehzangi, A., López, Y., Lal, S.P., *et al.*, 2017. PSSM-Suc: Accurately predicting succinylation using position specific scoring matrix into bigram for feature extraction. Journal of Theoretical Biology 425, 97–102.

Dehzangi, A., López, Y., Lal, S., *et al.*, 2018. Improving succinylation prediction accuracy by incorporating the secondary structure via helix, strand and coil, and evolutionary information from profile bigrams. PLOS ONE 13, e0191900.

DeLuca, D.S., Levin, J.Z., Sivachenko, A., *et al.*, 2012. RNA-SeQC: RNA-seq metrics for quality control and process optimization. Bioinformatics 28, 1530–1532.

Depeursinge, A., Foncubierta-Rodriguez, A., Ville, D.V.D., Müller, H., 2014. Three-dimensional solid texture analysis in biomedical imaging: Review and opportunities. Medical Image Analysis 18, 176–196.

Diaz, A., Nellore, A., Song, J.S., 2012. CHANCE: Comprehensive software for quality control and validation of ChIP-seq data. Genome Biology, 13. . p. R98.

Ding, C., Peng, H., 2005. Minimum redundancy feature selection from microarray gene expression data. Journal of Bioinformatics and Computational Biology 3, 185–205.

Disfani, F.M., Hsu, W.L., Mizianty, M.J., *et al.*, 2012. MoRFpred, a computational tool for sequence-based prediction and characterization of short disorder-to-order transitioning binding regions in proteins. Bioinformatics 28, i75–i83.

Dobin, A., Davis, C.A., Schlesinger, F., *et al.*, 2013. STAR: Ultrafast universal RNA-seq aligner. Bioinformatics 29, 15–21.

Dosztányi, Z., Mészáros, B., Simon, I., 2009. ANCHOR: Web server for predicting protein binding regions in disordered proteins. Bioinformatics 25, 2745–2746.

Dulyakarn, P., Rangsanseri, Y., 2001. Fuzzy C-means clustering using spatial information with application to remote sensing. In: Proceedings of the 22nd Asian Conference on Remote Sensing.

Du, P., Gu, S., Jiao, Y., 2014. PseAAC-General: Fast building various modes of general form of Chou's pseudo-amino acid composition for large-scale protein datasets. International Journal of Molecular Sciences 15, 3495–3506.

Dyson, H.J., Wright, E.P., 2005. Intrinsically unstructured proteins and their functions. Nature Reviews Molecular Cell Biology 6, 197–208.

Eberwine, J., Sul, J.Y., Bartfai, T., Kim, J., 2014. The promise of single-cell sequencing. Nature Methods 11, 25–27.

Echeverri, C.J., Perrimon, N., 2006. High-throughput RNAi screening in cultured cells: A user's guide. Nature Reviews Genetics 7, 373–384.

F.Dorn, J., Danuser, G., Yang, G., 2008. Computational processing and analysis of dynamic fluorescence image data. Methods in Cell Biology 85, 497–538.

Fabregat, A., Sidiropoulos, K., Garapati, P., *et al.*, 2016. The reactome pathway knowledgebase. Nucleic Acids Research 44, D481–D487.

Feng, X., Grossman, R., Stein, L., 2011. PeakRanger: A cloud-enabled peak caller for ChIP-seq data. BMC Bioinformatics 12, 139.

Fonville, J.M., Carter, C.L., Pizarro, L., *et al.*, 2013. Hyperspectral visualization of mass spectrometry imaging data. Analytical Chemistry 85, 1415–1423.

Forbes, S.A., Bhamra, G., Bamford, S., *et al.*, 2008. The Catalogue of Somatic Mutations in Cancer (COSMIC). In: HAINES, J.L. (Ed.), Current Protocols In Human Genetics.

Fowlkes, C.C., Hendriks, C.L.L., Keränen, S.V.E., *et al.*, 2008. A quantitative spatiotemporal atlas of gene expression in the *Drosophila* blastoderm. Cell 133, 364–374.

Auton, A., Brooks, L.D., Durbin, R.M., *et al.*, 2015. A global reference for human genetic variation. Nature 526, 68–74.

German, M.A., Pillay, M., Jeong, D.H., *et al.*, 2008. Global identification of microRNA-target RNA pairs by parallel analysis of RNA ends. Nature Biotechnology 26, 941–946.

Ginestet, C., 2011. ggplot2: Elegant graphics for data analysis. Journal of the Royal Statistical Society Series A 174, 245.

Glaser, J.R., Glaser, E.M., 1990. Neuron imaging with neurolucida – A PC-based system for image combining microscopy. Computerized Medical Imaging and Graphics 14, 307–317.

Hagberg, A., Swart, P.J., Chult, D.S., 2008. Exploring network structure, dynamics, and function using NetworkX. In: Proceedings of the 7th Python in Science Conference.

Hannon, 2010. FASTX-Toolkit: FASTQ/A short-reads pre-processing tools. Available at: http://hannonlab.cshl.edu/fastx_toolkit/.

Hastie, T., Friedman, J., Tibshirani, R., 2001b. Support vector machines and flexible discriminants. The Elements of Statistical Learning. New York: Springer.

Haury, A.C., Gestraud, P., Vert, J.P., 2011. The influence of feature selection methods on accuracy, stability and interpretability of molecular signatures. PLoS ONE 6, e28210.

Hell, S.W., 2003. Toward fluorescence nanoscopy. Nature Biotechnology 21, 1347–1355.

Hunter, J.D., 2007. Matplotlib: A 2D graphics environment. Computing in Science & Engineering 9, 90–95.

Hurd, P.J., Nelson, C.J., 2009. Advantages of next-generation sequencing versus the microarray in epigenetic research. Briefings in Functional Genomics & Proteomics 8, 174–183.

Hwang, S., Kim, E., Lee, I., Marcotte, E.M., 2015. Systematic comparison of variant calling pipelines using gold standard personal exome variants. Scientific Reports 5, 17875.

Imamura, M., Shigemizu, D., Tsunoda, T., *et al.*, 2013. Assessing the clinical utility of a genetic risk score constructed using 49 susceptibility alleles for type 2 diabetes in a Japanese population. The Journal of Clinical Endocrinology and Metabolism 98, E1667–E1673.

International HapMap Consortium, 2005. A haplotype map of the human genome. Nature 437, 1299–1320.

Jiang, H., Wang, F., Dyer, N.P., Wong, W.H., 2010. CisGenome Browser: A flexible tool for genomic data visualization. Bioinformatics 26, 1781–1782.

Kanehisa, M., Sato, Y., Kawashima, M., Furumichi, M., Tanabe, M., 2016. KEGG as a reference resource for gene and protein annotation. Nucleic Acids Research 44, D457–D462.

Kass, M., Witkin, A., Terzopoulos, D., 1988. Snakes: Active contour models. International Journal of Computer Vision 1, 321–331.

Kauffmann, A., 2009. arrayQualityMetrics – A bioconductor package for quality assessment of microarray data. Bioinformatics 25, 415–416.

Kauffmann, A., Huber, W., 2010. Microarray data quality control improves the detection of differentially expressed genes. Genomics 95, 138–142.

Kawashima, S., Pokarowski, P., Pokarowska, M., *et al.*, 2008. AAindex: Amino acid index database, progress report 2008. Nucleic Acids Research 36, D202–D205.

Kharchenko, P.V., Tolstorukov, M.Y., Park, P.J., 2008. Design and analysis of ChIP-seq experiments for DNA-binding proteins. Nature Biotechnology 26, 1351–1359.

Kidd, B.A., Readhead, B.P., Eden, C., Parekh, S., Dudley, J.T., 2015. Integrative network modeling approaches to personalized cancer medicine. Personalized Medicine 12, 245–257.

Koboldt, D.C., Zhang, Q., Larson, D.E., *et al.*, 2012. VarScan 2: Somatic mutation and copy number alteration discovery in cancer by exome sequencing. Genome Research 22, 568–576.

Kong, L., Wang, J., Zhao, S., *et al.*, 2012. ABrowse – a customizable next-generation genome browser framework. BMC Bioinformatics 13, 2.

Kuncheva, L.I., 2014. Combining Pattern Classifiers: Methods and Algorithms. New Jersey: John Wiley & Sons.

Landt, S.G., Marinov, G.K., Kundaje, A., *et al.*, 2012. ChIP-seq guidelines and practices of the ENCODE and modENCODE consortia. Genome Research 22, 1813–1831.

Langfelder, P., Horvath, S., 2008. WGCNA: an R package for weighted correlation network analysis. BMC Bioinformatics 9, 559.

Langmead, B., Salzberg, S.L., 2012. Fast gapped-read alignment with Bowtie 2. Nature Methods 9, 357–359.

Larson, D.E., Harris, C.C., Chen, K., *et al.*, 2012. SomaticSniper: Identification of somatic point mutations in whole genome sequencing data. Bioinformatics 28, 311–317.

Learned-Miller, E., 2006. Data driven image models through continuous joint alignment. IEEE Transactions on Pattern Analysis and Machine Intelligence 28, 236–250.

Lee, R.V.D., Buljan, M., Lang, B., *et al.*, 2014. Classification of intrinsically disordered regions and proteins. Chemical Reviews 114, 6589–6631.

Lee, S., Emond, M.J., Bamshad, M.J., *et al.*, 2012. Optimal unified approach for rare-variant association testing with application to small-sample case-control whole-exome sequencing studies. American Journal of Human Genetics 91, 224–237.

Lee, E., Helt, G.A., Reese, J.T., *et al.*, 2013. Web Apollo: A web-based genomic annotation editing platform. Genome Biology 14, R93.

Lever, J., Krzywinski, M., Altman, N., 2017. Points of Significance: Principal component analysis. Nature Methods 14, 641–642.

Liang, K., Keleş, S., 2012. Detecting differential binding of transcription factors with ChIP-seq. Bioinformatics 28, 121–122.

Liang, J., Mcinerney, T., Terzopoulos, D., 2006. United Snakes. Medical Image Analysis 10, 215–233.

Liao, Y., Smyth, G.K., Shi, W., 2014. featureCounts: An efficient general purpose program for assigning sequence reads to genomic features. Bioinformatics 30, 923–930.

Lin, S.M., Du, P., Huber, W., Kibbe, W.A., 2008. Model-based variance-stabilizing transformation for Illumina microarray data. Nucleic Acids Research 36, e11.

Liu, B., Liu, F., Wang, X., Chen, J., 2015. Pse-in-One: A web server for generating various modes of pseudo components of DNA, RNA, and protein sequences. Nucleic Acids Research 43, W65–W71.

Li, Q., Brown, J.B., Huang, H., Bickel, P.J., 2011. Measuring reproducibility of high-throughput experiments. The Annals of Applied Statistics 5, 1752–1779.

Li, H., Durbin, R., 2009. Fast and accurate short read alignment with Burrows–Wheeler transform. Bioinformatics 25, 1754–1760.

Li, H., Handsaker, B., Wysoker, A., et al., 2009a. The Sequence Alignment/Map format and SAMtools. Bioinformatics 25, 2078–2079.

Li, B., Leal, S.M., 2008. Methods for detecting associations with rare variants for common diseases: Application to analysis of sequence data. American Journal of Human Genetics 83, 311–321.

Li, H., Ruan, J., Durbin, R., 2008. Mapping short DNA sequencing reads and calling variants using mapping quality scores. Genome Research 18, 1851–1858.

Li, R., Yu, C., Li, Y., et al., 2009b. SOAP2: An improved ultrafast tool for short read alignment. Bioinformatics 25, 1966–1967.

Long, F., Peng, H., Liu, X., Kim, S., Myers, G., 2008. Automatic Recognition of Cells (ARC) for 3D Images of C. elegans. In: Vingron, M., Wong, L. (Eds.), Research in Computational Molecular Biology. Berlin, Heidelberg: Springer.

Long, F., Peng, H., Sudar, D., Lelièvre, S.A., Knowles, D.W., 2007a. Phenotype clustering of breast epithelial cells in confocal images based on nuclear protein distribution analysis. BMC Cell Biology 8, S3.

López, Y., Dehzangi, A., Lal, S.P., et al., 2017. SucStruct: Prediction of succinylated lysine residues by using structural properties of amino acids. Analytical Biochemistry 527, 24–32.

López, Y., Sharma, A., Dehzangi, A., et al., 2018. Success: Evolutionary and structural properties of amino acids prove effective for succinylation site prediction. BMC Genomics 19, 923.

Love, M.I., Huber, W., Anders, S., 2014. Moderated estimation of fold change and dispersion for RNA-seq data with DESeq2. Genome Biology 15, 550.

Lyons, J., Paliwal, K.K., Dehzangi, A., et al., 2016. Protein fold recognition using HMM–HMM alignment and dynamic programming. Journal of Theoretical Biology 393, 67–74.

Machanick, P., Bailey, T.L., 2011. MEME-ChIP: Motif analysis of large DNA datasets. Bioinformatics 27, 1696–1697.

Madsen, B.E., Browning, S.R., 2009. A groupwise association test for rare mutations using a weighted sum statistic. PLoS Genetics 5, e1000384.

Malhis, N., Gsponer, J., 2015. Computational identification of MoRFs in protein sequences. Bioinformatics 31, 1738–1744.

Malhis, N., Jacobson, M., Gsponer, J., 2016. MoRFchibi SYSTEM: Software tools for the identification of MoRFs in protein sequences. Nucleic Acids Research 44, W488–W493.

Marchini, J., Howie, B., Myers, S., Mcvean, G., Donnelly, P., 2007. A new multipoint method for genome-wide association studies by imputation of genotypes. Nature Genetics 39, 906–913.

Marschall, T., Costa, I.G., Canzar, S., et al., 2012. CLEVER: Clique-enumerating variant finder. Bioinformatics 28, 2875–2882.

Martin, M., 2012. Cutadapt removes adapter sequences from high-throughput sequencing reads. Bioinformatics in Action 17, 10–12.

Ma, S., Kosorok, M.R., 2009. Identification of differential gene pathways with principal component analysis. Bioinformatics 25, 882–889.

Mckenna, A., Hanna, M., Banks, E., et al., 2010. The Genome Analysis Toolkit: A MapReduce framework for analyzing next-generation DNA sequencing data. Genome Research 20, 1297–1303.

Meijering, E., 2012. Cell segmentation: 50 years down the road. IEEE Signal Processing Magazine 29, 140–145.

Meijering, E., Jacob, M., Sarria, J.-C.F., et al., 2004. Design and validation of a tool for neurite tracing and analysis in fluorescence microscopy images. Cytometry Part A 58A, 167–176.

Metzker, M.L., 2010. Sequencing technologies – the next generation. Nature Reviews Genetics 11, 31–46.

Moffat, J., Grueneberg, D.A., Yang, X., et al., 2006. A lentiviral RNAi library for human and mouse genes applied to an arrayed viral high-content screen. Cell 124, 1283–1298.

Morgenthaler, S., Thilly, W.G., 2007. A strategy to discover genes that carry multi-allelic or mono-allelic risk for common diseases: A cohort allelic sums test (CAST). Mutation Research 615, 28–56.

Neumann, B., Walter, T., Hériché, J.-K., et al., 2010. Phenotypic profiling of the human genome by time-lapse microscopy reveals cell division genes. Nature 464, 721–727.

Newton-Cheh, C., Johnson, T., Gateva, V., et al., 2009. Genome-wide association study identifies eight loci associated with blood pressure. Nature Genetics 41, 666–676.

Ng, L., Pathak, S., Kuan, C., et al., 2007. Neuroinformatics for genome-wide 3-D gene expression mapping in the mouse brain. IEEE/ACM Transactions on Computational Biology and Bioinformatics 4, 382–393.

Ozaki, K., Ohnishi, Y., Iida, A., et al., 2002. Functional SNPs in the lymphotoxin-alpha gene that are associated with susceptibility to myocardial infarction. Nature Genetics 32, 650–654.

Pabinger, S., Dander, A., Fischer, M., et al., 2014. A survey of tools for variant analysis of next-generation genome sequencing data. Briefings in Bioinformatics 15, 256–278.

Pedersen, B.S., Layer, R.M., Quinlan, A.R., 2016. Vcfanno: fast, flexible annotation of genetic variants. Genome Biology 17, 118.

Peng, H., Long, F., Ding, C., 2005b. Feature selection based on mutual information criteria of max-dependency, max-relevance, and min-redundancy. IEEE Transactions on Pattern Analysis and Machine Intelligence 27, 1226–1238.

Peng, H., Long, F., Eisen, M.B., Myers, E.W., 2006. Clustering gene expression patterns of fly embryos. In: Proceedings of the 3rd IEEE International Symposium on Biomedical Imaging: Nano to Macro, pp. 1144–1147.

Pimentel, H., Bray, N.L., Puente, S., Melsted, P., Pachter, L., 2017. Differential analysis of RNA-seq incorporating quantification uncertainty. Nature Methods 14, 687–690.

Pincus, Z., Theriot, J.A., 2007. Comparison of quantitative methods for cell-shape analysis. Journal of Microscopy 227, 140–156.

Podolskiy, D.I., Lobanov, A.V., Kryukov, G.V., Gladyshev, V.N., 2016. Analysis of cancer genomes reveals basic features of human aging and its role in cancer development. Nature Communications 7, 12157.

Polikar, R., 2006. Ensemble based systems in decision making. IEEE Circuits and Systems Magazine 6, 21–45.

Pratt, W.K., 2014. Introduction to Digital Image Processing. CRC Press Taylor & Francis Group.

Price, A.L., Kryukov, G.V., De Bakker, P.I., et al., 2010. Pooled association tests for rare variants in exon-resequencing studies. American Journal of Human Genetics 86, 832–838.

Purcell, S., Neale, B., Todd-Brown, K., et al., 2007. PLINK: A tool set for whole-genome association and population-based linkage analyses. American Journal of Human Genetics 81, 559–575.

Qin, Z.S., Jianjun, Y., Shen, J., et al., 2010. HPeak: An HMM-based algorithm for defining read-enriched regions in ChIP-Seq data. BMC Bioinformatics 11, 369.

Quinlan, A.R., Hall, I.M., 2010. BEDTools: A flexible suite of utilities for comparing genomic features. Bioinformatics 26, 841–842.

Qu, L., Long, F., Peng, H., 2015. 3-D Registration of biological images and models: Registration of microscopic images and its uses in segmentation and annotation. IEEE Signal Processing Magazine 32, 70–77.

Rashid, N.U., Giresi, P.G., Ibrahim, J.G., Sun, W., Lieb, J.D., 2011. ZINBA integrates local covariates with DNA-seq data to identify broad and narrow regions of enrichment, even within amplified genomic regions. Genome Biology 12, R67.

Remmert, M., Biegert, A., Hauser, A., Söding, J., 2011. HHblits: Lightning-fast iterative protein sequence searching by HMM-HMM alignment. Nature Methods 9, 173–175.

Ritchie, M.E., Diyagama, D., Neilson, J., et al., 2006. Empirical array quality weights in the analysis of microarray data. BMC Bioinformatics 7, 261.

Ritchie, M.E., Phipson, B., Wu, D., et al., 2015. limma powers differential expression analyses for RNA-sequencing and microarray studies. Nucleic Acids Research 43.

Ritchie, M.E., Silver, J., Oshlack, A., et al., 2007. A comparison of background correction methods for two-colour microarrays. Bioinformatics 23, 2700–2707.

Rohr, K., Fornefett, M., Stiehl, H.S., 2003. Spline-based elastic image registration: Integration of landmark errors and orientation attributes. Computer Vision and Image Understanding 90, 153–168.

Van Rooden, S.M., Heiser, W.J., Kok, J.N., et al., 2010. The identification of Parkinson's disease subtypes using cluster analysis: A systematic review. Movement Disorders 25, 969–978.

Roy, S., Coldren, C., Karunamurthy, A., *et al.*, 2018. Standards and guidelines for validating next-generation sequencing bioinformatics pipelines. The Journal of Molecular Diagnostics 20, 4–27.

Roy, S., Laframboise, W.A., Nikiforov, Y.E., *et al.*, 2016. Next-generation sequencing informatics challenges and strategies for implementation in a clinical environment. Archives of Pathology & Laboratory Medicine 140, 958–975.

Ruffier, M., Kähäri, A., Komorowska, M., *et al.*, 2017. Ensembl core software resources: Storage and programmatic access for DNA sequence and genome annotation. Database 2017.bax020.

Rusk, N., Kiermer, V., 2008. Primer: Sequencing – the next generation. Nature Methods 5, 15.

Rust, M.J., Bates, M., Zhuang, X., 2006. Sub-diffraction-limit imaging by stochastic optical reconstruction microscopy (STORM). Nature Methods 3, 793–796.

Salvado, J., Roque, B., 2005. Detection of calcifications in digital mammograms using wavelet analysis and contrast enhancement. In: Proceedings of the IEEE International Workshop on Intelligent Signal Processing.

Sathirapongsasuti, J.F., Lee, H., Horst, B.A.J., *et al.*, 2011. Exome sequencing-based copy-number variation and loss of heterozygosity detection: ExomeCNV. Bioinformatics 27, 2648–2654.

Schölkopf, B., Zien, A., 2006. Introduction to semi-supervised learning. In: Chapelle, O., Schölkopf, B., Zien, A. (Eds.), Semi-Supervised Learning. MIT Press.

Sepp, K.J., Hong, P., Lizarraga, S.B., *et al.*, 2008. Identification of neural outgrowth genes using genome-wide RNAi. PLoS Genetics 4, e1000111.

Shalon, D., Smith, S.J., Brown, P.O., 1996. A DNA microarray system for analyzing complex DNA samples using two-color fluorescent probe hybridization. Genome Research 6, 639–645.

Shamir, L., Delaney, J.D., Orlov, N., Eckley, D.M., Goldberg, I.G., 2010. Pattern Recognition software and techniques for biological image analysis. PLoS Computational Biology 6, e1000974.

Shannon, P., Markiel, A., Ozier, O., *et al.*, 2003. Cytoscape: A software environment for integrated models of biomolecular interaction networks. Genome Research 13, 2498–2504.

Shao, Z., Zhang, Y., Yuan, G.-C., Orkin, S.H., Waxman, D.J., 2012. MAnorm: A robust model for quantitative comparison of ChIP-Seq data sets. Genome Biology 13, R16.

Sharan, R., Ulitsky, I., Shamir, R., 2007. Network-based prediction of protein function. Molecular Systems Biology 3, 88.

Sharma, R., Bayarjargal, M., Tsunoda, T., Patil, A., Sharma, A., 2018a. MoRFPred-plus: Computational identification of MoRFs in protein sequences using physicochemical properties and HMM profiles. Journal of Theoretical Biology 437, 9–16.

Sharma, A., Boroevich, K., Shigemizu, D., *et al.*, 2017a. Hierarchical maximum likelihood clustering approach. IEEE Transactions on Biomedical Engineering 64, 112–122.

Sharma, R., Dehzangi, A., Lyons, J., *et al.*, 2015. Predict Gram-positive and Gram-negative subcellular localization via incorporating evolutionary information and physicochemical features into Chou's general PseAAC. IEEE Transactions on Nanobioscience 14, 915–926.

Sharma, A., Imoto, S., Miyano, S., 2012a. A between-class overlapping filter-based method for transcriptome data analysis. Journal of Bioinformatics and Computational Biology 10, 1250010.

Sharma, A., Imoto, S., Miyano, S., 2012b. A filter based feature selection algorithm using null space of covariance matrix for DNA microarray gene expression data. Current Bioinformatics 7, 289–294.

Sharma, A., Imoto, S., Miyano, S., 2012c. A top-r feature selection algorithm for microarray gene expression data. IEEE/ACM Transactions on Computational Biology and Bioinformatics 9, 754–764.

Sharma, A., Imoto, S., Miyano, S., Sharma, V., 2012d. Null space based feature selection method for gene expression data. International Journal of Machine Learning and Cybernetics 3, 269–276.

Sharma, A., Kamola, P.J., Tsunoda, T., 2017b. 2D-EM clustering approach for high-dimensional data through folding feature vectors. BMC Bioinformatics. 18, 547.

Sharma, A., Koh, C.H., Imoto, S., Miyano, S., 2011. Strategy of finding optimal number of features on gene expression data. Electronics Letters 47, 480–482.

Sharma, R., Kumar, S., Tsunoda, T., Patil, A., Sharma, A., 2016b. Predicting MoRFs in protein sequences using HMM profiles. BMC Bioinformatics 17, 504.

Sharma, A., López, Y., Tsunoda, T., 2017c. Divisive hierarchical maximum likelihood clustering. BMC Bioinformatics 18, 546.

Sharma, A., Lyons, J., Dehzangi, A., Paliwal, K.K., 2013. A feature extraction technique using bi-gram probabilities of position specific scoring matrix for protein fold recognition. Journal of Theoretical Biology 320, 41–46.

Sharma, A., Paliwal, K.K., 2007. Fast principal component analysis using fixed-point algorithm. Pattern Recognition Letters 28, 1151–1155.

Sharma, A., Paliwal, K.K., 2011. A gene selection algorithm using Bayesian classification approach. American Journal of Applied Sciences 9, 127–131.

Sharma, A., Paliwal, K.K., Imoto, S., Miyano, S., 2014. A feature selection method using improved regularized linear discriminant analysis. Machine Vision and Applications 25, 775–786.

Sharma, R., Raicar, G., Tsunoda, T., Patil, A., Sharma, A., 2018b. OPAL: prediction of MoRF regions in intrinsically disordered protein sequences. Bioinformatics 34, 1850–1858.

Sharma, A., Shigemizu, D., Boroevich, K.A., *et al.*, 2016a. Stepwise iterative maximum likelihood clustering approach. BMC Bioinformatics 17, 319.

Sherry, S.T., Ward, M.H., Kholodov, M., *et al.*, 2001. dbSNP: The NCBI database of genetic variation. Nucleic Acids Research 29, 308–311.

Shigemizu, D., Abe, T., Morizono, T., *et al.*, 2014. The construction of risk prediction models using GWAS data and its application to a type 2 diabetes prospective cohort. PLoS ONE 9, e92549.

Silver, J.D., Ritchie, M.E., Smyth, G.K., 2009. Microarray background correction: Maximum likelihood estimation for the normal-exponential convolution. Biostatistics 10, 352–363.

Slenter, D.N., Kutmon, M., Hanspers, K., *et al.*, 2018. WikiPathways: A multifaceted pathway database bridging metabolomics to other omics research. Nucleic Acids Research 46, D661–D667.

Soneson, C., Love, M.I., Robinson, M.D., 2015. Differential analyses for RNA-seq: transcript-level estimates improve gene-level inferences. F1000Research 4, 1521.

Spyrou, C., Stark, R., Lynch, A., Tavaré, S., 2009. BayesPeak: Bayesian analysis of ChIP-seq data. BMC Bioinformatics 10, 299.

Subramanian, A., Tamayo, P., Mootha, V.K., *et al.*, 2005. Gene set enrichment analysis: A knowledge-based approach for interpreting genome-wide expression profiles. Proceedings of the National Academy of Sciences of the United States of America 102, 15545–15550.

Sun, C., Medvedev, P., 2017. VarMatch: Robust matching of small variant datasets using flexible scoring schemes. Bioinformatics 33, 1301–1308.

Tarca, A.L., Bhatti, G., Romero, R., 2013. A comparison of gene set analysis methods in terms of sensitivity, prioritization and specificity. PLoS ONE 8, e79217.

Thomas-Chollier, M., Darbo, E., Herrmann, C., *et al.*, 2012. A complete workflow for the analysis of full-size ChIP-seq (and similar) data sets using peak-motifs. Nature Protocols 7, 1551–1568.

Uversky, V., 2014. Introduction to Intrinsically Disordered Proteins (IDPs). Chemical Reviews 114, 6557–6560.

Vidal, M., Cusick, M.E., Barabasi, A.L., 2011. Interactome networks and human disease. Cell 144, 986–998.

Viola, P., Wells, W., 1997. Alignment by maximization of mutual information. International Journal of Computer Vision 24, 137–154.

Walter, T., Shattuck, D.W., Baldock, R., *et al.*, 2010. Visualization of image data from cells to organisms. Nature Methods 7, S26–S41.

Wang, K., Li, M., Hakonarson, H., 2010. ANNOVAR: functional annotation of genetic variants from high-throughput sequencing data. Nucleic Acids Research 38, e164.

Wang, B., Mezlini, A.M., Demir, F., *et al.*, 2014. Similarity network fusion for aggregating data types on a genomic scale. Nature Methods 11, 333–337.

Wright, P.E., Dyson, H.J., 2015. Intrinsically disordered proteins in cellular signalling and regulation. Nature Reviews Molecular Cell Biology 16, 18–29.

Wu, M.C., Lee, S., Cai, T., *et al.*, 2011. Rare-variant association testing for sequencing data with the sequence kernel association test. American Journal of Human Genetics 89, 82–93.

Xu, S., Grullon, S., Ge, K., Peng, W., 2014. Spatial clustering for identification of ChIP-Enriched Regions (SICER) to map regions of histone methylation patterns in embryonic stem cells. In: Kidder B. (Eds.), Stem Cell Transcriptional Networks, Humana Press, New York.

Yang, Y., Chongxun, Z., Lin, P., 2004. A novel fuzzy C-means clustering algorithm for image thresholding. Measurement Science Review 4, 11–19.

Yang, Y., Heffernan, R., Paliwal, K., et al., 2017. SPIDER2: A package to predict secondary structure, accessible surface area and main-chain torsional angles by deep neural networks. Methods in Molecular Biology 1484, 55–63.

Yu, D., Kim, M., Xiao, G., Hwang, T.H., 2013. Review of biological network data and its applications. Genomics & Informatics 11, 200–210.

Zambelli, F., Pesole, G., Pavesi, G., 2013. Motif discovery and transcription factor binding sites before and after the next-generation sequencing era. Briefings in Bioinformatics 14, 225–237.

Zhang, Y., Liu, T., Meyer, C.A., et al., 2008. Model-based analysis of ChIP-Seq (MACS). Genome Biology 9, R137.

Zhou, J., Peng, H., 2007. Automatic recognition and annotation of gene expression patterns of fly embryos. Bioinformatics 23, 589–596.

Zhu, L.J., Gazin, C., Lawson, N.D., et al., 2010. ChIPpeakAnno: a Bioconductor package to annotate ChIP-seq and ChIP-chip data. BMC Bioinformatics 11, 237.

Zhu, Z., Zhang, F., Hu, H., et al., 2016. Integration of summary data from GWAS and eQTL studies predicts complex trait gene targets. Nature Genetics 48, 481–487.

Relevant Websites

www.r-project.org
    R Project.
www.bioconductor.org
    Bioconductor.

Constructing Computational Pipelines

ChuangKee Ong, European Bioinformatics Institute (EMBL-EBI), Hinxton, United Kingdom
Russell S Hamilton, University of Cambridge, Cambridge, United Kingdom

Introduction

The processing and analysis of data, such as from next-generation sequencing experiments requires multiple steps, many of which have complex sets of requirements. Running these steps in an ad-hoc manner can be very repetitive, time consuming and prone to human error. These shortcomings can be overcome through the utilization of computational pipeline tools, designed to streamline multiple complex analysis steps by linking the individual components into a single robust, efficient and reproducible workflow.

Dedicated pipelines remove the repetitiveness of the analysis and a single command can run a multiple-step pipeline on thousands of samples, whilst at the same time eliminating human error in the manual specification of the parameters required by the pipeline. As the pipeline runs the expectation is that a log file is generated with the version of the tools used, specified parameters, genome version, warning and error messages. These logs record the provenance of the analysis permitting the exact same analysis to be performed by researchers without access to the same hardware or pipeline tool.

In this article, we outline the features of several pipeline frameworks in terms of their job running efficiency and reproducibility. However, the choice of pipeline tools should also take into account the accompanying information provided by the pipeline tool project, for example, user documentation and resources provided by the user community. The development of pipeline frameworks and the defining of individual pipelines have many of the same requirements as the bioinformatics tools the pipelines call. For example, good documentation including manuals, quick start guides and code commenting make implementing the pipelines more manageable (Karimzadeh and Hoffman, 2017). Consideration should also be made to the reproducibility of the software, support for standard file formats, log file and version tracking (List *et al.*, 2017). The future adoption and support of the pipeline tool/framework will depend on its ease of use and ability for the users to write their own new pipelines.

Four key requirements we consider to be essential for a computational pipeline tool are:

1. Log provenance of analysis (e.g., version, parameters, genome release).
2. Standardized analysis across experiments.
3. Customizable, user created pipelines.
4. Utilize job scheduling where available.

Other important pipeline tool features include job dependencies where jobs await the execution of the steps upstream in the pipeline producing the required input. Non-dependent jobs can be run in parallel. In combination with a job scheduler this allows the individual steps in a pipeline to run as efficiently as possible. Check-pointing is also a very desirable feature, where pipelines can be restarted from the failure point rather than having to execute the entire pipeline from the start (Leipzig, 2016).

The primary take home message from this article is that to achieve robust and reproducible bioinformatics analyses it is vital to make use of a dedicated pipeline tool. Furthermore, the most appropriate tool should be selected based on the available computer infrastructure, user experience and project size.

Definitions of Hardware Levels, Project Sizes and User Experience Levels

One of the first considerations for choosing a pipeline framework to implement is the hardware available to run the pipelines (**Fig. 1**). This may be at the modest level of a single laptop for small scale project or prototyping right up to large, many thousand central processing unit (CPU) high performance computing (HPC) clusters. Cloud based solutions can scale beyond typical HPC installations if resources are available. Here we define four levels of hardware to aid selecting the most appropriate framework for the hardware available.

- Level 1: Laptop. Multicore (2 +), RAM (8 GB +).
- Level 2: Node. Multi-processor (1 − 2), Multicore (4 +), RAM (64 GB +).
- Level 3: HPC. Multi-processor, Multi-nodes (2 +, typically 100 s), RAM (64 GB +).
- Level 4: Cloud. Multi-processor, Multi-node (2 +) RAM (64 Gb +).

A further consideration is the project size which could range from a small RNA-Seq experiment consisting of six samples (e.g., 3 control and 3 case), up to a large-scale cohort study including many thousands of samples. Unless there are dedicated systems administrators available to install and maintain a pipeline environment the ease of install and usage are important factors in the choice of pipeline framework. User experience can range from a bench biologist wanting to analyze their data in a robust and reproducible manner up to seasoned bioinformaticians running pipelines on a production level scale for example at the EBI working towards the Ensembl releases on a three-month cycle.

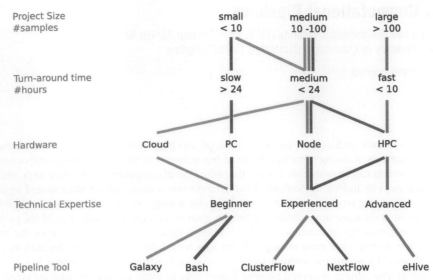

Fig. 1 Decision flowchart for choosing a suitable pipeline tool. There are many routes through the decision chart as each project or situation will have unique and changing requirements. We have highlighted five routes we consider to lead to the most appropriate choice for some typical environments. The red route is the least optimal as no dedicated pipeline framework is utilized.

Pipeline Tools

In this section, we will discuss a selection of popular pipeline tools and highlight their strengths and weaknesses. We will also introduce more generally applicable resources such as virtualisation and cloud based frameworks which are particularly well suited to developing bioinformatics pipelines.

Each pipeline tool uses its own terminology for the elements comprising a fully functional workflow or pipeline. To simplify the terminology, we define some common terms and concepts.

- Module/process: an independent, self-contained task in a pipeline, for example, the adapter and quality trimming of fastq files.
- Pipeline/workflow: constructed by linking together modules/processes to achieve an objective. **Fig. 3** depicts a simple RNA-seq data processing pipeline.
- Pipeline tool/framework: an implementation of multiple pipelines or workflows with necessary supporting libraries. A pipeline framework can also include other features such as viewing and creating figures from the analyses.
- Job scheduler: software to control and manage unattended background execution of jobs. A job scheduler will queue jobs until the requested resources (processor and memory) are available. Examples of job scheduling software are Simple Linux Utility for Resource Management (SLURM), Grid Engine (SGE), Portable Batch System (PBS) and Load Sharing Facility (LSF).
- Serial/parallel job processing: a job can run as serial processes, where each instruction is performed in turn; or in parallel where instructions are performed at the same time on different or multi-node processors.

Ad-Hoc/Shell Scripts

At the simplest level, a collection of tools can be combined into a pipeline using shell scripts, a set of commands to be run by the Linux Shell (e.g., BASH). These are often simple to create and require customisation for each project. There are many advanced features that can be incorporated into shell scripts. However, scripts lack the two main features of an efficient data processing pipeline: the ability to launch jobs on the completion of dependent jobs and check-pointing (Leipzig, 2016). With this in mind, and the difficulty in writing and maintaining scripts can be avoided by using dedicated workflow/ pipeline tools.

ClusterFlow

ClusterFlow was developed as an easy to use and install pipelining system for bioinformatics applications (Ewels *et al.*, 2016), and can be run on any level of hardware, with and without a dedicated job scheduling system. Internally, ClusterFlow uses pre-defined modules to build pipelines which are run as shell scripts tailored to the system hardware. For example, on a laptop the pipeline would run in serial for a set number of CPU cores. On a full cluster the bash script would launch the pipeline steps in parallel with queuing controlled by the job scheduling system. There are currently over 40 modules defined in ClusterFlow, using over 25 bioinformatics tools and there are over thirty predefined pipelines, an example of a simple RNA-Seq workflow is shown in **Fig. 3**. Writing custom modules involves the tool command and options to be defined in a Perl module, requiring a moderate knowledge of coding. Once created, modules can be included in pipelines defined as a nested list of tools to be run. The indentation and nesting defines the order the tools must be run and their dependencies. For example, a trimming step must complete before an alignment is started. As a pipeline completes a log file is generated capturing any log output from the tools in the pipeline as well as version information for the tools run. This is harvested at run time so produces the actual tool and genome version used. An email notification system runs when the job has completed, or of any issues that occurred during the run. ClusterFlow is unable to re-queue failed jobs, but does report the errors in log files.

Nextflow

NextFlow is a domain independent pipeline tool with strong support for bioinformatics applications (Di Tommaso et al., 2017) with tasks such as operations on common bioinformatics file formats are included as part of the core distribution. Pre-made bioinformatics pipelines are available from the Nextflow user community and are curated on the NextFlow website. The installation and initial set-up are non-trivial and require an experienced bioinformatician with systems administration skills. However, once set up NextFlow provides a very robust system for running pipelines with check-pointing allowing pipelines to be restarted from any point if failures are encountered. Modules can be written in any language (e.g., Perl, Python, Bash) and can use existing scripts, this has an advantage of not requiring new modules to be specifically written for Nextflow. Modules are then incorporated into pipelines in the NextFlow 'dataflow programming model' build as an operating system and hardware independent Java Virtual Machine. Nextflow is also compatible with Docker, permitting pipelines to be scaled up to a full HPC system or to cloud instances.

Bpipe

Bpipe (Sadedin et al., 2012) is a Java/Groovy based pipeline tool for bioinformatics, designed to take existing command line tools and shell scripts and wrap them into robust pipelines. The syntax has been selected to ease the transition from existing shell script based pipelines into Bpipe. Each task of the pipeline is written as a separate module allowing new pipelines to easily be built from existing tasks. Check-pointing is implemented so jobs can be restarted from a failure, in addition to the generation of log files as the pipelines proceeds. Non-interdependent tasks can be run in parallel and are compatible with job scheduling tools to fully optimise running jobs on different scale hardware. The tasks and pipelines are hardware independent so can be easily shared across different architectures.

Snakemake

Snakemake (Köster and Rahmann, 2012) is a scalable pipeline system based on the Python language with in-built check-pointing. The specification of the number of cores/threads on the hardware and the job scheduling system enables snakemake to scale from single core platforms to large multi-node clusters. For each snakemake run a directed acyclic graph (DAG) is generated with nodes representing the specified jobs to be run. A useful feature is the ability to export the DAG as an image for the pipeline to allow visualisation of the structure of the pipeline (Similar to **Fig. 3**). In this way, non-dependent jobs can be run in parallel, and with further configuration of the multi-threaded nature of some programs CPU usage can be optimised. The check-pointing system permits pipelines to be restarted, and with an output file check, pipelines can be re-started from the last successfully completed step rather than having to restart the entire pipeline. If a step of the pipeline fails then snakemake performs an automatic cleanup of output files from these incomplete jobs. Users can create and distribute snakemake workflows via code repositories such as GitHub, however to date no central repository for user-contributed pipelines exists.

eHive

eHive (Severin et al., 2010) is a Perl workflow management system, utilising job schedulers such as LSF to submit jobs to the compute clusters. Large compute clusters work on the concept of a centralised job queue and a job controller. Bottlenecks arise in the job controller as cluster nodes need explicit instructions for each and every job execution. A few seconds latency between job submission and execution can translate into a significant overhead when the scheduling system needs to handle millions of jobs. The core concept of eHive is that jobs are not scheduled by central controller, instead are modelled on a honeybee queen in a hive with her worker bees. The queen will create workers using a job creation/selection algorithm by observing the central blackboard. It is designed with the aim of moving job scheduling away a from centralised controller yet retaining the ability to monitor jobs as they progress. Eventually a system emerges with very small (3 ms) job overhead, fault tolerance and optimised utilization of computing clusters with more than 1000 cores.

The main console for eHive, the beekeeper, creates workers as required and submits them to the compute cluster, reporting their progress. In this model, workers need not be aware of the existence of other workers, rather only the steps prior and downstream of itself in the pipeline. Each worker generates and stores partial solutions to problems communicated indirectly through the central blackboard. Workers are autonomous and have the ability to create additional jobs, analyses, dataflow and control rules as they run. A MySQL database is used as the central blackboard detailing the jobs and processes to be run in the pipeline. In a centralised pipeline tool, a job will retrieve input data from a shared resource and in some cases store results into a common database. This

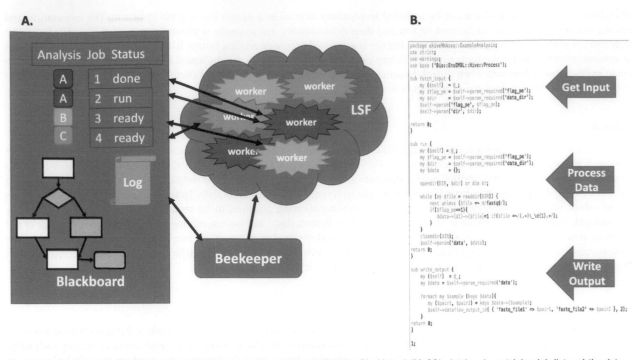

Fig. 2 Architecture of *eHive* Pipeline Tool. (A) Different components of *eHive*, the Blackboard (MySQL database) containing job list and the data flow rules; *beekeeper*, console that create workers and submit jobs to compute clusters; Workers, which run in the LSF job scheduling system. (B) A typical eHive Analysis module. Three key stages in a typical *eHive* analysis module lifecycle.

has the potential to create bottlenecks if there are a large number of jobs running at once. In *eHive*, the database can anticipate significant numbers of concurrent write requests via the implementation of an InnoDB database engine to enable row-level-locking supporting concurrent table updates. Jobs can also be processed in batches to mitigate this issue. Once a worker is created, it will register its choice of analysis on the central blackboard and load the modules needed to execute the analysis. Subsequent workers will grab and execute jobs available from the central blackboard. As the jobs progress, workers log their process status on the blackboard, finally setting the job status to done once completed without errors (**Fig. 2**).

Through these optimisations *eHive* can easily handle tens of millions of jobs and has been successfully tested with SGE, PBS and the default LSF job scheduler. *eHive* has been used in several large scale international bioinformatics projects as a key infrastructure of the data coordination centre, for example, the Ensembl (Aken *et al.*, 2017) and Ensembl Genomes Project (Kersey *et al.*, 2016), the Functional Annotation of Animal Genomes project (FAANG) (Andersson *et al.*, 2015) and the International Genome Sample Resource (ISGR) (Clarke *et al.*, 2017), as well various other high throughput genomics and epigenomics projects. To illustrate *eHive*'s industry scale capacity; the *eHive* InterProScan pipeline (Jones *et al.*, 2014) is run every three months in Ensembl and Ensembl Genomes, where protein domain annotations are run for over 1000 genomes, against 11 million protein sequences. *eHive* chunks the sequences into smaller sets and runs the InterProScan protein domain identification. The resulting XML files of identified signatures are then parsed and stored in the respective genome databases. The pipeline usually runs for 7–10 days, requiring regular monitoring via *guiHive* (Cunningham *et al.*, 2015) or a MySQL interface to ensure the beekeeper is still alive, and creating workers needed to complete the pipeline. Failed beekeeper jobs are typically due to memory limits or missing files, but can be easily restarted with the check-pointing system.

Virtualization

Rather than run pipelines directly on the available hardware via a dedicated pipelining system such as those outlined above, virtualisation provides a layer of abstraction with benefits such as being agnostic to the local hardware and operating system (OS). In essence, virtualisation is the ability to run multiple virtual computers on a single computer (e.g., laptop). Containers are stripped down virtual machines just containing the required parts of the operating system to run the required programs. The main advantage of virtualisation is the portability and the popularity of tools such as Docker in the wider computing community have created a large user base with extensive online resources.

Docker

Docker containers are a method of packaging together the minimal required elements required to run a piece of software or pipeline such as the source code, runtime environment, system tools, and system libraries. This makes an efficient, lightweight, self-contained systems ensuring software will always run reproducibly, regardless of where it is deployed. Containers and Virtual Machines have a shared heritage so are similar as in having resource isolation and allocation benefits, however architectural differences have given containers the advantage of being both portable and efficient. Virtual Machines typically comprise the main application, binaries and libraries as well as the entire guest OS and can be tens of GBs, running independently of the host OS. Contrary to this, containers have the same capability of a Virtual Machine, excluding the full OS in favour of sharing a kernel with other containers, running as isolated processes in user space on the host operating system. A further advantage of containers is their ability to isolate applications from one another as well as the underlying hardware, providing an additional layer of protection for the application a.k.a secure by default.

Docker is utilized across many disciplines, not just bioinformatics, however there are several projects providing domain specific resources for bioinformatics pipelines. These range from tutorials and documentation to repositories of community created pipelines and containers for bioinformatics software (see Relevant Websites Section). Bio-Docklets (Kim *et al.*, 2017) are an effort to ease the creation of bioinformatics pipelines using Docker. Each tool in the pipeline is containerised in an individual *docklet*, with wrapper scripts combining the docklets into a pipeline.

Pipeline Cloud Environments

In a next generation sequencing project with a high number of samples and/or read depth is likely to require the availability of high performance computing hardware. If this is not available, or a rapid scale-up is required, then cloud based environments are an attractive alternative to local hardware. However, it is worth stating that as with all cloud based storage, the data may be located in a different country potentially violating the policies of data storage for many government organisations and charities. A key advantage of many of the available pipeline cloud environments is a graphical interface to run and create pipelines, rather than relying on command-line execution or coding.

Galaxy

Galaxy (Afgan *et al.*, 2016) is targeted at researchers who do not want to design and run pipelines via the command line as pipelines can be designed graphically via the Galaxy interface assessed via an Internet browser. There is a large user community providing implementations of individual bioinformatics tools as well as complete pipelines. The Galaxy team also present regular user and developer meetings ensuring a thriving community supporting the platform. Galaxy can be accessed via public servers, local installs or via cloud instances.

Seven Bridges and DNANexus

There are several commercial cloud-based bioinformatics environments, with Seven Bridges (see Relevant Websites Section) and DNANexus (see Relevant Websites Section) being the most widely known. Both provide a large range of pipelines for the most common types of NGS analysis. However, a completely novel/custom pipeline would require working closely with the commercial teams. An open source alternative, Arvardos (see Relevant Websites Section) can be installed and run on private cloud instances, or via a commercial partner Curoverse (see Relevant Websites Section). The main advantage of cloud solutions is the ability to instantly scale up analysis without having to worry about the underlying hardware, the cost of cloud deployments is usually on a cost-effective pay-*per*-usage model. The commercial solutions also allow users to interact via web-based graphical interfaces or the command line for more advanced users.

Pipeline Languages

Each of the pipeline tools introduced in this article require the pipelines to be defined and coded in a tool specific manner. While some effort has gone into making pipelines portable, e.g., the ability to import shell scripts into NextFlow, it is a very attractive prospect to define pipelines in a truly environment agnostic manner. To address this the common workflow language was, and continues to be developed.

Common Workflow Language

The Common Workflow Language (CWL) aims to standardise the language used to define pipelines and allow the sharing of pipelines across the different pipeline systems (Amstutz *et al.*, 2016). The vision is for a researcher with a pipeline developed in for example Clusterflow to be able to share the code with a researcher using Arvardos without needing to re-implement the pipeline from scratch. This inherent portability from using CWL is also advantageous if a pipeline on local hardware requires a rapid scale up to run on a cloud environment for a specific project. CWL is supported in NextFlow, Galaxy, Seven Bridges, DNANexus and Arvardos.

Worked Example

To highlight the differences of the implementations of workflow in a selection of pipeline tools we provide a worked example for a simple RNA-Seq pipeline as a bash script (**Fig. 3**), in *ClusterFlow* and in *eHive*. We provide example code and documentation for each pipeline tool on Github (see Relevant Websites Section). In our simple paired-end RNA-Seq example there are six main steps, with requirements for jobs to complete before the next can proceed (i.e., dependencies). The initial quality control is performed with FastQC and trim_galore. The alignment with HiSat2 is dependent on trim_galore completing. Post-alignment gene quantification using htseq-counts and quality assessment using Qualimap require the alignment step to complete. Finally, once all jobs in the pipeline are complete for a sample then a summary report is generated with MultiQC. In the bash script example, each step in the pipeline is executed sequentially as the job dependencies are not defined. Each step can run as multithreaded jobs, but the overall efficiency of the pipeline is far from optimal. In the *ClusterFlow* and *eHive* examples the jobs are executed in a dependency aware manner, allowing efficient deployment of the pipeline jobs across samples. *eHive*'s check-pointing system will automatically restart failed jobs, and with the further optimisations detailed above is particularly suited to very large scale projects.

With the recent development and rapid adoption of single cell RNA sequencing (scRNA-Seq) it is worth highlighting the differences to the worked example above in terms of the creation of a reproducible and robust pipeline. There are several scRNA-Seq tool suites available, for example: Seurat, Scater and Monocle (Zappia *et al.*, 2017), however these could benefit from tighter integration with high performance computing environments and the robustness of pipeline tools for reproducible analysis. As the number of single cells in a typical experiment can easily be over 100,000 depending on the sequencing protocol, particular attention must be given to the quality control steps including filtering, normalisation, and drop-out modelling so are a critical component of any single cell pipeline (Svensson *et al.*, 2017).

Discussion

When it comes to pipeline design, there are various tools available and considerations to be taken into account. Here we illustrate a selection of tools and outline some key metrics (**Table 1**), which we feel that can aid in the process of decision making. Depending on the importance of a certain metric(s) to the project, one could then decide on the most appropriate tool to use. For instance, due to a short delivery time-frame for a small size project, a tool that is easy to install, new modules and pipeline can be easily built are of paramount importance. With this in mind, one could then look at *ClusterFlow* as potential tool solution as it satisfies the requirements for logging and the use of a job scheduler. At the other end of the spectrum, when analysis reproducibility, tool robustness and re-queuing capabilities are essential, *eHive* or *Galaxy* are strong candidates. It is absolutely critical from the outset to have a clear understanding of the project characteristics, available resources and output delivery in order to make the optimal decision on the pipeline tool to use. The use of pipeline frameworks in designing computational pipelines will ease the management of multiple pipelines, reducing the need for manual intervention, therefore minimizing errors and increasing the robustness and reproducibility of

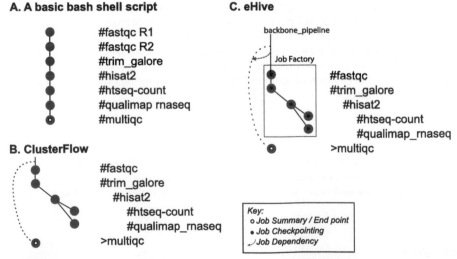

Fig. 3 A schematic highlighting the different job architectures for three pipeline tools. (A) Simple bash shell script with each of the pipeline steps executed in series requiring each job to be completed before launching the next. (B) *ClusterFlow* implements job dependencies, where jobs wait for their dependent job to be completed before launching. Non-dependent jobs can launch and run in parallel. A final step can be specified, in this case a MultiQC report, to run once all other jobs have completed. (C) *eHive* also has job dependencies, but with additional error checking and checkpointing. In this way pipeline jobs can be restarted from the last completed step. In all cases multithreading can be implemented in the specification of the tools being run, allowing within job parallelisation. Example code for each of the pipelines (A,B,C) can be freely accessed. Available at: https://github.com/darogan/ConstructingComputationalPipelines/).

Table 1   Comparison table for pipeline tool features

Metric	BASH	ClusterFlow	NextFlow	eHIVE	Galaxy
Ease of install	Easy	Easy	Moderate	Advanced	Moderate
Pre-made modules	No	Yes	Yes	Yes	Yes
Ease of writing modules	Easy	Moderate	Moderate	Advanced	Easy
Ease of writing pipelines	Easy	Easy	Moderate	Advanced	Easy
Use of queueing system	Partial	Yes	Yes	Yes	Yes
Checkpoints/re-queuing	No	No	Yes	Yes	Yes
Tool version logging	No	Yes	Yes	Yes	Yes
Pre-defined genome locations	No	Yes	Yes	Yes	Yes
Hardware level compatibility	1,2,3	1,2,3	1,2,3	2,3	2,3,4
Cloud compatibility	No	No	Yes	Yes	Yes
Inbuilt Docker support	No	No	Yes	No	Yes
Large scale projects	No	No	Yes	yes	Yes
Common Workflow language compatible	No	No	No	No	Yes
Under active development	N/A	Yes	Yes	Yes	Yes

Five options for running pipelines are compared for features supported by the tool as default. In many cases the feature compatibility is possible with customisation and an advanced level of expertise. Hardware levels are defined in the Introduction (1. Laptop, 2. Node, 3. HPC, 4. Cloud).

the analyses. The RNA-Seq worked example illustrated here is a basic implementation to demonstrate how a pipeline is constructed within three different frameworks. For examples of more comprehensive analysis pipelines, we recommend the GATK best practices for variant calling on whole genome and exome high-throughput sequencing projects (Auwera *et al.*, 2013). The variant calling pipeline includes many quality control steps such as marking duplicates, base quality recalibrations and filtering for variants. GATK also produce their own workflow data language (WDL) for constructing pipelines.

Future Directions

One of the key issues that must be addressed to ensure the widespread adoption of robust pipeline frameworks is the lack of interoperability of defined pipelines (e.g., RNA-Seq) between the different pipeline frameworks. Currently, it is not trivial to share a defined pipeline between frameworks, however with the standardization of languages for defining pipelines (e.g., CWL or WDL) and platform independent frameworks for running software (e.g., Biocontainers) there is a clear route to achieve this in the near future (Leprevost *et al.*, 2017).

Closing Remarks

The primary aim of this article has been to guide users into selecting the most suitable pipeline tool for their project and available resources. With all the advantages of automating robust bioinformatics pipelines it should be stated that this should not be at the expense of understanding the underlying processing and analyses being performed. Bioinformatics should never be thought of as a black-box, and careful though must be applied to ensuring the most appropriate tools are being used.

Acknowledgements

Russell Hamilton is funded by the Centre for Trophoblast Research (University of Cambridge). ChuangKee Ong is funded by Open Targets, European Bioinformatics Institute (EMBL-EBI). We would also like to thank Joseph Gardner and Malwina Prater for the critical reading of this article.

Appendix

Code and documentation to support our implementation of the worked example in Bash, *Clusterflow* and *eHive* are freely available from GitHub (see Relevant Websites Section).

See also: Computational Pipelines and Workflows in Bioinformatics. Computing for Bioinformatics. MapReduce in Computational Biology via Hadoop and Spark. Natural Language Processing Approaches in Bioinformatics

References

Afgan, E., Baker, D., van den Beek, M., et al., 2016. The Galaxy platform for accessible, reproducible and collaborative biomedical analyses: 2016 update. Nucleic Acids Res. 44, W3–W10. doi:10.1093/nar/gkw343.

Aken, B.L., Achuthan, P., Akanni, W., et al., 2017. Ensembl 2017. Nucleic Acids Res. 45, D635–D642. doi:10.1093/nar/gkw1104.

Amstutz, P., Crusoe, M.R., Tijanic, N., et al., 2016. Common Workflow Language. v1.0. doi:10.6084/M9.FIGSHARE.3115156.V2.

Andersson, L., Archibald, A.L., Bottema, C.D., et al., 2015. Coordinated international action to accelerate genome-to-phenome with FAANG, the Functional Annotation of Animal Genomes project. Genome Biol. 16, 57. doi:10.1186/s13059-015-0622-4.

Auwera, G.A., Van Der, Carneiro, M.O., Hartl, C., et al., 2013. From FastQ data to high-confidence variant calls: The genome analysis toolkit best practices pipeline. Curr. Protoc. Bioinform. 43. doi:10.1002/0471250953.bi1110s43.

Clarke, L., Fairley, S., Zheng-Bradley, X., et al., 2017. The international Genome sample resource (IGSR): A worldwide collection of genome variation incorporating the 1000 Genomes Project data. Nucleic Acids Res. 45, D854–D859. doi:10.1093/nar/gkw829.

Cunningham, F., Amode, M.R., Barrell, D., et al., 2015. Ensembl 2015. Nucleic Acids Res. 43, D662–D669. doi:10.1093/nar/gku1010.

Di Tommaso, P., Chatzou, M., Floden, E.W., et al., 2017. Nextflow enables reproducible computational workflows. Nat. Biotechnol. 35, 316–319. doi:10.1038/nbt.3820.

Ewels, P., Krueger, F., Käller, M., et al., 2016. Cluster flow: A user-friendly bioinformatics workflow tool. F1000Research 5, 2824. doi:10.12688/f1000research.10335.1.

Jones, P., Binns, D., Chang, H.Y., et al., 2014. InterProScan 5: Genome-scale protein function classification. Bioinformatics 30, 1236–1240. doi:10.1093/bioinformatics/btu031.

Karimzadeh, M., Hoffman, M.M., 2017. Top considerations for creating bioinformatics software documentation. Brief. Bioinform. bbw134. doi:10.1093/bib/bbw134.

Kersey, P.J., Allen, J.E., Armean, I., et al., 2016. Ensembl Genomes 2016: More genomes, more complexity. Nucleic Acids Res. 44, D574–D580. doi:10.1093/nar/gkv1209.

Kim, B., Ali, T., Lijeron, C., Afgan, E., Krampis, K., 2017. Bio-Docklets: Virtualization containers for single-step execution of NGS pipelines. bioRxiv. 0–8.

Köster, J., Rahmann, S., 2012. Snakemake – A scalable bioinformatics workflow engine. Bioinformatics 28, 2520–2522. doi:10.1093/bioinformatics/bts480.

Leipzig, J., 2016. A review of bioinformatic pipeline frameworks. Brief. Bioinform. bbw020. doi:10.1093/bib/bbw020.

Leprevost, F., da, V., Grüning, B.A., et al., 2017. BioContainers: An open-source and community-driven framework for software standardization. Bioinformatics 33, 1–3. doi:10.1093/bioinformatics/btx192.

List, M., Ebert, P., Albrecht, F., 2017. Ten simple rules for developing usable software in computational biology. PLOS Comput. Biol. 13, e1005265. doi:10.1371/journal.pcbi.1005265.

Sadedin, S.P., Pope, B., Oshlack, A., 2012. Bpipe: A tool for running and managing bioinformatics pipelines. Bioinformatics 28, 1525–1526. doi:10.1093/bioinformatics/bts167.

Severin, J., Beal, K., Vilella, A.J., et al., 2010. eHive: An artificial intelligence workflow system for genomic analysis. BMC Bioinform. 11, 240. doi:10.1186/1471-2105-11-240.

Svensson, V., Vento-Tormo, R., Teichmann, S.A., 2017. Exponential scaling of single-cell RNA-seq in the last decade. arXiv:1704.01379.

Zappia, L., Phipson, B., Oshlack, A., 2017. Exploring the single-cell RNA-seq analysis landscape with the scRNA- tools database. bioRxiv. doi:10.1101/206573.

Further Reading

Beaulieu-Jones, B.K., Greene, C.S., 2017. Reproducibility of computational workflows is automated using continuous analysis. Nat. Biotechnol. 35, 342–346. doi:10.1038/nbt.3780.

Ewels, P., Magnusson, M., Lundin, S., Käller, M., 2016. MultiQC: Summarize analysis results for multiple tools and samples in a single report. Bioinformatics 32, btw354. doi:10.1093/bioinformatics/btw354.

Hothorn, T., Leisch, F., 2011. Case studies in reproducibility. Brief. Bioinform. 12, 288–300. doi:10.1093/bib/bbq084.

Kim, Y., Poline, J., Dumas, G., 2017. Experimenting with reproducibility in bioinformatics. bioRxiv. 0–5. doi:10.1101/143503.

Merelli, I., Pérez-Sánchez, H., Gesing, S., D'Agostino, D., 2014. Latest advances in distributed, parallel, and graphic processing unit accelerated approaches to computational biology. Concurr. Comput. Pract. Exp. 26, 1699–1704. doi:10.1002/cpe.3111.

Pawlik, A., van Gelder, C.W.G., Nenadic, A., et al., 2017. Developing a strategy for computational lab skills training through Software and Data Carpentry: Experiences from the ELIXIR Pilot action. F1000Research 6, 1040. doi:10.12688/f1000research.11718.1.

Perez-riverol, Y., Wang, R., Sachsenberg, et al., Ten simple rules for taking advantage of GitHub. PLOS Comput. Biol. 5–11. Available at: https://doi.org/10.1371/journal.pcbi.1004947.

Piccolo, S.R., Frampton, M.B., 2016. Tools and techniques for computational reproducibility. Gigascience 5, 30. doi:10.1186/s13742-016-0135-4.

Sandve, G.K., Nekrutenko, A., Taylor, J., Hovig, E., 2013. Ten simple rules for reproducible computational research. PLOS Comput. Biol. 9, 1–4. doi:10.1371/journal.pcbi.1003285.

Wilson, G., Aruliah, D.A., Brown, C.T., et al., 2014. Best practices for scientific computing. PLOS Biol. 12. doi:10.1371/journal.pbio.1001745.

Relevant Websites

https://arvados.org/
Arvardos.

https://github.com/BioContainers/containers
BioContainers.

https://github.com/helios/bio-docker
BioDocker.

https://curoverse.com/
Curoverse.

https://github.com/sjackman/docker-bio
DockerBio.

https://www.dnanexus.com
DNANexus.

https://github.com/darogan/ConstructingComputationalPipelines
Github.

https://github.com/pditommaso/awesome-pipeline
Pditommaso/awesome pipeline.

https://www.sevenbridges.com/
Seven Bridges.

Biographical Sketch

ChuangKee is a proven research and informatics leader in the life science and pharma drug discovery space with hands on computational and informatics experience. In his role as Data Coordinator/Manager at OpenTargets (collaboration between EBI, GSK, Sanger Institute & Biogen), He manages data providers across various different groups, and drives data integration efforts. ChuangKee joined OpenTargets from Ensembl, one of the most successful large scale bioinformatics projects in history. Most recently he was the Senior Technical Officer in the Ensembl's production team, responsible for large scale processing pipelines, production infrastructure development, data coordination among sub-teams to ensure delivery of releases consisting of thousands genomes. Before Ensembl, ChuangKee was the Principal Scientist, VP at Sime Darby Technology Centre (SDTC). He headed the bioinformatics, data analysis department whose efforts were geared toward enhancing palm oil yield using high throughput assays such as NGS. Prior to joining SDTC, ChuangKee was a Senior Associate Scientist at Eli Lilly. He lead various cross-functional, -discipline drug discovery informatics projects to support target identification and validation in various therapeutic areas. Before Eli Lilly he was with Medical Research Council in Edinburgh. ChuangKee has a Masters in Bioinformatics from Chalmers University of Technology in Sweden.

Russell Hamilton heads the bioinformatics core facility at the Centre for Trophoblast Research (CTR), University of Cambridge. The focus of the CTR is the study of the placenta and maternal-fetal interactions during pregnancy and brings together over 25 Principal Investigators based in different departments within the University of Cambridge and Babraham Institute. He has previously worked in industry at Cambridge Epigenetix (CEGX) developing epigenetics tools to enable single base resolution sequencing of methyl-cytosine (mC) and hydroxymethyl-cytosine (hmC). Prior to this was a senior postdoc in the Department of Biochemistry at University of Oxford, working on the RNA structural motifs required for mRNA localization and their interaction with trans-acting protein factors. Russell received an MSc in Intelligent Systems from the University of Aberdeen and his PhD in bioinformatics from the University of Edinburgh. At each of his previous positions, Russell has set up bioinformatics infrastructure including pipelines for next-generation sequencing, RNA structure searches, protein structural modelling and a microscope imaging facility.

Pipeline of High Throughput Sequencing

ChuangKee Ong, European Bioinformatics Institute (EMBL-EBI), Hinxton, United Kingdom
Qi Bin Kwong, Ai Ling Ong, and Huey Ying Heng, Sime Darby Plantation R&D Centre, Selangor, Malaysia
Wai Yee Low, Davies Research Centre, University of Adelaide, Roseworthy, SA, Australia

Introduction

Advancements in sequencing technologies in recent years have created massive amount of sequenced data, which necessitate the development of efficient computational pipeline to mine the data. Preprocessing of raw next generation sequencing (NGS) data of large genomes such as that of humans is compute intensive. The bioinformatics bottleneck can be more time consuming than the time it takes to sequence the DNA and hence, the application of the right pipeline with features such as ease of setup and use, parallelization, job scheduling and tracking of compute processes is pivotal to move the field forward. To demonstrate and give readers a glimpse on the pros and cons of applying a pipeline to NGS data, this article will take as an example of five human exomes and preprocess them for single nucleotide variant (SNV) discovery. It starts with showing the painstaking process involved in running some common preprocessing software without stringing them together as a pipeline. Then, the application of pipeline for preprocessing in three different ways are discussed: Shell scripting, Galaxy (Afgan *et al.*, 2016) and eHive (Severin *et al.*, 2010). Among these three different methods, eHive can be considered as a frontier pipeline or workflow management system that has been deployed for use in big projects such as The Functional Annotation of Animal Genomes (FAANG) (Andersson *et al.*, 2015). The dataset and software used for this study are given in the Appendix.

NGS Preprocessing

One of the common tasks in resequencing studies is to align raw sequencing data (e.g., provided in FASTQ format) to a genome and then perform variant calling. This process is so common that the literature is replete with examples of methodology that involves preprocessing and there are many different tools that can be used to achieve this purpose. To provide as a sample case study, consider a scenario where researchers have sequenced a human exome using the Illumina technology; what then would be the steps required to go from raw reads to variant calls?

To start the preprocessing, a quality control check on the raw sequenced data is mandatory. A software tool known as FastQC (Andrews, 2010) can be used for this purpose. A sample command line format is as below:

```
$ fastqc <PE1> <PE2>
```

where <PE1> and <PE2> represents the front paired end and back paired end FASTQ files, respectively. Key aspects such as per base sequence quality, per base sequence content and Kmer content are given as HTML reports for users to evaluate sequence quality (Andrews, 2015). The presence of adapters is unwanted because only the insert sequences need to be analyzed. Adapters can be removed using Trim Galore! software (Krueger, 2015).

```
$ trim_galore –paired <PE1> <PE2>
```

The default output from Trim Galore! will be <PE1>_val_1.fq and <PE2>_val_2.fq. For this command with default parameters, TrimGalore! will auto-detect some common adapters such as Illumina universal, Nextera transposase and Illumina small RNA. Users may provide their own specific adapter sequences too. Additionally, by default sequences with quality score below Q20 will also be removed.

Prior to mapping, the reference genome <REF> needs to be indexed for quick access of its sequences, which is done using the command below.

```
$ bwa index <REF>
$ samtools faidx <REF>
```

The mapping of raw FASTQ reads to the reference genome can be done using BWA aligner (Li, 2013). BWA mem is used in this case because it is more suitable, faster and more accurate for sequences longer than 70 bp. Users can explore other options given in BWA and a myriad of other published aligners but such details are beyond the scope of this article.

```
$ bwa mem <REF> <PE1>_val_1.fq <PE2>_val_2.fq > mapped.sam
```

This is followed by the variant calling step where mapped.sam is the input. SNPs are called using samtools (Li *et al.*, 2009) and bcftools (Narasimhan *et al.*, 2016). The samtools view command converts the alignment file from SAM to BAM format, which represents a more compact way to store the data. Next, the samtools sort command will arrange the mapped alignment according to coordinate in ascending order along the chromosomes in the reference genome. The combination of samtools mpileup and bcftools view is to gather SNPs and visualize in vcf format.

```
$ samtools view -bT <REF> mapped.sam –o mapped.bam
$ samtools sort mapped.bam mapped.sort
$ samtools mpileup -uf <REF> mapped.sort.bam > output.mpileup
$ bcftools view -vcg output.mpileup > result.vcf
```

The vcf output contains all the SNPs found in the sample. However, it is not meaningful if it cannot be translated into biological significance. ANNOVAR (Wang *et al.*, 2010) is a collection of Perl scripts designed for functional annotation of the SNPs. The script converts the vcf format into input recognizable by ANNOVAR. Next, annotate_variation.pl performs annotations on the functions of the SNPs.

```
$ convert2annovar.pl –format vcf4 –includeinfo result.vcf > input.annovar
```

```
$ annotate_variation.pl –buildver hg19 input.annovar annovar/humandb -outfile result
```

Upon running the final command, two files will be generated, which are "result.variant_function" and the "result.exonic_variant_function". The first file contains all the potential gene-based functional annotation of the detected SNPs, and the second file gives additional information regarding the exonic SNPs detected.

Readers should take note that the steps outlined above illustrate some of the important steps for preprocessing but the gold standard version has additional steps such as base quality recalibration. For those interested in a tutorial that details these additional steps, refer in Low and Tammi (2017).

Application of a Pipeline for NGS Preprocessing Automation

Case Study With Shell Scripting

If one would like to perform large-scale analysis of multiple resequenced data, such as human exomes, instead of running commands one by one, users can write a Shell script (*.sh) that encompasses all the above commands. Shell script is a text file that serves as an overall controller for the pipeline of interest. Upon running the script, the written code will be interpreted and the pipeline will then be executed. Some of the usual Shell-script/command-line interpreters are the Bourne shell (sh), C Shell (csh) and the Bourne Again Shell (bash). In the example in **Box 1** below, the interpreter used is Bourne shell, as shown by the #!/bin/sh line on top.

This Shell script basically runs the pipeline for the preprocessing steps detailed in the preceding section. The difference is that a script is now being used to chain together a series of commands to process FASTQ files to get variant calls.

In Shell scripting, it is common to add an echo command, which prints out what the next step is, before running a new process. This allows for tracking of analysis progress or errors, and is particularly useful when a long Shell script is used. The input files for the Shell script can be passed from the command line through the usage of arguments/parameters. In this case, the script takes in two arguments, the FASTQ file and the reference genome file. The first argument is passed into the individual commands in the script as $1, whereas the second argument is passed on as $2. To ensure that two arguments are always passed into the script, the "if" statement starting at the second line of the script explains the usage, and that the script will automatically quits if there are lesser than two input arguments.

The main advantage of having a Shell script is that it reduces retyping of commands every time similar analysis needs to be carried out, and it can be set to run automatically at scheduled interval using cron (Keller, 1999). As compared to other workflow programs, setting up an analysis pipeline using Shell script has far lesser dependencies as compared to other workflow programs. Additionally, it is easier to customize. However, the disadvantage of this method is that there is no Graphical User Interface (GUI) and some programming skills are required. Furthermore, it is sometimes difficult to troubleshoot errors but this can be helped by writing code that can catch potential errors or trace for errors from log files but the script is not easy to interpret for novices.

Case Study With Galaxy

In the previous section, automation of various preprocessing steps using a Shell script is shown for one human exome dataset. In a real study, it is likely that multiple exome datasets will be used and as such some sort of looping is required to run the same analysis using different FASTQ input and saving the corresponding output. Although a Shell script can still be used for running multiple samples, the complexity of its use may have grown beyond what most can comfortably handle. In this section, a dedicated platform known as Galaxy will be used to demonstrate the same analysis and extending it to include multiple human exome samples.

Galaxy is an open, web-based platform for bioinformatics analysis that is implemented in Python programming language, which can be deployed on any UNIX system, from local computers to clusters to computer clouds. The web-based GUI of Galaxy

Box 1   Sample shell scripting for running bioinformatics analysis workflow.

```sh
#!/bin/sh
if [[ $# -lt 3 ]] ; then
 echo "USAGE: sh script.sh fastq_PE1 fastq_PE2 reference.fa"
 exit 1
fi
#This runs FastQC to check on quality of the FASTQ input file
echo "Running FastQC"
fastqc $1 $2
#Indexing the reference genome prior to mapping and SNP calling
echo "Indexing the reference genome"
bwa index $3
samtools faidx $3
#Set output prefix
prefix=`expr match "$2" '\(.*\)\_'`
#Running trim_galore filter
echo "Running sequence trimming"
trim_galore --paired $1 $2
#Mapping of the raw reads to the reference genome was done using BWA, followed by
SNP calling with samtools
echo "Running mapping and SNP calling"
bwa mem $3 $prefix\_1_val_1.fq $prefix\_2_val_2.fq | samtools view -bT $3 - | samtools
sort - tmp1.sort
samtools mpileup -uf $3 tmp1.sort.bam | bcftools view -vcg - > $prefix.vcf
#Functional annotation of the detected SNPs
echo "Running ANNOVAR"
annovar/convert2annovar.pl --format vcf4 --includeinfo $prefix.vcf > $prefix.annovar
annovar/annotate_variation.pl --buildver hg19 $prefix.annovar annovar/humandb -outfile
$prefix
echo "Analysis completed"
```

uses simple HTML markup that works with most web browsers. It can be accessed via the main public web server (see section Relevant Websites), or other publicly accessible Galaxy servers listed (see section Relevant Websites). It also can be installed locally by following the tutorial: see Relevant Websites section. Galaxy development team has created a portal named Galaxy Community Hub (see section Relevant Websites) that is a forum for discussion and allows researchers to share their analysis workflows.

One of the great features of Galaxy is the point-and-click interface that allows users without programming skills to manipulate data interactively. In addition, Galaxy supports for data uploads from a local computer and also import from external sources (**Fig. 1**). There are more than 650 tools available in the Galaxy server that enable users to perform a wide range of analyses on their data (Afgan *et al.*, 2016). The Galaxy Tool Shed (Blankenberg *et al.*, 2014) provides a platform where tool developers can share their tool configuration files and documentation (**Fig. 2**).

Users can create a workflow to string together the flow of output as input in other processes, either by using existing history or from scratch. This is done by using the Galaxy's graphical workflow editor. However, it is recommended that users should plan their analyses in advance if they would like to create the workflow from scratch. **Fig. 3** shows the workflow for preprocessing human exome datasets created in Galaxy workflow editor. When the workflow is properly setup, users can run the analysis using point-and-click on the interface. In this workflow, once the exome dataset is uploaded, Galaxy will run FastQC and Trim Galore! concurrently to check the quality and trim the sequences. Next, the output from trimming step will be automatically used as input for mapping to reference genome using bwa, and then call for SNP variants.

Galaxy has the feature of capturing the information of each analysis step, including the datasets, tools and parameters used. Its user interface makes it simple to monitor the status of each job. If a job has failed, the error details will be provided to help in

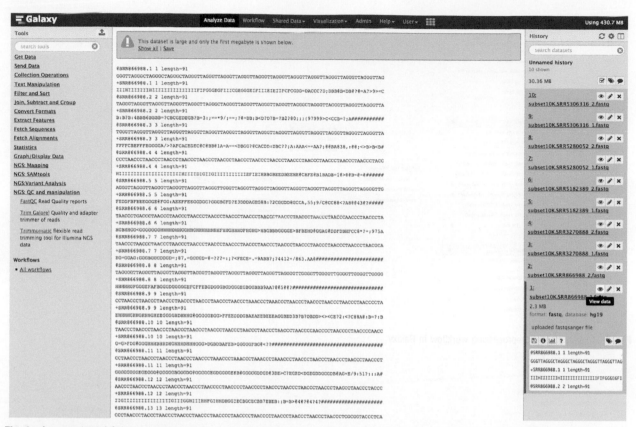

Fig. 1 A screenshot of Galaxy interface that shows the uploaded human exome datasets from a local computer. The left panel is a tool panel that contains the list of tools available in Galaxy. The center panel is a detail panel, showing the details of tools and data. The right panel is a history panel, showing the executed jobs and data.

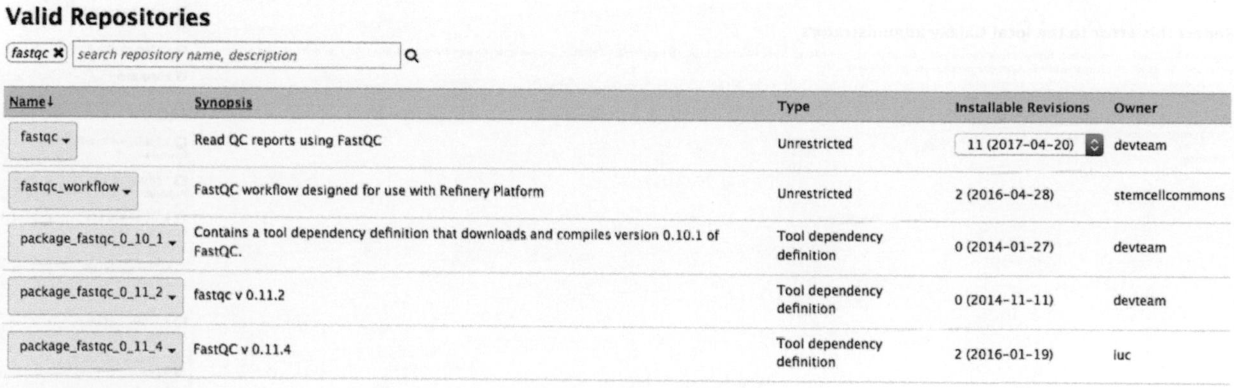

Valid Repositories

Name↓	Synopsis	Type	Installable Revisions	Owner
fastqc ▾	Read QC reports using FastQC	Unrestricted	11 (2017-04-20)	devteam
fastqc_workflow ▾	FastQC workflow designed for use with Refinery Platform	Unrestricted	2 (2016-04-28)	stemcellcommons
package_fastqc_0_10_1 ▾	Contains a tool dependency definition that downloads and compiles version 0.10.1 of FastQC.	Tool dependency definition	0 (2014-01-27)	devteam
package_fastqc_0_11_2 ▾	fastqc v 0.11.2	Tool dependency definition	0 (2014-11-11)	devteam
package_fastqc_0_11_4 ▾	FastQC v 0.11.4	Tool dependency definition	2 (2016-01-19)	iuc

Fig. 2 Galaxy Tool Shed allows the administrator to easily install a tool and its dependencies.

troubleshooting (**Fig. 4**). The feature of automatically tracked records allows for reproducible research (Sandve *et al.*, 2013), where other users can reproduce the same analysis.

Case Study With eHive

In situations where a large number of NGS datasets need to be processed in a short amount of time, for example, the 1000 Genomes project, a pipeline that is more suitable for heavy tasks is needed. One example is *eHive*, which is a workflow management system designed in Perl. It comes with features such as fault tolerant and distributed processing, which uses schedulers such as Load Sharing Facility (LSF) to submit jobs to the compute clusters (Severin *et al.*, 2010). *eHive* works on the principle that central controller does not perform job scheduling. Rather a queen creates autonomous "worker", which then create jobs by monitoring the central blackboard.

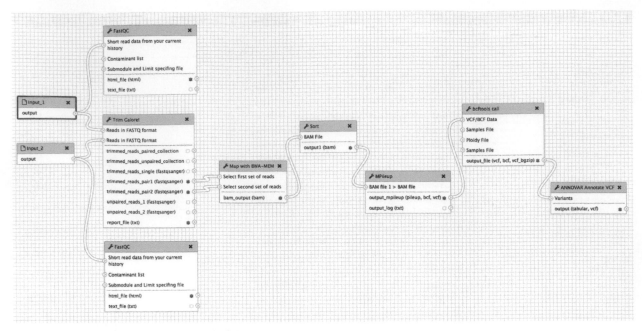

Fig. 3 Exome dataset preprocessing workflow in Galaxy.

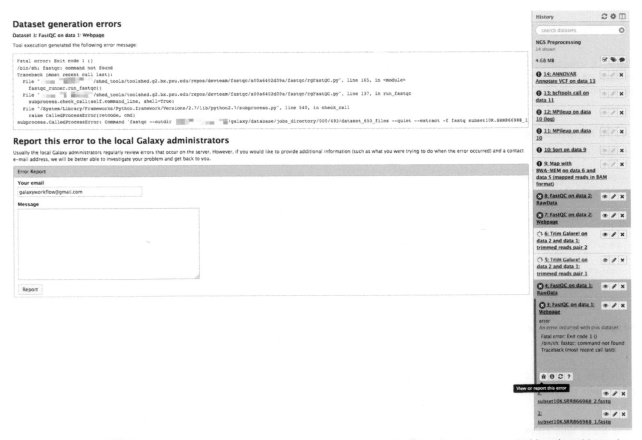

Fig. 4 A screenshot of Galaxy that shows an example of error messages due to a failed run. The status of jobs is marked by coloured boxes for a quick visualization of the overall run: Grey = in queue, Yellow = currently running, Green = completed, and Red = failed.

As a result, the system "behaves" like an insect hive with workers working on jobs. The advantage of the system is that it has very small (~3 ms) job submission overhead. The worker is central to the *eHive* model, once they are created by the *eHive console*, they are registered with the central blackboard. The blackboard will have information about various pipeline analysis, statistics of workers

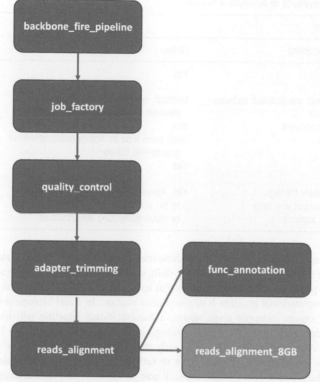

Fig. 5 A snapshot of an eHive workflow for processing of five human exomes.

registered to different analysis and jobs available for processing. Subsequently, the worker will load the code for a chosen analysis, register it on central blackboard and finally run jobs. Once completed, a worker can create new jobs and post it back to the blackboard for other workers. As workers progress through the processing modules within a job, the processing status is logged on the blackboard. Once a job is completed without errors, the worker will set the job status to "DONE". The primary strength of the blackboard model is that it provides more flexibility as no central controller is required. Though new workers are created centrally by *beekeeper*, it does not perform task distribution and has no visibility about the structure of the pipeline thus order of which the tasks should be solved. Workers have the liberty to alter structure of the pipeline at run-time and as they are fault tolerant, jobs can be re-executed up to a configurable number in the event of a failure before exiting the pipeline. Moreover, it allows automatic flow of jobs to cluster nodes with higher memory, if there is such a requirement.

Fig. 5 shows data flow of an *eHive* pipeline for the same five chosen human exome datasets mentioned in earlier sections. The "job_factory" is the analysis module, which will discover the raw sequencing data to be processed and create jobs with corresponding parameters (e.g., filenames). The "quality_control" analysis module will run the FASTQC steps for all the jobs in parallel, which upon completion of each will create new jobs for the "adapter_trimming" analysis module. Jobs of "adapter_trimming" analysis module, will start immediately when their corresponding "quality_control" jobs is completed. In other words, the dependency is at the job level instead of the analysis module level, which speeds up the whole processing pipeline. The "reads_alignment" analysis module will perform short reads alignment using bwa and should the computing node runs out of memory due to large dataset, the job will be "passed_on" to the next analysis module doing the same function but executed on a computing node with a larger memory, which in this case is 8 GB. The "func_annotation" module executes the ANNOVAR scripts similar to the above Shell scripting section. By default, each job will have a maximum retry attempt of 4 (configurable), until which the job status will be set to "FAILED." If a significant number of jobs are failing, the console will be terminated and users can investigate the failed jobs looking at the log messages to fix and resume the jobs as needed. The pipeline can be resumed from the state where the jobs failed using intermediate results if any, and hence removes the need to restart a pipeline from scratch, which is a great time saver especially when failure happens at later stage of the pipeline.

Discussion

The true list of potential ways to run a pipeline is not limited to the three methods outlined. A myriad of other workflow management systems exist and some of them are proprietary software that is beyond the scope here. This article focuses more on the usefulness of a computational pipeline to preprocess raw NGS data that nowadays comes in millions of reads. Whether users prefer to use the

Table 1   Comparison of different methods to automate a pipeline

Feature	Platform		
	Shell Scripting	*Galaxy*	*eHive*
Graphical User Interface (GUI) feature	No	Yes	Yes
Ease of setup	Easy, with pre-installed software or tools	Medium, with the advantage of publicly available tools and full integration	Medium
Error logging	Yes but indirect	Yes	Yes
Customization	Flexible	Need more time to incorporate customized scripts into Galaxy	Yes
Suitability for simple tasks	Yes	Yes	Not recommended
Scalable	Yes. Meant for high throughput and large scale analysis	Yes. Assumption is the users manage to set up the run on a cluster or cloud computing infrastructure	Yes. It has been used on projects with large datasets such as FAANG

ubiquitously applied Shell scripting method or resort to a workflow management system, such as Galaxy or eHive, depends on various factors that include complexity of the tasks, users' programming skills, ease of setup, errors troubleshooting and customization. **Table 1** details a comparison of the three pipeline methods and features that users will typically need to consider before choosing any pipeline.

The main reason to use a computational pipeline is to avoid time wastage. In a real biological experiment setting that involves NGS data, such as the human exome example given above, a computational pipeline will likely be designed or utilized by bioinformaticians who can understand instructions from biologists on what analyses need to be carried out. However, bioinformaticians are usually not the system administrator and as such, the pipeline designed is shared with those who understand and manage computer infrastructure to determine efficient ways to run the pipeline. In some projects, such as those that involve proprietary software, a part of the pipeline is essentially a 'black box' to the users and critical time bottleneck may not necessarily be in the pipeline itself but rather in the communication on how the data was processed. Sometimes even data transfer itself is time consuming, such those involving large alignment file in BAM format generated by a company that is in a country different than that of the user, who needs to be a custodian of such files for subsequent analyses. Efficiency from raw data to outcome requires consideration of external factors, such as data communication and transfer.

Conclusion

A computational pipeline is necessary to achieve efficiency in preprocessing of high throughput sequencing data, especially when dealing with multiple samples. The application of the right pipeline depends on complexity of the tasks, users' programming skills, ease of setup, error troubleshooting, customization and scalability.

Acknowledgement

We thank M. Farhan Sjaugi for his help on eHive installation.

Appendix

Sample Exome Datasets and Software

The human exome data was downloaded from the NCBI Sequence Read Archive (SRA). Here is a list of the SRA IDs: SRR3270888.sra, SRR5182389.sra, SRR5280052.sra, SRR5306316.sra, SRR866988.sra.

The FASTQ files can be obtained using NCBI SRAtoolkit as per sample commands:

```
$ ./sratoolkit.2.8.1–3-centos_linux64/bin/prefetch -v SRR5215189
$ ./sratoolkit.2.8.1–3-centos_linux64/bin/fastq-dump SRR3270888.sra –split-files
```

The software included in this study are given below:

- FastQC version 0.11.4 for quality control check of FASTQ files. The software is available at Babraham Bioinformatics website (see section Relevant Websites).

- Trim Galore! Version 0.4.4, downloadable at Babraham Bioinformatics website (see section Relevant Websites). This software served as automation of adapter and quality trimming of raw FASTQ sequences.
- BWA version 0.7.12 (see Section Relevant Websites). This software maps the raw NGS reads against a large reference genome (e.g., GCRH37, Hg19). BWA could map not only short reads (up to 100 bp) but also long reads (up to 1 Mbp). It uses the Burrow-Wheeler Transformation (BWT) algorithm for mapping reads. The input of BWA is a FASTQ file and the output is either a SAM or BAM file.
- Samtools version 0.1.18 (see section Relevant Websites). This software provides useful utilities to work with SAM and BAM files. It allows users to view, sort and make index of the BAM/SAM files. In addition, it is also possible to call variants by using mpileup and bcftools.
- ANNOVAR (version 2016 Feb01) is a program built for functional annotation of genetic variants acquired from NGS data and it is written in Perl. To download it, users need to register at ANNOVAR website.
- IGV version 2.3.72 is a visualization tool for SNVs data developed by the Broad Institute, which can be obtained at Integrative Genomics Viewer website.

See also: Computational Pipelines and Workflows in Bioinformatics. Constructing Computational Pipelines. Natural Language Processing Approaches in Bioinformatics

---

References

Afgan, E., *et al.*, 2016. The Galaxy platform for accessible, reproducible and collaborative biomedical analyses: 2016 update. Nucleic Acids Research 44 (W1), W3–W10.

Andersson, L., *et al.*, 2015. Coordinated international action to accelerate genome-to-phenome with FAANG, the Functional Annotation of Animal Genomes project. Genome Biology 16 (1), 57.

Andrews, S., 2010. FastQC: A quality control tool for high throughput sequence data.

Andrews, S., 2015. FastQC: A quality control tool for high throughput sequence data. Available at: http://www.bioinformatics.babraham.ac.uk/projects/fastqc.

Blankenberg, D., *et al.*, 2014. Dissemination of scientific software with Galaxy ToolShed. Genome Biology 15 (2), 403.

Keller, M.S., 1999. Take command: Cron: Job scheduler. Linux Journal 1999 (65es), 15.

Krueger, F., 2015. Trim Galore!: A wrapper tool around Cutadapt and FastQC to consistently apply quality and adapter trimming to FastQ files.

Li, H., *et al.*, 2009. The sequence alignment/map format and SAMtools. Bioinformatics 25 (16), 2078–2079.

Li, H., 2013. Aligning sequence reads, clone sequences and assembly contigs with BWA-MEM. arXiv preprint arXiv:1303.3997.

Low, L., Tammi, M., 2017. Bioinformatics: A Practical Handbook of Next Generation Sequencing and Its Applications. World Scientific.

Narasimhan, V., *et al.*, 2016. BCFtools/RoH: A hidden Markov model approach for detecting autozygosity from next-generation sequencing data. Bioinformatics. btw044.

Sandve, G.K., *et al.*, 2013. Ten simple rules for reproducible computational research. PLOS Computational Biology 9 (10), e1003285.

Severin, J., *et al.*, 2010. eHive: An artificial intelligence workflow system for genomic analysis. BMC Bioinformatics 11 (1), 240.

Wang, K., Li, M., Hakonarson, H., 2010. ANNOVAR: Functional annotation of genetic variants from high-throughput sequencing data. Nucleic Acids Research 38 (16), e164.

Relevant Websites

http://www.openbioinformatics.org/annovar/annovar_download_form.php
    ANNOVAR.
http://www.bioinformatics.babraham.ac.uk/projects/fastqc/
    Babraham Bioinformatics.
http://www.bioinformatics.babraham.ac.uk/projects/trim_galore/
    Babraham Bioinformatics.
http://bio-bwa.sourceforge.net/
    Burrows Wheeler Aligner.
https://usegalaxy.org
    Galaxy.
https://galaxyproject.org/public-galaxy-servers/
    Galaxy Community Hub.
http://getgalaxy.org
    Galaxy Community Hub.
https://galaxyproject.org/
    Galaxy Community Hub.
https://www.broadinstitute.org/igv/
    Integrative Genomics Viewer.
http://samtools.sourceforge.net/
    SAMtools.

Genome Annotation: Perspective From Bacterial Genomes

Alan Christoffels and Peter van Heusden, University of the Western Cape, Cape Town, South Africa

Introduction

Advances in sequencing technologies have accelerated the generation of genomic data for a myriad of species in record time. The Genomes Online Database (https://gold.jgi.doe.gov/) GOLD provides comprehensive access to information regarding genome and metagenome sequencing projects, and their associated metadata. For example, as of 1st May 2018 the GOLD database contained 10,204 completely sequenced bacterial genomes. Access to these genomic resources allow scientists to compare genomes in different biomedical, environmental and/or geographical contexts and driving the development of comparative and visualization tools that underpin the field of comparative genomics. Therefore, it is important to accurately define the location and structure of genes in a genome and map these at different levels to proteins, function and pathways.

Genome annotation refers to the extraction of biological information from nucleotide sequencing data. Medigue and Moszer (2007) define a two-component hierarchy for genome annotation; namely, (i) a static view of genome annotation versus (ii) a dynamic view of genome annotation.

Static View of Genome Annotation

A range of gene prediction tools is used to predict the location of a gene (i.e., protein coding region or functional RNA). The predicted genes are used in sequence similarity searches against databases to assign a cellular function to the gene product. Functional assignment includes chemical and structural properties of proteins, sub-cellular localization, biological functions in a cell and protein domain identification.

Caveats to this approach

Gene prediction tools can miss small genes or genes with unusual nucleotide composition. For example the smallest gene identified is 39 nucleotides long PatS peptide (Yoon and Golden, 1998), yet gene prediction algorithms avoid such a short gene length parameter setting to optimize its performance (Tripp et al., 2015). Furthermore, genome sequencing projects could be incomplete i.e., draft assembly and contain sequencing errors that will impact the accuracy of gene prediction tools.

Protein function assignment through sequence similarity search uses a similarity threshold score to limit spurious results. Accuracy of the annotations is improved by using annotations of model organisms that are manually curated; such as, data in RefSeq (Pruitt et al., 2007) and UniProt (The UniProt Consortium, 2007).

Protein domain identification could lead to a single domain being shared by two unrelated proteins. The overall protein domain organisation is required to remove false positive functional assignment.

Dynamic View of Genome Annotation

The annotations obtained in Section "1" are enriched for biological context by integrating information at the level of regulatory and metabolic networks, and protein-protein interactions. Chromosome context is also used to improve genome annotations especially when sequence identity is low. For example, co-location genes in different genomes, gene order and gene fusion analysis allows for more accurate assignment of orthologues. These co-localized genes tend to be co-expressed and can provide evidence for protein interactions that feed into reconstruction of protein interaction networks. Annotations stemming from integrated information can be accessed through warehouses that facilitate exploration of the data via queries against a range of annotation attributes (O'Malley and Soyer, 2012; Triplet and Butler, 2011). Intermine (Smith et al., 2012), is a framework that allows construction of such warehouses. More recently this framework was used as the bases for INDIGO – an Integrated data warehouse for microbial genomes (Alam et al., 2013).

Genome Annotation Software

Genome annotation pipelines vary in their degree to which they are automated. Initial development of annotation pipelines included MAGPIE (Gaasterland and Sensen, 1996), GENEQUIZ (Hoersch et al., 2000), AUTOFACT (Koski et al., 2005), and BASys (Van Domselaar et al., 2005). The latter is a web-based system for annotating bacterial chromosomes. Many of these tools do not allow users to edit the underlying annotations. Often editing applications are independent of the annotation database. For example, annotation and editing browsers such as ARTEMIS (Berriman and Rutherford, 2003) and Apollo (ref) provide a platform for reviewing and editing annotations but do not generate the annotations. Instead the annotations are imported from a GFF formatted file or database.

A combination of automated and manual annotation platforms include commercial systems such as ERGO (Overbeek *et al.*, 2003) or Pedant-Pro (successor of PEDANT (Frishman *et al.*, 2001)), and open-source systems, such as GenDB (Meyer *et al.*, 2003), Manatee (TIGR, unpublished), SABIA (Almeida *et al.*, 2004) and AGMIAL (Bryson *et al.*, 2006). Many of these annotation tools have other dependencies or the annotation pipeline requires a range of tools to be stitched together so that inputs and outputs are clearly defined. The installation of an array of tools (**Fig. 1**) required for annotation pipelines have been simplified with the availability of the conda package manager and the bioconda package channel. A package channel is a collection of precompiled software packages that can be installed by conda. The bioconda project creates conda packages for bioinformatics software, released through the conda package channel of the same name.

Curated Data Repositories for Genome Annotation

Data collections provide the basis for comprehensive genome annotation. These databases can be categorized as follows:

(1) Nucleotide Resources

The International nucleotide sequence database collection (see "Relevant Websites section") is a collaboration among DDBJ, EMBL and GENBANK. Other resources such as RefSeq (Pruitt *et al.*, 2007) at NCBI provide a non-redundant integrated set of nucleotides and proteins for a range of organisms.

(2) Protein Resources

UniProt (The UniProt consortium, 2007) originated from a merger between SwissProt and PIR protein databanks. This resource represents an expertly curated annotation resource, inclusion of the relevant literature and numerous cross-references. The unprecedented volume of data that required curation had to be further sub-divided into two collections namely:

    (i) UniProtKB/SwissProt – manually validated protein entries, and

    (ii) UniProtKB/TrEMBL – computationally annotated records

(3) Protein domain Resources

InterPro (Finn *et al.*, 2017) provides a unified resource that links databases such as PFAM (Finn *et al.*, 2016) and Prosite (Sigrist *et al.*, 2013). These proteins are organized into protein families based on their protein domain signatures.

(4) Cluster of orthologous groups

Proteins are clustered based on BLASTP comparison of all proteins against all. Clusters are generated if a minimum of three distantly related organisms are present (Tatusov *et al.*, 2003).

(5) Metabolic Pathways

These are provide by KEGG (Kanehisa *et al.*, 2017) and BioCyc (Karp *et al.*, 2015).

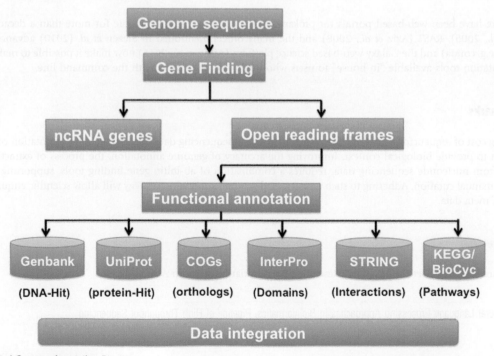

Fig. 1 Integrated Genome Annotation Pipeline.

(6) Protein interactions
    STRING database integrates predicted and known protein interaction data (von Mering *et al.*, 2007).
(7) Structural databases
    PDB (Berman *et al.*, 2007) stores 3-D protein structures.

Stepwise Approach to Genome Annotation

Genome annotation is preceded by a process of genome assembly using a reference genome-based method or de novo approach. The annotation of the assembled genome (**Fig. 1**) starts with identifying and masking RNA genes using RNAmmer (Lagesen *et al.*, 2007) and tRNAScanSE (Schattner *et al.*, 2005). Gene finding tools; such as, Prodigal (Hyatt *et al.*, 2010), GeneMark (Besemer *et al.*, 2001) and MetageneAnnotator (Noguchi *et al.*, 2008); are used to identified open reading frames (ORFs) in the genome sequence. These ORFs are BLAST searched against databases such as GENBANK and UniProt to identify putative functions and protein evidence. The ORFs are mapped to metabolic pathways using a KEGG database. Protein domains are identified through InterProScan searches. This search assigns GO terms to each of the protein domains and these features are later used to carry out functional enrichment analyses. ORFs are searched against the conserved domain database (Marchler-Bauer *et al.*, 2013) that includes COGs to identify corresponding orthologs.

Future Directions

In 2017 the NCBI announced that they would be re-annotating the 89732 bacterial genomes available in the Genbank repository using a new version of their automated prokaryotic genome annotation pipeline (PGAP). Analysis of the set of non-redundant proteins derived from this annotation exercise yielded a set of automated annotation rules that allow for rapid application of the best possible annotation for novel proteins (Richter and Rosselló-Móra, 2009). The future of prokaryotic genome annotation will almost certainly involve the application of curated biological knowledge for the development of heuristics for such multi-level annotation rules. Even these rules, however, only allow annotation of some 53% of the prokaryotic proteins in ReqSeq.

One obstacle facing annotators of de-novo assembled prokaryotic genomes is the difficulty in accessing expertise of biocuration communities, such as the one contributing to the NCBI rule engine described above. Historically the worlds of automated genome annotation and manual curation of annotation have been far apart. The emergence of rule engines (and possible in the future machine learning (Yip *et al.*, 2013) promises to accelerate the work of curators and bring the two worlds of annotation closer together.

Improved automated pipelines (e.g. Prokka (Seemann, 2014) and DFAST (Tanizawa, 2018)) and acceleration of pipeline components such as homology search tools (e.g. RapSearch (Ye *et al.*, 2011), DIAMOND (Buchfink 2014) and GHOSTX (Suzuki, 2014)) are addressing the need for faster annotation which in turn is driven by the decline in cost and increase in volume of DNA sequencing.

While there have been web-based portals for prokaryotic genome annotation available for more than a decade (e.g. MaGe (Vallenet *et al.*, 2006), RAST (Aziz *et al.*, 2008) and the many others mentioned in Siezen *et al.* (2010) advances in package deployment (e.g. conda) and the Galaxy web-based science platform (Afgan *et al.*, 2016) now make it possible to make prokaryotic genome annotation tools available "in house" to users who might not be familiar with the command line.

Closing Remarks

The decreasing cost of sequencing drives the production of genomic sequencing data such that genome annotation continues to be a requirement to provide biological context. Improving the accuracy of genome annotation, the process of extracting biological information from nucleotide sequencing data, requires a combination of ab-initio gene finding tools, supporting experimental evidence and manual curation. Adhering to such an integrated genome annotation strategy will allow scientific enquiry based on a rich source of meta data.

Acknowledgement

The authors are funded under the DST/NRF Research Chairs Initiative of South Africa.

See also: Natural Language Processing Approaches in Bioinformatics. Pipeline of High Throughput Sequencing

References

Afgan, E., Baker, D., van den Beek, M., *et al.*, 2016. Nucleic Acids Res. 44: Web Server issue. W3–W10. doi:10.1093/nar/gkw343.

Alam, I., Antunes, A., Kamau, A.A., Baalawi, W., Kalkatawi, M., *et al.*, 2013. INDIGO – Integrated data warehouse of microbial genomes with examples from the red sea extremophiles. PLOS ONE 8 (12), e82210. doi:10.1371/journal.pone.0082210.

Almeida, L.G., Paixao, R., Souza, R.C., *et al.*, 2004. A system for automated bacterial (genome) integrated annotation- SABIA. Bioinformatics 20, 2832e2833.

Aziz, R.K., Bartels, D., Best, A.A., *et al.*, 2008. The RAST Server: Rapid Annotations using Subsystems Technology. BMC Genomics 9, 75. doi:10.1186/1471-2164-9-75.

Berman, H., Henrick, K., Nakamura, H., Markley, J.L., 2007. The worldwide Protein Data Bank (wwPDB): Ensuring a single, uniform archive of PDB data. Nucleic Acids Res. 35, D301eD303.

Berriman, M., Rutherford, K., 2003. Viewing and annotating sequence data with Artemis. Brief. Bioinform. 4, 124e132.

Besemer, J., Lomsadze, A., Borodovsky, M., 2001. GeneMarkS: A selftraining method for prediction of gene starts in microbial genomes. Implications for finding sequence motifs in regulatory regions. Nucleic Acids Res. 29, 2607–2618.

Bryson, K., Loux, V., Bossy, R., *et al.*, 2006. AGMIAL: Implementing an annotation strategy for prokaryote genomes as a distributed system. Nucleic Acids Res. 34, 3533e3545.

Finn, R.D., Attwood, T.K., Babbitt, P.C., *et al.*, 2017. InterPro in 2017 – Beyond protein family and domain annotations. Nucleic Acids Res. 45, D190–D199.

Finn, R.D., Coggill, P., Eberhardt, R.Y., *et al.*, 2016. The Pfam protein families database: Towards a more sustainable future. Nucleic Acids Res. 44, D279–D285.

Frishman, D., Albermann, K., Hani, J., *et al.*, 2001. Functional and structural genomics using PEDANT. Bioinformatics 17, 44e57.

Gaasterland, T., Sensen, C.W., 1996. Fully automated genome analysis. that reflects user needs and preferences. A detailed introduction to the MAGPIE system architecture. Biochimie 78, 302e310.

Hoersch, S., Leroy, C., Brown, N.P., Andrade, M.A., Sander, C., 2000. The GeneQuiz web server: Protein functional analysis through the Web. Trends Biochem. Sci. 25, 33e35.

Hyatt, D., Chen, G.L., Locascio, P.F., Land, M.L., Larimer, F.W., *et al.*, 2010. Prodigal: Prokaryotic gene recognition and translation initiation site identification. BMC Bioinform. 11, 119.

Kanehisa, M., Furumichi, M., Tanabe, M., Sato, Y., Morishima, K., 2017. KEGG: New perspectives on genomes, pathways, diseases and drugs. Nucleic Acids Res. 45, D353–D361.

Karp, P.D., Latendresse, M., Paley, S.M., *et al.*, 2015. Pathway tools version 19.0: Integrated Software for pathway/genome informatics and systems biology. Brief. Bioinform..

Koski, L.B., Gray, M.W., Lang, B.F., Burger, G., 2005. AutoFACT: An automatic functional annotation and classification tool. BMC Bioinform. 6, 51.

Lagesen, K., Hallin, P., Rødland, E.A., Staerfeldt, H.H., Rognes, T., *et al.*, 2007. RNAmmer: Consistent and rapid annotation of ribosomal RNA genes. Nucleic Acids Res. 35, 3100–3108.

Marchler-Bauer, A., Zheng, C., Chitsaz, F., *et al.*, 2013. CDD: Conserved domains and protein three-dimensional structure. Nucleic Acids Res. 41, D348–D352.

Medigue, C., Moszer, I., 2007. Annotation, comparison and databases for hundreds of bacterial genomes. Res. Microbiol. 158, 724–736.

Meyer, F., Goesmann, A., McHardy, A.C., *et al.*, 2003. GenDBdan open source genome annotation system for prokaryote genomes. Nucleic Acids Res. 31, 2187e2195.

Noguchi, H., Taniguchi, T., Itoh, T., 2008. MetaGeneAnnotator: Detecting species-specific patterns of ribosomal binding site for precise gene prediction in anonymous prokaryotic and phage genomes. DNA Res. 15, 387–396.

O'Malley, M.A., Soyer, O.S., 2012. The roles of integration in molecular systems biology. Studies in History and Philosophy of Science Part C: Studies in History and Philosophy of Biological and Biomedical Sciences 43, 58–68. doi:10.1016/j.shpsc.2011.10.006.

Overbeek, R., Larsen, N., Walunas, T., *et al.*, 2003. The ERGO genome analysis and discovery system. Nucleic Acids Res. 31, 164e171.

Pruitt, K.D., Tatusova, T., Maglott, D.R., 2007. NCBI reference sequences (RefSeq): A curated non-redundant sequence database of genomes, transcripts and proteins. Nucleic Acids Res. 35, D61eD65.

Richter, M., Rosselló-Móra, R., 2009. Shifting the genomic gold standard for the prokaryotic species definition. PNAS 106 (45), 19126–19131. doi:10.1073/pnas.0906412106.

Schattner, P., Brooks, A.N., Lowe, T.M., 2005. The tRNAscan-SE, snoscan and snoGPS web servers for the detection of tRNAs and snoRNAs. Nucleic Acids Res. 33, W686–W689.

Seemann, T., 2014. Prokka: Rapid prokaryotic genome annotation. Bioinformatics 30 (14), 2068–2069. doi:10.1093/bioinformatics/btu153.

Siezen, R.J., van Hijum, S.A.F.T., 2010. Genome (re-)annotation and open-source annotation pipelines. Microbial Biotechnology 3 (4), 362–369. doi:10.1111/j.1751-7915.2010.00191.x.

Sigrist, C.J.A., de Castro, E., Cerutti, L., *et al.*, 2013. New and continuing developments at PROSITE. Nucleic Acids Res. 41, D344–D347.

Smith, R.N., Aleksic, J., Butano, D., *et al.*, 2012. InterMine: A flexible data warehouse system for the integration and analysis of heterogeneous biological data. Bioinformatics 28, 3163–3165. doi:10.1093/bioinformatics/bts577.

Suzuki, S., Kakuta, M., Ishida, T., Akiyama, Y., 2014. GHOSTX: An Improved Sequence Homology Search Algorithm Using a Query Suffix Array and a Database Suffix Array. PLoS ONE 9 (8), e103833. doi:10.1371/journal.pone.0103833.

Tatusov, R.L., Fedorova, N.D., Jackson, J.D., *et al.*, 2003. The COG database: An updated version includes eukaryotes. BMC Bioinform. 4, 41.

Tanizawa., Y., Fujisawa, T., Nakamura, Y., 2017. DFAST: A flexible prokaryotic genome annotation pipeline for faster genome publication. Bioinformatics 34 (6), 1037–1039. doi:10.1093/bioinformatics/btx713.

The UniProt Consortium, 2007. The universal protein resource (Uni-Prot). Nucleic Acids Res. 35, D193eD197.

Triplet T., Butler G., 2011. Systems biology warehousing: Challenges and strategies toward effective data integration. In: Proceedings of the 3rd International Conference on Advances in Databases, Knowledge, and Data Applications, St. Maarten. IARIA. pp 34–40.

Vallenet, D., Labarre, L., Rouy, Z., *et al.*, 2006. MaGe: A microbial genome annotation system supported by synteny results. Nucleic Acids Res 34 (1), 53–65. doi:10.1093/nar/gkj406.

Van Domselaar, G.H., Stothard, P., Shrivastava, S., *et al.*, 2005. BASys: A web server for automated bacterial genome annotation. Nucleic Acids Res. 33, W455eW459.

Von Mering, C., Jensen, L.J., Kuhn, M., *et al.*, 2007. STRING 7- recent developments in the integration and prediction of protein interactions. Nucleic Acids Res. 35, D358eD362.

Yip, K.Y., Cheng, C., Gerstein, M., 2013. Machine learning and genome annotation: a match meant to be? Genome Biology 14, 205. doi:10.1186/gb-2013-14-5-205.

Yoon, H.S., Golden, J.W., 1998. Heterocyst pattern formation controlled by a diffusible peptide. Science 282, 935–938. doi:10.1126/science.282.5390.935.

Relevant Websites

https://www.climb.ac.uk/
   Cloud infrastructure for microbial bioinformatics.
https://gold.jgi.doe.gov/
   Genomes Online Database.

https://bioconda.github.io/recipes.html#recipes
  Packages available in the Bioconda channel.
http://www.insdc.org
  INSDC.
https://bioconda.github.io/recipes.html%23recipes
  Packages available in the Bioconda channel.

Biographical Sketch

Alan Christoffels After completing my studies in South Africa in 2001, I moved to Singapore for a postdoc with a focus on genome evolution. During this time I contributed to the annotation and genome analysis of the Pufferfish genome and developed method for detecting genome duplication events. This methodology was later used in other international genome projects after I established my laboratory in Singapore in 2004. In 2007 I returned to South Africa and established my group at the University of the Western Cape at the South African National Bioinformatics Institute. For the following 8 years, I was part of an international execute team driving the genome sequencing and analysis of the Tsetse genome. As of 2013, the focus of the lab has shifted to bacterial genomes where most of my funding is directed at *M. tuberculosis*. My bioinformatics laboratory focuses on building tools and analyzing data that leads to a better understanding of human-M. tuberculosis interaction with a focus on functional non-coding RNA, drug target identification and genome evolution. Underpinning these Tuberculosis projects are methods to analyze next generation sequencing data.

Peter van Heusden I first joined the South African National Bioinformatics Institute as a computer systems administrator in 1996 and was soon involved in assisting with the bioinformatics research of the Institute. In the past decade I have assisted with annotating the genome of the African coelacanth (*Latimeria chalumnae*) and that of the Asian sea bass (*Lates calcarifer*). Since 2014 I have led a research software engineering team at SANBI with a focus on automating scientific workflows, specifically those related to analysis *Mycobacterium tuberculosis* genomic data.

Next Generation Sequencing Data Analysis

Ranjeev Hari and Suhanya Parthasarathy, Perdana University, Selangor, Malaysia

Introduction

The era of next generation sequencing (NGS) began following the first reports of this innovative technique in 2005 (Margulies *et al.*, 2005; Shendure and Ji, 2008). The high-throughput NGS technology, which uses parallel amplification and sequencing yields shorter read lengths, giving an average raw error rates of 1%–1.5% (Shendure and Ji, 2008) when compared to conventional Sanger sequencing protocols, which can generate to 1000 bp of 99.999% per base accuracies. While automation attempts of traditional dideoxy DNA sequencing by Sanger method improved the efficiency of DNA sequencing; however, in terms of cost and time, NGS technology was regarded as superior. An early method called massively parallel sequencing (MPS) that was introduced by Lynxgen Therapeutics set the stage for high throughput sequencing (Brenner *et al.*, 2000). The first NGS machine, the GS20, that was made available for researchers in 2005 by 454 Life Sciences (Basel, Switzerland) is based on large-scale parallel pyrosequencing by microbeads in micro-droplets of water in oil emulsion (Henson *et al.*, 2012).

The major NGS technology platforms in the market for whole-genome sequencing are primarily from brand names such as Illumina, Roche 454, Solid and IonTorrent. Each platform has its advantages and disadvantages and cost implications in terms of reliability, time and money (**Table 1**). Depending on each NGS platform, they offer values that may be attractive for specific purposes. For instance, the Ion Torrent is often positioned as a general purpose sequencer as well as in diagnostic protocols due to the quicker turnaround time (Tarabeux *et al.*, 2014). However, longer reads technology offered by Illumina and Roche are desirable but the cost involved for Roche 454 FLX is very steep rendering it impractical for large scale genome projects. Reads from Pacific Bioscience machine, PacBio, are generally not used in large genome projects for direct sequencing but can be useful in resolving repetitive regions and ambiguous regions due to capability of generating very long read lengths (**Table 1**).

NGS Process Workflow

The common processes involved in general NGS platforms are library preparation, library amplification, and sequencing (Figure 2.3). The starting material for library preparation can be from either RNA or DNA (genomic source or PCR-amplified). In the case of RNA, it has to be transcribed into cDNA because as of now, NGS machines sequence only DNA directly. Since target library molecules sequenced on each NGS platform are required to be in specific lengths, genomic DNA requires fractionation and size selection, which is performed by sonication, nebulization, or enzymatic techniques followed by gel electrophoresis and excision. For instance, Illumina NGs platform's standard fragment size is in the range of 300 and 550 bp including adapters. Generally, libraries are built by adding NGS platform-specific DNA adapters to the DNA molecules. These adapters facilitate the binding of the library fragments to a surface such as a microbead (454, Ion PGM, SOLiD) or a glass slide (Illumina, SOLiD).

However, depending on the specific NGS platform, the library construction step has to be customised to fit the sequencing protocol. Generally, DNA library construction directly depend on its applications and can be divided mainly into fragment libraries and mate-paired libraries. In fragment libraries, target genomic sequences are fragmented to smaller sizes typically up to 5 times the NGS platform's read length capabilities. Subsequently, sequencing adapters are attached to these fragments allowing the NGS platform to sequence from the adaptor tags. Typically, fragment libraries are of single end and paired-end. With adaptor tags at both forward and reverse sites, NGS platforms are able to sequence from both ends in paired-end libraries. The applications of fragment libraries are mainly for variant calling, copy number detection and genome reconstruction. While other types of NGS

Table 1 Comparison between different NGS platforms

	454 FLX	*HiSeq2000*	*Solid 5500XL*	*IonTorrent (318 Chip)*	*PacBio*
Company	Roche	Illumina	Life technologies	Life technologies	Pacific biosciences
Nucleotides/Run	700 Mbp	540–600 Gbp	180 Gbp	800 Mbp	0.5–1 Gbp
Maximum read length	700 bp	2 × 100 bp	75 + 35 bp	200 bp	10 kbp–>40 kbp
Pairs	2 × 150 bp	2 × 150 bp	2 × 60 bp	N/A	
Run time	23 hours	11 days	12–16 days	4.5 hours	30 m–4 hours
Reagent cost per Mbp (USD)	7	0.04	0.07	1	0.13–0.60
Advantages	–Read length	–High throughput	–Low cost/base	–Less expensive	–Read length
	–Fast	–Read length	–Accuracy	–Fast	–Fast
Disadvantages	–Expensive	–High DNA concentration	–Slow	–Homopolymer errors	–Error rate
	–Homopolymer errors	–Short reads	–Palindromic errors		
	–Low throughput		–Short reads		

sequencing techniques may exist, the fundamental principles are similar in fragment library construction. Other techniques may involve intermediary steps such as fragment capture, immune-hybridizations or reverse transcription.

In mate-pair library construction, target DNA sequences are fragmented to size more than 1000 bp that are often longer than the read length capacities of the NGS platforms. The required fragment size is excised from a gel electrophoresis run of the sheared DNA corresponding to the intended library size usually 2 kbp, 5 kbp or 10 kbp. These isolated DNA fragments are circularised by ligation through addition of biotinylated adapters to the ends to promote sequence specific ligation instead of ligating across fragments. Once again, the circularised DNA are fragmented and biotinylated fragments are purified by affinity capture. Sequencing adapters are added to the size selected sequences. The manipulation preformed during the library construction step allows identification of the terminal sequences of the circularised DNA by sequencing. Having known the sequence length *a priori*, computational algorithms can help differentiate large scale genomic rearrangements from a reference sequence besides typically being used to guide the scaffolding process in a genome assembly.

In the sequencing step, having known adaptor sequences allows the amplification of library fragments either by emulsion PCR (emPCR) or bridge PCR which are methods specific to the NGS platforms. Commonly, irrespective of platforms, NGS exploits parallelism in a factor of ten thousand to billions of library fragments. Generally, this is achieved by reiterated cycles of nucleotide addition using DNA polymerases or ligases (SOLiD), detection of incorporated nucleotides and washing steps. The extensive washing and repetitive steps, albeit automatic, may thus take sequencing to complete from hours to days. Base calling is the process of algorithmically deciding the incorporated nucleotide from the signal intensities that are detected during sequencing process.

Every NGS platform relies on slightly different strategies to generate and detect signals (Luo *et al.*, 2012; Merriman *et al.*, 2012; Ronaghi *et al.*, 1998). For instance, the chemistry used by Illumina and SOLiD sequencing is similar to the principles of sequencing by synthesis. Using four separate fluorescent-labelled nucleotides, its flushed over the glass slide and fluorescence signals are repetitively captured when nucleotides become incorporated to target sequences. In contrast, flooding of non-labelled nucleotides in 454 and Ion PGM sequencing are detected by pyrophosphate or proton release as part of its unique chemistry. Typically, the proton release is measured as a pH change by the semiconductor chip of the Ion Torrent instrument (Merriman *et al.*, 2012). On the other hand, pyrophosphate signal in the 454 system relies on chemistry of the enzyme luciferase to induce light signals (Ronaghi *et al.*, 1998). Altogether, these signals respective to each platform will be converted into basecalls and converted into raw sequencing data that is generally output in FASTQ format that includes the basecall qualities along with the DNA sequence.

While many platforms exist, markedly there are many advantages of NGS, compared to the conventional Sanger sequencing, such as: (i) NGS permits a considerably higher degree of parallelism than Sanger's conventional capillary-based sequencing. (ii) Removal of bottlenecks and limitations in older methods (*E. coli* transformation and colony picking) by *in vitro* construction of a sequencing library, followed by in vitro clonal amplification further enforcing parallelism in the workflow (iii) NGS system usually uses reagents that operate on immobilized target on arrays in microliter quantities, which costs are gained back over the full set of sequencing features on the array because the volume per feature are in the range of picoliters to femtoliters. Overall, these advantages translate into intensely lower costs for DNA sequence production using NGS technologies (Shendure and Ji, 2008). Therefore, in any NGS projects, the high-throughput nature of the method is favoured (**Figs. 1** and **2**).

Typical Data Analysis Workflow for NGS

NGS analysis utilize bioinformatics approaches in order to convert signals from the machine to meaningful information that involve signal conversion to data, annotations or catalogued information, and actionable knowledge. Primarily, the NGS bioinformatics analysis is divided into three distinct phases as primary, secondary and tertiary analyses. In the primary analyses, raw data from the sequencers are converted into nucleotide base and short read data. Secondary analyses apply detailed bioinformatics methodology specific to the NGS technique that was employed which may involve read alignments or read assembly. Usually, secondary analyses have the most complex analyses workflow and is usually run in a sequence as a pipeline. Besides, depending on the type of NGS technique that are employed, the analysis pipeline may differ greatly. For example, RNA-seq data, which characterizes transcriptomes, differ in secondary analysis approach compared to ChIP-seq data, which investigates genome-wide epigenetic mechanisms. Lastly, by tertiary analyses, the previous results obtained can be associated and understood in a biological context. However, tertiary bioinformatics analyses can be an iterative process that involve rigorous statistical and computational biology methods.

Sequence Generation

The initial primary analysis is usually transient as the sequencing machines detectors receives the signals obtained from the high throughput reactions. Thus, the base-calling and recording process is tightly integrated with the sequencing instruments resulting in quality scores corresponding to the short reads nucleotide sequence being output parallelly. The primary analysis software is installed by machine vendors on the workstation supporting the sequencing instrument. The software can be run in high-performance cluster systems for faster results. Besides converting raw signals to base calls, some software tools include demultiplexing of multiple samples into a single pooled and indexed run (Dodt *et al.*, 2012).

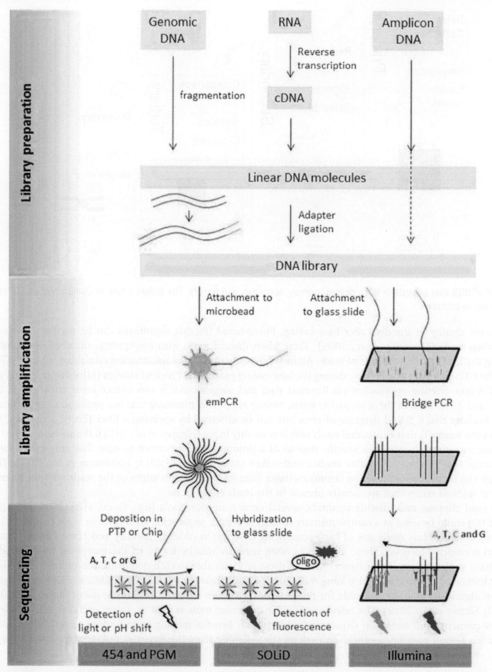

Fig. 1 Schematic diagram of the process involved in common NGS platforms. Adapted from Knief, C., 2014. Analysis of plant microbe interactions in the era of next generation sequencing technologies. Plant Genet. Genom. 5, 216. Available at: https://doi.org/10.3389/fpls.2014.00216.

NGS Raw Data Pre-Processing

As described earlier, NGS platforms suffer from higher error rates compared to Sanger sequencing (Nakamura *et al.*, 2011; Shendure and Ji, 2008). However, as part of primary analysis, different approaches and algorithms have been developed to compensate and spot these errors (Margulies *et al.*, 2005). Moreover, bases that have inaccuracy less than 0.1% can be carefully chosen algorithmically. As a simple approach, error-rates can be decreased by performing the DNA sequencing with high coverage, of at least 20–60-fold, depending on the sequencing project's goal (Luo *et al.*, 2012; Margulies *et al.*, 2005; Voelkerding *et al.*, 2009). Notably, each sequencing read can be categorised as a distinct genotype but in fact could be the result of sequencing error. Thus, it is very important to use established methods in differentiating these two causes of variation as it may lead to inaccurate results when flawed.

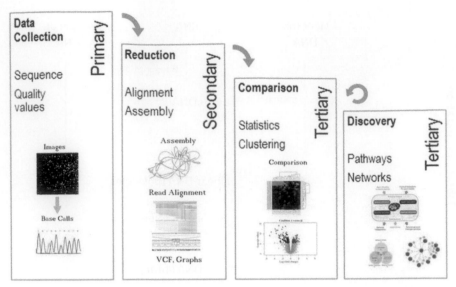

Fig. 2 Workflow of NGS data analysis in three phases: primary, secondary and tertiary. The tertiary phase of Comparison and Discovery is indicated as an iterative process.

To improve the quality of the data after base-calling, Phred-based filtering algorithms can be used to filter or remove low quality sequencing reads (Margulies *et al.*, 2005). These filters discard reads with low-quality, uncalled, and ambiguous bases besides clipping the lower quality 3'-ends of reads. All such filters use the quality information contained in the FASTQ file that are computed by the NGS platform at each base during the base calling procedure. Previous studies (Minoche *et al.*, 2011) have shown the effect of different filtering approaches on Illumina data and suggests that it can reduce error rates to less than 0.2% by eliminating around 15%–20% of the low-quality bases, mostly via 3'-end trimming that are prone to errors. Another study has supported the findings that a 5-fold decrease of error rate can be observed by applying a filter (Phred score of Q30, with 0.1% likelihood of a false basecall) that eliminated reads with low quality bases (Nguyen *et al.*, 2011). It may be useful to note that low quality bases are sometimes localised in specific regions of a genome. It is important to note that removal of these reads may introduce potential bias in the quantitative studies undertaken (Minoche *et al.*, 2011; Nakamura *et al.*, 2011). Therefore, read clipping strategy can be used to remove the erroneous bases from the left or right edges of the reads without filtering the whole reads in order to address errors that are usually present in the reads edges alone.

Apart from read clipping and filtering methods, several error correction tools (e.g., Coral, HiTEC, Musket, Quake, RACER, Reptile, or SHREC) could be used as a complementary strategy to reduce sequencing error rates in reads (Knief, 2014). Generally, these error correction methods make use of high sequencing coverage in order to identify and correct errors using the laws of probability and statistics. Moreover, these algorithms often consider quality scores of the examined bases besides looking at neighbouring base quality values. For instance, some of these tools are able to correct substitution errors in Illumina sequencing data (Ilie and Molnar, 2013; Liu *et al.*, 2013; Yang *et al.*, 2010) while others (Coral, HSHREC, KEC, and ET) are designed to include indel correction algorithms that are available for the analysis of Roche's 454 and IonTorrent data (Salmela, 2010; Salmela and Schröder, 2011; Skums *et al.*, 2012). The relevance of error correction tools is seen as a very useful strategy in *de novo* genome sequencing, resequencing and amplicon sequencing projects with benefits ranging from finding more optimal assembly in the DBG and reducing overall memory footprint to perform the assembly stage (Skums *et al.*, 2012; Yang *et al.*, 2010).

Genome Assembly

After the pre-processing of sequence reads, we can assemble the pre-processed reads into contigs. The process of assembly of sequencing reads generated from NGS technology involves the reduction of redundant data by contiguously placing reads by overlapping them adjacent to each other in an optimal way (Miller *et al.*, 2010). Instead of reads, when contigs (assembled set of reads) undergo the previously described process with long length information, it is known as scaffolding. In other words, it is a process of reconstructing the target as such to groups reads into contigs and contigs into scaffolds.

Generally, the size and accuracy of the contigs and scaffolds are important statistics in genome assemblies (Miller *et al.*, 2010). The quality of genome assemblies is usually described by maximum length, average length, combined total length, and N50. The contig N50 is the length of the smallest contig in the set that contains the fewest (of the largest) contigs whose joint length represents at least 50% of the assembly (Miller *et al.*, 2010). Generally, larger N50 values imply a higher quality genome assembly that describes lesser overall fragments. Typical high-coverage genome projects have N50 values that range in megabases; however, they are dependent on the genome size and is not a good measure to compare between unrelated assemblies instead of the same. Assembly accuracy is tough to quantity. Nevertheless, mapping the assembled contigs/scaffolds to reference genomes is useful to examine its quality if the references exist.

As outlined earlier, an assembly is an ordered data construction that maps the sequencing data to a supposed reconstruction of the target (He *et al.*, 2013). Contigs are reconstructed sequences from sequence alignment of reads which give rise to a consensus sequence. The scaffolds is a higher order organisation of sequences which define the contig order and orientation and the sizes of the gaps between contigs. The scaffolds represent more contiguous sequences mimicking the physical genome composition. Scaffold sequences could have N's in the gaps between contigs. The number of consecutive N's may show the gap length estimate during the assembly process based on the bridging of mate pair reads (Miller *et al.*, 2010).

There are many well-established software for assembling sequencing reads into contigs/scaffolds. In general, these genome assemblers can be grouped into three categories based on their approaches (Miller *et al.*, 2010): (1) The Overlap/Layout/Consensus (OLC) approaches depend on an overlap graph; (2) the *de* Bruijn Graph (DBG) use some form of *k*-mer graph; and, (3) the greedy graph algorithms can use OLC or DBG (**Table 2**).

There are many factors that need to be considered when choosing the most appropriate genome assembler especially when considering for large whole genome sequencing project. Among these factors are the choice of algorithm, compatibility with the NGS platform, the support of the assembly of large genomes, and parallel-computing support for speeding-up the assembly (Zerbino and Birney, 2008). Generally, the choice of algorithm and software will directly determine the memory requirements and speed of assembly. In general, DBG assemblers are faster but require large amount of memory compared to OLC assemblers.

Read Mapping

Whenever a reference genome becomes available, instead of a *de novo* assembly strategy, reads are mapped or aligned to the reference genome prior to subsequent analysis steps. The goal of mapping is to realign the vast number of reads back to the respective regions it likely originated from. The mapping of the reads to the reference genome typically involves the alignment of millions of short reads to the genome using fast algorithms. The algorithms are able to function parallelly while taking into account mutations such as polymorphisms, insertions and deletions in order to produce the alignment. In well-known aligners, for example BLAST, the individual query sequence is searched against a reference database using hash tables and seed and extend approaches. With NGS data, often similar methods are adapted to scale the alignment of short query sequences that are in the millions against a single reference genome of large sequences. Advances in mapping algorithms using various other techniques has improved alignment speed while reducing memory and space requirements. Examples of mapping software that are well known and used in NGS data includes SOAP2 (Short Oligonucleotide Alignment Program), BWA (Burrow-Wheels Alignment), NovoAlign and Bowtie 2.

The widely used format of storing mapping information of the reads to the genome is SAM (Sequence Alignment Map) format or its compressed binary form called BAM. While the BAM file is smaller and optimized for machine reading, the SAM file is human readable albeit slower for computer operations. There are 11 mandatory fields in the SAM format specification. Commonly, SAMtools software is used to manipulate and read both BAM and SAM formats.

Typically, mapping of reads to the reference genome is followed by collecting data about the mapping statistics. The summary statistics that is mainly of interest is the percentage of aligned reads, or the mapping rate. The mapping rate of reads to the reference genome are usually only 60%–75%. Besides the limitation due to the intrinsic properties of NGS data and technique that it was generated from, the inability to map to the reference genome can be ascribed to challenging regions in the genome, such as repeat rich regions, that aligners are not able to map to. Moreover, short read lengths in most high throughput NGS technology limits the alignment in mapping to span a small region hence limiting its coverage to convenient areas of the genome. Besides that, limitations such as NGS sequencing error, algorithmic robustness, mutational load and variation contributes to the low mapping rate.

The mapping file generated can be further inspected by region in-depth using visualization tools such as genome viewers which plot pileups (the stacked alignment of the reads). Visualization of reads mapped, for instance, can be important in diagnosing problems in read alignment in certain regions, detecting duplicates, and visualizing variations. Commonly used genome browsers that enable the reading of SAM files include Integrated Genome Viewer (IGV), and Tablet while some web-based browser that achieve similar visualizations include JBrowse, NGB and UCSC genome browser.

Table 2   Summary of assembly software used for *de novo* assembly of genomes

Assembler	Algorithm	Preferred data	Multithreading	Target genome
SGA	OLC	Illumina	Yes	Large
SOAPdenovo2	DBG	Illumina	Yes	Large
ALLPATHS-LG	DBG	Illumina	No	Large
CLC	DBG	Mixed	No	Large
SSAKE, SSHARCGS and VCAKE	Greedy	Illumina	No	Small
Edena	OLC	Illumina	No	Small
Newbler	OLC	454	No	Large
CABOG	OLC	Mixed	No	Large
Euler	DBG	454 + Sanger	No	Small
Velvet	DBG	Illumina	No	Small
ABySS	DBG	Illumina	Yes	Large

Tertiary Analysis

The tertiary process of analysing NGS data can be quite diverse depending on the scenario and context of a study. Generally, the reads that are representative of the underlying annotations will characterize the functional aspects of the study. As such, the corresponding statistics used are usually descriptive. In other cases, where a comparison is being made to a reference or a control, rigorous statistical tests are employed taking into account read counts in the target regions representative in each treatment groups. Applying statistical models to identify bias, accounting covariates and testing for significant difference are common steps in comparative analysis. The resulting outcomes of the analysis may provide a collection of target annotations or genes. Such a gene list can be subsequently analysed for enrichment in regards to gene ontology (GO) terms to infer the collective function, biological process and cellular compartmentalization. With such a gene list, the pathways being affected can also be mapped to grasp a better biological understanding of the process. In other derivative NGS techniques such as ChIP-seq or Hi-C, tertiary analysis may additionally involve deriving profiles that are commonly occurring in the interactions being observed. Thus, new motifs, structural interactions and regulatory signals that are being generated for a particular condition can be characterized. NGS techniques when applied to a population could derive meaningful interaction of evolutionary forces besides characterizing the differences in genetic composition either in terms of polymorphisms when observing the same species or taxonomy when studying metagenomics.

Conclusion

Approaches to NGS data analysis are diverse and dependant on the technology and methods being employed. Nevertheless, among the multiple stages that are involved in NGS data analysis, steps in primary and secondary analysis is generally a prerequisite in all NGS projects. Therefore, primary and secondary analyses must be carefully performed in order to prevent errors being carried over to tertiary analysis. In tertiary analysis, insights can be generated from the inclusion of annotation, network, and interaction information from external databases to expand on gene lists and profiles found in earlier steps. Collectively, these steps are required frequently, hence, independent bioinformatics labs create analysis pipelines for their in-house routine analyses. However, as NGS technology grows and improves, the methods for analyses may require further evaluation and integration with latest technologies.

> *See also*: Computational Pipelines and Workflows in Bioinformatics. Constructing Computational Pipelines. Experimental Platforms for Extracting Biological Data: Mass Spectrometry, Microarray, Next Generation Sequencing. Genome Annotation: Perspective From Bacterial Genomes. Natural Language Processing Approaches in Bioinformatics. Pipeline of High Throughput Sequencing

Reference

Brenner, S., Johnson, M., Bridgham, J., *et al.*, 2000. Gene expression analysis by massively parallel signature sequencing (MPSS) on microbead arrays. Nat. Biotechnol. 18, 630–634. Available at: https://doi.org/10.1038/76469.

Dodt, M., Roehr, J.T., Ahmed, R., Dieterich, C., 2012. FLEXBAR – Flexible barcode and adapter processing for next-generation sequencing platforms. Biology 1, 895–905. Available at: https://doi.org/10.3390/biology1030895.

Henson, J., Tischler, G., Ning, Z., 2012. Next-generation sequencing and large genome assemblies. Pharmacogenomics 13, 901–915. Available at: https://doi.org/10.2217/pgs.12.72.

He, Y., Zhang, Z., Peng, X., Wu, F., Wang, J., 2013. De novo assembly methods for next generation sequencing data. Tsinghua Sci. Technol. 18, 500–514. Available at: https://doi.org/10.1109/TST.2013.6616523.

Ilie, L., Molnar, M., 2013. RACER: Rapid and accurate correction of errors in reads. Bioinformatics 29, 2490–2493. https://doi.org/10.1093/bioinformatics/btt407.

Knief, C., 2014. Analysis of plant microbe interactions in the era of next generation sequencing technologies. Plant Genet. Genom. 5, 216. Available at: https://doi.org/10.3389/fpls.2014.00216.

Liu, Y., Schröder, J., Schmidt, B., 2013. Musket: a multistage k-mer spectrum-based error corrector for Illumina sequence data. Bioinformatics 29. https://doi.org/10.1093/bioinformatics/bts690.

Luo, C., Tsementzi, D., Kyrpides, N., Read, T., Konstantinidis, K.T., 2012. Direct comparisons of Illumina vs. Roche 454 sequencing technologies on the same microbial community DNA sample. PLOS ONE 7, e30087. Available at: https://doi.org/10.1371/journal.pone.0030087.

Margulies, E.H., Maduro, V.V.B., Thomas, P.J., *et al.*, 2005. Comparative sequencing provides insights about the structure and conservation of marsupial and monotreme genomes. Proc. Natl. Acad. Sci. USA 102, 3354–3359. Available at: https://doi.org/10.1073/pnas.0408539102.

Merriman, B., Rothberg, J.M., Ion Torrent R&D Team, 2012. Progress in ion torrent semiconductor chip based sequencing. Electrophoresis 33, 3397–3417. Available at: https://doi.org/10.1002/elps.201200424.

Miller, J.R., Koren, S., Sutton, G., 2010. Assembly algorithms for next-generation sequencing data. Genomics 95, 315–327. Available at: https://doi.org/10.1016/j.ygeno.2010.03.001.

Minoche, A.E., Dohm, J.C., Himmelbauer, H., 2011. Evaluation of genomic high-throughput sequencing data generated on Illumina HiSeq and genome analyzer systems. Genome Biol. 12, R112. Available at: https://doi.org/10.1186/gb-2011-12-11-r112.

Nakamura, K., Oshima, T., Morimoto, T., *et al.*, 2011. Sequence-specific error profile of Illumina sequencers. Nucleic Acids Res. 39, e90. Available at: https://doi.org/10.1093/nar/gkr344.

Nguyen, P., Ma, J., Pei, D., *et al.*, 2011. Identification of errors introduced during high throughput sequencing of the T cell receptor repertoire. BMC Genom. 12, 106. Available at: https://doi.org/10.1186/1471-2164-12-106.

Ronaghi, M., Uhlén, M., Nyrén, P., 1998. A sequencing method based on real-time pyrophosphate. Science 281, 363–365. Available at: https://doi.org/10.1126/science.281.5375.363.

Salmela, L., 2010. Correction of sequencing errors in a mixed set of reads. Bioinformatics 26, 1284–1290.

Salmela, L., Schröder, J., 2011. Correcting errors in short reads by multiple alignments. Bioinformatics 27, 1455–1461.

Shendure, J., Ji, H., 2008. Next-generation DNA sequencing. Nat. Biotechnol. 26, 1135–1145. Available at: https://doi.org/10.1038/nbt1486.

Skums, P., Dimitrova, Z., Campo, D.S., et al., 2012. Efficient error correction for next-generation sequencing of viral amplicons, in: BMC Bioinformatics. BioMed Central. p. S6.

Tarabeux, J., Zeitouni, B., Moncoutier, V., et al., 2014. Streamlined ion torrent PGM-based diagnostics: BRCA1 and BRCA2 genes as a model. Eur. J. Hum. Genet. 22, 535–541. Available at: https://doi.org/10.1038/ejhg.2013.181.

Voelkerding, K.V., Dames, S.A., Durtschi, J.D., 2009. Next-generation sequencing: From basic research to diagnostics. Clin. Chem. 55, 641–658. Available at: https://doi.org/10.1373/clinchem.2008.112789.

Yang, X., Dorman, K.S., Aluru, S., 2010. Reptile: representative tiling for short read error correction. Bioinformatics 26, 2526–2533.

Zerbino, D.R., Birney, E., 2008. Velvet: Algorithms for de novo short read assembly using de Bruijn graphs. Genome Res. 18, 821–829. Available at: https://doi.org/10.1101/gr.074492.107.

Exome Sequencing Data Analysis

Anita Sathyanarayanan, Institute of Health and Biomedical Innovation and School of Biomedical Sciences, Queensland University of Technology, Brisbane, QLD, Australia.
Srikanth Manda and Mukta Poojary, Institute of Bioinformatics, Bangalore, India
Shivashankar H Nagaraj, Institute of Health and Biomedical Innovation and School of Biomedical Sciences, Queensland University of Technology, Brisbane, QD, Australia and Translational Research Institute, Brisbane, QLD, Australia

Abbreviations

BAM	Binary Alignment/Map	SAM	Sequence Alignment/Map
BWT	Burrows Wheeler Transform	SNP	Single Nucleotide Polymorphism
CNV	Copy Number Variation	SNV	Single Nucleotide Variation
dbSNP	Single Nucleotide Polymorphism database	SRA	Sequence Read Archive
ExAC	Exome Aggregation Consortium	SV	Structural Variation
GATK	Genome Analysis ToolKit	VCF	Variant Call Format
Indel	Insertion or Deletion	WGS	Whole Genome Sequencing
OMIM	Online Mendelian Inheritance in Man	WES	Whole Exome Sequencing

Glossary

Alignment The process of mapping reads to a reference genome.

Complex diseases Otherwise known as multifactorial disorders. Contrast to Mendelian diseases, these diseases are caused due to multiple genes or mutations as well as environmental risk factors.

Germline variants Variants or mutations present in the germ cells.

Mendelian diseases Disorders caused due to mutation at a single locus and are inherited according to Mendel's law.

Reads The short sequence of nucleotide bases from a single molecule of DNA detected by the sequencers.

Somatic variants Variants exclusive to somatic cells and not present in germ cells.

Variant calling Variant calling refers to identification of bases in the sequencing reads which are different from the reference genome at that position.

Whole exome sequencing Sequencing only the protein coding region of an organism's genome.

Whole genome sequencing Sequencing the complete genome to identify the full DNA sequence of an organism.

Introduction

The human genome is composed of three billion base pairs, comprising both protein coding and non-coding regions. The advancement in sequencing techniques from traditional Sanger sequencing to massively parallel high-throughput methods has made genome sequencing faster, cheaper, and more informative, allowing for a more comprehensive understanding of human genetics. Genome sequencing has become a vital clinical tool for the identification of the genetic basis of diseases, facilitating the management and treatment of many previously intractable conditions. There are two primary methods used to identify particular allelic variants in a given individual: Whole Genome Sequencing (WGS) and Whole Exome Sequencing (WES). WGS involves the sequencing of the entire genome, while WES focuses specifically on sequencing only the coding (exonic) regions of the genome in a more a targeted approach. Both methods provide an unbiased means of variant identification to identify variants making them invaluable tools for precise personalized medicine.

The human exome comprises the entirety of the protein coding portion of the genome, which is just 1%–2% of the entire genome. The term exon derives from EXpressed regiON, i.e., the regions that are translated into protein products. These are generally the best studied and understood regions of the genome, and any mutation therein has the potential to disrupt normal protein function and to thereby cause disease. Given its more focused approach to genomic characterization, exome sequencing has emerged as a powerful tool in the recent years and has been utilized successfully to identify several severe and rare diseases associated with specific genetic variants in protein coding regions. The list of such diseases includes Miller Syndrome (Ng *et al.*, 2010b), Schinzel-Giedion syndrome (Hoischen *et al.*, 2010), Nonsyndromic hearing loss (Walsh *et al.*, 2010), Perrault syndrome (Pierce *et al.*, 2010), Sensenbrenner syndrome (Gilissen *et al.*, 2010), Kabuki syndrome (Ng *et al.*, 2010a), Progeroid syndrome (Puente *et al.*, 2011) and many others, each of which is caused by distinct mutations in specific proteins with serious physiological consequences. Exome sequencing thus provides a revolutionary means of characterizing the genomic landscapes of individuals with single base resolution, facilitating the identification of disease-associated mutations that allow for a more in-depth understanding of the root causes of a given disease, ultimately facilitating its treatment and management.

Background

There are two unbiased sequencing-based approaches for detecting genetic variations in an individual: Whole Genome Sequencing (WGS) and Whole Exome Sequencing (WES). While the human genome contains 3 billion bases, the human exome contains only 30 million bases (30 Mb). Despite phenomenal improvements in the accuracy and economic viability of genomic sequencing technologies, sequencing whole human genomes to a depth sufficient to identify novel variants associated with a given disease phenotype remains prohibitively resource-intensive both in terms of monetary and computational costs. WGS approaches are thus primarily employed for variant identification and related discoveries only in large genome sequencing laboratories and companies where such an approach is financially viable.

Advantages of Whole Exome Sequencing

WES technologies, in contrast, have helped to significantly reduce the time and resources required for actionable data – 20 human exomes can be sequenced in the same time required to sequence a single human genome. WES analysis significantly reduces the computational burden relative to a WGS analysis owing to the 99% reduction in the size of the sequenced regions within a given individual. Protein coding regions are better conserved between individuals (and across species) relative to intronic and non-coding regions, as the vital role of proteins in all aspects of human physiology renders these regions significantly more sensitive to the potentially deleterious effects of mutations. Indeed, more than 85% of disease-causing mutations in Mendelian diseases are located in coding regions of the genome. Given this enrichment for disease-associated mutations within the exome, WES provides an unbiased yet targeted approach to detect these variants, facilitating personalized and precision medicine at a fraction of the cost of WGS.

Exome Sequencing Analysis Workflow

The complete exome sequencing workflow begins with the extraction of DNA from a donor or patient of interest, and ends with the biological interpretation of identified variants through both experimental and computational approaches. The initial wet lab procedures involved in exome sequencing include genomic DNA extraction, DNA fragmentation, adaptor ligation, targeted exome capture, enrichment, and finally sequencing. The subsequent computational protocol involves the processing of raw sequencing reads to obtain a Variant Call Format (VCF) file that contains the list of identified variants within the given individual's exome. Intermediary steps include read quality control, alignment of sequenced data to a reference genome, post alignment clean-up (such as removal of duplicate reads), indel realignment, and base quality score recalibration, followed by variant calling, filtering, and annotation of the identified variants. Several in-depth guides regarding library preparation and sequencing are available in various published articles, and are an ideal resource for individuals performing WES (Parla *et al.*, 2011; Teer and Mullikin, 2010; Zhang *et al.*, 2015).

To begin a whole exome sequencing-based experiment, following the development of a careful experimental design which takes into account optimal patient/donor numbers and means of enriching for individuals with novel disease-associated variants, samples (blood, cheek swabs, etc.) must be collected from relevant individuals. After DNA is extracted from these samples, it is subjected to random fragmentation either via ultrasonication or with the help of transposons. Ensuring random fragmentation is important to avoid introducing sequencing artifacts. Artificial DNA linkers are added to the ends of all fragments to generate a shotgun library. Fragments containing coding sequences are then captured and enriched by commercially available hybridization-based capture kits. This target enrichment can be performed using in-solution or array-based capture techniques. For in-solution enrichment, a variety of probe definitions are available from different commercial companies such as Agilent, Illumina and NimbleGen. These enrichment strategies primarily differ in their specific genomic target regions covered, size, number of probes, and in their workflow design (see **Table 1**). The fragments of interest are hybridized to biotinylated DNA or RNA baits (depending on the exome capture kit used). The hybridized fragments are later recovered and enriched via affinity-based pull down, and are amplified prior to sequencing in order to generate a library of only captured exons.

Sequencing of the enriched fragments can be performed using a range of different sequencer platforms commercially available from Illumina, Life Technologies, or PacBio's SMRT. The information regarding the base identified at a particular position is stored in a raw data output file, the format of which varies based on the sequencer chosen. Regardless of the utilized sequencer, these files can be processed and analyzed using the data analysis pipelines tailored to answer experimental questions of interest. The steps of data analysis, starting from raw sequencer file outputs, are described further below.

Exome Sequencing Analysis

Quality Control/Pre-Processing

Sequencer outputs are known as nucleotide base calls, and are stored in the form of short nucleotide sequences called reads in file formats that vary based on the sequencing platform chosen. Generally accepted formats for read files are FASTQ and SRA (Sequence Read Archive). A number of different criteria can be used to assess read quality, including by measuring average read quality scores, GC content, presence of contaminating sequences and/or adaptor sequences, overrepresented k-mers, duplicated reads, and PCR artifacts.

Table 1   Exome capture platforms for human exome sequencing

	NimbleGen's SeqCap EZ exome v3.0 kit	Agilent's sure select human all Exon V6 kit	Illumina's TruSeq exome prep kit	Illumina's Nextera rapid capture exome and expanded kit
Probe size (bp)	55–105	114–126	95	95
Probe type	Biotinylated DNA	Biotinylated cRNA	Biotinylated DNA	Biotinylated DNA
Coverage strategy	High-density, overlapping probes	Adjacent probes	Gaps between probes	Gaps between probes
Fragmentation method	Ultrasonication	Ultrasonication	Ultrasonication	Transposons
Target region size (Mb, human)	64	60	45	62
Genomic DNA input required	1 ug	100 ng	100 ng	50 ng
Hybridization time (hours)	72	16	16	16
Reads remaining after filtering	66%	71.7%	54.8%	40.1%
Major strengths	• High sensitivity and specificity • Most uniform coverage in difficult regions	• Better coverage of indels • High alignment rate • Fewer duplicate reads than other platforms	• Good coverage of UTRs and miRNAs	• Good coverage of UTRs and miRNAs
Major weaknesses	• More duplicate reads than Agilent • Lower alignment rate than Agilent	• Fewer high-quality reads than NimbleGen	• High off-target enrichment	• High off-target enrichment • Coverage bias for high GC content areas reducing uniformity
Human support	Not required	Not required	Required	Required

The quality of a given base call is measured as a Phred quality score and indicates the probability of the base being called correctly. The scores generally range from 2 to 40 with higher scores indicating greater confidence in the call. A common practice is to filter out bases with Phred scores below 20, although individual preferences may lead some researchers to modulate this threshold. The removal of redundant reads and undesired sequences (such as 3′ adaptors, contaminants, or primers) is essential as contaminating sequences will not align to the genome resulting in poor alignment quality. Trimming low quality ends from reads is important as current sequencers are highly error-prone, with a significant dip in base quality at the 3′ ends of reads. With time it is likely that such technical issues will be resolved, allowing for even more cost-effective whole exome sequencing.

Other pre-processing alternatives include assessing the read GC content. A uniform GC content across reads signifies good sequencing without artifacts or contaminants. Contaminating sequences are identifiable by checking if the frequency of a k-mer (a short sequence of bases of length k) is unusually high relative to levels that would be predicted due to chance. Sequences matching known adaptor sequences should be trimmed before aligning the reads to a reference genome, as mentioned above.

It is necessary to carefully examine the quality of raw reads prior to alignment in order to obtain a high percentage of properly aligned reads. FastQC (Andrews, 2010) is a commonly used application that can examine the quality of read sequences. It reports several parameters such as sequence quality scores, GC content, length distribution, and duplication levels. Cutadapt (Martin, 2011) and Trimmomatic (Bolger et al., 2014) are readily available programs that allow for the detection and trimming of adaptor sequences in reads, facilitating downstream alignment and analysis.

Reference-Based Alignment

The next step following quality control is alignment of reads to a reference genome. For human samples, this process involves the matching of short sequences of bases to a published reference genome using an alignment program. This is a complex and computationally intensive task, as the software ultimately matches millions of short sequences to 3 billion possible positions within the reference genome. Successful alignment requires the utilization of an effective alignment algorithm that is both efficient at searching for perfect base matches as well as tolerant of imperfect matches. This latter consideration is particularly important, as the goal of whole exome sequencing is to identify novel single nucleotide polymorphisms (SNPs), which by definition will be distinct from those incorporated into the human reference genome. Such considerations also allow the algorithm to identify insertions or deletions within the genome that could also have physiological consequences. Computationally the algorithm must be fast, memory efficient, and strike an effective balance between accuracy and speed. These tools must also be capable of handling single end and paired end reads, as paired end reads are the most common approach to sequencing data generation. Based on the computational approach used for quick and memory efficient string matching, aligners can be broadly classified into hash-based method or Burrows-Wheeler Transform (BWT) method (**Table 2**). Hash-based methods create hash table either for the read sequences or for the reference genome and use them to identify the matches. Aligners such as SOAP (Li et al., 2008b), MAQ

Table 2   Commonly used alignment algorithms

Aligner	Description
Borrows-Wheeler Aligner (BWA)	Gapped alignment based on Borrows-Wheeler Transform. Consists of three algorithms: BWA-backtrack, BWA-SW, and BWA-MEM. BWA-MEM is the most recent and efficient algorithm among the three.
Bowtie (1 and 2)	Both Bowtie 1 and 2 are ultra-fast memory efficient aligners based on Borrows-Wheeler Transform. Bowtie 1 is short read ($\leq$ 50 bp) and ungapped aligner while Bowtie 2 allows gaps and has no restriction on read length.
SOAP (1,2 and 3)	While SOAP 1 is hash-based method, SOAP 2 and 3 are based on Borrows-Wheeler Transform. SOAP 2 is more memory efficient and utilizes lesser time than SOAP 1. SOAP 3 is the recent version which uses GPU processors.
MAQ	It is an ungapped short read aligner. It creates hash indexes of reads and scans the reference against the hashes to detect matches.
ELAND	Developed by Illumina company, it one of the first short read aligners. It performs ungapped alignment for reads of size 32bp. However, additional Perl scripts are provided to overcome the limitations. The source code is freely available for the machine buyers.
SHRiMP (1 and 2)	Performs Smith-Waterman local alignment algorithm for both letter space and colour space reads. While SHRiMP 1 indexes the reads, SHRiMP2 indexes the genome and is much faster. SHRiMP 2 also allows paired-end reads alignment and utilizes multi-threaded computation.
Novoalign	A commercial tool from Novocraft. It performs alignment by hashing the reference genome and is also capable of adaptor trimming and base quality trimming. It allows gaps and mismatches up to 50% of read length.

(Li et al., 2008a), ELAND, and SHRiMP (Rumble et al., 2009) are hash-based. BWT-based methods create a data structure called FM index for the genome sequence using data transformed using BWT and suffix array of the sequence. Popular aligners based on this approach are BWA (Li and Durbin, 2009), Bowtie2 (Langmead and Salzberg, 2012), and SOAP3 (Liu et al., 2012).

Once generated, alignment results containing the read sequences and their respective mapped locations on the reference genome can be stored in the human readable format known as Sequence Alignment/Map (SAM) or in the Binary Alignment/Map (BAM) binary format (Li et al., 2009). These alignment results then undergo further quality control, assessed based on a number of parameters including percentage of aligned reads, mapping quality, alignment scores, number of mismatches, and percentage of uniquely aligned reads. Successful mapping of 70%–90% of reads to the reference genome indicates good overall sequencing accuracy and absence of substantial amounts of contamination, thereby allowing for proper downstream analyses.

Several groups have reported on the comparative advantages of distinct aligners (Li and Homer, 2010; Fonseca et al., 2012; Flicek and Birney, 2009). These tools differ based on their sensitivity, speed, and indexing approach. Choosing the right aligner and optimal parameters based on the sample is vital for high quality alignments, as errors could be carried downstream to variant calling. However, depending on the specific experimental application being employed there may be more than one effective alignment algorithm available. For this reason it is important that individual investigators discuss the advantages and disadvantages of each aligner prior to choosing the one which they ultimately utilize.

Post Alignment Processing

To ensure the quality of identified genetic variants in sequenced and aligned samples, several optional post alignment processing steps can be performed. These include removal of PCR and other duplicates, local alignment around indels, and recalibration of base quality scores.

Removal of Duplicates

The initial steps of library preparation involve the shearing of DNA, ligation of adaptors to both ends of the sheared fragments, and amplification of these fragments via PCR. PCR amplification is performed in order to obtain enough target DNA for sequencing with good depth and coverage. This approach can, however, selectively amplify certain DNA fragments leading to PCR duplicates and an overall misrepresentation of the initial genetic sample. Such a biased selection can lead to a disproportionate amplification of a single allele while ignoring the other, resulting in incorrect allele identification. As a consequence it is necessary to remove these PCR duplicates before variant calling in order to avoid any bias in calculation of variant frequency. While polymerases used in modern PCR reactions are of high fidelity, there is inevitably a chance that any PCR reaction may also introduce novel mutation errors during amplification. These PCR artifacts are difficult to distinguish from true DNA content solely on the basis of sequence and alignment information, as it can be difficult to tell a novel variant apart from an in vitro PCR-induced mutation.

Programs such as SAMtools (rmdup) (Li et al., 2009) and Picard Tools (MarkDuplicates) can be used to remove the duplicates in silico so that they do not adversely affect sequence analyses or variant identification. These programs identify duplicates using information on the orientation and exact start site location on the forward and reverse read at their 5' and 3' positions respectively to properly establish whether a read is a duplicate or not. While SAMtools retains only the read with the highest mapping quality score, discarding their duplicates, Picard Tools simply sets a different flag for the highest scoring read pair and does not discard any reads from the file (Ebbert *et al.*, 2016; Li *et al.*, 2009). As with other software packages, experimental need and investigator preferences will inevitably drive appropriate software selection.

Local Realignment (Indel Realignment)

Sequencing reads are mapped to the reference genome independently of one another during alignment. As a result, there are a large number of erroneous alignments that typically accumulate around the locations of indels (insertions/deletions) or low complexity regions. The next step is to locate genomic regions containing indels and to improve their alignment quality. Indel alignments to the reference genome create gaps due to their novelty, and as a consequence of poor alignment they are prone to noise. Local realignment is one solution that can help improve the accuracy of these reads. In this procedure, the reads around the indels are realigned based on the alignment information of other reads present in the location or by local *de novo* assembly of all reads spanning the indel region along with construction of a consensus sequence for indel discovery. This provides a better chance to accurately align indels than does aligning them solely based on a reference genome, which will not be able to account for these novel sequences. Although this is an optional procedure, it is still advisable to perform realignment to obtain high quality variants, given that these are the desired outcome of most whole exome sequencing studies. Programs that perform indel realignment include IndelRealigner (GATK) (Mckenna *et al.*, 2010), Dindel (Albers *et al.*, 2011), and Novoalign.

Base Quality Score Recalibration (BQSR)

Each base called by the sequencing platform is assigned a Phred score which indicates the confidence of the base call to be error-free, as discussed above. This automated system, however, generates scores that are error-prone as they can be over- or under-estimated due to systematic errors. Although imperfect, Phred scores remain an important criteria for accurate variant calling, as bases with a low score still have a high probability of being called incorrectly. As variant callers depend greatly on the confidence of the base call, it is necessary to reconfirm the accuracy of the quality scores. BQSR is a process that applies machine learning to empirically model the errors and correct them accordingly, thereby markedly improving the accuracy of quality scores and boosting the quality of subsequent variant identification.

During recalibration, a covariation model based on the data and a set of known variants is constructed. Feeding in information on known variants will prevent the calling of real variant bases as base call errors. This covariation model is built based on quality score, position within the reads, and neighbouring nucleotides. Second, the base quality of the remaining mismatched bases are corrected based on this newly built model. It is common practice for investigators to generate before and after BQSR plots in order to visualise changes in base scoring for quality control purposes. Some commonly used tools are Recab (NGSUtils suite) (Breese and Liu, 2013), BaseRecalibrator (GATK) (Mckenna *et al.*, 2010), and ReQON (Bioconductor package) (Cabanski *et al.*, 2012).

Variant Analysis

A variant can be defined as a base in an individual's genome that is not the same as that in the reference genome. Variant calling refers to the identification of these mutated bases in the aligned reads, highlighting points that differ from the reference genome. To be called as a variant the base must have a good quality score and be well supported by multiple reads, thus minimizing the chance that the read is the result of poor alignment or other technical issues. Genomic variants or mutations can be of different types such as Single Nucleotide Variants (SNVs), insertion and deletion variants (indels), Copy Number Variants (CNVs), and large Structural Variants (SVs). The origin of these mutations may be either germline or somatic in nature. Germline variants, present in germ cells, are inherited and often related to familial diseases. Somatic mutations are often associated with tumour development, and are not heritable. The output of variant calling programs is a file containing several records, each of which represents a specific variant. Variant analysis consists of three major steps: Variant calling, annotation of variants, and prioritization of variants of interest depending on the constraints of a given study.

Variant calling

Variant calling refers to identification of bases in the sequencing reads which are different from the reference genome at that position. Variant calling can be performed using either single samples or multiple samples simultaneously depending on the experimental design and availability of computational resources/time constraints.

Germline variant calling

Germline variants correspond to the SNVs and indels in germ line cells. Briefly, germline variant calling tools compare each position of the sample genome to the reference genome and mathematically model the allele counts to obtain the genotype likelihood measures. Programs for identifying germline variants include UnifiedGenotyper (GATK), Haplotype caller (GATK) (Depristo *et al.*, 2011), FreeBayes (Garrison and Marth, 2012), SAMTools (Li *et al.*, 2009), Atals2 (Evani *et al.*, 2012), and VarScan 2 (Koboldt *et al.*, 2012).

Somatic variant calling

Somatic variants refer to the acquired mutations in somatic cells and are not transmitted to the progeny. As somatic variants play an important role in tumour initiation, development, and migration, somatic variant calling is widely used in cancer research and personalized medicine. It is highly recommended to have samples of both tumour and normal tissue/cells from a given patient in order to precisely identify only somatic variants while discarding the germline variants present in a given individual. Somatic variant calling programs detect variants using joint diploid genotype likelihoods or shared allele frequency between samples. Tools for somatic variants identification include MuTect (Cibulskis *et al.*, 2013), Strelka (Saunders *et al.*, 2012), deepSNV (Beerenwinkel *et al.*, 2015), and VarScan 2 (Koboldt *et al.*, 2012).

Variant annotation

Once variants are identified, they are annotated with attributes such as associated genomic features including tissue-specific expression, transcription factor binding sites, eQTLs, gene symbol, exonic function, and the specific amino acid change in question to facilitate the interpretation of their potential functional impact. Several tools are available for annotation of variant positions using information compiled from publicly available databases. They can also be used to calculate minor allele frequency (MAF) in normal populations, mine experimental evidence from clinical assays, predict potential deleterious variant functions, and analyze the frequency of the variant in oncogenic genes. Tools for annotating the variants are ANNOVAR (Wang *et al.*, 2010), MuTect (GATK), SnpEff (Cingolani *et al.*, 2012b), SnpSift (Cingolani *et al.*, 2012a), and VAT (Wang *et al.*, 2014), with ANNOVAR and MuTect being the most commonly used tools.

Variant filtration and prioritization

Typically a variant calling analysis will produce a list of thousands or millions of variants. This means that in addition to annotation, it is necessary to filter this list to obtain high confidence target variants that contribute to the disease or biological process under study. Variants are selected based on population frequency, coverage, supporting reads, and alignment score. They can also be prioritized according their predicted coding effect. Mutations that are likely to cause a loss of protein function such as nonsense mutations in conserved regions, splice mutations that lead to frameshift, and mutations that alter protein structure are often disease-causing variants. Disease-causing mutations can be identified based on experimental evidence from previous studies or by observing specific mutational patterns present in the pedigree of affected and unaffected individuals. Some tools available for prioritization include VAAST2 (Hu *et al.*, 2013), VarSifter (Teer *et al.*, 2011), KGGseq (Li *et al.*, 2012), gNOME, PLINK/SEQ, and Ingenuity Variant Analysis.

Complete Automated Pipelines

A major challenge for most laboratories after sequencing is the management of data in a structured, systematic manner for targeted computational analysis. The WES analysis pipeline requires the use of many different tools for different analysis steps, and its complex parameters need to be optimized for every run. As a consequence, advanced skills and a complete understanding of the tools available, their usage, as well as their relative advantages and disadvantages, is required. Data manipulation and interpretation of the results after each step in the processing pipeline is a potentially overwhelming task for inexperienced users.

The complexity of exome sequencing data analysis can be simplified by software suites which provide all tools required for each step of this processing pipeline in a unified package. Several WES data analysis pipelines are available in the public domain. SIMPLEX (Fischer *et al.*, 2012) is a cloud-based pipeline for single-end (SE) and paired-end (PE) exome sequencing data analysis available from Illumina and ABI SOLiD. SeqMule (Guo *et al.*, 2015) is a Linux-based, user-friendly pipeline for analyzing exome and genome sequencing data. It integrates five alignment and five variant calling algorithms to provide comprehensive analyses. It can be used for identifying both somatic and germ line variants and allows for comparison of results from the different included algorithms. This platform is very flexible, as it allows users to modify the configuration file in order to fine tune its parameters. Fastq2vcf (Gao *et al.*, 2015) is another open-source pipeline that incorporates several open-source tools that allow users to perform analyses from quality control of reads to variants annotation. Galaxy (Afgan *et al.*, 2016), an open source online platform, has a wide collection of tools integrated. Customizable WES pipelines can be created and executed online. Many commercial tools are available with automated WES analysis pipelines, such as CLC Genomics Workbench 9.5.3 by Qiagen, STRAND NGS by Strand Life Sciences Pvt. Ltd which can be installed locally and their modules can be updated by connecting to their servers as per user requirements. Ingenuity Variant Analysis software Ingenuity Systems provides analysis toolkit which directly connects to its database for analysis. Other commercial software programs include Partek and DNA nexus.

Repositories for Variant Storage and Annotation

The critical step in linking mutations to disease is the identification of rare pathogenic variants which are responsible for a disease of interest. This is generally achieved by filtering out known variants present in normal healthy individuals. Such filtering is done with the help of repositories which maintain databases of such variants. Some of the widely used repositories for such common variants are the Single Nucleotide Polymorphism database (dbSNP) (Sherry *et al.*, 2001) and the Exome Aggregation Consortium (ExAC) (Lek *et al.*, 2016). Also of note, the Online Mendelian Inheritance in Man (OMIM) (Hamosh *et al.*, 2005) is the largest repository of known pathogenic variants reported for human.

dbSNP database

dbSNP is the largest repository for simple single nucleotide variants, containing both disease causing mutations and neutral polymorphisms. The Reference SNP (refSNP) Cluster Report on each variant contains the location, sequence, alleles, experimental conditions, population frequency, and variant view. Links to several external databases such as HGBASE, TSC (The SNP Consortium, Ltd), variation initiative, and NCI CGAP-GAI are also available. The ANNOVAR tool can be used to annotate the list of variants with dbSNP and filter out the neutral variants and those with minor allele frequencies greater than 1% to obtain a comprehensive list of target variants.

ExAC database

A key challenge when identifying actionable mutations is that every individual carries several thousand mutations which may not be responsible for disease and are generally seen in a subset of healthy individuals. The ExAC database maintains the largest publicly available repository of human exomes representing populations around the world. Exomes of 60,706 individuals have been deeply sequenced and mined for variants in a uniform fashion. The ExAC browser can be used to mine actionable mutations by eliminating commonly occurring background mutations in the variant dataset.

OMIM database

OMIM is a continuously updated repository of human genes and their associated phenotypes, with a focus on the molecular relationships between genetic variation and phenotypic expression. The information available at OMIM is sourced from literature and is used to identify phenotypes associated with specific human genes. The data uses Mendelian Inheritance in Man (MIM) identifiers and provides concise information on a given gene's location, structure, function, available animal models, and relevant references.

Applications of Exome Sequencing

Discovery of Rare Variants in Mendelian Diseases and Complex Disorders

Exome sequencing has emerged as one of the most efficient strategies for deciphering the genetic causes of both simple Mendelian diseases and complex disorders. It has helped to link several diseases with their causal genes or variants, providing a cost-effective and high-throughput approach to relevant variant discovery. This approach can thus lead to deeper understanding of the mechanisms of disease, leading to improved diagnosis, and the development of superior preventive strategies or targeted therapeutics.

To identify causal variants, two types of exome sequencing sampling strategies are used: family-based sequencing and extreme phenotype sequencing. When multiple members of the same family are affected with a trait, then exome sequencing is performed for the most distantly related individuals. Distant relatives share fewer common genetic variants and hence allow identification of pathogenic variants with a greater amount of confidence. Sequencing a parent-offspring trio in which only the offspring is affected can also be conducted to identify variants responsible for complex diseases. The extreme phenotype sampling strategy involves sequencing the extreme phenotype samples of a trait i.e., samples on the either ends of a phenotype distribution (such as individuals with the most severe forms of a disease and normal controls). Alleles contributing to the extreme phenotypes are enriched, facilitating identification of casual variants.

Mendelian disorders arise from single mutations or a small number of mutations in select causal genes. Many studies have shown that exome sequencing can be successfully applied to discover causal genes in rare Mendelian disorders. The first such successful application of exome sequencing was the identification of the genetic root of the rare Mendelian Miller syndrome (Ng et al., 2010b). Exome sequencing of four affected individuals was performed, and the mutations on the responsible gene, DHODH, were discovered after filtering the exonic variants of the affected individuals against dbSNP and eight HapMap exomes.

Complex disorders are thought to be linked with single or multiple genes and/or a confluence of genetic and environmental risk factors. This results in a heterogeneity of both phenotypes and of the genes and factors involved, necessitating additional scrutiny when performing WES. Exome sequencing of large numbers of patient samples still makes such variant identification possible owing to its reduced costs relative to WGS, and its concomitant reduced analysis burdens. A successful application of WES for a complex phenotype was employed in the case of peripheral neuropathy in two male siblings born to healthy parents exhibiting this disease phenotype. Upon WES analysis, the casual mutation was revealed to be the deletion or substitution of arginine in the 1070th position on the PRX gene. This mutation is known to cause Dejerine-Sottas syndrome, or peripheral neuropathy (Williams et al., 2016). WES has also identified a number of causal genes for complex traits such as mental retardation (Vissers et al., 2010) and sporadic autism spectrum disorders (O'Roak et al., 2011).

Cancer is a heterogeneous disease with each tumour carrying a range of distinct somatic mutations in a number of different oncogenes and tumour suppressor genes including SNV's, short indels, copy number variants, and gene translocations. This makes it is a challenge to identify causal genes in cancer. The success of the Human Genome Project bolstered interest in understanding cancer exomes. The first cancer exome study analyzed 140 human acute myeloid leukemia (AML) WES samples and identified six known and seven novel mutations relevant for AML pathogenesis (Ley et al., 2003). Another early cancer exome study cataloged the landscape of genetic alterations that occur during tumorigenesis by studying the exomes of 11 colorectal and 11 breast tumors. They observed few recurrently mutated genes and several rarely mutated genes (Wood et al., 2007). This demonstrates the powerful capabilities of WES-based approaches in the context of complex disease, enabling the identification of potential novel driver mutations of cancer and underscoring the clinical utility of this tool.

Clinical Diagnosis

The success of WES in identifying genetic causes of disease has paved the way for its application as a diagnostic tool utilized for unbiased personalized medicine. Currently in a clinical setting WES is being used as a diagnostic tool for identifying casual genes and variants in patients afflicted with diseases that are suspected to be Mendelian in nature. It can also be used to identify dormant risk variants in patients even when symptoms are unobservable, particularly in patients with a family history of a given genetic disease. WES combined with pedigree information, through literature and relevant database searches, has been critical for diagnosis and variant or casual gene discovery in cases related to congenital heart disease, autism, epilepsy, brain malformation, neurodevelopmental deformities, and other neurological or congenital conditions.

Discussion Limitations of Exome Sequencing

As with every technology, exome sequencing also has limitations, and failure to identify disease-associated variants can occur for many reasons. One potential impediment to such analyses is the lack of knowledge of the full human transcriptome, due to an incomplete understanding of the exact locations of all protein coding regions. This makes comprehensively defining targets for WES challenging. Some of the technical reasons underlying potential assay failure include poor efficiency of capture probes, insufficient sequencing efficacy, and poor selection of target for sequencing. Analytical challenges include inadequate coverage at the casual variant location, identification of variants in low complexity regions, false positives due to misaligned reads, and poor separation of casual and non-casual alleles. Although the majority of known diseases are caused by mutations in the protein coding regions of genes, intronic regions are important and can also contribute to disease in certain instances. WES by definition precludes the possibility of identifying structural variants that arise in intergenic or intronic regions or on mitochondrial chromosomes.

Despite these limitations, WES remains a vital tool in clinical diagnostics due to its relatively low monetary and time costs relative to other sequencing approaches. As sequencing costs continue to decrease, computational resources become more available, and algorithms become more efficient it will inevitably become standard to perform WGS to establish gene-phenotype relations. Until technological advances permit for this approach, WES is a powerful tool that captures much of the utility and functionality of whole genome sequencing.

Future Directions

Advancements pertaining to Sequencing technology and large scale data analysis and management will significantly push the limits of exome sequencing applications. Improvements in sequencing methodologies will lead to production of longer reads, detection of longer indels, fewer errors during base call, high quality sequences and reliable reference genomes. With the decreasing costs and turnaround time for sequencing, usage of reference genomes specific to geographical population, ethnicity, etc., will become feasible thereby eliminating the use of a single reference genome during variant discovery. Additionally, integrated approach of WES and WGS will be increasingly applied to complement the short comings of the individual methods. Apart from WES and WGS methods, NGS is applied to other omics of cell such as the transcriptome, epigenome, proteome, and metabolome. It has already been recognised that integration of multi-omics data is crucial to get a holistic understanding of the disease state and its systems biology and multi-omics data integration will slowly become a routine in the foreseeable clinical space. With advent of NGS, there has been an enormous influx of data, making omic data handling and management undoubtedly one of the major challenges. The increasing data has led to the creation of global repositories for easier access. Efforts are also being made to create repositories with reliable multidimensional annotation and curation of phenotype. Parallel advancements in the fields such as artificial intelligence/machine learning, high performance computing and large scale data analysis will play major roles in data mining and knowledge extraction of sequencing data. Accordingly, we can look forward to a future where the current challenge of identifying of new Mendelian disorders and their causative genes will be easily resolved due to the collective effort, immense technological developments and progressive interdisciplinary research.

Closing Remarks

The field of genetics has witnessed remarkable progress in the past decade owing to the advancement in sequencing technology and computer science. With decreasing costs and increasing application of sequencing, whole exome sequencing has become an irreplaceable tool in the clinical space, giving faster, cheaper, and reliable results. However, translating the acquired knowledge in the clinical space is one of the biggest challenges being faced. A collective effort is required from researchers all around the globe to solve all Mendelian disorders, decipher the phenotype-genotype relationship, understand the disease mechanism and its systems biology which will ultimately translate the knowledge into better diagnostics and therapeutics.

See also: Computational Pipelines and Workflows in Bioinformatics. Constructing Computational Pipelines. Genome Annotation: Perspective From Bacterial Genomes. Natural Language Processing Approaches in Bioinformatics. Next Generation Sequencing Data Analysis. Pipeline of High Throughput Sequencing

References

Afgan, E., Baker, D., Van Den Beek, M., et al., 2016. The Galaxy platform for accessible, reproducible and collaborative biomedical analyses: 2016 update. Nucleic Acids Research 44, W3–W10.

Albers, C.A., Lunter, G., Macarthur, D.G., et al., 2011. Dindel: Accurate indel calls from short-read data. Genome Research 21, 961–973.

Andrews, S. 2010. FastQC: A quality control tool for high throughput sequence data.

Beerenwinkel, N., Jones, D., Martincorena, I., Gerstung, M. 2015. Package 'deepSNV'.

Bolger, A.M., Lohse, M., Usadel, B., 2014. Trimmomatic: A flexible trimmer for illumina sequence data. Bioinformatics 30, 2114–2120.

Breese, M.R., Liu, Y., 2013. NGSUtils: A software suite for analyzing and manipulating next-generation sequencing datasets. Bioinformatics 29, 494–496.

Cabanski, C.R., Cavin, K., Bizon, C., et al., 2012. ReQON: A bioconductor package for recalibrating quality scores from next-generation sequencing data. BMC Bioinformatics 13, 221.

Cibulskis, K., Lawrence, M.S., Carter, S.L., et al., 2013. Sensitive detection of somatic point mutations in impure and heterogeneous cancer samples. Nature Biotechnology 31, 213–219.

Cingolani, P., Patel, V.M., Coon, M., et al., 2012a. Using Drosophila melanogaster as a model for genotoxic chemical mutational studies with a new program, SnpSift. Frontiers in Genetics 3.

Cingolani, P., Platts, A., Wang, L.L., et al., 2012b. A program for annotating and predicting the effects of single nucleotide polymorphisms, SnpEff: SNPs in the genome of Drosophila melanogaster strain w1118; iso-2; iso-3. Fly 6, 80–92.

Depristo, M.A., Banks, E., Poplin, R., et al., 2011. A framework for variation discovery and genotyping using next-generation DNA sequencing data. Nature Genetics 43, 491–498.

Evani, U.S., Challis, D., Yu, J., et al., 2012. Atlas2 cloud: A framework for personal genome analysis in the cloud. BMC Genomics 13, S19.

Ebbert, M.T., Wadsworth, M.E., Staley, L.A., et al., 2016. Evaluating the necessity of PCR duplicate removal from next-generation sequencing data and a comparison of approaches. BMC bioinformatics 17 (7), 239.

Fischer, M., Snajder, R., Pabinger, S., et al., 2012. SIMPLEX: Cloud-enabled pipeline for the comprehensive analysis of exome sequencing data. PLOS ONE 7, e41948.

Flicek, P., Birney, E., 2009. Sense from sequence reads: Methods for alignment and assembly. Nature Methods 6, S6–S12.

Fonseca, N.A., Rung, J., Brazma, A., Marioni, J.C., 2012. Tools for mapping high-throughput sequencing data. Bioinformatics 28, 3169–3177.

Gao, X., Xu, J., Starmer, J., 2015. Fastq2vcf: A concise and transparent pipeline for whole-exome sequencing data analyses. BMC Research Notes 8, 72.

GARRISON, E., MARTH, G., 2012. Haplotype-based variant detection from short-read sequencing. arXiv preprint arXiv:1207.3907.

Gilissen, C., Arts, H.H., Hoischen, A., et al., 2010. Exome sequencing identifies WDR35 variants involved in Sensenbrenner syndrome. The American Journal of Human Genetics 87, 418–423.

Guo, Y., Ding, X., Shen, Y., Lyon, G.J., Wang, K., 2015. SeqMule: Automated pipeline for analysis of human exome/genome sequencing data. Scientific Reports 5.

Hamosh, A., Scott, A.F., Amberger, J.S., Bocchini, C.A., Mckusick, V.A., 2005. Online Mendelian Inheritance in Man (OMIM), a knowledgebase of human genes and genetic disorders. Nucleic Acids Research 33, D514–D517.

Hoischen, A., Van Bon, B.W., Gilissen, C., et al., 2010. De novo mutations of SETBP1 cause Schinzel-Giedion syndrome. Nature Genetics 42, 483.

Hu, H., Huff, C.D., Moore, B., et al., 2013. VAAST 2.0: Improved variant classification and disease-gene identification using a conservation-controlled amino acid substitution matrix. Genetic Epidemiology 37, 622–634.

Koboldt, D.C., Zhang, Q., Larson, D.E., et al., 2012. VarScan 2: Somatic mutation and copy number alteration discovery in cancer by exome sequencing. Genome Research 22, 568–576.

Langmead, B., Salzberg, S.L., 2012. Fast gapped-read alignment with Bowtie 2. Nature Methods 9, 357–359.

Lek, M., Karczewski, K.J., Minikel, E.V., et al., 2016. Analysis of protein-coding genetic variation in 60,706 humans. Nature 536, 285–291.

Ley, T.J., Minx, P.J., Walter, M.J., et al., 2003. A pilot study of high-throughput, sequence-based mutational profiling of primary human acute myeloid leukemia cell genomes. Proceedings of the National Academy of Sciences 100, 14275–14280.

Li, H., Durbin, R., 2009. Fast and accurate short read alignment with Burrows–Wheeler transform. Bioinformatics 25, 1754–1760.

Li, H., Handsaker, B., Wysoker, A., et al., 2009. The sequence alignment/map format and SAMtools. Bioinformatics 25, 2078–2079.

Li, H., Homer, N., 2010. A survey of sequence alignment algorithms for next-generation sequencing. Briefings in Bioinformatics 11, 473–483.

Li, H., Ruan, J., Durbin, R., 2008a. Mapping short DNA sequencing reads and calling variants using mapping quality scores. Genome Research 18, 1851–1858.

Li, M.-X., Gui, H.-S., Kwan, J.S., Bao, S.-Y., Sham, P.C., 2012. A comprehensive framework for prioritizing variants in exome sequencing studies of Mendelian diseases. Nucleic Acids Research 40, e53.

Li, R., Li, Y., Kristiansen, K., Wang, J., 2008b. SOAP: Short oligonucleotide alignment program. Bioinformatics 24, 713–714.

Liu, C.-M., Wong, T., Wu, E., et al., 2012. SOAP3: Ultra-fast GPU-based parallel alignment tool for short reads. Bioinformatics 28, 878–879.

Martin, M., 2011. Cutadapt removes adapter sequences from high-throughput sequencing reads. EMBnet Journal 17, 10–12.

Mckenna, A., Hanna, M., Banks, E., et al., 2010. The Genome Analysis Toolkit: A MapReduce framework for analyzing next-generation DNA sequencing data. Genome Research 20, 1297–1303.

Ng, S.B., Bigham, A.W., Buckingham, K.J., et al., 2010a. Exome sequencing identifies MLL2 mutations as a cause of Kabuki syndrome. Nature Genetics 42, 790–793.

Ng, S.B., Buckingham, K.J., Lee, C., et al., 2010b. Exome sequencing identifies the cause of a mendelian disorder. Nature Genetics 42, 30–35.

O'Roak, B.J., Deriziotis, P., Lee, C., et al., 2011. Exome sequencing in sporadic autism spectrum disorders identifies severe de novo mutations. Nature Genetics 43, 585–589.

Parla, J.S., Iossifov, I., Grabill, I., et al., 2011. A comparative analysis of exome capture. Genome Biology 12, R97.

Pierce, S.B., Walsh, T., Chisholm, K.M., et al., 2010. Mutations in the DBP-deficiency protein HSD17B4 cause ovarian dysgenesis, hearing loss, and ataxia of Perrault syndrome. The American Journal of Human Genetics 87, 282–288.

Puente, X.S., Quesada, V., Osorio, F.G., et al., 2011. Exome sequencing and functional analysis identifies BANF1 mutation as the cause of a hereditary progeroid syndrome. The American Journal of Human Genetics 88, 650–656.

Rumble, S.M., Lacroute, P., Dalca, A.V., et al., 2009. SHRiMP: Accurate mapping of short color-space reads. PLOS Computational Biology 5, e1000386.

Saunders, C.T., Wong, W.S., Swamy, S., et al., 2012. Strelka: Accurate somatic small-variant calling from sequenced tumor – Normal sample pairs. Bioinformatics, 28. . pp. 1811–1817.

Sherry, S.T., Ward, M.-H., Kholodov, M., et al., 2001. dbSNP: The NCBI database of genetic variation. Nucleic Acids Research 29, 308–311.

Teer, J.K., Green, E.D., Mullikin, J.C., Biesecker, L.G., 2011. VarSifter: Visualizing and analyzing exome-scale sequence variation data on a desktop computer. Bioinformatics 28, 599–600.

Teer, J.K., Mullikin, J.C., 2010. Exome sequencing: The sweet spot before whole genomes. Human Molecular Genetics 19, R145–R151.

Vissers, L.E., De Ligt, J., Gilissen, C., et al., 2010. A de novo paradigm for mental retardation. Nature Genetics 42, 1109–1112.

Walsh, T., Shahin, H., Elkan-Miller, T., *et al.*, 2010. Whole exome sequencing and homozygosity mapping identify mutation in the cell polarity protein GPSM2 as the cause of nonsyndromic hearing loss DFNB82. The American Journal of Human Genetics 87, 90–94.

Wang, G.T., Peng, B., Leal, S.M., 2014. Variant association tools for quality control and analysis of large-scale sequence and genotyping array data. The American Journal of Human Genetics 94, 770–783.

Wang, K., Li, M., Hakonarson, H., 2010. ANNOVAR: Functional annotation of genetic variants from high-throughput sequencing data. Nucleic Acids Research 38, e164.

Williams, H.J., Hurst, J.R., Ocaka, L., *et al.*, 2016. The use of whole-exome sequencing to disentangle complex phenotypes. European Journal of Human Genetics 24, 298.

Wood, L.D., Parsons, D.W., Jones, S., *et al.*, 2007. The genomic landscapes of human breast and colorectal cancers. Science 318, 1108–1113.

Zhang, G., Wang, J., Yang, J., *et al.*, 2015. Comparison and evaluation of two exome capture kits and sequencing platforms for variant calling. BMC Genomics 16, 581.

Further Reading

Bamshad, M.J., Ng, S.B., Bigham, A.W., *et al.*, 2011. Exome sequencing as a tool for Mendelian disease gene discovery. Nature Reviews Genetics 12, 745–755.

Biesecker, L.G., Green, R.C., 2014. Diagnostic clinical genome and exome sequencing. New England Journal of Medicine 370, 2418–2425.

Clark, M.J., Chen, R., Lam, H.Y., *et al.*, 2011. Performance comparison of exome DNA sequencing technologies. Nature biotechnology 29, 908–914.

Goodwin, S., Mcpherson, J.D., Mccombie, W.R., 2016. Coming of age: Ten years of next-generation sequencing technologies. Nature Reviews Genetics 17, 333–351.

Laurie, S., Fernandez-Callejo, M., Marco-Sola, S., *et al.*, 2016. From Wet-Lab to variations: Concordance and speed of bioinformatics pipelines for whole genome and whole exome sequencing. Human Mutation 37, 1263–1271.

Petersen, B.-S., Fredrich, B., Hoeppner, M.P., Ellinghaus, D., Franke, A., 2017. Opportunities and challenges of whole-genome and-exome sequencing. BMC Genetics 18, 14.

Rabbani, B., Tekin, M., Mahdieh, N., 2014. The promise of whole-exome sequencing in medical genetics. Journal of Human Genetics 59, 5–15.

Tennessen, J.A., Bigham, A.W., O'connor, T.D., *et al.*, 2012. Evolution and functional impact of rare coding variation from deep sequencing of human exomes. Science 337, 64–69.

Relevant Websites

http://annovar.openbioinformatics.org/en/latest/
    ANNOVAR.

https://www.hgsc.bcm.edu/software/atlas-2
    Atlas.

http://bio-bwa.sourceforge.net/
    Borrows-Wheeler Aligner.

http://bowtie-bio.sourceforge.net/index.shtml
    Bowtie.

https://www.qiagenbioinformatics.com/products/clc-genomics-workbench/
    CLC Genomics Workbench.

https://pypi.python.org/pypi/cutadapt
    Cutadapt.

https://www.ncbi.nlm.nih.gov/SNP/
    dbSNP.

https://bioconductor.org/packages/release/bioc/html/deepSNV.html
    deepSNV.

http://www.sanger.ac.uk/science/tools/dindel
    Dindel.

https://www.dnanexus.com/
    DNA Nexus.

http://exac.broadinstitute.org/
    ExAC.

https://sourceforge.net/projects/fastq2vcf/
    Fastq2vcf.

https://www.bioinformatics.babraham.ac.uk/projects/fastqc/
    FastQC.

https://github.com/ekg/freebayes
    FreeBayes.

https://software.broadinstitute.org/gatk/documentation/tooldocs/current/org_broadinstitute_gatk_tools_walkers_haplotypecaller_HaplotypeCaller.php
    HaplotypeCaller.

https://software.broadinstitute.org/gatk/documentation/tooldocs/current/org_broadinstitute_gatk_tools_walkers_indels_IndelRealigner.php
    IndelRealigner.

https://www.qiagenbioinformatics.com/products/ingenuity-variant-analysis/
    Ingenuity Variant Analysis.

http://grass.cgs.hku.hk/limx/kggseq/
    KGGSeq.

http://maq.sourceforge.net/maq-man.shtml
    MAQ.

https://software.broadinstitute.org/gatk/documentation/tooldocs/current/org_broadinstitute_gatk_tools_walkers_cancer_m2_MuTect2.php
    MuTect.

http://www.novocraft.com/products/novoalign/
    NovoAlign.

https://www.omim.org/
    OMIM.

http://www.partek.com/pgs
    Partek Genomics Suite.

http://broadinstitute.github.io/picard/
  Picard Tools.
http://atgu.mgh.harvard.edu/plinkseq/download.shtml
  Plink/Seq.
http://samtools.sourceforge.net/
  SamTools.
http://wglab.org/software/14-seqmule
  SeqMule.
http://compbio.cs.toronto.edu/shrimp/
  SHRiMP.
http://icbi.at/software/simplex/simplex.shtml
  Simplex.
http://snpeff.sourceforge.net/
  SnpEff.
http://snpeff.sourceforge.net/SnpSift.html
  SnpSift.
http://soap.genomics.org.cn/
  SOAP.
http://www.strand-ngs.com/
  StrandNGS.
https://github.com/Illumina/strelka
  Strelka.
http://www.usadellab.org/cms/?page=trimmomatic
  Trimmomatic.
https://software.broadinstitute.org/gatk/documentation/tooldocs/current/org_broadinstitute_gatk_tools_walkers_genotyper_UnifiedGenotyper.php
  UnifiedGenotyper.
http://www.yandell-lab.org/software/vaast.html
  VAAST2.
http://dkoboldt.github.io/varscan/
  VarScan.
https://research.nhgri.nih.gov/software/VarSifter/
  VarSifter.

Biographical Sketch

Anita Sathyanarayanan is pursuing her PhD in Bioinformatics at Queensland University of Technology, Australia. Her current area of research is application of computational methods to multi-omics data to understand cancer development and progression. Her research interests centres around the intersection of machine learning and high-throughput omics.

Srikanth Manda has completed his Masters in Biotechnology from Indian Institute of Technology, Bombay, thereafter, pursued a PhD in Bioinformatics from Institute of Bioinformatics, Bangalore and Johns Hopkins University, USA. During his PhD work he has analyzed datasets from Whole Genome (WGS), Whole Exome (WES), Transcriptome, epigenome, miRNAome, proteome and phosphoproteome. His research interests involve multi-omics data analysis, integration and interpretation from high-throughput platforms using available tools and cloud based workflows.

Mukta Poojary is a graduate student at CSIR-Institute of Genomics and Integrative Biology (CSIR-IGIB), New Delhi. She is a recipient of Bioinformatics National Certification (BINC). She works in the area of Genome informatics. Her academic interests spans RNA biology, Population genomics, Pharmacogenomics and Multi-omic data analysis.

Shivashankar H Nagaraj is Advanced Queensland Research Fellow at Queensland University of Technology. The focus of his group is on the development and application of bioinformatics approaches that utilize large amounts of data to solve problems in Genomics and Proteomics. He has developed multiple Bioinformatics solutions (e.g., ESTExplorer, EST2Secretome, PGTools) that are valuable and of practical utility to the wider scientific community.

Whole Genome Sequencing Analysis

Rui Yin, Chee Keong Kwoh, and Jie Zheng, Nanyang Technological University, Singapore

Introduction

The development of DNA sequencing has revolutionized the biological sciences and facilitated the discovery of gene functions. The first widely used DNA sequencing method was Sanger sequencing (Sanger et al., 1977; Slatko et al., 2001) developed in the 1980s in a manual way. Rapid shifts in the techniques of DNA sequencing made it possible for automated sequencing in the 1990s, which allowed the sequencing of whole genomes (Heather and Chain, 2016). Whole genome sequencing (WGS) is a laboratory process that determines the entire DNA sequence of an organism's genome at once. It involves uncovering the order of bases in a complete genome of an organism, which is backed by automatic DNA sequencing methods and computer techniques to assemble the tremendous biological sequence data (Saraswathy and Ramalingam, 2011). Whole genome shotgun sequencing was already in use in 1979 for small genomes ranging from 4000 to 7000 base pairs (Staden, 1979). In 1995, the first genome of *Haemophilus influenzae* was sequenced (Fleischmann et al., 1995). Later, the sequencing of nearly an entire human genome was completed in 2000 (Lander et al., 2001). However, early techniques for WGS were slow, labor-intensive, and expensive, especially in the era of extensive growth of genomic data (Kwong et al., 2015).

The advent and widespread use of next generation sequencing (NGS) techniques have greatly brought about the availability of whole genome analysis and significantly enhanced the capacity to perform efficient and low-cost WGS. Generally, NGS processes contain massively parallel sequencing, where millions of fragments of DNA from a single sample are sequenced (Moorthie et al., 2011). At the cellular level, it has been applied to the resequencing of previous reference strains and allows for the identification of all the potential mutations in an organism at the genomic level (Schuster, 2008). The genes in a genome usually don't work independently and their functions are not directly controlled by the promoter but rather many other regulatory elements such as the response elements, enhancers, and silencers (Saraswathy and Ramalingam, 2011). Therefore, the implementation of WGS will not only present better understanding of the function of all the genes in the cell, but also characterize the related information of DNA that is involved in gene expression. In addition, compared with whole exome sequencing (WES), WGS provides much more comprehensive information on genes by sequencing the noncoding DNA, which captures 98%–99% of the genome; most of the information about the function of noncoding DNA is still a mystery.

The power of NGS has broadened the scale of many applications in current work, including genetic variation (Dalca and Brudno, 2010; Alkan et al., 2011a,b), assembling new genomes or transcriptomes (Flicek and Birney, 2009), quantitative RNA-sequencing analysis (Pepke et al., 2009), epigenetic change identification (Meaburn and Schulz, 2012), etc. In this article, we only discuss the aspect of WGS application for processing genomic data related to genetic variation. The types of genetic variants mainly consist of single nucleotide polymorphisms (SNPs), indels (insertions or deletions), structural variants (duplications, deletions, and inversions), and copy number variants (CNVs) (Zafar et al., 2016; Hillier et al., 2008; Kidd et al., 2008). The inherited variation raises a great deal of risk for individual health that may cause both common and rare disease (Andrew et al., 2017). WGS renders multiple potential solutions by providing full-scale collection of genetic variants. Though the expense to conduct a large scale has decreased considerably, there is still much space for the reduction of the cost that could popularize the techniques and applications of WGS. Consequently, it is necessary to develop more advanced and efficient methodology and pipelines for processing and analyzing whole genomes.

Typical Computational Pipeline of Whole Wenome Sequencing

The exponential growth of NGS data has promoted the blossom and release of tools for genomic analysis in recent years. Numerous different workflows are now available to deal with high-throughput genome sequencing data in the distinct types (Leipzig, 2017), for example, shell script, tool-specific interface, and graphical workflow environment (Wang et al., 2009; Yoo et al., 2011; Goecks et al., 2010; Chard et al., 2008). A typical computational pipeline for WGS usually contains components such as data preparation, alignment and assembly, variant calling, annotation, and analysis. **Fig. 1** shows the detailed steps of the pipeline for WGS analysis.

Data Preparation

The first step in the pipeline of WGS is data preparation, more specifically, sample preparation. The samples of nucleotide vary greatly from source to quality, which requires professional kits that help to acquire the nucleic acid after purification processing. To obtain the sequences, the genomic materials need to be managed into a sample library that contains short fragments after purification (Van Dijk et al., 2014). The sample libraries usually require high quality and intact sequences at a sufficient amount that meets the requirements for performing the sequencing by instruments (Wong et al., 2012). The general procedures of library preparation consist of several steps. The first step is to split the source genomic material into required lengths and then conduct the end repair and ligation of oligonucleotide adapters to the ends of the fragments. Next is the enrichment of the adapter ligated

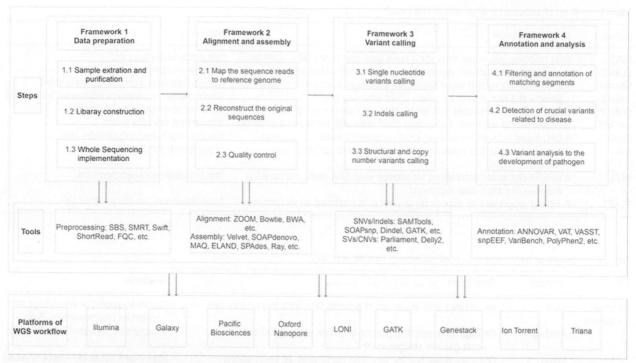

Fig. 1 A typical computational pipeline for whole genome sequencing.

library, and the final process is the validation and quantification of the results. Once the library construction is completed, large volumes of samples are sequenced in parallel by sequencing tools. The output of sequencing will be regulated in a standardized format such as FASTQ for alignment.

Alignment and Assembly

Once WGS data has been prepared, the alignment is set up that maps the reads of these samples to a reference genome. The length of reference genome could alter from thousands to billions of possible positions based on the species, so comparing plenty of short nucleotide reads to the reference genome is computationally intensive and time consuming (Kwong *et al.*, 2015). The implementation of alignment is usually using one or more specific algorithms aiming at the sequence reads characteristics. The hash-based (Flicek and Birney, 2009) and Burrows–Wheeler transform (BWT) (Li and Durbin, 2009) methods are the two most popular algorithms utilized as the core algorithm for many alignment software tools. The hash-based method builds either the hash table or input reads to scan the genome reference or in reverse. The software that uses hash table includes mrFAST, SHRiMP (Alkan *et al.*, 2011a,b; Rumble *et al.*, 2009). Another widely used method is the BWT, which creates a suffix array by performing BWT to obtain transformed sequences as a new reference genome for mapping. The BWT method achieves a faster algorithm compared with the hash-based method and is adopted by BOWTIE/BOWTIE2, SOAP2, BWA (Li *et al.*, 2009a,b; Langmead *et al.*, 2009). In addition to these software packages, many more tools can be found in **Table 1**.

Whole genome assembly follows the step of sequence alignment. The purpose of assembly is to reconstruct the original sequences into large contiguous segments that can be ordered and oriented along each chromosome (Flicek and Birney, 2009). De novo assembly and reference-based assembly are the two main approaches to form longer continuous sequences. De novo assembly involves utilizing computational methods to align overlapping WGS reads for assembling known reads as contigs and order the contigs into the framework of the sequenced genome (Robertson *et al.*, 2010). Referenced-based assembly maps each read to a reference genome sequence and builds a consensus sequence, which is similar but not necessarily identical to the backbone reference (Ng and Kirkness, 2010). Many tools are released online for assembling based on the two algorithms. De novo assemblers include two types: Overlap graphs (Myers, 1995) and de Bruijn graphs (Pevzner *et al.*, 2001). The overlap graph method is used by Canu (Myers *et al.*, 2000) and Arachne (Jaffe *et al.*, 2003), which calculates all the pairwise overlaps between reads and presents the information in the graph. The de Bruijn graph splits reads into k-mers to form the nodes of a network, where k describes the length in bases of these subsequences. Commonly used software based on this method includes Velvet (Zerbino and Birney, 2008), SOAPdenovo (Luo *et al.*, 2012), and ABySS (Simpson *et al.*, 2009). Compared with de novo assemblers, referenced-based assemblers require fewer computational resources but are more challenging in dealing with novel sequences. Examples of referenced-based assemblers include MAQ, SeqMap, and RMAP (Flicek and Birney, 2009; Jiang and Wong, 2008; Smith *et al.*, 2009). We have summarized some frequently used assemblers in **Table 2**.

Table 1   A list of software for alignment of short reads to the reference genome

Software	Simple description	Resources
MAQ	Build mapping assemblies from short reads generated by the NGS machines	http://maq.sourceforge.net/
ELAND	Hash-based computational alignment program for short oligonucleotides	https://www.illumina.com/
Bowtie/	A short-read aligner that aligns short DNA sequences (reads) to the human	http://bowtiebio.sourceforge.net/index.shtml
Bowtie2	genome at a rate of over 25 million 35-bp reads per hour	http://bowtiebio.sourceforge.net/bowtie2/index.shtml
SHRiMP	Sequence aligner developed with the multitudinous short reads of NGS	http://compbio.cs.toronto.edu/shrimp/
mrFAST	Seed-and-extend alignment tool to map short reads with the Illumina platform	http://mrfast.sourceforge.net/
SOAP	A GPU-based software for aligning short reads with a reference sequence	http://soap.genomics.org.cn/index.html
BWA	A software package that maps low-divergent sequences against a large reference genome	https://github.com/lh3/bwa
SEAL	A suite of distributed applications for aligning short DNA reads, manipulating and analyzing short-read alignments	http://biodoop-seal.sourceforge.net/
BLAST	A suite of programs that align query sequences in a selected target database	https://blast.ncbi.nlm.nih.gov/Blast.cgi

Table 2   Review of most commonly used software in genome assembly

Type	Software	Description	Resources
De novo assembly	Canu	Reconstruct long sequences of genomic DNA from fragmentary data	http://wgs-assembler.sourceforge.net/wiki/index.php?title=Main_Page
	Arachne	Package for assembling genome sequence using paired-end whole-genome shotgun reads	https://github.com/cseed/arachne-pnr
	Velvet	Sequence assembler for very short reads using de Bruijn graphs	https://www.ebi.ac.uk/~zerbino/velvet/
	SOAPdenovo	Short-read assembly method for the human-sized genomes	http://soap.genomics.org.cn/soapdenovo.html
	ABySS	Assembles the very large data sets produced by sequencing individual human genomes	http://www.bcgsc.ca/platform/bioinfo/software/abyss
Reference-based	SeqMap	Map large amount of oligonucleotide to the genome	http://www-personal.umich.edu/~jianghui/seqmap/
	MAQ	Build mapping assemblies from short reads generated by NGS machines	http://maq.sourceforge.net/
	RMAP	Map reads with or without error probability information and supports paired-end reads	http://rulai.cshl.edu/rmap/
Other	SPAdes	Standard isolates and single-cell MDA bacteria assembler	http://cab.spbu.ru/software/spades/
	Assembly	Unique and stable identifier for the set of sequences that comprise a specific genome assembly	https://www.ncbi.nlm.nih.gov/assembly/
	GAML	Systematic combination of diverse sequencing datasets into a single assembly	http://compbio.fmph.uniba.sk/gaml/

Quality control of sequence reads must be executed during the whole workflow, from sample preparation to alignment and assembly, as well in variant calling and annotation. Many issues can occur when processing genomic data. For example, the reads could be misaligned when performing alignment and assembly, causing systematic error of the device in sequencing and machine cycle (Torri *et al.*, 2012). These problems could lead to the quality score per base and affect the accuracy of variant calling. Unifying the aligned reads into Sequence Alignment/Map or Binary Sequence Alignment/Map format is essential for quality control (Wang *et al.*, 2012). This process could provide us a clean, well sorted, and indexed file as output that could be used in the subsequent analysis. In addition, in some WGS workflows, advanced quality control is also required in recalibrating the base quality scores of sequence reads for variation.

Variant Calling

After the alignment and assembly of short reads, the next step is variant calling, which is a very important step in the WGS pipeline. Variant calling is a conclusion that there is a difference between target sequence and reference at a given position in an individual genome. It is implemented after genome sequence alignment and assembly and the output of variant calling is stored in a standardized generic format called variant call format . These aligned reads differ from genome reference and the variants occurring are probably related to a certain kind of disease or only simple natural mutations without any functional effect in the cell. Based on the characteristics of variants, several different variations are shown in **Table 3**, which include SNPs/variants, indels, larger structural variants, and CNVs. We give an overview of these four variant calling types and provide the corresponding software packages for the implementation of variant calling.

Table 3   Variant calling tooling for the detection of SNVs, indels, SVs, and CNVs

Calling Type	Software	Simple description	Resources
SNP/ Indel	GATK	A collection of command line for the analysis of variant discovery	https://software.broadinstitute.org/gatk/
	SAMtools	A suite of programs for interacting with high-throughput sequencing data	http://www.htslib.org/
	Isaac Variant Caller	Detects SNVs/indels from the aligned sequencing reads of a single diploid sample	https://github.com/sequencing/isaac_variant_caller
	SOAPsnp	Software package for detecting somatic mutation of SNVs by resequencing	http://soap.genomics.org.cn/soapsnp.html
	Dindel	A Bayesian method to call indels from short-read sequence data in individuals	https://github.com/genome/dindel-tgi
SV/CNV	Breakdancer	Detect indels ranging from 10 base pairs to 1 megabase pair via a single conventional approach	http://gmt.genome.wustl.edu/packages/breakdancer/
	iSVP	A pipeline that applies multiple tools for detecting structural variants	http://nagasakilab.csml.org/en/isvp
	Pindel	Detects breakpoints of large deletions, medium sized insertions, inversions	https://github.com/genome/pindel
	SvABA	Detects SVs from short-read sequencing data using genome-wide local assembly	https://github.com/walaj/svaba
	SVMerge	A pipeline detects SVs by integrating calls from existing SV callers	http://svmerge.sourceforge.net/

SNP calling aims to determine in which positions there are polymorphisms or at least one of the bases differs from a reference sequence to describe the genetic relationship between isolates (Nielsen *et al.*, 2011). Accurate calling of SNPs needs high-quality sequencing data, high coverage, and a thorough bioinformatics approach to identify the SNPs in a statistically relevant manner. Indel calling is also a very common form of variant calling that corresponds to the insertion or deletion of base pairs in the sequence of an organism (Hasan *et al.*, 2015). Compared with SNP calling, accurate indel calling is more challenging, because the occurrence rate of indels is almost 8 times lower than SNPs. Various approaches have been applied to perform SNP and indel calling. Bayesian probabilistic procedure is the most frequently used method in the software packages to implement SNP or indel calling. It calculates the score of probability on each genotype and selecting the genotype in the position with highest probability (Li, 2012). The tools include GATK, SOAPsnp, SAMtools, and Isaac Variant Caller (McKenna *et al.*, 2010; Li *et al.*, 2009a,b, 2008; Raczy *et al.*, 2013). In addition, the pattern growth approach is another common method for indel calling by computing the fragments compared to the reference genome from paired-end reads, such as Dindel (Albers *et al.*, 2011).

Moreover, SV/CNV calling is similar to SNP and indel calling. The structural variants have the potential to impact large stretches of sequence, disrupting genes and regulatory elements that are associated with genetic disorders and used as disease markers in clinical diagnosis of diseases. To call large-scale structural variants, which are the source of sequence variation, involving deletion, insertion, and rearrangement of genomic material, it uses discordant fragments and depends on the paired-end reads. By resolving discordant fragments into some breakpoints between fragments through mapping of each end of the paired-end read, the category of a structural variant can be deduced (Fiegler *et al.*, 2006). For example, chromosomal translocations are a type of large-scale SV involving rearrangement of chromosomes. They can disrupt sequences and create new fusion products. Several signature translocations have been identified as mutations that drive the development of disease. The methods that call the relevant variants mainly involve read pair, split read, read depth, and de novo assembly (Alkan *et al.*, 2011a,b). However, there is still a lack of computational framework for SV/CNV calling. Up to now, only a few computational tools have been available, such as Breakdancer, iSVP, Pindel, SvABA, and SVMerge (Chen *et al.*, 2009; Mimori *et al.*, 2013; Ye *et al.*, 2009; Wong *et al.*, 2010). Details of the software used for variant calling are listed in **Table 3**.

Annotation and Analysis

Once the variant calling is completed, the next crucial step is the annotation between the target genome and reference genome to find the potential differences. Genome annotation includes the identification of genome segments of known and probable open reading frames and matching the identified segments to the detected gene sequences from the existing databases (Kwong *et al.*, 2015). It needs to be annotated with biological information. These biological related data range from gene models to gene functions including the Kyoto Encyclopedia of Genes and Genomes (Kanehisa and Goto, 2000) and Gene Ontology (Primmer *et al.*, 2013). A typical genome annotation constitutes a significant effort recorded on the human genome sequences in the reports, which present considerably detailed genome information. The unit record for each genome annotation describes an individual gene and its protein product. Meanwhile, simple evidence of the assigned function for the variants may also be stored in the file, for example, boundary of domains and functionally characterized homolog, but the details of the information need further exploration. The process of annotation conceptually contains two parts, namely the computational part and the annotation part. The computational part consists of the data from genomes or specific transcriptomes that are used in parallel to create initial gene and transcript information. The annotation part is used to synthesize the information into a gene annotation by a set of rules in an annotation pipeline. Usually, the success of genome annotation strongly relies on the quality of genome assembly so that it will produce satisfying results in terms of near-complete genomes broken by small gaps.

The purpose of genome analysis is to explore the effect of genomic variants on wild-type gene function and further on overall individual health. The progress of WGS has been yielding an increasing number of genetic variants. Identification of the disease-associated variants and seeking their specific types, locations, potential effects, and functions is complicated and challenging because of issues such as complex genomic regions, inaccurate variant calling, detection of the phase of the locus, etc. The causation between genomic variants and disease association is the key point during the process of genomic annotation and analysis, which could help us acquire explicit understanding on variation effects of individuals (Albert and Kruglyak, 2015). Many excellent resources and programmable workflows are usable for the annotation and analysis of identified variants that differ by type. Almost all the tools can process SNPs and indels, but for SV annotations, only a few tools are available like ANNOVAR (Wang *et al.*, 2010) and VAT (Habegger *et al.*, 2012). Also, these tools could achieve distinct functions such as reference database annotation, evolutionary information, prediction of identified variant effect, allele frequency, chromosomal position regarding to the nearby site of interest (e.g., gene, segmental duplication, splice site, regulatory region, etc.) (Bromberg, 2013). All these findings or results are the outcomes of individual variants that can be used for the diagnosis of disease. Some common tools for the execution of annotation and analysis are shown in **Table 4**.

The frameworks above present the steps and provide available tools for the implementation in each process. Such processes sequentially linked together constitute the complete computational WGS workflow. A number of platforms have been developed for the processing of genome sequencing analysis that integrate and manage pipelines. The most widely used WGS platform may be Illumina, which achieves DNA colony amplification by bridge PCR, sequencing-by-synthesis, and fluorescence imaging (Lunter and Goodson, 2011). The types of Illumina instruments vary a lot in terms of the function and cost, including MiSeq, NextSeq, HiSeq, HiSeq X Ten, etc. The Ion Torrent platform, a competitor to Illumina, is similar to cyclic array platforms in amplifying DNA colonies on beads that are immobilized within wells on a patterned surface. This system utilizes a novel and nonoptical detection method, measuring the release of a hydrogen ion (Merriman *et al.*, 2012). Pacific Biosciences is another platform that offers comprehensive solutions and advanced applications of WGS for complete gene discovery. Though, the cost is more expensive than alternatives, the combination of long reads and minimal GC bias for large-scale WGS by Pacific Biosciences allows access to a substantially larger portion of human genetic variation, an intrinsic advantage over short-read sequencing technology (Carneiro *et al.*, 2012). Another noteworthy platform is Oxford Nanopore, which uses low quantities of input nucleotides and long reads without manipulation (Mikheyev and Tin, 2014). Besides, there are many other companies and communities that are keen on exploiting novel and advanced WGS technologies including Galaxy, LONI, GATK, Taverna, etc. (Giardine *et al.* 2005; Rex *et al.*, 2003; McKenna *et al.*, 2010; Oinn *et al.*, 2004), so we are optimistic for the prospects of WGS platform development in the future.

Clinical Workflow and Application

The application of WGS shows a broad range across different fields, including agriculture, food, public health, even in space for a variety of settings and reasons. In this article, we only discuss its clinical applications, which are closely related to human health and life. The clinical application of WGS represents the elucidation of the genomic determinants of humans' heritable makeup. In fact, many genome projects have been released concentrating on the use of WGS for diagnosing those with rare and common diseases, cancer, etc. We anticipate that this description will continue to advance our understanding of pathophysiology with WGS and realize its value in discovering genes and variants for underlying disease and improving public health.

Current clinical applications mainly consist of Mendelian diseases, complex diseases, and cancer (Wu *et al.*, 2016). The diagnosis of Mendelian disease is the most common application of genome sequencing of individual patients that has been successfully applied in the identification of causal mutations (Lupski *et al.*, 2010; Roach *et al.*, 2010). The largest collection of Mendelian disease contains 7000 distinct diseases that are characterized based on the OMIM database (Hamosh *et al.*, 2002).

Table 4   A list of available software in genome annotation

Software	Simple description	Sources
ANNOVAR	Utilizes up-to-date information to annotate genetic variants detected from diverse genomes	http://annovar.openbioinformatics.org/en/latest/
VAT	A computational framework to functionally annotate variants in personal genomes	http://vat.gersteinlab.org/
VARIANT	Provides annotation of variants from NGS based on several different databases and repositories	http://variant.bioinfo.cipf.es/
VAAST	Identifies damaged genes and their disease-causing variants in personal genome sequences	http://www.yandell-lab.org/software/vaast.html
snpEFF	Annotates and predicts the effects of SNP, indel, and MNP variants in genomic sequences	http://snpeff.sourceforge.net/
VariBench	A benchmark database for testing and training methods for variation effect prediction	http://structure.bmc.lu.se/VariBench/
PolyPhen/ PolyPhen-2	Algorithms that predict possible impact of an AAS on the structure and function of human protein based on sequence, phylogenetics, and structure	http://genetics.bwh.harvard.edu/pph2/
SeattleSeq	Annotate novel and known SNVs and small indels with biological functions, protein positions, etc	http://snp.gs.washington.edu/SeattleSeqAnnotation150/

Almost half of them are caused by unknown genetic elements. The diagnosis of Mendelian disease by WGS workflow includes the combination of gene information, variant function prediction, variant frequency, and evolutionary conservation. The rationale underneath is the assumption that the variants related to the Mendelian diseases that change the protein function on corresponding genes tend to be rare. Common or complex diseases are another type of clinical application affected by more than one variant. Genome-wide association studies explore complex disease due to the variants that contribute to disease susceptibility with modest effect size. However, genome-wide association only genotypes common variants. The technique of WGS makes it possible to annotate all variants, including rare and common variants, and guarantee the sequencing of real functional genes. The identification of cancer, regarded as an important type of complex disease, has been in great demand in recent years. Much attention has been paid using whole exome sequencing to detect multiple types of cancers such as breast cancer, gastric cancer, and prostate cancer (Barbieri *et al.*, 2012; Wang *et al.*, 2011; Thompson *et al.*, 2012). Although certain types of cancer detection have obtained immense success, it still exposes the issue that whole exome sequencing only focuses on the protein coding region and ignores the noncoding region, which blocks the wider and deeper study of cancer. With increasing development of sequencing technology, WGS is solving the issue of identifying noncoding regions that are frequently mutated across cancer types, which creates opportunities for personalized medicine in the future (Tsai *et al.*, 2016).

We provide the MedSeq Project, the first randomized clinical trial that integrating WGS into clinical medicine, as an example to draw the outline of WGS clinical workflow for healthy individuals and individuals with disease (Vassy *et al.*, 2014). The holistic view of clinical WGS workflow is depicted in **Fig. 2**; this mainly consists of five components, namely patients, hospitals, lab experiments, reports and feedback, and solutions.

Limitations and Future Development

With the rapid progress of genome sequencing techniques and powerful tools and platforms, there are still limitations that obstruct the widespread use of WGS. The first challenge is that WGS may not detect all of the variations in a genome. For example, variations that cause DNA repetitions or rearrangements can hardly be detected by WGS, which means you may have variants that could deceive you to a certain genetic condition that escapes detection. Also, occasionally a portion of a gene may not be readable by WGS and the variants could be missed. The second is the interpretation of genetic variants in genes, especially related to human disease. The lack of a test and comparison in clinical research is still an immense issue, although many relevant studies are frequently published on the meaning of biological variants (Krier *et al.*, 2016). The development of a standardized evaluation of

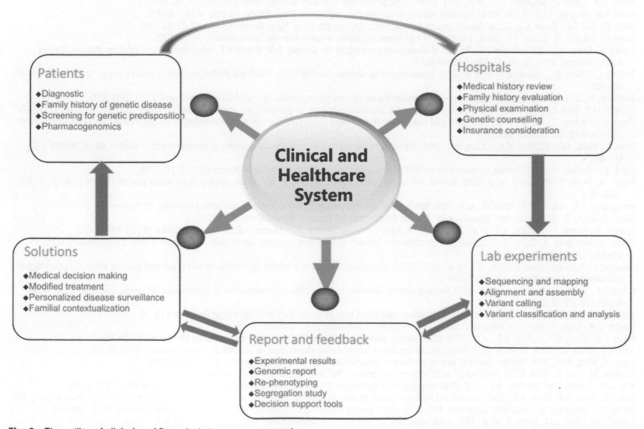

Fig. 2 The outline of clinical workflow of whole genome sequencing.

WGS pipelines for validation in clinics is of great significance to public health. The third remains the further improvement of methods and techniques for pipeline construction. WGS has extensively detected SNVs and indels, but for the identification of SVs and CNVs as well as genomic rearrangements, it remains in its infancy. Therefore, more innovative methods and advanced analysis techniques (such as deep WGS), which have not yet been applied as part of common workflow in most of the existing research and practical projects, need to be further explored.

Despite these challenges, we are still confident and looking forward to the bright future of WGS. We can expect continuous improvement on the steps of the WGS pipeline by sequencing technology and computational methods. New library construction enables sequencing by producing libraries with longer and more precise sizes and generating longer reads with less error rate. More efficient algorithms and stronger computation power could further reduce computing time and cost for genome sequencing, which will make WGS become routine in both genetics research and clinical application. After the enhancement in techniques and methods, there is no doubt that user-friendly and advanced workflows are the key to facilitate more widespread use of WGS. The unification of the pipeline with WGS in a shared and specified language, as well as common tools, will bring much convenience with the expanding community of users and producers of genomic data. This transition makes it possible that even small research teams or individuals with limited resources will be able to develop genomic studies and strengthen the use of WGS techniques in biology and related fields. As more multidimensional data and more-populated databases are generated (e.g., genetic pathways, functions, biomedical information) through research institutions and hospital networks, abundant variants will be detected, which will bring us a great chance for new discoveries to figure out the relation between variations and effects in certain diseases. In addition, the methods for storing and sharing WGS data seamlessly, construction of databases containing millions of individuals with diverse health networks using WGS, as well as the integration of genotypic and phenotypic information are also critical steps for the prosperity of future directions in WGS development.

See also: Computational Pipelines and Workflows in Bioinformatics. Constructing Computational Pipelines. Exome Sequencing Data Analysis. Genome Annotation: Perspective From Bacterial Genomes. Natural Language Processing Approaches in Bioinformatics. Next Generation Sequencing Data Analysis. Pipeline of High Throughput Sequencing

---

References

Albers, C.A., Lunter, G., MacArthur, D.G., et al., 2011. Dindel: Accurate indel calls from short-read data. Genome Research 21 (6), 961–973.

Albert, F.W., Kruglyak, L., 2015. The role of regulatory variation in complex traits and disease. Nature Reviews Genetics 16 (4), 197–212.

Alkan, C., Coe, B.P., Eichler, E.E., 2011a. Genome structural variation discovery and genotyping. Nature Reviews Genetics 12 (5), 363–376.

Alkan, C., Sajjadian, S., Eichler, E.E., 2011b. Limitations of next-generation genome sequence assembly. Nature Methods 8 (1), 61–65.

Dervan, A., Shendure, J., 2017. Chapter 3 – The state of whole-genome sequencing. In: Ginsburg, G.S., Willard, H.F. (Eds.), Genomic and Precision Medicine, third ed. Boston: Academic Press, pp. 45–62. ISBN 9780128006818.

Barbieri, C.E., Baca, S.C., Lawrence, M.S., et al., 2012. Exome sequencing identifies recurrent SPOP, FOXA1 and MED12 mutations in prostate cancer. Nature Genetics 44 (6), 685–689.

Bromberg, Y., 2013. Building a genome analysis pipeline to predict disease risk and prevent disease. Journal of Molecular Biology 425 (21), 3993–4005.

Carneiro, M.O., Russ, C., Ross, M.G., et al., 2012. Pacific biosciences sequencing technology for genotyping and variation discovery in human data. BMC Genomics 13 (1), 375.

Chard, K., Onyuksel, C., Tan, W., et al., 2008. Build grid enabled scientific workflows using gRAVI and taverna. In: Proceeding of the IEEE Fourth International Conference on eScience, 2008, pp. 614–619. IEEE.

Chen, K., Wallis, J.W., McLellan, M.D., Larson, et al., 2009. BreakDancer: An algorithm for high-resolution mapping of genomic structural variation. Nature Methods 6 (9), 677–681.

Dalca, A.V., Brudno, M., 2010. Genome variation discovery with high-throughput sequencing data. Briefings in Bioinformatics 11 (1), 3–14.

Fiegler, H., Redon, R., Andrews, D., et al., 2006. Accurate and reliable high-throughput detection of copy number variation in the human genome. Genome Research 16 (12), 1566–1574.

Fleischmann, R.D., Adams, M.D., White, O., et al., 1995. Whole-genome random sequencing and assembly of Haemophilus influenzae Rd. Science. 496–512.

Flicek, P., Birney, E., 2009. Sense from sequence reads: Methods for alignment and assembly. Nature Methods 6, S6–S12.

Giardine, B., Riemer, C., Hardison, R.C., et al., 2005. Galaxy: A platform for interactive large-scale genome analysis. Genome Research 15 (10), 1451–1455.

Goecks, J., Nekrutenko, A., Taylor, J., 2010. Galaxy: A comprehensive approach for supporting accessible, reproducible, and transparent computational research in the life sciences. Genome Biology 11 (8), R86.

Habegger, L., Balasubramanian, S., Chen, D.Z., et al., 2012. VAT: A computational framework to functionally annotate variants in personal genomes within a cloud-computing environment. Bioinformatics 28 (17), 2267–2269.

Hamosh, A., Scott, A.F., Amberger, J., et al., 2002. Online Mendelian Inheritance in Man (OMIM), a knowledgebase of human genes and genetic disorders. Nucleic Acids Research 30 (1), 52–55.

Hasan, M.S., Wu, X., Zhang, L., 2015. Performance evaluation of indel calling tools using real short-read data. Human Genomics 9 (1), 20.

Heather, J.M., Chain, B., 2016. The sequence of sequencers: The history of sequencing DNA. Genomics 107 (1), 1–8.

Hillier, L.W., Marth, G.T., Quinlan, A.R., et al., 2008. Whole-genome sequencing and variant discovery in C. elegans. Nature Methods 5 (2), 183–188.

Jaffe, D.B., Butler, J., Gnerre, S., et al., 2003. Whole-genome sequence assembly for mammalian genomes: Arachne 2. Genome Research 13 (1), 91–96.

Jiang, H., Wong, W.H., 2008. SeqMap: Mapping massive amount of oligonucleotides to the genome. Bioinformatics 24 (20), 2395–2396.

Kanehisa, M., Goto, S., 2000. KEGG: Kyoto encyclopedia of genes and genomes. Nucleic Acids Research 28 (1), 27–30.

Kidd, J.M., Cooper, G.M., Donahue, W.F., et al., 2008. Mapping and sequencing of structural variation from eight human genomes. Nature 453 (7191), 56–64.

Krier, J.B., Kalia, S.S., Green, R.C., 2016. Genomic sequencing in clinical practice: Applications, challenges, and opportunities. Dialogues in Clinical Neuroscience 18 (3), 299.

Kwong, J.C., McCallum, N., Sintchenko, V., Howden, B.P., 2015. Whole genome sequencing in clinical and public health microbiology. Pathology 47 (3), 199–210.

Lander, E.S., Linton, L.M., Birren, B., et al., 2001. Initial sequencing and analysis of the human genome. Nature 409 (6822), 860–921.

Langmead, B., Trapnell, C., Pop, M., Salzberg, S.L., 2009. Ultrafast and memory-efficient alignment of short DNA sequences to the human genome. Genome Biology 10 (3), R25.

Leipzig, J., 2017. A review of bioinformatic pipeline frameworks. Briefings in Bioinformatics 18 (3), 530–536.

Li, H., 2012. Exploring single-sample SNP and INDEL calling with whole-genome de novo assembly. Bioinformatics 28 (14), 1838–1844.

Li, H., Durbin, R., 2009. Fast and accurate short read alignment with Burrows–Wheeler transform. Bioinformatics 25 (14), 1754–1760.

Li, H., Handsaker, B., Wysoker, A., et al., 2009a. The sequence alignment/map format and SAMtools. Bioinformatics 25 (16), 2078–2079.

Li, R., Li, Y., Kristiansen, K., Wang, J., 2008. SOAP: Short oligonucleotide alignment program. Bioinformatics 24 (5), 713–714.

Li, R., Yu, C., Li, Y., et al., 2009b. SOAP2: An improved ultrafast tool for short read alignment. Bioinformatics 25 (15), 1966–1967.

Lunter, G., Goodson, M., 2011. Stampy: A statistical algorithm for sensitive and fast mapping of Illumina sequence reads. Genome Research 21 (6), 936–939.

Luo, R., Liu, B., Xie, Y., et al., 2012. SOAPdenovo2: An empirically improved memory-efficient short-read de novo assembler. Gigascience 1 (1), 18.

Lupski, J.R., Reid, J.G., Gonzaga-Jauregui, C., et al., 2010. Whole-genome sequencing in a patient with Charcot–Marie–Tooth neuropathy. New England Journal of Medicine 362 (13), 1181–1191.

McKenna, A., Hanna, M., Banks, E., et al., 2010. The Genome Analysis Toolkit: A MapReduce framework for analyzing next-generation DNA sequencing data. Genome Research 20 (9), 1297–1303.

Meaburn, E., Schulz, R., 2012. Next generation sequencing in epigenetics: Insights and challenges. In: Seminars in Cell & Developmental Biology, vol. 23 (2), pp. 192–199. Academic Press.

Merriman, B., Torrent, I., Rothberg, J.M., R&D Team, 2012. Progress in ion torrent semiconductor chip based sequencing. Electrophoresis 33 (23), 3397–3417.

Mikheyev, A.S., Tin, M.M., 2014. A first look at the Oxford Nanopore MinION sequencer. Molecular Ecology Resources 14 (6), 1097–1102.

Mimori, T., Nariai, N., Kojima, K., et al., 2013. iSVP: An integrated structural variant calling pipeline from high-throughput sequencing data. BMC Systems Biology 7 (6), S8.

Moorthie, S., Mattocks, C.J., Wright, C.F., 2011. Review of massively parallel DNA sequencing technologies. The HUGO Journal 5 (1-4), 1–12. http://doi.org/10.1007/s11568-011-9156-3.

Myers, E.W., 1995. Toward simplifying and accurately formulating fragment assembly. Journal of Computational Biology 2 (2), 275–290.

Myers, E.W., Sutton, G.G., Delcher, A.L., et al., 2000. A whole-genome assembly of Drosophila. Science 287 (5461), 2196–2204.

Ng, P.C., Kirkness, E.F., 2010. Whole genome sequencing. In: Genetic Variation. Humana Press, pp. 215–226.

Nielsen, R., Paul, J.S., Albrechtsen, A., Song, Y.S., 2011. Genotype and SNP calling from next-generation sequencing data. Nature Reviews Genetics 12 (6), 443–451.

Oinn, T., Addis, M., Ferris, J., et al., 2004. Taverna: A tool for the composition and enactment of bioinformatics workflows. Bioinformatics 20 (17), 3045–3054.

Pepke, S., Wold, B., Mortazavi, A., 2009. Computation for ChIP-seq and RNA-seq studies. Nature Methods 6, S22–S32.

Pevzner, P.A., Tang, H., Waterman, M.S., 2001. An Eulerian path approach to DNA fragment assembly. Proceedings of the National Academy of Sciences 98 (17), 9748–9753.

Primmer, C.R., Papakostas, S., Leder, E.H., Davis, M.J., Ragan, M.A., 2013. Annotated genes and nonannotated genomes: Cross-species use of Gene Ontology in ecology and evolution research. Molecular Ecology 22 (12), 3216–3241.

Raczy, C., Petrovski, R., Saunders, C.T., et al., 2013. Isaac: Ultra-fast whole-genome secondary analysis on Illumina sequencing platforms. Bioinformatics 29 (16), 2041–2043.

Rex, D.E., Ma, J.Q., Toga, A.W., 2003. The LONI pipeline processing environment. Neuroimage 19 (3), 1033–1048.

Roach, J.C., Glusman, G., Smit, A.F., et al., 2010. Analysis of genetic inheritance in a family quartet by whole-genome sequencing. Science 328 (5978), 636–639.

Robertson, G., Schein, J., Chiu, R., et al., 2010. De novo assembly and analysis of RNA-seq data. Nature Methods 7 (11), 909–912.

Rumble, S.M., Lacroute, P., Dalca, A.V., et al., 2009. SHRiMP: Accurate mapping of short color-space reads. PLOS Computational Biology 5 (5), e1000386.

Sanger, F., Nicklen, S., Coulson, A.R., 1977. DNA sequencing with chain-terminating inhibitors. Proceedings of the National Academy of Sciences 74 (12), 5463–5467.

Saraswathy, N., Ramalingam, P., 2011. Concepts and Techniques in Genomics and Proteomics. Elsevier.

Schuster, S.C., 2008. Next-generation sequencing transforms today's biology. Nature Methods 5 (1), 16–18.

Simpson, J.T., Wong, K., Jackman, S.D., et al., 2009. ABySS: A parallel assembler for short read sequence data. Genome Research 19 (6), 1117–1123.

Slatko, B.E., Albright, L.M., Tabor, S., Ju, J., 2001. DNA sequencing by the dideoxy method. Current Protocols in Molecular Biology. 4–7.

Smith, A.D., Chung, W.Y., Hodges, E., et al., 2009. Updates to the RMAP short-read mapping software. Bioinformatics 25 (21), 2841–2842.

Staden, R., 1979. A strategy of DNA sequencing employing computer programs. Nucleic Acids Research 6 (7), 2601–2610.

Thompson, E.R., Doyle, M.A., Ryland, G.L., et al., 2012. Exome sequencing identifies rare deleterious mutations in DNA repair genes FANCC and BLM as potential breast cancer susceptibility alleles. PLOS Genetics 8 (9), e1002894.

Torri, F., Dinov, I.D., Zamanyan, A., et al., 2012. Next generation sequence analysis and computational genomics using graphical pipeline workflows. Genes 3 (3), 545–575.

Tsai, E.A., Shakbatyan, R., Evans, J., et al., 2016. Bioinformatics workflow for clinical whole genome sequencing at partners healthcare personalized medicine. Journal of Personalized Medicine 6 (1), 12.

Van Dijk, E.L., Jaszczyszyn, Y., Thermes, C., 2014. Library preparation methods for next-generation sequencing: Tone down the bias. Experimental Cell Research 322 (1), 12–20.

Vassy, J.L., Lautenbach, D.M., McLaughlin, H.M., et al., 2014. The MedSeq Project: A randomized trial of integrating whole genome sequencing into clinical medicine. Trials 15 (1), 85.

Wang, D.L., Zender, C.S., Jenks, S.F., 2009. Efficient clustered server-side data analysis workflows using SWAMP. Earth Science Informatics 2 (3), 141–155.

Wang, K., Kan, J., Yuen, S.T., et al., 2011. Exome sequencing identifies frequent mutation of ARID1A in molecular subtypes of gastric cancer. Nature Genetics 43 (12), 1219–1223.

Wang, K., Li, M., Hakonarson, H., 2010. ANNOVAR: Functional annotation of genetic variants from high-throughput sequencing data. Nucleic Acids Research 38 (16), e164.

Wang, L., Wang, S., Li, W., 2012. RSeQC: Quality control of RNA-seq experiments. Bioinformatics 28 (16), 2184–2185.

Wong, K., Keane, T.M., Stalker, J., Adams, D.J., 2010. Enhanced structural variant and breakpoint detection using SVMerge by integration of multiple detection methods and local assembly. Genome Biology 11 (12), R128.

Wong, P.B., Wiley, E.O., Johnson, W.E., et al., 2012. Tissue sampling methods and standards for vertebrate genomics. GigaScience 1 (1), 8.

Wu, J., Wu, M., Chen, T., Jiang, R., 2016. Whole genome sequencing and its applications in medical genetics. Quantitative Biology 4 (2), 115–128.

Ye, K., Schulz, M.H., Long, Q., Apweiler, R., Ning, Z., 2009. Pindel: A pattern growth approach to detect break points of large deletions and medium sized insertions from paired-end short reads. Bioinformatics 25 (21), 2865–2871.

Yoo, J., Ha, I.C., Chang, G.T., et al., 2011. CNVAS: Copy Number Variation Analysis System – The analysis tool for genomic alteration with a powerful visualization module. BioChip Journal 5 (3), 265–270.

Zafar, H., Wang, Y., Nakhleh, L., Navin, N., Chen, K., 2016. Monovar: Single-nucleotide variant detection in single cells. Nature Methods 13 (6), 505–507.

Zerbino, D.R., Birney, E., 2008. Velvet: Algorithms for de novo short read assembly using de Bruijn graphs. Genome Research 18 (5), 821–829.

Metagenomic Analysis and its Applications

Arpita Ghosh, Eurofins Genomics India Pvt. Ltd., Bangalore, India and Centre for Bioinformatics, Perdana University, Selangor, Malaysia
Aditya Mehta, Eurofins Genomics India Pvt. Ltd., Bangalore, India
Asif M Khan, Perdana University, Selangor, Malaysia

Introduction

Metagenomic analysis is commonly used to investigate complex microbial communities sampled directly from the environment, without culturing or isolating a single organism. Microbes have important roles to play in various ecosystems, however, many remain to be characterized in detail. The term metagenomics was coined in 1998 (Handelsman et al., 1998); it helps to understand various aspects of a sample, and allows one to characterize the microbes in the given environmental sample. It helps identify the species present in the community and also provides insights about the metabolic activities and functional roles of the microbes in the environmental sample (Langille et al., 2013).

Current approaches allow one to understand the complex properties of the microbiota, their dynamics and function in the natural system. Various metagenomic approaches answer fundamental questions such as which organisms are present (Taxonomic diversity), and what roles they play (Functional metagenomics) (Vieites et al., 2008). The amplification of specific targeted genes such as (V1-V9) of 16S rRNA, 18S rRNA, ribosomal ITS, NifH, among others, by PCR before sequencing permit diversity analysis (Morgan and Huttenhower, 2012). The relative abundance of the most abundant microorganisms of a particular group is not necessarily associated with the importance of that group in the functioning of the community. The most abundant organisms may not always play the most critical role in a community, while organisms constituting only 0.1% of the community (e.g., nitrogen fixers) can have very important functions (Dinsdale et al., 2008).

Types of Metagenomics Studies

The two most commonly used methods of pathogen identification for high throughput data are (1) Amplicon based method which includes 16S ribosomal RNA for bacteria, internal transcribed spacer (ITS) and 18S region for fungi and eukaryotes, respectively, and (2) whole metagenomic shotgun sequencing.

Shotgun Metagenomics

Shotgun metagenomic analysis has the ability to identify the majority of the organisms (culturable and unculturable bacteria) in the environmental sample. A community biodiversity profile is created, which is further associated with functional composition analysis of organism lineages (i.e., genera or taxa) (Tringe et al., 2005). Shotgun metagenomic studies can be divided into two types: (1) Sequence-based screens, which describe the microbial diversity and genomes of a particular environmental sample, and (2) Functional screens, which identify the functional gene products, but do not determine from what species the genetic material originated (Madhavan et al., 2017). Before initiating a whole metagenomic study, an understanding of the potential microbial diversity and the relative abundance of species in the environmental sample is very important. For example, the metagenome of soil samples will consist of a more complex microbial community, than human skin. Hence, for proper coverage, more data must be generated in case of soil than for human skin. A higher sequencing depth also allows the detection of rare taxa (Sharpton, 2014). This makes shotgun metagenomic sequencing much more expensive than 16S sequencing, in order to achieve the coverage and depth needed for species identification (Quail et al., 2012).

Amplicon Based 16S

16S sequencing is a widely used technique that relies on the variable regions (V1-V9) of the bacterial 16S rRNA gene to make community-wide taxonomic assignments (Chakravorty et al., 2007). It is also used for microbial diversity analysis and has been used for various environmental samples, such as soil (Chong et al., 2012) and human gut (Dethlefsen et al., 2008), among others. Some degree of divergence is allowed during the sequence similarity assessment stage of the analysis; typically, nearly identical sequences (>97%) are clustered into Operational Taxonomical Units (OTU) (Morgan and Huttenhower, 2012). The limitation of this method is that, if any two organisms have the same 16S rRNA gene sequence, they may be classified as the same species in a 16S analysis, even if they are from different species. Because 16S analysis is based on the 16S rRNA gene, with OTUs defined as taxa, it is generally not possible to distinguish strains, nor, in some cases, closely related species. For example, *Escherichia coli* O157: H7 and *E. coli* K-12 cannot be differentiated based on 16S analysis (Weinstock, 2012), nor can *Shigella flexneri* be distinguished from *E. coli* (Hilton et al., 2016). The OTUs are analyzed at each taxonomic level, but are less precise at the species level (Ranjan et al., 2016).

Amplicon Based 18S/ITS

The 18S rRNA is one of the basic components of fungal cells and comprises both conserved and hypervariable regions. The internal transcribed spacer region, ITS, is located between the 18S and 5.8S rRNA genes and has a high degree of sequence variation. The 18S rRNA is mainly used for high resolution taxonomic studies of fungi, while the ITS region is widely used for analysing fungal diversity in environmental samples (Bromberg et al., 2015). Taxonomic studies of fungi are often based on the nuclear ribosomal gene cluster, which includes the 18S or small subunit (SSU), 5.8S subunit, and 28S or large subunit (LSU) rRNA genes. ITS1 and ITS2 have been found to be the most suitable markers for fungal phylogenetic analysis due to their variable sequences, conserved primers and multicopy nature (Cuadros-Orellana et al., 2013). Various pipelines, such as QIIME (Caporaso et al., 2010), MG-RAST (Glass et al., 2010) and Mothur (Schloss et al., 2009) are used to perform taxonomic and functional analysis (**Table 1**). In QIIME, the UNITE database is used as it includes fungal rDNA ITS sequences (Kõljalg et al., 2005). In addition to rRNA genes, other amplicon-based studies are performed in order to focus on specific functions such as nitrogen fixation activity, and diversity analysis of nitrogenase reductase (nifH) genes (Igai et al., 2016). Arbuscular mycorrhizal fungi have been found in a symbiotic relation with the roots of plants (Smith and Read, 2008) based on analyses of the fungal SSU rRNA gene (Vasar et al., 2017).

Metatranscriptomics and Metaproteomics

RNA-Seq analysis of microbial communities in a complex ecosystem is known as Metatranscriptomics (Zhang et al., 2017). Co-expression of gene clusters and transcript abundance, followed by functional annotation, can be studied in environmental samples (Oyserman et al., 2016). The quantitation of mRNA and pathway expression can be carried out using metatranscriptomics. The challenge associated with metatranscriptomic approaches is to get high quality RNA from environmental samples; given this, it is an efficient approach to elucidate gene expression, and to discover novel genes in the microbial community (Frias-Lopez et al., 2008; Tartar et al., 2009).

Table 1 List of tools and databases

Category	Tools	References
Assembly	IDBA-UD	Peng et al. (2012)
	MEGAHIT	Li et al. (2015)
	MetaVelvet	Namiki et al. (2012)
	MetaVelvet-SL	Sato and Sakakibara (2014)
	Ray Meta	Boisvert et al. (2012)
	SOAPdenovo2	Luo et al. (2012)
	Omega	Haider et al. (2014)
	metaSPAdes	Nurk et al. (2017)
	MetAMOS	Treangen et al. (2013)
Binning	SCIMM and PHYSCIMM	Kelley and Salzberg (2010)
	Phymm and PhymmBL	Brady and Salzberg (2009)
	CONCOCT	Alneberg et al. (2014)
	IMG/MER 4	Markowitz et al. (2013)
	MG-RAST	Glass et al. (2010)
	MEGAN	Huson and Weber (2013)
	MetaCluster	Wang et al. (2014)
Gene Prediction	MetaGeneMark	Zhu et al. (2010)
	Prodigal	Hyatt et al. (2010)
	FragGeneScan	Rho et al. (2010)
	Glimmer-MG	Kelley et al. (2011)
	Prokka	Seemann (2014)
OUT Picking & Clustering	QIIME	Caporaso et al. (2010)
	Mothur	Schloss et al. (2009)
Functional 16S analysis	PICRUSt	Langille et al. (2013)
Databases	SILVA	Quast et al. (2012)
	Greengenes	DeSantis et al. (2006)
	Ribosomal database (RDP)	Cole et al. (2006)
	KEGG	Ogata et al. (1999)
	SEED	Overbeek et al. (2005)
	eggnog	Powell et al. (2014)
	COG/KOG	Tatusov et al. (2000)
	PFAM	Bateman et al. (2004)
	TIGRFAM	Haft et al. (2003)
	UNITE	Kõljalg et al. (2013)

The study of the proteome expressed in the microbial community is known as Metaproteomics. This has been used to investigate microbial activities along with complex metabolic pathways in soil ecosystems (Zampieri et al., 2016). Community metaproteomics are emerging as complementary approaches to metagenomics and can provide large-scale characterization of proteins in the microbiota, such as in the human gut (Petriz and Franco, 2017). Metagenomics, along with metatranscriptomics and metaproteomics, provide insights into functional dynamics, prediction of the in situ microbial responses/activities, and the production capabilities of microbial communities (Simon and Daniel, 2011).

Analysis of the metagenome

In this section, we discuss the various analysis pipelines for the types of metagenomics studies shown in **Fig. 1** (credit to Oulas et al., 2015).

Shotgun Metagenomic Analysis

Metagenomics studies are carried out to investigate both known and unknown species, both culturable and unculturable, in the environmental sample studied. A *de novo* assembly of shorter reads may be carried out to obtain genomic contigs, followed by scaffolding, which is often performed to get a more compact and concise view of the sequenced environmental samples. Achieving full assemblies of the complete genomes present in the community is difficult, and is rarely possible except in simple communities, or with very deep sequencing (Tyson et al., 2004; Venter et al., 2004). In metagenomic studies, insight into the metabolic functions active in the environmental sample can be obtained based on the complete sequences of protein coding genes, as well as from the full operons present in the sequenced genomes (Oulas et al., 2015).

Pre-processing of sequence reads for metagenomics

The raw reads generated from the next generation sequencing platform are subjected to adapter trimming, quality filtration, and de-replication. If the metagenomic sample is isolated from a host organism, then host contamination is typically removed by aligning to the reference genome of the host organism using bowtie2 or other short-read mapper (Oulas et al., 2015).

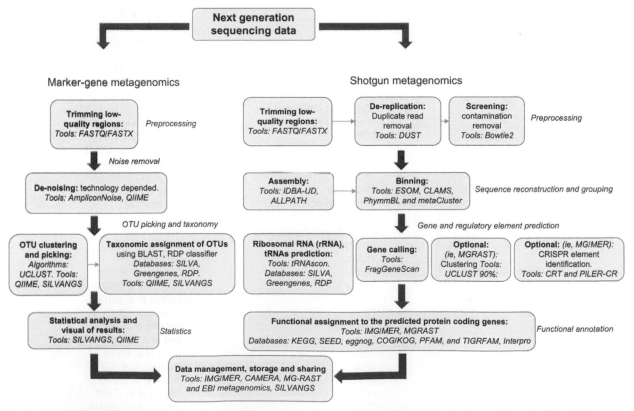

Fig. 1 The overview of the whole metagenomics and 16S analysis (marker-gene metagenomics). Reproduced from Oulas, A., Pavloudi, C., Polymenakou, P., *et al.*, 2015. Metagenomics: Tools and insights for analyzing next-generation sequencing data derived from biodiversity studies. Bioinformatics and Biology insights 9, 75.

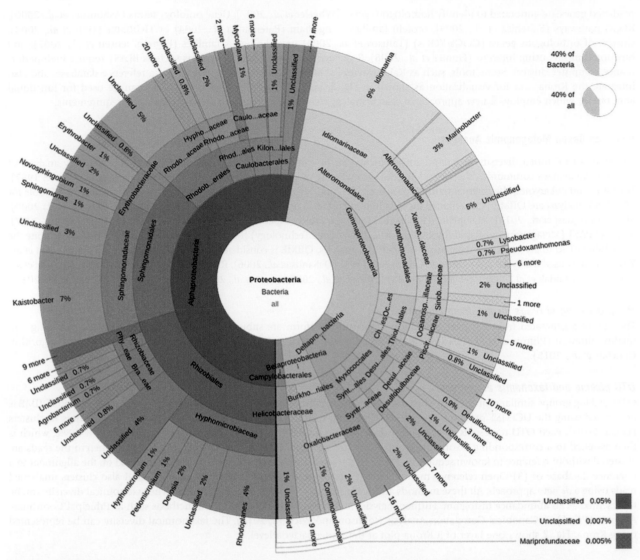

Fig. 2 Representation of Krona. Note: The 16S metagenome sample was analyzed using QIIME and displayed using Krona. The Taxonomy nodes are arranged from the top of the hierarchy at the center and progressing outward. The chart is zoomed to place the domain "Proteobacteria" at the root followed by the taxon.

De novo *assembly*

Assembly is computationally expensive and requires sophisticated algorithms, such as those based on de Bruijn graphs. Tools that are specifically designed for metagenomic applications are mainly built on de Bruijn graph algorithms. A few common metagenomics assembly tools include CLC workbench, Meta-Ray, MetaVelvet-SL, MetaVelvet, Meta-IDBA SOAP, and metaSPAdes (Nurk *et al.*, 2017; Zerbino and Birney, 2008; Luo *et al.*, 2012). A reference-guided assembly may be carried out when an appropriate reference genome is available (Nagarajan *et al.*, 2010).

Binning

The process of clustering reads or contigs into highly similar groups, and assigning the groups to specific species, subspecies or genera, is called binning. Two types of algorithms are available: (1) Composition-based binning and (2) Similarity-based binning. Certain binning tools deploy hybrid approaches which implement both kinds of algorithms (Oulas *et al.*, 2015). Composition-based binning groups, in a supervised or semi-supervised manner, the DNA fragments with similar composition. Similarity-based methods align the DNA fragments to NR database or reference sequences (Leung *et al.*, 2011).

Annotation

Prediction of CDS (coding DNA sequences), followed by functional assignment is carried out using similarity-based searches of query sequences against databases containing known functional and/or taxonomic information. The taxonomic information can be displayed using Krona, which displays hierarchical data as an interactive multilayered pie chart (Ondov *et al.*, 2011). The predicted genes are annotated to identify homologous genes (Wheeler *et al.*, 2007), Gene ontology terms (Ashburner *et al.*, 2000), KEGG pathways (Kanehisa et al., 2009), protein families using Pfam (Bateman *et al.*, 2004) or TIGRfams (Haft *et al.*, 2003), clusters of orthologous genes (COGs/KOGs) (Tatusov *et al.*, 2003) or orthologous families (Eggnog, Jensen *et al.*, 2007), and functional motifs using InterPro (Hunter *et al.*, 2008). Sequence similarity-based algorithms such as BLAST require high-performance computer clusters. Some tools, such as Kaiju (Menzel *et al.*, 2016), assign taxonomy using a reference database, and also integrate the Krona tool for visualization as shown in **Fig. 2**, and COGNIZER (Bose *et al.*, 2015) can be used for functional annotation, which employs a new approach of search strategy that helps in reducing the computational requirements.

Amplicon Based Metagenomic Analysis

The study of microbial diversity in natural environments can be carried out by targeting specific genes. For diversity analysis of bacteria and archaea community, the 16S rRNA gene is commonly used as it contains one or more variable regions (Woese, 1987). For fungi and eukaryotes, the internal transcribed spacer (ITS) and 18S rRNA gene are used, respectively. Commonly used tools for 16S rRNA analysis are QIIME (Quantitative Insights Into Microbial Ecology) (Caporaso *et al.*, 2010), Mothur (Schloss *et al.*, 2009), SILVAngs (Quast *et al.*, 2013), RDPipeline (Ribosomal Database Project Pipeline) (Cole *et al.*, 2013), MEGAN (Huson *et al.*, 2007), and MG-RAST (Metagenomics - Rapid Annotation using Subsystems Technology) (Meyer *et al.*, 2008) as listed in **Table 1**. Despite the availability of so many tools and databases for 16S rRNA analysis, QIIME is considered to be the "gold standard" (Nilakanta *et al.*, 2014). Widely used rRNA databases include Greengenes (16S) (DeSantis *et al.*, 2006), Ribosomal Database Project (16S) (Cole *et al.*, 2006, 2008; Maidak *et al.*, 1996), Silva (16S & 18S) (Pruesse *et al.*, 2007; Quast *et al.*, 2012) and UNITE (ITS) (Kõljalg *et al.*, 2013).

Pre-processing of reads for amplicon analysis

The raw files generated from the next generation sequencing platform are subjected to demultiplexing, adapter trimming and quality filtration (Plummer *et al.*, 2015). PCR product chimera detection and removal is carried out using UCHIME algorithm (Sinclair *et al.*, 2015).

OTU picking and taxonomic assignment

OTU picking groups similar sequences by clustering or a similarity-based method. OTU picking in the most popular tool QIIME is performed using the UCLUST program. The UCLUST program uses the USEARCH algorithm to assign the sequences to clusters (Edgar, 2010). Each OTU represents a cluster of sequences with similarity greater than a threshold, typically 97%–98%, which is then assigned to a corresponding taxonomic group. There are various OTU picking strategies: (1) *De novo*, wherein the reads are clustered without reference to known sequences. (2) Closed-reference, in which the reads are clustered based on the alignment to a reference database or (3) Open reference method, which clusters reads against a reference database and also clusters unaligned reads using a *de novo* approach. All these methods are incorporated in QIIME (Oulas *et al.*, 2015). The taxonomical diversity can be represented as an abundance histogram. Further analysis can be done with decomposition methods such as Principal Coordinate Analysis (PCoA) or Canonical Correlation Analysis (Johnson and Wichern, 2014). The taxonomical diversity can be represented using Krona, **Fig. 2** shows one layer of a Krona plot at the Proteobacteria level.

Statistical analysis

The taxonomic tree in Newick format can be obtained from QIIME, and can be visualised using any tree display tool, for instance FigTree (FigTree is available at: http://tree.bio.ed.ac.uk/software/figtree/). Alpha diversity measures variability within a single population, which measures richness, dominance, and evenness. Other diversity metrics include, for example, Phylogenetic Diversity (PD), Chao (1984) Shannon entropy (Gorelick, 2006), among others. Rarefaction analysis is used to assess the coverage of the microbial community in the sample. Rarefaction curves plot the sample size versus the estimated number of genera (Jaenicke *et al.*, 2011). Beta diversity is the diversity across many populations or samples, which is calculated using various matrices, such as unweighted and weighted UniFrac (Lozupone *et al.*, 2006) and PCoA (Principal Coordinate Analysis). It includes absolute or relative overlap between samples to estimate the taxa shared among them. Calculation of alpha and beta diversity is supported by QIIME.

Metagenomics Phylogenetic Analysis

The taxonomic methods can provide information at specific taxonomic hierarchy, such as phylum, class, order, family, genus and species (Darling *et al.*, 2014), whereas phylogenetic approaches help in identifying species and novel lineages at taxonomic levels (Darling *et al.*, 2014). Different tools used for the phylogenetic analysis of metagenomes are AmphoraNet (Kerepesi *et al.*, 2014), TIPP (taxonomic identification and phylogenetic profiling) (Nguyen *et al.*, 2014), and Phylosift (Darling *et al.*, 2014)), among others.

The PhyloSift database includes a set of "elite" gene families of Bacteria and Archaea, and also includes additional four sets of gene families *i.e.* 16S and 18S ribosomal RNA genes, mitochondrial gene families, eukaryote-specific gene families, and viral gene families. The metagenome reads are searched against the defined set of gene database to predict taxonomy. The query sequences are aligned with the reference genes in the database. The sequences are assigned on a phylogenic tree using Pplacer and taxonomic assignment is carried out (Darling *et al.*, 2014). This approach is based on statistical phylogenetic models *i.e.* Bayesian hypothesis testing and OTU-free analyses (Darling *et al.*, 2014). The AmphoraNet webserver uses the AMPHORA2 workflow for phylogenetic diversity analyses of metagenomic data (Wu and Eisen, 2008), where query sequences are aligned to bacterial and archaeal protein coding marker genes. Alignment to marker genes is carried out using a hidden Markov model trained on a reference database of fully sequenced bacterial genomes (Wu M and Eisen J 2008). The metagenomic reads are used as an input in AmphoraNet to search, align and mask the data against the HMM trained model, followed by phylogenic analysis using RaxML on the masked metagenomics sequence (Kembel *et al.*, 2011). Phylogenetic analysis is one of the critical steps in analysing metagenomics data, with applications in improved classification of sequences using phylogenetic methods, functional prediction of genes, and improved identification of OTUs, among others (Darling *et al.*, 2014).

Functional analysis

To predict the functional composition of microbial communities from the 16S profile, PICRUSt (Langille *et al.*, 2013) can be used. It uses an extended ancestral-state reconstruction algorithm, which predicts the gene families and then combines gene families to estimate the composite metagenome. The annotation of the predicted gene family counts are obtained from orthologous groups of gene families, KOGs, COGs, NOGs, or Pfam families (Langille *et al.*, 2013).

Metatranscriptomics/Metaproteomics Analysis

Metatranscriptomics allows the characterization and functionality analysis of the microbiome under study. It provides RNASeq-based measures of gene expression and regulation in the microbial community. The analysis used for metatranscriptomics is the same as in metagenomics (Simon and Daniel, 2011). The analysis can be carried in two approaches (1) *de novo* and (2) reference based. There are many *de novo* assembly tools, as listed in **Table 1**. Read alignment is carried out using standard short-read mapping tools such as bowtie2, or BWA. To study differentially expressed genes, statistical tools are used such as DESeq2 and edgeR (Bikel *et al.*, 2015).

Metaproteomics is the study of the total proteome expressed in the microbial community. This can be used to study metabolic pathways, and to identify enzymes present in unculturable microbes and communities (Simon and Daniel, 2011; Madhavan *et al.*, 2017).

The metaproteomic approach has four steps: sample collection, protein extraction, purification and fractionation; mass spectrometric (MS) analysis; and finally protein identification and further bioinformatics analyses. Raw data (SDS PAGE, MALDI-TOF-TOF, MS (LC-ESI-MS/MS)) are interpreted using software packages such as Mascot, SEQUEST and *de novo* analysis software such as PEAKS to identify peptides and proteins. There are two approaches for this: direct mass spectra based or *de novo* peptide sequence based, each of which is followed by a quantitative step, along with visualization of the complex functional information (Wang *et al.*, 2014a,b).

Application

Metagenomics has a wide range of applications from clinical to environmental samples, from food safety to industrial waste, and also has the ability to identify pathogens. For example: Lettuce has an immense number of viruses on it, which can infect various hosts, such as humans and animals. Metagenomics can detect human and animal viruses on lettuce samples, which can identify viral contamination of the green leaves in the field (Aw *et al.*, 2016). These approaches help to determine the source of microbial and viral contamination, and can be used to identify the critical steps where such contamination occurs, and to implement improved processes to ensure food quality and safety (Doyle *et al.*, 2017).

Metagenomics provides information about the diversity of organisms in environmental samples and has provided insights in industrial research. Functional metagenomics has been used for identification of several biocatalysts, which are available in the market, for example: laccases, esterases and nitrile hydratase (Fernández-Arrojo *et al.*, 2010). Novel cellulases with improved enzymatic characteristics have been identified; cellulose is an important component of plant biomass, and is the most abundant polymer in nature (Fang *et al.*, 2010). The use of metagenomics, metatranscriptomics and metaproteomics approaches enhance enzyme discovery and can be used to efficiently screen for highly active enzymes (Madhavan *et al.*, 2017). Recent studies (Devarapalli and Kumavath, 2015), have stated that metagenomics can be used as a bioremediation tool; in comparison with other approaches of bioremediation, metagenomics gave better degrading ratios. Metagenomics study help in identifying different widespread microorganism and their respective functions in polluted environment; these microorganisms are the best tools in nature to degrade toxic pollutants (Devarapalli and Kumavath, 2015).

Metagenomics has been used in clinical diagnostics. For example, metagenomic approaches have been used for identifying novel noninvasive diagnostic bacterial biomarkers from fecal samples, for diagnosis of colorectal cancer (Liang *et al.*, 2017). The 16S rRNA is a powerful approach for developing diagnostics, for example, for detecting bacterial bloodstream infections (bBSI) (Decuypere *et al.*, 2016). Viral metagenomics has the power to identify the root cause of novel epidemic diseases (Mokili *et al.*, 2012). Metagenomics is also used in medical or forensic investigations, and to solve challenges in the field of medicine, agriculture and ecology. Major applications of metaproteomics have included investigation of acid mine drainage biofilms, activated sludge, soil, human gut microbiota, and other environmental samples (Wilmes *et al.*, 2015).

Discussion and Future Direction

Microbes survive in a vast range of environmental conditions and are found throughout nature. Most of them are unculturable, so they are difficult to identify by traditional methods. Metagenomics is a molecular tool used to analyse DNA acquired from environmental samples, in order to study the community of microorganisms present, without the necessity of obtaining pure cultures. It is most often applied to bacteria, but can also be applied to archaea, viruses, and eukaryotes (Morgan and Huttenhower, 2012). Metagenomics provides a platform for studying the physiology and genetics of uncultured organisms. It can refine the approach of genomics and accelerates the rate of gene discovery. Metagenomics has a future in diagnostics, in which it could be applied to any specimen (for example plant, human, and *etc.*) to detect pathogens, such as bacteria, viruses, fungi, and parasites. Metagenomics in diagnostics has various challenges as there is wide range of abundance of different taxa in particular samples (Pallen, 2014). Identifying the causative agent of a new epidemic is one of the most important steps for effective response to disease outbreaks. Traditionally, virus discovery required propagation of the virus in cell culture, which has resulted in limited knowledge of viruses. Study of viral metagenomes suggests that the field of virology has explored much less than 1% of viral taxonomic diversity (Mokili *et al.*, 2012). The study of gene expression and protein production in the microbial community complement metagenomic analysis. Metatranscriptomics and metaproteomics approaches provide powerful tools for understanding the functional dynamics of microbial communities (Simon and Daniel, 2011).

Metaproteomics studies have not been used to their full potential in comparison to metagenomics and metatranscriptomics. Metaproteomics studies can provide deep insights into diverse biological questions regarding health and disease. Emerging technologies should improve the ability of metaproteomic approaches to handle the wide dynamic ranges of different metaproteomic samples, and also help in understanding protein modification (Wilmes *et al.*, 2015). Metaproteomics has emerged as complementary approach to metagenomics, which aims at the characterization of proteins from environmental microbiota (Petriz and Franco, 2017).

See also: Comparative Genomics Analysis. Functional Enrichment Analysis. Integrative Analysis of Multi-Omics Data. Large Scale Ecological Modeling With Viruses: A Review. Mapping the Environmental Microbiome. Natural Language Processing Approaches in Bioinformatics. Next Generation Sequencing Data Analysis. Pipeline of High Throughput Sequencing. Sequence Analysis. Sequence Composition. Whole Genome Sequencing Analysis

---

References

Alneberg, J., Bjarnason, B.S., De Bruijn, I., *et al.*, 2014. Binning metagenomic contigs by coverage and composition. Nature Methods 11 (11), 1144–1146.

Ashburner, M., Ball, C.A., Blake, J.A., *et al.*, 2000. Gene Ontology: Tool for the unification of biology. Nature Genetics 25 (1), 25.

Aw, T.G., Wengert, S., Rose, J.B., 2016. Metagenomic analysis of viruses associated with field-grown and retail lettuce identifies human and animal viruses. International Journal of Food Microbiology 223, 50–56.

Bateman, A., Coin, L., Durbin, R., *et al.*, 2004. The Pfam protein families database. Nucleic Acids Research 32 (suppl_1), [D138–D141].

Bikel, S., Valdez-Lara, A., Cornejo-Granados, F., *et al.*, 2015. Combining metagenomics, metatranscriptomics and viromics to explore novel microbial interactions: Towards a systems-level understanding of human microbiome. Computational and Structural Biotechnology Journal 13, 390–401.

Boisvert, S., Raymond, F., Godzaridis, É., Laviolette, F., Corbeil, J., 2012. Ray Meta: Scalable de novo metagenome assembly and profiling. Genome Biology 13 (12), R122.

Bose, T., Haque, M.M., Reddy, C.V.S.K., Mande, S.S., 2015. COGNIZER: A framework for functional annotation of metagenomic datasets. PLoS One 10 (11), e0142102.

Brady, A., Salzberg, S.L., 2009. Phymm and PhymmBL: Metagenomic phylogenetic classification with interpolated Markov models. Nature Methods 6 (9), 673–676.

Bromberg, J.S., Fricke, W.F., Brinkman, C.C., Simon, T., Mongodin, E.F., 2015. Microbiota [mdash] implications for immunity and transplantation. Nature Reviews Nephrology 11 (6), 342–353.

Caporaso, J.G., Kuczynski, J., Stombaugh, J., *et al.*, 2010. QIIME allows analysis of high-throughput community sequencing data. Nature Methods 7 (5), 335–336.

Chakravorty, S., Helb, D., Burday, M., Connell, N., Alland, D., 2007. A detailed analysis of 16S ribosomal RNA gene segments for the diagnosis of pathogenic bacteria. Journal of Microbiological Methods 69 (2), 330–339.

Chao, A., 1984. Nonparametric estimation of the number of classes in a population. Scandinavian Journal of Statistics. 265–270.

Chong, C.W., Pearce, D.A., Convey, P., Yew, W.C., Tan, I.K.P., 2012. Patterns in the distribution of soil bacterial 16S rRNA gene sequences from different regions of Antarctica. Geoderma 181, 45–55.

Cole, J.R., Chai, B., Farris, R.J., *et al.*, 2006. The ribosomal database project (RDP-II): Introducing myRDP space and quality controlled public data. Nucleic Acids Research 35 (suppl_1), D169–D172.

Cole, J.R., Wang, Q., Cardenas, E., *et al.*, 2008. The Ribosomal Database Project: Improved alignments and new tools for rRNA analysis. Nucleic Acids Research 37 (suppl_1), D141–D145.

Cole, J.R., Wang, Q., Fish, J.A., *et al.*, 2013. Ribosomal Database Project: Data and tools for high throughput rRNA analysis. Nucleic Acids Research 42 (D1), D633–D642.

Cuadros-Orellana, S., Leite, L.R., Smith, A., *et al.*, 2013. Assessment of fungal diversity in the environment using metagenomics: A decade in review. Fungal Genomics & Biology 3 (2), 1.

Darling, A.E., Jospin, G., Lowe, E., *et al.*, 2014. PhyloSift: phylogenetic analysis of genomes and metagenomes. PeerJ 2, e243.

Decuypere, S., Meehan, C.J., Van Puyvelde, S., *et al.*, 2016. Diagnosis of bacterial bloodstream infections: A 16S metagenomics approach. PLoS Neglected Tropical Diseases 10 (2), e0004470.

DeSantis, T.Z., Hugenholtz, P., Larsen, N., *et al.*, 2006. Greengenes, a chimera-checked 16S rRNA gene database and workbench compatible with ARB. Applied and Environmental Microbiology 72 (7), 5069–5072.

Dethlefsen, L., Huse, S., Sogin, M.L., Relman, D.A., 2008. The pervasive effects of an antibiotic on the human gut microbiota, as revealed by deep 16S rRNA sequencing. PLoS Biology 6 (11), e280.

Devarapalli, P., Kumavath, R.N., 2015. Metagenomics – A Technological Drift in Bioremediation. Advances in Bioremediation of Wastewater and Polluted Soil. Intech.

Dinsdale, E.A., Edwards, R.A., Hall, D., *et al.*, 2008. Functional metagenomic profiling of nine biomes. Nature 452 (7187), 629.

Doyle, C.J., O'Toole, P.W., Cotter, P.D., 2017. Metagenome-based surveillance and diagnostic approaches to studying the microbial ecology of food production and processing environments. Environmental Microbiology.

Edgar, R.C., 2010. Search and clustering orders of magnitude faster than BLAST. Bioinformatics 26 (19), 2460–2461.

Fang, Z., Fang, W., Liu, J., *et al.*, 2010. Cloning and characterization of a β-glucosidase from marine microbial metagenome with excellent glucose tolerance. Journal of Microbiology Biotechnology 20 (9), 1351–1358.

Fernández-Arrojo, L., Guazzaroni, M.E., López-Cortés, N., Beloqui, A., Ferrer, M., 2010. Metagenomic era for biocatalyst identification. Current Opinion in Biotechnology 21 (6), 725–733.

Frias-Lopez, J., Shi, Y., Tyson, G.W., *et al.*, 2008. Microbial community gene expression in ocean surface waters. Proceedings of the National Academy of Sciences 105 (10), 3805–3810.

Glass, E.M., Wilkening, J., Wilke, A., Antonopoulos, D., Meyer, F., 2010. Using the metagenomics RAST server (MG-RAST) for analyzing shotgun metagenomes. Cold Spring Harbor Protocols 2010 (1), pdb–prot5368.

Gorelick, R., 2006. Combining richness and abundance into a single diversity index using matrix analogues of Shannon's and Simpson's indices. Ecography 29 (4), 525–530.

Haft, D.H., Selengut, J.D., White, O., 2003. The TIGRFAMs database of protein families. Nucleic Acids Research 31 (1), 371–373.

Haider, B., Ahn, T.H., Bushnell, B., *et al.*, 2014. Omega: An Overlap-graph de novo Assembler for Metagenomics. Bioinformatics 30 (19), 2717–2722.

Handelsman, J., Rondon, M.R., Brady, S.F., Clardy, J., Goodman, R.M., 1998. Molecular biological access to the chemistry of unknown soil microbes: A new frontier for natural products. Chemistry & Biology 5 (10), R245–R249.

Hilton, S.K., Castro-Nallar, E., Pérez-Losada, M., *et al.*, 2016. Metataxonomic and metagenomic approaches vs. culture-based techniques for clinical pathology. Frontiers in Microbiology 7.

Hunter, S., Apweiler, R., Attwood, T.K., *et al.*, 2008. InterPro: The integrative protein signature atabase. Nucleic Acids Research 37 (suppl_1), D211–D215.

Huson, D.H., Auch, A.F., Qi, J., Schuster, S.C., 2007. MEGAN analysis of metagenomic data. Genome Research 17 (3), 377–386.

Huson, D.H., Weber, N., 2013. Microbial community analysis using MEGAN. Methods in Enzymology 531, 465–485.

Hyatt, D., Chen, G.L., LoCascio, P.F., *et al.*, 2010. Prodigal: Prokaryotic gene recognition and translation initiation site identification. BMC Bioinformatics 11 (1), 119.

Igai, K., Itakura, M., Nishijima, S., *et al.*, 2016. Nitrogen fixation and nifH diversity in human gut microbiota. Scientific Reports 6.

Jaenicke, S., Ander, C., Bekel, T., *et al.*, 2011. Comparative and joint analysis of two metagenomic datasets from a biogas fermenter obtained by 454-pyrosequencing. PloS one 6 (1), e14519.

Jensen, L.J., Julien, P., Kuhn, M., *et al.*, 2007. eggNOG: Automated construction and annotation of orthologous groups of genes. Nucleic Acids Research 36 (suppl_1), D250–D254.

Johnson, R.A., Wichern, D.W., 2014. Applied Multivariate Statistical Analysis, 4. Piscataway, NJ: Prentice-Hall.

Kanehisa, M., Goto, S., Furumichi, M., Tanabe, M., Hirakawa, M., 2009. KEGG for representation and analysis of molecular networks involving diseases and drugs. Nucleic Acids Research 38 (suppl_1), D355–D360.

Kelley, D.R., Liu, B., Delcher, A.L., Pop, M., Salzberg, S.L., 2011. Gene prediction with Glimmer for metagenomic sequences augmented by classification and clustering. Nucleic Acids Research 40 (1), [e9-e9].

Kelley, D.R., Salzberg, S.L., 2010. Clustering metagenomic sequences with interpolated Markov models. BMC Bioinformatics 11 (1), 544.

Kembel, S.W., Eisen, J.A., Pollard, K.S., Green, J.L., 2011. The phylogenetic diversity of metagenomes. PLoS One 6 (8), e23214.

Kerepesi, C., Banky, D., Grolmusz, V., 2014. AmphoraNet: the webserver implementation of the AMPHORA2 metagenomic workflow suite. Gene 533 (2), 538–540.

Kõljalg, U., Larsson, K.H., Abarenkov, K., *et al.*, 2005. UNITE: A database providing web-based methods for the molecular identification of ectomycorrhizal fungi. New Phytologist 166 (3), 1063–1068.

Kõljalg, U., Nilsson, R.H., Abarenkov, K., *et al.*, 2013. Towards a unified paradigm for sequence-based identification of fungi. Molecular Ecology 22 (21), 5271–5277.

Langille, M.G., Zaneveld, J., Caporaso, J.G., *et al.*, 2013. Predictive functional profiling of microbial communities using 16S rRNA marker gene sequences. Nature Biotechnology 31 (9), 814–821.

Leung, H.C., Yiu, S.M., Yang, B., *et al.*, 2011. A robust and accurate binning algorithm for metagenomic sequences with arbitrary species abundance ratio. Bioinformatics 27 (11), 1489–1495.

Liang, Q., Chiu, J., Chen, Y., *et al.*, 2017. Fecal bacteria act as novel biomarkers for noninvasive diagnosis of colorectal cancer. Clinical Cancer Research 23 (8), 2061–2070.

LI, D., Liu, C.M., Luo, R., Sadakane, K., Lam, T.W., 2015. MEGAHIT: An ultra-fast single-node solution for large and complex metagenomics assembly via succinct de Bruijn graph. Bioinformatics 31 (10), 1674–1676.

Lozupone, C., Hamady, M., Knight, R., 2006. UniFrac–an online tool for comparing microbial community diversity in a phylogenetic context. BMC Bioinformatics 7 (1), 371.

Luo, R., Liu, B., Xie, Y., *et al.*, 2012. SOAPdenovo2: An empirically improved memory-efficient short-read de novo assembler. Gigascience 1 (1), 18.

Madhavan, A., Sindhu, R., Parameswaran, B., Sukumaran, R.K., Pandey, A., 2017. Metagenome Analysis: A Powerful Tool for Enzyme Bioprospecting. Applied Biochemistry and Biotechnology. 1–16.

Maidak, B.L., Olsen, G.J., Larsen, N., *et al.*, 1996. The ribosomal database project (RDP). Nucleic Acids Research 24 (1), 82–85.

Markowitz, V.M., Chen, I.M.A., Chu, K., *et al.*, 2013. IMG/M 4 version of the integrated metagenome comparative analysis system. Nucleic Acids Research 42 (D1), D568–D573.

Menzel, P., Ng, K.L., Krogh, A., 2016. Fast and sensitive taxonomic classification for metagenomics with Kaiju. Nature Communications 7.

Meyer, F., Paarmann, D., D'Souza, M., *et al.*, 2008. The metagenomics RAST server – a public resource for the automatic phylogenetic and functional analysis of metagenomes. BMC Bioinformatics 9 (1), 386.

Mokili, J.L., Rohwer, F., Dutilh, B.E., 2012. Metagenomics and future perspectives in virus discovery. Current opinion in Virology 2 (1), 63–77.

Morgan, X.C., Huttenhower, C., 2012. Human microbiome analysis. PLOS Computational Biology 8 (12), e1002808.

Nagarajan, N., Cook, C., Di Bonaventura, M., *et al.*, 2010. Finishing genomes with limited resources: Lessons from an ensemble of microbial genomes. BMC Genomics 11 (1), 242.

Namiki, T., Hachiya, T., Tanaka, H., Sakakibara, Y., 2012. MetaVelvet: An extension of Velvet assembler to de novo metagenome assembly from short sequence reads. Nucleic Acids Research 40 (20), [e155-e155].

Nguyen, N.P., Mirarab, S., Liu, B., Pop, M., Warnow, T., 2014. TIPP: taxonomic identification and phylogenetic profiling. Bioinformatics 30 (24), 3548–3555.

Nilakanta, H., Drews, K.L., Firrell, S., Foulkes, M.A., Jablonski, K.A., 2014. A review of software for analyzing molecular sequences. BMC Research Notes 7 (1), 830.

Nurk, S., Meleshko, D., Korobeynikov, A., Pevzner, P.A., 2017. metaSPAdes: A new versatile metagenomic assembler. Genome Research 27 (5), 824–834.

Ogata, H., Goto, S., Sato, K., *et al.*, 1999. KEGG: Kyoto encyclopedia of genes and genomes. Nucleic acids Research 27 (1), 29–34.

Ondov, B.D., Bergman, N.H., Phillippy, A.M., 2011. Interactive metagenomic visualization in a Web browser. BMC Bioinformatics 12 (1), 385.

Oulas, A., Pavloudi, C., Polymenakou, P., *et al.*, 2015. Metagenomics: Tools and insights for analyzing next-generation sequencing data derived from biodiversity studies. Bioinformatics and Biology Insights 9, 75.

Overbeek, R., Begley, T., Butler, R.M., *et al.*, 2005. The subsystems approach to genome annotation and its use in the project to annotate 1000 genomes. Nucleic Acids Research 33 (17), 5691–5702.

Oyserman, B.O., Noguera, D.R., del Rio, T.G., Tringe, S.G., McMahon, K.D., 2016. Metatranscriptomic insights on gene expression and regulatory controls in Candidatus Accumulibacter phosphatis. The ISME Journal 10 (4), 810.

Pallen, M.J., 2014. Diagnostic metagenomics: Potential applications to bacterial, viral and parasitic infections. Parasitology 141 (14), 1856–1862.

Peng, Y., Leung, H.C., Yiu, S.M., Chin, F.Y., 2012. IDBA-UD: A de novo assembler for single-cell and metagenomic sequencing data with highly uneven depth. Bioinformatics 28 (11), 1420–1428.

Petriz, B.A., Franco, O.L., 2017. Metaproteomics as a Complementary Approach to Gut Microbiota in Health and Disease. Frontiers in Chemistry 5.

Plummer, E., Twin, J., Bulach, D.M., Garland, S.M., Tabrizi, S.N., 2015. A comparison of three bioinformatics pipelines for the analysis of preterm gut microbiota using 16S rRNA gene sequencing data. Journal of Proteomics & Bioinformatics 8 (12), 283.

Powell, S., Forslund, K., Szklarczyk, D., *et al.*, 2014. eggNOG v4. 0: Nested orthology inference across 3686 organisms. Nucleic Acids Research 42 (D1), D231–D239.

Pruesse, E., Quast, C., Knittel, K., *et al.*, 2007. SILVA: A comprehensive online resource for quality checked and aligned ribosomal RNA sequence data compatible with ARB. Nucleic Acids Research 35 (21), 7188–7196.

Quail, M.A., Smith, M., Coupland, P., *et al.*, 2012. A tale of three next generation sequencing platforms: Comparison of Ion Torrent, Pacific Biosciences and Illumina MiSeq sequencers. BMC Genomics 13 (1), 341.

Quast, C., Pruesse, E., Yilmaz, P., *et al.*, 2012. The SILVA ribosomal RNA gene database project: Improved data processing and web-based tools. Nucleic Acids Research 41 (D1), D590–D596.

Quast, C., Pruesse, E., Yilmaz, P., *et al.*, 2013. The 658 SILVA ribosomal RNA gene database project: Improved data processing and web-based tools. 659 Nucleic Acids Research 41, D590–D596. [660].

Ranjan, R., Rani, A., Metwally, A., McGee, H.S., Perkins, D.L., 2016. Analysis of the microbiome: Advantages of whole genome shotgun versus 16S amplicon sequencing. Biochemical and Biophysical Research Communications 469 (4), 967–977.

Rho, M., Tang, H., Ye, Y., 2010. FragGeneScan: Predicting genes in short and error-prone reads. Nucleic Acids Research 38 (20), [e191-e191].

Sato, K., Sakakibara, Y., 2014. MetaVelvet-SL: An extension of the Velvet assembler to a de novo metagenomic assembler utilizing supervised learning. DNA Research 22 (1), 69–77.

Schloss, P.D., Westcott, S.L., Ryabin, T., *et al.*, 2009. Introducing mothur: Open-source, platform-independent, community-supported software for describing and comparing microbial communities. Applied and Environmental Microbiology 75 (23), 7537–7541.

Seemann, T., 2014. Prokka: Rapid prokaryotic genome annotation. Bioinformatics 30 (14), 2068–2069.

Sharpton, T.J., 2014. An introduction to the analysis of shotgun metagenomic data. Frontiers in Plant Science 5.

Simon, C., Daniel, R., 2011. Metagenomic analyses: Past and future trends. Applied and Environmental Microbiology 77 (4), 1153–1161.

Sinclair, L., Osman, O.A., Bertilsson, S., Eiler, A., 2015. Microbial community composition and diversity via 16S rRNA gene amplicons: Evaluating the illumina platform. PlOS One 10 (2), e0116955.

Tartar, A., Wheeler, M.M., Zhou, X., *et al.*, 2009. Parallel metatranscriptome analyses of host and symbiont gene expression in the gut of the termite Reticulitermes flavipes. Biotechnology for Biofuels 2 (1), 25.

Tatusov, R.L., Fedorova, N.D., Jackson, J.D., *et al.*, 2003. The COG database: An updated version includes eukaryotes. BMC Bioinformatics 4 (1), 41.

Tatusov, R.L., Galperin, M.Y., Natale, D.A., Koonin, E.V., 2000. The COG database: A tool for genome-scale analysis of protein functions and evolution. Nucleic Acids Research 28 (1), 33–36.

Treangen, T.J., Koren, S., Sommer, D.D., *et al.*, 2013. MetAMOS: A modular and open source metagenomic assembly and analysis pipeline. Genome Biology 14 (1), R2.

Tringe, S.G., Von Mering, C., Kobayashi, A., *et al.*, 2005. Comparative metagenomics of microbial communities. Science 308 (5721), 554–557.

Tyson, G.W., Chapman, J., Hugenholtz, P., Allen, E.E., 2004. Community structure and metabolism through reconstruction of microbial genomes from the environment. Nature 428 (6978), 37.

Vasar, M., Andreson, R., Davison, J., *et al.*, 2017. Increased sequencing depth does not increase captured diversity of arbuscular mycorrhizal fungi. Mycorrhiza. 1–13.

Venter, J.C., Remington, K., Heidelberg, J.F., *et al.*, 2004. Environmental genome shotgun sequencing of the Sargasso Sea. Science 304 (5667), 66–74.

Vieites, J.M., Guazzaroni, M.E., Beloqui, A., Golyshin, P.N., Ferrer, M., 2008. Metagenomics approaches in systems microbiology. FEMS Microbiology Reviews 33 (1), 236–255.

Wang, D.Z., Xie, Z.X., Zhang, S.F., 2014a. Marine metaproteomics: Current status and future directions. Journal of Proteomics 97, 27–35.

Wang, Y., Leung, H.C.M., Yiu, S.M., Chin, F.Y.L., 2014b. MetaCluster-TA: Taxonomic annotation for metagenomic data based on assembly-assisted binning. BMC Genomics 15 (1), S12.

Weinstock, G.M., 2012. Genomic approaches to studying the human microbiota. Nature 489 (7415), 250.

Wheeler, D.L., Barrett, T., Benson, D.A., *et al.*, 2007. Database resources of the national center for biotechnology information. Nucleic Acids Research 36 (suppl_1), D13–D21.

Wilmes, P., Heintz-Buschart, A., Bond, P.L., 2015. A decade of metaproteomics: Where we stand and what the future holds. Proteomics 15 (20), 3409–3417.

Woese, C.R., 1987. Bacterial evolution. Microbiological Reviews 51 (2), 221.

Wu, M., Eisen, J., 2008. A simple, fast, and accurate method of phylogenomic inference. Genome Biology 9, R151.

Zampieri, E., Chiapello, M., Daghino, S., Bonfante, P., Mello, A., 2016. Soil metaproteomics reveals an inter-kingdom stress response to the presence of black truffles. Scientific Reports 6, 25773.

Zerbino, D.R., Birney, E., 2008. Velvet: Algorithms for de novo short read assembly using de Bruijn graphs. Genome Research 18 (5), 821–829.

Zhang, Y., Sun, J., Mu, H., Lun, J.C., Qiu, J.W., 2017. Molecular pathology of skeletal growth anomalies in the brain coral Platygyra carnosa: A meta-transcriptomic analysis. Marine Pollution Bulletin.

Zhu, W., Lomsadze, A., Borodovsky, M., 2010. Ab initio gene identification in metagenomic sequences. Nucleic Acids Research 38 (12), [e132-e132].

Further Reading

Blatter, M.C., Gerritsen, V.B., Palagi, P.M., Bougueleret, L., Xenarios, I., 2016. The Metagenomic Pizza: A simple recipe to introduce bioinformatics to the layman. EMBnet. journal 22, e864.

Darling, A.E., Jospin, G., Lowe, E., *et al.*, 2014. PhyloSift: Phylogenetic analysis of genomes and metagenomes. PeerJ 2, e243.

DeLong, E., 2013. Microbial Metagenomics, Metatranscriptomics, and Metaproteomics, 531. Academic Press.

Dudhagara, P., Bhavsar, S., Bhagat, C., *et al.*, 2015. Web resources for metagenomics studies. Genomics, Proteomics & Bioinformatics 13 (5), 296–303.

Howe, A., Chain, P.S., 2015. Challenges and opportunities in understanding microbial communities with metagenome assembly (accompanied by IPython Notebook tutorial). Frontiers in Microbiology 6.

Kembel, S.W., Eisen, J.A., Pollard, K.S., Green, J.L., 2011. The phylogenetic diversity of metagenomes. PLoS One 6 (8), e23214.

Kerepesi, C., Banky, D., Grolmusz, V., 2014. AmphoraNet: The webserver implementation of the AMPHORA2 metagenomic workflow suite. Gene 533 (2), 538–540.

Kuczynski, J., Stombaugh, J., Walters, W.A., *et al.*, 2012. Using QIIME to analyze 16S rRNA gene sequences from microbial communities. Current Protocols in Microbiology. 1E–5.

Marco, D. (Ed.), 2011. Metagenomics: Current Innovations and Future Trends. Horizon Scientific Press.

Wu, M., Eisen, J., 2008. A simple, fast, and accurate method of phylogenomic inference. Genome Biology 9, R151.

Nguyen, N.P., Mirarab, S., Liu, B., Pop, M., Warnow, T., 2014. TIPP: Taxonomic identification and phylogenetic profiling. Bioinformatics 30 (24), 3548–3555.

Relevant Websites

https://bioinformatics.ca/workshops/2015/analysis-metagenomic-data-2015
   Analysis of Metagenomic DataS.

https://ngs.csr.uky.edu/sites/default/files/Class_9_QIIME.pdf
   Analyzing Metagenomic Data with QIIME.

http://tree.bio.ed.ac.uk/software/figtree/
   FigTree.

http://qiime.org/1.2.1/tutorials/tutorial.html
   Qiime overview Tutorial.

Biographical Sketch

Arpita Ghosh is a Manager of Bioinformatics at Eurofins Genomics India Pvt Ltd/ Eurofins Clinical Genetics India Pvt. Ltd. She is also a PhD student at Perdana University, Malaysia. She has a rich research experience of more than seven years in various fields of genomics and clinical genetics data analysis using Next Generation Sequencing technology. She has published more than 15 international publications in different areas of genomics and clinical genetics. She has been working on cutting edge applications of genomics like amplicon based metagenomics (16S, ITS), whole metagenome, WGS, RNASeq, small RNA, GBS and Tilling, among others. Her current research is on virus metagenomics and to identify novel genes from viral genomes. Her primary research interest is in the field of genomics, application heat of which can be felt invarious fields such as molecular diagnostics and the study of the environment.

Aditya Mehta has more than five years of Industrial research experience in various fields of applied genomicsand translational genomics data analysis using various next generation sequencing platforms. He has worked on large scale data analysis projects like RNASeq, whole genome, Metagenomicsand 16S/18S analysis using high throughput sequencing data. He has extensive experience in analysing metagenomics and 16S rRNA data generated on Illumina platform. He has carried out large scale data analysis of various metagenomics samples like soil, water and the human gut and identified microbial diversity, their relative abundance in sample and also deciphering the gene functions. He has in depth knowledge of various metagenomics tools, software and databases that are widely used for microbial data analysis and taxonomical identification from experimental sample. He has designed new strategic approaches and workflow steps for microbial data analysis, including further downstream analysis.

Dr. Mohammad Asif Khan is currently appointed as the Director of the Perdana University Center for Bioinformatics (PU-CBi), Malaysia, and a Visiting Scientist for the Department of Pharmacology and Molecular Sciences, Johns Hopkins University School of Medicine (JHUSOM), USA. His research interests are in the area of biological data warehousing and applications of bioinformatics to the study of immune responses, vaccines, venom toxins, drug design, and disease biomarkers. He has contributed in the development of several novel bioinformatics methodologies, tools, and specialized databases, and currently has three patent applications granted.

Integrative Analysis of Multi-Omics Data

Lokesh P Tripathi, Tsuyoshi Esaki, Mari N Itoh, Yi-An Chen, and Kenji Mizuguchi, National Institutes of Biomedical Innovation, Health and Nutrition, Osaka, Japan

Introduction

Biomolecular interactions among elementary units of a living system such as DNA, RNA, proteins, lipids and also small molecule metabolites make up the different organisational levels of the cellular networks such as microRNA (miRNA)-target interactions (MTIs), protein-protein interactions (PPIs), transcription factor (TF)-target gene interactions and protein-chemical compound (small molecule) interactions (PCIs); such interactions underlie the complexity and functioning of all biological processes. The key step in biology is to understand how these different components come together and how they interact with each other and define the emergent behaviour of the living systems.

The quest to uncover the mechanisms underlying complex biological processes and the proliferation of various high-throughput "omics" experiments have resulted in an unprecedented surge in the diversity, volume and complexity of *genomics*, *transcriptomics*, *proteomics* and *metabolomics* data among others. *Genomics* data provide an overview of the complete set of genetic instructions provided by the DNA including the variants within; *transcriptomics* data provide insights into gene expression patterns; *proteomics* data examine the cellular dynamics of proteins and their interactions and *metabolomics* can be used to determine the differences between the levels of thousands of molecules between healthy and diseased conditions. The availability of such data have, therefore, opened up a myriad of opportunities for new biological discoveries.

Typically, omics datasets are analysed separately using varied statistical and computational methods and approaches. The analysis of PPI Networks (PPIN) (Huttlin *et al.*, 2017, 2015; Rolland *et al.*, 2014), genetic interactions (Boucher and Jenna, 2013), gene co-expression networks (van Dam *et al.*, 2017; Serin *et al.*, 2016) and metabolic interaction networks (Krumsiek *et al.*, 2016), among others, have provided valuable biological insights into the set-up of the cellular machinery. However, the single-datatype analyses only offer glimpses into one of the many layers that govern the cellular machinery; they do not take into account the relationships and interactions between different biological entities across different organisational layers. Therefore, combining different types of omics data into a single analytical framework provides an opportunity to simultaneously examine the multiple cellular organisational layers, understand the complex interactions between them and gain deeper insights into how their combined influence determines the behaviour of the biological systems (Yan *et al.*, 2017; Civelek and Lusis, 2014; Zhu *et al.*, 2012). Such integration can also facilitate a better understanding of how living systems adapt and modulate their responses to different environments and also help reduce the noise and false positives emanating from single source data sets.

A systems biology-based multi-omics data analysis approach seeks to integrate disparate omics data with bioinformatics tools for data manipulation and pattern discovery into an integrative data analysis pipeline to derive conceptual systems level models of genes and biological processes. Such integrative models can empower the researchers to predict complex traits, understand genotype-phenotype correlations, gain the knowledge of biological pathways involved in different traits and diseases and therefore, help prioritise biologically and therapeutically relevant genes and proteins (Krumsiek *et al.*, 2016; Kopczynski *et al.*, 2017; Sun and Hu, 2016; van Kampen and Moerland, 2016; Fukushima *et al.*, 2014; Berger *et al.*, 2013) (**Fig. 1**).

In this review we will discuss the different types of omics data and how they have been individually analysed. We will then discuss how the analysis of large data sets from different omics platforms has been performed using different approaches such as network modelling and pathway analysis. We finally discuss the future trends in the field.

High Throughput Omics Datatypes and Methodologies

Genomics

Every biological function has its basis in the genetic information of an organism. A better understanding of the genetic determinants of cellular processes including diseases is therefore necessary to gain the knowledge of biological systems, unravel disease mechanisms and develop effective therapeutic approaches. To achieve this, researchers have for long sought to determine the sequences of individual genes of interest. With the advent of high-throughput DNA sequencing technologies, it became possible to sequence the whole genome that is the complete set of DNA within a cell or an organism. Thus, the focus has shifted from investigating individual genes to mapping, annotation and characterisation of the whole genome, a study called *genomics*. The availability and analysis of whole genome sequence data have contributed immensely to the understanding and evolution of gene function in different species and disease mechanisms. Comparative genomics refers to the comparison and analysis of genomes from different species to gain a better understanding of the genomic organisation and conservation and evolution of gene and genomic functions that would have contributed to speciation, adaptation and evolution and to similarity and differences across species (Meadows and Lindblad-Toh, 2017). The advances in genomics technologies, especially the proliferation of low-cost NGS platforms (Levy and Myers, 2016) have led to an abundance of high-quality sequence data that have enhanced the identification of

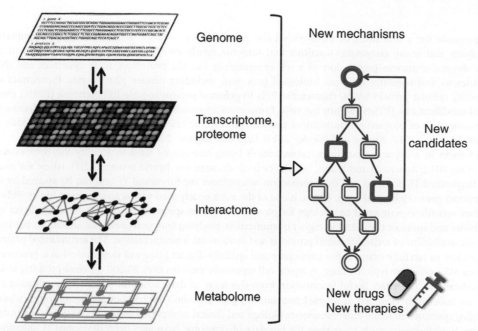

Fig. 1 High-throughput omics technologies provide large scale mapping of heterogenous molecular-level data. Computational methods for integrative multi-omics data analyses aim to uncover relationships across different cellular organisation layers represented by different omics datatypes to hypothesise the pathways and mechanisms underlying complex biological processes, which can then be leveraged to pinpoint biologically and therapeutically relevant genes and proteins (such as potential drug targets).

a large number of sequence and structural variants and are rapidly redefining the understanding of genotype-phenotype relationships (Shameer *et al.*, 2016).

Although genomics sequences have provided unprecedented insights into the gene function and evolution, they do not provide the context of these functional aspects such as spatio-temporal expression of different genes and changes in gene expression in response to different biological cues. To address these questions, genomics revolution was thus, soon followed by an increasing number of high-throughput studies that started mapping genome-wide gene expression profiles in specific cells and tissues in different biological contexts.

Transcriptomics

The genetic blueprint of an organism is encoded within its genome, but is expressed via transcription i.e., copying of the information from DNA into RNA that forms the key intermediate between the DNA and the protein. The sum total of RNA transcript population of a cell is known as Transcriptome and the study of transcriptome is known as *transcriptomics*. The two major and most widely used technologies for transcriptomics analysis are microarray and RNA-seq (Lowe *et al.*, 2017). Microarrays determine the abundance of mRNAs from a given sample, cell or a tissue via their hybridisation to an array of oligonucleotide DNA sequences or 'probes' that are immobilised on a solid surface (Lowe *et al.*, 2017; Schulze and Downward, 2001; Slonim and Yanai, 2009). DNA microarrays have emerged as a powerful medium for genomic and biomedical research to investigate the gene expression states underlying different physiological processes, for the characterisation of gene function and biomarker identification (Trevino *et al.*, 2007) and also for whole genome comparisons to investigate genomic variations (Gresham *et al.*, 2008). Another widely used technology to quantify the transcriptome is RNA-Seq that combines the usage of NGS with computational analytical tools to determine the presence and abundance of transcripts within a biological sample (Lowe *et al.*, 2017). Lately, RNA-Seq has emerged as the method of choice for large scale transcriptome mapping and for the identification of allele-specific expression, gene fusions and detecting alternatively spliced variants and non-coding RNAs even at the single-cell level (Hrdlickova *et al.*, 2017; Spies and Ciaudo, 2015).

With the rapid advances in transcriptomics technologies, there have been proliferating attempts at surveying the gene expression landscape across multiple tissues, cells and physiological processes such as mapping of genetic variation and its impact on the gene expression landscape in different tissues by the Genotype-Tissue Expression (GTEx) project (Consortium, 2013) and the Functional annotation of the mammalian genome (FANTOM) project (Consortium *et al.*, 2014). The availability of huge amounts of gene expression profiles from diverse physiological states have permitted the researchers to construct gene co-expression networks to assign functional annotations to different genes and to prioritise candidates for biological and clinical research (van Dam *et al.*, 2017).

Transcriptomics technologies measure the changes in the abundance of mRNA. However, most of the cellular functions are typically regulated at the level of proteins and thus, transcriptomic analyses often provides only an indirect measure of the cellular physiology. This limitation in turn has led to the development of high-throughput methodologies to simultaneously measure and understand the activities of a large number of proteins within a cell or an organism.

Proteomics

Proteins are responsible for a multitude of tasks within the cell. PPIs, for instance, are central to the organisation of macro-molecular complexes and many enzymatic reactions that underlie nearly every cellular process. The goal of *proteomics* is to understand how the entire protein population of a cell or organism, i.e., the proteome, their dynamics and their interactions together contributes to and regulates different biological processes, including disease phenotypes. Proteomics can be used to identify and quantify cellular protein levels, characterise PPIs to generate proteome-scale PPI Network (PPIN) maps or to profile post-translational modifications (PTMs) within the cells. Proteomics approaches have, thus, emerged as effective tools in studies involving the investigation of biomedical, nutritional sciences, pathogenic infection, host-pathogen interactions, and molecular biology (Jean Beltran *et al.*, 2017; Moore and Weeks, 2011; Lum and Cristea, 2016).

With rapid advances in analytical capabilities, proteomics is being increasingly used to identify the components of biological systems (Sabido *et al.*, 2012; Aebersold and Mann, 2016). For instance, yeast two-hybrid system (Y2H), where the proteins of interest are fused to the fragmented TF domains and their interaction reconstitutes the functional TF and can be assayed by the downstream expression of a reporter gene (Fields and Song, 1989), is one of the most widely used techniques to detect binary PPIs on a proteome-wide scale. Another versatile experimental technology for proteomics is mass spectrometry (MS), which can detect variable proteins with higher sensitivity and measure the values in higher quantification. Studying temporal proteome alterations has become a popular approach due to the availability of well-established protocols and modern MS instrumentation. The accumulated proteomics data have enabled the researchers to carefully examine the temporally and spatially distinct phases of dynamic cellular processes. However, the data obtained from MS studies are typically huge. A typical cell reportedly contains over 20,000 different proteins, isoforms, and post-translational modifications. To extract useful information from this array of data, powerful protein quantification approaches have emerged, which are collectively classified as *targeted proteomics*; *targeted proteomics* approaches are becoming increasingly popular to address wide-ranging questions in many different systems biology and clinical studies (Ebhardt *et al.*, 2015). As the instrumentation has improved, the new bioinformatics tools to analyse the big data of proteome have also been developed (Calderon-Gonzalez *et al.*, 2016). Integrated MS approaches, antibody-based affinity purification of protein complexes and cross-linking and protein array techniques have contributed towards elucidating complex networks of virus-host protein associations during infection for a wide range of RNA and DNA viruses (Lum and Cristea, 2016). The labelling method is also one of the most useful methods to quantify protein levels, through the use of stable isotope amino acid labelled with C_{13}, H_2, or N_{16} (Bantscheff *et al.*, 2012). These methods have immensely contributed to important biological discoveries and to the design of new therapeutics.

Metabolomics

Metabolomics is the newest of the 'omics' sciences. The metabolome refers to the sum total of low molecular weight compounds or metabolites such as amino acids, sugars, lipids etc. within a biological system (Krumsiek *et al.*, 2016). Metabolic compounds are typically substrates and by-products of biological processes and enzymatic reactions; they are widely involved in feedback regulatory processes in the cell and being the downstream products often directly influence the cellular or organismal phenotype and thus, metabolome is often regarded as the link between genotype and phenotype (Krumsiek *et al.*, 2016). Metabolomics aims to characterise the type and abundance of metabolites within a biological system at a specified time and under specific environmental conditions, thereby helping gain an understanding of varied metabolic processes (van Rijswijk *et al.*, 2017) and how their dysregulation may be correlated with the onset and progression of diseases (Tolstikov, 2016). *Metabolomics* is being increasingly used to investigate and understand diverse traits such as genetic variation and their correlation with metabolite concentrations (Suhre *et al.*, 2011; Kastenmuller *et al.*, 2015), gene expression patterns (Cavill *et al.*, 2016), biomarker and drug discovery (Wishart, 2016) and assessment of drug safety and efficacy (Ramirez *et al.*, 2013) and even personalised medicine (Tolstikov, 2016; Wishart, 2016).

As with proteomics, rapid strides in MS technologies have facilitated the detection and characterisation of a wide range of metabolites from various biological and clinical samples (Krumsiek *et al.*, 2016; Tolstikov, 2016; Wang *et al.*, 2015; Zampieri *et al.*, 2017) and also the development of new statistical and computational methods to store and analyse the huge amounts of emerging metabolomics data (Krumsiek *et al.*, 2016; Tolstikov, 2016; Xia *et al.*, 2015).

Integrative Analysis of High Throughput Omics Data

The availability of huge amounts of different types of omics data and their analyses have significantly contributed to advance our fundamental understanding of biological systems. However, the analyses of individual datasets offer limited and often disparate insights into the functions of different biological entities, with only a limited insight into how the different entities communicate with each other across different organisational layers. The first step towards an integrative multi-omics data analysis is the integration of different omics datatypes onto a single platform.

Integration of High-Throughput Data

Biological databases have emerged as invaluable resources for compiling, storing and distributing ever increasing amounts of omics data. To achieve multi-omics data analysis, the data from different omics databases must be linked together onto a single platform. However, the heterogeneity and often inconsistencies of the data generated from the different high-throughput technologies and the formats used to store, manage and query them in different repositories makes the integration of multi-omics data and their analyses a non-trivial challenge. Despite the challenges, integrative data analyses promise holistic and more informative insights into disease biology and drug discovery (Ritchie *et al.*, 2015). Therefore, there have been innumerable efforts to develop new computational tools and approaches to integrate and analyse diverse biological data types that often differ in scope, design, content, analytical abilities as well as the targeted research audience (Chen *et al.*, 2011, 2016; Ge *et al.*, 2003; Gerstein *et al.*, 2002; Smith *et al.*, 2012; Huang da *et al.*, 2009; Stein, 2003; Triplet and Butler, 2014).

Typically, the integration of different biological datatypes involves first identifying common elements among them that can be used to build relationships between the different types of biological entities. Among the many different frameworks for integrating and storing biological data, are the data warehouses that compile different biological datatypes onto a common platform, facilitate a wide range of queries linking different datatypes and different functional attributes and can produce a unified output for the user (Stein, 2003; Triplet and Butler, 2014). For instance, TargetMine is an integrative data analysis platform based on the Intermine framework (Smith *et al.*, 2012) that features different omics data types and analytical functions for gene set analysis and biological knowledge discovery (Chen *et al.*, 2011, 2016).

However, most integrated databases are equipped with limited data analyses capabilities and therefore there have been many attempts to develop more sophisticated standalone tools for integrative multi-omics data analyses that can be combined into an overall pipeline to link data generation to storage, analysis and prioritisation of biologically and therapeutically relevant candidates such as genes, transcripts, proteins and metabolites.

Analysis of Integrated Omics Data

A wide range of computational approaches have been developed for integrative analysis of multi-omics data to reduce the dimensionality of the large omics data sets, to identify biologically meaningful patterns and to prioritise candidate gene, proteins and biomolecules of interest (Ritchie *et al.*, 2015; Huang *et al.*, 2017). Broadly, such methods fall into unsupervised approaches such as clustering (Ronan *et al.*, 2016) and matrix factorisation (Li *et al.*, 2012) and supervised integrative analysis methods such as those based on network-based modelling (Robinson and Nielsen, 2016) or machine learning based algorithms (Lin and Lane, 2017). We discuss some of these approaches below.

Unsupervised Integration and Analysis of Omics Data

Unsupervised methods for data integration do not require a training dataset, rather they aim to analyse the data to uncover hidden patterns and/or underlying data structures and to gain and understand the relationships between different biological entities (Ritchie *et al.*, 2015; Huang *et al.*, 2017; Ronan *et al.*, 2016; Kirk *et al.*, 2012; Lock and Dunson, 2013). Clustering is one of the most widely used unsupervised methods for exploring patterns in large omics datasets and to identify subsets of correlated biological entities such as co-expressed or co-functional genes that are relevant to specific disease and cellular processes (Ronan *et al.*, 2016). Clustering approaches for integrative omics data analysis typically fall in the category of joint clustering approaches that leverage shared data features and relationships across diverse biological datatypes to analyse multi-dimensional biological data. As an example, the iCluster method simultaneously performs data integration and dimensionality reduction via a join latent variable to capture biologically and clinically relevant sub-clusters (Shen *et al.*, 2012).

However, methods that exploit shared data structures to integrate and correlate biological data types may often overlook patterns and features that are unique to individual datatypes. This problem has led to the development of methods that are based on the Bayesian approaches to integrative omics data analysis that simultaneously take into account correlations across different datasets and datatypes as well as source-specific features for integrative clustering of biological datatypes (Kirk *et al.*, 2012; Lock and Dunson, 2013; Ray *et al.*, 2014).

Network-Based Models of Integrative Omics Data Analysis

Network models form an important component of supervised integrative biological data analysis. A network consists of *nodes* that represent different biological entities (gene, RNA molecules, proteins, metabolites etc.) that are connected with each other via *edges* that represent the biological connectivities (physical and/or genetic) between the individual entities, the edges can include PPIs, TF-TG interactions, MTIs and PCIs among others. Typically, network models lie at the heart of the systems biology approaches since they closely reflect genetic, physical and chemical relationships that exists between biological entities within and across different cellular organisations layers. Consequently, a wide range of network-based approaches and tools have been developed to collate and analyse large amounts of biological data to obtain a deeper understanding of cellular physiology and pathogenesis of various diseases (Yan *et al.*, 2017; Ritchie *et al.*, 2015; Huang *et al.*, 2017; Robinson and Nielsen, 2016).

Conclusions

The rapid strides in experimental technologies that can map and quantify the different organisational layers of the living system have contributed to the rapidly increasing scale and sensitivity of omics data. A better understanding of the living systems can only come from a combined approach that seeks to integrate and analyse the different omics datatypes to unravel the complex networks that link different cellular organisational layers and drive the functioning of the cellular machinery. Consequently a large number of computational tools and pipelines using both supervised and unsupervised approaches have been developed for integrative analysis of multi-dimensional omics data.

However, several challenges persist in extracting biologically meaningful information from the analysis of multi-omics data.. For instance, the experimental platforms used to generate omics data and biological databases that are used to annotate them are far from comprehensive in their coverage of the biological systems. Additionally, the protocols for sample preparation, performing omics experiments and processing the raw omics data and their normalisation can vary substantially among researchers, which may often lead to difficulties with data sharing, analysis and reproducibility. Nevertheless, further advances in the field will facilitate more holistic approaches that can be applied to obtain deeper insights into the dynamics of complex relationships across multiple cellular organisational layers to gain more knowledge of the mechanisms underlying key biological processes including onset and pathogenesis of diseases.

See also: Biological Database Searching. Computational Pipelines and Workflows in Bioinformatics. Computational Systems Biology Applications. Constructing Computational Pipelines. Coupling Cell Division to Metabolic Pathways Through Transcription. Exome Sequencing Data Analysis. Genome Annotation: Perspective From Bacterial Genomes. Host-Pathogen Interactions. Information Retrieval in Life Sciences. Integrative Bioinformatics. Integrative Bioinformatics of Transcriptome: Databases, Tools and Pipelines. Natural Language Processing Approaches in Bioinformatics. Next Generation Sequencing Data Analysis. Pipeline of High Throughput Sequencing. Studies of Body Systems. Whole Genome Sequencing Analysis

---

References

Aebersold, R., Mann, M., 2016. Mass-spectrometric exploration of proteome structure and function. Nature 537, 347–355.

Bantscheff, M., *et al.*, 2012. Quantitative mass spectrometry in proteomics: Critical review update from 2007 to the present. Anal. Bioanal. Chem. 404 (4). 939–965.

Berger, B., Peng, J., Singh, M., 2013. Computational solutions for omics data. Nat. Rev. Genet. 14, 333–346.

Boucher, B., Jenna, S., 2013. Genetic interaction networks: Better understand to better predict. Front. Genet. 4, 290.

Calderon-Gonzalez, K.G., *et al.*, 2016. Bioinformatics tools for proteomics data interpretation. Adv. Exp. Med. Biol. 919, 281–341.

Cavill, R., *et al.*, 2016. Transcriptomic and metabolomic data integration. Brief. Bioinform. 17, 891–901.

Chen, Y.A., Tripathi, L.P., Mizuguchi, K., 2011. TargetMine, an integrated data warehouse for candidate gene prioritisation and target discovery. PLOS ONE 6 (3). e17844.

Chen, Y.A., Tripathi, L.P., Mizuguchi, K., 2016. An integrative data analysis platform for gene set analysis and knowledge discovery in a data warehouse framework. Database (Oxford) 2016.

Civelek, M., Lusis, A.J., 2014. Systems genetics approaches to understand complex traits. Nat. Rev. Genet. 15, 34–48.

Consortium, G.T., 2013. The Genotype-Tissue Expression (GTEx) project. Nat. Genet. 45, 580–585.

Consortium, F., *et al.*, 2014. A promoter-level mammalian expression atlas. Nature 507, 462–470.

Ebhardt, H.A., *et al.*, 2015. Applications of targeted proteomics in systems biology and translational medicine. Proteomics 15, 3193–3208.

Fields, S., Song, O., 1989. A novel genetic system to detect protein-protein interactions. Nature 340, 245–246.

Fukushima, A., Kanaya, S., Nishida, K., 2014. Integrated network analysis and effective tools in plant systems biology. Front. Plant Sci. 5, 598.

Ge, H., Walhout, A.J., Vidal, M., 2003. Integrating 'omic' information: A bridge between genomics and systems biology. Trends Genet. 19, 551–560.

Gresham, D., Dunham, M.J., Botstein, D., 2008. Comparing whole genomes using DNA microarrays. Nat. Rev. Genet. 9, 291–302.

Gerstein, M., Lan, N., Jansen, R., 2002. Proteomics. Integrating interactomes. Science 295, 284–287.

Hrdlickova, R., Toloue, M., Tian, B., 2017. RNA-seq methods for transcriptome analysis. Wiley Interdiscip. Rev. RNA 8 (1).

Huang da, W., Sherman, B.T., Lempicki, R.A., 2009. Systematic and integrative analysis of large gene lists using DAVID bioinformatics resources. Nat. Protoc. 4, 44–57.

Huang, S., Chaudhary, K., Garmire, L.X., 2017. More is better: Recent progress in multi-omics data integration methods. Front. Genet. 8, 84.

Huttlin, E.L., *et al.*, 2017. Architecture of the human interactome defines protein communities and disease networks. Nature 545, 505–509.

Huttlin, E.L., *et al.*, 2015. The BioPlex network: A systematic exploration of the human interactome. Cell 162, 425–440.

Jean Beltran, P.M., *et al.*, 2017. Proteomics and integrative omic approaches for understanding host-pathogen interactions and infectious diseases. Mol. Syst. Biol. 13, 922.

Kastenmuller, G., *et al.*, 2015. Genetics of human metabolism: An update. Hum. Mol. Genet. 24, R93–R101.

Kirk, P., *et al.*, 2012. Bayesian correlated clustering to integrate multiple datasets. Bioinformatics 28, 3290–3297.

Kopczynski, D., *et al.*, 2017. Multi-OMICS: A critical technical perspective on integrative lipidomics approaches. Biochim. Biophys. Acta 1862, 808–811.

Krumsiek, J., Bartel, J., Theis, F.J., 2016. Computational approaches for systems metabolomics. Curr. Opin. Biotechnol. 39, 198–206.

Levy, S.E., Myers, R.M., 2016. Advancements in next-generation sequencing. Annu. Rev. Genom. Hum. Genet. 17, 95–115.

Li, W., *et al.*, 2012. Identifying multi-layer gene regulatory modules from multi-dimensional genomic data. Bioinformatics 28, 2458–2466.

Lin, E., Lane, H.Y., 2017. Machine learning and systems genomics approaches for multi-omics data. Biomark. Res. 5, 2.

Lock, E.F., Dunson, D.B., 2013. Bayesian consensus clustering. Bioinformatics 29, 2610–2616.

Lowe, R., *et al.*, 2017. Transcriptomics technologies. PLOS Comput. Biol. 13 (5). e1005457.

Lum, K.K., Cristea, I.M., 2016. Proteomic approaches to uncovering virus-host protein interactions during the progression of viral infection. Expert Rev. Proteom. 13, 325–340.

Meadows, J.R.S., Lindblad-Toh, K., 2017. Dissecting evolution and disease using comparative vertebrate genomics. Nat. Rev. Genet. 18, 624–636.

Moore, J.B., Weeks, M.E., 2011. Proteomics and systems biology: Current and future applications in the nutritional sciences. Adv. Nutr. 2, 355–364.

Ramirez, T., *et al.*, 2013. Metabolomics in toxicology and preclinical research. ALTEX 30, 209–225.

Ray, P., *et al.*, 2014. Bayesian joint analysis of heterogeneous genomics data. Bioinformatics 30, 1370–1376.

Ritchie, M.D., *et al.*, 2015. Methods of integrating data to uncover genotype-phenotype interactions. Nat. Rev. Genet. 16, 85–97.

Robinson, J.L., Nielsen, J., 2016. Integrative analysis of human omics data using biomolecular networks. Mol. Biosyst. 12, 2953–2964.

Rolland, T., *et al.*, 2014. A proteome-scale map of the human interactome network. Cell 159, 1212–1226.

Ronan, T., Qi, Z., Naegle, K.M., 2016. Avoiding common pitfalls when clustering biological data. Sci. Signal. 9 (432). re6.

Sabido, E., Selevsek, N., Aebersold, R., 2012. Mass spectrometry-based proteomics for systems biology. Curr. Opin. Biotechnol. 23, 591–597.

Schulze, A., Downward, J., 2001. Navigating gene expression using microarrays – A technology review. Nat. Cell Biol. 3, E190–E195.

Serin, E.A., et al., 2016. Learning from co-expression networks: Possibilities and challenges. Front. Plant Sci. 7, 444.

Shameer, K., et al., 2016. Interpreting functional effects of coding variants: Challenges in proteome-scale prediction, annotation and assessment. Brief. Bioinform. 17, 841–862.

Shen, R., et al., 2012. Integrative subtype discovery in glioblastoma using iCluster. PLOS One 7 (4). e35236.

Slonim, D.K., Yanai, I., 2009. Getting started in gene expression microarray analysis. PLOS Comput. Biol. 5 (10). e1000543.

Smith, R.N., et al., 2012. InterMine: A flexible data warehouse system for the integration and analysis of heterogeneous biological data. Bioinformatics 28, 3163–3165.

Spies, D., Ciaudo, C., 2015. Dynamics in transcriptomics: Advancements in RNA-seq time course and downstream analysis. Comput. Struct. Biotechnol. J. 13, 469–477.

Stein, L.D., 2003. Integrating biological databases. Nat. Rev. Genet. 4, 337–345.

Suhre, K., et al., 2011. Human metabolic individuality in biomedical and pharmaceutical research. Nature 477, 54–60.

Sun, Y.V., Hu, Y.J., 2016. Integrative analysis of multi-omics data for discovery and functional studies of complex human diseases. Adv. Genet. 93, 147–190.

Tolstikov, V., 2016. Metabolomics: Bridging the gap between pharmaceutical development and population health. Metabolites 6 (3).

Trevino, V., Falciani, F., Barrera-Saldana, H.A., 2007. DNA microarrays: A powerful genomic tool for biomedical and clinical research. Mol. Med. 13, 527–541.

Triplet, T., Butler, G., 2014. A review of genomic data warehousing systems. Brief. Bioinform. 15, 471–483.

van Dam, S., et al., 2017. Gene co-expression analysis for functional classification and gene-disease predictions. Brief. Bioinform.

van Kampen, A.H., Moerland, P.D., 2016. Taking bioinformatics to systems medicine. Methods Mol. Biol. 1386, 17–41.

van Rijswijk, M., et al., 2017. The future of metabolomics in ELIXIR. F1000Res 6.

Wang, Y., et al., 2015. Current state of the art of mass spectrometry-based metabolomics studies – A review focusing on wide coverage, high throughput and easy identification. RSC Adv. 5, 78728–78737.

Wishart, D.S., 2016. Emerging applications of metabolomics in drug discovery and precision medicine. Nat. Rev. Drug Discov. 15, 473–484.

Xia, J., et al., 2015. MetaboAnalyst 3.0 – Making metabolomics more meaningful. Nucleic Acids Res. 43, W251–W257.

Yan, J., et al., 2017. Network approaches to systems biology analysis of complex disease: Integrative methods for multi-omics data. Brief. Bioinform.

Zampieri, M., et al., 2017. Frontiers of high-throughput metabolomics. Curr. Opin. Chem. Biol. 36, 15–23.

Zhu, J., et al., 2012. Stitching together multiple data dimensions reveals interacting metabolomic and transcriptomic networks that modulate cell regulation. PLOS Biol. 10 (4). e1001301.

Profiling the Gut Microbiome: Practice and Potential

Toral Manvar, Xcelris Labs Ltd., Ahmedabad, India and Gujarat University, Ahmedabad, India
Vijay Lakhujani, Xcelris Labs Ltd., Ahmedabad, India

Acronyms

BLAST	Basic Local Alignment Search Tool	PacBio	Pacific Biosciences
COPE	Connecting Overlapping Paired End reads	PcoA	Principal Coordinates Analysis
DGGE	Denaturing Gradient Gel Electrophoresis	PCR	Polymerase Chain Reaction
FLASH	Fast Length Adjustment of Short Reads	PICRUSt	Phylogenetic Investigation of Communities by Reconstruction of Unobserved States
FMT	Fecal Microbiota Transplantation	QIIME	Quantitative Insights Into Microbial Ecology
GI	Gastrointestinal	qPCR	Quantitative Polymerase Chain Reaction
GO	Gene Ontology	R	R Programming
HMM	Hidden Markov Model	RDP	Ribosomal Database Project
HMP	Human Microbiome Project	SAS	Statistical Analysis System
IBD	Inflammatory Bowel Diseases	SCFA	Short Chain Fatty Acid
KEGG	Kyoto Encyclopedia of Genes and Genomes	SMRT	Single-Molecule Real-Time
MetaHit	Metagenome Human Intestinal Tract Project	SOLiD	Sequencing by Oligo/Ligation and Detection
MG-RAST	Metagenomics-Rapid Annotations Using Subsystems Technology	SSCP	Single-Strand Conformation Polymorphism
		T2D	Type 2 Diabetes
NAST	Nearest Alignment Space Termination	TGGE	Temperature Gradient Gel Electrophoresis
NGS	Next Generation Sequencing	T-RFLP	Terminal Restriction Fragment Length Polymorphism
OTU	Operational Taxonomic Unit		

Introduction

Gut profiling is the study of unique microbial fingerprints found inside the human gut with the objective of understanding their associations with well-being and disorder. There seems to be a never ending debate on the actual number of microorganisms in the human body, specifically in the gastrointestinal (GI) tract (Sender et al., 2016). The latter accounts for more than a thousand (~ 1000–1150) different bacterial species (Sánchez et al., 2017; Qin et al., 2010) with Firmicutes, Bacteroidetes, Actinobacteria, and Proteobacteria as common occurring phyla (Arumugam et al., 2011). It is believed that there are around 3.3 million unique genes in human gut which is 150 times more than the genes in human genome (Zhu et al., 2010a, b). Researchers are intrigued to know that no two individuals have exactly the same composition of bacterial species in their guts just as the fingerprints. The gut microflora have a vital role to play in wide variety of metabolic, trophic and protective functions which includes: (i) Facilitating withdrawal of energy from non digestible polysaccharides producing short chain fatty acid (SCFAs), vitamins and antioxidants (ii) detoxification of the deleterious xenobiotics iii) modulation and development of immune-system vi) Epithelial cell growth and differentiation iv) secretion of anti-microbial products, providing the barrier effect against the pathogenic bacteria through the development of colonization resistance (v) nerve regulation, controlling mood and behavior (Guarner and Malagelada, 2003; Ly et al., 2011; Sun and Chang, 2014; Vernocchi et al., 2016; Mayer et al., 2014).

Microbiome research suggest that dysbiotic shifts i.e., the changes in the make-up of gut microbiota in terms of number or categorization may imbalance the homeostatic harmony causing conditions such as obesity (Ly et al., 2011; Alard et al., 2016), inflammatory bowel diseases (IBD) (Knights et al., 2013; Ferreira et al., 2014; Norman et al., 2015), allergy and asthma (Abrahamsson et al., 2014; Ly et al., 2011), chronic brain diseases (Mayer et al., 2014), colorectal cancer (Sobhani et al., 2011), type II diabetes (Qin et al., 2012; Karlsson et al., 2013; Moreno-Indias et al., 2014; Musso et al., 2010), rheumatoid arthritis (Scher and Abramson, 2011), fatty liver disease (Miele et al., 2009), lesional skin (Ganju et al., 2016) and numerous other diseases (**Fig. 1**). Thus, to understand the basis of dysbiotic shifts, it is important to first discover and characterize these communities by answering the following key questions: (1) Who is there in the gut? (2) What roles are they playing? (3) How they affect the gut functionally? (4) How their abundance changes with disease conditions? Because of the scale, complexity and the impact gut microbes has on an individual, the ecosystem of the colon has been the most diligently studied body habitat (Lloyd-Price et al., 2016).

Background

The time since the microscopic organisms have been discovered during 1665–1683 by Robert Hooke and Antoni Van Leeuwenhoek (Gest, 2004), mankind has travelled for more than 300 years to understand the integral relationship of them with us. There is a deep-seated alliance of human beings with the cohort of microorganisms, often called the microbiome (Lederberg, 2000), and hence it will be not be an exaggeration to call the microbiome as the "second genome" (Grice and Segre, 2012; Zhu et al., 2010a,b). While human beings share 99.9% similarity with each other at the genome level, our gut microbes can be very

Encyclopedia of Bioinformatics and Computational Biology, Volume 3   doi:10.1016/B978-0-12-809633-8.20503-7

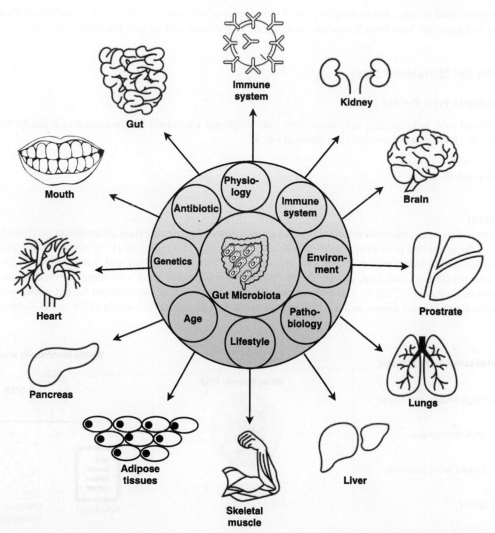

Fig. 1 The ecosystem of gut microbiome. At the centre lies the core gut microbiota. The inner small circles represent the factors that affect the composition and diversity of the gut microbes. The figures projecting out from the outer circle represent the diverse class of body organs affected by the gut microbiome interactions with human host.

much different providing us different phenotypes. The gastrointestinal tract which is sterile at birth (Ly *et al.*, 2011) starts the very first colonization right after the birth and in the following few days after delivery. Studies have shown that this colonization is largely dependent on the way of delivery (natural or c-section) and the kind of food provided in infancy (mother's milk or formula) and adulthood (vegetarian or non-vegetarian) (Jandhyala *et al.*, 2015).

A number of large scale collaborative projects have been initiated reinforcing our understanding of functional prospective of microbiota on human health. It includes "Metagenome Human Intestinal Tract project" (MetaHit project: see "Relevant Websites section") initiated in year 2010 having considered 124 European adults stool samples most of which were healthy individuals. This project was funded by the European Seventh Framework Program until 2012. Its objective was to understand the link between the human intestinal microbiota and two disorders of increasing incidence in Europe namely inflammatory bowel disease and obesity. Later in 2012, the "Human Microbiome Project" (HMP: see "Relevant Websites section") was launched to define microbes existing in 5 major body sites of 242 healthy adult from United States using 16S and shotgun metagenome approach. By end of 2013, the study of European population has begun under MyNewGut project (see "Relevant Websites section") with an aim to identify specific dietary strategies to improve the long-term health of the population. One more project entitled "American Gut Project" was conceived in 2012 which is the world's largest crowd-funded citizen science project. The participants of this project are American citizens who learn about their own microbiome and also contribute for samples and money required for executing the project smoothly.

Although there are number of molecular techniques ranging from culturing to fingerprinting, DNA microarray and clone sequencing which have been used since last many years, Next Generation Sequencing (NGS) has given a new insight into study of gut microbes. Several sequencing approaches have been deployed so far including shotgun metagenomics, microbial transcriptomics, whole genome microbial sequencing and marker gene sequencing. Additionally, NGS has also lead to the generation of giga bytes or even terabytes of data. Hence, it becomes essential to process, manipulate, analyze, visualize and store the sequencing data in a structured and meaningful manner. It is at this point where bioinformatics approaches are playing a pivotal role and various scientific methods, tools and protocols have been formulated to study the microbiome and achieve the desired outputs.

Approaches for Gut Microbiome Study

Molecular Techniques From Pre-ngs to NGS

Before the advent of NGS technologies, early researchers have employed a number of techniques which can be broadly divided into two categories (Rastogi and Sani, 2011) as given in **Fig. 2**:

1. Culture dependent,
2. Culture-independent.

Culture dependent

The basis of culture dependent methods is isolation of microbes followed by inferring their composition on standard commercial growth media under controlled laboratory conditions (Handelsman, 2004; Kirk *et al.*, 2004). To maximize the cultivable fraction of microbial communities, many improvements have been made in cultivation method and culture media so far to mimic the natural environments (Rastogi and Sani, 2011). This methodology remained as golden standard for many years for characterization of microbes (Fraher *et al.*, 2012). However, culture dependent approach is not preferred for gut microbiota study as this ecosystem is considered as most diverse and it contains large number of unculturable bacteria (70%–80%) (Eckburg *et al.*, 2005;

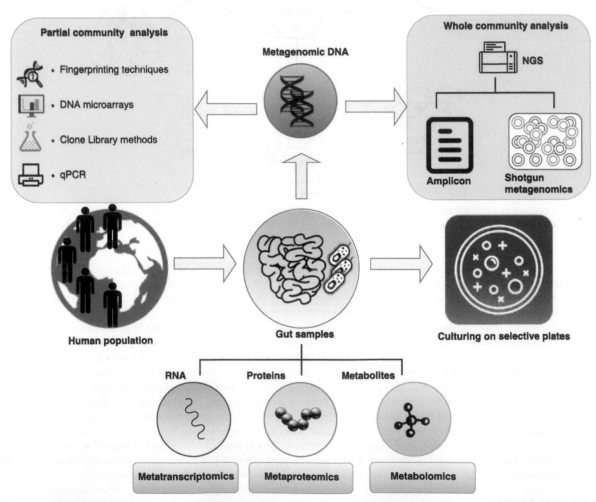

Fig. 2 Approaches for gut microbiome study. Pictorial representation of the different approaches (partial/whole community analysis) to study gut microbiome. Apart from DNA samples (metagenomics), RNA (metatranscriptomics study), protein (metaproteomics study) and metabolite (metabolomics study) samples are often useful to get a complete picture of the gut microbial interactions. Note: Modified from Rousseau, C., Butel, M.J., 2015. High-throughput techniques for studying of gut microbiota. Advances in Probiotic Technology 146.

Hayashi et al.,2002; Suau et al., 1999). Due to this shortcoming there was paradigm shift from culture dependent to culture independent methods.

Culture independent

The basis of culture-independent method is isolation of nucleic acid to analyze selected marker genes such as 16S rRNA or any other functional genes (for example, gyrase beta subunit or recombinase (A) to characterize prokaryotes community. In general, this molecular technique can be divided into (1) partial community analysis approaches (fingerprinting, clone library method DNA microarray, qPCR) (2) whole community analysis approaches (whole genome sequencing, metagenomics, metatranscriptomics, metaproteomics and metabolomics) depending upon the strength of techniques to exhibit the microbial diversity and their function (Rastogi and Sani, 2011).

Partial community analysis approaches

(a) *Fingerprinting techniques*:

Fingerprinting techniques namely denaturing or temperature gradient gel electrophoresis (DGGE/TTGE), terminal restriction fragment length polymorphism (T-RFLP), automated rRNA intergenic Spacer Analysis (ARISA), Amplified ribosomal DNA restriction analysis (ARDRA) and single-strand conformation polymorphism (SSCP) are commonly implemented to study complex microbial ecosystem like GI (Zoetendal et al., 2004). These are cheap and rapid methods and thus are preferred even today when large number of samples are involved and aim of the study is just to identify dominant bacterial group (more than 1%) (Hamady and Knight, 2009). Studies implementing these techniques have revealed that species richness increases along the length of the gut (Rousseau and Butel, 2015). However, the main drawback of these techniques is that data from different studies cannot be combined and thus compared.

(b) *Diversity microarrays*:

Diversity microarray is one of the promising techniques to study gut microbes (Zoetendal et al., 2004). It works on the principle of hybridization of probes (representing known genes attached to the glass surface) with DNA or RNA present in sample detected by means of fluorescence. HuGChip and PhyloChip are commonly used microarrays for microbiome studies (Tottey et al., 2013; Palmer et al., 2007). In 2003, for the first time (Call et al., 2003) scrutinized the antibiotic resistance genes in intestinal microbiota using microarray. IBD, a disorder of gut microbiota was also studied in Kang et al. (2010). using phylogenetic microarray. Main shortcoming of this technique is that the sequences to be used in probe designing have to be known, though if not at specific level but at upper level (phylum or family). Thus, this technique cannot be used for undiscovered microbes (DeSantis et al., 2007). However, its potential to process number of samples simultaneously makes it favorable method for many studies.

(c) *Clone Library Method*:

Here16S rRNA gene is amplified from the samples and then cloned followed by its sequencing. 16S rRNA database for instance Ribosomal Database Project (RDP), Greengenes, GenBank are then used to identify microbes represented by cloned sequences (DeSantis et al., 2007). Suau et al. were the first to characterize microbes in gut utilizing Sanger sequencing in the year 1999. Though, it is considered as "golden standard" for preliminary diversity study, the drawback of using this technique is that it requires large number of clones to be prepared and sequenced even to capture half of the diversity of sample making it labor-intensive and expensive technique (Rousseau and Butel, 2015).

Whole community analysis approaches

Since the completion of human genome project in 2003, a significant progress has been made in the field of human health and bioinformatics which was further fueled by the emergence of next generation sequencing (NGS) techniques. NGS has enabled quick analysis of huge number of samples with falling costs. This characteristic made it the most feasible and convincing method for studying uncultured gut microbial communities with no prior knowledge of the organism (Mandal et al., 2015; Frey et al., 2014). Gradually, this revolutionary technology resulted in development of new field of genomics called "metagenomics", defined as direct genetic analysis of genomes present in particular ecology eliminating the need for cultivating clonal cultures. Based on the aim of study, metagenomics can be divided into (i) Marker gene amplification metagenomics or meta-genetics (Handelsman, 2009) which is used for identification and abundance analysis of bacterial community. It is primarily based on the diversity of one gene (e.g., 16S rRNA or functional genes like amoA/B, nirK, nirS and nosZ etc.) obtained after PCR amplification. (ii) Full shotgun metagenomics (Sun and Xia, 2015) which provides access to the functional gene composition of microbial communities giving much broader description than phylogenetic surveys.

(i) *Marker gene amplification metagenomics*

Since Woese and Fox (1977) first pioneered the use 16S rRNA gene in classifying microbes, it is regarded as the most versatile phylogenetic marker for microbial classification as (i) it is ubiquitous in bacteria (ii) its function is conserved over time and (iii) its length (~ 1500 bp) is appropriate for isolation, sequencing and subsequent bioinformatics analysis (Janda and Abbott, 2007). The 16S rRNA gene includes 9 hyper variable regions labeled as V1–V9 ranging from about 30–100 base pairs. Though, this gene is mostly conserved, the hyper variable regions can change in a very short evolutionary period and thus provides an advantageous and efficient way for microbe identification. Most 16S studies operate on one of these hyper variable regions at any given time due to technical constraints. Marker gene metagenomics is the preferable choice for diversity analysis as it targets specific region and thus, it is cost effective and computationally easy to analyze. However it restricts the knowledge to only particular region studied, not providing any information of functional and metabolic aspects of microbial community present in the same.

(ii) *Full shotgun metagenomics*

As the word suggests, in full shotgun metagenomics, complete DNA including functional genes and phylogenetic markers are studied as a whole, thereby in addition to identification of microbes, it can provide information about the function of this microbial community. It is a perfect substitute to cumbersome cloning method requiring large amount of genomic DNA to sequence.

In the last decade, many studies have been carried out to analyze gut microbiota diversity using both the functional and phylogenetic approach using different NGS platforms. Metagenomics (DNA based) can be further combined with metatran-scriptomics (mRNA based), metaproteomics (protein based) and metabolomics (metabolism based) to analyze composition, function, expressed activities to provide insights into bacteria-host interactions that may lead to disease (Wang *et al.*, 2015; Franzosa *et al.*, 2015). Currently five high throughput sequencing platforms are used for studying the gut microbiome diversity namely Illumina (e.g., GA II, HiSeq, MiSeq, NextSeq500), 454 Life Sciences Roche (GS FLX Titanium sequencer), Applied Biosystems SOLiD, life technologies' ion torrent personal genome machine (PGM) and Pacific Bioscience's (PacBio) Single-Molecule Real-Time (SMRT) (Medini *et al.*, 2008; Hodkinson and Grice, 2015). Out of these, Illumina is the choice of most of the researchers as it gives high throughput data and advantage of read length up to 300 bp. All these NGS technologies have already been reviewed pre-eminently by Mardis (2008) and Metzker (2010). The impact of different sequencing platforms for microbial analysis has also been reviewed and discussed in detail by Allali *et al.* (2017) and Clooney *et al.* (2016).

Bioinformatics Approaches to Study the Gut Microbiome

Computational tools, techniques and algorithms are frequently employed to understand and interpret biological data. The complexity and amount of data generated through latest sequencing technologies make it difficult to manually analyze and visualize data to extract meaningful results. Therefore, bioinformatics methodologies have been constantly evolving in various aspects and microbiome study is no exception. Broadly, bioinformatics approaches could be categorized into (i) Marker gene analysis (using a specific and ubiquitous gene across the microbial world, for e.g., 16S rRNA and ITS region) and (ii) Metagenomic analysis (Oulas *et al.*, 2015; Thomas *et al.*, 2012), as discussed briefly below:

Marker gene analysis (e.g., : rRNA or ITS region)

Popular bioinformatics tools employed for analysis of phylogenetic markers like rRNA amplicon and internal transcribed spacer (ITS) are MEGAN (Huson *et al.*, 2007), Mothur (Schloss *et al.*, 2009), MG-RAST (Glass *et al.*, 2010) and QIIME (Caporaso *et al.*, 2010). Among these, QIIME is the most widely used and established pipeline due to its continuous support and development, well written documentation and ease of use. Though, every tool has its unique core algorithm, there is a basic set of analysis steps (**Fig. 3**) which most of the tools use and is described below:

(1) *Pre-processing of sequencing data*:

Pre-processing includes trimming of sequencing reads according to quality, stitching the reads to generate longer stretches and removal of chimeras. FastQC (see "Relevant Websites section") and NGS Toolkit (Patel and Jain, 2012) are some of the most commonly used fastq quality assessment tools. After surveying the data, reads need to be trimmed for adapter sequences and filtered on the basis of quality or length as per experimental requirements. For this purpose, few tools like Cutadapt (Martin *et al.*, 2011), Trimmomatic (Bolger *et al.*, 2014) and FASTX Toolkit (see "Relevant Websites section") are frequently used. Some of the tools like NGS Toolkit and Trim Galore (Krueger, 2015) come with dual functionality per-forming quality assessment along with trimming, thus reducing an extra step. Studies suggest that longer sequence could capture much more information than the shorter ones which are typically 100–300 base pairs. Hence, paired reads could be stitched generating a single long stretch by exploiting the overlap between the paired reads. Several software are available to achieve the same including PEAR (Zhang *et al.*, 2013), FLASH (Magoč and Salzberg, 2011), bbmerge tool from BBMAP (Bushnell), PANDASeq (Masella *et al.*, 2012), COPE (Liu *et al.*, 2012a,b), UPARSE merge (Edgar, 2013) and fastq-join (Aronesty, 2011). All of them vary on the basis of sensitivity, performance and stitching percentage and could be used according to the experimental needs. Though, some of these tools may have high merging rate at default parameters, however, the rate of false positives may be high. Out of them, BBMerge has lower false positive rate than PEAR, FLASH and fastq-join. COPE is quite comparable or slightly better than FLASH in terms of overall performance, however, it is unstable at N=0. Following stitching, the subsequent pre-processing step is the removal of chimeric sequences which are PCR artifacts. Two or more biological DNA sequences may join incorrectly during PCR cycle to generate artificial novel sequence and may further lead to misinterpretation of data. For chimera identification, mainly two approaches are employed viz. reference based and de novo (absence of reference database having chimera free sequences). In case of reference based analysis, databases such as Gold (see "Relevant Websites section") and RDP (Maidak *et al.*, 1996) are generally used. However, de novo analysis is preferred method when no information is present for particular type of metagenome sample. Pintail (Ashelford *et al.*, 2005) and DECIPHER (see "Relevant Websites section") work using reference based approach and others such as USEARCH and UCHIME (Edgar, 2010; Edgar *et al.*, 2011), ChimeraSlayer (Haas *et al.*, 2011) and Perseus (Quince *et al.*, 2011) can work either way. The advantage of UCHIME is that it works equally well with both ITS sequences and 16S

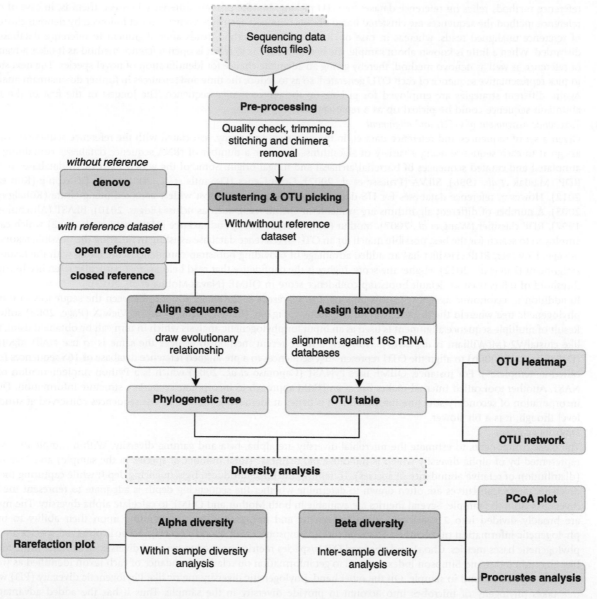

Fig. 3 Bioinformatics workflow for 16S rRNA marker gene studies. The analysis starts from pre-processing of raw sequencing reads followed by clustering and OTU picking with suitable strategies. Taxonomy is assigned by alignment methods and generating phylogenetic tree to draw evolutionary relationships. Diversity analysis (alpha and beta) is useful to study inter and intra sample diversity.

amplicon. It is also the default method when USEARCH is used in QIIME (Navas-Molina *et al.*, 2013). Chimera identification is a crucial step and the tool to remove it should be carefully chosen.

(2) *Clustering and OTU picking*

The word OTU stands for Operational Taxonomic Unit and there are different views on the origin and the exact meaning of the same which is out of the scope of this discussion. However, in context to metagenomics, OTU can represent an individual organism, a named taxonomic group i.e. species or genus, or a group with undetermined evolutionary relationships sharing common characters. Hence, it is often up to a scientist to put a proper context to OTU with the study. Generally, gut samples are obtained in batches and hence are often multiplexed. Such samples are first de-multiplexed (reads are assigned to samples based on unique barcode attached to the sequences) followed by OTU picking step which is basically clustering of similar sequences at (typically) 97% identify or more. However, the identity threshold of 97% may be considered for revision taking into account the increased number of high quality 16S sequences till date (Edgar, 2017).

Sequences thus clustered are considered to represent the same bacterial species (Janda and Abbott, 2007). Methods for OTU picking may vary widely and the most commonly used tool QIIME supports three different approaches, viz (i) de novo, (ii) open reference and (iii) closed reference, all of them uses UCLUST as default algorithm. As the name suggests, denovo method is solely based on pair wise identity among sequences in the absence of a reference dataset. While open and closed reference methods relies on reference dataset for OTU picking. But the primary difference between them is, in case of open reference method the sequences are clustered based on hits obtained against reference dataset followed by denovo clustering of reference unaligned reads, whereas in case of closed reference method, reads after alignment to reference database are discarded. When a little is known about sample, the best approach is to select is open reference method as it takes advantage of reference as well as denovo method, thereby giving an adequate chance for identification of novel species. The next step is to pick representative sequence of each OTU generated, so as to reduce the time and resources in further downstream analysis. Again, different strategies are employed for picking up the representative sequence. The longest or the first or the most abundant sequence could be picked up as a representative.

(3) *Taxonomic assignment of OTUs and alignment*

Given a set of sequences and reference dataset, in the next step, taxonomy, associated with the reference sequences, can be assigned to each sequence using a variety of algorithms. There are a number of rRNA sequence databases containing well annotated and curated sequences of bacterial/archaeal and fungal origin. Some of the widely used rRNA databases include RDP (Maidak *et al.*, 1996), SILVA (Pruesse *et al.*, 2007), GreenGenes (DeSantis *et al.*, 2006a) and EzTaxon-e (Kim et al., 2012). However, reference databases for ITS data analysis are quite few; most widely accepted being Unite (Kõljalg *et al.*, 2005). A number of different algorithms are available in QIIME itself, such as uclust (Edgar, 2010), BLAST (Altschul *et al.*, 1997), RDP classifier (Wang *et al.*, 2007), Mothur (Schloss *et al.*, 2009) and tax2tree (McDonald *et al.*, 2012) which can be employed to search for the best possible match for an OTU in reference database assisting in inferring the possible taxonomic lineage. However, RDP classifier has an added advantage of providing bootstrap confidence score along with the taxonomy assignment (Lan *et al.*, 2012). Higher the score, higher is the confidence that read belongs to a particular reference lineage. A threshold of 0.8 is used as default bootstrap confidence score in QIIME (Navas-Molina *et al.*, 2013).

In addition to taxonomic assignment, it is important to represent evolutionary distance between the sequences in form of phylogenetic tree wherein the distance can be visualized in FigTree (Rambaut, 2009) or TreeView X (Page, 2002) software. Result of multiple sequence alignment is used as an input for phylogenetic analysis which in turn can be obtained using tools like clustalW2 (McWilliam *et al.*, 2013). However, a more recent method to achieve the same is to use NAST algorithm (DeSantis *et al.*, 2006b) to align the OTU representative sequences to a pre-aligned reference database of 16S sequences (often called a "template"). For instance, QIIME uses PyNAST (Caporaso *et al.*, 2009) which is a Python implementation of the NAST. Another tool called Infernal makes use of an HMM approach to incorporate secondary structure information. Due to incorporation of secondary structure information, it is better at identifying variable rRNAs sequences conserved at structural level though, it is a bit slower.

(4) *Diversity analysis:*

The basic components to estimate the microbial diversity are alpha, beta and gamma diversity. Within sample diversity is represented by of alpha diversity which is indicative of "richness" (total number of species in the sample) and "evenness" (distribution of relative abundance of species). To remove the bias introduced by sequencing depth while capturing the true diversity, rarefaction curves are often drawn to determine whether the sequencing depth is adequate to represent the total diversity within the sample. Several metrics are available in both Mothur and QIIME to calculate alpha diversity. The metrics are broadly divided into 2 categories, viz. phylogenetic and non-phylogenetic, depending upon their ability to utilize phylogenetic information of microbes. Shannon index, Simpson's index, Good's coverage, chao1, observed species are non-phylogenetic bases metrics. Choa1 and observed OTUs/species metrics are used to get total diversity in sample, while metrics like Shannon index and Simpson index are used to get information on relative abundance of each taxon identified as well as diversity captured found in sample. On the other hand, phylogenetic diversity metric like Phylogenetic diversity (PD) whole tree takes phylogeny of microbes into account to provide diversity in the sample. Thus it has the added advantage of providing divergence-based analysis (Lozupone and Knight, 2008) for sequences which are different in base composition but similar at metabolite level.

Beta diversity is a term for the inter-sample comparison or across environmental sample comparison which is estimated by calculating the distance between samples using popular metrics like Unifrac (Weighted and UnWeighted), Bray-Curtis, Euclidean and Abundance-Jaccard. Like alpha diversity, beta diversity can also be divided as phylogenetic and non-phylogenetic based methods. Metric such as Jaccard provides richness estimation and Bray-Curtis, Euclidean can provide richness as well as evenness estimation among samples thereby giving better idea about the differences shared by different samples. However, Unifrac metrics like Unweighted and Weighted are phylogenetic based metrics for qualitative as well as quantitative beta diversity analysis respectively (Lozupone and Knight, 2008). Gamma diversity provides the total species diversity found across all samples.

(5) *Statistical analysis and visualization:*

The final step in broad characterization of complex microbial population is correlating gut microbiome with diseased or normal metabolic profile in human using different statistics and visual aids. MG-RAST (Glass *et al.*, 2010) performs a comprehensive analysis and at the end provides a detailed report which is publication ready. Similarly QIIME provides python based programs for 3D visualization of the correlation between the samples using principal coordinates analysis (PcoA). Further, procrustes analysis (Gower, 1975) is often performed to compare weighted and unweighted UniFrac PCoA plots generated by the same processing pipeline adding another dimension. PICRUSt (Langille *et al.*, 2013) analysis could also be carried out to derive functional aspect of sample using 16s rRNA gene information. The visualizations and further statistical tests are not limited to the popularly available tools. There are in fact, a number of open sources and commercial tools/programs/packages like R, SAS and MATLAB available to extend the understanding. Finally, programming in high level languages like Python cannot be ignored and in fact the complete QIIME pipeline is being written in Python. Advanced, Python packages like NumPy and SciPy are often used parallel.

Metagenomic analysis

(1) *Metagenomic assembly*:

Unlike, marker gene study involving analysis of specific region of genome, metagenomics is study of complete set of genomes from a cohort of microbes within an environmental sample. Though the third generation sequencing techniques (PacBio and Oxford Nanopore) have come up with longer reads, the assembly of overlapping reads into continuous or semi-continuous genome fragments also known as contigs or scaffolds is essential. Assembly of the reads allows an exhaustive analysis by reliably assigning specific functions or taxa as compared to gene fragments or unassembled reads. This step can be accomplished using any of the two approaches viz. *de novo* or reference based/guided. While a reference based approach is suitable in the presence of already sequenced reference genome to be used as a road map for genome reconstruction, a *de novo* assembly is preferred in the absence of the same. Assemblers are further categorized based on the type of algorithm they implement (i) de-bruijn graph based & (ii) Overlap Consensus Layout (OLC) (Li *et al.*, 2012). De-bruijn graph works by dividing reads into subsequences (kmers), making it appropriate approach for short reads. While, OLC works best with long reads (>300 bp). Tools such as Newbler (Chaisson and Pevzner, 2008), MIRA (Chevreux *et al.*, 1999) or are mostly employed for performing referenced based assemblies. Traditionally, for de novo assembly, assemblers such as SOAPde-novo2 (Luo *et al.*, 2012), SPAdes (Bankevich *et al.*, 2012), Velvet (Zerbino and Birney, 2008) and commercial tool like CLC genomics workbench are popularly used. However, for metagenomic samples, assembly poses challenges due to various reasons. Relative abundance of microorganisms in a sample is not always even, which results in some genomes being sequenced at a greater depth and coverage as compared to the rest. This problem usually boils down to either misassembling of metagenome or entirely missing out the less abundant species. This scenario worsens when sample contains microbes of related strain sharing most of their genomic content. Another challenge for metagenomic assembly is the computational constraint that is inherent with the diversity of microbes (Howe and Chain, 2015). To tackle these problems, the improved class of assembly tools, such as metaSPAdes (Nurk *et al.*, 2017), MEGAHIT v1.0 (Li *et al.*, 2016), IDBA-UD (Peng *et al.*, 2012), MetaVelvet (Namiki *et al.*, 2012), Meta Ray (Boisvert *et al.*, 2012) and Omega (Haider *et al.*, 2014) were developed. Recently developed tool, metaSPAdes address all these issues and provides competent result capturing low abundance microbes but, it cannot handle multiple libraries at a time. Whereas IDBA-UD takes uncompressed fasta files as input and doesn't support fastq format which is most common output from the latest NGS platforms. Similar is the issue with Omega which accepts uncompressed fasta and fastq format, but neither supports its compressed version nor aid with multithreading. On the other hand, Omega works on OLC approach preferred by researchers working with long reads. Few tools like Metavelvet and Megahit, are required to specify maximum kmer to support during or before source code compilation. Assembler results vary greatly depending upon the sample and its microbe content (simple or complex). However, recent study by Vollmers *et al.* (2017) shows that tools like IDBA-UD, Megahit and metaSPAdes employing multi kmer approach provide better results in terms of diversity captured when dealing with sample having high complexity. Still, metagenome assembly has scope for improvements in terms of computational performance and accuracy of assembling reads.

(2) *Binning*

Some of the most common challenges to metagenomic assembly are the uneven coverage across the sample, errors introduced during sequencing and stretches of repeated sequences (Brubach *et al.*, 2017). Hence, another approach called "binning" has been introduced which essentially means to group reads or contigs into so called "bins" and assigning them to operational taxonomic units (OTUs). The primary objective of binning is to group together the fragments belonging to same organism based on information such as sequence similarity, sequence composition or read coverage (Dröge and McHardy, 2012). Clustering and data representation are the two components of binning; where clustering involves bringing together the fragments like contigs or scaffolds followed by grouping these clusters with data representation approaches into taxonomic bins (Sangwan *et al.*, 2016). This approach is considered better for capturing novel microbes in the sample. However, precision of binning highly depends upon the quality of metagenome assembly. According to the availability of pre-existing bins derived from the genomics sequences, the binning algorithms are further classified into (i) supervised binning, when bins are already available & (ii) unsupervised binning, when no pre-existing bins are available. There are a number of tools and pipeline that implements binning process such as MG-RAST (Glass *et al.*, 2010), TACAO (Diaz *et al.*, 2009), MetaPhyler (Liu *et al.*, 2010), PhyloPythia (Patil *et al.*, 2012), SOrt-ITEMS (Monzoorul Haque *et al.*, 2009), IMG/M (Markowitz *et al.*, 2013), CARMA3 (Gerlach and Stoye, 2011), S-GSOM (Chan *et al.*, 2008), MEGAN (Huson *et al.*, 2007) and PhymmBL (Brady and Salzberg, 2009) etc. Use of long reads generated from 3rd generation sequencing platform like Pacbio RS II for metagenome analysis can result in improvement of assembly which in turn can help achieving accurate binning and taxonomy assignment (Frank *et al.*, 2016). Tools like CARMA3 and PhymmBL uses combination of two approaches for the process of binning from which one is BLAST, thus it provides added advantage in taxonomic classification (Teeling and Glöckner, 2012).

(3) *Annotation*:

One of the most important steps in gut microbiome study is the identification and subsequent annotation of the coding regions within the metagenome. A number of tools are available for gene identification such as MetaGeneMark (Zhu *et al.*,

2010a,b), Prodigal (Hyatt et al., 2010) and Metagene (Noguchi et al., 2006). Another tool called FragGeneScan (Rho et al., 2010) has been implemented in MG/RAST and IMG-ER which is considered better as compared to Metagene because it can handle sequencing error introduced by NGS technology. Additionally, it can work at read as well as assembly level. Non-coding RNAs such as tRNAs are commonly identified using the tools like tRNAScan (Lowe and Eddy, 1997). However, rRNAs can be predicted by comparing sequences to curated rRNA sequence database like Greengenes, SILVA and RDP. Functional annotation is performed by aligning the coding sequences against reference databases to perform homology searches usually with BLAST program. A recently developed alternative for blastx/blastp is Diamond (Buchfink et al., 2015) which is 20,000 times faster than BLAST and is very often used for larger datasets. Of course, high performance computing clusters or commercial cloud computing services like Amazon EC2 (Walker, 2008) have significantly speeded up the time taken to perform these tasks. In the list of standalone programs, COGNIZER (Bose et al., 2015) is an impressive addition since it enables direct derivation of KEGG, Pfam and GO from COG categorizations. Additionally clustered regularly interspaced short palindromic repeats (CRISPRs), a regulatory element can also be identified using specific tools like CRISPR recognition tool (CRT) (Bland et al., 2007). The main limitation of most of these annotation tools is that they assume metagenome data to contain more of bacterias and archeas and thus eukaryotes like fungus having complex genomic structure interspersed with intron are ignored to some extent.

Case Study: A Core Gut Microbiome in Obese and Lean Twins

As represented by Mandal et al. (2015), many publications have demonstrated the association of gut microbes with obesity as compared to other diseases. Thus, here we present a case study carried out by Turnbaugh et al., in 2008 considering obese and lean twins to show the effect of gut microbiota on obesity/leanness. Two set of individuals were examined in this study (i) 154 individuals (31 monozygotic twin pairs, 23 dizygotic twin pairs and 46 samples of their mothers (if available) at two time points and (ii) 18 individuals (3 lean and 3 obese European ancestry monozygotic twin pairs along with their mothers). Monozygotic, dizygotic co-twins and parent–offspring pairs were examined for research as they provide an appealing model for determining the core gut microbes and influence of genotype and shared environment on microbe composition.

Molecular technique and sequencing:

Set (i) of 154 individual samples: 16S rRNA sequencing approach using ABI 3730xl capillary sequencer as well as 16S rRNA V2 variable region13 and V6 hypervariable region1 using Roche 454 FLX instrument.

Set (ii) of 18 individual samples: Shotgun pyrosequencing using Roche 454 FLX/Titanium.

Findings:

- Not a single phylotype was found among all the sample whose abundance was more than 0.5%.
- Samples taken from the same individual at different time point's subsequently exhibited stable phylotypes. However variation was witness in relative abundance of the principal gut bacterial phyla.
- Obesity was marked by notable decrease in the level of diversity. Besides lower proportion of Bacteroidetes and a higher proportion of Actinobacteria in obese compared with lean individuals of both ancestries.
- High level of similarity at functional metabolic level was observed in contrary to excessive diversity concerning relative abundance of bacterial phylum.

This study revealed that, rather than at the phylotype level, the core gut microbiome prevail at the level of shared genes and metabolites.

Application of Gut Microbiome in Healthcare and Medicine

With the increased incidence of use/misuse of antibiotics as a treatment for different diseases, some major health issues have been raised. It is well established fact that bacteria are gradually developing resistance against many antibiotics. In Salyers et al. (2004) revealed that gut microbiota may act as a reservoir of antibiotic resistance when antibiotics pass through the colon. Widely used broad spectrum antibiotics as a side effect kills commensal and 'beneficial bacteria' along with pathogens thus influencing complete microbial community in gut (Shetty et al., 2013). In adults, disruption of gut microbes may lead to pathogenic infection (Robinson and Young, 2010). Antibiotic like ciprofloxacin, when used in excess can lead to reduction in diversity and evenness of bacterial community in gut (Dethlefsen et al., 2008). Hence knowing the fact that antibiotics can derange the protective microbes and increase susceptibility to infection, highlighted the importance of so called 'microbial interference treatment' (Bengmark, 1998). In last decades, our insight of gut microbes and their role in health and patho-physiology has refined a lot. With increased research, it is known that some disease condition can even be treated or improved using specific types of bacteria as a food component or supplement known as "probiotics" (AFRC, 1989). This term is derived from the Greek word 'biotikos' meaning 'for life' i.e., it is used to denote microbes that upon ingestion in requisite amount promotes well being beyond those of inherent fundamental nutrition, boosting gastrointestinal (GI) system (Conly and Johnston, 2004). They are likely to show positive impact upon a range of acute and chronic pathologies (**Table 1**). The health

Table 1   Diseases and their associated bacteria.

Disease	Name of prevalent bacteria	Reference	Probiotics
Type 2 diabetes	Akkermansia muciniphila Bacteroides intestinalis Bacteroides sp. 20_3 Clostridium bolteae Clostridium ramosum Clostridium sp. HGF2 Clostridium symbiosum Clostridium hathewayi Desulfovibrio sp. 3_1_syn3 Eggerthella lenta Escherichia coli	Qin et al. (2012) Mandal et al. (2015)	Lactobacillus acidophilis, Lactobacillus rhamnosus, Lactobacillus casei, Bacillus longum, Bacillus breve, Lactobacillus sporogenes (Zhang, Q., Wu, Y. and Fei, X., 2016)
Obesity/IBD/CD	Acidimicrobidae ellin 7143 Actinobacterium GWS-BW-H99 Actinomyces oxydans Bacillus licheniformis Drinking water bacterium Y7 Gamma proteobacterium DD103 Nocardioides sp. NS/27 Novosphingobium sp. K39 Pseudomonas straminea Sphingomonas sp. A01 Ruminococcus gnavus	Frank et al. (2007) Joossens et al. (2011) Zhang et al. (2015) Mandal et al. (2015)	Bacteroides spp. (Walker and Parkhill, 2013)
Colorectal cancer	Acinetobacter johnsonii Anaerococcus murdochii Bacteroides fragilis Bacteroides vulgatus Butyrate-producing bacterium A2–166 Dialister pneumosintes Enterococcus faecalis Fusobacterium nucleatum E9_12 Fusobacterium periodonticum Gemella morbillorum Lachnospira pectinoschiza Parvimonas micra ATCC 3,3270 Peptostreptococcus stomatis Shigella sonne Acidaminobacter Phascolarctobacterium Citrobacter farmer Akkermansia muciniphila	Mandal et al. (2015) Weir et al. (2013) Hemarajata and Versalovic (2013) Wang et al. (2012) Wu et al. (2009) Balamurugan et al. (2008)	Bifidobacterium longum (Singh et al., 1997)

(Continued)

Table 1 Continued

Disease	Name of prevalent bacteria	Reference	Probiotics
Prostate cancer	*Helicobacter hepaticus*	Poutahidis *et al.* (2013)	
HIV	*Escherichia. coli*	Zajac *et al.* (2007)	*Lactobacillus rhamnosus GR-1* (Hemsworth *et al.*, 2011)
	Proteus mirabilis	Vujkovic-Cvijin *et al.* (2013)	
	Citrobacter freundii	Gori *et al.* (2008)	
	Staphylococcus spp.	Wolf *et al.* (1998)	
	Enterobacter aerogenes		
	Salmonella spp.		
	Serratia spp.		
	Shigella spp.		
	Klebsiella spp.		
Autism	Campylobacter spp.	Heberling *et al.* (2013)	
	Candida albicans	De Angelis *et al.* (2013)	
	Pseudomonas aeruginosa	Finegold (2011)	
	Clostridium spp	Song *et al.* (2004)	
	Bacteroides vulgatus		
	Desulfovibrio desulfuricans		
	Desulfovibrio fairfieldensis		
	Desulfovibrio piger		
	Caloramator spp.		
	Sarcina spp.		
	Alistipes spp.		
	Akkermansia spp.		
Chronic heart disease	*Escherichia coli*	Krack *et al.* (2005)	
	Klebsiella pneumonia		
	Streptococcus viridians		
Symptomatic atherosclerosis	Escherichia coli	Karlsson *et al.* (2012)	
	Eubacterium rectale	Mandal *et al.* (2015)	
	Eubacterium siraeum		
	Faecalibacterium prausnitzii		
	Ruminococcus bromii		
	Ruminococcus sp. 5_1_39BFAA		
Liver disease (Nonalcoholic steatohepatitis–NASH)	Escherichia coli	Wu *et al.* (2008)	
Infectious diarrhea (children)	*Escherichia coli*	Sánchez *et al.* (2017)	*Lactobacillus rhamnosus GG*
	Salmonella spp.		*Saccharomyces boulardii* and *Lactobacillus reuteri DSM 1,7938*
	Campylobacter spp.		(Szajewska *et al.*, 2014)
	Shigella spp.		

Note: Modified from Mandal, R.S., Saha, S. Das, S., 2015. Metagenomic surveys of gut microbiota. Genomics, proteomics & bioinformatics 13 (3),148–158.

benefits of these bacteria are strain specific and thus even a change of strain can affect the outcome (Guarner and Malagelada, 2003). The evidence that, probiotics can be used as effective treatment came after studying patients suffering from diarrhoea. It was observed that in case of acute gastroenteritis in children, the use of either *Lactobacillus rhamnosus* or *Lactobacillus reuteri*, or *Lactobacillus casei* significantly decreased the duration of diarrhoea (Raza *et al.*, 1995; Shornikova *et al.*, 1997; Pedone *et al.*, 1999). It is assumed that diet induced obesity might also be reversed with use of specific diet or by manipulation of gut microbiota by mean of probiotics. Ait-belgnaoui *et al.* (2009) have shown that *Lactobacillus farciminis* taken as a probiotics can affect spinal neuronal activation. Supply of specific lactobacillus along with oat fiber was observed to significantly lower infections associated with pancreatitis, liver transplants and abdominal surgery (Rayes *et al.*, 2005; Rayes, 2004; Olah *et al.*, 2002). Consequently, probiotics can either be used as a replacement or to augment antibiotic effect to re-impose and promote the beneficial microbes in our bodies against diseases condition (Reid, 2006). Deciphering all these advantageous effects, probiotics can be considered as important part of overall care of the patient. Therefore, the study of gut microbiome in different population is vital to apprehend the mechanisms of action and basal of our microbiota for the development of indigenous probiotic strains to be further used for improvement of disease condition.

Gibson and Roberfroid (1995), first introduced the term "prebiotic" explained as nondigestible food ingredient when ingested in body promotes host well-being by nourishing the growth and/or activity of one or a confined number of bacteria in the colon. Prebiotics may include oligosaccharides (like oligofructose, galacto-oligosaccharides) peptides and lipids which could alter endogenous biochemical pathways, by remodeling the specific intestinal microbial communities residing in the colon (Versalovic and Wilson, 2008). List of prebiotics may extend to use of some type resistant starches and sugar alcohols. They may work by blocking the pathogen binding and providing nutrients to useful gut microbes. To infer the mechanism of working of prebiotics, altered activities can be evaluated by structural to functional studies using metagenomics, metaproteomics and metabolomics approach. It was observed that, when transgalactosylated disaccharides was used as a prebiotics, there was increase in number of Bifidobacteria and Lactobacillus whereas decrease in Bacteroides sp. and Candida sp. (Ito *et al.*, 1993). Only side effect of use of prebiotics is increased gas production. However when dealing with prebiotics one need to focus more on understanding its sufficiency, gut passage time and osmotic regularity. Similar to probiotics, studies to determine effective dosage and duration of probiotic exposure showing its effect is necessitate (Reid *et al.*, 2003).

When combination of probiotics with prebiotics is used together for management of microflora, they are known as synbiotics which exemplifies synergism. Theoretically, if prebiotics are taken together with suited probiotics, they may boost the activity of probiotics and their survival along with GI inhabitant microbiota. It is known that synbiotics elevate the number of balanced gut microbiota and also improve immunomodulating ability (Zhang *et al.*, 2010).

However, currently the process of Fecal Microbiota Transplantation (FMT) is in trend. It implicates transplantation of fecal microbiont from healthy individual to recipient in order to refurbish healthy microbiota community and thus deliberate its health benefits (Bakken *et al.*, 2011; Smits *et al.*, 2013). Although FMT was first introduced in year 1958 by Eiseman *et al.* for the treatment of pseudomembranous colitis (Eiseman *et al.*, 1958), but recently it received attention when it offered promising solution against recurring *Clostridium difficile* infection (Smits *et al.*, 2013; Bakken *et al.*, 2011). Due to some trepidations associated with FMT like patient acceptance, infectious potential and treatment standardization, its use is restricted only in case of failure of traditional therapies (Ji and Nielsen, 2015). Being natural and considerably economical treatment, it is favorable to use (Kelly *et al.*, 2015). It is anticipated that in near future, FMT may come-up as a fruitful treatment for other conditions like IBD, obesity, metabolic syndrome and functional gastrointestinal disorders (Gupta *et al.*, 2016).

Future of Gut Microbiome Research

Following the discussion so far, it is evident that studying the gut microbiome has significantly changed our views on how we associate health conditions with their root causes (Zhang *et al.*, 2015). The deeper we have dug into it, the better we have understood the striking correlations of gut microbiota with chronic (Guinane and Cotter, 2013) as well as acute disorders (Shukla *et al.*, 2017). With a detailed understanding of the human microbiome landscape, the possibility of synthetic microbiome modulating the health should not come as a surprise (Waldor *et al.*, 2015). New attempts have already been taken for microbiome replacement therapies, both from natural (Vrieze *et al.*, 2012) and synthetic source (Petrof *et al.*, 2013) with promising results. However, further research is of course required for it to become a routine medical practice and overcoming the inherent limitations. Researchers are further narrowing down stool microbiota ensemble to scientifically validated set of beneficial or rather remedial microorganisms which may be a paradigm shift in medical practices. A recent UNICEF survey (Source: UNICEF/WHO/World Bank Joint Child Malnutrition Estimates, May 2017 edition) suggests that nearly half of all deaths in children under 5 years attributes to under nutrition which translates into the unnecessary loss of about 3 million young lives a year. One can imagine the outcome of such studies to repair the defective gut of such undernourished children along with the food restoring health. Finally, we may also redefine the formal definition of the food we consume by essentially adding the details of gut microbiome associations. With all that said, there are certain aspects which need to be thoroughly considered while drawing conclusions. Firstly, gut studies are mostly carried out by fecal sampling which only represents the luminal microbiota which considerably differs from the mucosa-associated microbiota. Secondly, it is very crucial for viral and fungal species to be taken into consideration along with the bacterial species while studying the gut microbiome. And finally, a large numbers of varying human populations needs to be considered for sampling to establish microbiome-health relationships using combination of techniques to screen transcripts, proteins and metabolites along with the genomic sequences. On the technical side, there is a need for fast paced high performance yet sensitive bioinformatics tools to capture the information as efficiently as possible. The good news is that bioinformatics tools and methods to analyze the microbiome data are evolving in parallel with next generation wet-lab techniques to extract required samples. Hence, there is no doubt that computational techniques will continue to play a major role in the extraction of meaningful information from constantly piling up data.

Closing Remarks

With a number of human gut profiling studies being carried out, it is evident that microbes present in GI has major role to play in human well-being and disease condition. A large number of collaborative projects have been initiated to dig deeper into the understanding of function of these microbes and how their composition is impacted by diet, age, environment etc. Advancement of sequencing methodology, dropping sequencing cost and availability of easy to use bioinformatics tools has encouraged analysis of large number of gut metagenome samples simultaneously. Phylogenetic marker gene studies using next generation sequencing are routinely undertaken as a first choice to get taxonomy profile of a gut sample, answering basic question "who is there". But owing to the limitation of 16S rDNA gene study to answer some of the crucial question like 'how they function' and 'how they interact with gut ecosystem', approaches including whole metagenome, metatranscriptome, metaproteome and metabolomic are required. Thus to get a bigger and clear picture of overall activities of microbes and their involvement in human health, it is necessary to understand which genes are expressed and which metabolites are produced by particular microbe community. Advance bioinformatics analysis and statistical tools and software have made it possible to decode biological information from large number of samples to understand mechanism and mode of action of these microbes. With the ever increasing amount of data generation for gut profiling, certain limitations and issues of existing tools need to be overcome to meet the ever increasing demand. More and more information collected for these microbes is also helping to extend the dimension of their potential and use in health care industries. Thereby, it has given a strong hint that gut microbes study cannot be ignored while moving towards the era of personalized medicine.

Acknowledgment

We would like to thank Xcelris Labs Ltd., Ahmedabad, India for providing the resources and support. We would also like to thank the bioinformatics team at Xcelris Labs for their constant support and motivation.

See also: Computational Pipelines and Workflows in Bioinformatics. Constructing Computational Pipelines. Ecosystem Monitoring Through Predictive Modeling. Functional Enrichment Analysis. Information Retrieval in Life Sciences. Integrative Analysis of Multi-Omics Data. Large Scale Ecological Modeling With Viruses: A Review. Mapping the Environmental Microbiome. Metagenomic Analysis and its Applications. Natural Language Processing Approaches in Bioinformatics. Next Generation Sequencing Data Analysis. Pipeline of High Throughput Sequencing. Sequence Analysis. Sequence Composition. Studies of Body Systems. Whole Genome Sequencing Analysis

References

Abrahamsson, T.R., Jakobsson, H.E., Andersson, A.F., *et al.*, 2014. Low gut microbiota diversity in early infancy precedes asthma at school age. Clinical & Experimental Allergy 44 (6), 842–850.

AFRC, R.F., 1989. Probiotics in man and animals. Journal of Applied Microbiology 66 (5), 365–378.

Ait-belgnaoui, A., Eutamene, H., Houdeau, E., *et al.*, 2009. Lactobacillus farciminis treatment attenuates stress-induced overexpression of Fos protein in spinal and supraspinal sites after colorectal distension in rats. Neurogastroenterology & Motility 21 (5), 567.

Alard, J., Lehrter, V., Rhimi, M., *et al.*, 2016. Beneficial metabolic effects of selected probiotics on diet-induced obesity and insulin resistance in mice are associated with improvement of dysbiotic gut microbiota. Environmental Microbiology 18 (5), 1484–1497.

Allali, I., Arnold, J.W., Roach, J., *et al.*, 2017. A comparison of sequencing platforms and bioinformatics pipelines for compositional analysis of the gut microbiome. BMC Microbiology 17 (1), 194.

Altschul, S.F., Madden, T.L., Schäffer, A.A., *et al.*, 1997. Gapped BLAST and PSI-BLAST: A new generation of protein database search programs. Nucleic acids Research 25 (17), 3389–3402.

Aronesty, E., 2011. ea-utils: Command-Line Tools for Processing Biological Sequencing Data. Durham, NC: Expression Analysis.

Arumugam, M., Raes, J., Pelletier, E., *et al.*, 2011. Enterotypes of the human gut microbiome. Nature 473 (7346), 174.

Asheiford, K.E., Chuzhanova, N.A., Fry, J.C., Jones, A.J., Weightman, A.J., 2005. At least 1 in 20 16S rRNA sequence records currently held in public repositories is estimated to contain substantial anomalies. Applied and Environmental Microbiology 71 (12), 7724–7736.

Bakken, J.S., Borody, T., Brandt, L.J., *et al.*, 2011. Treating Clostridium difficile infection with fecal microbiota transplantation. Clinical Gastroenterology and Hepatology 9 (12), 1044–1049.

Balamurugan, R., Rajendiran, E., George, S., Samuel, G.V., Ramakrishna, B.S., 2008. Real-time polymerase chain reaction quantification of specific butyrate-producing bacteria, Desulfovibrio and Enterococcus faecalis in the feces of patients with colorectal cancer. Journal of Gastroenterology and Hepatology 23 (8pt1), 1298–1303.

Bankevich, A., Nurk, S., Antipov, D., et al., 2012. SPAdes: A new genome assembly algorithm and its applications to single-cell sequencing. Journal of Computational Biology 19 (5), 455–477. BBMap - Bushnell B. - sourceforge.net/projects/bbmap/.

Bengmark, S., 1998. Ecological control of the gastrointestinal tract.The role of probiotic flora. Gut 42 (1), 2–7.

Bland, C., Ramsey, T.L., Sabree, F., et al., 2007. CRISPR recognition tool (CRT): A tool for automatic detection of clustered regularly interspaced palindromic repeats. BMC Bioinformatics 8 (1), 209.

Boisvert, S., Raymond, F., Godzaridis, É., Laviolette, F., Corbeil, J., 2012. Ray Meta: Scalable de novo metagenome assembly and profiling. Genome Biology 13 (12), R122.

Bolger, A.M., Lohse, M., Usadel, B., 2014. Trimmomatic: A flexible trimmer for Illumina sequence data. Bioinformatics 30 (15), 2114–2120.

Bose, T., Haque, M.M., Reddy, C.V.S.K., Mande, S.S., 2015. COGNIZER: A framework for functional annotation of metagenomic datasets. PLOS ONE 10 (11), e0142102.

Brady, A., Salzberg, S.L., 2009. Phymm and PhymmBL: Metagenomic phylogenetic classification with interpolated Markov models. Nature Methods 6 (9), 673–676.

Brubach, B., Ghurye, J., Pop, M., Srinivasan, A., 2017. Better greedy sequence clustering with fast banded alignment. In: Proceedings of the LIPIcs-Leibniz International Proceedings in Informatics (vol. 88). Schloss Dagstuhl-Leibniz-Zentrum fuer Informatik.

Buchfink, B., Xie, C., Huson, D.H., 2015. Fast and sensitive protein alignment using DIAMOND. Nature Methods 12 (1), 59–60.

Call, D.R., Borucki, M.K., Loge, F.J., 2003. Detection of bacterial pathogens in environmental samples using DNA microarrays. Journal of Microbiological Methods 53 (2), 235–243.

Caporaso, J.G., Bittinger, K., Bushman, F.D., et al., 2009. PyNAST: A flexible tool for aligning sequences to a template alignment. Bioinformatics 26 (2), 266–267.

Caporaso, J.G., Kuczynski, J., Stombaugh, J., et al., 2010. QIIME allows analysis of high-throughput community sequencing data. Nature Methods 7 (5), 335–336.

Chaisson, M.J., Pevzner, P.A., 2008. Short read fragment assembly of bacterial genomes. Genome Research 18 (2), 324–330.

Chan, C.K.K., Hsu, A.L., Halgamuge, S.K., Tang, S.L., 2008. Binning sequences using very sparse labels within a metagenome. BMC Bioinformatics 9 (1), 215.

Chevreux, B., Wetter, T., Suhai, S., 1999. Genome sequence assembly using trace signals and additional sequence information. German Conference on Bioinformatics 99, 45–56.

Clooney, A.G., Fouhy, F., Sleator, R.D., et al., 2016. Comparing apples and oranges?: Next generation sequencing and its impact on microbiome analysis. PLOS ONE 11 (2), e0148028.

Conly, J.M., Johnston, B.L., 2004. Coming full circle: From antibiotics to probiotics and prebiotics. Canadian Journal of Infectious Diseases and Medical Microbiology 15 (3), 161–163.

De Angelis, M., Piccolo, M., Vannini, L., et al., 2013. Fecal microbiota and metabolome of children with autism and pervasive developmental disorder not otherwise specified. PLOS ONE 8 (10), e76993.

DeSantis, T.Z., Brodie, E.L., Moberg, J.P., et al., 2007. High-density universal 16S rRNA microarray analysis reveals broader diversity than typical clone library when sampling the environment. Microbial Ecology 53 (3), 371–383.

DeSantis, T.Z., Hugenholtz, P., Larsen, N., et al., 2006a. Greengenes, a chimera-checked 16S rRNA gene database and workbench compatible with ARB. Applied and Environmental Microbiology 72 (7), 5069–5072.

DeSantis, T.Z., Hugenholtz, P., Keller, K., et al., 2006b. NAST: A multiple sequence alignment server for comparative analysis of 16S rRNA genes. Nucleic Acids Research 34 (Suppl_2), W394–W399.

Dethlefsen, L., Huse, S., Sogin, M.L., Relman, D.A., 2008. The pervasive effects of an antibiotic on the human gut microbiota, as revealed by deep 16S rRNA sequencing. PLOS Biology 6 (11), e280.

Diaz, N.N., Krause, L., Goesmann, A., Niehaus, K., Nattkemper, T.W., 2009. TACOA – Taxonomic classification of environmental genomic fragments using a kernelized nearest neighbor approach. BMC Bioinformatics 10 (1), 56.

Dröge, J., McHardy, A.C., 2012. Taxonomic binning of metagenome samples generated by next-generation sequencing technologies. Briefings in Bioinformatics 13 (6), 646–655.

Eckburg, P.B., Bik, E.M., Bernstein, C.N., et al., 2005. Diversity of the human intestinal microbial flora. Science 308 (5728), 1635–1638.

Edgar, R.C., 2010. Search and clustering orders of magnitude faster than BLAST. Bioinformatics 26 (19), 2460–2461.

Edgar, R.C., 2013. UPARSE: Highly accurate OTU sequences from microbial amplicon reads. Nature Methods 10 (10), 996–998.

Edgar, R.C., 2017. Updating the 97% identity threshold for 16S ribosomal RNA OTUs. bioRxiv. 192211.

Edgar, R.C., Haas, B.J., Clemente, J.C., Quince, C., Knight, R., 2011. UCHIME improves sensitivity and speed of chimera detection. Bioinformatics 27 (16), 2194–2200.

Eiseman, Á., Silen, W., Bascom, G.S., Kauvar, A.J., 1958. Fecal enema as an adjunct in the treatment of pseudomembranous enterocolitis. Surgery 44 (5), 854–859.

Ferreira, C.M., Vieira, A.T., Vinolo, M.A.R., et al., 2014. The central role of the gut microbiota in chronic inflammatory diseases. Journal of Immunology Research. 2014.

Finegold, S.M., 2011. State of the art; microbiology in health and disease intestinal bacterial flora in autism. Anaerobe 17 (6), 367–368.

Fraher, M.H., O'toole, P.W., Quigley, E.M., 2012. Techniques used to characterize the gut microbiota: A guide for the clinician. Nature Reviews Gastroenterology and Hepatology 9 (6), 312–322.

Frank, D.N., Amand, A.L.S., Feldman, R.A., et al., 2007. Molecular-phylogenetic characterization of microbial community imbalances in human inflammatory bowel diseases. Proceedings of the National Academy of Sciences 104 (34), 13780–13785.

Frank, J.A., Pan, Y., Tooming-Klunderud, A., et al., 2016. Improved metagenome assemblies and taxonomic binning using long-read circular consensus sequence data. Scientific Reports 6, 25373.

Franzosa, E.A., Hsu, T., Sirota-Madi, A., et al., 2015. Sequencing and beyond: Integrating molecular 'omics' for microbial community profiling. Nature Reviews Microbiology 13 (6), 360.

Frey, K.G., Herrera-Galeano, J.E., Redden, C.L., et al., 2014. Comparison of three next-generation sequencing platforms for metagenomic sequencing and identification of pathogens in blood. BMC Genomics 15 (1), 96.

Ganju, P., Nagpal, S., Mohammed, M.H., et al., 2016. Microbial community profiling shows dysbiosis in the lesional skin of Vitiligo subjects. Scientific Reports 6, 18761.

Gerlach, W., Stoye, J., 2011. Taxonomic classification of metagenomic shotgun sequences with CARMA3. Nucleic Acids Research 39 (14), e91.

Gest, H., 2004. The discovery of microorganisms by Robert Hooke and Antoni Van Leeuwenhoek, fellows of the Royal Society. Notes and Records of the Royal Society 58 (2), 187–201.

Gibson, G.R., Roberfroid, M.B., 1995. Dietary modulation of the human colonic microbiota: Introducing the concept of prebiotics. The Journal of Nutrition 125 (6), 1401.

Glass, E.M., Wilkening, J., Wilke, A., Antonopoulos, D., Meyer, F., 2010. Using the metagenomics RAST server (MG-RAST) for analyzing shotgun metagenomes. Cold Spring Harbor Protocols 2010 (1), pp.pdb-prot5368.

Gori, A., Tincati, C., Rizzardini, G., et al., 2008. Early impairment of gut function and gut flora supporting a role for alteration of gastrointestinal mucosa in human immunodeficiency virus pathogenesis. Journal of Clinical Microbiology 46 (2), 757–758.

Gower, J.C., 1975. Generalized procrustes analysis. Psychometrika 40 (1), 33–51.

Grice, E.A., Segre, J.A., 2012. The human microbiome: Our second genome. Annual Review of Genomics and Human Genetics 13, 151–170.

Guarner, F., Malagelada, J.R., 2003. Gut flora in health and disease. The Lancet 361 (9356), 512–519.

Guinane, C.M., Cotter, P.D., 2013. Role of the gut microbiota in health and chronic gastrointestinal disease: Understanding a hidden metabolic organ. Therapeutic Advances in Gastroenterology 6 (4), 295–308.

Gupta, S., Allen-Vercoe, E., Petrof, E.O., 2016. Fecal microbiota transplantation: In perspective. Therapeutic Advances in Gastroenterology 9 (2), 229–239.

Haas, B.J., Gevers, D., Earl, A.M., *et al.*, 2011. Chimeric 16S rRNA sequence formation and detection in Sanger and 454-pyrosequenced PCR amplicons. Genome Research 21 (3), 494–504.

Haider, B., Ahn, T.H., Bushnell, B., *et al.*, 2014. Omega: An overlap-graph de novo assembler for metagenomics. Bioinformatics 30 (19), 2717–2722.

Hamady, M., Knight, R., 2009. Microbial community profiling for human microbiome projects: Tools, techniques, and challenges. Genome Research 19 (7), 1141–1152.

Handelsman, J., 2004. Metagenomics: Application of genomics to uncultured microorganisms. Microbiology and Molecular Biology Reviews 68 (4), 669–685.

Handelsman, J., 2009. Metagenetics: Spending our inheritance on the future. Microbial Biotechnology 2 (2), 138–139.

Hayashi, H., Sakamoto, M., Benno, Y., 2002. Phylogenetic analysis of the human gut microbiota using 16S rDNA clone libraries and strictly anaerobic culture-based methods. Microbiology and Immunology 46 (8), 535–548.

Heberling, C.A., Dhurjati, P.S., Sasser, M., 2013. Hypothesis for a systems connectivity model of autism spectrum disorder pathogenesis: Links to gut bacteria, oxidative stress, and intestinal permeability. Medical Hypotheses 80 (3), 264–270.

Hemarajata, P., Versalovic, J., 2013. Effects of probiotics on gut microbiota: Mechanisms of intestinal immunomodulation and neuromodulation. Therapeutic Advances in Gastroenterology 6 (1), 39–51.

Hemsworth, J., Hekmat, S., Reid, G., 2011. The development of micronutrient supplemented probiotic yogurt for people living with HIV: Laboratory testing and sensory evaluation. Innovative Food Science & Emerging Technologies 12 (1), 79–84.

Hodkinson, B.P., Grice, E.A., 2015. Next-generation sequencing: A review of technologies and tools for wound microbiome research. Advances in Wound Care 4 (1), 50–58.

Howe, A., Chain, P.S., 2015. Challenges and opportunities in understanding microbial communities with metagenome assembly (accompanied by IPython Notebook tutorial). Frontiers in Microbiology 6.

Huson, D.H., Auch, A.F., Qi, J., Schuster, S.C., 2007. MEGAN analysis of metagenomic data. Genome Research 17 (3), 377–386.

Hyatt, D., Chen, G.L., LoCascio, P.F., *et al.*, 2010. Prodigal: Prokaryotic gene recognition and translation initiation site identification. BMC Bioinformatics 11 (1), 119.

Ito, M., Kimura, M., Deguchi, Y., *et al.*, 1993. Effects of transgalactosylated disaccharides on the human intestinal microflora and their metabolism. Journal of Nutritional Science and Vitaminology 39 (3), 279–288.

Janda, J.M., Abbott, S.L., 2007. 16S rRNA gene sequencing for bacterial identification in the diagnostic laboratory: Pluses, perils, and pitfalls. Journal of Clinical Microbiology 45 (9), 2761–2764.

Jandhyala, S.M., Talukdar, R., Subramanyam, C., *et al.*, 2015. Role of the normal gut microbiota. World Journal of Gastroenterology 21 (29), 8787.

Ji, B., Nielsen, J., 2015. From next-generation sequencing to systematic modeling of the gut microbiome. Frontiers in Genetics 6, 219.

Joossens, M., Huys, G., Cnockaert, M., *et al.*, 2011. Dysbiosis of the faecal microbiota in patients with Crohn's disease and their unaffected relatives. Gut, pp.gut-2010.

Kang, S., Denman, S.E., Morrison, M., *et al.*, 2010. Dysbiosis of fecal microbiota in Crohn's disease patients as revealed by a custom phylogenetic microarray. Inflammatory Bowel Diseases 16 (12), 2034–2042.

Karlsson, F.H., Fåk, F., Nookaew, I., *et al.*, 2012. Symptomatic atherosclerosis is associated with an altered gut metagenome. Nature Communications 3, 1245.

Karlsson, F., Tremaroli, V., Nielsen, J., Bäckhed, F., 2013. Assessing the human gut microbiota in metabolic diseases. Diabetes 62 (10), 3341–3349.

Kelly, C.R., Kahn, S., Kashyap, P., *et al.*, 2015. Update on fecal microbiota transplantation 2015: Indications, methodologies, mechanisms, and outlook. Gastroenterology 149 (1), 223–237.

Kim, O.S., Cho, Y.J., Lee, K., *et al.*, 2012. Introducing EzTaxon-e: A prokaryotic 16S rRNA gene sequence database with phylotypes that represent uncultured species. International Journal of Systematic and Evolutionary Microbiology 62 (3), 716–721.

Kirk, J.L., Beaudette, L.A., Hart, M., *et al.*, 2004. Methods of studying soil microbial diversity. Journal of Microbiological Methods 58 (2), 169–188.

Knights, D., Lassen, K.G., Xavier, R.J., 2013. Advances in inflammatory bowel disease pathogenesis: Linking host genetics and the microbiome. Gut 62 (10), 1505–1510.

Kõljalg, U., Larsson, K.H., Abarenkov, K., *et al.*, 2005. UNITE: A database providing web-based methods for the molecular identification of ectomycorrhizal fungi. New Phytologist 166 (3), 1063–1068.

Krack, A., Sharma, R., Figulla, H.R., Anker, S.D., 2005. The importance of the gastrointestinal system in the pathogenesis of heart failure. European Heart Journal 26 (22), 2368–2374.

Krueger, F., 2015. Trim galore. In: Proceedings of a Wrapper Tool Around Cutadapt and FastQC to Consistently Apply Quality and Adapter Trimming to FastQ Files.

Langille, M.G., Zaneveld, J., Caporaso, J.G., *et al.*, 2013. Predictive functional profiling of microbial communities using 16S rRNA marker gene sequences. Nature Biotechnology 31 (9), 814–821.

Lan, Y., Wang, Q., Cole, J.R., Rosen, G.L., 2012. Using the RDP classifier to predict taxonomic novelty and reduce the search space for finding novel organisms. PLOS ONE 7 (3), e32491.

Lederberg, Joshua., 2000. Infectious history. Science 288 (5464), 287–293.

Li, D., Luo, R., Liu, C.M., *et al.*, 2016. MEGAHIT v1. 0: A fast and scalable metagenome assembler driven by advanced methodologies and community practices. Methods 102, 3–11.

Liu, B., Gibbons, T., Ghodsi, M., Pop, M., 2010. MetaPhyler: Taxonomic profiling for metagenomic sequences. In: Proceedings of the IEEE International Conference on Bioinformatics and Biomedicine (BIBM), pp. 95–100. IEEE.

Liu, B., Yuan, J., Yiu, S.M., *et al.*, 2012a. COPE: An accurate k-mer-based pair-end reads connection tool to facilitate genome assembly. Bioinformatics 28 (22), 2870–2874.

Liu, L., Li, Y., Li, S., *et al.*, 2012b. Comparison of next-generation sequencing systems. BioMed Research International. 2012.

Li, Z., Chen, Y., Mu, D., *et al.*, 2012. Comparison of the two major classes of assembly algorithms: Overlap – Layout – Consensus and de-bruijn-graph. Briefings in Functional Genomics 11 (1), 25–37.

Lloyd-Price, J., Abu-Ali, G., Huttenhower, C., 2016. The healthy human microbiome. Genome Medicine 8 (1), 51.

Lowe, T.M., Eddy, S.R., 1997. tRNAscan-SE: A program for improved detection of transfer RNA genes in genomic sequence. Nucleic Acids Research 25 (5), 955–964.

Lozupone, C.A., Knight, R., 2008. Species divergence and the measurement of microbial diversity. FEMS Microbiology Reviews 32 (4), 557–578.

Luo, R., Liu, B., Xie, Y., *et al.*, 2012. SOAPdenovo2: An empirically improved memory-efficient short-read de novo assembler. Gigascience 1 (1), 18.

Ly, N.P., Litonjua, A., Gold, D.R., Celedón, J.C., 2011. Gut microbiota, probiotics, and vitamin D: Interrelated exposures influencing allergy, asthma, and obesity? Journal of Allergy and Clinical Immunology 127 (5), 1087–1094.

Magoč, T., Salzberg, S.L., 2011. FLASH: Fast length adjustment of short reads to improve genome assemblies. Bioinformatics 27 (21), 2957–2963.

Maidak, B.L., Olsen, G.J., Larsen, N., *et al.*, 1996. The ribosomal database project (RDP). Nucleic Acids Research 24 (1), 82–85.

Mandal, R.S., Saha, S., Das, S., 2015. Metagenomic surveys of gut microbiota. Genomics, Proteomics & Bioinformatics 13 (3), 148–158.

Mardis, E.R., 2008. The impact of next-generation sequencing technology on genetics. Trends in Genetics 24 (3), 133–141.

Markowitz, V.M., Chen, I.M.A., Palaniappan, K., *et al.*, 2013. IMG 4 version of the integrated microbial genomes comparative analysis system. Nucleic Acids Research 42 (D1), D560–D567.

Martin, M., 2011. Cutadapt removes adapter sequences from high-throughput sequencing reads. EMBnet Journal 17 (1), 10–12.

Masella, A.P., Bartram, A.K., Truszkowski, J.M., Brown, D.G., Neufeld, J.D., 2012. PANDAseq: Paired-end assembler for illumina sequences. BMC Bioinformatics 13 (1), 31.

Mayer, E.A., Knight, R., Mazmanian, S.K., Cryan, J.F., Tillisch, K., 2014. Gut microbes and the brain: Paradigm shift in neuroscience. Journal of Neuroscience 34 (46), 15490–15496.

McDonald, D., Price, M.N., Goodrich, J., *et al.*, 2012. An improved Greengenes taxonomy with explicit ranks for ecological and evolutionary analyses of bacteria and archaea. The ISME Journal 6 (3), 610–618.

McWilliam, H., Li, W., Uludag, M., *et al.*, 2013. Analysis tool web services from the EMBL-EBI. Nucleic Acids Research 41 (W1), W597–W600.

Medini, D., Serruto, D., Parkhill, J., *et al.*, 2008. Microbiology in the post-genomic era. Nature Reviews Microbiology 6 (6), 419.

Metzker, M.L., 2010. Sequencing technologies – The next generation. Nature Reviews Genetics 11 (1), 31.

Miele, L., Valenza, V., La Torre, G., *et al.*, 2009. Increased intestinal permeability and tight junction alterations in nonalcoholic fatty liver disease. Hepatology 49 (6), 1877–1887.

Monzoorul Haque, M., Ghosh, T.S., Komanduri, D., Mande, S.S., 2009. SOrt-ITEMS: Sequence orthology based approach for improved taxonomic estimation of metagenomic sequences. Bioinformatics 25 (14), 1722–1730.

Moreno-Indias, I., Cardona, F., Tinahones, F.J., Queipo-Ortuño, M.I., 2014. Impact of the gut microbiota on the development of obesity and type 2 diabetes mellitus. Frontiers in Microbiology 5.

Musso, G., Gambino, R., Cassader, M., 2010. Obesity, diabetes, and gut microbiota. Diabetes Care 33 (10), 2277–2284.

Namiki, T., Hachiya, T., Tanaka, H., Sakakibara, Y., 2012. MetaVelvet: An extension of velvet assembler to de novo metagenome assembly from short sequence reads. Nucleic Acids Research 40 (20), e155.

Navas-Molina, J.A., Peralta-Sánchez, J.M., González, A., *et al.*, 2013. Advancing our understanding of the human microbiome using QIIME. Methods in Enzymology 531, 371.

Noguchi, H., Park, J., Takagi, T., 2006. MetaGene: Prokaryotic gene finding from environmental genome shotgun sequences. Nucleic Acids Research 34 (19), 5623–5630.

Norman, J.M., Handley, S.A., Baldridge, M.T., *et al.*, 2015. Disease-specific alterations in the enteric virome in inflammatory bowel disease. Cell 160 (3), 447–460.

Nurk, S., Meleshko, D., Korobeynikov, A., Pevzner, P.A., 2017. metaSPAdes: A new versatile metagenomic assembler. Genome Research 27 (5), 824–834.

Olah, A., Belagyi, T., Issekutz, A., Gamal, M.E., Bengmark, S., 2002. Randomized clinical trial of specific lactobacillus and fibre supplement to early enteral nutrition in patients with acute pancreatitis. British Journal of Surgery 89 (9), 1103–1107.

Oulas, A., Pavloudi, C., Polymenakou, P., *et al.*, 2015. Metagenomics: Tools and insights for analyzing next-generation sequencing data derived from biodiversity studies. Bioinformatics and Biology Insights 9, 75.

Page, R.D., 2002. Visualizing phylogenetic trees using TreeView. In: Proceedings of the Current Protocols in Bioinformatics, pp. 6.2.1–6.2.15.

Palmer, C., Bik, E.M., DiGiulio, D.B., 2007. Development of the human infant intestinal microbiota. PLoS biology 5 (7), p.e177.

Patel, R.K., Jain, M., *et al.*, 2012. NGS QC toolkit: A toolkit for quality control of next generation sequencing data. PLOS ONE 7 (2), e30619.

Patil, K.R., Roune, L., McHardy, A.C., 2012. The PhyloPythiaS web server for taxonomic assignment of metagenome sequences. PLOS ONE 7 (6), e38581.

Pedone, C.A., Bernabeu, A.O., Postaire, E.R., Bouley, C.F., Reinert, P., 1999. The effect of supplementation with milk fermented by Lactobacillus casei (strain DN-114 001) on acute diarrhoea in children attending day care centres. International Journal of Clinical Practice 53 (3), 179–184.

Peng, Y., Leung, H.C., Yiu, S.M., Chin, F.Y., 2012. IDBA-UD: A de novo assembler for single-cell and metagenomic sequencing data with highly uneven depth. Bioinformatics 28 (11), 1420–1428.

Petrof, E.O., Gloor, G.B., Vanner, S.J., *et al.*, 2013. Stool substitute transplant therapy for the eradication of Clostridium difficile infection: 'RePOOPulating' the gut. Microbiome 1 (1), 3.

Poutahidis, T., Cappelle, K., Levkovich, T., *et al.*, 2013. Pathogenic intestinal bacteria enhance prostate cancer development via systemic activation of immune cells in mice. PLOS ONE 8 (8), e73933.

Pruesse, E., Quast, C., Knittel, K., *et al.*, 2007. SILVA: A comprehensive online resource for quality checked and aligned ribosomal RNA sequence data compatible with ARB. Nucleic Acids Research 35 (21), 7188–7196.

Qin, J., Li, Y., Cai, Z., *et al.*, 2012. A metagenome-wide association study of gut microbiota in type 2 diabetes. Nature 490 (7418), 55–60.

Qin, J., Li, R., Raes, J., *et al.*, 2010. A human gut microbial gene catalog established by metagenomic sequencing. Nature 464 (7285), 59.

Quince, C., Lanzen, A., Davenport, R.J., Turnbaugh, P.J., 2011. Removing noise from pyrosequenced amplicons. BMC Bioinformatics 12 (1), 38.

Rambaut, A., 2009. FigTree. v1. 3.1. Available at: http://tree.bio.ed.ac.uk/software/figtree.

Rastogi, G., Sani, R.K., 2011. Molecular techniques to assess microbial community structure, function, and dynamics in the environment. In: Proceedings of the Microbes and Microbial Technology, pp.29–57. New York: Springer.

Rayes, N., 2004. Lactobacilli and Fibers – A strong couple against bacterial infections in patients with major abdominal surgery. Nutrition 20 (6), 579–580.

Rayes, N., Seehofer, D., Theruvath, T., *et al.*, 2005. Supply of pre-and probiotics reduces bacterial infection rates after liver transplantation – A randomized, double-blind trial. American Journal of Transplantation 5 (1), 125–130.

Raza, S., Graham, S.M., Allen, S.J., *et al.*, 1995. Lactobacillus GG promotes recovery from acute nonbloody diarrhea in Pakistan. The Pediatric Infectious Disease Journal 14 (2), 107–111.

Reid, G., 2006. Probiotics to prevent the need for, and augment the use of, antibiotics. Canadian Journal of Infectious Diseases and Medical Microbiology 17 (5), 291–295.

Reid, G., Sanders, M.E., Gaskins, H.R., *et al.*, 2003. New scientific paradigms for probiotics and prebiotics. Journal of Clinical Gastroenterology 37 (2), 105–118.

Rho, M., Tang, H., Ye, Y., 2010. FragGeneScan: Predicting genes in short and error-prone reads. Nucleic Acids Research 38 (20), e191.

Robinson, C.J., Young, V.B., 2010. Antibiotic administration alters the community structure of the gastrointestinal microbiota. Gut Microbes 1 (4), 279–284.

Rousseau, C., Butel, M.J., 2015. High-throughput techniques for studying gut microbiota. Advances in Probiotic Technology. 146.

Salyers, A.A., Gupta, A., Wang, Y., 2004. Human intestinal bacteria as reservoirs for antibiotic resistance genes. Trends in microbiology 12 (9), 412–416.

Sánchez, B., Delgado, S., Blanco-Míguez, A., *et al.*, 2017. Probiotics, gut microbiota, and their influence on host health and disease. Molecular Nutrition & Food Research 61 (1),

Sangwan, N., Xia, F., Gilbert, J.A., 2016. Recovering complete and draft population genomes from metagenome datasets. Microbiome 4 (1), 8.

Scher, J.U., Abramson, S.B., 2011. The microbiome and rheumatoid arthritis. Nature Reviews Rheumatology 7 (10), 569–578.

Schloss, P.D., Westcott, S.L., Ryabin, T., *et al.*, 2009. Introducing mothur: Open-source, platform-independent, community-supported software for describing and comparing microbial communities. Applied and Environmental Microbiology 75 (23), 7537–7541.

Sender, R., Fuchs, S., Milo, R., 2016. Revised estimates for the number of human and bacteria cells in the body. PLOS Biology 14 (8), e1002533.

Shetty, S.A., Marathe, N.P., Shouche, Y.S., 2013. Opportunities and challenges for gut microbiome studies in the Indian population. Microbiome 1 (1), 24.

Shornikova, A.V., Casas, I.A., Isolauri, E., Mykkänen, H., Vesikari, T., 1997. Lactobacillus reuteri as a therapeutic agent in acute diarrhea in young children. Journal of Pediatric Gastroenterology and Nutrition 24 (4), 399–404.

Shukla, S.D., Budden, K.F., Neal, R., Hansbro, P.M., 2017. Microbiome effects on immunity, health and disease in the lung. Clinical & Translational Immunology 6 (3), e133.

Singh, J., Rivenson, A., Tomita, M., *et al.*, 1997. Bifidobacterium longum, a lactic acid-producing intestinal bacterium inhibits colon cancer and modulates the intermediate biomarkers of colon carcinogenesis. Carcinogenesis 18 (4), 833–841.

Smits, L.P., Bouter, K.E., de Vos, W.M., Borody, T.J., Nieuwdorp, M., 2013. Therapeutic potential of fecal microbiota transplantation. Gastroenterology 145 (5), 946–953.

Sobhani, I., Tap, J., Roudot-Thoraval, F., *et al.*, 2011. Microbial dysbiosis in colorectal cancer (CRC) patients. PLOS ONE 6 (1), e16393.

Song, Y., Liu, C., Finegold, S.M., 2004. Real-time PCR quantitation of clostridia in feces of autistic children. Applied and Environmental Microbiology 70 (11), 6459–6465.

Suau, A., Bonnet, R., Sutren, M., *et al.*, 1999. Direct analysis of genes encoding 16S rRNA from complex communities reveals many novel molecular species within the human gut. Applied and Environmental Microbiology 65 (11), 4799–4807.

Sun, F., Xia, L.C., 2015. Accurate genome relative abundance estimation based on shotgun metagenomic reads. In: Proceedings of the Encyclopedia of Metagenomics, pp. 21–25. US: Springer

Sun, J., Chang, E.B., 2014. Exploring gut microbes in human health and disease: Pushing the envelope. Genes & Diseases 1 (2), 132–139.

Szajewska, H., Guarino, A., Hojsak, I., *et al.*, 2014. Use of probiotics for management of acute gastroenteritis: A position paper by the ESPGHAN working group for Probiotics and Prebiotics. Journal of Pediatric Gastroenterology and Nutrition 58 (4), 531–539.

Teeling, H., Glöckner, F.O., 2012. Current opportunities and challenges in microbial metagenome analysis – A bioinformatic perspective. Briefings in Bioinformatics 13 (6), 728–742.

Thomas, T., Gilbert, J., Meyer, F., 2012. Metagenomics-a guide from sampling to data analysis. Microbial Informatics and Experimentation 2 (1), 3.

Tottey, W., Denonfoux, J., Jaziri, F., *et al.*, 2013. The human gut chip "HuGChip", an explorative phylogenetic microarray for determining gut microbiome diversity at family level. PLOS ONE 8 (5), e62544.

Vernocchi, P., Del Chierico, F., Putignani, L., 2016. Gut microbiota profiling: Metabolomics based approach to unravel compounds affecting human health. Frontiers in Microbiology 7.

Versalovic, J., Wilson, M., 2008. Therapeutic Microbiology: Probiotics and Related Strategies. ASM Press.

Vollmers, J., Wiegand, S., Kaster, A.K., 2017. Comparing and evaluating metagenome assembly tools from a microbiologist's perspective-not only size matters!. PLOS ONE 12 (1), e0169662.

Vrieze, A., Van Nood, E., Holleman, F., *et al.*, 2012. Transfer of intestinal microbiota from lean donors increases insulin sensitivity in individuals with metabolic syndrome. Gastroenterology 143 (4), 913–916.

Vujkovic-Cvijin, I., Dunham, R.M., Iwai, S., *et al.*, 2013. Dysbiosis of the gut microbiota is associated with HIV disease progression and tryptophan catabolism. Science Translational Medicine 5 (193), 193ra91.

Waldor, M.K., Tyson, G., Borenstein, E., *et al.*, 2015. Where next for microbiome research? PLOS Biology 13 (1), e1002050.

Walker, A.W., Parkhill, J., 2013. Fighting obesity with bacteria. Science 341 (6150), 1069–1070.

Walker, E., 2008. Benchmarking amazon EC2 for high-performance scientific computing. USENIX Login 33 (5), 18–23.

Wang, Q., Garrity, G.M., Tiedje, J.M., Cole, J.R., 2007. Naive Bayesian classifier for rapid assignment of rRNA sequences into the new bacterial taxonomy. Applied and Environmental Microbiology 73 (16), 5261–5267.

Wang, T., Cai, G., Qiu, Y., *et al.*, 2012. Structural segregation of gut microbiota between colorectal cancer patients and healthy volunteers. The ISME Journal 6 (2), 320.

Wang, W.L., Xu, S.Y., Ren, Z.G., *et al.*, 2015. Application of metagenomics in the human gut microbiome. World Journal of Gastroenterology 21 (3), 803.

Weir, T.L., Manter, D.K., Sheflin, A.M., *et al.*, 2013. Stool microbiome and metabolome differences between colorectal cancer patients and healthy adults. PLOS ONE 8 (8), e70803.

Woese, C.R., Fox, G.E., 1977. Phylogenetic structure of the prokaryotic domain: The primary kingdoms. Proceedings of the National Academy of Sciences 74 (11), 5088–5090.

Wolf, B.W., Wheeler, K.B., Ataya, D.G., Garleb, K.A., 1998. Safety and tolerance of Lactobacillus reuteri supplementation to a population infected with the human immunodeficiency virus. Food and Chemical Toxicology 36 (12), 1085–1094.

Wu, S., Rhee, K.J., Albesiano, E., *et al.*, 2009. A human colonic commensal promotes colon tumorigenesis via activation of T helper type 17 T cell responses. Nature Medicine 15 (9), 1016–1022.

Wu, W.C., Zhao, W., Li, S., 2008. Small intestinal bacteria overgrowth decreases small intestinal motility in the NASH rats. World Journal of Gastroenterology 14 (2), 313.

Zajac, V., Stevurkova, V., Matelova, L., Ujhazy, E., 2007. Detection of HIV-1 sequences in intestinal bacteria of HIV/AIDS patients. Neuroendocrinology Letters 28 (5), 591–595.

Zerbino, D.R., Birney, E., 2008. Velvet: Algorithms for de novo short read assembly using de Bruijn graphs. Genome Research 18 (5), 821–829.

Zhang, J., Kobert, K., Flouri, T., Stamatakis, A., 2013. PEAR: A fast and accurate Illumina Paired-End reAd mergeR. Bioinformatics 30 (5), 614–620.

Zhang, M.M., Cheng, J.Q., Lu, Y.R., *et al.*, 2010. Use of pre-, pro-and synbiotics in patients with acute pancreatitis: A meta-analysis. World Journal of Gastroenterology 16 (31), 3970.

Zhang, Y.J., Li, S., Gan, R.Y., *et al.*, 2015. Impacts of gut bacteria on human health and diseases. International Journal of Molecular Sciences 16 (4), 7493–7519.

Zhang, Q., Wu, Y., Fei, X., 2016. Effect of probiotics on glucose metabolism in patients with type 2 diabetes mellitus: a meta-analysis of randomized controlled trials. Medicina 52 (1), 28–34.

Zhu, B., Wang, X., Li, L., 2010a. Human gut microbiome: The second genome of human body. Protein & Cell 1 (8), 718–725.

Zhu, W., Lomsadze, A., Borodovsky, M., 2010b. Ab initio gene identification in metagenomic sequences. Nucleic Acids Research 38 (12), e132.

Zoetendal, E.G., Collier, C.T., Koike, S., Mackie, R.I., Gaskins, H.R., 2004. Molecular ecological analysis of the gastrointestinal microbiota: A review. The Journal of Nutrition 134 (2), 465–472.

Further Reading

de Groot, P.F., Frissen, M.N., de Clercq, N.C., Nieuwdorp, M., 2017. Fecal microbiota transplantation in metabolic syndrome: History, present and future. Gut Microbes. 1–15.

Gonzalez, C.G., Zhang, L., Elias, J.E., 2017. From mystery to mechanism: Can proteomics build systems-level understanding of our gut microbes?.

Ley, R.E., Hamady, M., Lozupone, C., *et al.*, 2008. Evolution of mammals and their gut microbes. Science 320 (5883), 1647–1651.

Li, M., Wang, B., Zhang, M., *et al.*, 2008. Symbiotic gut microbes modulate human metabolic phenotypes. Proceedings of the National Academy of Sciences 105 (6), 2117–2122.

Nagpal, R., Yadav, H., Marotta, F., 2014. Gut microbiota: The next-gen frontier in preventive and therapeutic medicine? Frontiers in Medicine 1, 15.

O'Sullivan, D.J., 2000. Methods for analysis of the intestinal microflora. Current Issues in Intestinal Microbiology 1 (2), 39–50.

Roumpeka, D.D., Wallace, R.J., Escalettes, F., Fotheringham, I., Watson, M., 2017. A review of bioinformatics tools for bio-prospecting from metagenomic sequence data. Frontiers in Genetics 8, 23.

Santamaria, M., Fosso, B., Consiglio, A., *et al.*, 2012. Reference databases for taxonomic assignment in metagenomics. Briefings in Bioinformatics 13 (6), 682–695.

Tuohy, K., Del Rio, D., 2014. Diet-Microbe Interactions in the Gut: Effects on Human Health and Disease. Academic Press.

Wu, H.J., Wu, E., 2012. The role of gut microbiota in immune homeostasis and autoimmunity. Gut Microbes 3 (1), 4–14.

Yatsunenko, T., Rey, F.E., Manary, M.J., *et al.*, 2012. Human gut microbiome viewed across age and geography. Nature 486 (7402), 222–227.

Zoetendal, E.G., Rajilić-Stojanović, M., De Vos, W.M., 2008. High-throughput diversity and functionality analysis of the gastrointestinal tract microbiota. Gut 57 (11), 1605–1615.

Relevant Websites

http://www.bioinformatics.babraham.ac.uk/projects/fastqc
    Babraham Bioinformatics.
http://DECIPHER.cee.wisc.edu
    DECIPHER.

http://hannonlab.cshl.edu/fastx_toolkit/index.html
FASTX-Toolkit.
http://www.metahit.eu/
MetaHIT.
http://www.mynewgut.eu
MyNewGut.
http://hmpdacc.org/
NIH Human Microbiome Project.
http://sourceforge.net/project/showfiles.php?group_id=262346
SOURCEFORGE.

Biographical Sketch

Toral Manvar is a registered doctorate student at Gujarat University, Ahmedabad, India. She has more than 7 years of experience in CRO research and bioinformatics. She is working as team leader in NGS bioinformatics division at Xcelris Labs Ltd., Gujarat, India. She has completed her Master's in Bioinformatics in 2009 from Sardar Patel University, V.V Nagar, Gujarat, India. She has special interest in Next Generation Sequencing data analysis involving different DNA and RNA based applications and particularly metagenomics. She has experience in teaching and is currently involved in mentoring and tutoring bioinformatics to graduate and undergraduate students.

Vijay Lakhujani is a certified bioinformatician (Dept. of Biotechnology, Govt. Of India) with deep interest in Genomics and next generation sequencing technologies. He has 6.5 + years of industry experience working on design, implementation and analysis of microarray data and high-throughput NGS data. He is working as Project Scientist in NGS bioinformatics division at Xcelris Labs Ltd., Gujarat, India. He has completed his Masters in Bioinformatics in 2011 from University Of Pune, Maharashtra, India. He has special interest in computational process automation, programming and visualization. He has been formally certified as "lecturer" (CSIR-NET-JRF + LS, Govt. of India) and is involved in providing bioinformatics knowledge sharing sessions and bioinformatics trainings to graduate and undergraduate students.

Functional Enrichment Analysis

Srikanth Manda, Institute of Bioinformatics, Bangalore, India
Daliah Michael, Indian Institute of Science, Bangalore, India
Sudhir Jadhao, Institute of Health and Biomedical Innovation, School of Biomedical Sciences, Queensland University of Technology, Brisbane, QLD, Australia
Shivashankar H Nagaraj, Institute of Health and Biomedical Innovation, School of Biomedical Sciences, Queensland University of Technology, Brisbane and Australia Translational Research Institute, Woolloongabba, QLD, Australia

Abbreviations

BH	Benjamin Hochberg	GSEA	Gene set enrichment analysis
BLAST	Basic local alignment search tool	JSP	Java Server Pages
CRAN	Comprehensive R Archive Network	MEA	Modular enrichment analysis
DAVID	Database for Annotation, Visualization and Integration discovery	NCBI	National Center for Biotechnology Information
FDR	False discovery rate	NGS	Next-generation sequencing
GO	Gene ontology	SEA	Singular enrichment analysis
		SQL	Server Query Language

Introduction

Biological systems are complex entities with several levels of complexity inter-linked and integrated to perform diverse tasks which are monitored and coordinated closely by complex regulatory systems. The organismal level dynamics are result of complex interactions between network of genes, proteins and other biological macro and micro-molecules. These interactions across different omic levels regulate the organism's form and functions and any rewiring leads to disruption of the entire system leading to different disorders depending upon the nature of change. A comprehensive understanding of the different regulatory systems including genomics, proteomics, and metabolomics coupled with the integration of this information into a unified model will lead to better understanding of the resultant phenome at an organismal level. Hence, it is increasingly evident that a systems approach is needed to gain a deeper insight into any biological state of interest. A holistic systems approach allows us to integrate the information collected from different omic studies in order to visualize and understand the complete landscape at the organismal level (Rhee et al., 2008).

Systems level probing is now possible owing to the tremendous technological advances in high throughput experimentation. Studies yielding complex proteomic and genomic datasets help us gain insight into the dynamic changes in the landscape including differential expression and activation of specific pathways depending on the biological situation. The cost of these high throughput omic or multi-omic studies has also fallen dramatically over recent years, making them increasingly affordable and sensitive. This has resulted in a huge deluge of data generated from these high throughput omic studies being performed by investigators who are increasingly motivated to gain systems-level insights into their experimental systems. While generating omic data has become far easier, the difficulty in interpreting the results of such experiments has risen dramatically with the size of datasets, at times proving to be overwhelming for unexperienced researchers.

The analysis of any high throughput experiment ultimately converges upon the identification of all any significantly dysregulated molecules (e.g., genes, proteins, etc.) which are speculated to serve as possible leads that may shed light on the cellular dynamics in the particular biological context of experimental interest. A common analytical approach often hinges on studying differentially expressed genes to identify biomarkers or unique signatures that characterize a specific phenotype. Understanding how individual biomolecules influence a specific phenotype can be invaluable in the advancement of scientific understanding, but understanding the complex interactions and cumulative effects of all biomolecules present within a given system can be just as important despite being a more difficult analytical task. Manual annotation and examination of the roles of each of the dysregulated molecules along with interpretation of their collective roles in a given system is very tedious and time-consuming. It requires thorough study of both extant literature and available databases in order to gather information regarding the functional roles of all the molecules of interest (Hill et al., 2010; Hoehndorf et al., 2015).

Establishing the functional roles of each of the molecules of interest in a particular experimental context is essential in order to draw any conclusions or inferences from the data. When attempting to identify molecules of interest in a complex high throughput dataset, a functional enrichment analysis is the most commonly used approach for analysis and interpretation of biological. Functional enrichment analysis is possible due to the development of unified biological ontologies by the Gene Ontology (GO) Consortium which remains same across eukaryotes. The aim of the Gene Ontology Consortium was to develop, maintain and update well structured, precisely defined terms – also known as ontologies – that articulate the roles of biological molecules across different species (Gene Ontology Consortium, 2015). The GO Consortium is discussed in detail later in the article.

Functional enrichment analysis using the GO database was rendered possible by the emergence of bioinformatics tools that can retrieve information from the GO database. With the advent of these tools it became possible to summarize the information regarding all biological activities in which a particular molecule is known to participate. This information can then be condensed into a succinct enrichment summary. This analysis involves the use of a statistical approach to investigate abundantly represented classes of biological macromolecules such as genes, proteins or metabolites actively involved in different biological processes, molecular functions and cellular compartments. This approach allows us to generate a more holistic view of an experimental system, letting us visualize the biological roles of the differentially expressed biological macromolecules and deduce the significantly enriched biological themes. The different enrichment techniques used by different tools to assess enrichment are described below.

Types of Enrichment

There are three algorithms for performing enrichment analysis: Singular enrichment analysis (SEA), Gene set enrichment analysis (GSEA), Modular enrichment analysis (MEA) (Tipney and Hunter, 2010).

SEA

SEA is a relatively simple, easy-to-use approach to enrichment that is the most traditionally utilized. An SEA analysis takes a list of genes with particular values (e.g., Fold-change values) as the inputs and iteratively procures the associated annotation terms from the GO database for each of these genes. This approach estimates a p-value for each of the retrieved annotation terms by comparing the observed frequency of a term with the frequency expected by random chance. All the terms beyond a threshold (usually p-value $< = 0.05$) are considered to be significantly enriched. Statistical tests that are used to facilitate the identification of significantly enriched GO terms include the Chi-square test, Fischer's Exact Test, Binomial Probability or Hypergeometric distribution. A more detailed discussion of the different statistical methods used for enrichment analyses can be found in the later sections of this article. Once compiled, each of the significantly enriched annotation terms associated with each of the genes in the input gene list are then listed in form of a table. One caveat to this approach is that it ignores the hierarchical relationships between the annotation terms, and it can thus lead to redundancy within the enriched terms owing to association of multiple terms with a single biological process. Some of the tools that use this approach are: Onto-Express, FuncAssociate 2.0 and BiNGO (Berriz et al., 2009; Draghici et al., 2003; Maere et al., 2005).

GSEA

The GSEA approach is best-suited to a comparison-based analysis between two classes of data, multiple scenarios of data points or a single dataset across a series of timepoints. This approach requires a biological metric (e.g., Fold-change or expression) for each biomolecule of interest in order to rank them. A maximum enrichment score (MES) for all genes in a particular category is generated as an output of the GSEA analysis. Once MES scores are compiled, a p-valuebased assessment is done by comparing the ranked MES to the randomly generated MES distributions to assess for enrichment for particular terms beyond what would be expected due to chance. Unlike SEA, GSEA analyses determine whether the ranked list of genes share a particular annotation and form gene sets, reducing the redundancy that can arise from similar GO terms in SEA analyses.

Tools such as GSEA/P-GSEA, GeneTrail use this approach for enrichment analysis (Keller et al., 2008; Mootha et al., 2003; Stöckel et al., 2016; Subramanian et al., 2005).

Modular Enrichment Analysis (MEA)

The MEA approach considers the relationships between the different annotation terms during enrichment. Thus, this approach has better sensitivity and specificity owing to the reduction in the redundancy inherent in SEA/GSEA analyses. This modular approach allows the analysis software to deduce the biological theme in a much more refined manner as it considers the relationship between the terms, rather than just processing individual terms in the two above mentioned processes. Tools such as Ontologizer and GeneCodis use this approach (Bauer et al., 2008; Carmona-Saez et al., 2007).

Steps for Enrichment Analysis

Functional enrichment analysis can be performed using a range of tools that make use of different enrichment strategies. While the details of each protocol differ, these tools share common basic principles that are outlined below.

The starting point of any enrichment analysis is the generation of raw input data to be analyzed in the form of a list of biomolecules. Depending on the nature of study, enrichment analysis can be performed using lists of genes, proteins or metabolites. The list of molecules used can be ranked or unranked depending upon the enrichment algorithm employed by the tool. The tool to be used also should be selected carefully on the basis of the expected results from the analysis (Yang et al., 2008).

Step 1: Calculation of Enrichment Score

The selection of genes to be used for downstream analysis using any tool and algorithm needs to be carefully compiled, as the entire functional analysis will be based on this list. The choice of using a ranked or unranked list depends upon the desired outcome expected and the tool being used for analysis. To ensure that meaningful and specific results can be obtained, a background dataset should be included in the analyses. This background dataset is the list of all the molecules identified in the study, including the significantly dysregulated or important as well as the identified molecules of interest. The background database serves to improve the accuracy of the enrichment score and nullify any biases introduced in capturing the molecules due to experimental procedures.

Once this gene list has been generated and provided to the analysis software, ontology terms for each molecule are fetched from the GO database. These terms encompass a range of molecule descriptors including their functions, the processes/pathways in which they participate or the cellular compartments where they are localized. Ontology terms for the query and background lists are compared to assess the enrichment of different terms and processes. The enriched processes/pathways are those that are overrepresented in the query dataset relative to the background dataset. The enrichment score is a quantified value for each of the ontology term found to be associated by the query molecules.

Step 2: Estimation of Enrichment Score Significance

The statistical significance of the enrichment score can be calculated by using Binomial, Fischer's exact, Hypergeometric or Chi-square tests. The Binomial probability is used when the list of background molecules is large. The Fischer exact, Chi-square and Hypergeometric distributions are better suited to analyses with smaller background datasets. The statistical significance of the enrichment score is quantified with the help of a p-value denoting the extent to which the occurrence of the enrichment of a term is likely to be due to random chance. All terms below a chosen p-value threshold, typically 0.05 (representing a 5% chance of a given enrichment being due to chance), are considered to be significantly enriched. For a more stringent analysis, the p-value threshold can be further decreased to 0.01 or lesser. Many tools also implement alternative mathematical approaches. The user should decide the best suitable statistical method for the dataset.

Step 3: Adjustment for Multiple Hypothesis Testing

As multiple comparisons are being made simultaneously, adjusting p-values to account for false discovery rate (FDR) is necessary in enrichment analyses. FDR is used to control the family-wise error rate, and, an FDR threshold of 1% allows only 1% of the values to be observed by chance when drawn according to the null hypothesis. To account for this FDR, multiple hypothesis correction is applied to the results of the above statistical analysis. The majority of functional enrichment analysis tools perform such corrections using Bonferroni, Benjamini-Hochberg and also Holm, Q-value, and Permutation correction algorithms (de Leeuw et al., 2016).

Gene Ontology Consortium

The Gene Ontology Consortium ("see Relevant Websites section") was developed to provide a comprehensive resource for functional enrichment analysis. It is a collaborative effort that annotates biological macromolecules on the basis of experimental evidence to describe their different biological roles.

GO annotations describes the molecular functions contributing to different biological processes and cellular compartments where these occur. It also includes references to the experimental evidence supporting these associations. The GO consortium has painstakingly addressed the constant need for the development, maintenance and improvement of consistent annotations across species. This group has successfully compiled functional information from over 460,000 species including plants, animals and microorganisms (Gene Ontology Consortium, 2015).

Several commercial and open-source tools have been developed to facilitate quicker functional enrichment analyses, allowing researchers to probe the complexity of their large datasets. In the following sections we describe several tools which can be used for such analysis. **Table 1** provides the list of widely used tools for functional enrichment.

DAVID

The Database for Annotation, Visualization and Integration Discovery (DAVID) was released in 2003 with the aim of providing users with a simple user interface for quick biological interpretation of large datasets. The DAVID knowledgebase integrates a broad range of publically available annotation resources in a centralized location, thus enhancing the quality of high-throughput functional annotation analysis. The entire DAVID is freely available for download in simple text format ("see Relevant Websites section") and is updated frequently. It also provides a number of powerful tools which researchers can use to comprehensively annotate large gene sets from different biological angles. The DAVID Bioinformatics Resources is available for public access at website provided in "Relevant Websites section" (Huang et al., 2007, 2008, 2009).

AmiGO

AmiGO ("see Relevant Websites section") is an open source web-based application developed and maintained by the GO Consortium to query, browse and visualize ontologies and related gene product annotation (association) data. It features a BLAST search, Term Enrichment and GO Slimmer tools and the GO Online SQL Environment. It displays the distribution of annotations

Table 1   List of widely used Bioinformatics tools in the enrichment analysis. Each tool has their distinct algorithm and features; the general procedure of the tools is take query gene list processed it using algorithm and statistics against their annotation database to generate resulting enriched gene set

Tools	Year of publication	Citation	Statistical Method	Tool output
DAVID	2003	6078	Fisher's exact test	P-value with Enrichment score for each cluster in HTML
BiNGO	2005	2475	Hypergeometric test/ binomial	Network of enriched biological process
GOrilla	2009	1359	Hypergeometric test	Colored hierarchical structure of enriched biological process
Blast2GO	2008	997	Fisher's exact test	Annotation in CSV file
WebGestalt	2017	833	Fisher's exact test	Network of enriched biological process
ToppGene Suite	2009	816	Hypergeometric test with Bonferroni correction	P-value with Enriched category
GENECODIS	2007	439	Hypergeometric test/χ^2 test of independence	P-value with Enriched category
Ontologizer	2008	396	Fisher's exact test/ the novel parent–child method	Colored hierarchical structure of enriched biological process
Enrichr	2016	273	Fuzzy Enrichment analysis	Enriched category with cluster grams
MetPA	2010	220	Centrality measure	Network of chemical compounds with metabolites
DIANA-miRPath	2015	212	Fisher's exact test	Annotation in CSV file
FunRich	2015	153	Hypergeometric test/ Bonferroni	Enriched biological process with Venn diagrams, column, bar, pie and doughnut charts as well as interaction network and heatmap images.
INRICH	2012	148	Permutation approach	P-value with Enriched category
EasyGO	2007	133	Hypergeometric Test	Colored hierarchical structure of enriched biological process
GO-Elite	2012	127	Hypergeometric test/ Fisher's exact test	Network of enriched biological process
KEA	2009	97	Fisher's exact test	Network of enriched biological process
GeneTrailExpress	2008	91	Hypergeometric test/Fisher's exact test	Network of enriched biological process
HTSanalyzeR	2011	53	Hypergeometric test	Enrichment map and Network of enriched biological process

associated with a term and its children in both graphical and tabular formats via a bar chart viewer. It is a server-based Perl application that retrieves information from a database using go-perl and go-db-perl. It is publicly available at website provided in "Relevant Websites section" (Carbon et al., 2009).

GOrilla

GOrilla is a web-based application developed using Java. It is publicly available at: "See Relevant Websites Section". It currently supports 8 organisms: *Homo sapiens*, *Mus musculus*, *Rattus norvegicus* and other model organisms such as *Saccharomyces cerevisiae*, *Caenorhabditis elegans*, *Drosophila melanogaster* and *Arabidopsis thaliana*. Functional analysis can be performed using this tool with either of two approaches. The first approach involves using a ranked list of genes enriched via the mHG statistics employed by GOrilla. The second approach involves the generally followed comparison of target and customized background dataset which is analyzed using a hypergeometric model employed by the tool. Thus, the input for GOrilla can be either a single ranked list of genes or two sets of genes (target and background). The output consists of color-coded trimmed Directed acyclic graph (DAG) of all annotated GO terms generated with the help of GraphViz tool. The color codes denote the level of significance of enriched GO term and the nodes are linked to the corresponding entry in a table. This table includes the enriched GO terms, p-values for enrichment and associated annotated genes. The results can be exported in excel format (Eden et al., 2009).

FunRich

FunRich is a user-friendly, Windows-based, standalone application allowing users to perform enrichment analysis on their desktops. It is publicly available at: "See Relevant Websites Section" It allows users to perform functional enrichment analyses and interaction network analyses on background databases without any restrictions on genomic, proteomic or metabolomics data. Users are given an option to select the database. It provides three database options: the FunRich database containing only human annotations, the UniProt database equipped with support for 20 different taxonomic levels and a Custom database that can be customized according to the user's requirements. This tool was developed in C# language using Microsoft. NET library. A hypergeometric distribution test is used to evaluate the statistical significance of enriched and depleted terms. False Discovery Rate (FDR) is implemented to correct for multiple testing by Bonferroni and Benjamini-Hochberg (BH) method. It provides a graphical representation of the data in the form of scalable Venn diagrams, column graphs, heatmap, bar graphs, pie chart and doughnut charts with customizable font, scale and color. Results can be saved in publication quality images and excel sheets (Pathan *et al.*, 2015).

GOplot

R is a commonly used platform by the community for data analysis and for the generation of high quality graphical representations of data. GOplot imports several R packages and is based on the graphical package, ggplot2, enabling users to generate a variety of multilayered graphs. This approach works with two types of input: Molecule lists with their expression levels, and results of functional enrichment analyses. It generates outputs offering different levels of detail: Bar plots or Bubble plots can be constructed to visualize the most enriched categories and Circle, Chord or Cluster plots can offer a more detailed representation of the analyzed results. The Circle plot has two layers: The inner layer is a bar plot representing the statistical significance of enriched terms, and the Outer layer displays the expression levels of particular molecules. The Chord plot has GO terms and molecules connected with ribbons wherever applicable. The Cluster plot displays a circular dendrogram clustered on the basis of their expression profile along with another layer of the associated GO terms. The R package GOplot is available via CRAN-The Comprehensive R Archive Network provided in "Relevant Websites section".

BiNGO

Biological Networks Gene Ontology tool (BiNGO) is a flexible, extendable, open-source Java tool to determine significantly overrepresented GO terms in a set of genes or a subgraph of a given biological network. It maps the functional annotations of gene sets on a GO hierarchy to produce a customizable visual representation in Cytoscape. It provides annotations for a wide range of organisms and these annotations are parsed from GO information available at NCBI. It provides two statistical tests for evaluating the significance of the associated GO terms: hypergeometric and binomial tests. Both of these tests generate p-values as a score for the statistical significance of the enrichment of the GO term. Multiple testing corrections are then applied to discard Type I errors. Multiple testing can be done by applying Bonferroni correction or FDR by BH correction. BiNGO results can be visualized in Cytoscape or can be saved in a tab-delimited text file. It is distributed under GNU General Public License and can be downloaded as a Cytoscape plugin (Maere *et al.*, 2005).

Blast2GO

Blast2GO ("see Relevant Websites section") is a biologist-oriented, high throughput, quality data-mining tool which can be used for functional annotation of a wide range of organisms. It is an operating system independent Java Application made available in Java Web Start (JWS).

GO annotation in Blast2GO proceeds through three basic steps: search for homologues by BLAST, GO term mapping and actual annotation. Blast2GO uses the Basic Local Alignment Search Tool (BLAST) to find sequences similar to your query set. A local BLAST or Web-based BLAST can be performed with parameters adjusted according to user's requirement. The BLAST results can be saved in a file in different formats.

Mapping is done to retrieve the GO annotations for high scoring BLAST hits. Resultant accessions retrieved after BLAST are then used to retrieve gene names, symbols and other IDs. These are then searched against the GO database.

Annotation is done to select the GO terms from the GO pool obtained by the mapping step and assigning them to the query sequences. GO annotation is carried out by applying an annotation rule (AR) to the found ontology terms. This rule seeks to find the most specific annotations with a particular selected level of reliability. For each candidate GO an annotation score (AS) is computed. The annotation rule provides a general framework for annotation but depends completely on how the different parameters at the AS are set. The functionality of InterPro annotations in Blast2GO allows retrieval domain/motif information in a sequence-wise manner. Corresponding GO terms are then transferred to the sequences and merged with already compiled GO terms. Blast2GO provides EC annotation through the direct mapping available at the GO website. Additionally, the KEGG map module allows for the display of enzymatic functions in the context of the metabolic pathways in which they participate. Visualization of the BLAST2GO results can be constructed with the help of interactive directed acyclic graphs (DAG), pie charts and bar graphs which can be customized and filtered.

Most of its functionalities are available for free access at website provided in "Relevant Websites section" (Gotz *et al.*, 2008).

Case Study

Having seen the importance and application of functional enrichment analysis, the challenge now lies in the selection of the right tool for a particular analysis. There are plethora of tools that have been developed in the past to perform enrichment analyses, and many more are emerging at a considerable rate. While most of the tools employ the same general approach, they differ in the way they represent the output and the interpretation of this enrichment dataset (Khatri and Draghici, 2005). Each of these tools has their own advantages and limitations. Thus, at the time of use, one should also have a clear understanding of the disparity between tools and choose the most appropriate tool that would best serve the user's research requirements. There are two excellent review articles (Khatri and Draghici, 2005; Huang *et al.*, 2009) on these tools, that should be consulted when selecting the analytical approach to employ for a particular dataset.

One of the most popular tools used worldwide is DAVID (Huang *et al.*, 2007, 2009), discussed above. For the convenience of the readers we present here a demonstration of the tool using publically available sample input data (i.e., the set of genes) derived from an earlier study (Gardina *et al.*, 2006), primarily to exemplify the use of the tool. DAVID can be accessed at the URL provided in "Relevant Websites section".

The study by Gardina *et al.*, identified 160 differentially expressed genes in 20 pairs of tumor and normal colon cancer samples. This case study uses this set of 160 differentially expressed genes to demonstrate functional enrichment analysis using DAVID (Huang *et al.*, 2007, 2009).

The 'Home' page of DAVID (Huang *et al.*, 2007, 2009) has two main options – 'Functional Annotation' and 'Gene Functional Classification'. The steps to follow are outlined below:

(1) To begin, click on the 'Functional Annotation' option. A page opens up which will prompt the user to either paste a list of genes or upload a file containing the list of genes. The 'Select Identifier' asks the users to choose the appropriate type of gene ID that the input gene list uses. In the 'List Type', the user has to select whether the input gene list is a gene list or is to be used as the background gene set. Then click on 'Submit' (**Fig. 1**). The default database set as the background is the *Homo sapiens* genome database. However, the users may select different databases, according to the nature of their search and study. Choosing and setting up the right background for the analysis is a very crucial step. The general rule of thumb is to set a large background database such as the whole genome, as the results obtained will have more significant p-values as opposed to those resulting from concise background datasets (Huang *et al.*, 2009).

(2) This analysis will produce an 'Annotation Summary Results' page that displays categories indicates that the genes have been annotated in **Fig. 2**. Users may choose to see additional results there.

(3) Upon clicking the 'Functional Annotation Chart', the user can view a report that displays the annotation terms and the annotation database where the associated genes were mapped. It also displays the number and percentage of genes involved out of the total genes in the input list and the related terms list. The p-value of each result is displayed: the smaller the p-value the more enriched (**Fig. 3a**) a term is. Clicking on each annotation result will provide a list of genes from the input gene list that are associated with that particular annotation term (**Fig. 3b**).

(4) The 'Functional Annotation Table' provides, for each input gene, the annotation terms, the database in which it is oriented, related genes and the species of interest (**Fig. 4**).

(5) The annotation of the genes based on the Enrichment score is provided upon clicking the 'Functional Annotation Clustering' option. Here, the genes are clustered under an enrichment score, with a higher enrichment being the one with the higher

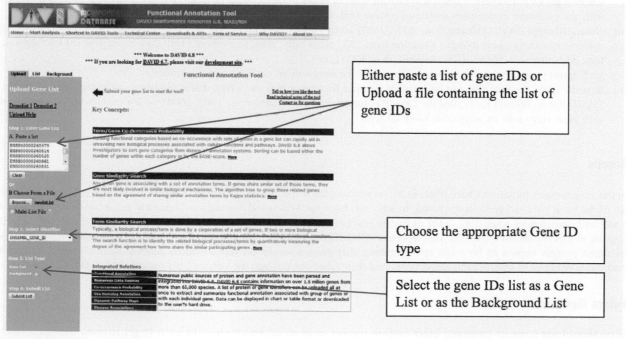

Fig. 1 Input page.

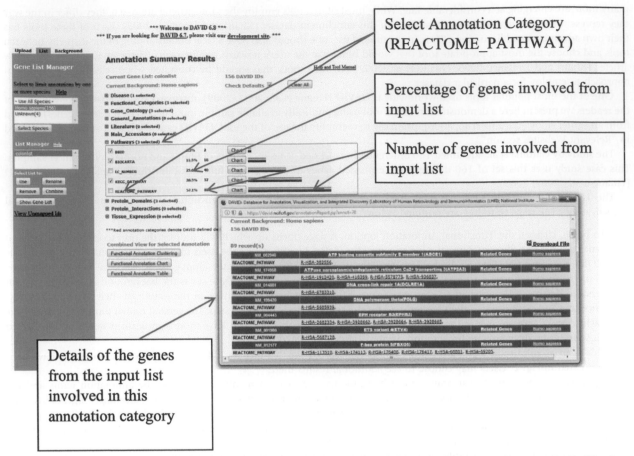

Fig. 2 The Annotation Summary page provides results on various functional annotation categories that the input genes have mapped with. Here, the 'Pathways' category shows the results of all the genes involved in the mentioned pathways, from the input gene list (i.e., 89 genes out of 156 genes).

value. The database associated as well as the number of genes involved, related terms and the p-values are also displayed. Clicking on each annotation result will provide a list of genes from the input gene list that fall under that particular cluster, with the particular enrichment score and p-value (**Fig. 5**).

(6) Note: Although DAVID (Huang *et al.*, 2007, 2009) accepts a very large input gene list, the Functional Annotation Clustering option requires the users to input a maximum of 3000 genes only. Thus, users should split their input gene list into separate files, such that each file contains no more than 3000 genes.

(7) Each result page provides an option to download the results in an easily documented manner.

(8) In some cases, the user may not be aware of the gene ID type or may use a type that is not listed out in the Gene Identifier. DAVID has an in-built tool called the Gene ID Conversion Tool (Huang *et al.*, 2007, 2009), which enables the conversion of each gene entry into an acceptable Gene ID type.

Results

In the 'Functional Annotation Chart' (**Figs. 3a,b**), on selecting the first annotation result with the lowest p-value (i.e., 8.9E − 8), the list of the most enriched genes is displayed. In addition, from the 'Functional Annotation Clustering' result, on selecting the first result with enrichment score 3.12, a list of highly enriched genes is displayed. As an example, let us take the first gene which appears in this cluster, NM_014750. This represents DLG (Discs Large Homolog)-associated protein 5, which is a hepatoma up-regulated protein known to be a cell cycle regulator that plays a significant role in carcinogenesis. Similarly, users can gain invaluable volumes of information about genes and their functions through the various links provided by DAVID's results.

Future Directions

Users should test some of these and other tools in parallel or in an integrated mode in order to get relevant biological inter-pretations that best encapsulate their datasets. The databases described in this text are not comprehensive or exhaustive, and

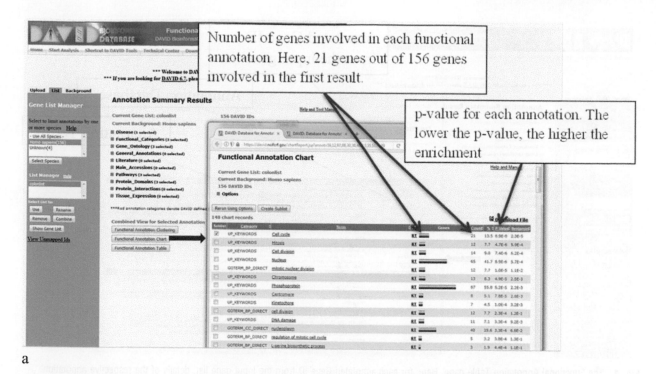

a

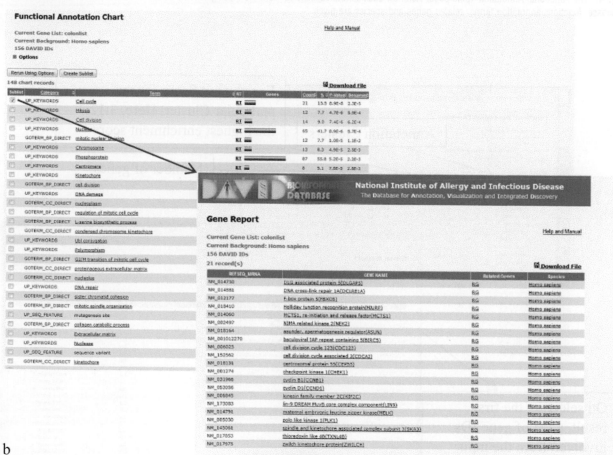

b

Fig. 3 (a). Functional Annotation Chart. (b). Gene Report generated from the first result on the Functional Annotation Chart page. The list of gene IDs for the particular functional annotation "Cell Cycle" along with the Gene names and related genes is displayed here.

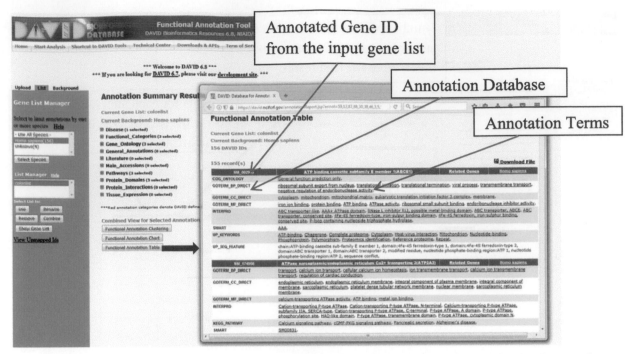

Fig. 4 The Functional Annotation Table page. Here, for each annotated Gene ID from the input gene list, details of the respective annotation database, functions/annotation terms, related genes and species are given.

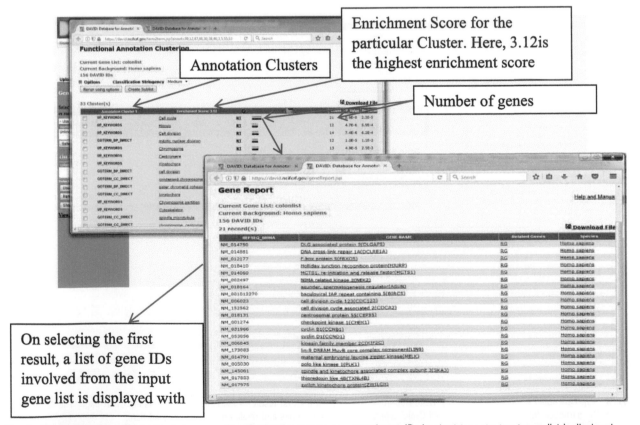

Fig. 5 The Functional Annotation Clustering page. On selecting the first result, a list of gene IDs involved from the input gene list is displayed with all details.

Table 2   Link of Enrichment analysis tools

Tools	Link
DAVID	https://david.ncifcrf.gov/
GOrilla	http://cbl-gorilla.cs.technion.ac.il/
FunRich	http://www.funrich.org/
BiNGO	https://www.psb.ugent.be/cbd/papers/BiNGO/Home.html
Blast2GO	https://www.blast2go.com/
WebGestalt	http://www.webgestalt.org/option.php
EasyGO	http://bioinformatics.cau.edu.cn/easygo/
ToppGene Suite	https://toppgene.cchmc.org/
Enrichr	http://amp.pharm.mssm.edu/Enrichr/
INRICH	https://atgu.mgh.harvard.edu/inrich/
GO-Elite	http://www.genmapp.org/go_elite/
HTSanalyzeR	https://bioconductor.org/packages/release/bioc/html/HTSanalyzeR.html
MetPA	http://www.metaboanalyst.ca/
KEA	http://amp.pharm.mssm.edu/X2K/
DIANA-miRPath	http://snf-515788.vm.okeanos.grnet.gr/
Ontologizer	http://ontologizer.de/
GeneTrailExpress	https://genetrail2.bioinf.uni-sb.de/
GENECODIS	http://genecodis.cnb.csic.es/

should instead serve as a starting point for users to develop their own analytical workflows. Users should also keep in mind that GO annotations and databases are constantly being updated, so using different versions of the same resource may result in different outputs depending on temporal constraints. As new technologies continue to emerge and the cost of high-throughput experiments continues to fall, there will be a constant refinement of existing annotations to fit new advancements in scientific understanding. As such, using the most up-to-date resources is always recommended.

Closing Remarks

This article focuses on the various methods used for enrichment analysis and some of the popular tools and their properties Table 2. Using a test-case dataset, the steps involved in performing a functional enrichment analysis using the DAVID databases is depicted. A functional enrichment analysis is the initial step in any high-throughput experiment, allowing us to narrow down to specific set of genes/functions/pathways of relevance to the problem in hand. The information provided in this article could be considered as a fundamental resource which can be built upon to facilitate the functional enrichment analysis of any datasets.

See also: Computational Pipelines and Workflows in Bioinformatics. Exome Sequencing Data Analysis. Functional Enrichment Analysis Methods. Gene Prioritization Tools. Gene Prioritization Using Semantic Similarity. Integrative Analysis of Multi-Omics Data. Natural Language Processing Approaches in Bioinformatics. Next Generation Sequencing Data Analysis. Pipeline of High Throughput Sequencing. Whole Genome Sequencing Analysis

References

Bauer, S., Grossmann, S., Vingron, M., Robinson, P.N., 2008. Ontologizer 2.0 – A multifunctional tool for GO term enrichment analysis and data exploration. Bioinformatics 24, 1650–1651.

Berriz, G.F., Beaver, J.E., Cenik, C., Tasan, M., Roth, F.P., 2009. Next generation software for functional trend analysis. Bioinformatics 25, 3043–3044.

Carbon, S., Ireland, A., Mungall, C.J., et al., 2009. AmiGO: Online access to ontology and annotation data. Bioinformatics 25, 288–289.

Carmona-Saez, P., Chagoyen, M., Tirado, F., Carazo, J.M., Pascual-Montano, A., 2007. GENECODIS: A web-based tool for finding significant concurrent annotations in gene lists. Genome Biol. 8, R3.

Draghici, S., Khatri, P., Bhavsar, P., et al., 2003. Onto-Tools, the toolkit of the modern biologist: Onto-Express, Onto-Compare, Onto-Design and Onto-Translate. Nucleic Acids Res. 31, 3775–3781.

Eden, E., Navon, R., Steinfeld, I., Lipson, D., Yakhini, Z., 2009. GOrilla: A tool for discovery and visualization of enriched GO terms in ranked gene lists. BMC Bioinform. 10, 48.

Gardina, P.J., Clark, T.A., Shimada, B., et al., 2006. Alternative splicing and differential gene expression in colon cancer detected by a whole genome exon array. BMC Genomics 7, 325.

Gene Ontology Consortium, 2015. Gene Ontology Consortium: Going forward. Nucleic Acids Res. 43, D1049–D1056.

Gotz, S., Garcia-Gomez, J.M., Terol, J., et al., 2008. High-throughput functional annotation and data mining with the Blast2GO suite. Nucleic Acids Res. 36, 3420–3435.

Hill, D.P., Berardini, T.Z., Howe, D.G., Van Auken, K.M., 2010. Representing ontogeny through ontology: A developmental biologist's guide to the gene ontology. Mol. Reprod. Dev. 77, 314–329.

Hoehndorf, R., Schofield, P.N., Gkoutos, G.V., 2015. The role of ontologies in biological and biomedical research: A functional perspective. Brief. Bioinform. 16, 1069–1080.

Huang, D.W., Sherman, B.T., Lempicki, R.A., 2008. Systematic and integrative analysis of large gene lists using DAVID bioinformatics resources. Nat. Protoc. 4, 44–57.

Huang, D.W., Sherman, B.T., Lempicki, R.A., 2009. Bioinformatics enrichment tools: Paths toward the comprehensive functional analysis of large gene lists. Nucleic Acids Res 37, 1–13.

Huang, D.W., Sherman, B.T., Tan, Q., et al., 2007. DAVID Bioinformatics Resources: Expanded annotation database and novel algorithms to better extract biology from large gene lists. Nucleic Acids Res. 35, W169–W175.

Keller, A., Backes, C., Al-Awadhi, M., et al., 2008. GeneTrailExpress: A web-based pipeline for the statistical evaluation of microarray experiments. BMC Bioinform. 9, 552.

Khatri, P., Draghici, S., et al., 2005. Ontological analysis of gene expression data: current tools, limitations, and open problems. Bioinformatics 21, 3587–3595.

de Leeuw, C.A., Neale, B.M., Heskes, T., Posthuma, D., 2016. The statistical properties of gene-set analysis. Nat. Rev. Genet. 17, 353–364.

Maere, S., Heymans, K., Kuiper, M., 2005. BiNGO: A Cytoscape plugin to assess overrepresentation of Gene Ontology categories in Biological Networks. Bioinformatics 21, 3448–3449.

Mootha, V.K., Lindgren, C.M., Eriksson, K.-F., et al., 2003. PGC-1 [alpha]-responsive genes involved in oxidative phosphorylation are coordinately downregulated in human diabetes. Nat. Genet. 34, 267.

Pathan, M., Keerthikumar, S., Ang, C.-S., et al., 2015. FunRich: An open access standalone functional enrichment and interaction network analysis tool. Proteomics 15, 2597–2601.

Rhee, S.Y., Wood, V., Dolinski, K., Draghici, S., 2008. Use and misuse of the gene ontology annotations. Nat. Rev. Genet. 9, 509–515.

Stöckel, D., Kehl, T., Trampert, P., et al., 2016. Multi-omics enrichment analysis using the GeneTrail2 web service. Bioinformatics 32, 1502–1508.

Subramanian, A., Tamayo, P., Mootha, V.K., et al., 2005. Gene set enrichment analysis: A knowledge-based approach for interpreting genome-wide expression profiles. Proc. Natl. Acad. Sci. 102, 15545–15550.

Tipney, H., Hunter, L., 2010. An introduction to effective use of enrichment analysis software. Hum. Genomics 4, 202.

Yang, D., Li, Y., Xiao, H., et al., 2008. Gaining confidence in biological interpretation of the microarray data: The functional consistence of the significant GO categories. Bioinformatics 24, 265–271.

Relevant Websites

http://amigo.geneontology.org/amigo/
  AmiGO Gene Ontology.
https://www.blast2go.com/
  Blast2GO.
http://cran.r-project.org/web/packages/GOplot
  CRAN-R - R Project.
https://david.ncifcrf.gov/
  DAVID Functional Annotation Bioinformatics Microarray Analysis.
http://david.abcc.ncifcrf.gov/knowledgebase
  DAVID Knowledgebase.
http://www.funrich.org/
  FunRich.
http://www.geneontology.org
  Gene Ontology Consortium.
http://cbl-gorilla.cs.technion.ac.il/
  GOrilla.

Biographical Sketch

Srikanth Manda has completed his Masters in Biotechnology from Indian Institute of Technology, Bombay, thereafter, pursued a PhD in Bioinformatics from Institute of Bioinformatics, Bangalore and Johns Hopkins University, USA. During his Ph.D. work he has analyzed datasets from Whole Genome (WGS), Whole Exome (WES), Transcriptome, epigenome, miRNAome, proteome and phosphoproteome. His research interests involve multi-omics data analysis, integration and interpretation from high-throughput platforms using available tools and cloud based workflows.

Sudhir Jadhao is persuing PhD in Genome Informatics at Queensland university of Technology. He specializes in NextGen sequencing and have analyzed data from diverse platforms (Illumina, PacBio, and Ion Torrent) and approaches (WGS, RNA-seq, miRNA, ChIP-seq, Microarray, Exome Sequencing, CNV). In his previous role as Research Assistant, Sudhir worked on understanding the role of non-coding RNA in regulation of the prostate cancer at the University of Macau.

Shivashankar H. Nagaraj is Advanced Queensland Research Fellow at Queensland University of Technology. The focus of his group is on the development and application of bioinformatics approaches that utilize large amounts of data to solve problems in Genomics and Proteomics. He has developed multiple Bioinformatics solutions (e.g., ESTExplorer, EST2Secretome, PGTools) that are valuable and of practical utility to the wider scientific community.

Prediction of Coding and Non-Coding RNA

Ranjeev Hari, Perdana University, Selangor, Malaysia
Suhanya Parthasarathy, Monash University Malaysia, Segamat, Malaysia

Introduction

Early biologists who primarily focused on prokaryotes noted that the majority (85%–90%) of genes were protein-coding and had them accounted for the major cellular processes. However, while complexity of organisms as driven by evolution became higher, the proportion of coding genes reduced gradually in relation to genome size (Mattick and Makunin, 2006). In one of the largest efforts to characterise human deoxyribonucleic acid (DNA), the Encyclopaedia of DNA Elements (ENCODE) project delineates that only about 2%–3% of the human genome are responsible for coding proteins. These genes which are transcribed appear minute in quantity when compared to the transcription of the non-coding regions which are at least 75% of the total genome (Djebali *et al.*, 2012).

The Central Dogma of Molecular Biology states that the genes from the genome (DNA) shall be transcribed into ribonucleic acid (RNA) molecules as per the quantum and mechanistic laws of physics and chemistry. Proteins are required to catalyse various cellular processes, and they are made when these RNAs called messenger RNAs (mRNA) are translated into amino acid sequence. The sudden discovery of non-coding RNAs (ncRNAs) in 1950s, however, were used to dispute the centrality of the Central Dogma. The infamous terms used for these non-coding DNA regions in the genome were "junk DNA" and is coupled with transcriptional "noise" for its RNA counterpart. By the 1970, there were key developments which suggested the role of ncRNAs in gene expression regulation of eukaryotes (Britten and Davidson, 1969; Kohne, 1970; Tomkins *et al.*, 1969). Till date, several possible functions are known for ncRNAs namely as epigenetic, transcriptional and post-transcriptional regulators often participating in DNA replication, splicing, translation, chromosome structure stability, and genome defence (Cheng *et al.*, 2005; ENCODE, 2007; Morris, 2012; Washietl *et al.*, 2007). Moreover, ncRNAs are also thought to have complex roles in cancer and other diseases. As a result, huge efforts are ongoing in trying to understand better the various classes of ncRNAs of its roles and functions in living systems.

RNA Universe

RNA is one of the three essential biopolymers apart from DNA and protein for biological life and are intermediaries to DNA and protein function as per the central dogma. It is an important catalyst for various biological processes and in some instances, once phosphorylated it can even become a subunit of ATP, NADH, and other metabolic compounds. Being commonly found in single-stranded form, it is flexible to take on a 3-dimensional structure better than the double-stranded DNA. Consequently, its structure has protein-like hierarchy that are defined into secondary and tertiary level of structure. Some of the diverse types of secondary structural elements are hairpin loops, 180° bend backbone, internal loops where sequences cannot form base pairs, multibranch loops where two or more regions form a close structure, and other bulge loops. These secondary structural elements can display distinct functions in a cell and are usually structurally conserved (Mathews *et al.*, 2004).

With diverse functions, and as new RNA are being discovered and studied there are different types of RNA classification systems that emerged. Most commonly, RNAs are classified by function and size. Functionally; as examples, RNAs; such as, messenger RNA (mRNA); better known as coding gene or coding RNA are involved in protein synthesis, ribosomal RNA (rRNA) that produce ribosome and aid mRNA by interacting with tRNA during translation, transfer RNA (tRNA) that are in triplet base carrying amino acid precursors for protein anabolism, RNA that involved in post-transcriptional activity are small nuclear RNA (snRNA) that are important in introns removal of heterogenous nuclear RNA (hnRNA), small nucleolar RNA (snoRNA) are essential in RNA mutation, ribonuclease P (RNase P) acts as a ribozyme that cleaves precursor sequences of tRNA, telomerase RNA (TER) are involved in eukaryotic RNA function of extending telomeres and small-interfering RNA (siRNA) are gene silencers and regulators. RNAs are also divided based on size into three groups; which is small ncRNAs, medium ncRNAs, and long ncRNAs (Akman and Erson Bensan, 2014; Brosius and Raabe, 2016; Gomes *et al.*, 2013a; Ma *et al.*, 2013; Santosh *et al.* 2015). An instance of the organisation of the RNA landscape by size is described in **Fig. 1**.

Coding RNA

Central Dogma proposed by Francis Crick explained the conversion flow from DNA which carries genetic information to protein which is a functional product (Crick, 1970). It is also a 2-key steps gene expression process, where transcription produces mRNA by RNA polymerase and translation convert information from mRNA into protein sequence. While RNA mediates majority of the transfer of information based on the proposed model by Crick (**Table 1**), wherever RNA is being expressed with no translation to protein, it is then largely labelled simply as RNA or non-coding RNA (ncRNA).

In coding genes, DNA will be transcribed into pre-mRNA; an immature single strand of mRNA, which will be processed into mature mRNA transcripts that are functional. In eukaryotes, 3'-end cleavage of transcripts generated by RNA polymerase II (pol II)

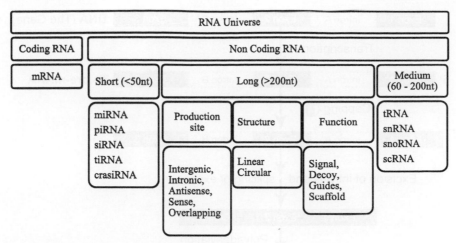

Fig. 1 RNA universe classification based on coding and non-coding RNA.

Table 1   Nine possible transfers in three classes as per Crick's central dogma

Class	Possible transfer	
General transfer	DNA replication	DNA –> DNA
	Transcription	DNA –> mRNA
	Translation	mRNA –> Protein
Special transfer	RNA replication	RNA –> RNA
	Reverse transcriptase	RNA –> DNA
	Protein synthesis without mRNA template	DNA –> Protein
Unknown transfer		Protein –> Protein
		Protein –> RNA
		Protein –> DNA

Source: Reproduced from Crick, F., 1970. Central dogma of molecular biology. Nature 227, 561–563.

is a universal step of gene expression that proceeds through the recognition of cis-acting elements of the pre-messenger RNA (mRNA). It will then undergo 5'-capping, followed by intron removal and methylation, as well as 3'-cleavage and polyadenylation (**Fig. 2**; Millevoi and Vagner, 2009). A mature mRNA, depending on the host organism, can be translated to protein based on a triplet sequence called codon for each amino acid by a specific codon to amino acid translation table.

Gene prediction programs makes use of the molecular and structural signatures of genes as important features in software algorithms predicting protein coding mRNA transcripts. Other approaches based on sequence similarity (homology) search by using BLAST searches are commonly used especially when high quality data is available in a sequence database of genes, EST or protein. However, since only half of genes being discovered have significant homology to databases, *ab initio* gene prediction methods are used instead. Gene prediction programs that are using algorithms such as dynamic programming, Hidden Markov Models (HMM), and neural networks includes GeneID, GENSCAN, FGENESH, and Grail (Blanco *et al.*, 2007; Burge and Karlin, 1997; Salamov and Solovyev, 1998; Xu *et al.*, 1996).

Non-Coding RNA

Essentially, RNA or ncRNA is a functional RNA molecule that are functional without having to translate into protein. Common functional RNA that are involved in cellular housekeeping includes the transfer RNA (tRNA) and ribosomal (rRNA) which are known to be involved with mRNA during translation. The many classes of ncRNAs have diverse yet essential roles in biological processes, including ribonucleoprotein (RNP) in translation, snoRNA in alternative RNA splicing regulation, Y RNAs in DNA replication, enhancer RNAs (eRNAs) which promote gene expression in gene regulation and other epigenetic ncRNAs such as miRNA, siRNA, piRNA and lncRNA involved in modifications to various DNA processes (Collins *et al.*, 2011; Storz, 2002). However, of the many ncRNAs being newly identified, most have no known function and are simply identified as junk RNA (Palazzo and Lee, 2015). Nevertheless, large bodies of evidence are being accrued that implicate ncRNA such as miRNAs and snoRNAs in diseases; such as, Autism, Alzheimer's and even some type of cancers (Ding *et al.*, 2008; Nakatani *et al.*, 2009; Shen *et al.*, 2009) (**Fig. 3**).

In previous studies, efforts in identifying ncRNAs often centred in experiments involving complementary DNA (cDNA) cloning and genomic tiling arrays (Lund *et al.*, 2014; Yazaki *et al.*2007). Some experimental strategies utilize *in vitro* translation to distinguish between ncRNAs and mRNAs where positive translation indicate that a transcript is an mRNA (Borsani *et al.*, 1991;

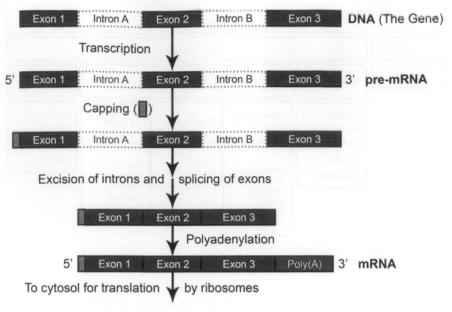

Fig. 2 The transcription process of information from DNA to RNA.

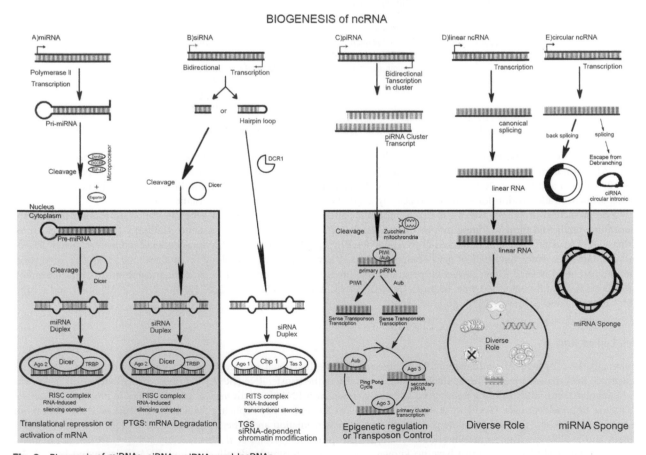

Fig. 3 Biogenesis of miRNAs, siRNAs, piRNAs and lncRNAs.

Galindo *et al.*2007; Tupy *et al.*2005). These experiments are often time-consuming and costly, requiring enough RNA samples while being limited to identifying long ncRNAs (lncRNAs). Researchers are increasingly using computational methods to offset these limitations by incorporating them in their experimental methods especially with the reduction in cost of high-throughput technologies such as next generation sequencing (NGS).

Coding and Non-Coding Prediction Approaches

Differentiating non-coding and coding regions in a genome can be approached computationally, moreover, it may be viewed as a classic type of statistical categorisation problem. Computationally, identifying and cataloguing vast information from genomic and transcriptomic data can be mainly divided into *ab initio* and evidence-based prediction methods while some are based on a hybrid of both methods. Generally, in *ab initio* prediction, the algorithm distinguishes from coding and non-coding genes relatively quickly from the genomic and transcript sequences provided as input. The prediction is derived upon known features of the coding gene such as the start and stop codons, open reading frame, splice and polyadenylation sites. Such *a priori* information will be applied as features in machine learning algorithms for better prediction accuracy. In contrast, evidence-based prediction method would use known information from DNA/RNA and protein sequences to generate predictions by mapping and comparison. In order to curtail the high false positive rates in *ab initio* prediction methods, supported by dwindling costs of NGS, evidence-based prediction is made practical for application in larger datasets. Furthermore, the application of both *ab initio* and evidence-based prediction into a hybrid approach is a natural progression in the field of gene prediction where, for instance, the use of gene expression evidence and subsequent genome mapping in generating better *ab initio* gene models is having widespread attention. Given transcript RNA sequences, many prediction software can predict its class of coding potential with relatively high-accuracy.

Several tools are available to discriminate mRNA and RNA which work on diverse set of features which are often shared in its approaches (Fan and Zhang, 2015). Often some software tools; such as, CNCTDiscriminator which utilizes machine learning as an ensemble of several statistical features of base composition, open-reading frame (ORF), and secondary structures in generating its predictions (Biswas *et al.*, 2013). Other example of software widely used in distinguishing coding and non-coding transcripts are COME (Hu *et al.*, 2017), CPC (Kang *et al.*, 2017; Kong *et al.*, 2007), CNCI (Sun *et al.*, 2013), CPAT (Wang *et al.*, 2013b), PhyloCSF (Lin *et al.*, 2011), PLEK (Li *et al.*, 2014), FEELnc (Wucher *et al.*, 2017), Lncrna-ID (Achawanantakun *et al.*, 2015) and PORTRAIT (Arrial *et al.*, 2009). These tools attempt to achieve similar goals of classifying mRNA and RNA, however, the focus for some are in specific organisms and RNA classes while others are general purpose classifiers.

Besides differentiating coding and non-coding RNAs, these computational methods could also be used in identifying and cataloguing functional RNAs by its class (**Fig. 4**). Evidence-based methods utilize homology information of the nucleotide sequences and sometimes its structural properties as well. Homology-based software tools using sequence homology includes Basic Local Alignment Search Tool (BLAST) (Johnson *et al.*, 2008), SSearch (Goujon *et al.*, 2010), BLAST-like alignment tool (BLAT) (Kent, 2002); while structural homology tools that usually have better prediction accuracy include INFERNAL (Nawrocki *et al.*, 2009) and RSearch (Klein and Eddy, 2003). Apart from homology-based software, ncRNA can be identified using *ab initio* algorithms such as CRITICA (Badger and Olsen, 1999) and ESTscan (Iseli *et al.*, 1999) based on sequence features; MiPred (Jiang *et al.*, 2007), Mfold (Zuker, 2003) and RNAfold (Hofacker, 2003) based on structure while miRDeep (Friedländer *et al.*, 2011) and snoSeeker (Yang *et al.*, 2006) based on sequence features from deep sequencing data (Wang *et al.*, 2013a). Moreover, hybrid integration of both homology and *ab initio* algorithms in RNA prediction is also applied in some software such as MASTR (Lindgreen *et al.*, 2007), pTRNApred (Gupta *et al.*, 2014), and Infernal (Nawrocki *et al.*, 2009).

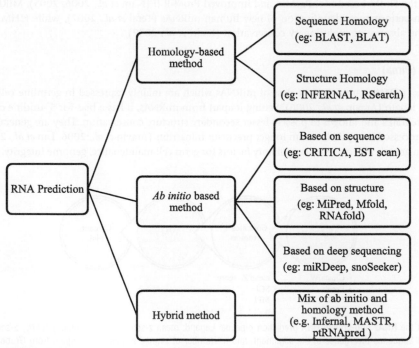

Fig. 4 Software tools for ncRNA prediction is divided into three methods: homology-based, ab initio, and hybrid method.

Small RNA

Sequences of RNAs within 50 nucleotides are classified as small non-coding RNA and are known to primarily control stability of mRNA translation by repressing or activating binding of ribosome to mRNAs (Storz *et al.*, 2004). Example of small ncRNAs that are commonly found in eukaryotes are microRNA (miRNA), piwi-interacting RNA (piRNA), short-interfering RNA (siRNA), tRNA-derived stress-induced RNA (tiRNA), and centromere repeat-associated small RNA (crasiRNA). The three major types of small ncRNAs play important role in gene silencing pathways especially in eukaryotes and protecting cell/genome against viruses, mobile repetitive DNA sequences, retro-elements and transposons are miRNAs, siRNAs and piRNAs (Gomes *et al.*, 2013b; Moazed, 2009).

One of the general purpose bioinformatics software that can used to predict small ncRNA is RNAz (Gruber *et al.*, 2010; Washietl *et al.*, 2005). RNAz uses a combined approach of support vector machines (SVM) regression with binary classification technique and applies minimum free energy (MFE) structural prediction algorithms. Two other important features used by RNAz in this approach are RNA's intrinsic unusual thermodynamic stability (by comparing MFE of native sequence to large number of random identical in length and base composition sequences) and structural conservation (by using RNAalifold) (Gruber *et al.*, 2010; Washietl *et al.*2007, 2005). **Fig. 5** is given to better illustrate an example of sRNA prediction workflow using RNAz.

Microrna (Mirna)

As one of the most studied class of ncRNA, microRNA (miRNA) are small, endogenous, single-stranded RNAs approximately 22 nucleotides/bases in size. They are found in both animals and plants and are evolutionary conserved units (Baulcombe, 2004; Zhang *et al.*, 2007). As small regulatory molecules, they are expressed independently, possess their own promoters and can be regulated by a distinctive set of transcription factors (Gulyaeva and Kushlinskiy, 2016). The target of miRNA commonly is messenger RNA (mRNA).

MicroRNAs functionally govern cell proliferation (Hwang and Mendell, 2006), differentiation and apoptosis (Xia *et al.*, 2017). They are sometimes related in regulation and reprogramming of cellular metabolism in cancer. In some instances, deregulated miRNAs have been correlated with cancers. For example several types of miRNAs that have been proved to be up regulated in cancerous tissues such as let-7e, miR-151p, miR-222, miR-21, miR-155, and miR-221 (Sarkar *et al.*, 2010). This RNA class is well known in affecting transcription levels in animals exerted by major silencing mechanism from destabilization through a cleavage-independent process (MacFarlane and Murphy, 2010). Moreover, miRNAs are noted in diverse functions in cellular life including cell cycle, development, signal transduction, metabolism, metastasis, cell proliferation, differentiation and apoptosis (Mahmoudi and Cairns, 2016).

Computationally, several prediction algorithms have been developed in identifying miRNAs. For instance, miRscan compares the identified putative structures with known miRNA features like 3′ and 5′-stem conservation while another tool, miRseeker, attempts to selects hairpins sharing similar nucleotide divergence patterns to a reference set (Lai *et al.*, 2003; Lim *et al.*2003; Terai *et al.*, 2007). These two main tools identify sequences that can form hairpin structures based on RNAfold and Mfold based on the conserved intragenic sequences. Besides that, there are several tools that have been developed to predict miRNAs for a variety of species, for example, the HMM-based tool ProMir, and improved ProMiR II (Nam *et al.*, 2006, 2005), MiRRim is another HMM-based to achieve high-performance identification of new human miRNAs (Terai *et al.*, 2007), while HHMMiR predicts de novo miRNA hairpins in the absence of evolutionary conservation (Kadri *et al.*, 2009).

Piwi-Interacting RNA (Pirna)

Piwi-interacting RNAs (piRNAs) are a distinct class of miRNAs which are mainly expressed in germline cells with approximately 24–32 nucleotides in length (Aravin *et al.*, 2006). Setting it apart from miRNAs, it has a bias for 5′-uridine common to piRNAs in vertebrates and invertebrates and known to possess lesser secondary structure conservation. They are generally detected with Piwi proteins as they get processed into piRNAs from longer precursor transcripts (Aravin *et al.*, 2006; Lau *et al.*, 2006). Piwi-interacting RNAs are important in genetic and epigenetic regulatory factors for germ cell maintenance, genome integrity, mRNA stability, DNA

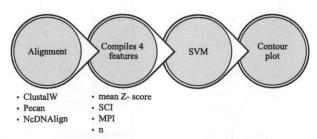

Fig. 5 The workflow of the RNAz non-coding RNA prediction pipeline. Legend: mean z-score: average folding energy z-score, SCI: Structure conservation index, MPI: Sequence divergence of the alignment, and n: Number of aligned sequences. Adapted from Gruber, A.R., Findeiss, S., Washietl, S., Hofacker, I.L., Stadler, P.F., 2010. RNAz 2.0: Improved noncoding RNA detection. Biocomputing 2010, 69–79.

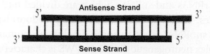

Fig. 6 General structure of siRNA.

methylation and retrotransposon control (Zuo *et al.*, 2016). It has some role in gene silencing and are involved in cancer pathways such as piRNAs piR-651 found to be overexpressed in many of cancer cell lines, piR-823 seen in many types of cancer development, and piR-Hep1 is up regulated in hepatic cell carcinoma (Cordeiro *et al.*, 2016; Ng *et al.*, 2016). Having such significance, computational methods offer quick identification of putative piRNA sequences.

Generally, a few of the computational prediction tools for piRNAs include Luo's method, Betel's method, piRNApredictor and Piano. Each attempt to differentiate transposon-derived piRNAs from non-piRNAs from different sequence and physiochemical features such as spectrum profile, mismatch profile, subsequence profile, position-specific scoring matrix, pseudo dinucleotide composition, and local structure-sequence triplet elements (Betel *et al.*, 2007; Luo *et al.*, 2016; Wang *et al.*, 2014; Zhang *et al.*, 2011). Recently, IpiRId webserver tool improved on several of the previous software tools prediction accuracy on human, mouse and fly datasets (Boucheham *et al.*, 2017).

Short Interfering RNA (Sirna)

Short interfering RNAs are generated from dsRNAs (double strand RNAs) and consist of two RNA strands which is antisense and a sense strand that form a duplex 19–25 bp in length with 3' dinucleotide overhangs as shown in **Fig. 6**. The antisense strand is a perfect reverse complement of the intended target mRNA.

Some of the functions and roles of siRNAs are mainly in post-transcriptional gene silencing (PTGS) or translational inhibition, protection from exogenous DNA, participation in epigenetic mechanisms and to maintain genome integrity via transcriptional silencing. Due to its ability to knockout genes, it has been exploited for commercial applications to rapidly study gene function *in vivo*. Thus, much of the computational applications of siRNA is in the design of optimal targeting of siRNA sequences to knockout genes. Thereafter, prediction of siRNAs can be used to develop screening protocols that can be used to find novel pathway, validating targets of cellular processes associated to diseases such as cancer, HIV infection, or hepatitis.

Computational prediction for siRNA is Sylamer, method to find significantly over or under-represented words in sequences according to a sorted gene list. Usually used to find significant enrichment or depletion of microRNA or siRNA seed sequences from microarray expression data.

Medium Non-Coding RNA

Mid-size RNA class have lengths that range from 60 to 200 nt which include transfer RNA (tRNA), small nucleolar RNA (snoRNA), small nuclear RNA (snRNA) and small cytoplasmic RNA (scRNA) (Bhan and Mandal, 2014).

Transfer RNA (tRNA)

The transfer RNA (tRNA) is a common RNA molecule 76–90 nt in length and serves as an adaptor molecule between mRNA and protein. During translation, tRNA acts as a carrier of amino acids to growing polypeptide chain. Besides that, tRNA is also known to be involved in non-protein synthetic processes in retrovirus life cycle. (Sharp *et al.*, 1985).

The tRNA has a cloverleaf structure which consists of four helices and three hairpin loops. The four helices are the acceptor (AA) helix (or stem) carrying charged amino acid by the cognate aminoacyl synthetase, the dihydrouridine (D) hairpin containing the modified base dihydrouracil; the anticodon (AC) hairpin having the apical loop that presents the anticodon triplets; and the thymine (T) hairpin containing the thymine base unusual in RNAs (Westhof and Auffinger, 2001). By having such highly conserved structural characteristics, established computational tools to predict tRNA from sequences are available such as tRNAscan SE and ARAGORN (Laslett and Canback, 2004; Lowe and Eddy, 1997).

As tRNA perform essential biological functions, mutation of tRNA may cause serious human disease, including pathological stress injuries, cancer and neurodegenerative disease. A special bioinformatics tool for tRNA sequence modification investigation is tRNAmodpred. The tool allows the prediction of post-transcriptional modifications of tRNAs in regards to position and modification type (Machnicka *et al.*, 2016).

Small Nucleolar RNA (Snorna)

Small Nucleolar RNA (snoRNA) is one of the medium-sized RNA which is approximately 60 to 170 nt in size and prominent in both Archae and Eukaryotes, however, absent in bacteria (Jorjani *et al.*, 2016; Bhattacharya *et al.*2016). The locus of snoRNA biosynthesis in yeast originates from a monocistron while for plants in a polycistron. Mainly, snoRNAs play an important role in guiding other

RNA's chemical modification particularly in rRNAs and snRNAs, which are divided into three motif-based classes of antisense C/D box with 2'-O-methylation of ribonucleotides, antisense H/ACA box with pseudouridylation and small Cajal body-specific RNAs (Bhattacharya et al., 2016). Loss of copy of snoRNAs leads to some debilitating human diseases such as Prader-Willi (PWS) and Angelman (AS) syndrome. Implicating complex neurogenetic disorders, PWS is characterized by intellectual impairment, obesity and type 2 diabetes, and short stature while AS symptoms show mental retardation or small head and specific appearance (Ding et al., 2008; Skryabin et al., 2007). In PWS, the cause is attributed to gene imprinting epigenetics on chromosome 15q11.2 and micro-deletion of the paternally inherited 29 copies of SNORD116. On the other hand, AS is attributed to the loss of maternal region chromosome 15 of Ube3A gene. Conversely, duplication of MBII52 snoRNA closely related to common neuropsychiatric disorder with impaired communication disorder, autism by affecting the serotonin 2c receptor (Nakatani et al., 2009).

A number of bioinformatics tool are available for snoRNA detection such as snoScan for C/D box methylation-guide snoRNAs and snoGPS servers for H/ACA pseudouridylation-guide snoRNAs. (Schattner et al., 2005). Besides that, snoSeeker includes two programs (CDseeker and ACAseeker) for screening alignments of whole genome putative snoRNA candidates in order to identify snoRNAs (Yang et al., 2006). Apart from this, snoReport, which is one of the bioinformatics snoRNAs approach with unknown targets, allow to recognize two major classes snoRNAs with combination of RNA secondary structure prediction and snoRNABase collection (Hertel et al., 2007).

Small Nuclear RNA (Snrna)

Small nuclear RNA (snRNA) is one of the small RNA with an average size of 150 nt. Eukaryotic genomes code for a variety of non-coding RNAs and snRNA is a class of highly abundant RNA, localized in the nucleus with important functions in intron splicing and other RNA processing (Maniatis and Reed, 1987). Generally, in transcript splicing, snRNA presents as a ribonucleoprotein particles (snRNPs) along with additional proteins that form a large particulate complex (spliceosome) bound to the unspliced primary RNA transcripts in order to mediate the process. Besides splicing, additional evidence indicate snRNPs function in nuclear maturation of primary transcripts in mRNAs, gene expression regulation, splice donor in non-canonical systems and in 3'-end processing of replication-dependent histone mRNAs (Buratti and Baralle, 2010; Ideue et al., 2012; Lasda and Blumenthal, 2011).

Long Non-Coding RNA

Transcribed RNAs with more than 200 nt long are generally classified as long non-coding RNA (lncRNA). This class of RNA is large and diverse and could be further classified by position of transcription (Intergenic, Intronic, Antisense, Sense and Overlapping ncRNAs) (Fig. 7), structure of RNA (Linear, Circular) and functionality (Bhan and Mandal, 2014; Peschansky and Wahlestedt, 2014). When functionally classified, there are four subcategories divided by mode of action; such as, lncRNAs, which act as either signals, decoys, guides, or scaffolds (Nie et al., 2015).

Alteration in lncRNAs is closely related to human neurological disease, cancer as well as aging. Over expressed of lncRNAs which located on chromosome 2q32 causes prostate cancer apart from abnormal of lncRNAs splicing event allow tumour-suppressor lncRNAs, metastasis associated lung adenocarcinoma transcript 1 (MALAT1) widely involved of lung cancer, pancreatic cancer and cervical cancer. Besides, MEG3, HOTAIR, and lincRNA-p21 act as oncogenic ncRNAs to allow them associated with disease susceptibility. For instance, loss and imprinted MEG3 may contribute to tumour progression; such as meningiomas, colorectal carcinoma, and type 1 diabetes, respectively. (Bhan and Mandal, 2014; Chen et al., 2016). Autosomal dominant facioscapulohumeral muscular dystrophy (FSHD) is caused by deletion of chromosome 4q35; yet, Duchenne muscular dystrophy occur commonly and severely due to deregulation of lncRNAs expression. (Neguembor et al., 2014). In addition, elevated antisense lncRNA transcript of beta secretase 1 (BACE1) is correlated to Alzheimer's disease (Faghihi et al., 2008).

As outlined previously, the identification and study of lncRNAs is of major relevance to human biology and disease since they represent an extensive, largely unexplored, and functional component of the genome (Mattick and Makunin, 2006; Ponting et al., 2009). For instance, although some lncRNAs have been shown to affect in human diseases, these studies are limited by the lack of lncRNA annotations. Therefore, the identification of high-quality catalogues of lncRNAs and its expression in tissues is important work. On the contrary, similar information for protein-coding genes has long been obtainable.

In order to facilitate the growing interest in ncRNA and particularly lncRNA, generating high-confidence catalogues of lncRNA for further study is crucial. Genome sequencing efforts in association with RNA-seq in several studies were able to catalogue lncRNA of various genomes of the sponge, mouse, bovine, and human. These studies have shown that a large portion of these genomes are actually transcribed and could aid the discovery of many more non-coding transcripts (Carninci et al., 2005; Harrow et al., 2006). Furthermore, some studies have focused on large intergenic non-coding RNAs (lincRNAs) (Ponjavic et al., 2007; Guttman et al., 2009; Khalil et al., 2009; Orom et al., 2010), the non-coding transcripts which are away from protein-coding regions.

Recent advances in whole-transcriptome RNA sequencing (RNA-seq) and computational methods for transcriptome reconstruction now provide an opportunity to expansively annotate and characterize lncRNA transcripts (Garber et al., 2011; Guttman et al., 2010; Trapnell et al.2010). Certainly, an initial application of this method in three mouse cell types characterized the gene structure of more than a thousand mouse lincRNAs, most of which were not identified before (Guttman et al., 2010). With logical frameworks that have

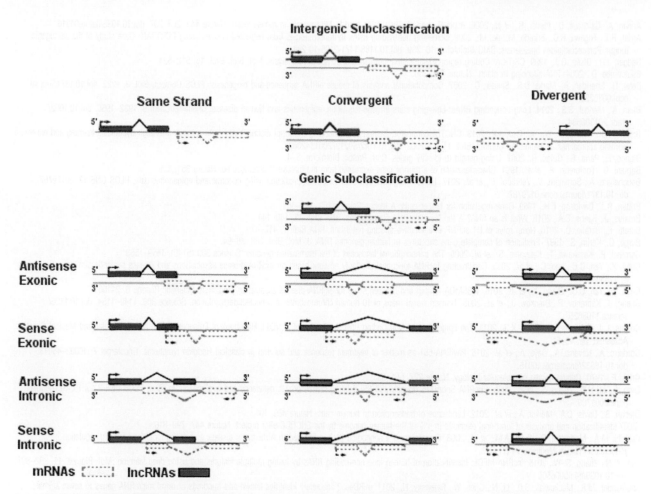

Fig. 7 Classification of lncRNA by transcript expression position in relation to gene and strand origin.

been thoroughly established in previous studies, it is now possible to catalogue and curate high-confidence lncRNA (Pauli *et al.*, 2012). Generally, a well-designed filtering pipeline can be used to arrive at putative lncRNA that can be further assessed for protein-coding capacity. The final set that exhibit poor protein-coding potential will remain as high-confidence lncRNA.

Many studies employ their own pipeline and criteria for filtering their transcript dataset from RNAseq. However, lately there has been software programs that execute the workflow systematically to catalogue the lncRNA; such as, lncrna-screen, FEELnc, and Annocript (Gong *et al.*, 2017; Peng *et al.*2017; Wucher *et al.*, 2017). Generally, the lncRNA identification pipeline will require the assembly of reads into transcripts models which will then be merged, low-confidence transcripts removed, both potential and actual protein-coding transcripts removed, and having the final set of lncRNA transcripts classified (Ulitsky, 2016).

Besides computational identification, since lncRNAs are known to contribute widely in human diseases, computational methods to predict association with diseases are also available. LDAP (lncRNA-disease association prediction) is proposed to predict interaction between lncRNA with susceptibility disease and uses Smith-Waterman algorithm to calculate sequence similarity and several methods to calculate disease similarity (Lan *et al.*, 2016). Apart from LDAP, LRLSLDA (Laplacian Regularized Least Squares for lncRNA-Disease Association) that associates functionally similar disease with lncRNA as well as LNCSIM (LRLSLDA-lncRNA Functional Similarity Calculation Model) that calculate semantic similarity between associated disease are powerful computational approach which could help find probable relationship of lncRNA to diseases (Chen *et al.*, 2015).

See also: Characterizing and Functional Assignment of Noncoding RNAs. Natural Language Processing Approaches in Bioinformatics

References

Achawanantakun, R., Chen, J., Sun, Y., Zhang, Y., 2015. LncRNA-ID: Long non-coding RNA IDentification using balanced random forests. Bioinform. Oxf. Engl. 31, 3897–3905. doi:10.1093/bioinformatics/btv480.
Akman, H.B., Erson Bensan, A.E., 2014. Noncoding RNAs and cancer. Turk. J. Biol. 38, 817–828. doi:10.3906/biy-1404-104.

Aravin, A., Gaidatzis, D., Pfeffer, S., et al., 2006. A novel class of small RNAs bind to MILI protein in mouse testes. Nature 442, 203–207. doi:10.1038/nature04916.

Arrial, R.T., Togawa, R.C., Brigido, M., de, M., 2009. Screening non-coding RNAs in transcriptomes from neglected species using PORTRAIT: Case study of the pathogenic fungus Paracoccidioides brasiliensis. BMC Bioinform. 10, 239. doi:10.1186/1471-2105-10-239.

Badger, J.H., Olsen, G.J., 1999. CRITICA: Coding region identification tool invoking comparative analysis. Mol. Biol. Evol. 16, 512–524.

Baulcombe, D., 2004. RNA silencing in plants. Nature 431, 356.

Betel, D., Sheridan, R., Marks, D.S., Sander, C., 2007. Computational analysis of mouse piRNA sequence and biogenesis. PLOS Comput. Biol. 3, e222. doi:10.1371/journal.pcbi.0030222.

Bhan, A., Mandal, S.S., 2014. Long noncoding RNAs: Emerging stars in gene regulation, epigenetics and human disease. ChemMedChem 9, 1932–1956. doi:10.1002/cmdc.201300534.

Biswas, A.K., Zhang, B., Wu, X., Gao, J.X., 2013. CNCTDiscriminator: Coding and noncoding transcript discriminator – An excursion through hypothesis learning and ensemble learning approaches. J. Bioinform. Comput. Biol. 11, 1342002. doi:10.1142/S021972001342002X.

Blanco, E., Parra, G., Guigó, R., 2007. Using geneid to identify genes. Curr. Protoc. Bioinform. 3–4.

Borsani, G., Tonlorenzi, R., et al., 1991. Characterization of a murine gene expressed from the inactive X chromosome. Nature 351, 325.

Boucheham, A., Sommard, V., Zehraoui, F., et al., 2017. IpiRId: Integrative approach for piRNA prediction using genomic and epigenomic data. PLOS ONE 12, e0179787. doi:10.1371/journal.pone.0179787.

Britten, R.J., Davidson, E.H., 1969. Gene regulation for higher cells: A theory. Science 165, 349–357.

Brosius, J., Raabe, C.A., 2016. What is an RNA? A top layer for RNA classification. RNA Biol. 13, 140–144.

Buratti, E., Baralle, D., 2010. Novel roles of U1 snRNP in alternative splicing regulation. RNA Biol. 7, 412–419.

Burge, C., Karlin, S., 1997. Prediction of complete gene structures in human genomic DNA. J. Mol. Biol. 268, 78–94.

Carninci, P., Kasukawa, T., Katayama, S., et al., 2005. The transcriptional landscape of the mammalian genome. Science 309 (5740), 1559–1563.

Chen, X., Yan, C.C., Luo, C., et al., 2015. Constructing lncRNA functional similarity network based on lncRNA-disease associations and disease semantic similarity. Sci. Rep. 5, 11338.

Chen, X., Yan, C.C., Zhang, X., et al., 2016. WBSMDA: Within and between score for MiRNA-disease association prediction. Scientific Reports 6, 21106.

Cheng, J., Kapranov, P., Drenkow, J., et al., 2005. Transcriptional maps of 10 human chromosomes at 5-nucleotide resolution. Science 308, 1149–1154. doi:10.1126/science.1108625.

Collins, L.J., Schönfeld, B., Chen, X.S., 2011. The Epigenetics of Non-Coding RNA. In: Tollefsbol, T. (Ed.), Handbook of Epigenetics: The New Molecular and Medical Genetics. Academic, pp. 49–61.

Cordeiro, A., Navarro, A., Gaya, A., et al., 2016. PiwiRNA-651 as marker of treatment response and survival in classical Hodgkin lymphoma. Oncotarget 7, 46002–46013. doi:10.18632/oncotarget.10015.

Crick, F., 1970. Central dogma of molecular biology. Nature 227, 561–563.

Ding, F., Li, H.H., Zhang, S., et al., 2008. SnoRNA Snord116 (Pwcr1/MBII-85) deletion causes growth deficiency and hyperphagia in mice. PLOS ONE 3.doi:10.1371/journal.pone.0001709.

Djebali, S., Davis, C.A., Merkel, A., et al., 2012. Landscape of transcription in human cells. Nature 489, 101.

2007.Identification and analysis of functional elements in 1% of the human genome by the ENCODE pilot project. Nature 447, 799–816.

Faghihi, M.A., Modarresi, F., Khalil, A.M., et al., 2008. Expression of a noncoding RNA is elevated in Alzheimer's disease and drives rapid feed-forward regulation of β-secretase. Nature Medicine 14 (7), 723.

Fan, X.-N., Zhang, S.-W., 2015. lncRNA-MFDL: Identification of human long non-coding RNAs by fusing multiple features and using deep learning. Mol. Biosyst. 11, 892–897. doi:10.1039/c4mb00650j.

Friedländer, M.R., Mackowiak, S.D., Li, N., Chen, W., Rajewsky, N., 2011. miRDeep2 accurately identifies known and hundreds of novel microRNA genes in seven animal clades. Nucleic Acids Res. 40, 37–52.

Galindo, M.I., Pueyo, J.I., Fouix, S., Bishop, S.A., Couso, J.P., 2007. Peptides encoded by short ORFs control development and define a new eukaryotic gene family. PLOS Biol. 5, e106.

Garber, M., Grabherr, M.G., Guttman, M., Trapnell, C., 2011. Computational methods for transcriptome annotation and quantification using RNA-seq. Nat. Methods 8, 469–477.

Gomes, A.Q., Nolasco, S., Soares, H., 2013a. Non-coding RNAs: Multi-tasking molecules in the cell. Int. J. Mol. Sci. 14, 16010–16039.

Gomes, C.P.D.C., Cho, J.-H., Hood, L.E., et al., 2013b. A Review of computational tools in microRNA discovery. Front. Genet. 4.doi:10.3389/fgene.2013.00081.

Gong, Y., Huang, H.-T., Liang, Y., et al., 2017. lncRNA-screen: An interactive platform for computationally screening long non-coding RNAs in large genomics datasets. BMC Genom. 18. doi:10.1186/s12864-017-3817-0.

Goujon, M., McWilliam, H., Li, W., et al., 2010. A new bioinformatics analysis tools framework at EMBL – EBI. Nucleic Acids Res. 38, W695–W699.

Gruber, A.R., Findeiss, S., Washietl, S., Hofacker, I.L., Stadler, P.F., 2010. RNAz 2.0: Improved noncoding RNA detection. Biocomputing 2010, 69–79.

Gulyaeva, L.F., Kushlinskiy, N.E., 2016. Regulatory mechanisms of microRNA expression. J. Transl. Med. 14.doi:10.1186/s12967-016-0893-x.

Gupta, Y., Witte, M., Möller, S., et al., 2014. ptRNApred: Computational identification and classification of post-transcriptional RNA. Nucleic Acids Res. 42, e167.

Guttman, M., Amit, I., Garber, M., et al., 2009. Chromatin signature reveals over a thousand highly conserved large non-coding RNAs in mammals. Nature 458 (7235), 223.

Guttman, M., Garber, M., Levin, J.Z., et al., 2010. Ab initio reconstruction of cell type-specific transcriptomes in mouse reveals the conserved multi-exonic structure of lincRNAs. Nat. Biotechnol. 28, 503–510.

Harrow, J., Denoeud, F., Frankish, A., et al., 2006. GENCODE: Producing a reference annotation for ENCODE. Genome Biology 7 (1), S4.

Hertel, J., Hofacker, I.L., Stadler, P.F., 2007. SnoReport: Computational identification of snoRNAs with unknown targets. Bioinformatics 24 (2), 158–164.

Hofacker, I.L., 2003. Vienna RNA secondary structure server. Nucleic Acids Res. 31, 3429–3431.

Hu, L., Xu, Z., Hu, B., Lu, Z.J., 2017. COME: A robust coding potential calculation tool for lncRNA identification and characterization based on multiple features. Nucleic Acids Res. 45, e2. doi:10.1093/nar/gkw798.

Hwang, H.-W., Mendell, J.T., 2006. MicroRNAs in cell proliferation, cell death, and tumorigenesis. Br. J. Cancer 94, 776–780. doi:10.1038/sj.bjc.6603023.

Ideue, T., Adachi, S., Naganuma, T., et al., 2012. U7 small nuclear ribonucleoprotein represses histone gene transcription in cell cycle-arrested cells. Proc. Natl. Acad. Sci. USA 109, 5693–5698. doi:10.1073/pnas.1200523109.

Iseli, C., Jongeneel, C.V., Bucher, P., 1999. ESTScan: A program for detecting, evaluating, and reconstructing potential coding regions in EST sequences. ISMB. 138–148.

Jiang, P., Wu, H., Wang, W., et al., 2007. MiPred: Classification of real and pseudo microRNA precursors using random forest prediction model with combined features. Nucleic Acids Res. 35, W339–W344.

Johnson, M., Zaretskaya, I., Raytselis, Y., et al., 2008. NCBI BLAST: A better web interface. Nucleic Acids Res. 36, W5–W9.

Jorjani, H., Kehr, S., Jedlinski, D.J., et al., 2016. An updated human snoRNAome. Nucleic Acids Res. 44, 5068–5082.

Kadri, S., Hinman, V., Benos, P.V., 2009. HHMMiR: Efficient de novo prediction of microRNAs using hierarchical hidden Markov models. BMC Bioinform. 10 (Suppl 1), S35. doi:10.1186/1471-2105-10-S1-S35.

Kang, Y.-J., Yang, D.-C., Kong, L., et al., 2017. CPC2: A fast and accurate coding potential calculator based on sequence intrinsic features. Nucleic Acids Res. 45 (W1), W12–W16. doi:10.1093/nar/gkx428.

Kent, W.J., 2002. BLAT – The BLAST-like alignment tool. Genome Res. 12, 656–664.

Khalil, A.M., Guttman, M., Huarte, M., *et al.*, 2009. Many human large intergenic noncoding RNAs associate with chromatin-modifying complexes and affect gene expression. Proceedings of the National Academy of Sciences 106 (28), 11667–11672.

Klein, R.J., Eddy, S.R., 2003. RSEARCH: Finding homologs of single structured RNA sequences. BMC Bioinform. 4, 44.

Kohne, D.E., 1970. Evolution of higher-organism DNA. Q. Rev. Biophys. 3, 327–375.

Kong, L., Zhang, Y., Ye, Z.-Q., *et al.*, 2007. CPC: Assess the protein-coding potential of transcripts using sequence features and support vector machine. Nucleic Acids Res. 35, W345–W349. doi:10.1093/nar/gkm391.

Lai, E.C., Tomancak, P., Williams, R.W., Rubin, G.M., 2003. Computational identification of Drosophila microRNA genes. Genome Biol. 4, R42. doi:10.1186/gb-2003-4-7-r42.

Lan, W., Li, M., Zhao, K., *et al.*, 2016. LDAP: A web server for lncRNA-disease association prediction. Bioinformatics 33, 458–460.

Lasda, E.L., Blumenthal, T., 2011. Trans-splicing. Wiley Interdiscip. Rev. RNA 2, 417–434.

Laslett, D., Canback, B., 2004. ARAGORN, a program to detect tRNA genes and tmRNA genes in nucleotide sequences. Nucleic Acids Res. 32, 11–16. doi:10.1093/nar/gkh152.

Lau, N.C., Seto, A.G., Kim, J., *et al.*, 2006. Characterization of the piRNA complex from rat testes. Science 313, 363–367.

Li, A., Zhang, J., Zhou, Z., 2014. PLEK: A tool for predicting long non-coding RNAs and messenger RNAs based on an improved k-mer scheme. BMC Bioinform. 15, 311. doi:10.1186/1471-2105-15-311.

Lim, L.P., Lau, N.C., Weinstein, E.G., *et al.*, 2003. The microRNAs of Caenorhabditis elegans. Genes Dev. 17, 991–1008. doi:10.1101/gad.1074403.

Lindgreen, S., Gardner, P.P., Krogh, A., 2007. MASTR: Multiple alignment and structure prediction of non-coding RNAs using simulated annealing. Bioinformatics 23, 3304–3311.

Lin, M.F., Jungreis, I., Kellis, M., 2011. PhyloCSF: A comparative genomics method to distinguish protein coding and non-coding regions. Bioinforma. Oxf. Engl. 27, i275–i282. doi:10.1093/bioinformatics/btr209.

Lowe, T.M., Eddy, S.R., 1997. tRNAscan-SE: A program for improved detection of transfer RNA genes in genomic sequence. Nucleic Acids Res. 25, 955–964.

Lund, S.H., Gudbjartsson, D.F., Rafnar, T., *et al.*, 2014. A method for detecting long non-coding RNAs with tiled RNA expression microarrays. PLOS ONE 9, e99899. doi:10.1371/journal.pone.0099899.

Luo, L., Li, D., Zhang, W., *et al.*, 2016. Accurate prediction of transposon-derived piRNAs by integrating various sequential and physicochemical features. PLOS ONE 11. doi:10.1371/journal.pone.0153268.

MacFarlane, L.-A., Murphy, P.R., 2010. MicroRNA: Biogenesis, function and role in cancer. Curr. Genom. 11, 537–561. doi:10.2174/138920210793175895.

Machnicka, M.A., Dunin-Horkawicz, S., de Crécy-Lagard, V., Bujnicki, J.M., 2016. tRNAmodpred: A computational method for predicting posttranscriptional modifications in tRNAs. Methods 107, 34–41.

Mahmoudi, E., Cairns, M.J., 2016. MiR-137: An important player in neural development and neoplastic transformation. Mol. Psychiatry 22, 44–55. doi:10.1038/mp.2016.150.

Ma, L., Bajic, V.B., Zhang, Z., 2013. On the classification of long non-coding RNAs. RNA Biol. 10, 924–933. doi:10.4161/rna.24604.

Maniatis, T., Reed, R., 1987. The role of small nuclear ribonucleoprotein particles in pre-mRNA splicing. Nature 325, 673–678. doi:10.1038/325673a0.

Mathews, D.H., Disney, M.D., Childs, J.L., *et al.*, 2004. Incorporating chemical modification constraints into a dynamic programming algorithm for prediction of RNA secondary structure. Proceedings of the National Academy of Sciences of the United States of America 101 (19), 7287–7292.

Mattick, J.S., Makunin, I.V., 2006. Non-coding RNA. Hum. Mol. Genet. 15, R17–R29.

Millevoi, S., Vagner, S., 2009. Molecular mechanisms of eukaryotic pre-mRNA 3′ end processing regulation. Nucleic Acids Res. 38, 2757–2774. doi:10.1093/nar/gkp1176.

Moazed, D., 2009. Small RNAs in transcriptional gene silencing and genome defence. Nature 457, 413–420. doi:10.1038/nature07756.

Morris, K.V., 2012. Non-Coding RNAs and Epigenetic Regulation of Gene Expression: Drivers of Natural Selection. Norfolk, UK: Caister Academic Press.

Nakatani, J., Tamada, K., Hatanaka, F., *et al.*, 2009. Abnormal behavior in a chromosome- engineered mouse model for human 15q11-13 duplication seen in autism. Cell 137, 1235–1246. doi:10.1016/j.cell.2009.04.024.

Nam, J.-W., Kim, J., Kim, S.-K., Zhang, B.-T., 2006. ProMiR II: A web server for the probabilistic prediction of clustered, nonclustered, conserved and nonconserved microRNAs. Nucleic Acids Res. 34, W455–W458. doi:10.1093/nar/gkl321.

Nam, J.-W., Shin, K.-R., Han, J., *et al.*, 2005. Human microRNA prediction through a probabilistic co-learning model of sequence and structure. Nucleic Acids Res. 33, 3570–3581. doi:10.1093/nar/gki668.

Nawrocki, E.P., Kolbe, D.L., Eddy, S.R., 2009. Infernal 1.0: Inference of RNA alignments. Bioinformatics 25, 1335–1337.

Neguembor, M.V., Jothi, M., Gabellini, D., 2014. Long noncoding RNAs, emerging players in muscle differentiation and disease. Skeletal Muscle 4 (1), 8.

Ng, K.W., Anderson, C., Marshall, E.A., *et al.*, 2016. Piwi-interacting RNAs in cancer: Emerging functions and clinical utility. Mol. Cancer 15.doi:10.1186/s12943-016-0491-9.

Nie, M., Deng, Z.-L., Liu, J., *et al.*, 2015. Noncoding RNAs, emerging regulators of skeletal muscle development and diseases. BioMed Res. Int. 2015, e676575. doi:10.1155/2015/676575.

Orom, U.A., Derrien, T., Beringer, M., *et al.*, 2010. Long noncoding RNAs with enhancer-like function in human cells. Cell 143 (1), 46–58.

Palazzo, A.F., Lee, E.S., 2015. Non-coding RNA: What is functional and what is junk? Front. Genet. 5, 1–11. doi:10.3389/fgene.2015.00002.

Bhattacharya, D.P., Canzler, S., Kehr, S., *et al.*, 2016. Phylogenetic distribution of plant snoRNA families. BMC Genomics 17, 969. doi:10.1186/s12864-016-3301-2.

Pauli, A., Valen, E., Lin, M.F., *et al.*, 2012. Systematic identification of long noncoding RNAs expressed during zebrafish embryogenesis. Genome Res. 22, 577–591.

Peng, X., Sun, K., Zhou, J., Sun, H., Wang, H., 2017. Bioinformatics for novel long intergenic noncoding RNA (lincRNA) identification in skeletal muscle cells. In: Proceedings of the Muscle Stem Cells, Methods in Molecular Biology, pp.355–362. New York, NY: Humana Press.

Peschansky, V.J., Wahlestedt, C., 2014. Non-coding RNAs as direct and indirect modulators of epigenetic regulation. Epigenetics 9, 3–12. doi:10.4161/epi.27473.

Ponjavic, J., Ponting, C.P., Lunter, G., 2007. Functionality or transcriptional noise? Evidence for selection within long noncoding RNAs. Genome Research 17 (5), 556–565.

Ponting, C.P., Oliver, P.L., Reik, W., 2009. Evolution and functions of long noncoding RNAs. Cell 136, 629–641.

Salamov, A., Solovyev, V., 1998. Fgenesh multiple gene prediction program.

Santosh, B., Varshney, A., Yadava, P.K., 2015. Non-coding RNAs: Biological functions and applications. Cell Biochem. Funct. 33, 14–22. doi:10.1002/cbf.3079.

Sarkar, F.H., Li, Y., Wang, Z., Kong, D., Ali, S., 2010. Implication of microRNAs in drug resistance for designing novel cancer therapy. Drug Resist. Update 13, 57–66. doi:10.1016/j.drup.2010.02.001.

Schattner, P., Brooks, A.N., Lowe, T.M., 2005. The tRNAscan-SE, snoscan and snoGPS web servers for the detection of tRNAs and snoRNAs. Nucleic Acids Research 33 (suppl_2), W686–W689.

Sharp, S.J., Schaack, J., Cooley, L., Burke, D.J., Söll, D., 1985. Structure and transcription of eukaryotic tRNA genes. CRC Crit. Rev. Biochem. 19, 107–144. doi:10.3109/10409238509082541.

Shen, J., Ambrosone, C.B., Zhao, H., 2009. Novel genetic variants in microRNA genes and familial breast cancer. Int. J. Cancer 124, 1178–1182. doi:10.1002/ijc.24008.

Skryabin, B.V., Gubar, L.V., Seeger, B., *et al.*, 2007. Deletion of the MBII-85 snoRNA gene cluster in mice results in postnatal growth retardation. PLOS Genet. 3, 2529–2539. doi:10.1371/journal.pgen.0030235.

Storz, G., 2002. An expanding universe of noncoding RNAs. Science 296, 1260–1263. doi:10.1126/science.1072249.

Storz, G., Opdyke, J.A., Zhang, A., 2004. Controlling mRNA stability and translation with small, noncoding RNAs. Curr. Opin. Microbiol. 7, 140–144. doi:10.1016/j.mib.2004.02.015.

Sun, L., Luo, H., Bu, D., *et al.*, 2013. Utilizing sequence intrinsic composition to classify protein-coding and long non-coding transcripts. Nucleic Acids Res. 41, e166. doi:10.1093/nar/gkt646.

Terai, G., Komori, T., Asai, K., Kin, T., 2007. miRRim: A novel system to find conserved miRNAs with high sensitivity and specificity. RNA N.Y.N 13, 2081–2090. doi:10.1261/rna.655107.

Tomkins, G.M., Gelehrter, T.D., Granner, D., et al., 1969. Control of specific gene expression in higher organisms. Science 166, 1474–1480.

Trapnell, C., Williams, B.A., Pertea, G., et al., 2010. Transcript assembly and quantification by RNA-Seq reveals unannotated transcripts and isoform switching during cell differentiation. Nat. Biotechnol. 28, 511–515. doi:10.1038/nbt.1621.

Tupy, J.L., Bailey, A.M., Dailey, G., et al., 2005. Identification of putative noncoding polyadenylated transcripts in Drosophila melanogaster. Proc. Natl. Acad. Sci. USA 102, 5495–5500.

Ulitsky, I., 2016. Evolution to the rescue: Using comparative genomics to understand long non-coding RNAs. Nat. Rev. Genet. 17, 601–614. doi:10.1038/nrg.2016.85.

Wang, C., Wei, L., Guo, M., Zou, Q., 2013a. Computational approaches in detecting non- coding RNA. Curr. Genom. 14, 371–377. doi:10.2174/13892029113149990005.

Wang, K., Liang, C., Liu, J., et al., 2014. Prediction of piRNAs using transposon interaction and a support vector machine. BMC Bioinform. 15, 419. doi:10.1186/s12859-014-0419-6.

Wang, L., Park, H.J., Dasari, S., et al., 2013b. CPAT: Coding-Potential Assessment Tool using an alignment-free logistic regression model. Nucleic Acids Res. 41, e74. doi:10.1093/nar/gkt006.

Washietl, S., Hofacker, I.L., Stadler, P.F., 2005. Fast and reliable prediction of noncoding RNAs. Proc. Natl. Acad. Sci. USA 102, 2454–2459. doi:10.1073/pnas.0409169102.

Washietl, S., Pedersen, J.S., Korbel, J.O., et al., 2007. Structured RNAs in the ENCODE selected regions of the human genome. Genome Res. 17, 852–864. doi:10.1101/gr.5650707.

Westhof, E., Auffinger, P., 2001. Transfer RNA Structure. eLS. 1–11. doi:10.1002/9780470015902.a0000527.pub2.

Wucher, V., Legeai, F., Hédan, B., et al., 2017. FEELnc: A tool for long non-coding RNA annotation and its application to the dog transcriptome. Nucleic Acids Res. 45, e57. doi:10.1093/nar/gkw1306. e57.

Xia, W., Zhou, J., Luo, H., et al., 2017. MicroRNA-32 promotes cell proliferation, migration and suppresses apoptosis in breast cancer cells by targeting FBXW7. Cancer Cell Int. 17.doi:10.1186/s12935-017-0383-0.

Xu, Y., Mural, R.J., Einstein, J.R., Shah, M.B., Uberbacher, E.C., 1996. GRAIL: A multi-agent neural network system for gene identification. Proc. IEEE 84, 1544–1552.

Yang, J.H., Zhang, X.C., Huang, Z.P., et al., 2006. snoSeeker: An advanced computational package for screening of guide and orphan snoRNA genes in the human genome. Nucleic Acids Res. 34, 5112–5123. doi:10.1093/nar/gkl672.

Yazaki, J., Gregory, B.D., Ecker, J.R., 2007. Mapping the genome landscape using tiling array technology. Curr. Opin. Plant Biol. 10, 534–542. doi:10.1016/j.pbi.2007.07.006.

Zhang, B., Wang, Q., Pan, X., 2007. MicroRNAs and their regulatory roles in animals and plants. J. Cell. Physiol. 210, 279–289.

Zhang, Y., Wang, X., Kang, L., 2011. A k-mer scheme to predict piRNAs and characterize locust piRNAs. Bioinform. Oxf. Engl. 27, 771–776. doi:10.1093/bioinformatics/btr016.

Zuker, M., 2003. Mfold web server for nucleic acid folding and hybridization prediction. Nucleic Acids Res. 31, 3406–3415.

Zuo, L., Wang, Z., Tan, Y., Chen, X., Luo, X., 2016. piRNAs and their functions in the brain. Int. J. Hum. Genet. 16, 53–60.

Vaccine Target Discovery

Li C Chong, Universiti Putra Malaysia, Serdang, Malaysia
Asif M Khan, Perdana University, Selangor, Malaysia and John Hopkins University, Baltimore, MD, United States

Introduction

Vaccination is one of the most efficacious medical interventions that have decreased human morbidity and mortality in all regions of the world. It not only has dramatically reduced the incidence of numerous diseases (Hilleman, 1985; Andre et al., 2008), such as measles, diphteria, mumps, rubella, tetanus, yellow fever, pertussis, and poliomyelitis, but also eradicated the dreaded smallpox viral infection (Strassburg, 1980). Efforts are currently also focused on developing vaccines for treatment of other diseases (Ada, 2003). This triumph over infectious diseases has been achieved by using either killed or attenuated conventional vaccines. A conventional or prophylactic vaccination is based on deliberate exposure to non-virulent form of the pathogen to establish immunity from subsequent exposure to the virulent form of the pathogen (Lee et al., 2012). This approach requires little knowledge of the molecular nature of the individual pathogen antigens or the immune responses they elicit. To date, this approach has undoubtedly been the most successful.

There is, however, an ongoing trend towards emerging infectious diseases (Fauci, 2001; Fauci et al., 2005) against humankind in different parts of the world. These diseases are caused by the emergence of new pathogens, resurgence of old ones, constantly mutating pathogens, drug-resistant pathogens, and even include pathogens used as agents of bioterrorism. Previously undescribed pathogens, such as severe acute respiratory syndrome (SARS), bird flu (avian influenza), mad cow, and HIV/AIDS, are appearing at an increasing frequency. On the other hand, old diseases such as ebola, hanta, dengue and cholera, among others, are invading populations from which they have disappeared or cross species barrier to invade new species. Occasionally, pathogens mutate (or recombine) and then they adapt and show up as new variants that evade the host's acquired immunity. The annual influenza epidemics are generally due to genetically drifting strains of influenza that differ slightly from previous strains (Bouvier and Palese, 2008). The development of drug-resistance pathogens, such as malaria, pneumococci, enterococci, and tuberculosis, has increased over the years, partly due to the widespread and inappropriate use of drugs (Knobler et al., 2003). Moreover, the pathogens responsible for the emerging infectious diseases are also of potential use as bioterrorist weapon (Ryan, 2008). For these reasons, emerging infectious diseases continue to pose threats to public health (Morens and Fauci, 2013). Therefore, there is a need for more effective vaccines to help reduce human morbidity and mortality from emerging infectious diseases.

The last decade has seen significant advances in new technologies for the development of new vaccines. These technologies, combined with our understanding of host response to foreign antigens, have laid the foundation for rapid advances in vaccinology. Few potential candidate approaches for this new family of vaccines (Arnon and Ben-yedidia, 2003; Minichiello, 2002; Babiuk, 1999; Nandy and Basak, 2016) are subunit vaccines, genetically engineered live vaccines, and polynucleotide (DNA or genetic) vaccines. All these new directions in vaccine development have something in common; their most important challenge is the discovery of key antigens from the array of proteins encoded by the pathogen genome that are able to elicit protective immune response against these pathogens and are effective for majority of the human population. The presence of genetic variation in the genes of the host immune system across the human population and the genomes of the pathogen variants make this a multi-dimensional and a combinatorial problem.

Since 1980s, the focus of vaccine design has been on the pathogen's variable domains, mutants, multivalent coverage and not so much on conserved regions (Plotkin, 2005). However, a large body of data is building up in the field of vaccine design and epitope prediction that points to the neglected aspect of conserved epitopes as important targets of vaccine development. In fact, evidence is accumulating that while many variable regions are highly antigenic, sufficiently large number of them are actually non-immunoprotective and have been exploited by viruses and other pathogens for immune escape and may lead to immuno-pathology (Haydon and Woolhouse, 1998). Conserved epitopes were thought to be un-important due to their lack of immuno-genicity (Bona et al., 1998; Li et al., 2011). However, the immunogenicity of such conserved epitopes especially those which are immune-protective and conserved amongst many variants and mutant strains, can be boosted using adjuvants, which are chemicals or approved drug molecules. Moreover, conserved epitopes also help address the issues of ethnicity ("pan-haplotype responsive") compared to variable epitopes (Khan et al., 2008). In addition, the conserved epitopes can circumvent vaccine design issues of escape mutants and the need of using the latest strains. In particular, if a set of conserved, immunogenic, and immunoprotective epitopes are suitably boosted, they will not elicit mutations in the pathogen, and thus can be reasonably predicted to remain unchanged in the next season of infection. The possibility of extended efficacy of vaccines would be a tremendous advance for the vaccine industry and will potentially serve the global population with protection against infections (Sylvester-Hvid et al., 2002; De Groot et al., 2004; Sette et al., 2001; Raman et al., 2014; Khan et al., 2017).

Vaccine informatics, a fledgling sub-field of reverse vaccinology, has the potential to develop effective vaccines (Hegde et al., 2017; Khan et al., 2017). With the rapid expansion of vaccine related data (host and pathogen) stemming from both classical and high-throughput genomic/proteomic approaches, identifying conserved, robust, immunogenic, and immunoprotective epitopes manually from this large data pool is inefficient. Vaccine informatics is a practical science for designing new vaccines with a focus on bioinformatics-driven acquisition, manipulation and analysis of data related to the immune system and disease agents (Raman et al., 2014). It provides a means for systematic study of big data, pre-screening of targets, and facilitates experimental design for validation by a small number of key experiments. The bioinformatics support can be divided into two, the standard bioinformatics support and the more specialised immunoinformatics support (Petrovsky et al., 2003). The standard support includes basic bioinformatics functions, such as sequence comparison and alignment, database searching, hunting for patterns and profiles, 3D-structure analysis and modeling, and data annotation (reviewed in Brusic and Petrovsky (2003)). Immunoinformatics is a more targeted bioinformatics support with an emphasis on data-warehousing and mining of immunological data, such as prediction of immunogenicity (Soria-Guerra et al., 2015; Brusic and Petrovsky, 2003). Vaccine researchers are taking advantage of these bioinformatics approaches, in combination with experimental validation, to discover and facilitate better understanding of the components of the human immunome, which then aid in the design of new vaccines. The immunome can be defined as the complete set of genes and proteins of the immune system. Highly accurate target predictions can diminish discovery cost by 10–20 folds (De Groot et al., 2002; Kast et al., 1994).

Background

In the human and higher vertebrate host, the major functions of the immune system are the maintenance of homeostasis, surveillance and tolerance to self-structures, and defence followed by immunity against pathogens (Yatim and Lakkis, 2015). The immune system is widely distributed in the body and comprises of immune organs, tissues, and cells, connected as a complex, but tightly regulated network (Jerne, 1993; NIH, 2003; Nicholson, 2016). In general, the processes that take place at the molecular level and cellular level largely initiate and regulate the function of the immune system. A healthy immune system will discriminate 'non-self' or foreign antigenic proteins from those that are normally present ('self') in an organism and will raise appropriate responses. The number of self-structures is large, but finite; the number of non-self structures is practically infinite. In the cell, both self and non-self proteins are digested by the proteasomes into short peptide fragments, which are then bound by major histocompatibility complex (MHC) molecules to form peptide/MHC complexes and are displayed on the surface of host cells (Vigneron and Van den Eynde, 2014). These peptides are recognition labels, which display the contents of host cells to T cells of the immune system. The presence of non-self peptides is a prerequisite for the initiation of immune responses. Peptides produced by degradation of intracellular proteins bind MHC class I molecules and are recognised by CD8$^+$ T cell receptor (Shastri et al., 2002; Chowell et al., 2015; Blum et al., 2013). MHC class II molecules present peptides, produced by degradation of proteins of extracellular origin, on the surface of antigen-presenting cells to CD4$^+$ T cells (reviewed in Lennon-Duménil et al. (2002)). A major function of CD8$^+$ T cells is to recognize and destroy cells infected by pathogens (Nicholson, 2016). Peptides displayed by the MHC class II molecules mainly serve to regulate immune responses; they are crucial for the initiation, enhancement and suppression of immune responses.

Driven by methods of molecular and cell biology, significant advances in the understanding of immunological processes have been made during the last two decades. This progress over the years resulted in the continuous accumulation of huge amount of immunological data obtained experimentally. This growing number of immunological data and the high complexity of the functional and structural foundation of the immune processes created a need for improved data management to enable advance data analysis. The need to manage and analyse this growing amount of complex data has led to the development of a number of immunological databases (Brusic et al., 2000), such as SYFPEITHI and MCHPEP, IMGT and FIMM, and complex computational models (Petrovsky and Brusic, 2002). The purpose of immunological databases is to facilitate the collection of, access to, and use of immunologically relevant data. One of the applications of the databases in immunology is for vaccine research and development by using complex computational models in combination with experimental approaches to help precise our understanding of antigen presentation and recognition by the immune system.

The combined effort between experimental and computational immunology provided us with a new perspective to designing vaccines that will be effective across demographic boundaries. Previously, the extreme degree of polymorphism observed in the MHC posed limitations for the development of such a vaccine because the ability to trigger an effective T-cell response is partly determined by the MHC phenotype of the individual and different individuals have different MHC allele (Macdonald et al., 2001; Marrack et al., 2017). The MHC genes are the most polymorphic of all human genes, with more than 10,000 alleles known (as of Feb 2018), and are important in increasing the range of responses that different individuals can mount. In humans, this polymorphism results from concentrated amino acid substitutions in the peptide-binding groove of human leukocyte antigen (HLA, the human MHC system) molecules that produce variability in peptide binding and presentation to T cells (MacDonald et al., 2000). Over the years, few groups have investigated the possibility of a functional classification of HLA polymorphism based on peptide-binding specificities. It was found that majority of HLA alleles (both class I and II) could be grouped into 18 or more different 'supertypes', purely on the basis of similarities in their peptide binding specificity (Lund et al., 2004). It has been suggested that the majority of all major human populations can be covered by only few HLA supertypes, where the different members of each supertype bind similar peptides ('promiscuous peptides') for presentation to T-cell (Sette et al., 1999). Further, latest developments show evidence for presence of "immunological hot-spots" (Srinivasan et al., 2004) in antigens. Immunological hot-spots are defined as antigenic regions possessing multiple promiscuous peptides that are supertype specific. This area of research raises the prospect of identifying key pathogenic antigens that possess immunological hot-spots as best candidates for vaccine design as it will provide protection at the population level, irrespective of ethnicity.

The humoral response involves antibodies produced by B-cells, which recognize both linear and conformational B-cell epitopes on the surface of the pathogen. Conformational neutralizing epitopes are the primary focus of various vaccine research for protective humoral responses. However, unlike linear B-cell epitopes and T-cell epitopes, reliable computational tools for prediction of conformational epitopes are limited (Kulkarni-Kale *et al.*, 2005; Zhang *et al.*, 2011).

As for the pathogens, the last decade witnessed the rapid expansion of sequence data at our disposal, stemming from both genomic and proteomic approaches, enabling analysis to map key antigens that are potential targets for protective immune responses. The genomic sequences of a large number of pathogens that threaten public health have been completed or are impending completion. For example, the whole genome of over 7,475 viruses have been sequenced and deposited in the major public database Entrez Genome (see "Relevant Website section"). The data derived from the genome/proteome sequencing and related projects for a particular species of pathogen, such as West Nile Virus, is the missing gap towards the development of vaccines effective against the majority of the variants currently known within that pathogenic species and probably against novel ones that are yet to emerge (Koo *et al.*, 2009). Such vaccines will be much superior to the current generation of vaccines, which are solely based on a single or few antigens providing protection only against certain variants of a pathogen and therefore might elicit too narrow a breadth of response to provide protection from the remaining diverse variants of the same pathogen species (Doolan, 2003).

We have made significant progress in understanding the processes in the host that are involved in mounting an immune response. However, we are still far from having a good understanding of the natural complexity of the pathogens. A good starting point would be by utilizing the pathogens genomic/proteomic data to study their sequence diversity, and identify antigens containing conserved and variable immunological hot-spots. To fully realize the promise of the available datasets for such study, we would require the development of appropriate technologies for systematically converting genomic/proteomic data into protective vaccines. Recently, systematic genome-wide approach to identify the key antigens of a pathogenic species from the numerous variant sequences of the same pathogen have been reported (Dhanda *et al.*, 2017; Rizwan *et al.*, 2017; Goodswen *et al.*, 2014; Vivona *et al.*, 2006; Del Tordello *et al.*, 2016; Maria *et al.*, 2017; Doolan, 2003; Raman *et al.*, 2014; Koo *et al.*, 2009; Khan *et al.*, 2017). The selected key antigens will represent the minimal representative sets of target sequences required to provide immunity against the majority of the existing variants of a particular pathogen species.

Bioinformatics is an inter-disciplinary field that is essential for the analysis and interpretation of complex and large quantity of biological data generated by functional studies and high throughput technologies. It is used to propose the next sets of experiments and, most importantly, to derive better understanding of biological processes. As stated, the number of pathogen sequence data in public databases is increasing rapidly, however, experimental approaches to study this large data pool for the development of immune interventions are time-consuming, costly and almost impractical. Through combination of bioinformatics and experimental approaches, it is possible to select key experiments and help optimize experimental design. Computer algorithms are increasingly used to speed-up the process of knowledge discovery by helping to identify critical experiments for testing hypothesis built upon the result of computational screening. A number of successful examples for application of computer models to study immunological problems have been described in Brusic *et al.* (2005). Such examples illustrate the power of computational approach to complex problems involving potentially vast datasets with potential biases, errors and discrepancies.

A Computational Framework for Vaccine Target Discovery

Reverse vaccinology, a bottom-up genomic approach, has been successfully applied to the development of vaccines against pathogens that were previously not suited to such development (Vernikos, 2008; Rappuoli and Covacci, 2003; Rappuoli, 2001; Del Tordello *et al.*, 2016). The pre-requisite for this approach is the sequence data of the target pathogen, which acts as input to various bioinformatics algorithms for prediction of putative antigens that are likely to be successful vaccine targets. These candidates can then be validated by a small number of key experiments in the lab. The approach has been successfully applied to the development of universal vaccines against group B Streptococcus (Maione *et al.*, 2005) and vaccine candidates against MenB (Pizza *et al.*, 2000), among others (Rappuoli and Covacci, 2003). Reverse vaccinology is a promising method for the high-throughput discovery of candidate vaccine targets that have the potential to mirror the dynamics and antigenic diversity of the target pathogen population, which includes the diversity of the interacting partner, the immune system. However, a big challenge to this end is the need to understand how vaccine developers can cover antigenic diversity and develop a systematic approach to rationally screen pathogen data to select candidate vaccine targets that cover the diversity.

Over the years, a number of bioinformatics pipelines have been designed that predict vaccine candidates both rapidly and efficiently. VacSol (Rizwan *et al.*, 2017), NERVE (Vivona *et al.*, 2006), and Vacceed (Goodswen *et al.*, 2014) are examples of such pipelines for proteomes of bacterial or eukaryotic pathogens and these pipelines are highly configurable and scalable (Zaharieva *et al.*, 2017). They include multiple steps and integrate various algorithms for analysis and comparison. Shortlisted candidate vaccine targets are ranked for prioritization towards experimental validation. These pipelines are expected to improve the vaccine target discovery process.

The general characteristics desired for a candidate vaccine target are (i) highly conserved; (ii) pathogen-specific; (iii) important for structure/function; (iv) immune-relevant; and (v) antigenically similar to circulating strains. Highly conserved targets are less likely to mutate and escape immune recognition. This is particularly so if they are important for structure and function, suggesting a robust historical conservation. High conservation also reduces the possibility of altered-peptide ligand (APL) effect from variant epitopes of the same pathogen species (Sloan-Lancaster and Allen, 1996; Evavold *et al.*, 1993; Rothman, 2004). Variants may also originate from other pathogens, in particular those that co-circulate or co-infect with the pathogen of interest and if they belong to the same family. In vaccine design, epitopes common to other pathogens could either be useful by inducing cross-protection, or detrimental by inducing altered-ligand effect. Thus, potential vaccine targets should be analyzed for specificity to the target pathogen. The definition of virus species-specific vaccine targets can be further expanded to exclude those with one amino acid mismatch to human sequences in order to avoid possibility of molecular mimicry. Antigenic mismatch between a vaccine and circulating strains has been shown to increases the risk of disease outbreak by 1000-fold compared to immunization using identical strains (Park et al., 2004). Thus, it is important to assess the extent of antigenic identity between the candidate vaccine targets and the circulating strains.

Typically, a generic semi-automated computational framework comprises of three key components: data collection, data processing, and data analysis (Khan, 2005, 2009; Khan et al., 2006, 2017). **Fig. 1** illustrates the workflow of the framework and **Fig. 2** provides a non-comprehensive list of commonly used tools. Data collection would involve the user providing a set of sequences (aligned or unaligned) of the pathogen of interest for analysis. The sequences could be a single protein dataset, multiple or the complete proteome. Additionally, comparative analyses of the sequences can be performed between subtypes/groups of the pathogen. The sequences can be retrieved from public repositories, primary or specialist databases, such as the NCBI Entrez Protein database (NCBI Resource Coordinators, 2017) or Influenza Research Database (IRD) (Zhang et al., 2017), respectively. User can also provide sequences derived from their experimental work, not available in public databases. Typically, downloaded data would comprise full-length or partial sequences, and the corresponding metadata. Data processing would involve removal of duplicate sequences from the dataset, and for comparative analysis, the merging of the input sequences will be required prior to the alignment step. Multiple sequence alignment will be carried out using an existing tool that is robust in dealing with large sequence data, such as (Sievers et al., 2011; Katoh et al., 2017; Edgar, 2004; Do et al., 2005) Clustal Omega, MAFFT, MUSCLE or PROBCONS. The output alignment quality will be manually inspected for any errors and/or misalignments, which are common when dealing with partial sequences. Henceforth, the data would be ready for analyses, which can involve performing a diversity analysis, such as by measuring entropy values (Heiny et al., 2007; Hu et al., 2013; Khan et al., 2008; Koo et al., 2009) and quantifying variant motifs for each, user-defined, k-mer positions in the alignment. The results of these analyses will be plotted as an output for the user, providing a holistic view of the diversity, including variant distribution. The user can define a preferred conservation threshold for selection of highly conserved sequences. These selected sequences are then analyzed for distribution of variants in nature (Khan et al., 2008; Koo et al., 2009), including matches to human proteins, enabling the identification of pathogen specific, highly conserved sequences. The robust nature of the historical conservation can be assessed by performing functional and structural analysis (Sprenger et al., 2008; Hung and Link, 2011; Wizemann et al., 1999; Sachdeva et al., 2005; Monterrubio-López et al., 2015; He, 2014; Tang et al., 2014; Maria et al., 2017). The relevance of the identified potential candidate vaccine targets for use against current circulating strains can be assessed by measuring the incidence of the candidate targets in the corresponding sequences of recent strains of the virus of interest (Khan et al., 2017). The antigenicity/immunogenicity of the candidate sequences are predicted to assess their immune relevance. Experimental validation includes matching the predicted epitopes with reported epitopes in public databases, such as the Immune Epitope Database (IEBD) or SYFPEITHI, or performing quantitative measurements of the pre-selected candidate peptides by generating synthetic constructs and testing for their immunogenicity, such as by use of HLA transgenic animal models that express specific HLA alleles (Rosloniec et al., 1997; Lefranc et al., 2009; Gourlay et al., 2017; Khan, 2005).

Immunoinformatics

Bioinformatics tools can facilitate the process of epitope mapping by identifying peptides that can potentially elicit T-cell responses. Binding of epitopes to HLA antigens is highly allele-specific; core peptide-binding motifs (usually between 8- and 11-mers, most often 9-mers) have been defined experimentally for a number of HLA class I and class II alleles and incorporated into computational algorithms, allowing to predict candidate HLA-binding epitopes in silico from protein sequences (Parker et al., 1994; Rammensee et al., 1999; Sturniolo et al., 1999; Zhang et al., 2005; Nielsen et al., 2010; Karosiene et al., 2013; Paul et al., 2013, 2015a,b; Andreatta et al., 2015; Andreatta and Nielsen, 2015; Pro et al., 2015; Trolle et al., 2015; Abelin et al., 2017; Jurtz et al., 2017; Fleri et al., 2017). More recently, quantifiable predictive features of TCR$\alpha\beta$ binding to HLA/epitope complexes have been also described (Birnbaum et al., 2014; Dash et al., 2017; Glanville et al., 2017; Gee et al., 2017).

Two main categories of specialized immunoinformatics tools are available for prediction of MHC binding peptides – methods based on identifying patterns in sequences of binding peptides, and those that employ three-dimensional (3D) structures to model peptide/MHC interactions (Tong et al., 2007; Liljeroos et al., 2015; Gourlay et al., 2017). Pattern-based methods includes binding motifs, quantitative matrices, decision trees, artificial neural networks (ANNs), hidden Markov models (HMMs) and support vector machines (SVMs), among others. In contrast, the structure based methods are theoretically rooted and include homology modeling, docking and 3D threading techniques (Dominguez et al., 2003; De Vries et al., 2010; Agostino et al., 2016; Khan and Ranganathan, 2010; Liljeroos et al., 2015; Gourlay et al., 2017). Although less accurate, pattern based approaches are over-represented in the literature due to higher complexity in development and longer computational time of the more accurate structure-based approaches (Ranganathan and Tong, 2007; Maria et al., 2017), including the sheer difference in the availability of linear versus structural data.

For a given sequence, typically all possible overlapping 9-mer (and later, 8- to 11- mer) peptide sequences are extracted. Epitope prediction for HLA class I and class II alleles are performed using benchmarked prediction models, including, for HLA

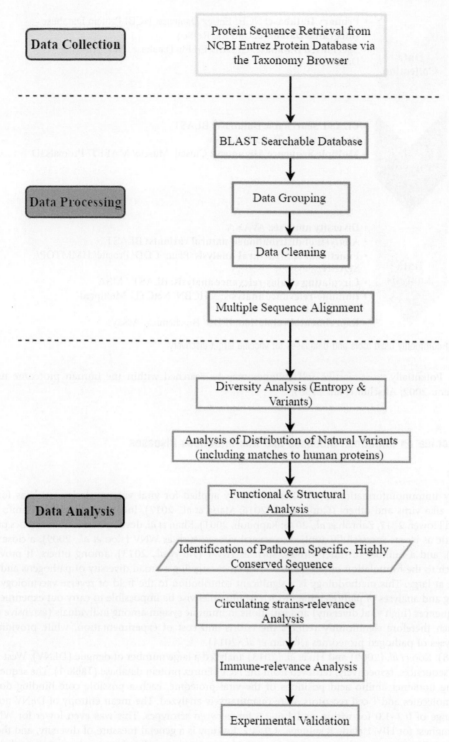

Fig. 1 Computational framework for vaccine target discovery.

class I epitopes, the artificial neural network (ANN)-trained NetMHCpan (version 4.0) (Andreatta et al., 2015; Trolle et al., 2015; Jurtz et al., 2017), and for HLA class II epitopes, NetMHCIIpan (Karosiene et al., 2013; Andreatta and Nielsen, 2015), and the allele-specific consensus percentile ranks of all algorithms queried by the Immune Epitope Database and Analysis Resource (IEDB) tools (combination of NN-align, SMM-align, and CombLib/Sturniolo) (Paul et al., 2015a,b). Additionally, proteasome cleavage (Hakenberg et al., 2003; Nussbaum et al., 2001; Nielsen et al., 2005) and TAP binding predictions (Zhang et al., 2006; Bhasin et al., 2007; Bhasin and Raghava, 2004) will be performed for priority ranking. Several tools, such as NetCTL (Larsen et al., 2005), integrate these various predictions into one and predict for HLA supertypes, which are groups of HLA alleles with similar peptide

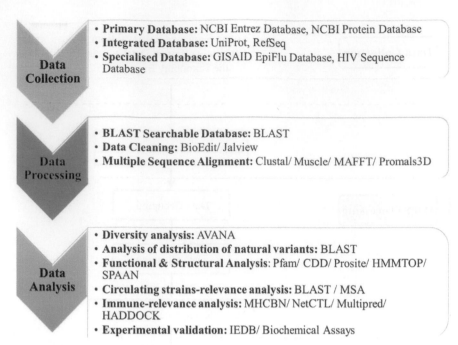

Fig. 2 An example of commonly used tools and databases for vaccine target discovery.

binding specificity. Potentially cross-reactive self epitopes may be searched within the human proteome using BLAST/BLAT alignment tools (Kent, 2002; Altschul *et al.*, 1990).

Case Studies: Vaccine on Infectious Diseases and Non-Infectious Diseases

Infectious Diseases

Reverse vaccinology immunoinformatics approaches are widely applied for viral vaccine design, such as for influenza virus, chikungunya virus, zika virus and others (Gupta *et al.*, 2016; María *et al.*, 2017), including parasites (Damfo *et al.*, 2017) and bacteria (Mistry and Flower, 2017; Zahroh *et al.*, 2016; Rappuoli, 2001). Khan *et al.* developed a bioinformatics pipeline for DENV, which proved generic as it was successfully applied to several viruses, such as WNV (Koo *et al.*, 2009), a close relative of DENV (Khan *et al.*, 2008), and a number of other viruses, such as HIV-1 (Hu *et al.*, 2013), among others. It provides a novel and generalized approach to the formulation of peptide-based vaccines targeting a broad diversity of pathogens and applicable to the human population at large. This methodology is a significant contribution to the field of reverse vaccinology as it enables the systematic screening and analyses of pathogen data which would otherwise be impossible to carry out experimentally, due to too many pathogen sequences (high viral diversity) and variations in immune system among individuals (extensive polymorphism of HLA). This approach therefore significantly reduces the efforts and cost of experimentation, while providing for systematic screening and analyses of pathogen proteomes (Raman *et al.*, 2014).

Khan *et al.* (2008), Koo *et al.* (2009) and Hu *et al.* (2013) analyzed a large number of dengue (DENV), West Nile virus (WNV) and clade B HIV-1, sequences, respectively, retrieved from the NCBI Entrez protein database (**Table 1**). The sequences were aligned and the overlapping nonamer amino acid positions of the viral proteome, each a possible core binding domain for human leukocyte antigen molecules and T-cell receptors, were quantitatively analyzed. The mean entropy of DENV nonamer sequences was low, with a range of 0.2–1.0 for within and 1.6–2.6 for between serotypes. This was even lower for WNV, ranging from 0.2– 0.5, with the highest for HIV-1 clade B subtype, 1.9–4.2. Entropy is a general measure of diversity, and the data provided a holistic overview viral diversity across the proteome. Accordingly, the incidence of variants to the most prevalent, index sequence at the aligned nonamer positions was the lowest for WNV (intra: $\leq 10\%$) and the highest for HIV-1 clade B (intra: ~80%–99%); the variants incidence within each DENV serotype was comparable to WNV, but between serotypes (~60%–80%) was closer to HIV-1 clade B subtype. Forty-four (44) sequences (pan-DENV sequences) identical in 80% or more of all recorded DENV sequences represented 15% of the DENV polyprotein length. The proportion (34%) was much higher for WNV and at complete conservation (100% incidence). Notably, at similar incidence level ($> =80\%$ incidence) to DENV, although pan-clade, ~35% of the intra HIV-1 clade B proteome was highly conserved. The proportion of these conserved sequences that were immune-relevant showed an inverse relationship: DENV (59% matched 9aa or more of 45 class I and II reported epitopes), WNV (50% matched 9aa or more of 57 class I and II reported epitopes), and HIV-1 clade B (37% matched 9aa or more of 73 class I and II reported epitopes). Khan *et al.* (2008) highlighted that conservation analysis should go beyond the species of interest, extending to all those

Table 1 Key summary results of vaccine target discovery study on Dengue virus (DENV), West Nile virus (WNV) and clade B HIV-1.

Category	DENV (Khan et al., 2008)	WNV (Koo et al., 2009)	HIV-1 clade B (Hu et al., 2013)
Mean nonamer entropy	Intra: 0.2–1.0 Inter: 1.6–2.6	Intra: 0.23–0.51	Intra: 1.9–4.2
General variants incidence trend % of the proteome covered by conserved sequences	Inter: ~60%–80% Pan-clade: 15% (> =80% incidence)	Intra: <10% Intra: 34% (=100 % incidence)	Intra: ~80%–99% Intra: 35% (> =80% incidence)
Immune relevance	(26/44) 59% matched 9aa or more of 45 class I and II reported epitopes	(44/88) 50% matched 9aa or more of 57 class I and II reported epitopes	(29/78) 37% matched 9aa or more of 73 class I and II reported epitopes
No. of other viral species matched by the conserved sequences	(27/44) 61% matched 64 flaviviruses	(67/88) 76% of the sequences matched 68 flaviviruses	(74/78) 95% matched 9 deltaviruses
No. of pathogen specific conserved sequences	17	21	4

other species that are evolutionarily related as they may act as variants to the conserved epitopes identified. This step is necessary to identify conserved epitope sequences that are pathogen specific, with none or minimal number of variant sequences within or across other pathogen species. Variant epitopes are hypothesized to cause deleterious immune responses. Many of the conserved sequences matched nine consecutive amino acids of many (flaviviruses; family of WNV and DENV) to few (deltaviruses; genus of HIV-1) other related viruses, leaving only 17, 21 and 4 pathogen specific conserved sequences for DENV, WNV and HIV-1 clade B subtype, respectively.

Non-Infectious Diseases

According to World Health Organization (WHO), non-infectious diseases, especially chronic diseases will lead the disability by 2020. Hence, diseases such as cancers, obesity, neurodegenerative disease addictions and others have become a recent focus of vaccine development (Barrett, 2016). Cancer is the most common non-infectious disease that leads death world-wide. Due to the advanced technology and success of *in silico* methods in infectious disease vaccine design, computational approaches have been applied in study of cancer vaccine design. For example, VaccImm was developed as a bioinformatics approach to simulate peptide vaccination in cancer therapy (von Eichborn *et al.*, 2013). In addition, modeling approaches using computational biology, such as Sim Triplex and MetastaSim model are important to understand the molecular interactions at the cellular and molecular level (Pappalardo *et al.*, 2013; Sankar *et al.*, 2013). Adekiya *et al.* (2017) reports a recent example of a study that included bioinformatics analysis in cancer vaccine development.

Conclusion: Vaccine Informatics and Future Vaccines

Future vaccines will be minimalistic in approach by focusing on key parts of the pathogen, such as regions containing epitopes that cover antigenic diversity and, thus, will target immunologically similar subgroups of the human population and multiple pathogen variants. This is evident from the trend observed in evolution of vaccine strategies, which has seen a shift from whole organisms to recombinant proteins, and further towards the ultimate in minimalist vaccinology, the peptide/epitope/multi-epitope based vaccines. The minimalist approach is also expected to cover the safety concerns that are associated with the traditional vaccine approach of using whole organism (Sette and Fikes, 2003; Dertzbaugh, 1998). Vectored vaccines, suitable for 'combination immunization' that are produced by recombinant DNA technology and contain multivalent minimal antigens to protect against multiple infections, are considered to be the future of vaccinology (Kutzler and Weiner, 2008). The future will bring increased integration of vaccine research with advances in immunology, molecular biology, genomics, proteomics, informatics, and high-throughput instrumentation, collective defined as the emerging field of "vaccinomics", which is hailed to be responsible for the next 'golden age' in vaccinology (Poland *et al.*, 2008). Awareness of the novel technological possibilities in vaccine research is also expected to grow. Future vaccinology will be based on detailed understanding of immune function, optimal stimulation of immune responses (using adjuvants) and precise mapping and rational selection of immune targets (Brusic *et al.*, 2005). To achieve this, vaccine development will routinely be conducted through large-scale functional studies supported by genomics, proteomics, and informatics techniques prior to clinical trials. This will provide an increased range of immune targets for vaccine design. The author expects the emergence of new generation of vaccines to be personalised to both the genetic make-up of the human population and of the disease agents. In summary, vaccinology will experience rapid progress and will eventually deliver benefits to patients from improved diagnosis, treatment and prevention of diseases.

See also: Computational Pipelines and Workflows in Bioinformatics. Extraction of Immune Epitope Information. Host-Pathogen Interactions. Natural Language Processing Approaches in Bioinformatics

References

Abelin, J.G., *et al.*, 2017. Mass spectrometry profiling of HLA-associated peptidomes in mono-allelic cells enables more accurate epitope prediction. Immunity 46 (2). 315–326.

Ada, G., 2003. Progress towards achieving new vaccine and vaccination goals. Internal Medicine Journal 33, 297–304.

Adekiya, T., *et al.*, 2017. Structural analysis and epitope prediction of MHC class-1-chain related protein-a for cancer vaccine development. Vaccines 6 (1). 1.

Agostino, M., *et al.*, 2016. Optimization of protein-protein docking for predicting Fc-protein interactions. Journal of Molecular Recognition 29 (11). 555–568.

Altschul, S.F., *et al.*, 1990. Basic local alignment search tool. Journal of Molecular Biology 215 (3). 403–410.

Andre, F.E., *et al.*, 2008. Vaccination greatly reduces disease, disability, death and inequity worldwide. Bulletin of the World Health Organization 86, 140–146.

Andreatta, M., *et al.*, 2015. Accurate pan-specific prediction of peptide-MHC class II binding affinity with improved binding core identification. Immunogenetics 67 (11–12). 641–650.

Andreatta, M., Nielsen, M., 2015. Gapped sequence alignment using artificial neural networks: Application to the MHC class I system. Bioinformatics 32 (4). 511–517.

Arnon, R., Ben-yedidia, T., 2003. Old and new vaccine approaches. International Immunopharmacology 3, 1195–1204.

Babiuk, L.A., 1999. Broadening the approaches to developing more effective vaccines. Vaccine 17, 1587–1595.

Barrett, A.D.T., 2016. Vaccinology in the twenty-first century. npj Vaccines 1 (1). 16009.

Bhasin, M., Lata, S., Raghava, G.P.S., 2007. TAPPred prediction of TAP-binding peptides in antigens. Methods in Molecular Biology 409, 381–386.

Bhasin, M., Raghava, G.P.S., 2004. SVM based method for predicting HLA-DRB1*0401 binding peptides in an antigen sequence. Bioinformatics 20 (3). 421–423.

Birnbaum, M.E., *et al.*, 2014. Deconstructing the peptide-MHC specificity of t cell recognition. Cell 157 (5). 1073–1087.

Blum, J.S., Wearsch, P.A., Cresswell, P., 2013. Pathways of antigen processing. Annual Review of Immunology 31, 443–473.

Bona, C.A., Casares, S., Brumeanu, T.D., 1998. Towards development of T-cell vaccines. Immunology Today 19 (3). 126–133.

Bouvier, N., Palese, P., 2008. The biology of influenza viruses. Vaccine 26, D49–D53.

Brusic, V., August, J.T., Petrovsky, N., 2005. Information technologies for vaccine research. Expert Review of Vaccines 4 (3). 407–417.

Brusic, V., Petrovsky, N., 2003. Immunoinformatics–The new kid in town. Novartis Foundation Symposium 254, 3–22. 98-101, 250-252.

Brusic, V., Zeleznikow, J., Petrovsky, N., 2000. Molecular immunology databases and data repositories. Journal of Immunological Methods 238, 17–28.

Chowell, D., *et al.*, 2015. TCR contact residue hydrophobicity is a hallmark of immunogenic CD8+ T cell epitopes. Proceedings of the National Academy of Sciences of the United States of America 112 (14). E1754–E1762.

Damfo, S.A., *et al.*, 2017. In silico design of knowledge-based Plasmodium falciparum epitope ensemble vaccines. Journal of Molecular Graphics and Modelling 78, 195–205.

Dash, P., *et al.*, 2017. Quantifiable predictive features define epitope-specific T cell receptor repertoires. Nature 547 (7661). 89–93.

Dertzbaugh, M.T., 1998. Genetically engineered vaccines: An overview. Plasmid 39 (2). 100–113.

Dhanda, S.K., *et al.*, 2017. Novel in silico tools for designing peptide-based subunit vaccines and immunotherapeutics. Briefings in Bioinformatics 18 (3). 467–478.

Do, C.B., Mahabhashyam, M.S., Brudno, M., Batzoglou, S., 2005. ProbCons: Probabilistic consistency-based multiple sequence alignment. Genome Res. 15 (2). 330–340. PubMed PMID: 15687296; PubMed Central PMCID: PMC546535.

Dominguez, C., Boelens, R., Bonvin, A.M.J.J., 2003. HADDOCK: A protein-protein docking approach based on biochemical or biophysical information. Journal of the American Chemical Society 125 (7). 1731–1737.

Doolan, D.L., 2003. Utilization of genomic sequence information to develop malaria vaccines. Journal of Experimental Biology 206 (21). 3789–3802.

Edgar, R.C., 2004. MUSCLE: A multiple sequence alignment method with reduced time and space complexity. BMC Bioinformatics. 5, 113. PubMed PMID: 15318951; PubMed Central PMCID: PMC517706.

von Eichborn, J., *et al.*, 2013. VaccImm: Simulating peptide vaccination in cancer therapy. BMC Bioinformatics 14.

Evavold, B.D., Sloan-Lancaster, J., Allen, P.M., 1993. Tickling the TCR: Selective T-cell functions stimulated by altered peptide ligands. Immunology Today 14 (12). 602–609.

Fauci, A.S., 2001. Infectious diseases: Considerations for the 21st Century. Clinical Infectious Diseases 32, 675–685.

Fauci, A.S., Touchette, N.A., Folkers, G.K., 2005. Emerging infectious diseases: A 10-year perspective from the National Institute of Allergy and Infectious Diseases. Emerging Infectious Diseases 11 (4). 519–525.

Fleri, W., *et al.*, 2017. The immune epitope database: How data are entered and retrieved. Journal of Immunology Research 2017.

Gee, M.H., *et al.*, 2017. Antigen identification for orphan T cell receptors expressed on tumor-infiltrating lymphocytes. Cell.

Glanville, J., *et al.*, 2017. Identifying specificity groups in the T cell receptor repertoire. Nature 547 (7661). 94–98.

Goodswen, S.J., Kennedy, P.J., Ellis, J.T., 2014. Vacceed: A high-throughput in silico vaccine candidate discovery pipeline for eukaryotic pathogens based on reverse vaccinology. Bioinformatics 30 (16). 2381–2383.

Gourlay, L., *et al.*, 2017. Structure and computation in immunoreagent design: From diagnostics to vaccines. Trends in Biotechnology 35 (12). 1208–1220.

De Groot, A.S., *et al.*, 2002. Immuno-informatics: Mining genomes for vaccine components. Immunology and Cell Biology 80 (3). 255–269.

De Groot, A.S., *et al.*, 2004. Engineering immunogenic consensus T helper epitopes for a cross-clade HIV vaccine. Methods 34, 476–487.

Gupta, A.K., *et al.*, 2016. ZikaVR: An integrated Zika virus resource for genomics, proteomics, phylogenetic and therapeutic analysis. Scientific Reports 6.

Hakenberg, J., *et al.*, 2003. MAPPP: MHC class I antigenic peptide processing prediction. Applied Bioinformatics 2 (3). 155–158.

Haydon, D.T., Woolhouse, M.E., 1998. Immune avoidance strategies in RNA viruses: Fitness continuums arising from trade-offs between immunogenicity and antigenic variability. J. Theor. Biol. 193, 601–612.

He, Y., 2014. Bacterial whole-genome determination and applications. Molecular Medical Microbiology: Second Edition. 357–368.

Hegde, N.R., *et al.*, 2017. The use of databases, data mining and immunoinformatics in vaccinology: Where are we? Expert Opinion on Drug Discovery 13 (2). 117–130.

Heiny, A., *et al.*, 2007. Evolutionarily conserved protein sequences of influenza a viruses, avian and human, as vaccine targets. PLOS ONE 2 (11). e1190. Available at: http://www.ncbi.nlm.nih.gov/pubmed/18030326.

Hilleman, M.R., 1985. Newer directions in vaccine development and utilization. Journal of Infectious Diseases 151 (3). 407–419.

Hu, Y., *et al.*, 2013. Dissecting the dynamics of HIV-1 protein sequence diversity. PLOS ONE 8 (4).

Hung, M.-C., Link, W., 2011. Protein localization in disease and therapy. Journal of Cell Science 124 (20). 3381–3392.

Jerne, N.K., 1993. The generative grammar of the immune system. Scandinavian Journal of Immunology 38 (1). 2–8.

Jurtz, V., *et al.*, 2017. NetMHCpan-4.0: Improved peptide–MHC class I interaction predictions integrating eluted ligand and peptide binding affinity data. The Journal of Immunology 199 (9). 3360–3368.

Katoh, K., Rozewicki, J., Yamada, K.D., 2017. MAFFT online service: Multiple sequence alignment, interactive sequence choice and visualization. Brief Bioinform. doi:10.1093/bib/bbx108 [Epub ahead of print] PubMed PMID: 28968734.

Karosiene, E., et al., 2013. NetMHCIIpan-3.0, a common pan-specific MHC class II prediction method including all three human MHC class II isotypes, HLA-DR, HLA-DP and HLA-DQ. Immunogenetics 65 (10). 711–724.

Kast, W.M., et al., 1994. Role of HLA-A motifs in identification of potential CTL epitopes in human papillomavirus type 16 E6 and E7 proteins. Journal of Immunology 152 (8). 3904–3912.

Kent, W.J., 2002. BLAT – The BLAST-like alignment tool. Genome Research 12, 656–664.

Khan, A.M., 2005. Mapping targets of immune responses in complete dengue viral genomes. MSc Thesis, National University of Singapore. Available at: http://www.scholarbank.nus.edu.sg/bitstream/handle/10635/15081/MohammadAsifKhan(KHAN AM_Thesis.PDF).pdf?sequence=1.

Khan, A.M., 2009. Antigenic diversity of dengue virus: Implications for vaccine design. PhD Thesis, National University of Singapore. Available at: http://scholarbank.nus.edu.sg/handle/10635/17142.

Khan, A.M., et al., 2006. A systematic bioinformatics approach for selection of epitope-based vaccine targets. Cellular Immunology 244 (2). 141–147. Available at: http://www.sciencedirect.com/science/article/B6WCF-4NH6NCY-2/2/081b67baf4faf7b5e9da5c0dd3ea404f.

Khan, A.M., et al., 2008. Conservation and variability of dengue virus proteins: Implications for vaccine design. PLOS Neglected Tropical Diseases 2 (8). e272. Available at: http://www.ncbi.nlm.nih.gov/pubmed/18698358.

Khan, A.M., et al., 2017. Analysis of viral diversity for vaccine target discovery. BMC Medical Genomics 10 (Suppl. 4). S78.

Khan, J.M., Ranganathan, S., 2010. PDOCK: A new technique for rapid and accurate docking of peptide ligands to major histocompatibility complexes. Immunome Research 6 (1). S2. doi: 10.1186/1745-7580-6-S1-S2.

Knobler, S.L., et al., 2003. The resistance phenomenon in microbes and infectious disease vectors: Implications for human health and strategies for containment. National Academies Press 336 (9). 309.

Koo, Q.Y., et al., 2009. Conservation and variability of West Nile virus proteins. PLOS ONE 4 (4). e5352.

Kulkarni-Kale, U., Bhosle, S., Kolaskar, A.S., 2005. CEP: A conformational epitope prediction server. Nucleic Acids Research 33 (Suppl. 2).

Kutzler, M.A., Weiner, D.B., 2008. DNA vaccines: Ready for prime time? Nature Reviews Genetics 9 (10). 776–788.

Larsen, M.V., et al., 2005. An integrative approach to CTL epitope prediction: A combined algorithm integrating MHC class I binding, TAP transport efficiency, and proteasomal cleavage predictions. European Journal of Immunology 35 (8). 2295–2303.

Lee, N.H., et al., 2012. A review of vaccine development and research for industry animals in Korea. Clinical and Experimental Vaccine Research 1, 18–34.

Lefranc, M.P., et al., 2009. IMGT®, the international ImMunoGeneTics information system®. Nucleic Acids Research 37 (Suppl. 1).

Lennon-Duménil, A.-M., et al., 2002. Analysis of protease activity in live antigen-presenting cells shows regulation of the phagosomal proteolytic contents during dendritic cell activation. The Journal of Experimental Medicine 196 (4). 529–540.

Li, F., Finnefrock, A.C., Dubey, S.A., et al., 2011. Mapping HIV-1 vaccine induced T-cell responses: Bias towards less-conserved regions and potential impact on vaccine efficacy in the Step study. PLoS One. 6 (6). e20479. doi:10.1371/journal.pone.0020479. Epub 2011 Jun 10. PubMed PMID: 21695251; PubMed Central PMCID: PMC3112144.

Liljeroos, L., et al., 2015. Structural and computational biology in the design of immunogenic vaccine antigens. Journal of Immunology Research 2015.

Lund, O., et al., 2004. Definition of supertypes for HLA molecules using clustering of specificity matrices. Immunogenetics 55 (12). 797–810.

MacDonald, K.S., et al., 2000. Influence of HLA supertypes on susceptibility and resistance to human immunodeficiency virus type 1 infection. The Journal of Infectious Diseases 181 (5). 1581–1589.

MacDonald, K.S., et al., 2001. Human leucocyte antigen supertypes and immune susceptibility to HIV-1, implications for vaccine design. DNA Sequence 79, 151–157.

Maione, D., et al., 2005. Immunology: Identification of a universal group B streptococcus vaccine by multiple genome screen. Science 309 (5731). 148–150.

María, R.R., et al., 2017. The impact of bioinformatics on vaccine design and development. In: Afrin, F. (Ed.), Vaccines. Place: IntechOpen, pp. 123–145. doi:10.5772/intechopen.69273. Available from: https://www.intechopen.com/books/vaccines/the-impact-of-bioinformatics-on-vaccine-design-and-development.

Marrack, P., et al., 2017. The somatically generated portion of T cell receptor CDR3α contributes to the MHC allele specificity of the T cell receptor. eLife 6.

Minichiello, V., 2002. New vaccine technology–what do you need to know? Journal of the American Academy of Nurse Practitioners 14 (2). 73–81.

Mistry, J., Flower, D.R., 2017. Designing epitope ensemble vaccines against TB by selection: Prioritizing antigens using predicted immunogenicity. Bioinformation 13 (7). 220–223.

Monterrubio-López, G.P., González-Y-Merchand, J.A., Ribas-Aparicio, R.M., 2015. Identification of novel potential vaccine candidates against tuberculosis based on reverse vaccinology. BioMed Research International 2015.

Morens, D.M., Fauci, A.S., 2013. Emerging infectious diseases: Threats to human health and global stability. PLOS Pathogens 9 (7). e1003467.

Nandy, A., Basak, S.C., 2016. A brief review of computer-assisted approaches to rational design of peptide vaccines. International Journal of Molecular Sciences 17 (5).

2017.Database resources of the national center for biotechnology information. Nucleic Acids Research 45 (D1). D12–D17.

Nicholson, L.B., 2016. The immune system. Essays in Biochemistry 60 (3). 275–301.

Nielsen, M., et al., 2005. The role of the proteasome in generating cytotoxic T-cell epitopes: Insights obtained from improved predictions of proteasomal cleavage. Immunogenetics 57 (1–2). 33–41.

Nielsen, M., et al., 2010. MHC Class II epitope predictive algorithms. Immunology 130 (3). 319–328.

NIH, 2003. Understanding the Immune System How It Works. NIH. pp. 1–7.

Nussbaum, A.K., et al., 2001. PAProC: A prediction algorithm for proteasomal cleavages available on the WWW. Immunogenetics 53 (2). 87–94.

Pappalardo, F., Chiacchio, F., Motta, S., 2013. Cancer vaccines: State of the art of the computational modeling approaches. BioMed Research International 2013, 106407.

Park, A.W., et al., 2004. The effects of strain heterology on the epidemiology of equine influenza in a vaccinated population. Proceedings of the Royal Society B: Biological Sciences 271 (1548). 1547–1555.

Parker, K.C., Bednarek, M.A., Coligan, J.E., 1994. Scheme for ranking potential HLA-A2 binding peptides based on independent binding of individual peptide side-chains. Journal of Immunology 152 (1). 163–175.

Paul, S., Dillon, M.B.C., et al., 2015a. A population response analysis approach to assign class II HLA-Epitope restrictions. The Journal of Immunology 194 (12). 6164–6176.

Paul, S., Lindestam Arlehamn, C.S., et al., 2015b. Development and validation of a broad scheme for prediction of HLA class II restricted T cell epitopes. Journal of Immunological Methods 422, 28–34.

Paul, S., et al., 2013. HLA class I alleles are associated with peptide-binding repertoires of different size, affinity, and immunogenicity. The Journal of Immunology 191 (12). 5831–5839.

Petrovsky, N., Brusic, V., 2002. Computational immunology: The coming of age. Immunology and Cell Biology 80 (3). 248–254.

Petrovsky, N., Schönbach, C., Brusic, V., 2003. Bioinformatic strategies for better understanding of immune function. In Silico Biology 3 (4). 411–416.

Pizza, M., et al., 2000. Identification of vaccine candidates against serogroup B meningococcus by whole-genome sequencing. Science 287 (5459). 1816–1820.

Plotkin, S.A., 2005. Vaccines: Past, present and future. Nature Medicine 11 (4 Suppl.). S5–S11.

Poland, G.A., Ovsyannikova, I.G., Jacobson, R.M., 2008. Personalized vaccines: The emerging field of vaccinomics. Expert Opinion on Biological Therapy 8 (11). 1659–1667.

Pro, S.C., et al., 2015. Automatic generation of validated specific epitope sets. Journal of Immunology Research 2015, 763461.

Raman, H., et al., 2014. Bioinformatics for vaccine target discovery. Asia Pacific Biotech News 18 (9). 25–53.

Rammensee, H.-G., et al., 1999. SYFPEITHI: Database for MHC ligands and peptide motifs. Immunogenetics 50 (3–4). 213–219.

Ranganathan, S., Tong, J.C., 2007. A practical guide to structure-based prediction of MHC-binding peptides. Methods in Molecular Biology 409, 301–308.

Rappuoli, R., 2001. Reverse vaccinology, a genome-based approach to vaccine development. Vaccine 19 (17–19). 2688–2691.

Rappuoli, R., Covacci, A., 2003. Reverse vaccinology and genomics. Science 302 (5645). 602.

Rizwan, M., et al., 2017. VacSol: A high throughput in silico pipeline to predict potential therapeutic targets in prokaryotic pathogens using subtractive reverse vaccinology. BMC Bioinformatics 18 (1)..

Rosloniec, E.F., et al., 1997. An HLA-DR1 transgene confers susceptibility to collagen-induced arthritis elicited with human type II collagen. The Journal of Experimental Medicine 185 (6). 1113–1122.

Rothman, A.L., 2004. Dengue: Defining protective versus pathologic immunity. Journal of Clinical Investigation 113 (7). 946–951.

Ryan, C.P., 2008. Zoonoses likely to be used in bioterrorism. Public Health Reports 123 (3). 276–281.

Sachdeva, G., et al., 2005. SPAAN: A software program for prediction of adhesins and adhesin-like proteins using neural networks. Bioinformatics 21 (4). 483–491.

Sankar, S., Nayanar, S., Balasubramanian, S., 2013. Current trends in cancer vaccines – a bioinformatics perspective. Asian Pacific Journal of Cancer Prevention 14 (7). 4041–4047.

Sette, A., et al., 2001. The development of multi-epitope vaccines: Epitope identification, vaccine design and clinical evaluation. Biologicals. 271–276.

Sette, A., Fikes, J., 2003. Epitope-based vaccines: An update on epitope identification, vaccine design and delivery. Current Opinion in Immunology 15 (4). 461–470.

Sette, A., Sidney, J., 1999. Nine major HLA class I supertypes account for the vast preponderance of HLA-A and -B polymorphism. Immunogenetics 50, 201–212.

Shastri, N., Schwab, S., Serwold, T., 2002. Producing nature's gene-chips: The generation of peptides for display by MHC class I molecules. Annual Review of Immunology 20 (1). 463–493. Available at:.http://arjournals.annualreviews.org/doi/abs/10.1146/annurev.immunol.20.100301.064819.

Sievers, F., Wilm, A., Dineen, D., et al., 2011. Fast, scalable generation of high-quality protein multiple sequence alignments using Clustal Omega. Mol. Syst. Biol. 7, 539. doi:10.1038/msb.2011.75. PubMed PMID: 21988835; PubMed Central PMCID: PMC3261699.

Sloan-Lancaster, J., Allen, P.M., 1996. Altered peptide ligand-induced partial T cell activation: Molecular mechanisms and role in T cell biology. Annual Review of Immunology 14, 1–27.

Soria-Guerra, R.E., et al., 2015. An overview of bioinformatics tools for epitope prediction: Implications on vaccine development. Journal of Biomedical Informatics 53, 405–414.

Sprenger, J., et al., 2008. LOCATE: A mammalian protein subcellular localization database. Nucleic Acids Research 36 (Suppl. 1). D230–D233.

Srinivasan, K.N., et al., 2004. Prediction of class I T-cell epitopes: Evidence of presence of immunological hot spots inside antigens. Bioinformatics 20 (Suppl. 1).

Strassburg, M.A., 1980. The global eradication of smallpox. American Journal of Infection Control 10 (2). 53–59.

Sturniolo, T., et al., 1999. Generation of tissue-specific and promiscuous HLA ligand databases using DNA microarrays and virtual HLA class II matrices. Nature Biotechnology 17 (6). 555–561.

Sylvester-Hvid, C., et al., 2002. Establishment of a quantitative ELISA capable of determining peptide – MHC class I interaction. Tissue Antigens 59, 251–258.

Tang, Y.W., Sussman, M., Liu, D., Poxton, I., Schwartzman, J. (Eds.), 2014. Molecular Medical Microbiology, second edn. Academic Press.

Tong, J.C., Tan, T.W., Ranganathan, S., 2007. Methods and protocols for prediction of immunogenic epitopes. Briefings in Bioinformatics 8 (2). 96–108.

Del Tordello, E., Rappuoli, R., Delany, I., 2016. Reverse vaccinology: Exploiting genomes for vaccine design. Human Vaccines: Emerging Technologies in Design and Development. 65–86.

Trolle, T., et al., 2015. Automated benchmarking of peptide-MHC class I binding predictions. Bioinformatics 31 (13). 2174–2181.

Vernikos, G.S., 2008. Genome watch: Overtake in reverse gear. Nature Reviews Microbiology 6 (5). 334–335.

Vigneron, N., Van den Eynde, B.J., 2014. Proteasome subtypes and regulators in the processing of antigenic peptides presented by class I molecules of the major histocompatibility complex. Biomolecules 4 (4). 994–1025.

Vivona, S., Bernante, F., Filippini, F., 2006. NERVE: New enhanced reverse vaccinology environment. BMC Biotechnology 6, 35.

De Vries, S.J., Van Dijk, M., Bonvin, A.M.J.J., 2010. The HADDOCK web server for data-driven biomolecular docking. Nature Protocols 5 (5). 883–897.

Wizemann, T.M., Adamou, J.E., Langermann, S., 1999. Adhesins as targets for vaccine development. Emerging Infectious Diseases 5 (3). 395–403.

Yatim, K.M., Lakkis, F.G., 2015. A brief journey through the immune system. Clinical Journal of the American Society of Nephrology 10 (7). 1274–1281.

Zaharieva, N., et al., 2017. Immunogenicity prediction by VaxiJen: A ten year overview. Journal of Proteomics & Bioinformatics 10 (11). 298–310.

Zahroh, H., et al., 2016. Immunoinformatics approach in designing epitopebased vaccine against meningitis-inducing bacteria (Streptococcus pneumoniae, Neisseria meningitidis,and Haemophilus influenzae type b). Drug Target Insights 10, 19–29.

Zhang, G., et al., 2005. MULTIPRED: A computational system for prediction of promiscuous HLA binding peptides. Nucleic Acids Res 33 (Web Server issue). W172–W179. Available at: http://www.ncbi.nlm.nih.gov/pubmed/15980449.

Zhang, G.L., et al., 2006. PRED(TAP): A system for prediction of peptide binding to the human transporter associated with antigen processing. Immunome Research 2 (1). 3.

Zhang, W., et al., 2011. Prediction of conformational B-cell epitopes from 3D structures by random forests with a distance-based feature. BMC Bioinformatics 12.

Zhang, Y., et al., 2017. Influenza research database: An integrated bioinformatics resource for influenza virus research. Nucleic Acids Research 45 (D1). D466–D474.

Further Reading

Aparicio, R., et al., 2017. World's largest science, technology & medicine open access book publisher. The impact of bioinformatics on vaccine design and development.

Barrett, A.D.T., 2016. Vaccinology in the twenty-first century. NPJ Vaccines 1 (1). 16009.

Brusic, V., August, J.T., Petrovsky, N., 2005. Information technologies for vaccine research. Expert Review of Vaccines 4 (3). 407–417.

Brusic, V., Petrovsky, N., 2003. Immunoinformatics – The new kid in town. Novartis Foundation Symposium 254, 13–22. 98–101, 250–252.

Brusic, V., Zeleznikow, J., Petrovsky, N., 2000. Molecular immunology databases and data repositories. Journal of Immunological Methods 238, 17–28.

Dhanda, S.K., et al., 2017. Novel in silico tools for designing peptide-based subunit vaccines and immunotherapeutics. Briefings in Bioinformatics 18 (3). 467–478.

Gourlay, L., et al., 2017. Structure and computation in immunoreagent design: From diagnostics to vaccines. Trends in Biotechnology 35 (12). 1208–1220.

Hegde, N.R., et al., 2017. The use of databases, data mining and immunoinformatics in vaccinology: Where are we? Expert Opinion on Drug Discovery 13 (2). 117–130.

Khan, A.M., et al., 2017. Analysis of viral diversity for vaccine target discovery. BMC Medical Genomics 10 (Suppl. 4). S78.

Mistry, J., Flower, D.R., 2017. Designing epitope ensemble vaccines against TB by selection: Prioritizing antigens using predicted immunogenicity. Bioinformation 13 (7). 220–223.

Tong, J.C., Ranganathan, S., 2013. Computer-Aided Vaccine Design, Woodhead Publishing Series In Biomedicine No. 23. Cambridge, UK: Woodhead, pp. 1–164.

Relevant Website

www.ncbi.nlm.nih.gov/genomes/VIRUSES/viruses.html
Viral Genomes.

Biographical Sketch

Chong Li Chuin is a Biomedical Science undergraduate student from Faculty of Medicine and Health Sciences, UPM. As part of her undergraduate studies, she completed an internship at Perdana University Centre for Bioinformatics (PU-CBi), Malaysia. She continued to be involved with the Centre to build on her passion for bioinformatics.

Associate Professor Dr. Mohammad Asif Khan is currently the Dean of the Perdana University School of Data Sciences, the Director of Perdana University Centre for Bioinformatics (PU-CBi), Malaysia, and a Visiting Scientist at Johns Hopkins University School of Medicine (JHUSOM), USA. He obtained his PhD in Bioinformatics from the National University of Singapore (NUS), and did his postdoctoral fellowships at NUS and JHUSOM. Dr. Khan's research interests are in the area of biological data warehousing and applications of bioinformatics to the study of immune responses, vaccines, venom toxins, drug design, and disease biomarkers.

Protocol for Protein Structure Modelling

Amara Jabeen, Abidali Mohamedali, and **Shoba Ranganathan,** Macquarie University, Sydney, NSW, Australia

Introduction

Protein structure has four levels of organization. The primary structure is represented by sequence of amino acids bound together by peptide bonds. When backbone atoms of one amino acid residue make hydrogen bonds with the backbone atoms of other residues, α-helices and β-pleated sheets are formed that comprise the secondary structure of a protein. These secondary structural elements are connected by loop regions. The folding of secondary structure elements into 3-dimensional (3D) space yields tertiary structure of a protein. In some proteins, folded chains of more than one polypeptide interact with each other to form quaternary structure. Protein structure dictates its function (Voet *et al.*, 2016). Mutations that alter the structure of a protein can lead to alteration of function which can either be detrimental or beneficial, therefore a thorough understanding of protein structure is mandatory to have insight into the biology of life (Starr *et al.*, 2011). Moreover, a 3D structure serves as an important starting point for insights into essential features of an evolutionary protein family, thereby establishing a possibility of identification of even remotely related proteins through structural similarities (Lacapere, 2017).

Protein structures that are determined through experimental methodologies (primarily by X-ray crystallography (XRC), nuclear magnetic resonance spectroscopy (NMR) and electron microscopy) are often submitted to the Protein databank (PDB) which is the largest repository for experimentally determined structures of proteins, nucleic acids and other complex assemblies (Berman *et al.*, 2000). There are numerous derived databases representing PDB files for specific families of proteins and their related information: for instance, PDBTM has transmembrane proteins selection of PDB (Kozma *et al.*, 2012).

Despite the rapid increase in the percentage of structures determined from different experimental methods (**Table 1**), there is still a vast gap between protein sequence (99,261,416 UniProt entries as on December 2017) and structure (125,799 protein PDB entries as on December 2017) entries. Some classes of proteins are significantly under-represented in the PDB: for instance, membrane proteins represent 40% of the human proteome (Lacapere, 2017) but only 702 structures (as on July 2017) have been solved experimentally. This is primarily due to the difficulty in crystallizing these proteins. Olfactory receptors, which represent the largest family of G protein coupled receptors (GPCRs) do not have a single experimentally solved structure. The lack of solved structures of proteins have long been recognized as a bottleneck in rational drug design; for instance, casein kinase II (CK2) has been extensively studied due to its implications in cancer, with potential inhibitors searched by testing against CK2. The CK2 XRC structure (PDB ID: 3AT2) has paved the way for discovery and optimization of its inhibitors through structure-based drug designing (Cozza, 2017).

Computational approaches can be used to predict the structure of the protein at a fraction of the cost and time compared to the experimental methods. Though these methods are not as accurate as experimental methods, the quality and efficiency of structure prediction in the past few years has demonstrated that it can be a viable complement to experimental methods (Khor *et al.*, 2015). The majority of structure-prediction methods provide structural templates closely matching the query protein sequence. This article provides the protocol for structure prediction of a protein through template-based modelling, with the basic aim of providing practical guide to readers to use computational approaches for structure prediction.

Methods for Protein Structure Prediction

Protein structure prediction is the method of inference of protein's 3D structure from its amino acid sequence through the use of computational algorithms. The 3D structure of a protein is predicted on the basis of two principles; the laws of physics and evolution. According to physical principles, protein folds into a stable and well-formed structure by minimizing the energy, while according to evolutionary principles, a protein molecule is a consequence of gradual changes in sequence and structure over the

Table 1 Experimental methods for protein entries in the Protein Databank

Experimental method	Number of structures resolved[a]
X-ray crystallography	111,712
Nuclear magnetic resonance spectroscopy	10,476
Electron microscopy	1,233
Hybrid	102
Other	199
Total	123,722

[a]As on 4 September 2017.

course of time. These two principles set up the foundation of the two protein structure prediction methods that are template-based modelling (homology modelling and threading method) and template free modelling (*ab initio* modelling), respectively (Illergård *et al.*, 2009). Hybrid methods utilize both of these methods. The selection of the methods depends primarily upon the availability of the templates structures in PDB.

Protein structure prediction took its ground with the thermodynamics hypothesis proposed by an American biochemist Christian Anfinsen in 1962. This hypothesis was based on his work conducted in 1954 on folding of bovine pancreatic ribonuclease into 3D conformation, i.e., native conformation (Anfinsen *et al.*, 1954), and then in 1961 he reported refolding of unfolded bovine pancreatic ribonuclease A into its native conformation (Scheraga, 2014). During the Anfinsen's Nobel acceptance speech in 1972 he talked about the dependence of 3D conformation upon amino acid sequence, which motivated different groups to work on protein structure prediction problem. One of the earliest efforts was done by Gibson and Scheraga in 1967 in finding thermodynamically stable conformation of protein by using different computer searching techniques (Wooley and Ye, 2007). The first success in the area of protein fold prediction from its amino acid sequence came in 1975 when Levitt and Warshel folded bovine pancreatic trypsin inhibitor (58 residues long) using energy minimization. In 1969 Browne and his co-workers exploited the observation that proteins that share sequence similarities share similar structure, to predict the structure of α-lactalbumin using the X-ray structure of lysozyme as a template, and this laid the foundation for comparative modelling (Guo *et al.*, 2008). After the prediction of the first homology model, continuous improvements have been made, from semi-automated to fully automated homology modelling. Homology (Greer, 1981) was the first semi-automated program and Modeller (Šali and Blundell, 1993) was the first fully automated program. The first ever fully automated server with web interface was then built in 1993, named SWISS-MODEL (Guex *et al.*, 2009). Great number of programs and fully automated servers are now available for solving protein structure prediction problem.

To bridge the gap between protein sequences and structures and to encourage the development of fast, efficient and accurate structure prediction methods, a community-wide global protein structure prediction experiment known as the Critical Assessment of protein Structure Prediction, or CASP was started in 1994, with the sequences of protein structures about to be experimentally solved offered as targets for prediction. Participants then submit their predicted models which are then compared to experimentally determined structures (Moult *et al.*, 2016). The main classes of protein structure prediction methods are briefly described below.

Homology Modelling

Homology modelling has proven to be the most successful approach for protein structure prediction but it requires that a template exists in PDB (Fiser, 2010), such that, the better the template, the more accurate the prediction. This approach is greatly benefited by the fact that structure of at least one member of almost all the families of proteins have been deduced experimentally which can be used as a template for modelling the other members of that particular family (Song *et al.*, 2013).

Threading

Threading relies on the observation that a limited number of folds are present in nature due to which even remotely homologous proteins have similar structures (Kelley and Sternberg, 2009). Protein threading methods are based on a *Z-score* which tests the possibility of target protein sequence to fold in the structure that is similar to the template structure. The *Z-score* represents the distance between optimal alignment score and mean alignment score that is obtained by random shuffling of a target sequence. This method involves building up databases for representative, non-redundant template structures, followed by devising a fitness scoring function which is based on the knowledge of known sequence to structure relationships. The scoring function is then minimized by finding the optimal alignment between the target and template and in the end, best template is selected based on all the template sequence alignments (Markstein and Xu, 2006).

Ab initio Methods

When a matching template cannot be found for a query sequence by use of homology or threading approaches, the *ab initio* methods are used to model the structure. These template-free methods rely on a set of core principles that are based on folding energetics and statistical tendencies of conformational characteristics demonstrated by experimental structures (Lee *et al.*, 2017). The general steps include devising an accurate energy function to estimate which model structures are thermodynamically stable, using an efficient search method that can identify lowest energy conformations, and selecting the near native conformation from a pool of structure decoys.

Ab initio methods are the least accurate of all the structure prediction methods and have limitations of protein size, and therefore is only used to model smaller proteins/peptides (Lee *et al.*, 2017).

Over the past decade substantial improvement has been made in the performance of different protein structure prediction servers. **Table 2** lists the top ten automated structure prediction servers according to the recent CASP 12 ranking.

Table 2   Top 10 automated structure prediction servers according to CASP 12 ranking[a]

Server	Rank (based on sum Z-score)	Protein size limit	URL
Zhang server	1	1500	http://zhanglab.ccmb.med.umich.edu/I-TASSER/
QUARK	2	150	http://zhanglab.ccmb.med.umich.edu/QUARK/
BAKER-ROSETTA SERVER	3	650	http://robetta.bakerlab.org/
GOAL	4		Not available publicly
RAPTORX	5	2500	http://RaptorX.uchicago.edu/
ToyPred_email	6		Not available publicly
MULTICOM-CONSTRCUT	7		Not available publicly
MULTICOM-CLUSTER	8	No limit	http://sysbio.rnet.missouri.edu/multicom_cluster/
MULTICOM-NOVEL	9		Not available publicly
IntFOLD4	10	2000	http://www.reading.ac.uk/bioinf/IntFOLD/

[a]Ranking is based on analysis of Z-score for GDT_TS.

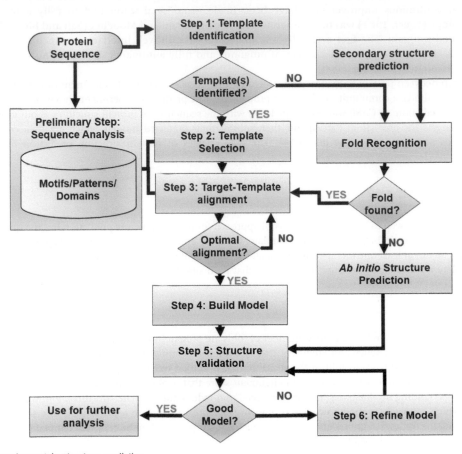

Fig. 1   Flow diagram for protein structure prediction.

Once a 3D structure for a protein sequence has been predicted using any of the three methods described above, the quality of the predicted structure needs to be thoroughly checked. CASP has been instrumental in developing methods for evaluating the quality and accuracy of structural models (Schwede, 2013).

Given a protein sequence with unknown structure, predicting its 3D structure is a laborious task, especially due to continuous improvements in structural knowledge and prediction methods as a result of advances in the area of structural bioinformatics. We present a comprehensive protocol for structure modelling, exemplified by a case study.

Protocol for Protein Structure Modelling

Given a protein sequence with unknown structure, the following protocol can be used to predict its 3D structure (**Fig. 1**), with each step elaborated in the following sub-sections.

Preliminary Step: Sequence Analysis

Analyzing the target sequence assists in providing useful biological information which can be further utilized in template selection and sequence alignment. The features that can be examined within the target sequence are as follows:

Protein family analysis

It has been established that two protein sequences of a length of over 100 amino acids that share more than 30% identity are predicted to have a similar structure and function (Pearson, 2013). Such proteins are called homologues ("siblings") and are assumed to have evolved from a common ancestor. When the sequence identity between two proteins is within and below 20%–35%, they fall in the twilight ("cousins") zone (Bahar et al., 2017). The structure relatedness is not obvious from sequence relationship in this case and therefore can be inferred from structural alignment. Structure is three to 10 times more conserved than sequence because amino acid changes in the primary sequence are reflected in the structure in terms of type and location of the changes in 3D space. Even a single amino acid mutation could affect the structure completely, but if physicochemical properties remain conserved, the structure remains unaffected (Illergård et al., 2009). For example, haemoglobin from a trematode which binds and transports oxygen (PDB: 1H97) has only 12.1% sequence identity with the haemoglobin of an annelid (PDB: 2GTL), which is part of a larger protein, erythrocruorin (3.6 million Da) and performs other functions in addition to binding and transporting oxygen. However, both share similar structures (RMSD: 2.3 Å), are part of the globin-like superfamily and have similar function (Sousounis et al., 2012). Despite the low sequence identity, proteins with a similar structure and function have remarkable conservation in the active site residues such that if an accurate model of the active site can be obtained, it can be utilized to elucidate the protein's function and ligands.

Conservation of residues important for structure and function

The function of a protein depends on the localization in space of a few key residues that are conserved through evolution and occupy identical positions in corresponding structures, usually in a solvent accessible cavity. Some residues are important for the stability of the protein fold or for formation of quaternary structures. If a protein contains buried charged residues that are conserved among homologues, such residues are also usually important for maintaining function (Isom and Dohlman, 2015).

Motifs and patterns

Identification of patterns and motifs can be done through databases (listed in Section Useful Resources) and literature searches. These patterns can then be mapped onto a template to have optimal alignment (Taylor, 1992).

Domain analysis

Protein domains represent the autonomously folding functional units of a protein, which can be present as a repeated unit or in combination with other domains (Marchler-Bauer et al., 2012). Protein sequence of length greater than 150 must be checked for the occurrence of multiple domains.

Template Identification

Template structure defines the framework for 3D structure prediction of a target protein. Templates are identified by aligning the target (query) sequence with sequences of available structures in PDB. The three available methods for template identification by alignment are summarized in **Table 3**.

Sequence-based methods are more specific but less sensitive than profile-based methods, which are more sensitive but less specific than structure-based methods. Basic Local Alignment Search Tool (BLAST) search results give clues of templates and region of high similarity but for model building we must align the target and template sequences globally. Every domain of the query protein must have a template to model it. If for any domain a template does not exist, it cannot be modelled by homology or comparative modelling. Homologue identification can be improved by splitting the long sequences into domains as determined by comparison with domain databases, and then searching a homologue for each domain.

Criteria for defining a homologue

The following parameters should be considered while defining the homology between two proteins:

Table 3 Methods for template identification

Alignment methodology	Description	Example
Sequence-based	Suitable for high identity	Protein BLAST
Profile-based	Suitable twilight-zone proteins	psi-BLAST, SAM, HHSEARCH, FFAS
Structure-based	Incorporates structural features for instance, secondary structure and solvent accessibility	RAPTOR, SPARKS, MUSTER, LOMETS

1. Alignment score and e-value: high alignment scores and low e-values (rule of thumb: <0.005) are usually desired.
2. Domain coverage: the aligned region between the two proteins must cover at least 60% of the structural domain involved.
3. Gaps: fewer gaps are better as they result in a higher quality model. Long and contiguous insertion/deletion ("indels") regions are preferred to several short indels, for generating a better structural model. Templates with fewer gaps and reasonable similarity scores are preferred over the templates with high scores and but too many gaps.

Template identification for small proteins
Small proteins lack a hydrophobic core and are stabilized by disulphide bridges, between cysteine side chains (Thangudu *et al.*, 2008) or by binding metal ions. Thus, while identifying templates for small proteins, the conservation should be restricted to the cysteine residues involved in making the disulphide bridges, and to residues that are involved in binding metal ions without which the proteins would not be able to fold properly. The size of the loops between the conserved cysteine residues is also crucial as gaps in such regions can affect the predicted model. The right modelling approach for small proteins must be able to produce a model with disulphide bridges or metal ions present intact, to make it biologically relevant.

Targets without homologues

If no considerable homologue is retrieved for the target by any of above tools, then its secondary structure can be predicted, which can give clues about class of the protein and order of occurrence of secondary structure elements that can then be used for matching with a fold, predicted by fold recognition methods (Section Useful Resources). If this also does not help, then *ab initio* methods can be used for model building. The regions of target sequence which does not have any template can be built up using an *ab initio* approach.

Template Selection

If only one template is identified, then model should be built with this template, otherwise appropriate template(s) may be selected from the pools of templates. For selection of templates a number of factors need to be considered, which include:

Sequence similarity
Multiple sequence alignment of all the domains of potential templates and target sequence can be performed and utilized in building a phylogenetic tree which can then depict the most similar structure that can be used for model building.

Similarity in secondary structure
A template with similar secondary structure as the predicted secondary structure of the target can be prioritised.

Bounded ligands
If the ultimate goal of structure prediction is receptor and ligand interactions studies, then a template that has the same binding ligand (if any) as of the protein of interest should be preferred.

Resolution of template structure
High resolution XRC structures are preferred over low resolution structures. Similarly, XRC structures are preferred over NMR. But if only NMR structures are available, the "average" NMR structure must be chosen for model building as NMR protein structures are often submitted in PDB as ensembles of models.

Presence of missing residues
Missing residues (if any) information is present in REMARK 465 in the header section of a PDB file. Missing residues information can also be seen by using most PDB viewer. If missing residues are present, then an alternate template should be selected, otherwise more than one template should be used to fill in the gaps. If the ultimate goal of structure prediction is to study protein interactions, then no missing residues should be present in the binding sites of the template.

Multiple templates
Optimal use of multiple templates can increase the accuracy of the developed model. If every template is providing unique information and there are minimal overlapping residues between templates, they can be selected for building a model. Superimposing Cα atoms can reveal the unique information each template is contributing. Other features to look at are insertions, variation in the length of secondary structure elements and different conformational loops. Few of the programs can build model by using multiple templates like Modeller, IntFOLD and M4T (Fiser, 2010). If sequence identity falls below 40%, multiple template usage is favorable but above this identity a single template will usually suffice (Fiser, 2010).

Target-Template Alignment

The most crucial task in modelling that guides the model building and determines the quality of a model is target to template alignment. When sequence identity between target and template drops below 40%, accurate alignment is critical. Incorrect alignment of even a single residue can result in error of approximately 4 Å in the resulting model (Fiser, 2010).

For optimal alignment, the profile of target sequence can be generated by aligning it with its close homologues through multiple sequence alignment (MSA) through any MSA tool like T-COFFEE or ClustalW, which can show the conserved and variable parts of the target sequence. As structure-based alignment is more significant than sequence-based alignment, it is good to align all the selected templates structurally by using UCSF Chimera. Structure-based sequence alignment (SSA) can then be extracted from already aligned structures in UCSF Chimera and aligned with multiple sequence alignment (MSA) of target sequence using profile alignment without any modification of alignment within SSA or MSA. The target-template alignment can now be extracted from this profile. The following checks must be performed to improve the quality of the alignment.

Residue conservation

a. Analysis of positions of identical and similar residues in terms of chemical similarity, charge, size and nature.
b. Presence of functional regions, motifs and patterns must be analyzed preferably by mapping available experimental information.
c. Histidine-rich sites often binds metal ions that are necessary for proper folding of small proteins (Section Template identification for small proteins) while proline has a structural role in guiding the protein folding. Therefore, the conservation of cysteine, proline and histidine residues must be checked for small proteins.

Gaps in alignment

Small gaps (indels) separating few residues should be combined into a long gap. Different sequence alignment methods (e.g., T-COFFEE or ClustalW) can provide clues regarding aggregation of gaps.

Gaps in secondary structures

If there are any indels present within α-helices or β-strands, they must be moved to the closest loop. Indels are normally placed at the end of the loop where the backbone is turning around to have a better quality model. These indels can be mapped onto the template by visualizing through any PDB viewer.

If multiple templates are chosen, then they all must be superimposed for structure alignment using any structure alignment tool such as UCSF Chimera. Structure-based sequence alignment can be extracted and can be used for model building, this alignment is different from sequence based alignment and provides improved results especially in case of low homology. Final target-template alignment is then passed to the next step of model construction.

Model Building

A number of tools are available for constructing a model on the basis of target-template alignment. **Table 4** summarizes the features of different programs used for modelling. Programs such as Modeller and I-TASSER provide a model refinement feature, in addition to model building. Others like WhatIF and MOE include the structure validation feature as well. Numerous webservers are also there that take in query sequence as an input and pass it through a pipeline of different programs for template identification, sequence alignment, model building, structure validation and refinement. The webservers used for automated structure prediction are summarized in **Table 5**. The most popular ones are I-TASSER, Robetta and Swiss model. A few servers such as I-TASSER and Swiss model even allow the user to select the template of their choice. Webservers like Bhageerath-H follow a hybrid approach of modelling, i.e., modelling is based on a template but if template is not spanning the query sequence somewhere, *ab initio* modelling will then be used to provide a complete model.

Structure Quality Analysis

It is essential to first evaluate the quality of the predicted model before using it for further analysis. The main features of the predicted model that can be assessed include bond lengths, bond angles, torsion angles, atomic clashes, distribution of hydrophobic and polar residues (Feig, 2016). Numerous webservers and tools are available to validate the protein structural model (**Table 6**). Each server validates different features like stereo-chemical correctness or knowledge-based statistical measures that have been derived from experimentally solved high resolution structures and has defined threshold for validation of the model (Schwede, 2013). For instance, the PSVS server calculates *Z-score* for protein structure validation that is based on a set of 252 X-ray structures <500 residues, of resolution <=1.80 Å, R-factor <=0.25 and R-free <=0.28 and models with positive scores are considered as good models. Many webservers also integrate several tools into one platform, such as protein structure analysis and validation (ProTSAV) and protein structure validation software suite (PSVS). To evaluate the performance of quality validation tools, quality validation category was introduced in CASP7 and from then onwards performance of quality validation servers have been evaluated in CASP every 2 years (Mcguffin *et al.*, 2013).

Table 4 Programs available for protein structure modelling

Method	OS	Freely available	Single/multiple templates	Method used	Key features
Modeller Webb and Sali (2014)	Windows, Mac, UNIX/Linux	Free for academia	Both	Modelling by satisfaction of spatial restraints	1. Most frequently used 2. Protein sequences and/or structures comparison 3. Clustering of proteins 4. Sequence databases searching 5. Model refinement 6. Model Loops
WHATIF Vriend (1990)	Windows, Linux	No	Single	CONCOORD (generation of geometric bonds from template and modelling on the basis of geometric bonds)	1. Display, manipulate and analyze small molecules, proteins, nucleic acids, and their interactions. 2. Cannot model indels 3. Structure validation
ICM Abagyan et al. (1994)	Windows, Mac, UNIX/Linux	Under academic licence	Single	Global optimization	1. Interface for molecular modelling, fully-flexible ligand and receptor docking, virtual ligand screening
MOE Molecular Operating Environment (MOE) (2017)	Windows, Mac, Linux	No	Both	Segment matching procedure (Levitt, 1992)	1. Highly interactive 2. Homology detection 3. Structure- based alignment facility 4. Side chain and loop modelling 5. Structure validation
I-TASSER Yang et al. (2015)	Linux	Free for academia	Both	Replica-exchange Monte-Carlo simulation technique	1. Integrated package for protein structure and function prediction 2. Use multiple threading technique to identify template 3. Model refinement
Nest Petrey et al. (2003)	Linux	Free for academia	Both	Artificial evolution algorithm	1. Side chain modelling 2. Loop modelling 3. Rapid model building

Table 5   Webservers available for protein structure modelling

Server	Domain boundary prediction	Template identification	Method for Sequence-template alignment	Method for model generation	Model refinement	Quality assessment
I-TASSER Zhang (2008)	Built-in process	LOMETS (User can also provide template) v	PPA Decoy-based optimized potential	Replica-exchange Monte carlo simulation technique	REMO	C-score[a]
Robetta Chivian et al. (2003)	Ginzu	BLAST, Psi-BLAST, FFAS03 and 3d-Jurry	K*Sync	Rosetta fragment-insertion technique1	–	DISOPRED
RaptorX Peng and Xu (2011)	Pfam database searching	Statistical learning methods[b]	CNFpred	MODELLER	–	DISOPRED
Seok server Ko et al. (2012)	GalaxyDom	HHsearch	Promals3D	GalaxyCassiopeia	GalaxyRefine	GalaxyQA
IntFOLD4 Mcguffin et al. (2015)	DomFOLD3	SP3, SPARKS2, HHsearch, COMA, SPARKSX, CNFsearch and LOMETS	SP3, SPARKS2, COMA and HHSEARCH	Modellerv9.8	–	ModFOLDclust2 (for single template models), ModFOLD6_rank QA and DISO-clust3
Bhagheerath-H Jayaram et al. (2014)	None	pGenthreader, ffas spark-x, HHSearch	substitution scoring matrix based on chemical properties of amino acids	Modeller for targets having templates and bhagheerath ab initio modelling method for stretches without template	Quantum mechanics (PM6) based loop bond angle optimization, Scwrl4 and Sander module of AMBER10	PROTSAV
Swiss model Biasini et al. (2014)	–	BLAST and HHblits (User can also provide template)	BLAST and HHblits	ProMod-II and MODELLER	–	QMEAN

[a]This is based on threading alignments and convergence of I-TASSER's structural assembly refinement simulations.

[b]These methods incorporate profile information, predicted secondary structure, solvent accessibility, amino acid physico-chemical properties.

Table 6   Webservers for protein structure validation

Webserver	Tools integrated	Output	Threshold	URL
ProTSAV (Singh et al., 2016)	Procheck ProSA-web ERRAT Verify 3D dDFire Naccess MolProbity D2N ProQ	Quality assessment plot	Green area: 0-2 Å. Yellow area: 2-5 Å. Orange area: 5-8 Å. Red area: >8 Å.	http://www.scfbio-iitd. res.in/software/ proteomics/protsav.jsp
	PSN-QA	ProTSAV score	Range: 0 to 1 0: Good quality 1: low quality	
PSVS (Bhattacharya et al., 2007)	PDBStat RPF DSSP PROCHECKG- factors MolProbity	Ramachandran plot summary PROCHECKG-factors	>85% in conformationally allowed region Z-score > − 3	http://psvs − 1_5-dev. nesg.org/
	Verify 3D Prosall	MolProbity clashscore	Z-score > − 3	
	PDB validation software	RMS deviation for bond lengths	<0.02 Å	
		RMS deviation for bond angles	<4°	
Molprobity (Davis et al., 2007)	None	Clash score Cβ deviations >0.25 Å Bad bonds Bad angles Ramachandran favored Favored rotamers	Range : 0 (worst) − 100 (best) 0 0 <0.1% >98% >98%	http://molprobity. biochem.duke.edu/

Structure Refinement

Structure refinement is based on the quality report. The goal of refinement is to improve the predicted model in a way that it has accurate side chain orientations and high stereo-chemical quality so that it might get closer to the native structure (Carlsen and Røgen, 2015). The following are two strategies used for structure refinement:

Potential energy minimization and molecular dynamics

Potential energy minimization (PEM) techniques are used to eliminate high energies in the predicted model and achieve local minima that is closer to native structure. Molecular dynamics (MD) is comparatively computationally expensive among all refinement techniques, but it is the most prevalent strategy for refinement (Feig, 2017). FG-MD (Zhang et al., 2011) is one of the examples of MD-based refinement server.

Structure optimization

Poor quality regions reported by quality checks can specifically be targeted and optimized iteratively to improve the model. Secondary structure elements and hydrogen bonding networks can be optimized. One example of refinement method using structure optimization approach and energy minimization is 3DRefine (Bhattacharya and Cheng, 2013). Editing target-template alignment and rebuilding a model iteratively can often improve the built model. Structure optimization after the MD is more useful for improving overall quality of the fold (Feig, 2017).

Success Stories of Protein Structure Modelling

Protein structure prediction methods are successfully bridging up the sequence-structure gaps by complementing experimental methods. Few examples of successful model predictions are given below to show how these methods are revolutionizing the research in structural biology.

Homology Modelling Using a Single Template

A structural model for DORN1 (plant purinoreceptor) was predicted through homology modelling (Tanaka *et al.*, 2016) and used to predict the extracellular ATP (eATP) binding pocket in DORN1, and key residues involved in binding. Blind docking and different tools for ligand pocket prediction were then used to predict the eATP binding pocket in the predicted model. Predicted binding pocket was then validated by site directed mutagenesis of key residues. Results showed the accuracy of modelled ligand binding pocket.

Homology Modelling Using Multiple Templates

The structure for integrin $\alpha v\beta 6$ was predicted through homology modelling by using multiple templates (Sowmya *et al.*, 2014). The specific interaction of integrin $\alpha v\beta 6$ and uPAR is known to be associated with cancer progression and was studied using the predicted structure. The crystal structure of the extracellular domains was subsequently determined (PDB ID: 4UM9) and the RMSD between the predicted and experimental structures is <1 Å, demonstrating the accuracy of the predicted model.

Ab initio Modelling

The structure of CT296 protein was predicted by *ab initio* modelling through the I-TASSER server (Kemege *et al.*, 2011). CT296 is present in *Chlamydia trachomatis,* which is a bacterial pathogen responsible for non-heritable blindness. It was previously suggested that CT296 shows similarity to the ferric uptake regulator and has DNA binding motifs. The predicted model was not consistent with this information. The XRC of CT296 was then determined at a resolution of 1.8 Å, supporting CT296 not having functional similarity to the ferric uptake regulator and also having DNA binding sites. When compared, the predicted model had significant similarity to the XRC (RMSD: 2.72 Å).

Threading-Based Homology Modelling

The β_1-adrenergic receptor (β_1-AR) belongs to GPCR superfamily and is known to play an important role in cardiovascular function and disease, serving as a drug target for the management of cardiovascular diseases. Through threading-based homology modelling approach, a 3D model for β_1-AR was constructed that was further utilized in docking four agonists (Carmoterol, Dobutamine, Isoprenaline and Salbutamol) to study the binding modes of β_1-AR (Ul-Haq *et al.*, 2015). The human β_1-AR structural model assisted the authors to understand its binding mechanism, for future targeted structure-based drug molecule development.

Let's Start to Model:

Given the poor representation of membrane proteins in the PDB and the complications involved in building a model for protein with multiple transmembrane segments, the example chosen to illustrate the steps involved in building a 3D model of a protein is that of a membrane protein.

Case Study

GPCRs represent the largest family of membrane proteins and are targets for almost half of the drugs (Tautermann, 2014). There are a total 130,314 GPCR protein sequences from multiple organisms, including *Homo sapiens,* available in UniProt (as on August 2017), but only 436 crystal structures of GPCRs are present in GPCRdb, which includes 44 unique crystallized receptors and 43 unique ligand-receptor complexes, indicating a large sequence structure gap. GPCRs consist of seven transmembrane (Schmiedeberg *et al.*, 2007) helices that are connected through three extracellular loops (ECLs) and three intracellular loops (ICLs) with extracellular N-terminus and intracellular C-terminus (Clark, 2017). Short wave sensitive opsin is one of the GPCR whose structure is predicted through homology modelling, with consideration of motifs and patterns, and in this case study is used as an example.

Obtaining Target Sequence

Download the amino acid sequence of the target, i.e., short wave sensitive opsin (OPSB_BOVIN) in FASTA Format from UniProt (UniProt ID: P51490, see Relevant Website section).

Sequence

a. Use TMSEG (Bernhofer *et al.*, 2016) to predict transmembrane regions of OPSB_BOVIN. Enter query sequence in FASTA format and select transmembrane helices option.

b. Use Predictprotein (see Relevant Websites section) to confirm transmembrane regions and to predict secondary structure of non-membrane segments.

c. Motifs and patters can be predicted by number of available webservers and their knowledge can also be gained from available literature. Each TM of GPCR contains at least one motif that can be very helpful for generating optimal alignment (Van Der Kant and Vriend, 2014). **Table 7** shows the motifs retrieved from the literature. Patterns/motifs predicted from different webservers are shown in **Table 8** (only strong matches are shown).

d. Extracellular part of GPCRs are involved in ligand recognition and binding. The ligand binding pockets are extremely diverse among GPCR members in terms of shape and features for recognition of varied ligands (Katritch *et al.*, 2012). Despite the diverse ligands, residues 3.32, 3.33, 3.36, 6.48, 6.51 and 7.39 (numbered according to Ballesteros–Weinstein numbering (Ballesteros and Weinstein, 1995)) are known to make consensus interactions with ligands among class A GPCRs. Residues from other transmembrane regions tend to interact with specific ligands to a varied extent. Therefore, TM3, TM6 and TM7 serve as a consensus cradle for the ligand binding pocket. Alteration of residues in these specific topological positions leads to ligand specificity in different receptors (Venkatakrishnan *et al.*, 2013). OPSB_BOVIN sequence is represented in **Fig. 2** with predicted TM regions, motifs, consensus ligand binding pocket and cysteine residues involved in the formation of disulphide bridges.

Table 7   Motifs of GPCR sequences retrieved from the literature

TM	Motif
ECL2	Disulphide bridge between TM3 (Cys$^{3.25}$) (Ballesteros and Weinstein, 1995) and ECL2 (Venkatakrishnan *et al.*, 2013)
1	GXXXN (de March *et al.*, 2015)
2	NLXXXD (Miguel *et al.*, 2017)
3	DRY (Deupi *et al.*, 2007)
	SX$_3$LX$_2$IX$_2$D(E,H)RY (Costanzi, 2012)
4	WX$_{8,9}$P (Costanzi, 2012)
5	FX$_2$PX$_7$Y (Costanzi, 2012)
6	CWXP (Miguel *et al.*, 2017)
	FX$_2$CW(Y,F)XP (Costanzi, 2012)
7	NPXXY (Sato, 2016)

Table 8   Predicted motifs and patterns

Webserver used	Predicted pattern/feature	Sequence/location
ScanProsite	Disulphide bridge	108 & 185
	G_Protein_Recep_F1_1	VTGwSLAFLAFERYlil (121–137)
	Opsin Retinal Binding Site	IpaFfSKSACvyNPiiY (288–304)
MotifScan	G_PROTEIN_RECEP_F1_1	121–137
	OPSIN *Visual pigments*	288–304
	7tm_1	52–304

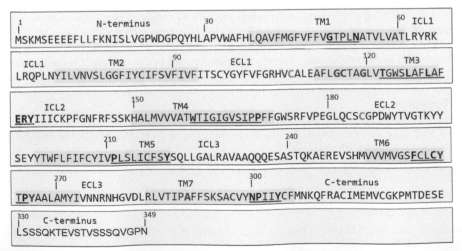

Fig. 2   OPSB_BOVIN sequence features. Predicted TM regions (highlighted in yellow), motifs (bold text) and patterns (underlined), cysteine residues involved in disulphide bridge formation (green) and consensus ligand binding cradle of class A GPCRs (red) are shown.

Template Identification and Selection

a. Run BLAST against Protein databank to retrieve the potential templates. OPSB_BOVIN has 44% sequence identity and 92% query coverage with bovine rhodopsin (PDB ID: 3OAX) according to BLAST results. Due to high sequence identity, query coverage and completeness of structure, 3OAX can be selected as a template, but there is another structure of bovine rhodopsin deposited in PDB (PDB ID: 1U19) with a resolution of 2.2 Å while 3OAX has a resolution of 2.6 Å. Due to the better resolution than 3OAX, 1U19 is selected as template for modelling OPSB_BOVIN.

b. Download the PDB file of 1U19 from Protein databank (see Relevant Websites section).

Target Template Alignment

a. Before alignment, the PDB file must be edited, if needed. For example, if the template has multiple chains and one of the chains is selected to serve as a template, then the rest of the chains must be deleted by use of the PDB visualizer such as UCSF Chimera. The PDB file 1U19 has two chains A and B, since we only need chain A, chain B is deleted by selecting the chain B in UCSF Chimera and then deleting it. If the PDB file contains any protein that is co-crystalized with the template protein, then it must also be removed. Additionally, all non-standard residues must be removed except the ligands (if required) and metals ions as they are important for folding specially for small proteins. Non-standard residues are present in the form of HETATM record in the PDB file and can be deleted using any text editor. There is one modified residue (HETATM) in the PDB file of 1U19 (line number 871–873), labelled as X in the sequence, it should also be removed. There might be some missing residues in the template, so the structure derived sequence of the template will be used which can be retrieved by clicking sequence in the tools tab in UCSF Chimera and saving it into a separate file. The gaps will be inserted in place of missing residues before alignment. There are no missing residues in 1U19.

b. The MSA webserver, T-COFFEE, is used to align OPSB_BOVIN and 1U19. The membrane protein option is selected before submitting the sequence.

c. Knowledge of motifs, patterns and ligand binding cradle gained during sequence analysis step can now be used to optimize the alignment between query and template. Motifs in OPSB_BOVIN are well aligned to 1U19. Due to the high sequence identity, there are no insertions and deletions in the predicted transmembrane regions. The only gaps present in alignment are within the N- and C-termini, which can be ignored, as these regions are usually not conserved in membrane proteins. According to the alignment between 1U19 and OPSB_BOVIN (Fig. 3), the last five residues of OPSB_BOVIN do not have a corresponding residue from the template, and thus these residues will not be modelled due to lack of matching template residues. These residues can be removed from alignment before model building.

Model Building, the Manual Way

Build the model of OPSB_BOVIN using Modeller, by following the tutorial provided (see Relevant Website section). It is better to build multiple models (say 5) and then select the final model on the basis of the lowest objective function (Fig. 4).

```
OPSB_BOVIN   MSKMSEEEEFLLFKNISL--VGPWDGPQYHLAPVWAFHLQAVFMGFVFFVGTPLNATVLVATLRYRKLRQPLNYILVNVS  78
1U19         MNGTEGPNFYVPFSNKTGVVRSPFEAPQYYLAEPWQFSMLAAYMFLLIMLGFPINFLTLYVTVQHKKLRTPLNYILLNLA  80
             *.  . : :: *.*  :     .*::.***:**  * * : *.:* ::::* *:* .* .*:::*** ******:*::

OPSB_BOVIN   LGGFIYCIFSVFIVFITSCYGYFVFGRHVCALEAFLGCTAGLVTGWSLAFLAFERYIIICKPFGNRFSSKHALMVVVAT  158
1U19         VADLFMVFGGFTTTLYTSLHGYFVFGPTGCNLEGFFATLGGEIALWSLVVLAIERYVVVCKPMSNFRFGENHAIMGVAFT  160
             :...:: :  . ..  .: ** :******  __  *  **.**:.   .* :: ***..**:***:::***. ****  ..**.:* *.  *

OPSB_BOVIN   WTIGIGVSIPPFFGWSRFVPEGLQCSCGPDWYTVGTKYYSEYYTWFLFIFCYIVPLSLICFSYSQLLGALRAVAAQQQES  238
1U19         WVMALACAAPPLVGWSRYIPEGMQCSCGIDYYTPHEETNNESFVIYMFVVHFIIPLIVIFFCYGQLVFTVKEAAAQQQES  240
             *.:.:. :  **:.  ****.:***.***** *.**  :  * :. :.**. .:*:** :* *.*.**. ::: .*******

OPSB_BOVIN   ASTQKAEREVSHMVVVMVGSFCLCYTPYAALAMYIVNNRNHGVDLRLVTIPAFFSKSACVYNPIIYCFMNKQFRACIMEM  318
1U19         ATTQKAEKEVTRMVIIMVIAFLICWLPYAGVAFYIFTHQGSDFGPIFMTIPAFFAKTSAVYNPVIYIMMNKQFRNCMVTT  320
             *:*****.**:**.:***::. :. .*: ***.:*.**..:: .:  :********.*.:.****.**.*:****** *.::

OPSB_BOVIN   VC-GK-PMTDESELSSSQKTEVSTVSSSQVGPN  349
1U19         LCCGKNPLGDDEASTTVSKTETSQVAPA-----  348
             :* ** *: *:. :: .***.* *:.
```

Fig. 3 Alignment of Bovine rhodopsin (1U19: A) and OPSB_BOVIN sequence given as an input to Modeller. TM regions of 1U19 and predicted TM regions of OPSB_BOVIN are highlighted in yellow with disulphide bridge forming cysteine residues (green), motifs of both sequences (bold text), patterns (underlined), ligand binding cradle of OPSB_BOVIN (red), ligand binding pocket of 1U19 (blue) and residues without a template are highlighted in red. Disulphide bridge is indicated by a dashed line.

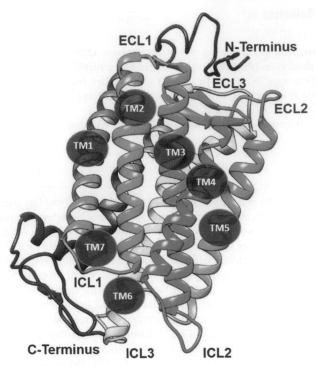

Fig. 4 OPSB_BOVIN model, from manual model building.

Structure Validation

a. Use PSVS server to validate the structure. PROCHECK program present in PSVS server reports the conformationally allowed regions of the residues. High quality X-ray structures have at least 85% of the residues in conformationally allowed regions (Sowmya *et al.*, 2014). For the predicted model, 99.7% of the residues are in conformationally allowed regions as reported by PROCHECK, including 88.3% of which are favorable and 11.4% are in allowed regions. RMSD for bond lengths and bond angles is 0.019 Å and 2.1° respectively, which should be lower than 0.02 Å and 4° for a good quality structure.
b. Closeness of the template and query determines the accuracy of the predicted structure, which is often measured by either Root Mean Square Deviation (RMSD) or global distance test (GDT_TS). The greater the similarity between the template and the query, the higher is the resolution. Sequence similarity over 50% and RMSD ≤ 1 Å corresponds to high resolution structure. If similarity is between 30% and 50% and RMSD ≤ 1.5 Å the resolution is medium (Carlsen and Røgen, 2015). The RMSD between the OPSB_BOVIN and 1U19 is 0.267 Å. RMSD can be retrieved by superimposing the predicted structure and template structure in UCSF Chimera (PDB visualizer).
c. Use the Molprobity server to look for favored and poor rotamers which are the low energy conformations of side-chain dihedral angles. The correct assignment of rotamers to each amino acid is essential for a thermodynamically stable structure (Bhuyan and Gao, 2011). The quality of predicted side chain can be analyzed by identifying the favored rotamers in the 3D structure of a protein (Harder *et al.*, 2010).
d. Use the ProTSAV server that gives a normalized average *Z-score* based on ten diversified structure validation programs. A *Z-score* closer to 0 represents a good quality structure. The manual model for OPSB_BOVIN has a *Z-score* of 0.5846 (**Table 9**).
e. Literature: It is observed that TM3 and ECL2 are connected together by a disulphide bridge (**Fig. 5**), which is the characteristic of majority of class A GPCRs (Venkatakrishnan *et al.*, 2013).

Automated Structure Prediction

Plenty of online servers are available that take a target sequence as an input and pass it to a pipeline of various programs to predict the 3D structure of the target protein. Almost all such webservers have a user-friendly interface. It is important that one should select the server carefully to have a good model. Top ranked servers (according to CASP ranking) were used in this case study to predict the model of OPSB_BOVIN, namely I-TASSER, RaptorX, and IntFOLD, among others. It should be noted that in this case, we allowed the servers to select the best template(s). The comparisons of structure validation results for predicted structures according to the steps in Section Structure Validation by use of the automated servers and the manual modelling is shown in **Table 9**.

Table 9   Comparison of structure validation results of manual modelling and automated modelling

Description		Manual model	RaptorX	IntFOLD	I-TASSER
Ramachandran plot (PSVS)	Favored (%)	88.3	92.5	85.4	82.5
	Allowed (%)	11.4	6.9	13.0	17.5
	Outliers (%)	0.3	0.6	1.6	0.0
RMSD for bond lengths (Å) (PSVS)		0.019	0.020	0.019	0.014
RMSD for bond angles (PSVS)		2.2°	3.0°	2.2°	2.3°
Favored rotamers (%) (Molprobity)		91.06	87.75	87.75	78.15
ProTSAV score (ProTSAV)		0.5846	0.5907	0.6042	0.5593
RMSD (Å)		0.260	1.605	0.203	1.177
Template(s) used		1U19 (Bovine Rhodopsin)	4ZWJ (Human rhodopsin)	2G87 (Bathorhodopsin)	Multiple[a]

[a]4ZWJ (Human Rhodopsin); 1GZM (Bovine Rhodopsin); 1U19 (Bovine Rhodopsin); 2KS9 (Substance P receptor); 2G87 (Bathorhodopsin).

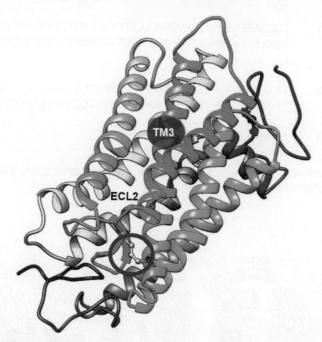

Fig. 5   Disulphide bridge between ECL2 and TM3.

For all the predicted models by the automated servers and the manual modelling, more than 90% of the residues were in the allowed regions according to PROCHECK embedded in PSVS server. The RMSD for bond lengths and bong angles from native structures for all the models were good but there were not enough favored rotamers, which should be more than 98%, suggesting that the side chains need refinement. In the manually predicted model, the favored rotamers were comparatively better than the automated models.

N- and C-Termini

The automated RaptorX server predicted long N- and C-termini as compared to the other predictions, it is because of the long indels present in the alignment of both termini between the OPSB_BOVIN and the template 4ZWJ selected by the server. Only few residues in N-terminus are modelled on the basis of template (4ZWJ) as seen in the alignment (**Fig. 6**).

Helical Bundle

According to both the manual and automated models, the predicted TM1, TM2 and TM4 are modelled in the same manner and have the same positions in each predicted model. There are slight differences in the start and end positions of TM3 between the manually predicted model and the I-TASSER model. There was a variation in the prediction of TM5, where I-TASSER and RaptorX had predicted a long TM5 as compared to the manual and IntFOLD server predictions. This is because the template (4ZWJ) chosen by the automated servers had a long TM5 (**Fig. 6**). The start and the end of TM6 was the same across all the predictions, except for I-TASSER which had only

```
OPSB_BOVIN    -----------MSKMSEEEEFLLFKNISLVGPWDGPQYHLAPVWAFHLQAV
4ZWJ          FSNATGVVRS--------------------PFEYPQYYLAEPWQFSMLAA

OPSB_BOVIN    FMGFVFFVGTPLNATVLVATLRYRKLRQPLNYILVNVSLGGFIYCIFSVF
4ZWJ          YMFLLIVLGFPINFLTLYVTVQHKKLRTPLNYILLNLAVADLFMVLGGFT

OPSB_BOVIN    IVFITSCYGYFVFGRHVCALEAFLGCTAGLVTGWSLAFLAFERYIIICKP
4ZWJ          STLYTSLHGYFVFGPTGCNLQGFFATLGGEIALWSLVVLAIERYVVVCKP

OPSB_BOVIN    FGNRFSSKHALMVVVATWTIGIGVSIPPFFGWSRFVPEGLQCSCGPDWY
4ZWJ          MSNFRFGENHAIMGVAFTWVMALACAAPPLAGWSRYIPEGLQCSCGIDYY

OPSB_BOVIN    TVGTKYYSEYYTWFLFIFCYIVPLSLICFSYSQLLGALRAVAAQQQESAS
4ZWJ          TLKPEVNNESFVIYMFVVHFTIPMIIIFFCYGQLVFTVKEAAAQQQESAT

OPSB_BOVIN    TQKAEREVSHMVVVMVGSFCLCYTPYAALAMYIVNNRNHGVDLRLVTIPA
4ZWJ          TQKAEKEVTRMVIIYVIAFLICWVPYASVAFYIFTHQGSCFGPIFMTIPA

OPSB_BOVIN    FFSKSACVYNPIIYCFMNKQFRACIMEMVCG-----------KPMTDESEL
4ZWJ          FFAKSAAIYNPVIYIMMNKQFRNCMLTTICCGKNVIFKKVS---------

OPSB_BOVIN    SSSQKTEVSTVSSSQVGPN
4ZWJ          -------------------
```

Fig. 6 Alignment of OPSB_BOVIN with 4ZWJ used by RaptorX to generate the 3D model of OPSB_BOVIN. N-terminus, C-terminus and TM5 of both OPSB_BOVIN and 4ZWJ are highlighted in yellow.

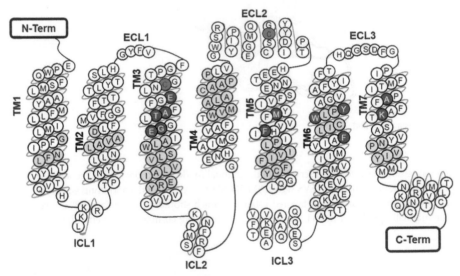

Fig. 7 Snake plot for 1U19, showing motifs/patterns (yellow), cysteine residues involved in disulphide bonding (green) and residues in ligand binding site (blue).

one residue difference. The start position of TM7 was the same for all the predictions, but there was a disagreement in the end position. TM boundaries of each predicted model can be seen clearly through snake plots in **Figs. 7–9**. Snake plots for 1U19 and OPSB_BOVIN are downloaded from GPCRdb (Munk *et al.*, 2016) and edited according to the predicted models.

Intracellular Loops

The structure of the predicted intracellular loop was nearly similar in all the models, except intracellular loop 3(ICL3 in **Fig. 9**) of models predicted by RaptorX and I-TASSER, where in these models the TM5 was longer, and thus the ICL3 was shorter, compared to the other two predicted models (**Fig. 10**).

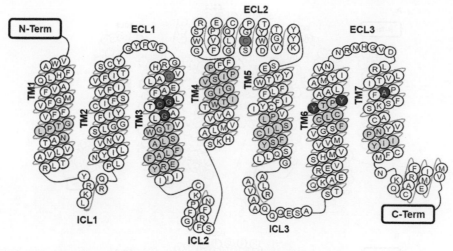

Fig. 8 Snake plot for manual model, showing motifs/patterns (yellow), cysteine residues involved in disulphide bonding (green) and residues in ligand binding site (red).

Disulphide Bridges

All of the predicted models had a single disulphide bridge between cysteine residues at positions 108 and 185. Thus, all models were consistent in building a viable disulphide bridge between the correct cysteine residues.

Secondary Structure Elements

All predicted models contained 7TM helices. Two β-strands were present in ECL2 of all the predicted models. According to the I-TASSER prediction, two more β-strands were present in the N-terminus. One small helix was present in ECL2 in a model predicted by RaptorX.

Automated Versus Manual Modelling

Automated modelling is convenient when high sequence identity exists between the query and the template, but for low sequence identity cases, manual modelling is preferable for the following reasons:

i. Alignment editing is required in most of the cases. For instance, in a model predicted by RaptorX, the C-terminus and N-terminus can be improved by adjusting the gaps in alignment. Many automated servers do not allow alignment editing.
ii. A careful study of template is required for its selection (Section Template Selection). We can see from the case study that the manual *versus* automated selection of the template affected the model; for example, resulting difference in the length of predicted TM5 by RaptorX and I-TASSER automated servers due to the different templates. Most of the automated servers focus on sequence identity between the target and template for selection; only some incorporate additional features, such as secondary structure and solvent accessibility, among others. Some automated servers do allow the user to specify the templates, but this might be risky as it can often result in a bad model if the template selection criteria are not well applied (Fasnacht *et al.*, 2014).
iii. Many servers do not allow use of multiple templates.
iv. Servers normally take one to several days for predicting the structure depending upon the load on the server, but through manual prediction, models can be built quickly as compared to automated servers.

Despite the above facts, automated servers do provide models that can give clues about the structure of a protein and in many instances, can serve as a first guess, before careful manual model building.

Conclusion

Enormous advancement has been witnessed in the area of protein structure prediction methods over the past decade. The nor-epinephrine transporter (NET), a drug target for various mood related and behavioral disorders, such as depression, is a notable success story in the application of such prediction methods. There was not a single good resolution atomic structure available for NET.

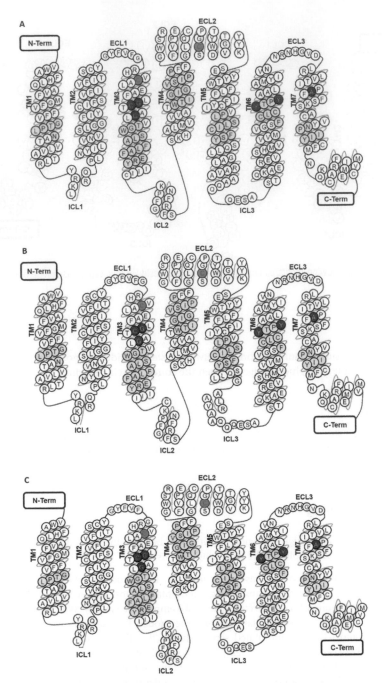

Fig. 9 Snake plots for RaptorX (A), IntFOLD (B) and I-TASSER (C) models, showing motifs/patterns (yellow), cysteine residues involved in disulphide bonding (green) and residues in ligand binding site (red).

Computational model of NET was constructed by use of the X-ray structure of leucine transporter LeuT from *Aquifex aeolicus* as a template. The built model was then used for virtual ligand screening against the binding site, which resulted in the identification of 10 already tested NET inhibitors and five novel ligands. Predicted ligands were then validated experimentally to be the potential inhibitors of NET (Schlessinger *et al.*, 2011). Despite the continuous progress in this field, there are cases where the proteins can be difficult to model. For example, *HpUreI*, a proton gated urea channel from *Helicobacter pylori* known to be involved in gastric infection, was one of the targets for CASP round 10. The X-ray structure of *HpUreI* showed a novel fold which was not predicted with accuracy by any of the template based modelling approach; and was predicted with little accuracy by the template free approach I-TASSER, but less than one third of the residues were in proximity to the corresponding X-ray structure (Kryshtafovych *et al.*, 2014). With continuous improvement in protein structure prediction methods, these challenges are hoped to be addressed. For example, numerous methods are now available for modelling membrane proteins; RosettaMP (Alford *et al.*, 2015) is one such method.

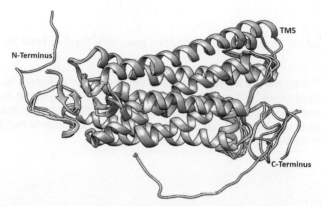

Fig. 10 Superimposition of model structures from IntFOLD (blue), I-TASSER (brown), RaptorX (green) and manual mode (pink).

Table 10   Useful resources for protein structure prediction and modelling

Step	Resource	URL
Sequence analysis resources	HHMM TOP (Topology prediction)	http://www.enzim.hu/hmmtop/
	TMHMM (Topology prediction)	http://www.cbs.dtu.dk/services/TMHMM/
	Consurf (Conserved buried/exposed residue prediction)	http://consurf.tau.ac.il/2016/
	Interpro (Domain prediction)	https://www.ebi.ac.uk/interpro/
	PRINTS (Protein families database)	http://130.88.97.239/PRINTS/index.php
	MOTIFSCAN (Motif prediction)	http://myhits.isb-sib.ch/cgi-bin/motif_scan
	SCANProsite (Motif prediction)	http://prosite.expasy.org/scanprosite/
	JPRED (Secondary structure prediction)	http://www.compbio.dundee.ac.uk/jpred/
	PSiPred (Secondary structure prediction)	http://bioinf.cs.ucl.ac.uk/psipred/
Template identification	BLAST	https://blast.ncbi.nlm.nih.gov/Blast.cgi
	Psi-BLAST	https://www.ebi.ac.uk/Tools/sss/psiblast/
	LOMETS	http://zhanglab.ccmb.med.umich.edu/LOMETS/
	MUSTER	http://zhanglab.ccmb.med.umich.edu/MUSTER/
	COMPASS	http://prodata.swmed.edu/compass/compass.php
	HMMER	http://hmmer.org/
	RAPTORX	http://RaptorX.uchicago.edu/
Multiple sequence alignment/profile construction	MAFT	https://www.ebi.ac.uk/Tools/msa/mafft/
	CLUSTAL Omega	https://www.ebi.ac.uk/Tools/msa/clustalo/
	MUSCLE	https://www.ebi.ac.uk/Tools/msa/muscle/
	T-COFFEE	http://tcoffee.crg.cat/
	SALIGN	https://modbase.compbio.ucsf.edu/salign/
	Promals3D	http://prodata.swmed.edu/promals3d/promals3d.php
3D model building	Homology Modelling	See **Tables 4, 5**
	PHYRE2 (Fold recognition)	https://modbase.compbio.ucsf.edu/modweb/
	pGenThreader (Fold recognition)	http://www.chemogenomix.com/chemogenomix/GenThreader.html
	ORION (Fold recognition)	http://www.dsimb.inserm.fr/ORION/
	Robetta (*Ab initio*)	http://robetta.bakerlab.org/
	QUARK (*Ab initio*)	https://zhanglab.ccmb.med.umich.edu/QUARK/
Structure refinement	GalaxyRefine	http://galaxy.seoklab.org/cgi-bin/submit.cgi?type=REFINE
	ModRefiner	http://zhanglab.ccmb.med.umich.edu/ModRefiner/
	3DRefine	http://sysbio.rnet.missouri.edu/3Drefine/
	REFINEpro	http://sysbio.rnet.missouri.edu/REFINEpro/
	PREFMD	http://feiglab.org/prefmd
	FG-MD	http://zhanglab.ccmb.med.umich.edu/FG-MD/
Structure validation	See **Table 6**	
PDB visualizers	Pymol	https://www.pymol.org/
	RASMOL	http://www.openrasmol.org/
	Discovery studio	http://accelrys.com/products/collaborative-science/biovia-discovery-studio/
	SwissPDB viewer	http://spdbv.vital-it.ch/
	Chimera	https://www.cgl.ucsf.edu/chimera/

Useful Resources

A list of resources for each step of the protein structure modelling protocol is listed in **Table 10**.

See also: Algorithms for Structure Comparison and Analysis: Prediction of Tertiary Structures of Proteins. Biomolecular Structures: Prediction, Identification and Analyses. Cloud-Based Molecular Modeling Systems. Computational Protein Engineering Approaches for Effective Design of New Molecules. Drug Repurposing and Multi-Target Therapies. In Silico Identification of Novel Inhibitors. Natural Language Processing Approaches in Bioinformatics. Protein Design. Small Molecule Drug Design. Structure-Based Design of Peptide Inhibitors for Protein Arginine Deiminase Type IV (PAD4). Study of The Variability of The Native Protein Structure

References

Abagyan, R., Totrov, M., Kuznetsov, D., 1994. ICM – A new method for protein modeling and design: Applications to docking and structure prediction from the distorted native conformation. Journal of Computational Chemistry 15, 488–506.

Alford, R.F., Leman, J.K., Weitzner, B.D., et al., 2015. An integrated framework advancing membrane protein modeling and design. PLOS Computational Biology 11, e1004398.

Anfinsen, C.B., Redfield, R.R., Choate, W.L., Page, J., Carroll, W.R., 1954. Studies on the gross structure, cross-linkages, and terminal sequences in ribonuclease. Journal of Biological Chemistry 207, 201–210.

Bahar, I., Jernigan, R.L., Dill, K.A., 2017. Protein Actions: Principles and Modeling. New York: Garland Science.

Ballesteros, J., Weinstein, H., 1995. Integrated methods for modeling G-protein coupled receptors. Methods in Neuroscience 25, 366–428.

Berman, H.M., Westbrook, J., Feng, Z., et al., 2000. The protein data bank. Nucleic Acids Research 28, 235–242.

Bernhofer, M., Kloppmann, E., Reeb, J., Rost, B., 2016. TMSEG: Novel prediction of transmembrane helices. Proteins: Structure, Function, and Bioinformatics 84, 1706–1716.

Bhattacharya, D., Cheng, J., 2013. 3Drefine: Consistent protein structure refinement by optimizing hydrogen bonding network and atomic-level energy minimization. Proteins: Structure, Function, and Bioinformatics 81, 119–131.

Bhattacharya, A., Tejero, R., Montelione, G.T., 2007. Evaluating protein structures determined by structural genomics consortia. Proteins: Structure, Function, and Bioinformatics 66, 778–795.

Bhuyan, M.S.I., Gao, X., 2011. A protein-dependent side-chain rotamer library. BMC Bioinformatics 12, S10.

Biasini, M., Bienert, S., Waterhouse, A., et al., 2014. SWISS-MODEL: Modelling protein tertiary and quaternary structure using evolutionary information. Nucleic Acids Research 42. W252–W259.

Carlsen, M., Røgen, P., 2015. Protein structure refinement by optimization. Proteins: Structure, Function, and Bioinformatics 83, 1616–1624.

Chivian, D., Kim, D.E., Malmström, L., et al., 2003. Automated prediction of CASP-5 structures using the Robetta server. Proteins: Structure, Function, and Bioinformatics 53, 524–533.

Clark, T., 2017. G-Protein coupled receptors: Answers from simulations. Beilstein Journal of Organic Chemistry 13, 1071–1078.

Costanzi, S., 2012. Homology modeling of class a G protein-coupled receptors. Methods in Molecular Biology 857, 259–279.

Cozza, G., 2017. The development of CK2 inhibitors: From traditional pharmacology to in silico rational drug design. Pharmaceuticals (Basel) 10, 26.

Davis, I.W., Leaver-Fay, A., Chen, V.B., et al., 2007. MolProbity: All-atom contacts and structure validation for proteins and nucleic acids. Nucleic Acids Research 35, W375–W383.

Deupi, X., Dolker, N., LUZ Lopez-Rodriguez, M., et al., 2007. Structural models of class AG protein-coupled receptors as a tool for drug design: Insights on transmembrane bundle plasticity. Current Topics in Medicinal Chemistry 7, 991–998.

Fasnacht, M., Butenhof, K., Goupil-Lamy, A., et al., 2014. Automated antibody structure prediction using Accelrys tools: Results and best practices. Proteins: Structure, Function, and Bioinformatics 82, 1583–1598.

Feig, M., 2016. Local protein structure refinement via molecular dynamics simulations with locPREFMD. Journal of Chemical Information and Modeling 56, 1304–1312.

Feig, M., 2017. Computational protein structure refinement: Almost there, yet still so far to go. Wiley Interdisciplinary Reviews: Computational Molecular Science 7, e1307.

Fiser, A., 2010. Template-based protein structure modeling. Methods in Molecular Biology 673, 73–94.

Greer, J., 1981. Comparative model-building of the mammalian serine proteases. Journal of Molecular Biology 153, 1027–1042.

Guex, N., Peitsch, M.C., Schwede, T., 2009. Automated comparative protein structure modeling with SWISS-MODEL and Swiss-PdbViewer: A historical perspective. Electrophoresis 30 Suppl 1, S162–S73.

Guo, J.-T., Ellrott, K., Xu, Y., 2008. A historical perspective of template-based protein structure prediction. Methods in Molecular Biology 413, 3–42.

Harder, T., Boomsma, W., Paluszewski, M., et al., 2010. Beyond rotamers: A generative, probabilistic model of side chains in proteins. BMC Bioinformatics 11, 306.

Illergård, K., Ardell, D.H., Elofsson, A., 2009. Structure is three to ten times more conserved than sequence – a study of structural response in protein cores. Proteins: Structure, Function, and Bioinformatics 77, 499–508.

Isom, D.G., Dohlman, H.G., 2015. Buried ionizable networks are an ancient hallmark of G protein-coupled receptor activation. Proceedings of the National Academy of Sciences 112, 5702–5707.

Jayaram, B., Dhingra, P., Mishra, A., et al., 2014. Bhageerath-H: A homology/ab initio hybrid server for predicting tertiary structures of monomeric soluble proteins. BMC Bioinformatics 15, S7.

Katritch, V., Cherezov, V., Stevens, R.C., 2012. Diversity and modularity of G protein-coupled receptor structures. Trends in Pharmacological Sciences 33, 17–27.

Kelley, L.A., Sternberg, M.J., 2009. Protein structure prediction on the Web: A case study using the Phyre server. Nature Protocols 4, 363–371.

Kemege, K.E., Hickey, J.M., Lovell, S., et al., 2011. Ab initio structural modeling of and experimental validation for Chlamydia trachomatis protein CT296 reveal structural similarity to Fe(II) 2-oxoglutarate-dependent enzymes. Journal of Bacteriology 193, 6517–6528.

Khor, B.Y., Tye, G.J., Lim, T.S., Choong, Y.S., 2015. General overview on structure prediction of twilight-zone proteins. Theoretical Biology and Medical Modelling 12, 15.

Kozma, D., Simon, I., Tusnády, G.E., 2012. PDBTM: Protein Data Bank of transmembrane proteins after 8 years. Nucleic Acids Research 41, D524–D529.

Ko, J., Park, H., Heo, L., Seok, C., 2012. GalaxyWEB server for protein structure prediction and refinement. Nucleic Acids Research 40 (Webserver issue). W294–W297.

Kryshtafovych, A., Moult, J., Bales, P., et al., 2014. Challenging the state of the art in protein structure prediction: Highlights of experimental target structures for the 10th critical assessment of techniques for protein structure prediction experiment CASP10. Proteins: Structure, Function, and Bioinformatics 82, 26–42.

Lacapere, J.J., 2017. Membrane Protein Structure and Function Characterization: Methods and Protocols. New York: Springer.

Lee, J., Freddolino, P.L., Zhang, Y., 2017. Ab Initio protein structure prediction. In: J. RIGDEN, D. (Ed.), From Protein Structure to Function With Bioinformatics. Dordrecht, Neterlands: Springer.

Levitt, M., 1992. Accurate modeling of protein conformation by automatic segment matching. Journal of Molecular Biology 226, 507–533.

Marchler-Bauer, A., Zheng, C., Chitsaz, F., et al., 2012. CDD: Conserved domains and protein three-dimensional structure. Nucleic Acids Research 41, D348–D352.

de March, C.A., Kim, S.K., Antonczak, S., *et al.*, 2015. G protein-coupled odorant receptors: From sequence to structure. Protein Science 24, 1543–1548.

Markstein, P., Xu, Y. 2006. *Computational Systems Bioinformatics*. London: Imperial College Press.

Mcguffin, L.J., Atkins, J.D., Salehe, B.R., Shuid, A.N., Roche, D.B., 2015. IntFOLD: An integrated server for modelling protein structures and functions from amino acid sequences. Nucleic Acids Research 43, W169–W173.

Mcguffin, L.J., Buenavista, M.T., Roche, D.B., 2013. The ModFOLD4 server for the quality assessment of 3D protein models. Nucleic Acids Research 41, W368–W372.

Miguel, R.N., Sanders, J., Furmaniak, J., Smith, B.R., 2017. Structure and activation of the TSH receptor transmembrane domain. Autoimmunity Highlights 8, 2.

Molecular Operating Environment (MOE), 2017. 2013.08; Chemical Computing Group ULC. 1010 Sherbooke St. West, Suite #910, Montreal, QC, Canada, H3A 2R7.

Moult, J., Fidelis, K., Kryshtafovych, A., Schwede, T., Tramontano, A., 2016. Critical assessment of methods of protein structure prediction: Progress and new directions in round XI. Proteins: Structure, Function, and Bioinformatics 84, 4–14.

Munk, C., Isberg, V., Mordalski, S., *et al.*, 2016. GPCRdb: The G protein-coupled receptor database – An introduction. British Journal of Pharmacology 173, 2195–2207.

Pearson, W.R., 2013. An introduction to sequence similarity ("homology") searching. Current Protocols in Bioinformatics. 3.1.1–3.1.8.

Peng, J., Xu, J., 2011. RaptorX: Exploiting structure information for protein alignment by statistical inference. Proteins: Structure, Function, and Bioinformatics 79, 161–171.

Petrey, D., Xiang, Z., Tang, C.L., *et al.*, 2003. Using multiple structure alignments, fast model building, and energetic analysis in fold recognition and homology modeling. Proteins: Structure, Function, and Bioinformatics 53, 430–435.

Šali, A., Blundell, T.L., 1993. Comparative protein modelling by satisfaction of spatial restraints. Journal of Molecular Biology 234, 779–815.

Sato, T., Kawasaki, T., Mine, S., Matsumura, H., 2016. Functional role of the C-terminal amphipathic helix 8 of olfactory receptors and other G protein-coupled receptors. International Journal of Molecular Sciences 17, 1930.

Scheraga H.A., 2014. Simulations of the folding of proteins: A historical perspective In: LIWO, A. (ed.) Computational Methods to Study the Structure and Dynamics of Biomolecules and Biomolecular Processes: From Bioinformatics to Molecular Quantum Mechanics. Berlin, Heidelberg: Springer.

Schlessinger, A., Geier, E., Fan, H., *et al.*, 2011. Structure-based discovery of prescription drugs that interact with the norepinephrine transporter, NET. Proceedings of the National Academy of Sciences, 108. pp. 15810–15815.

Schmiedeberg, K., Shirokova, E., Weber, H.-P., *et al.*, 2007. Structural determinants of odorant recognition by the human olfactory receptors OR1A1 and OR1A2. Journal of Structural Biology 159, 400–412.

Schwede, T., 2013. Protein modeling: What happened to the "protein structure gap"? Structure 21, 1531–1540.

Singh, A., Kaushik, R., Mishra, A., Shanker, A., Jayaram, B., 2016. ProTSAV: A protein tertiary structure analysis and validation server. Biochimica et Biophysica Acta (BBA)-Proteins and Proteomics 1864, 11–19.

Song, Y., Dimaio, F., Wang, R.Y.-R., *et al.*, 2013. High-resolution comparative modeling with RosettaCM. Structure, 21. pp. 1735–1742.

Sousounis, K., Haney, C.E., Cao, J., Sunchu, B., Tsonis, P.A., 2012. Conservation of the three-dimensional structure in non-homologous or unrelated proteins. Human Genomics 6, 10.

Sowmya, G., Khan, J.M., Anand, S., *et al.*, 2014. A site for direct integrin $\alpha v\beta 6 \cdot$ uPAR interaction from structural modelling and docking. Journal of Structural Biology 185, 327–335.

Starr, C., Taggart, R., Evers, C., Starr, L., 2011. Biology: The Unity and Diversity of Life. 12th ed. Belmont: Brooks/Cole.

Tanaka, K., Cao, Y., Cho, S.-H., Xu, D., Stacey, G., 2016. Computational analysis of the ligand binding site of the extracellular ATP receptor, DORN1. PLOS ONE 11, e0161894.

Tautermann, C.S., 2014. GPCR structures in drug design, emerging opportunities with new structures. Bioorganic & Medicinal Chemistry Letters 24, 4073–4079.

Taylor W., Patterns in Protein Sequence and Structure 1992, Berlin, Heidelberg, Springer-Verlag.

Thangudu, R.R., Manoharan, M., Srinivasan, N., *et al.*, 2008. Analysis on conservation of disulphide bonds and their structural features in homologous protein domain families. BMC Structural Biology 8, 55.

Ul-Haq, Z., Saeed, M., Halim, S.A., Khan, W., 2015. 3D structure prediction of human β1-adrenergic receptor via threading-based homology modeling for implications in structure-based drug designing. PLOS ONE 10, e0122223.

Van Der Kant, R., Vriend, G., 2014. Alpha-bulges in G protein-coupled receptors. International Journal of Molecular Sciences 15, 7841–7864.

Venkatakrishnan, A., Deupi, X., Lebon, G., *et al.*, 2013. Molecular signatures of G-protein-coupled receptors. Nature 494, 185–194.

Voet, D., Voet, J.G., Pratt, C.W., 2016. Fundamentals of biochemistry: Life at the molecular level, Life at the Molecular Level, fifth ed. Wiley.

Vriend, G., 1990. WHAT IF: A molecular modeling and drug design program. Journal of Molecular Graphics 8, 52–56.

Webb, B., Sali, A., 2014. Protein structure modeling with MODELLER. Methods in Molecular Biology 1137, 1–15.

Wooley, J.C., Ye, Y., 2007. A historical perspective and overview of protein structure prediction In: XU, Y., XU, D. & LIANG, J. (eds.) Computational Methods for Protein Structure Prediction and Modeling: vol. 1: Basic Characterization. New York: Springer.

Yang, J., Yan, R., Roy, A., *et al.*, 2015. The I-TASSER Suite: Protein structure and function prediction. Nature Methods 12, 7–8.

Zhang, J., Liang, Y., Zhang, Y., 2011. Atomic-level protein structure refinement using fragment-guided molecular dynamics conformation sampling. Structure 19, 1784–1795.

Zhang, Y., 2008. I-TASSER server for protein 3D structure prediction. BMC Bioinformatics 9, 40.

Further Reading

Childers, M.C., Daggett, V., 2017. Insights from molecular dynamics simulations for computational protein design. Molecular Systems Design & Engineering 2, 9–33.

Bujnicki, J.M. (Ed.), 2008. Prediction of Protein Structures, Functions, and Interactions. John Wiley & Sons.

Dakal, T.C., Kumar, R., Ramotar, D., 2017. Structural modeling of human organic cation transporters. Computational Biology and Chemistry 68, 153–163.

Eswar, N., Eramian, D., Webb, B., *et al.*, 2008. Protein structure modeling with MODELLER. Structural Proteomics: High-Throughput Methods. 145–159.

França, T.C.C., 2015. Homology modeling: An important tool for the drug discovery. Journal of Biomolecular Structure and Dynamics 33 (8), 1780–1793.

Mackenzie, C.O., Grigoryan, G., 2017. Protein structural motifs in prediction and design. Current Opinion in Structural Biology 44, 161–167.

Platform, A.E., 2005. Introduction to the Discovery Studio Visualizer. *San Diego, California, USA*: Accelrys Software Inc.

Rangwala, H., Karypis, G. (Eds.), 2011. Introduction to Protein Structure Prediction: Methods and Algorithms 18. John Wiley & Sons.

Schmidt, T., Bergner, A., Schwede, T., 2014. Modelling three-dimensional protein structures for applications in drug design. Drug Discovery Today 19, 890–897.

Sheehan, D., O'sullivan, S., 2011. Online homology modelling as a means of bridging the sequence-structure gap. Bioengineered Bugs 2 (6), 299–305.

Stansfeld, P.J., 2017. Computational studies of membrane proteins: From sequence to structure to simulation. Current Opinion in Structural Biology 45, 133–141.

Venko, K., Choudhury, A.R., Novič, M., 2017. Computational approaches for revealing the structure of membrane transporters: Case study on Bilitranslocase. Computational and Structural Biotechnology Journal 15, 232–242.

Relevant Websites

https://salilab.org/modeller/tutorial/
    Modeller.

https://www.predictprotein.org
   Predictprotein.
https://www.rcsb.org/pdb/explore/explore.do?structureId=1u19
   Protein Data Bank.
http://www.UniProt.org/UniProt/P51490
   Uniprot.

Biographical Sketch

Amara Jabeen is a PhD student in the Department of Chemistry and Biomolecular sciences at Macquarie University. She is working on functional annotation of odorant receptors using bioinformatics approaches. She is predicting the structures of olfactory receptors through computational methods. She has worked on genome wide analysis of T6SS proteins in *Acidovorax avenae* subsp. *avenae*, *Acidovorax avenae* subsp. *citrulli* AACOO1 and *Acidovorax avenae* subsp. *avenae* ATCC19860 through bioinformatics approaches. She has also worked on structure prediction of Lipase H and bioinformatics analysis of Lipase H and Extracellular matrix protein 1 (ECM1).

Abidali Mohamedali is Lecturer at Macquarie University in the Faculty of Science and Engineering. He completed his PhD in 2010 studying, using proteomics, the effects of single mutations in mouse model on brain development in the autism spectrum disorder, Rett syndrome. He then returned to Macquarie University undertaking a post-doc to study the biology of metastasis in colorectal cancer using proteomics and to determine novel therapeutic targets and develop novel technologies to examine the plasma proteome.

Shoba Ranganathan holds a Chair in Bioinformatics at Macquarie University since 2004. She has held research and academic positions in India, United States, Singapore and Australia, as well as a consultancy in industry. Shoba's research addresses several key areas of bioinformatics to understand biological systems using computational approaches. Her group has achieved both experience and expertise in different aspects of computational biology, ranging from metabolites and small molecules to biochemical networks, pathway analysis and computational systems biology. She has authored as well as edited several books, as well as contributed several articles to Springer's Encyclopedia of Systems Biology. She is currently the Editor-in-Chief of Elsevier's Encyclopedia of Bioinformatics and Computational Biology, as well as the Bioinformatics Section Editor for Elsevier's Reference Module in Life Sciences.

Structure-Based Drug Design Workflow

Ari Hardianto, Macquarie University, Sydney, NSW, Australia and Universitas Padjadjaran, Jatinangor, Indonesia
Muhammad Yusuf, Universitas Padjadjaran, Jatinangor, Indonesia
Fei Liu and Shoba Ranganathan, Macquarie University, Sydney, NSW, Australia

Introduction

Drug discovery in pharmaceutical companies was dominated by the process of generating synthetic compounds through combinatorial chemistry where many trials and errors occur, with a hope obtaining new active compounds (Li, 2013). It was a long way with a lot of efforts which spends time, money, and labor. For an illustration, pharmaceutical companies typically required 10–15 years with expenditure around US$800 to US$1.8 billion to release a drug to the market (Macalino *et al.*, 2015). With advances in high-throughput crystallography, computer hardware, and molecular modeling software, a new approach was introduced in the drug development by employing the three-dimensional (3D) structure of the biological target to design active molecules rationally. This method is called structure-based drug design (SBDD). SBDD started to flourish after the discovery of an HIV protease inhibitor (saquinavir) which exploited the 3D structure of the target macromolecule in its rational design (Li, 2013). Since then, SBDD has become an established tool which accelerates the process of drug development. Nowadays, SBDD is an integral part of the drug discovery and development in many modern pharmaceutical companies (Macalino *et al.*, 2015; Muegge *et al.*, 2017). **Fig. 1** summarizes the workflow for SBDD which includes target selection, target structure evaluation, binding site identification, molecular docking and scoring, and lead compound optimization to generate new drug.

Steps Involved in the Process of SBDD

Drug Target Selection

Selection of drug targets is the first step in SBDD. It is an essential part because SBDD relies on the 3D of target macromolecules in the process of drug design. Drug targets can be enzymes, receptors, ion channels, transport proteins, DNA/RNA and the ribosome, or targets of monoclonal antibodies (Imming *et al.*, 2006). Drug targets are identified and validated through direct biochemical approaches, genetic interaction, computational inference techniques or combination of these methods. These methods are comprehensively reviewed by Schenone (Schenone *et al.*, 2013). A thorough literature survey can assists in the selection of drug targets associated with the small molecules of interest.

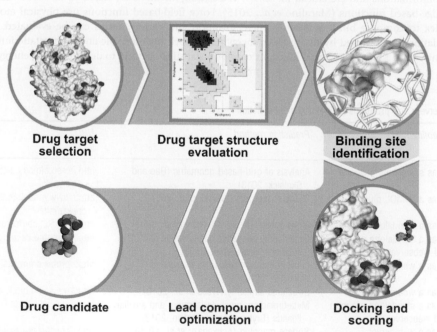

**Drug target
selection**

**Drug target structure
evaluation**

**Binding site
identification**

Drug candidate

**Lead compound
optimization**

**Docking and
scoring**

Fig. 1 Workflow of structure-based drug design (SBDD).

Evaluation of Drug Target Structures

Once the drug target has been identified, the next step is obtaining its 3D-structure from the Protein Data Bank (PDB; see "Relevant Websites section") or Cambridge Crystallographic Data Center (see "Relevant Websites section"). Experimental methods for determining the drug target structures are X-ray crystallography, nuclear magnetic resonance (NMR), and cryo-electron microscopy (EM) approaches. Crystal structures are the widely used source of structural information for drug design (Anderson, 2003; Petsko and Ringe, 2010). The quality of crystal structures is usually assessed from their resolutions, R factors, coordinate errors, temperature factors, and chemical correctness (Anderson, 2003). These parameters are usually reported in the 'REMARK' part of the PDB file. Crystal structure with resolution up to 2.5 Å is acceptable for drug design. The R factor and R_{free}, which reflect the correlation between the model and experiment, should be below 25 and 28%, respectively. The coordinate error must be between 0.2 and 0.3 Å. Temperature factors of atoms, which indicate an atomic position error, are less than the average temperature factor for the molecule. Stereochemical deviations of bond angles and lengths are less than 3° and 0.015 Å, respectively, whereas planar atoms should be less than 0.015 Å out of the plane. Ramachandran plot is then used to assess the chemical correctness of backbone φ and ψ angles where the percentage of at least 90% in the most favored regions are preferred (Laskowski et al., 2001).

However, if experimental structures are unavailable, comparative modeling, threading, or *ab initio* protein modeling is used to generate 3D-models for drug targets. The same evaluation parameters are applied to the generated models. A great number of programs are available for protein structure validation, for instance, PROCHECK (Laskowski et al., 2001) and WHATIF (Rodriguez et al., 1998).

Binding Site Identification

The binding site is usually a hollow part or pocket of the drug target where the small molecule or ligand binds (Macalino et al., 2015). The features of the binding site that are important for ligand binding include potential H-bond donors and acceptors, unique hydrophobic surfaces and molecular surface size (Anderson, 2003; Macalino et al., 2015). The knowledge of ligand binding site and its features are essential in SBDD and can be extracted from experimental structures and mutation studies. However, the information of ligand binding site may be unavailable. Fortunately, *in silico* approaches are there that can be used to predict potential binding sites. These approaches are implemented in many programs or online servers. A list of binding site prediction servers and programs are summarized in **Table 1**.

Molecular Docking

Once the drug target and its binding site are identified, structures of small molecules (ligands) are modified *in silico*. The modified ligands are usually subjected to molecular docking to predict binding modes and affinities of ligands (Forli et al., 2016). Molecular docking methodologies (listed in **Table 2**) consist of searching algorithms and scoring functions. These searching algorithms explore possible conformations of small molecules while interacting with residues in the binding site. The scoring functions then rank the possible conformations and are crucial for SBDD. The scoring functions are classified into force field-based, empirical-based, and knowledge-based functions (Macalino et al., 2015). Force field-based functions use physical atomic contacts in the target-ligand complex to compute binding affinity, where solvation and entropy terms can be evaluated. In empirical-based functions, the calculation is performed by fitting fewer energy terms, such hydrophobic and electrostatic interactions, to experimental binding affinity data. Knowledge-based functions employ a statistical method to derive binding energy from a training set of protein-ligand.

Table 1   Popular servers and programs for binding site prediction

Program/ server	Availability	Prediction method	URL
Cavitator	Free as standalone program	Analysis of grid-based geometric (Gao and Skolnick, 2013)	http://cssb.biology.gatech.edu/Cavitator
PocketFinder	Free as a PyMOL plugin	Shape descriptors (Weisel et al., 2007)	http://www.modeling.leeds.ac.uk/pocketfinder/
fpocket	Free as a standalone program	Alpha sphere theory (Guilloux et al., 2009)	http://fpocket.sourceforge.net/
ConCavity	Free as a standalone program and webserver	Evolutionary sequence conservation and 3D structure (Capra et al., 2009)	http://compbio.cs.princeton.edu/concavity/
ProBis	Free as a web server	Local structural alignments (Konc and Janežič, 2010)	http://probis.cmm.ki.si/index.php
3DLigandSite	Free as a web server	Structures similarity (Wass et al., 2010)	http://www.sbg.bio.ic.ac.uk/~3dligandsite/
eFindSite	Free as a standalone program and webserver	Meta-threading, machine learning, and auxiliary ligands (Brylinski and Feinstein, 2013)	http://brylinski.cct.lsu.edu/efindsite
ConSurf	Free as a web server	Surface-mapping (Ashkenazy et al., 2016)	http://consurf.tau.ac.il/2016/

Table 2   Available molecular docking packages

Program	Availability	Website
AutoDock	Free	http://autodock.scripps.edu/
AutoDock Vina	Free	http://vina.scripps.edu/
DOCK	Free	http://dock.compbio.ucsf.edu/
ICM	Commercial	http://www.molsoft.com/
cDocker	Commercial	http://accelrys.com
LigandFit	Commercial	http://accelrys.com
LibDock	Commercial	http://accelrys.com
FLIPDock	Free	http://flipdock.scripps.edu/

Table 3   ADMET prediction programs and webservers

Program/webserver	Availability	Websites
SwissADME	Free as a webserver	http://www.swissadme.ch/
admetSAR	Free as a standalone software	http://lmmd.ecust.edu.cn/admetsar1/
FAF-Drugs4	Free as a webservers	http://fafdrugs4.mti.univ-paris-diderot.fr/
ALOGPS	Free as a webservers	http://www.vcclab.org/lab/alogps/
QikProp	Commercial	https://www.schrodinger.com/
ADMET Predictor	Commercial	http://www.simulations-plus.com/software/admet-property-prediction-qsar/
ADMET and predictive toxicology	Commercial	http://accelrys.com/products/collaborative-science/biovia-discovery-studio/qsar-admet-and-predictive-toxicology.html

Lead Compound Optimization

The lead compound suggested by molecular docking is then subjected to a cycle of optimization. The compound must be synthesized and assessed by both *in vivo* and *in vitro* experiments. After these experiments conducted, the step returns to the computational stages. Another analog can be developed and estimated for their binding affinity through molecular docking. Since molecular docking roughly estimates the binding affinity of binding for ligands to the target macromolecule, another sophisticated approach like molecular dynamics or free energy perturbation may be required to obtain more realistic conformations of new analogs or binding affinity predictions (Forli *et al.*, 2016). Subsequently, the analogs are synthesized in the laboratory and assayed for their binding affinities. These computational and experiment are iteratively performed until the desired binding affinity of the ligand is reached (Macalino *et al.*, 2015).

At the final step of lead compound optimization, analyses of absorption, distribution, metabolism, excretion, and toxicity (ADMET) are highly required (Macalino *et al.*, 2015). After being administered to the body, drugs may need to absorb properly by crossing various barriers like a gastrointestinal tract to enter the bloodstream. Through bloodstream, drugs are then distributed to their effector sites in muscles or organs where they are metabolized and then excreted. Few of the drug metabolisms may result in toxic compounds which can be hazardous. There are many web servers and programs available for predicting ADMET, for instance, QikProp, SwissADME, and ADMET Predictor. Thus, ADMET estimation can be optionally performed before synthesis step for prioritizing compounds suggested by molecular docking (**Table 3**).

Practical Applications of SBDD in Pharmaceutical Industry

HIV Anti-Viral Drug

SBDD has engendered the pharmaceutical industry with many successes for instance drugs for HIV, influenza, and cancer. The discovery of an antiviral drug for HIV was the leading example and the milestone for the establishment of SBDD. Advancements in crystallography technique lead to the determination of structure for HIV protease in the late 1980s. Saquinavir, the first anti-HIV drug was developed using the crystal structure of the protease. Since then the further development assisted by SBDD have yielded nine FDA-approved anti-HIV drugs the latest one is darunavir (Li, 2013).

Influenza Anti-Viral Drug

SBDD has also contributed to the discovery of influenza antiviral drugs. By using the crystal structure of neuraminidase (NA), zanamivir was designed from 2-deoxy-2,3-didehydro-N-acetylneuraminic acid (DANA) as the lead compound. The knowledge

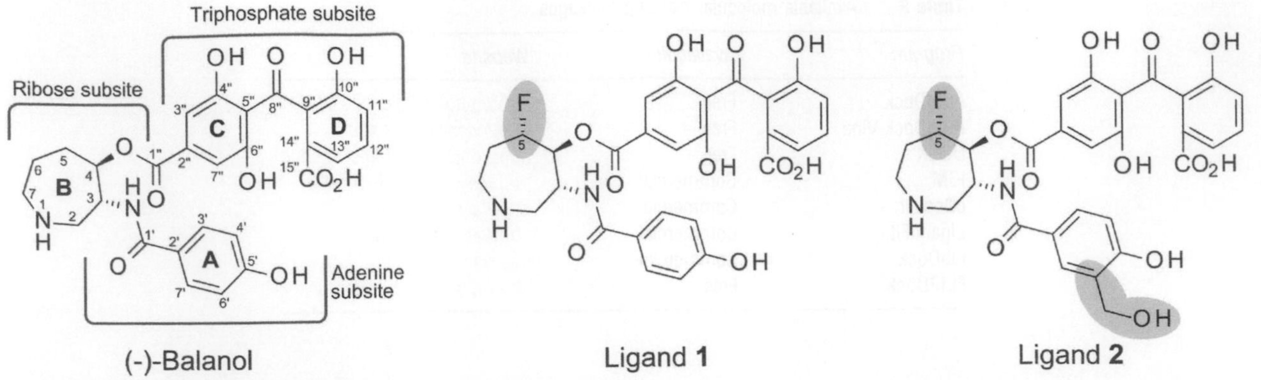

Fig. 2 Structures of balanol and its fluorinated analogs. The balanol structure has been divided into three moieties that correspond to different subsites based on its structural overlay with ATP.

extracted from the crystal structures of NA in complex with DANA and zanamivir also helped in the design of oseltamivir which has a more improved bioavailability than zanamivir. After the discovery of oseltamivir (OTV), the overlaid crystal structure of a furanose isomer with DANA in complex with N9 subtype revealed that the four functional groups (side chains) in both complexes had similar orientation and interactions in the binding site. Therefore, it was concluded that the central ring is not an absolute factor in the development of potential NA inhibitors. Instead, it is the relative position of the functional groups in the active site which is important (Babu *et al.*, 2000). For this reason, cyclopentane-based compounds (different central ring from the previous compounds) were developed and as a result peramivir was discovered. In 2006, FDA approved the usage of peramivir in the injectable formulation (Itzstein and Thomson, 2009).

Case Study

To illustrate SBDD, protein kinase C ε (PKCε) is employed as an example. Unlike other PKC isoforms that possess ambiguous roles in cancer development, PKCε shows clear oncogenic activities and is implicated in invasion and metastasis of cancer cells, such as human breast, glioma, and renal carcinoma (Garg *et al.*, 2014). A fungal natural product, called balanol, was discovered to competitively inhibit PKCε targeting its ATP site (Kulanthaivel *et al.*, 1993). However, the compound also unselectively inhibits other PKC isoforms. Interestingly, a stereospecific fluorination on balanol yielded an analog (hereafter mentioned as ligand **1**) with enhanced activity and selectivity to PKCε (Patel *et al.*, 2017).

The structure of balanol is an ATP mimic and divided into benzamide (ring A), azepane (ring B), and benzophenone (ring C and D) moieties. It completely occupies the ATP binding site (Taylor *et al.*, 2004). In particular, the benzamide moiety replaces the adenine subsite, whereas the azepane and the benzophenone moieties fill the ribose and the triphosphate subsites, respectively (**Fig. 2**).

Here, SBDD is utilized to design another new analog of balanol with improved binding activity to PKCε. Since the experimental structure of PKCε is unavailable, its 3D model was generated using homology modeling. To build the model, two crystal structures, a mouse protein kinase A (PDB ID 1BX6) and a human PKCθ (3TXO), were used as templates. The details about homology modeling method are presented in another article of this book.

The following part is dedicated to demonstrate how SBDD, using a molecular docking approach assists in predicting binding affinity of ligand **1** and another analog of fluorinated balanol (ligand **2**). A widely used program AutoDock (Forli *et al.*, 2016) is used in this case study. Autodock is freely available and can be downloaded from "see Relevant Websites section". Discovery Studio Visualizer and AutoDockTools are utilized in the molecular docking preparation and analysis. Discovery Studio Visualizer is freely distributed at "see Relevant Websites section", whereas AutoDockTools (ADT) which is part of MGLTools can be downloaded from "see Relevant Websites section". Coordinate files of the ligands and PKCε are provided as SBDD.zip.

Ligand Preparation

1. Create the coordinate files for ligands. The coordinates for the two ligands used in this case study were generated using homology modeling, which included a ligand mapping from the template 1BX6 to the resulting homology model of PKCε. The balanol structure was modified in Discovery Studio Visualizer to yield two fluorinated balanol analogs as ligands for PKCε. The first ligand is balanol with a fluorine atom on the position of C(5S) which is provided as ligand_1.pdb. It was prepared by the following steps (**Fig. 3**): open the balanol structure (bal.pdb) in Discovery Studio Visualizer program, select C5, on the menu bar choose 'Chemistry → Hydrogens → Add', then select the hydrogen atom on the position of C(5S), on the menu bar select 'Chemistry → Element → F' (**Fig. 3**). Ligand **2** is the further modification of the first ligand with an additional hydroxymethyl on the benzamide moiety. The coordinate file of this ligand is provided as ligand_2.pdb. Both ligands have negative charges on

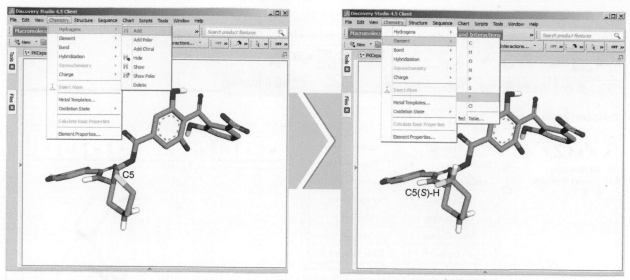

Fig. 3 Steps in incorporating the fluorine substituent to the azepane ring of balanol. Fluorine was added to the position C5(*S*).

the phenolic C6″OH and carboxylic C15″O$_2$H and a positive charge on the secondary amine N1 as suggested by our previous investigation (Hardianto *et al.*, 2017).

2. Load the coordinate file of the first ligand (ligand_1.pdb) to ADT. On ADT menu, choose 'Ligand → Input → Open' and select 'PDB files' for the file type, then browse to the folder where ligand_1.pdb is located, select the file and click 'Open'. ADT will add charges if required, merge nonpolar hydrogens, and assign suitable atom types. The ligand will appear in the viewer window. Click 'OK' on the popup window.

3. Prepare the PDBQT file for the first ligand (ligand_1.pdb). To do this, select 'Ligand → Torsion Tree → Detect Root' which will identify the center of the torsion tree. For this study case, we use the default torsional degrees of freedom. However, if a customization of such degree of freedom is needed, select 'Ligand → Torsion Tree → Choose Torsions'. Rotatable bonds are denoted in green and rigid ones are in the red, whereas non-rotatable bonds that are potentially rotatable are in magenta. Click the bonds to change the rotation flexibility. Click 'Done' to complete this step. Select 'Ligand → Output → Save as PDBQT', and then choose 'Save' to write the file ligand_1.pdbqt.

Receptor Preparation

Prepare the coordinate file of the receptor, i.e., PKCε. The coordinate file for receptor was generated using a homology modeling approach and is provided as PKCepsilon.pdb. Open the file by clicking 'Grid → Macromolecule → Open', and choose 'PDB files (.pdb)' for the file type. Click on file PKCepsilon.pdb and click 'Open'. A popup window will appear, click 'Save' to write the file PKCepsilon.pdbqt (**Fig. 4**).

Grid Maps Preparation and Generation

1. Prepare a grid parameter for generating the atomic affinity maps. Select 'Grid → Macromolecule → Choose' and choose 'PKCepsilon' in the popup window. Select 'Grid → Set Map Types → Choose Ligand' and choose 'bal_1c'. Set the grid box of the search space by selecting 'Grid → Grid Box', which prompts a window for defining the center and size of the box. Choose 'Center → Center on Ligand' to define a minimal box. To adjust the size and center of the box, drag left the thumbwheels to decrease or right to increase the value. Choose 'File → Close Saving Current'. Select 'Output → Save GPF' to save the grid parameter file as 'ligand_1.gpf'.

2. Run AutoGrid from the command line. Open a terminal window and go to the directory where the coordinate files and grid parameter file (ligand_1.gpf) are located. Make sure executable file of AutoGrid (autogrid4) is in the same directory. Type the following command:

```
autogrid4.exe -p ligand_1.gpf -l ligand_1.glg
```

Molecular Docking

1. Create a docking parameter file. Select the receptor PDBQT file by clicking 'Docking → Macromolecule → Set Rigid Filename' and choose 'PKCepsilon.pdbqt' in the directory where it is located. For the ligand, click 'Docking → Ligand → Choose' and

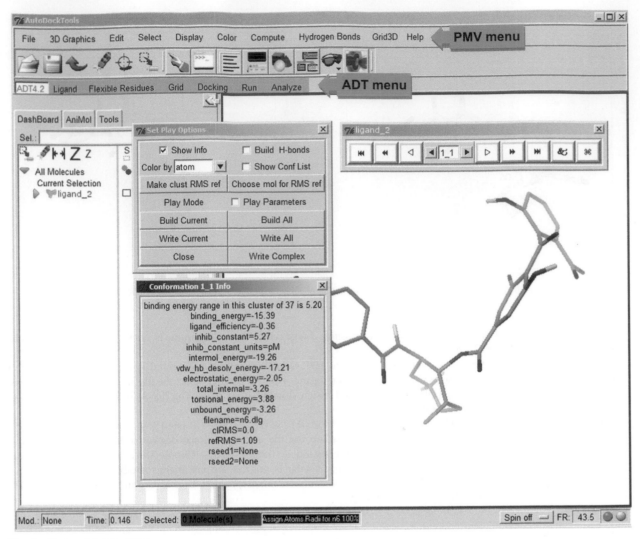

Fig. 4 Display of AutoDockTools.

select 'ligand_1', and accept the default ligand docking parameters. To set searching parameters, click 'Docking → Search Parameters → Genetic Algorithm Parameters', change 'Number of GA Runs' to 50, and accept the rest default parameters. Then click 'Docking → Docking Parameters' and use default parameters. Select 'Docking → Output → Lamarckian GA' to write the docking parameter file as 'ligand_1.dpf'.

2. Run AutoDock from the command line. In a terminal window, go to the directory containing the coordinate files and docking parameter (ligand_1.dpf). By assuming AutoDock (autodock4.exe) is in the same directory with the coordinate files and docking parameter, type the following command

```
autodock4.exe -p ligand_1.dpf -l ligand_1.dlg
```

Analysis

1. Visualize the molecular docking results. Load the results by selecting 'Analyze → Dockings → Open' and choose the ligand_1. dlg file. Select 'Analyze → Conformations → Play Ranked By Energy' to visualize the docking result. Click '&'-like button to open 'Set Play Options' panel, then check 'Show info' to display 'conformation info' dialog box which contains predicted binding energy and its components. When displaying the conformation 1, on the Set Play Options dialog box, click 'Build Current' and save the conformation of docked ligand 1 as conf1_ligand_1.pdbqt in your current working directory.

2. Visualize docking pose cluster based on binding energy values. To do this, select 'Analyze → Clustering → Show'.

3. Visualize ligand-protein interaction in Discovery Studio Visualizer. On Discovery Studio Visualizer, click 'File → Open' and select conf1_ligand_1.pdbqt in your working directory. On the left side of Discovery Studio Visualizer window, click 'View Interactions' and then 'Ligand interactions'.s

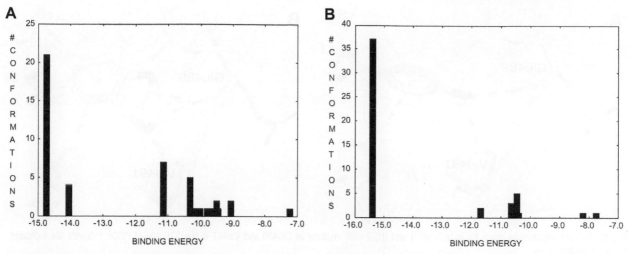

Fig. 5 Binding-energy-based clustering of docking poses of ligands (A) **1** and (B) **2** in the ATP site of PKCε.

For ligand **2**, steps in sections "Ligand Preparation" to "Molecular Docking" are applied to predict the binding affinity of this balanol analog, except Section "Ligand Preparation" step 1.

Discussion

Ligand **1** has an experimental binding affinity of 0.40 nM to PKCε. Molecular docking using AutoDock suggests 15 pose clusters based on predicted binding energy for this ligand when it is bound to the ATP site of PKCε. Binding energy values of the clusters span between −7.0 and −15 kcal/mol. The main cluster contains 21 poses with predicted binding energy values near −15 kcal/mol (**Fig. 5(A)**), which are the most negative among the others. In this cluster, the strongest docking pose has a binding energy of −14.74 kcal/mol. According to AutoDock result, the docking pose shows an intermolecular energy of −18.02 kcal/mol, a van der Waals and hydrogen bond (H-bond) desolvation energy of −15.90 kcal/mol, electrostatic energy of −2.12 kcal/mol, total internal energy of −1.96 kcal/mol, torsional energy of 3.28 kcal/mol, and unbound energy of −1.96 kcal/mol.

Visual inspection of this docking pose in the ATP site of PKCε suggests that the hydroxyl group on the benzamide moiety (C5'OH) interacts via two H-bonds with Glu489 and Val491 in the adenine subsite (**Fig. 6(A)**). The benzamide moiety may interact more tightly by introducing an additional hydroxyl group adjacent to C5'OH. The presence of such additional hydrogen group may strengthen the binding of balanol analog to PKCε. However, introducing such hydroxyl group may be problematic, since the presence of two adjacent hydroxyl groups in the benzamide moiety may lead to the unstable compound. Thus the additional hydroxyl group is incorporated as a hydroxymethyl substituent on the benzamide moiety to form the second ligand. The coordinate file of the second ligand is provided as ligand_2.pdb.

Molecular docking of the second ligand to PKCε predicted that the incorporation of the hydroxymethyl group results in an improved binding affinity to this protein kinase. Binding-energy-based grouping in ADT categorizes the resulting docking poses into seven clusters (**Fig. 5(B)**). The major cluster contains 37 docking poses with predicted binding energy values negative than −15 kcal/mol, which shows stronger interaction than the ligand1. Binding energy components of the second ligand are stronger than those of the first ligand such as intermolecular and desolvation energy which is −18.02 and −15.90 kcal/mol, respectively. Furthermore, visual assessment using Discovery Studio Visualizer shows that the presence of an additional hydroxyl group, as a hydroxymethyl substituent, enhances the H-bond interactions between the benzamide moiety and the ATP site of PKCε (**Fig. 6(B)**). This increased interaction resulted in greater binding affinity of the second ligand to PKCε.

Future Directions

In SBDD, molecular docking is a relatively fast and computationally cheap method in the rational drug design process to predict binding modes and affinities of small molecules to the drug targets of interest. However, with the continuous improvement of hardware, other approaches that were previously considered as computationally expensive and demanding are becoming feasible and cheaper. For instance, molecular dynamics simulation (MD), which is supported by the advance development of graphical processing unit (GPU) cards, is now more affordable (Le Grand et al., 2013). Thus, MD can more be routinely applied in SBDD. MD can accommodate protein flexibility and solvation effects, which normally cause problems in scoring and ranking of small molecules while using docking approach (Macalino et al., 2015). Additionally, the development of the accelerated MD versions alleviates the energy barrier issue in conventional one (Miao et al., 2015).

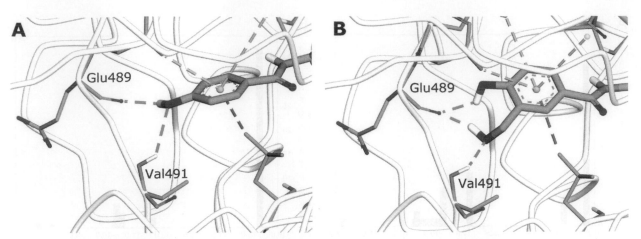

Fig. 6 H-bond interactions made by ligands (A) **1** and (B) **2** with residues of Glu489 and Val491 in the ATP site of PKCε. H-bonds are indicated by green dashed lines.

Another approach in computer-aided drug design is ligand-based drug design (LBDD) which utilizes a set of small molecules with a particular activity and does not need the prior knowledge of the drug target structure. Combining SBDD and LBDD may generate a better outcome in finding novel drug candidates (Macalino *et al.*, 2015).

Closing Remarks

SBDD is a great tool which complements experimental method in the discovery of promising drug candidates. It is now revolutionizing the discovery and development of therapeutic agents by employing the protein structure in the rational drug design. The method reduces the time required as well as failure rate in drug discovery and development. Here, SBDD workflow which includes drug target selection, binding site identification, molecular docking, and ADMET has been described. The practical illustration of molecular docking as a standard tool in SBDD has also been demonstrated.

See also: Algorithms for Structure Comparison and Analysis: Docking. Computational Pipelines and Workflows in Bioinformatics. Host-Pathogen Interactions. Natural Language Processing Approaches in Bioinformatics

---

References

Anderson, A.C., 2003. The process of structure-based drug design. Chemistry & Biology 10, 787–797.

Ashkenazy, H., Abadi, S., Martz, E., *et al.*, 2016. ConSurf 2016: An improved methodology to estimate and visualize evolutionary conservation in macromolecules. Nucleic Acids Research 44, W344–W350.

Babu, Y.S., Chand, P., Bantia, S., *et al.*, 2000. Discovery of a novel, highly potent, orally active, and selective influenza neuraminidase inhibitor through structure-based drug design. Journal of Medicinal Chemistry 43, 482–3486.

Brylinski, M., Feinstein, W., 2013. eFindSite: Improved prediction of ligand binding sites in protein models using meta-threading, learning and auxiliary ligands. Journal of Computer-Aided Molecular Design 27, 551–567.

Capra, J.A., Laskowski, R.A., Thornton, J.M., Singh, M., Funkhouser, T.A., 2009. Predicting protein ligand binding sites by combining evolutionary sequence conservation and 3D structure. PLOS Computational Biology 5, e1000585.

Forli, S., Huey, R., Pique, M.E., *et al.*, 2016. Computational protein-ligand docking and virtual drug screening with the AutoDock suite. Nature Protocols 11, 905–919.

Gao, M., Skolnick, J., 2013. APoc: Large-scale identification of similar protein pocket. Bioinformatics 29, 597–604.

Garg, R., Benedetti, L.G., Abera, M.B., *et al.*, 2014. Protein kinase C and cancer: What we know and what we do not. Oncogene 33, 5225–5237.

Guilloux, V., Le, Schmidtke, P., Tuffery, P., 2009. Fpocket: An open source platform for ligand pocket detection. BMC Bioinformatics 10, 168.

Hardianto, A., Yusuf, M., Liu, F., Ranganathan, S., 2017. Exploration of charge states of balanol analogues acting as ATP-competitive inhibitors in kinases. BMC Bioinformatics. 28, 18 (Suppl 16), 572. http://dx.doi.org/10.1186/s12859-017-1955-7.

Imming, P., Sinning, C., Meyer, A., 2006. Drugs, their targets and the nature and number of drug targets. Nature Reviews Drug Discovery 5, 821–834.

Itzstein, M., Thomson, R., 2009. Anti-influenza drugs: The development of sialidase inhibitors. In: Kräusslich, H.-G., Bartenschlager, R. (Eds.), Antiviral Strategies. Berlin: Springer, pp. 111–154.

Konc, J., Janežič, D., 2010. ProBis: A web server for detection of structurally similar protein binding sites. Nucleic Acids Research 3, W436–W440.

Kulanthaivel, P., Hallock, Y.F., Boros, C., *et al.*, 1993. Balanol: A novel and potent inhibitor of protein kinase C from the fungus Verticillium balanoides. Journal of the American Chemical Society 115, 6452–6453.

Laskowski, R.A., MacArthur, M.W., Thornton, J.M., 2001. PROCHECK: Validation of protein structure coordinates. In: Rossmann, M.G., Arnold, E.D. (Eds.), International Tables of Crystallography, vol. F. Crystallography of Biological Macromolecules. Netherlands: Kluwer Academic Publishers, pp. 722–725.

Le Grand, S., Götz, A.W., Walker, R.C., 2013. SPFP: Speed without compromise – A mixed precision model for GPU accelerated molecular dynamics simulations. Journal of Chemical Theory and Computation 184, 374–380.

Li, J.J., 2013. History of drug discovery. In: ELs. Chichester: John Wiley & Sons, Ltd., pp. 1–42.

Macalino, S.J.Y., Gosu, V., Hong, S., Choi, S., 2015. Role of computer-aided drug design in modern drug discovery. Archives of Pharmacal Research 38, 1686–1701.
Miao, Y., Feher, V.A., McCammon, J.A., 2015. Gaussian accelerated molecular dynamics: Unconstrained enhanced sampling and free energy calculation. Journal of Chemical Theory and Computation 11, 3584–3595.
Muegge, I., Bergner, A., Kriegl, J.M., 2017. Computer-aided drug design at Boehringer Ingelheim. Journal of Computer-Aided Molecular Design 31, 275–285.
Patel, A.R., Hardianto, A., Ranganathan, S., Liu, F., 2017. Divergent response of homologous ATP sites to stereospecific ligand fluorination for selectivity enhancement. Organic & Biomolecular Chemistry 15, 1570–1574.
Petsko, G.A., Ringe, D., 2010. X-ray crystallography in the service of structure-based drug design. In: Merz, K.M., Ringe, D., Reynolds, C.H. (Eds.), Drug Design: Structure- and Ligand-Based Approaches. New York: Cambridge University Press, pp. 17–29.
Rodriguez, R., Chinea, G., Lopez, N., Pons, T., Vriend, G., 1998. Homology modeling, model and software evaluation: Three related resources. Bioinformatics 14, 523–528.
Schenone, M., Dančík, V., Wagner, B.K., Clemons, P., 2013. Target identification and mechanism of action in chemical biology and drug discovery. Nature Chemical Biology 9, 232–240.
Taylor, S.S., Yang, J., Wu, J., et al., 2004. PKA: A portrait of protein kinase dynamics. Biochimica et Biophysica Acta – Proteins and Proteomics 1697, 259–269.
Wass, M.N., Kelley, L.A., Sternberg, M.J., 2010. 3DLigandSite: Predicting ligand-binding sites. Nucleic Acids Research 38, W469–W473.
Weisel, M., Proschak, E., Schneider, G., 2007. PocketPicker: Analysis of ligand binding-sites with shape descriptors. Chemistry Central Journal 1.

Further Reading

Forli, S., Huey, R., Pique, M.E., et al., 2016. Computational protein-ligand docking and virtual drug screening with the AutoDock suite. Nature Protocols 11, 905–919.
Li, J.J., 2013. History of drug discovery. In: eLs. Chichester: John Wiley & Sons, Ltd., pp. 1–42.
Macalino, S.J.Y., Gosu, V., Hong, S., Choi, S., 2015. Role of computer-aided drug design in modern drug discovery. Archives of Pharmacal Research 38, 1686–1701.
Merz, K.M., Ringe, D., Reynolds, C.H., 2010. Drug Design: Structure- and Ligand-Based Approaches. New York: Cambridge University Press.
Muegge, I., Bergner, A., Kriegl, J.M., 2017. Computer-aided drug design at Boehringer Ingelheim. Journal of Computer-Aided Molecular Design 31, 275–285.

Relevant Websites

http://autodock.scripps.edu/
 AutoDock.
http://accelrys.com/products/collaborative-science/biovia-discovery-studio/visualization-download.php
 Discovery Studio Visualization.
http://mgltools.scripps.edu
 MGLTools Website.
http://www.rcsb.org/
 RCSB PDB.
http://www.ccdc.cam.ac.uk/
 The Cambridge Crystallographic Data Centre (CCDC).

Biographical Sketch

Ari Hardianto is a Lecturer in the Department of Chemistry, Universitas Padjadjaran, Indonesia. Ari Hardianto received his PhD from the Department of Chemistry and Biomolecular Sciences at Macquarie University. He has worked on the development of protein kinase C ε inhibitors using structural bioinformatics methods such as homology modeling, molecular docking, and molecular dynamics simulation. He also has research interest in immunoinformatics, chemometrics, and applications of data science in chemistry and molecular biology.

Muhammad Yusuf is a Lecturer in the Department of Chemistry, Universitas Padjadjaran, Indonesia. He is currently the head of Bioinformatics Division at the Research Center of Molecular Biotechnology and Bioinformatics, Universitas Padjadjaran. Muhammad Yusuf received his PhD from the School of Pharmaceutical Sciences, Universiti Sains Malaysia. He has worked on homology modeling, molecular docking, and molecular dynamics simulation to study the behavior of the oseltamivir-resistance neuraminidase, a drug target of influenza virus. He also has a research interest in the molecular modeling study of protein engineering, diagnostics, therapeutics, natural compounds, and rare-earth metal separation.

Fei Liu is a Senior Lecturer in the Department of Molecular Sciences, Macquarie University. She did her PhD studies in Organic Chemistry at Yale University, USA. After her PhD, she moved to Boston, Massachusetts as an NIH postdoctoral fellow to work on new biosynthetic approaches in molecular medicine at the Harvard Medical School. In 2004, Fei moved from Boston to Sydney and is currently a teaching/research academic at Macquarie. The current phase of her research focuses on developing efficient synthetic methods for accessing small molecules with useful properties in chemistry and biology. Her long-term interest in chemical proteomics along with its applications in basic biological discovery and medicine and synthesis of novel candidate cancer drugs.

Shoba Ranganathan holds a Chair in Bioinformatics at Macquarie University since 2004. She has held research and academic positions in India, USA, Singapore and Australia as well as a consultancy in industry. Shoba's research addresses several key areas of bioinformatics to understand biological systems using computational approaches. Her group has achieved both experience and expertise in different aspects of computational biology, ranging from metabolites and small molecules to biochemical networks, pathway analysis and computational systems biology. She has authored as well as edited several books in as well as contributed several articles to Springer's Encyclopedia of Systems Biology. She is currently the Editor-in-Chief of Elsevier's Encyclopedia of Bioinformatics and Computational Biology as well as the Bioinformatics Section Editor for Elsevier's Reference Module in Life Sciences.

Network-Based Analysis for Biological Discovery

Lokesh P Tripathi, Yi-An Chen, and Kenji Mizuguchi, National Institutes of Biomedical Innovation, Health and Nutrition, Osaka, Japan
Yoichi Murakami, Tokyo University of Information Sciences, Wakaba-ku, Chiba, Japan

Introduction

Biological processes are complex systems, involving many interactions among elementary units of a living system; these include biological macromolecules such as DNA, RNA, proteins, lipids and also small molecule metabolites. To describe such processes, a common representation is a network model in which, the participating biomolecules are represented as *nodes* and the relationships or links between them as *edges*. Proteins are the most important biological building blocks and they carry out their functions in the cells by interacting with each other. Therefore, it is not surprising that the largest amount of biomolecular interaction data is available for PPIs and consequently, the substantial chunk of biological network analysis encompasses the construction and analysis of PPI networks (PPINs). PPIs are crucial to the formation of macromolecular structures and enzymatic complexes that form the basis of nearly every cellular process ranging from signal transduction and cellular transport to catalysing metabolic reactions, activating or inhibiting other proteins and biomolecular synthesis. PPIs are thus essential to homeostasis and their dysregulation typically leads to cellular dysfunction and is often associated with various diseases. A systematic mapping of protein interactomes, i.e., the entirety of PPIs in a cell or an organism, is necessary to gain a deeper understanding of the roles of PPIs and PPINs in fundamental cellular processes. It also enables a better understanding of the genotype-phenotype relationships and the perturbations that are involved with the onset of complex diseases.

Owing to their high specificity, PPIs are also promising targets to develop drugs that attuned to specific disease-related pathways (Jubb *et al.*, 2015; Wells and McClendon, 2007; Murakami *et al.*, 2017). However, in this review, we will focus on reconstruction and analysis of PPINs and their applications in interpreting available biological data to gain a deeper understanding of cellular processes and disease mechanisms. We first discuss how experimentally defined PPIN data have been generated and utilised for knowledge discovery. Next, we will discuss why *in silico* methods for PPI characterisation are important in a PPIN-based biological research. We will conclude with how future mapping efforts focussing on a more dynamic analysis of PPINs will shape the field.

Experimental Methods to Generate Proteome-Scale Interaction Maps

A variety of powerful experimental techniques are now available to characterise PPIs. Initially, however, interactions between protein pairs were described by independent studies that employed small-scale biochemical or genetic experiments (Koh *et al.*, 2012). The steady improvements in experimental methodologies and the development of new technologies that were more amenable to PPI mapping on a larger scale, such as yeast two-hybrid system (Y2H) (Fields and Song, 1989) (see below), have allowed rapidly increasing amounts of PPIs to be characterised. However, the advent of high-throughput genome sequencing technologies and the genomics breakthrough at the turn of the millennium was a milestone that paved the way for the PPI characterisation on a proteome-wide scale. The appearance of the first draft model organism genome sequences and the accompanying collection of genome-wide open reading frames (ORFs), coupled with the availability of robust, high-throughput PPI detection methods allowed the PPI mapping to truly take off (Luck *et al.*, 2017). Thus, proteome-scale interaction maps have been generated for different proteomes using available experimental techniques that are amenable to large-scale interactome mapping (Vidal *et al.*, 2011; Huttlin *et al.* 2015; Rolland *et al.* 2014).

The experimental methods for PPI mapping can be broadly classified into two groups. The first group consists of methods that are capable of simultaneously investigating a large number of PPIs, often on an interactome scale, whereas the second group consists of methods that are more suited to deeply examine individual PPIs (Tuncbag *et al.*, 2009). The Y2H system is one of the most widely used methods to map binary PPIs. Y2H is an *in vivo* method based on the reconstitution of a functional transcription factor (TF) following an interaction between two proteins and the subsequent activation of reporter genes controlled by the TF (Fields and Song, 1989). It is a scalable and relatively inexpensive method that is well suited to detecting binary interactions between proteins and therefore facilitates the characterisation of physiologically relevant PPIs. Unsurprisingly, Y2H has been the method of choice for generating proteome-wide binary interaction maps for a number of model organisms such as *E. coli* (Rajagopala *et al.*, 2014), Yeast (Uetz *et al.*, 2000; Ito *et al.* 2001; Yu *et al.*, 2008; Vo *et al.*, 2016), *C. elegans* (Li *et al.*, 2004), Drosophila (Formstecher *et al.*, 2005), *Arabidopsis thaliana* (Arabidopsis Interactome Mapping Consortium, 2011) and human (Vidal *et al.*, 2011; Huttlin *et al.*, 2015; Rolland *et al.*, 2014). However, Y2H suffers from a few notable shortcomings; it is less amenable to capturing PPIs involving extracellular or membrane proteins, PPIs that require proper folding as a part of protein complex subunits, or PPIs that require post-translational modifications (PTMs). To overcome the limitations of Y2H and to study different types of PPIs, several Y2H variants such as the mammalian cell-based two-hybrid assay (Luo *et al.*, 1997), the membrane-anchored two-hybrid assay (Snider *et al.*, 2010), and the three-hybrid assay (Maruta *et al.*, 2016) have been developed.

PPIs can also be mapped on an interactomic scale by Affinity Purification – Mass Spectrometry (AP-MS) that involves biochemical purification of the epitope-tagged target proteins from the cells, followed by the identification of the components of the purified protein complexes (including proteins interacting with the target protein) using mass-spectrometry analysis (Dunham *et al.*, 2012). AP-MS method has been widely used to characterise protein complexes on a large scale in different species including yeast, Drosophila and human (Guruharsha *et al.*, 2011; Krogan *et al.*, 2006; Ewing *et al.*, 2007). To overcome non-specific detection of co-purified proteins, two-step tandem affinity protein purification systems have been developed (Burckstummer *et al.*, 2006). This approach allows the preparation of a substantially pure target protein complex and reduces the background signals. The quantitative mass-spectrometry analysis also has been used to identify different contaminants (Trinkle-Mulcahy *et al.*, 2008). However, AP-MS data may not always detect binary interactions and often reflects only steady state PPI dynamics, thereby, potentially missing weak and transient interactions.

Another approach is to employ co-fractionation and mass spectrometry to characterise protein complexes. In this method, cellular extracts are subject to intense co-fractionation by using biochemical separation methods such as chromatography and a precise co-elution of proteins is used to determine PPIs. A distinct advantage of this method over AP-MS is that it allows a mapping of dynamic PPIs and the determination of the size of the protein complexes owing to the use of size-exclusion chromatography (Yang *et al.*, 2015). Thus, this method has been used to map protein complexes on a proteome-wide scale in different organisms such as yeast and human (Doerr, 2012; Havugimana *et al.*, 2012; Phanse *et al.*, 2016).

Eventually, a combination of different methods will provide a more comprehensive protein interaction map, since each method will likely lead to the exploration of different aspects of the interactome.

PPIN-Based Network Analysis

PPINs assembled from the experimentally characterised PPI data are an important avenue to understand the organisation of cellular events and the biology of the living systems and complex diseases. PPI data extracted from the proteomic literature and compiled within the expert-curated resources are highly useful in uncovering functional PPINs and for guiding subsequent research. However, such data are scattered across multiple databases that differ in scope and content, i.e., the type and number of PPIs they contain, the number of organisms that are covered and the experimental and computational methods that were used for PPI characterisation. Therefore, combining different PPI maps is necessary to obtain a complete view of protein interactomes (Razick *et al.*, 2008; Chen *et al.*, 2011; Chen *et al.*, 2016).

However, the combined PPI datasets will likely be noisy and include many false positives that are inherent in experimentally characterised PPIs and therefore, the assembled PPI data must be carefully assessed before using them for PPIN analyses. A relatively simple and commonly used approach is to consider only those PPIs that are determined by at least two different experimental methods or reported in the literature in two different publications (Chen *et al.*, 2016). Biophysical data from the experimentally determined structures of interacting proteins can be useful since they offer detailed insights into how PPIs are formed at the atomic scale (De Las Rivas and Fontanillo, 2010; Erijman *et al.*, 2014; Moal *et al.*, 2011, 2013), but such data are available for very few protein complexes. It is also important to view and analyse the PPIN data in the proper spatiotemporal context such as cellular/tissue specificity, protein subcellular localisation, gene expression patterns, homologous associations and PTMs (Schaefer *et al.*, 2013). A number of studies have employed PPIN analysis to probe a broad spectrum of biomolecular processes and seek answers to key biological questions **(Fig. 1)**.

Network Topology

A typical PPIN is an undirected graph with each protein represented as a *node* and each interaction between two proteins represented as an *edge* **(Fig. 1)**. This wiring or the connectivity of the different proteins within a PPIN is referred to as network topology. There is a strong correlation between the topological properties of a network and its functioning. Therefore, graph theory concepts such as *node degree distribution*, *betweenness centrality* and *shortest path length* have been used to identify key determinants of network function (Raman, 2010) and also to better understand network perturbations. Network 'hubs' are highly connected proteins with many PPIs (that is, they have a high *node degree*); they are therefore likely to have a greater influence on network functioning via multiple interactions. Network 'bottlenecks' are proteins with high *betweenness centrality*; they regulate the flow of signalling information across the network and therefore, represent key nodes for communication (Yu *et al.*, 2007) **(Fig. 1(a))**. Thus, analysing network topologies can be a source of new discoveries such as identifying novel biomarkers and potential drug targets (Csermely *et al.*, 2013; Kotlyar *et al.*2012; Charitou *et al.*, 2016; Gebicke-Haerter, 2016; Hakes *et al.*, 2008). Network topologies have been employed to identify novel disease-associated genes (Vidal *et al.*, 2011; Feldman *et al.*, 2008; Sarajlic *et al.*, 2013) and also to better understand the organisation of localised cellular networks. For example, Gupta *et al.* (2015) mapped the centriole-cilium protein interaction landscape by generating a PPIN consisting of >7000 interactions and using network topology analysis, which led to the discovery of novel insights into human centrosome and cilia biology.

Understanding Disease Mechanisms Based on Network Neighbourhood

An important outcome of using PPIN topology to investigate disease mechanisms is the disease module hypothesis, which is based on the observation that genes associated with the same disease preferentially interact with each other and tend to form

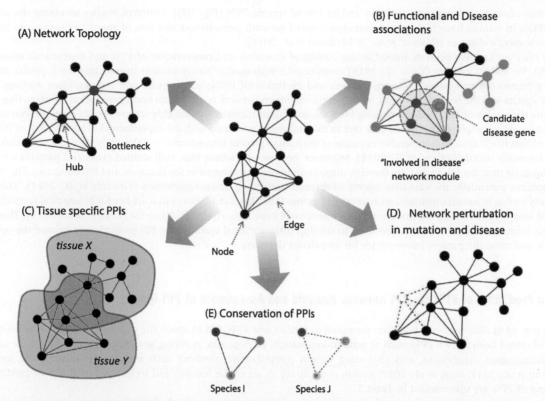

(A) Network Topology

Bottleneck

Hub

(C) Tissue specific PPIs

tissue X

tissue Y

Node

Edge

(B) Functional and Disease associations

Candidate disease gene

"Involved in disease" network module

(D) Network perturbation in mutation and disease

(E) Conservation of PPIs

Species I

Species J

Figure 1 Applications of PPIN-based analysis using large scale protein interactome maps. A reference interactome network is usually illustrated as proteins represented as *nodes* (solid circles) interacting with other proteins via PPIs represented as *edges* (solid lines). Applications of PPINs include (a) Investigating protein function and essentiality using network topology, (b) Understanding disease mechanisms by network neighbourhood, (c) Investigating the context specificity of PPIs such as in the context of cell/tissue-specific interactions (d) PPIN rewiring caused by mutation and/or disease and (e) Leveraging orthologous gene associations to map PPIs across species.

well-connected clusters in the same network neighbourhood (Barabasi *et al.*, 2011; Ideker and Sharan, 2008; Menche *et al.*, 2015) **(Fig. 1(b))**. The disease module hypothesis has attracted much interest from the researchers, since a given set of disease-causing genes can provide a deeper insight into related diseases. This is carried out by collating other disease-causing genes, by defining tightly interconnecting communities of functionally related or disease-related proteins and then retrieving the uncharacterised neighbouring genes connected with the initial "seed" genes by *shortest paths*. For instance, Huttlin and colleagues constructed BioPlex, a network of experimentally derived human PPIs and defined many protein communities and subnetworks that enabled functional characterisation of poorly characterised human proteins, including many with novel roles in human diseases such as cancer and hypertensive disease (Huttlin *et al.*, 2015, 2017). Rolland and co-workers also demonstrated that known cancer-associated genes are highly interconnected in the human protein interactome (Rolland *et al.*, 2014).

Context-Specificity of Protein Interactomes

Complex diseases are usually very site-specific and mostly impact specific cells and/or tissues (Goh *et al.*, 2007; Magger *et al.*, 2012). Therefore, it is necessary to examine the PPI data, in cellular and tissue context, such as cell/tissue-specific expression of proteins, the relative abundance of alternatively spliced isoforms and PTMs and their impact on the interactome of different cells and tissues. Magger and co-workers, for instance, observed that using tissue-specific PPI networks, greatly enhanced the prioritisation of candidate disease-causing genes compared with generic PPINs and also highlight novel tissue-disease associations (Magger *et al.*, 2012).

PPIN Rewiring During Disease, Mutation and Evolution

The rapid proliferation of high-quality sequence data generation using low-cost Next Generation Sequencing (NGS) experimental platforms coupled with speedy bioinformatics methods have contributed to the mapping of a large number of sequence and structural variants associated with clinically relevant phenotypes and diseases. Although there is a limited understanding of causal relationships between various mutations and diseases, it has been well established that functional variants may often impact overall protein functions including PPIs (Shameer *et al.*, 2016). Comparative PPIN analysis, therefore, offers a promising avenue to examine the genotype-phenotype relationships underlying key biological processes and the causative mechanisms of disease-causing mutations emanating from the gain and/or loss of specific PPIs (**Fig. 1(d)**). Different studies involving the analysis of global PPINs in human have highlighted mutation-induced network perturbation and loss of specific PPIs that can be reliably linked with specific diseases (Rolland *et al.*, 2014; Sahni *et al.*, 2015).

PPIN rewiring has also been examined in the context of evolution and conservation of PPIs and interactions across species (**Fig. 1(e)**). Vo and co-workers (Vo *et al.*, 2016) constructed a high-quality binary protein interactome for *S. pombe* and implemented a framework to compare the organisation and evolution of PPINs across yeast and human. Their findings revealed extensive species-specific network rewiring and novel paradigms on network co-evolution and conservation of interacting proteins.

Despite the wealth of knowledge emerging from the analysis of increasingly available large-scale PPI data, the known protein interactomes are incomplete. This is not only due to the challenges associated with the experimental determination of PPIs, it was speculated that to obtain a comprehensive coverage of the human protein interactome, ~ 200 million protein pairs would need to be experimentally tested (Rolland *et al.*, 2014). Moreover, because of systemic bias, well studied genes and proteins are screened more frequently than the others and are thereby, disproportionately represented in the literature and PPI databases. This has led to other proteins, potentially the causative agents of diseases, remaining under-represented (Edwards *et al.*, 2011). This issue is particularly visible in model organisms such as rat and mouse (Murakami *et al.*, 2017) that are key for biomedical research and it is estimated that only $\sim 10\%$ of the human protein interactome have been characterised so far (Kotlyar *et al.*, 2015). Therefore, to generate a complete interactome, it is necessary to develop computational methods for PPI prediction to expand the coverage of PPI space and mine the protein interactomes for knowledge discovery.

In Silico Prediction of PPIs for PPI Network Analysis and Assessment of PPI Quality

A wide range of *in silico* methods has been proposed to predict new PPIs and to assess the quality of existing PPIs using various features obtained from known PPIs, such as gene co-localisation, phylogenetic profiling, gene fusion, domain-domain interaction (DDI), homologous interactions, and also using various computational methods such as machine learning and text mining (Murakami *et al.*, 2017; Peng *et al.*, 2017; Keskin *et al.*, 2016). A list of the features and techniques used for the prediction and assessment of PPIs are summarised in **Table 1**.

In silico methods can be broadly classified into two types: Low-resolution methods that offer a simple binary classification to determine whether a given pair of proteins interact or not, and the high-resolution methods that can predict the detailed interatomic interactions between proteins (Vakser, 2014). The former can generally predict a large number of PPIs at lower cost and in much less time than experimental methods, and are also applicable to the assessment of a large number of existing PPIs. The latter can predict PPIs based on their structural and physicochemical complementarities, i.e., protein docking (Tuncbag *et al.*, 2009; Keskin *et al.*, 2016), and require protein structural information, and therefore, are expensive approaches for characterising the entire interactome.

Although recent advances in docking methodologies have produced reliable protein complex models, docking proteins with large conformational changes and/or without prior knowledge of the PPI sites (*ab initio* docking) remains a non-trivial task (Janin *et al.*, 2003; Janin and Wodak, 2007). To achieve this task, molecular dynamics (MD) simulations, which take into consideration the physical movements of atoms in proteins, have been used to elucidate the precise positions of atoms involved in the interaction; MD simulations, however, are computational resource intensive and therefore, unsuitable for whole interactome modelling.

Consequently, most of the existing *in silico* methods applicable to interactome modelling and PPI assessment rely heavily on previously known PPIs and on primary protein sequence information, which is more widely available than structural information. Below, we discuss the underlying principles of different low-resolution widely applicable *in silico* PPI prediction methods for PPIN analysis.

Table 1   A list of the features and techniques used for the prediction and assessment of PPIs

Utilised feature	*Fundamental concepts*
Protein structure	Structural and physicochemical complementarities.
Interologue	Orthologous PPIs among different species: If two proteins are known to interact in a species X and are conserved in a species Y, these proteins may likely interact in the species Y.
Domain information	Domain-domain interactions, since domains are directly involved in the intermolecular interactions.
Gene neighbourhood	Two proteins are likely to interact when their genes are located in the same region of genome.
Phylogenetic similarity	Functionally related proteins, i.e., interacting proteins, tend to be inherited together during evolution and co-evolve through the interaction. Thus, they have similar topological phylogenetic profiles.
Gene fusion (Domain fusion)	Separate genes can be fused to form a single chimeric gene, which is called as "Rosetta Stone".
Function annotation	Interacting proteins tend to have shared functional annotations since they are often involved in the same biological processes.
Text mining	Grammatical rules to retrieve the co-occurrence of predefined genes or proteins, and the relationship between these entities in repositories such as literature and various databases.
Machine learning	Training a classifier on a set of known PPI data to predict whether or not a given pair of proteins interact, using informative features extracted from the training PPI dataset.

Interologue-Based Methods

Orthologous proteins are descended from a common ancestral gene as a consequence of speciation, and they are believed to retain similarity in structure and function (Fitch, 2000; Koonin, 2005; Watson et al., 2005; Webber and Ponting, 2004), including PPIs. *Interologue-based methods* predict PPIs and assess the quality of existing PPIs based on the biological principle of orthologous PPIs (*interologue*) across different species, that is, if two or more proteins are known to interact in a species *I* and if they have identifiable orthologues in species *J*, the orthologous proteins may also potentially interact in species *J* (**Fig. 1(e)**). This approach is similar to those used for gene function annotation, where a gene function is inferred from the function of homologous genes in other species. A large amount of PPI data are currently available in public databases (Salwinski et al., 2004; Licata et al., 2012; Aranda et al., 2010; Szklarczyk et al., 2015; Chatr-Aryamontri et al., 2017), where orthologous PPIs can be identified. This approach is useful in transferring the annotation of PPIs from one species to another species of interest; for example, it has been applied to predict PPIs in human cancer proteins (Jonsson and Bates, 2006). The accuracy of this approach depends on the reliability of the interactions, so it is considered to be inappropriate for the prediction of transient interactions because such interactions are poorly conserved across species (Keskin et al., 2016). Thus, other features, such as domain co-occurrences, gene co-expression or functional similarity, can be integrated into this approach to assess PPIs and the co-localisation of the proteins predicted to interact, as implemented in PPI-Search (Chen et al., 2009), BIPS (Garcia-Garcia et al., 2012), I2D (Brown and Jurisica, 2005) and PSOPIA (Murakami and Mizuguchi, 2014) (**Table 2**).

Domain-Based Methods

Protein domains are independent evolutionary units, which define protein function. Multiple studies have demonstrated that domain-domain interactions (DDIs) are useful for predicting PPIs, since domains are directly involved in the intermolecular interactions (Memisevic et al., 2013; Shoemaker and Panchenko, 2007). The *domain-based methods* can identify PPIs without relying on homologous interactions that exist in public databases, unlike the *interologue-based approaches*. To use DDIs for the prediction of new PPIs, most methods annotate protein sequences using domain databases such as Pfam (Finn et al., 2016), SCOP2 (Andreeva et al., 2014) and CATH (Sillitoe et al., 2015). There are two types of *domain-based approaches* (Shoemaker and Panchenko, 2007). First type consists of the *association approach-based methods* that are based on the idea that certain domains are frequently observed in interacting proteins and therefore can be used as markers to predict new PPIs (Sprinzak and Margalit, 2001). However, this approach does not consider the relationships of all possible domain pairs in interacting pairs, and also the missing domain pairs not observed in known interacting pairs. The second type is the *Bayesian network approach*, where the interaction probabilities of all possible domain pairs are estimated using the Maximum Likelihood Estimation (Burger and van Nimwegen, 2008; Deng et al., 2002). The accuracy of this approach depends on the reliability of the domain assignments, so a sufficient coverage of domain databases is necessary to obtain sufficient true positives and negatives. This approach can also be used to assess the quality of PPIs since an interaction can be deemed more reliable if they contain domain pairs found in known PPIs in the database (Ng et al., 2003).

In recognition of the limitations of the *domain-based approaches*, a new set of PPI prediction methods have been developed, which are based on the principle of short co-occurring polypeptide regions as mediators of PPIs (Pitre et al., 2012; Schoenrock et al.2014). A distinct advantage of these methods is that unlike the classical *domain-based approaches*, they are designed to predict PPIs solely on the basis of primary sequence and are thus, not handicapped by the absence of characterised protein domains; these methods are therefore much useful for large-scale PPI prediction. For instance, Schoenrock and colleagues (Schoenrock et al.,

Table 2   A selection of *in silico* prediction web servers that are useful for PPI network analysis

Available in silico *prediction web servers for PPI network analysis*

Web server	Method, URL (http://)
BIPS: Biana Interolog Prediction *Server* (Garcia-Garcia et al., 2012)	Interologue (across multiple species)/domain/functional annotation http://sbi.imim.es/web/index.php/research/servers/bips
I2D: Interolog Interaction Database (Brown and Jurisica, 2007)	Interologues (across seven species; human, rat, mouse, fly, worm, yeast and hhv8) http://ophid.utoronto.ca/ophidv2.204
InterologFinder (Wiles et al., 2010)	Interologues (across five species; human, mouse, fly, worm and yeast) http://interologfinder.org/simpleIfWS
PPI-Search: Protein-Protein Interaction Search (Chen et al., 2009)	Interologues (across multiple species)/domain/functional annotation http://140.113.15.76/ppisearch*
PSOPIA: Prediction Server of Protein-Protein Interactions (Murakami and Mizuguchi, 2014)	Homologues (within the human genome)/domain/the shortest path between two homologous proteins http://mizuguchilab.org/PSOPIA*
MirrorTree Server (Ochoa and Pazos, 2010)	Phylogenetic similarity http://csbg.cnb.csic.es/mtserver/

*These servers accept only a single protein pair per submission.

2014) designed a tool to predict human PPINs and validated their prediction results experimentally. They further employed their computationally predicted human PPINs for the prediction of gene functions and formations of PPI complexes in human diseases, some of which were validated by follow-up experimental assays (Schoenrock *et al.*, 2014).

Gene Neighbourhood-Based Methods

Gene co-localisation-based methods are based on the idea that two proteins are likely to interact when their genes are located in the same region of the genome (Tamames *et al.*, 1997). This approach requires a number of genome sequences to predict and assess PPIs using information about the conservation of gene locations, and confidence increases with increasing genome sequences. Although this approach can predict new PPIs without relying on known PPIs reported in the literature or available in databases, it would not be applicable to the eukaryotic genomes, since there is no tangible evidence that two genes which encode for interacting proteins are always co-localised within a genome. Although this approach is simple in comparison with other *in silico* approaches, it often fails to detect interactions between distantly located genes and often generates a high amount of false negatives in the eukaryotic genomes (Zahiri *et al.*, 2013).

Phylogenetic Similarity-Based Methods

There are two types of *phylogenetic similarity-based approaches*. One is the *phylogenetic tree-based approach* (also known as the *mirror tree* approach), which is based on the idea that interacting proteins tend to co-evolve through the interaction and thus have similar topological phylogenetic tree profiles (Sato *et al.*, 2005; Pazos and Valencia, 2001; Goh and Cohen, 2002), as implemented in MirrorTree (Ochoa and Pazos, 2010) **(Table 2)**. However, when a pair of proteins co-evolve through the speciation events even if they do not interact, a large number of false positives are created due to the generation of similar mirror trees (Ochoa and Pazos, 2014). The elimination of non-specific tree similarities have been attempted by different methods, for example, the 16S rRNA tree is used as a representation of the speciation process to normalise the non-specific similarities by subtracting their phylogenetic distances from the distance matrices for a pair of proteins (Sato *et al.*, 2005; Pazos *et al.*, 2005). The second one is the *phylogenetic profile-based approach* that is based on the assumption that functionally related proteins tend to be inherited together during evolution. A phylogenetic profile represents the conservation of a certain protein in various species. Thus, if two proteins are functionally related, they are more likely to have similar phylogenetic profiles (Juan *et al.*, 2008). However, the outcomes of this approach are largely dependent on the number of the species used to construct phylogenetic profiles. Thus, this approach is not very suitable for eukaryotic proteins since there are comparatively fewer eukaryotes with complete genomic sequences than prokaryotes (Muley and Ranjan, 2012).

Gene Fusion-Based Methods

Gene fusion (domain fusion)-based approaches are based on the genetic observation that independent genes can combine or "fuse" together to form a single chimeric gene, known as "Rosetta Stone". The method is based on the observation that two separate proteins are functionally related and are likely to interact if certain proteins in a given species consist of co-localised domains otherwise mapped to different proteins in another species (Enright *et al.*, 1999; Marcotte *et al.*, 1999; Chia and Kolatkar, 2004). Although the gene fusion is an informative feature of the functional relationships between different proteins, it requires a mapping of domain architecture across different genomes and is usually only applicable to those proteins corresponding to well-characterised protein domain families.

Function Annotation-Based Methods

Function annotation-based methods are based on the observation that interacting proteins tend to significantly share function annotations since they are involved in the same biological processes (Peng *et al.*, 2017). This method is often used to assess the quality of existing PPIs and also evaluate the reliability of different sources with experimentally determined PPIs, for example, the reliability is evaluated by computing the faction of interacting proteins that have at least one identical function (Nabieva *et al.*, 2005). Gene Ontology (GO) can be used to define functional similarity between two proteins to assess the quality of existing PPIs (Cho *et al.*, 2007). However, this approach cannot reliably evaluate the quality of PPIs where the interacting proteins are annotated with many different GO terms (Peng *et al.*, 2017).

Text Mining-Based Methods

Text mining-based approaches use grammatical rules to retrieve the co-occurrence of predefined entities, i.e., in biology, genes or proteins, and the relationship between these entities in repositories such as literature and various databases (Papanikolaou *et al.*, 2015). An interaction between two proteins (A, B) can be ascertained if the grammatical rules, such as "A interaction verb B" or "interaction between A and B", are used in the repositories. Although such approaches cannot retrieve PPIs not described in the repositories, they may be able to infer potentially novel PPIs in a given species based on homologous PPIs in another species. For example, this approach has been used to automatically extract host-pathogen interactions from the biomedical literature (Thieu *et al.*, 2012), and also used in the STRING database to retrieve predicted interactions from the literature (Szklarczyk *et al.*, 2017).

Machine Learning-Based Methods

Machine learning-based methods train a classifier on a set of known PPI data to predict whether a given pair of proteins is likely to interact or not. In this approach, various types of features (descriptors) are combined and used to train the classifier, such as the positions of amino acids, the degree of the conservation and the physicochemical characteristics of proteins, the localisation of proteins, domains within proteins or the phylogenetic profile, and so on. Many different machine learning techniques, such as support vector machine (SVM), Naïve Bayes (NB), neural networks (NN), K-nearest neighbors (KNN) and random forest (RF) have been used to imbibe the informative features that can distinguish between true and false interactions. For example, the NB integrating protein domain data, gene expression data and functional annotation data has been applied to the human interactome network analysis to identify PPIs and subnetworks relevant to human cancer (Rhodes *et al.*, 2005). The KNN has been applied to identify human hereditary disease-genes based on topological features, which describe a protein in PPINs (Xu and Li, 2006). Furthermore, an ensemble learning approach, which combines multiple scores obtained from different classifiers trained on different machine learning techniques can be effective (Peng *et al.*, 2017). For example, an ensemble learning method which utilises four classifiers trained using RF, NB, SVM and multilayer perceptron (MLP, a type of NN with multi layers), has been applied to the prediction of PPIs between human and the hepatitis C virus (HCV) proteins (Emamjomeh *et al.*, 2014). The high quality of the training dataset, i.e., informative and unbiased, is crucial for accurate assessments and predictions, as well as for the evaluation of the machine learning models. The testing dataset, for example, is classified into three types by examining if the interacting partner proteins in the dataset are similar to the proteins in the training dataset or not (Hamp and Rost, 2015; Park and Marcotte, 2012). Such a classification offers an effective mechanism not only to evaluate the models but also to prepare high-quality datasets.

Different *in silico* methods based on various types of protein sequence information can be used to predict new PPIs and assess the quality of existing PPIs. Although some methods are more suitable for prokaryotes than eukaryotes, the confidence scores assigned to existing PPIs or to pairs of potentially interacting proteins can be useful to ascertain the reliability of the inferred interactomes for the subsequent PPIN analysis.

Conclusions and Future Prospects

A proteome-wide mapping of PPIs and leveraging them in PPIN-based analyses can help to gain knowledge of the genotype-phenotype relationships and the functioning of complex biological systems. Publicly available PPI data are expected to grow substantially and more comprehensive interactome maps are likely to become available in the near future. Consequently, the accuracy and efficacy of the various *in silico* PPI prediction and scoring methods will also likely improve with the increasing amounts of genomic and proteomics data that are likely to become available in the near future. As PPI mapping transitions from capturing steady state associations to dynamic interactions, it will become increasingly necessary to take additional parameters such as protein isoforms, spatiotemporal expression, localisation and interaction and perhaps even the "strength" of the PPIs into consideration to maximise the robustness of biological insights obtained from the PPIN-based analyses.

See also: Algorithms for Graph and Network Analysis: Clustering and Search of Motifs in Graphs. Algorithms for Graph and Network Analysis: Graph Alignment. Algorithms for Graph and Network Analysis: Graph Indexes/Descriptors. Algorithms for Graph and Network Analysis: Traversing/Searching/Sampling Graphs. Natural Language Processing Approaches in Bioinformatics. Network-Based Analysis of Host-Pathogen Interactions

---

References

Andreeva, A., *et al.*, 2014. SCOP2 prototype: A new approach to protein structure mining. Nucleic Acids Res. 42 (Database issue), D310–D314.
Arabidopsis Interactome Mapping Consortium, C., 2011. Evidence for network evolution in an Arabidopsis interactome map. Science 333 (6042), 601–607.
Aranda, B., *et al.*, 2010. The IntAct molecular interaction database in 2010. Nucleic Acids Res. 38 (Database issue), D525–D531.
Barabasi, A.L., Gulbahce, N., Loscalzo, J., 2011. Network medicine: A network-based approach to human disease. Nat. Rev. Genet. 12 (1), 56–68.
Brown, K.R., Jurisica, I., 2005. Online predicted human interaction database. Bioinformatics 21 (9), 2076–2082.
Brown, K.R., Jurisica, I., 2007. Unequal evolutionary conservation of human protein interactions in interologous networks. Genome Biol. 8 (5), R95.
Burckstummer, T., *et al.*, 2006. An efficient tandem affinity purification procedure for interaction proteomics in mammalian cells. Nat. Methods 3 (12), 1013–1019.
Burger, L., van Nimwegen, E., 2008. Accurate prediction of protein-protein interactions from sequence alignments using a Bayesian method. Mol. Syst. Biol. 4, 165.
Charitou, T., Bryan, K., Lynn, D.J., 2016. Using biological networks to integrate, visualize and analyze genomics data. Genet. Sel. Evol. 48, 27.
Chatr-Aryamontri, A., *et al.*, 2017. The BioGRID interaction database: 2017 update. Nucleic Acids Res. 45 (D1), D369–D379.
Chen, Y.A., Tripathi, L.P., Mizuguchi, K., 2011. TargetMine, an integrated data warehouse for candidate gene prioritisation and target discovery. PLOS ONE 6 (3), e17844.
Chen, Y.A., Tripathi, L.P., Mizuguchi, K., 2016. An integrative data analysis platform for gene set analysis and knowledge discovery in a data warehouse framework. Database (Oxf.) 2016.

Chen, C.C., *et al.*, 2009. PPISearch: A web server for searching homologous protein-protein interactions across multiple species. Nucleic Acids Res. 37 (Web Server issue), W369–W375.

Chia, J.M., Kolatkar, P.R., 2004. Implications for domain fusion protein-protein interactions based on structural information. BMC Bioinform. 5, 161.

Cho, Y.R., *et al.*, 2007. Semantic integration to identify overlapping functional modules in protein interaction networks. BMC Bioinform. 8, 265.

Csermely, P., *et al.*, 2013. Structure and dynamics of molecular networks: A novel paradigm of drug discovery: A comprehensive review. Pharmacol. Ther. 138 (3), 333–408.

De Las Rivas, J., Fontanillo, C., 2010. Protein-protein interactions essentials: Key concepts to building and analyzing interactome networks. PLOS Comput. Biol. 6 (6), e1000807.

Deng, M., *et al.*, 2002. Inferring domain-domain interactions from protein-protein interactions. Genome Res. 12 (10), 1540–1548.

Doerr, A., 2012. Interactomes by mass spectrometry. Nat. Methods 9 (11), 1043.

Dunham, W.H., Mullin, M., Gingras, A.C., 2012. Affinity-purification coupled to mass spectrometry: Basic principles and strategies. Proteomics 12 (10), 1576–1590.

Edwards, A.M., *et al.*, 2011. Too many roads not taken. Nature 470 (7333), 163–165.

Emarnjomeh, A., *et al.*, 2014. Predicting protein-protein interactions between human and hepatitis C virus via an ensemble learning method. Mol. Biosyst. 10 (12), 3147–3154.

Enright, A.J., *et al.*, 1999. Protein interaction maps for complete genomes based on gene fusion events. Nature 402 (6757), 86–90.

Erijman, A., Rosenthal, E., Shifman, J.M., 2014. How structure defines affinity in protein-protein interactions. PLOS ONE 9 (10), e110085.

Ewing, R.M., *et al.*, 2007. Large-scale mapping of human protein-protein interactions by mass spectrometry. Mol. Syst. Biol. 3, 89.

Feldman, I., Rzhetsky, A., Vitkup, D., 2008. Network properties of genes harboring inherited disease mutations. Proc. Natl. Acad. Sci. USA 105 (11), 4323–4328.

Fields, S., Song, O., 1989. A novel genetic system to detect protein-protein interactions. Nature 340 (6230), 245–246.

Finn, R.D., *et al.*, 2016. The Pfam protein families database: Towards a more sustainable future. Nucleic Acids Res. 44 (D1), D279–D285.

Fitch, W.M., 2000. Homology a personal view on some of the problems. Trends Genet. 16 (5), 227–231.

Formstecher, E., *et al.*, 2005. Protein interaction mapping: A Drosophila case study. Genome Res. 15 (3), 376–384.

Garcia-Garcia, J., *et al.*, 2012. BIPS: BIANA Interolog Prediction Server. A tool for protein-protein interaction inference. Nucleic Acids Res. 40 (Web Server issue), W147–W151.

Gebicke-Haerter, P.J., 2016. Systems psychopharmacology: A network approach to developing novel therapies. World J. Psychiatry 6 (1), 66–83.

Goh, C.S., Cohen, F.E., 2002. Co-evolutionary analysis reveals insights into protein-protein interactions. J. Mol. Biol. 324 (1), 177–192.

Goh, K.I., *et al.*, 2007. The human disease network. Proc. Natl. Acad. Sci. USA 104 (21), 8685–8690.

Gupta, G.D., *et al.*, 2015. A dynamic protein interaction landscape of the human centrosome-cilium interface. Cell 163 (6), 1484–1499.

Guruharsha, K.G., *et al.*, 2011. A protein complex network of Drosophila melanogaster. Cell 147 (3), 690–703.

Hakes, L., *et al.*, 2008. Protein-protein interaction networks and biology – What's the connection? Nat. Biotechnol. 26 (1), 69–72.

Hamp, T., Rost, B., 2015. Evolutionary profiles improve protein-protein interaction prediction from sequence. Bioinformatics 31 (12), 1945–1950.

Havugimana, P.C., *et al.*, 2012. A census of human soluble protein complexes. Cell 150 (5), 1068–1081.

Huttlin, E.L., *et al.*, 2015. The BioPlex network: A systematic exploration of the human interactome. Cell 162 (2), 425–440.

Huttlin, E.L., *et al.*, 2017. Architecture of the human interactome defines protein communities and disease networks. Nature 545 (7655), 505–509.

Ideker, T., Sharan, R., 2008. Protein networks in disease. Genome Res. 18 (4), 644–652.

Ito, T., *et al.*, 2001. A comprehensive two-hybrid analysis to explore the yeast protein interactome. Proc. Natl. Acad. Sci. USA 98 (8), 4569–4574.

Janin, J., *et al.*, 2003. CAPRI: A Critical Assessment of PRedicted Interactions. Proteins 52 (1), 2–9.

Janin, J., Wodak, S., 2007. The third CAPRI assessment meeting Toronto, Canada, April 20–21, 2007. Structure 15 (7), 755–759.

Jonsson, P.F., Bates, P.A., 2006. Global topological features of cancer proteins in the human interactome. Bioinformatics 22 (18), 2291–2297.

Juan, D., Pazos, F., Valencia, A., 2008. High-confidence prediction of global interactomes based on genome-wide coevolutionary networks. Proc. Natl. Acad. Sci. USA 105 (3), 934–939.

Jubb, H., Blundell, T.L., Ascher, D.B., 2015. Flexibility and small pockets at protein-protein interfaces: New insights into druggability. Prog. Biophys. Mol. Biol. 119 (1), 2–9.

Keskin, O., Tuncbag, N., Gursoy, A., 2016. Predicting protein-protein interactions from the molecular to the proteome level. Chem. Rev. 116 (8), 4884–4909.

Koh, G.C., *et al.*, 2012. Analyzing protein-protein interaction networks. J. Proteome Res. 11 (4), 2014–2031.

Koonin, E.V., 2005. Orthologs, paralogs, and evolutionary genomics. Annu. Rev. Genet. 39, 309–338.

Kotlyar, M., *et al.*, 2015. In silico prediction of physical protein interactions and characterization of interactome orphans. Nat. Methods 12 (1), 79–84.

Kotlyar, M., Fortney, K., Jurisica, I., 2012. Network-based characterization of drug-regulated genes, drug targets, and toxicity. Methods 57 (4), 499–507.

Krogan, N.J., *et al.*, 2006. Global landscape of protein complexes in the yeast Saccharomyces cerevisiae. Nature 440 (7084), 637–643.

Li, S., *et al.*, 2004. A map of the interactome network of the metazoan C. elegans. Science 303 (5657), 540–543.

Licata, L., *et al.*, 2012. MINT, the molecular interaction database: 2012 update. Nucleic Acids Res 40 (Database issue), D857–D861.

Luck, K., *et al.*, 2017. Proteome-scale human interactomics. Trends Biochem. Sci. 42 (5), 342–354.

Luo, Y., *et al.*, 1997. Mammalian two-hybrid system: A complementary approach to the yeast two-hybrid system. Biotechniques 22 (2), 350–352.

Magger, O., *et al.*, 2012. Enhancing the prioritization of disease-causing genes through tissue specific protein interaction networks. PLOS Comput. Biol. 8 (9), e1002690.

Marcotte, E.M., *et al.*, 1999. Detecting protein function and protein-protein interactions from genome sequences. Science 285 (5428), 751–753.

Maruta, N., Trusov, Y., Botella, J.R., 2016. Yeast three-hybrid system for the detection of protein-protein interactions. Methods Mol. Biol. 1363, 145–154.

Memisevic, V., Wallqvist, A., Reifman, J., 2013. Reconstituting protein interaction networks using parameter-dependent domain-domain interactions. BMC Bioinform. 14, 154.

Menche, J., *et al.*, 2015. Disease networks. Uncovering disease-disease relationships through the incomplete interactome. Science 347 (6224), 1257601.

Moal, I.H., *et al.*, 2013. Scoring functions for protein-protein interactions. Curr. Opin. Struct. Biol. 23 (6), 862–867.

Moal, I.H., Agius, R., Bates, P.A., 2011. Protein-protein binding affinity prediction on a diverse set of structures. Bioinformatics 27 (21), 3002–3009.

Muley, V.Y., Ranjan, A., 2012. Effect of reference genome selection on the performance of computational methods for genome-wide protein-protein interaction prediction. PLOS ONE 7 (7), e42057.

Murakami, Y., *et al.*, 2017. Network analysis and in silico prediction of protein-protein interactions with applications in drug discovery. Curr. Opin. Struct. Biol. 44, 134–142.

Murakami, Y., Mizuguchi, K., 2014. Homology-based prediction of interactions between proteins using Averaged One-Dependence Estimators. BMC Bioinform. 15, 213.

Nabieva, E., *et al.*, 2005. Whole-proteome prediction of protein function via graph-theoretic analysis of interaction maps. Bioinformatics 21 (Suppl 1), i302–i310.

Ng, S.K., *et al.*, 2003. InterDom: A database of putative interacting protein domains for validating predicted protein interactions and complexes. Nucleic Acids Res. 31 (1), 251–254.

Ochoa, D., Pazos, F., 2010. Studying the co-evolution of protein families with the Mirrortree web server. Bioinformatics 26 (10), 1370–1371.

Ochoa, D., Pazos, F., 2014. Practical aspects of protein co-evolution. Front. Cell Dev. Biol. 2, 14.

Papanikolaou, N., *et al.*, 2015. Protein-protein interaction predictions using text mining methods. Methods 74, 47–53.

Park, Y., Marcotte, E.M., 2012. Flaws in evaluation schemes for pair-input computational predictions. Nat. Methods 9 (12), 1134–1136.

Pazos, F., *et al.*, 2005. Assessing protein co-evolution in the context of the tree of life assists in the prediction of the interactome. J. Mol. Biol. 352 (4), 1002–1015.

Pazos, F., Valencia, A., 2001. Similarity of phylogenetic trees as indicator of protein-protein interaction. Protein Eng. 14 (9), 609–614.

Peng, X., *et al.*, 2017. Protein-protein interactions: Detection, reliability assessment and applications. Brief Bioinform 18 (5), 798–819.

Phanse, S., *et al.*, 2016. Proteome-wide dataset supporting the study of ancient metazoan macromolecular complexes. Data Brief. 6, 715–721.

Pitre, S., *et al.*, 2012. Short Co-occurring polypeptide regions can predict global protein interaction maps. Sci. Rep. 2, 239.

Rajagopala, S.V., *et al.*, 2014. The binary protein-protein interaction landscape of Escherichia coli. Nat. Biotechnol. 32 (3), 285–290.

Raman, K., 2010. Construction and analysis of protein-protein interaction networks. Autom. Exp. 2 (1), 2.

Razick, S., Magklaras, G., Donaldson, I.M., 2008. iRefIndex: A consolidated protein interaction database with provenance. BMC Bioinform. 9, 405.

Rhodes, D.R., et al., 2005. Probabilistic model of the human protein-protein interaction network. Nat. Biotechnol. 23 (8), 951–959.

Rolland, T., et al., 2014. A proteome-scale map of the human interactome network. Cell 159 (5), 1212–1226.

Sahni, N., et al., 2015. Widespread macromolecular interaction perturbations in human genetic disorders. Cell 161 (3), 647–660.

Salwinski, L., et al., 2004. The Database of interacting proteins: 2004 update. Nucleic Acids Res. 32 (Database issue), D449–D451.

Sarajlic, A., et al., 2013. Network topology reveals key cardiovascular disease genes. PLOS ONE 8 (8), e71537.

Sato, T., et al., 2005. The inference of protein-protein interactions by co-evolutionary analysis is improved by excluding the information about the phylogenetic relationships. Bioinformatics 21 (17), 3482–3489.

Schaefer, M.H., et al., 2013. Adding protein context to the human protein-protein interaction network to reveal meaningful interactions. PLOS Comput. Biol. 9 (1), e1002860.

Schoenrock, A., et al., 2014. Efficient prediction of human protein-protein interactions at a global scale. BMC Bioinform. 15, 383.

Shameer, K., et al., 2016. Interpreting functional effects of coding variants: Challenges in proteome-scale prediction, annotation and assessment. Brief. Bioinform. 17 (5), 841–862.

Shoemaker, B.A., Panchenko, A.R., 2007. Deciphering protein-protein interactions. Part II. Computational methods to predict protein and domain interaction partners. PLOS Comput. Biol. 3 (4), e43.

Sillitoe, I., et al., 2015. CATH: Comprehensive structural and functional annotations for genome sequences. Nucleic Acids Res. 43 (Database issue), D376–D381

Snider, J., et al., 2010. Detecting interactions with membrane proteins using a membrane two-hybrid assay in yeast. Nat. Protoc. 5 (7), 1281–1293.

Sprinzak, E., Margalit, H., 2001. Correlated sequence-signatures as markers of protein-protein interaction. J. Mol. Biol. 311 (4), 681–692.

Szklarczyk, D., et al., 2015. STRING v10: Protein-protein interaction networks, integrated over the tree of life. Nucleic Acids Res. 43 (Database issue), D447. v52.

Szklarczyk, D., et al., 2017. The STRING database in 2017: Quality-controlled protein-protein association networks, made broadly accessible. Nucleic Acids Res. 45 (D1), D362–D368.

Tamames, J., et al., 1997. Conserved clusters of functionally related genes in two bacterial genomes. J. Mol. Evol. 44 (1), 66–73.

Thieu, T., et al., 2012. Literature mining of host-pathogen interactions: Comparing feature-based supervised learning and language-based approaches. Bioinformatics 28 (6), 867–875.

Trinkle-Mulcahy, L., et al., 2008. Identifying specific protein interaction partners using quantitative mass spectrometry and bead proteomes. J. Cell Biol. 183 (2), 223–239.

Tuncbag, N., et al., 2009. A survey of available tools and web servers for analysis of protein-protein interactions and interfaces. Brief Bioinform. 10 (3), 217–232.

Uetz, P., et al., 2000. A comprehensive analysis of protein-protein interactions in Saccharomyces cerevisiae. Nature 403 (6770), 623–627.

Vakser, I.A., 2014. Protein-protein docking: From interaction to interactome. Biophys. J. 107 (8), 1785–1793.

Vidal, M., Cusick, M.E., Barabasi, A.L., 2011. Interactome networks and human disease. Cell 144 (6), 986–998.

Vo, T.V., et al., 2016. A Proteome-wide fission yeast interactome reveals network evolution principles from yeasts to human. Cell 164 (1–2), 310–323.

Watson, J.D., Laskowski, R.A., Thornton, J.M., 2005. Predicting protein function from sequence and structural data. Curr. Opin. Struct. Biol. 15 (3), 275–284.

Webber, C., Ponting, C.P., 2004. Genes and homology. Curr. Biol. 14 (9), R332–R333.

Wells, J.A., McClendon, C.L., 2007. Reaching for high-hanging fruit in drug discovery at protein-protein interfaces. Nature 450 (7172), 1001–1009.

Wiles, A.M., et al., 2010. Building and analyzing protein interactome networks by cross-species comparisons. BMC Syst. Biol. 4, 36.

Xu, J., Li, Y., 2006. Discovering disease-genes by topological features in human protein-protein interaction network. Bioinformatics 22 (22), 2800–2805.

Yang, J., Wagner, S.A., Beli, P., 2015. Illuminating spatial and temporal organization of protein interaction networks by mass spectrometry-based proteomics. Front. Genet. 6, 344.

Yu, H., et al., 2007. The importance of bottlenecks in protein networks: Correlation with gene essentiality and expression dynamics. PLOS Comput. Biol. 3 (4), e59.

Yu, H., et al., 2008. High-quality binary protein interaction map of the yeast interactome network. Science 322 (5898), 104–110.

Zahiri, J., Bozorgmehr, J.H., Masoudi-Nejad, A., 2013. Computational prediction of protein-protein interaction networks: Algo-rithms and resources. Curr. Genom. 14 (6), 397–414.

Sequence Analysis

Andrey D Prjibelski, Anton I Korobeynikov, and Alla L Lapidus, St. Petersburg State University, St Petersburg, Russia

Glossary

Adjusted p-value The lowest familywise significance level, at which a certain comparison will be considered as statistically significant as part of the multiple comparison testing.

Alignment score A measure that reflects the level of similarity between sequences.

Contig Long genomic fragment, usually generated by the genome assembly software.

Copy number variation (CNV) An alteration between the number of the same genomic fragment being repeated in the genome within the population.

de Bruijn graph An approach used for *de novo* sequence assembly from short reads.

De novo genome assembly The process of constructing the genome sequence directly from the sequencing reads without any supplementary information.

Differential expression analysis A process of studying changes in expression of the genes between samples, usually under different conditions.

Duplication A rearrangement event in which a genomic fragment is copied into the same chromosome.

Edit distance The minimum number of operations (insertions, deletions or substitutions) needed to turn one sequence into another.

FASTA format A text-based file format for storing biological sequences.

GC content The percentage of cytosine and guanine nucleotides relative to the total length of nucleic sequence.

Genome rearrangement A large genomic mutation, which alternates the whole chromosomes or their long fragments.

Graph simplification The process of removing erroneous edges from the graph (usually referred to de Bruijn graph).

Hamming distance The number of positions in two strings of the same length, in which the symbols do not match.

Hybrid assembly An approach for *de novo genome assembly* using multiple different sequencing technologies simultaneously.

Indel Insertion or deletion.

Inversion A rearrangement event in which a genomic fragment is reversed within the chromosome.

k-mer A sequence of length k.

Metagenomics A field of genomics, which studies genomes of the entire bacterial communities (or other samples containing different species).

Misassembly An error in the assembly when two distant genomic fragments are joined into a single contigs/scaffold.

N50 The maximum length X for which the collection of all contigs of length $>=$ X covers at least 50% of the assembly.

Overlap-Layout-Consensus approach (OLC) An *de novo* genome assembly method used for long sequencing reads.

Paired-end reads A couple of reads sequenced from the different ends of the same genomic fragment (typically from different strands); also can be referred to as left and right reads, or *mate reads*.

Phylogenetic tree A tree that demonstrates evolutionary relationships between selected biological species.

Read alignment (read mapping) The process of aligning sequencing reads to a longer sequence (typically reference genome) to detect the position, from which the read was originally sequences.

Read mapping See *read alignment*.

Repeat resolution The process resolving ambiguities during the assembly, which are caused by the genomic repeats.

SAM/BAM formats Formats for storing read alignment data. SAM is a text-based format and BAM is a compressed binary format.

Scaffold An ordered set of contigs, typically separated by regions with unknown bases (N).

Scaffolding The process of ordering *contigs* into *scaffolds*.

Sequence alignment The process of detecting similarities between biological sequences.

Single nucleotide polymorphism (SNP) A variation in a single position in the genome that appears in appreciable part of the population.

Strand-specific RNA-Seq A method for sequencing RNA molecules, from which it is possible to deduce the strand on which the gene is located.

String graph An approach used for *de novo* sequence assembly from short reads.

Synteny block A set of consecutive genes on the chromosome, which are typically inherited together and preserved by rearrangement events.

Translocation A rearrangement event in which a genomic fragment is exchanged with a fragment from another chromosome.

Universal single copy-ortholog A gene, which does not have paralogs and is typical for a given set of organisms.

VCF/BCF formats Formats for storing variations and mutations. VCF is a text-based format and BCF is a compressed binary format.

Introduction to Sequence Analysis

Sequence analysis is a term that comprehensively represents computational analysis of a DNA, RNA or peptide sequence, to extract knowledge about its properties, biological function, structure and evolution. To carry out sequence analysis efficiently, it is important to first understand the source of the data, i.e., the different experimental methods used for determining the biological sequence. We then need to follow analytical strategies, depending on whether the sequence is genomic, transcriptomic or proteomic. Databases currently warehousing the enormous data on these biomolecules will need to be first checked for the presence of similar sequences, which might direct experimental assays for functional investigations. Software tools and web services are often used for carrying of the bioinformatics analysis. After analysis of DNA, RNA and protein sequences, it is important to understand how they are connected by protein to genome mapping. The small organic molecules or metabolites that are essential for organisms to live and grow also need to be studied in the context of their interaction with genes and proteins, *via* metabolic pathways. This article aims to provide an overview of sequence analysis, at the DNA, RNA and proteins levels, with metabolic pathways describing their interplay.

Nucleic Acid Sequencing

DNA Sequencing Technologies

DNA sequencing is the process of determining the order of nucleotide bases of molecules of DNA. If the DNA of the whole genome of an organism is used as the DNA of interest, then the process is referred to as genomic sequencing. This process is currently widely used both in fundamental biological research and in many applications. Information about the primary DNA sequence is a crucial piece of data used in such areas of research as medical studies, gene therapy, drug development, evolutionary studies, agriculture, improvement of nutritional quality, biotechnology, forensic and many other.

First-generation sequencing

The era of DNA sequencing began about 30 years ago, when two methods of primary DNA structure determination appeared almost simultaneously. The one developed by A. Maxam and W. Gilbert at Harvard University was based on the use of chemical modifications of DNA. The other method was published by F. Sanger and A. Coulson from Cambridge and is called the chain-termination method. These methods were named 1st generation sequencing (Heather and Chain, 2016).

And although over time, both the Gilbert and the Sanger DNA sequencing methods have gone through a number of significant changes (one of which was the automation of the Sanger DNA method that assured its wider application), first generation sequencing methods continued to remain labor intensive, had a low throughput speed and were very expensive. To overcome these limitations and in response to the National Human Genome Research Institute (NGHRI) call to lower the cost of sequencing of an individual human genome to $1000, with an intermediate goal of reducing the cost of sequencing a mammalian-sized genome to $100,000, next generation sequencing technologies (NGS) were rapidly developed and began to be used in pyrosequencing, base-by-base sequencing by synthesis (SBS), sequencing by ligation, nanopore sequencing, and single-molecule sequencing by synthesis in real time strategies.

These newest sequencing technologies that are currently at different stages of development and implementation can be split into two groups: Second generation sequencing and the third generation approaches.

Second-generation sequencing

Compared to the traditional Sanger sequencing, the greatest advantage of the second generation sequencing is a very high level of parallelization: up to 10^7 reactions in one experiment. In addition, the minuscule volume of the individual wells (picoliters), within which the sequencing reactions are run and the high data density (10,000 times higher, than in case of the latest microelectrophoresis-based capillary instruments) significantly decrease the volume of reagents needed to perform the reactions. Another positive aspect of the second generation methods is the ability to circumvent DNA cloning and propagation in *Escherichia coli* cells, thus avoiding the problems of biased genome coverage due to the presence of genomic areas, which are hard or even impossible to clone in E. coli (so called unclonable areas). The downside of these technologies, as compared with the Sanger approach, however, is the length of the produced reads.

The 454 Genome Sequencer 20 System instrument (the first commercial NGS platform) produced reads of about 110 bp. The latest GS FLX Titanium chemistry (Margulies *et al.*, 2005) has managed to increase read length up to 1 kb (454 Life Sciences was shut down in 2013 and 454 sequencing instruments are not supported any longer). Meanwhile, technologies using SBS and sequencing by ligation (Applied Biosystem SOLiD; polony-based approaches) produced reads of only 25–50 bp long (Shendure *et al.*, 2005; Valouev *et al.*, 2008). This meant that although 454 sequencing has been successfully applied to de novo genome sequencing resulting in a gapped assembly with an error rate of about 1/3000–1/5000 bp, the ultra-short reads produced by Solexa technology appeared to be of use for resequencing purposes only, in this case a high-quality reference sequence would be present for alignment. The use of 25–50 bp reads for de novo genome sequencing appeared to be very problematic.

After being acquired by Illumina, the Solexa technology was renamed to Illumina technology. This approach uses the SBS sequencing to generate massively parallel genomic data and detect single bases as they are incorporated into growing DNA strands. Read lengths vary from 100 bp to 300 bp depending on the sequencing instrument used (MiSeq, NextSeq 500, different HiSeq). The low error rate of Illumina reads ($\leq 0.1\%$) makes this sequencing technology very attractive for a number of applications including de novo genome assembly.

Ion Torrent is yet another NGS approach (Rothberg *et al.*, 2011). It uses the semiconductor sequencing technology of SBS. The Ion PGM sequencer detects changes in pH when a nucleotide is incorporated into the DNA molecules and a proton is released.

This technology produces reads of 400 bp long with about 1% error rate, allowing single nucleotide polymorphism (SNP) detection as well as whole genome assembly.

The second Ion Torrent instrument released in 2012, the Ion Proton, produces shorter reads (200 bp), but provides 10 time larger (∼10 Gb) output than its predecessor. The read length provided by recently developed Ion S5 and Ion S5 XL Systems (www.thermofisher.com) is ranging from 200 bp to 600 bp depending on the chip type and the output can be as high as 10–15 Gb.

Third-generation sequencing

Among the numerous methods on the drawing board, special attention should be given to real-time sequencing of DNA molecules. Such methods use very small amounts of genomic DNA and require supersensitive detection methods. The success of these methods wholly depends on the quality of the genomic DNA used in the experiment: if the DNA is damaged while being isolated, the resulting sequence will be corrupt. In theory, the read length produced by this type of technology should be equal to that of a full genome.

PacBio (SMRT) sequencing is one of the first real-time single-molecule sequencing techniques capable of generating long reads (10–15 Kb) without requiring any amplification steps. Additionally, its unique ability to distinguish methylated bases from normal nucleotides (Levene *et al.*, 2003) opens up the possibility of studying the epigenetic potential of different organisms. Read error rate is high, but errors are random and thus can be corrected via an increase in coverage. Long reads play a crucial role in the gap closing step of the whole genome assembly and PacBio gave genome finishing, a step that for several years was set aside as time-consuming and not cost efficient, a much needed boost.

The UK company Oxford Nanopore Technologies developed a next generation sequencing approach based on nanopores. The MinION system allows to produce more than 3 Gbp of data from a single run. The resulting reads are of a variable length and can be up to 900,000 bases long. The current error rate of nanopore reads is 5%–15%. It was observed that this technology produces systematic sequencing errors, which end up being more challenging to correct bioinformatically than random ones.

The list of companies and university-based groups of researchers working on improving sequencing technology goes on and on. Some of them have already managed to achieve commercial success, others are still only working on approaching this goal and many have either already failed to do so or will end up failing eventually (Lapidus, 2015). In most cases a combination of different sequencing approaches allows to produce a high-quality sequence fairly quickly and at very low cost.

Rna-Seq

RNA molecules play a significant role in all living cells. Messenger RNA (mRNA) for example is responsible for translating the genetic information stored in DNA into proteins composed of different combinations of 20 amino acids, each of which has its own type of transfer RNA (tRNA) that binds and transports them to the growing polypeptide chain when needed. Ribosomal RNA (rRNA) is an integral part of both large and small subunits of ribosomes – A complex molecule responsible for protein synthesis in cells.

Transcriptomics allows to study the nature and amount of each of the RNA molecules in a given cell under a specific condition and at a given moment. The RNA sequencing (RNA-seq) approach uses next-generation sequencing (NGS) to perform direct sequencing of cDNA fragments (Hrdlickova *et al.*, 2017).

RNA-seq can detect: (i) Gene expression level; (ii) transcript abundance; (iii) alternative splicing that causes transcriptional diversity in eukaryotes; (iv) different isoform usage; (v) single nucleotide variations; (vi) fusion genes; (vii) post-transcriptional modifications. It can identify genes, exons, splicing events, ncRNAs, novel genes or transcripts.

A typical RNA-Seq experiment consists of RNA isolation and purification, assessment of the RNA purity and yield, enrichment of target RNAs (through polyA selection, size selection, or removal of non-target sequences through hybridization to probes), fragmentation of RNA, amplification, sequencing, followed by data analysis that in its turn includes quality control, read alignment to a reference genome or known transcripts, transcript quantification and *differential expression analysis* (Kukurba, 2015).

Most of the methods used for RNA-seq data analysis rely on well-annotated reference genomes and on accurate gene models of model organisms. The *de novo* transcriptome assembly approach helps to reconstruct the sequence of the expressed transcripts and is used when reference genomes are not available.

Sequencing Data Formats

The simplest and one of the most common formats for storing nucleic and amino acid sequences is the *FASTA format* (see "Relevant Websites section"). Typically FASTA files have ".fasta" or ".fa" extensions, but other extensions, such as ".fna" for nucleic sequences and ".faa" for proteins are also sometimes used. A single entry in a FASTA file contains the sequence name (sequence ID) and the sequence itself. Sequence names may also contain some meta information, such as for example sequence length. When the sequence is long, it is stored in multiple lines for added legibility. FASTA files can contain an unlimited number of sequence entries.

Sequencing reads can also be stored in the *FASTQ format* (see "Relevant Websites section") that contains information about reads quality in addition to read sequence and read ID. In the process of sequencing, the sequencer can estimate the probability of each nucleotide being detected incorrectly. The decimal logarithm of the error probability is then rounded to the nearest integer, added to a fixed offset and written to the FASTQ file as the corresponding ASCII character. However, there are several different formats for storing quality values, which vary by offset values and the way the error probability is converted to an integer number. Read ID in FASTQ file may contain additional information about the reads. For example, Illumina sequencer stores flowcell lane number, tile number, coordinates of the cluster and the information about read pairing (if reads are *paired*).

There are two possible ways to store *paired-end reads* in FASTQ files. The most common method stores left and right reads in the two separate files. The order of the reads in both files should be the same, i.e., first read from the file with left reads is a mate for the first read from the file with right reads. Paired reads can also be saved into a single file (called interlaced FASTQ file), in which left and right reads are placed one after another.

Since both FASTA and FASTQ formats are text formats, they typically require a huge amount of disk space. To save space, FASTQ files are usually either compressed using standard archiver software, or converted to SRA or unmapped BAM binary formats.

Beside FASTA/FASTQ, there exists a large variety of file formats suitable for storing supplementary information, such as sequence alignments, genomic variations and genome annotation. Some of these formats will be described further throughout the article.

Analyzing Genomic Sequences

Sequence Alignment

Classic alignment algorithms

Sequence alignment is the process of comparing and detecting similarities between biological sequences. What "similarities" are being detected will depend on the goals of the particular alignment process. Sequence alignment appears to be extremely useful in a number of bioinformatics applications.

For example, the simplest way to compare two sequences of the same length is to calculate the number of matching symbols. The value that measures the degree of sequence similarity is called the *alignment score* of two sequences. The opposite value, corresponding to the level of dissimilarity between sequences, is usually referred to as the *distance* between sequences. The number of non-matching characters is called the *Hamming distance*. **Fig. 1** shows an example of two sequences with Hamming distance (Bookstein *et al.*, 2002) equal to 3.

It is, however, worth noting that comparing sequence characters position by position as described above can barely be referred to as alignment process, since it does not take into account such typical biological events as deletions and insertions. The classical notion of sequence alignment includes calculating the so called *edit distance*, which generally corresponds to the minimal number of substitution, insertions and deletions needed to turn one sequence into another. **Fig. 2** demonstrates an example of two sequences with edit distance equal to 3.

The problems of computing edit distance and various types of sequence alignment have exact solutions, e.g., (Smith and Waterman, 1981) and (Needleman and Wunsch, 1970) algorithms. Since these algorithms were initially developed for protein-protein alignment and later adapter for DNA sequence alignment, they are described in the section 'Protein-protein alignment'. In most real-life cases, however, these algorithms appear to be impractical for DNA alignment due their running time and memory requirements.

BLAST and similar database search methods

To overcome the limitations of the classic alignment algorithms, which are usually used for rather short sequences, new methods and heuristics were developed. By heuristic algorithm we imply a non-exact solution, which works faster than exact algorithms (sometimes much faster) and provides biologically meaningful results.

Undoubtedly, the most popular sequence alignment tool in bioinformatics is the BLAST algorithm (Altschul *et al.*, 1990) and its variations, such as BLASTN (Acland *et al.*, 2014) and MegaBLAST (Morgulis *et al.*, 2008). The paper that describes the first version of the BLAST algorithm now has more than 60 thousand citations and the count keeps going up. Various modifications of the BLAST algorithms are used for aligning amino acid sequences to nucleic sequences (tblastn) and vice versa (blastx). BLAST is

ATTCGGATCTCA
ATTCGGCACTGA

Fig. 1 Example of two sequences with Hamming distances equal to 3.

ATTC-GATCTCA
ATTCGGAACT-A

Fig. 2 Example of two sequences with edit distances equal to 3.

widely used on the NCBI web site for searching sequences in various databases, such as 16s rRNA sequences and the nucleotide collection (all assembled genomes).

Beside the BLAST family algorithms, multiple alignment methods for various goals were developed during the past 20 years. Depending on the biological problem and alignment objective, different methods employ different algorithms and heuristic ideas, such as suffix trees and suffix arrays, k-mer indexing, seed-and-extend approaches and Hidden Markov Models. More information about specific sequence alignment algorithms can be found in Section "De Novo Transcriptome Assembly" (protein sequence alignment) and Section "Sequencing Data Formats" (mapping sequencing reads to the reference genome).

Comparative genomics

Nucleic sequence alignment algorithms are widely used in comparative genomics and phylogenetic studies. Comparative genomics studies similarities between two or more genomes at the level of large *rearrangement* events, such as *inversions*, *duplications*, *translocations*, large insertions and deletions. Since the comparative genomics usually does not take into account small structural variations and *single nucleotide polymorphisms* (SNPs), it requires a specific kind of alignment software. These methods typically detect *synteny blocks* – long sequences shared between genomes being compared. Indeed, those sequences may have differences at the nucleotide level, but are still highly similar overall. The genomes are then represented as a sequence of synteny blocks and rearrangements are detected (Hannenhalli and Pevzner, 1999).

Phylogenetic studies use various multiple sequence alignment methods to detect the level of sequence dissimilarity. The distance between compared sequences is used to construct *phylogenetic trees*, in which the length of the branches typically correspond to the distance between analyzed sequences. To construct a biologically meaningful and realistic tree, various clustering methods can be used as well as different sequences may be provided as input (Felsenstein, 1981; Kumar *et al.*, 1994). Phylogenetic studies can be done using whole genomes and rearrangement events, genes and proteins sequences, or even SNPs for closely related organisms.

Preprocessing Sequencing Data

Quality control of sequencing data

Regardless of what technology, protocol or sample was used to generate sequencing data, quality control remains an integral part of every experiment. When performed correctly during the early stages of a project, quality control helps save time and thus, money. There have been many cases when false conclusions were made due to the poor quality of initial data, and, as a known saying states, "garbage in – garbage out", meaning that great results do not come from low-quality data.

FastQC is one of the most popular tools for basic quality control of different kinds of sequencing data (Andrews, 2010). FastQC does not require any additional data, such as a reference genome, and the QC is performed based on just a FASTQ file with sequences and corresponding quality values. Below we will take a look at several important statistics produced by FastQC, how to interpret them and what the differences between high- and low- quality data are.

The first and one of the most important plots is the per base sequence quality plot. It demonstrates the average quality value amongst the reads. Illumina reads typically have lower quality and a higher number of sequencing errors towards the end of the read. **Fig. 3** demonstrates the plot of a per base sequence quality distribution of a normal Illumina dataset, while **Fig. 4** gives an example of low-quality Illumina reads and shows the significant drop in the average quality towards reads' end.

One of the basic, but very important nucleic sequence properties is the *GC content*. It is calculated as the total number of guanine and cytosine nucleotides relative to the total sequence length. The per sequence GC content plot is usually used to detect the presence of contamination in the sample. In case of non-contaminated sequencing data, the GC content distribution is typically bell-shaped and matches the theoretical distribution (**Fig. 5**). In the presence of contamination this distribution may contain several separate peaks, each of which would correspond to a different genome with different GC content (**Fig. 6**).

The following group of statistics and plots is typically used to detect a very common problem – The presence of sequencing adapters in the reads. These statistics include per base sequence content, adapter content, k-mer content and overrepresented sequences. The figures below demonstrate how sequence content plots look when working with clean data (**Fig. 7**) and with reads containing adapters (**Fig. 8**).

Adapter and quality trimming

As was demonstrated, sequencing adapters and low-quality ends (for Illumina reads) are the common problems that often arise when analyzing sequencing data. Both of them may significantly affect performance and the quality of the results generated during the next steps of the analysis, such as, for example, genome assembly. Therefore, during the preprocessing step low-quality ends are clipped and the adapters are removed.

One of the tools used for read trimming is called Trimmomatic (Bolger *et al.*, 2014). This tool is capable of clipping reads using quality values and removing adapters from both single-end and paired-end reads. One of the most useful methods for trimming reads is the detection of low-quality ends based on the average quality in the sliding window of a fixed size. A read is cut once the average quality in a window drops below a given threshold. **Fig. 9** demonstrates what the per base sequence quality plot looks like once the reads have been trimmed (plot for original reads is shown on **Fig. 4**). To remove the adapters from the reads a FASTA file with the adapter sequences needs to be fed into Trimmomatic. Other adapter-removing tools, such as cutadapt (Martin, 2011) or NxTrim (O'Connell *et al.*, 2015), can also be used.

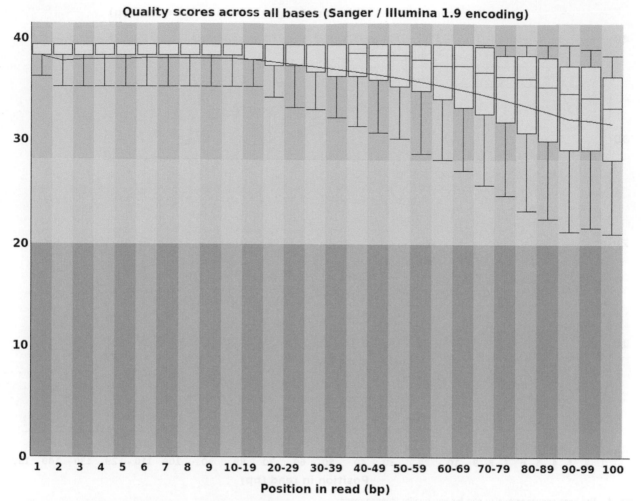

Fig. 3 Per-base sequence quality plot for normal Illumina reads.

Filtering contamination

Another typical problem for sequencing data is contamination – the presence of reads from the genomes of species you did not intend to sequence. Read contamination usually occurs when the sample has not been completely purified and contains the DNA of other organisms. As mentioned above, in cases when the unwanted genome contaminant has a different GC content, its presence can be easily detected using the per sequence GC content plot in FastQC. Otherwise, contamination may be detected using *read alignment* (see next section) or once the genome has been assembled.

In order to filter out the contaminants, one needs to have a database to screen the reads against. In most cases, a reference genome of the suspected contaminant can be used for this purpose. Contaminant reads can be cleaned using read alignment or using a simple tool called bbduk from the bbtools package (Bushnell, 2014).

Mapping Sequencing Data

Goals and problems of short reads alignment

The problem of aligning a read to a reference genome can be reformulated as an attempt to find the position, from which the read was originally sequences. *Read alignment* (or *read mapping*) is essential for many biological and medical applications, such as detecting genomic variations in the sequenced organism and phylogenetic studies.

Although both the local and the global alignments have exact solutions, these algorithms have a quadratic running time and memory consumption, which makes them inapplicable for read alignment due to the large size of genomic sequences (e.g., human genome is almost 3 Gbp long). Additionally, a single sequencing library may contain up to 100 million reads. Thus, in order to perform read alignment for the entire dataset in an observable amount of time, every separate read alignment has to be performed extremely efficiently. Several techniques used to speed up read alignment are discussed in the next section.

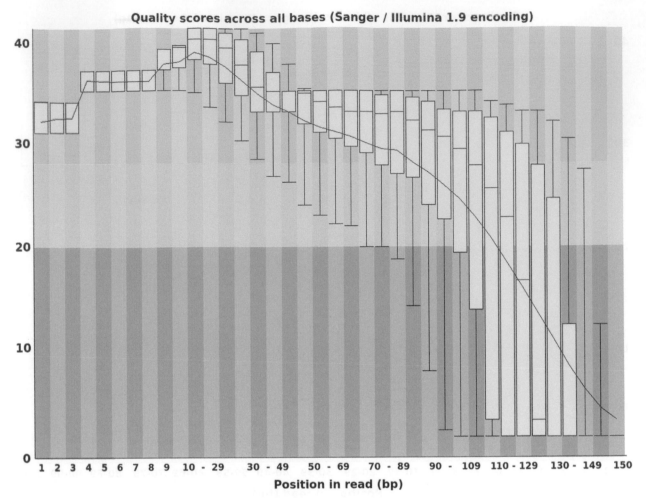

Fig. 4 Per-base sequence quality plot for low-quality Illumina reads.

The problem of read alignment is further complicated by the differences between the reference genome and the genome being analyzed, sequencing errors and genomic repeats. Reads corresponding to repetitive regions can be mapped to several genomic locations and are typically ignored.

In this section we discuss several approaches and tools that are designed for the purpose of aligning reads obtained with different sequencing technologies.

Alignment file formats

Files containing information about the alignment of reads to the reference sequence are typically stored using a specific file format called SAM. SAM files start with a header, which contains all the necessary supplementary information (e.g., lengths of chromosomes in the reference genome). Information about each read alignment is written as a separate line and contains such information as: The position and the strand of the read on the chromosome, name of the chromosome, read ID, the read sequence itself and the corresponding quality string, the information about the mate read (for paired reads) and other supplementary data. Complete information can be found in the SAM format specification.

Since SAM is a text format, it may require a huge amount of disk space, especially when the input files contain hundreds of millions of reads. To reduce disk usage, the binary BAM format was implemented. Typically, BAM files occupy up to 5 times less spaces than SAM files with the same amount of information. SAM/BAM files can be manipulated, converted and processed using a popular package called samtools (Li *et al.*, 2009).

Short read alignment

Modern short read alignment software is based on the same principles as internet search engines – Indexing the content to enable faster query search. Preprocessing of long genomic sequence allows to rapidly search for any of the reads. The genome is often indexed using a suffix array, the Burrows-Wheeler transform, the *FM-index* (Ferragina *et al.*, 2004) or a variation of these algorithms. Since the size of a genome may be large, the preprocessing step may take a significant amount of time, but on the up side, it

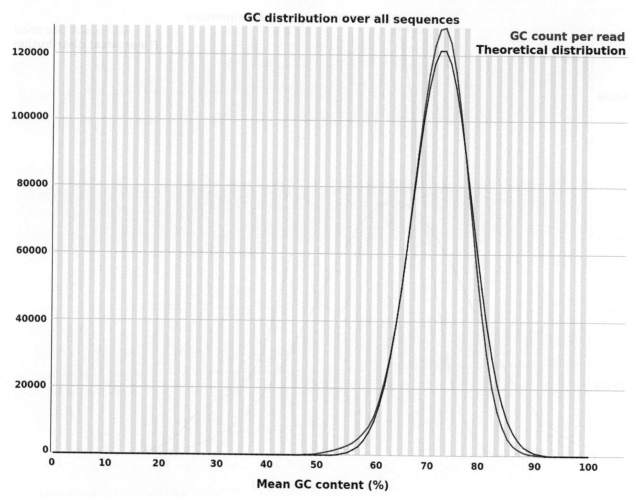

Fig. 5 GC content plot for normal Illumina reads.

needs to be computed only once. Once the index is computed, the read alignment itself can be performed quickly and in parallel, which allows to process reads simultaneously using multiple threads.

The most popular tools for aligning genomic reads are Bowtie2 (Langmead and Salzberg, 2012), various bwa algorithms (Li and Durbin, 2009; Li, 2013), bbmap (Bushnell, 2014) and others. In the case of Ion Torrent sequencing technology TMap can also be used as an alternative. Although comparisons demonstrating the differences in speed and accuracy between a number of popular aligners were published, the final selection of the read alignment software typically comes down to a personal preference based on individual experience.

Variation calling

The main application of short read alignment is detecting different types of genomic variations: *single nucleotide polymorphism* (SNP) sites, small insertions and deletions (*indels*), *copy number variations* (CNV). These kinds of events may have significant biological meaning and thus are of high interest as topics of investigation. For example, a change of single nucleotide in rpoB gene of *Mycobacterium tuberculosis* makes it resistant to Rifampicin.

To perform a variation calling, read alignments are sorted, the BAM files are then indexed, the reads are piled up and the variations are detected by comparing them to the reference sequence. Discovered variations are then filtered based on the specific parameters of the final objective. Filtering criteria may depend on such factors as, for example, the average coverage depth of the sequencing library or the organism ploidy. Details on the different variation calling pipelines can be found in the documentation for the Genome Analysis Toolkit (McKenna *et al.*, 2010).

Discovered genomic variations are typically stored in the VCF file format, or in the compressed BCF binary format. The vcftools toolkit is often used to filter and process these files (Danecek *et al.*, 2011). However, the process of calling SNPs on its own does not provide any biologically meaningful insights. In order to understand the effect of the discovered mutation, SNPs need to be annotated. Annotation of the genomic variations can be performed, using several existing databases (e.g., dbSNP, Ensembl Variation) and tools (e.g., SNPeff (Cingolani *et al.*, 2012), ANNOVAR (Wang *et al.*, 2012)), the selection of which will depend on the types of mutation discovered and its expected effect. *De novo* annotation is also possible, but typically requires a large number of samples to be examined in order to determine the associations between the particular variation and the studied effect (e.g., antibiotic resistance).

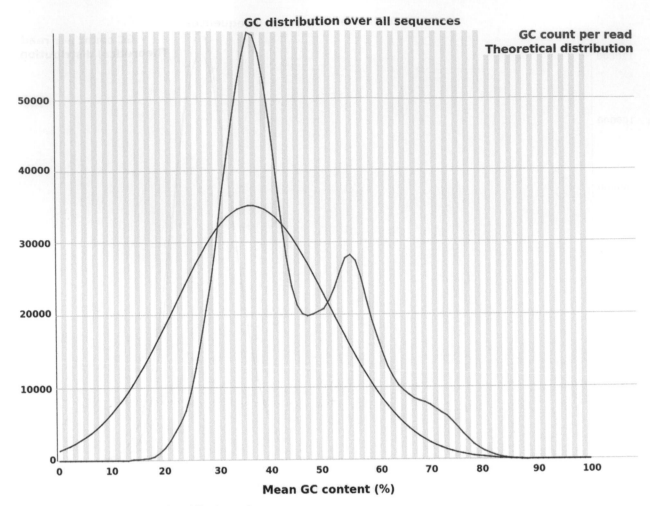

Fig. 6 GC content plot for contaminated Illumina reads.

In addition, once the variations are called, it may be useful to visualize them in a genome browser. Genome browsers are designed to display various genomic features along the chromosomes, such as genes and isoforms. Each genome browser is typically developed to address one particular need and is not universal. For example, to view and examine SNP sites a simple browser called Tablet (Milne *et al.*, 2009) may be used. Alternatively, more sophisticated browsers, such as IGV (Thorvaldsdóttir *et al.*, 2013) or UCSC (Kent *et al.*, 2002) genome browsers can be used.

QC using read alignment

Another possible application of read mapping is an additional QC of sequencing library and calculation of various statistics that cannot be computed without a reference genome. For, example, the number of unaligned, uniquely aligned and multiply aligned reads, faction of the genome covered and substitution error frequencies.

Read alignments may also be used to estimate coverage depth along the genome. **Figs. 10** and **11** show two coverage plots for different E.coli sequencing datasets. On both plots each dot represents an average coverage depth in the window of 1 kbp. **Fig. 10** demonstrates the coverage distribution for a conventional isolate dataset (uniform coverage distribution and more than 99% of genome covered), while plot on **Fig. 11** is constructed using the single-cell MDA-amplified sequencing data (only 96% of genome is covered and coverage depth is highly uneven due to non-uniform amplification process).

Another useful statistic that can be obtained via read alignment is the information about the insert size distribution. **Fig. 12** demonstrates the insert size distribution of an E.coli dataset with an average insert size of 215 bp and a standard deviation of 10 bp.

Plots and statistics shown above may be used to identify problems that cannot be detected using basic QC analysis, such as, for example, problems with size selection and coverage gaps.

Long error-prone read alignment

Reads generated by PacBio and Oxford Nanopore technologies significantly differ from those generated by the previous NGS technologies in terms of read length and accuracy. Alignment tools listed in the previous sections were designed especially for short reads with a rather low error rate and did not perform well out-of-the-box.

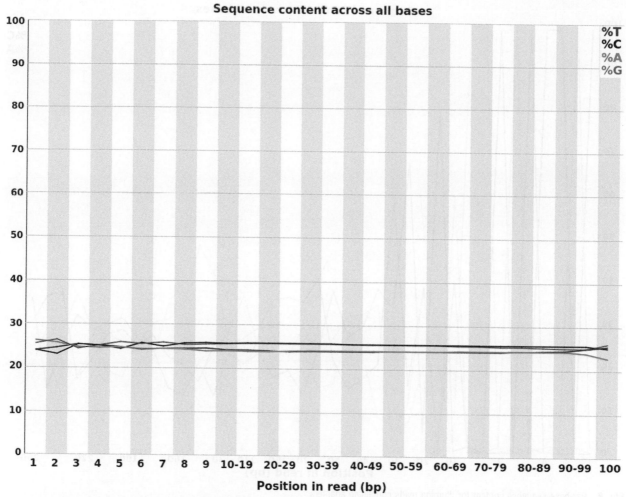

Fig. 7 Per-base sequence content for normal Illumina reads.

Therefore, several new tools were developed for alignment of long error-prone reads, e.g., GraphMap (Sović *et al.*, 2016) and minimap (Li, 2016). The later one is known for mapping reads without outputting actual alignments, which dramatically improves its performance. In addition, the bwa mem algorithm was modified and tuned to support the new family of sequencing technologies. However, due to an extremely high error rate, PacBio and Oxford Nanopores are not the best pieces of technology for calling SNPs and other small variations.

De Novo Genome Assembly

One of the first applications that genome sequencing was intended for is the *de novo genome assembly*. Currently, the problem of assembling a genome from scratch still cannot be considered as completely solved. Even now, in the age of biotechnological and computational progress, a path from the raw biological sample to the finished genome may require years of work and substantial financial resources.

The problem of *de novo* assembly is one of the most popular and algorithmically challenging in computational biology. Dozens of tools were developed during the sequencing era, and yet none of those tools can be named as the best genome assembler in the world for all cases. It is hardly possible to create a universal genome assembler due to the differences in the genomes being sequences, research goals and sequencing technologies.

Despite all recent advances in biotechnology and bioinformatics, it is rarely possible to generate a complete assembly of all chromosomes from raw reads. The key reasons are (i) the presence of genomic repeats and (ii) various sequencing errors and biases. Assembly tools typically generate long genomic regions called *contigs* (stored in FASTA format). The contigs can be further ordered and joined into *scaffolds*, even when the exact genomic sequence and distance between them is unknown. The unspecified nucleotide is usually denoted as an N symbol in the output FASTA file. The scaffolding step is typically performed by long-range sequencing libraries, e.g., mate-pairs.

De novo assembly using long reads

The most intuitive way of solving de novo genome assembly problem is to join overlapping reads with each other one by one – in the same way as jigsaw puzzles are assembled. The approach that implements this simple idea is called *Overlap-Layout-Consensus*

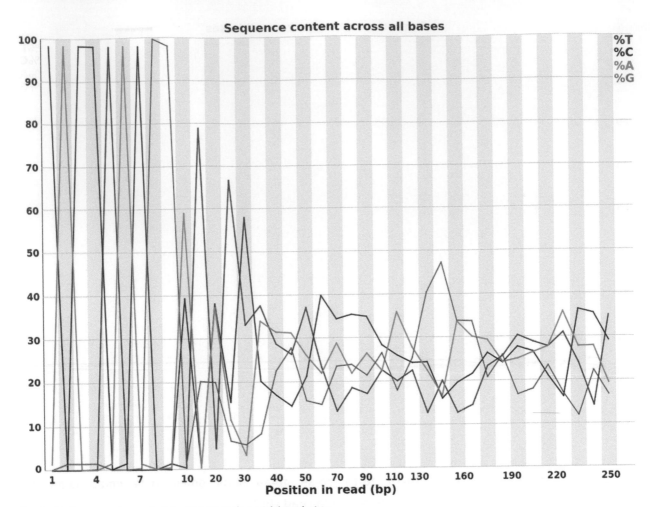

Fig. 8 Per-base sequence content for Illumina reads containing adapters.

(OLC), because it consists of the three consecutive stages. During the first step possible overlaps between all reads are detected, which is typically done using BLAST or similar algorithms. Afterwards, the algorithm constructs an overlap graph in order to determine the layout of the reads, which is then used to compute the consensus sequence and to obtain the resulting contigs. The OLC approach was implemented in multiple popular assembly tools, e.g., Celera (Myers *et al.*, 2000).

As was previously described, Sanger sequencing yields accurate reads up to 1 kbp, typically with low coverage. These characteristics allow to assemble Sanger reads using the OLC approach, which was successfully carried out in multiple groundbreaking genome assembly projects, such as the human genome project. Currently, genomes assembled from Sanger reads with the OLC approach remain the golden standard of genome assembly.

However, this algorithm requires significant computational resources for detecting overlaps between all reads. Although several optimizations can be done to speed up this step, it is still hardly possible to calculate all overlaps for high-covered NGS datasets.

The OLC approach was brought back to life by the recent emergence of the third-generation sequencing technologies – PacBio and Oxford Nanopore. Although Sanger sequencing differs significantly from these novel technologies in terms of error rate and read length, a modified OLC approach appeared to be very useful for their assembly. The main modification compared to the previous implementations of OLC was introduced in the overlap stage, which now implies the alignment of the reads with an extremely high error rate. OLC was successfully reused in such *de novo* assemblers as Canu (Koren *et al.*, 2017) and miniasm (Li, 2016).

De novo assembly using short reads

During the NGS era, sequencing became cheaper, and therefore available to more researchers worldwide. At the same time, it brought multiple algorithmic challenges to computational biology. The problem of *de novo* genome assembly was not an exception. The OLC approach appeared to be impractical for NGS data due to the extreme amount of reads and their short length.

Pevzner *et al.* (2001) proposed to apply the *de Bruijn graph* to the problem of *de novo* genome assembly from short reads. To construct a de Bruijn graph the reads are shredded into a set of smaller sequences of a fixed length k (called *k-mers*), which represent vertices of the graph. In comparison to the overlap graph, the process of constructing a de Bruijn graph does not include

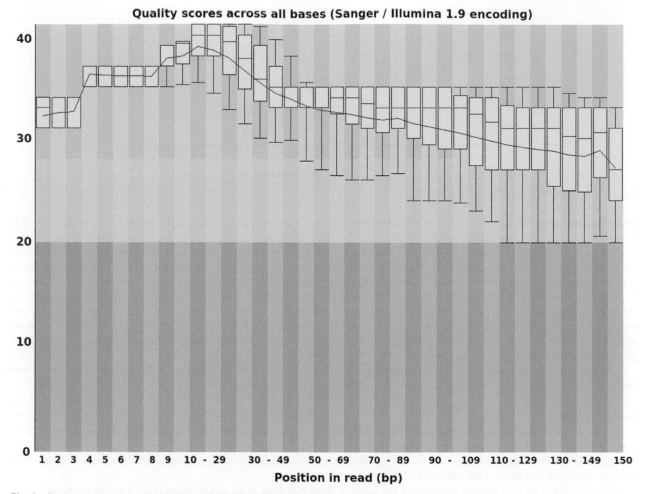

Fig. 9 Per-base sequence quality plot for quality-trimmed Illumina reads.

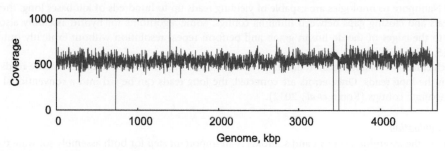

Fig. 10 Coverage depth along the genome for isolate *E.coli* dataset.

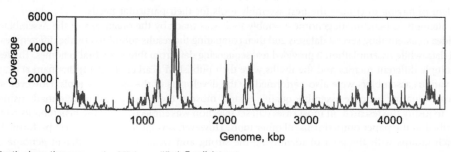

Fig. 11 Coverage depth along the genome for MDA-amplified *E.coli* dataset.

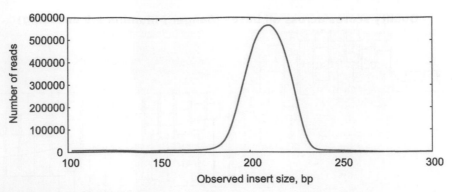

Fig. 12 Insert size distribution for isolate *E.coli* dataset.

read alignment stage, which greatly reduces running time. Since each k-mer is stored only once, the de Bruijn graph approach appears to be more memory-efficient than OLC and therefore suitable for high-coverage datasets with millions of reads.

Although the idea of using the de Bruijn graph was a breakthrough and revolutionized the field of *de novo* genome assembly, its application to real data necessitated the development of several additional algorithms and heuristics. For example, the de Bruijn graph approach appeared to be sensitive to sequencing errors. Each substitution error in a single read creates a number of erroneous non-genomic k-mers, which have to be removed. The process of cleaning the graph from these erroneous k-mers is called *graph simplification*. Once the graph is simplified, *repeat resolution* and *scaffolding* steps are performed to extract contigs and scaffolds from the graph with the help of, for example, read-pairs (Bresler *et al.*, 2012; Prjibelski *et al.*, 2014). The de Bruijn graph approach is implemented in many state-of-the-art genome assembly tools, such as Velvet (Zerbino and Birney, 2008), ABySS (Simpson *et al.*, 2009), SOAPdenovo (Luo *et al.*, 2012) and SPAdes (Nurk *et al.*, 2013).

It is worth noting, that later, in 2005, another similar concept called *String graph* was proposed by Myers (2005). In 2010 it was successfully adapted for use with real data and implemented in the SGA tool (Simpson and Durbin, 2012).

Hybrid assembly

Emergence of novel sequencing technologies also brought the possibility to perform *hybrid assembly* – A process of assembling genomes using reads from different sequencing technologies simultaneously. Hybrid assembly may be useful when long-read libraries have low coverage depth (e.g., less than 20x), which may be insufficient for constructing a reliable consensus string using the OLC approach due to the high error-rate of the reads.

Currently, there are two distinct approaches for utilizing short and long reads simultaneously. In the first approach, short accurate NGS reads are assembled using existing assembly tools to obtain accurate contigs with a small number of substitution and indel errors. Afterwards, long error-prone reads are mapped to these contigs and used for repeat resolution and scaffolding. Since PacBio and Oxford Nanopore technologies are capable of yielding reads up to hundreds of kilobases long, they can be useful for resolving long repeats and closing gaps between Illumina contigs. Some algorithms for hybrid assembly also consider aligning long reads directly to the edges of the de Bruijn graph and perform repeat resolution without explicitly outputting the contigs (Antipov *et al.*, 2015; Wick *et al.*, 2017).

Another approach consists of mapping short accurate reads (typically Illumina) onto long error-prone reads in order to correct sequencing errors in the long reads. Once errors are corrected, the long reads can be fed into a conventional OLC assembler to generate long and accurate contigs (Koren *et al.*, 2012).

Genome assembly evaluation

Assessing the quality of the assembled contigs and scaffolds is an important step for both assembly software developers and their users. By evaluating assemblers on various datasets the developers may gain a better understanding of the disadvantages and weak points of their software, improve it and benchmark against other tools to convince the scientific community that their assembler performs better on a specific variety of datasets. This also means that researchers involved in projects requiring genome assembly now face the problem of having to choose the best assembly tools for their particular needs.

One of the first attempts to benchmark genome assembly tools was made by the organizers of the Assemblathon competitions, who suggested the idea of assembling several datasets and then comparing the results submitted by the different teams. Assemblathon 1 offered simulated data, while Assemblathon 2 provided real sequencing data from three vertebrate genomes. The resulted contigs were compared using multiple different metrics and the results were then published (Earl *et al.*, 2011; Bradnam *et al.*, 2013).

Benchmarks of various assemblers were also performed by the developers of the assembly tools. However, since until recently no standard tool for evaluating genome assembly quality existed, most of these comparisons were made using custom in-house scripts. In addition, to justify the research, in most cases dataset selection was subjective and the benchmarks typically revealed that the assembler described in the paper outperforms all other tools. However, several benchmarks were performed and published by independent research groups with the goal of identifying the strong and weak points of different genome assembly software (Salzberg *et al.*, 2012; Magoc *et al.*, 2013).

In 2012 GAGE (Salzberg *et al.*, 2012) and QUAST (Gurevich *et al.*, 2013) tools were developed to allow researchers to perform genome assembly quality evaluation on their own. These tools are mostly designed for assessing assemblies of model organisms, i.e., when the reference genome is known. Reference-based quality evaluation allows to perform an excessive analysis of the assemblies by providing a number of informative metrics, such as the fraction of the genome covered, *misassemblies* statistics as well as mismatch and indel error rates.

While reference-based assembly evaluation is useful for testing and comparing genome assemblers, *de novo* evaluation is an integral part of the genome assembly projects. In general, there are three different approaches for reference-free assembly quality assessment. The first one includes calculation of basic statistics (e.g., total assembly length, *N50*) and is useful for initial quality control of the assembly. Another method relies on mapping the raw reads back to the assembly and estimating the likelihood of this particular assembly being generated by the given reads (Hunt *et al.*, 2013). The last group of methods involve counting genes in the assembled sequences. The BUSCO tool (Simão *et al.*, 2015) is designed for detecting the presence of *universal single-copy orthologs*, typical for the specified kingdom, phylum or class. Such tools as GeneMark (Lukashin and Borodovsky, 1998) and Glimmer (Delcher *et al.*, 1999) identify genes *de novo* using Hidden Markov Models (see Section "Genome Annotation" for more information).

Assembly of microbial genomes

Microbial genomes are known for their rather simple repeat structures (compared to the eukaryotic genomes) and therefore are easier to assemble. Since most of the repeats in bacterial genomes do not exceed 7 kbp in length, it is usually possible to assemble a complete bacterial genome with the help of either a mate-pair library (Vasilinetc *et al.*, 2015) with a large insert size or long-read sequencing data (Antipov *et al.*, 2015; Wick *et al.*, 2017). Current Illumina Nextera Mate-Pair protocol allows to obtain a complete bacterial genome using only a single short-read sequencing library (Vasilinetc *et al.*, 2015). At the same time, a single PacBio or Oxford Nanopore library with a decent coverage depth (e.g., higher than 20x–30x) also allows to obtain a complete bacterial genome in most cases.

To generate a sequencing library for a prokaryotic organism millions of identical cells are needed. However, nowadays most of known bacteria cannot be cultivated in the lab. To generate enough genomic material for the sequencing experiment, bacterial genome from a single cell can be amplified using for example the Multiple Displacement Amplification method (Lizardi and Yale University, 2000). Compared to the conventional isolate datasets, the reads obtained via the MDA technology typically have a highly uneven coverage depth across the genome, which complicates the assembly process. To address the problem of single-cell bacterial assembly SPAdes (Nurk *et al.*, 2013) and IDBA-UD (Peng *et al.*, 2012) assemblers were developed. Recently, a first bacterial genome was completely assembled and finished using only single-cell sequencing data (Woyke, 2010).

Assembling metagenomes

In real life, bacteria typically exist within large communities that may contain thousands of different species. Sequencing and studying the whole community at once is called *metagenomics*. Until recently, metagenomic studies mostly included such research goals as detecting the variety of species (e.g., using 16s rRNA genes) and their abundances within the specific community. The development of MEGAHIT (Li *et al.*, 2015) and metaSPAdes (Nurk *et al.*, 2017) assemblers allows to obtain decent bacterial assemblies from metagenomic datasets.

Metagenome assembly is characterized by such challenges as the presence of related strains within the community, conservative genomic regions shared between different species and uneven coverage depth due to variations in the abundances of the different bacteria in the sample. In addition, metagenomic datasets typically contain enormous amount of reads to capture genomic information for underrepresented bacteria. Since the total length of all genomes within the community may be similar to the length of a mammalian genome, metagenome assembly appears to be an extremely challenging problem not only regarding the quality of the resulting contigs, but in terms of computational resources required as well.

Assembly of eukaryotes

Eukaryotic genomes are known for their complex repeat structures, which complicate the problem of genome assembly by a margin. For example, the human genome contains various repeat families, such as ALUs (short 300 bp repeats with over a million copies in the genome), other short interspersed nuclear elements (SINEs), long interspersed nuclear elements (LINEs, typically about 7 kbp long), terminal repeats and various tandem repeats. To resolve such repeats eukaryotic genomes are assembled using a large variety of sequencing data: mate-pair libraries with different insert sizes, fosmid mate-pairs and genomic maps.

Genome Annotation

Assembled from short sequenced fragments genomic DNA contains all of the information about the metabolism of the organism, its development and responses to external stimuli. Most of these functions are carried out by proteins encoded within the genomic sequence. This means that the primary goal of any genome analysis is to identify protein encoding genes, determine their functions and then define and characterize the sections of DNA that regulate the amounts of these proteins being synthesized based on an exact point in time and conditions. This process is called *genome annotation*. At the start of the annotation process all possible start and end codons that delimit the parameters of protein encoding genes are identified. This stage is called *ORF calling* and will be described in more detail in the "Markov models and gene prediction" section.

It is important to keep in mind that ORF calling methods used for bacterial genomes cannot be applied to eukaryotic genomes, since the latter contain both coding (exons) and non-coding regions (introns). Introns are also significantly longer than exons (e.g., exons take up about 2% of the entire length of the human genome). Information, such as the frequency of encountering particular amino acids and synonymous codons and the knowledge of the length of the exons and introns is used in combination with other statistical data to identify genes in eukaryotic genomes. Despite the fact that genome annotation using statistical identification rules yields only very approximate data, it is still of great value as part of the whole process.

The best way to tackle this task is to compare the sequences of several different, but related genomes. Since exons and introns evolve with different speed (exons, evolve comparatively slower than non-coding segments, aka introns), we can use this information to highlight similar regions by comparing genome sequences to each other and as such, identify the overall location of the exons. The delimitations of these coding regions are then further refined via statistical methods.

Comparative analysis is also of help when trying to predict the function of the particular proteins encoded by the genes. If the level of similarity between the new protein and a previously researched and well described one (studied in a laboratory setting) is high, they can be considered as similar and are likely to have identical functions. The lower the degree of similarity between proteins, the more different their functions will be. To make sure that two protein coding genes from two different genomes are in fact the same gene, we must make sure that neither of these genes has a closer relative in a different genome. This stands true even if the function of these proteins is extremely similar. The quality and accuracy of such analysis is directly dependent on the availability of a large amount of high quality whole genome assembly reference data.

High quality predictions of protein functions play a crucial role in a large number of theoretical and experimental studies, such as for example research aiming to gain a deeper understanding of the underlying biochemical conditions related to numerous genetic diseases.

Not all genes in a genome encode proteins. Thus, instead of synthesizing protein, non-coding RNA genes are responsible for the production of functional RNA products. Non-coding RNA genes can be predicted by using various programs tRNAscan-SE (Lowe and Eddy, 1997), RNammer (Lagesen *et al.*, 2007) and BLAST (Altschul *et al.*, 1990) and data sources, as well as performing homology-based searches in such databases as Rfam (Burge *et al.*, 2013), the plant snoRNA database (Brown *et al.*, 2003) (for plant genomes), GenBank (Benson *et al.*, 2004) and ASRG (Wang and Brendel, 2004). RNA sequencing reads (if available) can be further mapped against the appropriate databases to strengthen the generated predictions.

The comparative sequence analysis approach coupled with functional genomics experiments allows annotating non-protein coding genomic regions.

A number of comprehensive annotation systems are available for carrying out functional annotation (see Further reading) for the interested reader to consider and use.

Markov models and gene prediction

Knowledge of the intrinsic gene structure is the main mechanism used in gene prediction. Indeed, the majority of genes have ATG (methionine) as a starting codon, though sometimes GTG and TTG are used as alternative starting codons. Certainly, there may be multiple ATG, GTG, or TGT codons in a frame, which means that the presence of these codons at the beginning of the frame does not necessarily give a proper indication of the translation initiation site. Therefore, another type of DNA structure, also associated with the translation initiation event, has to be used in addition to nucleotide content. One of such features is the ribosomal binding site (RBS) located upstream of the translation start codon. Knowing the ribosome binding site can help to determine the start codon. Each protein coding region ends in a stop codon that causes translation to stop. There are three possible stop codons, namely, TAG, TAA, and TGA, and all three of them are fairly easy to identify.

Manual prokaryotic gene identification relies on brute-force determination of ORFs and major features related to prokaryotic genes. As a part of this approach the DNA is first translated in all six possible frames (three frames on one strand and three frames on the opposite strand). It is worth mentioning that in a noncoding region a stop codon occurs on average every twenty codons, which means that a frame longer than thirty codons without any stop codons could be considered as putative gene coding region. The putative frame is further manually confirmed by the presence of other features such as a start codon and the RBS sequence.

Markov models can be very helpful in providing a probabilistic description of a gene sequence. A *Markov model* describes the probability distribution of nucleotides in a DNA sequence, where the conditional probability of a nucleotide occurring in a particular sequence position depends only on the nucleotides at k previous positions. The value k is called the *order* of a Markov model. This mean that a zero-order Markov model implies that each of the bases occur independently with a given probability. This is a typical situation for noncoding parts of a genome. A first-order Markov model (or *Markov chain*) stipulates that the probability of the occurrence of a particular base will depend only on the base preceding it. A second-order model looks at the preceding two bases to determine the probability of occurrence of the following base. This model is a better fit for the codons in a coding sequence.

The use of the Markov models in gene finding exploits the idea that oligonucleotide distributions in the coding regions are different from those for the noncoding regions. Indeed, having the Markov models that describes the structure of coding and non-coding regions (these can be represented with Markov models of different orders) we can calculate the probabilities of occurrence of a particular sequence under these models. Comparing these probabilities or, better yet, calculating the likelihood ratio we could decide whether the particular sequence is a part of a coding region, or not. Since a fixed-order Markov model describes the probability of a particular nucleotide that depends on previous k nucleotides, the longer the nucleotide sequence, the more accurately the internal structure can be described for the coding region. Therefore, the higher the order of a Markov model, the better it can predict genes.

A protein-encoding gene is formed by nucleotides organized in triplets as codons, hence the more effective Markov models are constructed from the sets of three nucleotides, explaining the observed distributions of trimers or hexamers, and so on. The parameters of a Markov model have to be trained using a set of sequences with known gene locations. Once the parameters of the model are established, the model can be used to estimate the probabilities of trimers or hexamers in a new sequence.

Under normal circumstances the pairs of codons tend to correlate, and as a result, the frequency of a particular six nucleotides appearing together in a coding region can be much higher than occurring by random chance. As a result, a fifth-order Markov model, which calculates the probability of hexamer bases, can detect nucleotide correlations typical for coding regions more accurately and is in fact most often used (Wang *et al.*, 2004).

A potential problem of using a high-order Markov chain is that if there are not enough hexamers, which happens in short gene sequences, the method's efficacy might be limited. One way to deal with this limitation is a variable-length Markov model also known as the *interpolated Markov model* (IMM). The IMM samples the largest number of sequence patterns with Markov model orders (k) ranging from 1 to 8 and uses a weighting scheme, placing less weight on rare k-mers (outlining the worse accuracy of corresponding probability estimation) and more weight on more frequent k-mers. The probability produced by the final model is the sum of probabilities of all weighted k-mers. In other words, this method has more flexibility in using Markov models depending on the amount of data available. Higher-order models are used when there is an abundant amount of data and lower-order models are used when the amount of data is smaller (Salzberg *et al.*, 1998).

Surprisingly, the gene content and length distribution of prokaryotic genes can vary a lot. The majority of genes are in the 100–500 amino acids range with a nucleotide distribution derived from the GC content of the organism. However, there are atypical genes that are shorter or longer and have a variety of nucleotide frequency profiles. These genes tend to escape detection using the gene models trained on the typical data. Moreover, the models trained on the whole spectrum of the genes tend to produce worse results due to reduced precision. Ideally, to describe all genes in a genome fully more than one Markov model is needed. The standard way to combine different Markov models (that would represent typical and atypical nucleotide distributions) is via *Hidden Markov Models* (HMM).

A HMM combines two or more Markov models within only one consisting of observed states and others representing unobserved (or "hidden") states that influence the outcome of the observed states (such unobserved state could be, for example, the type of the gene, or a particular part in the gene the nucleotide composition of which would differ from the other parts). In an HMM, as in a Markov model, the probability of going from one state to another state is the transition probability. Each state may be composed of a number of elements. For nucleotide sequences, there are four possible symbols, namely A, T, G, and C in each state. For amino acid sequences, there are twenty possible symbols. The probability value associated with the occurrence of each of the symbols in each state is called the emission probability. To calculate the total probability of a particular path of the model, both transition and emission probabilities linking all the "hidden" as well as observed states need to be taken into account.

The most popular prokaryotic gene prediction/ORF calling software are: Glimmer is based on interpolated Markov models (Salzberg *et al.*, 1998). GeneMark (Lukashin and Borodovsky, 1998) uses inhomogeneous three-periodic Markov chain models of protein-coding DNA sequences and could be viewed as an approximation of an HMM approach (Azad and Borodovsky, 2004).

Analyzing Transcriptomic Sequences

Quality Control of Rna-Seq

Initial quality control of RNA-Seq data can be performed using the same FastQC tool (Andrews, 2010), as used for genomic data. However, the FastQC reports for RNA-Seq data should be interpreted somewhat differently, compared to the genomic data. The main differentiating criteria for RNA-Seq data is the uneven coverage depth and the presence of ribosomal RNA sequences. Due to their high abundance, rRNA reads may introduce additional peaks into the GC content plot (**Fig. 13**), as well as create non-uniform k-mer content (**Fig. 14**).

The presence of unwanted rRNA reads is a typical problem for RNA-Seq experiments. Some sequencing protocols aim to filter out rRNAs during sample preparation, but such approach, however, may only remove a fraction of the rRNA reads from the dataset. Reads from rRNAs can be removed as contamination using, for example, the bbduk script from the bbtools package (see Section "Sequencing Data Formats". for the details), with known rRNA sequences provided as the database.

Aligning RNA Sequences

While alignment of prokaryotic RNA sequences to the reference genome can be performed with the same algorithms and methods used for DNA sequence alignment, the process of mapping eukaryotic RNA differs significantly due to the presence of splicing events. To support long insertions and skip intronic sequences splicing alignment algorithms are required. The most popular software tools for RNA to DNA mapping are BLAT (Kent, 2002), GMAP (Wu and Watanabe, 2005) and Splign (Kapustin *et al.*, 2008).

The problem of mapping eukaryotic RNA-Seq reads to the reference genome is further exacerbated by their short length and the presence of sequencing errors. One of the first tools for mapping RNA-Seq reads – TopHat – was based on the Bowtie aligner for genomic reads (Trapnell *et al.*, 2009) Later, STAR (Dobin *et al.*, 2013) and Hisat (Kim *et al.*, 2015) aligners were developed specifically to address the problem of rapid and accurate mapping of RNA-Seq data. All listed tools can take the gene database in

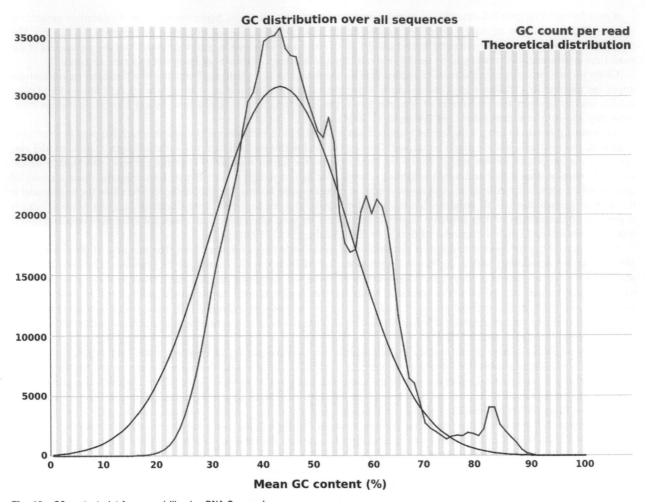

Fig. 13 GC content plot for normal Illumina RNA-Seq reads.

GFF format as input in addition to the reference genome, which increases the accuracy of the alignments and is especially true in the case of reads containing the splice junctions.

Mapping RNA-Seq reads can be of use as an additional reference based quality control. For example, the qualimap (Okonechnikov *et al.*, 2015) tool calculates such statistics as fractions of exonic, intronic and intergenic reads, gene coverage profile and splice junction distribution. The RSeQC (Wang *et al.*, 2012) can also be used as an alternative tool. In addition to the statistics listed above, it is capable of determining the insert size for paired-end RNA-Seq reads, estimate mismatch content and detect whether RNA-Seq data is *strand-specific* or not. In strand-specific RNA-Seq experiment the reads are sequenced either from the same or from the opposite strand of the gene that produces the RNA, which then allows to detect actual gene strand. RNA-Seq alignment can also be used to detect fusion genes – chimeric genes that can appear during genomic rearrangements in cancer cells (Kim and Salzberg, 2011).

Gene Counting and Differential Expression

The main application of RNA-Seq is the estimation of gene expression levels and *differential expression analysis* between multiple samples. Differential expression analysis implies the comparison of expression levels of the same genes/isoforms between samples under different conditions, such as cells under different treatments, healthy and ill patients, patients before and after medical treatment. The number of samples analyzed is the key to a successful analysis as only a correct choice will fully take advantage of RNA-Seq possibilities. To perform the differential expression analysis, a study requires at least three biological samples for each condition analyzed. This is because, when comparing gene expression between the different conditions, sample specific differences may affect the analysis and thus lead to inadequate conclusions, since these differences may not be related to the subject of research. Having an appropriate number of samples for each condition will reduce the impact of sample specific variability on the analysis. Both biological and technical variabilities within the samples can be reduced by normalization. The number of samples analyzed is also essential for the statistical tests required by any differential expression analysis. Most of them need at least three or more samples per condition to provide a statistically sound result. Less samples will suffice only for obtaining exploratory results, while more samples will increase the power of the analysis.

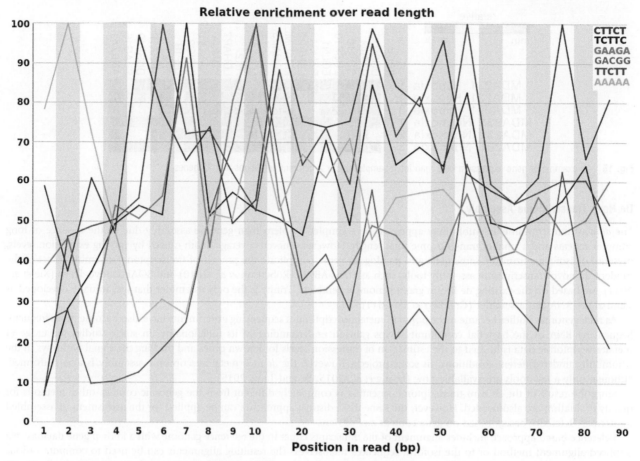

Fig. 14 k-mer distribution for normal Illumina RNA-Seq reads.

Since the isoforms of a gene contain the same exons, assigning each read to a specific isoform is much more complicated task than assigning those reads to the corresponding gene. Therefore, most RNA-Seq pipelines focus on gene level analysis, consisting of several steps.

Firstly, RNA-Seq reads are mapped to the reference genome ignoring reads that map equally well to more than one genomic location (multi-mappers) and assigned to the genes from the database. Afterwards, the number of reads assigned to each gene are counted, e.g., using htseq-count (Anders *et al.*, 2015). Some tools also allow to perform quantification without actually mapping the reads to the reference genome (Bray *et al.*, 2016). The gene counts can be normalized, usually by sequencing depth and gene length. The normalized counts are used to estimate relative change of the expression levels between different samples with a statistical test, e.g., a t-test or a test created specifically for RNA-Seq data. State-of-the-art software tools such as DESeq2 (Love *et al.*, 2014) and edgeR (Robinson *et al.*, 2010) require unnormalized raw counts and perform themselves the normalization step.

The results of the differential analysis are typically represented as a table with genes as rows and several values for each gene. Among these numbers, the most important are the measure of the change in gene expression between the conditions (usually a log fold-change) and the result of the statistical test, usually an *adjusted p-value*. Since thousands of tests are made, the adjusted p-value indicates the significance of the difference in expression (p-values are calculated for null-hypotheses stating that the expression level is the same for all conditions). The decision for calling a gene differentially expressed is not straightforward: it depends on arbitrary threshold values for both log fold-change (how much the expression has to change) and adjusted p-value (how many false positives can be tolerated).

Another way of exploring differential expression analysis results is using a heat map (see example in **Fig. 15**). Table rows correspond to the genes being examined, and each column corresponds to a single sample. Cells color represents estimated genes expression levels. The table is usually sorted according to the change in expression level between different conditions.

One of the possible biases that can significantly affect the results of differential expression analysis is the so called batch effect. The batch effect takes place when the difference between samples is caused by sample preparation or sequencing protocols, flowcell inconsistencies, variations between sequencer runs (Dündar *et al.*, 2015). These factors may lead to inappropriate calculation of expression levels and therefore, misleading interpretation of the results. *In silico* removal of the batch effect is implemented in various differential expression analysis toolkits, e.g., Deseq2 (Love *et al.*, 2014).

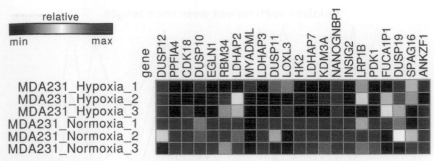

Fig. 15   An example of gene expression heat map for 6 samples under 2 different conditions and 22 genes.

De Novo Transcriptome Assembly

The *de novo* transcriptome assembly may appear to be a simpler problem than genome assembly due to the absence of long complex repeats and a smaller transcriptome total length. However, uneven coverage depth caused by varying expression levels, presence of isoforms from the same gene and paralogous genes complicate the process of transcriptome assembly. Most of the modern de novo transcriptome assembly tools, such as Trans-ABySS (Robertson *et al.*, 2010) and SOAPdenovo-Trans (Xie *et al.*, 2014), are based on the existing de Bruijn graph genome assemblers. Trinity is the only assembler that was initially developed as stand-alone RNA-Seq assembler (Grabherr *et al.*, 2011).

As metagenomic studies became more popular, metatranscriptomics sequencing experiments have also become more frequent. Sequencing RNA of the bacterial community helps gain an understanding of its functionality. In some studies the usage of metatranscriptomic data is limited to the estimation of expression levels for known genes and tracking the signal pathways in the community under different conditions. In some projects, however, the *de novo* metatranscriptome assembly is also performed, although only a few tools are available now (Leung *et al.*, 2015; Ye and Tang, 2015).

Since the result of the *de novo* transcriptome assembly is completely different from the genomic contigs, other methods for quality evaluation are also needed. However, the same three distinct approaches can be applied for the assessment of assembled transcripts: Reference-based, based on gene content and *de novo*.

Reference-based approach includes alignment of the transcripts either to the reference genome with a known gene database via a spliced alignment method or to the isoform sequences themselves. The resulting alignments can be used to compute various statistics and metrics, such as *misassembled* transcripts, number of assembled genes and isoforms, duplication ratio along with mismatch and indel error rate. Recently developed rnaQUAST (Bushmanova *et al.*, 2016) and Transrate (Smith-Unna *et al.*, 2016) tools are designed specifically for the reference-based quality evaluation of *de novo* transcriptome assemblies.

Similar to the genome assemblies, the gene content can be estimated using BUSCO (Simão *et al.*, 2015), which allows to search for single-copy orthologs that are universal for the specific group of organisms. *De novo* gene identification can be performed with a modified version of a popular tool GeneMark, called GeneMarkS-T (Tang *et al.*, 2015). *De novo* quality evaluation based on raw reads for RNA-Seq assemblies is implemented in such tools as Transrate (Smith-Unna *et al.*, 2016) and Detonate (Li *et al.*, 2014).

Protein Data Analysis

All living cells contain proteins that are of a great importance for all biological objects. The structure of proteins is very complex and includes several levels of organization. The primary structure of a protein is usually represented as a string of amino acids starting from the amino-terminal (N-terminal) to the carboxyl-terminal (C-terminal) of the protein. It can be obtained as a result of the direct sequencing of the protein or deduced from the corresponding DNA or mRNA, since the order of bases on a DNA strand specifies the order in which the amino acids are linked together during translation. The amino acid sequence of proteins or peptides is basic information to understand proteins or peptides and predict its post-translational modifications and functions.

Protein Sequencing Technologies

The process of determination of the amino acid sequence is known as protein sequencing. Amino acids may be represented by a single- or three-letter codes. It is worth to mention that sequencing methods were originally developed specifically with proteins in mind, since people thought that proteins were the main genetic material. Researchers believed that the structure of DNA was too simple (composed of only four nucleotides) to play this role comparing to proteins, that can be built of 20 different amino-acids and thus have a higher heterogeneity as molecules. All protein sequencing methods can be divided into two groups: one group provides N-terminus sequence of a protein, while the second group of methods is used to sequence and identify the entirety of the protein. A label-cleavage method for protein sequencing was developed by Pehr Edman in 1950s (Edman *et al.*, 1950).

Edman degradation procedure (**Fig. 16**) is based on a three-stage reaction that labels and removes the N-terminal residue of a polypeptide, which can then be identified as a phenylthiohydantoin (PTH – Edman reagent) derivative.

Phenyl isothiocyanate, $C_6H_5N=C=S$, is a reagent that permits the progressive removal and identification of the N-terminal amino acid, leaving the rest of the chain unaffected. The truncated peptide after the first degradation has a new N-terminal amino acid that can again react with phenyl isothiocyanate and thus makes progressive removal of the subsequent amino acids possible. This technique cannot be applied if the N-terminus is modified. Removed amino-acid residues are then identified by chromatography (Berg *et al.*, 2002).

Edman sequencing is automated (Niall, 1973) and uses a protein sequenator that allows sequencing peptides of about 5–50 amino acids long. Polypeptides longer than 50–70 amino acids must be cleaved into smaller peptides before sequencing. Use of multiple endopeptidases for the same protein to break up long peptides allows obtaining overlapping fragments of peptide that can be used to produce final sequence. To be sequenced the peptide is adsorbed onto a solid surface.

Edman approach is known for impurities that commonly occur in the first round of degradation. Despite this fact, it remains a valuable tool for characterizing a protein's N-terminus and is still the most reliable, and accurate protein and peptide sequencing method that provides an unambiguous sequence read and is widely used for quality control purposes.

Another method for peptide end-group analysis was developed by Fred Sanger (Ryle *et al.*, 1955) who was awarded the 1958 Nobel Prize for Chemistry for sequencing insulin that was performed with the developed approach. Sanger method uses chemical derivatives to selectively label the N-terminus of a protein with the yellow dye fluorodinitrobenzene, followed by hydrolysis, and electrophoretic or chromatographic separation of the labeled N-terminal amino acid residue. Multiple rounds of partial protein hydrolysis, fractionation, and terminal amino acid determination lead to complete sequence of a protein. There is no robust method to sequence a protein or peptide from its C-terminus because carboxypeptidases – enzymes that are used as part of these methods – can remove only specific individual C-terminal amino acids (Bergman *et al.*, 2003).

Reconstructing Proteins From Mass-Spectra

Mass spectrometry (MS) methods are now the most widely used for protein sequencing and identification. Mass spectrometry is an analytical method that measures mass-to-charge ratio for ions in gas phase. MS breaks up peptides into individual amino acids using electric current, collects the released amino acids in mass spectrometer detector to be individually identified by their unique mass. The development of MS technology allowed to sequence the entire set of proteins of a living organism and thus became the trigger for the emergence of proteomics. (Tran *et al.*, 2017).

There are currently two major types of MS approaches to protein sequencing (**Fig. 17**): the *bottom-up* approach for the analysis of peptide mixtures from digested proteins and *top-down* mass spectrometry that is used to analyze intact proteins.

The bottom-up approach starts from the proteolytic digestion of proteins that creates complex peptide samples, which are then used in combination with high-throughput liquid chromatography (LC) and tandem MS* (LC-MS/MS; LC–MALDI MS/MS,

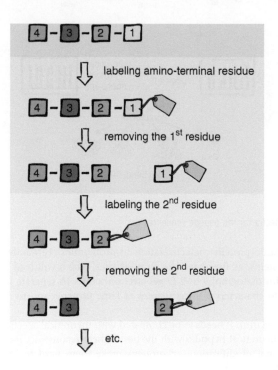

labeling amino-terminal residue

removing the 1st residue

labeling the 2nd residue

removing the 2nd residue

etc.

Fig. 16 Edman degradation procedure.

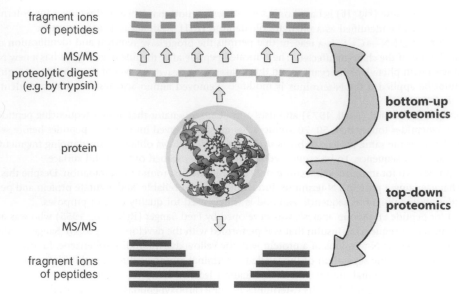

Fig. 17 MS approaches to protein sequencing.

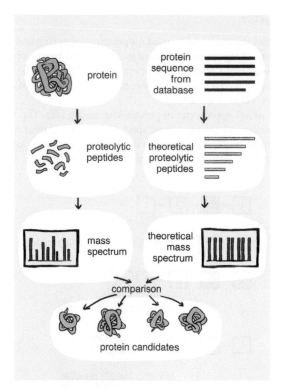

Fig. 18 Theoretical and experimental spectra for the peptide sequence.

MALDI TOF/TOF) to enable large-scale protein characterization in proteomics (Fernández-Puente *et al.*, 2014). This approach should not be applied for small proteins, as they have less cleavage sites, which will lead to an insufficient amount of peptides.

The top-down MS uses liquid chromatography or 2-D gel electrophoresis to separate intact proteins from complex samples. This approach is successfully used to characterize the structures of large proteins and to detect post-translational modifications (Aken *et al.*, 2016).

To analyze an experimental MS spectrum it needs to be compared with theoretical spectra for each of the peptides in a database (see "Relevant Websites" section). Theoretical peptides with the best fit help reconstruct the sequence of the experimental peptide (**Fig. 18**). Numerous post-translational modifications of proteins make them hard to be identified in databases and create a challenging computational problem.

The main goal of peptide sequencing is to reconstruct the amino acid sequence of a peptide. This goal can be achieved by using data of MS/MS spectrum and the peptide mass. Each tandem mass spectrum covers only a short part of the protein and to reconstruct the primary structure one has to assemble tandem mass spectra of overlapping peptides generated from multiple proteolytic digestions of the protein. Sounds like a DNA assembly task. Doesn't it? Here too we are trying to reconstruct a long sequence from many small fragments. In the case of protein assembly this approach is called top-down MS. To continue the analogy with genomic assembly, we should mention that top-down tandem mass spectra rarely provide full coverage of a protein. Bottom-up tandem mass spectra are used to increase sequence coverage (Liu et al., 2014).

Experiments using MS technologies produce huge amount of very complex data and require specialised software for their analysis (for example: PepNovo, PEAKS, NovoHMM, MSNovo, pNovo, UniNovo, Novor and DeepNovo (Tran et al., 2017)). Noisy and ambiguous MS/MS spectra cause additional computational challenges and require improved algorithms.

To find out more about the current tools that help retrieve long sequence fragments of the target proteins from sets of bottom-up and top-down MS/MS spectra see publications in further readings.

Mapping Proteins to Genome

Proteomics is a science that studies the protein composition of biological objects, as well as the modifications and the structural and functional properties of proteins. The uniqueness of the mass spectrometry pictures of products produced by proteolytic protein hydrolysis for each protein is used to analyze them against theoretical mass spectrum collected in databases.

One of the main goals when studying protein is to match the protein to the gene its coding. Knowledge of the mass of the whole protein does not provide reliable information due to the insufficient accuracy of the measurement or the presence of modifications. Therefore, researches use a mass spectrometry peptide map of a protein that consists of mass values of peptides obtained as a result of highly specific hydrolysis (chemical or enzymatic) of a protein. Such sets are called "MS-peptide fingerprints".

The main approach of protein identification by mass-spectrometry is to compare the real, experimentally obtained mass spectrum with the theoretical ones from the database that correspond to the known proteins.

Existing algorithms and corresponding programs that allow the identification of proteins by their mass spectra can be divided into three main groups:

1. Programs using the protein proteolytic peptide fingerprint (MASCOT (Perkins et al., 1999). ProFound (Zhang and Chait, 2000)),
2. Programs that work with the peptide fingerprint and MS/MS spectra (MASCOT, MS-Fit (see "Relevant Websites" section),
3. Programs that work with the MS/MS spectra only (SEQUEST (see "Relevant Websites" section), PepFrag (see "Relevant Websites" section), MS-Tag (see "Relevant Websites" section), Sherpa (Taylor et al., 1996).

All programs mentioned above use publicly available databases of amino acid sequences of proteins or nucleotide sequences of genes. Some of the most popular programs that contain protein sequences are: UniProt, a powerful database of annotated proteins (see "Relevant Websites" section); UniProtKB (see "Relevant Websites" section), a database that consists of Swiss-Prot (a collection of manually annotated and curated sequences) and TrEMBL (automatically annotated protein sequences translated from the nucleic acid sequences stored in EMBL) (Bairoch and Apweiler, 2000); UniRef, which contains sequence clusters for fast sequence similarity searches (see "Relevant Websites" section) and UniParc, a sequence archive of sequences and their identifiers (see "Relevant Websites" section); Protein Sequence Database (PSD) in the Protein Identification Resource (PIR, Barker et al., 1999), containing annotated protein sequences; NCBI nr protein database, including entries from the non-redundant GenBank translations (see "Relevant Websites" section), UniProt, PIR (Barker et al., 1999), Protein Research Foundation (PRF) in Japan (see "Relevant Websites" section), and the Protein Data Bank (PDB, see "Relevant Websites" section). Only entries with absolutely identical sequences are merged (Xu, 2004). Most of these databases also provide a sequence search tools.

Protein-Protein Alignment

Pairwise sequence alignment is a fundamental component of many bioinformatics problems. It is extremely useful in structural, functional, and evolutionary analyses of sequences since it provides information about the level of similarity between two sequences.

The overall goal of pairwise sequence alignment is to find the best "pairing" of two sequences of DNA, RNA, or protein, maximizing the number of similar characters. To achieve this, one sequence needs to be spread relative to the other to find the positions where maximal correspondence can be found. There are two main alignment strategies that are most oftenly used: global alignment and local alignment.

In *global alignment*, the two sequences to be aligned are assumed to be generally similar over the entirety of their length. Alignment is carried out from the start and till the end of both sequences to find the best possible alignment across the entire length between the two sequences. This method is more applicable for aligning two closely related sequences of (roughly) the same length. Note that this method is not suitable for identifying the highly similar local regions between the two sequences.

Local alignment, on the other hand, does not assume that the two sequences in question are similar over their entire length. In fact, it only determines regions with the highest level of similarity between the two sequences and aligns only these regions without taking into account the alignment of the rest of the sequences. This approach can be used for aligning more divergent sequences with the goal of searching for conserved patterns in DNA or protein sequences.

The way the alignment algorithms (both global and local) are implemented is fundamentally similar, with the exception of the optimization strategy used in aligning similar residues. Typically the alignment is performed by means of *dynamic programming*.

Dynamic programming is a method that determines the optimal alignment by matching two sequences against each other to identify for all possible pairs of matching characters between them. During this process a two-dimensional matrix is created and the two sequences to be compared are both laid out of the two axes. The symbols are then matched in according to the particular *scoring matrix*. Alignment scores are calculated one row at a time. The process starts with the first row of one sequence, which is used to scan through the entire length of the other sequence. The matching scores are calculated. The scanning of the second row takes into account the scores previously obtained during the first round. The best score is put into the bottom right corner of an intermediate matrix. This process is iterated until values for all the cells are filled. The scores are thus accumulated along a diagonal going from the upper left corner to the lower right corner. Once the matrix with the scores has been computed, the next step is to find the path that represents the optimal alignment. This is done by tracing back through the matrix in reverse order from the lower right-hand corner toward the origin of the matrix in the upper left-hand corner. The best matching path is the one that has the maximum total score. If two or more paths reach the same highest score, one is chosen arbitrarily to represent the best alignment. The path can also move horizontally or vertically at a certain point, which corresponds to the introduction of a gap or an insertion or deletion for one of the two sequences.

Gap penalties

Alignment between sequences often involves adding *gaps* that represent insertions and deletions. Note that special care should be taken when allowing gaps within the scoring scheme: if the gap penalty values are set too low, the gaps can become too numerous to allow even non-related sequences to be matched up with high similarity scores. If the penalty values are set too high, gaps may become too difficult to appear, which would stand in the way of the creation of a reasonable alignment.

Another factor to consider is the cost difference between opening a gap and extending an existing gap. Normally a gap opening should have a much higher penalty than a gap extension. This is based on the rationale that if insertions and deletions ever occur, several adjacent residues are likely to have been inserted or deleted together. These differential gap penalties are also referred to as affine gap penalties. Under normal circumstances separate gap penalty values are assigned for introducing and extending gaps. For example, one may use a $-12/-1$ scheme, in which the gap opening penalty is equal to -12 and the gap extension penalty is given the value of -1. The total gap penalty W is a linear function of gap length, which is calculated as $W = \gamma + \delta \times (l-1)$, where γ is the gap opening penalty, δ is the gap extension penalty, and l is the length of the gap (Gotoh, 1982). Besides the affine gap penalty, a constant gap penalty is sometimes also used, which assigns the same score for each gap position regardless whether it is an opening or an extension. In addition to that, end gaps can be allowed to be free (their inclusion will have zero penalty) to avoid getting unrealistic alignments.

Dynamic programming for global alignment

The classical global pairwise alignment algorithm using dynamic programming is known as the Needleman – Wunsch algorithm (Needleman and Wunsch, 1970). The aim this algorithm is to identify the optimal alignment is obtained over the entire lengths of the two sequences. It must extend from the beginning to the end of both sequences to achieve the highest total score. In other words, the alignment path has to go from the bottom right corner of the matrix to the top left corner. The possible drawback of focusing on trying to get a maximal score for the full-length sequence alignment is the risk of missing the best local similarities, which means that this strategy is only suitable for aligning two closely related sequences that are of the same length.

Dynamic programming for local alignment

In a regular sequence alignment, the level of divergence between the two sequences is not known in advance. The lengths of the two sequences may also differ. In cases such as these, it is of more value to identify the regional similarities between the two sequences than to try finding a match that would include all of the symbols. The dynamic programming approach to local alignment is known as Smith – Waterman algorithm (Smith and Waterman, 1981). In this algorithm, positive scores are assigned to matching symbols and zeros to mismatches. No negative scores are used. Occasionally, several optimally aligned segments with best scores are obtained. As in the global alignment, the final result is influenced by the choice of the scoring systems used. The goal of a local alignment is to get the highest alignment score locally, which may be at the expense of the highest possible overall score for a full-length alignment. This approach may be suitable for aligning divergent sequences or sequences with multiple domains that may be of different origins.

Scoring matrices

In the dynamic programming approach the alignment procedure has to make use of a scoring system, which represents a set of values used for the purpose of quantifying the likelihood of one symbol being substituted by another in an alignment. The scoring system is called a *substitution matrix* and is derived from the statistical analysis of symbol substitution data from sets of reliable alignments of highly related sequences. Scoring matrices for nucleotide sequences are relatively simple: a positive value or high score is given for a match and a negative value or low score for a mismatch. This assignment is based on the assumption that the frequencies of mutation are equal for all bases. However, this assumption may not be realistic; typically transitions (substitutions between purines and purines or between pyrimidines and pyrimidines) occur more frequently than transversions (substitutions between purines and pyrimidines). Therefore, a more sophisticated statistical model with different probability values to reflect the two types of mutations is needed.

Scoring matrices for amino acids are much more complicated because the scoring systems have to reflect both the properties of amino acid residues, as well as the likelihood of certain residues being substituted among the homologous sequences. Certain amino acids with similar chemical properties can be more easily substituted than those having vastly different characteristics. Substitutions among similar residues are likely to preserve the essential functional and structural features. Substitutions between residues of different chemical properties, however, are more likely to cause changes (and even disruptions) to the structure and function. Such type of substitution is less likely to be favored by evolution since it is more likely to yield nonfunctional proteins.

For example, phenylalanine, tyrosine, and tryptophan all share aromatic ring structures. Because of their chemical similarities, they can be easily substituted for one another without changing the regular function and structure of the protein. Similarly, arginine, lysine, and histidine are all large basic residues and there is a high probability of them being freely interchanged. The hydrophobic residue group includes methionine, isoleucine, leucine, and valine. Small and polar residues include serine, threonine, and cysteine. Residues within these groups have high a likelihoods of being substituted for each other. However, cysteine contains a sulfhydryl group that plays a role in metal binding, as well as active site, and disulfide bond formation. Substitution of cysteine with other residues therefore often reduces the enzymatic activity or destabilizes the protein structure. This residue is thus very rarely substituted. Small and nonpolar residues such as glycine and proline are also unique since their presence often disrupts regular protein secondary structures and therefore the substitutions with these residues do not frequently occur.

Amino acid scoring matrices

Amino acid substitution matrices are 20×20 and have been developed to reflect the likelihood of residue substitutions. There are two possible types of amino acid substitution matrices: one type is based on the interchangeability of the genetic code or amino acid properties, and the other is derived from empirical studies of amino acid substitutions. Although the two different approaches have a certain degree of overlap, surprisingly, the first approach, based on the genetic code or the chemical features of amino acids, has been shown to be less accurate than the second approach, which is based on the comparison of actual amino acid substitutions among related proteins.

The empirical amino acid scoring matrices, which include PAM (Dayhoff *et al.*, 1978) and BLOSUM (Henikoff and Henikoff, 1992) matrices, are derived from actual alignments of highly similar sequences. By analyzing the frequencies of amino acid substitutions in these alignments, a scoring system can be developed by giving a higher score to more likely substitutions and correspondingly lower scores for rare ones.

Statistical significance of a sequence alignment

Once a sequence alignment showing some degree of similarity is achieved, it is important to double check whether the observed sequence alignment is indeed sound or could have been occurred by pure chance. A truly statistically significant sequence alignment might be able to provide some results connected with the homology between the sequences being aligned.

To solve this problem one must make use of a procedure designed to assist with the estimation of the probabilistic distribution of the alignment scores of the two unrelated sequences of the same length. By calculating alignment scores of a large number of unrelated pairs of sequences, a distribution model of the randomized sequence scores can be derived. It turns out that the distribution in question is the so-called Gumbel distribution (or Generalized extreme value distribution of type I) for which a mathematical expression is available. This means that given a sequence similarity value the statistical significance can be accurately estimated (Altschul *et al.*, 1990).

Multiple sequence alignment

A natural extension of pairwise alignment is multiple sequence alignment, which aims to align multiple related sequences to achieve their optimal matching. Usually such related sequences are identified through a database similarity searching. As the process generates multiple matching sequence pairs, it is often necessary to somehow turn separate pairwise alignments into a single alignment, which arranges sequences in such a way that evolutionarily equivalent positions across all sequences are matched.

The multiple sequence alignment has the unique advantage of being able to reveal more biological information than many of the pairwise alignments. For example, it allows to identify conserved sequence patterns and motifs in the whole sequence family, which would not be easy to detect when comparing only two of the sequences. Many conserved and functionally critical amino acid residues can be identified in a protein multiple alignment. Multiple sequence alignment is also an essential prerequisite to carrying out phylogenetic analysis of sequence families and prediction of protein secondary and tertiary structures.

It is theoretically possible to use dynamic programming to align any number of sequences in the similar way as for pairwise alignment. However, it is worth keeping in mind that the amount of computing time and memory required will increase exponentially the more sequences are being compared. As a consequence, full dynamic programming usually cannot be applied for datasets of more than 10–25 sequences. In practice, heuristic approaches are most often used that provide suboptimal, but still extremely useful solutions. There are different approaches that could be used to perform multiple sequence alignment. For the sake of the simplicity we will describe only one, namely, the *progressive alignment* approach (Feng and Doolittle, 1996).

Progressive alignment depends on the stepwise assembly of multiple alignment and is heuristic in nature. It speeds up the alignment of multiple sequences through a multistep process. It first conducts pairwise alignments for each possible pair of sequences using the Needleman–Wunsch global alignment method and records these similarity scores from the pairwise comparisons. The scores can be, for example, a percent identity or similarity scores based on a particular substitution matrix. Both do correlate with the evolutionary distances between the sequences. The scores are then converted into evolutionary distances to generate a distance matrix for all the sequences involved. A simple phylogenetic analysis is then performed based on the distance matrix to group sequences based on pairwise distance scores. As a result, a phylogenetic tree is generated using the neighbor-joining method. The tree reflects the evolutionary proximity among all the sequences.

Despite the fact that the resulting tree will only be an approximation, it still can be used as a guide for directing realignment of the sequences. For that reason, it is often referred to as a *guide tree*. According to the guide tree, the two most closely related sequences are first re-aligned using the Needleman – Wunsch algorithm. To align additional sequences, the two already aligned sequences are converted to a consensus sequence with fixed gap positions. The consensus is then treated as a single sequence in the subsequent step. In the following step, the next closest sequence based on the guide tree is aligned with the consensus sequence using dynamic programming. More distant sequences or sequence profiles are subsequently added one at a time in accordance with their relative positions on the guide tree. After realignment with a new sequence using dynamic programming, a new consensus is derived, which is then used for the next round of alignment. The process is repeated until all the sequences are aligned.

See sections "Further readings" and "Software" for the list and details of software tools and web portals used in nucleotide and protein sequence alignment.

Metabolic Pathways Analysis

The functions of about half of the genes in a bacterium can be reliably insinuated by comparing them to reference databases. This approach allows to compile an overall approximation of the metabolic map of the organism, which describes the substances the bacterium is able to synthesize on its own, the substances it needs to absorb from its environment, what constitutes its source of energy etc. These maps can then be further refined and cleaned of any possible errors by adjusting the similarity and other criteria.

The results of these studies can be used in such fields as biotechnology, agronomy, pharmaceutics and medicine. The analysis of the metabolic pathways of commercial strains helps optimize the release of the intended product of interest. For example, enzymes that trigger key reactions in pathogens can be used as potential targets for new types of antibiotics.

Metabolic Pathways

Series of interactions between molecules in a cell that lead to assembly of new molecules in a cell, turn genes on and off, maintain and control the flow of information, energy and biochemical compounds are called biological pathways.

The most common types of biological pathways are involved in the metabolism of a cell (metabolic pathways), gene expression regulation (genetic pathways) and signal transmission (signal transduction pathways).

Metabolism can be defined as a series of chemical transformations of matter and energy taken from the environment aimed to maintain an organism's life. Metabolic pathways in their turn are a series of biochemical reactions that convert substrates into products.

Metabolism can be conditionally divided into two opposite streams of transformations: anabolism and catabolism.

Anabolism refers to all processes involved in the creation of new substances, cells and tissues in the body. Examples of anabolism include synthesis of proteins and hormones, creation of new cells, accumulation of fats, and creation of new muscle fibers. The sum of all processes in the body that lead to the creation of any new substances and tissues is called anabolism.

On the flip side we have catabolism, which encompasses the processes involved in splitting complex substances into simpler ones, as well as decay of old cell parts and tissues of the body. An example of catabolism is the breakdown of fats and carbohydrates to produce energy, which in turn can be used for the synthesis of the substances of use to the organism, the creation of cells and the overall renewal of the body. It follows that both anabolism and catabolism are very closely interrelated to each other. The most important metabolic pathways in humans are: glycolysis, citric acid cycle (Krebs' cycle), oxidative phosphorylation, pentose phosphate pathway, urea cycle, fatty acid β-oxidation, gluconeogenesis.

The most convenient way to investigate metabolic pathways is by analyzing metabolic models. They contain all the information about the reactions that can occur in a cell, how the reactions are related to each other, the activity of which genes can regulate the reactions, which of the reactions relate to standard metabolic pathways, and which are the most important, how they are combined into metabolic pathways and how they interact with each other.

Regulation of metabolic pathways is achieved through complex interactions of a large number of factors. As a result of the proper functioning of all metabolic pathways, the cell can maintain a stable homeostasis and properly respond to changes in the external environment. The availability of a large volume of genomic information (assembled genomes) facilitates the study of metabolism regulation. Based on this information, whole genome metabolic models generalizing the available ideas about metabolism and its regulation are constructed. Such models include a list of all possible reactions, a set of rules for the regulation of individual reactions, thermodynamic limitations that determine possible directions of reactions.

Methods of metabolic models analysis can be subdivided into two groups: qualitative (topological analysis, flux balance analysis, structural kinetic models) and quantitative (structural kinetic models, kinetic models) (Tomar and De, 2014). A number of methods also use information about the atomic structure of metabolites. They allow to analyze the transition from individual metabolites to biochemical reactions.

The development of bioinformatics methods to interpret data led to the development of metabolic pathway analysis methodologies, including structural and stoichiometric analysis, metabolic flux analysis, metabolic control analysis, and several kinetic modeling based analysis. The article written by Dr. Namrata Tomar and Dr. Rajat K. (Tomar and De, 2014), provides the comprehensive survey on the existing metabolic pathway analysis methodologies.

A review of the most common approaches for the construction of computational models of metabolic systems can be found in (Rice *et al.*, 2008).

Metabolic Databases

Metabolic models can be obtained from different sources.

The KEGG database contains a large amount of information on metabolic reactions. It includes several separate databases, such as: KEGG REACTION – with information on biochemical reactions; KEGG COMPOUND and KEGG GLYCAN – about metabolites; KEGG ENZYME – about enzymes; KEGG GENES – about the genes; KEGG PATHWAY and KEGG MODULES – about metabolic pathways.

This database was developed for bioinformatics analysis in genomics, metagenomics, metabolomics, modeling and simulation in systems biology, and translational research in drug development. It contains about 4000 organisms, including 123 animals. The database is curated and requires a paid license for full access. Some information is available for free via the web interface and the program interface (Kanehisa *et al.*, 2008, 2012, 2014, 2016, 2017). One can analyze new sequenses (DNA or protein) against metadata stored in the KEGG database by mapping them to the known pathways, models, orthologs and so on (See "Relevant Websites" Section) by linking new genomes to well curated known pathways.

The BioCyc database is similar to the KEGG database. It contains about 7600 organism-specific bases. Some of them are manually curated, including the base containing human data. Another ones, including the mouse DB, are partially supervised.

The metabolic models are also stored in the EBI BioModels Database. This free to use DB contains about 2500 whole genome metabolic models in SBML format, but all of them are generated automatically from KEGG and MetaCyc databases.

The Reactome database is another free database with information on metabolic and molecular pathways. This carefully curated database focuses mainly on human biology. Data from the database can be downloaded in SBML and other formats.

There are several end to end data pipelines dedicated to help with the complex task of metabolic pathways analysis (Poskar *et al.*, 2014; Abubucker *et al.*, 2016).

Gene Ontology

Gene ontology (GO) is a major bioinformatics initiative to unify the representation of gene and gene product attributes across all species (see "Relevant Websites" section).

Because the complexity of biological systems and the sizes of the datasets that need to be analyzed continue to grow, biomedical research is becoming increasingly dependent on knowledge stored in computable form. The Gene Ontology (GO) project is a collaborative effort to address the need for consistent descriptions of gene functions and gene products across different databases. The GO knowledgebase is composed of three primary components:

1. *Gene Ontology*, which provides the logical structure of the biological functions ('terms'). It is structured as a directed acyclic graph where each term has defined relationships to one or more other terms in the same domain and sometimes to other domains. The ontology includes data on: *cellular components; molecular functions* and *biological processes* (see "Relevant Websites" section).

   Molecular function corresponds to activities that can be performed by the individual gene products or by the assembled complexes of gene products.

   A biological process in GO is not the same as a pathway since GO does not include information about the dynamics or the dependencies, both of which would be required to fully describe a pathway.

   The GO vocabulary is species-neutral, and includes terms applicable to prokaryotes and eukaryotes, single or multicellular organisms.

2. *GO annotations* are evidence-based statements relating a specific gene product (a protein, non-coding RNA, or macromolecular complex, which we referred as 'genes' for simplicity) to a specific ontology term.

3. *Tools* that facilitate the creation, maintenance and use of ontologies. Software being developed aims to help edit and perform logic based analysis of ontologies, provide web access to the ontology and its annotations, and analyze data using the information in the GO knowledgebase to support biomedical research.

Ontologies can be browsed using a range of web-based browsers (see "Relevant Websites" section).

The overall goal of GO is to create a comprehensive model of biological systems. Currently, the GO knowledgebase includes experimental findings from almost 140,000 published papers (see "Relevant Websites" section), represented by over 600,000 experimentally-supported GO annotations, on the basis of which an additional 6 million functional annotations for a diverse set of organisms spanning the tree of life can be inferred.

That said, it is worth mentioning that GO does not store gene sequences and is not a catalog of gene products. GO describes how gene products behave in a cellular/organism context. The use of GO terms by the collaborating databases provides controlled vocabularies that are structured to facilitate querying at different levels and also to allow annotators to assign properties to genes or gene products at different levels, depending on the depth of knowledge about the particular entity.

Conclusions

Due to the rapid evolution of new methodologies in molecular and computational biology evolve, the aim of this article was to only provide a general overview of sequence analysis at the DNA, RNA, and protein and metabolic pathways level.

We have attempted to briefly cover both the general approaches, and the most popular and powerful tools that are currently being used to analyze large amounts of data from labs around the world.

Acknowledgement

Authors are grateful to our colleague Elena Strelnikova for her help with **Figs. 16, 17** and **18**. This work was supported by Russian Science Foundation (grant number 14–50–00069).

See also: Algorithms for Strings and Sequences: Multiple Alignment. Algorithms for Strings and Sequences: Pairwise Alignment. Natural Language Processing Approaches in Bioinformatics

References

Abubucker, S., Segata, N., Goll, J., *et al.*, 2016. Metabolic reconstruction for metagenomic data and its application to the human microbiome. PLOS Comput. Biol. 8 (6), e1002358.

Acland, A., Agarwala, R., *et al.*, 2014. Database resources of the National Center for Biotechnology Information. Nucleic Acids Res 42, D7–D17.

Aken, B.L., Ayling, S., Barrell, D., *et al.*, 2016. The Ensembl gene annotation system. Database J. Biol. Databases Curation 2016, baw093.

Altschul, S.F., Gish, W., Miller, W., Myers, E.W., Lipman, D.J., 1990. Basic local alignment search tool. J. Mol. Biol. 215, 403–410.

Anders, S., Pyl, P.T., Huber, W., 2015. HTSeq – A python framework to work with high-throughput sequencing data. Bioinformatics 31 (2), 166–169.

Andrews S., 2010. FastQC: A quality control tool for high throughput sequence data. Available online at: http://www.bioinformatics.babraham.ac.uk/projects/fastqc.

Antipov, D., Korobeynikov, A., McLean, J.S., Pevzner, P.A., 2015. hybridSPAdes: An algorithm for hybrid assembly of short and long reads. Bioinformatics 32 (7), 1009–1015.

Azad, R.K., Borodovsky, M., 2004. Probabilistic methods of identifying genes in prokaryotic genomes: Connections to the HMM theory. Brief. Bioinform. 5, 118–130.

Barker, W.C., Garavelli, J.S., McGarvey, P.B., *et al.*, 1999. The PIR-international protein sequence database. Nucleic Acids Res. 27 (1), 39–43.

Benson, D.A., Karsch-Mizrachi, I., Lipman, D.J., Ostell, J., Wheeler, D.L., 2004. GenBank: Update. Nucleic Acids Res. 32, D23–D26.

Berg, J., Tymoczko, J., Stryer, L., 2002. Biochemistry, 5th ed. New York: W.H. Freeman.

Bergman, T., Cederlund, E., Jörnvall, H., Fowler, E., 2003. Current protocols in protein science. (Chapter 11, Unit 11.8).

Bairoch, A., Apweiler, R., 2000. The SWISS-PROT protein sequence database and its supplement TrEMBL in 2000. Nucleic Acids Res. 28 (1), 45–48.

Bolger, A.M., Lohse, M., Usadel, B., 2014. Trimmomatic: A flexible trimmer for illumina sequence data. Bioinformatics 30 (15), 2114–2120.

Bookstein, A., Kulyukin, V.A., Raita, T., 2002. Generalized hamming distance. Inform. Retr. 5, 353.

Bradnam, K.R., Fass, J.N., Alexandrov, A., *et al.*, 2013. Assemblathon 2: Evaluating de novo methods of genome assembly in three vertebrate species. GigaScience 2 (1), 10.

Bray, N.L., Pimentel, H., Melsted, P., Pachter, L., 2016. Near-optimal probabilistic RNA-seq quantification. Nat. Biotechnol. 34 (5), 525–527.

Bresler, M.A., Sheehan, S., Chan, A.H., Song, Y.S., 2012. Telescoper: De novo assembly of highly repetitive regions. Bioinformatics 28 (18), i311–i317.

Brown, J.W.S., Echeverria, M., Qu, L.-H., *et al.*, 2003. Plant snoRNA database. Nucleic Acids Res. 31, 432–435.

Burge, S.W., Daub, J., Eberhardt, R., *et al.*, 2013. Rfam 11.0: 10 years of RNA families. Nucleic Acids Res. 41, D226–D232.

Bushnell, B., 2014. BBTools: A suite of fast, multithreadedbioinformatics tools designed for analysis of DNA and 1NA sequencedata. Available online at: https://jgi.doe.gov/data-and-tools/bbtools/.

Bushmanova, E., Antipov, D., Lapidus, A., Suvorov, V., Prjibelski, A.D., 2016. rnaQUAST: A quality assessment tool for de novo transcriptome assemblies. Bioinformatics 32 (14), 2210–2212.

Cingolani, P., Platts, A., Wang, L.L., *et al.*, 2012. A program for annotating and predicting the effects of single nucleotide polymorphisms, SnpEff: SNPs in the genome of Drosophila melanogaster strain w1118; iso-2; iso-3. Fly 6 (2), 80–92.

Danecek, P., Auton, A., Abecasis, G., *et al.*, 2011. The variant call format and VCFtools. Bioinformatics 27 (15), 2156–2158.

Dayhoff, M.O., Schwartz, R.M., Orcutt, B.C., 1978. A model for evolutionary change in proteins. In: Dayhoff, Margaret O. (Ed.), Atlas of Protein Sequence and Structure, vol. 5. Washington DC: National Biochemical Research Foundation, pp. 345–352.

Delcher, A.L., Harmon, D., Kasif, S., White, O., Salzberg, S.L., 1999. Improved microbial gene identification with GLIMMER. Nucleic Acids Res. 27 (23), 4636–4641.

Dobin, A., Davis, C.A., Schlesinger, F., *et al.*, 2013. STAR: Ultrafast universal RNA-seq aligner. Bioinformatics 29 (1), 15–21.

Dündar, F., Skrabanek, L., Zumbo, P., 2015. Applied Bioinformatics Core/Weill Cornell Medical College. Applied Bioinformatics Core/Weill Cornell Medical College. pp. 1–67.

Earl, D., Bradnam, K., John, J.S., *et al.*, 2011. Assemblathon 1: A competitive assessment of de novo short read assembly methods. Genome Res. 21 (12), 2224–2241.

Edman, P., Högfeldt, E., Sillén, L.G., Kinell, P.-O., 1950. Method for determination of the amino acid sequence in peptides. Acta Chem. Scand. 4, 283–293.

Felsenstein, J., 1981. Evolutionary trees from DNA sequences: A maximum likelihood approach. J. Mol. Evol. 17 (6), 368–376.

Feng, D.-F., Doolittle, R.F., 1996. Doolittle progressive alignment of amino acid sequences and construction of phylogenetic trees from them. In: Proceedings of the Methods in Enzymology, 266, pp. 368–382. Academic Press.

Fernández-Puente, P., Mateos, J., Blanco, F.J., Ruiz-Romero, C., 2014. LC-MALDI-TOF/TOF for shotgun proteomics. Methods Mol. Biol. 2014 (1156), 27–38.

Ferragina, P., Manzini, G., Mäkinen, V., Navarro, G., 2004. An alphabet-friendly FM-index. In: Proceedings of the String Processing and Information Retrieval, p. 228. Berlin/Heidelberg: Springer.

Gotoh, O., 1982. An improved algorithm for matching biological sequences. J. Mol. Biol. 162, 705–708.

Grabherr, M.G., Haas, B.J., Yassour, M., et al., 2011. Full-length transcriptome assembly from RNA-Seq data without a reference genome. Nat. Biotechnol. 29 (7), 644–652.

Gurevich, A., Saveliev, V., Vyahhi, N., Tesler, G., 2013. QUAST: Quality assessment tool for genome assemblies. Bioinformatics 29 (8), 1072–1075.

Hannenhalli, S., Pevzner, P.A., 1999. Transforming cabbage into turnip: Polynomial algorithm for sorting signed permutations by reversals. J. ACM (JACM) 46 (1), 1–27.

Heather, J.M., Chain, B., 2016. The sequence of sequencers: The history of sequencing DNA. Genomics 107 (1), 1–8. doi:10.1016/j.ygeno.2015.11.003.

Henikoff, S., Henikoff, J.G., 1992. Amino acid substitution matrices from protein blocks. PNAS 89, 10915–10919.

Hrdlickova, R., Toloue, M., Tian, B., 2017. RNA-Seq methods for transcriptome analysis. WIREs RNA 8 (1), doi:10.1002/wrna.1364. Jan.

Hunt, M., Kikuchi, T., Sanders, M., et al., 2013. REAPR: A universal tool for genome assembly evaluation. Genome Biol. 14 (5), R47.

Kanehisa, M., Araki, M., Goto, S., et al., 2008. KEGG for linking genomes to life and the environment. Nucleic Acids Res. 36, D480–D484.

Kanehisa, M., Goto, S., Sato, Y., Furumichi, M., Tanabe, M., 2012. KEGG for integration and interpretation of large-scale molecular datasets. Nucleic Acids Res. 40, D109–D114.

Kanehisa, M., Goto, S., Sato, Y., et al., 2014. Data, information, knowledge and principle: Back to metabolism in KEGG. Nucleic Acids Res. 42, D199–D205.

Kanehisa, M., Sato, Y., Kawashima, M., Furumichi, M., Tanabe, M., 2016. KEGG as a reference resource for gene and protein annotation. Nucleic Acids Res. 44, D457–D462.

Kanehisa, M., Furumichi, M., Tanabe, M., Sato, Y., Morishima, K., 2017. KEGG: New perspectives on genomes, pathways, diseases and drugs. Nucleic Acids Res. 45, D353–D361.

Kapustin, Y., Souvorov, A., Tatusova, T., Lipman, D., 2008. Splign: Algorithms for computing spliced alignments with identification of paralogs. Biol. Direct 3 (1), 20.

Kent, W.J., 2002. BLAT – The BLAST-like alignment tool. Genome Res. 12 (4), 656–664.

Kent, W.J., Sugnet, C.W., Furey, T.S., et al., 2002. The human genome browser at UCSC. Genome Res. 12 (6), 996–1006.

Kim, D., Salzberg, S.L., 2011. TopHat-Fusion: An algorithm for discovery of novel fusion transcripts. Genome Biol. 12 (8), R72.

Kim, D., Langmead, B., Salzberg, S.L., 2015. HISAT: A fast spliced aligner with low memory requirements. Nat. Methods 12 (4), 357–360.

Koren, S., Schatz, M.C., Walenz, B.P., et al., 2012. Hybrid error correction and de novo assembly of single-molecule sequencing reads. Nat. Biotechnol. 30 (7), 693–700.

Koren, S., Walenz, B.P., Berlin, K., et al., 2017. Canu: Scalable and accurate long-read assembly via adaptive k-mer weighting and repeat separation. Genome Res. 27 (5), 722–736.

Kukurba, K.R., Montgomery, S.B., 2015. RNA Sequencing and Analysis. Cold Spring Harb Protoc. 11, 951–969.

Kumar, S., Tamura, K., Nei, M., 1994. MEGA: Molecular evolutionary genetics analysis software for microcomputers. Bioinformatics 10 (2), 189–191.

Lagesen, K., Hallin, P., Rødland, E.A., et al., 2007. RNAmmer: Consistent and rapid annotation of ribosomal RNA genes. Nucleic Acids Res. 35, 3100–3108.

Langmead, B., Salzberg, S.L., 2012. Fast gapped-read alignment with Bowtie 2. Nat. Methods 9 (4), 357–359.

Lapidus, A.L., 2015. Genome Sequence Databases: Sequencing and Assembly. Reference Module in Biomedical Sciences. Oxford: Elsevier, Available at: http://www.sciencedirect.com/science/article/pii/B9780128012383024958.

Leung, H.C., Yiu, S.M., Chin, F.Y., 2015. IDBA-MTP: A hybrid metatranscriptomic assembler based on protein information. J. Comput. Biol. 22 (5), 367–376.

Levene, M.J., Korlach, J., Turner, S.W., et al., 2003. Zero-mode waveguides for single-molecule analysis at high concentrations. Science 299, 682–686.

Li, B., Fillmore, N., Bai, Y., et al., 2014. Evaluation of de novo transcriptome assemblies from RNA-Seq data. Genome Biol. 15 (12), 553.

Li, D., Liu, C.M., Luo, R., Sadakane, K., Lam, T.W., 2015. MEGAHIT: An ultra-fast single-node solution for large and complex metagenomics assembly via succinct de Bruijn graph. Bioinformatics 31 (10), 1674–1676.

Li, H., 2013. Aligning sequence reads, clone sequences and assembly contigs with BWA-MEM. Available from: http://arxiv.org/abs/1303.3997.

Li, H., 2016. Minimap and miniasm: Fast mapping and de novo assembly for noisy long sequences. Bioinformatics 32 (14), 2103–2110.

Li, H., Durbin, R., 2009. Fast and accurate short read alignment with Burrows – Wheeler transform. Bioinformatics 25 (14), 1754–1760.

Li, H., Handsaker, B., Wysoker, A., et al., 2009. The sequence alignment/map format and SAMtools. Bioinformatics 25 (16), 2078–2079.

Liu, X., Dekker, L.J., Wu, S., et al., 2014. De novo protein sequencing by combining top-down and bottom-up tandem mass spectra. J. Proteome Res. 13 (7), 3241–3248.

Lizardi, P.M., 2000. Multiple displacement amplification. Yale University, U.S. Patent 6,124,120.

Love, M.I., Huber, W., Anders, S., 2014. Moderated estimation of fold change and dispersion for RNA-seq data with DESeq2. Genome Biol. 15 (12), 550.

Lowe, T.M., Eddy, S.R., 1997. tRNAscan-SE: A program for improved detection of transfer RNA genes in genomic sequence. Nucleic Acids Res. 25, 955–964.

Lukashin, A.V., Borodovsky, M., 1998. GeneMark.hmm: New solutions for gene finding. Nucleic Acids Res. 26 (4), 1107–1115.

Luo, R., Liu, B., Xie, Y., et al., 2012. SOAPdenovo2: An empirically improved memory-efficient short-read de novo assembler. Gigascience 1 (1), 18.

Magoc, T., Pabinger, S., Canzar, S., et al., 2013. GAGE-B: An evaluation of genome assemblers for bacterial organisms. Bioinformatics 29 (14), 1718–1725.

Margulies, M., Egholm, M., Altman, W.E., et al., 2005. Genome sequencing in microfabricated high-density picolitre reactors. Nature 437, 376–380.

Martin, M., 2011. Cutadapt removes adapter sequences from high-throughput sequencing reads. EMBnet J. 17 (1), 10.

McKenna, A., Hanna, M., Banks, E., et al., 2010. The genome analysis toolkit: A MapReduce framework for analyzing next-generation DNA sequencing data. Genome Res. 20 (9), 1297–1303.

Milne, I., Bayer, M., Cardle, L., et al., 2009. Tablet – Next generation sequence assembly visualization. Bioinformatics 26 (3), 401–402.

Morgulis, A., Coulouris, G., Raytselis, Y., et al., 2008. Database indexing for production MegaBLAST searches. Bioinformatics 24 (16), 1757–1764.

Myers, E., 2005. The fragment assembly string graph. Bioinformatics 21 (S2), ii79–ii85.

Myers, E.W., Sutton, G.G., Delcher, A.L., et al., 2000. A whole-genome assembly of Drosophila. Science 287 (5461), 2196–2204.

Needleman, S.B., Wunsch, C.D., 1970. A general method applicable to the search for similarities in the amino acid sequence of two proteins. J. Mol. Biol. 48 (3), 443–453.

Niall, H.D., 1973. Automated Edman degradation: The protein sequenator. Methods Enzymol. 27, 942–1010.

Nurk, S., Bankevich, A., Antipov, D., et al., 2013. Assembling single-cell genomes and mini-metagenomes from chimeric MDA products. J. Comput. Biol. 20 (10), 714–737.

Nurk, S., Meleshko, D., Korobeynikov, A., Pevzner, P.A., 2017. metaSPAdes: A new versatile metagenomic assembler. Genome Res. 27 (5), 824–834.

O'Connell, J., Schulz-Trieglaff, O., Carlson, E., et al., 2015. NxTrim: Optimized trimming of illumina mate pair reads. Bioinformatics 31 (12), 2035–2037.

Okonechnikov, K., Conesa, A., García-Alcalde, F., 2015. Qualimap 2: Advanced multi-sample quality control for high-throughput sequencing data. Bioinformatics 32 (2), 292–294.

Peng, Y., Leung, H.C., Yiu, S.M., Chin, F.Y., 2012. IDBA-UD: A de novo assembler for single-cell and metagenomic sequencing data with highly uneven depth. Bioinformatics 28 (11), 1420–1428.

Perkins, D.N., Pappin, D.J.C., Creasy, D.M., Cottrell, J.S., 1999. Probability-based protein identification by searching sequence databases using mass spectrometry data. Electrophoresis 20, 3551–3567.

Pevzner, P.A., Tang, H., Waterman, M.S., 2001. An Eulerian path approach to DNA fragment assembly. Proc. Natl. Acad. Sci. 98 (17), 9748–9753.

Poskar, C.H., Huege, J., Krach, C., Shachar-Hill, Y., Junker, B.H., 2014. High-throughput data pipelines for metabolic flux analysis in plants. Methods Mol. Biol. 1090, 223–246.

Prjibelski, A.D., Vasilinetc, I., Bankevich, A., et al., 2014. ExSPAnder: A universal repeat resolver for DNA fragment assembly. Bioinformatics 30 (12), i293–i301.

Rice, S.A., Steuer, R., Junker, B.H., 2008. Computational models of Metabolism: Stability and regulation in metabolic. Networks. doi:10.1002/9780470475935.ch3.

Robertson, G., Schein, J., Chiu, R., et al., 2010. De novo assembly and analysis of RNA-seq data. Nat. Methods 7 (11), 909–912.

Robinson, M.D., McCarthy, D.J., Smyth, G.K., 2010. edgeR: A bioconductor package for differential expression analysis of digital gene expression data. Bioinformatics 26 (1), 139–140.

Rothberg, J.M., Hinz, W., Rearick, T.M., et al., 2011. An integrated semiconductor device enabling non-optical genome sequencing. Nature 475, 348–352.

Ryle, A.P., Sanger, F., Smith, L.F., Kitai, R., 1955. The disulphide bonds of insulin. Biochem. J. 60 (4), 541–556.

Salzberg, S., Delcher, A., Kasif, S., White, O., 1998. Microbial gene identification using interpolated Markov models. Nucleic Acids Res. 26 (2), 544–548.

Salzberg, S.L., Phillippy, A.M., Zimin, A., et al., 2012. GAGE: A critical evaluation of genome assemblies and assembly algorithms. Genome Res. 22 (3), 557–567.

Shendure, J., Porreca, G.J., Reppas, N.B., et al., 2005. Accurate multiplex polony sequencing of an evolved bacterial genome. Science 309, 1728–1732.

Simão, F.A., Waterhouse, R.M., Ioannidis, P., Kriventseva, E.V., Zdobnov, E.M., 2015. BUSCO: Assessing genome assembly and annotation completeness with single-copy orthologs. Bioinformatics 31 (19), 3210–3212.

Simpson, J., Durbin, R., 2012. Efficient de novo assembly of large genomes using compressed data structures. Genome Res. 22, 549–556.

Simpson, J.T., Wong, K., Jackman, S.D., et al., 2009. ABySS: A parallel assembler for short read sequence data. Genome Res. 19 (6), 1117–1123.

Smith, T.F., Waterman, M.S., 1981. Identification of common molecular subsequences. J. Mol. Biol. 147 (1), 195–197.

Smith-Unna, R., Boursnell, C., Patro, R., Hibberd, J.M., Kelly, S., 2016. TransRate: Reference-free quality assessment of de novo transcriptome assemblies. Genome Res. 26 (8), 1134–1144.

Sović, I., Šikić, M., Wilm, A., et al., 2016. Fast and sensitive mapping of nanopore sequencing reads with GraphMap. Nat. Commun. 7, 11307.

Tang, S., Lomsadze, A., Borodovsky, M., 2015. Identification of protein coding regions in RNA transcripts. Nucleic Acids Res. 43 (12), e78.

Taylor, J.A., Walsh, K.A., Johnson, R.S., 1996. Sherpa: A macintosh-based expert system for the interpretation of electrospray ionization LC/MS and MS/MS data from protein digests. Rapid Commun. Mass Spectrom. 10, 679–687.

Thorvaldsdóttir, H., Robinson, J.T., Mesirov, J.P., 2013. Integrative Genomics Viewer (IGV): High-performance genomics data visualization and exploration. Brief. Bioinform. 14 (2), 178–192.

Tomar, N., De, R.K., 2014. A comprehensive view on metabolic pathway analysis methodologies. Curr. Bioinform. 9, 295–305.

Tran, N.H., Zhang, X., Xin, L., Shan, B., Li, V., 2017. De novo peptide sequencing by deep learning. Proc. Natl. Acad. Sci. 114 (31), 8247–8252.

Trapnell, C., Pachter, L., Salzberg, S.L., 2009. TopHat: Discovering splice junctions with RNA-Seq. Bioinformatics 25 (9), 1105–1111.

Valouev, A., Ichikawa, J., Tonthat, J., et al., 2008. A high-resolution, nucleosome position map of C. elegans reveals a lack of universal sequence-dictated positioning. Genome Res. 18, 1051–1063.

Vasilinetc, I., Prjibelski, A.D., Gurevich, A., Korobeynikov, A., Pevzner, P.A., 2015. Assembling short reads from jumping libraries with large insert sizes. Bioinformatics 31 (20), 3262–3268.

Wang, B.-B., Brendel, V., 2004. The ASRG database: Identification and survey of Arabidopsis thaliana genes involved in pre-mRNA splicing. Genome Biol. 5, R102.

Wang, L., Wang, S., Li, W., 2012. RSeQC: Quality control of RNA-seq experiments. Bioinformatics 28 (16), 2184–2185.

Wang, Z., Chen, Y., Li, Y., 2004. A brief review of computational gene prediction methods. Genom. Prot. Bioinform. 4, 216–221.

Wick, R.R., Judd, L.M., Gorrie, C.L., Holt, K.E., 2017. Unicycler: Resolving bacterial genome assemblies from short and long sequencing reads. PLOS Comput. Biol. 13 (6), e1005595.

Woyke, T., Tighe, D., Mavromatis, K., et al., 2010. One Bacterial Cell, One Complete Genome. PLoS ONE 5 (4), e10314.

Wu, T.D., Watanabe, C.K., 2005. GMAP: A genomic mapping and alignment program for mRNA and EST sequences. Bioinformatics 21 (9), 1859–1875.

Xie, Y., Wu, G., Tang, J., et al., 2014. SOAPdenovo-Trans: De novo transcriptome assembly with short RNA-Seq reads. Bioinformatics 30 (12), 1660–1666.

Xu, D., 2004. Protein Databases on the Internet. Curr. Protoc. Mol. Biol.. 19.4), (CHAPTER: Unit–19.4. PMC. Web. 2 Nov. 2017).

Ye, Y., Tang, H., 2015. Utilizing de Bruijn graph of metagenome assembly for metatranscriptome analysis. Bioinformatics 32 (7), 1001–1008.

Zhang, W., Chait, B.T., 2000. ProFound: An expert system for protein identification using mass spectrometric peptide mapping information. Analyt. Chem. 72, 2482–2489.

Zerbino, D.R., Birney, E., 2008. Velvet: Algorithms for de novo short read assembly using de Bruijn graphs. Genome Res. 18 (5), 821–829.

Further Reading

Brudno, M., Malde, S., Poliakov, A., et al., 2003. Glocal alignment: Finding rearrangements during alignment. Bioinformatics 19 (Suppl. 1), i54–i62. 90001.

Dohrmann, J., Puchin, J., Singh, R., 2015. Global multiple protein-protein interaction network alignment by combining pairwise network alignments. BMC Bioinform. 16 (Suppl. 13), S11.

Dündar, F., Skrabanek, L., Zumbo, P., 2015. Introduction to Differential Gene Expression Analysis Using RNA-Seq. Applied Bioinformatics Core/Weill Cornell Medical College.

Faisal, F.E., Zhao, H., Milenkovic, T., 2015. Global Network Alignment in the Context of Aging. IEEE/ACM Trans. Comput. Biol. Bioinform. 12 (1), 40–52.

Jones, N.C., Pevzner, P., 2004. An introduction to bioinformatics algorithms. MIT press.

Peris, G., Marzal, A., 2014. Statistical significance of normalized global alignment. J. Comput. Biol. 21 (3), 257–268.

Vyatkina, K., 2017. De novo sequencing of top-down tandem mass spectra: A next step towards retrieving a complete protein sequence. Proteomes 5 (1), 6.

Software

Alignment

a. MUMmer http://mummer.sourceforge.net/
b. Minimap2 https://github.com/lh3/minimap2
c. NCBI BLAST https://blast.ncbi.nlm.nih.gov/
d. Bushnell, B., 2014. BBMap: a fast, accurate, splice-aware aligner. https://sourceforge.net/projects/bbmap/
e. List of sequence alignment software https://en.wikipedia.org/wiki/List_of_sequence_alignment_software

Pairwise alignment

f. CLUSTALW/CLUSTALW2/CLUSTALO https://www.ebi.ac.uk/Tools/msa/clustalo/
g. T-COFFEE http://www.tcoffee.org/
i. MAFFT https://www.ebi.ac.uk/Tools/msa/mafft/
h. MUSCLE https://www.ebi.ac.uk/Tools/msa/muscle/

Reads QC

a. Bushnell, B., 2014. BBTools software package https://sourceforge.net/projects/bbtools/
b. Andrews, S., 2010. FastQC: a quality control tool for high throughput sequence data. https://www.bioinformatics.babraham
   ac.uk/projects/fastqc/.

Functional annotation systems

a. BioConductor - https://www.bioconductor.org/
b. DAVID - https://david.ncifcrf.gov/summary.jsp
c. Quevillon, E., Silventoinen, V., Pillai,S., Harte, N., Mulder, N., Apweiler, R., Lopez, R. 2005. InterProScan: protein domains
   identifier. Nucleic Acids Res. 33(Web Server issue):W116–20. https://github.com/ebi-pf-team/interproscan
d. Ensembl: http://uswest.ensembl.org/index.html

Relevant Websites

https://biocyc.org/
   BioCyc database.
https://www.ebi.ac.uk
   EBI BioModels Database.
https://en.wikipedia.org/wiki/FASTA_format
   FASTA format.
https://en.wikipedia.org/wiki/FASTQ_format
   FASTQ format.
http://www.geneontology.org/page/introduction-go-resource
   Gene Ontology Consortium.
ftp://ftp.geneontology.org
   Gene Ontology Consortium.
http://www.genome.jp/kegg/ko.html
   KEGG.
www.genome.jp
   KEGG database.
http://www.ncbi.nlm.nih.gov
   NCBI - NIH.
https://www.nanoporetech.com/
   Oxford Nanopore Technologies.
https://omictools.com/pepfrag-tool
   PepFrag.
https://en.wikibooks.org/wiki/Proteomics/Protein_Identification_-_Mass_Spectrometry/Databases
   Proteomics/Protein Identification.
http://prospector.ucsf.edu/
   ProteinProspector.
http://prospector.ucsf.edu/
   ProteinProspector.
http://www.rcsb.org/pdb
   RCSB PDB.
sbml.org
   SBML format.
https://omictools.com/sequest-tool
   SEQUEST.
http://www.illumina.com
   Solexa technology.
https://www.proteinresearch.net/
   The Protein Research Foundation.
http://www.uniprot.org/
   UniProt.
http://www.uniprot.org/uniprot/
   UniProtKB.
http://www.uniprot.org/
   UniProt.
http://www.uniprot.org/uniprot/
   UniProt.
https://www.uniprot.org/help/uniref
   UniProt.
https://www.uniprot.org/help/uniparc
   UniProt.

Biographical Sketch

Andrey Prjibelski (formal transliteration Przhevalsky) received BSc degree in informatics from St. Petersburg State Technical University in 2010 and MSc in applied mathematics and physics from St. Petersburg Academic University in 2012. In 2011 he started an internship at Algorithmic Biology Lab led by Prof. Pavel Pevzner in St. Petersburg Academic University and then continued to work there as a junior research fellow. In 2014 the whole laboratory moved to St. Petersburg University and became Center for Algorithmic Biotechnologies (CAB). Andrey participated in development of one of the main lab projects – SPAdes de novo genome assembler and in 2014 received outstanding student paper award at ISMB 2014, Boston. Later he participated developing SPAdes-based de novo transcriptome assembler and improving SPAdes for large genome assembly. Andrey also teaches "NGS data analysis" for master students St. Petersburg Academic University and participates in various bioinformatics workshops and schools as a teacher and co-organizer.

Anton Korobeynikov received the MSc and PhD degrees in applied mathematics from St. Petersburg State University, Russia, in 2007 and 2010, respectively. He started to work at St. Petersburg State University in 2007, where he currently holds the position of Associate Professor of Statistical Modeling Department, School of Mathematics and Mechanics. The main areas of research interests of Dr. Korobeynikov are computational and applied statistics, including time series analysis, efficient implementation of algorithms of computation statistics and probabilistic methods in bioinformatics.

In 2012 he joined Algorithmic Biology Laboratory at St. Petersburg Academic University. The laboratory led by Prof. P. Pevzner is developing SPAdes – a novel de novo assembler suitable for single cell and multi cell data among other tools. In 2014 the whole laboratory moved to St. Petersburg University and became Center for Algorithmic Biotechnologies. Currently Anton is a SPAdes team leader and oversees the technical questions related to SPAdes development.

Professor Alla Lapidus holds a PhD in Molecular Biology from the Institute for Genetics and Selection of Industrial Microorganisms (IGSIM) and an MS Degree in Physics from the Moscow Engineering Physics Institute. Her primary areas of expertise include high-throughput DNA sequencing, genome structure analysis, reference quality genome assembly, bioinformatics. Currently the deputy-director of the Center for Algorithmic Biotechnology, St. Petersburg State University, Dr. Lapidus was previously an Associate professor at Fox Chase Cancer Center. From 2003 Dr. Lapidus has been applying high-throughput DNA sequencing, genome-wide analysis and bioinformatics to the study of microbial and fungal genomes and metagenomic communities by optimizing data QC, data analysis and de-novo assemblies at Joint Genome Institute (JGI). She has spearheaded multiple projects using NGS to optimize data QC, analysis and de-novo assemblies, created microbial finishing pipeline from the ground up and was the mind behind the development of the next generation de-novo assembly algorithms.

Previously she served as the Director of Sequencing Center, Integrated Genomics, as a Senior Research Scientist at the INRA, France, at The University of Chicago and at the IGSIM, Moscow. Professor Lapidus has authored several on-line courses on Bioinformatics and is a lead of the MS program "Bioinformatics" at SPbU. She also authored and co-authored over 350 papers and patents.

Sequence Composition

Jin Xing Lim and Bryan T Li, Temasek Polytechnic, Singapore
Maurice HT Ling, Colossus Technologies, LLP, Singapore

Introduction

Since the sequencing of *Escherichia coli* (Moxon and Higgins, 1997) and *Plasmodium falciparum* (Cowman and Crabb, 2002) genome, DNA sequence has been commonly known as the "blueprint of life" as DNA is the hereditary molecule for cellular life. Hence, logically should contain all the information necessary to infer the activities of life even though such inference may not be obvious. Despite so, a lot of information about the regulation of a gene, as well as the function of the gene product may be derived from its sequence. For example, common response elements across multiple genes at the promoter region suggest induction by the same external stimulus (Domenech *et al.*, 2001). In this article, we will look at various DNA sequence features at the DNA and review several recent applications where sequence features are used. Through these applications, we can appreciate that sequence composition is an integral aspect of sequence analysis.

DNA Sequence Composition

In this section, we will look at 6 major DNA sequence composition features: promoter, enhancer, ribosome binding site, coding sequence, terminator, methylation sites and CpG islands.

Promoter is a short DNA region of 100–1000 base-pairs upstream of the coding sequence that triggers gene transcription. Hence, identifying the promoter indicates the start of transcriptional activity leading to the start of a potential mRNA molecule. A desktop tool capable of finding promoter is ProSOM (Abeel *et al.*, 2008). The core promoter has exclusive features that cannot be found in other sequences when comparing with the average structural profile based on based stacking energy of transcribed. The program that is used for ProSOM is able to distinctly differentiate between the structural profiles of promoter sequences and other genomic sequences. It is done based on unsupervised clustering of physical properties of DNA by using self-organising maps. Additional tests on the ENCODE regions of the human genome yield high precision, showing 98% of all predictions made by ProSOM can be associated with transcriptionally active regions (Abeel *et al.*, 2008). Another tool that we can use is CoreBoost_HM (Wang *et al.*, 2009). It is a web-based tool that is an upgraded version of CoreBoost (Zhao *et al.*, 2007), which predicts core-promoters by applying a boosting technique with stumps, using both the small-scale and large-scale DNA sequence features. CoreBoost_HM uses the same technique as CoreBoost but with the addition of histone modification features as well. CoreBoost_HM can be used to identify and characterise the core-promoters of both coding and noncoding genes with high sensitivity and specificity at high resolution (Wang *et al.*, 2009). ChromHMM (Ernst and Kellis, 2012) characterises chromatin states, it can facilitate the biological characterization of each state by automatically computing state enrichments for large-scale functional and annotation datasets (Ernst and Kellis, 2012). Hence, ChromHMM is also able to locate promoter.

Enhancer is a short DNA region of 50–1500 base-pairs that increases the chance of occurrence of a particular gene's transcription through binding by a type of proteins called activators. One tool that can help us locate enhancers is ChromHMM (Ernst and Kellis, 2012). It is a desktop software that discovers and characterises chromatin states from multiple chromatin datasets through automation. Based on a multivariate Hidden Markov Model, ChromHMM accurately models the existence of each chromatin mark. As a result, it can then be used to annotate a genome in one or more cell types orderly; hence locating sequence features such as enhancers (Ernst and Kellis, 2012). Another tool that can locate enhancers is EnhancerPred (Jia and He, 2016). It is a web-based tool that differentiates between enhancers and non-enhancers and measures enhancer's strength with overall accuracies of 77.39% and 68.19% respectively. From combination of bi-profile Bayes and pseudo-nucleotide composition, it presents as a binary classification problem and EnhancerPred solves it using a machine learning algorithm, which is a two-step rapper-based feature selection method (Jia and He, 2016).

Ribosome binding site (RBS) is a nucleotide sequence upstream of an mRNA transcript's start codon, which engages a ribosome during protein translation's initiation. One web-based tool we can use to locate RBS is the Ribosome Binding Site Calculator (Salis, 2011). It is a design method that predicts and controls bacteria's translation initiation and protein expression. For each start codon in a mRNA transcript, the method can foresee the translation initiation's rate. A targeted translation initiation rate of a synthetic RBS sequence can be achieved through optimization method. Through the RBS calculator, a protein coding sequence's translation rate may be logically controlled across a 100,000 fold range (Salis, 2011; Salis *et al.*, 2009). Another desktop tool that we can use is Estimated Locations of Pattern Hits (ELPH; see "Relevant Websites sections"), which takes a set of DNA or protein sequences, up to thousands of sequences, as input and locates motifs using Gibbs sampling. The program seeks through the set of sequences for the most common motif, assuming that each sequence contains one copy of the motif. ELPH can also be used to find patterns such as RBSs and exon splicing enhancers (ESEs).

Coding sequence (CDS) of a gene is the portion of a gene's DNA, which comprised of exons, that is used to code for protein. One web tool that we can use to find CDS is ORFFinder by NCBI (see "Relevant Websites sections"). An open reading frame (ORF) is the portion of a DNA sequence, in continuous, non-overlapping triplets called codons, that has the potential to be translated to protein. By finding ORFs, it is equivalent of find the potential CDSs of a gene. ORF finder is a graphical analysis tool which seeks for ORFs in your input DNA sequence. Other than returning the range of each ORF, it gives its protein translation as well. The predicted protein is verified using SMART BLAST or regular BLASTP. However, the web version of the ORF finder is limited to sequences up to 50 kb long. Another web tool that we can use is ORFPredictor (Min *et al.*, 2005). It is designed to locate protein-coding segments in expressed sequence tag (EST)-derived sequences. For query sequences with a hit in BLASTX, the program predicts the CDS based on the translation reading frames classified in BLASTX alignments. Otherwise, it predicts the most probable CDS based on the inherent signals of the query sequences. The output includes the predicted peptide sequences in the FASTA format and a definition line that consists of the query ID, the translation reading frame and the range of the CDS. However, the ORFPredictor web server is limited to data of file size up to 20 Mb. For datasets exceeding the limitations, there is a standalone desktop version available for download (Min *et al.*, 2005).

Transcription terminator is a DNA segment that indicates the end of a gene or operon during transcription. Together with the preceding promoter, they delimit the transcriptional boundaries. This segment produces signals in the newly synthesized mRNA that initiate processes which break the mRNA off from the transcriptional complex to intervene transcriptional termination. One web-based tool we can use to locate transcription terminal is ARNold (Naville *et al.*, 2011). Rho–independent termination is an important mechanism in bacteria that causes RNA transcription to terminate and release the newly transcribed RNA. ARNold is able to locate rho-independent terminators in DNA sequences. This search method incorporates two complementary prediction programs, Erpin and RNAmotif, and performs approximately as well as more complex methods while begin available to the non-specialist. Erpin (Gautheret and Lambert, 2001) generates a lod-score profile and seeks high scoring instances of the profile in the user's sequence with a structure-annotated alignment of 1200 terminator sequences from *Bacillus subtilis* and *Escherichia coli* as training set. On the other hand, RNAmotif (Macke *et al.*, 2001) uses a descriptor developed by Lesnik *et al.* (2001) to recognise terminators. RNAmotif matches are scored using the sequence contents of T-rich region and stability of the stem loop region, with an empirical score cutoff is defined to accept or reject matches. The free energy of the predicted terminator stem-loop structure using RNAfold (Hofacker *et al.*, 1994) is generated to provide a uniform scoring scheme for Erpin and RNAmotif hits. Another way to locate transcription terminators is through WebGeSTer DB (Mitra *et al.*, 2011). It is one of the largest database of intrinsic transcription terminators. The database consists of a million terminators found from 1060 bacterial genome sequences and 798 plasmids. Both graphic and tabular results on putative terminators can be generated and are arranged in tiers to allow easy retrieval. An interactive map has been integrated to visualise the distribution of terminators across the whole genome (Mitra *et al.*, 2011).

DNA methylation happens when a methyl group is added to either one of the DNA's bases, cytosine or adenine. Methylation can modify the activity of a DNA region without changing the sequence. The process commonly is used to repress gene transcription when located in a gene promoter. Methylation is necessary for normal development and gene expression control such as genomic imprinting and X-chromosome inactivation (for males). One desktop tool that we can use BS-Seeker2 (Guo *et al.*, 2013), an updated version of BS-Seeker (Chen *et al.*, 2010). It is used to map the bisulfite-treated reads and generate DNA methylomes – nucleic acids that undergo methylation modifications. Together with high-throughput sequencing, bisulfite treatment provides a useful approach for studying DNA methylation at base resolution across the genome. The use of libraries such as whole genome bisulfite sequencing (WGBS) and reduced represented bisulfite sequencing (RRBS) to generate DNA methylomes improves mappability, efficiency and accuracy of the reads. BS-Seeker2 also is equipped with additional function to filter out reads with incomplete bisulfite conversion. This will minimise the overestimation of DNA methylation levels (Guo *et al.*, 2013). Another desktop tool that we can use is MethGo (Liao *et al.*, 2015). Similar to BS-Seeker2, this software tool analyse bisulfite sequencing (BS-Seq) data from WBGS and RRBS and provides 9 analyses (both genomic and epigenomic) in 5 major modules to profile (epi) genome. The 9 analyses include coverage distribution of each cytosine, global cytosine methylation level, cytosine methylation level distribution, cytosine methylation level of genomic elements, chromosome-wide cytosine methylation level distribution, gene-centric cytosine methylation level, cytosine methylation levels at transcription factor binding sites (TFBSs), single nucleotide polymorphism (SNP) calling and copy number variation (CNV) calling (Liao *et al.*, 2015).

Besides adenine, cytosine can also be methylated. CpG islands are segments of DNA where a cytosine nucleotide is followed by a guanine nucleotide linearly along its 5′ to 3′ direction. Cytosine methylation often occurs in CpG islands; hence, finding CpG islands is synonymous to finding cytosine methylation sites. One accurate and fast desktop tool that we can use to identify CpG islands is CpGTLBO (Yang *et al.*, 2017). First, CpGTLBO uses clustering approach to identify CpG island candidates, which effectively cut down the large amount of redundant DNA fragments. Then it uses teaching-learning-based-optimization (TLBO) to accurately predict CpG islands among promising CpG island candidates. CpGTLBO performs more accurate and faster than many CpG island detection methods, that detect based on sliding window and clustering technology, as the accuracy of these methods is proportional to the time required (Yang *et al.*, 2017). Another desktop tool we can use is CpGcluser (Hackenberg *et al.*, 2006), which CpGTLBO (Yang *et al.*, 2017) is built on. This algorithm predicts directly CpG clusters based on the physical distance between neighbouring CpGs on the chromosome. A p-value is given to each of these clusters and the most statistically significant ones can be predicted as CpG islands. As CpGcluster only uses integer arithmetic method, it is a fast and computationally efficient algorithm to predict statistically significant clusters of CpGs. Furthermore, all CpG islands predicted by the algorithm start and end with a CpG dinucleotides, which should be relevant for a genomic feature whose functionality is based directly on CpG dinucleotides (Hackenberg *et al.*, 2006).

Secondary structure is the set of interactions between nucleotide bases, i.e., which parts of strands are likely to bind to each other. In DNA double helix, secondary structure is responsible for the 3-dimensional shape of the nucleic acids. One web-based tool that we can use is Kinefold (Xayaphoummine *et al.*, 2005). It simulates stochastic folding of nucleic acids on second to minute time scales. Simulations of renaturation or co-transcriptional folding paths are done at the level of helix formation and dissociation in agreement with the seminal experimental results. Efficient predictions of pseudoknots and topologically "entangled" helices are done, taking into considerations due to simple geometrical and topological constraints. Simulations launched are automatically stopped from time to time to allow users to have the freedom to choose to continue incomplete simulations or modify recommended options provided by the server in their initial query. The web server provides detailed output that include a series of low free energy structures, an online animated folding path and a programmable trajectory plot focusing on a few helices of interest to each user (Xayaphoummine *et al.*, 2005). We can use another desktop tool called Unified Nucleic Acid Folding or abbreviated to UNAFold (Markham and Zuker, 2008). This software package combines different programs to simulate folding, hybridization, and melting pathways for one or two-stranded nucleic acid sequences (DNA or RNA). Folding prediction for single-stranded RNA or DNA merges free energy minimization, partition function calculations and stochastic sampling. Images of secondary structures, hybridizations, and dot plots may be computed using common formats. The program computes not only melting temperatures, but also full melting profiles. UV absorbance at 260 nm, heat capacity change and different molecular species' mole fractions are generated as a function of temperature. The software is "command line" driven. Underlying complied programs may be used independently, or in special combinations with the use of Perl scripts (Markham and Zuker, 2008).

Applications of Sequence Composition

The application of sequence composition is extensive. In this section, four recent studies are highlighted to showcase the applications of sequence composition analysis. Eukaryotic RNA often undergo RNA processing to form mature mRNA, and one of the important steps is splicing, which is to excise the introns from the immature RNA and join the resulting exons. Hence, identifying the intron/exon boundaries on a sequence is useful to computing the resulting peptide from genomic sequence. A study (Zafrir and Tuller, 2015) using 4 fungi; *Saccharomyces cerevisiae*, *Schizosaccharomyces pombe*, *Aspergillus nidulans*, and *Candida albicans*; found that intron/exon boundaries often exhibit weak RNA folding and a decrease in GC content. This suggests that current RNA sequence analysis tools, such as RNAfold (Hofacker *et al.*, 1994) and ViennaRNA (Lorenz *et al.*, 2011), may be useful for other purposes.

The ability to predict gene expression from sequence is useful to have (Ling and Poh, 2014), especially when experimentally derived expression data is lacking. A study (Su *et al.*, 2016) proposed to use DNA sequence features; such as histone modifications, DNA methylation, DNA accessibility, transcription factors, and trinucleotide composition; in a support vector machine to predict gene expression. Su *et al.* (2016) achieved a predictive accuracy of 95.96% on human embryonic stem cell line H1, presenting the work as a predictive model for binary classification into high or low expression when experimentally derived expression data is lacking.

Assembly of reads from next generation sequencing experiments often results in large sequence fragments, known as contigs, rather than entire genome. Each contig is considered as an operational taxonomic unit and related contigs needs to be binned together for further analysis. Several software for binning contigs exist and some tools; such as CONCOCT (Alneberg *et al.*, 2014), employed sequence composition in its computation. In this case, sequence composition is used a data point for computation, which acts like a compression of the sequence has the effect of reducing the feature space compared to using raw sequences. Recently, a new tool known as COCACOLA (Lu *et al.*, 2017) that incorporates sequence composition had been proposed, and demonstrated a precision of 99.78% and a recall of 99.93%, compared to precision of 93.43% and recall of 99.6% from CONCOCT.

Many eukaryotes contains accessory chromosomes, known as B chromosomes, in contrast to standard chromosomes or A chromosomes (Houben, 2017). Sequence analysis of several B chromosomes revealed B chromosomes contains DNA originating from standard chromosomes, such as in rye (Klemme *et al.*, 2013). This suggests that B chromosomes may serve an evolutionary purpose and further demonstrates that sequence analysis is an important aspect of evolutionary genetics (Ruban *et al.*, 2017).

See also: Natural Language Processing Approaches in Bioinformatics. Sequence Analysis

References

Abeel, T., Saeys, Y., Rouzé, P., Van de Peer, Y., 2008. ProSOM: Core promoter prediction based on unsupervised clustering of DNA physical profiles. Bioinformatics 24, i24–i31.

Alneberg, J., Bjarnason, B.S., de Bruijn, I., *et al.*, 2014. Binning metagenomic contigs by coverage and composition. Nat. Methods 11, 1144–1146.

Chen, P.-Y., Cokus, S.J., Pellegrini, M., 2010. BS seeker: Precise mapping for bisulfite sequencing. BMC Bioinform. 11, 203.

Cowman, A.F., Crabb, B.S., 2002. The Plasmodium falciparum genome – A blueprint for erythrocyte invasion. Science 298, 126–128.

Domenech, V.S., Nylen, E.S., White, J.C., *et al.*, 2001. Calcitonin gene-related peptide expression in sepsis: Postulation of microbial infection-specific response elements within the calcitonin I gene promoter. J. Investig. Med. 49, 514–521.

Ernst, J., Kellis, M., 2012. ChromHMM: Automating chromatin-state discovery and characterization. Nat. Methods 9, 215–216.

Gautheret, D., Lambert, A., 2001. Direct RNA motif definition and identification from multiple sequence alignments using secondary structure profiles. J. Mol. Biol. 313, 1003–1011.

Guo, W., Fiziev, P., Yan, W., et al., 2013. BS-Seeker2: A versatile aligning pipeline for bisulfite sequencing data. BMC Genom. 14, 774.

Hackenberg, M., Previti, C., Luque-Escamilla, P.L., et al., 2006. CpGcluster: A distance-based algorithm for CpG-island detection. BMC Bioinform. 7, 446.

Hofacker, I.L., Fontana, W., Stadler, P.F., et al., 1994. Fast folding and comparison of RNA secondary structures. Monatshefte Chem./Chem. Mon. 125, 167–188.

Houben, A., 2017. B chromosomes – A matter of chromosome drive. Front. Plant Sci. 8, 210.

Jia, C., He, W., 2016. EnhancerPred: A predictor for discovering enhancers based on the combination and selection of multiple features. Sci. Rep. 6, 38741.

Klemme, S., Banaei-Moghaddam, A.M., Macas, J., et al., 2013. High-copy sequences reveal distinct evolution of the rye B chromosome. New Phytol. 199, 550–558.

Lesnik, E.A., Sampath, R., Levene, H.B., et al., 2001. Prediction of rho-independent transcriptional terminators in Escherichia coli. Nucleic Acids Res. 29, 3583–3594.

Liao, W.-W., Yen, M.-R., Ju, E., et al., 2015. MethGo: A comprehensive tool for analyzing whole-genome bisulfite sequencing data. BMC Genom. 16, S11.

Ling, M.H., Poh, C.L., 2014. A predictor for predicting Escherichia coli transcriptome and the effects of gene perturbations. BMC Bioinform. 15, 140.

Lorenz, R., Bernhart, S.H., Höner zu Siederdissen, C., et al., 2011. ViennaRNA package 2.0. Algorithms Mol. Biol.: AMB 6, 26.

Lu, Y.Y., Chen, T., Fuhrman, J.A., Sun, F., 2017. COCACOLA: Binning metagenomic contigs using sequence composition, read coverage, co-alignment and paired-end read linkage. Bioinformatics 33, 791–798.

Macke, T.J., Ecker, D.J., Gutell, R.R., et al., 2001. RNAMotif, an RNA secondary structure definition and search algorithm. Nucleic Acids Res. 29, 4724–4735.

Markham, N.R., Zuker, M., 2008. UNAFold: Software for nucleic acid folding and hybridization. Methods Mol. Biol. 453, 3–31.

Min, X.J., Butler, G., Storms, R., Tsang, A., 2005. OrfPredictor: Predicting protein-coding regions in EST-derived sequences. Nucleic Acids Res. 33, W677–W680.

Mitra, A., Kesarwani, A.K., Pal, D., Nagaraja, V., 2011. WebGeSTer DB – A transcription terminator database. Nucleic Acids Res. 39, D129–D135.

Moxon, E.R., Higgins, C.F., 1997. E. coli genome sequence. A blueprint for life. Nature 389, 120–121.

Naville, M., Ghuillot-Gaudeffroy, A., Marchais, A., Gautheret, D., 2011. ARNold: A web tool for the prediction of Rho-independent transcription terminators. RNA Biol. 8, 11–13.

Ruban, A., Schmutzer, T., Scholz, U., Houben, A., 2017. How next-generation sequencing has aided our understanding of the sequence composition and origin of B chromosomes. Genes (Basel) 8.

Salis, H.M., 2011. The ribosome binding site calculator. Methods Enzymol. 498, 19–42.

Salis, H.M., Mirsky, E.A., Voigt, C.A., 2009. Automated design of synthetic ribosome binding sites to control protein expression. Nat. Biotechnol. 27, 946–950.

Su, W.-X., Li, Q.-Z., Zhang, L.-Q., et al., 2016. Gene expression classification using epigenetic features and DNA sequence composition in the human embryonic stem cell line H1. Gene 592, 227–234.

Wang, X., Xuan, Z., Zhao, X., Li, Y., Zhang, M.Q., 2009. High-resolution human core-promoter prediction with CoreBoost_HM. Genome Res. 19, 266–275.

Xayaphoummine, A., Bucher, T., Isambert, H., 2005. Kinefold web server for RNA/DNA folding path and structure prediction including pseudoknots and knots. Nucleic Acids Res. 33, W605–W610.

Yang, C.-H., Chiang, Y.-C., Chuang, L.-Y., Lin, Y.-D., 2017. A CpGCluster-teaching-learning-based optimization for prediction of CpG islands in the human genome. J. Comput. Biol.

Zafrir, Z., Tuller, T., 2015. Nucleotide sequence composition adjacent to intronic splice sites improves splicing efficiency via its effect on pre-mRNA local folding in fungi. RNA 21, 1704–1718.

Zhao, X., Xuan, Z., Zhang, M.Q., 2007. Boosting with stumps for predicting transcription start sites. Genome Biol. 8, R17.

Relevant Websites

http://www.cbcb.umd.edu/software/ELPH/
ELPH User Manual.
https://www.ncbi.nlm.nih.gov/orffinder/
National Center for Biotechnology Information.

Codon Usage

Raimi M Redwan, Faculty of Agro-based Industry, University of Malaysia, Kelantan, Malaysia
Suhanya Parthasarathy and Ranjeev Hari, Perdana University, Selangor, Malaysia

Introduction

A genome contains all the necessary information required for a system to function optimally at any given condition. The central dogma skeleton dictates the flow of genetic information from genome to protein via RNA. The 20 amino acids are decoded within the genome using the combination of the four letters of DNA language in three base pair combinations (i.e., triplets of bases), known as DNA codons. One feature of the DNA codons is that the code is degenerate as one amino acid can be coded by more than one codon. Redundancy of the codons can be explained from the excessive 64 possible combination of the four nucleotide base pairs in a triplet base ($4^3 = 64$) to represent the 20 amino acids. As a consequence, only methionine and trypsin are encoded by a single codon, whereas the other 18 amino acids are encoded by more than one codon. The genetic code table showed that the degeneracy mostly occurred due to variation in the third base of the codons. It is due to this redundancy that different DNA sequences can still produce identical protein sequences, a situation known to be synonymous mutation.

As the DNA sequences become accessible through sequencing, information regarding the codon usage in the coding sequences can be obtained. This data led to the discovery that these codons are not being used equally uniform throughout the genome. Earlier studies have identified the presence of preferred codons to encode for specific amino acids. Variation of choice of codons to represent amino acids is not only observed among species from different taxonomic group, but also showed significant variation among individuals of the same species, across different genes in the same genome and even across regions in the same gene. Nevertheless, the codon bias is most prominent in species from different taxonomic groups even in proteins with identical function. This phenomenon of species-specific codon choice is known as "codon dialect," which signifies the codon-usage bias observed across different organisms (Ikemura, 1985).

GC Content and Codon-Usage Bias

Earlier, the study of codon usage focused on the DNA composition at the last base pair of the codons, the position where degeneracy mostly occurred. In relation to that, preference of the base content at this location also distinguished the codon bias observed in monocots and dicots. In monocots, 16 amino acids favor G + C at the third degenerate base, whereas in dicots only 7 out of 18 amino acids prefer G + C at this base (Murray et al., 1989; Tyson and Dhindsa, 1995). Nonetheless, when there is C at the second codon's base, both groups of plants avoid G in their last codon's base as dinucleotide combination of CG may results in methylation of the DNA. Dinucleotide combination of CG is not only avoided in plants but also other higher eukaryotes, where methylation plays a role in gene regulation. Preference of base in choice of synonymous codons is known to be related to its GC content. In *Mycoplasma*, which is known to be AT rich at 60%–75%, has codon preferences toward A and T in various coding region (Muto et al., 1986). Furthermore, homologous cDNA of human gene sequences derived from different tissue sample contained 80% amino acid sequence similarity but with significant G + C content variation. In consequences, the sequences were also identified to have significant variation of codon bias, especially at the third codons (Kudla et al., 2009). This observation supports that the total G + C content in genome or within genes is the determinants of the variation in codon usage. This variation is hypothesized to be attributed by the mutational mechanism that directly controlled the GC content throughout the genome (Chen et al., 2004). Positive correlation between the GC content and the codon usage is advantageous as the GC content data can be exploited to predict the reading frame and the coding strands of DNA sequences (Bibb et al., 1984). Recently, a study highlighted the important role of the genome's GC content to influence the genome-wide codon-usage bias in the mammalian cell (Rudolph et al., 2016).

Influence of tRNA Abundance on Codon Bias

Another determinant of the codon-usage variation is the tRNA abundance. As an adapter molecule to link the mRNA to the amino acid in protein synthesis, the abundance of the complementary tRNA molecules are directly related to the frequency of codons (Ikemura, 1985). The investigation was based on the finding that codon bias is the most extreme in highly expressed genes where translational efficiency would be a priority. The finding established a selection-based hypothesis that the selection of optimal codons in a certain gene is a function of the gene's adaptation to the complementary tRNA molecule available to increase efficiency of the protein synthesis. Following this observation, a metric known as tRNA adaptation index (tAI) was developed to analyze the correlation between the abundance of tRNAs and translational efficiency (dos Reis et al., 2004). The metric measures the copy number of tRNA genes, which is assumed to be correlated with tRNA abundance in cells.

It also takes into consideration the efficiency of the binding between the codon–anticodon and the possibility of the imperfect match between the codon–anticodon at the third position (i.e., Crick's wobble rules) (Crick, 1966). Most importantly, the metric enables genome-wide estimation of translational efficiency through the abundance of tRNAs, which is directly related to codon bias. The metric has been used successfully to predict translation efficiency of 2800 yeast orthologous genes based on the measures of tRNA adaptation to conform the codon usage (Man and Pilpel, 2007). Moreover, the metric has also been shown to be in correlation with the ratio of protein to mRNA level in *Saccharomyces cerevisiae*, which has been able to support the tRNA adaptation hypothesis (Tuller *et al.*, 2010b).

The tRNA adaptation theory to shape the codon composition in genes is not applicable universally across all kingdoms. The hypothesis could explain variation of codon composition in most of the prokaryotes tested (Andersson and Kurland, 1990) but not in eukaryotes. Kanaya *et al.* (2001) showed that different eukaryotes have different selectional forces to determine their codon composition. In his study, only *Schizosaccharomyces pombe* and *Caenorhabditis elegans* showed positive correlation patterns of codon usage and tRNA gene number. On the other hand, *Drosophila melanogaster* showed the important influence of C or G base in the third codons to shape its codon usage. *Xenopus laevis* and *Homo sapiens* showed the role of isochore structure of mRNA produced to influence their codon composition (Kanaya *et al.*, 2001). It was suggested that multicellular organisms of eukaryotes have higher tRNA gene redundancy, which posits lower selection pressure to compose their codons based on the tRNA availability (Quax *et al.*, 2015). In addition, the disparity of determinants for codon composition may also be related to the different strength of optimal codon bias in eukaryotic genome as was shown in Dos Reis and Wernisch (2009). Nevertheless, recent evidence showed that translational selection (i.e., mechanism of translational optimization based on the natural selection of the codon usage) was identified to be the positive factor contributing to codon bias in housekeeping-genes of human (Ma *et al.*, 2014), contradicting the previous findings (Kanaya *et al.*, 2001). Moreover, the hypothesis is favored by the finding that there is a preference to employ the same tRNA leading to repetitive use of a similar set of optimal codons as a way to optimize translation speed especially in regions of highly expressed genes (Cannarrozzi *et al.*, 2010). Preferential optimal codons identified in highly expressed genes were also identified to be limited by the availability of tRNAs to increase its translational efficiency (Qian *et al.*, 2012).

Codon Adaptation in Composition of Codon

Composition of codon in genes is known to affect the fate of the protein being synthesized as it influences level of expression, protein folding, and the regulation of protein expression. This observation led to the same common question as the translational selection as discussed above and that is the role of codon bias in determination of the proteins' expression level. As a consequence, each species has its own set of "preferred codons" identified within the highly expressed genes that is assumed to translate efficiently to ensure optimal protein synthesis. Relative to the finding, a matrix known as codon adaptation index (CAI) was developed to assess the relative adaptation of individual codons encoding a certain amino acid. The index measures the ratio of the codon's frequency to the frequency of its other synonymous codons. The index was measured from the highly expressed genes as the set of reference and the CAI for a gene can then be derived through the geometric mean of the relative adaptiveness values of all the codon within the gene (Sharp and Li, 1987). Similar to tAI, CAI also enables prediction of gene expression level but on the basis of the choice of codons encoding the gene (Sen *et al.*, 2007; Wu *et al.*, 2005). The index was also shown to be highly correlated to mRNA concentration of most of the genes tested in Coghlan and Wolfe (2000) and in microarray study of Martín-Galiano *et al.* (2004). Nonetheless, the CAI index has its own caveats to its predictive power. This is due to the fact that the index relies on a set of reference genes to derive its index, which might imposed limited value to predict expression for genes not reflected in the reference set (Martín-Galiano *et al.*, 2004). The index also failed to include other positive factors influencing the expression value of the composed codons (Ermolaeva, 2001). Consequently, few studies showed a disparity of CAI index and the actual expression value of the genes tested (dos Reis *et al.*, 2003; Kudla *et al.*, 2009). Nonetheless, the index is still widely used as a prediction tool especially in de novo gene synthesis, whereby the CAI value is taken into consideration in the codon optimization algorithm (Chung and Lee, 2012; Condon and Thachuk, 2012; Nandagopal and Elowitz, 2011). The algorithm is developed based on several known factors to influence the expression level of genes based on the composition of codons, other than just the CAI. In addition, there are also other indexes developed to predict expression value based on the codon usage. Some of the alternatives to CAI are relative codon-usage bias (Roymondal *et al.*, 2009), expression measure E(g) (Roymondal *et al.*, 2009), relative codon adaptation (Fox and Erill, 2010) and modified relative codon bias strength (Das *et al.*, 2017).

Positive correlation of the codon composition and its expression level implied that synonymous mutation among orthologous gene products, be it across different individuals or tissues, may no longer be considered as silent (Chamary *et al.*, 2006; Kimchi-Sarfaty *et al.*, 2007; Shields *et al.*, 1988). The choice of codons, even though they are synonymous with respect to amino acids they encode, the information determines the mRNA structure and stability and affecting the protein structure, and its folding kinetics. This was depicted in a study when 154 synthetic orthologous genes with various synonymous variants in their codon showed different level of mRNA level and degradation rates (Kudla *et al.*, 2009). It is important to note that the variant was not entirely caused by the composition of preferred codons throughout the genes but due to the variation in the ribosomal binding site that changed the stability of mRNA folding.

Codon Ramp at Translational Initiation

In separate studies, investigation of coding sequences from both prokaryotes and eukaryotes revealed a presence of evolutionarily conserved codon composition known as "ramp" at the 5′ end of the sequences (Tuller et al., 2010a). The author highlights the role of codon composition in controlling translation efficiency through codon and tRNA adaptation and also via the presence of codon ramp as a mean to reduce ribosomal traffic jams in the beginning of translation. Even though the feature is evolutionarily conserved across domains of life, the ramp may not be universally present in all genes in every genome but only in highly expressed genes as inspected in the study. It was also suggested that the ramp functions to sense the abundance of tRNAs and changes its ramp's design in response to the different conditions based on the observation that different functional genes contained different design of the ramp. The condition-specific ramp is still an open question and thus far no study has yet validated the claim.

Study of translational efficiency and codon usage advance forward with the emerging new techniques of ribosome profiling. The technique used deep sequencing technologies to profile in vivo translation (Ingolia, 2014). By using the approach, a study was able to prove slower elongation rate upon reduction of heavily used tRNA and at the beginning of a message (i.e., ramp) (Pop et al., 2014). Moreover, another two studies were also able to validate the slower translational elongation rate of the nonoptimal or the rare codons that have low respective tRNA population (Dana and Tuller, 2014; Gardin et al., 2014).

Bioinformatics Tools to Analyze Codon Usage

As described earlier, CAI is one of the indexes used apart from several other measures of codon usage. There are a large number of indices that cover a wide area of underlying biological features (Roth et al., 2012). Typically, these indices are used to denote a measure of departure from an expected value, for instance, of codon distribution based on nucleotide frequencies. Similarly, some indices measure the closeness to a hypothetical optimal codon state. In turn, such measures get compared to preferred codon usage of reference set of genes that may be optimal, highly expressed, in a specifically defined group or, on the contrary, genes encompassing the whole genome.

While a large amount of codon measures has been developed, the choice of the index will depend on the goal being achieved as every index has its specific aspect of codon usage being measured. The CAI has been widely used and known for its usage of measuring codon-usage bias (Cannarrozzi et al., 2010; Friberg et al., 2004). Several other complementary indices provide a measure of understanding diversity and recommend using an ensemble of features to better classify aspects such as translational efficiency (Roth et al., 2012; Tuller et al., 2010a). Having diverse methods of measuring codon usage requires benchmarks in order to test its statistical performance in achieving the goals comparatively. Some studies have described comparisons across measures, however, the coverage across the many indices available is still lacking (Comeron and Aguadé, 1998; Supek and Vlahoviček, 2005; Suzuki et al., 2008). Partly, this is due to the scarce availability of reproducible computational implementation of those measures by the authors in the form of programming scripts or software.

Nevertheless, there are a few tools that have the ability to calculate the desired indices easily based on DNA sequences. INCA provides the ability to calculate CAI and effective Nc (ENC) besides the ability to apply principal component analysis (PCA), self-organizing maps, and 3D scatterplot to visualize any correlations in the high-dimensional data being presented (Supek and Vlahoviček, 2004). Moreover, Dnasp, a multipurpose population genetics software program, can compute relative synonymous codon usage, ENC, codon bias index, and the scaled chi square (Morton, 1993; Sharp et al., 1986; Shields et al., 1988; Wright, 1990). Other software tools that offer similar calculation of indices are GCUA, ACUA, and CodonW (McInerney, 1998; Peden, 1997; Vetrivel et al., 2007). Most of this software includes some statistical analysis method such as multivariate analysis, PCA, and correspondence analyses (CA). Comparison of statistical methods for CA showed that within-group CA performed well in identifying new factors contributing to variation and horizontal transfers of genes more accurately (Suzuki et al., 2008). To support the use of the analysis, an online resource to perform such analysis is available Pôle Bioinformatique Lyonnais server (Charif et al., 2005).

Bioinformatics Tools to Optimize Codon Usage in DNA

Besides serving the specific purposes to better understand codon variation, researchers may use the principle behind the finding to synthesize artificial DNA. Codon bias does not affect the amino acid sequence itself, nevertheless, it may have impact in protein production. Directly, the biotech application to optimize the DNA sequence is crucial for optimal production of target protein in bioreactors. For such purposes, there are software programs that aid in returning the optimal form of codon usage for a DNA sequence such as DNAworks and OPTIMIZER (Hoover and Lubkowski, 2002; Puigbò et al., 2007). DNAWorks has a standard threshold that it uses in the optimization step to pick the two highest frequency codons for encoding the amino acid. In contrast, OPTIMIZER server provides precomputed tables for around 150 prokaryotic genomes that are found to be under strong translational selection while optimizing all codons while introducing the most minimum changes to the DNA submitted.

Applications in Systems and Synthetic Biology

Through natural selection, optimal codon usages for diverse types of genes and organisms were formed. While the codon optimization field is inevitably moving away from older ideas that synthetic genes should contain mostly of high-frequency codons, the real challenge remains on methods in replicating high protein production for robust production systems in biotechnology. There could be many features that are important for synthetic gene design such as synonymous codon cooccurrence bias, nonsynonymous codon pair bias, tRNA-associated properties, and expression (Quax *et al.*, 2015). However, there is a lack of attention of incorporating these features in synthetic biology. For instance, recording of tRNA-associated properties such as charged tRNA and regular tRNA abundance levels in high protein expression conditions will provide hints for better codon optimization to maintain tRNA levels for increased production of target protein. Besides that, application of the "codon harmonization" principles could be better suited in achieving efficiency in robust yet demanding heterologous production environments (Angov *et al.*, 2008; Quax *et al.*, 2015).

Some of the exciting implications of better rational gene design in synthetic biology are the creation of synthetic biosynthetic pathways, gene circuits, or even entirely new genomes. Realistically, timely expression of functionally networked genes is crucial in the design of such biocircuitry. Some progress made in differential codon bias and differentially expressed prokaryotic cistrons may provide blueprints for designing synthetic operons to express these circuits or pathways (Li *et al.*, 2014; Quax *et al.*, 2013). Moreover, rapid advances in DNA assembly recently allowed the assembly and transplantation of complete synthetic genomes (Gibson, 2014). Essentially, such a protocol enables the redesign of genomes from scratch and allows its reemergence from another compatible host. Nevertheless, better understanding of codon bias could be helpful in the systematic design of an optimally functional synthetic genome by incorporating sensible modules that consider codon usage, tRNA gene levels, and tRNA-modifying enzymes.

Conclusion

The study of translational efficiency and codon usage is still an open debate. Several studies are in support of the selection theory in codon composition while others refuted and claim other features of the mRNAs are more significant to contribute in its efficiency. Nonetheless as technologies advance forward and more techniques prevail, the question demands more evidence to fulfill the answer. The understanding of codon composition is important not only for de novo gene synthesis but to understand the regulation of genes in different conditions, information that seems to be hidden in what used to be a silent mutation. Furthermore, in the future, codon usage principles might find relevance in synthetic biology, for instance in optimizing the production of target proteins.

See also: Natural Language Processing Approaches in Bioinformatics. Sequence Analysis. Sequence Composition

---

References

Andersson, S.G., Kurland, C.G., 1990. Codon preferences in free-living microorganisms. Microbiology Reviews 285, 198–210.

Angov, E., Hillier, C.J., Kincaid, R.L., Lyon, J.A., 2008. Heterologous protein expression is enhanced by harmonizing the codon usage frequencies of the target gene with those of the expression host. PLOS ONE 3, e2189.

Bibb, M.J., Findlay, P.R., Johnson, M.W., 1984. The relationship between base composition and codon usage in bacterial genes and its use for the simple and reliable identification of protein-coding sequences. Gene 30, 157–166.

Cannarrozzi, G., Schraudolph, N.N., Faty, M., *et al.*, 2010. A role for codon order in translation dynamics. Cell 141, 355–367. Available at: https://doiorg/10.1016/j.cell.2010.02.036.

Chamary, J.V., Parmley, J.L., Hurst, L.D., 2006. Hearing silence: Non-neutral evolution at synonymous sites in mammals. Nature Reviews Genetics 7, 98–108.

Charif, D., Thioulouse, J., Lobry, J.R., Perrière, G., 2005. Online synonymous codon usage analyses with the ade4 and seqinR packages. Bioinformatics 21, 545–547. Available at: https://doi.org/10.1093/bioinformatics/bti037.

Chen, S.L., Lee, W., Hottes, A.K., Shapiro, L., McAdams, H.H., 2004. Codon usage between genomes is constrained by genome-wide mutational processes. Proceedings of the National Academy of Sciences of the United States of America 101, 3480–3485. Available at: https://doi.org/10.1073/pnas.0307827100.

Chung, B.K.-S., Lee, D.-Y., 2012. Computational codon optimization of synthetic gene for protein expression. BMC Systems Biology 6, 134. Available at: https://doi.org/10.1186/1752-0509-6-134.

Coghlan, A., Wolfe, K.H., 2000. Relationship of codon bias to mRNA concentration and protein length in Saccharomyces cerevisiae. Yeast 16, 1131–1145. Available at: https://doi.org/10.1002/1097-0061(20000915)16:12 1131::AID-YEA609 3.0.CO;2-F.

Comeron, J.M., Aguadé, M., 1998. An evaluation of measures of synonymous codon usage bias. Journal of Molecular Evolution 47, 268–274.

Condon, A., Thachuk, C., 2012. Efficient codon optimization with motif engineering. Journal of Discrete Algorithms 16, 104–112. Available at: https://doi.org/https://doi.org/10.1016/j.jda.2012.04.017.

Crick, F.H., 1966. Codon–anticodon pairing: The wobble hypothesis. Journal of Molecular Evolution 19, 548–555.

Dana, A., Tuller, T., 2014. The effect of tRNA levels on decoding times of mRNA codons. Nucleic Acids Research 42, 9171–9181. Available at: https://doi.org/10.1093/nar/gku646.

Das, S., Chottopadhyay, B., Sahoo, S., 2017. Comparative analysis of predicted gene expression among crenarchaeal genomes. Genomics Information 15, 38–47.

Ermolaeva, M.D., 2001. Synonymous codon usage in bacteria. Current Issues in Molecular Biology 3, 91–97.

Fox, J.M., Erill, I., 2010. Relative codon adaptation: A generic codon bias index for prediction of gene expression. DNA Research: An International Journal for Rapid Publication of Reports on Genes and Genomes 17, 185–196. Available at: https://doi.org/10.1093/dnares/dsq012.

Friberg, M., von Rohr, P., Gonnet, G., 2004. Limitations of codon adaptation index and other coding DNA-based features for prediction of protein expression in Saccharomyces cerevisiae. Yeast 21, 1083–1093.

Gardin, J., Yeasmin, R., Yurovsky, A., et al., 2014. Measurement of average decoding rates of the 61 sense codons in vivo. eLife. 3. Available at: https://doi.org/10.7554/eLife.03735.

Gibson, D.G., 2014. Programming biological operating systems: Genome design, assembly and activation. Nature Methods 11, 521–526.

Hoover, D.M., Lubkowski, J., 2002. DNAWorks: An automated method for designing oligonucleotides for PCR-based gene synthesis. Nucleic Acids Research 30, e43.

Ikemura, T., 1985. Codon usage and tRNA content in unicellular and multicellular organisms. Molecular Biology and Evolution 2, 13–34. Available at: https://doi.org/10.1093/oxfordjournals.molbev.a040335.

Ingolia, N.T., 2014. Ribosome profiling: New views of translation, from single codons to genome scale. Nature Reviews Genetics 15, 205–213. Available at: https://doi.org/10.1038/nrg3645.

Kanaya, S., Yamada, Y., Kinouchi, M., Kudo, Y., Ikemura, T., 2001. Codon usage and tRNA genes in eukaryotes: Correlation of codon usage diversity with translation efficiency and with CG-dinucleotide usage as assessed by multivariate analysis. Journal of Molecular Evolution 53, 290–298. Available at: https://doi.org/10.1007/s002390010219.

Kimchi-Sarfaty, C., Oh, J.M., Kim, I.-W., et al., 2007. A "silent" polymorphism in the MDR1 gene changes substrate specificity. Science 315, 525–528. Available at: https://doi.org/10.1126/science.1135308.

Kudla, G., Murray, A.W., Tollervey, D., Plotkin, J.B., 2009. Coding-sequence determinants of gene expression in Escherichia coli. Science 324, 255 LP–255258. Available at: https://doi.org/10.1126/science.1170160.

Li, G.-W., Burkhardt, D., Gross, C., Weissman, J.S., 2014. Quantifying absolute protein synthesis rates reveals principles underlying allocation of cellular resources. Cell 157, 624–635.

Man, O., Pilpel, Y., 2007. Differential translation efficiency of orthologous genes is involved in phenotypic divergence of yeast species. Nature Genetics 39, 415–421. Available at: https://doi.org/10.1038/ng1967.

Martín-Galiano, A.J., Wells, J.M., de la Campa, A.G., 2004. Relationship between codon biased genes, microarray expression values and physiological characteristics of Streptococcus pneumoniae. Microbiology 150, 2313–2325. Available at: https://doi.org/10.1099/mic.0.27097-0.

Ma, L., Cui, P., Zhu, J., Zhang, Z., Zhang, Z., 2014. Translational selection in human: More pronounced in housekeeping genes. Biology Direct 9, 17. Available at: https://doi.org/10.1186/1745-6150-9-17.

McInerney, J.O., 1998. GCUA: General codon usage analysis. Bioinformatics 14, 372–373.

Morton, B.R., 1993. Chloroplast DNA codon use: Evidence for selection at the psb A locus based on tRNA availability. Journal of Molecular Evolution 37, 273–280.

Murray, E.E., Lotzer, J., Eberle, M., 1989. Codon usage in plant genes. Nucleic Acids Research 17, 477–498.

Muto, A., Yamao, F., Hori, H., Osawa, S., 1986. Gene organization of Mycoplasma capricolum. Advances in Biophysics 21, 49–56.

Nandagopal, N., Elowitz, M.B., 2011. Synthetic biology: Integrated gene circuits. Science. 333. Available at: https://doi.org/10.1126/science.1207084.

Peden, J., 1997. CodonW: Correspondence Analysis of Codon Usage. United Kingdom: Nottingham University.

Pop, C., Rouskin, S., Ingolia, N.T., et al., 2014. Causal signals between codon bias, mRNA structure, and the efficiency of translation and elongation. Molecular Systems Biology 10, 770. Available at: https://doi.org/10.15252/msb.20145524.

Puigbò, P., Guzmán, E., Romeu, A., Garcia-Vallvé, S., 2007. OPTIMIZER: A web server for optimizing the codon usage of DNA sequences. Nucleic Acids Research 35, W126–W131. Available at: https://doi.org/10.1093/nar/gkm219.

Qian, W., Yang, J.-R., Pearson, N.M., Maclean, C., Zhang, J., 2012. Balanced codon usage optimizes eukaryotic translational efficiency. PLOS Genetics 8, e1002603.

Quax, T.E.F., Claassens, N.J., Söll, D., van der Oost, J., 2015. Codon bias as a means to fine-tune gene expression. Molecular Cell 59, 149–161. Available at: https://doi.org/10.1002/aur.1474.Replication.

Quax, T.E.F., Wolf, Y.I., Koehorst, J.J., et al., 2013. Differential translation tunes uneven production of operon-encoded proteins. Cell Reports 4, 938–944. Available at: https://doi.org/10.1016/j.celrep.2013.07.049.

dos Reis, M., Savva, R., Wernisch, L., 2004. Solving the riddle of codon usage preferences: A test for translational selection. Nucleic Acids Research 32, 5036–5044. Available at: https://doi.org/10.1093/nar/gkh834.

Dos Reis, M., Wernisch, L., 2009. Estimating translational selection in eukaryotic genomes. Molecular Biology and Evolution 26, 451–461. Available at: https://doi.org/10.1093/molbev/msn272.

dos Reis, M., Wernisch, L., Savva, R., 2003. Unexpected correlations between gene expression and codon usage bias from microarray data for the whole Escherichia coli K-12 genome. Nucleic Acids Research 31, 6976–6985.

Roth, A., Anisimova, M., Cannarozzi, G.M., 2012. Measuring codon usage bias. In: Codon Evolution: Mechanisms and Models. NY: Oxford University Press Inc., pp. 189–217.

Roymondal, U., Das, S., Sahoo, S., 2009. Predicting gene expression level from relative codon usage bias: An application to Escherichia coli genome. DNA Research 16, 13–30. Available at: https://doi.org/10.1093/dnares/dsn029.

Rudolph, K.L.M., Schmitt, B.M., Villar, D., et al., 2016. Codon-driven translational efficiency is stable across diverse mammalian cell states. PLOS Genetics 12, 1–23. Available at: https://doi.org/10.1371/journal.pgen.1006024.

Sen, G., Sur, S., Bose, D., et al., 2007. Analysis of codon usage patterns and predicted highly expressed genes for six phytopathogenic Xanthomonas genomes shows a high degree of conservation. In Silico Biology 7, 547–558.

Sharp, P.M., Li, W.H., 1987. The codon Adaptation Index – A measure of directional synonymous codon usage bias, and its potential applications. Nucleic Acids Research 15, 1281–1295.

Sharp, P.M., Tuohy, T.M., Mosurski, K.R., 1986. Codon usage in yeast: Cluster analysis clearly differentiates highly and lowly expressed genes. Nucleic Acids Research 14, 5125–5143.

Shields, D.C., Sharp, P.M., Higgins, D.G., Wright, F., 1988. "Silent" sites in Drosophila genes are not neutral: Evidence of selection among synonymous codons. Molecular Biology and Evolution 5, 704–716.

Supek, F., Vlahoviček, K., 2004. INCA: Synonymous codon usage analysis and clustering by means of self-organizing map. Bioinformatics 20, 2329–2330.

Supek, F., Vlahoviček, K., 2005. Comparison of codon usage measures and their applicability in prediction of microbial gene expressivity. BMC Bioinformatics 6, 182. Available at: https://doi.org/10.1186/1471-2105-6-182.

Suzuki, H., Brown, C.J., Forney, L.J., Top, E.M., 2008. Comparison of correspondence analysis methods for synonymous codon usage in bacteria. DNA Research: An International Journal for Rapid Publication of Reports on Genes and Genomes 15, 357–365. Available at: https://doi.org/10.1093/dnares/dsn028.

Tuller, T., Carmi, A., Vestsigian, K., et al., 2010a. An evolutionarily conserved mechanism for controlling the efficiency of protein translation. Cell 141, 344–354. Available at: https://doi.org/10.1016/j.cell.2010.03.031.

Tuller, T., Waldman, Y.Y., Kupiec, M., Ruppin, E., 2010b. Translation efficiency is determined by both codon bias and folding energy. Proceedings of the National Academy of Sciences of the United States of America 107, 3645–3650. Available at: https://doi.org/10.1073/pnas.0909910107.

Tyson, H., Dhindsa, R., 1995. Codon usage in plant peroxidase genes. DNA sequencing 5, 339–351. Available at: https://doi.org/10.3109/10425179509020865.

Vetrivel, U., Arunkumar, V., Dorairaj, S., 2007. ACUA: A software tool for automated codon usage analysis. Bioinformation 2, 62–63.

Wright, F., 1990. The "effective number of codons" used in a gene. Gene 87, 23–29.

Wu, G., Culley, D.E., Zhang, W., 2005. Predicted highly expressed genes in the genomes of Streptomyces coelicolor and Streptomyces avermitilis and the implications for their metabolism. Microbiology 151, 2175–2187. Available at: https://doi.org/10.1099/mic.0.27833-0.

Identification of Sequence Patterns, Motifs and Domains

Michael Gribskov, Purdue University, West Lafayette, IN, United States

Introduction

The development of protein and nucleic acid sequencing has revolutionized our understanding of macromolecular function. Sequence-based analyses are so powerful that it has been estimated that over 95% of our biochemical understanding of the protein function comes from such analyses. The power of sequence analysis is intimately tied to the evolutionary process. While the mutation process is not chemically random, it is random with respect to whether mutations occur in non-coding regions, genes, or regions that encode functionally important parts of proteins (such as active site residues). The process of selection is decidedly non-random; mutations that disrupt vital cellular processes, such as changes in transcriptional regulatory regions, structurally or functionally important parts of proteins, or epigenetic regulation are generally eliminated from the population (i.e., the organism bearing these mutation shows reduced fitness). The result is that structurally and functionally important sequence residues in proteins, the corresponding nucleotides that encode these regions in DNA, and important regulatory factor binding sites in DNA and RNA, all accumulate mutations at a slower rate than less critical regions. These regions thus appear *conserved*, and it is this conservation that is exploited by sequence-based methods for identifying patterns, motifs, and domains. Furthermore, conserved regions can often be directly associated with the specific molecular function that causes their conservation, making them extremely useful for predicting molecular properties from sequence.

In this article we will use the term *motif*, to cover all kinds of motifs, patterns, and domains, and focus on motifs that can be identified in macromolecular sequences. The definition of *motif* in computational biology is essentially the same as in common English usage – "A dominant or recurring idea in an artistic work (see "Relevant Websites section")". Sequence motifs can be found because they repeatedly occur, with limited sequence variation, many times in the same molecule or in different molecules. A critical sequence region that occurs only once is very difficult to define and associate with functional information.

Nucleic acid and protein motifs have very different properties. One of the most salient differences is due to the difference in the size of the nucleic acid and protein alphabets, four bases versus twenty amino acid residues. The difference in alphabet size means that, for any specific motif, the background of randomly matching (false positive) sequences will be higher in nucleic acids than in proteins. In addition, the pitch of the DNA helix, 10.4 bases/turn in A-form DNA, suggests that a protein interacting with the base-pairs in the major groove of the DNA can interrogate only five to six consecutive bases (assuming it does not wrap around the DNA); Not coincidentally, many transcription factor binding sites are about six bases long (or dimeric sites with two six base regions). The small alphabet and the short length of nucleic acid motifs makes the identification of such motifs challenging. Proteins, on the other hand have a larger alphabet, and the size of protein motifs is often larger. Structurally, conserved regions of proteins tend to lie in the folded core of the protein; typically a protein chain requires 6–12 residues to cross the protein core, where there are many constraints on acceptable mutations due to the very tight packing of the protein interior. Upon reaching the surface, the chain typically makes a bend or turn and reenters the protein core. The residues at turns and other surface exposed segments tend to show much weaker evolutionary constraints because they are free to move in the solvent. Surface residues also tend to be *hydrophilic* whereas core residues tend to be *hydrophobic*. This pattern of protein structure produces conserved regions that are much longer than in DNA, but which include a certain amount of internal length variation (commonly called *gaps*), due to the less conserved turn and surface regions. It is noteworthy that at surface turns, very large insertions of additional sequence often occur without disrupting the folded structure of the protein. The twenty letter protein alphabet and larger size of protein motifs makes it easier to confidently identify them in practice.

Transcription factor binding sites (TFBS) are the most important class of DNA motifs, due to their importance in gene regulation. Other DNA motifs of interest include transcription and translation start sites, splicing signals, terminator regions (although some of these actually function at the RNA level). Broader sequence patterns such as CG rich "islands", patterns associated with 3D structure (bending and twisting of the helix), and sequence isochores, local DNA regions with different base composition, have also received attention. Motifs in RNA have received less attention in general, and can be either sequence-based, as in DNA, or related to the formation of internally base-paired structures.

In proteins, sequence motifs have been derived on many different scales ranging from the sites of post-translational modifications (single amino acid residues), active sites (several residues), to domains (dozens to hundreds of residues) and whole proteins (hundreds of residues).

Measuring Classification Quality

Pattern/motif/domain recognition is usually treated as a two-class supervised learning problem where the goal is to label each letter of a sequence, either nucleic acid or protein, as either belonging to a motif (positive), or belonging to a background model (negative). After classification, each letter in the sequence is considered to be true positive (TP; labeled as motif, part of motif), false negative (FN; labeled as background, part of motif), false positive (FP; labeled as motif, part of background), or true negative (TN; labeled as background, part of background), based on comparison to correctly labeled (gold-standard) training data. The success of the classification is measured in the same way as most machine learning methods, *i.e.*, in terms of precision

(TP/TP + FP) and recall (TP/TP + FN). The terms sensitivity, which is the same as recall, and specificity are also used. The definition of specificity is inconsistent in the literature, sometimes being defined as the same as precision, and sometimes defined as the correct negative fraction (TN/TN + FN). Precision and recall, since they are unambiguous, are therefore preferred. Usually there are many more negative examples in the training data than positive examples, for example, a gene region may contain only one TFBS (covering 10–12 bases), and tens of thousands of bases of non-TFBS bases. This *class imbalance* means that even methods with very high recall (sensitivity), may not work well in practice because the false positive rate is too high (i.e., low precision). Indeed, a method that only misclassifies 1/1000 of the negative bases, may easily generate far more false positives than true positives.

There is usually a tradeoff between precision and recall. For instance, one may achieve very high recall by simply predicting all bases as belonging to the motif. One may also achieve high precision by predicting only the strongest sites as belonging to a motif, but at the cost of misclassifying many true, but weaker, sites as non-motif. Approaches that consider both precision and recall in evaluating classification quality are preferred over simply looking at the recall since they cannot be "gamed" by tuning a method to be high recall/low precision. The most widely used method that considers both precision both precision and recall is the Receiver Operating Characteristic, ROC (Zweig and Campbell, 1993; Gribskov and Robinson, 1996), and the area under the ROC curve, or AUC. This statistic has an attractive statistical interpretation; AUC is equivalent to a Wilcoxon test and is the probability that a random positive will score higher than a random negative. It is well known that ROC and AUC tend to perform poorly when there is a large degree of class imbalance; in this case, Mean Average Precision, MAP, is often preferred. Another commonly reported measure of classification quality is the F_1 score (also referred to as F-score, F-measure, accuracy, or Sørensen–Dice similarity coefficient), which is the harmonic mean of precision and recall $\left(F_1 = \frac{2 \cdot Precision \cdot Recall}{Precision + Recall} = \frac{2\ TP}{2\ TP + FN + FP}\right)$; F_1 considers false positives and false negatives to be equally costly, which is usually not true when class imbalance is large, and can be misleading in many practical situations.

The precision and recall seen on the gold standard training data often overestimates the efficacy of the classification due to *overfitting*. An unbiased estimate of classification quality therefore requires *cross validation*, a procedure in which a portion of the data is not used in training, and held out for use only in testing. It is important that the training and test data be independent; in the sequence motif context this requires that highly similar sequences (probable *homologs*) not occur in both training and test sets. Such sequences are usually identified by screening with sequence comparison programs such as Blast (Altschul *et al.*, 1990, 1997).

Models

When considered as a two-class problem, motif identification considers two feature distributions: the motif, or *foreground*, distribution and the non-motif or *background*, distribution. In a Bayesian context, the background model is the prior probability of the features, and the foreground model is the conditional probability of the features in the model class. The discrimination between these distributions can be measured in many ways, among the most common are log-odds (log(*foreground/background*)), and Bayesian posterior probability $\left(\frac{P_{back}P_{for}}{\sum P_{back}P_{for}}\right)$. Log-odds statistics are particularly useful as the sum of the values over a series of sequence positions gives the relative probability that the sequence arises from the foreground or background model. The scoring matrices used in sequence alignment and database searching, such as the Dayhoff PAM (Dayhoff *et al.*, 1978) and the BLOSUM (Henikoff and Henikoff, 1992) matrices, are log-odds matrices allowing alignment scores to be interpreted in terms of the relative probability that the aligned sequences are homologous (foreground model) or unrelated (background model).

Background Model

The features are most commonly single amino acid residues, but may be physical-chemical characteristics, probabilities estimated by a prior analysis, or higher order combinations such as words (substrings). For protein sequences, the background model usually assumes that there is no positional correlation between amino acid residues, i.e., that each position is *iid* with respect to all others. While this assumption is known to be incorrect, there are in fact strong correlations between amino acid residues in proteins (in fact these are the basis of many secondary structure prediction methods), it often is sufficient in practice. Another option is to use the observed non-motif sequences to generate the background distribution as in the FastA (Pearson, 1996) sequence comparison program. For nucleic acids, it is well known that there are pronounced correlations between adjacent bases, most notably in the case of the avoidance of CG dinucleotides in eukaryotic sequences. The encoding of protein sequences imposes additional correlations. It is therefore common to use an order 3 to 5 Markov model for the background model. Use of such models is also common in *ab initio gene modeling* where exons, introns, and intergenic regions are separately modeled (most frequently with a 5th order Markov model).

Motif (foreground) Model

Consensus Sequence

Consensus sequence models date to the earliest days of sequencing and are still in use today. Consensus sequences represent a motif as a single sequence where only one base or amino acid residue is permitted at each position. Many restriction enzyme cut sites are effectively modeled in this way (consider, e.g., the *Eco*RI site: ĜAATC). As more sequences became available, it was common to use consensus sequences to model promoters and other DNA signals by aligning examples of the signal, and using the most common base at each position as the consensus sequence (**Fig. 1**). Such consensus sequences were often referred to as "boxes", for instance the Pribnow Box (Pribnow, 1975) (now known as the − 10 region of the *E. coli* promoter), TATAAT, CAAT (Graves *et al.*, 1986) box, TATA (Lifton *et al.*, 1978) box, and many others.

Because they are concise, consensus sequences are often shown in the literature to mark the position of a motif in a sequence. However, they are a very weak method for motif identification. First, they discard all information about the frequency of the letters at different positions of the motif. For instance, in the consensus sequence for the *E. coli* promoter, TATAAT, the final T is almost 100% conserved, indicating it has very high functional significance. One the other hand, the T at the third position, is not even present in a majority promoters − A, C, G, and T occur almost equally, indicating that this position is essentially irrelevant. Second, consensus sequences do not include a background model − overprediction of promoters in regions that are simply A/T rich is common − consensus sequences do not take into account that a sequence such as TATAAT occurs much more frequently at random in A/T rich regions. Third, consensus sequence do not generalize well. Only a fraction of known sequences precisely match the consensus sequence, and allowing mismatches or *gaps* greatly increases the number of false positive predictions, a problem that is exacerbated by the loss of information discussed, above.

Regular Expression

Regular expressions address some of the inadequacies of consensus sequences by admitting the possibility of several different letters matching at each position of the motif, and by allowing a limited number of variable spaces within the motif. The most important collection of regular expression patterns is found in the Prosite (Xenarios, 2013) database. Because of its high visibility, the Prosite syntax is probably the most widely used for protein sequences (**Fig. 2**), and is often used for nucleic acid sequences, as well. For the promoter sequence described above, we could write a regular expression such as [TC]-A-X-[AT]-{G}-T, and the combined − 35 and − 10 regions of the promoter could be written as T-T-[GT]-[CA]-{G}-[AT]-X(16,18)-[TC]-A-X-[AT]-{G}-T (compare to **Fig. 3**).

One of the advantages of regular expression representations is that efficient algorithms for identifying matches to regular expressions in text corpora are available in most programming languages, and in the UNIX operating system (*grep*). In principle, disregarding setup time, regular expression matching can be $O(n)$, where n is the length of the corpus.

In spite of their superiority to consensus sequence representations, regular expression representations suffer from similar problems. Although multiple characters can be allowed (or forbidden) at each position, there is no way to distinguish between letters that are allowed at very different frequencies (for instance the difference in the frequency of C and T in the first position of the − 10 element in **Fig. 3** (Oliphant and Struhl, 1988)). Regular expressions also do not incorporate a background model, and permitting incomplete matching typically gives rise to huge numbers of false positive matches. In spite of these drawbacks, the excellent compendium of functional motifs found in the Prosite database (ProDoc) has provided a fundamental resource for both protein annotation and validation of sequence matching algorithms.

ATATT**ATG**	sequence 1
G**TACTTTG**	sequence 2
TC**AC**A**GTA**	sequence 3
TT**A**G**TCTC**	sequence 4
C**TA**A**CTTC**	sequence 5
TACTTT	consensus

Fig. 1   Consensus sequence. Five sequences from the E. coli − 10 promoter region and the majority-rule consensus sequence. Bases matching the consensus are sown in bold. Note that no sequence in the training set exactly matches the consensus.

X	indicates a match to any letter
[]	enclose sets of allowed matching letters
{}	enclose sets of forbidden letters
(*min,max*)	indicates the preceding letter must occur a minimum of *min* times and a maximum of *max* times. (*min*) indicates a letter must occur *min* or more times.
-	separates sequence positions
<	marks the beginning of the sequence
>	marks the end position of the sequence

Fig. 2   Prosite regular expression (pattern) syntax.

```
A. -35                          -10
   G  1  4 42  2  2  8  ...   3  1 11  7  6  2 G
   C  0  4  3 15 32 11  ...  15  2 14  8 24  1 C
   A  0  3  1 33 11 16  ...   1 47 13 21 12  2 A
   T 57 47 12  8 13 23 .....  33  2 14 16 10 47 T

B.
   15  16  17  18  19   spacing
    2  18  59  26   5   count
```

Fig. 3 PSSM of E. coli Promoter elements. A. Numbers indicate counts of each base at each position. B. The numbers in the lower row indicate the counts of promoters with the indicated spacing (top row) between the −10 and −35 elements.

Regular expression matches are usually evaluated as simply a match or non-match, and the regular expressions in databases such as Prosite are manually tuned to provide high recall and precision. Calculating the exact probability of matching to regular expressions is complex (see Sewell and Durbin (1995)), but it is clear that allowing even a single unmatched position often dramatically increases the number of false positive matches, causing a great reduction in match precision.

Position Specific Scoring Matrix

PSSMs, also known as Positional Weight Matrices, PWM, and Position Specific Weight Matrices, PSWM, represent motifs as a vector of values for every possible character at each position of the motifs. In literature, PSSMs are often shown with the columns corresponding to positions and rows corresponding to the possible letters; computationally they are more often transposed so that the rows correspond to sequence positions and the columns to letters. The values in the PSSM can be of several kinds – among the most common are: simple counts, probabilities (i.e., each column sums to 1), or log-odds scores (log of the relative probabilities of the character in positive examples of the motif divided by the probabilities of the character in a background model). PSSMs retain all position independent information present in the training data, but do not incorporate information about correlated positions. PSSMs can be matched with sequences using dynamic programming alignment approaches [EPS30004], with complexity $O(nm)$ time, where n is the length of the database, and m is the number of positions in the motif PSSM. Empirical analysis suggests that the score distribution for PSSMs follows an extreme value distribution, similarly to local dynamic programming alignments (Altschul and Gish, 1996). The term profile (see next section) is sometimes used for PSSMs, although this usage is confusing.

Profile

Profile (Gribskov et al., 1987) and Profile Hidden Markov Models, PHMMs, are PSSMs that have additional information representing position-specific the weights/probabilities of insertion/deletion. For PHMMs, this additional information specifies the transition probabilities between the match states (which have the position specific probabilities of the letters) and to and from insert and delete states. Some kinds of profiles/HMMs contain additional information describing probabilities of insertion and deletions, resulting in additional columns. In order to keep the file human-readable, these motif representations may use more than one line per position in the sequence. Profiles and PHMMs can be matched using the same kind of dynamic programming algorithms used for PSSMs (Wang and Dunbrack, 2004), but it is customary to discuss PHMMs in terms of the Viterbi (Viterbi, 1967; Rabiner, 1989) and Baum-Welch (Baum et al., 1970) algorithms.

Large molecular structures, such as protein domains, are most often defined using the profile approach because of the incorporation of positions specific indels in such models. In general, whole proteins and proteins domains may have insertions at any sequence position exposed on the surface of the protein – such large indels are seen in many families (see, for instance, for instance the ubiquitin specific protease family (Ye et al., 2009)).

Sequence Logos

Examining and discerning the pattern of conservation in a PSSM or profile is difficult due to the large number of values. Sequence Logos (Schneider and Stephens, 1990) are a widely used graphical representation in which the letters at each position of the motif are displayed with different heights depending on their conservation. Conservation can be measured in a variety of ways such as letter frequency or information content ($H = -\sum_i p_i \log p_i$).

Learning Approaches

Multiple Alignment Based

Many motif learning approaches rely on multiple sequence alignments [EPS30005], MSAs, as a starting point. Several issues with MSAs affect one's ability to extract motif descriptions from MSAs.

One of the most important concerns is sampling. Even today, when thousands of complete genomes have been sequenced, the motif training data (i.e., the known sequences) is often very uneven with respect to the range of taxa from which sequences are drawn, and with respect to the presence of many close homologs (or even exact duplicate sequences). If not dealt with, these sampling issues tend to bias the motifs towards certain subclasses of sequences, and may compromise the ability of the learning algorithm to generalize. There are two main approaches to address sampling bias: selecting a less biased subset of sequences for training, or weighting sequences according to the amount of independent information they contain. Selecting a representative subset of sequences with less bias can be done manually, usually relying on taxonomic or other external information (for example, biochemical or structural properties of proteins), or automatically based on pairwise sequence comparisons. One of the most popular automatic methods is CD-HIT (Li *et al.*, 2001), see **Fig. 4**. Clearly this approach does not produce a completely unbiased representative set since the original distribution of sequences still has a strong effect.

Many methods have been successfully used for sequence weighting (Sibbald and Argos, 1990; Henikoff and Henikoff, 1994; Thompson *et al.*, 1994a,b). Many approaches rely on a distance-based tree [EPS10149], calculated using alignment scores from pairwise alignments or the MSA. The method introduced by Thompson *et al.* (1994a,b) in the Clustal V multiple alignment program, and Henikoff and Henikoff's position-based sequence weights (Henikoff and Henikoff, 1994), which do not require a tree, have been widely used **(Fig. 5)**.

Position specific weights are first calculated for the letters at each aligned position in each sequence. The weight is

$$w = \sum_{p=1}^{LENGTH} \sum_{i}^{alphabet} \frac{1}{k_p n_{i,p}}$$

where k_p is the number of distinct letters at position p, and $n_{i,p}$ is the number of occurances of letter i at position p

While the use of weighting to account for sampling bias is widely accepted, it does not appear that the weights need to be highly accurate, probably due to the high degree of biological variation in evolutionary rates.

In addition to bias, sequence training sets may also suffer from undersampling – the total number of sequences may be small, and letters/words that occur at very low frequencies are not observed. This problem is often treated by replacing the observed letter counts with a modified count that includes a pseudocount or prior. One common adjustment, commonly called a "plus one prior" is to add one to every letter count. Unless the total counts are very large, such a pseudocount is probably an overcorrection. Another common approach is to add one letter count distributed according to the overall letter distribution (i.e., the pseudocount sums to one across all letters).

Another concern with MSAs is the presence of errors in the alignment, especially near to insertions and deletions. In the case of regular expression representations, misalignment can be a severe problem and causes serious degradation of both precision and recall. The misalignment issue is exacerbated by the inclusion of sequences with errors, very distantly related sequences, or even sequences that are unrelated, in the training set. The latter problem is more frequent that one might think because training sequences are often selected by noisy biological criteria (such as co-expression) – the presence of incorrectly labeled training examples is therefore very common in biological contexts.

Consensus sequences and regular expression motif descriptions usually focus on short, highly conserved sequences. Often these are selected manually (see "Relevant Websites section"), based on an initial multiple alignment and/or expert knowledge, followed by

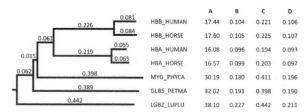

	A	B	C	D
HBB_HUMAN	17.44	0.104	0.221	0.106
HBB_HORSE	17.60	0.105	0.225	0.107
HBA_HUMAN	16.08	0.096	0.194	0.093
HBA_HORSE	16.57	0.099	0.203	0.097
MYG_PHYCA	30.19	0.180	0.411	0.196
GLB5_PETMA	32.02	0.191	0.398	0.190
LGB2_LUPLU	38.10	0.227	0.442	0.211

Fig. 4 Sequence weights. The tree shows a group of globin proteins (Thompson *et al.*). A. position-based weights, un-normalized. B. position-based weights, normalized to sum to 1. C. Clustal tree-based weights, un-normalized. D. Tree-based weights normalized to sum to 1.

1. Measure similarities between sequences using Blast or a dynamic programming alignment
2. For each sequence, determine the number of neighbors. Sequences are neighbors if their alignment score is higher that a user selected threshold
3. Find the available sequence with the most neighbors and add it the representative set.
4. Mark all of its neighbors as unavailable
5. Repeat 3-4 until no sequences remain available

Fig. 5 CD-Hit method of selecting unbiased representative sequences.

iterative database searching to validate that the pattern separates positive and negative examples. A problem with this manual approach is that if may not generalize well because only letters that occur at a position, in the training data, are included in the pattern. A new sequence that contains a chemically similar but novel amino acid residue may therefore not be recognized. In addition, as true positive examples accumulate, with continuing growth in the number of sequences, one typically finds that an increasing number of letters are allowed at each position leading to a concomitant increase in false positive matches (i.e., lower precision). This problem is typically solved by splitting the pattern into two more specific patterns that each recognize a subset of the training examples.

Generalization, the ability to detect examples of a motif that do not precisely match any of the training examples is one of the primary goals of motif identification. Generalization is particularly difficult when the number of training examples is small, or drawn from a limited taxonomic range so that the sequence diversity is low. A common approach to this is to use external knowledge about the chemical/mutational similarity of the amino acid residues to augment the training observations. This approach has been called *regularization* (Karplus, 1995), although it differs significantly from the L_1 and L_2 regularization approaches typically used in machine learning to restrict the complexity of the model parameterization [EPS30012]. In the case of regular expression patterns, regularization often augments the set of allowed letters observed at a position with additional letters that are chemically similar, but were not observed. For instance, it is common to predefine classes of amino acid residues such as hydrophobic = [ILMV], basic = [HKR], aromatic = [FWY], acid/amide = [DNEQ], hydrophilic = [HKRDNEQSTWY], etc. A column in a multiple sequence that contains, for instance, Isoleucine (I), Methionine (M) and Valine (V), might be defined as belonging to the hydrophobic class [ILMV], even though Leucine (L) was not observed. A more sophisticated approach, incorporated in the EMotif program (Huang and Brutlag, 2001; Nevill-Manning *et al.*, 1998) matches multiple overlapping classes to the observed set of letters and chooses the best matching class. These approaches are regularizations in the sense that they reduce the original 5×10^{18} possible character classes to around 10 classes.

For PSSMs, mixture models based on empirical observations of amino acid substitutions are commonly used. Fitting the observed data to a Dirichlet mixture distribution is a common approach. A mixture distribution is a weighted combination of simpler base models, in this case the base models are Dirichlet distributions. The probability of the "true" letter distribution at a position $P(\vec{x})$ is given by

$$P(\vec{x}) = \frac{\sum_j w_j P_j(\vec{x})}{\sum_j w_j}$$

where the $P_j(\vec{x})$ are the probabilities predicted by the base models and w_j are weights that indicate the importance of the model in the mixture. $P_j(\vec{x})$ is a Dirichlet distribution.

$$P(\vec{x}) = \frac{\sum_{i=1}^{20} p_i^{\alpha-1}}{Z}$$

where the p_i and w_j are empirically determined based on known "good" multiple alignments drawn from the BLOCKs database, HSSP, or expert protein family multiple alignments (Brown *et al.*, 1993; Sjölander *et al.*, 1996).

For a vector of observed letter counts, $\vec{n}$, and M base Dirichlet distributions, the estimated true frequency of letter i, $\hat{P}(x_i)$

$$\hat{P}(x_i) = \sum_{j=1}^{k} P(\vec{\alpha}_j | \vec{n}) \frac{n_i + \alpha_{ij}}{|\vec{n}| + |\vec{\alpha}_j|} = \sum_{j=1}^{M} \left(\frac{w_j P(\vec{n} | \alpha_j)}{\sum_k w_k P(\vec{n} | \alpha_k)} \right) \frac{n_i + \alpha_{ij}}{|\vec{n}| + |\vec{\alpha}_j|}$$

Another approach to learning a PSSM is the evolutionary profile (Gribskov and Veretnik, 1996), in which the Dayhoff PAM evolutionary model is used a source of known biological patterns of residue substitution. Briefly, for each column in the alignment, the probability of the observed letter frequencies expected for each possible ancestral residue, at different evolutionary distance from 1 PAM to 1024 PAM, are used to choose the components of a mixture model, weighted by the probabilities. The mixture probabilities are then used to form log-odds scores using expected random frequencies of the letters as the background. This approach has also been generalized to use a continuous estimate of the evolutionary distance rather than a fixed set of PAM matrices (Eskin *et al.*, 2001).

In some cases, either due to a poor multiple sequence alignment, or because of biological or functional divergence within the set of training sequences, an aligned position may represent two or more distinct patterns of conserved letters. When this occurs, it has been argued that is desirable to replace the actual observed letter frequencies (or pseudocount) with the probabilities that are dominated by the probabilities derived from a known, biologically relevant, prior distribution. This approach was termed the megaprior heuristic (Bailey and Gribskov, 1996), and has been implemented in MEME, evolutionary profiles, and HMMs.

Non-Alignment Approaches

Protein motifs are most commonly extracted from an initial multiple sequence alignment, but sometimes the training sequences are not strictly homologous, or the sequences contain repeated sequences, rearrangements, or other common situations that disrupt alignment approaches. For nucleic acid sequences, it is usually difficult or impossible to construct an accurate multiple alignment due to the small nucleic acid alphabet, four letters, and the rapid evolution of non-coding regions (such as promoter or enhancer regions in which one might want to find transcription factor binding sites). In these cases, it is necessary to use a learning approach that simultaneously learns both the motif locations and the motif pattern itself. The most widely used approaches, expectation maximization and Gibbs sampling, learn a PSSM motif, without gaps, based on a set of training sequences.

Expectation-Maximization is a general purpose optimization approach that learns a locally optimal pattern that maximizes the probability of the data given the pattern, i.e., the likelihood. With sequences, the pattern is a PSSM giving the probability of each letter at each position of the motif for a pre-determined motif length. EM, as the name implies, is an iterative two-stage algorithm. In the first step, given the current pattern, the probability that each position of each sequence was generated by the pattern is calculated. In the second, the pattern is re-estimated based on the probabilities determined in the first step. The probability weighted frequencies of the letters at each position of the PSSM represent the maximum likelihood estimate of the pattern. The updated pattern is then used to recalculate the probabilities that each position is a site, and the two step process iterated to convergence. The total likelihood is guaranteed to remain equal or increase at each iteration so this can be recognized as a greedy, loca hill-climbingl, process. EM has a number of advantages: it needs little or no prior information about the pattern to be found (except its length), it typically converges rapidly, and it is adaptable to many kinds of patterns including repeated patterns and patterns that are not present in every sequence. It also has disadvantages: it is a locally optimal method, it is sensitive to initial conditions, and the width of the pattern must typically be known in advance. Typically EM approaches overcome the issues of local optimality and sensitivity to initial conditions by repeating the training multiple times using randomized initial conditions each time. Patterns with the highest total likelihood, or that are found repeatedly, are assumed to be the globally optimal solution (although obviously one cannot be sure).

The MEME program (Bailey and Elkan, 1994) incorporates several clever enhancements that improve the performance of this general EM approach with biological sequence motifs. The first insight is that the desired conserved motif must be present in the training set. Rather than using randomized initial PSSMs, MEME comprehensively samples sequences from the training set and creates the initial PSSMs by mixing the sequence with the background frequency distribution. Then several cycles of EM are performed and the partially trained PSSMs are inspected to identify which ones are converging, taking advantage of the rapid convergence of EM; only these PSSMs are iterated to convergence. The second issue has to do with the motif length. Since this is an input parameter for the EM, the only option is to sample a large number of lengths and to choose the length that maximizes the likelihood (including a correction for model complexity). Finally, especially when considering gap-free motifs, most training sets contain multiple motifs – for instance, two conserved motifs with a variable spacing, such as the E. coli promoter, cannot be learned as a single PSSM. To solve this problem, MEME iteratively identifies multiple motifs, and uses probabilistic erasing to remove each motif from the training data after it is discovered. In probabilistic erasing, after the PSSM has converged, the probability, $P(S_{ij}/PSSM)$, that each position, j, of each of the training sequences, S_i, was generated by the motif is evaluated, and the weight of that position is decreased to $1- P(S_{ij}/PSSM)$.

Another method for learning both the motif and the motif locations is the Gibbs sampler (Lawrence et al., 1993) (GS), which uses a Markov chain Monte Carlo (MCMC) sampling approach. GS can be looked on as a stochastic version of EM. As with EM, a motif width, W, is defined. Each width W word in each sequence is a possible location of the motif, and the probability of each of these positions is calculated identically to the E-step in EM. The probability of generating each word assuming some background distribution, for instance the random expected frequencies of the bases or amino acids, is also calculated. The ratio of these probabilities can be considered to be weights on each possible width-W word. The initial PSSM is constructed by randomly selecting words according to these weights, and at each step, one word is randomly replaced, the probabilities and weights recalculated. This is very similar to the process used in EM, but rather than using the probabilities of all words across the sequences, only a specific group of sampled positions is used. GS is typically slow to converge, often requiring thousands of cycles for even modest numbers and lengths of sequences. Extensions to the original GS procedure that allow multiple motifs to be learned, and that allow the motif width to be optimized have been developed (Neuwald et al., 1995).

Because of the small nucleotide alphabet, motif finding in nucleic acids often incorporates the identification of kmer words that are statistically overrepresented in a training set, where k is typically in the range of 5 to 8 bases. These approaches are widely used, for instance, in defining promoter elements and transcription factor binding sites (TFBS). Because all words are evaluated, word based methods have the theoretical advantage of discovering a globally optimal pattern rather than the locally optimal patterns found by EM and GS. In practice, the advantages are less clear due to the pronounced word preferences of nucleic acid sequences, and the weak conservation of many DNA motifs. Because of the relatively strong word-preference of DNA sequences, even in non-conserved regions, it is critical to include a background model; typically a 5th or 6th order Markov model is used (Sinha and Tompa, 2002). An important issue with word probability based methods is that any ambiguity in the motif, such as a position which is not highly conserved, splits the occurrences of the motif into multiple words. Clearly, this weakens the distinction between the conserved words and the background, reducing the chance that the motif will be detected as significantly overrepresented. In principal one can identify words that represent ambiguous images of a conserved site (Pavesi et al., 2004) but it remains difficult to distinguish such ambiguous patterns. Because of their short length, and the small alphabet, it is common to try to use additional information to constrain the patterns that are identified. The most common constraint has been to require an internal dyad symmetry (van Helden et al., 2000), since many DNA binding proteins possess such symmetry. Most word-based approaches, similarly to PSSM-based approaches, also assume that the positions of a motif are independent which is not necessarily correct.

Validation

Assessment of the classification ability of a program has been one of the most difficult areas in both computational and systems biology. Gold standard data are, themselves, often calculated by a computational learning method. A new method that is better, appears to make many false positive label assignments when compared to an older inferior standard. Still, just assigning more class labels, or predicting more positives, measures only the recall of a method and says nothing about precision. As discussed above, this leads to serious overestimation of the usefulness of a method. With protein motifs it has been common to use two kinds of standards. The first approach relies on the documentation associated with the PROSITE database, much of which is carefully hand curated. Although PROSITE signatures are based on these data, the data include annotations of false negatives, that is, sequences that should be positive but did not match the PROSITE signature of pattern. This inclusion of both the easy positives (that can be identified with regular expressions), and the difficult positives, which cannot, has made the PROSITE annotation very useful. Another approach is to use the three-dimensional structure databases CATH (Dawson *et al.*, 2017) and SCOP (Fox *et al.*, 2014) to define groups of related proteins. While it is still not clear that all proteins with similar three-dimensional structures are actually related, or whether some protein folds are somehow just energetically favorable, a classification method with the highest recall/ precision vs the structural classification is still likely to be the best. For nucleic acid motifs, validation vs gold standard data is more problematic. While a number of compendia of promoter sites and TFBS exist, the counts for particular motifs are often low, and the motifs themselves have often been identified by the multiple alignment or overrepresented word approaches described above. In a few cases, laboratory experiments have been conducted to find short oligonucleotides that physically bind to specific proteins, or that can be pulled down by their bind (as in ChIP-Seq). These datasets are still somewhat difficult to interpret since the exact binding site is usually not determined, and because most sequence-specific nucleic acid binding-proteins have also have high non-sequence specific binding, as well.

See also: Biological Database Searching. DNA Barcoding: Bioinformatics Workflows for Beginners. Functional Enrichment Analysis. Identifying Functional Relationships Via the Annotation and Comparison of Three-Dimensional Amino Acid Arrangements in Protein Structures. Natural Language Processing Approaches in Bioinformatics. Sequence Analysis. Sequence Composition

References

Altschul, S.F., Gish, W., 1996. Local alignment statistics. Methods Enzymol. 266, 460–480.

Altschul, S.F., Gish, W., Miller, W., Myers, E.W., Lipman, D.J., 1990. Basic local alignment search tool. J. Mol. Biol. 5 (215), 403–410.

Altschul, S.F., Madden, T.L., Schäffer, A.A., *et al.*, 1997. Gapped BLAST and PSI-BLAST: A new generation of protein database search programs. Nucleic Acids Res. 25, 3389–3402.

Bailey, T.L., Elkan, C., 1994. Fitting a mixture model by expectation maximization to discover motifs in biopolymers. In: Proceedings of the Second International Conference on Intelligent Systems for Molecular Biology, pp. 28–36. AAAI Press.

Bailey, T.L., Gribskov, M., 1996. The megaprior heuristic for discovering protein sequence patterns. Proc. Int. Conf. Intell. Syst. Mol. Biol. 4, 15–24.

Baum, L., Petrie, T., Soules, G., Weiss, N., 1970. A maximization technique occurring in the statistical analysis of probabilistic functions of Markov chains. Ann. Math. Stat. 41, 164–171.

Brown, M., Hughey, R., Krogh, A., *et al.*, 1993. Using Dirichlet mixture priors to derive hidden Markov models for protein families. Proc. Int. Conf. Intell. Syst. Mol. Biol. 1, 47–55.

Dawson, N.L., Lewis, T.E., Das, S., *et al.*, 2017. CATH: An expanded resource to predict protein function through structure and sequence. Nucleic Acids Res. 45, D289–D295.

Dayhoff, M.O., Schwartz, R.M., Orcutt, B.C., 1978. A model of evolutionary change in proteins. In: Dayhoff, M.O. (Ed.), Atlas of Protein Sequence and Structure, vol. 5(3). Washington, DC: National Biomedical Research Foundation, pp. 345–352.

Eskin, E., Grundy, W.N., Singer, Y., 2001. Using mixtures of common ancestors for estimating the probabilities of discrete events in biological sequences. Bioinformatics 17 (Suppl. 1), S65–S73.

Fox, N.K., Brenner, S.E., Chandonia, J.M., 2014. SCOPe: Structural Classification of Proteins—Extended, integrating SCOP and ASTRAL data and classification of new structures. Nucleic Acids Res. 42, D304–D309.

Graves, B.J., Johnson, P.F., McKnight, S.L., 1986. Homologous recognition of a promoter domain common to the MSV LTR and the HSV tk gene. Cell 44, 565–576.

Gribskov, M., McLachlan, A.D., Eisenberg, D., 1987. Profile analysis: Detection of distantly related proteins. Proc. Natl. Acad. Sci. USA 84, 4355–4358.

Gribskov, M., Robinson, N.L., 1996. Use of receiver operating characteristic (ROC) analysis to evaluate sequence matching. Comput. Chem. 20, 25–33.

Gribskov, M., Veretnik, S., 1996. Identification of sequence patterns with profile analysis. Methods Enzymol. 266, 198–212.

Henikoff, S., Henikoff, J.G., 1992. Amino acid substitution matrices from protein blocks. Proc. Natl. Acad. Sci. USA 89, 10915–10919.

Henikoff, S., Henikoff, J.G., 1994. Position-based sequence weights. J. Mol. Biol. 243, 574–578.

Huang, J.Y., Brutlag, D.L., 2001. The EMOTIF database. Nucleic Acids Res. 29, 202–204.

Karplus, K., 1995. Evaluating regularizers for estimating distributions of amino acids. Proc. Int. Conf. Intell. Syst. Mol. Biol. 3, 188–196.

Lawrence, C.E., Altschul, S.F., Boguski, M.S., *et al.*, 1993. Detecting subtle sequence signals: A Gibbs sampling strategy for multiple alignment. Science 262, 208–214.

Lifton, R.P., Goldberg, M.L., Karp, R.W., Hogness, D.S., 1978. The organization of the histone genes in Drosophila melanogaster: Functional and evolutionary implications. Cold Spring Harb. Symp. Quant. Biol. 42, 1047–1051.

Li, W., Jaroszewski, L., Godzik, A., 2001. Clustering of highly homologous sequences to reduce the size of large protein databases. Bioinformatics 17, 282–283.

Neuwald, A.F., Liu, J.S., Lawrence, C.E., 1995. Gibbs motif sampling: Detection of bacterial outer membrane protein repeats. Protein Sci. 4, 1618–1632.

Nevill-Manning, C.G., Wu, T.D., Brutlag, D.L., 1998. Highly specific protein sequence motifs for genome analysis. Proc. Natl. Acad. Sci. USA 95, 5865–5871.

Oliphant, A.R., Struhl, K., 1988. Defining the consensus sequences of E. coli promoter elements by random selection. Nucleic Acids Res. 16, 7673–7683.

Pavesi, G., Mereghetti, P., Mauri, G., Pesole, G., 2004. Weeder Web: Discovery of transcription factor binding sites in a set of sequences from co-regulated genes. Nucleic Acids Res. 32, W199–W203.

Pearson, W.R., 1996. Effective protein sequence comparison. Methods Enzymol. 266, 227–258.

Pribnow, D., 1975. Nucleotide sequence of an RNA polymerase binding site at an early T7 promoter. Proc. Natl. Acad. Sci. USA 72, 784–788.

Rabiner, L.R., 1989. A tutorial on hidden Markov models and selected applications in speech recognition. Proc. IEEE 77, 257–286.

Schneider, T.D., Stephens, R.M., 1990. Sequence logos: A new way to display consensus sequences. Nucleic Acids Res. 18, 6097–6100.

Sewell, R.F., Durbin, R., 1995. Method for calculation of probability of matching a bounded regular expression in a random data string. J. Comput. Biol. 2, 25–31.

Sibbald, P.R., Argos, P., 1990. Weighting aligned protein or nucleic acid sequences to correct for unequal representation. J. Mol. Biol. 216, 813–818.

Sinha, S., Tompa, M., 2002. Discovery of novel transcription factor binding sites by statistical overrepresentation. Nucleic Acids Res. 30, 5549–5560.

Sjölander, K., Karplus, K., Brown, M., et al., 1996. Dirichlet mixtures: A method for improved detection of weak but significant protein sequence homology. Comput Appl. Biosci. 12, 327–345.

Thompson, J.D., Higgins, D.G., Gibson, T.J., 1994a. Improved sensitivity of profile searches through the use of sequence weights and gap excision. Comput. Appl. Biosci. 10, 19–29.

Thompson, J.D., Higgins, D.G., Gibson, T.J., 1994b. CLUSTAL W – Improving the sensitivity of progressive multiple sequence alignment through sequence weighting, position-specific gap penalties and weight matrix choice. Nucleic Acids Res. 22, 4673–4680.

van Helden, J., Rios, A.F., Collado-Vides, J., 2000. Discovering regulatory elements in noncoding sequences by analysis of spaced dyads. Nucleic Acids Res. 28, 1808–1818.

Viterbi, A.J., 1967. Error bounds for convolutional codes and an asymptotically optimum decoding algorithm. IEEE Trans. Inf. Theory 13, 260–269.

Wang, G., Dunbrack, R.L., 2004. Scoring profile-to-profile sequence alignments. Protein Sci. 13, 1612–1626.

Xenarios, I., 2013. New and continuing developments at PROSITE. Nucleic Acids Res. 41 (Database issue), D344–D347.

Ye, Y., Scheel, H., Hofmann, K., Komander, D., 2009. Dissection of USP catalytic domains reveals five common insertion points. Mol. Biosyst. 5, 1797–1808.

Zweig, M.H., Campbell, G., 1993. Receiver-operating characteristic (ROC) plots: A fundamental evaluation tool in clinical medicine. Clin Chem. 39, 561–577.

Relevant Websites

https://en.oxforddictionaries.com/definition/motif
 motif.

http://prosite.expasy.org/prosuser.html
 PROSITE user manual ExPASy.

Epigenetics: Analysis of Cytosine Modifications at Single Base Resolution

Malwina Prater and **Russell S Hamilton,** University of Cambridge, Cambridge, United Kingdom

Introduction

All DNA nucleotides can undergo covalent modifications *in vivo*, with 5-methylcytosine (5mC) being the most investigated and understood of the modifications. In eukaryotes, 5mC is most commonly methylated in a CpG context, however it can also be modified in non-CpG contexts (CHH and CHG methylation) (Guo *et al.*, 2014). Other known DNA nucleotide modifications include adenine that can be converted to N6-methyladenine (6mA), and thymine to 5-hydroxymethyluracil (5hmU) (Sood *et al.*, 2016).

With the advent of next generation sequencing, it is possible to interrogate DNA modifications on a genomic scale and at single base resolution. In this article, we outline methods for interrogating cytosine modifications with particular emphasis on the important and emerging interest in 5-hydroxymethylcytosine (5hmC), 5-formylcytosine (5fC) and 5-carboxylcytosine (5caC) and the downstream bioinformatics analysis.

Some of the existing methylation data including 5mC, 5hmC and 5caC generated by large epigenetic-focused consortia can be viewed and downloaded. Among these, BLUEPRINT is a key player in sharing DNA methylation data, providing a database to browse and download raw data, analysis files or explore data on the BLUEPRINT Data Analysis Portal. Genome tracks are also provided for visualizing the data in UCSC or Ensembl. Other epigenetic data consortia that can provide DNA methylation data (mostly WGBS-seq) include NIH Roadmap, ENCODE and International Human Epigenome Consortium (IHEC) (Adams *et al.*, 2012; Bernstein *et al.*, 2010; Consortium *et al.*, 2012). DeepBlue Epigenomic Data Server enables centralized access to these and more databases (Albrecht *et al.*, 2017).

It is worth noting that nucleotide modifications are also found in RNA molecules (Frye *et al.*, 2016). Many of the analyses outlined in this article will be applicable to RNA, however we focus our attention to the cytosine modifications in DNA.

Cytosine Modifications

The covalent modifications of cytosine of greatest biological interest are to the 5' position. These modifications are of particular interest as they have been shown to regulate development and disease, and more recently aging. Correlative DNA methylation levels at specific loci proved to be valuable tool for predicting the speed of aging in human and mouse (Horvath, 2013; Stubbs *et al.*, 2017). The concept of epigenetic clock was taken a step further into development of commercial test, that is now available to individuals (see Section Relevant Websites).

Starting from unmodified cytosine, a series of enzyme driven reactions lead to 4 distinct modifications and can be returned to an unmodified cytosine (**Fig. 1**). 5mC is established *de novo* by DNA methyltransferase enzymes (DNMTs): DNMT3a, DNMT3b and DNMT3L (Goll and Bestor, 2005), and its maintenance is controlled by DNMT1 (Delgado-Olguín *et al.*, 2012; Liang *et al.*, 2002). 5mC can be reversed to unmodified C via two alternative mechanisms: passive demethylation as a consequence of lack of maintenance as the cells replicate; or active demethylation, which involves oxidative DNA demethylation mediated by ten-eleven translocation (TET) family of enzymes (Kohli and Zhang, 2013). TET enzymes (5mC hydroxylases) can catalyze the stepwise oxidation of 5mC to 5hmC, 5fC and 5caC (He *et al.*, 2011; Ito *et al.*, 2011; Tahiliani *et al.*, 2009). The conversion of 5fC and 5caC to unmethylated C is thought to be facilitated by excision of modified cytosine by thymine DNA glycosylase (TDG), followed by base excision repair mechanisms (BER) (Weber *et al.*, 2016).

5-methylcytosine: 5mC

The addition of methyl group to the 5' position of cytosine in 5mC is stable and has been shown to play important role in development, tissue specificity, aging and disease. The majority of methylation in mammals occurs in a CpG context, which are distributed non-randomly (Guo *et al.*, 2013, 2014). Most of the mammalian genomes are methylated (Li and Zhang, 2014), but CpG island regions (CGIs) with high density of CpGs usually remain unmethylated and are predominantly associated with gene promoters. Methylation of cytosine is associated with silenced chromatin, but the role of DNA methylation depends on its location within the transcriptional unit. In general, highly methylated DNA in close proximity to the transcription start site is associated with long-term silencing of genes (Raynal *et al.*, 2012). In contrast, methylation of the gene body is associated with transcriptional activity and alternative splicing (Ball *et al.*, 2009; Hahn *et al.*, 2011). Interestingly, 5mC can inhibit binding of methylation-sensitive transcription factors to their target sites, and also promote binding of others, especially those involved in embryonic and organism development (Yin *et al.*, 2017). A further biological role of 5mC is the regulation of imprinted genes (Paulsen and Ferguson-Smith, 2001). The 5mC is also thought to have protective role for genome stability and to act as a defense mechanism against transposons (Bourc'his and Bestor, 2004; Lavie *et al.*, 2005; Turelli *et al.*, 2014; Walsh *et al.*, 1998). It is also clear that 5mC and histone modifications crosstalk, but in mammals this relationship is complex and interdependent (Du *et al.*, 2015; Li and Zhang, 2014).

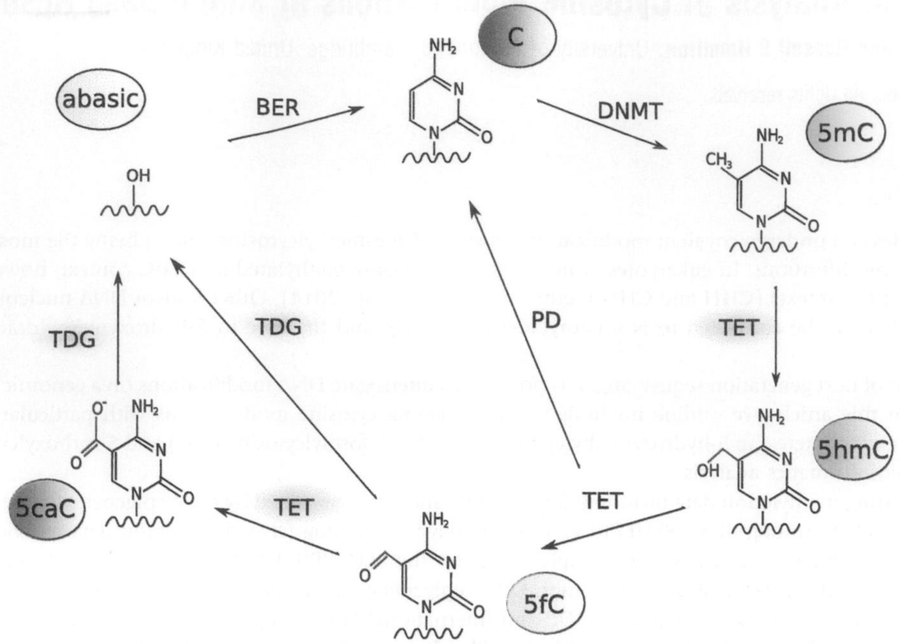

Fig. 1 Cytosine can be methylated at the 5th position by DNA methyltransferases: Dnmt1 as a maintenance process, or *de novo* by Dnmt3a or Dnmt3b. Resulting 5mC bases can be iteratively oxidised by TET enzymes in the process of active demethylation, resulting in 5hmC, 5fC and finally 5caC products. In the process of passive dilution (PD), 5hmC (and similarly 5fC and 5caC, not shown) can be demethylated to C during the course of DNA replication. 5caC, and also 5fC, can be deaminated to thymine and excised by thymine DNA glycosylase (TDG). The abasic site can be filled with unmodified deoxycytidine triphosphate (dCTP) by the base excision machinery (BER).

5-hydroxymethylcytosine: 5hmC

Recent years have brought evidence that 5hmC is not only an oxidation product of 5mC, but is chemically stable, with a distinct distribution in the genome, forming a stable epigenetic mark in its own right (Bachman *et al.*, 2014). In Embryonic Stem Cells (ESC) cells, 5hmC is enriched at differentiation-associated enhancers (Madzo *et al.*, 2014; Sérandour *et al.*, 2012; Stroud *et al.*, 2011; Szulwach *et al.*, 2011) and bivalent promoters of genes repressed at ESC cells, but activated upon differentiation (Wu *et al.*, 2011). 5hmC is also hypothesized to have a role in protection of genome integrity by marking sites for DNA damage (Kafer *et al.*, 2016). Levels of 5hmC are very tissue specific, with highest prevalence in central nervous system (brain). The differences in 5hmC levels within brain itself are pronounced enough to distinguish between specific brain regions (Lunnon *et al.*, 2016; Spiers and Hannon, 2017).

5-formylcytosine: 5fC and 5-carboxylcytosine: 5caC

The functions of 5fC and 5caC are still unclear, but recent research hints that they may be more than mere oxidation products. In mouse ESCs, 5fC is enriched in enhancer regions marked by H3K4me1 and H3K27ac (Iurlaro *et al.*, 2016). Furthermore, 5fC and 5caC have been shown to affect the rate and substrate specificity of RNA polymerase II processivity (Kellinger *et al.*, 2012; Wang *et al.*, 2015). Chromatin modifiers and transcriptional regulators have been identified as proteins binding to 5fC, suggesting a potential role of 5fC in gene regulation (Iurlaro *et al.*, 2013). Although the role of 5caC still needs to be elucidated, it has been hypothesized to be involved in regulating alternative splicing via CTCF preferential binding to 5caC (Marina and Oberdoerffer, 2016; Spruijt *et al.*, 2013).

Experimental Methods to Assay DNA Modifications in Genome

Bisulfite conversion alone can no longer claim to be a gold standard in 5mC detection as it co-detects 5mC and 5hmC modifications, leaving a confounded signal. To address this limitation of bisulfite-only conversion, several methods have been developed to distinguish between the distinct cytosine modifications (with focus on 5mC and 5hmC). A recent review compares a selection of 5hmC specific profiling techniques (Skvortsova *et al.*, 2017), in this article we focus on techniques compatible with 5hmC, 5fC and 5caC profiling (Table 1).

Bisulfite and oxidative bisulfite sequencing is able to discriminate between 5mC and 5hmC. In standard bisulfite conversion (BS), both 5mC and 5hmC are protected and are read in sequencing as C. The oxidant *potassium perruthenate* is used to convert 5hmC to 5fC, which is read as T in sequencing after BS conversion (same as unmethylated C, 5fC and 5caC) (oxBS). 5hmC levels

Table 1   Comparison of methods for assaying cytosine modifications using array or next-generation sequencing platforms

	Detection of				Modified base sequenced as					Bisulfite-based	Cost	Methylome coverage	Depth of seq required	SNP detection	Limitations	Comments/Strengths	Description
	5mC	5hmC	5fC	5caC	C	5mC	5fC	5caC	5hmC								
EPIC array	Y	Y	Y*	N	T	C	T	T	BS: C, oxBS: T	Y	low	850k		N	oxBS-redBS does not differentiate between 5caC and unmodified C; human only	cost-effective	Hybridisation of BS/oxBS DNA to arrays
RRBS-seq/RRHP	Y	Y	Y*	N	T	C	T	T	BS: C, oxBS: T	Y	mid	~ 12 M	30X	Y	oxBS-redBS does not differentiate between 5caC and unmodified C; Position limited by proximity to enzymes' recognition sites	cost-effective	MspI digestion, Library prep amplification, NGS
WG	Y	Y	Y*	N	T	C	T	T	BS: C, oxBS: T	Y	high	28 M	30X	Y	oxBS-redBS does not differentiate between 5caC and unmodified C; high cost	Compatible with single cell as input (not for OxBS due to coverage limitations)	Evaluates methylation levels of almost all CpGs
Targeted	Y	Y	Y*	N	T	C	T	T	BS: C, oxBS: T	Y	mid	Kit defined	30X	Y	oxBS-redBS does not differentiate between 5caC and unmodified C	cost-effective	Enrichment/library prep -> NGS
MeDIP-seq	Y	Y	Y	Y	–	–	–	–	–	N	mid			Y	Biased toward hypermethylated regions, not suitable for very low 5hmC, 100 bp resolution; Limited by antibody specificity	bisulfite-free	Anti–5(h)mC antibody to methylated CpG sites followed by NGS
TAB-Seq	Y	Y	N	N	T	BS: C, TAB: T	T	T	C	N	high			Y	Accuracy limited by efficiency of Tet enzyme	limitations of using enzymes	5hmC labelling with b-GT, TET oxidation, BS conversion, NGS
PacBio SMRT	Y	Y	Y	Y	C	5mC	5fC	5caC	5hmC	N	high			Y	High cost, throughput limitations	bisulfite-free; no DNA amplification, long reads, multiple modifications detected	Direct detection of modified bases by assessing activity of DNA polymerase
Nanopore	Y	Y	Y	Y	C	5mC	5fC	5caC	5hmC	N	high			Y	High error rate, processivity/ throughput, cost	bisulfite-free; long reads, multiple modifications detected	Direct detection of modified bases via ion current as passes through pore

*indicates with redBS.

can be quantified by subtracting BS from oxBS signals for each cytosine position (Booth et al., 2012). An associated method to map 5fC is redBS-seq, which utilises chemical reduction of 5fC to 5hmC using *sodium borohydride* (Booth et al., 2014). As a result, 5fC is read as C after BS conversion (same as 5hmC and 5mC). Thus, 5fC levels can be quantified by subtracting redBS from the BS signal. Whole genome sequencing of oxBS and redBS provide the most accurate and least biased 5hmC distribution across the genome, but the associated sequencing costs are very high due to high coverage requirements. OxBS and redBS treatments are also compatible with arrays (e.g., Illumina 450K and EPIC arrays) or in combination with Reduced Representation Bisulfite Sequencing (RRBS) and enrichment methods (e.g., Roche Nimblegen SeqCap)(See **Table 1**) (Gross et al., 2016; Spiers and Hannon, 2017; Stewart et al., 2015). The enrichment methods provide a more cost-effective way of assaying methylation levels than for whole genome. BS/oxBS sequencing, however, is not the only method to interrogate 5hmC distribution at a genome scale. TAB-seq, detects 5hmC directly by converting 5hmC to 5-glucosylmethylcytosine with β-glucosyltransferase first (read as C), followed by oxidation of 5mC and 5fC to 5caC by TET enzymes, and BS-seq (Yu et al., 2012a,b). A subtraction of the 5hmC from the BS signal is required to call the 5mC. Several methods to map 5fC and 5caC have been proposed, including *M.SssI* methylase-assisted BS-seq (MAB-seq and caMAB-seq) and chemical-modification-assisted bisulfite sequencing (fCAB-seq and caCAB-seq). Single base resolution methods are mainly bisulfite or enzyme conversion based, but recently novel technologies with the ability to directly detect nucleotide modifications have been developed (e.g. Pacific Biosciences SMRT and Oxford Nanopore) (Rand et al., 2017; Simpson et al., 2017; Song et al., 2012a). These methods currently do not have the per cytosine accuracy of, for example, bs/oxBS, however are likely to be the methods of choice in the future and are introduced further in the Discussion. Although bisulfite-based methods to identify and quantify DNA methylation are the current gold standard, their usage has some caveats. Bisulfite conversion itself introduces a range of systematic sequencing biases by DNA degradation. For example, DNA degradation induced by bisulfite conversion depletes more regions with unmethylated cytosines, while incomplete conversion can lead to overestimation of methylated cytosines. On top of these, methylation status of specific CpG-rich regions may cause their under- or over-estimation in WGBS experiments. These biases are even more pronounced during library amplification step (Olova et al., 2017).

If single base resolution is not required, several other 5hmC detection methods could be considered: antibody immuno-precipitation (h)MeDIP-seq (Bock et al., 2010); or selective labelling and pulldown (e.g., hMe-Seal) (Han et al., 2016; Song et al., 2012b). Analysis packages such as MeDIPS (Lienhard et al., 2014) provide a suite of tools to analyse (h)MeDIP-seq data including the identification of differentially methylated regions. Although not offering base resolution and lacking sensitivity for regions with low enrichment, antibody immunoprecipitation can enrich for each of DNA modifications with specific antibody, ensuring high specificity at low cost (Tan et al., 2013). Independent of the chosen method it is good practice to validate methylation calls at a locus-specific level with methods such as bisulfite pyrosequencing (Strogantsev et al., 2015).

Analysis

Quality Control and Mapping to the Genome

With all the methods detailed in **Table 1**, the first step is to map the experimental output to a reference genome. In the case of array based methods, the reported individual probes are mapped to the genome via a lookup table of locations provided by the manufacturer. With second and third generation sequencing methods, the read sequences have to be aligned to a reference genome.

Array methods

Mapping of probes to their genomic locations doesn't require an explicit alignment step as is required with NGS data; instead the probe genomic locations are provided in the manufacturer supplied manifests for the arrays. The quality control steps required for the analysis of the array data is centered around removing poorly performing probes and corrections to batch effects due to bead detection on the chip. There are also control probes on the chip which should be interrogated for a variety of QC metrics. Illumina's Infinium HumanMethylation 450K and MethylationEPIC array chips are based on two distinct probe designs for assaying the methylation status of CpGs requiring normalization to match the differing methylation profiles. Illumina methylation arrays can be analysed using missMethyl (Phipson et al., 2015) or Chip Analysis Methylation Pipeline (ChAMP) (Morris et al., 2014). Both missMethyl and ChAMP R packages accept raw IDAT format files as input and integrate a selection of normalization methods (e.g. SWAN or BMIQ), differential methylation analysis and gene set analysis. Batch effects are corrected using Combat (Johnson et al., 2007) in ChAMP and RUVm (Maksimovic et al., 2015) in missMethyl which is designed to correct unknown source of variation as well as batch effects. ChAMP can additionally identify copy number alterations present in a dataset. Both packages provide the methylation states of the probes passing the QC steps.

Next generation sequencing

Standard steps in BS-seq data analysis are: adapter and sequence trimming, assurance of reads quality, alignment of the reads to the reference genome and methylation calling. We discuss each of these steps in the sections below. **Fig. 2** outlines a typical pipeline for the analysis of BS-seq data.

Trimming

Bisulfite conversion itself can introduce biases, as less efficient bisulfite conversion at 5' ends is commonly observed, and this could be misinterpreted as high methylation calls. Also, in any paired-end directional BS-Seq, 5' overhangs created by sonication are

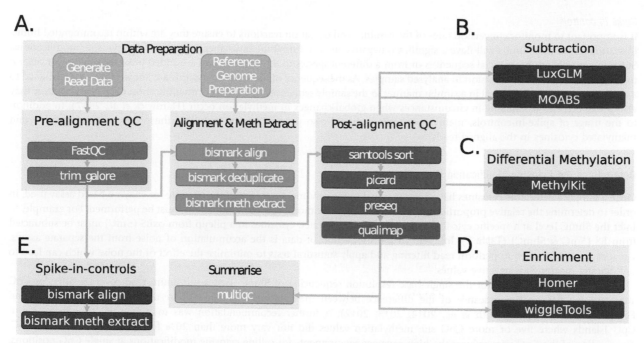

Fig. 2 A typical analysis pipeline for bisulfite based assays for detecting modified cytosine positions. A. Quality control and alignments steps. B. LuxGLM and MOABS are able to perform the required subtraction between different bisulfite based assays to call, e.g., 5hmC. C. Example software for calculating differential methylation between sample groups (e.g., case and control). D. Enrichment for cytosine modifications and histone marks can be performed with programs such as Homer and wiggleTools.

filled with unmodified C during end-repair step in library preparation, which can introduce biases in the genuine methylation state of cytosine at both ends of sequenced reads. Similarly, in RRBS, enzymatic reaction of *MspI* also creates 5′ overhangs, and the missing positions are filled with unmodified C, but not of the true genomic cytosine. Additional consideration is also required for the sequencing of Post-Bisulfite Adapter Tagging (PBAT) libraries. Random priming step can introduce biases in base composition and thus in detecting methylation levels, which are affected mostly at the 5′ end of all reads. Therefore, it's important to trim affected bases (length of random oligo primers) from the libraries before the alignment step to remove methylation biases. With tools such as Trim Galore! (see Relevant Websites) and Cutadapt (Martin, 2011) all of the biases can be efficiently removed.

Aligners and methylation callers

Mapping of the bisulfite converted reads to a reference genome is challenging due to C to T conversion and therefore reduced sequence complexity. In the course of bisulfite treatment, the top and bottom strands become non-complementary and their PCR amplification products differ, resulting in 4 different sequences: original top (OT), original bottom (OB), complementary top (CT) and complementary bottom (CB) strands. Different aligners approach these issues slightly differently, but arguably the most widely used is Bismark (Krueger and Andrews, 2011). Bismark is considered to be a conservative aligner, with expected alignment rates of around 80% (human), and may be a good choice as its very well supported by the developers. Bismark also has tools to extract methylation calls and distinguishes between the different cytosine contexts: CpG, CHH and CGH. methylKit can perform the methylation calls directly from aligned BAM files as well as import methylation calls from Bismark (Akalin *et al.*, 2012). This is particularly convenient for creating pipelines as methylKit is primarily utilised for differential methylation analysis (see Section Differential Methylation). Alternatively, BWA-Meth offers more lenient aligning with rates (e.g., upwards of 90% (human) as it performs soft-clipping). This tool can be very useful if investigating genomic variants and may allow more reads to be aligned, but also some reads may be incorrectly mapped to genomic regions like repetitive regions.

The presence of SNPs can contribute to the miscalling of cytosine modifications, especially through C to T substitutions. Therefore, knowing the positions of common SNPs, for example, from dbSNP (Sherry *et al.*, 2001), can be utilised to mask these positions in SNP aware alignment/calling software such as Bis-SNP (Liu *et al.*, 2012).

In order for 5hmC, 5fC and 5caC to be accurately called in bisulfite based sequencing, there is a requirement for high read coverage to separate the true methylation signal from background noise (Discussed below). The high cost of sequencing to achieve the required coverage can be ameliorated with tools such as BSmooth (Hansen *et al.*, 2012). BSmooth provides an entire pipeline from the raw reads, through alignment to differential methylation calling. However, the feature of particular interest is the smoothing of the methylation signal across regions to improve the precision of calling the methylation status of cytosine modifications. In this way, low coverage regions can be included in the differential methylation calling, where they may have been excluded in Fisher's Exact test based methods (Discussed below).

Spike in controls

It is important to monitor conversion rates of the bisulfite and oxidation reactions to ensure they are within recommended limits. Deviations from these limits will have a significant negative impact during the downstream calling of the cytosine modifications. Spike-in-controls can be artificial sequences or from a different species to the samples, and are added prior to bisulfite conversion to assay the efficiency of conversion in analysed samples. As the sequence of the spike-in-controls are known they can be aligned to a control reference and analysed in a similar manner to the sample sequences. The absolute quantification of spike-in-controls may also prove even more valuable in circumstances when global changes in methylation occur (Hardwick *et al.*, 2017). In addition to the usage of spike-in-controls, methylation callers should also provide reports including the proportions of cytosine and methylated cytosines in the aligned reads.

Determining the Cytosine Modification Proportions

Once a sample's detectable cytosines have been mapped to the genome, regardless of the bisulfite- or enzyme-based assay used, in order to determine the relative proportions of the assayed cytosine modifications, subtractions must be performed. For example, to infer the 5hmC level at a specific cytosine, the number of methylated cytosines in a pileup from oxBS (5mC) must be subtracted from BS (5mC & 5hmC) **(Table 2)**. Inherent in the subtraction of data is the accumulation of noise from the separate assays. Great care must be taken to perform read filtering and apply statistical tests to minimize the effect of the noise which can lead to biologically meaningless negative values.

The original publications for the single-base resolution sequencing of 5hmC used a minimum read coverage filter for CpG sites and for statistical significance of the difference between the bisulfite and oxidation results; Benjamini-Hochberg and Fisher's tests were used (Booth *et al.*, 2014, 2013, 2012). A further recommendation was to pool CpG sites from within CpG Islands where five or more CpG site methylation values did not vary more than 20% for 5mC and 10% for 5hmC. The pooling of the CpG sites reduces the high coverage requirements for calling cytosine modifications at single CpG positions. Coverage of over 500 reads would be required to reliably detect below 5% hmC, where pooling enables detection of hmC down to 1% (Booth *et al.*, 2013). This protocol, which we refer to as the Booth method, for read coverage and statistical testing should be considered the minimum requirement for performing a subtraction and is applicable to both array and NGS approaches.

Methylation arrays

The analysis results from MissMethyl and ChAMP, as detailed above, provide the methylation status of each of the assayed CpG site on the array. However, neither method performs the subtractions required to call the proportions of 5hmC, 5fC or 5caC modifications. To address this, two related methods were developed for the validation of the compatibility of the oxBS treatment on the 450K array (Field *et al.*, 2015; Stewart *et al.*, 2015). Subtractions between BS and oxBS to call 5hmC are performed for CpG sites with a methylation difference over a threshold ($\Delta\beta > 0.3$). This filtering has the effect of minimizing the number of negative values in a similar manner to the Booth approach for NGS. A more recent package, OxyBS (Houseman *et al.*, 2016), utilises maximum likelihood estimates to call 5hmC from matched BS and oxBS samples. This method goes beyond naïve threshold filtering by modelling the methylation states (5C, 5mC, 5hmC) in the BS and oxBS paired samples.

Next-generation sequencing

There are several tools available for performing the subtractions required to make 5hmC calls **(Table 2)**. MLML (Qu *et al.*, 2013) is one of the earliest methods for estimating 5mC and 5hmC levels and has been developed for BS/oxBS, TAB-Seq and a combination of BS/oxBS and TAB-Seq. Maximum likelihood estimates are used to model the methylation states, and at sites with negative values the latent variables are used to approximate the MLE. oxBS-MLE (Xu *et al.*, 2016) uses binomial modelling of paired BS and oxBS samples and is applicable to both array and sequencing methods. The method is related to OxyBS, but overcomes the CPU time constraints enabling studies to be performed on much larger sample sizes. MOABS (Sun *et al.*, 2014) was

Table 2   Comparison table of a selection of subtraction methods for calling cytosine modifications. A variety of modelling approaches are used: Maximum Likelihood Estimates (MLE), Hidden Markov Models (HMM), General Linear Models (GLM). None of the methods have been applied and published for 5fC, and 5caC, however, they should be in theory, with optimizations applicable

	Statistical significance	Negative value filtering/modelling	Utilises biological replicates	Array/NGS/Both	5mC/5hmC/5fC/5caC/All
Booth Methods	Y	Filtering	No	NGS	All
OxBS-Array	Y	Filtering	No	Array	5mC/5hmC
Oxy-BS	Y	Modelling (MLE)	No	Array	5mC/5hmC
oxBS-MLE	Y	Modelling (MLE)	No	Both	5mC/5hmC
MLML	Y	Modelling (MLE)	No	Both	5mC/5hmC
MOABS	Y	Modelling (Beta-binomial)	Yes	NGS	5mC/5hmC
H(O)TA	Y	Modelling (hMM)	Time points	NGS	5mC/5hmC
LuxGLM	Y	Modelling (GLM)	Yes	NGS	All

primarily designed to improve the calling of 5mC sites in traditional bisulfite sequencing, however an extension to the beta-binomial method permits 5hmC calling. MOABS also takes into account biological replicates in methylation calls to account for biological variation. H(O)TA (Kyriakopoulos et al., 2017) employs hidden Markov Models (hMM) of the methylation states of the cytosines in BS and oxBS paired samples across experimental time points. LuxGLM (Äijö et al., 2016a,b) is one of the more recently published methods and was designed to work with a variety of chemical and enzymatic treatments followed by sequencing. A general linear model (GLM) is able to capture all cytosine modification methylation states across replicates to estimate the proportions of the modifications assayed.

Differential Methylation

Differentially Methylated Positions (DMPs) or Regions (DMRs) are genomic regions exhibiting distinct methylation states between biological samples, and are thought to have the potential to regulate gene expression. Depending on the samples interrogated, DMRs can be further classified into, e.g., tissue-specific, allele-specific, developmental stage or disease-associated (such as cancer-specific DMRs). Genome wide association studies have shown specific DMRs to be associated with disease states, while locus-specific studies confirmed their functional roles in regulating gene expression. Clear links have been made between DMRs and diseases such as systemic lupus erythematosus, cancer, aging, obesity, inflammatory bowel disease (Baba et al., 2010; Jeffries et al., 2011; McKinney et al., 2015; Soubry et al., 2015; Stirzaker et al., 2016; Ventham et al., 2016). Several DMRs have proved to be valuable epigenetic biomarkers with clinical applications (Barault et al., 2015; Church et al., 2014; Dietrich et al., 2012; Imperiale et al., 2014; Kristensen et al., 2016). Patterns of 5hmC are tissue specific and associate with tissue, organ and developmental stage functionality. For example, in placenta, maternal DNA methylation regulates development of early trophoblast, while unique 5mC and 5hmC patterns of placenta associate with birth weight (Branco et al., 2016; Fogarty et al., 2015; Green et al., 2016; Piyasena et al., 2015; Zhu et al., 2015). The latter example points a valid point how important is to discriminate between 5mC and 5hmC and that bisulfite-seq data (non-discriminative between 5mC and 5hmC) should be treated very carefully.

Determining the locations of the cytosine modifications on the genome is of particular interest in development, however it is often desirable to perform a comparison across conditions. For example, comparisons across tissues, investigating the effect of a gene knockout with CRISPR or in biomarker discovery in a disease case and control. There are a wealth of methods for finding differentially methylated genomic regions. Typically, these require more hands-on tailoring for the most appropriate comparisons in the study in hand and are often supplied as R packages. All the methods highlighted below perform multiple testing correction. BiSeq is designed for RRBS data analysis and performs DMR finding using the Wald statistic from the beta-binomial regression fit R package (Hebestreit et al., 2013). BSmooth searches for bumps on smoothed t-like scores of methylation profiles to find DMRs (Hansen et al., 2012). methylSig is an R package for calling DMRs with likelihood ratio test (and also a beta-binomial approach) (Park et al., 2014). methylKit, an R package, identifies DMRs with logistic regression and Fisher's exact tests (Akalin et al., 2012). methylKit can also directly input methylation calls from Bismark making it suitable for integrating into a pipeline. methylPipe employs Wilcoxon or Kruskal–Wallis paired non-parametric test to identify DMRs and the predicted DMRs can be in silico tested for validation with compEpiTools (Kishore et al., 2015).

It is important to state that the identification of DMRs is only a discovery step; further experimental validation is essential. Once a large whole genome case/control study has identified and validated a DMR/biomarker it can be incorporated into a targeted panel to greatly reduce the cost for diagnostic purposes.

Interpretation

Genomic Distribution of Cytosine Modifications

Once the detectable cytosines modifications have been mapped and processed to provide relative proportions of the measurable modifications, it is then desirable to look for where they accumulate in the genome and interpret the biological significance in the context of the experiment being performed. Genome tracks such as RefSeq genes (intron/exon), promoters, enhancers, repeats (inc Alu LINE elements), CpG Islands, Shores, Shelves can be downloaded in BED format from the UCSC Genome Browser (Raney et al., 2014). Tools such as bedTools2 can then be used to perform intersections with the elements of choice to address specific biological questions such as: are 5hmC sites enriched in promoters as compared to enhancers? (Quinlan and Hall, 2010).

Correlation With ChIP-Seq

Chromatin immunoprecipitation followed by high throughput sequencing (ChIP-seq) provides genomic locations of histone marks such as H3K4me3 found in promoters under active transcription and H3K27ac marking active over poised enhancers. Studies performing methylation sequencing are often coupled with ChIP-Seq for the specific tissue or cell type of interest (Guo et al., 2017). In order to determine the co-localization of cytosine modifications with the histone marks tools such as wiggleTools (Zerbino et al., 2014), Homer (Heinz et al., 2010), bedTools2 (Quinlan and Hall, 2010), and GIGGLE (Layer et al., 2017) can be used.

Correlation With RNA-Seq

DNA methylation analysis alone may be difficult to interpret, as DNA modifications can exert different effects depending on their position relative to the genes. To make a compelling case for the role of the assayed cytosine modifications on gene expression, it is recommended to perform a matched sample RNA-Seq experiment. Bulk RNA-Seq or transcription start site (TSS) specific CAGE-Seq enable the effect on gene expression in differentially methylated regions to be quantified (Steyaert et al., 2016). The integrative transcriptional-epigenomic studies and their bioinformatics analyses are far more challenging in the single-cell approaches, but promising methods are under development (Angermueller et al., 2016; Clark et al., 2016; Hu et al., 2016).

Allelic Expression

Not all genes are expressed from both alleles. Some genes are expressed in a parent-of-origin specific manner and do not follow classical Mendelian inheritance. These are known as imprinted genes and since both active and repressed copies of imprinted genes can co-exist in the same nucleus, they are particularly suited as a model system to study epigenetic gene regulation. Imprinted genes have been shown to play a role in the growth of the placenta and the development of the embryo, as well as having postnatal behavioral and physiological functions (Frost and Moore, 2010; Garfield et al., 2011; Li et al., 1999).

As imprinted genes are expressed from one allele, they are more susceptible to mutations and dysregulation, coinciding with their abnormal expression in diseases and cancer. A common feature found in imprinted gene clusters are imprinting control regions (ICRs) that are differentially methylated on both alleles (and so they are differentially methylated regions, DMRs). Parent of origin specific methylation is established in germline and contributes to allele specific expression of imprinted genes. Also, some loci exhibit non-imprinted allelic methylation that occurs at random. This phenomenon can be partially explained by existence of SNPs with CpGs (Rouhi et al., 2006; Shoemaker et al., 2010; Strogantsev et al., 2015). To computationally determine the parental origin of an allele, the reads must be aligned to the genome of each parent. In human samples, genotyping permits the parental origin of the allele to be resolved. It is also possible to use triploidies to take advantage of parental genomic contributions (Yuen et al., 2011). In mouse, the use of hybrid crosses allows the parental origin of the gene of interest to be resolved (Kobayashi et al., 2009).

Discussion

In this article, competing methods for assaying DNA modifications were reviewed, many of which are able to assay cytosine modifications at single base resolution. However, there are limitations to the current methods, such as the requirement for chemical or enzymatic treatments, PCR amplification and high depth sequencing, all requiring computational tools to account for these sources of deviation from the true biological signal.

In mammals, cytosine modifications are predominantly found at CpG sites, and often clustered in CpG islands. These regions are therefore of low complexity due to the enrichment of CpG sites making the unique mapping of short-reads difficult, or impossible, leaving gaps in assaying the methylome. To cover these gaps, new sequencing technologies such as long-read sequencing (see Section Future Directions) are required, and accompanying bioinformatics tools to assay the nucleotide modifications need to be developed. Tool development will be key to unlocking these previously un-mappable regions of genomes.

Importantly, cytosine modifications at single base resolution need to be carefully interpreted, ideally with orthogonal methods such as ChIP-Seq or RNA-Seq, as well as with allelic expression. Together, they make powerful tools to dissect roles of DNA modifications in epigenetic regulation of gene expression.

Future Directions

Emerging technologies, such as the long-read sequencing technologies, are rapidly approaching the accuracy of the short-read based methods for methylation sequencing. A further development expected over the next few years is the ability to detect all cytosine modifications within single cells. Methods have recently been developed to assay 5mC in single cells and further developments have permitted the simultaneous sequencing the methylome and transcriptome from the same cell.

Long-Read Sequencing

Cytosines undergoing modifications are often located in clusters (e.g., CpG islands) which are therefore repetitive in nature. Short-read based methods are unable to uniquely map short reads to repetitive regions, resulting in the under representation of these important regions. Long-read based methods such as Pacific Biosciences single-molecule real-time sequencing (SMRT) and Oxford Nanopore do not suffer from this limitation as the reads can be 10's or 100's of kilobases in length and can therefore span and uniquely map to these CpG dense regions. A further key advantage is the ability to directly assess the methylation status of cytosines without the need for treatments such as bisulfite, or enzymatic modification. SMRT sequencing measures the incorporation of nucleotides in real time and is able to distinguish between each of the modification states of cytosine and adenine (Fang *et al.*, 2012; Suzuki *et al.*, 2015), while Nanopore technology detects DNA bases, including modified cytosines, by measuring electrostatic charge as a DNA strand passes through a protein nanopore (Rand *et al.*, 2017; Simpson *et al.*, 2017). The challenge now is to develop new bioinformatics methods for long-read sequencing such as high accuracy base calling of methylated bases

Single Cell Sequencing

Methods have been developed to assay 5mC in single cells using bisulfite treatments (Smallwood *et al.*, 2014). However, to date, only TAB-Seq is able to assay 5hmC in single cell treatments as the bisulfite methods are too harsh and unable to achieve the required read depths for the subtractions (Clark *et al.*, 2016). More recent methods, e.g., G&T-Seq, have been developed to simultaneously sequence the genome and transcriptome (Macaulay *et al.*, 2015). In the future, it will hopefully be possible to simultaneously assay all the levels of epigenetic detail of a single cell such as cytosine modifications, histone marks, chromatin structure and 3D genome arrangements in combination with the transcriptome, genome and proteome (Clark *et al.*, 2016). As with long-read sequencing methods the challenge for the bioinformatics community is to develop new multi-modal methods to simultaneously analyse the multi-ome data sets derived from single cells.

Closing Remarks

The current state-of-the-art methods for interrogating cytosine modifications rely on chemical or enzymatic treatments accompanied with PCR amplification. Future gold standard methods will undoubtedly forgo these treatments and directly infer the methylation status of DNA and RNA nucleotides from the native molecules. The current, and future methods, will continue to further our understanding of the biological role of nucleotide modifications and their impact in human disease. Perhaps, most excitingly, these modification marks could be edited with systems such as CRISPR-CAS9 to treat a wide range of diseases.

Acknowledgements

Russell S. Hamilton and Malwina Prater are funded by the Centre for Trophoblast Research (University of Cambridge).

See also: Natural Language Processing Approaches in Bioinformatics

References

Adams, D., Altucci, L., Antonarakis, S.E., *et al.*, 2012. BLUEPRINT to decode the epigenetic signature written in blood. Nat. Biotechnol. 30, 224–226. doi:10.1038/nbt.2153.

Äijö, T., Huang, Y., Mannerström, H., *et al.*, 2016a. A probabilistic generative model for quantification of DNA modifications enables analysis of demethylation pathways. Genome Biol. 17, 49. doi:10.1186/s13059-016-0911-6.

Äijö, T., Yue, X., Rao, A., Lähdesmäki, H., 2016b. LuxGLM: A probabilistic covariate model for quantification of DNA methylation modifications with complex experimental designs. Bioinformatics 32, i511–i519. doi:10.1093/bioinformatics/btw468.

Akalin, A., Kormaksson, M., Li, S., *et al.*, 2012. methylKit: A comprehensive R package for the analysis of genome-wide DNA methylation profiles. Genome Biol. 13, R87. doi:10.1186/gb-2012-13-10-r87.

Albrecht, F., List, M., Bock, C., Lengauer, T., 2017. DeepBlueR: Large-scale epigenomic analysis in R. Bioinformatics 33, 2063–2064. doi:10.1093/bioinformatics/btx099.

Angermueller, C., Clark, S.J., Lee, H.J., *et al.*, 2016. Parallel single-cell sequencing links transcriptional and epigenetic heterogeneity. Nat. Methods 13, 229–232. doi:10.1038/nmeth.3728.

Baba, Y., Nosho, K., Shima, K., *et al.*, 2010. Hypomethylation of the IGF2 DMR in colorectal tumors, detected by bisulfite pyrosequencing, is associated with poor prognosis. Gastroenterology 139, 1855–1864. doi:10.1053/j.gastro.2010.07.050.

Bachman, M., Uribe-Lewis, S., Yang, X., *et al.*, 2014. 5-Hydroxymethylcytosine is a predominantly stable DNA modification. Nat. Chem. 6, 1049–1055. doi:10.1038/nchem.2064.

Ball, M.P., Li, J.B., Gao, Y., *et al.*, 2009. Targeted and genome-scale strategies reveal gene-body methylation signatures in human cells. Nat. Biotechnol. 27, 361–368. doi:10.1038/nbt.1533.

Barault, L., Amatu, A., Bleeker, F.E., *et al.*, 2015. Digital PCR quantification of MGMT methylation refines prediction of clinical benefit from alkylating agents in glioblastoma and metastatic colorectal cancer. Ann. Oncol. 26, 1994–1999. doi:10.1093/annonc/mdv272.

Bernstein, B.E., Stamatoyannopoulos, J.A., Costello, J.F., *et al.*, 2010. The NIH roadmap epigenomics mapping consortium. Nat. Biotechnol. 28, 1045–1048. doi:10.1038/nbt1010-1045.

Bock, C., Tomazou, E.M., Brinkman, A.B., *et al.*, 2010. Quantitative comparison of genome-wide DNA methylation mapping technologies. Nat. Biotechnol. 28, 1106–1114. doi:10.1038/nbt.1681.

Booth, M.J., Branco, M.R., Ficz, G., *et al.*, 2012. Quantitative sequencing of 5-methylcytosine and 5-hydroxymethylcytosine at single-base resolution. Science 336 (80-), 934–937. doi:10.1126/science.1220671.

Booth, M.J., Marsico, G., Bachman, M., Beraldi, D., Balasubramanian, S., 2014. Quantitative sequencing of 5-formylcytosine in DNA at single-base resolution. Nat. Chem. 6, 435–440. doi:10.1038/nchem.1893.

Booth, M.J., Ost, T.W.B., Beraldi, D., et al., 2013. Oxidative bisulfite sequencing of 5-methylcytosine and 5-hydroxymethylcytosine. Nat. Protoc. 8, 1841–1851. doi:10.1038/nprot.2013.115.

Bourc'his, D., Bestor, T.H., 2004. Meiotic catastrophe and retrotransposon reactivation in male germ cells lacking Dnmt3L. Nature 431, 96–99. doi:10.1038/nature02886.

Branco, M.R., King, M., Perez-garcia, V., et al., 2016. Maternal DNA methylation regulates early trophoblast development article maternal DNA methylation regulates. Dev. Cell 36, 152–163. doi:10.1016/j.devcel.2015.12.027.

Church, T.R., Wandell, M., Lofton-Day, C., et al., 2014. Prospective evaluation of methylated SEPT9 in plasma for detection of asymptomatic colorectal cancer. Gut 63, 317–325. doi:10.1136/gutjnl-2012-304149.

Clark, S.J., Lee, H.J., Smallwood, S.A., Kelsey, G., Reik, W., 2016. Single-cell epigenomics: Powerful new methods for understanding gene regulation and cell identity. Genome Biol. 17, 72. doi:10.1186/s13059-016-0944-x.

Consortium, E.N.C.O.D.E.P., Bernstein, B.E., Birney, E., et al., 2012. An integrated encyclopedia of DNA elements in the human genome. Nature 489, 57–74. doi:10.1038/nature11247.

Delgado-Olguín, P., Huang, Y., Li, X., et al., 2012. Epigenetic repression of cardiac progenitor gene expression by Ezh2 is required for postnatal cardiac homeostasis. Nat. Genet. 44, 343–347. doi:10.1038/ng.1068.

Dietrich, D., Kneip, C., Raji, O., et al., 2012. Performance evaluation of the DNA methylation biomarker SHOX2 for the aid in diagnosis of lung cancer based on the analysis of bronchial aspirates. Int. J. Oncol. 40, 825–832. doi:10.3892/ijo.2011.1264.

Du, J., Johnson, L.M., Jacobsen, S.E., Patel, D.J., 2015. DNA methylation pathways and their crosstalk with histone methylation. Nat. Rev. Mol. Cell Biol. 16, 519–532. doi:10.1038/nrm4043.

Fang, G., Munera, D., Friedman, D.I., et al., 2012. Genome-wide mapping of methylated adenine residues in pathogenic Escherichia coli using single-molecule real-time sequencing. Nat. Biotechnol. 30, 1232–1239. doi:10.1038/nbt.2432.

Field, S.F., Beraldi, D., Bachman, M., et al., 2015. Accurate measurement of 5-methylcytosine and 5-hydroxymethylcytosine in human cerebellum DNA by oxidative bisulfite on an array (OxBS-Array). PLOS ONE 10, 1–12. doi:10.1371/journal.pone.0118202.

Fogarty, N.M.E., Burton, G.J., Ferguson-Smith, A.C., 2015. Different epigenetic states define syncytiotrophoblast and cytotrophoblast nuclei in the trophoblast of the human placenta. Placenta 36, 796–802. doi:10.1016/j.placenta.2015.05.006.

Frost, J.M., Moore, G.E., 2010. The importance of imprinting in the human placenta. PLOS Genet. 6, 1–9. doi:10.1371/journal.pgen.1001015.

Frye, M., Jaffrey, S.R., Pan, T., Rechavi, G., Suzuki, T., 2016. RNA modifications: What have we learned and where are we headed? Nat. Rev. Genet. 17, 365–372. doi:10.1038/nrg.2016.47.

Garfield, A.S., Cowley, M., Smith, F.M., et al., 2011. Distinct physiological and behavioural functions for parental alleles of imprinted Grb10. Nature 469, 534. doi:10.1038/nature09651. [U101].

Goll, M.G., Bestor, T.H., 2005. Eukaryotic cytosine methyltransferases. Annu. Rev. Biochem. 74, 481–514. doi:10.1146/annurev.biochem.74.010904.153721.

Green, B.B., Houseman, E.A., Johnson, K.C., et al., 2016. Hydroxymethylation is uniquely distributed within term placenta, and is associated with gene expression. FASEB J. 30, 1–11. doi:10.1096/fj.201600310R.

Gross, J.A., Lefebvre, F., Lutz, P.-E., et al., 2016. Variations in 5-methylcytosine and 5-hydroxymethylcytosine among human brain, blood, and saliva using oxBS and the Infinium MethylationEPIC array. Biol. Methods Protoc. bpw002. doi:10.1093/biomethods/bpw002.

Guo, H., Hu, B., Yan, L., et al., 2017. DNA methylation and chromatin accessibility profiling of mouse and human fetal germ cells. Cell Res. 27, 165–183. doi:10.1038/cr.2016.128.

Guo, J.U., Su, Y., Shin, J.H., et al., 2013. Distribution, recognition and regulation of non-CpG methylation in the adult mammalian brain. Nat. Neurosci. 17, 215–222. doi:10.1038/nn.3607.

Guo, W., Chung, W.Y., Qian, M., Pellegrini, M., Zhang, M.Q., 2014. Characterizing the strand-specific distribution of non-CpG methylation in human pluripotent cells. Nucleic Acids Res. 42, 3009–3016. doi:10.1093/nar/gkt1306.

Hahn, M.A., Wu, X., Li, A.X., Hahn, T., Pfeifer, G.P., 2011. Relationship between gene body DNA methylation and intragenic H3K9ME3 and H3K36ME3 chromatin marks. PLOS ONE. 6. doi:10.1371/journal.pone.0018844.

Hansen, K.D., Langmead, B., Irizarry, R.A., et al., 2012. BSmooth: From whole genome bisulfite sequencing reads to differentially methylated regions. Genome Biol. 13, R83. doi:10.1186/gb-2012-13-10-r83.

Han, D., Lu, X., Shih, A.H., et al., 2016. A highly sensitive and robust method for genome-wide 5hmC profiling of rare cell populations. Mol. Cell 63, 711–719. doi:10.1016/j.molcel.2016.06.028.

Hardwick, S.A., Deveson, I.W., Mercer, T.R., 2017. Reference standards for next-generation sequencing. Nat. Rev. Genet. 18, 473–484. doi:10.1038/nrg.2017.44.

Hebestreit, K., Dugas, M., Klein, H.U., 2013. Detection of significantly differentially methylated regions in targeted bisulfite sequencing data. Bioinformatics 29, 1647–1653. doi:10.1093/bioinformatics/btt263.

Heinz, S., Benner, C., Spann, N., et al., 2010. Article simple combinations of lineage-determining transcription factors prime cis-regulatory elements required for macrophage and B cell identities. Mol. Cell 38, 576–589. doi:10.1016/j.molcel.2010.05.004.

He, Y.-F., Li, B.-Z., Li, Z., et al., 2011. Tet-Mediated Formation of 5-Carboxylcytosine and Its Excision by TDG in Mammalian DNA. Science 333 (80-), 1303–1307. doi:10.1126/science.1210944.

Horvath, S., 2013. DNA methylation age of human tissues and cell types. Genome Biol. 14, R115. doi:10.1186/gb-2013-14-10-r115.

Houseman, E.A., Johnson, K.C., Christensen, B.C., 2016. OxyBS: Estimation of 5-methylcytosine and 5-hydroxymethylcytosine from tandem-treated oxidative bisulfite and bisulfite DNA. Bioinformatics 32, 2505–2507. doi:10.1093/bioinformatics/btw158.

Hu, Y., Huang, K., An, Q., et al., 2016. Simultaneous profiling of transcriptome and DNA methylome from a single cell. Genome Biol. 17, 88. doi:10.1186/s13059-016-0950-z.

Imperiale, T.F., Ransohoff, D.F., Itzkowitz, S.H., et al., 2014. Multitarget stool DNA testing for colorectal-cancer screening. N. Engl. J. Med. 370, 1287–1297. doi:10.1056/NEJMoa1311194.

Ito, S., Shen, L., Dai, Q., et al., 2011. Tet proteins can convert 5-methylcytosine to 5-formylcytosine and 5-carboxylcytosine. Science 333 (80-), 1300–1303. doi:10.1126/science.1210597.

Iurlaro, M., Ficz, G., Oxley, D., et al., 2013. A screen for hydroxymethylcytosine and formylcytosine binding proteins suggests functions in transcription and chromatin regulation. Genome Biol. 14, R119. doi:10.1186/gb-2013-14-10-r119.

Iurlaro, M., McInroy, G.R., Burgess, H.E., et al., 2016. In vivo genome-wide profiling reveals a tissue-specific role for 5-formylcytosine. Genome Biol. 17, 141. doi:10.1186/s13059-016-1001-5.

Jeffries, M.A., Dozmorov, M., Tang, Y., et al., 2011. Genome-wide DNA methylation patterns in CD4 + T cells from patients with systemic lupus erythematosus. Epigenetics 6, 593–601. doi:10.4161/epi.6.5.15374.

Johnson, W.E., Li, C., Rabinovic, A., 2007. Adjusting batch effects in microarray expression data using empirical Bayes methods. Biostatistics 8, 118–127. doi:10.1093/biostatistics/kxj037.

Kafer, G.R., Li, X., Horii, T., et al., 2016. 5-Hydroxymethylcytosine marks sites of DNA damage and promotes genome stability. Cell Rep. 14, 1283–1292. doi:10.1016/j.celrep.2016.01.035.

Kellinger, M.W., Song, C.-X., Chong, J., et al., 2012. 5-formylcytosine and 5-carboxylcytosine reduce the rate and substrate specificity of RNA polymerase II transcription. Nat. Struct. Mol. Biol. 19, 831–833. doi:10.1038/nsmb.2346.

Kishore, K., de Pretis, S., Lister, R., et al., 2015. methylPipe and compEpiTools: A suite of R packages for the integrative analysis of epigenomics data. BMC Bioinform. 16, 1–11. doi:10.1186/s12859-015-0742-6.

Kobayashi, H., Yamada, K., Morita, S., *et al.*, 2009. Identification of the mouse paternally expressed imprinted gene Zdbf2 on chromosome 1 and its imprinted human homolog ZDBF2 on chromosome 2. Genomics 93, 461–472. doi:10.1016/j.ygeno.2008.12.012.

Kohli, R.M., Zhang, Y., 2013. TET enzymes, TDG and the dynamics of DNA demethylation. Nature 502, 472–479. doi:10.1038/nature12750.

Kristensen, L.S., Hansen, J.W., Kristensen, S.S., *et al.*, 2016. Aberrant methylation of cell-free circulating DNA in plasma predicts poor outcome in diffuse large B cell lymphoma. Clin. Epigenetics 8, 95. doi:10.1186/s13148-016-0261-y.

Krueger, F., Andrews, S.R., 2011. Bismark: A flexible aligner and methylation caller for Bisulfite-Seq applications. Bioinformatics 27, 1571–1572. doi:10.1093/bioinformatics/btr167.

Kyriakopoulos, C., Giehr, P., Wolf, V., 2017. H(O)TA: Estimation of DNA methylation and hydroxylation levels and efficiencies from time course data. Bioinformatics 33, btx042. doi:10.1093/bioinformatics/btx042.

Lavie, L., Kitova, M., Maldener, E., Meese, E., Mayer, J., 2005. CpG methylation directly regulates transcriptional activity of the human endogenous retrovirus family HERV-K (HML-2). J. Virol. 79, 876. doi:10.1128/JVI.79.2.876.

Layer, R.M., Pedersen, B.S., DiSera, T., *et al.*, 2017. GIGGLE: A search engine for large-scale integrated genome analysis. bioRxiv. doi:10.1101/157735.

Liang, G., Chan, M.F., Tomigahara, Y., *et al.*, 2002. Cooperativity between DNA methyltransferases in the maintenance methylation of repetitive elements cooperativity between DNA methyltransferases in the maintenance methylation of repetitive elements. Mol. Cell. Biol. 22, 480. doi:10.1128/MCB.22.2.480.

Lienhard, M., Grimm, C., Morkel, M., Herwig, R., Chavez, L., 2014. MEDIPS: Genome-wide differential coverage analysis of sequencing data derived from DNA enrichment experiments. Bioinformatics 30, 284–286. doi:10.1093/bioinformatics/btt650.

Li, E., Zhang, Y., 2014. DNA methylation in mammals. Cold Spring Harb. Perspect. Biol 6, a019133. doi:10.1101/cshperspect.a019133. [a019133].

Li, L., Keverne, E.B., Aparicio, S. a., *et al.*, 1999. Regulation of maternal behavior and offspring growth by paternally expressed Peg3. Science 284, 330–333. doi:10.1126/science.284.5412.330.

Liu, Y., Siegmund, K.D., Laird, P.W., Berman, B.P., 2012. Bis-SNP: Combined DNA methylation and SNP calling for Bisulfite-seq data. Genome Biol. 13, R61. doi:10.1186/gb-2012-13-7-r61.

Lunnon, K., Hannon, E., Smith, R.G., *et al.*, 2016. Variation in 5-hydroxymethylcytosine across human cortex and cerebellum. Genome Biol. 17, 27. doi:10.1186/s13059-016-0871-x.

Macaulay, I.C., Haerty, W., Kumar, P., *et al.*, 2015. G&T-seq: Parallel sequencing of single-cell genomes and transcriptomes. Nat. Methods 12, 519–522. doi:10.1038/nmeth.3370.

Madzo, J., Liu, H., Rodriguez, A., *et al.*, 2014. Hydroxymethylation at gene regulatory regions directs stem/early progenitor cell commitment during erythropoiesis. Cell Rep. 6, 231–244. doi:10.1016/j.celrep.2013.11.044.

Maksimovic, J., Gagnon-Bartsch, J.A., Speed, T.P., Oshlack, A., 2015. Removing unwanted variation in a differential methylation analysis of Illumina HumanMethylation450 array data. Nucleic Acids Res. 43, e106. doi:10.1093/nar/gkv526.

Marina, R.J., Oberdoerffer, S., 2016. Epigenomics meets splicing through the TETs and CTCF. Cell Cycle 15, 1397–1399. doi:10.1080/15384101.2016.1171650.

Martin, M., 2011. Cutadapt removes adapter sequences from high-throughput sequencing reads. EMBnet J. 17, 10. doi:10.14806/ej.17.1.200.

McKinney, B.C., Lin, C.-W., Oh, H., *et al.*, 2015. Hypermethylation of BDNF and SST genes in the orbital frontal cortex of older individuals: A putative mechanism for declining gene expression with age. Neuropsychopharmacology 40, 2604–2613. doi:10.1038/npp.2015.107.

Morris, T.J., Butcher, L.M., Feber, A., *et al.*, 2014. ChAMP: 450k chip analysis methylation pipeline. Bioinformatics 30, 428–430. doi:10.1093/bioinformatics/btt684.

Olova, N., Krueger, F., Andrews, S., *et al.*, 2017. Comparison of whole-genome bisulfite sequencing library preparation strategies identifies sources of biases affecting DNA methylation data. Bioarxiv. doi:10.1101/165449.

Park, Y., Figueroa, M.E., Rozek, L.S., Sartor, M. a., 2014. MethylSig: A whole genome DNA methylation analysis pipeline. Bioinformatics 30, 1–8. doi:10.1093/bioinformatics/btu339.

Paulsen, M., Ferguson-Smith, A., 2001. DNA methylation in genomic imprinting, development, and disease. J. Pathol. 195, 97–110. doi:10.1002/path.890.

Phipson, B., Maksimovic, J., Oshlack, A., 2015. missMethyl: An R package for analyzing data from Illumina's HumanMethylation450 platform. Bioinformatics 32, btv560. doi:10.1093/bioinformatics/btv560.

Piyasena, C., Reynolds, R.M., Khulan, B., *et al.*, 2015. Placental 5-methylcytosine and 5-hydroxymethylcytosine patterns associate with size at birth. Epigenetics 10, 692–697. doi:10.1080/15592294.2015.1062963.

Quinlan, A.R., Hall, I.M., 2010. BEDTools: A flexible suite of utilities for comparing genomic features. Bioinformatics 26, 841–842. doi:10.1093/bioinformatics/btq033.

Qu, J., Zhou, M., Song, Q., Hong, E.E., Smith, A.D., 2013. MLML: Consistent simultaneous estimates of DNA methylation and hydroxymethylation. Bioinformatics 29, 2645–2646. doi:10.1093/bioinformatics/btt459.

Rand, A.C., Jain, M., Eizenga, J.M., *et al.*, 2017. Mapping DNA methylation with high-throughput nanopore sequencing. Nat. Methods. 1–6. doi:10.1038/nmeth.4189.

Raney, B.J., Dreszer, T.R., Barber, G.P., *et al.*, 2014. Track data hubs enable visualization of user-defined genome-wide annotations on the UCSC genome browser. Bioinformatics 30, 1003–1005. doi:10.1093/bioinformatics/btt637.

Raynal, N.J.M., Si, J., Taby, R.F., *et al.*, 2012. DNA methylation does not stably lock gene expression but instead serves as a molecular mark for gene silencing memory. Cancer Res. 72, 1170–1181. doi:10.1158/0008-5472.CAN-11-3248.

Rouhi, A., Gagnier, L., Takei, F., Mager, D.L., 2006. Evidence for epigenetic maintenance of Ly49a monoallelic gene expression. J. Immunol. 176, 2991–2999. doi:10.4049/jimmunol.176.5.2991.

Sérandour, A.A., Avner, S., Oger, F., *et al.*, 2012. Dynamic hydroxymethylation of deoxyribonucleic acid marks differentiation-associated enhancers. Nucleic Acids Res. 40, 8255–8265. doi:10.1093/nar/gks595.

Sherry, S.T., Ward, M.H., Kholodov, M., *et al.*, 2001. dbSNP: The NCBI database of genetic variation. Nucleic Acids Res. 29, 308–311. doi:10.1093/nar/29.1.308.

Shoemaker, R., Deng, J., Wang, W., Zhang, K., 2010. Allele-specific methylation is prevalent and is contributed by CpG-SNPs in the human genome. Genome Res. 20, 883–889. doi:10.1101/gr.104695.109.

Simpson, J.T., Workman, R.E., Zuzarte, P.C., *et al.*, 2017. Detecting DNA cytosine methylation using nanopore sequencing. Nat. Methods. 1–7. doi:10.1038/nmeth.4184.

Skvortsova, K., Zotenko, E., Luu, P.-L., *et al.*, 2017. Comprehensive evaluation of genome-wide 5-hydroxymethylcytosine profiling approaches in human DNA. Epigenetics Chromatin 10, 16. doi:10.1186/s13072-017-0123-7.

Smallwood, S.A., Lee, H.J., Angermueller, C., *et al.*, 2014. Single-cell genome-wide bisulfite sequencing for assessing epigenetic heterogeneity. Nat. Methods 11, 817–820. doi:10.1038/nmeth.3035.

Song, C.-X., Clark, T.A., Lu, X.-Y., *et al.*, 2012a. Sensitive and specific single-molecule sequencing of 5-hydroxymethylcytosine. Nat. Methods 9, 75–77. doi:10.1038/nmeth.1779.

Song, C.-X., Yi, C., He, C., 2012b. Mapping recently identified nucleotide variants in the genome and transcriptome. Nat. Biotechnol. 30, 1107–1116. doi:10.1038/nbt.2398.

Sood, A.J., Viner, C., Hoffman, M.M., 2016. DNAmod: The DNA modification database. bioRxiv 1–13. doi:10.1101/071712.

Soubry, A., Murphy, S.K., Wang, F., *et al.*, 2015. Newborns of obese parents have altered DNA methylation patterns at imprinted genes. Int. J. Obes. (Lond) 39, 650–657. doi:10.1038/ijo.2013.193.

Spiers, H., Hannon, E., 2017. 5-hydroxymethylcytosine is highly dynamic across human fetal brain development Helen. Bioarxiv. doi:10.1101/126169.

Spruijt, C.G., Gnerlich, F., Smits, A.H., *et al.*, 2013. Dynamic readers for 5-(Hydroxy)methylcytosine and its oxidized derivatives. Cell 152, 1146–1159. doi:10.1016/j.cell.2013.02.004.

Steyaert, S., Diddens, J., Galle, J., *et al.*, 2016. A genome-wide search for epigenetically regulated genes in zebra finch using MethylCap-seq and RNA-seq. Sci. Rep. 6, 20957. doi:10.1038/srep20957.

Stewart, S.K., Morris, T.J., Guilhamon, P., *et al.*, 2015. OxBS-450K: A method for analysing hydroxymethylation using 450K BeadChips. Methods 72, 9–15. doi:10.1016/j.ymeth.2014.08.009.

Stirzaker, C., Zotenko, E., Clark, S.J., 2016. Genome-wide DNA methylation profiling in triple-negative breast cancer reveals epigenetic signatures with important clinical value. Mol. Cell. Oncol. 3, e1038424. doi:10.1080/23723556.2015.1038424.

Strogantsev, R., Krueger, F., Yamazawa, K., et al., 2015. Allele-specific binding of ZFP57 in the epigenetic regulation of imprinted and non-imprinted monoallelic expression. Genome Biol. 16, 112. doi:10.1186/s13059-015-0672-7.

Stroud, H., Feng, S., Morey Kinney, S., Pradhan, S., Jacobsen, S.E., 2011. 5-Hydroxymethylcytosine is associated with enhancers and gene bodies in human embryonic stem cells. Genome Biol. 12, R54. doi:10.1186/gb-2011-12-6-r54.

Stubbs, T.M., Bonder, M.J., Stark, A., et al., 2017. Multi-tissue DNA methylation age predictor in mouse. Genome Biol. 18, 68. doi:10.1186/s13059-017-1203-5.

Sun, D., Xi, Y., Rodriguez, B., et al., 2014. MOABS: Model based analysis of bisulfite sequencing data. Genome Biol. 15, R38. doi:10.1186/gb-2014-15-2-r38.

Suzuki, Y., Korlach, J., Turner, S.W., et al., 2015. AgIn: Measuring the Landscape of CpG methylation of individual repetitive elements. bioRxiv 32, 18531. doi:10.1101/018531.

Szulwach, K.E., Li, X., Li, Y., et al., 2011. Integrating 5-hydroxymethylcytosine into the epigenomic landscape of human embryonic stem cells. PLOS Genet. 7. doi:10.1371/journal.pgen.1002154.

Tahiliani, M., Koh, K.P., Shen, Y., et al., 2009. Conversion of 5-methylcytosine to 5-hydroxymethylcytosine in mammalian DNA by MLL partner TET1. Science 324 (80-), 930–935. doi:10.1126/science.1170116.

Tan, L., Xiong, L., Xu, W., et al., 2013. Genome-wide comparison of DNA hydroxymethylation in mouse embryonic stem cells and neural progenitor cells by a new comparative hMeDIP-seq method. Nucleic Acids Res. 41, 1–12. doi:10.1093/nar/gkt091.

Turelli, P., Castro-diaz, N., Marzetta, F., et al., 2014. Interplay of TRIM28 and DNA methylation in controlling human endogenous retroelements Interplay of TRIM28 and DNA methylation in controlling human endogenous retroelements. Genome Res. 1260–1270. doi:10.1101/gr.172833.114.

Ventham, N.T., Kennedy, N.A., Adams, A.T., et al., 2016. Integrative epigenome-wide analysis demonstrates that DNA methylation may mediate genetic risk in inflammatory bowel disease. Nat. Commun. 7, 13507. doi:10.1038/ncomms13507.

Walsh, C.P., Chaillet, J.R., Bestor, T.H., 1998. No title. Nat. Genet. 20, 116–117. doi:10.1038/2413.

Wang, L., Zhou, Y., Xu, L., et al., 2015. Molecular basis for 5-carboxycytosine recognition by RNA polymerase II elongation complex. Nature. doi:10.1038/nature14482.

Weber, A.R., Krawczyk, C., Robertson, A.B., et al., 2016. Biochemical reconstitution of TET1–TDG–BER-dependent active DNA demethylation reveals a highly coordinated mechanism. Nat. Commun. 7, 10806. doi:10.1038/ncomms10806.

Wu, H., D'Alessio, A.C., Ito, S., et al., 2011. Genome-wide analysis of distribution reveals its dual function in transcriptional regulation in mouse embryonic stem cells. Genes Dev. 25, 679–684. doi:10.1101/gad.2036011.GENES.

Xu, Z., Taylor, J.A., Leung, Y.-K., Ho, S.-M., Niu, L., 2016. oxBS-MLE: An efficient method to estimate 5-methylcytosine and 5-hydroxymethylcytosine in paired bisulfite and oxidative bisulfite treated DNA. Bioinformatics 32, btw527. doi:10.1093/bioinformatics/btw527.

Yin, Y., Morgunova, E., Jolma, A., et al., 2017. Impact of cytosine methylation on DNA binding specificities of human transcription factors. Science 356 (80-), eaaj2239. doi:10.1126/science.aaj2239.

Yuen, R.K., Jiang, R., Penaherrera, M.S., McFadden, D.E., Robinson, W.P., 2011. Genome-wide mapping of imprinted differentially methylated regions by DNA methylation profiling of human placentas from triploidies. Epigenetics. Chromatin 4, 10. doi:10.1186/1756-8935-4-10.

Yu, M., Hon, G.C., Szulwach, K.E., et al., 2012a. Tet-assisted bisulfite sequencing of 5-hydroxymethylcytosine. Nat. Protoc. 7, 2159–2170. doi:10.1038/nprot.2012.137.

Yu, M., Hon, G.C., Szulwach, K.E., et al., 2012b. Base-resolution analysis of 5-hydroxymethylcytosine in the mammalian genome. Cell 149, 1368–1380. doi:10.1016/j.cell.2012.04.027.

Zerbino, D.R., Johnson, N., Juettemann, T., Wilder, S.P., Flicek, P., 2014. WiggleTools: Parallel processing of large collections of genome-wide datasets for visualization and statistical analysis. Bioinformatics 30, 1008–1009. doi:10.1093/bioinformatics/btt737.

Zhu, L., Lv, R., Kong, L., et al., 2015. Genome-wide mapping of 5mC and 5hmC identified differentially modified genomic regions in late-onset severe preeclampsia: a pilot study. PLOS ONE 10, 1–15. doi:10.1371/journal.pone.0134119.

Further Reading

Bird, A., 2007. Perceptions of epigenetics. Nature 447, 396–398. doi:10.1038/nature05913.

Bock, C., Halbritter, F., Carmona, F.J., et al., 2016. Quantitative comparison of DNA methylation assays for biomarker development and clinical applications. Nat. Biotechnol. doi:10.1038/nbt.3605.

Chen, D.-P., Lin, Y.-C., Fann, C.S.J., 2016. Methods for identifying differentially methylated regions for sequence- and array-based data. Brief. Funct. Genomics 15, elw018. doi:10.1093/bfgp/elw018.

Guy, J., Gan, J., Selfridge, J., Cobb, S., Bird, A., 2007. Reversal of neurological defects in a mouse model of Rett syndrome. Science 315 (80-), 1143–1147. doi:10.1126/science.1138389.

Inoue, A., Jiang, L., Lu, F., Suzuki, T., Zhang, Y., 2017. Maternal H3K27me3 controls DNA methylation-independent imprinting. Nature. doi:10.1038/nature23262.

Kriaucionis, S., Heintz, N., 2009. The nuclear DNA base 5-hydroxymethylcytosine is present in Purkinje neurons and the brain. Science 324, 929–930. doi:10.1126/science.1169786.

Miska, E.A., Ferguson-smith, A.C., 2016. Transgenerational inheritance: models and mechanisms of non-DNA sequence-based inheritance. Science 354, 778–782. doi:10.1126/science.aaf4945.

Robinson, M.D., Kahraman, A., Law, C.W., et al., 2014. MINI REVIEW: Statistical methods for detecting differentially methylated loci and regions. bioRxiv 5, 7120. doi:10.1101/007120.

Wreczycka, K., Gosdschan, A., Yusuf, D., Platform, B., Group, B., 2017. Strategies for analyzing bisulfite sequencing data. Bioarxiv. doi:10.1101/109512.

Relevant Websites

http://www.cegx.co.uk
    Cambridge Epigenetix.
https://www.pmgenomics.ca/hoffmanlab/proj/dnamod/
    DNAmod.
http://ihec-epigenomes.org/
    International Human Epigenome Consortium.
https://sequencing.qcfail.com/
    QCFail.
https://swiftbiosci.com/
    Swift Biosciences.

https://www.wisegeneusa.com/5hmc
WiseGene.
http://www.zymoresearch.com/services/epigenetic-aging-clock
Zymo Research.

Biographical Sketch

Malwina Prater is a bioinformatician at the Centre for Trophoblast Research, University of Cambridge. Her previous work at Cambridge Epigenetix (CEGX) involved developing technologies that enable accurate quantification of methylcytosine (mC) and hydroxymethylcytosine (hmC) at a single base resolution. Prior to this, she was undertaking her PhD at Cancer Research UK Cambridge Institute, University of Cambridge. Her work focused on long non-coding RNAs and epigenetic regulation of gene expression. She has also been involved in projects investigating control of protein expression in yeast (University of Edinburgh) and ribosome biogenesis in plants (Goethe University in Frankfurt).

Russell Hamilton heads the bioinformatics core facility at the Centre for Trophoblast Research (CTR), University of Cambridge. The focus of the CTR is the study of the placenta and maternal-fetal interactions during pregnancy and brings together over 25 Principal Investigators based in different departments within the University of Cambridge and Babraham Institute. He has previously worked in industry at Cambridge Epigenetix (CEGX) developing epigenetics tools to enable single base resolution sequencing of methylcytosine (mC) and hydroxymethylcytosine (hmC). Prior to this was a senior postdoc in the Department of Biochemistry at University of Oxford, working on the RNA structural motifs required for mRNA localization and their interaction with trans-acting protein factors. Russell received an MSc in Intelligent Systems from the University of Aberdeen and his PhD in bioinformatics from the University of Edinburgh. At each of his previous positions, Russell has set up bioinformatics infrastructure including pipelines for next-generation sequencing, RNA structure searches, protein structural modelling and a microscope imaging facility.

Comparative Epigenomics

Yutaka Saito, National Institute of Advanced Industrial Science and Technology (AIST), Koto-ku, Japan and National Institute of Advanced Industrial Science and Technology (AIST), Shinjuku-ku, Japan

Nomenclature		HiC	High-throughput chromosome conformation capture
ChIP	Chromatin immunoprecipitation		
DEG	Differentially expressed gene	IHEC	International human epigenome consortium
DMC	Differentially methylated cytosine	NGS	Next-generation sequencing
DMR	Differentially methylated region	SRA	Sequence read archive
ENCODE	Encyclopedia of DNA elements	TPM	Transcripts per million
FPKM	Fragments per kilobase million	TSS	Transcription start site
GEO	Gene expression omnibus		

Introduction

The analysis of epigenomic data often involves the comparison with other epigenomic data. For example, consider the analysis of DNA methylation data where a certain genomic locus is detected to have a methylation level lower than its flanking regions. Such a locus is regarded as a candidate of cis-regulatory elements. However, further insights into its regulatory role are difficult to obtain solely from DNA methylation data. In such cases, it is useful to compare DNA methylation data with histone modification data. If the locus has H3K4me3, it is inferred as a promoter that regulates the expression of neighboring genes. Alternatively, the locus may have H3K4me1, suggesting that it is an enhancer regulating the expression of distal genes. Epigenomic data can also be compared between different cell types. For example, consider that the DNA methylation data were collected from stem cells, and are compared with those from differentiated cells. If the locus shows an increased methylation level in the differentiated cells, its function is predicted to be related to the differentiation from the stem cells. These examples clearly demonstrate that the comparison of epigenomic data is a powerful approach in epigenome research.

This article aims to describe conventional methods for comparing epigenomic data. We show practical issues that arise in real-life analysis settings, and explain how to address these problems. A review of widely-used software for various kinds of epigenomic data is provided. We also provide a review of public epigenomic databases that can be used as a reference for the comparison with in-house epigenomic data. Finally, we present a case study where mesenchymal stem cells and mature fat cells are compared using DNA methylation, histone modification, transcription factor binding, and gene expression data. The study provides an example of how to combine each analysis task in constructing the whole analysis for addressing a specific research question.

Background

Epigenetic Modification

The knowledge on epigenetic modification is necessary to interpret the results of epigenomic data analysis. Table 1 summarizes representative epigenetic modifications and their known functions in gene regulation.

Table 1 Epigenetic modifications and their functions in gene regulation

Epigenetic modification	Indication	Experimental technology
H3K4me3	Promoter	ChIP-seq
H3K4me1	Enhancer	
H3K27ac	Activated	
H3K9me3	Heterochromatin	
H3K27me3	Repressed	
H3K36me3	Active gene body	
DNA methylation, promoter	Repressed	Bisulfite-seq, Infinium BeadChip
DNA methylation, gene body	Activated (in some cell types)	

Encyclopedia of Bioinformatics and Computational Biology, Volume 3   doi:10.1016/B978-0-12-809633-8.20112-X

Several kinds of histone modification have established regulatory roles. H3K4me3 and H3K4me1 are histone modifications that indicate promoters and enhancers, respectively. H3K27ac is a hallmark of active chromatins. Genomic loci that harbor both H3K4me1 and H3K27ac are called active enhancers, suggesting that genes regulated by these enhancers are activated. On the other hand, genomic loci that have H3K4me1 but lack H3K27ac are sometimes called "primed" enhancers, meaning that these loci have the potential to function as enhancers although their target genes are still not activated in the cell type of interest. H3K9me3 and H3K27me3 are hallmarks of repressed chromatins. H3K9me3 tends to be observed at heterochromatic regions consistently repressed in a broad range of cell types, while H3K27me3 indicates a temporal repression in specific cell types. As a last example, H3K36me3 is observed at actively transcribed gene bodies.

The function of DNA methylation is more complicated and context-dependent in comparison to histone modification. In general, DNA methylation is considered to modulate the binding affinity of transcription factors either positively or negatively, and its regulatory outcome depends on the function of transcription factors such as activators or repressors. For example, if a transcription factor with an activator function preferentially binds to unmethylated DNA, an increase in DNA methylation will decrease the transcription factor's affinity for that region, thereby repressing gene expression. Despite this complexity, some genome-wide associations are known between DNA methylation and gene expression. DNA methylation at promoters is associated with the repression of gene expression. Inversely, DNA methylation at gene bodies is associated with the activation of gene expression in some cell types.

There are many other kinds of epigenetic modification not included in **Table 1**. For histone modification, there are a variety of "non-standard" modifications such as phosphorylation, ubiquitination, and sumoylation. See Zentner and Henikoff (2013) for a recent review. While DNA methylation usually refers to cytosine methylation in the CpG context (cytosines followed by guanines), other kinds of DNA methylation are known to be important in some cell types and/or organisms. These include cytosine methylation in the non-CpG context (Jang *et al.*, 2017) and hydroxymethylation (Guibert and Weber, 2013). In addition, it is important to be aware that the current knowledge on epigenetic modification has mainly been obtained from studies on model organisms such as mammals and yeasts. Therefore, one should be careful when analyzing epigenomic data from non-model organisms where epigenetic modifications may have unknown functions.

It is common to incorporate transcription factor binding data into epigenomic data analysis even though they are not strictly considered to be epigenomic data. This is because transcription factor binding and epigenetic modification are closely related to each other. For example, the binding affinity of some transcription factors is known to be modulated by DNA methylation, and some transcription factors are known to induce histone modification at the binding sites. Gene expression data are also regularly utilized in epigenomic data analysis. Since a major function of epigenetic modification is gene regulation, gene expression data are useful to analyze the regulatory outcome of epigenetic modification in the cell type of interest.

Experimental Technology and Raw Data Processing

The understanding of experimental technologies for measuring epigenomic data is a prerequisite for selecting the appropriate methods for analyzing the data. **Table 1** includes experimental technologies used for various epigenetic modifications. Most kinds of epigenomic data are measured by next-generation sequencing (NGS) or microarray-based technologies. Histone modification and transcription factor binding are measured by chromatin-immunoprecipitation sequencing (ChIP-seq) where DNA fragments bound by a specific protein are extracted by an antibody prior to sequencing. DNA methylation is measured by bisulfite sequencing (bisulfite-seq) where unmethylated cytosines are chemically converted and sequenced as thymines. DNA methylation can also be measured by a microarray-based technology called Illumina Infinium BeadChip. Gene expression is measured either by NGS (RNA-seq) or microarrays.

Raw data generated by these experimental technologies are fastq files for NGS, and platform-dependent files for microarrays (e.g., tab-delimited text files for Agilent microarrays, and CEL files for Affymetrix microarrays). With appropriate data processing, they can be transformed into signal values along genomic positions. For example, DNA methylation data are represented as a methylation level (also referred to as a methylation ratio, a methylation rate, or a beta value) for each cytosine position, which is a value ranging from 0 to 1 that indicates the fraction of methylated cytosines in a cell population. Similarly, gene expression data are represented as an expression level for each gene that is linked to its genomic position. In this article, we focus our discussion on the comparison of epigenomic data, assuming that input data are already represented as signal values. Therefore, the detail in raw data processing such as read mapping falls outside the scope of this article. However, it is still important to be aware of the experimental technology used for measuring the epigenomic data since some downstream analyses need care depending on different experimental technologies. For example, conventional methods for the detection of differentially expressed genes (DEGs) are different for RNA-seq and microarray data. In such cases, we explain the analyses separately for each experimental technology.

Application

In this section, we first describe practical issues in the comparative analysis of epigenomic data. Then, we provide a review of widely-used software for each kind of epigenomic data (The list of all software discussed in this article is given in Appendix). Finally, we provide a review of public epigenomic databases.

Comparative Analysis: Correlation and Difference

A useful method for comparing epigenomic data is to evaluate the correlation between two epigenomic datasets. For example, consider two DNA methylation datasets, each of which represents methylation levels measured from a certain cell type. The correlation coefficient between the methylation levels can be used as a similarity measure between the two cell types.

Another method for the comparative analysis is to detect differences between two epigenomic datasets at specific genomic loci. For example, one can calculate the difference in methylation levels between two cell types at each cytosine position. Cytosines with large differences in methylation levels are called differentially methylated cytosines (DMCs). Methylation differences can be detected not only for a cytosine position but also for a window of a certain length using methylation levels averaged over the region. In such cases, detected regions are called differentially methylated regions (DMRs).

Defining Windows

As shown in the above example of DNA methylation, signal values computed from epigenomic data are often averaged or summed over the windows of genomic regions. Therefore, how windows are defined is an important practical issue. The most general method for defining windows is a sliding-window approach where windows are defined as fixed-length regions (e.g., 1000 bp) with a certain step size (e.g., 500 bp). Another conventional method is to define windows based on their positions relative to genes. For example, fixed-length windows around transcription start sites (TSSs) are often used for analyzing promoters. Windows are sometimes defined using other genomic elements (e.g., retrotransposons) to specifically analyze their epigenomic profiles.

Windows can also be defined using epigenomic data themselves. Some tools are designed to detect DMRs without pre-specifying regions of interest by determining the boundaries of DMRs solely from DNA methylation data. Detected DMRs can be used as windows for analyzing other kinds of epigenomic data such as transcription factor binding. Similarly, one can detect transcription factor binding sites from ChIP-seq data, and use these sites as windows for analyzing DNA methylation.

Biological Replicates

Biological replicates refer to parallel measurements of biologically distinct samples produced from the same experimental condition. It is well known that the comparative analysis of omics data becomes more accurate and reproducible by using replicates. A simple method for utilizing replicates is to average signal values from individual replicates. However, this method fails to incorporate the information of variance among replicates. Most tools for detecting DEGs utilize the variance information for evaluating a statistical significance (i.e., p-value). For DMC and DMR detection, some tools support replicates for evaluating p-values while others do not.

Biological replicates should be distinguished from technical replicates that refer to repeated measurements from the same biological sample. While averaging technical replicates can reduce the experimental noise of measurements, their variance information is not effective to increase the power of statistical testing. This is because the variance among technical replicates does not represent biological variation. See Blainey *et al.* (2014) for a detailed discussion on handling biological and technical replicates.

Although replicates are useful, their availability is sometimes limited in real-life analysis settings. This is especially true for epigenomic data measured by newer technologies with higher experimental costs. For example, while replicates are quite common for microarrays, they are relatively limited for DNA methylation data measured by bisulfite-seq (e.g., few or no replicates are available). In such cases, one needs to resort to replicate-free analysis where the difference in methylation levels between single samples is used for detecting DMCs and DMRs.

DNA Methylation

Raw data processing of bisulfite-seq is performed by software such as Bismark (Krueger and Andrews, 2011), BSMAP (Xi and Li, 2009), and Bisulfighter (Saito *et al.*, 2014). These tools map bisulfite-seq reads to a reference genome, and calculate a methylation level for each cytosine position based on the mapping results. The detection of DMCs and DMRs is conducted with software such as BSmooth (Hansen *et al.*, 2012) and ComMet (Saito and Mituyama, 2015). These tools are capable of *de novo* DMR detection without pre-specifying windows. BSmooth supports replicate-aware analysis but is not applicable to data without replicates, while ComMet supports replicate-free analysis but cannot utilize replicate information. We refer to the review (Tsuji and Weng, 2016) for other tools available for bisulfite-seq data.

Raw data processing of Infinium BeadChip is performed by software such as IMA (Wang *et al.*, 2012) and Minfi (Aryee *et al.*, 2014). These tools compute methylation levels at individual cytosine positions (often referred to as beta values), and average methylation levels for various gene-related windows including promoters and gene bodies. The detection of differential methylation for Infinium BeadChip is usually conducted with these windows using methods originally developed for gene expression microarrays. For example, IMA detects DMCs and DMRs using the limma method (Ritchie *et al.*, 2015) developed for detecting DEGs. DMR detection without pre-specified windows is not common for Infinium BeadChip data, perhaps due to a limited number of measurable cytosine positions, although some tools are developed for this purpose (Morris *et al.*, 2014). See the review (Dedeurwaerder *et al.*, 2014) for other Infinium BeadChip data analysis tools.

DNA methylation data are commonly compared with gene expression data. Since DNA methylation at promoters is associated with gene repression, the inverse correlation between methylation levels and expression levels are used in many studies. Similarly,

DMCs and DMRs between cell types can be compared with DEGs. However, it is important to be aware that the association between DNA methylation and gene expression is evident but not so strong. Therefore, it is often the case that one fails to detect an inverse correlation between methylation levels and expression levels. A practical tip here is to focus on the top-ranked genes. For example, the comparison of methylation levels between the top 10% of genes with the highest expression levels and the bottom 10% of genes with the lowest expression levels will result in a clear difference between the two groups. A similar issue also applies when comparing DMCs and DMRs with DEGs between different cell types.

Histone Modification and Transcription Factor Binding

Read mapping for ChIP-seq is performed by software such as Bowtie (Langmead et al., 2009) and BWA (Li and Durbin, 2009). Signal values for ChIP-seq data are the fraction of mapped read counts in the ChIP sample (i.e., immunoprecipitated by an antibody) divided by those in the input sample (i.e., sequenced without immunoprecipitation). This task is conducted by software such as MACS (Zhang et al., 2008), SICER (Zang et al., 2009), and DROMPA (Nakato et al., 2013). Other tools for ChIP-seq data are reviewed in Nakato and Shirahige (2017).

An important task in ChIP-seq data analysis is peak detection where genomic regions enriched with signal values are determined by comparing read mapping results between ChIP samples and input samples. The above tools for computing signal values also support peak detection. However, it is worth noting that peak detection is a difficult task, and it is often the case that peaks detected by different tools show a strong disagreement in their numbers and positions. This is partly because the characteristics of peaks are different for various DNA-binding proteins: some proteins produce sharp peaks with signal values highly enriched in short regions, while others produce broad peaks showing an intermediate enrichment throughout long regions. Due to this difficulty, signal values are sometimes directly used for downstream analyses without peak detection. Nonetheless, peaks are useful as windows for comparing ChIP-seq data with other epigenomic data.

Histone modification data are frequently compared with DNA methylation data. For example, one can calculate the methylation levels at H3K4me1 peaks for measuring their enhancer activity. Similarly, methylation levels at transcription factor peaks are used for surveying the interplay between transcription factor binding and DNA methylation. The detection of DMRs can also be conducted using ChIP-seq peaks as windows. Since peak detection involves the technical difficulties as explained above, sliding windows are also used instead of peaks. For this purpose, sliding windows with the highest enrichment of ChIP signals (e.g., the top 10%) are used for calculating methylation levels.

Gene Expression

Read mapping for RNA-seq is performed by software such as TopHat2 (Kim et al., 2013) and STAR (Dobin et al., 2013). Expression levels are measured as fragments per kilobase million (FPKM) computed by Cufflinks (Trapnell et al., 2010), or transcripts per million (TPM) computed by RSEM (Li and Dewey, 2011). DEGs can be detected by tools like Cuffdiff (Trapnell et al., 2013), edgeR (Robinson et al., 2010) and DEGseq (Wang et al., 2010), all of which support replicates. Compared to bisulfite-seq and ChIP-seq data, there are numerous tools available for RNA-seq data. See Conesa et al. (2016) for the recent review.

Raw data processing of gene expression microarrays is performed by software such as limma (Ritchie et al., 2015) and affy (Gautier et al., 2004). limma supports various types of microarrays produced by Agilent, while affy is a widely-used package for Affymetrix microarrays. limma is also a conventional tool for detecting DEGs with support for replicates.

Gene expression data are used in epigenomic data analysis for evaluating the regulatory outcome of epigenetic modification. For example, when a genomic locus is detected as an enhancer candidate with a high H3K4me1 signal and a low DNA methylation level, its influence on gene expression can be evaluated by RNA-seq or microarray data.

Chromatin State Estimation

One of the goals of epigenomic data analysis is to annotate genomic loci with some "chromatin states". For example, one can annotate loci with high H3K9me3 signals and DNA methylation levels as the "heterochromatin state", and loci with high H3K4me1 and H3K27ac signals accompanied by low DNA methylation levels as the "active enhancer state". Chromatin state estimation is a task for doing such annotations by integrating various kinds of epigenomic data. ChromHMM (Ernst and Kellis, 2012) is a software that is commonly used for chromatin state estimation.

Public Databases

It is effective to incorporate public epigenomic data into the analysis of in-house epigenomic data. For example, even if you only have DNA methylation data, you may find histone modification data measured from the same cell type in public databases, allowing the comparative analysis between the datasets. Epigenomic data published in previous studies are deposited in the Gene Expression Omnibus (GEO) database where raw NGS data (fastq files) can be found by following a hyperlink to the Sequence Read Archive (SRA) database. In practice, it is important to be aware that the word search functionality in GEO and SRA sometimes fails to retrieve relevant data. Thus, it is highly recommended that general search engines (e.g., Google) are used in combination with GEO and SRA. In addition, it is useful to visit the web portals of international epigenome projects, including International Human Epigenome Consortium (IHEC), Encyclopedia of DNA Elements (ENCODE), Roadmap Epigenomics, and BLUEPRINT Epigenome. These web portals organize various kinds of epigenomic data as a form of the "experiment matrix" where rows and columns represent cell types (e.g., embryonic stem cells) and experimental technologies (e.g., bisulfite-seq), respectively, so that one can easily find epigenomic data of their interest. The URLs of these databases and web portals are given in Relevant Websites.

Case Study

In the previous sections, many tasks in the comparative analysis of epigenomic data were explained separately. In practice, however, these tasks need to be combined for addressing a specific research question. Here, we show such an example using a case study. The study is the re-analysis of the data from Takada *et al.* (2014) where human adipose-derived stem cells (ADSCs) are compared to mature fat cells differentiated from ADSCs (FatCs) based on various types of epigenomic data. The purpose of the study is to find epigenetic markers that characterize the differentiation from ADSCs to FatCs.

Data

For ADSCs and FatCs, DNA methylation and gene expression data were measured by bisulfite-seq and RNA-seq, respectively. These were in-house data produced by the authors of the original study, and deposited in the SRA database with the accession number SRP003529. The authors also used histone modification and transcription factor binding data from FatCs. These were public data measured by ChIP-seq, and were downloaded from the SRA database with the accession number SRP002343. Replicates were not available for these datasets. For bisulfite-seq data, read mapping and the calculation of methylation levels were performed by Bisulfighter (Saito *et al.*, 2014). Read mapping for RNA-seq data was performed by TopHat2 (Kim *et al.*, 2013), and expression levels (FPKM) were calculated by Cufflinks (Trapnell *et al.*, 2010). Read mapping for ChIP-seq data was conducted by Bowtie (Langmead *et al.*, 2009), and peaks were detected by MACS (Zhang *et al.*, 2008).

Comparison of DNA Methylation and Gene Expression

We first compared DNA methylation with gene expression in ADSCs. The methylation levels of promoters and gene bodies were calculated for all genes. Promoter windows were defined as regions around the TSSs from -1000 bp upstream to $+500$ bp downstream, while gene body windows were defined as regions from $+2000$ bp downstream of the TSSs to the corresponding transcription termination sites. We then compared FPKM between the top 10% of genes with the highest methylation levels, and the bottom 10% of genes with the lowest methylation levels (**Fig. 1**). As expected, genes with highly methylated promoters tended to have low FPKM values, while genes with highly methylated gene bodies tended to have high FPKM values.

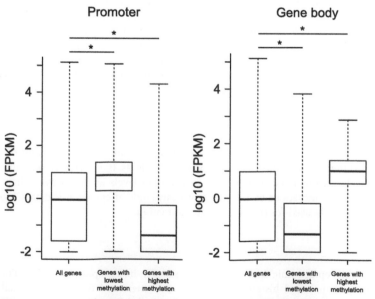

Fig. 1 Comparison of expression levels between the genes with the highest and the lowest methylation levels in ADSCs. Expression levels (FPKM) were compared for all genes, the top 10% of genes with the highest methylation levels, and the bottom 10% of genes with the lowest methylation levels. The analysis was conducted separately for promoter methylation and gene body methylation. *: $P < 1e-100$ (Mann-Whitney U test).

Comparison of DNA Methylation Between Cell Types

We next compared DNA methylation between ADSCs and FatCs using promoter methylation levels. Only small differences in promoter methylation levels were observed between ADSCs and FatCs (**Fig. 2**). For reference, when a similar analysis was conducted between ADSCs and induced pluripotent stem cells (iPSCs), promoter methylation levels were more diverse. This was surprising because when we compared gene expression using FPKM, similar levels of correlation were detected for the two comparisons (Pearson correlation coefficients: 0.79 for ADSCs versus FatCs, and 0.88 for ADSCs versus iPSCs). These results suggest that differential methylation between ADSCs and FatCs occurs at specific genomic loci other than promoters.

Comparison of DNA Methylation at Transcription Factor Binding Sites

To find specific loci harboring differential methylation between ADSCs and FatCs, we used ChIP-seq data for PPARγ, a transcription factor known to function as a master regulator of fat cell differentiation. PPARγ peaks were detected in FatCs, and then these peaks were used as windows for differential methylation analysis between ADSCs and FatCs. Interestingly, specific hypomethylation was found at PPARγ peaks (**Fig. 3**). A similar analysis was also conducted using ChIP-seq data for H3K4me3 that indicates general promoters, but the hypomethylation was not observed. Therefore, these results demonstrated that specific hypomethylation at PPARγ binding sites represents epigenetic markers for fat cell differentiation.

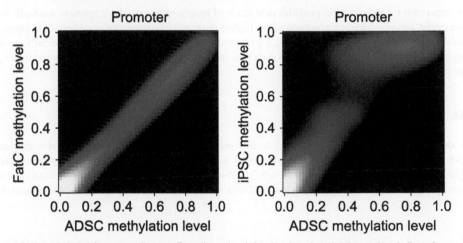

Fig. 2 Comparison of DNA methylation between cell types. Two-dimensional density plot where brighter colors indicate larger numbers of promoters with corresponding methylation levels. (Left) Promoter methylation levels were compared between ADSCs and FatCs. (Right) A similar analysis was conducted between ADSCs and iPSCs.

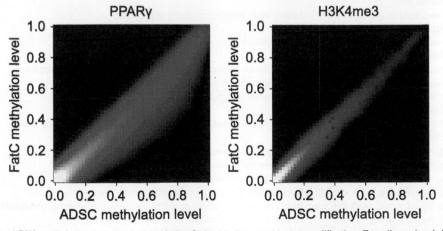

Fig. 3 Comparison of DNA methylation in light of transcription factor binding and histone modification. Two-dimensional density plot similar to Fig. 2. (Left) Methylation levels at PPARγ peaks. The bright colors in the bottom-right of the plot region indicate the hypomethylation of PPARγ binding sites in FatCs compared to ADSCs. (Right) Methylation levels at H3K4me3 peaks. Hypomethylation was not observed.

Discussion

The comparative analysis of epigenomic data involves several practical issues including how to define windows and how to handle biological replicates. As for replicates, some tools do not support replicates, especially for epigenomic data from relatively new experimental technologies. However, there is a general framework called IDR (Li *et al.*, 2011) that can extend replicate-free methods to replicate-aware versions. Indeed, IDR is extensively used for ChIP-seq data in the ENCODE project where peaks detected from individual replicates are integrated so that reliable peaks showing an agreement among all replicates are retained in the final result.

Another practical issue yet to be addressed in this article is the problem of batch effects. Batch effects refer to the difference detected between data due to artifacts such as those introduced from the laboratory environments (e.g., the difference in the dates of experiments, and/or the difference in the persons who conducted experiments). Batch effects are problematic because they may cover up true biological differences between epigenomic data. ComBat (Johnson *et al.*, 2007) and SVA (Leek and Storey, 2007) are widely-used methods for the detection and the correction of batch effects. The consideration of batch effects is necessary not only for the comparison between in-house and public data but also for the comparison of in-house data measured in different laboratory environments.

Future Directions

The advent of new experimental technologies provides new kinds of epigenomic data. An important example of new epigenomic data is three-dimensional genome structures measured by high-throughput chromosome conformation capture (HiC). See the review (de Wit and de Laat, 2012) for HiC and related experimental technologies. HiC data are especially useful for associating distal enhancers to their target genes. The utilization of such emerging epigenomic data will make comparative epigenomics more powerful in future studies.

Closing Remarks

In this article, we described conventional methods for comparing epigenomic data with a review of widely-used software and databases. There are many possible ways to compare epigenomic data depending on what kind of epigenomic data and which cell type are used in the comparison. An important point is to combine individual analysis tasks to construct the whole analysis in order to reach a specific research goal. The case study using ADSCs and FatCs provided an example of such analyses conducted in a research setting.

Appendix

The summary of software described in this article

Name	Analysis	URL
Bismark	Bisulfite-seq, read mapping, methylation level	http://www.bioinformatics.babraham.ac.uk/projects/bismark
BSMAP	Bisulfite-seq, read mapping, methylation level	https://code.google.com/archive/p/bsmap
Bisulfighter	Bisulfite-seq, read mapping, methylation level	https://github.com/yutaka-saito/Bisulfighter
BSmooth	Bisulfite-seq, DMC/DMR detection	http://bioconductor.org/packages/release/bioc/html/bsseq.html
ComMet	Bisulfite-seq, DMC/DMR detection	https://github.com/yutaka-saito/ComMet
IMA	Infinium BeadChip, methylation level, DMC/DMR detection	https://www.rforge.net/IMA
Minfi	Infinium BeadChip, methylation level, DMC/DMR detection	http://bioconductor.org/packages/release/bioc/html/minfi.html
Bowtie	ChIP-seq, read mapping	http://bowtie-bio.sourceforge.net/index.shtml
BWA	ChIP-seq, read mapping	http://bio-bwa.sourceforge.net/
MACS	ChIP-seq, signal value, peak detection	https://github.com/taoliu/MACS
SICER	ChIP-seq, signal value, peak detection	http://home.gwu.edu/~wpeng/Software.htm
DROMPA	ChIP-seq, signal value, peak detection	http://www.iam.u-tokyo.ac.jp/chromosomeinformatics/rnakato/drompa
TopHat2	RNA-seq, read mapping	http://ccb.jhu.edu/software/tophat/index.shtml
STAR	RNA-seq, read mapping	https://github.com/alexdobin/STAR
Cufflinks	RNA-seq, expression level	https://github.com/cole-trapnell-lab/cufflinks
RSEM	RNA-seq, expression level	http://deweylab.github.io/RSEM

Cuffdiff	RNA-seq, DEG detection	https://github.com/cole-trapnell-lab/cufflinks
edgeR	RNA-seq, DEG detection	https://bioconductor.org/packages/release/bioc/html/edgeR.html
DEGseq	RNA-seq, DEG detection	https://bioconductor.org/packages/release/bioc/html/DEGseq.html
limma	Microarray, expression level, DEG detection, Agilent	https://bioconductor.org/packages/release/bioc/html/limma.html
affy	Microarray, expression level, DEG detection, Affymetrix	https://bioconductor.org/packages/release/bioc/html/affy.html
ChromHMM	Chromatin state estimation from various epigenomic data	http://compbio.mit.edu/ChromHMM
IDR	To extend replicate-free methods to replicate-aware versions	https://sites.google.com/site/anshulkundaje/projects/idr
ComBAT/SVA	To remove batch effects	http://bioconductor.org/packages/release/bioc/html/sva.html

See also: Epigenetics: Analysis of Cytosine Modifications at Single Base Resolution. Exome Sequencing Data Analysis. Functional Enrichment Analysis. Integrative Analysis of Multi-Omics Data. Natural Language Processing Approaches in Bioinformatics. Next Generation Sequencing Data Analysis. Whole Genome Sequencing Analysis

References

Aryee, M.J., Jaffe, A.E., Corrada-Bravo, H., *et al.*, 2014. Minfi: A flexible and comprehensive Bioconductor package for the analysis of Infinium DNA methylation microarrays. Bioinformatics 30 (10), 1363–1369. doi:10.1093/bioinformatics/btu049.

Blainey, P., Krzywinski, M., Altman, N., 2014. Points of significance: Replication. Nat. Methods 11 (9), 879–880. doi:10.1038/nmeth.3091.

Conesa, A., Madrigal, P., Tarazona, S., *et al.*, 2016. A survey of best practices for RNA-seq data analysis. Genome Biol. 17, 13. doi:10.1186/s13059-016-0881-8.

Dedeurwaerder, S., Defrance, M., Bizet, M., *et al.*, 2014. A comprehensive overview of Infinium HumanMethylation450 data processing. Brief Bioinform. 15 (6), 929–941. doi:10.1093/bib/bbt054.

de Wit, E., de Laat, W., 2012. A decade of 3C technologies: Insights into nuclear organization. Genes Dev. 26 (1), 11–24. doi:10.1101/gad.179804.111.

Dobin, A., Davis, C.A., Schlesinger, F., *et al.*, 2013. STAR: Ultrafast universal RNA-seq aligner. Bioinformatics 29 (1), 15–21. doi:10.1093/bioinformatics/bts635.

Ernst, J., Kellis, M., 2012. ChromHMM: Automating chromatin-state discovery and characterization. Nat. Methods 9 (3), 215–216. doi:10.1038/nmeth.1906.

Gautier, L., Cope, L., Bolstad, B.M., Irizarry, R.A., 2004. Affy - analysis of Affymetrix GeneChip data at the probe level. Bioinformatics 20 (3), 307–315. doi:10.1093/bioinformatics/btg405.

Guibert, S., Weber, M., 2013. Functions of DNA methylation and hydroxymethylation in mammalian development. Curr. Top. Dev. Biol. 104, 47–83. doi:10.1016/B978-0-12-416027-9.00002-4.

Hansen, K.D., Langmead, B., Irizarry, R.A., 2012. BSmooth: From whole genome bisulfite sequencing reads to differentially methylated regions. Genome Biol. 13 (10), R83. doi:10.1186/gb-2012-13-10-r83.

Jang, H.S., Shin, W.J., Lee, J.E., Do, J.T., 2017. CpG and Non-CpG methylation in epigenetic gene regulation and brain function. Genes 8 (6), doi:10.3390/genes8060148. pii: E148.

Johnson, W.E., Li, C., Rabinovic, A., 2007. Adjusting batch effects in microarray expression data using empirical Bayes methods. Biostatistics 8 (1), 118–127. doi:10.1093/biostatistics/kxj037.

Kim, D., Pertea, G., Trapnell, C., *et al.*, 2013. TopHat2: Accurate alignment of transcriptomes in the presence of insertions, deletions and gene fusions. Genome Biol. 14 (4), R36. doi:10.1186/gb-2013-14-4-r36.

Krueger, F., Andrews, S.R., 2011. Bismark: A flexible aligner and methylation caller for Bisulfite-Seq applications. Bioinformatics 27 (11), 1571–1572. doi:10.1093/bioinformatics/btr167.

Langmead, B., Trapnell, C., Pop, M., Salzberg, S.L., 2009. Ultrafast and memory-efficient alignment of short DNA sequences to the human genome. Genome Biol. 10 (3), R25. doi:10.1186/gb-2009-10-3-r25.

Leek, J.T., Storey, J.D., 2007. Capturing heterogeneity in gene expression studies by surrogate variable analysis. PLOS Genet. 3 (9), 1724–1735. doi:10.1371/journal.pgen.0030161.

Li, B., Dewey, C.N., 2011. RSEM: Accurate transcript quantification from RNA-Seq data with or without a reference genome. BMC Bioinform. 12, 323. doi:10.1186/1471-2105-12-323.

Li, H., Durbin, R., 2009. Fast and accurate short read alignment with Burrows-Wheeler transform. Bioinformatics 25 (14), 1754–1760. doi:10.1093/bioinformatics/btp324.

Li, Q., Brown, J.B., Huang, H., Bickel, P.J., 2011. Measuring reproducibility of high-throughput experiments. Ann. Appl. Stat. 5 (3), 1752–1779. doi:10.1214/11-aoas466.

Morris, T.J., Butcher, L.M., Feber, A., *et al.*, 2014. ChAMP: 450k chip analysis methylation pipeline. Bioinformatics 30 (3), 428–430. doi:10.1093/bioinformatics/btt684.

Nakato, R., Itoh, T., Shirahige, K., 2013. DROMPA: Easy-to-handle peak calling and visualization software for the computational analysis and validation of ChIP-seq data. Genes Cells 18 (7), 589–601. doi:10.1111/gtc.12058.

Nakato, R., Shirahige, K., 2017. Recent advances in ChIP-seq analysis: From quality management to whole-genome annotation. Brief Bioinform. 18 (2), 279–290. doi:10.1093/bib/bbw023.

Ritchie, M.E., Phipson, B., Wu, D., *et al.*, 2015. Limma powers differential expression analyses for RNA-sequencing and microarray studies. Nucleic Acids Res. 43 (7), e47. doi:10.1093/nar/gkv007.

Robinson, M.D., McCarthy, D.J., Smyth, G.K., 2010. edgeR: A bioconductor package for differential expression analysis of digital gene expression data. Bioinformatics 26 (1), 139–140. doi:10.1093/bioinformatics/btp616.

Saito, Y., Mituyama, T., 2015. Detection of differentially methylated regions from bisulfite-seq data by hidden Markov models incorporating genome-wide methylation level distributions. BMC Genomics 16 (Suppl 12), S3. doi: 10.1186/1471-2164-16-S12-S3.

Saito, Y., Tsuji, J., Mituyama, T., 2014. Bisulfighter: Accurate detection of methylated cytosines and differentially methylated regions. Nucleic Acids Res. 42 (6), e45. doi:10.1093/nar/gkt1373.

Takada, H., Saito, Y., Mituyama, T., *et al.*, 2014. Methylome, transcriptome, and PPARg cistrome analyses reveal two epigenetic transitions in fat cells. Epigenetics 9 (9), 1195–1206. doi:10.4161/epi.29856.

Trapnell, C., Hendrickson, D.G., Sauvageau, M., *et al.*, 2013. Differential analysis of gene regulation at transcript resolution with RNA-seq. Nat. Biotechnol. 31 (1), 46–53. doi:10.1038/nbt.2450.

Trapnell, C., Williams, B.A., Pertea, G., *et al.*, 2010. Transcript assembly and quantification by RNA-Seq reveals unannotated transcripts and isoform switching during cell differentiation. Nat. Biotechnol. 28 (5), 511–515. doi:10.1038/nbt.1621.

Tsuji, J., Weng, Z., 2016. Evaluation of preprocessing, mapping and postprocessing algorithms for analyzing whole genome bisulfite sequencing data. Brief Bioinform. 17 (6), 938–952. doi:10.1093/bib/bbv103.

Wang, D., Yan, L., Hu, Q., et al., 2012. IMA: An R package for high-throughput analysis of Illumina's 450K Infinium methylation data. Bioinformatics 28 (5), 729–730. doi:10.1093/bioinformatics/bts013.

Wang, L., Feng, Z., Wang, X., Wang, X., Zhang, X., 2010. DEGseq: An R package for identifying differentially expressed genes from RNA-seq data. Bioinformatics 26 (1), 136–138. doi:10.1093/bioinformatics/btp612.

Xi, Y., Li, W., 2009. BSMAP: Whole genome bisulfite sequence MAPping program. BMC Bioinform. 10, 232. doi:10.1186/1471-2105-10-232.

Zang, C., Schones, D.E., Zeng, C., et al., 2009. A clustering approach for identification of enriched domains from histone modification ChIP-Seq data. Bioinformatics 25 (15), 1952–1958. doi:10.1093/bioinformatics/btp340.

Zentner, G.E., Henikoff, S., 2013. Regulation of nucleosome dynamics by histone modifications. Nat. Struct. Mol. Biol. 20 (3), 259–266. doi:10.1038/nsmb.2470.

Zhang, Y., Liu, T., Meyer, C.A., et al., 2008. Model-based analysis of ChIP-Seq (MACS). Genome Biol. 9 (9), R137. doi:10.1186/gb-2008-9-9-r137.

Further Reading

Blainey, P., Krzywinski, M., Altman, N., 2014. Points of significance: Replication. Nat. Methods 11 (9), 879–880. doi:10.1038/nmeth.3091.

Conesa, A., Madrigal, P., Tarazona, S., et al., 2016. A survey of best practices for RNA-seq data analysis. Genome Biol. 17, 13. doi:10.1186/s13059-016-0881-8.

Dedeurwaerder, S., Defrance, M., Bizet, M., et al., 2014. A comprehensive overview of Infinium HumanMethylation450 data processing. Brief Bioinform. 15 (6), 929–941. doi:10.1093/bib/bbt054.

de Wit, E.1., de Laat, W., 2012. A decade of 3C technologies: Insights into nuclear organization. Genes Dev. 26 (1), 11–24. doi:10.1101/gad.179804.111.

Guibert, S., Weber, M., 2013. Functions of DNA methylation and hydroxymethylation in mammalian development. Curr. Top. Dev. Biol. 104, 47–83. doi:10.1016/B978-0-12-416027-9.00002-4.

Jang, H.S., Shin, W.J., Lee, J.E., Do, J.T., 2017. CpG and Non-CpG methylation in epigenetic gene regulation and brain function. Genes 8 (6), doi:10.3390/genes8060148. [pii: E148].

Nakato, R., Shirahige, K., 2017. Recent advances in ChIP-seq analysis: From quality management to whole-genome annotation. Brief Bioinform. 18 (2), 279–290. doi:10.1093/bib/bbw023.

Tsuji, J., Weng, Z., 2016. Evaluation of preprocessing, mapping and postprocessing algorithms for analyzing whole genome bisulfite sequencing data. Brief Bioinform. 17 (6), 938–952. doi:10.1093/bib/bbv103.

Zentner, G.E., Henikoff, S., 2013. Regulation of nucleosome dynamics by histone modifications. Nat. Struct. Mol. Biol. 20 (3), 259–266. doi:10.1038/nsmb.2470.

Relevant Websites

http://www.blueprint-epigenome.eu/
    BLUEPRINT Epigenome.
https://www.encodeproject.org/
    ENCODE.
http://ihec-epigenomes.org/
    IHEC.
https://www.ncbi.nlm.nih.gov/geo/
    GEO.
https://www.ncbi.nlm.nih.gov/sra
    SRA.
http://www.roadmapepigenomics.org/
    Roadmap Epigenomics.

Biographical Sketch

Yutaka Saito received his Ph.D. in 2012 from Keio University, Japan. He joined the National Institute of Advanced Industrial Science and Technology (AIST), Japan, as a post-doctoral researcher. Currently, he is a tenure-track researcher at AIST. His research interest is the development of bioinformatics methods for analyzing the function of noncoding genomic regions such as noncoding RNAs and epigenetic modifications.

Genetics and Population Analysis

Fotis Tsetsos, Democritus University of Thrace, Alexandroupolis, Greece
Petros Drineas and Peristera Paschou, Purdue University, West Lafayette, IN, United States

Nomenclature

Common Variant-Common Disease (CDCV) A hypothesis that common variants must be in the genetic background of disease of high prevalence in a population.

Copy Number Variant (CNV) A structural variation within DNA where sections of the genome have been deleted or duplicated in comparison to a reference genome.

Genetic architecture A collective term encompassing the number, frequencies, and effect sizes of causal alleles for a complex phenotype.

Genome Wide Association Study (GWAS) A study that evaluates the genomes of a large population, usually in search of disease-linked genes.

Haplotype An array of alleles that are transmitted together, hence highly-correlated, in a population.

Hardy-Weinberg Equilibrium (HWE) The law that states that allele and genotype frequencies in a population will remain constant from generation to generation in the absence of other evolutionary influences.

Heterozygosity The proportion of heterozygous individuals in each population simply by counting alleles.

Identity by Descent (IBD) The state where two individuals carry the same genetic segment because they have inherited it from a common ancestor.

Linkage Disequilibrium (LD) The non-random association of alleles at different loci in a given population.

Mendelian Following Mendelian inheritance, namely single-gene characteristics that often run in families.

Microarray A sequencing technique involving attaching DNA or RNA fragments to a slide or membrane.

Next Generation Sequencing (NGS) The collective term for modern DNA sequencing technology that can sequence millions of DNA fragments at once in a short amount of time.

Principal Component Analysis (PCA) A technique used to emphasize variation and bring out strong patterns in a dataset by reducing its dimensions.

Quality control (QC) Procedure that examines the data and ascertains its validity, by filtering out substandard data.

Reticulate evolution The concept of the partial merging of lineages that leads to genetic relationships better represented by a network.

Single Nucleotide Polymorphisms (SNP) A type of SNV defined by occurring with high frequency within a population without occurring in the majority of individuals.

Single Nucleotide Variants (SNV) Single Nucleotide Variant. A variant from the reference genome that only differs by a single base.

Whole Genome Sequencing (WGS) A type of NGS which sequences the entirety of the sample genome, both coding and non-coding regions.

Introduction

Population genetics can be defined as the study of patterns of genetic variation to explain genetic divergence within and between different groups of organisms. Its principal methodology includes genetic assessment both across populations and among individuals, and investigating the mechanics of the influence exerted by evolutionary factors on genetic variation.

The early attempts at studying genetic variation were limited to the phenotypes of traits that were clearly heritable, with the most popular trait being the blood groups. ABO, the most prominent blood group classification system, was identified by Landsteiner (1900), leading to a Nobel Prize award in 1930 for this discovery. Incidentally, Landsteiner did not recognize the heritable identity of the trait, which was identified by Dungern and Hirschfeld (1910). Hirschfeld and Hirschfeld (1919) performed the first ever study of human genetic variation using the ABO grouping system as a variable. Later on, molecular techniques enabled the use of genetic markers to identify genetic variation, albeit at a very limited scale. The technological advancements of the last decade have enabled us to efficiently examine large amounts of genetic markers using microarrays or by means of Whole Genome Sequencing (WGS), so that we can affordably and efficiently assess the genome-wide variation patterns to investigate the distribution of variation within and between populations. With these recent staggering technological leaps, we have also witnessed a shift towards the examination of rare variants. Furthermore, the incorporation of ancient genetic data at a large scale has led to the formation of the newly created fields of archaeogenomics and palaeogenomics.

The current scientific era is inundated with genomic data, aimed to be used towards the identification of the genetic background of disease. The alleles that get associated with disease are an important part of the total genetic variation distributed in and across populations, and as such, are influenced by demographic events and natural genetic forces. Population genetics can also supply robust models for hypotheses concerning disease pathogenesis, which can effectively steer medical efforts towards disease prevention and treatment. Studies of linkage disequilibrium patterns in disease gene identification, combined with our knowledge of the human genetic variation, can effectively aid us in our search for disease-causing genes, providing us with deep insight for the investigation of genetic trait mechanics and heritability.

In this article, we provide an overview of the software tools most commonly used in population genetics that are backed by robust algorithms, a description of the steps used when applying them to avoid pitfalls and analytic biases, along with assessment cautions to avoid interpretation biases, but also a brief recital of the fundamental concepts and perspectives of population genetics.

Quantifying Genetic Variation and Perspectives

Population genetics is a discipline that aims to address the issue of inter- and intra-population differences. Hence, it is important to set some boundaries of perspective, by citing some cases that portray the spectrum of genetic differences.

On the one end of the spectrum, identical twins differ, at least at the conception level, at practically none of their DNA base pairs. Any pair of unrelated humans differs at approximately one in a thousand base pairs, being approximately 99.9% identical at the DNA level. From this rate, it can be extrapolated that for any haploid sequence, there are approximately 3 million variants, as indeed evidenced by Prado-Martinez et al. (2013). The latest estimates by the 1000 Genomes Project Consortium (2015) have revised that number to the range of 4–5 million, depending on the internal variation of the studied population.

Compared with the chimp, humans are approximately 99% similar for aligned DNA-bases, and by including structural variants, the percentage is reduced to approximately 95% similarity. Interestingly, humans present significantly reduced variation than the other major grade ape species, and can be considered to be relatively lacking in genetic diversity as showcased by Prado-Martinez et al. (2013).

So naturally, our focus shifts next to inquiring about the percentage of the variation shared among major human groups in different geographical continents. Xing et al. (2009) addressed this inquiry by studying four major well-populated regions of the world, namely Africa, Europe, East Asia, and India. They reported that approximately 80% of relatively common variants are seen in all four of these groups, while 88% are seen in at least three groups, and more than 90% are shared in at least two groups. More variation is present in the African samples, with almost seven percent of the common variants seen only in the African subset, while only half percent were seen in any non-African group, which a commonly observed feature in population genetics.

Genetic variation is most commonly partitioned based on the nature and the allelic frequency of the variants. The 1000 Genomes Project Consortium (2015) released the final version of their very dense public WGS panel of world-wide reference populations, cataloguing an impressive amount of genetic variants present in the human genome. The overwhelming majority of the catalogued variants affect one nucleotide, hence called Single Nucleotide Variants (SNVs). Designation of a variant as common or rare is not solidly consistent, with the most common threshold of classification being an allelic frequency of 1%.

Common variants are an invaluable tool for genetic investigative efforts, since they facilitate the detection of constraints in their flow. Rare variation proves to be more challenging to assess properly. The study by Sudmant et al. (2015) exploring the distribution of rare variants, showed that for major continental populations, the great majority of SNVs were found to be population-specific. For frequencies less than two percent, fewer than five percent of alleles are actually shared between any two pairs of continents, which is intuitively sensible because these rare variants arose relatively recently. In the case of rare allele analysis in our genetic studies and our disease-related studies, we need to consider that most rare alleles will tend to be population-specific rather than shared across populations.

Fundamental Concepts Overview

In order to analyze and interpret genomic data, a deep understanding of the structure of the genome is needed, as well as the forces shaping its variation and its function.

In the middle of the previous century, Wright (1955) identified four major factors of evolution, namely mutation, natural selection, genetic drift and gene flow. Mutation is the main force that creates variation in the genome. Natural selection acts by selecting in favor of variants that are beneficial, and selecting against variants that are harmful. Genetic drift introduces the stochastic element in evolution, with populations of limited size presenting significant changes over time in allelic frequencies. And lastly there is gene flow, the transmission of genetic material from one population to another which can be regarded as the homogenizing force. The result of these factors is the complex landscape of individual-level, population-level, and species-level variation.

Landmark studies by Roach et al. (2010) and Conrad et al. (2011) have recently been able to directly estimate the human mutation rate by investigating WGS in a human family, comparing parents and offspring and discovering that the human mutation rate from generation-to-generation is in the order of approximately one in a hundred million base pairs per generation, meaning we transit with each gamete approximately 30–35 new DNA variants. That estimate has recently been confirmed in a number of subsequent studies so we can assert that we have an accurate estimate of the rate at which new variation enters the human genomes. The rest of the factors are heavily influenced by geography and demography, and their elucidation requires population genetics analysis.

Linkage Disequilibrium

Given the trans-generational dynamic state of the genome, it is important to infer loci that tend to accompany each other across generations and shape heredity. That inference can be performed by investigating the correlation between alleles and their associations. An array of alleles in different loci that are non-randomly associated with each other is termed a haplotype.

Linkage Disequilibrium (LD) is a term coined to describe the non-random association between alleles of genetic loci that lie in proximity to each other. Initially described by Lewontin and Kojima (1960) the term was an obscure part of genetics, until its resurface in modern genetics with the analysis of large-scale genomic data. The LD between two loci, A and B, can be quantified by the D_{AB} metric. If we define as $P_{A_1B_1}$ the frequency of haplotype A_1B_1, P_{A1} as the frequency of allele A_1, and P_{B_1} as the frequency of allele B_1, then D_{AB} is defined as:

$$D_{AB} = P_{A_1B_1} - P_{A_1}P_{B_1} \tag{1}$$

Based on this equation, when D_{AB} equals to 0, then the alleles are in linkage equilibrium, thus are in statistical independence, much similar to Hardy-Weinberg Equilibrium (HWE) premises. For its correct interpretation for non-zero values, the D_{AB} metric should then be normalized to accurately portray LD, since D_{AB} possible values are heavily influenced by the allelic frequencies. Lewontin and Kojima (1960) used the D'_{AB} statistic, which is the ratio of D_{AB} to its maximum possible absolute value. This metric does provide accurate results in the case of similar allelic frequencies, but could be inflated in the case of small sample number or if one of the alleles is rare.

Another very popular normalization method is the transformation of D_{AB} to the correlation coefficient r^2, by dividing the square of D_{AB} by the allelic frequencies in both loci. This equation is more sensitive for rare alleles, but could prove to be underpowered when detecting haplotypes that may contain rare alleles.

$$r^2 = \frac{D_{AB}^2}{P_{A1}P_{A2}P_{B1}P_{B2}} \tag{2}$$

Geneticists most often rely on both metrics to get a more complete reading on the linkage disequilibrium between two loci. It is worth stating that these descriptive statistics offer no explanation on the reason for these non-random associations between alleles, and a meaningful interpretation should include at least these two statistics, since each statistic has its own advantages. These equations can also be extended to include multiple loci for investigation, instead of only two. However, their practicality is limited, and regional LD is most commonly calculated with a pairwise model.

Haplotypic Phase

Regional LD analyses through D_{AB} reveal the extent of regions with LD-clustered SNVs, which are commonly referred to as haplotypic blocks. Haplotypic blocks are in essence the estimates of the haplotypic phase of the corresponding real genomes.

The use of haplotypic data is an excellent approach to maximize the information gained from genotyping and sequencing experiments, since the mechanics of heredity are largely powered through the transit of a single chromosome out of every chromosomal pair from each parent. Experimental methods to produced haplotypic phased data are still not adequately efficient and cost-effective, thus the haplotypes have to be estimated through statistical procedures from the genotypic data. The genotypic data produced are unphased, meaning that at heterozygosity there is no direct assumption on the parental derivation of each allele.

Haplotypic phase estimation can be performed by some well-established algorithms. Because of the statistical nature of the estimation, there are limits to the confidence levels for the haplotypic phase of the genotypes. The accurate estimation of haplotypes from high-throughput genomic data is an active field of computational and genetic research that is constantly improving. We will outline the methods used to identify haplotypes in a subsequent section of the article.

Analytic Methods and Strategies

The technological advents of the modern era have produced a wealth of data in the field of genetics. As with other big data fields, a main goal is the statistical exploration of the data and the inference of a meaningful interpretation. In this section we will outline the methods currently employed by population geneticists to investigate population genetics data.

Exploratory data analysis techniques are well established in genetics studies. In the case of population genetics, we mostly focus on graphical techniques, with one of the most important techniques being the ones pertaining to dimensionality reduction. Model-based clustering methods are equally well represented, with a variety of established algorithms used extensively. Of course, for the techniques to be used successfully, the datasets should be well maintained, with appropriate quality control steps that will minimize false-positive results and guide towards a meaningful interpretation of the data.

Quality Control

For quality control purposes, PLINK is an invaluable suite of software tools for the manipulation of genetic data, originally developed by Purcell *et al.* (2007) and further refined and augmented by Chang *et al.* (2015). It introduced the most popular format for storing and analyzing genotypic data, the binary PED format, providing high compression along with great computational efficiency.

In genome-wide population genetics, it is usually not feasible to generate all data from a specific institution, so in the majority of cases the bulk of the data derives from a variety of sources that are publically available, or available upon request. Specific care should be applied when merging datasets of different origin, since platform and batch differences could lead to false-positives in the analyses that could compromise our results. This necessitates specific quality control steps to avoid batch effects.

Merging multiple-origin datasets requires a streamlined procedure, since the merging process attends to two datasets at a time. The recommended routine is to first aim to merge together all the datasets that have derived from the same technology, e.g., datasets that have been genotyped on the same microarray chip, or datasets that have been sequenced using the same method. Even when merging datasets generated from the same technology, there are bound to be some markers that are overlapping, but with different annotation details, such as genomic mapping position. In that case, the recommended procedure is their removal, since this error most commonly is a result of a specific marker mapping to multiple regions in the genome. Then a batch effect quality control should be performed on these supersets separately, and then repeat the previous steps, with this step aiming to merge together supersets of each technology.

Avoiding batch effects can be a thorny endeavor, in a field that aims to identify cross-population variation. The study of the genetic background of population de facto includes the assumption of genetic flow barriers, so instinctively HWE cannot be utilized in studying batch effects, as the case would be in a common GWAS analytic protocol. In turn, we employ genome-wide missingness patterns to infer batch effects. First, a genome-wide dataset-spanning call rate threshold of 95% should be used for all markers, removing samples that fail to cross that threshold, in order to achieve a basic level of homogenization in our data. Then, an Identity-by-Missingness (IBM) matrix should be constructed, which is very similar to the Identity-by-Descent (IBD) matrix but differs in that the metric used is similarity in missingness patterns. Its visualization by using a heatmap then enables the identification of missingness clusters that could bias results in downstream analyses. In the case of cluster formation, the recommended routine is to perform of the same call rate threshold of 95% to the clustered sample subgroup and the removal of the culprit markers.

In population genetics, geographical and qualitative regularity in sampling is crucial. Even though researchers apply extensive care into avoiding irregularities, it is possible that sampling mishaps do occur. The construction of an IBD matrix enables the investigation of cryptic close genetic relationships between samples, e.g., relatives, that could confound the results, especially in the case of IBD segment detection. Another common phenomenon is the appearance of genetic outliers. These outliers should be examined carefully to validate their outlier status. Population genetic analysis is based on the average of the genetic background in a specific region, and it is possible that some rare variation could create outliers out of otherwise fine samples that just happen to have an inversion that distinguish them from other samples. Specific areas that are prone to structural variation are relatively well known, such as the 17q21 inversion, which population genetics is a separate subject in its own. Inclusion or exclusion of such areas from the analysis depends on the aim of the analysis.

It is also worth considering that the type of analyses that will be performed is highly dependent on the density and the number of markers. For dimensionality reduction methods, as well as modelling-based clustering methods, it has been shown by Patterson et al. (2006) that the number of markers to distinguish between different populations is inversely proportional to the genetic distance between the population. A useful metric for genetic distance is the F_{ST}, which will be described in the next sections.

Quality control is a very important aspect of population genetics, but its specifics are versatile, based on the aim of the analysis and the regional characteristics of the samples. Thus, it is strongly recommended that the aims of a population genetics analysis are extensively laid out before formulating a quality control strategy.

Dimensionality Reduction Methods

Traditional methods of phylogenetic analysis relied on data of low dimensionality. Current technology has since enabled the output of high-dimensional data, that are projected to scale upwards as time and technology progress. Dimensionality reduction methods facilitate modern genetic analysis and interpretation by converting large-scale genotypic data to a low number of elements. In this section we will cover the Principal Component Analysis (PCA) method, the most robust and representative method for dimensionality reduction, as well as some of its modifications that suit more specialized analytic protocols.

PCA has been in use in genetics for a long time, since the middle of the century, with Cavalli-Sforza et al. (1994) using it extensively in their landmark genetic studies. Notably, its earliest uses were on low dimensional data, condensing phenotypic, as well as genetic information. The technological advances of the past recent years has since shifted to analyzing large scale individual-level data. PCA was shown to be an excellent method to reduce the dimensionality of high throughput genetic data by Patterson et al. (2006), who developed the EIGENSOFT software suite to enable the easy application of the method on various popular genomics data formats.

PCA on genomic data can be affected by highly correlated markers and long-range high LD genetic regions. An efficient way to overcome such hurdles is to perform a pruning step to only keep SNPs that are relatively independent from each other in the genome. To avoid highly correlated markers, a simple implementation of a pruning step by specifying a window size of 200 SNPs, a window step of 5 SNPs, and a LD correlation r^2 value of 0.1 is sufficient.

Usually the genomic matrices that are used as input for PCA are nearly complete, with very low missing data. There are instances in population genetics, where specific samples cannot be fully covered, such as in the case of samples that are genotyped on specific markers, or in the case either of ancient and partially degraded nucleic samples. In such cases, these samples can be projected onto the eigenvectors calculated from the complete datasets. The best practice for PCA projection is using a least-squares approach to project the samples with missing data onto the calculated eigenvectors, so that the missing data will not be replaced by the average of the allelic frequencies in the reference data. This approach presents one drawback, referred to as shrinkage. Shrinkage is a notable phenomenon that occurs when solving by using the least-squares approach. An approximate method to efficiently address this problem was also implemented in the latest version of EIGENSOFT, which enables the more accurate projection of data when using the least squares approach.

The popularity of PCA for genetic analysis spawned many algorithms and methods to assess genetic data. Some notable modifications of PCA were designed to run on haplotypic phased data to also infer local ancestry. Haplotype resolving and haplotype-based methods will be described in the following sections, but it is worth mentioning such methods in this section, as the algorithms behind them are based on PCA. This different approach of PCA was utilized by Brisbin *et al.* (2012), in their software package PCAdmix. It is of note that PCA is only a part of this approach, and another step using a forward-backward HMM algorithm to assign ancestry is implemented. They proposed an algorithm that identifies LD-blocks of genetic data, used them as a guide to create genetic bins and perform PCA on every bin to identify patterns of shared inheritance. Using the forward-backward algorithm, PCAdmix is able to calculate the posterior probability for the shared ancestry for each bin by calculating the distance between populations.

PCA is a fast, non-parametric method of identifying population structure and substructure. However, PCA by itself does not assign ancestry to samples and is mostly used for a graphical representation of the data. Ancestry assignment can be achieved by using statistical clustering methods on the output of PCA.

Modelling-Based Methods

Genetic clustering methods can be roughly subdivided into two major groups, the modelling-based and the distance-based methods. Modelling-based methods use population genetic models to classify individuals into potential ancestry groups. Their inherent assumption is that the observations in each cluster are randomly drawn in a parametric model, and they aim to jointly infer the model parameters along with the cluster membership coefficients. Since they are based on population genetic models, they are traditionally more computationally expensive than PCA. Each computational run is based on the premise that each individual is the result of admixture from a number of different hypothetical ancestral populations. Based on this model, they produce an array of coefficients for each individual. Each coefficient is a quantified estimate for a calculated genetic contribution of a hypothetical ancestral population. The number of hypothetical ancestral populations is finite for each run of the algorithm, and will henceforth be referred to as the K value.

These individual membership coefficients for each ancestral population are probabilistic estimates and are translated into admixture proportions. These admixture proportion estimates for each individual are stored in matrices, referred to as Q matrices. These Q matrices can then be used to visualize and identify clusters of individual ancestries. Many approaches have been developed for this type of analysis, mainly differing on the statistical method employed, or their approximations. The choice of software depends on the nature of the constraints of the analysis, be it efficiency, resources, or depth of genome coverage.

Pritchard *et al.* (2000) developed STRUCTURE, the first software reported to use a model-based clustering method to identify population structure. STRUCTURE uses a bayesian approach and a Markov Chain Monte Carlo (MCMC) algorithm to sample the posterior distributions. The last extensions of the original STRUCTURE software were described by Hubisz *et al.* (2009), leading to the current version of STRUCTURE. The models employed by this version also allowed STRUCTURE to account for LD between markers. STRUCTURE was a novel approach to identifying population structure, and was met with great success when investigating strong population structure, though it presented significant flaws when population structure was weak. That success and shortcomings of STRUCTURE created a surge of ideas to increase accuracy and to expedite computational speeds, since the procedures followed by STRUCTURE were computationally intensive, and the number of the markers available for analysis were ever-increasing.

ADMIXTURE was developed by Alexander *et al.* (2009) as an alternative computational method, based on the likelihood approach employed by STRUCTURE. ADMIXTURE uses a maximum-likelihood approach instead of sampling the posterior distribution, employing a block relaxation algorithm to update the Q matrix. By combining a fast block relaxation strategy and a quasi-Newton convergence acceleration, while opting to compute standard error estimates rather than confidence intervals, ADMIXTURE achieves computational speeds up to two magnitudes greater than those of STRUCTURE, while being more accurate, especially in the case of weak structure.

Also responding to the need for better computational speeds and accuracy, Raj *et al.* (2014) described a new approximation method to accelerate and improve STRUCTURE, in a new software package named fastSTRUCTURE. FastSTRUCTURE introduces two new computational solutions that serve different analytic needs, the simple prior and the logistic prior. The simple prior can be used as a first investigative step, as computations with it are significantly faster, on par with those of ADMIXTURE. The logistic prior can then be used on specific Ks to identify subtle and weak population structure.

ADMIXTURE succeeded in significantly speeding up the runtime, in the order of $O(K^2Ln)$, where L is the number of loci and n the number of individual samples. A newer method, sNMF gained tract in the recent years, due to reducing the complexity to the order of $O(KLn)$, while being competitively accurate. sNMF is a method developed by Frichot *et al.* (2014) who used a sparse non-negative matrix factorization (NMF) algorithm and a least-squares optimization approach, an idea based on the theoretical connections between PCA, likelihood and NMF approaches. This method is able to compute admixture proportion estimates with similar accuracy to ADMIXTURE and STRUCTURE, while also being ten to thirty times faster. Additionally, sNMF appears to be adept at analyzing inbred lineages of samples, achieving more accurate results than its competitors. The rewards of using sNMF's algorithm in large datasets can be fully reaped when large numbers of K are considered.

Notably, these algorithms infer global scale ancestry, that is, they produce whole-genome estimates of ancestry, and do not identify the ancestry of particular genomic segments. To that end, the Chromopainter/fineSTRUCTURE approach was developed by Lawson *et al.* (2012). This approach involves the painting the chromosomes of each individual, creating a coancestry matrix by estimating the genetic relationships between all pairs, and using the matrix to infer groups. Practically, it requires the input of haplotypes instead of markers, which can be calculated by specialized software, such as BEAGLE developed by Browning and Browning (2007), SHAPEIT by Delaneau et al. (2013), fastPHASE by Scheet and Stephens (2006) or EAGLE by Loh et al. (2016). FineSTRUCTURE has two methods of operation, based on utilizing LD information or not. The unlinked method can outperform STRUCTURE in some cases when datasets with a large number of markers are used, but the core of fineSTRUCTURE's strength lies on its linked method, which has the power to identify subtle differences in population groups with finer population structure.

As with PCA-based methods, strong LD could be detrimental for these analyses. It is recommended to remove strongly linked markers, by specifying a genomic window, in the same fashion that was described for the PCA-based methods, albeit with a more permissive r^2 threshold. Care should be taken when setting LD thresholds, since most of those methods do not explicitly account for LD between markers. The authors of the methods often opt to conceptually partition LD based on its demographic implications. Hence, the LD attributable to ancestry differences between individuals is termed as *mixture LD*, the LD differences caused by recent admixture *admixture LD*, and the rest that is influenced by population history *background LD*. LD pruning can limit background LD, but again, if the aim is the intra-population investigation of genetic history, then it could prove to be detrimental for the analysis.

In the case of missing or masked genotypic data, both ADMIXTURE and sNMF fare very well when dealing with missing or masked genotypes, even it the presence of relatively high (<20%) genotypic missingness. Nevertheless, keeping the missingness thresholds to GWAS standards (<2%) is recommended for all of the aforementioned model-based methods.

Identity by Descent-Based Methods

IBD describes identity through common descent, although the IBD segments are not necessarily identical through the rise of mutations during transgenerational transmission. Since the number of mutations and events amassed in each segment is directly proportional to the generational distance to the common ancestor, that information can be leveraged to infer genetic distance. Analyzing IBD sharing patterns can provide insights into past demographic events, migrations and population size fluctuations.

The longer the IBD segments identified between individuals, the more recent the genetic relatedness among them. Shared IBD segments tend to be rare, but when analyzing large datasets, there is a higher probability of detecting them, and those segments can be relatively long. In a dataset with n individuals, the number of possible IBD sharing pairs is $\binom{n}{2}$. The number of samples needed for that type of analysis require fast and computationally efficient algorithms, so that these analyses can become feasible.

The IBD calculation method implemented by Purcell et al. (2007) has the advantage of being a fast method, that does not require phasing of the genotypic data. It implements a hidden Markov model for IBD to determine the posterior probabilities. However, it does not account for LD between markers and requires a previous LD pruning of the data, which can lead to a severe loss of information.

GERMLINE was developed by Gusev et al. (2009) and used a novel hashing and extension algorithm to detect IBD segments. This haplotypic dictionary approach greatly speeds up IBD detection, with the runtime being analogous to the number of samples, far reducing the amount of computations required by the theoretical model described above.

Browning and Browning (2013) developed a series of algorithms for efficient and accurate IBD detection, with the latest, most improved one being BEAGLE's RefinedIBD algorithm. The algorithms preceding RefinedIBD were computationally intensive and solely relied on hidden Markov models and posterior estimations. RefinedIBD investigates IBD sharing in two steps, one that incorporates GERMLINE's method, and a second refined step that performs the evaluation of the candidate segments produced by the previous step through a probabilistic approach. Due to its nature, RefinedIBD can deliver the highest accuracy of the aforementioned algorithms, while also being computationally efficient on large datasets.

In the case of datasets comprising of unrelated individuals, IBD sharing detection can produce a wealth of information about the demographics of the included populations as well as the evolutionary forces that act on specific areas in different population groups.

Distance-Based Methods

Distance-based methods attempt to measure descent, and they are based on the concepts behind IBD. These methods can be utilized to calculate the distances between all pairs of individuals to produce a population pairwise distance matrix, that can then be further manipulated into a graphical tree-based output. The phylogenetic concepts behind the distance-based methods can be difficult to grasp by an aspiring population geneticist, but they are the fundamentals of population genetics. Here we attempt a brief outline of the methods and their history.

Wright (1921) proposed the first method for distance measurement, the inbreeding coefficient. This measure was later extended to become the F-statistics, a well-established family of statistical methods for measuring population differentiation and the calculation of genetic distances. Introduced in the middle of the previous century independently by Wright (1949) and Malécot (1948), F-statistics are measures of differentiation, statistics used to calculate the amount of variation in the entire population that is attributable to population differences and subdivision. F-statistics can provide valuable insights into population differentiation and due to that they became the most applied methods in population genetics, leading to the spawning of an abundance of related statistics.

Several definitions exist for the F-statistics, and can be partitioned into three main coefficients. The most popular one is the F_{ST}, also referred to commonly as θ. It is defined as the proportion of genetic diversity due to cross-population difference in allelic frequencies, and is dependent on the deviation of the genotypic frequencies from the HWE, assuming linkage equilibrium.

The computational estimation of F_{ST} is complicated, and has been the subject of many published theoretical studies. A simplification of the estimator of F_{ST} was described by Weir and Cockerham (1984). For this simplification to be theoretically valid, a large number of populations are needed, with each population having an large sample size equal to that of the other populations. These assumptions lets us consider that $1/r$ and $1/\overline{n}$ can be ignored from the full formula, leading to this simplified form:

$$F_{ST} = \frac{\sigma_p^2}{\overline{p}(1-\overline{p})} \tag{3}$$

where σ_p^2 is the variance of the allelic state and $\overline{p}$ is the total average allelic frequency. This simplified form is rarely the one used, with most published estimates of F_{ST} using the full estimation formula. The estimator by Weir and Cockerham (1984) is the most commonly used estimator out of a series of published estimators by different authors, with each possessing different strengths and shortcomings. Markedly, the EIGENSOFT package implementation uses the estimator proposed by Hudson et al. (1992), with Bhatia et al. (2013) arguing in favor of its robustness to sample size fluctuations and it not leading to overestimations of F_{ST}.

These F_{ST} distances can then be incorporated and fitted to a tree. The inception of the tree-based representation can be traced to the studies of (Cavalli-Sforza and Edwards, 1967), that used F_{ST} distances to infer phylogenetic trees.

Patterson et al. (2012) built on the ideas of the F-statistics to develop a new distinct set of statistics, confusingly named also f-statistics -albeit with a lower-case f for notation- published as part of the ADMIXTOOLS package. This set includes a host of methods for distance measurement, the two population test f_2, the three-population test f_3, the four population test f_4 and the qpGraph. They were developed in a quest to infer treeness, admixture and its proportions, founder populations, and complex past demographic events. These methods were extremely successful, inspiring the publication of a series of high-impact papers on the study of modern and ancient population genetics. In brief, f_2 can be considered as a genetic drift measure, f_3 as an admixture test and f_4 as a test of admixture proportions and directionality. Before analyzing for admixture, it is important to test our populations with a treeness test, because in the case of complex admixture events, it is often very difficult to describe past demography with a phylogenetic tree. Even in the case of treeness, the proposed tree should be fit to the data with a certain confidence.

The qpGraph is an admixture graph fitting method that shares similarities with the TreeMix method. TreeMix was developed by Pickrell and Pritchard (2012) and constructs phylogenetic trees by incorporating migratory models. The main difference between those two methods is that while TreeMix explores the possible model space to identify the one that best describes and fits the data, qpGraph uses a proposed model and tests it to investigate its fit on the data. Those migratory models produced by TreeMix, can provide insights into possible admixture events, but provide no info for a proposed date, they are only suggested based on the allowances set by the researcher. Methods that can estimate and date migratory events have been also developed and methodologically constitute a group of their own.

Admixture Dating Methods

Admixed individuals carry the haplotypes of their ancestors, which can be identified by the investigation of LD patterns, namely ancestry tracts. Throughout the generations, the ancestry tracts in the genome can be broken and intercepted by recombination. Thus, in the case of admixed populations or individuals, it is plausible to infer admixture dates by investigating the length distributions of the ancestry tracts.

Dating admixture events between populations was traditionally practiced by studying historical evidence and subsequently reverse engineered to investigate genetic patterns in the data. High density genome-wide genetic data enabled the investigation of LD-blocks, enabling the study of breaks in haplotypes between different populations. This knowledge can be leveraged to measure the transgenerational decay of LD-blocks and infer relative admixture dates.

ROLLOFF is the first reported software to infer admixture dates based on LD decay. The method was first reported by Moorjani et al. (2011) and was later incorporated in the ADMIXTOOLS software package developed by Patterson et al. (2012) to enable admixture studies across human history. It aggregates pairwise LD measurements using a weighting scheme, to produce a weighted LD curve as a function of genetic distance. This results in an exponential LD decay, and, given a rate constant, it can be further used to infer admixture dates.

Loh et al. (2013) built on the ideas of ROLLOFF to develop ALDER, a more sensitive algorithm that incorporates the information of the amplitude of the weighted LD curve to interpret further admixture parameters, enabling inferences on history, such as admixture dates and admixture fractions, or even to infer phylogenetic relationships. The latest extension of the method, MALDER, is able to additionally infer multiple admixture events. ALDER performs very well for two-way admixture hypotheses, but is limited to admixture events less than five hundred generations ago.

The aforementioned methods are used on genotypic data and rely on LD calculations to produce the decay curves. However, they are susceptible to performance issues when dealing with large scale datasets. Newer approaches suggest that utilizing haplotype information can produce more efficient and accurate results. GLOBETROTTER is a method described by Hellenthal et al. (2014) that is based on the Chromopainter output to infer admixture dates. Chromopainter is an efficient method that can paint chromosomes based on an ancestry estimation model using large scale data of the tested population and surrogate populations. The resulting haplotypes are then used by GLOBETROTTER to estimate the pairwise likelihood of these haplotypes being painted by these surrogate populations. These haplotypes are analyzed at a range of genetic distances to produce coancestry curves, to an exponential decay curve output similar of the previous methods. The advantage of this method is that the admixing sources are modelled as a linear mixture of surrogate populations, which enables the non-exact sampling of the source populations and the use of larger geographical groups as surrogates. This method is best used to infer later dates of admixture, and produces a wealth of information, but can underperform when using less than 300,000 markers.

Instead of fitting an exponential LD-decay curve, Pugach *et al.* (2011) developed stepPCO by following a PCA-based approach. StepPCO applies PCA stepwise to identify block-like admixture signals and computes discreet wavelet transform to calculate frequencies and position from the sum of waves in each signal. The dominant frequencies are then compared to the calculated ones to generate the admixture rates. Sanderson *et al.* (2015) provided some extensions to the stepPCO method, accelerating the runtime and improving the statistical power when differentiating between separate admixture events, but limiting it to only two-way admixture hypotheses. StepPCO also requires haplotypes as input, which can be estimated with the appropriate software that were described in the *Modelling-based methods* section.

Each of these admixture dating methods possess various advantages and disadvantages, thus the use of multiple methods is recommended. A limitation that all these algorithms share is their inability to explore genetic events over 5000 years ago, which makes those algorithms better suited for more recent admixture events.

Network Analysis

Network theory, as the study of graphs for related discreet objects, can be applied to genetic data to infer relationships between the samples. The results of the previously mentioned analytic methods can be integrated towards the construction of nodes and edges to create interpretable graphs. Network analysis provides in depth visualizations for multi-dimensional data.

In population genetics, in the case of the aforementioned analytic strategies, we often resort to a specific series of assumptions, a major one of them being that populations emerge in the form of a tree and deriving from a set ancestral population and collectively refer to every other genetic influence as admixture. Network theory can aid the exploration of past demography, by employing the principles of reticulate evolution into our data. As described earlier, in many cases, there are no specific trees that can explain the data, with multiple lineages merging or converging to form new populations. In such cases, reticulate patterns of demography can occur. The integration of network theory into population genetics and phylogenetics can act as a valuable tool to address such issues.

Phylogenetic networks can be divided into two main categories, the unrooted and the rooted networks. Numerous methods have been developed for both types of networks, some of which have achieved popularity. Software packages have been constructed in an effort to encompass the most mainstream of them for the ease of the user. In this section we will briefly describe some of these approaches and the theory behind them.

SplitsTree is an interactive application developed by Huson and Bryant (2006), that infers unrooted networks from genetic data. It also includes the NeighborNet algorithm, which was introduced by Bryant (2003) to construct split networks from measured genetic distances. Dendroscope was also developed by Huson and Scornavacca (2012), with the goal of inferring rooted phylogenetic networks, integrating algorithms such as the CASS by Iersel *et al.* (2010), the cluster network by Huson and Rupp (2008), and the galled network by Huson *et al.* (2009). These programs can accept pairwise genetic distance matrices or sequence alignments to infer reticulated demography. A commonly chosen metric for these calculations is F_{ST}, as described in a previous section.

NetStruct is a newer package developed by Greenbaum *et al.* (2016) that draws from the community and modularity methods included in the *igraph* software package, described by Csárdi and Nepusz (2006), to create networks and infer population structure. For input it requires genotypes, in contrast to the previous methods, but it does not account for linkage disequilibrium, which is one of its shortcomings.

Paschou *et al.* (2014) and Stamatoyannopoulos *et al.* (2017) developed a different approach into network inference. Instead of using F_{ST} or traditional phylogenetic methods, they opted to infer networks from the output of PCA and ADMIXTURE. To form the networks, they identified the top few nearest neighbors of each sample by representing each sample with respect to the top K coefficients returned by PCA or ADMIXTURE, and then computing the distance of each sample to all other samples that do not belong in the same population. In the resulting network, an edge between two populations shows that the two populations share genetically related individuals, with thicker edges indicating a larger number of genetically close individuals, which gives insights into the pathways of inter-population genetic flow.

A newer method was introduced by Zhang *et al.* (2017), who deployed the ideas behind chromosome painting and NeighborNet to combine them using a markov clustering approach. This approach features the investigation of recombination events, an increased resolution of shared ancestry, and the determination of the number of clades.

Networks are an important part of population genetics and phylogenetics, since reticulate evolution is the rule, which most times in phylogenetics we tend to disregard because of the model assumptions and its complications. Networks deviate from the rigid tree-like structure, and lead to a broader concept of population emergence and admixture. Of course, no method escapes all biases, so careful examination, along with a global exploration of the data is recommended.

Scanning for Selection

The methods explored in the previous section have a limit to their detection timescale. When investigating events in the far past, the effect of the evolutionary selective forces becomes increasingly evident. In this section we describe microevolutionary theory in conjunction with its applications on population genetics.

Natural selection creates regions of strong LD, raising the possibility of reverse engineering information about natural selection in populations. Considering that a new variant arises on a chromosomal background, there will be SNPs nearby in strong LD that are highly probable to be shuffled by recombination into increasingly smaller haplotypes through generations, which are going to be associated with that variant. Under a neutral model, this variant is expected to increase in frequency gradually so that by the time it attains higher frequencies, it will be on a relatively small associated SNP haplotype background.

If there has been rapid positive selection for that variant, it will essentially drag the nearby SNPs along with it and we will be able to identify a region of high linkage disequilibrium because this variant has evolved quickly to high frequency, so quickly that recombination was late to reshuffle these nearby SNPs. This is one of the signatures that indicates a region that underwent recent and rapid selection. To avoid false positives, it is suggested to remove low complexity regions, as well as the highly-complex HLA region, due to our limited knowledge into their genetic mechanics.

The detection signatures of selection is a vast category of analytic methods that is further divided into three subcategories, the frequency-based methods, the linkage disequilibrium-based methods, and the population differentiation-based methods. It is of note that, when selecting the analytic method, the timescale over which we hypothesize that selection has acted upon is considered to have a major effect in our analysis. Each method by its inception has fundamental advantages and disadvantages. Methods that rely on population differentiation and allelic frequencies have an advantage in large timescales, due to their inherent assumptions.

By Allelic Frequency

Since a selected genomic region can affect the allelic distributions in populations, statistical tests investigating allelic frequency patterns were developed to detect deviations from the neutral theory of evolution. Tajima (1989) was the first to introduce such a selection metric, referred to as Tajima's D. It operates by comparing the average pairwise difference between samples to the number of segregating polymorphisms. It is the most popular metric to detect selection signals, and spawned an array of derivatives.

The H metric by Fay and Wu (2000), building on Tajima's D, compares the pairwise differences to the samples that are homozygous for the derived allele. H measures the deviation from neutrality as they manifest between high and intermediate allelic frequencies, while D between low and intermediate allelic frequencies. Continuing this line of thought, Zeng et al. (2006) introduced E, which measures between high and low allelic frequencies, while putting less weight on high allelic frequencies. The combination of all of these metrics can act as an indicator of population expansion and distinguish it from purifying selection.

Fu and Li (1993) developed two metrics, F^* and D^* for the examination of singleton mutations. The D^* metric compares the average pairwise differences to the singleton mutations, and the F^* compares the average nucleotide differences to the singleton mutations. Of these two statistics, F^* is considered to be the one with the greatest power. The R^2, introduced by Ramos-Onsins and Rozas (2002), also utilizes singleton information and improves upon the previous method by comparing the differences between the average nucleotide differences to the singletons in each sequence, and also accounting for ascertainment bias in the use of genotype microarrays.

The timescale on which these methods operate is indeed vast. Tajima's D can detect evidence of selection in the past 10,000 generations of human populations, while Fay and Wu's H can detect events up to 3000 generations in the past.

By Linkage Disequilibrium

Selective pressure can create extended regions of strong LD, with haplotypic segments that are consistently inherited through generations. By utilizing the information gained by extended haplotypes, it is possible to infer positive selective pressure.

Sabeti et al. (2002) proposed a statistic for the measurement of the decay of LD, called extended haplotype homozygosity (EHH), defined as the probability that two random haplotypes in the sample set are identical by descent. This statistic inspired the development of several influential methods. In the same study, Sabeti et al. (2002) developed the long-range haplotype (LHR) test to investigate EHH. Based on the assumption that recent events should have a clearer signal when they extend over 10 times that of the background LD segments (0.02cM), it can detect recent positive selection, typically up to 400 generations in the past. Expanding on EHH, Sabeti et al. (2007) also developed the cross-population extended haplotype homozygosity (XP-EHH) test, which examines variation in recombination rates by comparing haplotype lengths among populations to probe for variation in recombination rates. Voight et al. (2006) introduced the integrated haplotype score (iHS), a variation of EHH, which attained popularity. It calculates the integral of the EHH decay curve for the ancestral and the derived variants, to provide a measure of the unexpectedness of the haplotypes around a marker relative to the whole genome. These methods are designed to identify alleles that have attained high frequencies in such a rapid fashion that the LD around them has not decayed. While XP-EHH is more suitable with selective sweeps nearing fixation in one, but not all populations, iHS has the power to detect partial sweeps.

Leveraging the information gained by haplotypes, Fu (1997) based the calculation of his F_S on the infinite-sites mutation model to estimate the probability that a random individual would possess an equal or smaller number of alleles compared to the observed values. Fu's F_S is more powerful in detecting population expansions than Tajima's D, and also performs very well in large sample sizes. It is sensitive in the presence of recombination, which could also be used as a test for evidence of recombination. Dh is another measure that uses haplotypic information, introduced by Nei (1987). It is an unbiased haplotype diversity estimate, which computes the probability that two random haplotypes in the sample are different. In a more brute fashion, identified IBD segments, which can be obtained through the methodology described in the previous section, can also be utilized for the detection of selective sweeps. If a particular IBD segment is enriched in a specific population, then it could be evidence for selection.

These statistics can be significantly affected by erroneous recombination estimates, and as such, when recombination rates are unknown, it is preferred to rely on the statistics based on allelic frequency, preferably Tajima's D or the R^2. Additionally, as these methods are essentially based on LD, their investigative timescales are much lower than those based on allelic frequency.

By Population Differentiation

Selection patterns can be investigated through the direct measurement of the frequencies of the derived allele between populations. Given a common ancestor, we define the allele that was passed onto its descendants as ancestral, while the allele that was created by mutation as derived. The derived allele is subject to selection, either positive or negative. This difference between the frequencies observed between populations, the δDAF, can be utilized to leverage derived allele frequency differences to infer whether selection has occurred.

F_{ST}, described earlier, can also indicate if diversifying selection has occurred by cross-examining between populations. A genome-wide scan of single marker estimates of F_{ST} can identify regions where natural selection has favored specific alleles in specific populations, with a detection range of up to 3000 generations into the past. In order to properly identify selection signatures using this method, a proper genome-wide background should be specified, depending on the properties of the study. When identifying adaptation to a specific environment, a very similar population that resides in a different habitat should be selected as the background for comparison. F_{ST} can be highly variable when applied only to single loci to study selection, and counter-measure approaches propose utilizing sliding windows to report average or highest values, which can lead to the discarding of valuable information. As with the phylogenetic usage of F_{ST}, scrutiny of the appropriate estimators, as well as the markers to be used is recommended.

By Composite Scoring

Each of the previous categories and tests is designed to detect a particular type of signal. However, the selective process is not limited to a specific signal type, generating a multitude of signal types. The study of a single type of signal can limit the power and the resolution of our inquiries. To that end, there have been efforts to combine multiple metrics based off different approaches into one composite method to attain greater power and resolution.

The composite likelihood ratio test (CLR) is a statistical method introduced by Kim and Stephan (2002) to probe the reduction of variation in local regions, which divides the maximum composite likelihood under a model without selection by the maximum composite likelihood under selection. This approach was successful in utilizing the spatial variation patterns in the frequency spectrum, with the downside of being inefficient for large scale datasets and sensitive to recombination and mutation rate biases. Building on these ideas, Nielsen *et al.* (2005) modified the CLR method by opting to calculate the null hypothesis from the background of the input data. However, this method does not account for multiple populations, and as such Nielsen *et al.* (2009), with G2D, and Chen *et al.* (2010), with XP-CLR, provided extensions to account for cross-population comparisons. The XP-CLR is based on a model-based extension of F_{ST} to compare multilocus allelic frequencies between populations, and is able to capture the spatial patterns of frequency skews that emerge around given markers. XP-CLR is able to better avoid ascertainment bias and demographic uncertainties, while G2D is better suited for when detailed demographic models are available. Additionally, a computationally efficient implementation by Pavlidis *et al.* (2013), enables the application of the CLR method on very high density data, such as the ones produced by WGS.

Another strategy into composite scoring is the combination of many tests for a single site. Pybus *et al.* (2014) opted to use combine the results of a variety of methods, combining them using a ranking algorithm to evaluate their significance of the findings. Their method utilizes supervised algorithms in a hierarchical classification scheme, by maximizing the difference between different evolutionary scenarios.

The methods described in this section can be found in standalone executables by their authors, integrated in a variety of community packages of programming languages (e.g., R, python), or in software packages, for example selscan by Szpiech and Hernandez (2014), Sweep by Sabeti *et al.* (2007), Arlequin by Excoffier and Lischer (2010), and DnaSP by Rozas *et al.* (2017).

Assessment and Considerations

Assessment of PCA and PCA-derived methods mostly relies on the visualization of the components that capture the most variance. Notably, approximately ninety per cent of the total genotypic variance pertains to intra-population variance, which means that only a fraction of the top principal components will be useful for the correct interpretation of inter-population differences. In most cases, the top three principal components are indicative of population structure, which can be visualized either in a three-dimensional scatter plot, or a combination of two-dimensional scatter plots.

The assessment of model-based clustering methods is based on the use bar plots to visualize the ancestry coefficients that are contained in the Q matrices, which was also one of the major factor that contributed to their immense popularity. This in turn translates to multiple analysis runs for different Ks of hypothetical ancestral populations. ADMIXTURE's cross-validation procedure produces an error estimate that aids ancestry modelling. The lowest cross-validation error value is proposed to be the most sensible K value to be used for ancestry modelling. STRUCTURE and its derivatives rely on the calculation of the marginal likelihood for each K, where the greater the value, the better the fit of the data to the model.

Because of the model that they operate on and their inherent assumptions, model-based clustering methods are prone to misinterpretation. To address this issue, several points must be stressed. Since the K value is an estimate, there is no evidence that it is the true one. The true value of K is highly dependent on sampling and its geographical regularity. In the case that important population groups have been under-, over-, or even unsampled, K estimates will not lead to meaningful interpretation. Apart from its numerical value, the qualities of the K ancestral populations should also be considered. The K ancestral populations could, but could equally not have existed at all in history. These ancestral populations should not be considered homogeneous and unadmixed, and they may as well have been related to each other. The primary assumption of those methods is a unidirectional admixture model, which works in the case of simple population histories but can prove problematic in complex population histories. In such cases, they select the most prominent drift components as they are detected and regard them as ancestral, which can lead to populations close to ancestral frequencies to be regarded as admixed. These methods cannot discern between admixture, retrograde admixture, or population bottlenecks, which can heavily influence the resulting output.

The practicality of distance-based methods is sufficiently multifaceted. They can produce the branches of a phylogenetic tree, they can showcase the shared genetic drift between groups, and they can deduce complex demographic scenarios based on the coalescence times and the internal genealogical branch lengths. The complex nature of this range of interpretations though also raises some points of consideration. The choice of markers is critical for the type of analysis aimed for, with a notable example being the inclusion of genomic areas undergoing strong selection which can confound investigations into past demography. The presence of LD can also influence the analysis, with current software packages offering elegant solutions to this issue, such as the bootstrapping and the block-jackknife that can produce error measurements. Because the main method of interpretation is through eye examination, the distance measure and the choice of graphical representation may significantly affect the identified clusters. Because of their complex statistical nature, distance-based methods can occasionally be counter-intuitive, and as such, require a deep understanding of the concepts behind them.

In the case of the admixture dating methods, it needs to be stressed that they operate with specific hypotheses. One is that admixture happens in pulses, as single admixture events, and not at prolonged periods of rates. The second is that they take into account only unilateral admixture between pairs of populations. Third, since they require the use of surrogate populations to test their hypotheses, they can open the gates to a flood of biases, especially when selecting the surrogate populations, since most populations are already admixed. In that case, the modern populations should be carefully selected as surrogates and potential biases clearly stated. Their investigative past timeline is also limited, with 5000 years being the lowest bound in the range of inferred dates.

When probing selection sweeps, it is probable that while the neutrality tests can lead to the rejection of the null, the results could prove to be falsely positive. Demographic events may well interject in the performance of the algorithms, and to combat such possibilities, many methods that take into account demographic models have been implemented. Strong LD between a neutral and a selected variant can also create false-positives in the interpretation of the results. Confounding patterns of LD can also arise due to systematic biases. Using genotype microarray data often cause the oversight of markers with lower frequency, leading to ascertainment biases in the analysis.

In all cases, effective and regular sampling is very strongly recommended. All the cited methods are particularly sensitive on the samples used, the genetic differentiation between the populations, and, equally important, on the number of markers examined. Also of note is that the analytic choice of populations should be coupled with an appropriate density in markers. Genetic discrimination between subgroups of an ethnic group, requires a much higher density in markers than discriminating between different ethnic groups. As always, the global use of a variety of different methods is advised. As in the case of model-based clustering algorithms, different software use different estimation or approximation procedures to achieve computational efficiency. Different methods can capture mishaps and erroneous estimates produced by other methods, or can be particularly sensitive in specific genetic signals.

The Peopling of Europe as an Illustrative Case

The genetics of the European continent have provided prime illustrations of the capabilities that population genetics has when applied to study historical demographics. Archeogenetics and population genetics have been able, supported by palaeological and archaeological evidence, to give insight to the population movements that occurred from the transition of the Middle Paleolithic into the Upper Paleolithic and into the modern structure of anatomically modern humans.

Since the landmark studies by Cavalli-Sforza et al. (1994), it was evident that genetic components seem to follow continuous clines in Europe, a notion further reinforced by the whole-genome genotype analysis of Novembre et al. (2008). Cavalli-Sforza et al. (1994) proposed that these clines were the indications for the mass population movements of the Neolithic expansion into Europe, over the Mesolithic and Epipaleolithic populations. Present day knowledge now confirms these notions, albeit in a much more complicated manner than the one originally proposed.

The genetic ancestries of the modern Europeans can be traced to three major genetic influences as showcased by Lazaridis et al. (2014): the Mesolithic hunger-gatherers, the anatolian Neolithics, and the migrants from the steppe. To elaborate on these ancestries, a recapitulation of the current state of knowledge is in order.

There has been evidence of a wide distribution of anatomically modern humans by 43,000 BCE in Europe, as suggested by Benazzi et al. (2011). This Aurignacian culture is thought to have led to the disappearance of the Neanderthals in a multitude of ways.

The oldest genomic evidence available originates from this exact era, an individual from the geographic area of modern Romania named Oase 1. This individual was reported by Fu *et al.* (2015) to have 6%–9% Neanderthal ancestry, with genomic tracts extending over 50cM, indicating a Neanderthal ancestor 4–6 generations past. However, the genome of this individual suggests that this population did not contribute in an identifiable way to the genetics of the later humans. The Aurignacian culture was most likely succeeded by the Gravettian culture during the Upper Paleolithic era at approximately 35–30,000 BCE, which was most probably the last unified culture of Europe. Fu *et al.* (2016), analyzing 51 Eurasians that ranged from the Upper Paleolithic to the Mesolithic era (45,000–7000 BCE), reported that even though there was no detectable genetic influence by these early humans over the modern humans, these people were the likely descendants of a single founder population, with a 35,000 year-old human specimen representing the earliest discovered branch of this population. Fu *et al.* (2016) also identified a major shift in the peopling of Europe after the last Ice Age and during the major warming period, with the disappearance of the Gravettian culture, and migrants with a significant genetic component attributed to modern Near Eastern populations. This era was most likely the subject of intense population shifts, as it is proposed that the these recolonizers were replaced by the eventual future Mesolithic cultures. These Mesolithic cultures are proposed to be a medley of at least two ancestral sources after the last Ice Age period, though with no clear evidence of their origin. Analysis of genomic data from Mesolithic and later populations, such as the studies by Lipson *et al.* (2017), Lazaridis *et al.* (2014), Skoglund *et al.* (2012), Sánchez-Quinto *et al.* (2012) suggest a genomic diversity background that deviates from the one observed in modern humans, but similarly showing clinal patterns, following an east to west genetic cline.

The rise of the Neolithic Age in the fertile crescent, brought about a major population migration into Europe, initiating during the 8th millenium BCE, leading to the first agrarian societies in Europe by the 7th millenium BCE. These Neolithic migrants conveyed the agricultural technology and culture to the whole mainland of the European continent. Many studies, such as the ones by Gamba *et al.* (2014), Haak *et al.* (2015), Hofmanová *et al.* (2016), demonstrated the genetic entanglement of the Mesolithic and Neolithic ancestries into admixed populations with a 10%–25% Neolithic ancestral component. The exact route followed by the Neolithics was a matter of historical debate, with genetics supplying insights into the migrational routes, as Paschou *et al.* (2014) demonstrated genetic signatures of a maritime route of colonization that was followed by the Neolithics from the fertile crescent into Europe. This finding has also been supported by Hughey *et al.* (2013), who inferred from mitochondrial data that the Minoan population was indeed a population closely resembling the Neolithic and modern European populations.

The last genetic component of the modern Europeans derives from a genetic influence from the Eurasian steppe, around the 5th millenium BCE. The studies by Allentoft *et al.* (2015) and Haak *et al.* (2015), identified an ancestral component associated with the Yamnaya and the Afanasievo cultures, mostly appearing in the Northeastern and Central Europe. These steppe populations also show distinct signatures of admixture, themselves being an amalgamation of Mesolithic cultures from East Europe and the Caucasus, the Neolithic and later age Iranian fields, as well as modern population components. These suggest that the genetic flow followed a bidirectional route, instead of a unidirectional one.

The nature of the genetic influence over other populations does not always follow the same mechanics, with some genetic signatures involving abrupt genetic influences, and others gradual genetic assimilation. Especially in the case of the steppe genetic influx, the transitions appear to have occurred between relatively short timescales. Goldberg *et al.* (2017) and Saag *et al.* (2017) demonstrated that while the Neolithic migrations involved large numbers of males and females, the migrations from the steppe, as well as their genetic influence, were mostly of male origin.

Modern day European population structure is the result mainly of these major genetic influences, with the magnitude of these influences varying by region. The patterns of these genetic components shift based on the genetic flow from these major or from minor sources. Haak *et al.* (2015) reported a more prevalent Anatolian Neolithic ancestry in southern Europeans than in northern Europeans, and higher percentages of steppe ancestry in north-central Europeans than southern Europeans. The genetic clines initially observed by Cavalli-Sforza, led to the reveal of an intriguingly intricate genetic past of Europe, branching off to the study of the human history over all continents, enabling the exploration of the rise of the modern anatomical humans and their expansion all over the world. Population genetics contributed immensely to that end, supplying an overwhelming amount of data and analytic methods for the investigation and inference of past human demographics.

The study of population genetics has also been exercised on later generations of genetic history, into the medieval and more recent time periods, to investigate and elucidate historical controversies. Stamatoyannopoulos *et al.* (2017) tested the hypothesis set by Jakob Philipp Fallmerayer, a strong proponent of the theory of the eradication of medieval Peloponnesean Greek populations by Slavic and Avar invaders and the genetic discontinuity between medieval and modern Greeks. The results refuted those claims, indicating a strong genetic similarity of the modern Greeks with modern Sicilians and Italians and a clear differentiation from the genetics of the Slavic homeland. Population genetics also has the remarkable ability to produce historical controversies, such as the case of the remains of King Richard III of England, which were genetically investigated by King *et al.* (2014).

The study substantiated that, while the maternal royal line was continuous, the paternal one was surprisingly discontinuous, which laid doubts on the right of patrilineal succession of medieval English kings even into the modern royal family.

Application of Population Genetics in Disease

The exact mechanisms that link genetic variation to disease have been a major subject of debate, stemming from the era of classical genetics and reaching to modern genetics. Fisher (1919) laid the foundations for considering polygenic disorders and continuous phenotypes as a combination of multiple Mendelian loci. Expanding on these notions, Common Disease-Common Variant is a well established hypothesis, tracing its origins on multiple articles but mainly to the landmark paper by Reich and Lander (2001). In essence, it states that for a disease of high prevalence in a population, the genetic components that lead to it should be relatively common in that population.

Following the Common Disease-Common Variant hypothesis and its extensions, when investigating a multifactorial disease, a significant amount of its genetic background should rely on common variance. Since common variance is heavily influenced by demography and evolutionary forces, the implementation of population genetics becomes critical for the avoidance of a result riddled with false positives that can be attributed to population structure in the data.

When the analysis spans an extensive amount of the genome, such as in the case of a GWAS, the use of PCA or model-based clustering methods can sufficiently correct for inflation related to population stratification. Price *et al.* (2006) demonstrated that incorporating the output of the principal components for each individual as coefficients in an association model can alleviate the inflation effects. Alexander *et al.* (2009) also designed ADMIXTURE as a method competing with EIGENSOFT in the calculation of ancestry coefficient for association modelling. Nowadays, it is commonplace to use the output of PCA, or ADMIXTURE or related methods, as coefficients in a logistic regression association model to correct for inflation in the statistics.

However, a critical number of association studies are not performed in a genome-wide frame, especially in the case of replication studies that seek to validate results from GWAS in various populations. In that case, the use of PCA to identify SNPs that carry the inter- and intra-population variance, and their subsequent genotyping along with the investigated markers, is fundamental for the avoidance of bias and confounding related to population structure.

To that end, Paschou *et al.* (2007) developed a PCA-based methodology to infer ancestry informative markers (AIMs), that was able to identify the prime markers capturing the intercontinental and cross-population variance, efficiently reducing the number of markers required for structure identification to a mere handful, though these markers were in general not overlapping among regions. Paschou *et al.* (2008) applied the method in European-American datasets, effectively demonstrating that by using this method, 150–200 AIMs were sufficient to capture the fine details of stratification in individuals that derived their ancestry from Europe. Drineas *et al.* (2010) applied the method to successfully infer geographic coordinates of European population data by using a small subset of the markers, further showcasing the effectiveness of the method and the bridging between population and disease genetics. Through an extension of the method, Paschou *et al.* (2010) demonstrated its applicability in a portable worldwide setting, resulting in a significant reduction of required markers to capture broad and fine-scale stratification to less than 0.1% of the original dataset. These methods were very successful in denoting the power of PCA to decrease study expenditure and increase computational efficiency when controlling for stratification effects in association analyses.

Discussion

Population genetics has a deep impact on the whole field of genetics, shaping many of its fundamentals, and branching off into different subfields. Nowadays we can discern between population genetics, palaeogenetics, evolutionary genetics and spatial genetics. Palaeogenetics, or archeogenetics, as the genetic study of samples that predate the current era, since modern technology has enabled the isolation of DNA of appreciable quality from bone samples and the sequencing of their bases, and spatial genetics as the joint analysis of genetics and geographical space and the investigation of their interaction and co-dependence. We refrained from referring to spatial genetics methods, as we believe that they constitute a subfield of their own, and they would be outside the scope of population genetic analysis. We also skimmed the surface of palaeogenetics and evolutionary genetics, by mentioning some of the methods used for these analyses, that are overlapping with population genetics, but not delving into the complex theory required for their interpretation.

Originally, when drafting an article about population genetics analyses, a dilemma arises faced on the decision on how to classify and showcase the algorithms and the protocols, whether the criterion should be the depth level required of the genetic data, the form of the genetic data, or the algorithmic method on which the software is based on. In this guide, we opted for the latter. We focused mainly on the nature of the base method, than how many variants should be included in the dataset.

High-density data enable what is termed as local ancestry inference, namely the ability to infer the ancestry of specific genetic tracts all over the genome. Global ancestry inference is still very popular, and for a good reason, since the majority of variants are associated through LD, which means that global ancestry inference methods can work on thinner datasets, which is most commonly the case when conglomerating datasets.

Oftentimes, in interdisciplinary research, it is not uncommon that specific terms get misused or mixed. A notable example is referring to a method as "supervised". Pritchard *et al.* (2000) refer to the term to describe a method that incorporates information to the data that relates to their prior groupings. Other researchers refer to the term as the need to specify their own number of *K* ancestral populations. There is no correct or erroneous use of the term, as in both cases its use is justified, and we are just using this cautionary example to prevent misgivings when interpreting published analytic protocols.

We can apply the information gained from our studies of genetic variation that pertains to the use of LD in disease-gene mapping. LD essentially reflects the patterns of recombination occurring over many hundreds of generations, especially for closely linked loci, and we can use it to infer the distance between closely linked loci. Populations that were founded a long time ago had more evolutionary time for recombination to occur, which leads to less LD. Specific groups of populations have had a more rapid decay of LD between SNP pairs (1000 Genomes Project Consortium, 2015), which necessitates a population genetics view when pursuing and interpreting disease-associated genomic loci. Since many markers in the genome are in LD with each other, they can be considered redundant for our analyses, and we can get relatively complete coverage of a genome in a GWAS with approximately 1.5 million SNPs for African derived populations, and approximately a half million to a million SNPs for non-African populations. Thus, studies of population history can inform our design of these GWAS and our design of SNP microarrays.

It is important to note, that the most significant and impactful current scientific advances in human population genetics have been achieved through the study of SNVs. Such variants comprise the overwhelming majority of genetic variation, enabling the capture of a significant amount of variation for study. Another category of variation is the structural variation, with a substantial amount of variation existing at the structural level. These structural variants are more difficult to identify than SNVs, but, as Sudmant *et al.* (2015) reported in their study, we can estimate that in the average haploid human sequence, at least 9mb are affected by structural variants. When compared with the approximately 3.5mb in the average genome that are affected by SNVs, these structural variants, even though occurring less frequently in the genome, account for more differences than SNVs. And if we also consider Copy Number Variations (CNVs), where genetic segments can differ by multiple copies, each human is heterozygous for approximately 150 of those CNVs.

As rare variants tend to be population specific, we can investigate a lot about the functional significance of these genetic variants, because functional regions in the genome, whether coding or non-coding, tend to show more evidence of purifying selection. And we can actually use this information to more effectively identify functional regions of the genome.

The examples of CNVs and rare variation showcase the amount of genetic information that still eludes us. However, the modern technological advances have overcome that limitation, producing more global maps of genetic variation. With the avalanche of genetic data being generated daily, we can await for a wealth of knowledge to be generated in the following years, along with the development of methods that will be able to handle that level of data.

See also: Natural Language Processing Approaches in Bioinformatics

---

References

1000 Genomes Project Consortium, 2015. A global reference for human genetic variation. Nature 526 (7571), 68–74. doi:10.1038/nature15393.

Alexander, D.H., Novembre, J., Lange, K., 2009. Fast model-based estimation of ancestry in unrelated individuals. Genome Research 19 (9), 1655–1664. doi:10.1101/gr.094052.109.

Allentoft, M.E., Sikora, M., Sjögren, K.G., *et al.*, 2015. Population genomics of Bronze Age Eurasia. Nature 522, 167.

Benazzi, S., Douka, K., Fornai, C., *et al.*, 2011. Early dispersal of modern humans in Europe and implications for Neanderthal behaviour. Nature 479 (7374), 525–528. doi:10.1038/nature10617.

Bhatia, G., Patterson, N., Sankararaman, S., Price, A.L., 2013. Estimating and interpreting FST: The impact of rare variants. Genome Research 23 (9), 1514–1521. doi:10.1101/gr.154831.113.

Brisbin, A., Bryc, K., Byrnes, J., *et al.*, 2012. PCAdmix: Principal components-based assignment of ancestry along each chromosome in individuals with admixed ancestry from two or more populations. Human Biology 84 (4), 343–364. doi:10.3378/027.084.0401.

Browning, B.L., Browning, S.R., 2013. Improving the accuracy and efficiency of identity-by-descent detection in population data. Genetics 194 (2), 459–471. doi:10.1534/genetics.113.150029.

Browning, S.R., Browning, B.L., 2007. Rapid and accurate haplotype phasing and missing-data inference for whole-genome association studies by use of localized haplotype clustering. The American Journal of Human Genetics 81 (5), 1084–1097. doi:10.1086/521987.

Bryant, D., 2003. Neighbor-Net: An agglomerative method for the construction of phylogenetic networks. Molecular Biology and Evolution 21 (2), 255–265. doi:10.1093/molbev/msh018.

Cavalli-Sforza, L., Edwards, A., 1967. Phylogenetic analysis. Models and estimation procedures. The American Journal of Human Genetics 19 (3 Pt 1), 233–257. doi:10.1073/pnas.85.16.6002.

Cavalli-Sforza, L., Menozzi, P., Piazza, A., 1994. The History and Geography of Human Genes. Princeton University Press.

Chang, C.C., Chow, C.C., Tellier, L.C., *et al.*, 2015. Second-generation PLINK: Rising to the challenge of larger and richer datasets. Gigascience 4 (1), 7. doi:10.1186/s13742-015-0047-8.

Chen, H., Patterson, N., Reich, D., 2010. Population differentiation as a test for selective sweeps. Genome Research 20 (3), 393–402. doi:10.1101/gr.100545.109.

Conrad, D.F., Keebler, J.E.M., DePristo, M.A., *et al.*, 2011. Variation in genome-wide mutation rates within and between human families. Nature Genetics 43 (7), 712. doi:10.1038/ng.862.

Csárdi, G., Nepusz, T., 2006. The igraph software package for complex network research. InterJournal, Complex Systems 1695 (5), 1–9.

Delaneau, O., Zagury, J.F., Marchini, J., 2013. Improved whole-chromosome phasing for disease and population genetic studies. Nature Methods 10 (1), 5–6. doi:10.1038/nmeth.2307.

Drineas, P., Lewis, J., Paschou, P., 2010. Inferring geographic coordinates of origin for Europeans using small panels of ancestry informative markers. PLOS ONE 5, 8. doi:10.1371/journal.pone.0011892.

Dungern, E von., Hirschfeld, L., 1910. Uber vererbung gruppenspezifischer strukturen des blutes. Zeitschrift fur Immunitatsforschung und Experimentelle Therapie 6, 284–292.

Excoffier, L., Lischer, H.E.L., 2010. Arlequin suite ver 3.5: A new series of programs to perform population genetics analyses under Linux and Windows. Molecular Ecology Resources 10 (3), 564–567. doi:10.1111/j.1755-0998.2010.02847.x.

Fay, J.C., Wu, C.I., 2000. Hitchhiking under positive Darwinian selection. Genetics 155 (3), 1405–1413.

Fisher, R.A., 1919. XV. – The correlation between relatives on the supposition of Mendelian inheritance. Transactions of the Royal Society of Edinburgh 52 (2), 399–433.

Frichot, E., Mathieu, F., Trouillon, T., Bouchard, G., Francois, O., 2014. Fast and efficient estimation of individual ancestry coefficients. Genetics 196 (4), 973–983. doi:10.1534/genetics.113.160572.

Fu, Y.X., 1997. Statistical tests of neutrality of mutations against population growth, hitchhiking and background selection. Genetics 147 (2), 915–925.

Fu, Q., Hajdinjak, M., Moldovan, O.T., *et al.*, 2015. An early modern human from Romania with a recent Neanderthal ancestor. Nature 524 (7564), 216–219. doi:10.1038/nature14558.

Fu, Y.X., Li, W.H., 1993. Statistical tests of neutrality of mutations. Genetics 133 (3), 693–709. evolution.

Fu, Q., Posth, C., Hajdinjak, M., *et al.*, 2016. The genetic history of Ice Age Europe. Nature 534 (7606), 200–205. doi:10.1038/nature17993.

Gamba, C., Jones, E.R., Teasdale, M.D., *et al.*, 2014. Genome flux and stasis in a five millennium transect of European prehistory. Nature Communications 5. doi:10.1038/ncomms6257.

Goldberg, A., Gunther, T., Rosenberg, N.A., Jakobsson, M., 2017. Ancient X chromosomes reveal contrasting sex bias in Neolithic and Bronze Age Eurasian migrations. Proceedings of the National Academy of Sciences 114 (10), 2657–2662. doi:10.1073/pnas.1616392114.

Greenbaum, G., Templeton, A.R., Bar-David, S., 2016. Inference and analysis of population structure using genetic data and network theory. Genetics 202 (4), 1299–1312. doi:10.1534/genetics.115.182626.

Gusev, A., Lowe, J.K., Stoffel, M., et al., 2009. Whole population, genome-wide mapping of hidden relatedness. Genome Research 19 (2), 318–326. doi:10.1101/gr.081398.108.

Haak, W., Lazaridis, I., Patterson, N., et al., 2015. Massive migration from the steppe was a source for Indo-European languages in Europe. Nature 522 (7555), 207–211. doi:10.1038/nature14317.

Hellenthal, G., Busby, G.B.J., Band, G., et al., 2014. A genetic atlas of human admixture history. Science 343 (6172), 747–751. doi:10.1126/science.1243518.

Hirschfeld, L., Hirschfeld, H., 1919. Serological differences between the blood of different races. The result of researches on the Macedonian front. The Lancet 194 (5016), 675679.

Hofmanová, Z., Kreutzer, S., Hellenthal, G., et al., 2016. Early farmers from across Europe directly descended from Neolithic Aegeans. Proceedings of the National Academy of Sciences 113 (25), 6886–6891. doi:10.1073/pnas.1523951113.

Hubisz, M.J., Falush, D., Stephens, M., Pritchard, J.K., 2009. Inferring weak population structure with the assistance of sample group information. Molecular Ecology Resources 9 (5), 1322–1332. doi:10.1111/j.1755–0998.2009.02591.x.

Hudson, R.R., Slatkin, M., Maddison, W.P., 1992. Estimation of levels of gene flow from DNA sequence data. Genetics 132 (2), 583–589. PMC1205159.

Hughey, J.R., Paschou, P., Drineas, P., et al., 2013. A European population in minoan Bronze age crete. Archives of Hellenic Medicine 30 (4), 456–466. doi:10.1038/ncomms2871.

Huson, D.H., Bryant, D., 2006. Application of phylogenetic networks in evolutionary studies. Molecular Biology and Evolution 23 (2), 254–267. doi:10.1093/molbev/msj030.

Huson, D.H., Rupp, R., 2008. Summarizing multiple gene trees using cluster networks. In: Proceedings of the International Workshop on Algorithms in Bioinformatics, pp. 296–305. doi:10.1007/978–3–540–87361–7_25.

Huson, D.H., Rupp, R., Berry, V., Gambette, P., Paul, C., 2009. Computing galled networks from real data. Bioinformatics 25 (12), doi:10.1093/bioinformatics/btp217.

Huson, D.H., Scornavacca, C., 2012. Dendroscope 3: An interactive tool for rooted phylogenetic trees and networks. Systematic Biology 61 (6), 1061–1067. doi:10.1093/sysbio/sys062.

Iersel, L., van, Kelk, S., Rupp, R., Huson, D., 2010. Phylogenetic networks do not need to be complex: Using fewer reticulations to represent conflicting clusters. Bioinformatics 26 (12), doi:10.1093/bioinformatics/btq202.

Kim, Y., Stephan, W., 2002. Detecting a local signature of genetic hitchhiking along a recombining chromosome. Genetics 160 (2), 765–777.

King, T.E., Fortes, G.G., Balaresque, P., et al., 2014. Identification of the remains of King Richard III. Nature Communications 5. doi:10.1038/ncomms6631.

Landsteiner, K., 1900. "Zur Kenntnis der antifermentativen, lytischen und agglutinierenden Wirkungen des Blutseruns und der Lymphe". Zentralblatt Fur Bakteriologie 27, 357–362.

Lawson, D.J., Hellenthal, G., Myers, S., Falush, D., 2012. Inference of population structure using dense haplotype data. PLOS Genetics 8 (1), 11–17. doi:10.1371/journal.pgen.1002453.

Lazaridis, I., Patterson, N., Mittnik, A., et al., 2014. Ancient human genomes suggest three ancestral populations for present-day Europeans. Nature 513 (7518), 409–413. doi:10.1038/nature13673.

Lewontin, R.C., Kojima, Ki., 1960. The evolutionary dynamics of complex polymorphisms. Evolution 14 (4), 458–472.

Lipson, M., Szécsenyi-Nagy, A., Mallick, S., et al., 2017. Parallel palaeogenomic transects reveal complex genetic history of early European farmers. Nature 551 (7680), 368–372. doi:10.1038/nature24476.

Loh, P.R., Danecek, P., Palamara, P.F., et al., 2016. Reference-based phasing using the haplotype reference consortium panel. Nature Genetics 48 (11), 14431448. doi:10.1038/ng.3679.

Loh, P.R., Lipson, M., Patterson, N., et al., 2013. Inferring admixture histories of human populations using linkage disequilibrium. Genetics 193 (4), 1233–1254. doi:10.1534/genetics.112.147330.

Malécot, G., 1948. Les Mathematiques de L'heredite. Barneoud freres.

Moorjani, P., Patterson, N., Hirschhorn, J.N., et al., 2011. The history of african gene flow into Southern Europeans, Levantines, and Jews. PLOS Genetics 7 (4), 1–13. doi:10.1371/journal.pgen.1001373.

Nei, M., 1987. Molecular Evolutionary Genetics. Columbia University Press.

Nielsen, R., Hubisz, M.J., Hellmann, I., et al., 2009. Darwinian and demographic forces affecting human protein coding genes. Genome Research 19 (5), 838–849. doi:10.1101/gr.088336.108.

Nielsen, R., Williamson, S., Kim, Y., et al., 2005. Genomic scans for selective sweeps using SNP data. Genome Research 15 (11), 1566–1575. doi:10.1101/gr.4252305.

Novembre, J., Johnson, T., Bryc, K., et al., 2008. Genes mirror geography within Europe. Nature 456 (7218), 98–101. doi:10.1038/nature07331.

Paschou, P., Drineas, P., Lewis, J., et al., 2008. Tracing sub-structure in the European American population with PCA-informative markers. PLOS Genetics 4 (7), doi:10.1371/journal.pgen.1000114.

Paschou, P., Drineas, P., Yannaki, E., et al., 2014. Maritime route of colonization of Europe. Proceedings of the National Academy of Sciences 111 (25), 9211–9216. doi:10.1073/pnas.1320811111.

Paschou, P., Lewis, J., Javed, A., Drineas, P., 2010. Ancestry informative markers for fine-scale individual assignment to worldwide populations. Journal of Medical Genetics 47 (12), 835–847. doi:10.1136/jmg.2010.078212.

Paschou, P., Ziv, E., Burchard, E.G., et al., 2007. PCA-correlated SNPs for structure identification in worldwide human populations. PLOS Genetics 3 (9), 1672–1686. doi:10.1371/journal.pgen.0030160.

Patterson, N., Moorjani, P., Luo, Y., et al., 2012. Ancient admixture in human history. Genetics 192 (3), 10651093. doi:10.1534/genetics.112.145037.

Patterson, N., Price, A., Reich, D., 2006. Population structure and eigenanalysis. PLOS Genetics 2 (12), 2074–2093. doi:10.1371/journal.pgen.0020190.

Pavlidis, P., Živković, D., Stamatakis, A., Alachiotis, N., 2013. SweeD: Likelihood-based detection of selective sweeps in thousands of genomes. Molecular Biology and Evolution 30 (9), 2224–2234. doi:10.1093/molbev/mst112.

Pickrell, J.K., Pritchard, J.K., 2012. Inference of population splits and mixtures from genome-wide allele frequency data. PLOS Genetics 8 (11), e1002967. doi:10.1371/journal.pgen.1002967.

Prado-Martinez, J., Sudmant, P.H., Kidd, J.M., et al., 2013. Great ape genetic diversity and population history. Nature 499 (7459), 471–475. doi:10.1038/nature12228.

Price, A., Patterson, N., Plenge, R., et al., 2006. Principal components analysis corrects for stratification in genome-wide association studies. Nature Genetics 38 (8), 904–909. doi:10.1038/ng1847.

Pritchard, J.K., Stephens, M., Donnelly, P., 2000. Inference of population structure using multilocus genotype data. Genetics 155 (2), 945–959. doi:10.1111/j.1471–8286.2007.01758.x.

Pugach, I., Matveyev, R., Wollstein, A., Kayser, M., Stoneking, M., 2011. Dating the age of admixture via wavelet transform analysis of genome-wide data. Genome Biology 12 (2), doi:10.1186/gb-2011–12–2-r19.

Purcell, S., Neale, B., Todd-Brown, K., et al., 2007. PLINK: A tool set for whole-genome association and population-based linkage analyses. The American Journal of Human Genetics 81 (3), 559–575. doi:10.1086/519795.

Pybus, M., Dall'Olio, G.M., Luisi, P., et al., 2014. 1000 genomes selection browser 1.0: A genome browser dedicated to signatures of natural selection in modern humans. Nucleic Acids Research 42 (D1), 903–909. doi:10.1093/nar/gkt1188.

Raj, A., Stephens, M., Pritchard, J.K., 2014. FastSTRUCTURE: Variational inference of population structure in large SNP data sets. Genetics 197 (2), 573–589. doi:10.1534/genetics.114.164350.

Ramos-Onsins, S.E., Rozas, J., 2002. Statistical properties of new neutrality tests against population growth. Molecular Biology and Evolution 19 (12), 2092–2100. doi:10.1093/oxfordjournals.molbev.a004034.

Reich, D., Lander, E., 2001. On the allelic spectrum of human disease. Trends in Genetics 17 (9), 502–510.

Roach, J.C., Glusman, G., Smit, A.F.A., et al., 2010. Analysis of genetic inheritance in a family quartet by whole-genome sequencing. Science (New York, NY) 328 (5978), 636–639. doi:10.1126/science.1186802.

Rozas, J., Ferrer-Mata, A., Sanchez-DelBarrio, J.C., et al., 2017. DnaSP 6: DNA sequence polymorphism analysis of large data sets. Molecular Biology and Evolution 32, 3299–3302. doi:10.1093/molbev/msx248.

Saag, L., Varul, L., Scheib, C.L., et al., 2017. Extensive farming in Estonia started through a sex-biased migration from the Steppe. Current Biology 27 (14), 2185–2193. doi:10.1016/j.cub.2017.06.022. e6.

Sabeti, P.C., Reich, D.E., Higgins, J.M., et al., 2002. Detecting recent positive selection in the human genome from haplotype structure. Nature 419 (6909), 832–837. doi:10.1038/nature01027.1.

Sabeti, P.C., Varilly, P., Fry, B., et al., 2007. Genome-wide detection and characterization of positive selection in human populations. Nature 449 (7164), 913–918. doi:10.1038/nature06250.

Sánchez-Quinto, F., Schroeder, H., Ramirez, O., et al., 2012. Genomic affinities of two 7,000-year-old Iberian hunter-gatherers. Current Biology 22 (16), 1494–1499. doi:10.1016/j.cub.2012.06.005.

Sanderson, J., Sudoyo, H., Karafet, T.M., Hammer, M.F., Cox, M.P., 2015. Reconstructing past admixture processes from local genomic ancestry using wavelet transformation. Genetics 200 (2), 469–481. doi:10.1534/genetics.115.176842.

Scheet, P., Stephens, M., 2006. A fast and flexible statistical model for large-scale population genotype data: Applications to inferring missing genotypes and haplotypic phase. The American Journal of Human Genetics 78 (4), 629–644. doi:10.1086/502802.

Skoglund, P., MalmstrSm, H., Raghavan, M., et al., 2012. Origins and genetic legacy of neolithic farmers and hunter-gatherers in Europe. Science 336 (6080), 466–469. doi:10.1126/science.1216304.

Stamatoyannopoulos, G., Bose, A., Teodosiadis, A., et al., 2017. Genetics of the Peloponnesean populations and the theory of extinction of the medieval Peloponnesean Greeks. European Journal of Human Genetics 25, 637–645. doi:10.1038/ejhg.2017.18.

Sudmant, P.H., Rausch, T., Gardner, E.J., et al., 2015. An integrated map of structural variation in 2,504 human genomes. Nature 526 (7571), 75–81. doi:10.1038/nature15394.

Szpiech, Z.A., Hernandez, R.D., 2014. Selscan: An efficient multithreaded program to perform EHH-based scans for positive selection. Molecular Biology and Evolution 31 (10), 2824–2827. doi:10.1093/molbev/msu211.

Tajima, F., 1989. Statistical method for testing the neutral mutation hypothesis by DNA polymorphism. Genetics 123 (3), 585–595. PMC1203831.

Voight, B.F., Kudaravalli, S., Wen, X., Pritchard, J.K., 2006. A map of recent positive selection in the human genome. PLOS Biology 4 (3), 0446–0458. doi:10.1371/journal.pbio.0040072.

Weir, B.S., Cockerham, C.C., 1984. Estimating F-statistics for the analysis of population structure. Evolution 38 (6), 1358–1370.

Wright, S., 1921. Systems of mating. Genetics 6 (2), 111–178.

Wright, S., 1949. The genetical structure of populations. Annals of Eugenics 15 (1), 323354. doi:10.1111/j.1469–1809.1949.tb02451.x.

Wright, S. , 1955. Classification of the factors of evolution. In: Proceedings of the Cold Spring Harbor Symposia on Quantitative Biology, vol. 20, pp. 16 24. Cold Spring Harbor Laboratory Press.

Xing, J., Watkins, W.S., Witherspoon, D.J., et al., 2009. Fine-scaled human genetic structure revealed by SNP microarrays. Genome Research 19 (5), 815–825. doi:10.1101/gr.085589.108.

Zeng, K., Fu, Y.X., Shi, S., Wu, C.I., 2006. Statistical tests for detecting positive selection by utilizing high-frequency variants. Genetics 174 (3), 1431–1439. doi:10.1534/genetics.106.061432.

Zhang, J., Khan, A., Kennard, A., Grigg, M.E., Parkinson, J., 2017. PopNet: A Markov clustering approach to study population genetic structure. Molecular Biology and Evolution 34 (7), 1799–1811. doi:10.1093/molbev/msx110.

Further Reading

Casillas, S., Barbadilla, A., 2017. Molecular population genetics. doi:10.1534/genetics.116.196493.

Cavalli-Sforza, L., Menozzi, P., Piazza, A., 1994. The History and Geography of Human Genes. Princeton University Press.

Charlesworth, B., Charlesworth, D., 2017. Population genetics from 1966 to 2016. doi:10.1038/hdy.2016.55.

Dyer, R.J., 2015. Population Graphs and Landscape Genetics. Annual Review of Ecology, Evolution, and Systematics 46 (1), 327–342. doi:10.1146/annurev-ecolsys-112414-054150.

Holsinger, K.E., Weir, B.S., 2009. Genetics in geographically structured populations: Defining, estimating and interpreting FST. Nature Reviews Genetics 10 (9), 639–650. doi:10.1038/nrg2611.

Lawson, D.J., Falush, D., 2012. Population identification using genetic data. Annual Review of Genomics and Human Genetics 13 (1), 337–361. doi:10.1146/annurev-genom-082410-101510.

Nielsen R., Akey J.M., Jakobsson M., et al., 2017. Tracingthe peoplingofthe world throughgenomics. doi:10.1038/nature21347.

Ségurel, L., Bon, C., 2017. On the evolution of lactase persistence in humans. Annual Review of Genomics and Human Genetics 18 (1), 297–319. doi:10.1146/annurev-genom-091416-035340.

Population Analysis of Pharmacogenetic Polymorphisms

Zen H Lu and Naeem Shafqat, Universiti Brunei Darussalam, Bandar Seri Begawan, Brunei Darussalam
Nani Azman, Mark IR Petalcorin, and Lie Chen, PAPRSB Institute of Health Sciences, Universiti Brunei Darussalam, Bandar Seri Begawan, Brunei Darussalam

Overview

The practice of modern pharmacological treatment is very much a balancing act between the therapeutic benefit and toxicity or adverse effects of the prescribed drugs. While pharmacokinetic/-dynamic properties of drugs are usually balanced carefully with many exogenous and endogenous factors such as gender, age, weight, comorbid diseases, drug–drug interaction, etc., rarely are impacts of human genetic variation being taken into consideration when it comes to conventional prescription of medications. This is despite the fact that individuals' variation in genes involving in drug reactions/responses (pharmacogenes) within a population and/or among different ethnic groups have well been established to exert a direct impact on the metabolism and hence, the pharmacological efficacy and probable toxicity of drugs (Chung *et al.*, 2004; Hung *et al.*, 2006; Kaniwa *et al.*, 2013). In addition, manifestation of adverse drug reactions (ADRs) and drug efficacy can also vary geographically (Mizzi *et al.*, 2016).

To date, approximately 19,000 genetic variants from about 1600 human genes have been annotated in various databases to play either a direct or an indirect role in drug responses (Pharmgkb, 2017; Whirl-Carrillo *et al.*, 2012). As of December 2017, 255 of these variants are included in the labels of about 200 marketable drugs approved by the U.S. Food and Drug Administration (FDA) (Fda, 2017). This represents a mere 12% of the total number (1607) of FDA-approved drugs. In fact, population-wide genetic variation means that most of the medications are beneficial to only a subset of the treated patients; with the rest remaining either untreated or subsequently developing mild-to-serious ADRs (Schork, 2015; Spear *et al.*, 2001). The National Health Service in the UK has recently reported only 30%–60% "pharmaceutical effectiveness" for drug treatments (Hill, 2015).

"Imprecision" medicine is not only a leading cause of mortality and morbidity globally, the economic burden is enormous too. In the US alone, ADRs were estimated to cost up to approximately 30 billion US dollars annually (Sultana *et al.*, 2013). Until recently, the high costs and technological complexity associated with the precise identification, analysis, and interpretation of genetic variants have hindered the inclusion of these data in the wider pharmacological practices. However, with the advent of genomics technologies, especially that of sequencing and bioinformatics, a vast amount of data on population genetic polymorphism can now be generated. Together with the increasing availability of clinical phenotypes and pharmacosurveillance data, association between these variants and their impacts on drug efficacy and/or toxicity can now be resolved with a much higher resolution at a much lower cost.

This article aims to give a general overview on the population-wide approach to the fields of pharmacogenetics and pharmacogenomics. A particular focus is paid to the different bioinformatics methodologies used in the analysis of population genetic data.

Genetic Basis of Variability in Drug Response

Pharmacogenetics & Pharmacogenomics

The terms *pharmacogenetics* and *pharmacogenomics* are sometimes used interchangeably. The former describes the influence of genetic variants of a single gene or a number of genes on drug response. However, it is evident that many of these genes do interact, either directly or indirectly, and work within a network of drug pathways to contribute to the interindividual differences observed in drug response. Consequently, a comprehensive genome-wide approach, i.e., pharmacogenomics, involving not only the pharmacogenes but also their up- and downstream pathway genes is necessary.

In the simplest sense, for any drug to exert its therapeutic effect after entering the systemic circulation of the body, it has to bind to a certain receptor molecule before being delivered across the cellular membrane to reach and act upon its intended target; and finally with the unwanted end metabolites removed from the body. The cellular transport processes are carried out by the so-called pharmacokinetics (PK) genes, which can affect how a drug is being absorbed into the body and cells, distributed throughout its target sites, metabolized to either active or inactive forms, and excreted out of the body (**Fig. 1**). On the other hand, the effects of a drug on its targets and associated downstream pathways are mediated by pharmacodynamics (PD) genes (**Fig. 1**). Some of these PK and PD genes include ATP-binding cassette (ABC) and solute carrier (SLC) transporters, membrane targeting PDZ proteins, drug receptor families such as the G protein-coupled receptors (GPCRs) and various ion channels, and Phase I and II metabolizing enzymes. Among them, allelic variation in the different member genes of the Phase I enzyme cytochrome P450 (CYP450) family have alone been reported to affect the metabolism of up to approximately 25% of all drugs (Ingelman-Sundberg *et al.*, 2007).

Therefore the desirable therapeutic response to a drug is only elicited when both PK and PD genes are functioning as intended. However, variation in any of these genes may also result in "off target" effects that can cause adverse reactions (Karczewski *et al.*,

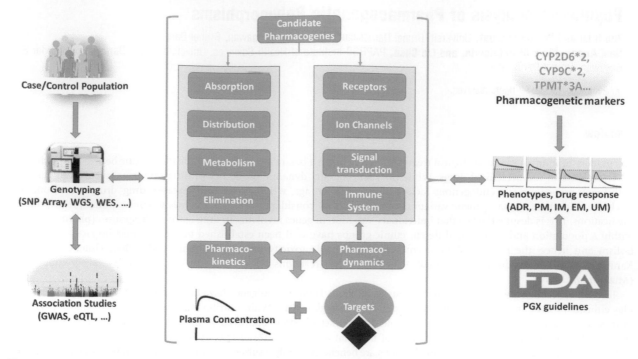

Fig. 1 A workflow of pharmacogenetics/-genomics. The workflow depicts the common steps typically taken to identify a pharmacogenetic allele responsible for a drug response in a population. Variants discovered through various genotyping platforms in patient and control groups are analyzed using the GWAS approach to identify probable causal candidate(s) in PK and/or PD genes. Functional details of these candidates need to be established and clinically validated before any clinical guidelines can be implemented.

2012). Such an "off target" effect may also be induced by a variant in a pharmacogene, which although itself is not involved in-direct interaction with the drug, is a member gene of the drug metabolizing pathway.

In general, pharmacogenetic variability can be broadly classified into three groups:

1. Inherited Mendelian monogenic traits, disorders, or ADRs that are affected by usually single rare coding variants;
2. Oligogenic traits affected by a few PK and/or PD genes; and
3. Complex multifactorial traits affected by not only many small-effect pharmacogenetic variants but possibly also epigenetic and environmental factors (Zhang and Nebert, 2017).

The complexity in predicting and identifying the three categories of pharmacogenetics increases as the number of genes and factors increases, ranging from simple statistical association between genotypes and pharmacological phenotypes to massive whole genome- or exome-wide association studies.

Workflow in Pharmacogenetics

Increasingly, pharmacogenomics research involving large number of patients across different population groups is believed to hold the key to the resolution of low pharmacological efficacy observed in many of today's drug treatments. Identification of pharmacogenetic variants usually adopts either the candidate gene or genome-wide approach. The former involves genotyping of either one or a few (sometimes up to hundreds of) genes using techniques ranging from PCR or SNP array to targeted next-generation sequencing (NGS). This is a workable approach when prior functional knowledge of the pharmacogenes and their related diseases or phenotypes is known. The latter, which sometimes is also known as the hypothesis-generating approach, uses various NGS methodologies to screen for genetic variants that include single-nucleotide variants (SNVs), insertion/deletions (indels), and structural variants (SVs) in the entire genome of patient (*e.g.*, drug responders, ADR patients) and control (e.g., nonresponder, extensive, or normal drug metabolizers) groups (**Fig. 1**). No prior knowledge about any of the genetic variants is necessary for this approach. Although discovery in nature, the genome-wide approach is especially useful for studying complex traits/diseases that are influenced by multiple genetic factors. Compared with the candidate gene approach, this latter approach allows the systematic testing of more hypotheses in order to discover novel associations. Discussion on the advantages and disadvantages of the two approaches and the technologies involved is provided elsewhere (Peters *et al.*, 2010; Yang *et al.*, 2016; Cohn *et al.*, 2017).

NGS technologies have the potential to discover millions of genetic variants in both diseased and healthy control individuals. Characterization of the effects of these variants on drug response forms the main objective of pharmacogenetic/-genomic studies. Whilst the number of methods and tools available for the analysis of genetic variants are too many to be adequately reviewed

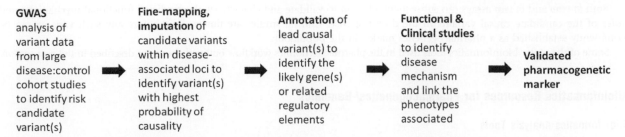

GWAS
analysis of variant data from large disease:control cohort studies to identify risk candidate variant(s) ➡

Fine-mapping, imputation of candidate variants within disease-associated loci to identify variant(s) with highest probability of causality ➡

Annotation of lead causal variant(s) to identify the likely gene(s) or related regulatory elements ➡

Functional & Clinical studies to identify disease mechanism and link the phenotypes associated ➡

Validated pharmacogenetic marker

Fig. 2 A workflow of pharmacogenetics GWAS. True causal candidate variants identified during initial GWAS analysis are usually difficult to distinguish as they cluster with neutral variants in LD. They may also be missing from the list. Fine-mapping process, including filling in the variant gaps using imputation tools, is necessary to refine this list. Functional annotation and studies are next performed to decipher the biological mechanisms behind the association of the variants and drug response.

here (Omicx, 2018; Henry *et al.*, 2014), some basic steps illustrated in **Fig. 2** are commonly adopted, especially for the genome-wide approach.

In the last decade, genome-wide association studies (GWAS) have been widely and successfully used in the identification of single-nucleotide polymorphisms (SNPs) in genes that are associated with a variety of human phenotypes or traits, including that of pharmacogenetic significance (Cooper *et al.*, 2008; Takeuchi *et al.*, 2009; Giacomini *et al.*, 2017). A total of 333 entries on SNP-trait associations for "Response to drug" are now held in the GWAS Catalog (Macarthur *et al.*, 2017).

Statistically, GWAS analysis is basically a straightforward null hypothesis test to identify variant data that lies at the far ends of the null distribution. These are the SNPs in which associations with the tested pharmacological outcome are considered statistically significant. A few factors should be taken into consideration when a pharmacogenomics GWAS is planned. They include the allelic frequency of the SNPs, effect size (small- or large-) of SNPs on the phenotypes, the need of large sample sizes or cohorts to provide the necessary statistical power to identify the candidate SNPs, characteristics (*e.g.*, treatment regimen, patient features such as ethnicity, etc.) of the population studied, and study design (either observational study or randomized controlled trial) (Motsinger-Reif *et al.*, 2013). Furthermore, it is also important to realize that pharmacogenomics GWAS may differ from most other diseased traits in such a way that (1) due the present of clinically well-defined phenotypes with known underlying mechanisms, the pharmacogenomic outcomes are often clear; and (2) association can be established with greater statistical confidence since larger genetic effects may exist in some of the pharmacogenomic phenotypes.

Although many tools have been developed over the years to deal with different forms of GWAS data, some widely used analytical features include distribution of allelic frequencies, Hardy–Weinberg equilibrium, analysis of association between single SNPs and haplotypes with different traits, etc. The results of GWAS analyses are typically presented in a graph as either a QQ or a Manhattan plot of *P*-values representing the association test of each genetic variant across a chromosomal region (Uitterlinden, 2016; Reed *et al.*, 2015).

However, one of the biggest drawbacks of GWAS analysis, including that for pharmacogenomics, is the large number of resulting candidate genetic variants; many of which are clustered in linkage disequilibrium (LD) in the implicated loci. Here, the haplotype structure of these loci makes the distinction between neutral and causal variants difficult (Spain and Barrett, 2015). In addition, rarely do any of the GWAS variants fall within protein-coding sequences. Instead, the vast majority of them are found in the noncoding segments of the human genome where functional details may be incomplete or lacking (Farh *et al.*, 2015); despite efforts such as ENCODE (Encode_Project_Consortium, 2011) and Fantom5 (Kawaji *et al.*, 2017) to annotate these regulatory regions. As a result, direct translation of GWAS variants into targetable pharmacogenetic markers is not always possible and further refinement of the list of candidate variants using methods such as fine-mapping and/or genotype is necessary.

In essence, fine-mapping aims to pinpoint the causal variants and/or genes that statistically are most likely to have a direct effect on the observed phenotype. However, before this can be done, many of the common variants in the loci should be genotyped or imputed with high confidence. This is especially important with GWAS summary data derived from medium- to low-coverage genotyping or whole genome sequencing datasets (Chan *et al.*, 2016). Using comprehensive genotype data such as the 1000 Genomes Project reference panels (1000_Genomes_Project_Consortium *et al.*, 2012), imputation allows variant gaps missing from the genotyping arrays or NGS to be filled in. This much improved dataset can then undergo either a step-wise conditional analysis in which SNPs with the lowest *P*-value or LD are conditioned iteratively till no more SNP is found to reach the threshold of the preassigned *P*-value or analysis using Bayesian methods to assign each of the SNPs with posterior probabilities of causality (Spain and Barrett, 2015).

However, the value of a GWAS/fine-mapping exercise is not fully realized until the underlying functional basis of the refined causal genetic variants and/or the target gene can be resolved with informed biological inference through some post-GWAS analysis. Among them are expression quantitative trait loci analysis, which attempts to correlate genetic variants on regulatory regions with quantitative changes in the expression of genes that are under the control of affected elements (Schroder *et al.*, 2013; Gtex_Consortium, 2015); genome-wide gene enrichment and pathway analysis to link a trait or phenotype to a pathway(s) instead of looking at single genes only (Postmus *et al.*, 2014; Di Iulio and Rotger, 2011); and protein–protein interaction analysis to predict drug repurposing (Pritchard *et al.*, 2017).

Both *in vitro* and *in vivo* assays can subsequently be run to validate and characterize the predicted functional mechanisms and roles of the candidate causal variants in the drug response. Clinical studies are finally done before any such variants can be confidently established as a pharmacogenetics marker in the population.

Some of the major bioinformatics tools used in the pharmacogenomics workflow outlined above are described in the next section.

Bioinformatics Resources for Pharmacogenetics/-Genomics

Bioinformatics Analysis Tools

GWAS are currently seen as one of the best methodologies for population analysis of pharmacogenetic polymorphisms. Advances in NGS technologies and the accompanying bioinformatics tools have allowed GWAS to be conducted with higher statistically precision. It is therefore not unexpected that nearly 500 tools have been developed to analyze various aspects of GWAS (Omicx, 2018). A few of the widely used ones are discussed below.

General GWAS analysis

PLINK: A free open-source whole genome GWAS toolset capable of performing analyses ranging from the very basic to the large-scale computationally demanding ones (Chang *et al.*, 2015; Purcell *et al.*, 2007). PLINK does not do any pre-GWAS analysis, such as genotype or CNV calling. It is a pure genotype/phenotype analytical tool with support for visualization, annotation, and management of results.

GenABEL: A software package based on the R statistical programming language; it is used for the statistical analyses of genome variation data (Aulchenko *et al.*, 2007). It contains subprograms to do to genome-wide association (GWA) analysis (GenABEL, ProbABEL, MixABEL, OmicABEL), meta-analysis (MetABEL), parallelization of GWA analyses (ParallABEL), management of very large files (DatABEL), and evaluation of prediction (PredictABEL). It also provides tools for visualizing the statistical output.

Bioconductor: Another R open-source and open development effort to provide a comprehensive collection of tools to analyze different types of high-throughput genomic data (*e.g.*, microarray, NGS genotypes) (Huber *et al.*, 2015). A number of R programs are included in Bioconductor to deal with association studies, including GWASTools (Gogarten *et al.*, 2012) and traseR (Chen and Qin, 2016).

Imputation

IMPUTE: The program or its latest version IMPUTE2 is a tool used for genotype imputation and phasing in GWAS/fine-mapping studies. It is based on dense marker sets such as haplotypes from the 1000 Genomes Project (Howie *et al.*, 2009). IMPUTE2 can achieve a higher accuracy and allow information across multiple reference panels to be combined while remaining computationally feasible.

BEAGLE: A software package that performs "genotype calling, genotype phasing, imputation of ungenotyped markers, and identity-by-descent segment detection" (Browning and Browning, 2016; Browning and Browning, 2007). It is capable of analyzing big genetic datasets containing hundreds of thousands of genotypes on thousands of samples.

MACH: The core function of this package is to perform genotype imputation and haplotype phasing in samples of unrelated individuals within a variety of populations (Li *et al.*, 2010). The software achieves this by using the HapMap sample or other densely genotyped individuals (*e.g.*, from the 1000 Genomes Project) as a reference. Simple tests of association can also be run using MACH.

Functional annotation of variants

Variant Effect Predictor: A powerful toolset developed by ENSEMBL to analyze, annotate, and prioritize genomic variants (SNPs, insertions, deletions, CNVs, or SVs) in both coding and noncoding regions (Mclaren *et al.*, 2016).

SnpEff: A toolbox containing different programs to annotate and predict the effects of genetic variants on genes and proteins (Cingolani *et al.*, 2012). It also allows annotation using the GWAS catalog (Nhgri-Ebi, 2018).

ANNOVAR: A tool to efficiently annotate genetic variants (SNVs and indels) (Wang *et al.*, 2010). Using update-to-date information, it assigns "functional consequences of genes, inferring cytogenetic bands, reporting functional importance scores, finding variants in conserved regions, or identifying variants reported in the 1000 Genomes Project and dbSNP."

Databases

For a long time, genetic variants associated with drug response have been deposited together with other data in various large-scale databases such as the dbSNP of NCBI and European Genome–Phenome Archive of EBI. However, the ever-increasing genetic and genomic data generated from population-wide sequencing and GWAS studies has seen the growth of dedicated pharmacogenomics-centric web resources. Some of these have been reviewed elsewhere (Zhang *et al.*, 2015; Potamias *et al.*, 2014; Sim *et al.*, 2011) and a few of the prominent ones are discussed here (**Table 1**).

PharmGKB (The Pharmacogenomics Knowledge Base) is a curated knowledge base providing organized information on the impacts of human genetic variations on drug response. It currently holds annotation for about 19,000 genetic variants (SNP, indel, repeat, haplotype). They are integrated into nearly 3500 genotype–phenotype relationships; 500 clinical prescriptions in the form of drug labelings, 98 genotype-based dosing recommendations, and 128 pathways showing the association of genotypes with PK

Table 1 Web-based Databases of Pharmacogenomics

Database (url)	Features	Reference
PharmGKB The Pharmacogenomics Knowledge base (https://www.pharmgkb.org/)	A curated knowledge base providing organized information on the impacts of human genetic variations on drug response. Among the vast resources, the database also contains clinical prescribing information detailing gene–drug associations, genotype–phenotype relationships, and dosing guidelines.	Whirl-Carrillo *et al.* (2012)
PharmVar Pharmacogene Variation Consortium (https://www.pharmvar.org/)	A central repository of haplotype structure and allelic variants of pharmacogenes. The database is a transition from the CYP-allele Database (http://www.cypalleles.ki.se/), which contains the nomenclature of human *CYP450* alleles.	Gaedigk *et al.* (2018); Sim *et al.* (2010)
DrugBank (https://www.drugbank.ca/)	A comprehensive bioinformatics and cheminformatics database containing information on drugs and drug targets. It also contains resources on pharmaco-genomics, -metabolomics, -transcriptomics, and -proteomics.	Wishart *et al.* (2018, 2006)
CPIC The Clinical Pharmacogenetics Implementation Consortium (https://cpicpgx.org/)	A detailed collection of regularly updated, peer-reviewed, and evidence-based clinical practice guidelines to facilitate the implementation of pharmacogenetic tests for patient care.	Relling and Klein (2011), Caudle *et al.* (2014)
SPHINX Sequence and Phenotype Integration Exchange (https://www.emergesphinx.org/)	A searchable catalog of inherited variants found in 82 important pharmacogenes of a large population cohort. In addition to the lists of genes, drugs, and pathways, SPHINX also contains such information as the implication of the genetic variations, drug interactions, and allelic frequencies of variants.	Rasmussen-Torvik, *et al.* (2014)
ePGA electronic Pharmacogenomics Assistant (http://www.epga.gr/)	A collection of public datasets linking the interactions between drug metabolizing status and the related haplotype information. The genotype-to-phenotype translation tool matches individual genotype profiles with known pharmacogenetics variation to give an indicative drug efficacy/toxicity summary.	Lakiotaki *et al.* (2016)
FDA Pharmacogenomic Biomarkers (https://www.fda.gov/Drugs/ScienceResearch/ucm572698.htm)	A table listing the pharmacogenomic biomarkers of FDA-approved drugs. Information includes clinical response, drug exposure variability, and dosing recommendation due either to germline or somatic variants of the pharmacogenes.	
PharmaADME Pharmacogenetics of Absorption, Distribution, Metabolism & Excretion genes (http://pharmaadme.org/)	An industry–academia effort that provides lists of standardized "evidence based" pharmacogenetics biomarkers that affect the absorption, distribution, metabolism, and excretion of drugs.	
PhID Pharmacology Interactions Database (http://phid.ditad.org/)	A database that allows visualization of complex network relationships among diseases, targets, drugs, genes, side effects, and pathways.	Deng *et al.* (2017)
GPCRdb G protein-coupled receptors (GPCRs) Database (http://gpcrdb.org/)	A comprehensive database containing data on genes, proteins, tertiary structures, ligand-receptors, and drug targets of GPCRs. The site also provides tools to select and study the impact of natural genetic variation for the drug targets of GPCRs.	Isberg *et al.* (2016), Hauser *et al.* (2018)
The NATs database The database of arylamine N-acetyltransferases (NATs) (http://nat.mbg.duth.gr/)	This database set up by The *NAT* Gene Nomenclature Committee covers the nomenclature and alleles of the polymorphic phase II xenobiotic metabolizing enzymes, arylamine NATs, from both eukaryotes, including those from the human, and prokaryotes.	Hein, *et al.* (2008)
PMT database The Pharmacogenetics of Membrane Transporters (http://pharmacogenetics.ucsf.edu/)	A database that provides information on both coding and noncoding genetic variants of solute carrier (SLC) transporters and ATP-binding cassette (ABC) transporters. Locations of the variants on the gene and secondary protein structure are also mapped. In addition, allelic frequencies in major racial and ethnic populations are also given.	Kroetz *et al.* (2010)
UGT-allele database The UDP-glucuronosyltransferaseAllele Nomenclature (https://www.pharmacogenomics.pha.ulaval.ca/ugt-alleles-nomenclature/)	A catalogue of human *UGT1A* and *UGT2B* haplotypes and SNPs. Information of pharmacogenetic relevance include allelic names, nucleotide changes, protein effects, genotype–phenotypes.	Mackenzie *et al.* (2005)

and PD of drugs; and 64 Very Important Pharmacogenes (VIP) where there is considerable evidence on the pharmacogenomics of each of the genes.

PharmVar (Pharmacogene Variation Consortium) is a central repository of haplotype structure and allelic variants of pharmacogenes. This updated database is a transition from the Human Cytochrome P450 (CYP) Allele Nomenclature Database (**Table 1**), which housed the nomenclature and genotypes of the human CYP450 alleles.

DrugBank is a comprehensive bioinformatics and cheminformatics database that encompasses information such as PK, PD, ADRs, ADEMT, etc., of drugs and drug targets. In addition, it also contains multiomics (pharmacogenomics, -metalobomics, -transcriptomics and -proteomics) resources on the drug–gene interactions.

CPIC (The Clinical Pharmacogenetics Implementation Consortium) is a consortial effort to address the difficulty in translating pharmacogenetic findings into actionable prescribing information for clinicians. The database provides detailed collection of regularly updated, peer-reviewed, and evidence-based clinical practice guidelines to facilitate the implementation of pharmacogenetic tests for patient care. A total of 34 guidelines and updates have been published to date (January 2018).

SPHINX (Sequence and Phenotype Integration Exchange) is a searchable catalogue of inherited variants in 82 very important pharmacogenes identified from large population studies. In addition, the database also contains such information as the implication of the genetic variations, drug interactions, allelic frequencies of variants, and pathways of metabolism and diseases.

ePGA (electronic Pharmacogenomics Assistant) is a collection of public datasets used to provide associations between the haplotypes/alleles and possible ADME reactions. The genotype-to-phenotype translation tool matches individual genotype profiles with known pharmacogenetics variation to give an indicative drug efficacy/toxicity summary.

FDA Pharmacogenomic Biomarkers is a table listing FDA-approved drugs with labelings containing information on the associated pharmacogenomic biomarkers. Other information on the labeling includes clinical response, drug exposure variability, and dosing recommendation due either to germline or somatic variants of pharmacogenes.

e-PKGene integrates information from different resources to allow quantitative analysis of how genetic variants of drug metabolizing enzymes and transporters impact on pharmacokinetic responses to drugs and metabolites. Where available, summaries of the impact of variants on drugs and metabolites in different populations are also provided.

PharmaADME (Pharmacogenetics of Absorption, Distribution, Metabolism & Excretion genes) is an industry–academia effort that provides a consensus core list of standardized "evidence based" pharmacogenetic biomarkers that have been shown to affect the absorption, distribution, metabolism, and excretion of drugs.

PhID (Pharmacology Interactions Database) is a database that allows visualization of complex network relationships among diseases, targets, drugs, genes, side effects, and pathways.

SuperCYP is a Cytochrome P450 database containing genetic variants of *CYP450* genes. The site also provide a tool to analyze interactions between CYP450 enzymes and drugs.

GPCRdb (GPCRs Database) is a comprehensive database containing data on genes, proteins, tertiary structures, ligand-receptor, and drug targets of GPCRs. The site also provides tools to select and study the impact of natural genetic variation for the drug targets of GPCRs.

The NATs database (The database of arylamine N-acetyltransferases (NATs)), set up by the *NAT* Gene Nomenclature Committee, covers the nomenclature and alleles of the polymorphic phase II xenobiotic metabolizing enzymes, arylamine NATs, from both eukaryotes, including those from the human, and prokaryotes.

PMT database (the Pharmacogenetics of Membrane Transporters) provides information on both coding and noncoding genetic variants of SLC transporters and ABC transporters. Locations of the variants on the gene and secondary protein structure are also mapped. In addition, allelic frequencies in major ethnic population groups are also given.

UGT-allele database (The UDP-glucuronosyltransferase Allele Nomenclature) is a catalogue of human *UGT1A* and *UGT2B* haplotypes and SNPs. Information of pharmacogenetic relevance includes allelic names, nucleotide changes, protein effects, genotype–phenotypes.

Pharmacogenetics in Practice

Although clinical implementation of pharmacogenomics is yet to be fully realized, there have been some success stories thus far. To date, the Clinical Pharmacogenetics Implementation Consortium has issued detailed practical guidelines for the application of pharmacogenetics in the therapeutic usage of 35 drugs (Relling and Klein, 2011; Drew, 2016). Among them is the genotyping of the highly variable major histocompatibility complex class I allele (*HLA*) (Becquemont, 2010) for abacavir (Watson *et al.*, 2009; Young *et al.*, 2008), carbamazepine (Phillips *et al.*, 2018), and allopurinol (Saito *et al.*, 2016; Hershfield *et al.*, 2013); the drugs prescribed for the treatment of HIV, epilepsy, and gout respectively. Approximately 5%–8% Caucasian and 0.26%–3.6% African American, Asian, and Hispanic HIV/AIDS patients with the *HLA-B*57:01* allele are affected by the abacavir hypersensitivity syndrome during the first 6 weeks of drug administration (Ma *et al.*, 2010). Screening for this allele prior to drug therapy is therefore recommended by various healthcare authorities worldwide (Martin *et al.*, 2012). On the other hand, patients harboring the *HLA-B*15:02* pharmacogenetic marker of Southeast Asian and Chinese origin are known to suffer from severe and potentially fatal carbamazepine-induced cutaneous adverse reactions such as toxic epidermal necrolysis (TEN) and Stevens–Johnson syndrome (SJS). This allele is present in approximately 10%–15% of the population groups in this region but <1% in the Japanese and Korean population; and it is largely absent in other non-Asian population groups (Chung *et al.*, 2004; Hung *et al.*, 2006; Kaniwa *et al.*, 2013). Similarly, allopurinol-induced TEN/SJS is more prevalent in Taiwanese and Southeast Asian patients with the *HLA-B*58:01* allele (Hung *et al.*, 2005; Tassaneeyakul *et al.*, 2009).

It is estimated that almost 60%–70% of all breast cancers are estrogen receptor (ER)-positive and therefore, inhibitors of ER signaling, such as tamoxifen (TAM), remain as one of the most widely prescribed drug treatment options for patients (Hertz *et al.*, 2017). TAM has been shown to reduce the recurrence and mortality rates by one third in both pre- and postmenopausal women (Goetz *et al.*, 2008). However, approximately 40% of patients are unresponsive to the treatment due to interindividual genetic variability (Hertz *et al.*, 2017). The highly polymorphic drug metabolizing gene *CYP2D6* (with > 160 alleles (Gaedigk *et al.*, 2018; Pharmgkb, 2017) has been implicated in this unsatisfactory treatment outcome (Rofaiel *et al.*, 2010). For instance, *CYP2D6*10* allele, which corresponds to a decreased enzyme activity and intermediate drug metabolism, is more prevalent amongst Asians and Africans; with the phenotype amounting to about 38%–70% (Rofaiel *et al.*, 2010). On the hand, the allele *CYP2D6*4*, which corresponds to a nonfunctional variant and hence a poor metabolism (PM) phenotype, is more prevalent amongst Caucasians (Fernandez-Santander *et al.*, 2013) than Asians (Lim *et al.*, 2011). Due to its obvious medical benefit, the US FDA has in fact approved pharmacogenetic testings for *CYP2D6* variants prior to treatment with tamoxifen (Rofaiel *et al.*, 2010).

In addition, pharmacogenomics research on a number of other drugs are currently undertaken by various large international consortia (Giacomini *et al.*, 2017). Translation of such efforts into more pharmacogenomic guidelines and clinical implementation should further expand the success stories.

Conclusions

The ability to interrogate genetic variation at a population scale over the last decade has seen a rapid paradigm shift in medicine, in particular the field of drug treatment, from the "one size fits all" approach to a more targeted and precise treatment tailored according to an individual's genetic and genomic profile. Although most patients have been shown to harbor at least one actionable pharmacogenetic variant (Van Driest *et al.*, 2014), clinical prediction of drug response due to these genotypes has only been applied to relatively few drugs, which exclude even many of the most commonly prescribed ones (Relling and Evans, 2015; Caudle *et al.*, 2014; Janssens and Van Duijn, 2008). In most of these cases, pharmacogenetic guidelines are only provided to drugs whereby a small number of large-effect contributing genetic variants can be confidently associated with a clearly defined set of phenotypes such as efficacy effects and ADRs.

Pharmacogenetic association between drugs and complex traits, such as type 2 diabetes (Florez, 2017) and irritable bowel syndrome (Rufini *et al.*, 2017), usually involves multiple genetic factors and accurate deciphering of such relationship remains challenging. Not only are the genotype–phenotype association marginal in many of the complex diseases, some pharmacogenetic variants also work in combination to exert their effects (Zhang and Nebert, 2017). In addition, many of pharmacological phenotypes can further be complicated by changes in gene expression (Gamazon *et al.*, 2010), epigenetic regulation (Cacabelos and Torrellas, 2015; Pisanu *et al.*, 2018), and protein–protein interactions (Shiota *et al.*, 2008) brought about by genetic variation in either the pharmacogenes or their associated pathway genes.

Although advances in NGS and GWAS technologies have enabled many more pharmacogenetic variants to be identified through the running of large-scale cohort studies and some even at a whole-nation level (Gudbjartsson *et al.*, 2015), this deluge of data is also accompanied by increases in biases and noise of the data. Therefore, improved computational methodologies that are capable of handling veracity of big genomic data are needed.

More importantly, variants identified in many of these large sample size studies are not always going to benefit pharmacogenomic GWAS due to the simple fact that the prevalence, and hence the availability, of large sample size is usually not possible with multidrugs induced diseases having clear defined adverse pharmacological phenotypes. This much needed statistical resolution provided by the sample size is further reduced when the interethnic genetic variation is also taken into consideration. Although some progresses have recently been made to provide a glimpse into the pharmacogenomics of various population groups across the world (Ramos *et al.*, 2014; Giacomini *et al.*, 2017), the number of individuals with ADRs sequenced within each of the different ethnic groups remains small. The trend of sequencing and fine-mapping of genetic variants in other non-European and ancestral populations is, therefore, expected to continue. Technologies such as improved GWAS, as well as whole genome and exome NGS, will aid in better translation of ethnicity-specific pharmacogenetic/-genomic findings into clinical practice (Chan *et al.*, 2015; Popejoy and Fullerton, 2016).

The field of pharmacogenomics is developing rapidly. However, continuous national-scale genotyping of population groups and whole genome/exome GWAS alone are not likely to result in widespread clinical application of pharmacogenomics. Further technological and methodological advancement in areas such as long read sequencing, imputation, and precision fine-mapping are needed to increase the quantity and quality of the pharmacogenomics variants. Coupled with a more integrated approach encompassing multiomics system biology, healthcare records, and artificial intelligence, pharmacogenomic data derived from population-wide analysis is expected to ultimately speed up the introduction of stratified, if not personalized, drug treatment in the near future.

See also: Genetics and Population Analysis. Natural Language Processing Approaches in Bioinformatics

---

References

Abecasis, G.R., Auton, A., Brooks, L.D., *et al.*, 2012.An integrated map of genetic variation from 1092 human genomes. Nature 491, 56–65.
Aulchenko, Y.S., Ripke, S., Isaacs, A., Van Duijn, C.M., 2007. GenABEL: An R library for genome-wide association analysis. Bioinformatics 23, 1294–1296.
Becquemont, L., 2010. HLA: A pharmacogenomics success story. Pharmacogenomics 11, 277–281.
Browning, B.L., Browning, S.R., 2016. Genotype imputation with millions of reference samples. American Journal of Human Genetics 98, 116–126.

Browning, S.R., Browning, B.L., 2007. Rapid and accurate haplotype phasing and missing-data inference for whole-genome association studies by use of localized haplotype clustering. American Journal of Human Genetics 81, 1084–1097.

Cacabelos, R., Torrellas, C., 2015. Epigenetics of aging and Alzheimer's disease: Implications for pharmacogenomics and drug response. International Journal of Molecular Sciences 16, 30483–30543.

Caudle, K.E., Klein, T.E., Hoffman, J.M., et al., 2014. Incorporation of pharmacogenomics into routine clinical practice: The Clinical Pharmacogenetics Implementation Consortium (CPIC) guideline development process. Current Drug Metabolism 15, 209–217.

Chan, A.W., Hamblin, M.T., Jannink, J.L., 2016. Evaluating imputation algorithms for low-depth Genotyping-By-Sequencing (GBS) data. PLOS ONE 11, e0160733.

Chan, S.L., Jin, S., Loh, M., Brunham, L.R., 2015. Progress in understanding the genomic basis for adverse drug reactions: A comprehensive review and focus on the role of ethnicity. Pharmacogenomics 16, 1161–1178.

Chang, C.C., Chow, C.C., Tellier, L.C., et al., 2015. Second-generation PLINK: Rising to the challenge of larger and richer datasets. Gigascience 4, 7.

Chen, L., Qin, Z.S., 2016. traseR: An R package for performing trait-associated SNP enrichment analysis in genomic intervals. Bioinformatics 32, 1214–1216.

Chung, W.H., Hung, S.I., Hong, H.S., et al., 2004. Medical genetics: A marker for Stevens-Johnson syndrome. Nature 428, 486.

Cingolani, P., Platts, A., Wang Le, L., et al., 2012. A program for annotating and predicting the effects of single nucleotide polymorphisms, SnpEff: SNPs in the genome of Drosophila melanogaster strain w1118; iso-2; iso-3. Fly (Austin) 6, 80–92.

Cohn, I., Paton, T.A., Marshall, C.R., et al., 2017. Genome sequencing as a platform for pharmacogenetic genotyping: A pediatric cohort study. NPJ Genomic Medicine 2, 19.

Cooper, G.M., Johnson, J.A., Langaee, T.Y., et al., 2008. A genome-wide scan for common genetic variants with a large influence on warfarin maintenance dose. Blood 112, 1022–1027.

Deng, Z., Tu, W., Deng, Z., Hu, Q.N., 2017. PhID: An open-access integrated pharmacology interactions database for drugs, targets, diseases, genes, side-effects, and pathways. Journal of Chemical Information and Modelling 57, 2395–2400.

Di Iulio, J., Rotger, M., 2011. Pharmacogenomics: What is next? Frontiers in Pharmacology 2, 86.

Drew, L., 2016. Pharmacogenetics: The right drug for you. Nature 537, S60–S62.

2011.A user's guide to the encyclopedia of DNA elements (ENCODE). PLOS Biology 9, e1001046.

Farh, K.K., Marson, A., Zhu, J., et al., 2015. Genetic and epigenetic fine mapping of causal autoimmune disease variants. Nature 518, 337–343.

Fda, 2017. Table of Pharmacogenomic Biomarkers in Drug Labeling [Online]. Available at: https://www.fda.gov/Drugs/ScienceResearch/ucm572698.htm (accessed 06.12.2017).

Fernandez-Santander, A., Gaibar, M., Novillo, A., et al., 2013. Relationship between genotypes Sult1a2 and Cyp2d6 and tamoxifen metabolism in breast cancer patients. PLOS ONE 8, e70183.

Florez, J.C., 2017. The pharmacogenetics of metformin. Diabetologia 60, 1648–1655.

Gaedigk, A., Ingelman-Sundberg, M., Miller, N.A., et al., 2018. The Pharmacogene Variation (PharmVar) Consortium: Incorporation of the Human Cytochrome P450 (CYP) allele nomenclature database. Clinical Pharmacology Therapeutics 103 (3), 399–401.

Gamazon, E.R., Huang, R.S., Cox, N.J., Dolan, M.E., 2010. Chemotherapeutic drug susceptibility associated SNPs are enriched in expression quantitative trait loci. Proceedings of the National Academy of Sciences of the United States of America 107, 9287–9292.

Giacomini, K.M., Yee, S.W., Mushiroda, T., et al., 2017. Genome-wide association studies of drug response and toxicity: An opportunity for genome medicine. Nature Reviews Drug Discovery 16, 1.

Goetz, M.P., Kamal, A., Ames, M.M., 2008. Tamoxifen pharmacogenomics: The role of CYP2D6 as a predictor of drug response. Clinical Pharmacology Therapeutics 83, 160–166.

Gogarten, S.M., Bhangale, T., Conomos, M.P., et al., 2012. GWASTools: An R/Bioconductor package for quality control and analysis of genome-wide association studies. Bioinformatics 28, 3329–3331.

2015.Human genomics. The Genotype-Tissue Expression (GTEx) pilot analysis: Multitissue gene regulation in humans. Science 348, 648–660.

Gudbjartsson, D.F., Helgason, H., Gudjonsson, S.A., et al., 2015. Large-scale whole-genome sequencing of the Icelandic population. Nature Genetics 47, 435–444.

Hauser, A.S., Chavali, S., Masuho, I., et al., 2018. Pharmacogenomics of GPCR drug targets. Cell 172 (1–2), 41–54.

Hein, D.W., Boukouvala, S., Grant, D.M., Minchin, R.F., Sim, E., 2008. Changes in consensus arylamine N-acetyltransferase gene nomenclature. Pharmacogenet Genomics 18, 367–368.

Henry, V.J., Bandrowski, A.E., Pepin, A.S., Gonzalez, B.J., Desfeux, A., 2014. OMICtools: An informative directory for multi-omic data analysis. Database (Oxford) 2014, bau069.

Hershfield, M.S., Callaghan, J.T., Tassaneeyakul, W., et al., 2013. Clinical Pharmacogenetics Implementation Consortium guidelines for human leukocyte antigen-B genotype and allopurinol dosing. Clinical Pharmacology and Therapeutics 93, 153–158.

Hertz, D.L., Kidwell, K.M., Hilsenbeck, S.G., et al., 2017. CYP2D6 genotype is not associated with survival in breast cancer patients treated with tamoxifen: Results from a population-based study. Breast Cancer Research and Treatment 166, 277–287.

Hill, S., 2015. Taking a more personalised approach to diagnosis and care [Online]. Available: https://www.england.nhs.uk/blog/sue-hill/ (accessed 20.07.2017).

Howie, B.N., Donnelly, P., Marchini, J., 2009. A flexible and accurate genotype imputation method for the next generation of genome-wide association studies. PLOS Genetics 5, e1000529.

Huber, W., Carey, V.J., Gentleman, R., et al., 2015. Orchestrating high-throughput genomic analysis with Bioconductor. Nature Methods 12, 115–121.

Hung, S.I., Chung, W.H., Jee, S.H., et al., 2006. Genetic susceptibility to carbamazepine-induced cutaneous adverse drug reactions. Pharmacogenet Genomics 16, 297–306.

Hung, S.I., Chung, W.H., Liou, L.B., et al., 2005. HLA-B*5801 allele as a genetic marker for severe cutaneous adverse reactions caused by allopurinol. Proceedings of the National Academy of Sciences of the United States of America 102, 4134–4139.

Ingelman-Sundberg, M., Sim, S.C., Gomez, A., Rodriguez-Antona, C., 2007. Influence of cytochrome P450 polymorphisms on drug therapies: Pharmacogenetic, pharmacoepigenetic and clinical aspects. Pharmacology and Therapeutics 116, 496–526.

Isberg, V., Mordalski, S., Munk, C., et al., 2016. GPCRdb: An information system for G protein-coupled receptors. Nucleic Acids Research 44, D356–D364.

Janssens, A.C., Van Duijn, C.M., 2008. Genome-based prediction of common diseases: Advances and prospects. Human Molecular Genetics 17, R166–R173.

Kaniwa, N., Sugiyama, E., Saito, Y., et al. 2013.Specific HLA types are associated with antiepileptic drug-induced Stevens-Johnson syndrome and toxic epidermal necrolysis in Japanese subjects. Pharmacogenomics 14, 1821–1831.

Karczewski, K.J., Daneshjou, R., Altman, R.B., 2012. Chapter 7: Pharmacogenomics. PLOS Computational Biology 8, e1002817.

Kawaji, H., Kasukawa, T., Forrest, A., Carninci, P., Hayashizaki, Y., 2017. The FANTOM5 collection, a data series underpinning mammalian transcriptome atlases in diverse cell types. Scientific Data 4, 170113.

Kroetz, D.L., Yee, S.W., Giacomini, K.M., 2010. The pharmacogenomics of membrane transporters project: Research at the interface of genomics and transporter pharmacology. Clinical Pharmacology and Therapeutics 87, 109–116.

Lakiotaki, K., Kartsaki, E., Kanterakis, A., et al., 2016. ePGA: A Web-Based Information System for Translational Pharmacogenomics. PLOS ONE 11, e0162801.

Li, Y., Willer, C.J., Ding, J., Scheet, P., Abecasis, G.R., 2010. MaCH: Using sequence and genotype data to estimate haplotypes and unobserved genotypes. Genetic Epidemiology 34, 816–834.

Lim, J.S., Chen, X.A., Singh, O., et al., 2011. Impact of CYP2D6, CYP3A5, CYP2C9 and CYP2C19 polymorphisms on tamoxifen pharmacokinetics in Asian breast cancer patients. British Journal of Clinical Pharmacology 71, 737–750.

Macarthur, J., Bowler, E., Cerezo, M., et al., 2017. The new NHGRI-EBI Catalog of published genome-wide association studies (GWAS Catalog). Nucleic Acids Research 45, D896–D901.

Mackenzie, P.I., Bock, K.W., Burchell, B., et al., 2005. Nomenclature update for the mammalian UDP glycosyltransferase (UGT) gene superfamily. Pharmacogenet Genomics 15, 677–685.

Martin, M.A., Klein, T.E., Dong, B.J., et al. 2012.Clinical pharmacogenetics implementation consortium guidelines for HLA-B genotype and abacavir dosing. Clinical Pharmacology and Therapeutics 91, 734–738.

Ma, J.D., Lee, K.C., Kuo, G.M., 2010. HLA-B*5701 testing to predict abacavir hypersensitivity. PLOS Currents 2, RRN1203.

Mclaren, W., Gil, L., Hunt, S.E., et al., 2016. The Ensembl Variant Effect Predictor. Genome Biology 17, 122.

Mizzi, C., Dalabira, E., Kumuthini, J., et al., 2016. A European spectrum of Pharmacogenomic biomarkers: Implications for clinical pharmacogenomics. PLOS ONE 11, e0162866.

Motsinger-Reif, A.A., Jorgenson, E., Relling, M.V., et al., 2013. Genome-wide association studies in pharmacogenomics: Successes and lessons. Pharmacogenet Genomics 23, 383–394.

Nhgri-Ebi. 2018. GWAS Catalog [Online]. Available at: http://www.ebi.ac.uk/gwas. (accessed).

Omicx, 2018. OMICtools [Online]. Available at: https://omictools.com/whole-genome-resequencing-category. (accessed 17.02.2018).

Peters, B.J., Rodin, A.S., De Boer, A., Maitland-Van Der Zee, A.H., 2010. Methodological and statistical issues in pharmacogenomics. Journal of Pharmacy and Pharmacology 62, 161–166.

Pharmgkb, 2017. PharmGKB: The Pharmacogenomics Knowledgebase [Online]. Available: https://www.pharmgkb.org/. (accessed 28.12.2017).

Phillips, E.J., Sukasem, C., Whirl-Carrillo, M., et al., 2018. Clinical Pharmacogenetics Implementation Consortium guideline for HLA genotype and use of carbamazepine and oxcarbazepine. 2017 update. Clinical Pharmacology Therapeutics 103 (4), 574–581.

Pisanu, C., Katsila, T., Patrinos, G.P., Squassina, A., 2018. Recent trends on the role of epigenomics, metabolomics and noncoding RNAs in rationalizing mood stabilizing treatment. Pharmacogenomics 19, 129–143.

Popejoy, A.B., Fullerton, S.M., 2016. Genomics is failing on diversity. Nature 538, 161–164.

Postmus, I., Trompet, S., Deshmukh, H.A., et al., 2014. Pharmacogenetic meta-analysis of genome-wide association studies of LDL cholesterol response to statins. Nature Communications 5, 5068.

Potamias, G., Lakiotaki, K., Katsila, T., et al., 2014. Deciphering next-generation pharmacogenomics: An information technology perspective. Open Biology 4, 140071.

Pritchard, J.E., O'mara, T.A., Glubb, D.M., 2017. Enhancing the Promise of Drug Repositioning through Genetics. Frontiers in Pharmacology 8, 896.

Purcell, S., Neale, B., Todd-Brown, K., et al., 2007. PLINK: A tool set for whole-genome association and population-based linkage analyses. American Journal of Human Genetics 81, 559–575.

Ramos, E., Doumatey, A., Elkahloun, A.G., et al., 2014. Pharmacogenomics, ancestry and clinical decision making for global populations. The Pharmacogenomics Journal 14, 217–222.

Rasmussen-Torvik, L.J., Stallings, S.C., Gordon, A.S., et al., 2014. Design and anticipated outcomes of the eMERGE-PGx project: A multicenter pilot for preemptive pharmacogenomics in electronic health record systems. Clinical Pharmacology Therapy 96, 482–489.

Reed, E., Nunez, S., Kulp, D., et al., 2015. A guide to genome-wide association analysis and post-analytic interrogation. Statistics in Medicine 34, 3769–3792.

Relling, M.V., Evans, W.E., 2015. Pharmacogenomics in the clinic. Nature 526, 343–350.

Relling, M.V., Klein, T.E., 2011. CPIC: Clinical Pharmacogenetics Implementation Consortium of the pharmacogenomics research network. Clinical Pharmacology Therapeutics 89, 464–467.

Rofaiel, S., Muo, E.N., Mousa, S.A., 2010. Pharmacogenetics in breast cancer: Steps toward personalized medicine in breast cancer management. Pharmacogenomics and Personalized Medicine 3, 129–143.

Rufini, S., Ciccacci, C., Novelli, G., Borgiani, P., 2017. Pharmacogenetics of inflammatory bowel disease: A focus on Crohn's disease. Pharmacogenomics 18, 1095–1114.

Saito, Y., Stamp, L.K., Caudle, K.E., et al. 2016.Clinical Pharmacogenetics Implementation Consortium (CPIC) guidelines for human leukocyte antigen B (HLA-B) genotype and allopurinol dosing: 2015 update. Clinical Pharmacology and Therapeutics 99, 36–37.

Schork, N.J., 2015. Personalized medicine: Time for one-person trials. Nature 520, 609–611.

Schroder, A., Klein, K., Winter, S., et al., 2013. Genomics of ADME gene expression: Mapping expression quantitative trait loci relevant for absorption, distribution, metabolism and excretion of drugs in human liver. The Pharmacogenomics Journal 13, 12–20.

Shiota, M., Kusakabe, H., Hikita, Y., et al., 2008. Pharmacogenomics of cardiovascular pharmacology: Molecular network analysis in pleiotropic effects of statin – An experimental elucidation of the pharmacologic action from protein-protein interaction analysis. Journal of Pharmacological Sciences 107, 15–19.

Sim, S.C., Altman, R.B., Ingelman-Sundberg, M., 2011. Databases in the area of pharmacogenetics. Human Mutation 32, 526–531.

Sim, S.C., Ingelman-Sundberg, M., 2010. The Human Cytochrome P450 (CYP) Allele Nomenclature website: A peer-reviewed database of CYP variants and their associated effects. Human Genomics 4, 278.

Spain, S.L., Barrett, J.C., 2015. Strategies for fine-mapping complex traits. Human Molecular Genetics 24, R111–R119.

Spear, B.B., Heath-Chiozzi, M., Huff, J., 2001. Clinical application of pharmacogenetics. Trends in Molecular Medicine 7, 201–204.

Sultana, J., Cutroneo, P., Trifiro, G., 2013. Clinical and economic burden of adverse drug reactions. Journal of Pharmacology and Pharmacotherapeutics 4, S73–S77.

Takeuchi, F., Mcginnis, R., Bourgeois, S., et al., 2009. A genome-wide association study confirms VKORC1, CYP2C9, and CYP4F2 as principal genetic determinants of warfarin dose. PLOS Genetics 5, e1000433.

Tassaneeyakul, W., Jantararoungtong, T., Chen, P., et al., 2009. Strong association between HLA-B*5801 and allopurinol-induced Stevens-Johnson syndrome and toxic epidermal necrolysis in a Thai population. PharmacoSgenet Genomics 19, 704–709.

Uitterlinden, A.G., 2016. An Introduction to Genome-Wide Association Studies: GWAS for Dummies. Seminars in Reproductive Medicine 34, 196–204.

Van Driest, S.L., Shi, Y., Bowton, E.A., et al., 2014. Clinically actionable genotypes among 10,000 patients with preemptive pharmacogenomic testing. Clinical Pharmacology & Therapeutics 95, 423–431.

Wang, K., Li, M., Hakonarson, H., 2010. ANNOVAR: Functional annotation of genetic variants from high-throughput sequencing data. Nucleic Acids Research 38, e164.

Watson, M.E., Patel, L.G., Ha, B., et al., 2009. A study of HIV provider attitudes toward HLA-B 5701 testing in the United States. AIDS Patient Care and STDs 23, 957–963.

Whirl-Carrillo, M., Mcdonagh, E.M., Hebert, J.M., et al., 2012. Pharmacogenomics knowledge for personalized medicine. Clinical Pharmacology & Therapeutics 92, 414–417.

Wishart, D.S., Feunang, Y.D., Guo, A.C., et al., 2018. DrugBank 5.0: A major update to the DrugBank database for 2018. Nucleic Acids Research 46 (D1), D1074–D1082.

Wishart, D.S., Knox, C., Guo, A.C., et al., 2006. DrugBank: A comprehensive resource for in silico drug discovery and exploration. Nucleic Acids Research 34, D668–D672.

Yang, W., Wu, G., Broeckel, U., et al., 2016. Comparison of genome sequencing and clinical genotyping for pharmacogenes. Clinical Pharmacology & Therapeutics 100, 380–388.

Young, B., Squires, K., Patel, P., et al., 2008. First large, multicenter, open-label study utilizing HLA-B*5701 screening for abacavir hypersensitivity in North America. AIDS 22, 1673–1675.

Zhang, G., Nebert, D.W., 2017. Personalized medicine: Genetic risk prediction of drug response. Pharmacology and Therapeutics 175, 75–90.

Zhang, G., Zhang, Y., Ling, Y., Jia, J., 2015. Web resources for pharmacogenomics. Genomics Proteomics Bioinformatics 13, 51–54.

Detecting and Annotating Rare Variants

Jieming Chen, Genentech Inc., South San Francisco, CA, United States
Akdes S Harmanci and Arif O Harmanci, The University of Texas Health Science Center at Houston, Houston, TX, United States

Introduction

For the past decade, genome-wide association studies (GWASes) have been the focus of large-scale genetic studies that are used to characterize the genomic architecture of traits and diseases (Visscher et al., 2012). These GWASes have been largely brought about by the use of single nucleotide polymorphism (SNP) microarrays, coupled with a wealth of computational tools to efficiently process and analyze the high throughput data on a large scale. SNP arrays have enabled the easy genotyping of millions of variants in the genomes of hundreds of individuals (International HapMap Consortium et al., 2007; The International HapMap 3 Consortium, 2010). As they typically need to know the sequence of these genomic locations to design the array probes, the variants detected are mainly common polymorphisms, which are defined to be at a minor allele frequency (MAF) of at least 5% in the human population. In general, less common polymorphisms are between MAF 1% and 5%, and rare variants are variation that occur with MAF of less than 1% in the human population.

As of 2016, the GWAS catalog from the National Human Genome Research Institute (NHGRI) houses published GWASes from about 2500 publications, for over 24000 SNP-trait associations (MacArthur et al., 2017). Despite this large number of trait and disease associations with common variants, much of the genetic contributions to these traits and diseases remain unexplained. Due to the initial focus on the common variants, variants with lower MAF in the human population have been thought to account for at least part of this "missing heritability" (Zuk et al., 2014). The 1000 Genomes Project sequenced 2504 healthy individuals from 26 ethnic populations. They found that while rare variation comprises only 5% of the total variation per individual, collectively, rare germline variants are in abundance in the general human population (1000 Genomes Project Consortium et al., 2015, 2012). Previously, rare variants have already been shown to play significant roles in human diseases and traits. Highly penetrant rare variants are known to cause Mendelian disorders; such as, cystic fibrosis (Castaldo et al., 1999; Soe and Gregoire-Bottex, 2017) and sickle cell anemia (Higgs and Wood, 2008); and common (and complex) diseases; such as, autism (Griswold et al., 2015) and Type 2 Diabetes (Steinthorsdottir et al., 2014). There is, however, an ascertainment bias that partially hindered the research of rare variants. This bias is largely due to the difficulty in detecting and identifying these variants for genotyping probe creation in microarrays, coupled with the appeal of finding and publishing the "low-hanging fruits" in association studies; that is, the associations of traits with more easily detected common variants. For these reasons, the community have, for a while, largely neglected this lower end of the allele frequency spectrum.

In more recent years, the advent and maturation of short-read DNA sequencing technologies have engendered the sequencing of entire genomes of thousands of individuals that can be interrogated multiple times (more deeply). Consequently, rare genomic variants can now be detected per individual more easily. An entire ecosystem of bioinformatic algorithms have also been developed to meet the challenges of automation, and facilitating the procedures of data collection, processing, visualization, and computational analyses. In this article, we will introduce a non-exhaustive array of ways that bioinformatics and computational biology have been harnessed to create tools and methodologies, specifically in detecting and annotating rare variation.

Detection of Rare Variation

Over the years, there has been evolving connotations and meanings of the use of terminologies to define 'nucleotide changes', such as 'mutation' and 'polymorphism' (Condit et al., 2002; Karki et al., 2015). This created confusion depending on the context such as the effect (disease-causing or neutral), allelic frequency (rare or polymorphic), and inheritance pattern (somatic or germline). In order to prevent further confusion, the American College of Medical Genetics and Genomics (ACMG), the Human Variome Project, the Human Genome Variation Society (HGVS) and the Human Genome Organization (HUGO) have published recommendations and guidelines in favor of the use of more neutral terms such as 'variant', 'alteration', and 'allelic variant', to refer more generically to nucleotide changes in the genome, which include both natural variations and mutations (Richards et al., 2015; den Dunnen et al., 2016; Li et al., 2017). Henceforth, we will be referring to any generic nucleotide change as a 'variant'.

Broadly, there are three types of variants in the human genome. These are single nucleotide substitutions (SNVs), small insertions/deletions (indels) of nucleotides, and structural variants that comprise translocation and/or inversion of long chunks of DNA sequences (SVs). In addition, SVs may cause amplification or loss of large chunks of DNA sequences. These are referred to as copy number variants (CNVs). Each variant type is then detected (or "called") using different bioinformatics methodologies. While the computational tools for the detection of rare variants are mostly generic variant calling methodologies for arrays and sequencing technologies, they have to be customized with appropriate considerations to cater to the specific underlying array and sequencing technologies, in order to more accurately detect variants with lower frequencies. Additionally, the use of in silico genotype imputation has also been proven to be extremely accurate in many instances, and thus provides a more cost-effective complement to array, and targeted and exome sequencing options. Hence, we will first review some of the challenges and strategies in rare variant detection. We will then discuss, in turn, the application of bioinformatics in microarray, sequencing and imputation technologies. Finally, there are non-germline variants that are also rare, for instance, somatic mutations. Hence, we include a section on somatic mutation calling in cancer research.

Challenges and Strategies in Rare Variant Detection

Rare variants occur in very low frequency in the population. Various human genetics efforts have defined the threshold of rarity slightly differently. For example, the 1000 Genomes Project defines <0.5% to be rare (The 1000 Genomes Project Consortium, 2012, 2015), while others have used <1% as the threshold (Agarwala et al., 2013; Chouraki and Seshadri, 2014; Bomba et al., 2017). The low occurrence of these variants in the population is, in itself, a challenge that initially hampered the high throughput detection of rare and novel variants using genotyping arrays. The advent of sequencing enabled *de novo* rare variant detection on a large scale. In order to detect rare variants, population scale sequencing is typically performed, followed by using efficient bioinformatic pipelines to pool all the sequenced reads and perform variant calling on the pooled data. In this approach, the sequencing errors (such as polymerase chain reaction amplifications) do not affect the variant calling because they are mostly independent between individuals, and using pooled data alleviates the severity of these errors. The computational tools for the pooled variant calling procedure are parametrized to have high sensitivity. Thus, pooled variant calling increases power to detect rare variants that have very low frequencies, and also help decrease the false positive rates of detection (1000 Genomes Project Consortium et al., 2015). The cost of sequencing can be decreased by performing a low coverage sequencing in each individual. This may, however, come at the cost of reduced power to detect rare variants.

In many cases, in order to circumvent the issue of cost and coverage, it may be useful to perform targeted sequencing; for example, exome sequencing. In such a way, the cost is decreased but only a particular region or regions of interest are sequenced; using the example of exome sequencing, only the exons are sequenced. This approach increases the power to detect variants (e.g., on the exons) by trading read depth coverage for genomic coverage. One downside of this approach is that the target capture technologies have non-uniform efficiency among different parts of the genome, for example, across different exons (Wang et al., 2017; Clark et al., 2011). This causes non-uniform genomic coverage, and complicates computational detection of some variants, such as in the detection of CNVs, which look for duplication or deleted regions (Wu et al., 2012). This approach is also not easily applicable for identifying complex SVs because of the low concordance between different methodologies and high false positive error rates. However, some studies have found that whole genome sequencing is less biased in identifying variants than exome sequencing (Belkadi et al., 2015).

An important aspect of detecting rare variants is also the characterization of low frequency haplotypes in the human genome. In order to identify rare haplotypes, it is necessary to have deeply catalogued population-specific genetic panels. Using these panels, the bioinformatics pipelines for variant calling can be combined with genetic imputation to detect rare variants more accurately (please refer to Section 'Genotype Imputation'). This greatly depends on our ability to build high quality population panels (The International HapMap 3 Consortium, 2010). Also, this approach may not work well for SVs and CNVs. CNVs do not correlate highly with other variants in the linkage disequilibrium blocks. For complex SVs, the understanding of their recombination rates and LD block is not yet very well-developed (Wineinger et al., 2011). Altogether, these render the imputation of SV and CNV genotypes less accurate than SNVs and indels.

Nonetheless, the use of sequencing technologies has spurred complementary strategies in microarrays, targeted sequencing and imputation to detect rare variants.

Microarrays

Microarrays require the knowledge of the genomic sequences for probe design. Hence, the initial microarrays for variant detection were more catered for common variants. With next-generation sequencing (NGS) efforts in obtaining rare variant sequences, many arrays have incorporated rare variant probes detected from NGS. This is also implemented in a more targeted, and context-specific manner, such as focusing on certain diseases, ethnicities or genomic regions. For example, bespoke customized genotyping arrays such as the Immunochip (Cortes and Brown, 2011), Illumina ExomeChip (Illumina, URL available in references), and the UK Biobank Axiom Array (Affymetrix, URL available in references) have probes that are specially designed for rare single nucleotide variants in different contexts. For larger SVs, the array comparative genomic hybridization technology (Banerjee, 2013) and the more recent SNP arrays from Illumina and Affymetrix have been used for detection of rare CNVs or SVs. These custom-built microarray chips allow for a cheaper and more focused option for the detection of rare variants. Moreover, rare variant detection in microarrays can conveniently capitalize on the bioinformatics methods and tools made for microarrays that have been well-characterized, and -utilized for almost two decades (LaFramboise, 2009).

In microarray data, preprocessing of the signal intensities from the probes consists of multiple steps, and needs to be executed before genotype calling. These include *in silico* background correction, resulting from technical artefacts such as non-specific probe hybridization (Owzar et al., 2008); normalization of the probes intensities, within and between chips, so that intensities can be compared across all chips (Carvalho et al., 2007; Hu and He, 2007; Staaf et al., 2008); removal of batch effects (Miclaus et al., 2010); quality control and outlier removal (Guo et al., 2014). There are bioinformatics tools that implement statistical methods for these preprocessing steps. For example, Robust Multiarray Analysis (RMA) uses parametric background correction, quantile normalization and robust fitting of a log-linear additive model (Irizarry *et al.*, 2003). There are also R packages conveniently available in Bioconductor (Huber *et al.*, 2015) streamlined for analyses in R (Morgan, 2016; Gentleman *et al.*, 2005). Following preprocessing, genotype calling tools can be implemented for clustering to call genotypes. These have included open source tools from academia (Teo, 2012; Wellcome Trust Case Control Consortium, 2007; Wang *et al.*, 2007), and proprietary software from companies such as BeadStudio, and Affymetrix clustering algorithms for different microarray platforms.

Exome/Whole Genome Sequencing

For variant detection in NGS technologies, the reads from sequencing experiments are mapped on the reference genome using short read mapping tools like BWA (Li *et al.*, 2008) and Bowtie (Langmead and Salzberg, 2012). In SNV detection, the SNVs are detected by finding the single nucleotide differences in the mapped reads compared to the reference genome (**Fig. 1**). Indels are detected by comparing the reference genome and the mapped reads to identify the insertions/deletions of nucleotides in the mapped reads (**Fig. 1**). The identification of SVs (and CNVs) requires detection of the breakpoints that correspond to DNA positions that formed the SVs. The mapped reads are analyzed to find breakpoints at the ends of SVs (**Fig. 1**). Currently, analysis of the paired end reads and fine mapping of breakpoints by splitting, and mapping the reads (split read mapping) are the most reliable ways to identify SVs. Finally, an SV is identified by careful analysis of mapping patterns of paired-end reads. These strategies are utilized by bioinformatics algorithms for detecting SVs, such as DELLY, PEMer, BreakDancer, and GenomeStrip (Rausch *et al.*, 2012; Korbel *et al.*, 2009; Alkan *et al.*, 2011; Handsaker *et al.*, 2011; Chen *et al.*, 2009). For the SVs that amplify and delete chunks of DNA, i.e., CNVs, analysis of the read depth has been successful, which is used by CNVnator to detect CNVs (Abyzov *et al.*, 2011).

The sensitivity of bioinformatics tools for variant detection is variable among different types of variants. Sensitivity of SNV detection using short read sequencing technologies is very high (1000 Genomes Project Consortium *et al.*, 2012, 2015). GATK (McKenna *et al.*, 2010) is currently the standard bioinformatics tool that is used for detecting SNVs. VarScan (Koboldt *et al.*, 2009) is another popular variant detection tool. The combination of the software packages GATK and dindel (Albers *et al.*, 2011) has been used in indel detection. The sensitivity of indel detection is high, albeit the false positive rates can be high as well (Hasan *et al.*, 2015). The accuracy of SV detection is hard to quantify as they differ depending on contexts, such as in diseased and normal individuals. This is mainly because there are currently no appropriate ground-truth references for SVs. Nonetheless, large-scale projects like the 1000 Genomes (1000 Genomes Project Consortium *et al.*, 2012) and The Cancer Genome Atlas (Collins, 2007) provide extremely useful SV sets for healthy and diseased genomes. In these datasets, it has been shown that the concordance of identified variants among different methods is generally modest (Tattini *et al.*, 2015). The most reliable strategy to identify SVs is to use multiple bioinformatics tools separately to detect the SVs. The SVs identified by each method are then merged. This method is effective in removing false positives at the expense of decreased sensitivity (Sudmant *et al.*, 2015).

The major hurdles for accurate variant calling can be divided into two categories. First, certain parts of human genome are hard to sequence experimentally. For example, DNA in heterochromatin regions cannot be easily fragmented while DNA library is being prepared (Shendure and Ji, 2008). A second hurdle is a bioinformatics problem, that is, a large fraction of the human genome is difficult to align to, because it contains repeated DNA sequences (de Koning *et al.*, 2011). This includes the transposable elements (such as Alu's), and segmental duplications of large chunks of human genome (Bailey and Eichler, 2006). The short reads that are sequenced from these regions cannot be uniquely mapped. Therefore, the variants in these regions are very hard, if not impossible, to detect. There are already bioinformatics methods developed to probabilistically assign reads in repeat regions. Even though these mitigate the effects of low mappability to a certain degree, short-read mapping to repeat regions remains an ongoing challenge.

The most promising (and logical) direction for the identification of variants in hard-to-map regions are long-read technologies, which include PacBio (Rhoads and Au, 2015), 10X (Zheng *et al.*, 2016), Illumina's Moleculo (McCoy *et al.*, 2014), and Oxford Nanopore (Feng *et al.*, 2015). However, these long-read technologies often have different strengths and weaknesses. For example, PacBio generates very long reads, but with high error rates, while the 10X technology creates linked reads that have very low error rates, but are not exactly contiguous. There have been some bioinformatics tools that calibrate errors and call variants using data from long-read technologies (English *et al.*, 2014). Integrative bioinformatics methods are also in development, which utilize multiple long-read technologies in concert, to identify highly complex SVs and variants in the repeat regions and highly polymorphic regions, such as HLA locus (Nelson *et al.*, 2015). In addition, graph-based bioinformatics tools that use de-bruijn graphs have been used successfully in whole genome assembly and transcriptome assembly of long-read sequencing data (Lin *et al.*, 2016; Gordon *et al.*, 2016). New bioinformatics methods are utilized in cancer genomics to computationally de-convolve complex structural variation patterns in unstable cancer genomes (Zheng *et al.*, 2016) (please refer to the Section 'Detection of somatic variants in cancer genomes' for more discussion). Hence, long-read technologies, while still yielding notable issues, are nonetheless very powerful, especially when they are used in conjunction with traditional NGS (Mostovoy *et al.*, 2016).

Genotype Imputation

Genotype imputation is the process of predicting the genotypes of genetic variants that were not directly interrogated experimentally. It was conceptualized from the observation that some genomic variation is frequently observed to be associated with each other in the human population, i.e., they are in linkage disequilibrium (LD), and that these highly correlated variants can be

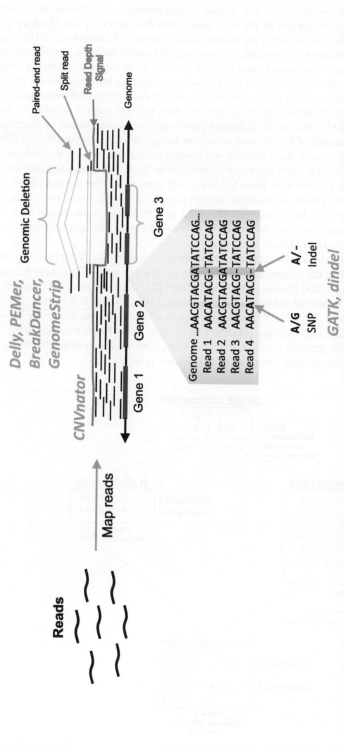

Fig. 1 Overview of a bioinformatic analysis of DNA sequencing reads in variant detection. First, the sequenced reads (wavy lines) are mapped to the genome (thick black line with arrowheads at termini) using read mapping tools. After mapping, the mapped reads (straight lines) at each location is counted to generate the read depth signal (blue line above the reads). A genomic deletion can be estimated when a drop in the read depth signal can be observed. Reads can be single-end (straight lines), or paired-end (reads connected by dashed lines with corners). When mapped to genes, reads can be 'split' (reads connected by straight dashed lines), due to exon–intron junctions (exons are denoted by thick red lines on genome). Here, we focus on a specific genomic region (blue inset) to illustrate an example of read alignment and detection of an SNV (shaded yellow) and indel (shaded orange). For the SNV, a nucleotide change from 'G' to 'A' is supported by 2 reads, while an 'A' nucleotide deletion is supported by 3 reads. Some of the bioinformatics tools that use paired-end reads, split reads, and read depth are shown in grey. Two methods that identify SNVs and indels are also shown (in grey below the blue inset).

inherited in haplotype blocks (Wall and Pritchard, 2003). The accuracy of imputation is contingent on both knowing the 'phase' (i.e., haplotypes) of the genetic markers, and the availability of accurate reference panels of LD patterns. Hence, there are two essential parts to *in silico* imputation: (1) the reference panel, and (2) the computational algorithm to estimate (or impute) the missing genotypes probabilistically, based on the haplotype information and LD patterns in the reference panel (**Fig. 2**).

Existing imputation reference panels are available, and already computationally constructed from large genotyping and sequencing studies (**Fig. 2**). The initial development of reference panels was first driven by the HapMap project for common variants (International HapMap Consortium *et al.*, 2007; The International HapMap 3 Consortium, 2010). Thus, imputation was skewed towards better estimation of genotypes from common variants. Further improvements in more recent years, particularly for the imputation of rare variants, came with the introduction of NGS and the 1000 Genomes Project (1000 Genomes Project Consortium *et al.*, 2012, 2015). Because imputation derives their genotype estimation from population allele frequencies, reference panels are typically built from larger consortia efforts with denser marker distribution and bigger and more diverse sample populations. They are constructed so that the allele frequencies of the genetic markers and LD patterns are better represented in accordance with ethnicities (Marchini and Howie, 2010). Reference panels can also be constructed by merging one's own dataset with a reference panel, especially if the sample of interest is of an admixed origin or ethnic populations not found in the existing panels. Previous studies have already employed these existing and merged reference panels to successfully obtain rare variant imputation (Li *et al.*, 2011; Chen *et al.*, 2013). There are many bioinformatics tools and methodologies now that adopt several strategies with merging reference panels. For example, there has been early work where the merged panels are modeled jointly (Ewing *et al.*, 2012), or by first treating the panels as references for each other, and then imputing one's data against the resultant panel (Howie *et al.*, 2009). There have also been strategies that used an ethnically diverse imputation panel, instead of a population-specific one, especially in situations where the dataset of interest is from an admixed population, or if the population of interest has a higher number of rare variants (Howie *et al.*, 2011).

There are many imputation tools currently available for use by the scientific community. They typically involve the following steps: phasing, which estimates the phase in the dataset of interest *in silico*, and then execute the genotype estimation process. There are many software for phasing, including MaCH (Li *et al.*, 2010), and SHAPEIT2 (Delaneau *et al.*, 2013). After phasing, the actual genotype imputation can be performed by several software, such as Minimac2 (Fuchsberger *et al.*, 2015), BEAGLE (Browning and Browning, 2011), and IMPUTE2 (Howie *et al.*, 2011). The performance and accuracy of these tools have been benchmarked and compared extensively in many publications over the years (Marchini and Howie, 2008; Roshyara *et al.*, 2016). Currently, there are also tools that use the biology of a specific genomic region to implement imputation, such as those that imputes genotypes in the complicated region of the major histocompatibility complex (MHC) (Karnes *et al.*, 2017).

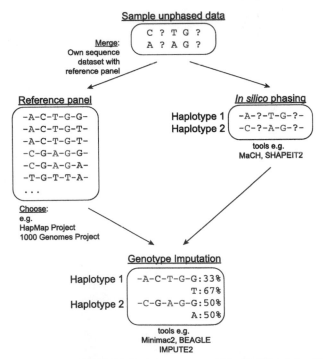

Fig. 2 General process of genotype imputation of rare variants. The process of imputation typically starts with a sample dataset that is usually unphased and contain missing genotypes (denoted by '?'). If the starting dataset is genotyped from a microarray, one can additionally sequence part of the dataset to merge with a selected reference panel, or choose from an existing reference panel, e.g., 1000 Genomes Project or HapMap Project. Concurrently, *in silico* phasing can done performed to estimate the haplotypes for each individual in the sample dataset using tools such as MaCH and SHAPEIT2. Finally, imputation software such as Minimac2, BEAGLE and IMPUTE2 can perform imputation to approximate the missing genotypes probabilistically, by comparing the user haplotypes to the reference haplotypes.

Detection of Somatic Variants in Cancer Genomes

So far, we have discussed mostly about the detection of rare germline variants. There is an additional set of non-germline mutations, i.e., somatic variants, which are heavily studied and researched particularly in cancer genomes. Cancer genomes typically harbor many types of somatic variants that run the gamut. Whole genome or exome sequencing are used to detect SNVs, CNVs, indels and SVs, whereas RNA-sequencing is ideal for detecting fusion transcript events.

Somatic variants can be detected in cancer, by comparing the genomic alterations in tumor samples with their matched normal samples. Somatic variant calling is a very challenging task, because of the complex nature of cancers. Tumor heterogeneity, normal cell contamination, sequencing and alignment errors might all limit the ability to detect somatic variants, especially since somatic variants can be present at very low allelic levels. Therefore, sensitivity in somatic variant calling is very important in cancer. There are various popular bioinformatics methods for calling somatic SNVs and indels in cancer. Both MuTect (Cibulskis *et al.*, 2013) and Strelka (Saunders *et al.*, 2012) use a Bayesian approach to detect somatic variants. MuTect is especially designed to detect variants with a very low allele fraction. SomaticSniper (Larson *et al.*, 2012) uses a Bayesian framework to combine the genotype likelihood of tumor samples and normal samples. VarScan2 (Koboldt *et al.*, 2009) has a heuristic approach based on thresholds for read depth, base quality, variant allele frequency and statistical significance. There are also different computational methods for identifying CNVs in cancer genomes. Some of them consider other factors in their detection algorithms, such as normal cell contamination, ploidy and clonality of the tumor cells. Some of the most popular CNV calling methods include ExomeCNV (Sathirapongsasuti *et al.*, 2011), CoNIFER (Krumm *et al.*, 2012), VarScan2 (Koboldt *et al.*, 2009) and CONTRA (Li *et al.*, 2012). For SV detection in cancer, BreakDancer (Chen *et al.*, 2009) and Delly (Rausch *et al.*, 2012), are widely used.

Another important computational challenge in cancer is distinguishing driver variants from passenger variants. Driver mutations provide growth advantage to a tumor cell, thus promoting cancer development. MUSIC (Dees *et al.*, 2012), MutSig (Lawrence *et al.*, 2013), CHASM (Carter *et al.*, 2009), SIFT (Ng and Henikoff, 2003), PolyPhen (Adzhubei *et al.*, 2013) and other tools aim to predict *in silico* whether a somatic mutation is a driver or passenger, and prioritize candidate variants for downstream experiments.

Annotation of Rare Variation

With large-scale variant detection from sequencing and array technologies, a looming challenge is the rapid and efficient functional annotation of these variants in a high throughput fashion. One of the goals of *in silico* functional annotation is to be able to rank and prioritize variants for downstream experimental validation. The functional impact of rare variants can be estimated computationally in several ways, including comparative sequence analysis, and guilt-by-association. A secondary objective of the annotation process is to assess possible clinical impact of the variants, particularly in the context of diseases. These are typically tested in rare variant association studies (RVAS).

Impact Estimation for Rare Variants

We can estimate the impact of rare variants bioinformatically in different genomic contexts, and approaches. Often, the functional consequences of variants can be assessed in the context of the functional elements that it resides, in a guilt-by-association fashion. This requires prior knowledge of functional genomic elements that are provided by bioinformatics databases such as RefSeq (O'Leary *et al.*, 2016), Ensembl (O'Leary *et al.*, 2016), GENCODE (Harrow *et al.*, 2012a,b), and ENCODE (Dunham *et al.*, 2012). For example, Annovar (Wang *et al.*, 2010) and Ensembl's Variant Effect Predictor (VEP) (McLaren *et al.*, 2016) map rare variants of interest onto basic genomic features. Given a list of rare variants with genomic locations on the human reference genome, VEP can assess the potential impact of the variants, depending on whether they reside in an exon, intron, splice site or untranslated region. If the rare variant is found in a coding region, VEP can output whether the variant will cause a synonymous or non-synonymous change in the protein sequence. In non-coding regions, variants can be associated with key elements such as enhancers, DNA-binding motifs, and promoters.

By comparing multiple sequences across species or within species, more quantitative tools were developed to examine the likelihood of a particular variant to be functionally impactful, based on the various biological properties and genomic contexts. For example, the GERP score measures the divergence or sequence conservation of every base in the human genome, based on sequence comparison across multiple primate genomes (Cooper *et al.*, 2005; Davydov *et al.*, 2010). SIFT uses the BLOSUM matrix, which is derived from comparing inter-species homologous sequences, to estimate the likelihood of non-synonymous variants being deleterious (Ng and Henikoff, 2001). PolyPhen2 (Adzhubei *et al.*, 2013) additionally uses information from the three-dimensional structure of a protein to further examine the impact of a coding variant. Other computational tools such as FATHMM (Shihab *et al.*, 2013), ENTPRISE (Zhou *et al.*, 2016), and MutationTaster (Schwarz *et al.*, 2014) are also more recent additions. Funseq2 (Fu *et al.*, 2014) provides a score for a non-coding variant based on the integration of multiple layers of information, such as the position of a variant in regulatory networks, and the disruptive effect of the variant on DNA-binding motifs. Combined Annotation Dependent Depletion (CADD) algorithm (Kircher *et al.*, 2014) also outputs a score based on a support vector machine classifier that integrates multiple annotations into its prediction. A non-exhaustive list of currently available bioinformatics tools for functional impact estimation is available in **Table 1**. There is also a recent strategy of aggregating and computing the enrichment of rare allele-specific variants across multiple individual genomes, in order to identify regions that exhibit allele-specific behavior (Chen *et al.*, 2016).

Table 1 Table of bioinformatics tools that can annotate and prioritize rare variants. This table provides a list of bioinformatics tools that can estimate the functional impact of variants in three broad categories, namely tools that can annotate variants in the coding and noncoding regions, and tools that gives a score for each nucleotide in the genome, allowing quantification and prioritization of variants

Software tool	Year first introduced	PubMed ID and citation
Coding-variant-based		
SIFT	2001	11337480 (Ng and Henikoff, 2001)
PolyPhen	2002	12202775 (Ramensky *et al.*, 2002)
MAPP	2005	15965030 (Stone and Sidow, 2005)
PMUT	2005	15879453 (Ferrer-Costa *et al.*, 2005)
PHD-SNP	2006	16895930 (Capriotti *et al.*, 2006)
SNAP	2007	17526529 (Bromberg and Rost, 2007)
MutPred	2009	19734154 (Li *et al.*, 2009)
SNPS&GO	2009	19514061 (Calabrese *et al.*, 2009)
MutationTaster	2010	19734154 (Schwarz *et al.*, 2010)
Condel	2011	21457909 (González-Pérez and López-Bigas, 2011)
MutationAssessor	2011	21727090 (Reva et al., 2011)
CAROL	2012	22261837 (Lopes *et al.*, 2012)
FATHMM	2013	23033316 (Shihab *et al.*, 2013)
PredictSNP	2014	24453961 (Bendl *et al.*, 2014)
CADD	2014	24487276 (Kircher *et al.*, 2014)
Noncoding-variant-based		
FunSeq	2013	PMC3947637 (Khurana *et al.*, 2013)
GWAVA	2014	24487584 (Ritchie *et al.*, 2014)
FATHMM-XF	2017	28968714 (Rogers *et al.*, 2017)
Nucleotide-based		
GERP	2005	15965027 (Cooper *et al.*, 2005)
PhastCons	2005	16024819 (Siepel *et al.*, 2005)
PhyloP	2010	19858363 (Pollard *et al.*, 2010)

RVAS Studies: Predicting Functions of Rare Variants

The association studies are very useful for understanding the functional impact of variants in the context of traits and diseases. For example, GWASes give clues about the phenotypic effects of variants. In these studies, there is a sample with the disease or trait that is studied, termed the 'case' sample. There is also the 'control' sample, which includes individuals who do not have the manifestation of the disease or trait. The bioinformatics tools for GWAS look for genetic variants that are enriched in the case sample compared to the control sample. The enrichment of the variants indicate that the trait or disease associates with the variant (Bush and Moore, 2012). As mentioned, GWASes have identified thousands of loci that correlate with diverse set of traits and diseases, and can be found in the GWAS catalog (MacArthur *et al.*, 2017).

The GWASes generally address common variants that have small phenotypic effects (**Fig. 3**). These variants support the common variant common disease hypothesis (Pritchard and Cox, 2002), where many common variants with small effects culminate to a disease phenotype. However, based on heritability estimates in twin studies, the variants identified so far have been unable to account for all genetic contributions. Hence, for a while, researchers have thought that this 'missing heritability' can be explained at least in part by the effects of rare variants. This forms the basis of the rare-variant-common-disease hypothesis, which attributes rare variants to diseases (Cirulli and Goldstein, 2010).

In order to identify the effects of rare variants in traits and diseases, it is necessary to consider allelic heterogeneity, where different rare variants can affect a gene and give rise to the same phenotypic presentation. Moreover, there may be multiple causal genes. A bioinformatics method similar to GWAS can be deployed on rare variants to associate them with diseases and traits. These are termed generally as rare variant association studies (RVAS). In RVAS, it is necessary to use very large case and control sample sizes in order to obtain enough statistical power to detect the enrichment of rare variant alleles in the case sample (Lin, 2016). This may generally turn out to be impractical, especially if the prevalence of the rare allele is infinitesimally small. One approach is to group rare variants into biological elements, such as genes or signaling pathways. After grouping, a statistical test is performed to evaluate whether the element is under higher "burden" in the case sample compared to the control sample. This way, the association is computed for a region or element of multiple related rare variants, rather than a single variant. Because the frequency that an element is affected by the rare variants is increased, such burdening also increases the power of detection (**Fig. 3**). Most notably, RVAS studies have been useful in psychiatric diseases such as Alzheimer's and Schizophrenia (Cruchaga *et al.*, 2014; Yang *et al.*, 2017; Singh *et al.*, 2017). SKAT (Wu *et al.*, 2011) is one of the most popular bioinformatics tools for performing various types of RVAS.

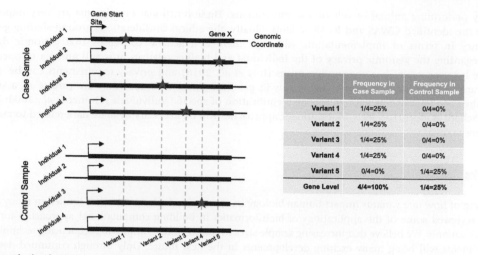

Fig. 3 Illustration of a burden test in a hypothetical RVAS study. This is a toy example showing the variants on a gene for eight individuals, four of whom are cases (with the trait or disease in question) and four are control samples. There are five mutations (red stars) in total that affect the gene X. The table summarizes the frequency of the variants in the case and control samples. Each mutation has a frequency of 25%, hence the individual mutations in the case sample do not show significant enrichment because each mutation is seen only once. However, when the mutations are counted on the gene as a whole, the case sample shows 4 times higher 'burden' compared to the control sample.

The accuracy of burden tests depends heavily on the precision and amount of element annotations. The annotations of protein coding genes on human genome can be assumed to be virtually complete (Harrow *et al.*, 2012a,b). It is, however, important to note that in the majority of GWAS and RVAS, variants are in non-coding regions of the genome (Zhang and Lupski, 2015). This implies that non-coding elements, like long non-coding RNAs and enhancers, must be studied in greater depth with respect to their functional roles. Moreover, the annotation of non-coding elements in the human genome is far from complete. Projects such as ENCODE (Bernstein *et al.*, 2012) and Roadmap Epigenome (Romanoski *et al.*, 2015) have been leading the way in the annotation of non-coding elements using functional genomics assays coupled with the corresponding bioinformatics pipelines, notably in ChIP-Seq (Harmanci *et al.*, 2014; Rozowsky *et al.*, 2009) and RNA-seq (Pepke *et al.*, 2009). Also, recent studies point to the importance of the three dimensional conformation of chromatin in genetic regulation (Belaghzal *et al.*, 2017). Taken altogether, understanding various non-coding elements can potentially enable a better delineation of the effects of rare variants when used in the RVAS studies.

One way to increase the power of RVAS studies is retrospectively combining results of previous RVAS studies. This bioinformatics analysis is referred to as meta-analysis of association studies (Begum *et al.*, 2012). Meta-analysis is very useful, because they make use of earlier association studies to increase the power of detection by increasing sample size. These methods combine the test statistics and p-values of individual studies to perform statistical test on the enrichment of rare variants in the pooled sample set. However, a major challenge is the computational adjustment for hidden covariates, such that the identified associations are based solely on genetic factors. Population stratification (Cardon and Palmer, 2003) and familial relationships (Manichaikul *et al.*, 2010) in the data are two major confounding factors that need to be adjusted for in association studies (Vilhjálmsson and Nordborg, 2013).

Future Directions

As more research is being performed for rare variation, an important future direction is the development of novel and more effective statistical methods that are suitable for new sequencing technologies. This will be especially imperative for the technologies that generate long reads, which will enable genomics regions that were originally difficult to be sequenced by short reads to be made accessible. Using long-reads technologies, we will also be able to identify more accurately rare SVs, which will add more to our understanding of how these large variants affect diseases.

These developments will also bring new challenges. The large-scale sequencing efforts will generate a large number of variants, whose effects cannot be fully and quickly understood with the current knowledge and technologies. The new high throughput functional assays (Shalem *et al.*, 2015) have great potential in generating new data resources that can be combined with computational methods to better understand the effects of variants. These studies will also clarify how we should approach the classifications of rare and common variants with respect to their utility in public health and epidemiology (Visscher *et al.*, 2012). In addition to better uncovering their effects, sharing the data associated with variants of unknown significance (VUS) with patients will also create ethical challenges. We need to create standards and privacy-preserving frameworks for sharing these data. Understanding rare VUS will be best enabled using experimental protocols that follow up on

RVAS studies, by performing animal or cell culture experiments. These functional experiments are very important to functionally validate the identified GWAS and RVAS variants. Finally, the ethical considerations around sharing genomic data is still in its infancy in terms of implementation. Although there is a general consensus that genomic data may have adverse effects regarding the genomic privacy of the individual and his/her relatives, it is still an area of open debate as to how the balance between open data sharing incentives (Joly *et al.*, 2016) and privacy requirements can be maintained. In particular, the rare variants are one of the key aspects in genomic privacy, because they are private to a small group of individuals, so they can be sensitive enough for the identification of specific individuals (Homer *et al.*, 2008; Harmanci and Gerstein, 2016; Schadt *et al.*, 2012). New bioinformatic approaches will be necessary to share data related to rare variants in a privacy-preserving manner.

Closing Remarks

Our understanding of how rare variants impact human biology has come very far but is also still limited in many regards. In this article, we have reviewed some of the applications of bioinformatics in building computational approaches for detection and annotation of rare variants. We believe that increasing sample sizes in cohort studies, improving sequencing technologies, and new functional experiments will bring many exciting developments in the near future. Only through continued development and improvement of both experimental and computational methodologies, can we break new grounds.

See also: Natural Language Processing Approaches in Bioinformatics

References

1000 Genomes Project Consortium, *et al.*, 2015. A global reference for human genetic variation. Nature 526 (7571), 68–74. doi:10.1038/nature15393.

Abecasis, G.R., *et al.*, 2012. An integrated map of genetic variation from 1,092 human genomes. Nature 491 (7422), 56–65. doi:10.1038/nature11632.

Abyzov, A., *et al.*, 2011. CNVnator: An approach to discover, genotype, and characterize typical and atypical CNVs from family and population genome sequencing. Genome Research 21 (6), 974–984. doi:10.1101/gr.114876.110.

Adzhubei, I., Jordan, D.M., Sunyaev, S.R., 2013. Predicting functional effect of human missense mutations using PolyPhen-2 (Chapter 7). In: Haines, J.L., *et al.*, Current Protocols in Human Genetics. doi:10.1002/0471142905.hg0720s76. p. Unit7.20

Affymetrix (no date) *UK Biobank Axiom Array*. Available at: http://www.ukbiobank.ac.uk/wp-content/uploads/2014/04/UK-Biobank-Axiom-Array-Datasheet-2014.pdf (Accessed: 8 December 2017).

Agarwala, V., *et al.*, 2013. Evaluating empirical bounds on complex disease genetic architecture. Nature Genetics 45 (12), 1418–1427. doi:10.1038/ng.2804.

Albers, C.A., *et al.*, 2011. Dindel: Accurate indel calls from short-read data. Genome Research 21 (6), 961–973. doi:10.1101/gr.112326.110.

Alkan, C., Coe, B.P., Eichler, E.E., 2011. Genome structural variation discovery and genotyping. Nature Reviews Genetics. 363–376. doi:10.1038/nrg2958.

Bailey, J.A., Eichler, E.E., 2006. Primate segmental duplications: Crucibles of evolution, diversity and disease. Nature Reviews Genetics. 552–564. doi:10.1038/nrg1895.

Banerjee, D., 2013. Array comparative genomic hybridization: An overview of protocols, applications, and technology trends. Methods in Molecular Biology (Clifton, N.J.) 973, 1–13. doi:10.1007/978-1-62703-281-0_1.

Begum, F., *et al.*, 2012. Comprehensive literature review and statistical considerations for GWAS meta-analysis. Nucleic Acids Research. 3777–3784. doi:10.1093/nar/gkr1255.

Belaghzal, H., Dekker, J., Gibcus, J.H., 2017. Hi-C 2.0: An optimized Hi-C procedure for high-resolution genome-wide mapping of chromosome conformation. Methods 123, 56–65. doi:10.1016/j.ymeth.2017.04.004.

Belkadi, A., *et al.*, 2015. Whole-genome sequencing is more powerful than whole-exome sequencing for detecting exome variants. Proceedings of the National Academy of Sciences of the United States of America 112 (17), 5473–5478. doi:10.1073/pnas.1418631112.

Bendl, J., *et al.*, 2014. PredictSNP: Robust and accurate consensus classifier for prediction of disease-related mutations. PLoS Computational Biology 10 (1), e1003440. doi:10.1371/journal.pcbi.1003440.

Bernstein, B.E., *et al.*, 2012. An integrated encyclopedia of DNA elements in the human genome. Nature 489, 57–74. doi:10.1038/nature11247.

Bomba, L., Walter, K., Soranzo, N., 2017. The impact of rare and low-frequency genetic variants in common disease. Genome Biology 18 (1), 77. doi:10.1186/s13059-017-1212-4.

Bromberg, Y., Rost, B., 2007. SNAP: Predict effect of non-synonymous polymorphisms on function. Nucleic Acids Research 35 (11), 3823–3835. doi:10.1093/nar/gkm238.

Browning, B.L., Browning, S.R., 2011. A fast, powerful method for detecting identity by descent. American Journal of Human Genetics 88 (2), 173–182. doi:10.1016/j.ajhg.2011.01.010.

Bush, W.S., Moore, J.H., 2012. Chapter 11: Genome-Wide Association Studies. PLoS Computational Biology 8 (12), doi:10.1371/journal.pcbi.1002822.

Calabrese, R., *et al.*, 2009. Functional annotations improve the predictive score of human disease-related mutations in proteins. Human Mutation 30 (8), 1237–1244. doi:10.1002/humu.21047.

Capriotti, E., Calabrese, R., Casadio, R., 2006. Predicting the insurgence of human genetic diseases associated to single point protein mutations with support vector machines and evolutionary information. Bioinformatics (Oxford, England) 22 (22), 2729–2734. doi:10.1093/bioinformatics/btl423.

Cardon, L.R., Palmer, L.J., 2003. Population stratification and spurious allelic association. Lancet. 598–604. doi:10.1016/S0140-6736(03)12520-2.

Carter, H., *et al.*, 2009. Cancer-specific high-throughput annotation of somatic mutations: Computational prediction of driver missense mutations. Cancer Research 69 (16), 6660–6667. doi:10.1158/0008-5472.CAN-09-1133.

Carvalho, B., *et al.*, 2007. Exploration, normalization, and genotype calls of high-density oligonucleotide SNP array data. Biostatistics (Oxford, England) 8 (2), 485–499. doi:10.1093/biostatistics/kxl042.

Castaldo, G., *et al.*, 1999. Detection of five rare cystic fibrosis mutations peculiar to Southern Italy: Implications in screening for the disease and phenotype characterization for patients with homozygote mutations. Clinical Chemistry 45 (7), 957–962. Available at.http://www.ncbi.nlm.nih.gov/pubmed/10388469

Chen, J., *et al.*, 2016. A uniform survey of allele-specific binding and expression over 1000-Genomes-Project individuals. Nature Communications 7, 11101. doi:10.1038/ncomms11101.

Chen, K., *et al.*, 2009. BreakDancer: An algorithm for high-resolution mapping of genomic structural variation. Nature Methods 6 (9), 677–681. doi:10.1038/nmeth.1363.

Chen, Z., et al., 2013. The G84E mutation of HOXB13 is associated with increased risk for prostate cancer: Results from the REDUCE trial. Carcinogenesis 34 (6), 1260–1264. doi:10.1093/carcin/bgt055.

Chouraki, V., Seshadri, S., 2014. Genetics of Alzheimer's disease. Advances in Genetics 87, 245–294. doi:10.1016/B978-0-12-800149-3.00005-6.

Cibulskis, K., et al., 2013. Sensitive detection of somatic point mutations in impure and heterogeneous cancer samples. Nature Biotechnology 31 (3), 213–219. doi:10.1038/nbt.2514.

Cirulli, E.T., Goldstein, D.B., 2010. Uncovering the roles of rare variants in common disease through whole-genome sequencing. Nature Reviews Genetics. 415–425. doi:10.1038/nrg2779.

Clark, M.J., et al., 2011. Performance comparison of exome DNA sequencing technologies. Nature Biotechnology 29 (10), 908–916. doi:10.1038/nbt.1975.

Collins, F.S., 2007. The Cancer Genome Atlas (TCGA). Online. 1–17.

Condit, C.M., et al., 2002. The changing meanings of "mutation:" A contextualized study of public discourse. Human Mutation 19 (1), 69–75. doi:10.1002/humu.10023.

Cooper, G.M., et al., 2005. Distribution and intensity of constraint in mammalian genomic sequence. Genome Research 15 (7), 901–913. doi:10.1101/gr.3577405.

Cortes, A., Brown, M.A., 2011. Promise and pitfalls of the Immunochip. Arthritis Research & Therapy 13 (1), 101. doi:10.1186/ar3204.

Cruchaga, C., et al., 2014. Rare coding variants in the phospholipase D3 gene confer risk for Alzheimer's disease. Nature 505 (7484), 550–554. doi:10.1038/nature12825.

Davydov, E.V. et al., 2010 Identifying a High Fraction of the Human Genome to be under Selective Constraint Using GERP++, PLoS Computational Biology. Edited by W. W. Wasserman, 6(12), e1001025. doi: 10.1371/journal.pcbi.1001025.

Dees, N.D., et al., 2012. MuSiC: Identifying mutational significance in cancer genomes. Genome Research 22 (8), 1589–1598. doi:10.1101/gr.134635.111.

Delaneau, O., Zagury, J.-F., Marchini, J., 2013. Improved whole-chromosome phasing for disease and population genetic studies. Nature Methods 10 (1), 5–6. doi:10.1038/nmeth.2307.

Dunham, I., et al., 2012. An integrated encyclopedia of DNA elements in the human genome. Nature. 57–74. doi:10.1038/nature11247.

den Dunnen, J.T., et al., 2016. HGVS Recommendations for the Description of Sequence Variants: 2016 Update. Human Mutation 37 (6), 564–569. doi:10.1002/humu.22981.

English, A.C., Salerno, W.J., Reid, J.G., 2014. PBHoney: Identifying genomic variants via long-read discordance and interrupted mapping. BMC Bioinformatics 15 (1), 180. doi:10.1186/1471-2105-15-180.

Ewing, C.M., et al., 2012. Germline mutations in HOXB13 and prostate-cancer risk,. The New England Journal of Medicine 366 (2), 141–149. doi:10.1056/NEJMoa1110000.

Feng, Y., et al., 2015. Nanopore-based fourth-generation DNA sequencing technology. Genomics, Proteomics and Bioinformatics. 4–16. doi:10.1016/j.gpb.2015.01.009.

Ferrer-Costa, C., et al., 2005. PMUT: A web-based tool for the annotation of pathological mutations on proteins,. Bioinformatics (Oxford, England) 21 (14), 3176–3178. doi:10.1093/bioinformatics/bti486.

Fu, Y. et al., 2014. FunSeq2 : A framework for prioritizing noncoding regulatory variants in cancer. doi: 10.1186/s13059-014-0480-5.

Fuchsberger, C., Abecasis, G.R., Hinds, D.A., 2015. minimac2: Faster genotype imputation. Bioinformatics (Oxford, England) 31 (5), 782–784. doi:10.1093/bioinformatics/btu704.

Gentleman, R., et al. (Eds.), 2005. Bioinformatics and Computational Biology Solutions Using R and Bioconductor. New York, NY: Springer New York. (Statistics for Biology and Health). doi: 10.1007/0-387-29362-0.

González-Pérez, A., López-Bigas, N., 2011. Improving the assessment of the outcome of nonsynonymous SNVs with a consensus deleteriousness score, Condel. American Journal of Human Genetics 88 (4), 440–449. doi:10.1016/j.ajhg.2011.03.004.

Gordon, D., et al., 2016. Long-read sequence assembly of the gorilla genome. Science 352 (6281), aae0344. doi:10.1126/science.aae0344. aae0344.

Griswold, A.J., et al., 2015. Targeted massively parallel sequencing of autism spectrum disorder-associated genes in a case control cohort reveals rare loss-of-function risk variants. Molecular Autism 6, 43. doi:10.1186/s13229-015-0034-z.

Guo, Y., et al., 2014. Illumina human exome genotyping array clustering and quality control. Nature Protocols 9 (11), 2643–2662. doi:10.1038/nprot.2014.174.

Handsaker, R.E., et al., 2011. Discovery and genotyping of genome structural polymorphism by sequencing on a population scale. Nature Genetics 43 (3), 269–276. doi:10.1038/ng.768.

Harmanci, A., Gerstein, M., 2016. Quantification of private information leakage from phenotype-genotype data: Linking attacks. Nature Methods 13 (3), 251–256. doi:10.1038/nmeth.3746.

Harmanci, A., Rozowsky, J., Gerstein, M., 2014. MUSIC: Identification of enriched regions in ChIP-Seq experiments using a mappability-corrected multiscale signal processing framework. Genome biology 15 (10), 474. doi:10.1186/s13059-014-0474-3.

Harrow, J., et al., 2012a. GENCODE: The reference human genome annotation for The ENCODE Project. Genome Research. 1760–1774.

Harrow, J., et al., 2012b. GENCODE: The reference human genome annotation for The ENCODE Project. Genome Research 22 (9), 1760–1774. doi:10.1101/gr.135350.111.

Hasan, M.S., Wu, X., Zhang, L., 2015. Performance evaluation of indel calling tools using real short-read data. Human Genomics 9 (1), 20. doi:10.1186/s40246-015-0042-2.

Higgs, D.R., Wood, W.G., 2008. Genetic complexity in sickle cell disease Proceedings of the National Academy of Sciences of the United States of America 105 (33), 11595–11596. doi:10.1073/pnas.0806633105.

Homer, N., et al., 2008. Resolving individuals contributing trace amounts of DNA to highly complex mixtures using high-density SNP genotyping microarrays. PLoS Genetics 4. doi:10.1371/journal.pgen.1000167.

Howie, B., Marchini, J., Stephens, M., 2011. Genotype imputation with thousands of genomes. G3 (Bethesda, Md.) 1 (6), 457–470. doi:10.1534/g3.111.001198.

Howie, B.N., Donnelly, P., Marchini, J., 2009. A flexible and accurate genotype imputation method for the next generation of genome-wide association studies. PLoS Genetics 5 (6), e1000529. doi:10.1371/journal.pgen.1000529.

Hu, J., He, X., 2007. Enhanced quantile normalization of microarray data to reduce loss of information in gene expression profiles. Biometrics 63 (1), 50–59. doi:10.1111/j.1541-0420.2006.00670.x.

Huber, W., et al., 2015. Orchestrating high-throughput genomic analysis with Bioconductor. Nature Methods 12 (2), 115–121. doi:10.1038/nmeth.3252.

Illumina (no date) Illumina Exome-2.4 BeadChip. Available at: https://www.illumina.com/documents/products/datasheets/datasheet_humanexome_beadchips.pdf (Accessed: 8 December 2017).

Irizarry, R.A., et al., 2003. Exploration, normalization, and summaries of high density oligonucleotide array probe level data. Biostatistics (Oxford, England) 4 (2), 249–264. doi:10.1093/biostatistics/4.2.249.

Joly, Y., et al., 2016. Are Data Sharing and Privacy Protection Mutually Exclusive? Cell. 1150–1154. doi:10.1016/j.cell.2016.11.004.

Karki, R., et al., 2015. Defining "mutation" and "polymorphism" in the era of personal genomics. BMC Medical Genomics 8, 37. doi:10.1186/s12920-015-0115-z.

Karnes, J.H., et al., 2017. Comparison of HLA allelic imputation programs. PloS One 12 (2), e0172444. doi:10.1371/journal.pone.0172444.

Khurana, E., et al., 2013. Integrative Annotation of Variants from 1092 Humans: Application to Cancer Genomics. Science 342 (6154), 1235587. doi:10.1126/science.1235587.

Kircher, M., et al., 2014. A general framework for estimating the relative pathogenicity of human genetic variants. Nature Genetics 46 (3), 310–315. doi:10.1038/ng.2892.

Koboldt, D.C., et al., 2009. VarScan: Variant detection in massively parallel sequencing of individual and pooled samples. Bioinformatics 25 (17), 2283–2285. doi:10.1093/bioinformatics/btp373.

de Koning, A.P.J., et al., 2011. Repetitive elements may comprise over Two-Thirds of the human genome. PLoS Genetics 7 (12), doi:10.1371/journal.pgen.1002384.

Korbel, J.O., et al., 2009. PEMer: A computational framework with simulation-based error models for inferring genomic structural variants from massive paired-end sequencing data. Genome Biology 10 (2), R23. doi:10.1186/gb-2009-10-2-r23.

Krumm, N., et al., 2012. Copy number variation detection and genotyping from exome sequence data. Genome Research 22 (8), 1525–1532. doi:10.1101/gr.138115.112.

LaFramboise, T., 2009. Single nucleotide polymorphism arrays: A decade of biological, computational and technological advances. Nucleic Acids Research 37 (13), 4181–4193. doi:10.1093/nar/gkp552.

Langmead, B., Salzberg, S.L., 2012. Fast gapped-read alignment with Bowtie 2. Nature Methods. 357–359. doi:10.1038/nmeth.1923.

Larson, D.E., et al., 2012. Somaticsniper: Identification of somatic point mutations in whole genome sequencing data. Bioinformatics 28 (3), 311–317. doi:10.1093/bioinformatics/btr665.

Lawrence, M.S., et al., 2013. Mutational heterogeneity in cancer and the search for new cancer-associated genes. Nature 499 (7457), 214–218. doi:10.1038/nature12213.

Li, B., et al., 2009. Automated inference of molecular mechanisms of disease from amino acid substitutions. Bioinformatics (Oxford, England) 25 (21), 2744–2750. doi:10.1093/bioinformatics/btp528.

Li, H., Ruan, J., Durbin, R., 2008. Mapping short DNA sequencing reads and calling variants using mapping quality scores. Genome Research 18 (11), 1851–1858. doi:10.1101/gr.078212.108.

Li, J., et al., 2012. CONTRA: Copy number analysis for targeted resequencing. Bioinformatics 28 (10), 1307–1313. doi:10.1093/bioinformatics/bts146.

Li, L., et al., 2011. Performance of genotype imputation for rare variants identified in exons and flanking regions of genes. PLoS One 6 (9), e24945. doi:10.1371/journal.pone.0024945.

Li, M.M., et al., 2017. Standards and Guidelines for the Interpretation and Reporting of Sequence Variants in Cancer: A Joint Consensus Recommendation of the Association for Molecular Pathology, American Society of Clinical Oncology, and College of American Pathologists. The Journal of Molecular Diagnostics : JMD 19 (1), 4–23. doi:10.1016/j.jmoldx.2016.10.002.

Li, Y., et al., 2010. MaCH: Using sequence and genotype data to estimate haplotypes and unobserved genotypes. Genetic Epidemiology 34 (8), 816–834. doi:10.1002/gepi.20533.

Lin, W.Y., 2016. Beyond Rare-Variant Association Testing: Pinpointing Rare Causal Variants in Case-Control Sequencing Study. Scientific Reports 6. doi:10.1038/srep21824.

Lin, Y., et al., 2016. Assembly of long error-prone reads using de Bruijn graphs. Proceedings of the National Academy of Sciences 113 (52), E8396–E8405. doi:10.1073/pnas.1604560113.

Lopes, M.C., et al., 2012. A combined functional annotation score for non-synonymous variants. Human Heredity 73 (1), 47–51. doi:10.1159/000334984.

MacArthur, J., et al., 2017. The new NHGRI-EBI Catalog of published genome-wide association studies (GWAS Catalog). Nucleic Acids Research 45 (D1), D896–D901. doi:10.1093/nar/gkw1133.

Manichaikul, A., et al., 2010. Robust relationship inference in genome-wide association studies. Bioinformatics 26 (22), 2867–2873. doi:10.1093/bioinformatics/btq559.

Marchini, J., Howie, B., 2008. Comparing Algorithms for Genotype Imputation. The American Journal of Human Genetics 83 (4), 535–539. doi:10.1016/j.ajhg.2008.09.007.

Marchini, J., Howie, B., 2010. Genotype imputation for genome-wide association studies. Nature Reviews. Genetics 11 (7), 499–511. doi:10.1038/nrg2796.

McCoy, R.C., et al., 2014. Illumina TruSeq synthetic long-reads empower de novo assembly and resolve complex, highly-repetitive transposable elements. PLoS One 9 (9), doi:10.1371/journal.pone.0106689.

McKenna, A., et al., 2010. The Genome Analysis Toolkit: A MapReduce framework for analyzing next-generation DNA sequencing data. Genome Research 20 (9), 1297–1303. doi:10.1101/gr.107524.110.

McLaren, W., et al., 2016. The Ensembl Variant Effect Predictor. Genome Biology 17 (1), 122. doi:10.1186/s13059-016-0974-4.

Miclaus, K., et al., 2010. Batch effects in the BRLMM genotype calling algorithm influence GWAS results for the Affymetrix 500K array. The Pharmacogenomics Journal 10 (4), 336–346. doi:10.1038/tpj.2010.36.

Morgan, A.P., 2016. argyle: An R Package for Analysis of Illumina Genotyping Arrays. G3&#58; Genes|Genomes|Genetics 6 (2), 281–286. doi:10.1534/g3.115.023739.

Mostovoy, Y., et al., 2016. A hybrid approach for de novo human genome sequence assembly and phasing. Nature Methods 13 (7), 587–590. doi:10.1038/nmeth.3865.

Nelson, W.C., et al., 2015. An integrated genotyping approach for HLA and other complex genetic systems. Human Immunology 76 (12), 928–938. doi:10.1016/j.humimm.2015.05.001.

Ng, P.C., Henikoff, S., 2001. Predicting deleterious amino acid substitutions. Genome Research 11 (5), 863–874. doi:10.1101/gr.176601.

Ng, P.C., Henikoff, S., 2003. SIFT: Predicting amino acid changes that affect protein function. Nucleic Acids Research 31 (13), 3812–3814. doi:10.1093/nar/gkg509.

O'Leary, N.A., et al., 2016. Reference sequence (RefSeq) database at NCBI: Current status, taxonomic expansion, and functional annotation. Nucleic Acids Research 44 (D1), D733–D745. doi:10.1093/nar/gkv1189.

Owzar, K., et al., 2008. Statistical challenges in preprocessing in microarray experiments in cancer. Clinical Cancer Research : An Official Journal of the American Association for Cancer Research 14 (19), 5959–5966. doi:10.1158/1078-0432.CCR-07-4532.

Pepke, S., Wold, B., Mortazavi, A., 2009. Computation for ChIP-seq and RNA-seq studies. Nature Methods 6, S22–S32. doi:10.1038/nmeth.1371.

Pollard, K.S., et al., 2010. Detection of nonneutral substitution rates on mammalian phylogenies. Genome Research 20 (1), 110–121. doi:10.1101/gr.097857.109.

Pritchard, J.K., Cox, N.J., 2002. The allelic architecture of human disease genes: Common disease-common variant...or not? Human Molecular Genetics 11 (20), 2417–2423. doi:10.1093/hmg/11.20.2417.

Ramensky, V., Bork, P., Sunyaev, S., 2002. Human non-synonymous SNPs: Server and survey. Nucleic Acids Research 30 (17), 3894–3900. Available at: http://www.ncbi.nlm.nih.gov/pubmed/12202775.

Rausch, T., et al., 2012. DELLY: Structural variant discovery by integrated paired-end and split-read analysis. Bioinformatics 28 (18), doi:10.1093/bioinformatics/bts378.

Reva, B., Antipin, Y., Sander, C., 2011. Predicting the functional impact of protein mutations: Application to cancer genomics. Nucleic Acids Research 39 (17), e118. doi:10.1093/nar/gkr407.

Rhoads, A., Au, K.F., 2015. PacBio Sequencing and Its Applications. Genomics, Proteomics and Bioinformatics. 278–289. doi:10.1016/j.gpb.2015.08.002.

Richards, S., et al., 2015. Standards and guidelines for the interpretation of sequence variants: A joint consensus recommendation of the American College of Medical Genetics and Genomics and the Association for Molecular Pathology. Genetics in Medicine : Official journal of the American College of Medical Genetics 17 (5), 405–424. doi:10.1038/gim.2015.30.

Ritchie, G.R.S., et al., 2014. Functional annotation of noncoding sequence variants. Nature Methods 11 (3), 294–296. doi:10.1038/nmeth.2832.

Rogers, M.F., et al., 2017. FATHMM-XF: Accurate prediction of pathogenic point mutations via extended features. Bioinformatics (Oxford, England). doi:10.1093/bioinformatics/btx536.

Romanoski, C.E., et al., 2015. Epigenomics: Roadmap for regulation. Nature 518 (7539), 314–316. doi:10.1038/518314a.

Roshyara, N.R., et al., 2016. Comparing performance of modern genotype imputation methods in different ethnicities. Scientific Reports 6 (1), 34386. doi:10.1038/srep34386.

Rozowsky, J., et al., 2009. PeakSeq enables systematic scoring of ChIP-seq experiments relative to controls. Nature Biotechnology 27, 66–75. doi:10.1038/nbt.1518.

Sathirapongsasuti, J.F., et al., 2011. Exome sequencing-based copy-number variation and loss of heterozygosity detection: ExomeCNV. Bioinformatics 27 (19), 2648–2654. doi:10.1093/bioinformatics/btr462.

Saunders, C.T., et al., 2012. Strelka: Accurate somatic small-variant calling from sequenced tumor-normal sample pairs. Bioinformatics 28 (14), 1811–1817. doi:10.1093/bioinformatics/bts271.

Schadt, E.E., Woo, S., Hao, K., 2012. Bayesian method to predict individual SNP genotypes from gene expression data. Nature Genetics. 603–608. doi:10.1038/ng.2248.

Schwarz, J.M., et al., 2010. MutationTaster evaluates disease-causing potential of sequence alterations. Nature Methods 7 (8), 575–576. doi:10.1038/nmeth0810-575.

Schwarz, J.M., et al., 2014. MutationTaster2: Mutation prediction for the deep-sequencing age. Nature Methods 11 (4), 361–362. doi:10.1038/nmeth.2890.

Shalem, O., Sanjana, N.E., Zhang, F., 2015. High-throughput functional genomics using CRISPR-Cas9. Nature Reviews Genetics. 299–311. doi:10.1038/nrg3899.

Shendure, J., Ji, H., 2008. Next-generation DNA sequencing. Nature Biotechnology 26 (10), 1135–1145. doi:10.1038/nbt1486.

Shihab, H.A., et al., 2013. Predicting the Functional, Molecular, and Phenotypic Consequences of Amino Acid Substitutions using Hidden Markov Models. Human Mutation 34 (1), 57–65. doi:10.1002/humu.22225.

Siepel, A., et al., 2005. Evolutionarily conserved elements in vertebrate, insect, worm, and yeast genomes. Genome Research 15 (8), 1034–1050. doi:10.1101/gr.3715005.

Singh, T., *et al.*, 2017. The contribution of rare variants to risk of schizophrenia in individuals with and without intellectual disability. Nature Genetics 49 (8), 1167–1173. doi:10.1038/ng.3903.

Soe, K., Gregoire-Bottex, M.M., 2017. A rare CFTR mutation associated with severe disease progression in a 10-year-old Hispanic patient. Clinical Case Reports 5 (2), 139–144. doi:10.1002/ccr3.764.

Staaf, J., *et al.*, 2008. Normalization of Illumina Infinium whole-genome SNP data improves copy number estimates and allelic intensity ratios. BMC Bioinformatics 9, 409. doi:10.1186/1471-2105-9-409.

Steinthorsdottir, V., *et al.*, 2014. Identification of low-frequency and rare sequence variants associated with elevated or reduced risk of type 2 diabetes. Nature Genetics 46 (3), 294–298. doi:10.1038/ng.2882.

Stone, E.A., Sidow, A., 2005. Physicochemical constraint violation by missense substitutions mediates impairment of protein function and disease severity. Genome Research 15 (7), 978–986. doi:10.1101/gr.3804205.

Sudmant, P.H., *et al.*, 2015. An integrated map of structural variation in 2,504 human genomes. Nature 526 (7571), 75–81. doi:10.1038/nature15394.

Tattini, L., D'Aurizio, R., Magi, A., 2015. Detection of Genomic Structural Variants from Next-Generation Sequencing Data. Frontiers in Bioengineering and Biotechnology. 3. doi:10.3389/fbioe.2015.00092.

Teo, Y.Y., 2012. Genotype calling for the Illumina platform. Methods in Molecular Biology (Clifton, N.J.) 850, 525–538. doi:10.1007/978-1-61779-555-8_29.

The 1000 Genomes Project Consortium, 2012. An integrated map of genetic variation. Nature 135, 0–9. doi:10.1038/nature11632.

The International HapMap 3 Consortium, 2010. Integrating common and rare genetic variation in diverse human populations. Nature 467 (7311), 52–58. doi:10.1038/nature09298.

Vilhjálmsson, B.J., Nordborg, M., 2013. The nature of confounding in genome-wide association studies. Nature Reviews Genetics. 1–2. doi:10.1038/nrg3382.

Visscher, P.M., *et al.*, 2012. Five years of GWAS discovery. American Journal of Human Genetics 90 (1), 7–24. doi:10.1016/j.ajhg.2011.11.029.

Wall, J.D., Pritchard, J.K., 2003. Haplotype blocks and linkage disequilibrium in the human genome. Nature Reviews. Genetics 4 (8), 587–597. doi:10.1038/nrg1123.

Wang, K., *et al.*, 2007. PennCNV: An integrated hidden Markov model designed for high-resolution copy number variation detection in whole-genome SNP genotyping data. Genome Research 17 (11), 1665–1674. doi:10.1101/gr.6861907.

Wang, K., Li, M., Hakonarson, H., 2010. ANNOVAR: Functional annotation of genetic variants from high-throughput sequencing data. Nucleic Acids Research 38 (16), e164. doi:10.1093/nar/gkq603.

Wang, Q., *et al.*, 2017. Novel metrics to measure coverage in whole exome sequencing datasets reveal local and global non-uniformity. Scientific Reports 7 (1), doi:10.1038/s41598-017-01005-x.

Wellcome Trust Case Control Consortium, 2007. Genome-wide association study of 14,000 cases of seven common diseases and 3,000 shared controls. Nature 447 (7145), 661–678. doi:10.1038/nature05911.

Wineinger, N.E., Pajewski, N.M., Tiwar, H.K., 2011. A method to assess linkage disequilibrium between CNVs and SNPs inside copy number variable regions. Frontiers in Genetics 2 (APR), doi:10.3389/fgene.2011.00017.

Wu, M.C., *et al.*, 2011. Rare variant association testing for sequencing data using the Sequence Kernel Association Test (SKAT). American Journal of Human Genetics 89, 82–93.

Wu, J., *et al.*, 2012. Copy Number Variation detection from 1000 Genomes project exon capture sequencing data. BMC Bioinformatics 13 (1), 305. doi:10.1186/1471-2105-13-305.

Yang, Z., *et al.*, 2017. Rare damaging variants in DNA repair and cell cycle pathways are associated with hippocampal and cognitive dysfunction: A combined genetic imaging study in first-episode treatment-naive patients with schizophrenia. Translational Psychiatry 7 (2), e1028. doi:10.1038/tp.2016.291.

Zhang, F., Lupski, J.R., 2015. Non-coding genetic variants in human disease. Human Molecular Genetics. R102–R110. doi:10.1093/hmg/ddv259.

Zheng, G.X.Y., *et al.*, 2016. Haplotyping germline and cancer genomes with high-throughput linked-read sequencing. Nature Biotechnology 34 (3), 303–311. doi:10.1038/nbt.3432.

Zhou, H., Gao, M., Skolnick, J., 2016. ENTPRISE: An Algorithm for Predicting Human Disease-Associated Amino Acid Substitutions from Sequence Entropy and Predicted Protein Structures. PloS One 11 (3), e0150965. doi:10.1371/journal.pone.0150965.

Zuk, O., *et al.*, 2014. Searching for missing heritability: Designing rare variant association studies. Proceedings of the National Academy of Sciences of the United States of America 111 (4), E455–E464. doi:10.1073/pnas.13225631111.

Predicting Non-Synonymous Single Nucleotide Variants Pathogenic Effects in Human Diseases

Marwa S Hassan, National Research Centre, Cairo, Egypt
AA Shaalan, Zagazig University, Zagazig, Egypt
MI Dessouky, Menoufia University, Menouf, Egypt
Abdelaziz E Abdelnaiem, Zagazig University, Zagazig, Egypt
Dalia A Abdel-Haleem, National Research Centre, Cairo, Egypt
Mahmoud ElHefnawi, Nile University, Giza, Egypt and National Research Centre, Cairo, Egypt.

Introduction

The recent advances in bioinformatics technologies produce a vast amount of genetic data. Since gene or protein variants are random and most variations have no harmful consequences, recognition of genetic deviations is usually an essential (Zhou et al., 2016). Variations in the protein have influence not only in the protein structure but also its stability and function. nsSNVs and mutations can affect protein function in an abundant way. Besides, early detection of nsSNVs and mutations can be helpful in diagnosing the illness at a first stage, prognosis, prevention, and treatment of illness (Kulshreshtha et al., 2016).

Bioinformatics analyses are necessary to predict contributing Amino Acid Substitutions (AAS) to human diseases for each genome (Kulshreshtha et al., 2016). Expecting the functional effect of AAS caused by nsSNVs is becoming increasingly significant as more and more novel variants are being discovered to discriminate disease-associated mutations with non-disease mutations (Kulshreshtha et al., 2016). One of the main challenges in the human genome is – to recognize functional effects of Single-nucleotide Variants (SNVs). Although some of the Variants found in genes assessed in the laboratory, many others have not evaluated for their possible damaging effects on protein structure and function (Hepp et al., 2015).

Several existing methods in this field established over the years for expecting the impact of SNVs on human health (Kulshreshtha et al., 2016). Nevertheless, they still have a high false prediction rate, which is overcome by computational approaches depend on combined features (Capriotti and Fariselli, 2017). Recently, these computational tools that are available on the website as web servers work on algorithms (a set of rules) can satisfy better predictions of the effect of SNVs if used combined from rather than alone (Kulshreshtha et al., 2016).

In this study, we present web servers that can use in predicting SNVs or mutated protein stability that causes diseases. Computational web servers based on machine learning techniques (MLTs) Support Vector Machine (SVM), Random Forest (RF), Hidden Markov Models (HMM) and Artificial Neural Network (ANN) and so on. The servers can categorize according to variant information into protein structure, evolutionary conservation, sequence parameters and Combined features (Kulshreshtha et al., 2016; Dong et al., 2015). Consensus tools (integration of various instruments) with specific to protein features may do better than others with unfocused component scores (Dong et al., 2015). By detecting diseases causing mutations, servers help to detect and understand genotype-phenotype associations, predict disease, and choose suitable treatments for patients.

Computational Approaches

A significant challenge is how to assess the disease relevance of genomic variations on a large scale. Single Nucleotide Variants (SNVs) are the most plentiful type of mutations in the human genome (Wang and Wei, 2016). The ability of computational tools to produce accurate and meaningful predictions at the protein level is not yet sufficient (Gallion et al., 2017). In the last years, many methods (Web servers) have been established to predict the effect of nsSNVs which considered as unsolved problems earlier. Among the most popular servers, both SIFT and PolyPhen were developed and updated in several studies (Ng, 2003; Xi et al., 2004; Li et al., 2009; Adzhubei et al., 2010; 2013, Sim et al., 2012; Gallion et al., 2017). Computational tools based on the MLT (SVM, RF, ANN, HMM and so on). It divided into several Techniques related to variants information, sequence homology, protein structure, combined features (structure and sequence) and consensus tool (scores of individual devices) as indicated in **(Fig. 1)**.

Sequence-Based Approaches

Nowadays, a huge amount of data generated from various genome sequencing projects which are utilized for making libraries or databases and further, applied for comparison of the query sequence to the target sequence (Kulshreshtha et al., 2016). *PhD-SNPg* was developed and compared with CADD and FATHMM by Capriotti and Fariselli (2017). It is a binary approach built on a Gradient Boosting algorithm. It can expect the effect of single and multiple SNVs from an input file included four elements, which indicate the chromosome, the position, reference and alternative alleles. Its output is a probability score between 0 and 1. When the score is > 0.5, the SNVs predicted as Pathogenic otherwise Benign. PhD-SNPg web server is a user-friendly interface to expect the influence of SNVs in coding and non-coding regions (Capriotti and Fariselli, 2017).

A web-based tool *Cancer-Specific high-throughput Annotation of Somatic Mutations (CHASM)* is a computational tool to recognize and prioritize those missense mutations best likely to produce functional changes that enhance tumor cell creation. The CHASM

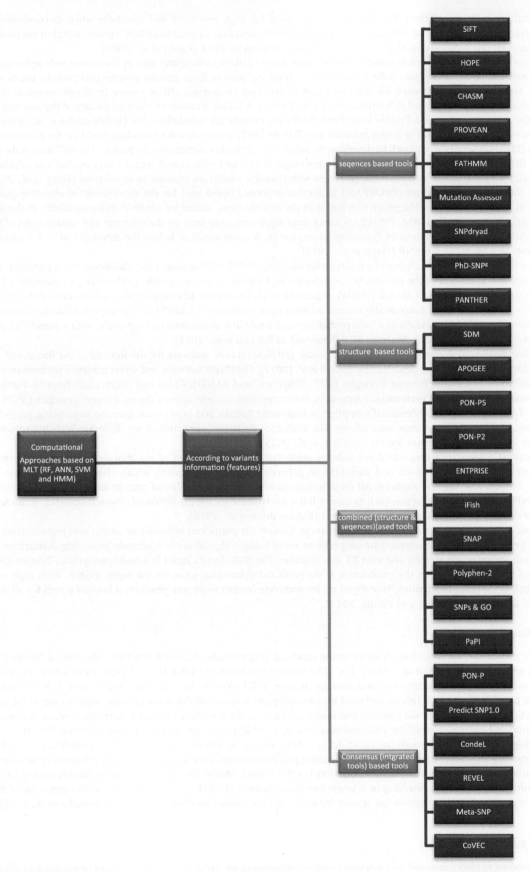

Fig. 1 Overall framework of the categories of computational approaches.

method built on a Random Forest classifier (RF). The method has high sensitivity and specificity when discriminating between known driver missense mutations and randomly created missense mutations (area under ROC curve >0.91). It outperforms other expectation methods in discriminating known oncogenic mutations in TP53 (Carter *et al.*, 2009).

The most straight forward tool is *Homotopy optimization method (HOPE)* where any user of the online web server can submit a sequence and mutation. It can also collect information about the protein from various sources (3D protein structure, UniProt Database, and DAS servers). It used for the prediction of standard phenotypic effects caused by single amino acid change. It discriminates between neutral and deleterious mutations. Further, it builds a model of mutated protein if the amount of identity between the query sequence and Protein Data Bank (PDB) file exceeds the threshold value (Kulshreshtha *et al.*, 2016).

Another sequence-based tool, *The Sorting Intolerant from Tolerant (SIFT)* uses a sequence homology based on the Numerous Sequence Alignment (MSA) conservation approach to classifying the nsSNVs as tolerated or damaged to the protein. The SIFT score is the normalized possibility that the amino acid change tolerated. The score ranges from 0 to 1 with a cutoff score of 0.05. Amino acid substitutions with (cutoff < 0.05) are predicted to be deleterious, and those with (cutoff > =0.05) are expected to be tolerated (Hepp *et al.*, 2015).

Protein Variation Effect Analyzer (PROVEAN) is another sequence based tool for the expectation of the damaging effect of variations in protein sequences. The prediction based on the modification, caused by a nsSNP, in the similarity of the sequence of related protein sequences in an MSA. PROVEAN uses a delta alignment score built on the reference and variant types of the protein sequence concerning the alignment of homologous sequences. A score equal or below the threshold of − 2.5 determines the classification as a deleterious nsSNP (Hepp *et al.*, 2015).

Another tool, *Protein Analysis Through Evolutionary Relationships (PANTHER)* evaluates the likelihood that a particular nsSNP will cause a functional alteration of the protein. It calculates the replacement Position-Specific Evolutionary Conservation (sub-PSEC) score built on a Hidden Markov Model (HMM) alignment of evolutionarily related proteins. Substitution with positive values (subPSEC > =0) is showed as functionally neutral; whereas negative values of (subPSEC < 0) expect deleterious substitutions. A subPSEC score (cutoff of-3) parallels to a 50% probability that a nsSNP is deleterious to the protein, with a possibility of causing a deleterious impact on the protein function (P deleterious) of 0.5 (Mi *et al.*, 2016).

Also, *Functional Analysis through Hidden Markov Models (FATHMM)* tool, software for the forecast of the functional impacts of protein missense variations, was described by Shihab *et al.* (2012). FATHMM Software and server achieved performance accuracies that outperformed traditional forecast strategies (SIFT, POlyPhen, and PANTHER) on two distinct benchmarks. Furthermore, in one benchmark, they achieved performance accuracies that outperform current state-of-the-art forecast strategies (SNPs & GO and MutPred). FATHMM Can be professionally applied to large-scale human and nonhuman genome sequencing projects with the other benefit of phenotypic outcome associations. The VariBench database is available at see "Relevant Websites section" and the SwissVar at see "Relevant Websites section" (Shihab *et al.*, 2013).

The Mutation Assessor tool also calculates stability score that predicts the effect of the mutation on protein. It relies on the evolutionary conservation approach and uses MSA to generate a conservation score, which classifies the mutation into three categories; neutral, low, high or medium. All these mutations affect the functionality of protein and their stability. This tool also used for SNPs associated with diseases such as cancer. It has its database for the prediction of diseases; however, it can retrieve data from other databases such as COSMIC and UniProt (Kulshreshtha *et al.*, 2016).

SNPdryad is a novel computational technique that can forecast the pernicious influence of amino acid replacements happened in human proteins. SNP dryad consistently outperforms other leading algorithms in accurately predicting deleterious nsSNVs. It uses different conservation scoring and uses RF as a classifier. The SNP dryad's input is a non-synonymous human SNP and the sequence of the human protein; the production is the predicted deleterious score for the input nsSNP. With high score value, predicted nsSNP be more deleterious. SNP dryad on the complete human proteome produces a forecast scores for all the possible amino acid substitutions (Wong and Zhang, 2014).

Structure-Based Approaches

These tools predict the stability changes by detecting structural properties as secondary structure. *Site-Directed Mutate (SDM)* web server was generated by Worth *et al.* (2011). The SDM server provides users with a fast and perfect evaluating the impact that a mutation will have on protein structure and stability. It gives a 3D view of the wild and mutant- sort. It is a worthy tool for recognizing possible illness associations and used for forecasting deleterious nsSNVs at the genome scale. To run SDM, clients must upload a wild-type structure and the position and amino acid type of the mutation. The returned results contain information about the local structural environment of the wild and mutant-sort, a stability score and illness associated forecast (Worth *et al.*, 2011).

The pathogenicity Prediction through Logistic Model tree (APOGEE) server was developed in 2017 by Castellana *et al.* APOGEE is a Machine Learning technique that outperforms all current prediction techniques in assessing the harmfulness of non-Synonymous genome variations. It based on the classification model of the Logistic Model Tree (LMT), which syndicates the logistic regression models with tree introduction resulting in a single tree (Castellana *et al.*, 2017). Structure-based tools cannot use if the protein cannot be crystallized; this limitation can resolve by using sequence-based prediction tools (Kulshreshtha *et al.*, 2016).

Combined Features Based Tools

Several preceding studies presented and assessed novel computational model that predict the impact of amino acid allelic variants on protein structure and function. Structural based approaches can utilize only when the structure is known. Otherwise, sequence-based approaches suggested. However, predicted the accuracy of sequence-based approaches is lower than the structure-based approaches. None of them is confirmed to be accurate and provide complete mutant protein analysis. The prediction accuracy can increase by using the right combination of features. Therefore, combined and consensus approaches are developed with increased accuracy and efficiency and for use in all situations (Kulshreshtha *et al.*, 2016).

PON-PS is the first generic tool for classification of amino acid substitutions associated with benign, severe, and less severe phenotypes. It combines the PON-P2 pathogenicity predictor and an ML model that classifies variants into three categories showed an accuracy of 61% in the test dataset which is higher than for existing tolerance prediction methods. PON-PS also helps to detect and understand genotype-phenotype correlations (Niroula and Vihinen, 2017).

PON-P2 is a new computational technique for sorting of amino acid variations in human proteins. It is a Machine Learning based classifier that clusters the variants into pathogenic, neutral and unknown classes, by Random Forest likelihood score. It is trained using pathogenic and neutral variants obtained from the VariBench dataset. It uses information about evolutionary conservation of sequences, biochemical properties of amino acids, physical and if available, functional annotations of variation sites. It consistently showed more significant performance in comparison to existing tools. In 10- fold cross-validation test, its accuracy and MCC are 0.86 and 0.71, respectively. PON-P2 is a powerful tool for showing and ranking deleterious variants (Niroula *et al.*, 2015).

ENTPRISE webserver can predict disease-associated/cancer driver variations. It also performs excellently and better than some of the established methods such as Mutation Assessor and PolyPhen-2 for cancer driver prediction on the COSMIC data. The combination of the parameters (amino acid type, sequence entropy and contacting the residue composition) makes ENTPRISE do well in allover tests (Zhou *et al.*, 2016).

Integrated Functional inference of SNVs in human (IFish) is also a new online web server, which had flexible functionalities and user-friendly interfaces that permit users to analyze large sets of nsSNVs rapidly. iFish could predict the pathogenicity of human nsSNVs with increased accuracy. It outperformed other existing techniques on independent benchmarking datasets. It supports the collection of genetic evidence into the expectation of pathogenicity using a Bayesian model. Inputs specified by the chromosome, position, reference allele and an alternative allele of each nsSNV. It also enables registered users to create their gene-specific classifiers using their variations, which is not available with other existing tools. (IFish) accomplished high accuracies and outperformed other existing tools (Wang and Wei, 2016).

Screening for Non-Acceptable Polymorphisms (SNAP) is also a neural network-based method for the expectation of the functional effects of nsSNVs. SNAP uses features for the residue conservation within sequence families as protein structure and annotations, when available. It receipts protein sequences and lists of mutants and delivers a score for each substitution, which can then convert into binary predictions of a neutral or non-neutral effect (Hepp *et al.*, 2015).

Polymorphism Phenotyping v2 (Polyphen-2) is a structure and sequence-based method that determines the structural and functional consequences of nsSNVs. The PolyPhen-2 that capable of analyzing vast volumes of data created by Next-generation sequencing projects calculates the probability that a Bayesian classifier damages a nsSNP. It is an automatic tool for the expectation of the probable effect of an amino acid exchange on the structure and function of a human protein (Adzhubei *et al.*, 2013).

Another combined based tool *SNPs & GO* is a method based on SVM to predict disease-related mutations from the protein sequence, which uses information derived from evolutionary information. Protein sequence and function as encoded in the Gene Ontology (GO) terms annotation to expect if a given mutation can be secret as disease-related or neutral (Hepp *et al.*, 2015). It was implemented and updated by Capriotti *et al.* (2012). Its input comprises the sequence and its structure (when available), a set of target variants and its functional Gene Ontology (GO) terms, while the output of the server delivers, for each protein variation, is the probabilities to be related to human diseases. It tested on a massive set of marked variations extracted from the SwissVar database. The results of the server are (79% and 83%) overall accuracy for the sequence-based and structure-based inputs, respectively (Capriotti *et al.*, 2013b).

Pseudo Amino Acid Composition (PaPI) is a new machine-learning tool to sort and score human coding variations by estimating the probability to damage their protein-related function. The combination of pseudo amino acid composition, evolutionary conservation, and homologous proteins based methods outperform various prediction techniques, and it is also able to score multiple variants such as deletions, insertions, and indels (Mi *et al.*, 2016). The Position-Specific Independent Count (PSIC) of the results of the server ranges from 0 to 1. The categorization of the nsSNVs results is probably damaging and possibly damaging (PSIC >0.5) or Benign (PSIC <0.5) (Hepp *et al.*, 2015).

Consensus Tools With Combined Features

Consensus tools based on the integration of various tools. It provides information that needs to design a novel protein with desired characteristic and stability (Kulshreshtha *et al.*, 2016). Some classifying tools have been improved their accuracy by integrating them with other tools. Where each tool built on the specific dataset, the combination of these individual tools in a consensus classifier is enough to improve the classification capacity. Many studies cooperate in this kind of classifications.

PON-P is a Meta classifier that combines the outputs from the five methods (SIFT, PhD-SNP, PolyPhen-2, SNAP and I-Mutant 3.0) to predict the possibility that a nsSNP will affect protein function and may so be disease-related. It utilizes RF for predicting whether variants affect functioning and lead to diseases. The (PON-P) classifies the nsSNVs as neutral, unclassified or pathogenic with a corresponding possibility of pathogenicity, and provides the data existing in the UniProt database for each entry (Hepp *et al.*, 2015).

Predict SNP1.0 is an SNP classifier technique that merges six forecast techniques (MAPP, PhD-SNP, PolyPhen-1, PolyPhen-2, SIFT, and SNAP) to gain a consensus expectation of the result of the amino acid substitution. The six prediction tools run by a dataset of non-redundant mutations. The individual confidence scores are transformed to percentages to allow comparison and the individual predictions combined in the consensus prediction. Most of these tools based on machine learning methods, primarily designed to classify neutral and deleterious mutations by sequence and structural parameters. It provides a consensus prediction with improved accuracy and efficiency over individual integrated tools (Bendl *et al.*, 2014).

Combined Annotation Dependent Depletion (Condel) is also a consensus tool which developed by integrating SIFT, PolyPhen-2, and Mutation Assessor. It collects, assembles and presents the results obtained by these tools. Condel can use as a web server or standalone tool (run on the computer after downloading).

Recently, *Rare Exome Variant Ensemble Learner (REVEL)* developed by Ioannidis *et al.* (2016) is a standard technique for expecting the pathogenicity of missense variants by individual tools. MutPred, FATHMM, VEST, Poly-Phen, SIFT, PROVEAN, Mutation Assessor, Mutation Taster, LRT, GERP, SiPhy, phyloP, and past Cons. REVEL had the best global performance as compared to any individual tool and seven ensemble methods: Meta SVM, MetaLR, KGGSeq, Condel, CADD, DANN, and Eigen. It is a standard technique that outperforms existing tools for distinguishing pathogenic variants from rare neutral variants (Ioannidis *et al.*, 2016).

Meta-SNP presented by Capriotti *et al.* (2013a,b) as a new approach for the discovery of illness-associated ns-SNVs that integrates four existing strategies: PANTHER, PhD-SNP, SIFT, and SNAP find that the Meta-SNP algorithm realizes better performance than the best single predictor. The results showed that the combination of forecasts from various resources is a good plan for the selection of high-reliability forecasts Capriotti *et al.* (2013a).

Consensus Variant Effect Classification (COVEC) is a Meta classifier that mixes the expected results of four methods SIFT, PolyPhen2, SNPs & GO and Mutation Assessor. The COVEC method outperforms unique methods and highlights the advantage of merging results from multiple tools. The SVM-based consensus classifier combines the raw output scores generated from these tools. The SVM model performs the classification using either a linear kernel or a radial based function (RBF) (Frousios *et al.*, 2013).

Consensus tools enhance accuracy and efficiency of the unique tools and predict the results better than any other tool. These tools provide a platform for comparing the results achieved by different tools in a familiar place and hence, reduce the efforts required to study the data by using different tools individually (Kulshreshtha *et al.*, 2016).

Web Servers as a Tool for Predicting the Snvs

Computational approaches, online web server, are tools for expecting the impact of SNVs on protein stability and function. After selecting the suitable database and determining the parameters affecting function and stability of the mutant protein, predicting the influence of SNVs on protein function and stability can do with the help of different computational approaches and tools. These tools are built on machine learning methods to detect and use non- redundant features that required for forecasting the effects of amino acid substitutes on protein function and classifying mutations as damaging or neutral (Kulshreshtha *et al.*, 2016).

Recent studies have indicated that the altering human behaviors have a significant influence on genetic variation (Bermejo *et al.*, 2014). Here, we launch a comprehensive review on an individual and ensemble servers for mutation analysis. We collect the most common unique tools in (**Table 1**) and ensemble tools in (**Table 2**) with their Web site, MLT that based on, Input parameters, Deleterious Threshold & Outputs, and references. The performance of the most widely used tools in predicting nsSNVs in (**Table 3**) through ACC (accuracy), AUC (Area under the curve), and MCC (Math well Correlation Coefficient). In additional to, Accuracy of the best singular and consensus tools that recently developed displayed in (**Fig. 2**).

Conclusion

In the last decade, many tools have been progressed to expect the effect of SNPs and mutation on genomic location, and on translated protein (synonymous and non-synonymous SNPs) that was considered as unsolved problems earlier (Kulshreshtha *et al.*, 2016). Recently, consensus tools have established by incorporating many tools together, which provided single window results for comparison purposes (Kaminker *et al.*, 2007). It also noted that the best ensemble scores not require a massive number of component scores to improve performance significantly, but need integrated component scores that are specific to protein features to be a marked improvement in performance. For example, KGGSeq, which integrated five module scores (SIFT, PolyPhen-2, LRT, Mutation Taster and PhyloP), performed healthy than (CADD), which integrated more than 40 component scores (Dong *et al.*, 2015).

In this review, we have performed a comprehensive study of several popular and recent prediction techniques to discriminate the pathogenic nsSNVs. It provides the fundamental knowledge based on sequence, structure and evolutionary relationship. These tools provide more reliable and accurate prediction due to compelling and comparing data from various tools.We found that some of them updated for already existing servers, others are the novel servers, while others are ensemble servers (integrated individual). Several previous studies have provided comparisons between many servers to highlight the most accurate and efficient servers and to combine them in an ensemble (Meta) server that enhances the expecting performance.

Finally, after doing a comprehensive review on all these categories of computational approaches, most studies conclude that Meta predictions are better than an individual tool. Many advanced computational approaches have been established over the years, to forecast the function and stability of a mutated protein. These methodologies based on structure, sequence features and combined features (both structure and sequence features) provide an accurate valuation of the influence of amino acid exchange on function and stability protein. By comparing the results, we realized from the range of servers performance (**Table 3**) and (**Fig. 2**) that REVEL, CADD, COVEC, Meta-SNP, PAPI, and Condel are better tools than other ensemble tools and PON-P2, SNP dryad, CHASM, PROVEAN, PhD-SNP^g, and Mutation Assessor are better tools than other individual tools. The consensus techniques have the highest overall performance.

Table 1 Shed lights on the most common individual tools with their main features as input parameters, MLT that based on, forecast scores and respective websites

ID	Server name	Website	MLT that based on	(Input features through the user)	Deleterious threshold & outputs	References
1	PON-PS	http://structure.bmc.lu.se/PON-PS	RF	Protein seqences and amino acid substitution.	Neutral, sever, non sever	Niroula and Vihinen (2017)
2	PhD-SNPg	http://snps.biofold.org/phdsnpg	Gradient boosting algorithm	chromosome position, and Protein variation (position, and First amino acid, and second amino acid variant)	If the probability is >0.5 then the SNV is predicted to be Pathogenic otherwise Benign	Capriotti and Fariselli (2017)
3	PON-P2	http://structure.bmc.lu.se/PON-P2/genomic_submission.html/	RF	Protein sequences and amino acid substitution.	Pathogenic, neutral or unknown tolerance	Niroula et al. (2015)
4	SNP dryad	http://snps.ccbr.utoronto.ca:8080/SNPdryad/DNAquery.html	RF	Human genome version, Chromosome location and variant allele	Deleterious forecast score (DPS)	Wong and Zhang (2014)
5	Polyphen-2	http://genetics.bwh.harvard.edu/pph2/	Empirical rules	Protein, SNP identifier or Protein sequence in FASTA format and positions of the substitution.	Probably damaging or Benign, or Possibly damaging, Sensitivity, specificity, Multiple sequence alignment and 3D Visualization	Adzhubei et al. (2013)
6	SNAP2	https://www.rostlab.org/services/SNAP/	ANN	Protein sequence	Non-neutral and neutral, Score and accuracy	Zhang et al. (2014)
7	Entprise	http://cssb.biology.gatech.edu/entprise	A boosted tree regression	Protein variation (First amino acid, position, and second amino acid variant) and protein RefSeq ID (not mRNA ID)	Pathogenicity score, deleterious (if score >0.45) and Sequence entropy	Zhou et al. (2016)
8	Mutation assessor	http://mutationassessor.org/r3/	Conservation method	Genome build, chromosome position, reference allele and substituted allele or Protein ID and variant.	(VC) Variant conservation score and (VS) Variant specificity score	Kulshreshtha et al. (2016), Reva et al. (2011)
9	SIFT	http://sift.jcvi.org/www/SIFT_help.html#SIFT_OUTPUT	Alignment scores	The original amino acid, the position of the substitution and the new amino acid.	Score (0–1). The predicted is damaging if the score <= 0.05 and tolerated if the score >0.05.	Hepp et al. (2015), Ng (2003), Kumar et al. (2009)
10	SNPs & GO	http://snps-and-go.biocomp.unibo.it/snps-and-go/	SVM	UniProt Accession Number, Mutation Position, Substituting residue and Wild-type residue.	Mutations are disease-related (If output =0) and neutral polymorphism (If output =1)	Calabrese et al. (2009), Capriotti et al. (2013b)
11	PROVEAN	http://provean.jcvi.org/protein_batch_submit.php?species=human	Delta alignment score	Query protein sequence in FASTA format, Position, reference amino acids and variant amino acids.	The forecast is deleterious if score <= −2.5 The forecast is neutral if score >= −2.5	Hepp et al. (2015)
12	FATHMM	http://fathmm.biocompute.org.uk/ fathmmMKL.htm Or http://fathmm.biocompute.org.uk/	HMM	Chromosome, position, reference base and mutant base	P-values in the range [0, 1]; standards above 0.5 (deleterious), while those under 0.5 (neutral or benign)	Shihab et al. (2013)
13	Mutpred	http://mutpred.mutdb.org/	RF	Protein sequence, list of amino acid substitutions and an email address	Score probability to determine neutral or disease variants	Li et al. (2009)

(Continued)

Table 1   Continued

ID	Server name	Website	MLT that based on	(Input features through the user)	Deleterious threshold & outputs	References
14	PANTHER	http://www.pantherdb.org/about.jsp	Alignment Scores HMM	Protein sequence and substitution	All GO annotations & Phylogenetic annotation	Mi et al. (2016)
15	CHASM	http://www.cravat.us	RF	A protein accession identifier, codon number, reference and variant amino acid residues	Score for each variant of a mixture of the known driver and synthetic passenger mutations	Carter et al. (2009), Wong et al. (2011)
16	Hope	http://www.cmbi.ru.nl/hope/method Or http://www.cmbi.ru.nl/hope/	Wicket web framework	FASTA seq & list of amino acid substitutions	The wild-type residue conserved or not, and annotation about the protein	
17	HANSA	http://hansa.cdfd.org.in:8080/	SVM	Protein IDs or FASTA seq and List of amino acid substitutions	Neutral or disease	Acharya and Nagarajaram (2012)
18	PMut	http://mmb2.pcb.ub.es:8080/PMut/	ANN	FASTA seq and list of amino acid substitutions	A pathogenicity directory ranging from 0 to 1 (directories >0.5 signal pathological mutations) and a confidence index (low or high)	Ferrer-Costa et al. (2005)
19	MuD (Mutation Detector)	http://mud.tau.ac.il/overview.php	RF	FASTA seq and list of variants (reference amino acids, Position, and amino acids)	Deleterious or neutral mutation	Wainreb et al. (2010)
20	VarMod (modeling the functional effects of non-synonymous variants)	http://www.wasslab.org/varmod/	SVM	FASTA sequence, Uniprot Id, and list of variants (reference amino acids, Position, and variant amino acids).	VarMod Probability	
21	EFIN (Evaluation of functional impact of non-synonymous SNPs)	http://147.8.193.83/EFIN/Query_DNA_loc.html	RF	Protein uniprot Accession id, reference amino acids, Position and variant amino acids	Damaging/neutral	
22	Ifish	http://ifish.cbi.pku.edu.cn/submit.html	SVM	Chromosome, Position, Reference Base and Mutant Base	Neutral or Deleterious	Wang and Wei (2016)
23	Net Disease SNP (a sequence conservation-based predictor of the pathogenicity of mutations)	http://www.cbs.dtu.dk/services/NetDiseaseSNP/	ANNs	FASTA seq and [protein uniprot Accession id] [AAref] [Loc] [AAvar]	(Score >= 0.5: disease; score <0.5: neutral)	

Table 2 Shed lights on the most common consensus tools with their main features as input parameters (output of individual tools), MLT that based on, forecast scores and respective websites

ID	Server Name	Website	MLT that based on	(Input parameters)	Deleterious threshold & outputs	References
1	CONDEL	http://bg.upf.edu/fannsdb/signin?next=%2Ffannsdb%2Fquery%2Fcondel Or http://bg.upf.edu/condel	A weighted average of the normalized notches of the individual methods (WAS)	A weighted average of the scores of Mutation Assessor and FATHMM.	(0.0 = Neutral, 1.0 = Deleterious)	Capriotti et al. (2013a)
2	Meta-SNP	Snps.biofold.org/metasnp/pages/help.html	RF	A score of PANTHER, PhD-SNP, SIFT, and SNAP	Disease-related orPolymorphicnon-synonymous SNVs.	Bendl et al. (2014)
3	PredictSNP	http://loschmidt.chemi.muni.cz/predictsnp	Weighted majority vote consensus	A score of PolyPhen-1, PolyPhen-2, SIFT, MAPP, PhD-SNP SNPs&GO	Confidence scores and neutral or deleterious	Lopes et al. (2012)
4	CAROL	http://www.sanger.ac.uk/resources/software/carol/	A weighted Z method	A score of SIFT, PolyPhen2	The scaled scores (Pk) range between Neutral (0) and Deleterious (0)	Dong et al. (2015)
5	Meta RL &Meta SVM	https://omictools.com/functional-forecasts-category	MMAF, linear kernel, radial kernel and polynomial kernel	A score of SIFT, PolyPhen-2, GERP ++, Mutation Taster, Mutation Assessor, FATHMM, LRT, SiPhy and PhyloP	D (Deleterious), N (Neutral) and U (Unknown)	Olatubosun et al. (2012)
6	PON-P	http://bioinf.uta.fi/PON-P/	RF	A score of SIFT, PolyPhen2, SNAP, PhD-SNP, and I-Mutant	(0.5) uncertain class,(0) maximally certain neutral variant effect And (1) absolute certainty variant is deleterious	Frousios et al. (2013)
7	Meta predict	http://www.folowsite.com/www.metapredict.eu	A weighted average of the normalized notches of the individual methods (WAS)	A score of SIFT, PolyPhen2, Condel, CHASM, mCluster, logRE, SNAP, and Mutation Assessor	(0.0 = Neutral, 1.0 = Deleterious)	Ioannidis et al. (2016)
8	COVEC	http://www.dcs.kcl.ac.uk/pg/frousiok/variants/index.html	Weighted majority Vote Score (WMV) & SVM	A Score of SIFT, PolyPhen2, SNPs and GO and Mutation Assessor	Damaging (+2), neutral (−2), intermediate (0)	Kircher et al. (2014)
9	REVEL	https://sites.google.com/site/revelgenomics/	RF	A score of MutPred, FATHMM, VEST, Poly-Phen, SIFT, PROVEAN, Mutation Assessor, MutationTaster, LRT, GERP, SiPhy, phyloP, and phastCons.	Disease variants or rare neutral variants	Quang et al. (2014)
10	CADD	http://cadd.gs.washington.edu/score	A linear kernel support vector machine (SVM)	SNVs	Functional, deleterious, and pathogenic variants	Jabot-Hanin et al. (2016)
11	DANN	https://cbcl.ics.uci.edu/public_data/DANN/	A deep neural network (DNN)	SNVs	"Simulated" or "observed" variants	Mi et al. (2016)
12	rfPred	http://www.sbim.fr/rfPred/	RF	A Score of SIFT, Polyphen2, LRT, PhyloP, and MutationTaster	Neutral or deleterious	Kaminker et al. (2007)
13	PAPI	http://papi.unipv.it/	RF	A scorePolyPhen2, SIFT, and RF	Damaging or tolerated and confidence score	
14	Can predict (Cancer predict)	https://www.gene.com/research/genentech/canpredict	RF	A score of SIFT, LogR.	Activating or inactivating variants,evaluate score, and GO log-odds score for each variation.	

Table 3   Shed lights on the performance of the best individual and ensemble tools as ACC (accuracy), AUC (Area under the curve), and MCC (Math well Correlation Coefficient)

NO.	Server name	% ACC	% AUC	% MCC
1	PhD–SNPg	86	92	72
2	iFish (integrated Functional inference of SNVs in human)	76.99	0.73	0.54
3	SNP dryad	89	70–94	–
4	Prophen1 (Polymorphism Phenotyping v1)	65.8–70	65–69	31–39
5	Prophen2 (Polymorphism Phenotypingv2)	62–75	63–94	27–75
6	SNAP (screening for Non – Acceptable Polymorphisms)	63.1–68	66.7–79	26.3–37
7	Entprise	62.6–74.2	67–81.8	25.4–49.3
8	Mutation Assessor	57–81	74–89	40.2 62
9	Mutation Taster	63.8–71.78	66.2–86	30.5–49
10	SIFT (sorting intolerant from tolerant)	64–75	66–87	30–82
11	SNPs & GO	82–83	89–93	65–68
12	PROVEAN (Protein Variation Effect Analyzer)	77.4–88	78.3–84	46–74
13	FATHMM (Functional Analysis Through Hidden Markov Models)	59.2–73.07	63.7–93	18.2–45
14	Mutpred	50.4–78.8	83.5–50.3	1–54
15	PANTHER (Protein Analysis Through Evolutionary Relationships)	75	84	52
16	KGGseq	–	87–92	–
17	PON–P2	86–95	–	71–80
18	PON–PS	61–65	–	22–29
19	CONDEL (Consensus Deleteriousness score of missense SNVs)	64–78	85–90	33–58
20	Meta–SNP	56.2–87	73–75	20.5–35.1
21	Predict–SNP	66.2–70.8	72–78	33.2–43.3
22	CAROL (Combined Annotation Scoring Tool)	74.5–85.2	–42–	64
23	Meta LR (Logistic Regression)	59.8	63.5–95.16	–
24	Meta SVM (Support Vector Machine)	58.2	63.08–93.3	–
25	PON–P	75	86	40–73
26	COVEC (Consensus Variant Effect Classification)	87	—	74
27	PaPI (Pseudo amino acid composition to score human protein–coding variants)	86.4	92.6	0.74
28	CHASM (Cancer–specific High–throughput Annotation of Somatic Mutations)	50–89	79–99.6	8–79
29	REVEL (Rare Exome Variant Ensemble Learner)	89	90–95.7	–
30	CADD (Combined Annotation Dependent Depletion)	76.20–87	77–92	0.53–74
31	DANN (Deep Artificial Neural Network)	66.1	70–95.6	–

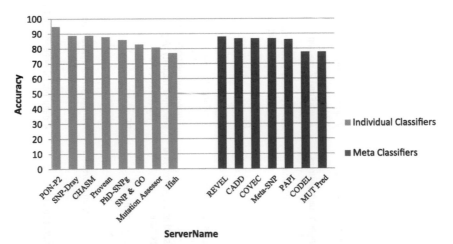

Fig. 2   Accuracy of the best individual and ensemble classifiers.

We concluded that consensus classifiers are better than single ones. We recommend using multiple prediction algorithms as well as more available genetic level information may help to enhance the predictive power. This review is a useful user guide for future studies based on web servers for prediction the impact of genetic variants in human diseases.

See also: Detecting and Annotating Rare Variants. Disease Biomarker Discovery. Identification and Extraction of Biomarker Information. Natural Language Processing Approaches in Bioinformatics. Prediction of Protein-Binding Sites in DNA Sequences. Single Nucleotide Polymorphism Typing

References

Acharya, V., Nagarajaram, H.A., 2012. Hansa: An automated method for discriminating disease and neutral human nsSNPs. Hum. Mutat. 33, 332–337.

Adzhubei, I., Jordan, D.M., Sunyaev, S.R., 2013. Predicting functional effect of human missense mutations using PolyPhen-2. Curr. Protoc. Hum. Genet. (Chapter 7: Unit7 20).

Adzhubei, I.A., Schmidt, S., Peshkin, L., et al., 2010. A method and server for predicting damaging missense mutations. Nat. Methods 7, 248–249.

Bendl, J., Stourac, J., Salanda, O., et al., 2014. PredictSNP: Robust and accurate consensus classifier for prediction of disease-related mutations. PLOS Comput. Biol. 10, e1003440.

Bermejo, C.N.H., Poch, O., Thompson, J., 2014. A comprehensive study of small non-frameshift insertions/deletions in proteins and prediction of their phenotypic effects by a machine learning method (KD4i). BMC Bioinform. 15, 111.

Calabrese, R., Capriotti, E., Fariselli, P., Martelli, P.L., Casadio, R., 2009. Functional annotations improve the predictive score of human disease-related mutations in proteins. Hum. Mutat. 30, 1237–1244.

Capriotti, E., Altman, R.B., Bromberg, Y., 2013a. Collective judgment predicts disease-associated single nucleotide variants. BMC Genom. 14 (Suppl 3), S2.

Capriotti, E., Calabrese, R., Fariselli, P., et al., 2013b. WS-SNPs&GO: A web server for predicting the deleterious effect of human protein variants using functional annotation. BMC Genom. 14 (Suppl 3), S6.

Capriotti, E., Fariselli, P., 2017. PhD-SNPg: A webserver and lightweight tool for scoring single nucleotide variants. Nucleic Acids Res. doi:10.1093/nar/gkx369.

Carter, H., Chen, S., Isik, L., et al., 2009. Cancer-specific high-throughput annotation of somatic mutations: Computational prediction of driver missense mutations. Cancer Res. 69, 6660–6667.

Castellana, S., Fusilli, C., Mazzoccoli, G., et al., 2017. High-confidence assessment of functional impact of human mitochondrial non-synonymous genome variations by APOGEE. PLOS Comput. Biol. 13, e1005628.

Dong, C., Wei, P., Jian, X., et al., 2015. Comparison and integration of deleteriousness prediction methods for nonsynonymous SNVs in whole exome sequencing studies. Hum. Mol. Genet. 24, 2125–2137.

Ferrer-Costa, C., Gelpi, J.L., Zamakola, L., et al., 2005. PMUT: A web-based tool for the annotation of pathological mutations on proteins. Bioinformatics 21, 3176–3178.

Frousios, K., Iliopoulos, C.S., Schlitt, T., Simpson, M.A., 2013. Predicting the functional consequences of non-synonymous DNA sequence variants – Evaluation of bioinformatics tools and development of a consensus strategy. Genomics 102, 223–228.

Gallion, J., Koire, A., Katsonis, P., et al., 2017. Predicting phenotype from genotype: Improving accuracy through more robust experimental and computational modeling. Hum. Mutat. 38, 569–580.

Hepp, D., Goncalves, G.L., de Freitas, T.R., 2015. Prediction of the damage-associated non-synonymous single nucleotide polymorphisms in the human MC1R gene. PLOS ONE 10, e0121812.

Ioannidis, N.M., Rothstein, J.H., Pejaver, V., et al., 2016. REVEL: An ensemble method for predicting the pathogenicity of rare missense variants. Am. J. Hum. Genet. 99, 877–885.

Jabot-Hanin, F., Varet, H., Tores, F., Alcais, A., Jais, J.-P., 2016. doi:10.1101/037127.

Kaminker, J.S., Zhang, Y., Waugh, A., et al., 2007. Distinguishing cancer-associated missense mutations from common polymorphisms. Cancer Res. 67, 465–473.

Kircher, M., Witten, D.M., Jain, P., et al., 2014. A general framework for estimating the relative pathogenicity of human genetic variants. Nat. Genet. 46, 310–315.

Kulshreshtha, S., Chaudhary, V., Goswami, G.K., Mathur, N., 2016. Computational approaches for predicting mutant protein stability. J. Comput. Aided Mol. Des. 30, 401–412.

Kumar, P., Henikoff, S., Ng, P.C., 2009. Predicting the effects of coding non-synonymous variants on protein function using the SIFT algorithm. Nat. Protoc. 4, 1073–1081.

Li, B., Krishnan, V.G., Mort, M.E., et al., 2009. Automated inference of molecular mechanisms of disease from amino acid substitutions. Bioinformatics 25, 2744–2750.

Lopes, M.C., Joyce, C., Ritchie, G.R., et al., 2012. A combined functional annotation score for non-synonymous variants. Hum. Hered. 73, 47–51.

Mi, H., Poudel, S., Muruganujan, A., Casagrande, J.T., Thomas, P.D., 2016. PANTHER version 10: Expanded protein families and functions, and analysis tools. Nucleic Acids Res. 44, D336–D342.

Ng, P.C., 2003. SIFT: Predicting amino acid changes that affect protein function. Nucleic Acids Res. 31, 3812–3814.

Niroula, A., Urolagin, S., Vihinen, M., 2015. PON-P2: Prediction method for fast and reliable identification of harmful variants. PLOS ONE 10, e0117380.

Niroula, A., Vihinen, M., 2017. Predicting severity of disease-causing variants. Hum. Mutat. 38, 357–364.

Olatubosun, A., Valiaho, J., Harkonen, J., Thusberg, J., Vihinen, M., 2012. PON-P: Integrated predictor for pathogenicity of missense variants. Hum. Mutat. 33, 1166–1174.

Quang, D., Chen, Y., Xie, X., 2015. DANN: A deep learning approach for annotating the pathogenicity of genetic variants. Bioinformatics 31, 761–763.

Reva, B., Antipin, Y., Sander, C., 2011. Predicting the functional impact of protein mutations: Application to cancer genomics. Nucleic Acids Res. 39, e118.

Shihab, H.A., Gough, J., Cooper, D.N., et al., 2013. Predicting the functional, molecular, and phenotypic consequences of amino acid substitutions using hidden Markov models. Hum. Mutat. 34, 57–65.

Sim, N.L., Kumar, P., Hu, J., et al., 2012. SIFT web server: Predicting effects of amino acid substitutions on proteins. Nucleic Acids Res. 40, W452–W457.

Wainreb, G., Ashkenazy, H., Bromberg, Y., et al., 2010. MuD: An interactive web server for the prediction of non-neutral substitutions using protein structural data. Nucleic Acids Res. 38, W523–W528.

Wang, M., Wei, L., 2016. iFish: Predicting the pathogenicity of human nonsynonymous variants using gene-specific/family-specific attributes and classifiers. Sci. Rep. 6, 31321.

Wong, W.C., Kim, D., Carter, H., et al., 2011. CHASM and SNVBox: Toolkit for detecting biologically important single nucleotide mutations in cancer. Bioinformatics 27, 2147–2148.

Wong, K.C., Zhang, Z., 2014. SNPdryad: Predicting deleterious non-synonymous human SNPs using only orthologous protein sequences. Bioinformatics 30, 1112–1119.

Worth, C.L., Preissner, R., Blundell, T.L., 2011. SDM – A server for predicting effects of mutations on protein stability and malfunction. Nucleic Acids Res. 39, W215–W222.

Xi, T., Jones, I.M., Mohrenweiser, H.W., 2004. Many amino acid substitution variants identified in DNA repair genes during human population screenings are predicted to impact protein function. Genomics 83, 970–979.

Zhang, J., Liu, J., Sun, J., et al., 2014. Identifying driver mutations from sequencing data of heterogeneous tumors in the era of personalized genome sequencing. Brief Bioinform. 15, 244–255.

Zhou, H., Gao, M., Skolnick, J., 2016. ENTPRISE. An algorithm for predicting human disease-associated amino acid substitutions from sequence entropy and predicted protein structures. PLOS ONE 11, e0150965.

Relevant Websites

http://bioinf.uta.fi/VariBench

A benchmark database for variations. Nair PS, Vihinen M. VariBench: A Benchmark Database for Variations. Hum Mutat. 2013, 34(1):42–9. PUBMED.

http://swissvar.expasy.org

ExPASy Bioinformatic Resource Portal.

Genome Analysis – Identification of Genes Involved in Host-Pathogen Protein-Protein Interaction Networks

Fransiskus Xaverius Ivan, Jie Zheng, and Chee-Keong Kwoh, Nanyang Technological University, Singapore
Vincent TK Chow, National University of Singapore, Singapore

Introduction

Among various types of molecular networks, host-pathogen protein-protein interaction (HP-PPI) networks have been considered as one of the most important types (Stebbins, 2005; Korkin et al., 2011; Zoraghi and Reiner, 2013) in the study of infectious diseases. Advances in understanding the nature of HP-PPIs could enlighten ourselves as to the principles of mechanisms for the infection mechanisms by pathogens. A few principles have been proposed, including the specificity and multiplicity of pathogen proteins in targeting the host proteins, and the preference of pathogen proteins in targeting the hubs of the host protein-protein interaction networks (Arnold et al., 2012). Recently, the centrality of a pathogen protein in the host-pathogen interactome, but not pathogen interactome, is shown to correlate with the fitness of the pathogen during in vivo infection (Asensio et al., 2017). Knowledge of such network wiring would pave the way for implementing network medicine which may provide novel strategies for determining therapeutic targets and altering a disease state to a normal state (Barabási et al., 2011).

To uncover HP-PPI networks, several high-throughput experimental techniques have been available and reviewed by Nicod et al. (2017). Of particular interest is the yeast two-hybrid (Y2H), an in vivo technique which detects an interaction based on the reconstitution of a functional transcription factor. This method has been used to uncover interactions between human proteins and proteins from varying viruses, including hepatitis C virus (De Chassey et al., 2008; Dolan et al., 2013), herpesvirus (Lee et al., 2011), influenza virus (Shapira et al., 2009) and various flaviviruses (Le Breton et al., 2011; Khadka et al., 2011; Mairiang et al., 2013) and oncoviruses (Calderwood et al., 2007; Gulbahce et al., 2012; Muller et al., 2012; Rozenblatt-Rosen et al., 2012). To some extent, it has also been limitedly used to uncover interactions between human proteins and effectors of varying bacteria and parasites, including Bacillus anthracis (Dyer et al., 2010), Burkholderia mallei (Memisević et al., 2013), Escherichia coli (Blasche et al., 2014), Francisella tularensis (Dyer et al., 2010; Wallqvist et al., 2015), Mycobacterium tuberculosis (Mehra et al., 2013), Yersinia pestis (Dyer et al., 2010; Yang et al., 2011), and Toxoplasma gondii (Liu et al., 2017). However, note that although Y2H technique can test the interaction between any pair of proteins, it may not capture the interactions between proteins that require posttranslational modification in their original organisms and proteins that are not localized in the nucleus.

In addition to Y2H, high-throughput proteomic approaches have also gained popularity for uncovering HP-PPIs in the recent years. Among them, mass spectrometry (MS) based methods are the most common ones. Unlike Y2H, MS methods can provide information related to posttranslational modifications and capture interactions in physiologically relevant conditions. Additionally, MS methods also allow quantification of proteome to compare changes of proteins complexes between biological conditions. Unfortunately, most MS methods are not highly sensitive and sometimes require high amounts of purified protein complexes that are hard to be obtained (Nicod et al., 2017). One of the most promising MS methods is coupled with affinity purification (AP), and it has been mainly used to study HP-PPIs during virus infections. These include infections by hepatitis C virus (Germain et al., 2014; Ramage et al., 2015), herpesvirus (Davis et al., 2015), HIV (Jäger et al., 2011; Kane et al., 2015), influenza virus (Watanabe et al., 2014), and various flaviviruses (Colpitts et al., 2011) and oncoviruses (Rozenblatt-Rosen et al., 2012; White et al., 2012a). Further highlights to the application of MS methods on resolving HP-PPIs can be found in Gerold et al. (2016). MS methods have also been limitedly used to study HP-PPIs during infections by bacteria and parasites, including Salmonella (Auweter et al., 2011), Chlamydia trachomatis (Mirrashidi et al., 2015) and Plasmodium falciparum (Swearingen et al., 2016).

Another emerging approach to identifying genes involved in HP-PPI networks is the dual RNA-seq technique which simultaneously captures transcripts in both the host and pathogen organisms (Westermann et al., 2017). The method has been applied to studying interactions between human/animal proteins and proteins from various pathogens, including Chlamydia trachomatis (Humphrys et al., 2013), Lawsonia intracellularis (Vannucci et al., 2013), Escherichia coli (Mavromatis et al., 2015), Mycobacterium bovis (Rienksma et al., 2015), Haemophilus influenzae (Baddal et al., 2015), Salmonella typhi (Avraham et al., 2015; Westermann et al., 2016) and Streptococcus pneumonia (Aprianto et al., 2016). For revealing the HP-PPI networks, a correlation between host's and pathogen's gene expression profiles can be reliably used; however, it must be noted that both direct and indirect interactions may be detected by the correlation methods (Reid and Berriman, 2013).

Despite their promising performance, experimental high-throughput approaches are costly and labor-intensive. Moreover, as discussed above, the resultant datasets may have inherent noises, biases and limited coverage (see Xing et al., 2016 for detailed discussions on technological issues and flaws of various experimental methods). Thus, in light of limited reliability and voluminous nature of HP-PPI data, predictive computational methods that integrate genome-wide data sources would be a great complement to the experimental techniques in exploring the full range of possible genes involved in HP-PPIs.

Here, we review the latest achievements in the integrated genome-wide computational prediction of HP-PPI networks. First, we describe a workflow for predicting HP-PPI networks and highlight two different principles for detecting interacting pairs of proteins. Secondly, we illustrate several case studies in the area of human infectious diseases and categorize them according to the types of pathogens. We highlight several aspects that need to be considered when uncovering related HP-PPI networks. Finally, we discuss issues on the methods, highlight efforts that have been made to address them, and outline future developmental works in the area.

Workflow for Predicting Host-Pathogen Protein-Protein Interactions

From a survey of the literature and previous literature reviews (Arnold et al., 2012; Zhou et al., 2013a; Nourani et al., 2015; Sen et al., 2016), we have recognized that a workflow for predicting genes involved in HP-PPI networks can be divided into four stages: (1) retrieval of host-pathogen genomes and PPI data, (2) detecting potential HP-PPIs, (3) filtering predicted HP-PPIs, and (4) validating predicted HP-PPIs. These stages are explained in detail in the following subsections.

Retrieval of Host-Pathogen Genomes/Proteomes and Protein-Protein Interaction Data

To conduct an investigation on HP-PPI networks, we must first collect genomes or proteomes of host and pathogen of interest. If available, such data can be retrieved from free genome or proteome repositories in NCBI (NCBI Resource Coordinators, 2017), ENA (Toribio et al., 2017), ENSEMBL (Kersey et al., 2016), or UniProt (The UniProt Consortium, 2017), as well as specialized ones such as CryptoDB (Heiges et al., 2006), ToxoDB (Gajria et al., 2008), PlasmoDB (Aurrecoechea et al., 2009), TubercuList (Lew et al., 2011), GeneDB (Logan-Klumpler et al., 2012), EuPathDB (Aurrecoechea et al., 2017), HIV Sequence Databases (Kuiken et al., 2003), and many others.

Next, we require protein-protein interaction (PPI) datasets that can be considered as the ground truth for predicting new HP-PPIs. A number of specialized or generalized databases have been available, and they mainly include intra-species protein-protein interaction data. Some databases that maintain HP-PPI datasets have also been developed, including PHISTO (Durmuş et al., 2013), VirHostNet (Guirimand et al., 2015), HPIDB (Ammari et al., 2016) and PHI-base (Urban et al., 2017). In addition to those databases, PDB (Rose et al., 2017) is also a valuable resource for collecting interaction data along with their protein structures; while 3did database (Mosca et al., 2014) a secondary database that provides information about 3D interacting domains extracted from PDB. The list of PPI databases that have been used for investigations and are still actively maintained is given in Table 1. One important note is that the databases may contain PPIs that are uncovered from literature by an automated text mining approach. A recent review of the development of text mining approaches for HP-PPI recovery from literatures is given by Durmuş et al. (2015).

Table 1   Repositories for gold standard intra-species and inter-species (host-pathogen) protein-protein interactions

Organisms	Database	Link	References
Any	Database of Interacting Proteins (DIP)	http://dip.mbi.ucla.edu/dip/	Salwinski et al. (2004)
Any	PIBASE	https://salilab.org/pibase	Davis and Sali (2005)
Any	Biologic Interaction and Network Analysis (BIANA)	http://sbi.imim.es/web/BIANA.php	Garcia-Garcia et al. (2010)
Any	Molecular INTeraction (MINT)	http://mint.bio.uniroma2.it/	Licata et al. (2012)
Any	Three-dimensional interacting domains (3did)	https://3did.irbbarcelona.org	Mosca et al. (2014)
Any	IntAct	https://www.ebi.ac.uk/intact/	Orchard et al. (2014)
Any	Biological General Repository for Interaction Datasets (BioGRID)	https://thebiogrid.org/	Chatr-Aryamontri et al. (2017)
Any	Protein Data Bank (PDB)	https://www.rcsb.org/	Rose et al. (2017)
Any-any	Host-Pathogen Interaction Database (HPIDB)	http://agbase.msstate.edu/hpi/main.html	Ammari et al. (2016)
Any-prokaryotic or eukaryotic pathogen	Pathogen-Host Interaction database (PHI-base)	http://www.phi-base.org/	Urban et al. (2017)
Any-virus	VirHostNet	http://virhostnet.prabi.fr/	Guirimand et al. (2015)
Bacteria	PATRIC	https://www.patricbrc.org/	Wattam et al. (2017)
Human	Human Protein Reference Database (HPRD)	http://www.hprd.org/	Prasad et al. (2009)
Human	Human Proteinpedia Interaction	http://www.humanproteinpedia.org/	Muthusamy) et al. (2013)
Human-any	PHISTO	http://www.phisto.org/	Durmuş et al. (2013)
Fly	Drosophila Interaction Database (DroID)	http://www.droidb.org/	Murali et al. (2011)
Mammals	MIPS mammalian protein-protein interaction database (MPPI)	http://mips.helmholtz-muenchen.de	Pagel et al. (2005)
Plasmodium falciparum	PlasmoDB	http://plasmodb.org	Aurrecoechea et al. (2009)

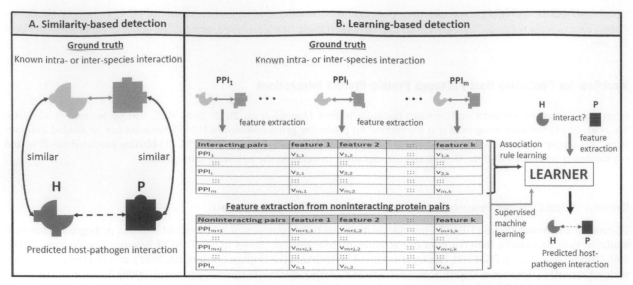

Fig. 1 Two principles for detecting potential HP-PPI between host protein H and pathogen protein P. (A) Similarity-based detection: H and P interact if each of them is similar to a different component of a known interacting protein pair. The similarity can be either based on sequences, domains, motifs, or structures. (B) Learning-based detection: The interaction between H and P is decided by a learner that is constructed using an association rule learning or a supervised machine learning approach. Association rule learning relies only on feature dataset extracted from known protein-protein interactions (PPIs), while supervised machine learning must be trained using feature datasets from both interacting and noninteracting protein pairs.

Detecting Potential Host-Pathogen Protein-Protein Interactions

At this stage, potential protein-protein interactions are detected by using known intra-species PPI or HP-PPI datasets as the ground truth. In general, there are two classes of methods for detecting potential interactions: similarity-based and learning-based methods. In principles, similarity-based methods compare the sequences, domains, motifs, or structures of candidate interacting protein pairs with those of known interacting protein pairs; while learning-based methods generate features from candidate and known interacting protein pairs for training a classifier or constructing rules for predictions. Illustration of these principles is presented in **Fig. 1**. Although both similarity- and learning-based approaches can be combined, here we explain each method separately.

Similarity-based detection methods

Similarity-based detection methods rely on the assumption that "If protein A and protein B are known to interact, and we have A' and B' are respectively similar to A and B in terms of sequence, domain, motif, or 3D information structures, then we may conclude that A' and B' are potential to interact". Sequence similarity indicates homology or evolutionary relationship between sequences, and thus the method is often referred to as a homology-based method. Predicted interactions by homology-based methods are called interologs. Several databases have been developed to store information on homologous sequences, which include OrthoMCL-DB (Fischer *et al.*, 2011), InParanoid (Sonnhammer and Östlund, 2015), NCBI HomoloGene (NCBI Resource Coordinators, 2017) and OrthoDB (Zdobnov *et al.*, 2017); and thus, inference on interologs could be eased with the presence of such databases. In the absence of homologous information, homology between a host or a pathogen protein with a known interacting protein can be assessed by using BLASTP (Altschul *et al.*, 1990). For capturing distant similarity, PSI-BLAST (Altschul *et al.*, 1997; Schäffer *et al.*, 2001) should be considered. Tools for quick ortholog (homolog due to speciation) assignments between two genomes from different species, which include free tools that are used to create OrthoDB, OrthoMCL-DB, and InParanoid, may also be employed.

Similarly, classification of domain or motif of protein sequences can be checked in domain or motif databases (especially Pfam database (Finn *et al.*, 2016)) and used for predicting protein-protein interactions. Domain or motif of new protein sequences (proteins that are not in the databases) can be classified using various domain or motif search tools, including TMHMM (Krogh *et al.*, 2001), ScanProsite (De Castro *et al.*, 2006), HMMER (Mistry *et al.*, 2013), InterProScan (Jones *et al.*, 2014), RPS-BLAST (Marchler-Bauer *et al.*, 2015) and ELM (Dinkel *et al.*, 2016). For 3D structure, similar protein structures in PDB can be obtained in Dali Database (Holm and Rosenström, 2010) or SCOP2 (Andreeva *et al.*, 2014), while similarity search for query protein structures against protein structures in PDB can be done using DaliLite (Holm *et al.*, 2008). DaliLite, or alternatively TM-align (Zhang and Skolnick, 2005) may also be used for comparing two protein structures in a local database; alternatively. If only protein sequences are available, 3D structures of the proteins can be first predicted before performing similarity search. The

Table 2   Repositories for similar protein sequences, domains, motifs and structures

Information	Database	Link	References
Homologous sequences	OrthoMCL-DB2	http://orthomcl.org	Fischer *et al.* (2011)
	InParanoid	http://inparanoid.sbc.su.se/cgi-in/index.cgi	Sonnhammer and Östlund (2015)
	NCBI HomoloGene	https://www.ncbi.nlm.nih.gov/homologene	NCBI Resource Coordinators (2017)
	OrthoDB	http://www.orthodb.org/	Zdobnov *et al.* (2017)
Domain and motif classification	MulPSSM	http://mulpssm.mbu.iisc.ernet.in/	Gowri *et al.* (2006)
	PROSITE	http://prosite.expasy.org/prosite.html	Sigrist *et al.* (2013)
	InterPro	http://www.ebi.ac.uk/interpro	Mitchell *et al.* (2015)
	Pfam	http://pfam.xfam.org/	Finn *et al.* (2016)
Structural classification	Dali Database	http://ekhidna.biocenter.helsinki.fi/dali/start	Holm and Rosenström (2010)
	SCOP2	http://scop2.mrc-lmb.cam.ac.uk/	Andreeva *et al.* (2014)

Table 3   Sequence, domain, motif and structure similarity search tools

Type of search	Tool	Link	References
Sequence	BLASTP	https://blast.ncbi.nlm.nih.gov/Blast.cgi	Altschul *et al.* (1990)
	Position-Specific Iterated BLAST (PSI-BLAST)	https://blast.ncbi.nlm.nih.gov/Blast.cgi	Altschul *et al.* (1997), Schäffer *et al.* (2001)
Domain and motif	TMHMM	http://www.cbs.dtu.dk/services/TMHMM/	Krogh *et al.* (2001)
	ScanProsite	http://prosite.expasy.org/scanprosite/	De Castro *et al.* (2006)
	HMMER	http://hmmer.org/	Mistry *et al.* (2013)
	InterProScan	http://www.ebi.ac.uk/interpro/search/sequence-search	Jones *et al.* (2014)
	Reverse Position-Specific BLAST (RPS-BLAST)	https://www.ncbi.nlm.nih.gov/Structure/cdd/docs/cdd_search.html	Marchler-Bauer *et al.* (2015)
	Eukaryotic Linear Motif (ELM) prediction tool	http://elm.eu.org/	Dinkel *et al.* (2016)
Structure	TM-align	https://zhanglab.ccmb.med.umich.edu/TM-align/	Zhang and Skolnick (2005)
	DaliLite	http://ekhidna2.biocenter.helsinki.fi/dali/	Holm *et al.* (2008)

prediction can be done by using software such as I-TASSER (Yang *et al.*, 2015) and MODELLER (Webb and Sali, 2016) and utilizing PDB's structural information as a template. Respectively, **Tables 2** and **3** summarize repositories and search tools that are available publicly.

Learning-based detection methods

Learning-based detection methods have been widely applied for predicting HP-PPIs. Supervised machine learning methods, such as logistic regression, multilayer perceptron, random forest and support vector machine, have been applied in the presence of positive and negative datasets (i.e., interacting and noninteracting protein pairs). Regardless of the methods they use, and whether it is a single-task or multi-task learning, or involves transfer learning or not, generation of features for labeled data is crucial to apply supervised learning-based methods. The features have been extracted from various resources, including features from interacting proteins (sequence, domain, and motif features), known HP-PPI data (HP-PPIs with experimental evidence), network topology (mainly from host interactome), Gene Ontology (GO) annotations, and other varying biological contexts. A summary of features that have been used for prediction is shown in **Table 4**. Among them, *k*-mer composition of host and pathogen proteins has been the most popular feature being used.

Nonetheless, some authors (Mukhopadhyay *et al.*, 2010, 2012, 2014; Mondal *et al.*, 2012; Ray *et al.*, 2012; Nouretdinov *et al.*, 2012) have argued that negative dataset or a list of noninteracting protein pairs cannot be defined precisely. In this case, they proposed the use of association rule learning, a data mining approach for discovering interesting relations between items in a large dataset. Highlights about their methods are presented in the case studies.

Filtering Predicted Host-Pathogen Protein-Protein Interactions

Detection methods usually come along with a threshold parameter that needs to be set in order to obtain potential interactions with significant evidence. For example, when using BLASTP for detecting homology or sequence similarity, we must determine a cut-off for E-value for reasonable results. The choice of the parameter is made to maximize the proportion of true interactions without getting a significant proportion of negative interactions. In addition to filters associated with detection methods,

Table 4   Features exploited for learning-based detections of host-pathogen protein-protein interactions

Source of information	Extracted features	References
Sequences	Statistics based on the k-mer composition of host and pathogen proteins	Dyer *et al.* (2011), Wuchty (2011), Cui *et al.* (2012), Kshirsagar *et al.* (2012, 2013, 2017), Barman *et al.* (2014), Coelho *et al.* (2014), Dong *et al.* (2015), Abbasi and Minhas (2016), Eid *et al.* (2016), Jindalertudomdee *et al.* (2016), Nourani *et al.* (2016), Chen *et al.* (2017)
	Sequence feature engineering (e.g., ProFET features (Ofer and Linial, 2015))	Abbasi and Minhas (2016)
	E-value of local similarity of pathogen protein to host protein and host protein's binding partners	Tastan *et al.* (2009), Qi *et al.* (2010), Kshirsagar *et al.* (2012), Nouretdinov *et al.* (2012)
	Statistics based on sequence homology (evolutionary features)	Kshirsagar *et al.* (2012), Coelho *et al.* (2014), Abbasi and Minhas (2016)
Domain and motif information	Statistics of interacting domains	Dyer *et al.* (2011), Kshirsagar *et al.* (2012), Barman *et al.* (2014), Coelho *et al.* (2014), Nourani *et al.* (2016)
	The presence of motif-ligand interactions	Tastan *et al.* (2009), Qi *et al.* (2010), Nouretdinov *et al.* (2012)
Known host-pathogen protein-protein interactions	Matrix representation of host-pathogen interactions	Tastan *et al.* (2009), Qi *et al.* (2010), Mukhopadhyay *et al.*, (2010, 2012, 2014), Mondal *et al.* (2012), Nouretdinov *et al.* (2012), Ray *et al.* (2012)
Network topology	Degree (centrality) of host protein in host PPI networks (or viral protein in known host-pathogen PPIs)	Tastan *et al.* (2009), Qi *et al.* (2010), Dyer *et al.* (2011), Kshirsagar *et al.*, (2012, 2013), Nouretdinov *et al.* (2012), Barman *et al.* (2014), Dong *et al.* (2015), Jindalertudomdee *et al.* (2016), Nourani *et al.* (2016)
	Clustering coefficient of host protein in host PPI networks	Tastan *et al.* (2009), Qi *et al.* (2010), Kshirsagar *et al.*, (2012, 2013), Nouretdinov *et al.* (2012), Jindalertudomdee *et al.* (2016)
	Betweenness centrality of host protein in host PPI networks	Tastan *et al.* (2009), Qi *et al.* (2010), Dyer *et al.* (2011), Kshirsagar *et al.*, (2012, 2013), Nouretdinov *et al.* (2012), Dong *et al.* (2015), Jindalertudomdee *et al.* (2016)
	Graphlet degree vector of host protein in host PPI networks	Jindalertudomdee *et al.* (2016)
Gene Ontology (GO) annotations	The count of the interacting proteins that belong to each GO term	Mei (2013), Mei and Zhu (2014a,b)
	The count of the co-occurrence of GO terms for interacting proteins	Kshirsagar *et al.* (2013)
	Pairwise GO similarity for interacting proteins	Tastan *et al.* (2009), Qi *et al.* (2010), Kshirsagar *et al.*, (2012, 2013), Nouretdinov *et al.* (2012), Coelho *et al.* (2014), Nourani *et al.* (2016)
	Neighbor GO similarity for interacting proteins	Tastan *et al.* (2009), Qi *et al.* (2010), Kshirsagar *et al.* (2012), Nouretdinov *et al.* (2012)
Other resources	Literature features – Concept profiles (co-occurrence statistics for interacting proteins) from abstracts of publications	Coelho *et al.* (2014)
	Gene expression features – Differential gene expression data under different control conditions	Tastan *et al.* (2009), Qi *et al.* (2010), Kshirsagar *et al.*, (2012, 2013), Nouretdinov *et al.* (2012)
	RNAi expression features – Significance of pathways or protein complexes involving host protein in RNAi screenings of infected host	Kshirsagar *et al.* (2012)
	Posttranslational modification features – Binary codes for encoding the presence of shared posttranslational modification between pathogen protein and host protein's binding partner	Tastan *et al.* (2009), Qi *et al.* (2010), Nouretdinov *et al.* (2012)
	Conserved pathways – Total number of pathways shared by host-pathogen pairs and their interologs in different organisms	Kshirsagar *et al.* (2012)
	Pathway membership	Nourani *et al.* (2016)
	Percentage of disorder regions of host and pathogen proteins	Barman *et al.* (2014)
	Tissue feature – Susceptibility of a tissue as a site of infection	Tastan *et al.* (2009), Qi *et al.* (2010), Nouretdinov *et al.* (2012)
	Structural features – A variety of features derived from the structural component of host-pathogen protein pairs	Halder *et al.* (2017)

biological-context-based and structural-based filters have also been widely applied, especially when similarity-based methods are used to detect potential HP-PPIs. Biological-context-based filters utilize information related to molecular characteristics, cellular localization and functions, tissue specificity, pathogenicity, and gene expressions. Structural-based filters can be as simple as homomeric information and as complex as a score that measures interaction strength between residues in the interface of interacting host and pathogen protein pairs.

Validating Predicted Host-Pathogen Protein-Protein Interactions

Several methods have been used to validate the results of predicted host-pathogen interactions. Among them, one of the common methods is literature validation, where predicted HP-PPIs are matched with reported interactions that have experimental evidence. Another popular method is the gene set enrichment or over-representation analyses. This is commonly done by computing the significance of the overlap between the set of predicted host genes involved in HP-PPI networks and the set of proteins belong to the same GO category using a hypergeometric distribution. Specifically, if N is the total number of genes associated with a host genome, M is the number of genes belongs to a specific GO category, n is the number of predicted host genes involved in HP-PPI networks, and x is the number of predicted genes in the GO category, then the significance of observing x or more predicted genes in the GO category is given by the following formula:

$$p - value = \sum_{j=x}^{n} \frac{\binom{M}{j}\binom{N-M}{n-j}}{\binom{N}{n}}$$

As an alternative to GO categories, other lists of genes may also be used for enrichment analyses. These include a list of genes appeared in the same pathway or obtained from expression profiling and RNAi screening.

Network analyses have also been used to assess the prediction results of interacting proteins. Common network topology measures such as degree, betweenness centrality, shortest path length, clustering and density coefficients, number of connected components, and scale-freeness of the networks have been calculated for intra-host or host-pathogen PPIs (see Costa *et al.*, 2007 for a survey of various network measurements). Some other interesting measures that have been proposed are the distribution of distances between host protein pairs interacting with a particular pathogen protein (and vice versa; Dyer *et al.*, 2007) and pathway participation coefficient that measures the diversity of the pathways for host protein's binding partners (Wuchty, 2011).

Some other methods for validating predicted interactions use aspects of data that are not exploited for predictions or filtering. For examples, Tyagi *et al.* (2009) used the superposition of predicted complex and template PDB structure to evaluate prediction results detected by homology- and domain-based methods, while Dyer *et al.* (2007) computed distribution of Spearman's correlation between the expression profiles of the protein pairs to evaluate predictions based on domain-based method. Additionally, methods for assessing the statistical significance of predicted interactions by using randomized interactions have also been proposed by Doolittle and Gomez (2010) and Itzhaki (2011).

Case Studies on Predicting Human-Pathogen Protein-Protein Interactions

To illustrate the application of the workflow for predicting HP-PPIs, we highlight their uses in uncovering protein-protein interactions that underlie human infectious diseases caused by viruses, bacteria, and parasites. **Table 5** lists studies that have been carried for each category of the pathogen. Depending on the type of the pathogen, a unique strategy might be applied to predict HP-PPIs.

Uncovering Human-Virus Protein-Protein Interactions

Human-virus interactions have been investigated for varying viruses, including dengue virus, Ebola virus, HIV, herpes simplex virus, influenza virus and varying oncoviruses (adenovirus, Epstein-Barr virus, hepatitis C virus, human papillomavirus, human T-lymphotropic virus, and Kaposi's sarcoma-associated herpesvirus). Among them, HIV has been widely studied and our discussion will focus on it. Different detection methods have been applied to identify potential interactions between human proteins and HIV proteins, including domain-/motif-based similarity (Evans *et al.*, 2009; Segura-Cabrera *et al.*, 2013; Becerra *et al.*, 2017), structural-based similarity (Doolittle and Gomez, 2010; Cui *et al.*, 2016), supervised machine learning (Tastan *et al.*, 2009; Qi *et al.*, 2010; Dyer *et al.*, 2011; Nouretdinov *et al.*, 2012; Mei, 2013; Abbasi and Minhas, 2016), and rule mining (Mukhopadhyay *et al.*, 2010, 2012, 2014; Mondal *et al.*, 2012; Ray *et al.*, 2012).

Of those methods, the domain-/motif-based similarity and rules mining have been uniquely carried out for HIV. Evans *et al.* (2009) and Becerra *et al.* (2017) proposed a method that is based on direct interactions between host-mimicked short eukaryotic linear motifs (ELMs or SLiMs) and cluster domains (CDs) that are present in HIV-1 and human proteins, respectively. Different types of filters for ELMs – including conservation level, rarity, and association with disordered regions – have also been assessed by Becerra *et al.* (2017), demonstrating that the majority of conserved ELMs are associated with disordered regions. On the other

Table 5   Predictive host pathogen protein-protein interaction studies related to human infectious diseases (categorized according to the types of pathogens)

Pathogen	Detection methods[a]	References
Viruses		
Adenovirus	Learning with RF and SVM	Abbasi and Minhas (2016)
Dengue virus	Structural-based method	Doolittle and Gomez (2011)
	Domain-/motif-based method	Segura-Cabrera et al. (2013)
Epstein-Barr Virus (EBV)	Domain-/motif-based method	Itzhaki (2011)
Ebola	Learning with DT, KNN, NB and SVM	Halder et al. (2017)
	Multitask learning	Kshirsagar et al. (2017)
Hepatitis C Virus (HCV)	Learning with SVM	Cui et al. (2012)
	Domain-/motif-based method	Segura-Cabrera et al. (2013)
	Multitask learning	Kshirsagar et al. (2017)
Human Immunodeficiency Virus (HIV)	Learning with RF	Tastan et al. (2009)
	Domain-/motif-based method	Evans et al. (2009), Segura-Cabrera et al. (2013), Becerra et al. (2017)
	Structural-based method	Doolittle and Gomez (2010), Cui et al. (2016)
	Learning with MLP	Qi et al. (2010)
	Learning with ARs	Mukhopadhyay et al., (2010, 2012, 2014), Mondal et al. (2012), Ray et al. (2012)
	Learning with SVM	Dyer et al. (2011)
	Learning with CP	Nouretdinov et al. (2012)
	Homology-based method and transfer learning	Mei (2013)
	Learning with RF and SVM	Abbasi and Minhas (2016)
Human Papillomavirus (HPV)	Learning with SVM	Cui et al. (2012), Dong et al. (2015)
	Domain-/motif-based method	Segura-Cabrera et al. (2013)
Herpes Simplex Virus (HSV)	Domain-/motif-based method	Itzhaki (2011)
Human T-cell Leukemia Virus (HTLV)	Homology-based method and transfer learning	Mei and Zhu (2014a)
Influenza	Structural-based method	De Chassey et al. (2013)
	Domain-/motif-based method	Segura-Cabrera et al. (2013)
	Multitask learning	Kshirsagar et al. (2017)
Kaposi's Sarcoma-associated Human Virus (KSHV)	Domain-/motif-based method	Itzhaki (2011)
Multiple types of viruses	Homology-based method	Franzosa and Xia (2011)
	Domain-/motif-based method	Segura-Cabrera et al. (2013)
	Learning with NB, RF and SVM	Barman et al. (2014)
	Learning with SVM	Eid et al. (2016)
	Learning with AMPKE	Nourani et al. (2016)
Bacteria		
Bacillus anthracis	Multitask learning	Kshirsagar et al. (2013)
	Learning with SCW and SGD	Jindalertudomdee et al. (2016)
	Learning with ELM, SDA, and SVM	Chen et al. (2017)
Clostridium difficile	Learning with ELM, SDA, and SVM	Chen et al. (2017)
Escherichia coli	Homology- and domain-/motif-based methods	Krishnadev and Srinivasan (2011)
	Learning with ELM, SDA, and SVM	Chen et al. (2017)
Francisella tularensis	Multitask learning	Kshirsagar et al. (2013)
	Learning with SCW and SGD	Jindalertudomdee et al. (2016)
Helicobacter pylori	Homology- and domain-/motif-based methods	Tyagi et al. (2009)
Microbes in oral cavity	Ensemble learning	Coelho et al. (2014)
Mycobacterium leprae	Structural-based method	Davis et al. (2007)
Mycobacterium tuberculosis	Structural-based method	Davis et al. (2007)
	Domain-/motif-based method	Zhou et al. (2013b)
	Homology-based method	Zhou et al. (2014)
	Homology- and domain-/motif-based methods	Huo et al. (2015)
	Structural-based method	Cui et al. (2016)
	Domain-/motif-based method	Mahajan and Mande (2017)
Salmonella	Homology- and domain-/motif-based methods	Schleker et al. (2012)
Salmonella typhi	Homology- and domain-/motif-based methods	Krishnadev and Srinivasan (2011)
	Multitask learning	Kshirsagar et al. (2013)
	Homology-based method and transfer learning	Mei and Zhu (2014b)
	Learning with SCW and SGD	Jindalertudomdee et al. (2016)

Table 5 Continued

Pathogen	Detection methods[a]	References
Yersinia pestis	Homology- and domain-/motif-based methods	Krishnadev and Srinivasan (2011)
	Multitask learning	Kshirsagar et al. (2013)
	Learning with SCW and SGD	Jindalertudomdee et al. (2016)
Parasites		
Aspergillus fumigatus	Homology-based method	Remmele et al. (2015)
Candida albicans	Homology-based method	Remmele et al. (2015)
Cryptosporidium spp.	Structural-based method	Davis et al. (2007)
Leishmania major	Structural-based method	Davis et al. (2007)
Plasmodium falciparum	Domain-/motif-based method	Dyer et al. (2007), Liu et al. (2014)
	Homology- and domain-/motif-based methods	Krishnadev and Srinivasan (2008)
	Homology-based method	Lee et al. (2008)
	Homology-based method and learning with RF	Wuchty (2011)
Plasmodium spp.	Structural-based method	Davis et al. (2007)
Trypanosoma spp.	Structural-based method	Davis et al. (2007)

[a]Acronyms for learning-based methods – AMPKE: adapted multiple kernel preserving embedding; ARs: association rules; CP: conformal predictor; DT: decision tree; ELM: extreme learning machine; KNN: k-nearest neighbor; MLP: multi-layer perceptron; NB: naïve Bayes; RF: random forest; SCW: soft confidence-weighted; SDA: stacked denoising autoencoder; SGD: stochastic gradient descent; SVM: support vector machine.

hand, Segura-Cabrera et al. (2013) utilized motif information from 3did datasets, in combination with a filter based on surface accessibility of motif residues.

The second method extracts association rules from only known interactions using a biclustering for predicting new interactions between HIV and human proteins (Mukhopadhyay et al., 2010, 2012, 2014; Mondal et al., 2012; Ray et al., 2012). For this, the known interactions are presented as a matrix with rows and columns represent the viral and human proteins, respectively. Each entry of the matrix indicates a type of interaction. For extracting association rules as done for market basket or transaction data analysis, we consider each row as a transaction and each column as an item. If we have $[HP_1 \, HP_2 \ldots HP_k] \rightarrow [HP_{k+1} \, HP_{k+2} \ldots HP_m]$ as a highly confident rule, where each HP_i represents a host protein, then we basically infer that HP_{k+1}, HP_{k+2}, ..., and HP_m interact with each of viral protein that interacts with each of HP_1, HP_2, ..., and HP_k.

Of particular interest from those studies is small overlaps between the sets of interactions predicted using different approaches, which is a standing issue in HP-PPI prediction (Mukhopadhyay et al., 2012, 2014; Segura-Cabrera et al., 2013). Despite such inconsistency, HP-PPI predictions that utilize homology-based detection method and structural information has helped to provide insights about structural principles governing the interactions between human and viral proteins (Franzosa and Xia, 2011). These include the characteristics of HP-PPI interfaces that mimic host's PPI interfaces, but they are governed by their own structural, functional and evolutionary principles.

Uncovering Human-Bacterial Protein-Protein Interactions

Various detection methods have been applied independently or in different combinations to uncover varying human-bacteria protein-protein interactions. Of interest, Zhou et al. (2013b) proposed a stringent domain-based prediction method. The method first detects the PPIs using the domain-domain interaction approach that employs Bayesian formula (Dyer et al., 2007; as explained in the next section). Then, a layer of assessment is applied; where for each predicted PPI, a score that indicates the strength of each interaction is calculated based on the interacting residues in their interaction interfaces extracted from the 3did database. Using this layer of assessment, the authors claim that the stringent method is better than the conventional one. A different layer of assessment has been proposed by Mahajan and Mande (2017). It employs the Smith-Waterman local alignment-based comparison of bacterial and human proteins with domain-domain interaction template sequences, and it is followed by the calculation of the geometric mean of the similarities for scoring the interaction.

In another human-M. tuberculosis PPIs study, Zhou et al. (2014) introduced a stringent homology-based method which predicts human-M. tuberculosis PPIs from known eukaryote-prokaryote inter-species PPIs. Such stringency takes into account the differences between (1) the structures of eukaryote and prokaryote genes, and (2) the interfaces of intra- and inter-species protein-protein interactions. The authors claimed that the stringent approach performs better than the conventional method that infers human-M. tuberculosis interologs from inter-species PPIs.

Uncovering Human-Parasites Protein-Protein Interactions

Studies in this category have frequently explored the interactions between human and Plasmodium falciparum, the deadliest Plasmodium that causes malaria disease. For detecting the interactions, the homology-, domain-, and structural-based methods have been employed independently by Davis et al. (2007), Dyer et al. (2007), Lee et al. (2008) and Liu et al. (2014). In addition, Krishnadev and Srinivasan (2008) have also combined homology- and domain-based methods for the detection, while Wuchty

(2011) applied a random forest classifier to a dataset containing the composition of amino acid triplet classes of interacting proteins in order to obtain more reliable interolog candidates.

Of interest, Dyer *et al.* (2007) applied the Bayesian formula to calculate the likelihood that the host and pathogen proteins interact given their domains. In particular, for host protein H and pathogen protein P that have domain h and p, respectively, the likelihood is computed as follows:

$$\Pr(I(P,H)|D(P,p) \cap D(H,h)) = \frac{\Pr(D(P,p) \cap D(H,h)|I(P,H))\Pr(I(P,H))}{\Pr(D(P,p) \cap D(H,h))}$$

where $I(P,H)$ denotes the event that protein P and H interact and $D(P,p) \cap D(H,h)$ denotes the event that protein P has domain p and protein H has domain h. Each term on the right-hand side can be calculated from intra-species PPIs and the domains present in each of the interacting proteins. If multiple pairs of domains (p_i, h_j) are contained in the pair of proteins, then the likelihood of the interaction is estimated by assuming the independence of domain pairs, which gives the following formula:

$$\Pr\big(I(P,H)| \cap_i \cap_j (D(P,p_i) \cap D(H,h_j))\big) = 1 - \prod_i \prod_j \big(1 - \Pr(I(P,H)|D(P,p_i) \cap D(H,h_j))\big)$$

The application of expectation-maximization algorithm to calculate this likelihood has also been proposed by Liu *et al.* (2014).

Another particular note from studies on human-*P. falciparum* PPIs is on how the candidate of interactions are further filtered with various biological contexts (Lee *et al.*, 2008; Krishnadev and Srinivasan, 2008; Wuchty, 2011; Liu *et al.*, 2014). These include filtering with: (1) various molecular characteristics of parasite proteins (e.g., the presence of transmembrane domains, signaling peptides and host cell-targeting signals); (2) cellular localization (proteins localized in nucleus or mitochondria are not expected to interact); (3) cellular functions (ubiquitin proteins, DNA polymerases, and splicing factors are not expected to interact); and (4) expression data in the corresponding human tissue and parasite's cell cycle stage (e.g., host proteins in liver tissue and parasite proteins in the sporozoite stage; host proteins in erythrocyte and pathogen proteins in merozoite stage).

Discussion

In the previous section, we illustrated the application of the workflow for HP-PPI prediction to investigating human-pathogen PPIs. One important observation is that a particular strategy may or may not be useful for prediction involving a particular type of pathogen, or a particular type of interaction. For example, the Bayesian method proposed by Dyer *et al.* (2007) may not be useful for investigating human-HIV interactions due to the absence of viral domains; instead, the utilization of ELMs or SLiMs would be more appropriate to capture host-viral interactions, such as works of Evans *et al.* (2009) and Becerra *et al.* (2017). For another example, we ought to utilize tools for predicting the presence of extracellular or trans-membrane domains if we focus on the interactions that drive invasion and intracellular signaling of bacteria or parasites. Hence, knowledge about biological and biochemical contexts would be very valuable when predicting HP-PPI networks (see Sen *et al.* (2016) for further insights).

Nonetheless, like other integrative genomic studies, computational HP-PPI studies are still in their infancy and many issues still need to be addressed before they become fruitful. First, each HP-PPI detection method comes with its own limitation. Sequence, domain, and motif similarity-based methods tend to produce many false positives; structure similarity-based methods are constrained by the available protein structures in the database; supervised learning methods lack definitive noninteracting datasets; lastly, association rule learning methods are limited by a small fraction of known interactions.

To cope with the high number of false positives produced by sequence-, domain- and motif-based similarity methods for detecting PPIs, the standard method being used is by filtering detected interactions. Various types of filters have been highlighted in the previous section, and filters based on biological context and structural information are the most popular ones. Another strategy to prevent the high number of false positives is to use a stringent criterion for PPI resources being used for comparison. For example, when predicting the interaction between human and bacterial proteins, we may follow the approach proposed by Zhou *et al.* (2014) which only uses known interactions between eukaryotic and bacterial proteins as gold standard PPIs.

Meanwhile, issues with scarcity and unavailability of gold standard data (in other words, missing data) for learning-based approaches have been resolved mainly by utilizing knowledge of homologous genes. Kshirsagar *et al.* (2012) have demonstrated that imputation of missing data for GO annotations and gene expression features with techniques that utilize homolog or cross-species information outperform other imputation techniques. In particular, they applied two phases of imputation: (1) cross-species information integration and (2) modeling-based imputation. The first phase is able to transfer a large number of cross-species attributes, but it still leaves missing values of gene expression for proteins whose homologs are unknown. The second phase estimates the rest of missing values by using a LASSO regularization technique. Mei (2013) also used homolog information features for missing data and demonstrated that prediction with a probability weighted ensemble learning that only utilizes homology features for training and testing has promising results, indicating the effectiveness of the approach. Mei and Zhu (2014a) further demonstrated the effectiveness of transferring homolog features as the second instance of proteins in predicting cross-species protein interactions using a multi-instance AdaBoost method.

As it is mentioned earlier, the lack of verifiable negative feature datasets for noninteracting protein pairs is also another problem in supervised machine learning methods for HP-PPI prediction. Assuming that the number of interacting host-pathogen protein pairs is far less than the number of noninteracting ones, such that the probability of randomly picking positive interaction is close to zero, it is very common to randomly choose the noninteracting pairs from the set of protein pairs with no interaction evidence. Nonetheless,

Yu *et al.* (2010) noted that the choice of noninteracting proteins in the training data may greatly influence the accuracy of the classifier or predictor due to the bias towards the interactions involving hub proteins in the positive dataset. To prevent the bias, Yu *et al.* (2010) performed a balanced random sampling that ensures each protein appears in the positive and negative datasets with the same frequency. In another study, Mei (2013) claimed that excluding the pairs from the same sub-cellular localization also allows the construction of a reliable and unbiased classifier. Furthermore, Eid *et al.* (2016) proposed the use of a dissimilarity threshold for alignment between pathogen protein pairs to pick unlikely interactions as negative examples. In particular, if pathogen protein y is known to interact with host protein h, and x and y are dissimilar, then we conclude that x is unlikely to interact with h.

In addition to missing data and the construction of negative dataset, practices of validating machine learning models have also been criticized. Note that the notion of validation here is different from the validation of predicted HP-PPIs in the presented workflow – validation in machine learning approach assesses how well a model has been trained, while validation in the workflow assesses the biological significance of predicted interactions. Abbasi and Minhas (2016) questioned the effectiveness of K-fold cross-validation for estimating the generalization ability of host-pathogen PPI prediction for proteins with no known interaction. In particular, they highlighted the possibility of K-fold cross-validation for not preventing both similarity and redundancy between training and testing examples within a fold, i.e., a protein in a test example in a fold can occur as part of another example in training. To resolve this, they proposed an alternative evaluation scheme called leave one pathogen protein out (LOPO) and demonstrated that it was more effective in modeling HP-PPI predictors. In relation to this proposed method, they have also proposed new performance metrics that include true hit rate (THR), false hit rate (FHR) and median rank of the first positive prediction (MRFPP), which were claimed to be more intuitive for biologists.

Another issue related to learning-based methods is feature representation, which is still an ongoing research area for bioinformatics overall. As mentioned earlier, k-mer composition – especially the conjoint triad – has become one of the most popular features being used. Nonetheless, the study by Yu *et al.* (2010) has highlighted a pitfall in using such simple sequence features since some hub proteins that appear many more times in the positive set than the negative sets will lead to unrealistic accuracy. This is demonstrated by the performance of SVM learning method on balanced random sampled negative interaction datasets that is lower than the performance on purely random negative interaction sampled datasets. In another study related to human-virus interactions, Barman *et al.* (2014) demonstrated that domain-domain association appears to be the best descriptor among 44 descriptors that include amino acid composition and association with disordered regions. In a more recent study, Jindalertudomdee *et al.* (2016) have explored the usefulness of graphlet degree vector (GDV), a network feature that represents the similarity of local topological structure between proteins in a host PPI. Such feature is claimed to increase the performance of stochastic gradient descent (SGD) and soft confidence-weighted (SCW) learning methods.

Finally, the major issue in applying integrative genomic approaches for predicting HP-PPIs is the fact that the overlap between predicted interactions from different approaches tend to be small, as exemplified by the human-HIV studies we discussed previously. Abstract models (e.g., the definition of the motif and the formulation of the learning method), filtering methods, and types of features extracted for interacting protein pairs and their interaction interfaces – all of them easily influence the outcome of the prediction. This issue is not yet resolved and should be paid attention to in the future.

Future Directions

Tremendous accumulation of biological data – including genomic data, 3D protein structures, and gold standard experimental HP-PPI data – could be expected to continue and their quality will be improved. On the other hand, the performance of integrative bioinformatics approach for predicting HP-PPIs would be enhanced and related algorithms are expected to be more accurate and effective. Thus, in the presence of cheaper genome data but the absence of costly gold standard protein-based interactome data, predictive methods provide an alternative to obtain valuable insights about the nature of specific HP-PPI networks, especially in the area of human infectious diseases. Hence, the development of bioinformatics tools and pipelines that allow a routine prediction and exploration of HP-PPI networks by life scientists would be expected in the next few years.

In addition to biological insights, the ultimate goal of uncovering HP-PPI networks is to drive the development of network medicine and personalized medicine for infectious diseases. Investigations of HP-PPI networks are expected to aid the discovery of new biomarkers and therapeutic targets based on gene essentiality and some other network principles. For example, it will assist the design of multiple drug combinations that target disease modules and re-route metabolic activity to compensate for the lost functions during a disease state (Barabási *et al.*, 2011). In relation to personalized medicine, a challenging problem in the prediction of HP-PPI networks is to take into account genetic make-up of both host and pathogen. A recent study by Recker *et al.* (2017) has clearly demonstrated the importance of both host and pathogen factors in determining the outcome of infections by Staphylococcus aureus. Hence, the ability to incorporate the host and pathogen genetic variations into HP-PPI network models should help us to understand further on why some pathogens become more virulent, or why some pathogens do not affect the host. Of interest, we like to uncover how small genetic changes could impact the activation or deactivation of disease modules. To some extent, this means that we attempt to measure the virulence of pathogens as defined by Casadevall and Pirofski (1999), i.e., the capacity of microbes to cause damage according to the interplay between unique host and pathogen properties. Such understanding will further drive the development of personalized medicine for infectious diseases, which has become more feasible these days.

Closing Remarks

We have presented recent progress in the development of computational prediction of HP-PPIs. Explicitly, we have differentiated two major principles In detection methods used in the prediction workflow for new HP-PPIs, i.e., similarity-based and learning-based methods. Case studies on human infectious diseases and some insights obtained from the studies are illustrated. Several issues on the approaches and some proposals for addressing the issues, mainly for learning based methods, are highlighted. One challenging problem to be resolved is the inconsistency of predicted HP-PPIs given by different methods. Nonetheless, while efforts for improvements are being made, existing workflows may be utilized to guide HP-PPI experimentation as well as gain further insights into principles underlying host-pathogen interactions. Finally, enhancements to the methods and overall workflows may allow us to advance the development of network and personalized medicine related to infectious diseases.

Acknowledgement

This project is supported by AcRF Tier 2 grant MOE2014-T2-2-023, Ministry of Education, Singapore.

See also: Host-Pathogen Interactions. Large Scale Ecological Modeling With Viruses: A Review. Mapping the Environmental Microbiome. Natural Language Processing Approaches in Bioinformatics. Next Generation Sequencing Data Analysis. Sequence Analysis

---

References

Abbasi, W.A., Minhas, F.U., 2016. Issues in performance evaluation for host-pathogen protein interaction prediction. Journal of Bioinformatics and Computational Biology 14 (3), 1650011.

Altschul, S.F., Madden, T.L., Schäffer, A.A., *et al.*, 1997. Gapped BLAST and PSI-BLAST: A new generation of protein database search programs. Nucleic Acids Research 25 (17), 3389–3402.

Altschul, S.F., Gish, W., Miller, W., Myers, E.W., Lipman, D.J., 1990. Basic local alignment search tool. Journal of Molecular Biology 215 (3), 403–410.

Ammari, M.G., Gresham, C.R., McCarthy, F.M., Nanduri, B., 2016. HPIDB 2.0: A curated database for host-pathogen interactions. Database (Oxford). (pii: baw103).

Andreeva, A., Howorth, D., Chothia, C., Kulesha, E., Murzin, A.G., 2014. SCOP2 prototype: A new approach to protein structure mining. Nucleic Acids Research 42 (Database issue), D310–D314.

Aprianto, R., Slager, J., Holsappel, S., Veening, J.W., 2016. Time-resolved dual RNA-seq reveals extensive rewiring of lung epithelial and pneumococcal transcriptomes during early infection. Genome Biology 17 (1), 198.

Arnold, R., Boonen, K., Sun, M.G., Kim, P.M., 2012. Computational analysis of interactomes: Current and future perspectives for bioinformatics approaches to model the host-pathogen interaction space. Methods 57 (4), 508–518.

Asensio, N.C., Giner, E.M., de Groot, N.S., Burgas, M.T., 2017. Centrality in the host-pathogen interactome is associated with pathogen fitness during infection. Nature Communications 8, 14092.

Aurrecoechea, C., Brestelli, J., Brunk, B.P., *et al.*, 2009. PlasmoDB: A functional genomic database for malaria parasites. Nucleic Acids Research 37 (Database issue), D539–D543.

Aurrecoechea, C., Barreto, A., Basenko, E.Y., *et al.*, 2017. EuPathDB: The eukaryotic pathogen genomics database resource. Nucleic Acids Research 45 (D1), D581–D591.

Auweter, S.D., Bhavsar, A.P., de Hoog, C.L., *et al.*, 2011. Quantitative mass spectrometry catalogues Salmonella pathogenicity island-2 effectors and identifies their cognate host binding partners. The Journal of Biological Chemistry 286 (27), 24023–24035.

Avraham, R., Haseley, N., Brown, D., *et al.*, 2015. Pathogen cell-to-cell variability drives heterogeneity in host immune responses. Cell 162 (6), 1309–1321.

Baddal, B., Muzzi, A., Censini, S., *et al.*, 2015. Dual RNA-seq of nontypeable haemophilus influenzae and host cell transcriptomes reveals novel insights into host-pathogen cross talk. mBio 6 (6), e01765-15.

Barabási, A.L., Gulbahce, N., Loscalzo, J., 2011. Network medicine: A network-based approach to human disease. Nature Reviews Genetics 12 (1), 56–68.

NCBI Resource Coordinators, 2017. Database resources of the National Center for Biotechnology Information. Nucleic Acids Research 45 (D1), D12–D17.

Barman, R.K., Saha, S., Das, S., 2014. Prediction of interactions between viral and host proteins using supervised machine learning methods. PLOS ONE 9 (11), e112034.

Becerra, A., Bucheli, V.A., Moreno, P.A., 2017. Prediction of virus-host protein-protein interactions mediated by short linear motifs. BMC Bioinformatics 18 (1), 163.

Blasche, S., Arens, S., Ceol, A., *et al.*, 2014. The EHEC-host interactome reveals novel targets for the translocated intimin receptor. Scientific Reports 4, 7531.

Calderwood, M.A., Venkatesan, K., Xing, L., *et al.*, 2007. Epstein-Barr virus and virus human protein interaction maps. Proceedings of the National Academy of Sciences of the United States of America 104 (18), 7606–7611.

Casadevall, A., Pirofski, L.A., 1999. Host-pathogen interactions: Redefining the basic concepts of virulence and pathogenicity. Infection and Immunity 67 (8), 3703–3713.

Chatr-Aryamontri, A., Oughtred, R., Boucher, L., *et al.*, 2017. The BioGRID interaction database: 2017 update. Nucleic Acids Research 45 (D1), D369–D379.

Chen H., Shen J., Wang L., Song J., 2017. Collaborative data analytics towards prediction of pathogen-host protein-protein interactions. In: Proceedings of the International Conference on Computer Supported Cooperative Work in Design, pp. 269–274. United States: IEEE.

Coelho, E.D., Arrais, J.P., Matos, S., *et al.*, 2014. Computational prediction of the human-microbial oral interactome. BMC Systems Biology 8, 24.

Colpitts, T.M., Cox, J., Nguyen, A., *et al.*, 2011. Use of a tandem affinity purification assay to detect interactions between West Nile and dengue viral proteins and proteins of the mosquito vector. Virology 417 (1), 179–187.

Costa, L.D.F., Rodrigues, F.A., Travieso, G., Boas, P.R.V., 2007. Characterization of complex networks: A survey of measurements. Advances in Physics 56 (1), 167–242.

Cui, G., Fang, C., Han, K., 2012. Prediction of protein-protein interactions between viruses and human by an SVM model. BMC Bioinformatics 13 (Suppl. 7), S5.

Cui, T., Li, W., Liu, L., Huang, Q., He, Z.G., 2016. Uncovering new pathogen-host protein-protein interactions by pairwise structure similarity. PLOS ONE 11 (1), e0147612.

Davis, F.P., Sali, A., 2005. PIBASE: A comprehensive database of structurally defined protein interfaces. Bioinformatics 21 (9), 1901–1907.

Davis, F.P., Barkan, D.T., Eswar, N., McKerrow, J.H., Sali, A., 2007. Host pathogen protein interactions predicted by comparative modeling. Protein Science 16 (12), 2585–2596.

Davis, Z.H., Verschueren, E., Jang, G.M., *et al.*, 2015. Global mapping of herpesvirus-host protein complexes reveals a transcription strategy for late genes. Molecular Cell 57 (2), 349–360.

De Castro, E., Sigrist, C.J., Gattiker, A., *et al.*, 2006. ScanProsite: Detection of PROSITE signature matches and ProRule-associated functional and structural residues in proteins. Nucleic Acids Research 34 (Web Server issue), W362–W365.

De Chassey, B., Navratil, V., Tafforeau, L., et al., 2008. Hepatitis C virus infection protein network. Molecular Systems Biology 4, 230.

De Chassey, B., Meyniel-Schicklin, L., Aublin-Gex, A., et al., 2013. Structure homology and interaction redundancy for discovering virus-host protein interactions. EMBO Reports 14 (10), 938–944.

Dinkel, H., Van Roey, K., Michael, S., et al., 2016. ELM 2016 – Data update and new functionality of the eukaryotic linear motif resource. Nucleic Acids Research 44 (D1), D294–D300.

Dolan, P.T., Zhang, C., Khadka, S., et al., 2013. Identification and comparative analysis of hepatitis C virus-host cell protein interactions. Molecular BioSystems 9 (12), 3199–3209.

Dong, Y., Kuang, Q., Dai, X., et al., 2015. Improving the understanding of pathogenesis of human papillomavirus 16 via mapping protein-protein interaction network. BioMed Research International 2015, 890381.

Doolittle, J.M., Gomez, S.M., 2010. Structural similarity-based predictions of protein interactions between HIV-1 and Homo sapiens. Virology Journal 7, 82.

Doolittle, J.M., Gomez, S.M., 2011. Mapping protein interactions between Dengue virus and its human and insect hosts. PLOS Neglected Tropical Diseases 5 (2), e954.

Durmuş, S., Çakır, T., Özgür, A., Guthke, R., 2015. A review on computational systems biology of pathogen-host interactions. Frontiers in Microbiology 6, 235.

Durmuş, T.S., Çakır, T., Ardiç, E., et al., 2013. PHISTO: Pathogen-host interaction search tool. Bioinformatics 29 (10), 1357–1358.

Dyer, M.D., Murali, T.M., Sobral, B.W., 2007. Computational prediction of host-pathogen protein-protein interactions. Bioinformatics 23 (13), i159–i166.

Dyer, M.D., Neff, C., Dufford, M., et al., 2010. The human-bacterial pathogen protein interaction networks of Bacillus anthracis, Francisella tularensis, and Yersinia pestis. PLOS ONE 5 (8), e12089.

Dyer, M.D., Murali, T.M., Sobral, B.W., 2011. Supervised learning and prediction of physical interactions between human and HIV proteins. Infection, Genetics and Evolution 11 (5), 917–923.

Eid, F.E., ElHefnawi, M., Heath, L.S., 2016. DeNovo: Virus-host sequence-based protein-protein interaction prediction. Bioinformatics 32 (8), 1144–1150.

Evans, P., Dampier, W., Ungar, L., Tozeren, A., 2009. Prediction of HIV-1 virus-host protein interactions using virus and host sequence motifs. BMC Medical Genomics 2, 27.

The UniProt Consortium, 2017. UniProt: The Universal Protein knowledgebase. Nucleic Acids Research 45 (D1), D158–D169.

Finn, R.D., Coggill, P., Eberhardt, R.Y., et al., 2016. The Pfam protein families database: Towards a more sustainable future. Nucleic Acids Research 44 (D1), D279–D285.

Fischer, S., Brunk, B.P., Chen, F., et al., 2011. Using OrthoMCL to assign proteins to OrthoMCL-DB groups or to cluster proteomes into new ortholog groups. Current Protocols in Bioinformatics. (Chapter 6: Unit 6.12.1–19).

Franzosa, E.A., Xia, Y., 2011. Structural principles within the human-virus protein-protein interaction network. Proceedings of the National Academy of Sciences of the United States of America 108 (26), 10538–10543.

Gajria, B., Bahl, A., Brestelli, J., et al., 2008. ToxoDB: An integrated Toxoplasma gondii database resource. Nucleic Acids Research 36 (Database issue), D553–D556.

Garcia-Garcia, J., Guney, E., Aragues, R., Planas-Iglesias, J., Oliva, B., 2010. Biana: A software framework for compiling biological interactions and analyzing networks. BMC Bioinformatics 11, 56.

Germain, M.A., Chatel-Chaix, L., Gagné, B., et al., 2014. Elucidating novel hepatitis C virus-host interactions using combined mass spectrometry and functional genomics approaches. Molecular and Cellular Proteomics 13 (1), 184–203.

Gerold, G., Bruening, J., Pietschmann, T., 2016. Decoding protein networks during virus entry by quantitative proteomics. Virus Research 218, 25–39.

Gowri, V.S., Krishnadev, O., Swamy, C.S., Srinivasan, N., 2006. MulPSSM: A database of multiple position-specific scoring matrices of protein domain families. Nucleic Acids Research 34 (Database issue), D243–D246.

Guirimand, T., Delmotte, S., Navratil, V., 2015. VirHostNet 2.0: Surfing on the web of virus/host molecular interactions data. Nucleic Acids Research 43 (Database issue), D583–D587.

Gulbahce, N., Yan, H., Dricot, A., et al., 2012. Viral perturbations of host networks reflect disease etiology. PLOS Computational Biology 8 (6), e1002531.

Halder, A.K., Dutta, P., Kundu, M., Basu, S., Nasipuri, M., 2017. Review of computational methods for virus-host protein interaction prediction: A case study on novel Ebola-human interactions. Briefings in Functional Genomics.

Heiges, M., Wang, H., Robinson, E., et al., 2006. CryptoDB: A Cryptosporidium bioinformatics resource update. Nucleic Acids Research 34 (Database issue), D419–D422.

Holm, L., Rosenström, P., 2010. Dali server: Conservation mapping in 3D. Nucleic Acids Research 38 (Web Server issue), W545–W549.

Holm, L., Kääriäinen, S., Rosenström, P., Schenkel, A., 2008. Searching protein structure databases with DaliLite v.3. Bioinformatics 24 (23), 2780–2781.

Humphrys, M.S., Creasy, T., Sun, Y., et al., 2013. Simultaneous transcriptional profiling of bacteria and their host cells. PLOS ONE 8 (12), e80597.

Huo, T., Liu, W., Guo, Y., et al., 2015. Prediction of host-pathogen protein interactions between Mycobacterium tuberculosis and Homo sapiens using sequence motifs. BMC Bioinformatics 16, 100.

Itzhaki, Z., 2011. Domain-domain interactions underlying herpesvirus-human protein-protein interaction networks. PLOS ONE 6 (7), e21724.

Jäger, S., Cimermancic, P., Gulbahce, N., et al., 2011. Global landscape of HIV-human protein complexes. Nature 481 (7381), 365–370.

Jindalertudomdee, J., Hayashida, M., Song, J., Akutsu, T., 2016. Host-pathogen protein interaction prediction based on local topology structures of a protein interaction network. In: Proceeding of International Conference on Bioinformatics and Bioengineering (BIBE), pp. 7–12. United States: IEEE.

Jones, P., Binns, D., Chang, H.Y., et al., 2014. InterProScan 5: Genome-scale protein function classification. Bioinformatics 30 (9), 1236–1240.

Kane, J.R., Stanley, D.J., Hultquist, J.F., et al., 2015. Lineage-specific viral hijacking of non-canonical E3 ubiquitin ligase cofactors in the evolution of Vif anti-APOBEC3 activity. Cell Reports 11 (8), 1236–1250.

Kersey, P.J., Allen, J.E., Armean, I., et al., 2016. Ensembl Genomes 2016: More genomes, more complexity. Nucleic Acids Research 44 (D1), D574–D580.

Khadka, S., Vangeloff, A.D., Zhang, C., et al., 2011. A physical interaction network of dengue virus and human proteins. Molecular and Cellular Proteomics 10 (12), M111.012187.

Korkin, D., Thieu, T., Joshi, S., Warren, S., 2011. Mining hostpathogen interactions. In: Yang, N.-S. (Ed.), Systems and Computational Biology – Molecular and Cellular Experimental Systems. Rijeka: InTech, pp. 163–184.

Krishnadev, O., Srinivasan, N., 2008. A data integration approach to predict host-pathogen protein-protein interactions: Application to recognize protein interactions between human and a malarial parasite. In Silico Biology 8 (3–4), 235–250.

Krishnadev, O., Srinivasan, N., 2011. Prediction of protein-protein interactions between human host and a pathogen and its application to three pathogenic bacteria. International Journal of Biological Macromolecules 48 (4), 613–619.

Krogh, A., Larsson, B., von Heijne, G., Sonnhammer, E.L., 2001. Predicting transmembrane protein topology with a hidden Markov model: Application to complete genomes. Journal of Molecular Biology 305 (3), 567–580.

Kshirsagar, M., Carbonell, J., Klein-Seetharaman, J., 2012. Techniques to cope with missing data in host-pathogen protein interaction prediction. Bioinformatics 28 (18), i466–i472.

Kshirsagar, M., Carbonell, J., Klein-Seetharaman, J., 2013. Multitask learning for host-pathogen protein interactions. Bioinformatics 29 (13), i217–i226.

Kshirsagar, M., Murugesan, K., Carbonell, J.G., Klein-Seetharaman, J., 2017. Multitask matrix completion for learning protein interactions across diseases. Journal of Computational Biology 24 (6), 501–514.

Kuiken, C., Korber, B., Shafer, R.W., 2003. HIV sequence databases. AIDS Reviews 5 (1), 52–61.

Le Breton, M., Meyniel-Schicklin, L., Deloire, A., et al., 2011. Flavivirus NS3 and NS5 proteins interaction network: A high-throughput yeast two-hybrid screen. BMC Microbiology 11, 234.

Lee, S., Salwinski, L., Zhang, C., et al., 2011. An integrated approach to elucidate the intra-viral and viral-cellular protein interaction networks of a gamma-herpesvirus. PLOS Pathogens 7 (10), e1002297.

Lee, S.A., Chan, C.H., Tsai, C.H., *et al.*, 2008. Ortholog-based protein-protein interaction prediction and its application to inter-species interactions. BMC Bioinformatics 9 (Suppl. 12), S11.

Lew, J.M., Kapopoulou, A., Jones, L.M., Cole, S.T., 2011. TubercuList – 10 years after. Tuberculosis (Edinb) 91 (1), 1–7.

Licata, L., Briganti, L., Peluso, D., *et al.*, 2012. MINT, the molecular interaction database: 2012 update. Nucleic Acids Research 40 (Database issue), D857–D861.

Liu, Q., Li, F.C., Elsheikha, H.M., Sun, M.M., Zhu, X.Q., 2017. Identification of host proteins interacting with Toxoplasma gondii GRA15 (TgGRA15) by yeast two-hybrid system. Parasit and Vectors 10 (1), 1.

Liu, X., Huang, Y., Liang, J., *et al.*, 2014. Computational prediction of protein interactions related to the invasion of erythrocytes by malarial parasites. BMC Bioinformatics 15, 393.

Logan-Klumpler, F.J., De Silva, N., Boehme, U., *et al.*, 2012. GeneDB – An annotation database for pathogens. Nucleic Acids Research 40 (Database issue), D98–D108.

Mahajan, G., Mande, S.C., 2017. Using structural knowledge in the protein data bank to inform the search for potential host-microbe protein interactions in sequence space: Application to Mycobacterium tuberculosis. BMC Bioinformatics 18 (1), 201.

Mairiang, D., Zhang, H., Sodja, A., *et al.*, 2013. Identification of new protein interactions between dengue fever virus and its hosts, human and mosquito. PLOS ONE 8 (1), e53535.

Marchler-Bauer, A., Derbyshire, M.K., Gonzales, N.R., *et al.*, 2015. CDD: NCBI's conserved domain database. Nucleic Acids Research 43 (Database issue), D222–D226.

Mavromatis, C.H., Bokil, N.J., Totsika, M., *et al.*, 2015. The co-transcriptome of uropathogenic Escherichia coli-infected mouse macrophages reveals new insights into host-pathogen interactions. Cellular Microbiology 17 (5), 730–746.

Mehra, A., Zahra, A., Thompson, V., *et al.*, 2013. Mycobacterium tuberculosis type VII secreted effector EsxH targets host ESCRT to impair trafficking. PLOS Pathogens 9 (10), e1003734.

Mei, S., 2013. Probability weighted ensemble transfer learning for predicting interactions between HIV-1 and human proteins. PLOS ONE 8 (11), e79606.

Mei, S., Zhu, H., 2014a. Computational reconstruction of proteome-wide protein interaction networks between HTLV retroviruses and Homo sapiens. BMC Bioinformatics 15, 245.

Mei, S., Zhu, H., 2014b. AdaBoost based multi-instance transfer learning for predicting proteome-wide interactions between Salmonella and human proteins. PLOS ONE 9 (10), e110488.

Memisević, V., Zavaljevski, N., Pieper, R., *et al.*, 2013. Novel Burkholderia mallei virulence factors linked to specific host-pathogen protein interactions. Molecular and Cellular Proteomics 12 (11), 3036–3051.

Mirrashidi, K.M., Elwell, C.A., Verschueren, E., *et al.*, 2015. Global mapping of the Inc-human interactome reveals that retromer restricts chlamydia infection. Cell Host and Microbe 18 (1), 109–121.

Mistry, J., Finn, R.D., Eddy, S.R., Bateman, A., Punta, M., 2013. Challenges in homology search: HMMER3 and convergent evolution of coiled-coil regions. Nucleic Acids Research 41 (12), e121.

Mitchell, A., Chang, H.Y., Daugherty, L., *et al.*, 2015. The InterPro protein families database: The classification resource after 15 years. Nucleic Acids Research 43 (Database issue), D213–D221.

Mondal, K.C., Pasquier, N., Mukhopadhyay, A., *et al.*, 2012. Prediction of protein interactions on HIV1 human PPI data using a novel closure-based integrated approach. In: Proceedings of the International Conference on Bioinformatics Models, Methods and Algorithms, pp. 164–173. Vilamoura.

Mosca, R., Céol, A., Stein, A., Olivella, R., Aloy, P., 2014. 3did: A catalog of domain-based interactions of known three-dimensional structure. Nucleic Acids Research 42 (Database issue), D374–D379.

Mukhopadhyay, A., Maulik, U., Bandyopadhyay, S., 2012. A novel biclustering approach to association rule mining for predicting HIV-1-human protein interactions. PLOS ONE 7 (4), e32289.

Mukhopadhyay, A., Ray, S., Maulik, U., 2014. Incorporating the type and direction information in predicting novel regulatory interactions between HIV-1 and human proteins using a biclustering approach. BMC Bioinformatics 15, 26.

Mukhopadhyay, A., Maulik, U., Bandyopadhyay, S., Eils, R., 2010. Mining association rules from HIV-human protein interactions. In: Proceeding of International Conference on Systems in Medicine and Biology, pp. 344–348. Kharagpur.

Muller, M., Jacob, Y., Jones, L., *et al.*, 2012. Large scale genotype comparison of human papillomavirus E2-host interaction networks provides new insights for e2 molecular functions. PLOS Pathogens 8 (6), e1002761.

Murali, T., Pacifico, S., Yu, J., *et al.*, 2011. DroID 2011: A comprehensive, integrated resource for protein, transcription factor, RNA and gene interactions for Drosophila. Nucleic Acids Research 39 (Database issue), D736–D743.

Muthusamy, B., Thomas, J.K., Prasad, T.S., Pandey, A., 2013. Access guide to human proteinpedia. Current Protocols in Bioinformatics. (Chapter 1: Unit 1.21).

Nicod, C., Banaei-Esfahani, A., Collins, B.C., 2017. Elucidation of host-pathogen protein-protein interactions to uncover mechanisms of host cell rewiring. Current Opinion in Microbiology 39, 7–15.

Nourani, E., Khunjush, F., Durmuş, S., 2015. Computational approaches for prediction of pathogen-host protein-protein interactions. Frontiers in Microbiology 6, 94.

Nourani, E., Khunjush, F., Durmuş, S., 2016. Computational prediction of virus-human protein-protein interactions using embedding kernelized heterogeneous data. Molecular BioSystems 12 (6), 1976–1986.

Nouretdinov, I., Gammerman, A., Qi, Y., Klein-Seetharaman, J., 2012. Determining confidence of predicted interactions between HIV-1 and human proteins using conformal method. Pacific Symposium on Biocomputing. 311–322.

Ofer, D., Linial, M., 2015. ProFET: Feature engineering captures high-level protein functions. Bioinformatics 31 (21), 3429–3436.

Orchard, S., Ammari, M., Aranda, B., *et al.*, 2014. The MIntAct project – IntAct as a common curation platform for 11 molecular interaction databases. Nucleic Acids Research 42 (Database issue), D358–D363.

Pagel, P., Kovac, S., Oesterheld, M., *et al.*, 2009. The MIPS mammalian protein-protein interaction database. Bioinformatics 21 (6), 832–834.

Prasad, T.S.K., Goel, R., Kandasamy, K., *et al.*, 2009. Human protein reference database – 2009 update. Nucleic Acids Research 37 (Database issue), D767–D772.

Qi, Y., Tastan, O., Carbonell, J.G., Klein-Seetharaman, J., Weston, J., 2010. Semi-supervised multi-task learning for predicting interactions between HIV-1 and human proteins. Bioinformatics 26 (18), i645–i652.

Ramage, H.R., Kumar, G.R., Verschueren, E., *et al.*, 2015. A combined proteomics/genomics approach links hepatitis C virus infection with nonsense-mediated mRNA decay. Molecular Cell 57 (2), 329–340.

Ray, S., Mukhopadhyay, A., Maulik, U., 2012. Predicting annotated HIV1 – Human PPIs using a biclustering approach to association rule mining. In: Proceedings of Third International Conference on Emerging Applications of Information Technology (EAIT), pp. 3–6. Kolkata.

Recker, M., Laabei, M., Toleman, M.S., *et al.*, 2017. Clonal differences in Staphylococcus aureus bacteraemia-associated mortality. Nature Microbiology 2 (10), 1381–1388.

Reid, A.J., Berriman, M., 2013. Genes involved in host-parasite interactions can be revealed by their correlated expression. Nucleic Acids Research 41 (3), 1508–1518.

Remmele, C.W., Luther, C.H., Balkenhol, J., *et al.*, 2015. Integrated inference and evaluation of host-fungi interaction networks. Frontiers in Microbiology 6, 764.

Rienksma, R.A., Suarez-Diez, M., Mollenkopf, H.J., *et al.*, 2015. Comprehensive insights into transcriptional adaptation of intracellular mycobacteria by microbe-enriched dual RNA sequencing. BMC Genomics 16, 34.

Rose, P.W., Prlić, A., Altunkaya, A., *et al.*, 2017. The RCSB protein data bank: Integrative view of protein, gene and 3D structural information. Nucleic Acids Research 45 (D1), D271–D281.

Rozenblatt-Rosen, O., Deo, R.C., Padi, M., *et al.*, 2012. Interpreting cancer genomes using systematic host network perturbations by tumour virus proteins. Nature 487 (7408), 491–495.

Salwinski, L., Miller, C.S., Smith, A.J., *et al.*, 2004. The database of interacting proteins: 2004 update. Nucleic Acids Research 32 (Database issue), D449–D451.

Schäffer, A.A., Aravind, L., Madden, T.L., *et al.*, 2001. Improving the accuracy of PSI-BLAST protein database searches with composition-based statistics and other refinements. Nucleic Acids Research 29 (14), 2994–3005.

Schleker, S., Garcia-Garcia, J., Klein-Seetharaman, J., Oliva, B., 2012. Prediction and comparison of Salmonella-human and Salmonella-Arabidopsis interactomes. Chemistry and Biodiversity 9 (5), 991–1018.

Segura-Cabrera, A., García-Pérez, C.A., Guo, X., Rodríguez-Pérez, M.A., 2013. A viral-human interactome based on structural motif-domain interactions captures the human infectome. PLOS ONE 8 (8), e71526.

Sen, R., Nayak, L., De, R.K., 2016. A review on host-pathogen interactions: Classification and prediction. European Journal of Clinical Microbiology & Infectious Diseases 35 (10), 1581–1599.

Shapira, S.D., Gat-Viks, I., Shum, B.O., et al., 2009. A physical and regulatory map of host-influenza interactions reveals pathways in H1N1 infection. Cell 139 (7), 1255–1267.

Sigrist, C.J., de Castro, E., Cerutti, L., et al., 2013. New and continuing developments at PROSITE. Nucleic Acids Research 41 (Database issue), D344–D347.

Sonnhammer, E.L., Östlund, G., 2015. InParanoid 8: Orthology analysis between 273 proteomes, mostly eukaryotic. Nucleic Acids Research 43 (Database issue), D234–D239.

Stebbins, C.E., 2005. Structural microbiology at the pathogen-host interface. Cellular Microbiology 7 (9), 1227–1236.

Swearingen, K.E., Lindner, S.E., Shi, L., et al., 2016. Interrogating the plasmodium sporozoite surface: Identification of surface-exposed proteins and demonstration of glycosylation on CSP and TRAP by mass spectrometry-based proteomics. PLOS Pathogens 12 (4), e1005606.

Tastan, O., Qi, Y., Carbonell, J.G., Klein-Seetharaman, J., 2009. Prediction of interactions between HIV-1 and human proteins by information integration. Pacific Symposium on Biocomputing. 516–527.

Toribio, A.L., Alako, B., Amid, C., et al., 2017. European nucleotide archive in 2016. Nucleic Acids Research 45 (D1), D32–D36.

Tyagi, N., Krishnadev, O., Srinivasan, N., 2009. Prediction of protein-protein interactions between Helicobacter pylori and a human host. Molecular BioSystems 5 (12), 1630–1635.

Urban, M., Cuzick, A., Rutherford, K., et al., 2017. PHI-base: A new interface and further additions for the multi-species pathogen-host interactions database. Nucleic Acids Research 45 (D1), D604–D610.

Vannucci, F.A., Foster, D.N., Gebhart, C.J., 2013. Laser microdissection coupled with RNA-seq analysis of porcine enterocytes infected with an obligate intracellular pathogen (Lawsonia intracellularis). BMC Genomics 14, 421.

Wallqvist, A., Memišević, V., Zavaljevski, N., et al., 2015. Using host-pathogen protein interactions to identify and characterize Francisella tularensis virulence factors. BMC Genomics 16, 1106.

Watanabe, T., Kawakami, E., Shoemaker, J.E., et al., 2014. Influenza virus-host interactome screen as a platform for antiviral drug development. Cell Host and Microbe 16 (6), 795–805.

Wattam, A.R., Davis, J.J., Assaf, R., et al., 2017. Improvements to PATRIC, the all-bacterial Bioinformatics Database and Analysis Resource Center. Nucleic Acids Research 45 (D1), D535–D542.

Webb, B., Sali, A., 2016. Comparative protein structure modeling using MODELLER. Current Protocols in Protein Science 86, 2.9.1–2.9.37.

Westermann, A.J., Förstner, K.U., Amman, F., et al., 2016. Dual RNA-seq unveils noncoding RNA functions in host-pathogen interactions. Nature 529 (7587), 496–501.

Westermann, A.J., Barquist, L., Vogel, J., 2017. Resolving host-pathogen interactions by dual RNA-seq. PLOS Pathogens 13 (2), e1006033.

White, E.A., Kramer, R.E., Tan, M.J., et al., 2012a. Comprehensive analysis of host cellular interactions with human papillomavirus E6 proteins identifies new E6 binding partners and reflects viral diversity. Journal of Virology 86 (24), 13174–13186.

White, E.A., Sowa, M.E., Tan, M.J., et al., 2012b. Systematic identification of interactions between host cell proteins and E7 oncoproteins from diverse human papillomaviruses. Proceedings of the National Academy of Sciences of the United States of America 109 (5), E260–E267.

Wuchty, S., 2011. Computational prediction of host-parasite protein interactions between P. falciparum and H. sapiens. PLOS ONE 6 (11), e26960.

Xing, S., Wallmeroth, N., Berendzen, K.W., Grefen, C., 2016. Techniques for the analysis of protein-protein interactions in vivo. Plant Physiology 171 (2), 727–758.

Yang, H., Ke, Y., Wang, J., et al., 2011. Insight into bacterial virulence mechanisms against host immune response via the Yersinia pestis-human protein-protein interaction network. Infection and Immunity 79 (11), 4413–4424.

Yang, J., Yan, R., Roy, A., et al., 2015. The I-TASSER Suite: Protein structure and function prediction. Nature Methods 12 (1), 7–8.

Yu, J., Guo, M., Needham, C.J., et al., 2010. Simple sequence-based kernels do not predict protein-protein interactions. Bioinformatics 26 (20), 2610–2614.

Zdobnov, E.M., Tegenfeldt, F., Kuznetsov, D., et al., 2017. OrthoDB v9.1: Cataloging evolutionary and functional annotations for animal, fungal, plant, archaeal, bacterial and viral orthologs. Nucleic Acids Research 45 (D1), D744–D749.

Zhang, Y., Skolnick, J., 2005. TM-align: A protein structure alignment algorithm based on the TM-score. Nucleic Acids Research 33 (7), 2302–2309.

Zhou, H., Jin, J., Wong, L., 2013a. Progress in computational studies of host-pathogen interactions. Journal of Bioinformatics and Computational Biology 11 (2), 1230001.

Zhou, H., Rezaei, J., Hugo, W., et al., 2013b. Stringent DDI-based prediction of H. sapiens-M. tuberculosis H37Rv protein-protein interactions. BMC Systems Biology 7 (Suppl. 6), S6.

Zhou, H., Gao, S., Nguyen, N.N., et al., 2014. Stringent homology-based prediction of H. sapiens-M. tuberculosis H37Rv protein-protein interactions. Biology Direct 9, 5.

Zoraghi, R., Reiner, N.E., 2013. Protein interaction networks as starting points to identify novel antimicrobial drug targets. Current Opinion in Microbiology 16 (5), 566–572.

Biographical Sketch

Dr. Fransiskus Xaverius Ivan is a Research Fellow in the School of Computer Science and Engineering, Nanyang Technological University (NTU), Singapore. He received Ph.D. in Computations and Systems Biology, Singapore-MIT Alliance (SMA) Programme from NTU in 2014, Master of Computing and Information Technology from the University of New South Wales (UNSW) in 2008, and Bachelor of Science in Mathematics from Bogor Agricultural University in 1999. His research interest is interdisciplinary life science, which is not limited to Bioinformatics, Genomic Data Science, Computational Systems Biology, and Computational Host-Pathogen Interactions. He has published in experimental and computational life science journals and conferences, including Genomics, Functional Integrative Genomics, IEEE Engineering in Medicine and Biology Conference (EMBC), and ACM Conference on Bioinformatics, Computational Biology, and Health Informatics (ACM BCB). Dr. Ivan has actively collaborated with scientists from various backgrounds, including Life Science and Biomedical Science.

Dr. Jie Zheng is a tenure-track assistant professor of School of Computer Science and Engineering, Nanyang Technological University (NTU), Singapore. He received PhD in 2006 from the University of California, Riverside and his B. Eng (honors) in 2000 from Zhejiang University in China, both in Computer Science. Before joining NTU in 2011, he was a research scientist at the National Center for Biotechnology Information (NCBI), National Library of Medicine (NLM), National Institutes of Health (NIH), USA. His research interests are Bioinformatics, Computational Systems Biology and Genomics, aiming to develop novel algorithms and *in silico* models to help answer Biomedical questions (e.g. how are cell fates decided in cancer and stem cells). He has published in top-tier journals such as Genome Biology, Molecular Biology & Evolution, Nucleic Acids Research, Bioinformatics, PLoS Computational Biology, etc. While trained as a Computer Scientist, Dr. Zheng maintains active and long-standing collaborations with Life Scientists.

Dr. Vincent T.K. Chow is a medical virologist and molecular biologist who graduated with MD, PhD, MBBS, MSc and FRCPath qualifications. Currently, he serves as Associate Professor and Education Director of Microbiology, and Principal Investigator of the Host and Pathogen Interactivity Laboratory at the Yong Loo Lin School of Medicine, National University of Singapore (NUS). Since 1996, he established the Human Genome Laboratory that has isolated and characterized several novel human genes and proteins. Dr. Chow previously served as President of the Asia-Pacific Society for Medical Virology, as well as Chair of the Virology Section of the International Society of Chemotherapy. His laboratory has published over 250 articles in international refereed journals, and has presented over 260 conference papers. He has received several awards (including the Murex Virologist Award, the Special Commendation Award and Faculty Research Excellence Award from NUS, the Singapore Society of Pathology – Becton Dickinson Award, and the Chan Yow Cheong Oration at the 6th Asia-Pacific Congress of Medical Virology). His recent research interests focus on the molecular genetics and infectomics of influenza pneumonia and of hand, foot and mouth disease, specifically on the cellular, molecular, and viral pathogenesis of severe influenza and enterovirus 71 infections.

Dr. Kwoh Chee Keong is in the School of Computer and Science Engineering, Nanyang Technology since 1993. He received his Bachelor degree in Electrical engineering (1st Class) and Master in Industrial System Engineering from the National University of Singapore in 1987 and 1991 respectively. He received his PhD from the Imperial College, University of London in 1995. His research interests include Data Analytics, Data Mining, and Graph-Based inference; applications areas include Bioinformatics and Biomedical Engineering. He has done significant research work the research areas of Bioinformatics and Computational Biology. He has been active as organizing member, referee and reviewer for a number of premier conferences and journals. Dr. Kwoh is a member of The Institution of Engineers Singapore, Association for Medical and Bio-Informatics, Imperial College Alumni Association of Singapore (ICAAS). He has provided many service to professional bodies, and the Singapore and was conferred the Public Service Medal, the President of Singapore in 2008 and the National Day Award Ministry of Education (Long Service Medal) in 2016.

Comparative Genomics Analysis

Hui San Ong, Perdana University, Selangor, Malaysia

Introduction

Deoxyribonucleic acid (DNA) is a nucleic acid that encodes the genetic information required to carry out activities in all living organisms. A DNA molecule are comprises of two strands, each run in the direction of 5′ to 3′ and are antiparallel. Both strands pair based on Watson-Crick complementarity; adenine (A) binds to thymine (T) while guanine (G) binds to cytosine (C). A genome can be defined as a complete collection of an organism's DNA, inclusive of the genes (the coding regions) and noncoding DNA. Genomics, on the other hand is an interdisciplinary field concerned with the study of the genes and intergenic regions as well as their structures, function and evolution.

The availability of genomics information from living organisms has led to the empowerment of comparative genomics analysis. The goal is to use related genomes en masse to achieve a better understanding of every individual genome in a dataset. It involves the comparison of more than one genome to uncover the similarities and differences between them. Comparison can be conducted for the entire genomes or the syntenic regions of various species or for various strains of the same species (Wei *et al.*, 2002). However, the scope of comparisons varies, as it can be carried out between the same species or across different kingdoms of living organisms. For example, the study of HSP90 chaperone family was carried out in Archaea, Bacteria, Protista, Plantae, Fungi and Animalia (Chen *et al.*, 2006). There are three distinct levels where the genome comparison can be carried out; in order to gain different viewpoint on an organism, (i) genomes structures at DNA and gene levels, and overall nucleotide statistics, (ii) coding regions and (iii) noncoding regions, including the prediction of the regulatory elements (Wei *et al.*, 2002; Loots *et al.*, 2002). In contrast to the former two, studies on noncoding regions are rather at infancy and much work needs to be done. It is only until late 20th century that we started to understand that regulatory sequences in noncoding regions play essential roles in the post-transcriptional processes (Wedemeyer *et al.*, 2000; Mazumder *et al.*, 2003).

Comparative genomics can be dated back to 1984 through the efforts led by Professor Wimmer to compare different virus genomes. The comparison was made between several animal picornaviruses and cowpea mosaic virus, a plant virus that causes the "mosaic" pattern on plant leaves (Argos *et al.*, 1984). Two years later, a large-scale study was carried out between the varicella-zoster virus that causes chickenpox in humans and the Epstein-Barr virus that is associated with diseases such as gastric cancer, nasopharyngeal carcinoma and Hodgkin's lymphoma (McGeoch and Davison, 1986). Ever since then, this approach has been employed extensively and its application encompasses various fields such as agriculture (Sharma *et al.*, 2014; Sorrells, 2006; Wang *et al.*, 2017), evolutionary study and disease study (Alfoldi and Lindblad-Toh, 2013).

The main objective of this article is to provide the readers an overview of how bioinformatics is applied to carry out comparative genomics, with a focus on agriculture and biomedical research. It begins with a brief historical background and provides the current status on some notable genome sequencing projects. This is not meant to serve as an exhaustive dossier on comparative genomics, but rather to serve as a guide on the topic from the application perspective.

Background

The Past and Present: From Sequence to Genomes

The earliest bacterial genomes *Haemophilus influenza* and *Mycoplasma genitalium* (Fleischmann *et al.*, 1995; Fraser *et al.*, 1995) were fully sequenced in 1995 and 8 years later, the first human genome sequencing project was concluded (International Human Genome Sequencing, 2004). Since then, several teams have taken on the challenge of initiating ambitious genome sequencing projects, such as the 100,000 Genomes Project by Genomics England to sequence genomes of 100,000 patients with rare disease, registered with the National Health Service (NHS) (England, 2016); another is the GenomeAsia 100 K project to sequence 100,000 individuals in the Asian population (see Relevant Website section).

The rapid surge in the number of sequencing projects has led to the generation of massive amount of data, evidenced by the increment of sequencing data depositions in the Sequence Read Archive (SRA) (Leinonen *et al.*, 2011) at National Center for Biotechnology Information (**Fig. 1**). Many other public databases that cater for the specific projects based on the organism being sequenced have also been developed, for instance the Ensembl Genomes (Hubbard *et al.*, 2002), Mouse Genome Database (MGD) (Bult *et al.*, 2008), Maize Genetics Database (MaizeGDB) (Lawrence *et al.*, 2004), UCSC Genome Browser Database (Karolchik *et al.*, 2003) and other specific human disease-related databases, such as The Cancer Genome Atlas (Cancer Genome Atlas Research, 2008) and International Cancer Genome Consortium (Zhang *et al.*, 2011).

These efforts exemplify how the sequencing projects have progressed at a rapid speed, largely owing to the vast reduction in the sequencing cost, which stands at USD 0.012 per megabase as of 31st July 2017 (Wetterstrand, 2017). In the last five years (from 1st August 2013 to 1st August 2017), we have seen publications with the word "genome sequencing" (in the title/abstract) recorded in the PubMed database increase by two folds; with a latest a total of 13,314 articles published. During the

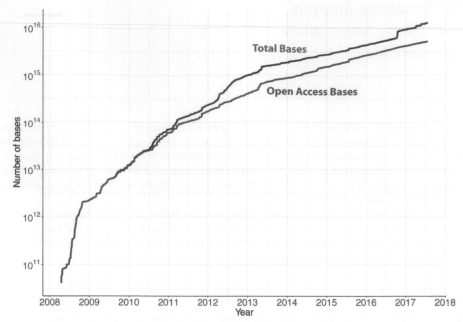

Fig. 1 The graph shows the growth in the Sequence Read Archive (SRA) database that stores raw sequencing data from high-throughput sequencing platforms from year 2008 to the present. The data used to plot this graph were extracted from Sequence Read Archive at https://www. ncbi.nlm.nih.gov/Traces/sra. The graph was built using R version 3.4.0. Reproduced from Leinonen, R., Sugawara, H., Shumwayand, M., International Nucleotide Sequence Database Collaboration, 2011. The sequence read archive. Nucleic Acids Res 39, D19–D21.

same time period, publications with the phrase "comparative genomics" in the title or abstract surged from 3546 articles to 5560 articles, an increment of approximately 57% from the year 2013. These figures indicate that one of the driving forces behind comparative genomics is the growth in the number of genome sequencing projects that provide the required genomics data.

Methods in Comparative Genomics

The process in comparative genomics frequently involves the alignment of DNA sequences; such as the use of pairwise alignment (e.g. Needle and Water Needleman and Wunsch, 1970; Smith and Waterman, 1981) to detect closely related genes. An extension of this sequence alignment is multiple sequence alignment (MSA) such as Clustal Omega (Sievers *et al.*, 2011) and T-coffee (Notredame *et al.*, 2000) where it can be used to detect conserved regions through the alignment of three or more sequences. Housekeeping genes are examples of regions in a genome that tend to be highly conserved and evolve slower than other genes such as the tissue-specific genes (Zhang and Li, 2004), mainly due to their roles in the maintenance of basic cellular functions and are essential for the existence of a cell.

Homology is another crucial term that is frequently integrated into genomics study. The detection of homologous genes is of fundamental importance in many fields of biology, particularly in comparative genomics. Homology refers to a relationship between genes due to a common ancestry and it can be applied in two major contexts, depending on whether the genes were separated through a speciation (ortholog) or duplication (paralog) event. Orthologous genes are usually detected using sequence similarity, and a gene is considered as ortholog of each other if they have the highest percentage of sequence similarity compared to others genes. Reciprocal best blast hits (Ward and Moreno-Hagelsieb, 2014; Horiike *et al.*, 2016) and domain based detection (Chen *et al.*, 2010) are among the standard protocols used to detect the orthologous genes. Unlike orthologous genes which preserve the same function throughout evolution, paralogous genes are the new genes that diverged after duplication events and later evolved into a new function. The procedures used in comparative genomics vary depending on the application, and the general workflow on the commonly used procedures is detailed in **Fig. 2**.

Applications of Comparative Genomics

Prokaryotes

Mycobacterium ulcerans causes Buruli ulcer, an infectious tropical disease that causes skin ulcers. Although much effort has been invested, the slow growing nature of *M. ulcerans* in experimental conditions has hampered the progress in conventional drug discovery methods. To address this problem, the comparative genomics technique has been deployed by Butt *et al.* (2012a) to

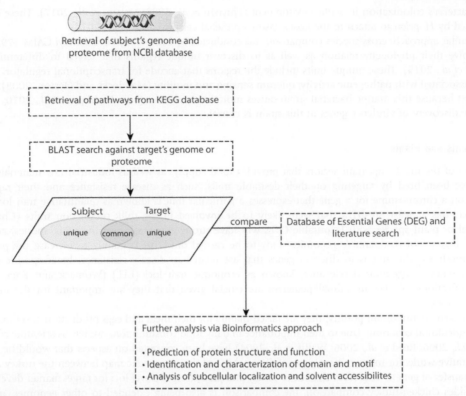

Fig. 2 General workflow of comparative genomics. It starts with the subject's genome and proteome as input and followed by the information retrieval from KEGG database. The BLAST search (e.g. BLASTP) against the target's proteome will reveal the existence of unique or common (shared) proteins between the subject and the target. Further bioinformatics analysis is often conducted on the proteins of interest.

identify novel therapeutic candidates against *M. ulcerans*, through homology searching of essential targets from twenty different bacteria that have no homology in human host. The group successfully discovered a total of 236 proteins based on these criteria as the potential drug and vaccine candidates against *M. ulcerans*. The comparison was done using a series of computational workflows which includes the homology blastp search and analysis of host and pathogenic metabolic pathways (Butt *et al.*, 2012a).

The study carried out on *Salmonella Typhimurium* LT2 and *Mycoplasma genitalium* were based on the similar approach to *M. ulcerans*, that is focusing on the identification of essential targets in the bacterial pathogens but have no homology in the human host. These studies are coupled with metabolic pathway analysis in order to pinpoint the unique biological pathways that are present in *S. Typhimurium* LT2 (Samal *et al.*, 2015) and *M. genitalium* as compared to the *Homo sapiens* (Butt *et al.*, 2012b). The workflows, which include the drug targets prioritization and homology modelling have successfully identified 13 proteins as vaccine candidates in *S. Typhimurium* LT2 (Samal *et al.*, 2015). *M. genitalium* is another human parasitic pathogen that is affiliated with sexually transmitted diseases. Hence, *in silico* comparative genomics is being employed because conventional drug discovery process is costly and bear few drug targets. This comparison against human host has identified 67 non-homologous essential proteins of *M. genitalium*, which could serve as potential drug design and vaccine targets against *M. genitalium* (Butt *et al.*, 2012b).

Concretely, comparative methods are employed to pinpoint genes of essential function amongst the pathogenic bacteria, even more so when there is an increasing emergence of reported antibiotic-resistant pathogenic microorganisms (Choudhury *et al.*, 2012; Martinez, 2008). In view of this, Glass *et al.* (2002) compiled a list of essential attributes of a good drug targets in the bacteria genomes, which includes the target (i) being essential for the disease, (ii) unique to the bacteria and significantly different from its corresponding orthologous genes in human and (iii) present in key pathogenic bacteria (Glass *et al.*, 2002). As proposed by the former examples, target selection is mainly done using computational approaches, for example, comparison of pathways, sequence and structural homology as well as cluster and motif analysis (Gerstein, 2000; Rosamond and Allsop, 2000; Gerstein and Jansen, 2000).

Genome comparison can also be made with the aim to identify species-specific features or single-copy (unique) genes of an organisms. In the context of comparative genomics, some of the unique genes can be referred as the genes with no homolog, even with its closely related species (Llorente *et al.*, 2000; Ong *et al.*, 2012). These genes can be used to provide insights into the niche adaptation of the specific phenotypes (Kahlke *et al.*, 2012) and virulence factors. *Helicobacter pylori*, a gram negative bacteria that colonizes gastric epithelium and causes a persistent inflammatory response (Ruggiero, 2010) is an example of bacteria that possess such unique feature in their genetic makeup. Given its distinctive role in pathogenicity, genome comparison was carried out between *Helicobacter pylori* and its two pathogenic counterparts; *Haemophilus influenza* and *Escherichia coli*. The work has successfully contributed in the identification of species-specific features such as acid tolerance and outer membrane family proteins, which are crucial for the bacteria's colonization in acidic environment (Huynen *et al.*, 1998; Matsuo *et al.*, 2017). These outer membrane proteins were used by *H. pylori* to attach to the host's gastric epithelial cells (Matsuo *et al.*, 2017).

In another similar approach, cross-species comparison was conducted by comparing *Vibrio harveyi* CAIM 1792 with its related genomes to resolve their phylogeny relation as well as to discover unique regions that served to differentiate these strains (Espinoza-Valles *et al.*, 2015). These unique traits include the regions that encode for transcriptional regulator, LysR, which was described to be associated with pathogenic activity, quorum sensing and motility (Maddocks and Oyston, 2008). *V. harveyi* CAIM 1792 is of interest because this marine bacterial strain causes mortality in shrimp (Soto-Rodriguez *et al.*, 2010; Moriarty, 1998), and therefore the discovery of virulence genes in this strain is crucial.

Agricultural Animals and Plants

Agriculture is one of the most important sectors that provides food supply, as well as industrial raw materials. Farm animals, for example, have been bred by targeting on their desirable traits, such as disease resistance and their rapid growth. The general location on a chromosome for a gene that expresses a particular trait is known as quantitative trait locus (QTL). Dairy cattle for instance, has at least 30 QTLs that were likely to be involved in the milk production traits (Chamberlain *et al.*, 2007). An animal or plant species with favourable QTLs will have strong advantage over the other species; and this serves as the basis for the urgency of comparative genomics study to be carried out. This is mainly to increase the production of the agricultural commodities. The aim is to discover genes that are related to disease resistance, breed-specific quantitative loci along with phenotypes of agricultural relevance, known as economic trait loci (ETL) (Womack and Kata, 1995; Womack, 1998). The identifications of ETLs in animal pedigrees are crucial given that they are important for the improvement and production of livestock.

Turkey and chicken are important poultry; they are raised mainly for their meat and eggs production and thus have significant contribution in agricultural economy. Due to their importance in daily food consumption, numerous scientific efforts (Reed *et al.*, 2005; Chaves *et al.*, 2006; Reed *et al.*, 2006; Wallis *et al.*, 2004) have been concerted on aspects that would be beneficial to the industry. Comparative works for instance have successfully established the cytogenetic map between the turkey and chicken that allowed for the transfer of genetic data from chicken to turkey and prediction of novel loci for target marker development (Griffin *et al.*, 2008). Besides chicken-turkey comparison, the comparison is also being extended to other genomes, including human genome (International Chicken Genome Sequencing, 2004).

Identification of orthologous genes is one of the common procedures in comparative analysis. Once the orthologous genes have been defined, the subsequent step is the identification of the conserved chromosomal regions that will lead to the generation of comparative map (Burt, 2002). If two genes are located on the same chromosome, the two are known as syntenic. The construction of cattle-human comparative map (Larkin *et al.*, 2003) assists in the adding of the cattle genome to the existing multispecies comparative genome studies, which is also inclusive of goat (Schibler *et al.*, 1998), pig (Pinton *et al.*, 2000; Ma *et al.*, 2011), and horse (Caetano *et al.*, 1999).

Besides agriculture livestock, identification of quantitative trait locus (QTLs) is also important in increasing crops yield, its tolerance against environmental stress and disease resistance, which would involve the construction of genetic maps of the crop species. To exemplify this, Hwang *et al.* (2006) successfully formulated a fine genetic map near Rsv4 gene in soybean by comparing against the genome of closely related model, legume *Lotus japonicas* (Hwang *et al.*, 2006). Rsv4 gene has profound economic value due its ability to confer resistance against all seven Soybean mosaic virus (SMV) strains (Ma *et al.*, 1995). Soybean [(*Glycine max L.* (*Merrill*)] is one of the major sources of edible oil and proteins and it is under severe threat from SMV that could affect its production worldwide (Hill and Whitham, 2014). Following the formulation of this genetic map near Rsv4 gene, the researchers are able to derive a new biomarker, AW307114A from the soybean expressed sequence tags (ESTs). This newly discovered marker is important because it is more closely linked to Rsv4 resistance gene in the soybeans (Hwang *et al.*, 2006) than the previously discovered biomarkers.

Bacterial wilt (BW) is yet another plant disease caused by *Ralstonia solanacearum* that affects pepper, tomato and eggplant (Hayward, 1991). To overcome this, researchers resequenced the plants that harbour resistance traits towards BW, in this case the pepper plant YCM344 (Kang *et al.*, 2016). Using the comparative analysis against the pepper reference genome sequence (version 1.55), they have successfully identified single nucleotide polymorphisms (SNP) that have the potential to cause BW resistance in pepper plant. Not only that, they could also pinpoint genomic regions of these SNP to be homologous to the known resistance genes in the tomato genomes, exemplified yet again by the use of comparative analysis to identify conserved regions across different genomes.

Jute (*Corchorus* sp.) is one of the pivotal sources of natural fibre, with the advantages such as high tensile strength, moderate heat resistance and biodegradable. Given that jute production has profound economic value, genomics comparison was carried out on two species of jute (*Corchorus olitorius* and *Corchorus capsularis*) against 13 others genomes including *Arabidopsis thaliana* and *Glycine max* (Islam *et al.*, 2017). Subsequent identification of homologous genes has led the team to propose a model for bast fibre biogenesis in jute (Islam *et al.*, 2017). The understanding of molecular basis of the fibre biogenesis enabled improvement to the breeding strategies of jute to meet the increasing demand of natural fibres in industry, as the annual global production of jute is up to 2.821 million tonnes for year 2014/15 (Food and Agriculture Organization of The United Nations, 2016).

Rice (*Oryza sativa*) is the staple food in Asia and the productions of rice are among the highest in Asian populations. A number of comparative genomics studies have been conducted on rice. For instance, the comparison between rice and Arabidopsis genomes using the phylogenetic comparisons reveals that certain families that are involved in the auxin homeostasis and plant development in Arabidopsis are missing from the rice genome (Nelson *et al.*, 2004). Another comparison of structural variation was conducted between rice and its closest relative in the genus Oryza (Hurwitz *et al.*, 2010). Together, this has resulted in the detailed catalog of structural variation across the Oryza family that can be used for forthcoming works in genome evolution, speciation, domestication and novel gene discovery (Hurwitz *et al.*, 2010).

Comparative genomics has showcased significant improvement in the plants yield production. This is of much dire urgency, as better yield of crops production would ensure better management of the famine outspread worldwide, with estimates about 795 million people from the 7.3 billion people in the world were affected from persistent undernourishment (Food and Agriculture Organization *et al.*, 2015)

Animal Models for Human Disease

From historical perspective, biologists remarkably benefited from the study of animals. Animal models (Perlman, 2016; Jiminez *et al.*, 2015; Schofield *et al.*, 2011; Iannaccone and Jacob, 2009; Shin and Fishman, 2002) are often used to get a better understanding on the diseases that are associated with human. For instance, nematode (*Caenorhabditis elegans*) is used as a model for studies such as in cancer research (Kyriakakis *et al.*, 2015) and in host-microbiome interactions at the apical surface of epithelial cells in the intestine (Pukkila-Worley and Ausubel, 2012). This interaction study is important because the immune defense system must be able to distinguish between pathogens and the harmless bacteria that are present in the mammalian intestine, in order to combat infection.

The use of human disease models in understanding the fundamental pathophysiology of a disease and the breakthrough of new therapeutic, signifies the need for comparative studies. For instance, the study of mouse genome involved the identification of QTLs for blood pressure that are known to contribute to hypertension (Wright *et al.*, 1999). This breakthrough has served as a precursor for the development of novel comparative genomics map for "candidate hypertension loci" in human based on the QTLs translation between rat model and human (Stoll *et al.*, 2000). It has then resulted in the prognostication of 26 chromosomal regions in human that are plausible to harbour hypertension genes (Stoll *et al.*, 2000), and thus can potentially be used for the development of new therapeutics.

Although rat and mouse remain the leading models to decipher the genetic basis of human diseases, zebrafish is yet another excellent model for human disease. This is mainly attributed to its optical clarity during embryogenesis, high productivity of large clutches of embryos and short generations time (Detrich *et al.*, 1999). On top of that, due to high genomic content similarity shared between zebrafish and human (approximately 70% the genes are orthologues) (Howe *et al.*, 2013), it offers huge opportunities for comparative analysis between these two genomes. Some of the applications of zebrafish as a model for better understanding of the human diseases would be the study of cardiovascular disease (Sehnert and Stainier, 2002; North and Zon, 2003), muscle disease (Guyon *et al.*, 2007; Kunkel *et al.*, 2006) and aging process (Keller and Murtha, 2004).

Animal models also served as valuable tools to study the biology and genetic aspects of human cancers, as well as for preclinical study of anti-cancer therapeutics (LeGendre-McGhee *et al.*, 2015; Steele *et al.*, 2005; Ruggeri *et al.*, 2014). Therefore, it is crucial to have animal data to be evaluated in the context of human cancers. Some initial cancer studies leverage on comparative genomics to identify orthologs of cancer genes (Pickeral *et al.*, 2000; Makalowski *et al.*, 1996), such as for the study of Wnt signalling pathway (Katoh and Katoh, 2005a,b). While other studies carry on with further analysis to define the syntenic region between the rat and human genomes and this helps to uncover the chromosomal regions for tumor and metastasis in the rat that are involved in human prostate cancer (Datta *et al.*, 2005).

In short, although human and animal models may have different physical appearance, but both share a certain degree of similarities in their genomes. It is these "similarities" that could give important clues on the development of the diseases in human and afford us an opportunity to treat these diseases more effectively. In fact, researchers are now able to find better treatment of human disease by recreating the human diseases in animal models, ensuring a better quality of life ever since for human.

Closing Remarks

The fundamental basis of comparative genomics is to identify the genes of interest that control traits variation and this is made possible through the ability to compare and contrast between one organism to another organism. Aided with the integration of genomics analysis, this translation is an exciting notion in gaining the momentum for the breakthrough in gene discovery for all domains of life, either for single-celled or multicellular organisms. The resulting genomics information is able to provide insights into the biology of an individual genome, benefitting the advances in human disease related study and greater yield improvement in agricultural animals, plant and crops.

See also: Exome Sequencing Data Analysis. Functional Enrichment Analysis. Genome Analysis – Identification of Genes Involved in Host-Pathogen Protein-Protein Interaction Networks. Integrative Analysis of Multi-Omics Data. Natural Language Processing Approaches in Bioinformatics. Next Generation Sequencing Data Analysis. Pipeline of High Throughput Sequencing. Sequence Analysis. Whole Genome Sequencing Analysis

References

Alfoldi, J., Lindblad-Toh, K., 2013. Comparative genomics as a tool to understand evolution and disease. Genome Res 23, 1063–1068.

Argos, P., Kamer, G., Nicklin, M.J., Wimmer, E., 1984. Similarity in gene organization and homology between proteins of animal picornaviruses and a plant comovirus suggest common ancestry of these virus families. Nucleic Acids Res 12, 7251–7267.

Bult, C.J., Eppig, J.T., Kadin, J.A., et al., 2008. The Mouse Genome Database (MGD): Mouse biology and model systems. Nucleic Acids Res 36, D724–D728.

Burt, D.W., 2002. Comparative mapping in farm animals. Brief Funct Genomic Proteomic 1, 159–168.

Butt, A.M., Nasrullah, I., Tahir, S., Tong, Y., 2012a. Comparative genomics analysis of *Mycobacterium ulcerans* for the identification of putative essential genes and therapeutic candidates. PLOS ONE 7, e43080.

Butt, A.M., Tahir, S., Nasrullah, I., et al., 2012b. Mycoplasma genitalium: A comparative genomics study of metabolic pathways for the identification of drug and vaccine targets. Infect Genet Evol 12, 53–62.

Caetano, A.R., Shiue, Y.L., Lyons, L.A., et al., 1999. A comparative gene map of the horse (*Equus caballus*). Genome Res 9, 1239–1249.

Chamberlain, A.J., McPartlan, H.C., Goddard, M.E., 2007. The number of loci that affect milk production traits in dairy cattle. Genetics 177, 1117–1123.

Chaves, L.D., Knutson, T.P., Krueth, S.B., Reed, K.M., 2006. Using the chicken genome sequence in the development and mapping of genetic markers in the turkey (*Meleagris gallopavo*). Anim Genet 37, 130–138.

Chen, B., Zhong, D., Monteiro, A., 2006. Comparative genomics and evolution of the HSP90 family of genes across all kingdoms of organisms. BMC Genom 7, 156.

Chen, T.W., Wu, T.H., Ng, W.V., Lin, W.C., 2010. DODO: An efficient orthologous genes assignment tool based on domain architectures. Domain based ortholog detection. BMC Bioinform 11 (Suppl. 7), S6.

Food and Agriculture Organization, International Fund for Agricultural Development, World Food Programme, International Fund for Agricultural Development & Program., W. F., 2015. The State of Food Insecurity in the World 2015. Strengthening the enabling environment for food security and nutrition. Rome: FAO.

Cancer Genome Atlas Research Network, N., 2008. Comprehensive genomic characterization defines human glioblastoma genes and core pathways. Nature 455, 1061–1068.

Choudhury, R., Panda, S., Singh, D.V., 2012. Emergence and dissemination of antibiotic resistance: A global problem. Indian J Med Microbiol 30, 384–390.

Datta, M.W., Suckow, M.A., Twigger, S., et al., 2005. Using comparative genomics to leverage animal models in the identification of cancer genes. Examples in prostate cancer. Cancer Genom Proteom 2, 137–144.

International Chicken Genome Sequencing Consortium, C., 2004. Sequence and comparative analysis of the chicken genome provide unique perspectives on vertebrate evolution. Nature 432, 695–716.

International Human Genome Sequencing Consortium, C., 2004. Finishing the euchromatic sequence of the human genome. Nature 431, 931–945.

Detrich 3rd, H.W., Westerfield, M., Zon, L.I., 1999. Overview of the zebrafish system. Methods Cell Biol 59, 3–10.

Food and Agriculture Organization of The United Nations, 2016. Jute, kenaf, sisal, abaca coir and allied fibres. Rome: FAO.

Genomics England, 2016. The 100,000 Genomes Project.

Espinoza-Valles, I., Vora, G.J., Lin, B., et al., 2015. Unique and conserved genome regions in *Vibrio harveyi* and related species in comparison with the shrimp pathogen *Vibrio harveyi* CAIM 1792. Microbiology 161, 1762–1779.

Fleischmann, R.D., Adams, M.D., White, O., et al., 1995. Whole-genome random sequencing and assembly of *Haemophilus influenzae* Rd. Science 269, 496–512.

Fraser, C.M., Gocayne, J.D., White, O., et al., 1995. The minimal gene complement of *Mycoplasma genitalium*. Science 270, 397–403.

Gerstein, M., 2000. Integrative database analysis in structural genomics. Nat Struct Biol. 7 Suppl), 960–963.

Gerstein, M., Jansen, R., 2000. The current excitement in bioinformatics-analysis of whole-genome expression data: How does it relate to protein structure and function? Curr Opin Struct Biol 10, 574–584.

Glass, J.I., Belanger, A.E., Robertson, G.T., 2002. *Streptococcus pneumoniae* as a genomics platform for broad-spectrum antibiotic discovery. Curr Opin Microbiol 5, 338–342.

Griffin, D.K., Robertson, L.B., Tempest, H.G., et al., 2008. Whole genome comparative studies between chicken and turkey and their implications for avian genome evolution. BMC Genomics 9, 168.

Guyon, J.R., Steffen, L.S., Howell, M.H., et al., 2007. Modeling human muscle disease in zebrafish. Biochim Biophys Acta 1772, 205–215.

Hayward, A.C., 1991. Biology and epidemiology of bacterial wilt caused by *Pseudomonas solanacearum*. Annu Rev Phytopathol 29, 65–87.

Hill, J.H., Whitham, S.A., 2014. Control of virus diseases in soybeans. Adv Virus Res 90, 355–390.

Horiike, T., Minai, R., Miyata, D., Nakamura, Y., Tateno, Y., 2016. Ortholog-Finder: A tool for constructing an ortholog data set. Genome Biol Evol 8, 446–457.

Howe, K., Clark, M.D., Torroja, C.F., et al., 2013. The zebrafish reference genome sequence and its relationship to the human genome. Nature 496, 498–503.

Hubbard, T., Barker, D., Birney, E., et al., 2002. The Ensembl genome database project. Nucleic Acids Res 30, 38–41.

Hurwitz, B.L., Kudrna, D., Yu, Y., et al., 2010. Rice structural variation: A comparative analysis of structural variation between rice and three of its closest relatives in the genus *Oryza*. Plant J 63, 990–1003.

Huynen, M., Dandekar, T., Bork, P., 1998. Differential genome analysis applied to the species-specific features of Helicobacter pylori. FEBS Lett 426, 1–5.

Hwang, T.Y., Moon, J.K., Yu, S., et al., 2006. Application of comparative genomics in developing molecular markers tightly linked to the virus resistance gene Rsv4 in soybean. Genome 49, 380–388.

Iannaccone, P.M., Jacob, H.J., 2009. Rats!. Dis Model Mech 2, 206–210.

Islam, M.S., Saito, J.A., Emdad, E.M., et al., 2017. Comparative genomics of two jute species and insight into fibre biogenesis. Nat Plants 3, 16223.

Jiminez, J.A., Uwiera, T.C., Douglas Inglis, G., Uwiera, R.R., 2015. Animal models to study acute and chronic intestinal inflammation in mammals. Gut Pathog 7, 29.

Kahlke, T., Goesmann, A., Hjerde, E., Willassen, N.P., Haugen, P., 2012. Unique core genomes of the bacterial family vibrionaceae: Insights into niche adaptation and speciation. BMC Genomics 13, 179.

Kang, Y.J., Ahn, Y.K., Kim, K.T., Jun, T.H., 2016. Resequencing of *Capsicum annuum* parental lines (YCM334 and Taean) for the genetic analysis of bacterial wilt resistance. BMC Plant Biol 16, 235.

Karolchik, D., Baertsch, R., Diekhans, M., et al., 2003. The UCSC Genome Browser Database. Nucleic Acids Res 31, 51–54.

Katoh, M., Katoh, M., 2005a. Comparative genomics on Wnt7a orthologs. Oncol Rep 13, 777–780.

Katoh, M., Katoh, M., 2005b. Comparative genomics on Wnt8a and Wnt8b genes. Int J Oncol 26, 1129–1133.

Keller, E.T., Murtha, J.M., 2004. The use of mature zebrafish (*Danio rerio*) as a model for human aging and disease. Comp Biochem Physiol C Toxicol Pharmacol 138, 335–341.

Kunkel, L.M., Bachrach, E., Bennett, R.R., Guyon, J., Steffen, L., 2006. Diagnosis and cell-based therapy for Duchenne muscular dystrophy in humans, mice, and zebrafish. J Hum Genet 51, 397–406.

Kyriakakis, E., Markaki, M., Tavernarakis, N., 2015. *Caenorhabditis elegans* as a model for cancer research. Mol Cell Oncol 2, e975027.

Larkin, D.M., Everts-van der Wind, A., Rebeiz, M., et al., 2003. A cattle-human comparative map built with cattle BAC-ends and human genome sequence. Genome Res 13, 1966–1972.

Lawrence, C.J., Dong, Q., Polacco, M.L., Seigfried, T.E., Brendel, V., 2004. MaizeGDB, the community database for maize genetics and genomics. Nucleic Acids Res 32, D393–D397.

LeGendre-McGhee, S., Rice, P.S., Wall, R.A., et al., 2015. Time-serial assessment of drug combination interventions in a mouse model of colorectal carcinogenesis using optical coherence tomography. Cancer Growth Metastasis 8, 63–80.

Leinonen, R., Sugawara, H., Shumway, M., , International Nucleotide Sequence Database Collaboration, C., 2011. The sequence read archive. Nucleic Acids Res 39, D19–D21.

Llorente, B., Durrens, P., Malpertuy, A., et al., 2000. Genomic exploration of the hemiascomycetous yeasts: 20. Evolution of gene redundancy compared to Saccharomyces cerevisiae. FEBS Lett 487, 122–133.

Loots, G.G., Ovcharenko, I., Pachter, L., Dubchak, I., Rubin, E.M., 2002. rVista for comparative sequence-based discovery of functional transcription factor binding sites. Genome Res 12, 832–839.

Ma, G., Chen, P., Buss, G.R., Tolin, S.A., 1995. Genetic characteristics of two genes for resistance to soybean mosaic virus in PI486355 soybean. Theor Appl Genet 91, 907–914.

Ma, J.G., Chang, T.C., Yasue, H., et al., 2011. A high-resolution comparative map of porcine chromosome 4 (SSC4). Anim Genet 42, 440–444.

Maddocks, S.E., Oyston, P.C., 2008. Structure and function of the LysR-type transcriptional regulator (LTTR) family proteins. Microbiology 154, 3609–3623.

Makalowski, W., Zhang, J., Boguski, M.S., 1996. Comparative analysis of 1196 orthologous mouse and human full-length mRNA and protein sequences. Genome Res 6, 846–857.

Martinez, J.L., 2008. Antibiotics and antibiotic resistance genes in natural environments. Science 321, 365–367.

Matsuo, Y., Kido, Y., Yamaoka, Y., 2017. Helicobacter pylori outer membrane protein-related pathogenesis. Toxins (Basel) 9.

Mazumder, B., Seshadri, V., Fox, P.L., 2003. Translational control by the 3'-UTR: The ends specify the means. Trends Biochem Sci 28, 91–98.

McGeoch, D.J., Davison, A.J., 1986. DNA sequence of the herpes simplex virus type 1 gene encoding glycoprotein gH, and identification of homologues in the genomes of varicella-zoster virus and Epstein-Barr virus. Nucleic Acids Res 14, 4281–4292.

Moriarty, D., 1998. Microbial ecology: Protecting the prawns in polluted ponds. Microbiol. Aust 19, 22–27.

Needleman, S.B., Wunsch, C.D., 1970. A general method applicable to the search for similarities in the amino acid sequence of two proteins. J Mol Biol 48, 443–453.

Nelson, D.R., Schuler, M.A., Paquette, S.M., Werck-Reichhart, D., Bak, S., 2004. Comparative genomics of rice and Arabidopsis. Analysis of 727 cytochrome P450 genes and pseudogenes from a monocot and a dicot. Plant Physiol 135, 756–772.

North, T.E., Zon, L.I., 2003. Modeling human hematopoietic and cardiovascular diseases in zebrafish. Dev Dyn 228, 568–583.

Notredame, C., Higgins, D.G., Heringa, J., 2000. T-Coffee: A novel method for fast and accurate multiple sequence alignment. J Mol Biol 302, 205–217.

Ong, H.S., Mohamed, R., Firdaus-Raih, M., 2012. Comparative genome sequence analysis reveals the extent of diversity and conservation for glycan-associated proteins in Burkholderia spp. Comp Funct Genomics 2012, 752867.

Perlman, R.L., 2016. Mouse models of human disease: An evolutionary perspective. Evol Med Public Health 2016, 170–176.

Pickeral, O.K., Li, J.Z., Barrow, I., et al., 2000. Classical oncogenes and tumor suppressor genes: A comparative genomics perspective. Neoplasia 2, 280–286.

Pinton, P., Schibler, L., Cribiu, E., Gellin, J., Yerle, M., 2000. Localization of 113 anchor loci in pigs: Improvement of the comparative map for humans, pigs, and goats. Mamm Genome 11, 306–315.

Pukkila-Worley, R., Ausubel, F.M., 2012. Immune defense mechanisms in the Caenorhabditis elegans intestinal epithelium. Curr Opin Immunol 24, 3–9.

Reed, K.M., Hall, M.K., Chaves, L.D., Knutson, T.P., 2006. Single nucleotide polymorphisms for integrative mapping in the Turkey (Meleagris gallopavo). Anim Biotechnol 17, 73–80.

Reed, K.M., Chaves, L.D., Hall, M.K., Knutson, T.P., Harry, D.E., 2005. A comparative genetic map of the turkey genome. Cytogenet Genome Res 111, 118–127.

Rosamond, J., Allsop, A., 2000. Harnessing the power of the genome in the search for new antibiotics. Science 287, 1973–1976.

Ruggeri, B.A., Camp, F., Miknyoczki, S., 2014. Animal models of disease: Pre-clinical animal models of cancer and their applications and utility in drug discovery. Biochem Pharmacol 87, 150–161.

Ruggiero, P., 2010. Helicobacter pylori and inflammation. Curr Pharm Des 16, 4225–4236.

Samal, H.B., Prava, J., Suar, M., Mahapatra, R.K., 2015. Comparative genomics study of Salmonella typhimurium LT2 for the identification of putative therapeutic candidates. J Theor Biol 369, 67–79.

Schibler, L., Vaiman, D., Oustry, A., Giraud-Delville, C., Cribiu, E.P., 1998. Comparative gene mapping: A fine-scale survey of chromosome rearrangements between ruminants and humans. Genome Res 8, 901–915.

Schofield, P.N., Sundberg, J.P., Hoehndorf, R., Gkoutos, G.V., 2011. New approaches to the representation and analysis of phenotype knowledge in human diseases and their animal models. Brief Funct Genomics 10, 258–265.

Sehnert, A.J., Stainier, D.Y., 2002. A window to the heart: Can zebrafish mutants help us understand heart disease in humans? Trends Genet 18, 491–494.

Sharma, A., Li, X., Lim, Y.P., 2014. Comparative genomics of Brassicaceae crops. Breed Sci 64, 3–13.

Shin, J.T., Fishman, M.C., 2002. From zebrafish to human: Modular medical models. Annu Rev Genomics Hum Genet 3, 311–340.

Sievers, F., Wilm, A., Dineen, D., et al., 2011. Fast, scalable generation of high-quality protein multiple sequence alignments using Clustal Omega. Mol Syst Biol 7, 539.

Smith, T.F., Waterman, M.S., 1981. Identification of common molecular subsequences. J Mol Biol 147, 195–197.

Sorrells, M.E., 2006. Applications of Comparative Genomics to Crop Improvement. Ames, IA: Blackwell Publishing.

Soto-Rodriguez, S.A., Gomez-Gil, B., Lozano, R., 2010. 'Bright-red' syndrome in Pacific white shrimp Litopenaeus vannamei is caused by Vibrio harveyi. Dis Aquat Organ 92, 11–19.

Steele, V.E., Lubet, R.A., Moon, R.C., 2005. Preclinical animal models for the development of cancer chemoprevention drugs. In: Kelloff, G.J., Hawk, E.T., Sigman, C.C. (Eds.), Cancer Chemoprevention: Volume 2: Strategies for Cancer Chemoprevention. Totowa, NJ: Humana Press.

Stoll, M., Kwitek-Black, A.E., Cowley Jr., A.W., et al., 2000. New target regions for human hypertension via comparative genomics. Genome Res 10, 473–482.

Wallis, J.W., Aerts, J., Groenen, M.A., et al., 2004. A physical map of the chicken genome. Nature 432, 761–764.

Wang, W., Cao, X.H., Miclaus, M., Xu, J., Xiong, W., 2017. The promise of agriculture genomics. Int J Genom 2017, 9743749.

Ward, N., Moreno-Hagelsieb, G., 2014. Quickly finding orthologs as reciprocal best hits with BLAT, LAST, and UBLAST: How much do we miss? PLOS ONE 9, e101850.

Wedemeyer, N., Schmitt-John, T., Evers, D., et al., 2000. Conservation of the 3'-untranslated region of the Rab1a gene in amniote vertebrates: Exceptional structure in marsupials and possible role for posttranscriptional regulation. FEBS Lett 477, 49–54.

Wei, L., Liu, Y., Dubchak, I., Shon, J., Park, J., 2002. Comparative genomics approaches to study organism similarities and differences. J Biomed Inform 35, 142–150.

Wetterstrand, K.A., 2017. DNA sequencing costs: Data from the NHGRI Genome Sequencing Program (GSP) 2017. Available at: www.genome.gov/sequencingcostsdata (accessed 05.12.17).

Womack, J.E., 1998. The cattle gene map. ILAR J 39, 153–159.

Womack, J.E., Kata, S.R., 1995. Bovine genome mapping: Evolutionary inference and the power of comparative genomics. Curr Opin Genet Dev 5, 725–733.

Wright, F.A., O'Connor, D.T., Roberts, E., et al., 1999. Genome scan for blood pressure loci in mice. Hypertension 34, 625–630.

Zhang, J., Baran, J., Cros, A., et al., 2011. International Cancer Genome Consortium Data Portal – A one-stop shop for cancer genomics data. Database (Oxford) 2011, bar026.

Zhang, L., Li, W.H., 2004. Mammalian housekeeping genes evolve more slowly than tissue-specific genes. Mol Biol Evol 21, 236–239.

Relevant Website

http://www.genomeasia100k.com/
GenomeAsia 100k.

Single Nucleotide Polymorphism Typing

Srilakshmi Srinivasan, Institute of Health and Biomedical Innovation and School of Biomedical Sciences, Queensland University of Technology, Brisbane, QLD, Australia
Jyotsna Batra, Institute of Health and Biomedical Innovation and School of Biomedical Sciences, Queensland University of Technology, Brisbane, QLD, Australia and Australian Prostate Cancer Research Centre – Queensland, Translational Research Institute, Woolloongabba, QLD, Australia

Abbreviations

ARMS	Amplification refractory mutation system	HRM	High-resolution melting curve
ASO	Allele-specific oligonucleotide	ISFET	Ion-sensitive field-effect transistor
AS-PCR	Allele-specific PCR	Mb	Mega bases
AS-SBE	Allele-specific single-base primer extension	NGS	Next generation sequencing
BAQ	Base alignment quality	OLA	Oligonucleotide ligation assay
bp	Base pair	ONT	Oxford Nanopore Technologies
CCD	Charged couple device	PCR	Polymerase chain reaction
CLR	Continuous long read	PGM	Personal genome machine
CMOS	Complementary metal-oxide-semiconductor	RFLP	Restricted-fragment length polymorphism
CRT	Cyclic reversible termination	SBL	Sequencing by ligation
dHPLC	Denaturing high-performance liquid chromatography	SBS	Sequencing-by-synthesis
		SMRT	Single-molecule real-time
dNTPs	Deoxy-nucleotide triphosphates	SMS	Single molecule sequencing
dsDNA	Double-stranded DNA	SNA	Single-nucleotide addition
FRET	Fluorescence resonance energy transfer	SNPs	Single nucleotide polymorphisms
GATK	Genome-analysis-toolkit	SSCP	Single-strand conformation polymorphism
Gb	Giga bases	ssDNA	Single-stranded
GWAS	Genome-wide association studies	ZMW	Zero-mode waveguides

Introduction

SNPs have emerged as important biomarkers to monitor disease prognosis and diagnosis. A SNP is a single base pair (bp) change either an insertion/deletion/substitution at a specific locus, with rare allele frequency usually $> 1\%$. These variations in DNA sequences may alter the genetic code and result in disease conditions or undesirable traits. Historically, a number of different SNP typing approaches have been used in both research and clinical laboratories (Srinivasan *et al.*, 2016). Presently, there is no single SNP genotyping method that is ideal for all research and/or clinical laboratory applications. Commonly used current chemistries include hybridization, primer extension, and cleavage methods coupled to various detection systems (Srinivasan and Batra, 2014). A multitude of innovations in these reagents and instrumentation have supported the initiation of the Human Genome Project and have led to more advanced technologies some of which are discussed in this review. However, the advanced technologies require a wide variety of algorithms for SNP detection from the raw data generated which is not crucial for the conventional methods. Thus we have categorized the SNP genotyping technologies into approaches that may or may not require computational algorithms for SNP detection as below.

Methods That do not Require Complex Computational Analysis

Amplification Refractory Mutation System (ARMS)

ARMS is an allele-specific polymerase chain reaction (PCR) for the detection of single base changes based on the use of sequence-specific PCR primers that allows amplification of template DNA only when the target allele is present. Thus, an ARMS primer can be designed specifically to amplify a specific member of a multi-allelic system. After PCR, the patterns of the PCR products (such as differences in length) allow differentiation of the alleles (Newton *et al.*, 1989).

High-Resolution Melting (HRM) Curve Analysis

HRM analysis is the technique introduced in 2003 to determine whether two PCR amplicons have identical sequences in the presence of a fluorescent reporter dye. Following amplification, the amplified product is exposed to an increasing gradient of temperature to reduce and denature the helicity of the double-stranded oligonucleotide, releasing the fluorescent dye (Montgomery *et al.*, 2007). Once released, the dye undergoes a conformational change that reduces the amount of fluorescence produced and a thermocycler will record the fluctuations in fluorescence and produce a melt-curve unique to the amplicon sequence analysed. HRM technique thus can compare the similarity of two amplicons by the melting curve of each oligonucleotide, length, and primary structure (Hjelmso *et al.*, 2014). The weak A-T bond is disrupted at a lower temperature than the G-C bond, and therefore, A-T–rich regions of the amplicon denature at lower temperatures than the G-C–rich regions (Wittwer *et al.*, 2003). The distribution of these A-T– or G-C–rich regions of the oligonucleotide dictates the resulting melt curve and can be used to compare the similarity of amplicons from multiple samples. Although, a simple, cost effective technique, SNPs at GC rich regions are difficult to detect as they introduce additional melting domains into the melting curve and only a small number of SNPs can be multiplexed at one time (Venables *et al.*, 2014).

Restricted Fragment Length Polymorphism (RFLP)

RFLP is a common choice of genotyping in regular laboratories for genetic association studies. RFLP is based on the technique that differentiates SNPs by analysis of patterns derived from cleavage of amplified DNA fragments by restriction enzymes (Chuang *et al.*, 2008). The samples may yield different sized fragments at the SNP site due to either creation or loss of a restriction endonuclease site because of the change in the genomic DNA (Awasthi *et al.*, 2014). To discriminate SNP by this assay, the restriction enzymes must be unique and recognize only one of the SNP containing sequences. This technique is a simple cost-effective method but requires large amount of sample DNA and manual mining for restriction enzyme sites is challenging and cumbersome (Ding *et al.*, 2017).

Invader Assay

Invader assay developed by Third Wave Technologies, Inc. uses fluorescence resonance energy transfer (FRET) detection and does not involve PCR, restriction digestion, or gel electrophoresis. The technology relies on the specificity of Cleavase® enzymes, that recognize and cleave structures that form when the 3′ end of an upstream "invading" oligonucleotide overlaps the hybridization site of the 5′ end of a downstream oligonucleotide probe by at least 1 bp (Hayashi *et al.*, 2017). This activity enables detection of single-nucleotide mismatches immediately upstream of the cleavage site on the downstream DNA strand because mispairing results in the formation of a noninvasive structure that the enzyme does not recognize as a cleavable substrate. The generation of the proper enzyme substrate is dependent on base-pairing at a critical position between the two oligonucleotides and the target nucleic acid, which provides the ability to discriminate single-base changes.

Single-Strand Conformation Polymorphism (SSCP)

SSCP is a simple and sensitive assay for SNP detection and genotyping. The principle is based on the conformation of the single-stranded DNA (ssDNA). In the presence of a single base change, the conformation of the ssDNA is changed and causes shift in the migration of the DNA under non-denaturing electrophoresis conditions. This results in different band patterns for wild type and mutant DNA samples (Choi and Jung, 2017). A simple SSCP involves four steps: 1) a PCR amplification of target DNA sequence, 2) denaturation of the PCR products, 3) self-annealing of the denatured DNA, and 4) detection in mobility difference of the ssDNA molecules under non-denaturing conditions (Gupta *et al.*, 2014). The DNA can be visualized by different mobility shifts by incorporating radio-isotopes, fluorescent dyes, capillary-based or silver staining.

Heteroduplex Analysis

Hetero-duplex analysis is a low-medium high-throughput SNP detection technique. During heteroduplex analysis, the target gene is PCR amplified and the amplified products are then denatured, re-annealed slowly to form four different double-stranded DNA molecules from the two alleles of the gene (Paniego *et al.*, 2015). In the presence of a heterozygous mutation, two homoduplexes comprising of two perfectly complementary strands (mutant-mutant and wildtype-wildtype) and two heteroduplexes, that contain a sequence mismatch or denaturation bubble (mutant-wildtype and wildtype-mutant) are formed (Palais *et al.*, 2005). The re-annealed DNA molecules on re-annealing can be separated by denaturing high-performance liquid chromatography (dHPLC), enzymatic (RNase cleavage assay), electrophoretic methods and chemical cleavage assays. Heteroduplexes can then be analysed by their differential mobility during electrophoresis, which allows the detection of sequence changes in comparison to the wild type (Velasco *et al.*, 2007).

Allele-Specific Hybridization (Taqman Assay)

Allele-specific hybridization is a technique based on discriminating between alleles at SNP using allele-specific oligonucleotide (ASO) probes and exploits the 5′ exonuclease activity of DNA polymerases (Gaudet *et al.*, 2009). Allele-specific PCR (AS-PCR) is achieved by PCR by an allele-specific primer rather than direct detection by a probe. Three primers are required, two to match the two alleles at the SNP site and the third to anneal to the opposite strand (Germer and Higuchi, 2003; Dhas *et al.*, 2015). Some of the tools used for designing AS primers are Tetra-primer, Visual-OMP and Primo SNP. Each of the two probes anneals to one allele to create a stable structure that would lead to its degradation by DNA polymerase, but when it anneals to the other allele, it forms a structure that is less stable so that the probe gets pushed off the template without being PCR amplified. A recent extension of the allele-specific expression is quantification of the allele-specific expression at mRNA level by fluorescence *in situ* analysis in a single-cell. Although simple and effective, the TaqMan assay requires substantial optimization and probe design remains largely empirical that makes it less preferable for large studies.

Allele-Specific Single-Base Primer Extension (AS-SBE)

AS-PCR makes use of the difference in extension between primers with matched and mismatched 3′ bases. AS-PCR requires two primers that anneal to the target with their 3′ bases matching the two alleles of an SNP. The allele-specific primers are labelled to enable their identification (Kisaki et al., 2010; Balschun et al., 2011). Allele-specific expression (ASE) can be conducted in situ on a chip when two allele-specific primers are anchored at different loci. SBE is considered to have a superior discrimination compared to ASE and is dependent on the sequence surrounding the polymorphism.

Oligonucleotide Ligation Assay (OLA)

OLA is a DNA dependent amplification that uses a set of four oligonucleotides, in the presence of a thermostable Taq DNA ligase, to detect SNP alleles. Any nucleotide variation at the ligation junction can be detected using a fluorescent or biotin labelling method (Dokuta et al., 2013; Mutsvangwa et al., 2014). The ligation occurs only when the 3′ detector nucleotide is complementary to the SNP nucleotide. Software such as GeneMapper are used for analyzing the raw data and calling SNP genotypes. Two fluorescent peaks in an electropherogram represents two alleles for a specific SNP (Tobler et al., 2005). A variation of this technique was recently reported and known as Heated OLA that uses a thermostable ligase and cycles of denaturation and hybridization for ligation and SNP detection (Beck et al., 2014).

Mid and High-Throughput Technologies Requiring Computational Analysis

Mid-throughput technologies that identified SNPs utilizing SBE are also desirable as modest multiplexing assays with minimal assay setup costs such as Sequenom MassARRAY platform (Clendenen et al., 2015; Miller et al., 2014). After PCR of the SNP region, a third primer is added that binds one position upstream of the SNP site and the four nucleotide bases linked to terminators are added. The nucleotide at the SNP is extended by an enzyme. The samples genotype is determined by hybridizing extended primers to a universal DNA array and by determining the identity of the extended base by hybridization pattern analysis. This can be used as second-tier applications such as validating hits after genome-wide association studies (GWAS) (Batra et al., 2011; Lose et al., 2012; Lose et al., 2013). SNP microarrays started more than two decades ago and have progressed from low-throughput to the current mid-throughput Affymetrix GeneChip SNP platforms, Illumina Golden Gate Assay or the Infinium Assay of Illumina to study thousands of SNPs simultaneously. In this approach the arrayed DNA is extended at the SNP site in a single extension reaction or the bar-coded oligos are hybridized to a universal array (Cutler et al., 2001; Bumgarner, 2013).

Here for the high-throughput technologies reviewed, initially, we discuss the physical method followed by the computational analysis for the SNP detection.

Sequencing by Ligation (SBL)

SBL approaches comprise the hybridization and ligation of labelled probes of varying lengths and short, known anchor sequences to a DNA strand (Tomkinson et al., 2006). The emission spectra by the fluorophore indicates its complementarity to the probe (Pu et al., 2015). In SBL, the DNA is clonally amplified on a solid surface, the presence of thousands of copies reduces the background noise. The probes encode one or two known bases, enabling complementary binding of the probe to the template. The anchor fragment encodes a sequence complementary to an adapter sequence and initiates ligation. After ligation, the template is imaged to identify the known base or bases in the probe (Landegren et al., 1988). A new cycle starts after removing the anchor–probe complex or removal of the fluorophore by a cleavage event and to restore the ligation site.

Next-generation sequencing (NGS) platforms based on SBL including, SOLiD and Complete Genomics systems utilizes deoxy-nucleotide triphosphates (dNTPs) that are probed multiple times (Valouev et al., 2008). In Complete Genomic's DNA nanoballs' technique, the sequences are obtained by probe-ligation, but the clonal DNA amplification is performed by rolling circle amplification unlike the bead or emulsion amplification. The rolling circle amplification generates long DNA chains with repetitive elements of template bordered by adapters which then assemble into nanoballs that are fixed to a slide and sequenced. Both SOLiD and Complete Genomics systems are termed to have a very high accuracy of ~99.9% and generate both single-end and paired-end sequencing (in which the sequence at both ends of each DNA cluster is recorded) (Drmanac et al., 2010; Liu et al., 2012). Although highly accurate, they still are reported to miss true variants (Wall et al., 2014) and false representation of AT-rich regions (Rieber et al., 2013). For example, SOLiD system display substitution errors and GC-rich under-representation (Harismendy et al., 2009). They also generate very short read lengths (~75 bp for SOLiD and 28–100 for Complete Genomics) limiting their wider application and longer run times.

Polony sequencing is a technique to amplify DNA in situ on a thin polyacrylamide film. The amplified DNA are localized in a gel and thus its mobility is restricted to the gel and form the so-called "polonies" for polymerase colonies (Shendure et al., 2005). On a single microscope slide nearly 5 million polonies can be formed. The read length by this technique is up to 13 bases per colony (Zhang et al., 2006) and multiplexing using this technique is also in use that combines polony amplification along with sequence-by-ligation method to sequence up to 14-base tags (Ruegger et al., 2012). The limitation associated with this technique is low throughput and high costs.

Sequencing-by-Synthesis (SBS)

SBS can be classified into cyclic reversible termination (CRT) or as single-nucleotide addition (SNA)

Cyclic reversible termination (CRT)

CRT utilizes terminator molecules similar to Sanger sequencing by blocking the ribose 3'-OH group thus preventing elongation (Seo *et al.*, 2005). To begin amplification, the DNA template need to be primed by a complementary sequence to adapter. This will initiate the binding of DNA polymerase to double stranded DNA (dsDNA). At each cycle, uniquely labelled dNTPs specific to each base are added after which the surface is imaged to identify the type of dNTP incorporated at each cluster (Guo *et al.*, 2008). The blocking group is then removed and a new cycle begins.

One example for this technique is Solexa Genome Analyzer uses a flow cell consisting of an optical transparent slide with 8 lanes of bound oligonucleotide anchors (Voelkerding *et al.*, 2009). Template DNA is sheared into 100 bp lengths and end-paired to generate 5'-phosphorylated blunt ends. The DNA fragments are then passed over complementary oligonucleotides bound to a flowcell and a follow-up solid phase PCR generates clusters of clonal populations from each of the individual flow-cell binding DNA strands. Sequencing is by SBS using fluorescent 'reversible-terminator' dNTPs that allows the sequencing to occur in a synchronous manner (Turcatti *et al.*, 2008). The incorporated nucleotide at each cycle is monitored by a charged couple device (CCD) by exciting fluorophores with laser light, before the removal of the fluorescent moiety and continuation to next step. Earlier Genome Analyzers were only capable of short reads (~35 bases long) but can produce paired-end data. NextSeq and MiniSeq platforms utilize two-colour labelling system and reduce the costs by reducing scanning to two colour channels. However, this results in a higher error rate and underperformance for less diverse samples. MiSeq has a low-throughput but less expensive with faster turnaround and longer read lengths (Balasubramanian, 2011; Quail *et al.*, 2012).

GeneReader (Qiagen) is envisioned for clinical application on cancer gene panels and is well optimized (Darwanto *et al.*, 2017). It's an all-in-one platform from sample preparation to analysis. The NGS platform is coupled with QIAcube for sample preparation. With a long run-time GeneReader is likely to have the same merits and demerits as the MiSeq platform providing a lower cost effective option per gigabase (Gb) sequenced (Mardis, 2017). The standard Genome Analyzer was later taken over by the HiSeq that is capable of a greater read length and depth but needs rigorous optimization and therefore is limited for fewer applications such as whole genome sequencing. Cancer panels (Novogene, USA) for personalized medicine that specifically targets cancer specific utilizing HiSeq for sequencing are currently available. This cancer panel called NovoPM™ is available for both tissues, liquid biopsy, FFPE and circulating DNA and is considered to be cost-effective service for cancer studies.

Single-nucleotide addition (SNA)

SNA relies on a single signal unlike CRT to incorporate dNTPs into an elongating strand. The nucleotides are added to a sequencing reaction to ascertain that only one dNTP is responsible for the signal. This doesn't require blocking of the dNTP as in CRT to prevent elongation. For the homopolymer regions that involves identical dNTPs, a proportional increase in the signal will be observed as the nucleotides get incorporated.

Pyrosequencing is a sequence-by-synthesis method for *de novo* DNA sequencing. The technique is based on the incorporation of nucleotides base by base by converting the production of pyrophosphate into light (Ronaghi *et al.*, 1998). The amount of pyrophosphate is proportional to the light produced (Royo *et al.*, 2007; Royo and Galan, 2009). The read length for pyrosequencing has an upper limit of 400 bases and has a better detection and accuracy compared to the conventional Sanger sequencing. However, the major concern with this technique is determining the number of incorporated nucleotides in homopolymeric regions as the light response is not linear after incorporation of more than 5–6 identical nucleotides. Further, the primers need to be checked for primer-dimer, self-looping and cross-hybridizations (Heather and Chain, 2016). One example utilizing this principle is 454 Pyrosequencer developed by Life Science in 2000. The 454 Pyrosequencer is the first commercial high throughput-next generation sequencing (HT-NGS) platform. This SNA method distributes beads bound to the template into a TiterPlate along with enzyme cocktail (Batra *et al.*, 2014). As a dNTP gets incorporated into a strand, enzymatic cascade occurs liberating a bioluminescence signal. The light is then detected by a CCD camera that records the number of nucleotides incorporated at a particular bead.

The Ion Torrent is the first sequencer without optical sensing (Rothberg *et al.*, 2011). To generate a signal the Ion Torrent detects the H^+ ions released after each dNTP incorporation. The resultant change in pH is recognised by an integrated ion-sensitive field-effect transistor (ISFET) and a complementary metal-oxide-semiconductor (CMOS). The change in the pH is proportional to the number of nucleotides identified. But this limits the accuracy in detection of the length of homopolymers. The 454 and Ion Torrent systems generate greater read lengths compared to other short-read sequencers with an average read length of 700 and 400 bp, respectively (Goodwin *et al.*, 2016). This offers advantage especially for sequencing repetitive DNA regions or complex DNA. However, insertion and deletion errors dominate for homopolymers although they are compared to be on par compared to other NGS platforms in sequencing non-homopolymers. The 454 sequencers could not compete with the upcoming new technologies in terms of yield or costs (Voelkerding *et al.*, 2010).

Ion Torrent platform offers a wide range of chips and instrument to consumer needs for chips ranging from ~50 megabase (Mb) to 15 Gb with a shorter runtime ~2–7 h, making it the faster than other current platforms (Stahl and Lundeberg, 2012). Some of them are currently used for clinical applications, transcriptome profiling and splice sites detection. The Ion Personal Genome Machine (PGM) and the Ion S5 series are some of the machines currently used for dedicated diagnostic applications

(Roy *et al.*, 2016). The Ion Proton and S5 devices cannot perform paired-end sequencing, thus limiting their application for elucidating long-range genomic or transcriptomic structure.

Long-Read Technologies

Genomic DNA harbors long repetitive elements, copy number alterations and structural variations that makes it highly complex. Short-read paired-end technologies are not sufficient to resolve these complex elements and require technologies that can deliver long-reads for resolution of the long structural features. Currently, there are mainly two types of long-read technologies: single-molecule real-time sequencing and synthetic long-reads

Single molecule real-time long reads

The first single molecule sequencing (SMS) was developed by Stephen Quake *et al.*, and later commercialized by Helicos BioSciences (Pushkarev *et al.*, 2009). In this technique, DNA template is attached to a planar surface, and fluorescent reversible terminator dNTPs are washed over one base at a time, imaged and cleaved before the next base is cycled. This is a slow and expensive technique but was the first sequencing technology of non-amplified DNA, thus avoiding errors and biases (Heather and Chain, 2016).

Currently the widely used long-read technology is the single-molecule real-time (SMRT) sequencing approach by Pacific Biosciences (PacBio). PacBio®RSII sequencer uses a flow cell with thousands of picolitre wells – zero-mode waveguides (ZMW). Short-read SBS techniques (Illumina sequencers) bind the DNA and allow polymerase to bind to the template, PacBio anchors the polymerase to the well and allows DNA to travel through the ZMW (Rhoads and Au, 2015; Larkin *et al.*, 2017). SMRT also uses a unique circular template for the polymerase to traverse repeatedly thus allowing the sequencing of DNA multiple times to generate continuous long read (CLR). The polymerase then cleaves the fluorophore bound to the dNTP incorporated. The average length of a CLR is 10–60 kb and depends on the polymerase half-life. The SMRT-sequencing reads are then mapped by tools such as BLASR that allows confident mapping of the reads to their reference sequence.

In 2014, a first consumer prototype of a nanopore sequencer to generate long-reads was released – the MinION, Oxford Nanopore Technologies (ONT). ONT directly sequences a native ssDNA by measuring the changes in the current as the bases are stringed through the nanopore by a molecular motor protein. ONT MinION uses a hairpin library structure, the DNA template and its complement are bound by a hairpin adapter similar to the PacBio circular DNA template (Oikonomopoulos *et al.*, 2016). The raw reads are then split into two "1D" reads ("template" and "complement") after removing the adapter (Laver *et al.*, 2015). Due to similar data features with PacBio, many researchers have utilized or are testing ONT in applications where PacBio has been applied. Because of the unique nature of ONT technique, as there are 1000 distinct signals, it has a large error rate ($\sim$30%) particularly for indel errors. Homopolymer sequencing also remains a challenge for ONT MinION and PacBio. Further the cost per base is higher than Illumina platforms and the per-base error rates are high (5%–15%) (Cornelis *et al.*, 2017). Recently, improvements and algorithms to improve the accuracy are in progress.

Synthetic long-reads

Synthetic approaches generate long-reads by library preparation that barcodes associate fragments to allow assembly computationally of a larger fragment. Large DNA fragments are partitioned into microtiter wells or into an emulsion with few molecules in each partition. The template fragments within individual partition are sheared and barcoded. This allows sequencing on existing short-read instruments, after which the data are split by barcoding and reassembled. By segregating fragments, complicated regions can be isolated allowing for them to be assembled locally. This reduce the breaks (gaps) in the obtained sequence data (Schatz *et al.*, 2010; English *et al.*, 2015). Two popular systems using this technique are the Illumina synthetic long-read sequencing platform and 10X Genomics emulsion-based system.

The Illumina Truseq Long-Read DNA partitions DNA into a microtiter plate and do not require special instrumentation whereas the 10X Genomics emulsion-based system use emulsion to partition DNA and use a microfluidic instrument for pre-sequencing reactions (Mccoy *et al.*, 2014). The DNA required for 10X Genomics is as little as 1 ng (nanogram) and can arbitrarily partition large DNA fragments ($\sim$100 kb) into micelles known as 'GEMs'. Each GEM would contain approximately 0.3x genome copies and a unique barcode. Within each GEM, smaller fragments of DNA are amplified. The reads are aligned and grouped together to form a series of anchored fragments across the original fragment. Grouped reads from each long fragment can be restacked, combining their individual coverage into an overall map. As the Illumina long-read approach relies on the existing instrument, the throughput and error profile are similar to those of the current short-read sequencers (Goodwin *et al.*, 2016). Depending on the method of DNA partition, higher coverage is required, thus is associated also with high costs using the Illumina long-read approach. The 10X Genomics uses less DNA but the partitioning is not very effective and can lead to surplus DNA within a droplet complicating deconvolution. This leads to ambiguity and makes analysis difficult.

Analysis of the SNP Data Generated by the Sequencers

The last few years have seen incredible progress in the development of algorithms and software to make sense of the short reads onto a reference sequence and to identify the differences between the individual and the reference. The complexity of genome makes it impossible to generate genetic maps that are based on the segregation of genetic variations through pedigrees that provided information about the order of sequences at specific loci and at the chromosomes scale. Most popular SNP callers are focused primarily on the high recovery of SNPs while keeping low false discovery rates.

De novo assembly to the reference genome

The first step in data analysis is alignment of the short sequences obtained from the sequencing methods to the existing reference genome. Alignment starts with indexing, following alignment. The common aligners are Bowtie2 and SOAP3-dp that index reference genome rather than sequenced reads, which is less time consuming as indexing reference needs to be performed only once, while indexing sequence has to performed for each sample individually (Luo *et al.*, 2013). Some of the indexing methods are suffix/prefix trie, enhanced suffix array, FM-*index* and hash table. The *suffix/prefix trie* is defined as a data structure representing the set of suffixes of a given string of characters, enabling fast matching of the string (a sequence read) to the reference genome. However for very large data, this method is not efficient and replaced by the enhanced suffix array approach that enables storing of large genome data. FM-*index* is considered to be better of the first three indexing methods and some popular software tools utilizing this algorithm are Bowtie, SOAP2 and SOAP3 (Chacon *et al.*, 2013). The hash table method is based on the seed-and-extend algorithm. Some of the algorithms in use using the hash table method are BFAST, MAQ, RMAP and SHRiMP (Wu, 2016).

Regardless of the indexing method, the alignment can be performed by many algorithms and the resulting alignment can be gapped or ungapped (Yorukoglu *et al.*, 2016). Alignment gaps are a result of genomic rearrangements, such as insertions/deletions. Allowing gaps in alignment is a preferred option by most alignment software tools. The first alignment tool, SHRiMP was able to perform alignment for single-end sequence and currently most of the algorithms support a paired-end alignment which considers both forward and reverse orders as a pair resulting in a longer piece of sequence and improving quality of alignment.

Post-alignment processing

The most commonly applied post-alignment methods include output file format converting, removing PCR artefacts or creating reports from the alignment process (Mielczarek and Szyda, 2016). These can be carried out using SAMtools package. SAMtools allows reducing the data set size and downstream compatibility with variant callers, such as Unified Genotyper (Genome Analysis Toolkit package) and other software tools (Cornish and Guda, 2015). A simple summary is generated to describe the alignment process (Bowtie2, SOAP2, and MOSAIK) and the description includes the total number of aligned reads, number of properly aligned reads, number of reads aligned only once. Summary statistics helps to assess the overall quality and accuracy of alignment. Removing PCR duplicates can be done by SAMtools rmdup tool (Ebbert *et al.*, 2016).

Pre-variant calling processing

To obtain reliable polymorphic variant calling, additional steps for SNP calling are recommended before the actual variant detection. Some alignment artefacts occur during alignment that may result in mismatching of different bases. These mismatches are most likely to be considered as SNPs (Nielsen *et al.*, 2011). To avoid this, local realignment tools are designed that allows realignment of reads at the site of the artefact to minimize the number of mismatching bases. A large amount of genomic DNA require realignment due to the presence of InDels with respect to the reference genome (Olson *et al.*, 2015). A sequencer may miscalculate the base quality expressed as the Phred score. Genome-analysis-toolkit (GATK) package tools recalibrate base quality scores to more accurate estimates to reduce the mismatches with the reference genome (Mckenna *et al.*, 2010; Maretty *et al.*, 2017). SAMtools provide a score for each base called a base alignment quality (BAQ) score, which is calculated as Phred-scaled probability for a base being misaligned. If a base is sub-optimally aligned to a different reference base, the BAQ score is low. Some programs do not allow pre-SNP calling step, two examples include SOAPsnp and Atlas-SNP2 (Yu and Sun, 2013).

SNP calling

Conventionally SNPs were identified by techniques such as microarrays. Today microarrays have tremendously progressed to process about hundreds of thousands of SNPs. Some of the platforms such as Affymetrix, Illumina based on microarray for SNP detection utilize software such as Dynamic Model software (100 K SNPs) that do not require any normalization step (Di *et al.*, 2005), Bayesian Robust Linear Model with Mahalanobis Distance Classifier algorithm for 500 K SNP arrays (Hong *et al.*, 2008) and GenCall algorithm (Teo *et al.*, 2007; Steemers and Gunderson, 2007). Recent NGS techniques have provided new avenues to identify a higher number of variants including the rare SNPs that are important for complex disease phenotypes. However, for a reliable detection of these variants require a high depth of coverage so as to differentiate them from sequencing errors. Multiple algorithms and software tools are currently available for SNP calling. SNP calling may be defined as the process of identifying regions differing from a reference sequence, while genotype calling refers to the determination of genotypes (Nielsen *et al.*, 2011). SNP and genotype callers are based on either heuristic or probabilistic methods.

Heuristic methods call variants are less commonly used than probabilistic methods and are based on multiple information sources associated with the data structure and quality. Example of software using heuristic approach is VarScan2 which is also a statistical test based on the number of reads for each allele (Durtschi *et al.*, 2013). A heuristic approach determines genotype based on thresholds for base quality (minimum 20), coverage (minimum 33), and allele frequency (minimum 0.08). After determining genotype, Fisher's exact test of read counts for each allele is analysed in comparison to the expected distribution based on the sequencing error alone.

Probabilistic method measures statistical uncertainty for called genotypes allowing to monitor the accuracy of genotype calling. Additionally, information regarding allele frequencies, linkage disequilibrium can be included in the analysis. Genotype calling is based on likelihood calculations and adopts Bayes' theorem (Maruki and Lynch, 2014). After realignment and quality score recalibration, the next step is to calculate likelihood for each possible genotype at each base (a homozygote for the reference allele, a homozygote for the minor allele or a heterozygote). In Bayesian framework, the computed likelihood is combined with a previous genotype probability to derive a posterior probability of a genotype (Nielsen *et al.*, 2012; Fumagalli *et al.*, 2013). SAMtools is an example of software including probabilistic approach. SAMtools mpileup collects data stored in input BAM (binary version of the Sequence Alignment Map format) files and computes likelihood of data for each possible genotype. Recently, a study compared thirteen pipelines and popular read aligners against twelve sequence data sets from a single genome. For the SNP calls from Illumina data sets, the BWA-MEM and SAMtools exhibited best performance and Freebayes aligner showed high quality for SNP calls. For SNPs from Ion Proton data set, SAMtools performed best including TVC (Hwang *et al.*, 2015). Thus, researchers must exhibit extreme care when choosing the appropriate algorithms for variant detection and analysis after sequencing.

Conclusion and Prospects

It is difficult to directly compare and suggest the best sequencing system between different platforms. This is because the technique to choose is to be weighed between the costs, coverage and accuracy. Different platforms may require different levels of accuracy to achieve the same level of accuracy and comparisons have to be made either by considering coverage or higher costs to achieve better accuracy. With the increasing research to develop robust sequencing technologies, it is certainly possible in near term that a relatively inexpensive, highly accurate with better coverage sequencer will be achievable that can be used in clinics.

NGS techniques are now becoming a routine part of biological research. These techniques is boosting research into areas which once was thought to be unachievable. Some sequencing-based technologies target single cells that will address many new and longstanding questions. For example, single-cell genomics will help to discover cell lineage relationships and single-cell transcriptomics will succeed in discovering marker-based cell types. In a decade, these technologies may enable high-throughput, multi-dimensional analyses of single cells that will produce comprehensive information of the cell lineage of higher organisms. Such studies will have profound implications to allow revolutionary science including precision medicine based on personalized genome sequencing.

Declaration of Interest

J. Batra is a National Health and Medical Research Council Career Development Fellow. S. Srinivasan is supported by an Advance QLD ECR Research Fellowship.

See also: Detecting and Annotating Rare Variants. Exome Sequencing Data Analysis. Functional Enrichment Analysis. Integrative Analysis of Multi-Omics Data. Natural Language Processing Approaches in Bioinformatics. Next Generation Sequencing Data Analysis. Sequence Analysis. Whole Genome Sequencing Analysis

References

Awasthi, S.P., Asakura, M., Neogi, S.B., *et al.*, 2014. Development of a PCR-restriction fragment length polymorphism assay for detection and subtyping of cholix toxin variant genes of Vibrio cholerae. J. Med. Microbiol. 63, 667–673.

Balasubramanian, S., 2011. Sequencing nucleic acids: From chemistry to medicine. Chem. Commun. (Camb.) 47, 7281–7286.

Balschun, K., Wenke, A.K., Rocken, C., Haag, J., 2011. Detection of KRAS and BRAF mutations in advanced colorectal cancer by allele-specific single-base primer extension. Expert Rev. Mol. Diagn. 11, 799–802.

Batra, J., Nagle, C.M., O'mara, T., *et al.*, 2011. A Kallikrein 15 (KLK15) single nucleotide polymorphism located close to a novel exon shows evidence of association with poor ovarian cancer survival. BMC Cancer 11, 119.

Batra, J., Srinivasan, S., Clements, J.A., 2014. Single nucleotide polymorphisms (SNPs). In: Jothy, G.M.Y.A.S. (Ed.), Molecular Testing in Cancer, 2014 ed. New York: Springer Science & Business.

Beck, I.A., Deng, W., Payant, R., *et al.*, 2014. Validation of an oligonucleotide ligation assay for quantification of human immunodeficiency virus type 1 drug-resistant mutants by use of massively parallel sequencing. J. Clin. Microbiol. 52, 2320–2327.

Bumgarner, R., 2013. Overview of DNA microarrays: Types, applications, and their future. Curr. Protoc. Mol. Biol. (Chapter 22, Unit 22 1).

Chacon, A., Moure, J.C., Espinosa, A., Hernandez, P., 2013. n-step FM-Index for faster pattern matching. In: Proceeding of 2013 International Conference on Computational Science, 18, pp. 70–79.

Choi, W., Jung, G.Y., 2017. Highly multiplex and sensitive SNP genotyping method using a three-color fluorescence-labeled ligase detection reaction coupled with conformation-sensitive CE. Electrophoresis 38, 513–520.

Chuang, L.Y., Yang, C.H., Tsui, K.H., *et al.*, 2008. Restriction enzyme mining for SNPs in genomes. Anticancer Res. 28, 2001–2007.

Clendenen, T.V., Rendleman, J., Ge, W., *et al.*, 2015. Genotyping of single nucleotide polymorphisms in DNA isolated from serum using sequenom MassARRAY technology. PLOS ONE 10, e0135943.

Cornelis, S., Gansemans, Y., Deleye, L., Deforce, D., Van Nieuwerburgh, F., 2017. Forensic SNP Genotyping using Nanopore MinION Sequencing. Sci. Rep. 7, 41759.

Cornish, A., Guda, C., 2015. A comparison of variant calling pipelines using genome in a bottle as a reference. Biomed. Res. Int.

Cutler, D.J., Zwick, M.E., Carrasquillo, M.M., et al., 2001. High-throughput variation detection and genotyping using microarrays. Genome Res. 11, 1913–1925.

Darwanto, A., Hein, A.M., Strauss, S., et al., 2017. Use of the QIAGEN GeneReader NGS system for detection of KRAS mutations, validated by the QIAGEN Therascreen PCR kit and alternative NGS platform. BMC Cancer 17.

Dhas, D.B., Ashmi, A.H., Bhat, B.V., Parija, S.C., Banupriya, N., 2015. Modified low cost SNP genotyping technique using cycle threshold (Ct) & melting temperature (Tm) values in allele specific real-time PCR. Indian J. Med. Res. 142, 555–562.

Di, X., Matsuzaki, H., Webster, T.A., et al., 2005. Dynamic model based algorithms for screening and genotyping over 100 K SNPs on oligonucleotide microarrays. Bioinformatics 21, 1958–1963.

Ding, M., Duan, X., Feng, X., Wang, P., Wang, W., 2017. Application of CRS-PCR-RFLP to identify CYP1A1 gene polymorphism. J. Clin. Lab. Anal.

Dokuta, S., Utaipat, U., Praparattanapan, J., et al., 2013. Improvement of the oligonucleotide ligation assay for detection of the M184V drug-resistant mutation in patients infected with human immunodeficiency virus type 1 subtype CRF01_AE. J. Virol. Methods 190, 20–28.

Drmanac, R., Sparks, A.B., Callow, M.J., et al., 2010. Human genome sequencing using unchained base reads on self-assembling DNA nanoarrays. Science 327, 78–81.

Durtschi, J., Margraf, R.L., Coonrod, E.M., Mallempati, K.C., Voelkerding, K.V., 2013. VarBin, a novel method for classifying true and false positive variants in NGS data. BMC Bioinform. 14.

Ebbert, M.T., Wadsworth, M.E., Staley, L.A., et al., I., 2016. Evaluating the necessity of PCR duplicate removal from next-generation sequencing data and a comparison of approaches. BMC Bioinform. 17, 239.

English, A.C., Salerno, W.J., Hampton, O.A., et al., 2015. Assessing structural variation in a personal genome-towards a human reference diploid genome. Bmc Genom. 16.

Fumagalli, M., Vieira, F.G., Korneliussen, T.S., et al., 2013. Quantifying population genetic differentiation from next-generation sequencing data. Genetics 195, 979.

Gaudet, M., Fara, A.G., Beritognolo, I., Sabatti, M., 2009. Allele-specific PCR in SNP genotyping. Methods Mol. Biol. 578, 415–424.

Germer, S., Higuchi, R., 2003. Homogeneous allele-specific PCR in SNP genotyping. Methods Mol. Biol. 212, 197–214.

Goodwin, S., Mcpherson, J.D., Mccombie, W.R., 2016. Coming of age: Ten years of next-generation sequencing technologies. Nat. Rev. Genet. 17, 333–351.

Guo, J., Xu, N., Li, Z., et al., 2008. Four-color DNA sequencing with 3′-O-modified nucleotide reversible terminators and chemically cleavable fluorescent dideoxynucleotides. Proc. Natl. Acad. Sci. USA 105, 9145–9150.

Gupta, V., Arora, R., Gochhait, S., Bairwa, N.K., Bamezai, R.N., 2014. Gel-based nonradioactive single-strand conformational polymorphism and mutation detection: Limitations and solutions. Methods Mol. Biol. 1105, 365–380.

Harismendy, O., Ng, P.C., Strausberg, R.L., et al., 2009. Evaluation of next generation sequencing platforms for population targeted sequencing studies. Genome Biol 10, R32.

Hayashi, K., Ishigami, M., Ishizu, Y., et al., 2017. A comparison of direct sequencing and Invader assay for Y93H mutation and response to interferon-free therapy in hepatitis C virus genotype 1b. J. Gastroenterol. Hepatol.

Heather, J.M., Chain, B., 2016. The sequence of sequencers: The history of sequencing DNA. Genomics 107, 1–8.

Hjelmso, M.H., Hansen, L.H., Baelum, J., et al., 2014. High-resolution melt analysis for rapid comparison of bacterial community compositions. Appl. Environ. Microbiol. 80, 3568–3575.

Hong, H., Su, Z., Ge, W., et al., 2008. Assessing batch effects of genotype calling algorithm BRLMM for the Affymetrix GeneChip Human Mapping 500 K array set using 270 HapMap samples. BMC Bioinform. 9, S17.

Hwang, S., Kim, E., Lee, I., Marcotte, E.M., 2015. Systematic comparison of variant calling pipelines using gold standard personal exome variants. Sci. Rep. 5, 17875.

Kisaki, O., Kato, S., Shinohara, K., et al., 2010. High-throughput single-base mismatch detection for genotyping of UDP-glucuronosyltransferase (UGT1A1) with probe capture assay coupled with modified allele-specific primer extension reaction (MASPER). J. Clin. Lab. Anal. 24, 85–91.

Landegren, U., Kaiser, R., Sanders, J., Hood, L., 1988. A ligase-mediated gene detection technique. Science 241, 1077–1080.

Larkin, J., Henley, R.Y., Jadhav, V., Korlach, J., Wanunu, M., 2017. Length-independent DNA packing into nanopore zero-mode waveguides for low-input DNA sequencing. Nat. Nanotechnol.

Laver, T., Harrison, J., O'neill, P.A., et al., 2015. Assessing the performance of the oxford nanopore technologies minion. Biomol. Detect. Quantif. 3, 1–8.

Liu, L., Li, Y., Li, S., et al., 2012. Comparison of next-generation sequencing systems. J. Biomed. Biotechnol. 2012, 251364.

Lose, F., Batra, J., O'mara, T., et al., 2013. Common variation in Kallikrein genes KLK5, KLK6, KLK12, and KLK13 and risk of prostate cancer and tumor aggressiveness. Urol. Oncol. 31, 635–643.

Lose, F., Lawrence, M.G., Srinivasan, S., et al., B., 2012. The kallikrein 14 gene is down-regulated by androgen receptor signalling and harbours genetic variation that is associated with prostate tumour aggressiveness. Biol. Chem. 393, 403–412.

Luo, R., Wong, T., Zhu, J., et al., 2013. SOAP3-dp: Fast, accurate and sensitive GPU-based short read aligner. PLOS ONE 8, e65632.

Mardis, E.R., 2017. DNA sequencing technologies: 2006–2016. Nat. Protoc. 12, 213–218.

Maretty, L., Jensen, J.M., Petersen, B., et al., 2017. Sequencing and de novo assembly of 150 genomes from Denmark as a population reference. Nature 548, 87–91.

Maruki, T., Lynch, M., 2014. Genome-wide estimation of linkage disequilibrium from population-level high-throughput sequencing data. Genetics 197, 1303. U421.

Mccoy, R.C., Taylor, R.W., Blauwkamp, T.A., et al., 2014. Illumina TruSeq synthetic long-reads empower de novo assembly and resolve complex, highly-repetitive transposable elements. PLOS ONE 9, e106689.

Mckenna, A., Hanna, M., Banks, E., et al., 2010. The genome analysis toolkit: A mapreduce framework for analyzing next-generation DNA sequencing data. Genome Res. 20, 1297–1303.

Mielczarek, M., Szyda, J., 2016. Review of alignment and SNP calling algorithms for next-generation sequencing data. J. Appl. Genet. 57, 71–79.

Miller, J.K., Buchner, N., Timms, L., et al., 2014. Use of Sequenom sample ID Plus(R) SNP genotyping in identification of FFPE tumor samples. PLOS ONE 9, e88163.

Montgomery, J., Wittwer, C.T., Palais, R., Zhou, L., 2007. Simultaneous mutation scanning and genotyping by high-resolution DNA melting analysis. Nat. Protoc. 2, 59–66.

Mutsvangwa, J., Beck, I.A., Gwanzura, L., et al., 2014. Optimization of the oligonucleotide ligation assay for the detection of nevirapine resistance mutations in Zimbabwean Human Immunodeficiency Virus type-1 subtype C. J. Virol. Methods 210, 36–39.

Newton, C.R., Graham, A., Heptinstall, L.E., et al., 1989. Analysis of any point mutation in DNA. The amplification refractory mutation system (ARMS). Nucleic Acids Res. 17, 2503–2516.

Nielsen, R., Korneliussen, T., Albrechtsen, A., Li, Y.R., Wang, J., 2012. SNP calling, genotype calling, and sample allele frequency estimation from new-generation sequencing data. PLOS ONE 7.

Nielsen, R., Paul, J.S., Albrechtsen, A., Song, Y.S., 2011. Genotype and SNP calling from next-generation sequencing data. Nat. Rev. Genet. 12, 443–451.

Oikonomopoulos, S., Wang, Y.C., Djambazian, H., Badescu, D., Ragoussis, J., 2016. Benchmarking of the Oxford Nanopore MinION sequencing for quantitative and qualitative assessment of cDNA populations. Sci. Rep. 6, 31602.

Olson, N.D., Lund, S.P., Colman, R.E., et al., 2015. Best practices for evaluating single nucleotide variant calling methods for microbial genomics. Front. Genet. 6, 235.

Palais, R.A., Liew, M.A., Wittwer, C.T., 2005. Quantitative heteroduplex analysis for single nucleotide polymorphism genotyping. Anal. Biochem. 346, 167–175.

Paniego, N., Fusari, C., Lia, V., Puebla, A., 2015. SNP genotyping by heteroduplex analysis. Methods Mol. Biol. 1245, 141–150.

Pu, D., Chen, J., Qian, X., Xiao, P., 2015. Probe optimization for sequencing by ligation. J. Biochem. 157, 357–364.

Pushkarev, D., Neff, N.F., Quake, S.R., 2009. Single-molecule sequencing of an individual human genome. Nat. Biotechnol. 27, 847. U101.

Quail, M.A., Smith, M., Coupland, P., et al., 2012. A tale of three next generation sequencing platforms: Comparison of Ion Torrent, Pacific Biosciences and Illumina MiSeq sequencers. BMC Genom. 13, 341.

Rhoads, A., Au, K.F., 2015. PacBio sequencing and its applications. Genom. Proteom. Bioinform. 13, 278–289.

Rieber, N., Zapatka, M., Lasitschka, B., *et al.*, 2013. Coverage bias and sensitivity of variant calling for four whole-genome sequencing technologies. PLOS One 8, e66621.

Ronaghi, M., Uhlen, M., Nyren, P., 1998. A sequencing method based on real-time pyrophosphate. Science 281, 363.

Rothberg, J.M., Hinz, W., Rearick, T.M., *et al.*, 2011. An integrated semiconductor device enabling non-optical genome sequencing. Nature 475, 348–352.

Roy, S., Laframboise, W.A., Nikiforov, Y.E., *et al.*, 2016. Next-generation sequencing informatics: Challenges and strategies for implementation in a clinical environment. Arch. Pathol. Lab. Med. 140, 958–975.

Royo, J.L., Galan, J.J., 2009. Pyrosequencing for SNP genotyping. Methods Mol. Biol. 578, 123–133.

Royo, J.L., Hidalgo, M., Ruiz, A., 2007. Pyrosequencing protocol using a universal biotinylated primer for mutation detection and SNP genotyping. Nat. Protoc. 2, 1734–1739.

Ruegger, P.M., Bent, E., Li, W., *et al.*, 2012. Improving oligonucleotide fingerprinting of rRNA genes by implementation of polony microarray technology. J. Microbiol. Methods 90, 235–240.

Schatz, M.C., Delcher, A.L., Salzberg, S.L., 2010. Assembly of large genomes using second-generation sequencing. Genome Res. 20, 1165–1173.

Seo, T.S., Bai, X.P., Kim, D.H., *et al.*, 2005. Four-color DNA sequencing by synthesis on a chip using photocleavable fluorescent nucleotides. Proc. Natl. Acad. Sci. USA 102, 5926–5931.

Shendure, J., Porreca, G.J., Reppas, N.B., *et al.*, 2005. Accurate multiplex polony sequencing of an evolved bacterial genome. Science 309, 1728–1732.

Srinivasan, S., Batra, J., 2014. Four generations of sequencing – Is it ready for the clinic yet? J. Next Gener. Seq. Appl.

Srinivasan, S., Clements, J.A., Batra, J., 2016. Single nucleotide polymorphisms in clinics: Fantasy or reality for cancer? Crit. Rev. Clin. Lab. Sci. 53, 29–39.

Stahl, P.L., Lundeberg, J., 2012. Toward the single-hour high-quality genome. Annu. Rev. Biochem. 81, 359–378.

Steemers, F.J., Gunderson, K.L., 2007. Whole genome genotyping technologies on the BeadArray platform. Biotechnol. J. 2, 41–49.

Teo, Y.Y., Inouye, M., Small, K.S., *et al.*, 2007. A genotype calling algorithm for the Illumina BeadArray platform. Bioinformatics 23, 2741–2746.

Tobler, A.R., Short, S., Andersen, M.R., *et al.*, 2005. The SNPlex genotyping system: A flexible and scalable platform for SNP genotyping. J. Biomol. Tech. 16, 398–406.

Tomkinson, A.E., Vijayakumar, S., Pascal, J.M., Ellenberger, T., 2006. DNA ligases: Structure, reaction mechanism, and function. Chem. Rev. 106, 687–699.

Turcatti, G., Romieu, A., Fedurco, M., Tairi, A.P., 2008. A new class of cleavable fluorescent nucleotides: Synthesis and optimization as reversible terminators for DNA sequencing by synthesis. Nucleic Acids Res. 36, e25.

Valouev, A., Ichikawa, J., Tonthat, T., *et al.*, 2008. A high-resolution, nucleosome position map of C. elegans reveals a lack of universal sequence-dictated positioning. Genome Res. 18, 1051–1063.

Velasco, E., Infante, M., Duran, M., *et al.*, 2007. Heteroduplex analysis by capillary array electrophoresis for rapid mutation detection in large multiexon genes. Nat. Protoc. 2, 237–246.

Venables, S.J., Mehta, B., Daniel, R., *et al.*, 2014. Assessment of high resolution melting analysis as a potential SNP genotyping technique in forensic casework. Electrophoresis 35, 3036–3043.

Voelkerding, K.V., Dames, S., Durtschi, J.D., 2010. Next generation sequencing for clinical diagnostics-principles and application to targeted resequencing for hypertrophic cardiomyopathy: A paper from the 2009 William Beaumont Hospital Symposium on Molecular Pathology. J. Mol. Diagn. 12, 539–551.

Voelkerding, K.V., Dames, S.A., Durtschi, J.D., 2009. Next-generation sequencing: From basic research to diagnostics. Clin. Chem. 55, 641–658.

Wall, J.D., Tang, L.F., Zerbe, B., *et al.*, 2014. Estimating genotype error rates from high-coverage next-generation sequence data. Genome Res. 24, 1734–1739.

Wittwer, C.T., Reed, G.H., Gundry, C.N., Vandersteen, J.G., Pryor, R.J., 2003. High-resolution genotyping by amplicon melting analysis using LCGreen. Clin. Chem. 49, 853–860.

Wu, T.D., 2016. Bitpacking techniques for indexing genomes: I. Hash tables. Algorithms Mol. Biol. 11.

Yorukoglu, D., Yu, Y.W., Peng, J., Berger, B., 2016. Compressive mapping for next-generation sequencing. Nat. Biotechnol. 34, 374–376.

Yu, X.Q., Sun, S.Y., 2013. Comparing a few SNP calling algorithms using low-coverage sequencing data. BMC Bioinform. 14.

Zhang, K., Zhu, J., Shendure, J., *et al.*, 2006. Long-range polony haplotyping of individual human chromosome molecules. Nat. Genet. 38, 382–387.

Genome-Wide Haplotype Association Study

Yongshuai Jiang and Jing Xu, Harbin Medical University, Harbin, China

Introduction

The single nucleotide polymorphism (SNP) is a concept in population genetics. It is a polymorphism of a single nucleotide at a specific chromosome position. A SNP locus is a specific chromosome location where the DNA base has two statuses (in most cases) in a population. With the development of high throughput SNP array technology (such as Affymetrix SNP array 6.0) (Nishida *et al.*, 2008) and whole-genome sequencing technology (such as second generation sequencing technology) (Kerstens *et al.*, 2009), the identification of millions (or tens of millions) of SNPs has facilitated the population genetics and medical genetics studies. With this background, the genome-wide association study (GWAS) has been developed and achieved great success (Welter *et al.*, 2014). Thousands of risk loci were successfully identified for complex diseases or phenotypes, such as breast cancer (Garcia-Closas *et al.*, 2013), type 2 diabetes (Cho *et al.*, 2011), and bone mineral density (Rivadeneira *et al.*, 2009). The GWAS focus on the association between single SNP locus and disease/phenotype. However, the single locus does not explain all the genetic risks. Therefore, the haplotype analysis is needed to identify the association between combination types of SNP alleles (multi-loci) and disease/phenotype, where a SNP allele is defined as the base status of one member of homologous chromosomes at a specific chromosome location. There are two alleles for a SNP locus in a population.

In the genome, a group of physically proximate SNPs often nonrandomly associate with each other to form a linkage disequilibrium (LD) block. For two SNP loci, the nonrandom association between SNP alleles at the two SNP loci is called LD. The human LD map for different human populations has been discussed in detail by the International HapMap Project (Altshuler *et al.*, 2010; Frazer *et al.*, 2007) and the 1000 Genomes Project (Abecasis *et al.*, 2010). The LD block may be the smallest heredity unit and is also known as a haplotype block, which is made up of a group of physically proximate SNPs. The SNPs in the LD block are in high LD with each other. A haplotype is defined as a collection of specific SNP alleles on a single chromosome. For k SNPs in a genomic region, if these SNPs are LE of each other, there will be 2^k haplotypes in the population. If the k SNPs are LD of each other, the types of haplotype will be less than 2^k. The genotype at a specific locus is defined as the combination of SNP alleles located on homologous chromosomes. We assume that there are two alleles at the locus: A and a. For an individual, there are three possible genotypes at the locus: AA (homozygote), Aa (heterozygote), and aa (homozygote). The relationships between SNP, allele, LD block, haplotype, and genotype can be found in **Fig. 1**. For k SNPs in a LD block region, the haplotypes will be less than 2^k. Currently, many genome-wide haplotype association studies have been successfully carried out for identifying the disease/phenotype related genes. For example, by using the genome-wide haplotype association studies strategy, Tregouet *et al.* identified the SLC22A3-LPAL2-LPA gene cluster (chromosome 6q26–q27) as a risk locus for coronary artery disease (Tregouet *et al.*, 2009), Lv *et al.* found that a haplotype TT (rs7090018 and rs2912759) at the gene FGFR2 locus had significant association with acute myeloid leukemia, and Sun *et al.* (2016) identified four oral squamous cell carcinoma related genes,that is, SERPINB9, SERPINE2, GAK, and HSP90B1. The genome-wide haplotype association study is an effective strategy for identifying susceptibility genes of complex diseases/phenotypes.

In general, there are six steps in genome-wide haplotype association study: Data preparation, quality control, LD block identification, haplotype frequency estimation, association test, and multiple testing corrections. Next, we will introduce the six parts in detail.

The Framework of Genome-Wide Haplotype Association Study

The framework of genome-wide haplotype association study includes the following steps (**Fig. 2**):

Data preparation

Phenotype data: The genome-wide haplotype association study supports both binomial phenotype (case-control) and continuous phenotype (quantitative).

Genotype data: The raw SNP genotypes can be obtained from the SNP array (such as Affymetrix SNP array 6.0) or whole-genome sequencing technology (such as second generation and third generation sequencing technology). SNP array can produce millions of SNPs, and sequencing can produce tens of millions of SNPs.

In general, the phenotype and genotype data can be shown as matrix in **Fig. 3**. We suppose that there are m samples and n SNPs. Then the genotype data consists of n rows (each row is a SNP) and $k+m$ columns (the first k columns are the basic information of SNPs, such as chr#, position and allele, and the last m columns are the genotypes of SNPs). The phenotype data consists of m rows (each row is a sample) and one column (phenotype).

Quality Control (QC)

In general, there were three commonly used criteria for filtering the raw SNP genotype data: (1) the percentage of individuals successfully genotyped $>75\%$, (2) Hardy – Weinberg equilibrium ($P > 0.001$), and (3) minor allele frequency (MAF, being the

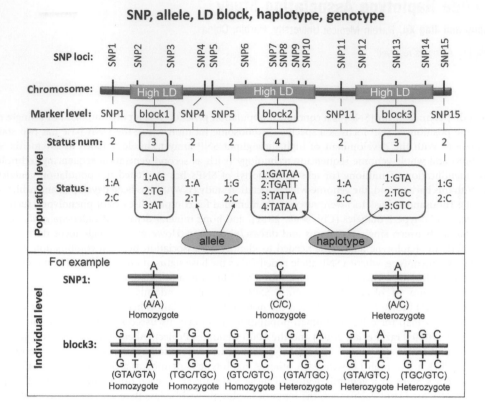

Fig. 1   The relationships between Single Nucleotide Polymorphism, allele, Linkage Disequilibrium block, haplotype, and genotype.

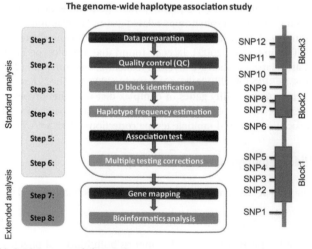

Fig. 2   The framework of genome-wide haplotype association study.

smaller of the two allele frequencies) >1%. These QC criteria ensure that the researchers can use high quality, stable, common SNPs (with the MAF > 0.01) to carry out the genome-wide haplotype association study.

Linkage disequilibrium block identification

The nonrandom association of alleles at different SNP loci is usually called LD (Slatkin, 2008). For two SNPs in LD, the frequency of association of their different alleles is higher or lower than random. A LD block (or haplotype block) is made up of a group of physically proximate SNPs that are highly LD to each other. In other words, the LDs between SNPs are higher within blocks and lower between blocks (Wang *et al.*, 2002).

The identification of the LD block is an important step in a genome-wide haplotype association study. There are many methods to identify LD blocks, such as Gabriel's confidence intervals method (Gabriel *et al.*, 2002), four-gamete test (FGT) (Wang *et al.*,

Genotype data

SNP	Chr#	position	Allele	Sample 1	Sample 2	Sample 3	...	Sample m
SNP 1	1	384531	A/T	AA	AA	AT	...	TT
SNP 2	1	396473	A/G	AG	AA	GG	...	AG
SNP 3	1	403251	C/G	CG	CC	CG	...	GG
...	...	...	...	...	...	...	...	...
SNP n-1	22	...	A/T	AT	TT	AA	...	TT
SNP n	22	...	A/C	AA	CC	AA	...	AC

Binomial phenotype (case-control)

sample	phenotype
Sample 1	Case
Sample 2	Case
Sample 3	Control
...	...
Sample m	Control

Continuous phenotype (quantitative)

sample	phenotype
Sample 1	1.78
Sample 2	1.92
Sample 3	1.69
...	...
Sample m	1.76

Fig. 3 The format of phenotype and genotype data.

2002), hidden Markov model (Daly *et al.*, 2001), and the dynamic programming algorithm (Zhang *et al.*, 2002). Although these algorithms can effectively identify haplotype blocks, they are still limited when millions or tens of millions of SNPs are encountered. This is because some blocks are often interrupted by limited computer memory or fixed size windows. To scan the whole-genome smoothly, Xu *et al.* (2016) developed an elastic sliding window method to avoid breaking the real block structure. Firstly, a fixed size sliding window was used to identify the LD blocks in the window. If the last locus in the window is not located in a block, the window was slid to the next locus. Otherwise, if the last locus in the window is located in an identified block, the block is likely to be broken by the border of the window. Then the window size was increased to twice the original fixed window size. The window size can be gradually increased until the last SNP is not in a block. By using this strategy, we can scan the entire genome and identify LD block using very little computer memory. Researchers can identify genome-wide LD blocks by using haplotype analysis software HAPLOTYPE 1.0 (see "Relevant Websites section").

Haplotype Frequency Estimation

At present, neither SNP chip technology nor the second generation sequencing technology can directly detect haplotypes. This is because the gametic phase is ambiguous when individual genotypes are both heterozygous at two SNP loci. Therefore, some important algorithms, such as expectation-maximization algorithms (EM) (Barrett *et al.*, 2005), Bayesian methods (Scheet and Stephens, 2006), and Markov models (Delaneau *et al.*, 2013), have been developed to phase the haplotype and estimate the haplotype frequency. The phased haplotype can be obtained from the software SHAPEIT (Delaneau *et al.*, 2013) and fastPHASE (Scheet and Stephens, 2006), and the frequency of haplotype can be estimated from the software Haploview (Barrett *et al.*, 2005) and HAPLOTYPE 1.0.

Association Test

For the case-control study, the Pearson's chi-square test can be used to identify the association between haplotype and phenotype. For a haplotype, we can estimate the haplotype frequency for case and control samples using methods mentioned above.

Then we can calculate the count of the haplotype in the case and control, and construct a fourfold table. The chi-square statistic measures for haplotype (this haplotype versus other haplotypes) and affection status (case versus control) can be found as following:

$$\chi^2 = \sum \frac{(observed - expected)^2}{expected}$$

Researchers can also calculated the odd ratio and 95% (confidence interval).

For continuous or quantitative phenotype, researchers can identify the association between haplotype and phenotype using linear regression and variance analysis.

Multiple Testing Corrections

Genome-wide haplotype association study will scan all of the chromosomes, identify the LD blocks, and check the association between each haplotype and phenotype/disease. Therefore, the multiple testing is a challenging issue in genome-wide haplotype association study. Many techniques can be used to correct multiple hypotheses, such as the Bonferroni (Kowalski and Enck, 2010) and Sidak corrections (Guo and Romano, 2007), false discovery rate (Benjamini et al., 2001), and permutation (Chen et al., 2006). The simplest and strictest method of correction is the Bonferroni correction. For each individual hypothesis, researchers can obtain significant results by using a significance level of α/N, where α is the overall significant level and N is the number of hypotheses (the number of haplotypes). If the researchers think the threshold is too strict, they can choose a relatively loose threshold and use a bioinformatics strategy to filter the candidate genes (see Section "Applications").

Applications

Identifying Complex Disease-Related Haplotype

One of the most important areas of application of the genome-wide haplotype association study is to identify the complex disease-related haplotypes. The disease-related haplotype can be classified into two categories: Risk haplotype and protective haplotype. A haplotype is labeled as risk (or protective) haplotype if the frequency of the haplotype in disease samples is higher (lower) than in control samples. The risk haplotype can increase the risk of disease, and the protective haplotype reduces disease risk.

Mapping Disease-Related Haplotype to Genes

Identifying the disease-related candidate gene is an important application for genome-wide haplotype association studies. The researchers can map the significant haplotypes to genes based on their chromosome location information. The information of start and end sites for all the human genes can be downloaded for the NCBI gene database (see "Relevant Websites section"). The SNP position can be downloaded from the NCBI SNP database (see "Relevant Websites section"). A notable problem is that the genome versions of gene and SNP must be consistent. A gene can be regarded as a candidate gene if the gene shares some chromosome fragment with a risk haplotype.

Analyzing the Gene Functions Using the Bioinformatics Strategy

After obtaining candidate genes, researchers can prioritize the candidate genes based on the correlation (such as sequence similarity and coexpression pattern) with known disease genes. The known disease genes can be obtained from some disease database, such as the Online Mendelian Inheritance (Amberger et al., 2015). The software Endeavor can be used to calculated the similarity between the candidate genes and the known genes from several aspects, such as protein–protein interactions, gene expression, sequence information, text-mining, and gene annotation information (Tranchevent et al., 2008).

Researchers can also analyze the gene functions using the gene annotation database, such as the GO (Gene Ontology) database (Blake and Harris, 2008) and KEGG pathway database (Kyoto Encyclopedia of Genes and Genomes) (Kanehisa and Goto, 2000). Some methods of gene enrichment analysis, such as hypergeometric test and enrichment disequilibrium (Jiang et al., 2012), can be used to identify the disease-related pathways and gene functional categories.

The Haplotype Analysis Software

Here we briefly introduce the most commonly used haplotype analysis software. Using this software, researchers can successfully perform haplotype analysis.

HAPLOTYPE can carry out genome-wide haplotype association study using an elastic sliding window method. The software can be downloaded at the website provided in "Relevant Websites section".

Haploview is one of the most commonly used haplotype analysis software programs. It supports single SNP and haplotype association tests for limited loci. The software can be downloaded at the website provided in "Relevant Websites section".

Plink can scan the whole-genome and carry out the genome-wide haplotype association study. The software can be downloaded at the website provided in "Relevant Websites section".

Shapeit can quickly estimate the phase of haplotype. The software can be downloaded at the website provided in "Relevant Websites section".

An Example

For better understanding the genome-wide haplotype association study, we describe an example. Previously, Wang et al. (2015) carried out a genome-wide haplotype association for 33 Chinese prostate cancer patients and 139 normal samples. All the samples are unrelated individuals. A total of 632,532 SNPs on 22 autosomal chromosomes had passed QC criteria (MAF > 1%, Hardy–Weinberg equilibrium P > 0.001, and call ratio >75 %). Then they scanned the whole-genome using a FGT and identified 138,072 LD blocks. For each block, an EM algorithm was used to estimate haplotype frequencies for prostate cancer samples and normal samples. There were total 558,565 haplotypes in the 138,072 LD blocks. For each haplotype, a chi-square test was used to obtain the significant haplotypes. At last, 794 haplotype were significantly associated with prostate cancer. These significant haplotypes were located in 694 LD blocks. To find the novel prostate cancer related gene, they mapped the significant haplotypes to genes based on physical position and obtained 454 candidate genes. Then Endeavor software was used to prioritize the candidate genes based on the similarity with 13 known prostate cancer genes. In the end, they identified seven novel susceptibility genes. Among these genes, the most significant gene is BLM in chr15. A haplotype GGTTACCCCTC (rs2270131, rs2073919, rs11073953, rs12592875, rs16944863, rs2238337, rs414634, rs401549, rs17183344, rs16944884, and rs16944888) on the BLM gene region has significant association with prostate cancer (P = 2.37E − 11). The haplotype frequency is 0.16 in prostate cancer samples, whereas it is only 0.0004 in normal samples. The haplotype is a risk haplotype. For other genes, we will not describe them in detail. For more details, please see the research report (Wang et al., 2015).

Discussion

The genome-wide haplotype association study is an important strategy for identifying diseases/traits related haplotypes (chromosome segments) and mapping candidate genes. However, there are still some technical limitations. The main reason is that current SNP detection techniques break the association between physically proximate SNPs. This directly leads to an unknown gametic phase when two SNPs are both heterozygous. Both SNP chip technology and second generation sequencing technology cannot solve this question. With the development of genome sequencing technology (perhaps the fourth or fifth generation sequencing technology), the haplotype will be sequenced directly rather than inferred, and haplotype analysis will become a hot issue.

In some cases, the researchers have only SNP genotype data for disease, and no control data. They can use some public genotype data in the same or similar population as control samples, such as the 1000 Genomes Project.

We will gradually share some learning materials and data on the HAPLOTYPE website provided in "Relevant Websites section".

Conclusions and Future Directions

Genome-wide haplotype association studies are an important tool in medical genetics studies.

When the haplotype can be directly sequenced, genome-wide haplotype analysis will become a very important analytical tool. In addition, the genome-wide haplotype association study framework will possibly be extended to other omics, such as the epigenome. For DNA methylation, there was also nonrandom association between neighboring methylation loci (we called methylation disequilibrium, MD). A group of methylation status (M: Methylation or U: Unmethylation) on a chromosome can also be defined as a methylation haplotype (meplotype). The genome-wide haplotype association study could be extended to the epigenome-wide meplotype association study. Related concepts can be seen in the framework for population epigenetic study (Zhao et al., 2018). The analysis program for meplotype and single methylation polymorphism (SMP) (Xu et al., 2018) can be found at EWAS website provided in "Relevant Websites section".

Acknowledgment

We thank Di Liu (Harbin Medical University, China) and Linna Zhao (Harbin Medical University, China) for their contributions to the figures and materials. This work was supported in part by the National Natural Science Foundation of China (Grant No. 91746113). The funder had no role in study design, data collection and analysis, decision to publish, or preparation of the manuscript.

See also: Comparative Genomics Analysis. Detecting and Annotating Rare Variants. Exome Sequencing Data Analysis. Functional Enrichment Analysis. Integrative Analysis of Multi-Omics Data. Natural Language Processing Approaches in Bioinformatics. Next Generation Sequencing Data Analysis. Single Nucleotide Polymorphism Typing. Whole Genome Sequencing Analysis

References

Abecasis, G.R., et al., 2010. A map of human genome variation from population-scale sequencing. Nature 467, 1061–1073.
Altshuler, D.M., et al., 2010. Integrating common and rare genetic variation in diverse human populations. Nature 467, 52–58.

Amberger, J.S., et al., 2015. OMIM.org: Online Mendelian Inheritance in Man (OMIM(R)), an online catalog of human genes and genetic disorders. Nucleic Acids Research 43, D789–D798.

Barrett, J.C., et al., 2005. Haploview: Analysis and visualization of LD and haplotype maps. Bioinformatics 21, 263–265.

Benjamini, Y., et al., 2001. Controlling the false discovery rate in behavior genetics research. Behavioural Brain Research 125, 279–284.

Blake, J.A., Harris, M.A., 2008. The Gene Ontology (GO) project: Structured vocabularies for molecular biology and their application to genome and expression analysis. Current Protocols in Bioinformatics. Chapter 7, Unit 7 2.

Chen, B.E., et al., 2006. Resampling-based multiple hypothesis testing procedures for genetic case-control association studies. Genetic Epidemiology 30, 495–507.

Cho, Y.S., et al., 2011. Meta-analysis of genome-wide association studies identifies eight new loci for type 2 diabetes in east Asians. Nature Genetics 44, 67–72.

Daly, M.J., et al., 2001. High-resolution haplotype structure in the human genome. Nature Genetics 29, 229–232.

Delaneau, O., Zagury, J.F., Marchini, J., 2013. Improved whole-chromosome phasing for disease and population genetic studies. Nature Methods 10, 5–6.

Frazer, K.A., et al., 2007. A second generation human haplotype map of over 3.1 million SNPs. Nature 449, 851–861.

Gabriel, S.B., et al., 2002. The structure of haplotype blocks in the human genome. Science 296, 2225–2229.

Garcia-Closas, M., et al., 2013. Genome-wide association studies identify four ER negative-specific breast cancer risk loci. Nature Genetics 45, 392–398.

Guo, W., Romano, J., 2007. A generalized Sidak-Holm procedure and control of generalized error rates under independence. Statistical Applications in Genetics and Molecular Biology 6.Article3.

Jiang, Y., et al., 2012. Enrichment Disequilibrium: A novel approach for measuring the degree of enrichment after gene enrichment test. Biochemical and Biophysical Research Communications 424, 563–567.

Kanehisa, M., Goto, S., 2000. KEGG: Kyoto encyclopedia of genes and genomes. Nucleic Acids Research 28, 27–30.

Kerstens, H.H., et al., 2009. Large scale single nucleotide polymorphism discovery in unsequenced genomes using second generation high throughput sequencing technology: Applied to Turkey. BMC Genomics 10, 479.

Kowalski, A., Enck, P., 2010. Statistical methods: Multiple significance tests and the Bonferroni procedure. Psychotherapie, Psychosomatik, Medizinische Psychologie 60, 286–287.

Nishida, N., et al., 2008. Evaluating the performance of Affymetrix SNP Array 6.0 platform with 400 Japanese individuals. BMC Genomics 9, 431.

Rivadeneira, F., et al., 2009. Twenty bone-mineral-density loci identified by large-scale meta-analysis of genome-wide association studies. Nature Genetics 41, 1199–1206.

Scheet, P., Stephens, M., 2006. A fast and flexible statistical model for large-scale population genotype data: Applications to inferring missing genotypes and haplotypic phase. American Journal of Human Genetics 78, 629–644.

Slatkin, M., 2008. Linkage disequilibrium – Understanding the evolutionary past and mapping the medical future. Nature Reviews Genetics 9, 477–485.

Sun, W., et al., 2016. Genome-wide haplotype association analysis identifies SERPINB9, SERPINE2, GAK, and HSP90B1 as novel risk genes for oral squamous cell carcinoma. Tumour Biology 37, 1845–1851.

Tranchevent, L.C., et al., 2008. ENDEAVOUR update: A web resource for gene prioritization in multiple species. Nucleic Acids Research 36, W377–W384.

Tregouet, D.A., et al., 2009. Genome-wide haplotype association study identifies the SLC22A3-LPAL2-LPA gene cluster as a risk locus for coronary artery disease. Nature Genetics 41, 283–285.

Wang, N., et al., 2002. Distribution of recombination crossovers and the origin of haplotype blocks: The interplay of population history, recombination, and mutation. American Journal of Human Genetics 71, 1227–1234.

Wang, Q., et al., 2015. Genome-wide haplotype association study identifies BLM as a risk gene for prostate cancer in Chinese population. Tumour Biology 36, 2703–2707.

Welter, D., et al., 2014. The NHGRI GWAS catalog, a curated resource of SNP-trait associations. Nucleic Acids Research 42, D1001–D1006.

Xu, J., et al., 2016. EWAS: Epigenome-wide association studies software 1.0 – Identifying the association between combinations of methylation levels and diseases. Scientific Reports 6, 37951.

Xu, J., et al., 2018. EWAS: Epigenome-wide association study software 2.0. Bioinformatics. https://doi.org/10.1093/bioinformatics/bty163.

Zhang, K., et al., 2002. A dynamic programming algorithm for haplotype block partitioning. Proceedings of the National Academy of Sciences of the United States of America 99, 7335–7339.

Zhao, L., et al., 2018. The framework for population epigenetic study. Briefings in Bioinformatics 19 (1), 89–100.

Relevant Websites

http://www.broadinstitute.org/haploview/
  BROAD INSTITUTE.
http://www.ewas.org.cn
  EWAS.
http://www.bioapp.org/ewas
  EWAS.
ftp://ftp.ncbi.nlm.nih.gov/gene
  Gene - NCBI.
http://www.haplotype.cn
  HAPLOTYPE1.0.
http://www.cog-genomics.org/plink
  PLINK.
https://mathgen.stats.ox.ac.uk/genetics_software/shapeit/shapeit.html
  SHAPEIT.
ftp://ftp.ncbi.nlm.nih.gov/snp
  SNP - NCBI FTP Site.

Prediction of Protein-Binding Sites in DNA Sequences

Kenta Nakai, The University of Tokyo, Tokyo, Japan

Introduction

In the nucleus of living cells, DNA molecules are specifically bound by a number of proteins to be functional. Of these, the most abundant ones are histones and their related proteins, which are important for organizing nuclear DNA into chromatins and for regulating their structure by epigenetic mechanisms. This topic is described in another article. Here we mainly deal with the binding of transcription factors (TFs) because it is critical in understanding how gene expression is regulated and has been extensively studied. The transcription-factor binding sites (TFBSs) are recognized as *cis*-elements in DNA sequences. Compared with a parallel problem of predicting DNA-binding regions in protein sequences or protein 3D structures, locating TFBSs in DNA sequences can be more difficult because the regions surrounding TFBSs are not necessarily similar between instances. In other words, (global) sequence alignment-based methods are not so effective, though so-called phylogenetic footprinting is effective when evolutionarily orthologous regions are compared (see below). Thus, a specialized field known as the motif-finding (or motif-discovery) problem has been formulated and studied well so far. In this problem, a set of DNA sequences, each of which is likely to contain at least one common TFBS, are given and these TFBSs which are recognized as an over-represented motif, i.e., a short sequence pattern with some statistical significance, are extracted. Typically, the input sequences are the potentially regulatory regions, such as the upstream 1000 bp-regions from the TSSs (transcriptional start sites), of co-expressed genes, i.e., genes which share s similar condition-specific expression and thus are likely to be regulated by a common mechanism, such as by a common transcription factor. As described below, many algorithms have been developed and their performances have been evaluated. More recently, the appearances of the NGS (next generation sequencing) technology, particularly the ChIP-seq (chromatin immuno-precipitation sequencing) technology, which enable to map the binding regions of a specified TF to the entire genome, have changed the situation of this field significantly. For one thing, the scale of the input sequences has been enlarged enormously. For another, a new need of algorithms for locating a TFBS in each ChIP-seq peak has emerged and algorithms specifically tailored for the ChIP-seq data analysis have been developed. In addition, demands for expanding the motif-finding problem to capture the more general architecture of gene regulatory regions have also emerged.

Many review articles have been written in this field. Of these, Zambelli *et al.* (2013) was written with a similar perspective with this article, though it is not so new. A more recent review by Liu *et al.* (2017) introduces recent advances, focusing on the algorithms for analysing ChIP-seq data.

How to Represent Motifs and the Problem of False Positives

The typical length of the binding sites of a monomeric TF is around 6 base pairs (bps) but the length of extracted *cis*-elements can become as long as 20 bps because TFs sometimes bind as a homodimer or a heterodimer. The homodimer binding motifs show the so-called palindromic feature and their central regions are sometimes close to random sequence, which can be regarded as a gap region. However, although the length of such 'gap's can even be varied, the length of sought TFBSs is practically assumed to be constant in motif-finding. In other words, variable gaps are not considered for aligning TFBSs in most cases.

Since the binding sequences of a TF are varied more or less, various ways have been used to represent its binding pattern. As described later, the way of how to represent the binding pattern (motif) is tightly related to the algorithms for finding it. Roughly speaking, there are two types of representing motifs: one is character-based and the other is numerical (profile-based).

The former character-based representation is related to the consensus-sequence representation, which shows the most frequent base at each position (in its simplest form). For example, the consensus sequence of the TATA-binding protein is known as 'TATAAT', though most of its known binding instances are not 'TATAAT'. It is well known that the frequency of base appearance at each position is not the same and thus sometimes bases that frequently appear are shown with capital letters while less frequent bases are shown in lower cases, such as 'TATAat', When the majority of the preference of bases is shared with two bases, they are sometimes shown with parentheses, such as 'TATaa(t/a)'. The IUPAC code for representing degenerate bases is often used (**Table 1**). These character-based (or pattern-based) representation is a subset of regular expressions in computer science and is relatively easier to be treated in computers. In motif finding, the binding pattern of a TF is sometimes assumed to be represented as the so-called (l, d)-pattern, where l is the length of the pattern (e.g., 6) and d is the maximum number of allowed mismatches from the consensus (e.g., 3).

On the other hand, in the numeric or profile-based representation, the so-called positional weight matrix (PWM) is the standard (it is often referred as a profile). A PWM is a matrix, such as $\{w_{i,j}\}$, $i=1,..,4$, $j=1,..,l$ for a motif with l-bases. The matrix element $w_{i,j}$ shows a score when base i appears at position j in the candidate instance. Typically, the score is proportional to the log-odds, which is the logarithm of the frequency of base i at position j in the set of known binding sequences for the TF divided by the background frequency of base i (for the base of the logarithm. 10 or 2 are often used). For each candidate binding site, the score at each position j is summed over the l positions, giving the score for the candidate. If this summed score exceeds a certain

Table 1   IUPAC codes for nucleotides

Code	Base
A	Adenine
C	Cytosine
G	Guanine
T (or U)	Thymine (or Uracil)
R	A or G
Y	C or T
S	G or C
W	A or T
K	G or T
M	A or C
B	C or G or T
D	A or G or T
H	A or C or T
V	A or C or G
N	Any base

threshold parameter, the candidate is predicted to be one of the binding sites. Note that this method adds the logarithms of base frequency; this means that it essentially calculates the probability of observing motifs assuming that the base appearance at each position is independent each other. Practically, the observed frequency of base i can become 0 just because the size of the known set is not large. In such a case, candidates containing such a position will never be predicted to be positive. To avoid this, a small number of artificial occurrence is added to all the matrix elements. These values are called pseudo-counts. According to a study based on simulated data, a value 0.8 was recommended for practical uses (Nishida *et al.*, 2009).

Obviously, the PWM representation contains more information than the (l, d)-representation. In fact, the predicted sites with higher scores are not only more likely to be the true binding sites but also more likely that the TF binds more strongly. Nevertheless, both of these representations suffer from the problem of too many false positives. Namely, in both representations, the binding motif tends to match to too many positions in the genome, many of which are not the true binding sites. In this sense, the matrices stored in public transcription factor databases, such as JASPAR and TRANSFAC, are useful but should be used carefully. Indeed, our fundamental assumption that the short sequence motif is the determinant of specificity for any transcription factor is not accurate at least *in vivo*; exactly the same sequences can be bound at one site while unbound at another. Then, what kind of information should we add? We still do not have accurate answer; it is unlikely that the inherent assumption of positional independence in the PWM representation is the main reason because the incorporation of inter-position dependency does not seem to solve the problem (Zhang and Marr, 1993), though there are a few ecent reports that the use of more flexible frameworks (e.g., HMM or deep learning) in motif representation improved the performance (Mathelier and Wasserman, 2013; Alipanahi *et al.*, 2015). Perhaps, the surrounding region with a relatively short range (say, $+/- 10$ bp) does not carry enough information. It is widely believed that the chromatin structure around the (relatively long-range) region is the key. Namely, if the surrounding chromatin is tightly packed and in an inactive state, the sites within it will not be bound but if it is in an open and active state, the sites within it will be more likely to be bound, though detailed confirmation has not been reported as far as the author notice. In this sense, phylogenetic conservation analyses of ChIP-seq data are useful to know what is happening. As an example, Schmidt *et al.* (2010) compared the binding profiles of CEBPA to the region around the PCK1 gene in the liver between five animals. There was a clear peak which is conserved between all five species at the 5′ position of the gene but, interestingly, there was also an unique upstream peak which is human-specific, for example. It is not known whether this peak shows an evolutionary acquisition of a new functional element or just shows a randomly appeared, non-functional binding site. Thus, we should mind that even ChIP peaks may not show functional sites and that evolutionary conservation is an effective information to detect functionally important peaks (though not all functional sites are necessary to be conserved).

Algorithms of Motif Finding

In the motif-finding problem, the length of the motif sought is usually given as an input parameter. Each of the input sequence is often assumed to contain (at least) one target binding site (i.e., an instance) but practically, it would be all right, of course, if some of the input sequences do not contain target sites. Based on the representation methods for DNA motifs, the algorithms for motif finding are roughly-divided into two categories: the character-string (or word)-based methods and the numeric profile-based methods. Although there have been more preceding attempts based on word-based approach, a pioneering work which formalized the problem is done in Hertz *et al.* (1990), where they proposed a way to find a kind of PWM which is formed by the instances of input sequences and gives the highest sum of scores intuitively (the method thus belongs to the profile-based category and the improved algorithm is later released as CONSENSUS). Then, two classical algorithms, MEME (Bailey and Elkan, 1994) and Gibbs sampler (Lawrence *et al.*, 1993), which use the Expectation Maximization algorithm and the Gibbs sampling algorithm, respectively, for optimizing the PWM, appeared. The basic idea of Gibbs sampler is first to randomly locate the instance position for each input sequence and make a PWM from them except one of them; then, the PWM is used to scan the excluded sequence; if another position gives higher score than the original instance. The instance of the sequence is updated with the probability determined by their score difference. Iterating this procedure many times, the PWM will happen to include target instances partially and will start to work efficiently to find the target instances in the remainder of sequences. Finally, the PWM will converge to the optimum one. A boom in this field had come after MEME and a number of algorithms have been developed. Practically, it is recommended to apply a motif finding algorithm with various parameter values and confirm these results by eyes. It would be even desirable to compare the results of multiple algorithms to confirm the stability of the extracted motifs (though there is no guarantee that frequently extracted motifs are more reliable). A tool has been released for helping such procedures (Okumura et al., 2007).

As described above, in the character-string-based approach, the problem is formalized to efficiently enumerate motifs in the form of the (l, d) pattern (Pevzner and Sze, 2000). This formalism is appealing to researchers with the background of computer science and many techniques have been applied to reduce its computational cost. One successful example of this approach is Weeder (Pavesi et al., 2001), which is proposed as a method to detect motifs with unknown length. In 2005, a relatively systematic evaluation of the performance of available algorithms was published, using various benchmark data (Tompa et al., 2005). Although there was not a single excellent algorithm for all purposes, the performance of Weeder was impressive.

However, with the appearance of the NGS (next generation sequencing) technology, including the ChIP-seq method, the situation has been changed. First, as noted above, more specialized software for the analysis of ChIP-seq data is required. Second and more importantly, the size of the input sequences has been enlarged enormously; for those large inputs, traditional software such as MEME and Weeder are not practical. Third, because the genome sequences of so many organisms have become available, comparison of orthologous regions between evolutionarily close organisms has become easier. Since the topic of phylogenetic footprinting is treated in another article, we do not describe about it further but just cite one pioneering work, which is even earlier than the establishment of the motif finding problem (Tagle et al., 1988) as well as one recent progress (Liu et al., 2016) in the field. Perhaps, the most popular tool for ChIP-seq motif finding is DREME by the author of MEME (Bailey, 2011). DREME belongs to the string (word)-based category and exhaustively finds top 100 words (of length l) which appear most significantly in the positive data compared with the negative data. Then, the top words are merged between similar ones to allow wild-card representation of a mismatch. DREME is also used in the MEME-ChIP web server, which integrates the two types of motif-finding algorithms, MEME and DREME (Machanick and Bailey, 2011), and it is included in a large collection of MEME-related tools, the MEME Suite (Bailey et al., 2015; **Fig. 1**). The peak-motif tool in the RSAT (Regulatory Sequence Analysis Tools) web server, which is also well-known, belongs to the string-based class but the found motifs are compiled to the form of PWM (Thomas-Chollier et al., 2012). As a pioneering example of numeric matrix-based approach for ChIP-seq peak detection, ChIPMunk, which is an iterative algorithm combining greedy optimization with bootstrapping, is famous (Kulakovskiy et al., 2010). ChIPMunk has been used to construct a comprehensive collection of TF specificity of human and mouse TFs (HOCOMOCO; Kulakovskiy et al., 2018). Another recent algorithm, DeepBind, employs a more general way of representing motifs than PWM and uses the deep learning algorithm, which is known to be quite powerful in various applications (Alipanahi et al., 2015). So far, systematic benchmarking attempts for ChIP-seq motif finders have not been reported well (but see Wilbanks and Facciotti, 2010), probably because of the difficulty in setting correct binding motifs except trivial cases. However, it would be true that, generally speaking, more recently released algorithms are more likely to be better in their performance/speed and that the combined use of algorithms based on different principles are also recommended (for reviews, see Tran and Huang, 2014; Liu et al., 2017, for example).

Variations of the Theme

One way to improve the sensitivity of motif detection is to improve the quality of background sequences, which are not random at all. For example, in the human genome, the frequency of the CpG dinucleotide is significantly fewer and many short repetitive sequence patterns exist. Markov-chain models have been used to capture these features. But there are also needs for more specific discriminative motif finding, where only motifs that significantly occur frequently in the positive dataset rather than the negative dataset are reported. For example, to extract motifs that are responsible for muscle-specific gene expression, ubiquitous signals, such as the TATA box, should not be extracted. Although the use of negative data has been attempted since very early years, the problem of discriminative motif finding can be a specific field to be explored (Redhead and Bailey, 2007; Huggins et al., 2011). The need may have become even more important for the analysis of condition-specific changes of ChIP-seq peaks. And related to this, there is also a great need to extract a set of multiple non-redundant motifs that co-occur in a set of regulatory regions of co-expressed genes and this problem is regarded as the cofactor motif finding. Note that even ordinary motif finders can detect multiple motifs independently. For example, a rather simple algorithm, such as DREME, has been shown to be effective in finding cofactor motifs (Bailey, 2011). Of course, there have been algorithms which can detect co-occurring motifs simultaneously, such as SIOMICS (Ding et al., 2015). This kind of approaches is also related to attempts to characterize the architecture (way of the placement of multiple TFBSs) in the upstream region of co-expressed genes. Some pioneering works were performed by Fickett and Wasserman (2000). Vandenbon and Nakai (2010) tried to systematically extract a set of rules on the combination and their relative placement of de novo motifs that can be used to distinguish a set of certain tissue-specific genes from the others. A similar approach was attempted to characterize the structure of cis regulatory modules that direct the

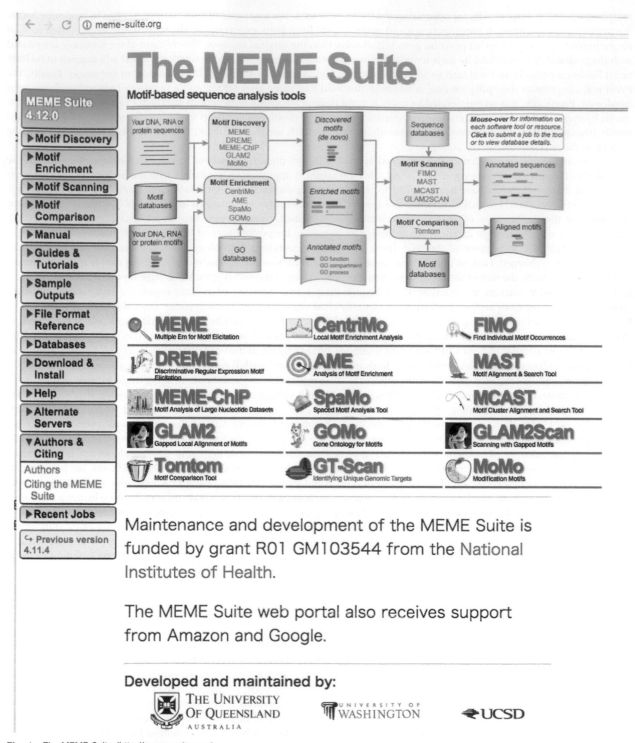

Fig. 1 The MEME Suite (http://meme-suite.org/).

developmental stage-specific expression of genes in *Drosophila* (Lopez *et al.*, 2017). With the advance of NGS technologies, such as the single-cell transcriptomics, this field should become more flourishing. An important remaining problem to be explored is to find motifs in enhancer regions. In spite of several large-scale experimental and computational studies, it is still a mystery on how transcription factors contribute to specify the enhancer activity (Kheradpour *et al.*, 2013). Systematic attempts to accumulate ChIP-seq and related data in several organisms, such as ENCODE, will offer a powerful foundation in the field (ENCODE Project Consortium, 2012). And future understanding on how the regulatory information is encoded in DNA would be undoubtedly useful in characterizing the relative importance of mutations/variations found in the non-coding regions of our genome, for example.

Concluding Remarks

Looking at the pace of publications in the field of motif-finding, this field has become to be regarded as a maturing field. The performance of the relevant software, however, is still not satisfactory at all. Especially, the problem of high false-positive rate must be overcome. As mentioned above, one important factor to be considered should be the chromatin states, which are closely related to the DNA looping structure, such as the TAD (topologically-associating domains; Dixon *et al.*, 2016). The chromatin states are predicted from a set of histone mark information, obtained by ChIP-seq. The DNA looping structure is also estimated with NGS-based technology, such as the Hi-C technology (reviewed in Han *et al.* (2018)). With the incorporation of such new advances, this field should experience another new boost in the near future.

Acknowledgement

This work was partly supported by Japan Society for the Promotion of Science (JSPS) KAKENHI Grant Number 17K00397.

See also: Natural Language Processing Approaches in Bioinformatics. Sequence Analysis. Sequence Composition

---

References

Alipanahi, B., Delong, A., Weirauch, M.T., Frey, B.J., 2015. Predicting the sequence specificities of DNA- and RNA-binding proteins by deep learning. Nat Biotechnol 33, 831–838.

Bailey, T.L., 2011. DREME: Motif discovery in transcription factor ChIP-seq data. Bioinformatics 27, 1653–1659.

Bailey, T.L., Johnson, J., Grant, C.E. & Noble, W.S., 2015. The MEME Suite. Nucleic Acids Res, 43, W39-W49.

Bailey, T.L., Elkan, C., 1994. Fitting a mixture model by expectation maximization to discover motifs in biopolymers. Proc. Int. Conf. Intell. Syst. Mol. Biol. 2, 28–36.

Ding, J., Dhillon, V., Li, X., Hu, H., 2015. Systematic discovery of cofactor motifs from ChIP-seq data by SIOMICS. Methods 79–80, 47–51.

Dixon, J.R., Gorkin, D.U., Ren, B., 2016. Chromatin domains: The unit of chromosome organization. Mol. Cell 62, 668–680.

ENCODE Project Consortium, 2012. An integrated encyclopedia of DNA elements in the human genome. Nature 489, 57–74.

Fickett, J.W., Wasserman, W.W., 2000. Discovery and modeling of transcriptional regulatory regions. Curr. Opin. Biotechnol. 11, 19–24.

Han, J., Zhang, Z., Wang, K., 2018. 3C and 3C-based techniques: The powerful tools for spatial genome organization deciphering. Mol. Cytogenet. 11, 21.

Hertz, G.Z., Hartzell, G.W., Stormo, G.D., 1990. Identification of consensus patterns in unaligned DNA sequences known to be functionally related. Comput. Appl. Biosci. 6, 81–92.

Huggins, P., Zhong, S., Shiff, I., *et al.*, 2011. DECOD: Fast and accurate discriminative DNA motif finding. Bioinformatics 27, 2361–2367.

Kheradpour, P., Ernst, J., Melnikov, A., *et al.*, 2013. Systematic dissection of regulatory motifs in 2000 predicted human enhancers using a massively parallel reporter assay. Genome Res. 23, 800–811.

Kulakovskiy, I.V., Boeva, V.A., Favorov, A.V., Makeev, V.J., 2010. Deep and wide digging for binding motifs in ChIP-Seq data. Bioinformatics 26, 2622–2623.

Kulakovskiy, I.V., Vorontsov, I.E., Yevshin, I.S., *et al.*, 2018. HOCOMOCO: Towards a complete collection of transcription factor binding models for human and mouse via large-scale ChIP-Seq analysis. Nucleic Acids Res 46, D252–D259.

Lawrence, C.E., Altschul, S.F., Boguski, M.S., *et al.*, 1993. Detecting subtle sequence signals: A Gibbs sampling strategy for multiple alignment. Science 262, 208–214.

Liu, B., Yang, J., Li, Y., Mcdermaid, A., Ma, Q., 2017. An algorithmic perspective of de novo cis-regulatory motif finding based on ChIP-seq data. Brief Bioinform.

Liu, B., Zhang, H., Zhou, C., *et al.*, 2016. An integrative and applicable phylogenetic footprinting framework for cis-regulatory motifs identification in prokaryotic genomes. BMC Genomics 17, 578.

Lopez, Y., Vandenbon, A., Nose, A., Nakai, K., 2017. Modeling the cis-regulatory modules of genes expressed in developmental stages of Drosophila melanogaster. PeerJ 5, e3389.

Machanick, P., Bailey, T.L., 2011. MEME-ChIP: Motif analysis of large DNA datasets. Bioinformatics 27, 1696–1697.

Mathelier, A., Wasserman, W.W., 2013. The next generation of transcription factor binding site prediction. PLoS Comput Biol, 9, e1003214.

Nishida, K., Frith, M.C., Nakai, K., 2009. Pseudocounts for transcription factor binding sites. Nucleic Acids Res. 37, 939–944.

Okumura, T., Makiguchi, H., Makita, Y., Yamashita, R., Nakai, K., 2007. Melina II: A web tool for comparisons among several predictive algorithms to find potential motifs from promoter regions. Nucleic Acids Res. 35, W227–W231.

Pavesi, G., Mauri, G., Pesole, G., 2001. An algorithm for finding signals of unknown length in DNA sequences. Bioinformatics 17 (Suppl. 1), S207–S214.

Pevzner, P.A., Sze, S.H., 2000. Combinatorial approaches to finding subtle signals in DNA sequences. Proc. Int. Conf. Intell. Syst. Mol. Biol. 8, 269–278.

Redhead, E., Bailey, T.L., 2007. Discriminative motif discovery in DNA and protein sequences using the DEME algorithm. BMC Bioinform. 8, 385.

Schmidt, D., Wilson, M.D., Ballester, B., *et al.*, 2010. Five-vertebrate ChIP-seq reveals the evolutionary dynamics of transcription factor binding. Science 328, 1036–1040.

Tagle, D.A., Koop, B.F., Goodman, M., *et al.*, 1988. Embryonic epsilon and gamma globin genes of a prosimian primate (Galago crassicaudatus). Nucleotide and amino acid sequences, developmental regulation and phylogenetic footprints. J. Mol. Biol. 203, 439–455.

Thomas-Chollier, M., Herrmann, C., Defrance, M., *et al.*, 2012. RSAT peak-motifs: Motif analysis in full-size ChIP-seq datasets. Nucleic Acids Res. 40, e31.

Tompa, M., Li, N., Bailey, T.L., *et al.*, 2005. Assessing computational tools for the discovery of transcription factor binding sites. Nat. Biotechnol. 23, 137–144.

Tran, N.T., Huang, C.H., 2014. A survey of motif finding Web tools for detecting binding site motifs in ChIP-Seq data. Biol Direct, 9, 4.

Vandenbon, A., Nakai, K., 2010. Modeling tissue-specific structural patterns in human and mouse promoters. Nucleic Acids Res. 38, 17–25.

Wilbanks, E.G., Facciotti, M.T., 2010. Evaluation of algorithm performance in ChIP-seq peak detection. PLoS One, 5, e11471.

Zambelli, F., Pesole, G., Pavesi, G., 2013. Motif discovery and transcription factor binding sites before and after the next-generation sequencing era. Brief. Bioinform. 14, 225–237.

Zhang, M.Q., Marr, T.G., 1993. A weight array method for splicing signal analysis. Comput. Appl. Biosci. 9, 499–509.

Genome-Wide Scanning of Gene Expression

Sung-J Park, The University of Tokyo, Tokyo, Japan

Introduction

Identifying genetic and epigenetic factors that impact molecular interplay and disease development is a high priority issue in the field of biological and medical sciences. As a solution to this issue, profiling of gene expression with microarray-based technologies has widely been adopted (Hoheisel, 2006). More recently, thanks to the improvement of next-generation sequencing (NGS) technologies, RNA sequencing (RNA-seq) has emerged as a new routine tool for the transcriptome profiling (Wang *et al.*, 2009). Beyond quantifying RNA population, RNA-seq facilitates to discover genome-wide alternative splicing isoforms, transcriptional start sites, epigenetic modifications, and allele specific transcripts. Currently, RNA-seq is gaining more popularity with growing demand of genome assays from communities.

It is often the case that billions of digital RNA fragments produced by NGS machines are computationally processed and statistically tested. Furthermore, to understand functional meaning of gene expression, incorporating multi-omics data that are rapidly increasing in quantity became inevitable. Thus, along with a well-designed experiment setting, successful transcriptome studies require to leverage bioinformatics and to carry out a pipeline that makes studies repeatable and transparent. In this regard, extensive community-wide efforts have been made to guide the effective usage of bioinformatics resources through developing online systems (Henry *et al.*, 2014; Cochrane *et al.*, 2016; Sloan *et al.*, 2016) and conducting benchmarks (Teng *et al.*, 2016; Williams *et al.*, 2016; Yan *et al.*, 2017). However, we frequently remain uncertain which background assumptions, statistical thresholds, or bioinformatics tools are appropriate to individual purposes (**Fig. 1**).

Herein, after succinctly briefing on the trends in NGS technology, we summarize recent progresses in scanning of genome-wide gene expression and in profiling of its functional importance. We focus on computational and statistical issues for filtering, mapping, quantifying, and annotating the RNA-seq outcomes. To help readers finding new opportunities and challenges, we provide a series of references that expedites understanding of each issue in detail. In addition, this article exemplifies a practical way of gene expression profiling with public data of spermatogenesis (**Fig. 2(A)**), which strives to avoid profound discussions on the germ cell development reviewed in excellent references (Bettegowda and Wilkinson, 2010; Saitou *et al.*, 2012; Bohacek and Mansuy, 2015; Ernst *et al.*, 2017).

Although we limit our scope of this review to transcriptome analysis, readers can also find attractive themes for processing of multi-omics data that gives a new multifaceted window to the identification of key factors. We expect that transcriptome atlases established by genome-wide scanning of gene expression provide fundamental resource to the extensive genomic studies that require the incorporation of large-scale heterogeneous datasets.

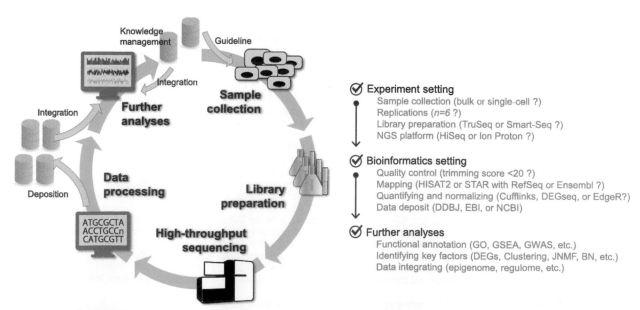

Fig. 1 Schematic representation of the routine scanning of genome-wide gene expression by NGS technology that requires appropriate setting of experiment and bioinformatics. Along with data sharing and integrating, an effective pipeline design is a critical facet in conducting NGS experiments. DEGs; Differentially Expressed Genes, JNMF; Joint Non-negative Matrix Factorization, BN; Bayesian Network.

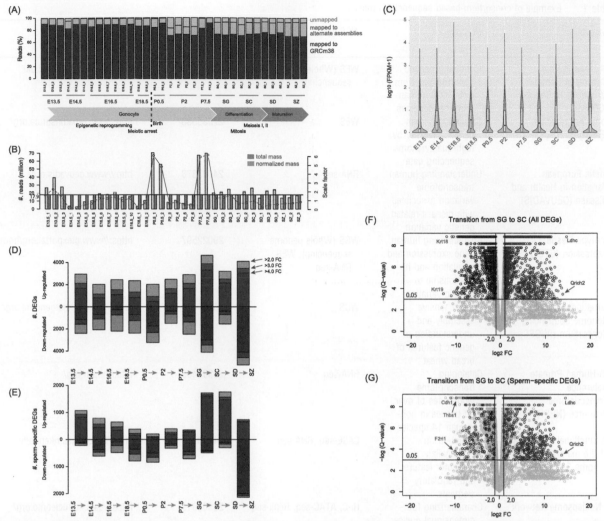

Fig. 2 An example of transcriptome analysis with HISAT2-Cufflinks2 pipeline. This example used public RNA-seq data of mouse spermatogenesis prepared at the time-points of embryonic day E13.5, E14.5, E16.5, E18.5, postnatal P0.5, P2, P7.5, Spermatogonia (SG), Spermatocytes (SC), Spermatids (SD), and Spermatozoa (SZ). (A) Schematic representation of male germ cell development, and read mappability of each replicate. (B) Normalized number of sequenced reads by scale factors. (C) Broad dynamic range of gene expression value FPKMs at each stage. (D) Differentially expressed genes (DEGs) in two consecutive stages (<0.05 FDR). (E) DEGs excluding genes expressed either MEF or Sertoli cells. (F) and (G) examples of volcano plot with Q-value and Fold-change (FC). FC is the FPKM ratio of SC/SG.

Genomic-Scale Transcriptome Profiling

Applications of High-Throughput Sequencing

The advent of massive parallel sequencing technology has led a new era of genome analysis, which can rapidly produce readouts of billions of DNA and RNA molecules. Since Sanger's success in sequencing a complete genome of virus (Sanger *et al.*, 1977), through a series of technical innovations (Mardis, 2013; Reuter *et al.*, 2015; Park *et al.*, 2016; Shendure *et al.*, 2017), the high-throughput sequencing also known as next-generation sequencing (NGS) is gaining more popularity with growing demand from academic and clinical communities (Koboldt *et al.*, 2013). Indeed, various consortium-based sequencing projects are ongoing towards specific goals (**Table 1**). They continuously manage the outcomes as public databases that provide new opportunities to unveil biological enigma.

The rapid progress in NGS technology has placed diverse features in commercialized machines (Loman *et al.*, 2012; Reuter *et al.*, 2015; Shendure *et al.*, 2017). For instance, Illumina platforms coupled with advanced experiment protocols, such as immunoprecipitation and enzyme reaction, produce relatively short genomic fragments (i.e., reads). On the other hand, synthetic long-read technologies, such as PacBio (Nakano *et al.*, 2017) and Oxford Nanopore Technologies (Loman and Watson, 2015), have emerged as a recent innovation of NGS technology. These NGS platforms often show trade-off features between pros and cons in throughput, cost per run, and signal-to-noise ratio (Mardis, 2013; Ross *et al.*, 2013; Reuter *et al.*, 2015). Thus, attention

Table 1   Example of consortium-based sequencing projects

Consortium	Purpose	NGS type	Reference (PMID)	Website
Cell Lines Project, Catalog of Somatic Mutations in Cancer (COSMIC)	Identifying genetic abnormalities from over 1000 human immortal cell lines	WES (Whole exome sequencing)	27727438	http://cancer.sanger.ac.uk/
Exome Aggregation (ExAC)	Cataloging human genetic diversity by high-quality exome sequencing data	WES	27535533	http://exac.broadinstitute.org/
Genetic European Variation in Health and Disease (GEUVADIS)	Understanding human transcriptome variation associated with disease-related genetic variation	RNA-seq	24037378	http://www.geuvadis.org/
Genotype-Tissue Expression (GTEx)	Characterizing human gene expression and regulation and its relationship to genetic variation	WGS (Whole genome sequencing), WES, RNA-seq	29022597	https://www.gtexportal.org/home/
International Wheat Genome Sequencing Consortium (IWGSC)	Comprehensive assembly and understanding of genetic features of bread wheat	WGS	25035484	https://www.wheatgenome.org/
Non-Human Primate Reference Transcriptome Resource (NHPRTR)	Cataloging transcriptome landscapes of over 20 tissues in non-human 14 species	RNA-seq	25392405	http://nhprtr.org/
The functional annotation of the mammalian genome 5 (FANTOM5)	Characterizing mammalian promoter features and regulatory elements	CASE-seq, RNA-seq	24670764	http://fantom.gsc.riken.jp/5/
4D Nucleosome Network	Characterizing four-dimensional nuclear architecture and its role in gene expression and cellular function	Hi-C, ATAC-seq, Repli-seq	28905911	https://data.4dnucleome.org/

needs to be paid to the choice of NGS platforms for maximizing the impact on genome sequencing projects, even though it is no doubt that their pervasive utilization will widely spread in communities.

The short-read technologies are frequently used to interrogate broad genome profiling; that is, polymorphism analysis by whole-genome and whole-exome sequencing (Lam *et al.*, 2012; Sudmant *et al.*, 2015), profiling of transcription factor (TF) occupancy (Park, 2009; Kidder *et al.*, 2011), profiling of genomic-scale transcriptome (Wang *et al.*, 2009). The NGS applications can also capture epigenetic variabilities, including DNA and RNA modifications (Laird, 2010; Frye *et al.*, 2016), chromatin accessibility (Buenrostro *et al.*, 2013), and chromosome 3D organization (Paulsen *et al.*, 2014; Ay and Noble, 2015). Although computationally intense, the long-read technologies demonstrate prominent performances in analyzing highly intricate genetic features (Sahraeian *et al.*, 2017); e.g., assembly of high-complex genome regions (McCoy *et al.*, 2014; Li *et al.*, 2015), detection of structural variations (Chaisson *et al.*, 2015), and identification of gene isoforms (Cho *et al.*, 2014; Xu *et al.*, 2015; Weirather *et al.*, 2017).

Profiling Transcriptome Landscape by RNA Sequencing

As a standard application of NGS, RNA sequencing (RNA-seq) enables the broad investigation of protein coding and non-coding transcripts on genomic scales. In this regard, microarray-based technology has been widely used (Hoheisel, 2006; Shi *et al.*, 2006), and is continuously improving its performance in (dis)concordant with RNA-seq outcomes (Marioni *et al.*, 2008; Wang *et al.*, 2014; Nazarov *et al.*, 2017). Although we expect synergistic and complementary effects of these two assays, RNA-seq offers comprehensive catalog of diverse RNA species, and depicts their transcriptomic and epitranscriptomic landscapes (Wang *et al.*, 2009; Ozsolak and Milos, 2011a; Helm and Motorin, 2017). In fact, recent large-scale RNA-seq projects have revealed remarkable biological characteristics, which includes pervasive transcriptomic feature (Djebali *et al.*, 2012), ingenious promoter usage (Yamashita *et al.*, 2011; Forrest *et al.*, 2014), disease-related transcripts (Weinstein *et al.*, 2013), and dynamic transcriptome waves (Park *et al.*, 2013).

In general, RNA-seq experiments first convert target RNAs into cDNAs that are further amplified. Then, they sequence the amplicons as reads that are computationally mapped on a reference genome. Consequently, the total number of reads mapped to single gene gives the degree of its expression. Of note, various alternative protocols have been developed, such as cDNA-conversion-free RNA-seq (Ozsolak and Milos, 2011b) and amplification-free RNA-seq (Mamanova *et al.*, 2010; Loman and Watson, 2015). Conventionally, RNAs are extracted from bulk cells by considering the cell homogeneity (Park *et al.*, 2013), giving averaged gene expression. Recently, RNA extraction from single cell has emerged (i.e., scRNA-seq) to address key biological issues (Tang *et al.*, 2009; Wang and Navin, 2015) including heterogeneous cell responses that are markedly observed in cancer diseases (Kim *et al.*, 2015), stem cells (Wen and Tang, 2016), and immune systems (Kadoki *et al.*, 2017; Papalexi and Satija, 2018).

Prior to the establishment of transcriptome profiles, researchers have to correct sequencing biases and errors that may occur due to the intrinsic feature of NGS applications (Li *et al.*, 2014; Seqc_Maqc-Iii_Consortium, 2014). To do so, guidelines suggested by the community emphasize many technical issues, such as the importance of multiple biological and technical replicates (Schurch *et al.*, 2016; Merino *et al.*, 2017), the impact of library preparation methods (Parekh *et al.*, 2016), the influence of reference genomes and annotations on downstream interpretation (Hardwick *et al.*, 2017), and the prevention of microbial contaminations (Strong *et al.*, 2014; Olarerin-George and Hogenesch, 2015). Although some issues appear to be highly complex, bioinformatics tools will greatly help the error detection and correction through practical computation and mathematics (Greenfield *et al.*, 2014; Finotello and Di Camillo, 2015; Conesa *et al.*, 2016; Pimentel *et al.*, 2017). One can find a list of related bioinformatics software from the web site of OMIC Tools (Henry *et al.*, 2014).

Bioinformatics for Transcriptome Analysis

Once genomic fragments were determined as reads, bioinformatics further analyzes these digital outcomes for answering biological questions. Thus, along with a well-designed experiment setting, successful NGS studies require to leverage bioinformatics tools and to carry out a pipeline that makes researches repeatable and transparent (Conesa *et al.*, 2016; Kulkarni and Frommolt, 2017). In RNA-seq experiments, the components of a typical pipeline consist of read quality control, mapping to a reference genome, and expression quantification.

The quality control (QC) of reads trims and discards erroneous bases. Since ambiguous base calling leads to misalignments and therefore misinterpretation, the base-call error probability defined as Phred score (Ewing and Green, 1998) is indispensable information. Even if reads include high-quality bases, some of the bases are potentially adapter-origin. For dealing with this issue, many solutions have been proposed; in particular, FastQC (see "Relevant Websites section"), Prinseq (Schmieder and Edwards, 2011), Cutadapt (see "Relevant Websites section"), FASTX-Toolkit (see "Relevant Websites section"), and Trimmomatic (Bolger *et al.*, 2014). Importantly, it should be known that the QC process affects gene expression profile (Williams *et al.*, 2016), which indicates the necessity of scrupulous care.

Spliced mapping tools (Dobin *et al.*, 2013; Kim *et al.*, 2013; Pertea *et al.*, 2016) align RNA-seq reads to a reference genome that includes gene annotations (e.g., exon-exon junctions). This reference-guided approach is helpful to minimize algorithmic biases associated with particular tools. The tools are also applicable to reconstructing transcripts without any reference annotations. This *de novo* transcriptome assembly is a powerful approach for detecting unknown transcripts as well as for novel organisms (Grabherr *et al.*, 2011; Xie *et al.*, 2014). It should be noted that some portion of total sequenced reads are not mapped to the reference genome but mapped to its alternate assemblies and contigs that have been unplaced in building the reference genome. For instance, **Fig. 2(A)** exhibits 66.8%–91.6% mappability with the mouse reference genome GRCm38 (2647.54 Mb in size), and shows that 8.1%–24.1% in total reads are mappable to the alternate sequences of GRCm38 downloadable from public databases (8373.72 Mb in size). This underlines the possibility that the reference-guided approach misses one fourth of transcriptome in a worse case, which requires further investigation on its impact.

To quantify gene- or transcript-level expression, the mapped reads are rigorously addressed in terms of read depth and transcript-width coverage. Since the short reads are results from random cutting of RNA molecules, the transcript length and total number of sequenced reads affect the quantification (Conesa *et al.*, 2016). Therefore, normalization within a sample as well as among samples is an essential process that is still actively developed (Mortazavi *et al.*, 2008; Trapnell *et al.*, 2010; Risso *et al.*, 2014; Teng *et al.*, 2016; Jin *et al.*, 2017). The units frequently used in the normalization include FPKM (Fragments Per Kilobase of transcript per Million mapped reads), RPKM (Reads Per Kilobase of transcript per Million mapped reads), TPM (Transcripts Per Million), CPM (Counts-Per-Million), and PPM (Parts Per Million).

For example, HISAT2-Cufflinks2 pipeline (Trapnell *et al.*, 2012; Pertea *et al.*, 2016) first merges all the transcript assemblies coming from multiple replicates of each sample. Then, Cufflinks package counts mapped reads incorporated with the merged assembly, and scales the counts using the median of the geometric means of fragment counts across all samples (Anders and Huber, 2010). In the case of **Fig. 2**, the total read number of each replicate was adjusted to $1.78725e + 07$ by a formula with each scale factor (**Fig. 2(B)**), which yields the broad dynamic range of gene expression value FPKMs that makes easy to detect differentially expressed genes (**Fig. 2(C)**).

Functional Profiling With Transcriptome Data

Identifying Differentially Expressed Genes

To scan biologically relevant genes, further investigation with a transcriptome profile may focus on categorizing gene expression changes. In this regard, the identification of differentially expressed genes (DEGs) between two samples is one of the most frequently used approaches, which employs a statistical model for the distributional approximation among biological replicates of the two samples. The statistical models, such as Poisson distribution, negative binomial distribution, Bayesian, and bootstrapping, have been embedded in a large number of tools (Marioni *et al.*, 2008; Hardcastle and Kelly, 2010; Robinson *et al.*, 2010; Wang *et al.*, 2010; Bray *et al.*, 2016; Dong *et al.*, 2016; Pimentel *et al.*, 2017). On the other hand, recent systematic benchmarks for these tools indicate that hidden factors underlying statistical assumption affect reproducibility and false discovery rate (FDR) in the DEG detection (Schurch *et al.*, 2016; Teng *et al.*, 2016; Jin *et al.*, 2017; Merino *et al.*, 2017; Pimentel *et al.*, 2017).

As an example, **Fig. 2(D)** shows the number of DEGs in consecutive stages, and **Fig. 2(E)** shows a subset of the DEGs excluding genes expressed (>3.0 FPKM) either in MEF or Sertoli cells, which indicates sperm-specific transcriptomic bursts at the mitotic and meiotic stage SG, SC, and SD (Margolin *et al.*, 2014). Cuffdiff (Trapnell *et al.*, 2012) defined these DEGs using two empirical thresholds; FPKM fold-change (FC) and Q-value. The Q-value denotes FDR in which Benjamini-Hochberg correction adjusted P-value of two-group t-test (Storey and Tibshirani, 2003). Volcano plot visualizing the effect of two thresholds is typically used to identify the most meaningful DEGs (**Fig. 2(F)** and **(G)**).

Grouping Gene Expression Patterns

Given a transcriptome profile from multiple cells and/or multiple time points, genes and transcripts often exhibit dynamic expression waves that DEGs can hardly explain. To decompose the profile into expression waves, bioinformatics of so-called spatio-temporal gene expression analysis employs various computational algorithms including principal component analysis, matrix decomposition, t-distributed stochastic neighbor embedding (t-SNE) analysis, and network analysis (Domazet-Loso and Tautz, 2010; Shapiro *et al.*, 2013; Hashimshony *et al.*, 2015; Chou *et al.*, 2016; van Dam *et al.*, 2017).

As a straightforward method, clustering analyses clearly show gene groups with similar expression patterns (Eisen *et al.*, 1998; Oyelade *et al.*, 2016). For instance, to prepare a clustering heatmap (**Fig. 3(A)**), FPKMs shown in **Fig. 2(C)** formatted a matrix Genes × Stages, and the matrix was converted into relative values by quantile normalization and matrix mean centering. Then, a clustering method grouped the matrix rows using Euclidian distance metric and hierarchical average linkage method (**Fig. 3(A)**). The method also grouped the matrix columns using Pearson's correlation coefficient, showing (dis)similarity of gene expression patterns among the developmental stages (**Fig. 3(B)**). As a result, one can trace gene clusters that may share biological functions (**Fig. 3(C)**). Of note, the clustering considered relative values without FPKM trimming and cutoff. Thus, absolute FPKMs of genes in a cluster might vary in degree even if their expression dynamics are highly similar. For example, Cluster 2 exhibits repressive FPKM distribution compared to Cluster 9 (**Fig. 3(C)**); 51.6% of genes in Cluster 2 (1503/2914) are <3.0 FPKM at E14.5. Consequently, expression filtering with a threshold may affect further interpretation.

Annotating Functional Importance of Genes

In order to reveal functional meaning of key genes, bioinformatics tools search functional genome databases with a gene list, and subsequently perform statistical tests to infer whether any biological annotations are enriched in the genes compared to a background gene set. The approaches include Gene Set Enrichment Analysis (GSEA), Gene Ontology (GO) enrichment analysis, and pathway signature analysis (Subramanian *et al.*, 2005; Huang da *et al.*, 2009; Hung *et al.*, 2012; Yu *et al.*, 2016; Kanehisa *et al.*, 2017). Remarkably, all of the methods exploit knowledge repositories that have become indispensable for interpreting biological functions. Therefore, opening and sharing functional annotations in a standardized data format are increasingly important.

A difficult consideration in the enrichment analysis is to reduce FDR by controlling a balance between false positives (type I error, incorrectly inferring *"enriched"* from truly *"not enriched"* results) and false negatives (type II error, incorrectly inferring *"not enriched"* from truly *"enriched"* results) (Storey and Tibshirani, 2003; Curtis *et al.*, 2005). Also, since repeat enrichment tests for a gene set with different biological terms increase the change of observing false positives, researchers might adjust raw P-values by such as Benjamini-Hochberg procedure and Bonferroni correction (Storey and Tibshirani, 2003; Schwartzman and Lin, 2011). However, the multiplicity correction needs an attention due to leading to contradictory results with higher type II error rate, which is still under argument along with the issue of what P-value threshold is appropriate to enrichment decisions (Perneger, 1998; Sterne and Davey Smith, 2001).

In **Fig. 3(A)**, among 16 clusters that the number of member genes is >100, ten clusters showed GO terms enriched by the tool of GOC (Gene Ontology Consortium, 2015), which indicates the involvement of common or unique biological processes (**Fig. 3(D)**). This enrichment analysis conducted Bonferroni correction, and picked up GO terms only if <0.001 FDR. When other options for statistical test were used, the results presented broader GO term enrichment including the result in **Fig. 3(D)**. Interestingly, genes in Cluster 8 transiently up-regulated at SG (Spermatogonia) are significantly involved in cell differentiation processes; at this stage, SG undergo mitotic proliferation and maturation (Ernst *et al.*, 2017). Also, Cluster 2 showing transient gene expression at E14.5 is

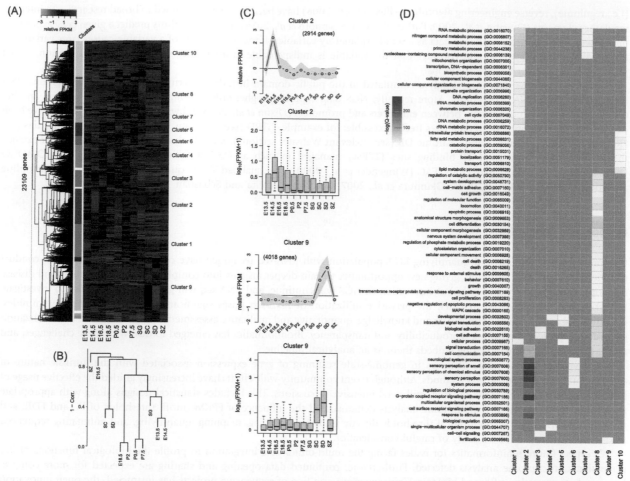

Fig. 3 An example of clustering analysis of transcriptome complexity. (A) Hierarchical clustering retrieving 16 clusters in which the number of genes in a cluster is over 100; among the clusters, 10 clusters showed significant GO term enrichment. (B) Dendrogram showing (dis)similarity of gene expression patterns among samples based on the distance of Pearson's correlation coefficient. (C) Examples of relative and absolute expression patterns; red line stands for the mean of relative FPKMs, and boxplot shows corresponding absolute FPKMs. (C) Result of GO term (biological process) enrichment analysis using Q-value of Bonferroni correction (<0.001).

involved in olfactory sensory activity. Indeed, over 500 olfactory receptors (ORs) are located in this cluster, and the genes without weakly expressed (<3.0 FPKM) still exhibited the enrichment of term *"sensory perception of smell"* (GO:0007608); FDR = 4.38e−10. Although ORs play importance roles in spermatogenesis (Fukuda and Touhara, 2006), unlike ORs highly expressed in Cluster 6, this activity might be related to epigenetic reprograming; at E14.5 and E15.5, DNA methylation is globally erased and rapidly re-acquired (Bohacek and Mansuy, 2015).

Integrating Transcriptome With Multi-Omics Data

As ENCODE has illustrated (Djebali *et al.*, 2012), complex intra- and inter-molecular crosstalk is observed among regulatory elements, which indicates the necessity of projection of other omics data (e.g., epigenomics, proteomics, and metabolomics) onto transcriptome data. Extensive efforts have therefore been made for emerging multi-omics importance that can be manifested by various NGS assays, and have expedited the understanding of a wide range of biological phenomena (Hasin *et al.*, 2017; Li *et al.*, 2018; Lowe *et al.*, 2017). For example, ICGC and GTEx consortia have released multi-omics datasets in unprecedented scale, facilitating studies in the association of molecular signatures and phenotypes across large number of different cancer types and tissues (International Cancer Genome Consortium *et al.*, 2010; GTEx Consortium, 2017; Li *et al.*, 2017).

We expect that biases led from the heterogeneous datasets introduce highly confounding results with low reproducibility. Therefore, to integrate the multi-omics data by reducing unfavorable effects is a hot topic in bioinformatics, and a line of researches has proposed advanced computational algorithms (Gomez-Cabrero *et al.*, 2014; Huang *et al.*, 2017). These include matrix factorization (Zhang *et al.*, 2012), graph- or kernel-based methods (Yan *et al.*, 2017), and machine learning approaches (Li *et al.*, 2018; Chaudhary *et al.*, 2018). In regard to the association between transcriptome and a set of regulatory elements (i.e., regulome), reverse engineering algorithms (Bussemaker, 2006) have been successfully applied in broad researches to infer key regulatory elements (Ouyang *et al.*, 2009; Park *et al.*, 2014; Sasamoto *et al.*, 2016). These algorithms predict a given gene expression profile with features from regulome data as a set of explanatory variables. If the removal test of a variable causes large variance in the predictive model, we should consider that the variable is indispensable factor for regulating the gene expression, which provides clues into further investigations.

Particular regulome data increasingly accumulated in the public domain include TF occupancy, histone modification, DNA methylation, and DNA accessibility. More recently, NGS data capturing higher-order chromatin organization became another omics data showing cooperativity between enhancers and promoters (Dixon *et al.*, 2015; Schwarzer *et al.*, 2017). These have been devoted to the development of databases freely accessible; for example, GTRD (see "Relevant Websites section"), ChIP-Atlas (see "Relevant Websites section") and Cistrome DB (see "Relevant Websites section"). Meta-analysis of the databases further extends the empirical information of TF binding sites (TFBSs) managed in such as JASPAR (Vlieghe *et al.*, 2006), HOCOMOCO (Kulakovskiy *et al.*, 2013) and TRANSFAC (Wingender *et al.*, 2000). The qualified TFBSs can be extensive resources for online analytical tools (Ho Sui *et al.*, 2005; Okumura *et al.*, 2007; Contreras-Moreira and Sebastian, 2016).

Outlook and Conclusions

Comprehensive cataloging and quantifying RNA population with RNA-seq technique have convinced communities to conduct routine gene expression profiling, giving new opportunities to gain deeper insights into complex molecular interplay and disease development. It is likely that technical innovation in NGS will continue, and RNA-seq will gain more popularity to investigate transcriptome complexity. In parallel, the pervasive utilization of RNA-seq poses significant challenges to the communities, including the management of huge data and knowledge, quantitative and qualitative assessment of outcomes, and standardization of analytical protocols ensuring reproducibility and transparency. Bioinformatics has emerged to deal with these challenges, and recent RNA-seq experiment setting embeds them as an analytical pipeline.

We have described a range of issues in genome-scale scanning of gene expression associated with the intrinsic nature of experimental and computational methods. Although recent community-wide efforts have increasingly guided the effective usage of bioinformatics resources, some of issues still need intensive discussions. This includes statistical designs along with appropriate thresholds; the example of transcriptome analysis demonstrated the influence of FPKM cutoff, thresholds of FC and FDR, and multiplicity correction. Such empirical thresholds directly impact on filtering, mapping, quantifying, and annotating sequenced reads, which indicates the necessity of careful consideration.

We expect future bioinformatics for issues facing the multi-omics data integration to profile the biological functions of key genes that transcriptome analysis detected. Furthermore, continued data opening and sharing are expected for more comprehensive characterization of broad biological consequences; as a line of sequencing projects has instructed, the open innovation coupled with Big Data paradigm will provide valuable resources for systematic reciprocal linking of multiple regulatory layers, and also for linking genotypes to phenotypes. Therefore, effective bioinformatics methods for the integration approaches are becoming more indispensable. Finally, we believe that researchers will actively conduct open sharing of gene expression atlases established by tackling the issues mentioned here, and the atlases will propel genome analysis studies in biological science and clinical setting.

Materials and Methods

Data Preparing

Illumina SRA files for 34 RNA-seq samples were prepared from NCBI GEO; embryonic day E13.5 (GSM1064457), E14.5 (ERP015330), E16.5 (ERP015330), E18.5 (ERP015330), postnatal P0.5 (DRP002386), P2 (ERP015330), P7.5 (DRP002386), Spermatogonia; SG (GSM1069640), Spermatocytes; SC (GSM1069641), Spermatids; SD (GSM1069642), Spermatozoa; SZ (GSM1069643), Mouse embryonic fibroblast; MEF (GSM1643254), and Sertoli; SL (GSM1069639). SRA toolkit (ver. 2.8.2–1) converted the SRA files into FASTQ files by using options "fastq-dump -split-files -A *accession*".

Rna-Seq Pipeline

Step1 (Quality control): Trimmomatic (ver. 0.36) assessed all the FASTQ files by using options "ILLUMINACLIP:*adapter_file*:2:30:10 LEADING:20 TRAILING:20 MINLEN:36".

Step2 (Mapping): HISAT2 (ver.2.0.5) coupled with Bowtie2 (ver. 2.2.9) mapped the reads of each replicate to the mouse reference genome GRCm38 with options "-k 1 –dta –dta-cufflinks", resulting 34 BAM files. After gathering unmapped reads from the BAMs by Samtools (ver. 1.5) with options "view -bf 4", Blastn (ver. 2.2.31) aligned the unmapped reads by using options "-evalue 0.001 -perc_identity 80 -max_target_seqs 1" and a pre-built database with alternative assemblies and contigs downloaded from ftp://ftp.ensembl.org/pub/ and ftp://ftp.ncbi.nlm.nih.gov/blast/db/.

Step 3 (Assembling and Quantifying): Cufflinks (ver. 2.2.1) with options "–total-hits-norm -b GRCm38.fa -G *RefSeq(release 80)*" assembled transcripts of each BAM, resulting 34 GTF (gene feature format) files. Cuffcompare (ver. 2.2.1) combined the 34

GTFs by using options "-C -T -R -r *RefSeq(release 80)* -s GRCm38.fa". Cuffquant (ver. 2.2.1) with options "-b GRCm38.fa *Combined_GTF*" quantified each BAM and created 34 CBX files. Finally, Cuffdiff (ver. 2.2.1) profiled FPKMs and DEGs from 34 CBXs by using options "–FDR 0.05 –library-norm-method geometric –compatible-hits-norm *Combined_GTF All_CBX_files*".

Bioinformatics Analysis

Clustering of gene expression performed R language function hclust; Euclidean distances among FPKMs of samples were adjusted by quantile normalization and mean centering, and the hierarchical average linkage method clustered genes. Sample clustering used Pearson's correlation coefficient as distances. The enrichment analysis of GO terms used the GOC web tool (see "Relevant Websites section") with the dataset "*PANTHER GO-Slim Biological Process*". Bonferroni correction that multiplies P-value of single Binomial test by the number of independent tests calculated FDR represented by Q-value.

Acknowledgement

The author thanks Prof. Kenta Nakai, the University of Tokyo, for helpful comments and discussions. Computational resources were provided by the supercomputer system SHIROKANE at Human Genome Center, the Institute of Medical Science, the University of Tokyo.

See also: Exome Sequencing Data Analysis. Functional Enrichment Analysis. Integrative Analysis of Multi-Omics Data. Natural Language Processing Approaches in Bioinformatics. Next Generation Sequencing Data Analysis. Whole Genome Sequencing Analysis

References

Anders, S., Huber, W., 2010. Differential expression analysis for sequence count data. Genome Biol. 11, R106.
Ay, F., Noble, W.S., 2015. Analysis methods for studying the 3D architecture of the genome. Genome Biol. 16, 183.
Bettegowda, A., Wilkinson, M.F., 2010. Transcription and post-transcriptional regulation of spermatogenesis. Philos. Trans. R Soc. Lond. B Biol. Sci. 365, 1637–1651.
Bohacek, J., Mansuy, I.M., 2015. Molecular insights into transgenerational non-genetic inheritance of acquired behaviours. Nat. Rev. Genet. 16, 641–652.
Bolger, A.M., Lohse, M., Usadel, B., 2014. Trimmomatic: A flexible trimmer for Illumina sequence data. Bioinformatics 30, 2114–2120.
Bray, N.L., Pimentel, H., Melsted, P., Pachter, L., 2016. Near-optimal probabilistic RNA-seq quantification. Nat. Biotechnol. 34, 525–527.
Buenrostro, J.D., Giresi, P.G., Zaba, L.C., Chang, H.Y., Greenleaf, W.J., 2013. Transposition of native chromatin for fast and sensitive epigenomic profiling of open chromatin, DNA-binding proteins and nucleosome position. Nat. Methods 10, 1213–1218.
Bussemaker, H.J., 2006. Modeling gene expression control using Omes Law. Mol. Syst. Biol. 2, 2006.0013.
Chaisson, M.J., Huddleston, J., Dennis, M.Y., et al., 2015. Resolving the complexity of the human genome using single-molecule sequencing. Nature 517, 608–611.
Chaudhary, K., Poirion, O.B., Lu, L., Garmire, L.X., 2018. Deep Learning based multi-omics integration robustly predicts survival in liver cancer. Clin. Cancer Res. 24 (6), 1248–1259.
Cho, H., Davis, J., Li, X., et al., 2014. High-resolution transcriptome analysis with long-read RNA sequencing. PLOS ONE 9, e108095.
Chou, S.J., Wang, C., Sintupisut, N., et al., 2016. Analysis of spatial-temporal gene expression patterns reveals dynamics and regionalization in developing mouse brain. Sci. Rep. 6, 19274.
Cochrane, G., Karsch-Mizrachi, I., Takagi, T., International Nucleotide Sequence Database Collaboration, 2016. The International Nucleotide Sequence Database Collaboration. Nucleic Acids Res. 44, D48–D50.
Conesa, A., Madrigal, P., Tarazona, S., et al., 2016. A survey of best practices for RNA-seq data analysis. Genome Biol. 17, 13.
Contreras-Moreira, B., Sebastian, A., 2016. FootprintDB: Analysis of plant cis-regulatory elements, transcription factors, and binding interfaces. Methods Mol. Biol. 1482, 259–277.
Curtis, R.K., Oresic, M., Vidal-Puig, A., 2005. Pathways to the analysis of microarray data. Trends Biotechnol. 23, 429–435.
Dixon, J.R., Jung, I., Selvaraj, S., et al., 2015. Chromatin architecture reorganization during stem cell differentiation. Nature 518, 331–336.
Djebali, S., Davis, C.A., Merkel, A., et al., 2012. Landscape of transcription in human cells. Nature 489, 101–108.
Dobin, A., Davis, C.A., Schlesinger, F., et al., 2013. STAR: Ultrafast universal RNA-seq aligner. Bioinformatics 29, 15–21.
Domazet-Loso, T., Tautz, D., 2010. A phylogenetically based transcriptome age index mirrors ontogenetic divergence patterns. Nature 468, 815–818.
Dong, K., Zhao, H., Tong, T., Wan, X., 2016. NBLDA: Negative binomial linear discriminant analysis for RNA-Seq data. BMC Bioinform. 17, 369.
Eisen, M.B., Spellman, P.T., Brown, P.O., Botstein, D., 1998. Cluster analysis and display of genome-wide expression patterns. Proc. Natl. Acad. Sci. USA 95, 14863–14868.
Ernst, C., Odom, D.T., Kutter, C., 2017. The emergence of piRNAs against transposon invasion to preserve mammalian genome integrity. Nat. Commun. 8, 1411.
Ewing, B., Green, P., 1998. Base-calling of automated sequencer traces using phred. II. Error probabilities. Genome Res. 8, 186–194.
Finotello, F., Di Camillo, B., 2015. Measuring differential gene expression with RNA-seq: Challenges and strategies for data analysis. Brief. Funct. Genomics 14, 130–142.
Forrest, A.R., Kawaji, H., Rehli, M., et al., 2014. The impact of rare variation on gene expression across tissues. Nature 507, 462–470.
Frye, M., Jaffrey, S.R., Pan, T., Rechavi, G., Suzuki, T., 2016. RNA modifications: What have we learned and where are we headed? Nat. Rev. Genet. 17, 365–372.
Fukuda, N., Touhara, K., 2006. Developmental expression patterns of testicular olfactory receptor genes during mouse spermatogenesis. Genes Cells 11, 71–81.
Gene Ontology Consortium, 2015. Gene Ontology Consortium: Going forward. Nucleic Acids Res. 43, D1049–D1056.
Gomez-Cabrero, D., Abugessaisa, I., Maier, D., et al., 2014. Data integration in the era of omics: Current and future challenges. BMC Syst. Biol. 8, I1.
Grabherr, M.G., Haas, B.J., Yassour, M., et al., 2011. Full-length transcriptome assembly from RNA-Seq data without a reference genome. Nat. Biotechnol. 29, 644–652.
Greenfield, P., Duesing, K., Papanicolaou, A., Bauer, D.C., 2014. Blue: Correcting sequencing errors using consensus and context. Bioinformatics 30, 2723–2732.
GTEx Consortium, 2017. Genetic effects on gene expression across human tissues. Nature 550, 204–213.
Hardcastle, T.J., Kelly, K.A., 2010. baySeq: Empirical Bayesian methods for identifying differential expression in sequence count data. BMC Bioinform. 11, 422.
Hardwick, S.A., Deveson, I.W., Mercer, T.R., 2017. Reference standards for next-generation sequencing. Nat. Rev. Genet. 18, 473–484.
Hashimshony, T., Feder, M., Levin, M., Hall, B.K., Yanai, I., 2015. Spatiotemporal transcriptomics reveals the evolutionary history of the endoderm germ layer. Nature 519, 219–222.
Hasin, Y., Seldin, M., Lusis, A., 2017. Multi-omics approaches to disease. Genome Biol. 18, 83.
Helm, M., Motorin, Y., 2017. Detecting RNA modifications in the epitranscriptome: Predict and validate. Nat. Rev. Genet. 18, 275–291.

Henry, V.J., Bandrowski, A.E., Pepin, A.S., Gonzalez, B.J., Desfeux, A., 2014. OMICtools: An informative directory for multi-omic data analysis. Database (Oxford) 2014, bau069.

Hoheisel, J.D., 2006. Microarray technology: Beyond transcript profiling and genotype analysis. Nat. Rev. Genet. 7, 200–210.

Ho Sui, S.J., Mortimer, J.R., Arenillas, D.J., et al., 2005. oPOSSUM: Identification of over-represented transcription factor binding sites in co-expressed genes. Nucleic Acids Res. 33, 3154–3164.

Huang da, W., Sherman, B.T., Lempicki, R.A., 2009. Systematic and integrative analysis of large gene lists using DAVID bioinformatics resources. Nat. Protoc. 4, 44–57.

Huang, S., Chaudhary, K., Garmire, L.X., 2017. More is better: Recent progress in multi-omics data integration methods. Front. Genet. 8, 84.

Hung, J.H., Yang, T.H., Hu, Z., Weng, Z., DeLisi, C., 2012. Gene set enrichment analysis: Performance evaluation and usage guidelines. Brief Bioinform. 13, 281–291.

Hudson, T.J., Anderson, W., Artez, A., et al., 2010. International Cancer Genome Consortium, International network of cancer genome projects. Nature 464, 993–998.

Jin, H., Wan, Y.W., Liu, Z., 2017. Comprehensive evaluation of RNA-seq quantification methods for linearity. BMC Bioinform. 18, 117.

Kadoki, M., Patil, A., Thaiss, C.C., et al., 2017. Organism-level analysis of vaccination reveals networks of protection across tissues. Cell 171, e21.

Kanehisa, M., Furumichi, M., Tanabe, M., Sato, Y., Morishima, K., 2017. KEGG: New perspectives on genomes, pathways, diseases and drugs. Nucleic Acids Res. 45, D353–D361.

Kidder, B.L., Hu, G., Zhao, K., 2011. ChIP-Seq: Technical considerations for obtaining high-quality data. Nat. Immunol. 12, 918–922.

Kim, D., Pertea, G., Trapnell, C., et al., 2013. TopHat2: Accurate alignment of transcriptomes in the presence of insertions, deletions and gene fusions. Genome Biol. 14, R36.

Kim, K.T., Lee, H.W., Lee, H.O., et al., 2015. Single-cell mRNA sequencing identifies subclonal heterogeneity in anti-cancer drug responses of lung adenocarcinoma cells. Genome Biol. 16, 127.

Koboldt, D.C., Steinberg, K.M., Larson, D.E., Wilson, R.K., Mardis, E.R., 2013. The next-generation sequencing revolution and its impact on genomics. Cell 155, 27–38.

Kulakovskiy, I.V., Medvedeva, Y.A., Schaefer, U., et al., 2013. HOCOMOCO: A comprehensive collection of human transcription factor binding sites models. Nucleic Acids Res. 41, D195–D202.

Kulkarni, P., Frommolt, P., 2017. Challenges in the setup of large-scale next-generation sequencing analysis workflows. Comput. Struct. Biotechnol. J. 15, 471–477.

Laird, P.W., 2010. Principles and challenges of genomewide DNA methylation analysis. Nat. Rev. Genet. 11, 191–203.

Lam, H.Y., Clark, M.J., Chen, R., et al., 2012. Performance comparison of whole-genome sequencing platforms. Nat. Biotechnol. 30, 78–82.

Li, H., Wang, X., Rukina, D., et al., 2018. An integrated systems genetics and omics toolkit to probe gene function. Cell Syst. 6 (1), 90–102.

Li, R., Hsieh, C.L., Young, A., et al., 2015. Illumina synthetic long read sequencing allows recovery of missing sequences even in the "Finished" C. elegans genome. Sci. Rep. 5, 10814.

Li, S., Labaj, P.P., Zumbo, P., et al., 2014. Detecting and correcting systematic variation in large-scale RNA sequencing data. Nat. Biotechnol. 32, 888–895.

Li, X., Kim, Y., Tsang, E.K., et al., 2017. The impact of rare variation on gene expression across tissues. Nature 550, 239–243.

Li, Y., Wu, F.X., Ngom, A., 2018. A review on machine learning principles for multi-view biological data integration. Brief. Bioinform. 1 (19), 325–340.

Loman, N.J., Misra, R.V., Dallman, T.J., et al., 2012. Performance comparison of benchtop high-throughput sequencing platforms. Nat. Biotechnol. 30, 434–439.

Loman, N.J., Watson, M., 2015. Successful test launch for nanopore sequencing. Nat. Methods 12, 303–304.

Lowe, E.K., Cuomo, C., Arnone, M.I., 2017. Omics approaches to study gene regulatory networks for development in echinoderms. Brief. Funct. Genom. 16, 299–308.

Mamanova, L., Andrews, R.M., James, K.D., et al., 2010. FRT-seq: Amplification-free, strand-specific transcriptome sequencing. Nat. Methods 7, 130–132.

Mardis, E.R., 2013. Next-generation sequencing platforms. Annu. Rev. Anal. Chem. (Palo Alto Calif) 6, 287–303.

Margolin, G., Khil, P.P., Kim, J., Bellani, M.A., Camerini-Otero, R.D., 2014. Integrated transcriptome analysis of mouse spermatogenesis. BMC Genom. 15, 39.

Marioni, J.C., Mason, C.E., Mane, S.M., Stephens, M., Gilad, Y., 2008. RNA-seq: An assessment of technical reproducibility and comparison with gene expression arrays. Genome Res. 18, 1509–1517.

McCoy, R.C., Taylor, R.W., Blauwkamp, T.A., et al., 2014. Illumina TruSeq synthetic long-reads empower de novo assembly and resolve complex, highly-repetitive transposable elements. PLOS ONE 9, e106689.

Merino, G.A., Conesa, A., Fernandez, E.A., 2017. A benchmarking of workflows for detecting differential splicing and differential expression at isoform level in human RNA-seq studies. Brief. Bioinform.

Mortazavi, A., Williams, B.A., McCue, K., Schaeffer, L., Wold, B., 2008. Mapping and quantifying mammalian transcriptomes by RNA-Seq. Nat .Methods 5, 621–628.

Nakano, K., Shiroma, A., Shimoji, M., et al., 2017. Advantages of genome sequencing by long-read sequencer using SMRT technology in medical area. Hum. Cell 30, 149–161.

Nazarov, P.V., Muller, A., Kaoma, T., et al., 2017. RNA sequencing and transcriptome arrays analyses show opposing results for alternative splicing in patient derived samples. BMC Genom. 18, 443.

Okumura, T., Makiguchi, H., Makita, Y., Yamashita, R., Nakai, K., 2007. Melina II: A web tool for comparisons among several predictive algorithms to find potential motifs from promoter regions. Nucleic Acids Res. 35, W227–W231.

Olarerin-George, A.O., Hogenesch, J.B., 2015. Assessing the prevalence of mycoplasma contamination in cell culture via a survey of NCBI's RNA-seq archive. Nucleic Acids Res. 43, 2535–2542.

Ouyang, Z., Zhou, Q., Wong, W.H., 2009. ChIP-Seq of transcription factors predicts absolute and differential gene expression in embryonic stem cells. Proc. Natl. Acad. Sci. USA 106, 21521–21526.

Oyelade, J., Isewon, I., Oladipupo, F., et al., 2016. Clustering algorithms: Their application to gene expression data. Bioinform. Biol. Insights 10, 237–253.

Ozsolak, F., Milos, P.M., 2011a. RNA sequencing: Advances, challenges and opportunities. Nat. Rev. Genet. 12, 87–98.

Ozsolak, F., Milos, P.M., 2011b. Single-molecule direct RNA sequencing without cDNA synthesis. Wiley Interdiscip. Rev. RNA 2, 565–570.

Papalexi, E., Satija, R., 2018. Single-cell RNA sequencing to explore immune cell heterogeneity. Nat. Rev. Immunol. 18 (1), 35–45.

Parekh, S., Ziegenhain, C., Vieth, B., Enard, W., Hellmann, I., 2016. The impact of amplification on differential expression analyses by RNA-seq. Sci. Rep. 6, 25533.

Park, P.J., 2009. ChIP-seq: Advantages and challenges of a maturing technology. Nat. Rev. Genet. 10, 669–680.

Park, S.J., Komata, M., Inoue, F., et al., 2013. Inferring the choreography of parental genomes during fertilization from ultralarge-scale whole-transcriptome analysis. Genes Dev. 27, 2736–2748.

Park, S.J., Saito-Adachi, M., Komiyama, Y., Nakai, K., 2016. Advances, practice, and clinical perspectives in high-throughput sequencing. Oral Dis. 22, 353–364.

Park, S.J., Umemoto, T., Saito-Adachi, M., et al., 2014. Computational promoter modeling identifies the modes of transcriptional regulation in hematopoietic stem cells. PLOS ONE 9, e93853.

Paulsen, J., Rodland, E.A., Holden, L., Holden, M., Hovig, E., 2014. A statistical model of ChIA-PET data for accurate detection of chromatin 3D interactions. Nucleic Acids Res. 42, e143.

Perneger, T.V., 1998. What's wrong with Bonferroni adjustments. BMJ 316, 1236–1238.

Pertea, M., Kim, D., Pertea, G.M., Leek, J.T., Salzberg, S.L., 2016. Transcript-level expression analysis of RNA-seq experiments with HISAT, StringTie and Ballgown. Nat. Protoc. 11, 1650–1667.

Pimentel, H., Bray, N.L., Puente, S., Melsted, P., Pachter, L., 2017. Differential analysis of RNA-seq incorporating quantification uncertainty. Nat. Methods 14, 687–690.

Reuter, J.A., Spacek, D.V., Snyder, M.P., 2015. High-throughput sequencing technologies. Mol. Cell 58, 586–597.

Risso, D., Ngai, J., Speed, T.P., Dudoit, S., 2014. Normalization of RNA-seq data using factor analysis of control genes or samples. Nat. Biotechnol. 32, 896–902.

Robinson, M.D., McCarthy, D.J., Smyth, G.K., 2010. edgeR: A bioconductor package for differential expression analysis of digital gene expression data. Bioinformatics 26, 139–140.

Ross, M.G., Russ, C., Costello, M., et al., 2013. Characterizing and measuring bias in sequence data. Genome Biol. 14, R51.

Sahraeian, S.M.E., Mohiyuddin, M., Sebra, R., et al., 2017. Gaining comprehensive biological insight into the transcriptome by performing a broad-spectrum RNA-seq analysis. Nat. Commun. 8, 59.

Saitou, M., Kagiwada, S., Kurimoto, K., 2012. Epigenetic reprogramming in mouse pre-implantation development and primordial germ cells. Development 139, 15–31.

Sanger, F., Air, G.M., Barrell, B.G., et al., 1977. Nucleotide sequence of bacteriophage phi X174 DNA. Nature 265, 687–695.

Sasamoto, Y., Hayashi, R., Park, S.J., *et al.*, 2016. PAX6 Isoforms, along with reprogramming factors, differentially regulate the induction of cornea-specific genes. Sci. Rep. 6, 20807.

Schmieder, R., Edwards, R., 2011. Quality control and preprocessing of metagenomic datasets. Bioinformatics 27, 863–864.

Schurch, N.J., Schofield, P., Gierlinski, M., *et al.*, 2016. How many biological replicates are needed in an RNA-seq experiment and which differential expression tool should you use? RNA 22, 839–851.

Schwartzman, A., Lin, X., 2011. The effect of correlation in false discovery rate estimation. Biometrika 98, 199–214.

Schwarzer, W., Abdennur, N., Goloborodko, A., *et al.*, 2017. Two independent modes of chromatin organization revealed by cohesin removal. Nature 551, 51–56.

Seqc_Maqc-Iii_Consortium, 2014. A comprehensive assessment of RNA-seq accuracy, reproducibility and information content by the Sequencing Quality Control Consortium. Nat. Biotechnol. 32, 903–914.

Shapiro, E., Biezuner, T., Linnarsson, S., 2013. Single-cell sequencing-based technologies will revolutionize whole-organism science. Nat. Rev. Genet. 14, 618–630.

Shendure, J., Balasubramanian, S., Church, G.M., *et al.*, 2017. DNA sequencing at 40: Past, present and future. Nature 550, 345–353.

Shi, L., Reid, L.H., Jones, W.D., *et al.*, 2006. The MicroArray Quality Control (MAQC) project shows inter- and intraplatform reproducibility of gene expression measurements. Nat. Biotechnol. 24, 1151–1161.

Sloan, C.A., Chan, E.T., Davidson, J.M., *et al.*, 2016. ENCODE data at the ENCODE portal. Nucleic Acids Res. 44, D726–D732.

Sterne, J.A., Davey Smith, G., 2001. Sifting the evidence-what's wrong with significance tests? BMJ 322, 226–231.

Storey, J.D., Tibshirani, R., 2003. Statistical significance for genomewide studies. Proc. Natl. Acad. Sci. USA 100, 9440–9445.

Strong, M.J., Xu, G., Morici, L., *et al.*, 2014. Microbial contamination in next generation sequencing: Implications for sequence-based analysis of clinical samples. PLOS Pathog. 10, e1004437.

Subramanian, A., Tamayo, P., Mootha, V.K., *et al.*, 2005. Gene set enrichment analysis: A knowledge-based approach for interpreting genome-wide expression profiles. Proc. Natl. Acad. Sci. USA 102, 15545–15550.

Sudmant, P.H., Rausch, T., Gardner, E.J., *et al.*, 2015. An integrated map of structural variation in 2,504 human genome. Nature 526, 75–81.

Tang, F., Barbacioru, C., Wang, Y., *et al.*, 2009. mRNA-Seq whole-transcriptome analysis of a single cell. Nat. Methods 6, 377–382.

Teng, M., Love, M.I., Davis, C.A., *et al.*, 2016. A benchmark for RNA-seq quantification pipelines. Genome Biol. 17, 74.

Trapnell, C., Roberts, A., Goff, L., *et al.*, 2012. Differential gene and transcript expression analysis of RNA-seq experiments with TopHat and Cufflinks. Nat. Protoc. 7, 562–578.

Trapnell, C., Williams, B.A., Pertea, G., *et al.*, 2010. Transcript assembly and quantification by RNA-Seq reveals unannotated transcripts and isoform switching during cell differentiation. Nat. Biotechnol. 28, 511–515.

van Dam, S., Vosa, U., van der Graaf, A., Franke, L., de Magalhaes, J.P., 2017. Gene co-expression analysis for functional classification and gene-disease predictions. Brief. Bioinform. 139.

Vlieghe, D., Sandelin, A., De Bleser, P.J., *et al.*, 2006. A new generation of JASPAR, the open-access repository for transcription factor binding site profiles. Nucleic Acids Res. 34, D95–D97.

Wang, C., Gong, B., Bushel, P.R., *et al.*, 2014. The concordance between RNA-seq and microarray data depends on chemical treatment and transcript abundance. Nat. Biotechnol. 32, 926–932.

Wang, L., Feng, Z., Wang, X., Wang, X., Zhang, X., 2010. DEGseq: An R package for identifying differentially expressed genes from RNA-seq data. Bioinformatics 26, 136–138.

Wang, Y., Navin, N.E., 2015. Advances and applications of single-cell sequencing technologies. Mol. Cell 58, 598–609.

Wang, Z., Gerstein, M., Snyder, M., 2009. RNA-Seq: A revolutionary tool for transcriptomics. Nat. Rev. Genet. 10, 57–63.

Weinstein, J.N., Collisson, E.A., Mills, G.B., *et al.*, 2013. The cancer genome Atlas pan-cancer analysis project. Nat. Genet. 45, 1113–1120.

Weirather, J.L., de Cesare, M., Wang, Y., *et al.*, 2017. Comprehensive comparison of Pacific Biosciences and Oxford Nanopore Technologies and their applications to transcriptome analysis. F1000Research 6, 100.

Wen, L., Tang, F., 2016. Single-cell sequencing in stem cell biology. Genome Biol. 17, 71.

Williams, C.R., Baccarella, A., Parrish, J.Z., Kim, C.C., 2016. Trimming of sequence reads alters RNA-Seq gene expression estimates. BMC Bioinform. 17, 103.

Wingender, E., Chen, X., Hehl, R., *et al.*, 2000. TRANSFAC: An integrated system for gene expression regulation. Nucleic Acids Res. 28, 316–319.

Xie, Y., Wu, G., Tang, J., *et al.*, 2014. SOAPdenovo-Trans: De novo transcriptome assembly with short RNA-Seq reads. Bioinformatics 30, 1660–1666.

Xu, Z., Peters, R.J., Weirather, J., *et al.*, 2015. Full-length transcriptome sequences and splice variants obtained by a combination of sequencing platforms applied to different root tissues of Salvia miltiorrhiza and tanshinone biosynthesis. Plant J. 82, 951–961.

Yamashita, R., Sathira, N.P., Kanai, A., *et al.*, 2011. Genome-wide characterization of transcriptional start sites in humans by integrative transcriptome analysis. Genome Res. 21, 775–789.

Yan, K.K., Zhao, H., Pang, H., 2017. A comparison of graph- and kernel-based -omics data integration algorithms for classifying complex traits. BMC Bioinform. 18, 539.

Yu, J., Gu, X., Yi, S., 2016. Ingenuity pathway analysis of gene expression profiles in distal nerve stump following nerve injury: Insights into Wallerian degeneration. Front. Cell Neurosci. 10, 274.

Zhang, S., Liu, C.C., Li, W., *et al.*, 2012. Discovery of multi-dimensional modules by integrative analysis of cancer genomic data. Nucleic Acids Res. 40, 9379–9391.

Relevant Websites

https://www.bioinformatics.babraham.ac.uk/projects/fastqc/
    Babraham Bioinformatics.
http://chip-atlas.org/
    ChIP-Atlas.
http://dc2.cistrome.org/
    Cistrome DB.
http://hannonlab.cshl.edu/fastx_toolkit/
    FASTX-Toolkit.
http://www.geneontology.org/
    Gene Ontology Consortium.

https://github.com/marcelm/cutadapt
   GitHub - marcelm/cutadapt.
http://gtrd.biouml.org/
   GTRD.

Biographical Sketch

Sung-Joon Park received the PhD degree in Engineering from Tokyo Institute of Technology, Tokyo, Japan, in 2005. He has worked as a researcher in Kobe University and Kyoto University. He is currently a senior assistant professor (project) in Human Genome Center, the Institute of Medical Science, the University of Tokyo. He is working on the field of genome information science, and has explored genome features and developed several databases devoted to embryogenesis and stem cell biology. His main research interest is to develop computational ways for interpreting biological information, especially for the functional analysis of gene expression and regulation with high-throughput sequencing data. He is a member of Information Processing Society of Japan (IPSJ), The Japan Society for Artificial Intelligence (JSAI), and Japanese Society for Bioinformatics (JSBi).

Metabolome Analysis

Camila Pereira Braga and Jiri Adamec, University of Nebraska-Lincoln, Lincoln, NE, United States

Introduction

Omics strategies have being used in different biological systems to generate knowledge about new biomarkers associated with diagnosis, disease progression, response to treatment (Reichel, 2011), and generally to understand biological processes and their regulation. In the OMICS arena, the proteome represents all proteins expressed in a cell, tissue, or organism, while the genome is associated with the genetic information (Wilkins *et al.*, 1996), the transcriptome with the RNA transcripts, and the metabolome with the metabolites. In this context, the Omics areas are referred to as proteomics, genomics, transcriptomics, and metabolomics. Recently, new terms have been introduced referring either to new areas (interactomics and topomics) or targeting specific class of the molecules (lipidomics and glycomics as a part of metabolomics or degradomics as a part of proteomics) (Nicholson *et al.*, 2007).

The primary focus of this article is on metabolomics – metabolome analysis, the most recently introduced strategy among the Omics. In 1998, Oliver *et al.* (1998) introduced the term metabolome analysis for functional genomics using a yeast model, associating the results of gene deletion or overexpression with the change in the relative concentration of metabolites. That same year, Tweeddale *et al.* (1998) used the term introduced by Oliver *et al.* (1998) (metabolome analysis) in analyzing *Escherichia coli* cell metabolites for phenotypic profiling. One year later, Nicholson *et al.* (1999) defined the term metabonomics as the "quantitative measurement of the dynamic multiparametric metabolic response of living systems to pathophysiological stimuli or genetic modification".

In 2001, such terms were clearly defined by Fiehn: metabolomics – the "metabolome of the biological system under study," metabolic fingerprinting – "a rapid classification of samples according to their origin or their biological relevance," metabolite profiling – the investigation of pre-defined metabolites (based in their association with a specific pathway or class of compounds), and metabolite target analysis – which aims "to study the primary effect of any alteration (e.g., a genetic mutation) directly" (Fiehn, 2001). Other terms have also appeared throughout the years, such as metabolic footprinting, which refers to exo metabolomes and secretomes (metabolites in extracellular fluids) (Kell *et al.*, 2005).

Metabolomics analysis can be categorized into two approaches, targeted and untargeted metabolomics. In targeted metabolomics, the metabolites selected for quantification are known and represent specific pathway(s) or class(es) of molecules. Untargeted metabolomics, on the other hand, is used to determine as many metabolites as possible and involves both metabolites quantification and their identification. (Cambiaghi *et al.*, 2017). Targeted metabolomics refers to absolute quantification (nM or mg mL^{-1}), specifically by using an internal standard and semiquantitative or quantitative analysis to detect known compounds related to specific pathways defined *a priori*, based on the hypotheses of the study (Roberts, *et al.*, 2012; Cambiaghi *et al.*, 2017). Untargeted metabolomics refers to the measure of all possible metabolites in a sample using relative quantification (fold change), and comparison between samples (Roberts *et al.*, 2012; Cambiaghi *et al.*, 2017). The challenges of untargeted metabolomics are metabolite identification, characterization of unknown small molecules, and the time needed to process the generated data (Roberts *et al.*, 2012).

Metabolome Analysis

Metabolome analysis involves several steps, as indicated in **Fig. 1**. The study starts with an experimental design that consists of two main steps (Goodacre *et al.*, 2007). The first step is to define the biological problem, generating the hypotheses of the study. Based on that, the second step involves various metabolomics approaches used in the analysis. These steps typically include sample preparation, sample analysis and data acquisition, data preprocessing, and data statistical analysis and interpretation.

Sample Preparation

Sample preparation is an important step in metabolome analysis, consisting of sample collection and metabolite extraction. Metabolite extraction depends on the sample type (cell, biological fluid, or tissues), the metabolomics approach defined in the experimental design, and can involve steps such as quenching (removal of proteins and their enzymatic activities by denaturation and precipitation), use of internal standards, and optional derivatization of specific classes of metabolites (Klassen *et al.*, 2017).

In the quenching step, the inactivation of the cellular metabolic and enzymatic activities is achieved by sample exposure to an acidic or alkaline solution, or/and cold ($< -40°C$) or hot solutions (Villas-Bôas *et al.*, 2006). Some examples are the use of cold methanol, liquid nitrogen, and perchloric acid. The choice of the method(s) usually depends on the stability of the metabolites targeted for analysis. If, for example, metabolites of interests are not stable at higher temperature or low pH, hot solution or acids are avoided in quenching steps. Liquid nitrogen and cold methanol are usually used for untargeted metabolomics as they represent relatively mild conditions and have a minimal impact on the stability of samples. The quenching step is often combined with extraction. For example, performing an extraction of both biomass and media will allow a simultaneous intracellular and

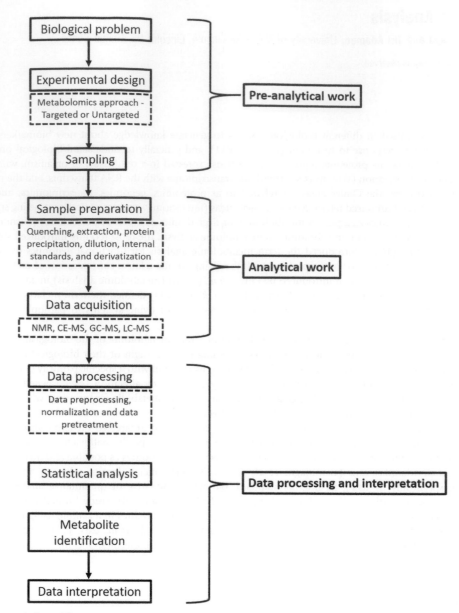

Fig. 1 Metabolome analysis workflow.

extracellular analysis. On the other hand, prior separation of the cellular components by, e.g., centrifugation will permit an intracellular analysis without the interference of extracellular compounds (Villas-Bôas *et al.*, 2005).

The most common solvents used to extract metabolites are organic solvents: polar solvents (methanol, ethanol, and mixtures of methanol-water) are used to extract polar metabolites, while non-polar solvents (chloroform, hexanes, and ethyl acetate) are employed to extract lipids (Villas-Bôas *et al.*, 2005, 2006). The selected extraction method should obtain the maximum quantity of intracellular metabolites to avoid loss of metabolites, and to be compatible with the analytical tools used for their quantification and identification (Villas-Bôas *et al.*, 2005, 2006). The concentration step (freeze-drying and reducing volume under vacuum using e.g., roto-vac) is recommended when an extraction method is used, as sample dilution can decrease metabolite concentrations under the detection limits, and affect the sensitivity and overall results. Furthermore, it is possible to analyze the metabolites of interest by using solid-phase extraction (SPE) and solid-phase micro-extraction (SPME) to concentrate the intracellular metabolites from a diluted sample.

Protein precipitation is an important step that removes proteins present in the sample, extracting the metabolites that can non-covalently bind to proteins by , and preserving the column when using liquid chromatography (LC) as an analytical method (Bruce *et al.*, 2008).

The derivatization step is particularly important in Gas Chromatography – Mass Spectrometry (GC–MS) based analytical techniques as the GC can separate only volatile compounds (Garcia and Barbas, 2011). In this case, silylation, alkylation, or other derivatization reactions can convert non-volatile compounds to volatile ones.

Microbial sample preparation

Winder et al. (2008) studied different methods of sample quenching by evaluating 60% aqueous methanol (−48°C), tricine-buffered (0.5 mM, pH 7.4) aqueous 60% methanol solution (−48°C), and boiling with ethanol (90°C); in combination with various extraction steps including 100% methanol (−48°C), methanol/chloroform (2:1), perchloric acid (0.25 M), and boiling with ethanol (90°C) and potassium hydroxide (0.25 M, 80°C). The study concluded that the procedure utilizing 60% aqueous methanol (−48°C) to quench the metabolism, and extraction with 100% methanol (−48°C) were the most appropriate methods to extract intracellular metabolites in Escherichia coli cultures (Winder et al., 2008). Li et al. (2013) found that the most appropriate quenching method for Bacillus licheniformis consisted of perchloric acid rather than hydrochloric and phosphoric acids. Another study suggested a cold glycerol-saline solution as a quenching method for analyzing intracellular metabolites in microbial cell cultures (e.g., Pseudomonas fluorescens – a gram-negative bacterium, Streptomyces coelicolor – a gram-positive bacterium, and Saccharomyces cerevisiae – baker's yeast) (Villas-Bôas and Bruheim, 2007).

Plants tissue sample preparation

The most common method used as for quenching to extract metabolites in plants after harvesting is snap-freezing the plant tissue with liquid nitrogen, and subsequent storage at −80°C (Jorge et al., 2016). In the extraction step, the most common solvents are chloroform, methanol, and water (2:1:1, v/v) to separate lipophilic (non-polar) and hydrophilic (polar) metabolites (Verpoorte et al., 2008).

Animal tissue sample preparation

For animal and human tissues, the primary methods used to quench metabolism are snap-freezing in liquid nitrogen and cold methanol (Stentiford et al., 2005; Wang et al., 2011). For the extraction of polar and non-polar metabolites, chloroform and methanol (2:1, v/v) has been demonstrated to be the most efficient solvent (van Ginneken et al., 2007; Atherton et al.2008).

Sample Analysis and Data Acquisition

Common analytical platforms employed for data acquisition in metabolome analysis are nuclear magnetic resonance (NMR) and mass spectrometry (MS) analysis, typically coupled with separation techniques such as gas chromatography (GC), high or ultra-performance liquid chromatography (HPLC or UPLC), or capillary electrophoresis (CE).

NMR based metabolomics

NMR is a relatively robust technique which is typically applied to studies such as metabolite fingerprinting, profiling, and metabolic flux analysis, involving different samples such as cell extracts, cell cultures, tissues, and biofluids. NMR is based on spin behavior of atomic nuclei in magnetic field which is represented by the resonance frequency. NMR is nondestructive, noninvasive and nonequilibrium method requiring minimal or no sample preparation to analyze various metabolites in the micromolar range (Reo, 2002; Beckonert et al., 2007). As NMR is a noninvasive method, it has been also used extensively in metabolomics analysis to diagnose diseases (Brindle et al., 2002; Gowda et al.2008; Capati et al., 2017).

NMR in metabolomics analysis exhibits highly reproducible and quantitative characteristics; molecular properties such as hydrophobicity and acid dissociation constant (pKa) do not influence NMR sensitivity (Pan and Raftery, 2007). The limitations of NMR in metabolomics analysis are due to poor sensitivity and spectral resolution (minimum spectral distance between two distinguishable peaks) that can compromise metabolite identification in complex samples. The sample preparation is the same for the most types of samples. To generate good NMR data, it is necessary to add an internal chemical shift standard, a phosphate buffer solution, and deuterated water (D_2O, the latter of which is used as a lock frequency for long-term magnetic field drifts (Heude et al., 2017).

The most common NMR spectroscopic methods used to quantify metabolites are one-dimensional proton NMR spectroscopy (1D NMR) and two-dimensional proton J-resolved NMR spectroscopy (2D Jres NMR). The advantages of 1D NMR are to provide a relatively good quantitative profile of the metabolites and rapid spectral acquisition. In addition, a single standard can be used for absolute quantification of the measured metabolites (Huang et al., 2015). On the other hand, the only more abundant metabolites can be detected (concentrations > 1–10 μM) , and peak overlap hinders metabolite identification (Gebregiworgis and Powers, 2012). 2D–1H Jres can partially resolve the peak overlaps observed in 1D–1H NMR by determining the peak intensity and properties, using the separation of chemical shifts and J coupling in two spectral dimensions to improve metabolite identification (Huang et al., 2014, 2015).

MS based metabolomics

In comparison to NMR, MS is more sensitive and specific. Furthermore, the increase in coverage of the metabolite analysis can potentially lead to the detection of thousands of metabolites. Every mass spectrometer consists of three integrated parts including 1/an ionization source that adds charge to molecules to be analyzed, 2/a mass analyzer that separates molecules based on their mass/charge ratio (m/z), and 3/a detector. Although direct injection is a rapid technique, often used in metabolomics analysis (in both targeted analysis and metabolite profiling – to quantify metabolites and elucidate metabolite structure), the major limitation is associated with low and inconsistent ionization efficiencies in complex biological samples (Zhang et al., 2012).

Therefore, the best results are achieved by using separation techniques such as GC, HPLC/UPLC, and CE (Zhang *et al.*, 2012) prior to MS analysis. Although this can be done using off-line separation followed, by MS analysis of individually collected fractions, an in-line setup that couples the separation and MS steps into one system is preferred, and leads to better results.

GC–MS metabolomics

GC–MS in metabolomics analysis can separate and detect volatile metabolites that occur naturally (alcohols, aldehydes, esters, etc.), or metabolites that become volatile after derivatization (semi-volatile metabolites – amides, amines, amino acids, sugars, organic acids, peptides, and lipids; and nonvolatile metabolites that are chemically modified to increase their stability in the high temperatures used in GC–MS analysis) (Villas-Bôas *et al.*, 2005; Zhang *et al.*, 2012). Over the years, the GC–MS approach has demonstrated robustness, high reproducibility, and it is relatively inexpensive (Villas-Bôas *et al.*, 2005; Zhang *et al.*, 2012). The basic principle of GC separation is based on the partition of specific molecules between gas and liquid phases at a given temperature, and the effect of the portioning on their movement through the GC column. Molecules in the gas phase move through the GC capillary column and are subsequently detected by MS. Because the molecules have different volatility, and partition differently between the gas and liquid phases depending on the temperature, applying an increasing temperature gradient on the GC column allows for the separation of molecules in time. GC capillary columns are selected based on the metabolite characteristics, such as polarity or volatility (Villas-Bôas *et al.*, 2005). For semi-volatile and non-volatile metabolites, the derivatization step needs to be included in the sample preparation. The methods used for derivatization include usually silylation (especially used with sugars – amino sugars, sugar alcohols, and phosphorylated sugars), and alkylation or esterification (used with polyfunctional amines and organic acids) (Villas-Bôas *et al.*, 2005). For untargeted metabolite profiling, the GC–MS approach involves sample extraction, sample derivatization and separation by GC, and ionization of the separated molecules, followed by detection and data evaluation (Kopka *et al.*, 2004). For targeted analyses, additional steps such as extraction with an organic solvent to enrich specific classes of metabolites, or adjustment of separation conditions, such as the use of long capillary columns (30–60 m), or/and sample injection at various, sample specific, temperatures may be necessary (Villas-Bôas *et al.*, 2005).

Using GC–MS techniques, Lv and Yang (2012) found potential biomarkers of breast cancer in free fatty acids (palmitic acid, stearic acid, and linoleic acid) using serum samples analyzed by GC–MS. Changes in sn-glycerol-3-phosphate in lipid metabolism were found in metabolomics analysis by GC–MS when comparing breast cancer and normal tissues (Brockmöller *et al.*, 2012). In addition, Dória *et al.* (2012) found lysophospholipids and saturated fatty acids in phosphatidylinositols using an Electrospray Ionization Mass Spectrometry (ESI-MS) and cell culture model. In 2012, Nishiumi *et al.* (2012) used GC–MS to analyze a serum-targeted metabolome in Colorectal Cancer (CRC) patients, and found 2-hydroxybutyrate, aspartic acid, kynurenine, and cystamine as potential biomarkers for early detection. Years later, the use of NMR-based fecal metabolomic fingerprinting in CRC patients led to the observation of reduced levels of acetate, butyrate, propionate, glucose, glutamine, and elevated quantities of succinate, proline, alanine, dimethylglycine, valine, glutamate, leucine, isoleucine and lactate. The changes in metabolite levels between samples from CRC patients and the control group can be associated with malabsorption of nutrients, disturbance in the bacterial ecology, and increased glycolysis and glutaminolysis (Lin *et al.*, 2016).

LC-MS metabolomics

In LC-MS, liquid samples are directly injected into the LC column and metabolites are separated based on their interaction with a stationary phase prior MS detection. The stationary phase is usually represented by spherical beads covered on the surface with specific functional groups that define the nature of the separation. Whilst polar metabolites are typically separated by ion exchange or Hydrophilic Interaction Chromatography (HILIC) columns, non-polar metabolites are separated by their hydrophobicity on Reverse Phase (RPLC) columns (C4, C8, or C18). Non-hydrophobic molecules without charge can be separated by Normal Phase Liquid Chromatography (NPLC). In all cases, the metabolites retained on the column are eluted by a solvent that disrupts metabolite-stationary phase interactions, and leads to metabolite release NPLC uses a solvent with a higher polarity than that of the stationary phase (nonpolar are eluted first), whereas RPLC uses a solvent with a lower polarity than the stationary phase (Lopes *et al.*, 2017). The ionization techniques applied in LC-MS are electrospray ionization (ESI), atmospheric pressure chemical ionization (APCI), and atmospheric pressure photoionization (APPI). These ionization processes do not modify or fragment biomolecules and therefore are considered to be soft ionization techniques. Although the most common technique is ESI (Villas-Bôas *et al.*, 2005; Lopes *et al.*, 2017), APPI and APCI are primary techniques that are used to analyze metabolites with limited ESI efficiency, such as Vitamin D and its metabolites (Adamec *et al.*, 2011).

The major difference between untargeted and targeted LC-MS approaches is the MS parameter setup. Untargeted metabolomics is designed to detect as many metabolites as possible, therefore the instrument is optimized for a broad range of molecular masses (m/z), typically set to 50–2200 m/z. Targeted metabolomics, on the other hand, is optimized for maximum sensitivity at the specific m/z of metabolite(s) of interest. Currently, two types of MS instruments, QQQ and qTRAP, are almost exclusively used for targeted analysis using techniques known as Selected Reaction Monitoring (SRM) and Multiple Reaction Monitoring (MRM). In these techniques, data is acquired from one or more specific product ions generated by fragmentation of selected precursor ion(s) (metabolite(s) of interest), with known m/z, using a multi-stage mass spectrometer (QQQ or qTRAP) (Hoffmann, 1996). In first stage, only ions with defined m/z are allowed to pass through to the second stage, in which the precursor ion is fragmented. In the third stage, only the intensities of fragments (product ions) corresponding to the original precursor ion are monitored and used for quantification.

LC-MS techniques are widely used in many biological studies. For example, using an untargeted metabolomic analysis of serum samples with 300 Type 2 Diabetes (T2D) patients and 300 healthy controls by UPLC-MS, the authors found lipids, hexose sugars, and purine nucleotides as biomarkers of T2D (Drogan *et al.*, 2015). Metabolomics studies conducted in Alzheimer's patients plasma samples identified desmosterol as a potential biomarker (Sato *et al.*, 2012). Although, LC-MS is very powerful tool, to increase a number of identified metabolites, the approach is often combined with GC–MS. Using both, LC-MS and GC–MS, lysophosphocholine, tryptophan, phytosphingosine, dihydrosphingosine, hexadecosphinganine, arachidonic acid, *N,N*-dimethylglycine, thymine, glutamine, glutamic acid, and cytidine were also identified as potential biomarkers of Alzheimer disease (Li *et al.*, 2010; Wang *et al.*, 2014).

Capillary electrophoresis (CE)-MS metabolomics

CE-MS is a separation technique that uses capillary electrophoresis to achieve high efficiency and selectivity, peak capacity (by resolving more peaks), fast analysis, and small sample volume, to analyze polar and ionic compounds without a derivatization step (Ramautar *et al.*, 2009). This technique can be used to analyze targeted and untargeted metabolites, such as amino acids, carbohydrates, vitamins, thiols, peptides, and nucleotides (Villas-Bôas *et al.*, 2005).

In CE, capillary zone electrophoresis (CZE), in which separation is based in differences in electrophoretic mobilities (neutral compounds are not separated), is the most used mode. Other modes include micellar electrokinetic chromatography (MEKC, separation of neutral compounds is possible), capillary isoelectric focusing (CIEF, where a pH gradient is used to separate amphiprotics), capillary isotachophoresis (CITP, for separation of small molecules and ions), capillary gel electrophoresis (CGE; large molecules and polymers can be analyzed using gels), and affinity capillary electrophoresis (ACE, which is based on biospecific interactions) (Rodrigues *et al.*, 2017).

Data Processing and Analysis

A critical component of any metabolomics platform is the link between the generation of data and realization of the value it contains. This link is filled with various bioinformatics and statistical tools specifically designed for metabolomics data mining. The individual steps involved in this process are typically data preprocessing, normalization, data pretreatment, and statistical analysis with interpretation and visualization (**Figs. 2** and **3**) (Karaman, 2017).

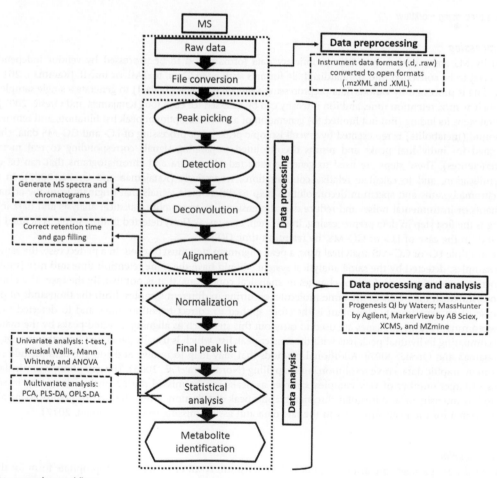

Fig. 2 MS data processing workflow.

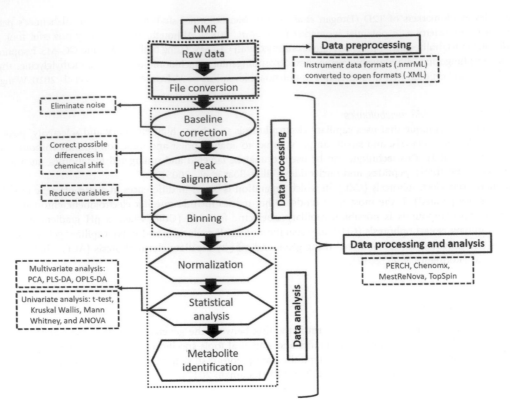

Fig. 3 NMR data processing workflow.

MS data preprocessing

Data generated by MS are collected in vendor proprietary data formats, and to be processed by vendor independent software packages, they need to be converted into standardized file formats such as mzData, mzXML or mzML (Karaman, 2017). Following the conversion, data is processed by various data preprocessing software packages (**Table 1**) to generate a single sample file in which characteristics such as m/z, retention time, and ion intensity can be accessed for each ion (Katajamaa and Orešič, 2007). The process consists of several steps including (but not limited to) generation of a peak list, optional peak list filtration, and removal of isotopes (as each compound (metabolite) is represented by several isotopic peaks). For processing of LC- and GC–MS data, chromatograms must be generated for individual peaks and results deconvoluted (separating signals corresponding to real metabolites from instrument interferences). These steps are used to generate extracted MS spectra and chromatograms that can be employed for metabolite identification, and to calculate relative concentrations, respectively (Katajamaa and Orešič, 2007). In addition, the generation of chromatograms and spectrum deconvolution help to differentiate signals that originate from the actual analytes, or from contaminants or instrumental noise, and reduce data dimensionality, to simplify statistical analysis and data interpretation.

Peak picking is the first step in data preprocessing. In this step, every peak (ion) detected in the sample is defined (assigned) by its m/z value and, in the case of LC- or GC–MS, by retention time (RT).

To compare multiple LC- or GC–MS analytical runs, a peak alignment step must be used. In a perfect case, the same metabolites from different samples, detected by the same analytical system, should have the same retention time and m/z (molecular mass). Due to the experimental variation and minor changes in analytical conditions, that is not usually the case. The objective of peak alignment is to distinguish the peaks of the same molecule, occurring in different samples, from the thousands of peaks detected during the course of an experiment. Alignment is therefore applied to correct retention times and to detected molecular mass variations between runs. Various strategies are used to carry out this step such as aligning detected peaks by the match score (join aligner), or by comparing individual peak lists with the master peak list, which is usually generated from the average of all aligned peak lists (Katajamaa and Orešič, 2007). Additional methods that may help to resolve and sort the data include summation or binning of chromatographic data, curve resolution, and gap filing (Nordström et al., 2006). The gap filling is particularly important step in analysis of larger number of very complex samples as peaks can be missed during peak picking step in some samples, primarily due to low intensity or/and irregular chromatographic peak distribution. When this occurs, preprocessing algorithms can be employed to search for the peak structures in the raw data and assign missing values (Karaman, 2017).

NMR data preprocessing

Currently, many software packages are available (**Table 1**) to transform NMR raw data to an appropriate form for the subsequent processing steps, including baseline correction, peak alignment, and binning.

Table 1   Software for metabolomics data processing

Name	Free or vendor	Description	Website
ACD	ACD Labs	Metabolomics with NMR data	http://www.acdlabs.com/resources/freeware/nmr_proc/
Analyst	SCIEX	Metabolomics with LC-MS data	https://sciex.com/products/software/analyst-software
Chenomx NMR	Chenomx	Metabolomics with NMR data	http://www.chenomx.com/
MarkerView	AB Sciex	Metabolomics with LC-MS data	https://sciex.com/products/software/markerview-software
MassHunter	Agilent	Metabolomics with all MS data	http://www.agilent.com/en/products/software-informatics/masshunter-suite/masshunter#0
MATLAB	The MathWorks Inc.	Metabolomics with MS and NMR data	https://www.mathworks.com/help/bioinfo/mass-spectrometry-and-bioanalytics.html
MET-IDEA	Free	Metabolomics with CE-MS, GC–MS and LC-MS data	http://bioinfo.noble.org/download/
MetaboAnalyst	Free	Metabolomics with MS and NMR data	http://www.metaboanalyst.ca/
metAlign	Free	Metabolomics with GC–MS and LC-MS data	https://www.metalign.nl
MestReNova	MestreLab Research	Metabolomics with LC-MS, GC–MS and NMR data	http://mestrelab.com/
MNova	MestreLab	Metabolomics with NMR data	http://mestrelab.com/software/mnova/nmr/
MS Resolver	Pattern Recognition Systems AS	Metabolomics with GC–MS and LC-MS data	http://www.prs.no/MS%20Resolver/MS%20Resolver.html
MSFACTs	Free	Metabolomics with GC–MS and LC-MS data	http://bioinfo.noble.org/download/
Mzmine	Free	Metabolomics with LC-MS data	http://mzmine.github.io/
PERCH	PERCH Solution Ltd	Metabolomics with NMR data	http://www.perchsolutions.com/
Progenesis QI	Waters	Metabolomics with LC-MS data	http://www.nonlinear.com/progenesis/qi/
TopSpin	Bruker. Free for academia and governmental institutions only	Metabolomics with NMR data	https://www.bruker.com/products/mr/nmr/nmr-software/software/topspin/overview.html
XCMS online	Free	Metabolomics with GC–MS and LC-MS data	https://xcmsonline.scripps.edu/

Baseline correction is applied to differentiate real peaks from instrumental noise. The most used baseline correction approaches is the frequency or time domain method, which can be easily applied to metabolomics spectra, subtracting a baseline estimation from the measured spectrum (Euceda et al., 2015). Additional procedures that employ steps such as noise removal and/or smoothing include iterative polynomial fitting and asymmetric least squares smoothing (AsLS) (Euceda et al., 2015).

During a relatively long time of NMR data acquisition process, resulting chemical shift can be affected by changes in pH, temperature and/or molecular interactions in the samples. This, in turn, creates a small variation in ppm spectra in different samples. Peak alignment methods are used to correct these differences. The alignment can be global (parametric time warping – PTW), in which the total spectrum is corrected, or the alignment can be carried out in each segment separately (correlation optimized warping – COW; icoshift) (Euceda et al., 2015; Karaman, 2017).

The binning step is important in facilitating data analysis through the reduction in the number of variables. In this case, the spectra generated in NMR are segmented into various bins and signal in each bin is calculated by the integration. This may, however, lead to the loss of resolution or/and to the risk of splitting a peak (Vu and Laukens, 2013; Karaman, 2017). Therefore, depending on the data, binning methods can be of equal size (0.005 and 0.05 ppm), or bin size can be determined for each interval, and the bins can represent either individual peaks or a groups of peaks (Euceda et al., 2015; Karaman, 2017).

Normalization

To minimize experimental variation in multi-sample quantitative analyses, it is necessary to normalize the data. Although several normalization methods including auto-scaling, use of a reference sample, log linear model, trimmed constant mean, and average intensity are available in software packages, the choice of the best method depends on the type of study and complexity of the samples. For example, by the addition of internal or external standards – samples can be normalized using the peak area/intensity of the known standard (Karaman, 2017). However, this method controls for variation due to sample preparation and analysis (technical variation), but not the sampling itself. Statistical models, on the other hand, allow one to normalize each sample with optimal scaling factors based on the complete database (Crawford and Morrison, 1968) in accordance with the unit vector norm generated by scaling each sample vector (variable – ion) (Scholz et al., 2004) or median (Wang et al., 2003) intensities, or by the maximum likelihood method (Orešič et al., 2004), without any internal/external standards.

Data pretreatment

Another very useful tool, particularly for extraction of relevant biological information and for results interpretation, is data pretreatment (van den Berg *et al.*, 2006). Complex samples contain thousands of metabolites with concentrations covering enormous dynamic range (difference between low abundant and high abundant metabolites). Problem is that changes in cellular function (phenotype) is often not proportional to the fold change and overall abundance of the metabolites. For example, regulatory molecules usually exist in very low concentrations and small fold change have tremendous impact on the cell behavior (induced proliferation, cell survival etc.). Structural molecules, on the other hand, can be present in high concentrations or significant fold change may have only a minimal impact for overall cellular functions. To correct for these disproportion, data pretreatment methods can be used. These methods usually consist of centering, scaling, and data transformation. In centering, the mean that centers the differences between the samples (high and low abundant metabolites) is adjusted, leaving only the relevant variation (van den Berg *et al.*, 2006). In scaling, each variable is divided by the scaling factor, leading to an adjustment in the fold differences in the various metabolites (van den Berg *et al.*, 2006). Scaling can be based on data dispersion measured as a scaling factor. In autoscaling, metabolites are scaled based on standard deviation and all metabolites become equally important. Pareto scaling, on the other hand, reducing the relevant importance of large values. It is based on standard deviation, however, larger changes are scaled less than small changes. Similarly, Vast scaling focusing primarily on metabolites with small fluctuations. Level scaling uses the mean concentration as the scaling factor emphasizing relative response and therefore ideal for biomarker discovery (van Ginneken *et al.*, 2007; Karaman, 2017). Data transformation consists of eliminating heteroscedastic noise. (van Ginneken *et al.*, 2007). The most common transformations used are nonlinear transformations, such as log transformation, for which multiplicative noise is converted to additive noise, and power transformations, in which the original data is replaced by the calculated square root. (van Ginneken *et al.*, 2007; Karaman, 2017). It is important to note, that the selection of the data pretreatment methods can significantly affect the interpretation of results the metabolomics studies, and strongly depends on the biological question to be answered, the properties of the data, and the statistical analysis applied to the pretreated data. Inappropriate choice of these methods can lead to data misinterpretation.

Statistical Analysis

To find significant differences among the sample groups, basic statistical methods are usually a part of metabolomics data analysis software packages. Statistical significance tests identify data elements that make significant contributions to the protein and/or metabolite profile of a sample, or that distinguish a group of samples from others.

Phenotypic grouping is also an important tool for the investigation of the underlying interrelationships within a large data set. Statistical methodologies that identify these groups or clusters are known as clustering techniques, and originate from multivariate statistics. Hierarchical clustering can be used to sort data out into previously unknown clusters. Clustering objects on subsets of attributes (COSA) is an unsupervised method to cluster samples, that is an enhancement to distance based clustering methods (Friedman and Meulman, 2004). COSA detects groups of objects that have preferentially close values in different, possibly overlapping, subsets of attributes. Other clustering methods such as Principal Component Analysis (PCA), k-means clustering, and self-organizing maps (SOM) are also included in many software packages. Multivariate analyses such as Principal Component Analysis (PCA), Partial Least Squares-Discriminant Analysis (PLS-DA), and Orthogonal Projection to Latent Structures (OPLS-DA), can be employed to corroborate applied univariate analyses, such as t-tests, Kruskal Wallis tests, Mann Whitney tests, and ANOVA (Alonso *et al.*, 2015). Unsupervised methods are often used to explore, summarize and find hidden relation between the data (Liland, 2011). For example, to detect pattern correlated with experimental conditions or disease, or to assess data quality, PCA can be used. In this case, PCA is considered as the unsupervised methods pointing out various sample patterns (Liland, 2011).

PLS-DA and OPLS-DA, on the other hand, are supervised methods (OPLS-DA was developed to improve PLS-DA) used to discriminate known classes (e.g. control vs disease). Unlike unsupervised methods, these methods are applied to classify, predict, and discover potential biomarkers (Ren *et al.*, 2015).

Metabolite Identification and Pathway Visualization

Metabolite identification is necessary for untargeted metabolite analysis, since the metabolites of interest are unknown when the biological problem is defined. The list of possible metabolites can be generated using free databases and libraries, using either measured molecular mass (m/z) of the unknown metabolites and their retention time (for LC- or GC–MS data), or from chemical shifts and coupling constants (for NMR data) (Moco *et al.*, 2007). Common databases and libraries used in metabolomics include the Human Metabolome Database (HMDB), Spectral Database for Organic Compounds (SDBS), Comprehensive Species-Metabolite Relationship Database (KNApSAcK), Metlin, Golm Metabolome Database , MassBank, MassTRIX, PubChem, Chenomx, Chemical Entities of Biological Interest (ChEBI), BioMagResBank, and Kyoto Encyclopedia of Genes and Genomes (KEGG) (**Fig. 4**) (Moco *et al.*, 2007; Klassen *et al.* 2017). For LC-MS experiments, the molecular mass of the metabolite is not sufficient for final identification as many compounds may have the same molecular mass, but differ in atomic composition and structure, Therefore, additional experiments using MS/MS techniques are necessary to analyze the fragmentation patterns of the metabolites of interest and their correctly identify them.

The final step in data analysis and interpretation is the visualization of the results, and identification of pathways associated with the biological response or regulation. The databases commonly used are the Kyoto Encyclopedia of Genes and Genomes (KEGG), MetaCyc, the Small Molecule Pathway Database (SMPDB), MetaboLights, and Reactome (**Fig. 4**).

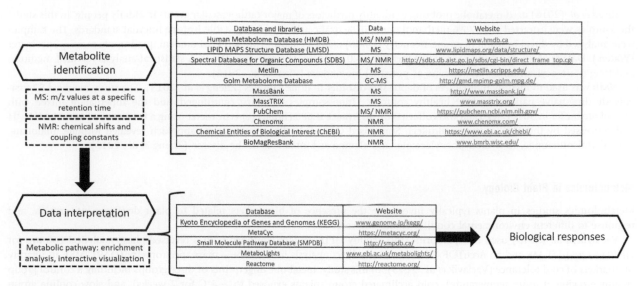

Fig. 4 Metabolite identification and data interpretation.

Applications

Metabolomics analyses have been applied in various research fields, such as medical research (diseases), plant biology, microbiology, toxicology, sustainable energy research etc. The focus primarily centers on the changes in the metabolite concentration, or their flux in specific pathways. Metabolomics data is important to the discovery of new biomarkers that can be associated with early diagnosis, progression, response to treatment, and to understand basic cellular processes and their regulation.

Metabolomics in Disease

In cancer, metabolomic analysis can be used to help to directly diagnose cancer stages from bodily fluids or histological samples. Colorectal cancer (CRC) is the third most commonly diagnosed cancer after lung and breast cancers; it also represents the fourth highest cancer-related cause of death (Siegel et al., 2017).

Qiu et al. (2009) combined two analytical techniques, GC–MS and LC-MS, to analyze the serum metabolome of patients with CRC. Collected serum samples were spiked with internal standards L-2-chlorophenylalanine and heptadecanoic acid, and metabolites were extracted with methanol/chloroform (3:1 ratio (v/v)). First, the sample aliquots were derivatized using methoxyamine and BSTFA, followed by injection and metabolite separation using a DB-5 ms capillary column (30 m × 250 μm, 0.25 μm film thickness) in GC–MS system (Agilent 6890N gas chromatography instrument coupled with a Pegasus HT time-of-flight mass spectrometer from Leco Corporation). MATLAB 7.0 was used to convert the acquired data to netCDF format, and the ChromaTOF software was used to perform data processing. For LC-MS (Acquity ultra performance liquid chromatography MS system, Waters) analysis, the serum samples were spiked with the internal standard L-2-chlorophenylalanine and metabolites extracted using methanol/acetonitrile (5:3 ratio (v/v)). Samples were injected into a 1.7-μm BEH C18 column and run in both positive and negative mode. Data acquisition was performed using the MassLynx software. The SIMCA-P software was used for PCA and OPLS-DA statistical analysis, in which CRC and healthy controls patients were compared. NIST MS Search 2.0 was used for metabolite identification. Five metabolites, including pyruvate, lactate, tryptophan, tyrosine, and uridine, were identified by both analytical techniques as potential biomarkers, and indicated perturbation in glycolysis, arginine, and proline metabolism, as well as in the metabolism of fatty acids (Qiu et al., 2009).

Urine is a biofluid commonly used in metabolomic analysis to identity biomarkers. Using urine samples and both GC–MS and LC-MS platforms, Cheng et al. (2012) identified citrate, hippurate, p-cresol, 2-aminobutyrate, myristate, putrescine, and kynurenate as potential biomarkers of CRC. Results suggest that the urinary metabolome of patients with CRC is potentially altered by metabolites derived from gut microbe–host co-metabolism (Cheng et al., 2012).

In another study, using urine samples from 401 patients with clinically diagnosed Parkinson's disease, 106 patients with idiopathic Parkinson's disease, and 104 healthy control participants, metabolome analysis was carried out by LC–MS (Luan et al., 2015). Urine samples were precipitated with methanol, and the supernatant injected in an LC-MS (Shimadzu Prominence LC system) coupled online to an LTQ Orbitrap Velos instrument (Thermo–Fisher Scientific), with which samples were analyzed in both positive and negative mode. Data analysis was conducted using XCMS and CAMERA software, with the R statistical package. The OPLS-DA and Human Metabolome Database were used to identify possible biomarkers, which included cortisol, 11-deoxycortisol, 21-deoxycortisol, histidine, urocanic acid, imidazoleacetic acid, and hydroxyphenylacetic acid (Luan et al., 2015).

Rizza *et al.* (2014) used metabolic profiling to identify predictors of major cardiovascular events in elderly people. In this study, the samples were extracted with 75% methanol and 0.01% oxalic acid containing stable isotope internal standards. The samples were analyzed by direct infusion mass spectrometry (DIMS) using a Quattro Ultima Pt ESI tandem quadrupole mass spectrometer (Waters). Data analysis was performed with MassLynx v4.0 and NeoLynx software. The PCA statistical analysis revealed medium- and long-chain acylcarnitines, and alanine as potential biomarkers (Rizza *et al.*, 2014).

NMR was used to identify biomarkers of depressive disorder in urine samples (Zheng *et al.*, 2013). The study involved 82 first-episode drug-naive patients and 82 healthy controls. Urine samples were first centrifuged, and the supernatant mixed with phosphate buffer in 90% D_2O. Data was collected on an Avance II 600 (Bruker) spectrometer using a frequency of 600.13 MHz ^1H and processed by the AMIX package (Bruker). Supervised OPLS-DA with a multivariate approach revealed formate, malonate, N-methylnicotinamide, m-hydroxyphenylacetate, and alanine as biomarkers of the disease (Zheng *et al.*, 2013).

Metabolomics in Plant Biology

Metabolomics studies in plants typically investigate the presence of biomarkers related to plant development, growth, and response to different environmental conditions and stressors.

Vaclavik *et al.* (2013) used two platforms, the Acquity UPLC system equipped with a reversed-phase analytical column for UHPLC–QqQ/LIT-MS and an AccuTOF -LP-TOF-MS for direct analysis in real time – mass spectrometry (DART–MS), to identify biomarkers of cold tolerance (Vaclavik *et al.*, 2013). In this study, metabolic fingerprints of three groups including a control group (plants growing at room temperature), cold acclimated group (plants exposed to − 4°C for 2 weeks), and slow cooling group (plants exposed to − 4°C for 8 h) of *Arabidopsis thaliana* were compared and evaluated. The metabolites were extracted using methanol (50 mg tissue/mL) and analyzed by UHPLC–QqQ/LIT MS. The acquired data was processed by the MarkerView software (AB SCIEX), using PCA and a *t*-test to compare the peak intensities among the groups. In addition, the DART–MS data was processed by the Mass Center software (version 1.3, JEOL), and STATISTICA software (version 8.0, StatSoft) was used for the PCA statistical analysis. To identify the structure of significantly affected metabolites, the authors used the MassLynx software (Waters), and isotope distribution, to estimate elemental composition (Vaclavik *et al.*, 2013). Whilst gluconapin was demonstrated to be biomarker of the cold sensitive phenotype, kaempferol-3,7-O-dirhamnoside and kaempferol-3-neohesperidoside-7-O-rhamnoside were identified as the biomarkers of high cold tolerance (Vaclavik *et al.*, 2013).

The plant metabolomics is associated with a high diversity of secondary metabolites also known as phytochemicals. Nakabayashi *et al.* (2009) studied *Arabidopsis thaliana* as a model for genome research, using non targeted metabolomics by 1D and 2D NMR, HRFABMS, FT-ESI-MS and GC–TOF-MS techniques. To maximize metabolome coverage, reduce the sample complexity, and enrich specific classes of metabolites, the authors used a series of extraction methods including methanol, n-hexane, ethyl acetate, chloroform containing 5% methanol and n-butanol. For example, the anthocyanin fraction was obtained by n-butanol extraction. A total of 37 compounds such as apocarotenoids, anthocyanins, carotenoids, chlorophyll derivatives, dicarboxylic acids, flavonols, galactolipids, glucosinolate, icosane, steroid, phenylpropanoids, and nucleosides were identified in this study (Nakabayashi *et al.*, 2009).

Metabolomics in Microbiology

Metabolomics in microbiology is a very important tool for understanding basic biological questions such as those for which microbes have been used as model organisms for many years. Recently, many studies also have focused on the improvement of microbes to produce alternative sources of energy, or to better understand microbial resistance to various antibiotics and identify new drug targets.

Ledala *et al.* (2014) used NMR as an analytical technique to investigate influence of iron and oxygen limitations on the metabolism of *Staphylococcus aureus*. Samples from two growth phases were harvested in this study, exponential (2 h) and post-exponential (6 h). Altogether, eight and four replicates, respectively, were used for one-dimensional 1H NMR and two-dimensional 1H-13C heteronuclear single quantum coherence (1H-13C HSQC) analyses. The samples were quenched in liquid nitrogen, and bacteria were collected using ice-cold 20 mM phosphate buffer. TMSP-d4 (3-(trimethylsilyl)propionic acid-2,2,3,3–d4) was used as an internal standard for both 1H NMR and 1H-13C HSQC experiments. For 1H NMR, the data was processed and analyzed by ACD/1D NMR manager version 12.0 (Advanced Chemistry Development), and 1H-13C HSQC data were processed using the NMRPipe software package. To identify the significant metabolite changes, t-tests, PCA, OPLS-DA, and unique structure (SUS) calculations were performed using the SIMCA 12.0_statistical package (Umetrics). Metabolite identification was achieved by comparison of measured chemical shifts with the chemical shift references from Human Metabolomics Database, Platform for RIKEN Metabolomics (PRIMe), and Biological Magnetic Resonance Data Bank (BMRB). The most significant changes in metabolite concentrations were found in the post-exponential phase, and were associated with the TCA cycle (Ledala *et al.*, 2014).

Stipetic *et al.* (2016) investigated differences in the metabolome of the planktonic and biofilm states of *Staphylococcus aureus*. The sample extraction was performed using chloroform/methanol/water (1:3:1 ratio (v/v/v)), followed by LC-MS analysis using a hydrophilic interaction liquid chromatography (HILIC). The MS data was analyzed using several packages including XCMS (peak picking), mzMatch (filtering and grouping), and R-scripts (filtering, post-processing and identification). In the statistical analysis step, PCA was implemented to compare the two states. Affected pathways were visualized in the KEGG, and suggested that the most prominent changes are in arginine biosynthesis (Stipetic *et al.*, 2016).

Closing Remarks

Metabolomics is the most recent OMICS strategy, and is being used to understand the molecular mechanisms of cellular processes in various biological systems. Whilst proteomics data determines the overall concentration of proteins in biological systems, it may not reflect their actual activities, as protein activities depend not only on their concentrations, but also on post-translational modification(s), protein-protein interactions, binding of activators, repressors, or co-factors, or changes in tertiary Therefore metabolomics, which directly measures these activities, brings a new dimension to our knowledge, helps to explain many regulatory events, and can map the complex relationships of individual molecules and pathways to predict cellular behavior and responses to various stimuli. Like the other OMICS techniques, the results of metabolomics strongly depend on the selected methodology. GC–MS and LC-MS approaches detect different classes of metabolites, and should be used as complementary techniques to increase metabolome coverage. Extraction methods can be used to decrease the complexity of the samples and focus on very specific molecules. Therefore, the choice of individual methods is the most critical aspect of metabolomics experimental design, and must be driven by biological questions. In summary, metabolomics represents a very valuable tool, however, careful selection of individual analytical and statistical steps is essential to understand the results and avoid their misinterpretation.

See also: Integrative Analysis of Multi-Omics Data. Natural Language Processing Approaches in Bioinformatics

---

References

Adamec, J., Jannasch, A., Huang, J., *et al.*, 2011. Development and optimization of an LC-MS/MS-based method for simultaneous quantification of vitamin D(2), vitamin D(3), 25-hydroxyvitamin D(2) and 25-hydroxyvitamin D(3). Journal of Separation Science 34, 11–20.

Alonso, A., Marsal, S., Julià, A., 2015. Analytical methods in untargeted metabolomics: State of the art in 2015. Frontiers in Bioengineering and Biotechnology 3, 1–20.

Atherton, H.J., Jones, O.A.H., Malik, S., Miska, E.A., Griffin, J.L., 2008. A comparative metabolomic study of NHR-49 in Caenorhabditis elegans and PPAR-α in the mouse. FEBS Letters 582, 1661–1666.

Beckonert, O., Keun, H.C., Ebbels, T.M.D., *et al.*, 2007. Metabolic profiling, metabolomic and metabonomic procedures for NMR spectroscopy of urine, plasma, serum and tissue extracts. Nature Protocols 2, 2692–2703.

Brindle, J.T., Antti, H., Holmes, E., *et al.*, 2002. Rapid and noninvasive diagnosis of the presence and severity of coronary heart disease using 1H NMR-based metabonomics. Nature Medicine 8, 1439–1445.

Brockmöller, S.F., Bucher, E., Müller, B.M., *et al.*, 2012. Integration of metabolomics and expression of glycerol-3-phosphate acyltransferase (GPAM) in breast cancer-link to patient survival, hormone receptor status, and metabolic profiling. Journal of Proteome Research 11, 850–860.

Bruce, S.J., Jonsson, P., Antti, H., *et al.*, 2008. Evaluation of a protocol for metabolic profiling studies on human blood plasma by combined ultra-performance liquid chromatography/mass spectrometry: From extraction to data analysis. Analytical Biochemistry 372, 237–249.

Cambiaghi, A., Ferrario, M., Masseroli, M., 2017. Analysis of metabolomic data: Tools, current strategies and future challenges for omics data integration. Briefings in Bioinformatics 18, 498–510.

Capati, A., Ijare, O.B., Bezabeh, T., 2017. Diagnostic applications of nuclear magnetic resonance-based urinary metabolomics. Magnetic Resonance Insights 10, 1–12.

Cheng, Y., Xie, G., Chen, T., *et al.*, 2012. Distinct urinary metabolic profile of human colorectal cancer. Journal of Proteome Research 11, 1354–1363.

Crawford, L.R., Morrison, J.D., 1968. Computer methods in analytical mass spectrometry. Identification of an unknown compound in a catalog. Analytical Chemistry 40, 1464–1469.

Dória, M.L., Cotrim, Z., Macedo, B., *et al.*, 2012. Lipidomic approach to identify patterns in phospholipid profiles and define class differences in mammary epithelial and breast cancer cells. Breast Cancer Research and Treatment 133, 635–648.

Drogan, D., Dunn, W.B., Lin, W., *et al.*, 2015. Untargeted metabolic profiling identifies altered serum metabolites of type 2 diabetes mellitus in a prospective, nested case control study. Clinical Chemistry 61, 487–497.

Euceda, L.R., Giskeødegård, G.F., Bathen, T.F., 2015. Preprocessing of NMR metabolomics data. Scandinavian Journal of Clinical and Laboratory Investigation 75, 193–203.

Fiehn, O., 2001. Combining genomics, metabolome analysis, and biochemical modelling to understand metabolic networks. Comparative and Functional Genomics 2, 155–168.

Friedman, J.H., Meulman, J.J., 2004. Clustering objects on subsets of attributes. Journal of the Royal Statistical Society: Series B (Statistical Methodology) 66, 815–839.

Garcia, A., Barbas, C., 2011. Gas chromatography-mass spectrometry (GC–MS)-based metabolomics. In: Metz, T.O. (Ed.), Metabolic Profiling: Methods and Protocols. Totowa, NJ: Humana Press, pp. 191–204.

Gebregiworgis, T., Powers, R., 2012. Application of NMR metabolomics to search for human disease biomarkers. Combinatorial Chemistry & High Throughput Screening 15, 595–610.

Goodacre, R., Broadhurst, D., Smilde, A.K., *et al.*, 2007. Proposed minimum reporting standards for data analysis in metabolomics. Metabolomics 3, 231–241.

Gowda, G.A.N., Zhang, S., Gu, H., *et al.*, 2008. Metabolomics-based methods for early disease diagnostics: A review. Expert Review of Molecular Diagnostics 8, 617–633.

Heude, C., Nath, J., Carrigan, J.B., Ludwig, C., 2017. Nuclear magnetic resonance strategies for metabolic analysis. In: Sussulini, A. (Ed.), Metabolomics: From Fundamentals to Clinical Applications. Cham: Springer International Publishing, pp. 45–76.

Hoffmann, E. de., 1996. Tandem mass spectrometry: A primer. Journal of Mass Spectrometry 31, 129–137.

Huang, Y., Cai, S., Zhang, Z., Chen, Z., 2014. High-Resolution two-dimensional J-resolved NMR spectroscopy for biological systems. Biophysical Journal 106, 2061–2070.

Huang, Y., Zhang, Z., Chen, H., *et al.*, 2015. A high-resolution 2D J-resolved NMR detection technique for metabolite analyses of biological samples. Scientific Reports 5, 8390.

Jorge, T.F., Mata, A.T., António, C., 2016. Mass spectrometry as a quantitative tool in plant metabolomics. Philosophical Transactions of the Royal Society A 374, 20150370.

Jorge, T.F., Rodrigues, J.A., Caldana, C., *et al.*, 2016. Mass spectrometry-based plant metabolomics: Metabolite responses to abiotic stress. Mass Spectrometry Reviews 35, 620–649.

Karaman, I., 2017. Preprocessing and pretreatment of metabolomics data for statistical analysis. In: Sussulini, A. (Ed.), Metabolomics: From Fundamentals to Clinical Applications. Springer International Publishing, pp. 145–161.

Katajamaa, M., Orešič, M., 2007. Data processing for mass spectrometry-based metabolomics. Journal of Chromatography A 1158, 318–328.

Kell, D.B., Brown, M., Davey, H.M., *et al.*, 2005. Metabolic footprinting and systems biology: The medium is the message. Nature Reviews Microbiology 3, 557–565.

Klassen, A., Faccio, A.T., Canuto, G.A.B., *et al.*, 2017. Metabolomics: Definitions and significance in systems biology. In: Sussulini, A. (Ed.), Metabolomics: From Fundamentals to Clinical Applications. Springer International Publishing, pp. 3–17.

Kopka, J., Fernie, A., Weckwerth, W., Gibon, Y., Stitt, M., 2004. Metabolite profiling in plant biology: Platforms and destinations. Genome Biology 5, 109.

Ledala, N., Zhang, B., Seravalli, J., Powers, R., Somerville, G.A., 2014. Influence of iron and aeration on Staphylococcus aureus growth, metabolism, and transcription. Journal of Bacteriology 196, 2178–2189.

Li, N., Liu, W., Li, W., *et al.*, 2010. Plasma metabolic profiling of Alzheimer's disease by liquid chromatography/mass spectrometry. Clinical Biochemistry 43, 992–997.

Li, X., Long, D., Ji, J., *et al.*, 2013. Sample preparation for the metabolomics investigation of poly-gamma-glutamate-producing Bacillus licheniformis by GC–MS. Journal of Microbiological Methods 94, 61–67.

Liland, K.H., 2011. Multivariate methods in metabolomics – From pre-processing to dimension reduction and statistical analysis. TrAC Trends in Analytical Chemistry 30, 827–841.

Lin, Y., Ma, C., Liu, C., *et al.*, 2016. NMR-based fecal metabolomics fingerprinting as predictors of earlier diagnosis in patients with colorectal cancer. Oncotarget 7, 29454.

Lopes, A.S., Cruz, E.C.S., Sussulini, A., Klassen, A., 2017. Metabolomic strategies involving mass spectrometry combined with liquid and gas chromatography. In: Sussulini, A. (Ed.), Metabolomics: From Fundamentals to Clinical Applications. Springer International Publishing, pp. 77–98.

Luan, H., Liu, L.F., Meng, N., *et al.*, 2015. LC-MS-based urinary metabolite signatures in idiopathic Parkinson's disease. Journal of Proteome Research 14, 467–478.

Lv, W., Yang, T., 2012. Identification of possible biomarkers for breast cancer from free fatty acid profiles determined by GC–MS and multivariate statistical analysis. Clinical Biochemistry 45, 127–133.

Moco, S., Vervoort, J., Moco, S., *et al.*, 2007. Metabolomics technologies and metabolite identification. TrAC – Trends in Analytical Chemistry 26, 855–866.

Nakabayashi, R., Kusano, M., Kobayashi, M., *et al.*, 2009. Metabolomics-oriented isolation and structure elucidation of 37 compounds including two anthocyanins from Arabidopsis thaliana. Phytochemistry 70, 1017–1029.

Nicholson, J.K., Holmes, E., Lindon, J.C., 2007. Metabonomics and metabolomics techniques and their applications in mammalian systems. In: Nicholson, J.K., Holmes, E. (Eds.), The Handbook of Metabonomics and Metabolomics. Amsterdam: Elsevier Science B.V, pp. 1–33.

Nicholson, J.K., Lindon, J.C., Holmes, E., 1999. Metabonomics': Understanding the metabolic responses of living systems to pathophysiological stimuli via multivariate statistical analysis of biological NMR spectroscopic data. Xenobiotica 29, 1181–1189.

Nishiumi, S., Kobayashi, T., Ikeda, A., *et al.*, 2012. A novel serum metabolomics-based diagnostic approach for colorectal cancer. PLOS ONE 7, e40459.

Nordström, A., O'Maille, G., Qin, C., Siuzdak, G., 2006. Non-linear data alignment for UPLC-MS and HPLC-MS based metabolomics: Application to endogenous and exogenous metabolites in human serum. Analytical Chemistry 78, 3289–3295.

Oliver, S.G., Winson, M.K., Kell, D.B., Baganz, F., 1998. Systematic functional analysis of the yeast genome. Trends in Biotechnology 16, 373–378.

Orešič, M., Clish, C.B., Davidov, E.J., *et al.*, 2004. Phenotype characterisation using integrated gene transcript, protein and metabolite profiling. Applied Bioinformatics 3, 205–217.

Pan, Z., Raftery, D., 2007. Comparing and combining NMR spectroscopy and mass spectrometry in metabolomics. Analytical and Bioanalytical Chemistry 387, 525–527.

Qiu, Y., Cai, G., Su, M., *et al.*, 2009. Serum metabolite profiling of human colorectal cancer using GC-TOFMS and UPLC-QTOFMS. Journal of Proteome Research 8, 4844–4850.

Ramautar, R., Somsen, G.W., de Jong, G.J., 2009. CE-MS in metabolomics. Electrophoresis 30, 276–291.

Reichel, C., 2011. OMICS-strategies and methods in the fight against doping. Forensic Science International 213, 20–34.

Ren, S., Hinzman, A.A., Kang, E.L., Szczesniak, R.D., Lu, L.J., 2015. Computational and statistical analysis of metabolomics data. Metabolomics 11, 1492–1513.

Reo, N.V., 2002. Nmr-based metabolomics. Drug and Chemical Toxicology 25, 375–382.

Rizza, S., Copetti, M., Rossi, C., *et al.*, 2014. Metabolomics signature improves the prediction of cardiovascular events in elderly subjects. Atherosclerosis 232, 260–264.

Roberts, L.D., Souza, A.L., Gerszten, R.E., Clish, C.B., 2012. Targeted metabolomics. Current Protocols in Molecular Biology. 1–24.

Rodrigues, K.T., Cieslarová, Z., Tavares, M.F.M., Simionato, A.V.C., 2017. Strategies involving mass spectrometry combined with capillary electrophoresis in metabolomics. In: Sussulini, A. (Ed.), Metabolomics: From Fundamentals to Clinical Applications. Cham: Springer International Publishing, pp. 99–141.

Sato, Y., Suzuki, I., Nakamura, T., *et al.*, 2012. Identification of a new plasma biomarker of Alzheimer's disease using metabolomics technology. The Journal of Lipid Research 53, 567–576.

Scholz, M., Gatzek, S., Sterling, A., Fiehn, O., Selbig, J., 2004. Metabolite fingerprinting: Detecting biological features by independent component analysis. Bioinformatics 20, 2447–2454.

Siegel, R.L., Miller, K.D., Fedewa, S.A., *et al.*, 2017. Colorectal cancer statistics, 2017. CA: A Cancer Journal for Clinicians 67, 177–193.

Stentiford, G.D., Viant, M.R., Ward, D.G., *et al.*, 2005. Liver tumors in wild flatfish: A histopathological, proteomic, and metabolomic study. Omics : A Journal of Integrative Biology 9, 281–299.

Stipetic, L.H., Dalby, M.J., Davies, R.L., *et al.*, 2016. A novel metabolomic approach used for the comparison of Staphylococcus aureus planktonic cells and biofilm samples. Metabolomics 12, 75.

Tweeddale, H., Notley-McRobb, L., Ferenci, T., 1998. Effect of slow growth on metabolism of Escherichia coli, as revealed by global metabolite pool ('metabolome') analysis. Journal of Bacteriology 180, 5109–5116.

Vaclavik, L., Mishra, A., Mishra, K.B., Hajslova, J., 2013. Mass spectrometry-based metabolomic fingerprinting for screening cold tolerance in Arabidopsis thaliana accessions. Analytical and Bioanalytical Chemistry 405, 2671–2683.

van den Berg, R.A., Hoefsloot, H.C.J.H., Westerhuis, J.A., Smilde, A.K., van der Werf, M.J., 2006. Centering, scaling, and transformations: Improving the biological information content of metabolomics data. BMC Genomics 7, 142.

van Ginneken, V., Verhey, E., Poelmann, R., *et al.*, 2007. Metabolomics (liver and blood profiling) in a mouse model in response to fasting: A study of hepatic steatosis. Biochimica et Biophysica Acta (BBA) - Molecular and Cell Biology of Lipids 1771, 1263–1270.

Verpoorte, R., Choi, Y.H., Mustafa, N.R., Kim, H.K., 2008. Metabolomics: Back to basics. Phytochemistry Reviews 7, 525–537.

Villas-Bôas, S.G., Bruheim, P., 2007. Cold glycerol–saline: The promising quenching solution for accurate intracellular metabolite analysis of microbial cells. Analytical Biochemistry 370, 87–97.

Villas-Bôas, S.G., Mas, S., Akesson, M., Smedsgaard, J., Nielsen, J., 2005. Mass spectrometry in metabolome analysis. Mass Spectrometry Reviews 24, 613–646.

Villas-Bôas, S.G., Roessner, U., Hansen, M.A., *et al.*, 2006. Sampling and sample preparation. In: Villas-Bôas, S.G., Nielsen, J., Smedsgaard, J., Hansen, M.A.E., Roessner-Tunali, U. (Eds.), Metabolome Analysis: An Introduction. Hoboken, NJ: John Wiley & Sons, Inc, pp. 39–82.

Vu, T.N., Laukens, K., 2013. Getting your peaks in line: A review of alignment methods for NMR spectral data. Metabolites 3, 259–276.

Wang, G., Zhou, Y., Huang, F.J., *et al.*, 2014. Plasma metabolite profiles of Alzheimer's disease and mild cognitive impairment. Journal of Proteome Research 13, 2649–2658.

Wang, J., Zhang, S., Li, Z., *et al.*, 2011. 1H NMR-based metabolomics of tumor tissue for the metabolic characterization of rat hepatocellular carcinoma formation and metastasis. Tumor Biology 32, 223–231.

Wang, W., Becker, C.H., Zhou, H., *et al.*, 2003. Quantification of proteins and metabolites by mass spectrometry without isotopic labeling or spiked standards. Analytical Chemistry 75, 4818–4826.

Wilkins, M.R., Sanchez, J.-C., Gooley, A.A., *et al.*, 1996. Progress with proteome projects: Why all proteins expressed by a genome should be identified and how to do it. In: Proceedings of the Biotechnology and Genetic Engineering Reviews, 13, pp. 19–50.

Winder, C.L., Dunn, W.B., Schuler, S., *et al.*, 2008. Global Metabolic profiling of escherichia coli cultures: An evaluation of methods for quenching and extraction of intracellular metabolites. Analytical Chemistry 80, 2939–2948.

Zhang, A., Sun, H., Wang, P., Han, Y., Wang, X., 2012. Modern analytical techniques in metabolomics analysis. The Analyst 137, 293–300.
Zheng, P., Wang, Y., Chen, L., *et al.*, 2013. Identification and validation of urinary metabolite biomarkers for major depressive disorder. Molecular & Cellular Proteomics 12, 207–214.

Further Reading

Fan, T.W.M., Lane, A.N., Higashi, R.M., 2012. The Handbook of Metabolomics. Springer.
Johnson, C.H., Ivanisevic, J., Siuzdak, G., 2016. Metabolomics: Beyond biomarkers and towards mechanisms. Nature Reviews Molecular Cell Biology 17, 451–459.
Lindon, J.C., Nicholson, J.K., Holmes, E., 2011. The handbook of Metabonomics and Metabolomics. Elsevier.
Smolinska, A., *et al.*, 2012. NMR and pattern recognition methods in metabolomics: From data acquisition to biomarker discovery: A review. Analytica Chimica Acta 750, 82–97.
Zhou, B., Xiao, J.F., Tuli, L., Ressom, H.W., 2012. LC-MS-based metabolomics. Molecular BioSystems 8, 470–481.

Relevant Websites

http://www.cytoscape.org/
    Cytoscape.
http://www.hmdb.ca/
    Human Metabolome Database (HMDB).
http://www.genome.jp/kegg/
    Kyoto Encyclopedia of Genes and Genomes (KEGG).
http://www.metaboanalyst.ca/faces/home.xhtml
    MetaboAnalyst.
http://reactome.org/
    Reactome.

Disease Biomarker Discovery

Tiratha R Singh and Ankita Shukla, Jaypee University of Information Technology, Solan, India
Bensellak Taoufik and Ahmed Moussa, École Nationale Des Sciences Appliquées de Tanger, Tangier, Morocco
Brigitte Vannier, University of Poitiers, Poitiers France

Metabolic Networks: A Background for Biomarkers

Network biology is a branch of science that deals with the interactions among biomolecules that include genes, transcripts, proteins, metabolites, etc. With the advent of system biology, networks are being used widely across many branches of biology (proteomics, genomics, transcriptomics, and metabolomics) as a convenient representation of the interaction between specific biological elements. These graphical representations denote the molecular-level blueprint of interactions and mechanisms of regulation inside a cell. These biological networks include gene regulatory network, transcriptomic network, protein–protein interaction network, and metabolic network. The network biology approach helped to cover the overall aspects of the necessary facets that need to be considered while finding the probable therapeutic intervention for the particular disease type. The interaction data come through the high-throughput methods that are gathered from individual studies and large-scale screens that finally get assembled into a topological form (i.e., network format) that holds significant biological properties. In a recent scenario, more attention has been given to the gene and protein networks to study a complex form of diseases (Shukla and Singh, 2017). Although it has been found that the metabolic networks seem to play a significant role in the complex disease regulation like in case of cancer's Warburg effect (Vander Heiden *et al.*, 2009), which signifies uncontrolled cell division even in anaerobic conditions that involve numerous metabolites and the reaction mechanisms. The metabolic network comprises of metabolites and enzymes that take the role of nodes and the reactions describing their transformations and is represented as directed edges in **Fig. 1** (Bourqui *et al.*, 2007).

Biochemical reactions happening inside a metabolic network allow an organism to grow, reproduce, and respond to the environment and maintain its structure (Xu *et al.*, 2016). In a biochemical pathway, the metabolic network centralizes its attention towards mass flow that generates essential components like amino acids, sugars, and lipids, and the energy required by the biochemical reactions (Zhu *et al.*, 2007). In a metabolic network, it's not only metabolites that perform the overall metabolism but there are genes and proteins too that commence their task in regulatory mechanisms; this is what makes the metabolic networks more efficient from the disease perspective and their immediate applications too for therapeutic interventions (Berkhout *et al.*, 2013). This shows that metabolic networks typically show the representation of not only metabolites but also for genes and proteins and therefore provide wide perspective in disease studies. In a cell, metabolism holds chemical processes by which cells break down food and nutrients into usable building blocks and then reassemble those building blocks to form the biological molecules known as metabolites (DeBerardinis and Thompson, 2012). The metabolites consumed are called the substrates of the reaction; however those produced are called the products. Most metabolic reactions do not occur spontaneously, or we can say that they occur at a very low rate; therefore enzymes are used to enhance the pace of the reaction to get it completed (Cooper, 2000). This breakdown and reassembly in a pathway entails a set of successive chemical reactions that convert initial inputs into useful end products via a series of steps and this complete set of reactions in the pathway forms the metabolic network (Sridharan *et al.*, 2015). To understand the interacting mechanism in a network it's necessary to understand the architecture of the network topology. In a metabolic network, nodes represent the chemicals produced and consumed by the reactions that include small molecules (i.e. carbohydrates, lipids, amino acids, and nucleotides), and the edges denote the metabolic flow or the regulatory effects of a specific reaction (Lee *et al.*, 2008). Understanding the complex network often requires a bottom-up approach that carries its path towards systems biology perspective (Shahzad and Loor, 2012). Thus there is need to examine a system, not only in terms of individual components but as a whole, which can be done by considering the elementary constituents individually as well as when they are connected. Numerous components of a system and their interactions are best characterized as networks and they are mainly represented as graphs where thousands of nodes are connected with thousands of vertices (Cho *et al.*, 2012).

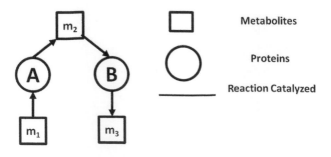

Fig. 1 Basic metabolic network.

Network analysis has suggested that biological networks have two imperative structural properties (Mahadevan and Palsson, 2005). First, it has been shown that several of these networks, including metabolic networks, are scale-free and possess a "small world" property (Barabasi and Oltvai, 2004). Second, scale-free networks are suggested to have high error tolerance and low attack tolerance (Crucitti *et al.*, 2004). In general, interactions in a network between biological entities (genes, transcripts, proteins, metabolites, etc.) can be classified on the basis of the nature of the interaction into two broad categories, i.e., influence networks and the flow networks. For influence networks, the nature of interactions are "influence-based" such as protein–protein interaction or signaling networks, i.e., connections mark the presence or absence of the reaction (Mahadevan and Palsson, 2005). This class might be extended with the case where the type of interaction is important in addition to presence or absence of the interaction, e.g., gene regulatory networks where transcription factors can either activate or repress gene expression. While in flow networks, where a specific variable like mass or energy flow may be conserved at each node, such as metabolic networks. However, it should be noted that the fundamental properties of biological networks in these two classes can be significantly different (Barabasi and Oltvai, 2004). It has been seen widely that along with the complete network graph, the subgraphs are also seen to play an essential functional role like network motifs (that represent most frequently occurring subgraph) and studies have shown the structural organization of the feedback loops (**Fig. 2**). Similarly, single-input and multiple-input motifs (**Fig. 2**) (Sehgal *et al.*, 2015) can influence the dynamics and the regulation of metabolic pathways (Beber *et al.*, 2012). For effective analysis it's important to model the network graphs correctly for which there are a wide variety of approaches depending on the features of interest through which network dynamics can be modeled, like for small networks with explicit kinetics, which can be modeled with differential equations, while for larger networks dynamics can be accessed by flux balance analysis or stochastic kinetic modeling (Boccaletti *et al.*, 2006). Also, for the case where only stoichiometric information is available, more basic approaches like network expansion or Petri nets can be utilized (Peleg *et al.*, 2005).

Varieties of graph representations are available in network biology but studies have shown that bipartite graph (**Fig. 3**) (two nodes represent metabolites with edges joining each metabolite to the reaction) is the most correct representation of the metabolic network (Veeramani and Bader, 2010). The edges in the representative graphs are directed because some metabolites (the substrates) go into the reaction and some (the products) come out of it. Metabolic networks are represented through nodes as metabolites and the links as reactions that are catalyzed by specific gene products; this representation is different from protein–protein interaction networks, where the nodes are the gene products and the links correspond to interactions. The analysis of protein–protein interaction networks has suggested that the deletion of the most highly connected proteins correlates well with a lethal phenotype (Mahadevan and Palsson, 2005). In contrast, a node in metabolic networks cannot be deleted by genetic techniques, but links can (Jeong *et al.*, 2001).

Now the question comes as to how the resultant computational network are formed and how their global representation is possible. The answer lies in the computer readable file formats for the biological networks, i.e., Systems Biology Markup Language (SBML), a global format which could be utilized for the reusability of network models. It is a XML-like machine-readable language that is proficient to represent models to be analyzed by a computer. SBML can represent metabolic networks, cell signaling pathways, regulatory networks, and many other kinds of systems (Hucka *et al.*, 2003). An increasing number of diseases are now

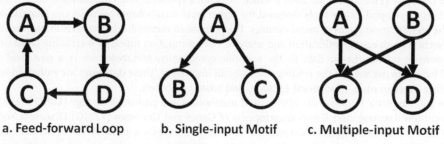

a. Feed-forward Loop   b. Single-input Motif   c. Multiple-input Motif

Fig. 2 Most frequent regulatory motif.

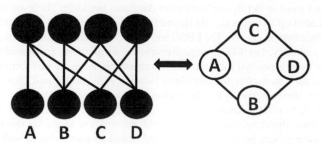

Fig. 3 Bipartite graph with corresponding simple representation.

seen to be a result of drastic perturbations of cellular functions that involve large sets of genes, where connections are complicated to understand. Diseases in particular like cancer, CVD, or diabetes causes huge perturbations in cell metabolism. Therefore, the study of metabolic networks primary perturbation in interactions and fluxes can aid better understanding of the physiopathology of such diseases. It notably permits an understanding of how and why alteration in activity or expression levels of a few enzymes can transmit substantial perturbations into entire cellular functions. Therefore these metabolites could have been proposed as putative biomarkers for the human diseases.

Metabolome Analysis: Computational Protocols and Methods

The metabolome comprises of the biochemical composition of the small-molecule metabolites present in a cell that are involved in the metabolic reaction mechanism and required for the maintenance, growth, and normal functioning of the cell (Mohney and Milburn, 2015). The metabolome was first described by Oliver and colleagues in 1998 (Oliver et al., 1998), during their pioneering work on yeast metabolism that therefore confers the discipline of metabolomics; that follows the analysis of the metabolome. Metabolomics is sometimes also called metabonomics or metabolic profiling (Lindon et al., 2011). Various experimental, statistical, and computational approaches have been discovered so far to perform the metabolome analysis. The most commonly used experimental techniques in metabolomics are mass spectrometry (MS), i.e., gas chromatography (GC–MS) or liquid chromatography (LC-MS), and nuclear magnetic resonance spectroscopy (NMR) spectra (Zhang et al., 2012). Along with this statistical approaches have been devised to perform the analysis and it comprises of various standard analysis methods such as t-test and ANOVA, as well as more sophisticated methodologies such as univariate and multivariate analysis methods (Bartel et al., 2013).

Also, bioinformatic approaches fall into the scenario due to the boom in high-throughput data and this includes databases for the data retrieval as well as web servers for carrying out the analysis (Maudsley et al., 2011). Tremendous efforts have been implemented to archive all types of biological data, i.e., genes, proteins, gene products, metabolites, etc. With the advent of the genomic era, the amount of biochemical knowledge has exploded in the last two decades, which has necessitated its storage in large databases. Variety of top-down (gene to protein to metabolite) and bottom-up (chemical entity to biological function) approaches have been implied resulting in a rich expanse of metabolic knowledge from the biochemical network (Cakir and Khatibipour, 2014). Bioinformatics is a pioneer in preserving the data obtained through the experimental or natural resources and also provided the numerous tools for the analysis purpose. The databases provide the contextual biochemical basis for metabolomics data interpretation. By providing information regarding metabolites like defining which enzymatic reactions consume or produce them, and which pathways they're involved in, researchers can use this data to interpret their experiments towards a higher level of annotation.

METLIN, was the first metabolomics database, was established in 2004 (Smith et al., 2005). Thereby in 2005, the Human Metabolome Project was launched to find and catalog all of the metabolites in human tissue and biofluids. This metabolite information is kept in the Human Metabolome Database, which produced its first draft in 2007 (Wishart et al., 2007). There are many databases containing metabolomics data, and each has different information, ranging from NMR and MS spectra to metabolic pathways. Additionally, and more specifically to the development of metabolomics, mass spectral databases like the Golm Metabolome Database (Hummel et al., 2007), which links mass spectrum and chromatographic retention time to specific compounds, have been developed. Some tools designed for higher level metabolomic analysis can take GC–MS spectra as input and use them for the identification stages of metabolomics. The purpose of metabolic databases is to organize the metabolites in a way that helps researchers in an easy identification and analysis. The information found in metabolite databases has continuously been updated to provide state-of-the-art data to the scientific community. Metabolomics is a new field and therefore new approaches are still being discovered and the existing ones are still improving. These databases are embraced with various types of information including concentration, anatomical location, and related disorders.

Other databases are MassBank (Horai et al., 2008), lipid metabolites and pathways strategy (LIPID-MAPS) (LIPID), Madison metabolomics consortium database, and Kyoto Encyclopedia of Genes and Genomes (KEGG) (Kanehisa and Goto, 2000). The major database till now is the KEGG, which is divided into several subdatabases with LIGAND, REACTION PAIR and PATHWAY being the most relevant to metabolomics (Booth et al., 2013). In KEGG however there is a dauntingly large sum, i.e., 10,664 reactions and 18,107 metabolites (Kanehisa and Goto, 2000). These databases have been undergoing continuous updation and annotation for and so contain a great deal of valuable information. KEGG and MetaCyc (Karp et al., 2002) are currently the largest (most number of organisms) and most in-depth comprehensive databases available. There are other databases too as Reactome (Joshi-Tope et al., 2005), Model SEED (Devoid et al., 2013), and BiGG (Schellenberger et al., 2010), that can be more useful than the large databases if a specific organism is desired. The KEGG and MetaCyc databases each contain a generalized conserved set of pathways based on metabolic pathways. For KEGG, organism-specific annotations are available to query while for MetaCyc, individual "Cyc" databases have been generated for a number of organisms, some are just computationally derived while others are extensively manually curated such as AraCyc for *Arabidopsis* (Mueller et al., 2003) and EcoCyc for *E.coli* strain *K-12 MGI655* (Karp et al., 2014). A more recent development is the cheminformatic databases like PubChem (Wang et al., 2009) and ChEBI (Degtyarenko et al., 2007), which provide a chemically ontological approach to catalog small molecules that are active in biological systems. These databases, therefore, can provide fruitful information regarding the metabolic datasets. Finally, it is important to note that these databases can be cross-referenced and linked to each other as well as against more widely known databases such as the well-known Chemical Abstract Service (CAS) among many others. Along with the above mentioned

Table 1 Selected databases and tools w.r.t metabolomics

Databases

BioCyc	Collection of 10992 Pathway/Genome Databases (PGDBs)	http://biocyc.org
BiGG Models	Knowledgebase of genome-scale metabolic network reconstructions.	http://bigg.ucsd.edu/
BMRB	Repository for data from nuclear magnetic resonance spectroscopy (NMR) spectroscopy on proteins, peptides, nucleic acids, and other biomolecules	http://www.bmrb.wisc.edu/
BRENDA	Comprehensive enzyme repository, provide metabolic pathway details	http://www.brenda-enzymes.info/index.php
ChEBI	Freely available dictionary of molecular entities focused on "small" chemical compounds	https://www.ebi.ac.uk/chebi/
DIMEdb	Database of biologically relevant metabolite structures and annotations	http://dimedb.ibers.aber.ac.uk/
DRUGBANK	Unique bioinformatics and cheminformatics resource that combines detailed drug (i.e., chemical, pharmacological, and pharmaceutical) data with comprehensive drug target (i.e., sequence, structure, and pathway) information	https://www.drugbank.ca/
ECMDB	Contains extensive metabolomic data and metabolic pathway diagrams about *Escherichia coli (strain K12, MG1655)*	http://ecmdb.ca/
GMD	Facilitates the search for and dissemination of reference mass spectra from biologically active metabolites quantified using gas chromatography coupled to mass spectrometry (MS)	http://gmd.mpimp-golm.mpg.de/
HMDB	Archive information about small-molecule metabolites found in the human body	http://www.hmdb.ca/
KEGG	Resource for understanding high-level functions and utilities of the biological system, such as the cell, the organism and the ecosystem, from molecular-level information	http://www.genome.jp/kegg/pathway.html
MANET	Maps evolutionary relationships of molecule (metabolic, protein) architectures directly onto biological networks	http://manet.illinois.edu/
MassBank	Contains high resolution mass spectral data	http://massbank.eu/MassBank/
MetaboLights	Database for metabolomics experiments and derived information	http://www.ebi.ac.uk/metabolights/
MetaNetX	Automated model construction and genome annotation for large-scale metabolic networks	http://www.metanetx.org/
Reactome	Navigable map of human biological pathways, ranging from metabolic processes to hormonal signaling	http://www.reactome.org
SMPDB	Support pathway elucidation and pathway discovery in metabolomics, transcriptomics, proteomics and systems biology	http://smpdb.ca/
YMDB	Manually curated database of small-molecule metabolites found in or produced by *Saccharomyces cerevisiae*	http://www.ymdb.ca/

Computational analysis tools

Arcadia	Visualization tool for metabolic pathways	http://arcadiapathways.sourceforge.net/
CellNetAnalyzer	MATLAB toolbox providing a various (partially unique) computational methods and algorithms for exploring structural and functional properties of metabolic, signaling, and regulatory networks	http://www.mpi-magdeburg.mpg.de/projects/cna/cna.html
GLAMM	Unified web interface for visualizing metabolic networks, reconstructing metabolic networks from annotated genome data, visualizing experimental data in the context of metabolic networks, and investigating the construction of novel, transgenic pathways	http://glamm.lbl.gov/
IMPaLA	Perform pathway overrepresentation and enrichment analysis with expression and/or metabolite data	http://impala.molgen.mpg.de
iPath	Web-based tool for the visualization, analysis and customization of the various pathways maps	http://pathways.embl.de
JDesigner	Graphical modeling environment for biochemical reaction networks	http://jdesigner.sourceforge.net/Site/JDesigner.html
KaPPA-View	Web-based analysis tool for integration of transcript and metabolite data on plant metabolic pathway	http://kpv.kazusa.or.jp/en/
LIPID MAPS	Online tools for lipid research	http://www.lipidmaps.org/tools/index.html
MapMan	A user-driven tool to display genomics data sets onto diagrams of metabolic pathways and other biological processes	http://mapman.gabipd.org/web/guest/mapman
MetaMapp	Mapping and visualizing metabolomic data by integrating information from biochemical pathways and chemical and mass spectral similarity	http://uranus.fiehnlab.ucdavis.edu:8080/MetaMapp/homePage
MetPA	A web-based metabolomics tool for pathway analysis and visualization	http://metpa.metabolomics.ca
MassTRIX	Annotate metabolites in high precision MS data	http://masstrix3.helmholtz-muenchen.de/masstrix3/
MetaboAnalyst	Web server designed to permit comprehensive metabolomic data analysis, visualization and interpretation	http://www.metaboanalyst.ca/MetaboAnalyst/
MetaPath Online	For the analysis of metabolic networks	https://scopes.biologie.hu-berlin.de/

(Continued)

Table 1   Continued

Databases

Meta P-server	A web based, easy-to-use analysis tool for the statistical analysis of metabolomics data	http://metabolomics.helmholtz-muenchen.de/metap2/
MetExplore	Find information about metabolite relationships in metabolic networks	http://metexplore.toulouse.inra.fr/metexplore/
Metscape	A plug-in for Cytoscape, used to visualize and interpret metabolomic data in the context of human metabolic networks	http://metscape.ncibi.org
MGV	A versatile generic graph viewer for multiomics data also it offers a comprehensive set of tools for analysis and visualization of graphs.	http://www.microarray-analysis.org/mayday
MPEA	Metabolite pathway enrichment analysis	http://ekhidna.biocenter.helsinki.fi/poxo/mpea/
MSEA	A web-based tool to identify biologically meaningful patterns in quantitative metabolomic data	http://www.msea.ca
Omix	Network drawing tool along with programmable visualization framework	http://www.omix-visualization.com/?from=http://www.13cflux.net#sthash.vLyVKteK.dpbs
Paintomics	A web based tool for the joint visualization of transcriptomics and metabolomics data	http://www.paintomics.org
TICL	A web tool for network-based interpretation of compound lists inferred by high-throughput metabolomics	http://mips.helmholtz-muenchen.de/proj/cmp/home.html
Vanted	Network visualization and analysis tool for creating and editing the network and mapping experimental data onto networks	https://immersive-analytics.infotech.monash.edu/vanted/

Table 2   PAM50 genes list

PAM50 genes

ACTR3B	CDCA1 (NUF2)	FOXA1	MDM2	PGR
ANLN	CDH3	FOXC1	MELK	PHGDH
BAG1	CENPF	GPR160	MIA	PTTG1
BCL2	CEP55	GRB7	MKI67	RRM2
BIRC5	CXXC5	KIF2C	MLPH	SFRP1
BLVRA	EGFR	KNTC2(NDC80)	MMP11	SLC39A6
CCNB1	ERBB2	KRT14	MYBL2	TMEM45B
CCNE1	ESR1	KRT17	MYC	TYMS
CDC20	EXO1	KRT5	NAT1	UBE2C
CDC6	FGFR4	MAPT	ORC6L(ORC6)	UBE2T

databases there are different types of databases built so far only the selected ones based upon accuracy and applications are mentioned in alphabetical order in **Table 1**.

Similarly, there are many computational tools available for the metabolic data handling like for building, editing, enrichment, and interpreting metabolic network models, including Arcadia (Villeger *et al.*, 2010), GLAMM (Bates *et al.*, 2011), CellNetAnalyzer (Klamt and von Kamp, 2011), MetaMapp (Barupal *et al.*, 2012), MetPA (Xia and Wishart, 2010a), Vanted (Rohn *et al.*, 2012) for network visualization. Likewise there are tools for drawing a network, Omix (Droste *et al.*, 2013) which have been widely used for creating a network model. TICL (Antonov *et al.*, 2009) is used for the interpretation of compound lists that are inferred by high-throughput metabolomics. Enrichment analysis could be done with the help of MSEA (Xia and Wishart, 2010b), MPEA (Kankainen *et al.*, 2011). MassTRIX (Suhre and Schmitt-Kopplin, 2008) performs the annotating metabolites in high precision MS data. There are other tools also, which have been mentioned in **Table 2** along with their descriptions.

Biomarker Discovery: A Challenge and Plausible Solutions Through Bioinformatics

Biomarkers are measured indicators of biological and pathogenic conditions or pharmacological responses to a therapeutic intervention (Strimbu and Tavel, 2010). Based on pathophysiological, epidemiological, therapeutic, or other scientific evidence they are intended to be useful in terms of clinical significance (i.e., to know whether they will benefit or harm) (Baumgartner *et al.*, 2011; Downing, 2001). Biomarkers have a generous impact on the care of patients; for those who are suspected to have the disease or those who have or have no visible disease symptoms (Baumgartner *et al.*, 2011). For a long time biomarkers have served as a plausible diagnostic key to unraveling disease conditions, especially in case of cancers. Depending on the condition type they can be categorized as diagnostic, prognostic, and screening biomarkers (Madu and Lu, 2010). Currently, screening biomarkers are of high interest due to their ability to predict future events, but there are only a few accepted biomarkers for disease screening available today (Melander *et al.*, 2009). Therefore it is necessary to have considerable search, verification, biological and biochemical interpretation, and independent validation of disease biomarkers, which requires advancement in high-throughput technologies. To achieve this goal there is necessity to have interdisciplinary expertise, which requires the teamwork of clinicians, biologists, biochemists, and bioinformaticians to carry out biomarker cohort studies with professional planning, implementation, and control. Bioinformatics plays a key role in the biomarker discovery process via bridging the gap between initial discovery phases such as experimental design, clinical study execution, and bioanalytics, including sample preparation, separation, high-throughput profiling, and independent validation of identified candidate biomarkers (Baumgartner *et al.*, 2011) (**Fig. 4**).

It is well known that a disease or a phenotype is rarely a consequence of an abnormality of a single gene or its expression but instead reflects the interactions of various processes in a complex network; such network could combine multiple genes (proteins) and metabolites. For example, plants can produce numerous metabolites to handle different environmental conditions however the biosynthetic pathways for most of these compounds have not yet been revealed (Schlapfer *et al.*, 2017). From these facts, the need for a disease signature, a set of compounds generally presented as a network, becomes evident. Such disease-specific signature could be helpful in understanding all its mechanisms and evolution and in an earlier diagnosis. Multiple works and frameworks aimed to either use genes expression or metabolic data to extract a set of disease-relevant compounds; it's safe to say biomarkers (Strimbu and Tavel, 2010). Identifying such crucial biomarkers responsible for disease characteristics and revealing its mechanisms can be used to infer its evolution and development and offers better targets for drug development, treatment individualization, and dose regimen. These biomarkers are selected by analytic methods or pathway and network-centric methods (Wang *et al.*, 2015). A typical case would be gene expression data of two pairs of samples in both disease and normal states help in discovering genes and metabolites which can be potential biomarkers (Li *et al.*, 2013; Shlomi, 2010; Li *et al.*, 2012). Cancer is a heterogeneous disease, for instance, breast cancer. Biomarkers at the DNA, RNA, and protein levels were developed to better understand the biology of breast cancer, leading to the possibility to classify the disease into subtypes and subgroups, which may lead to new therapeutic opportunities (Le Du *et al.*, 2013). Many tests are available for the diagnosis and each one is based on a set of genes; we can list some of most known ones such as PAM50. PAM50 stands for Prediction Analysis of Microarray 50 (Sweeney *et al.*, 2014), fifty genes were probed like *ACTR3B, ANLN, BAG1, BCL2, BIRC5*, etc. Elaborating a set of biomarkers allowed the development of many tools online (cbioportal (Gao *et al.*, 2013)) and offline, in libraries and packages. These tools offer the possibility of analyzing targeted datasets and understanding the disease stage. Machine learning tools are also a very effective way of dealing with such complex diseases, predicting treatment effectiveness and new treated disease trajectory. Since these, new models have been well designed, which fully explains the relationship between each biomarker.

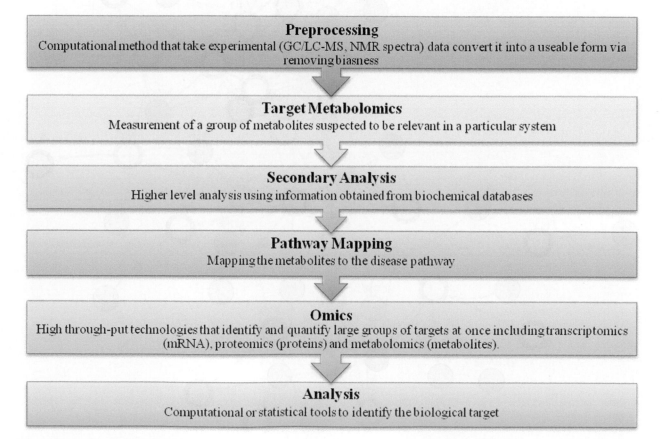

Fig. 4 Computational pipeline for metabolome analysis.

Gene Expression and Metabolic Network: Applications in Biomarker Discovery for Complex Diseases

DNA microarray technologies permit systematic approaches to the biological discovery that have a profound impact on biological research, pharmacology, and medicine (Yousef et al., 2014). The ability to obtain quantitative information from the complete transcription profile of cells provides a powerful means to explore basic biology, disease diagnosis, drug development, mold therapeutics to specific pathologies, and generate databases (Young, 2000). Gene expression studies bridge the gap between DNA information and its trait information by dissecting the biochemical pathways into intermediate components, that is, between genotype and phenotype (Xiong et al., 2001). The gene expression studies, therefore, open new avenues for identifying complex disease genes and biomarkers for disease diagnosis and also for assessing drug efficacy and toxicity. One particularly powerful application of gene expression analyses is in biomarker discovery, which can be used for disease risk assessment, early detection, prognosis, predicting response to therapy, and preventive measures.

For years, scientists studied one gene at a time and genes were indeed studied in isolation from the larger context of other involved genes. Nowadays, genomics via high-throughput techniques helps to study the genome of organisms as a whole thus allowing a wide picture of gene characteristics. One of the most popular high-throughput techniques are arrays, which are an orderly arrangement of a large number of samples allowing large-scale studies (Yousef et al., 2014). This gave rise to the genomic era, which emerged from the sequencing of genomes from many organisms. The development of the first arrays started many years ago to study a large number of genes at a time (Hergenhahn et al., 2003) and has widely expanded since then. Today the approach is also applicable to RNA probes, proteins, antibodies, and even biological samples allowing new types of research (Yousef et al., 2014). Currently, other types of high-throughput techniques are also developing, for instance, to study the transcripts and metabolites.

Today, genomics has induced two new paradigms in biology; the first paradigm is a new approach that allows the study of the complex network through which genes and proteins communicate. It is attained via an amalgamation of the researcher having expertise in the field of biology, engineering, chemistry, and computer science; this multidisciplinary approach allows the development of systems biology. The second paradigm is a direct consequence of information derived from genomics studies where raw data needs to be analyzed and then to be used in the systemic approach. This led the development of bioinformatics,

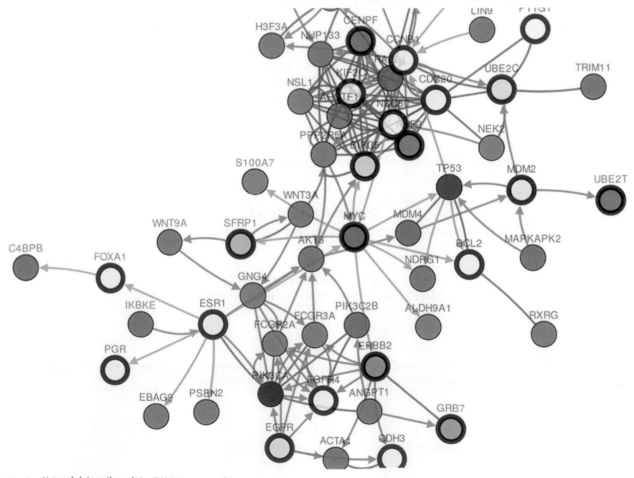

Fig. 5 Network interaction of the PAM50 genes set.

which requires the use of computers to manage biological information. The practical applications of gene expression analyses are numerous and only beginning to be realized. One particularly powerful application of gene expression analyses is in biomarker identification, which can be used for disease risk assessment, early detection, prognosis, prediction response to therapy, and preventative measures.

Therefore approaches to cancer biomarker discovery comprise genomics, epigenomics, transcriptomics, and proteomic analyses. Current efforts in the laboratory focus on the identification of biomarkers in chronic lymphocytic leukemia, lung cancer, and colon cancer (McDermott *et al.*, 2013). Along with the mRNA other small RNAs are also known to be a predictive indicator in disease studies; and it has been found that alterations in gene expression patterns due to dysregulation of miRNAs is a common cause in tumorigenesis (Chen *et al.*, 2012). High concentrations of cell-free miRNAs that originate from the primary tumor have been found in the plasma of cancer patients, and several lines of evidence indicate that plasma miRNAs are associated with specific vesicles called exosomes (Yang *et al.*, 2016). This led to the discovery of new biomarkers that comprises plasma miRNAs and seems to be promising in disease prognosis (Jeffrey, 2008). Recent discovery of quantifiable circulating cancer-associated miRNAs exposes the immense potential of their use as novel minimally invasive biomarkers for breast and other cancers (Heneghan *et al.*, 2009).

Discovery of Biomarkers Through Computational Pipeline: A Cancer Based Study

The classification of samples from gene expression datasets usually involves a small number of samples. The problem of selecting those biomarker genes that are vital for differentiating the different sample classes being compared poses a challenging problem in

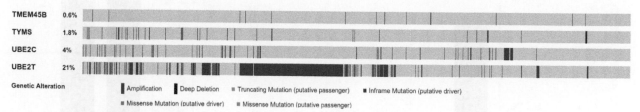

Fig. 6 Oncoprint for only four biomarkers.

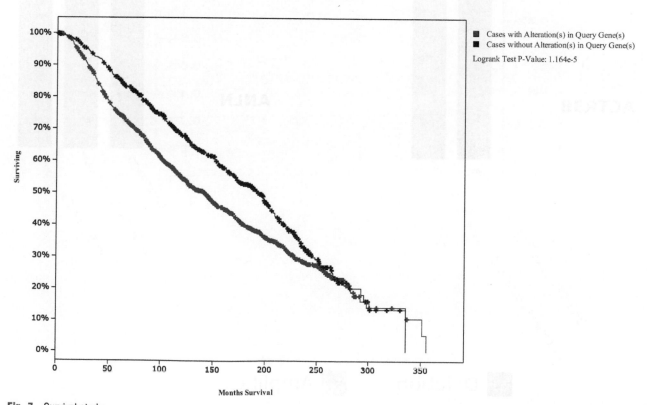

Fig. 7 Survival study.

case of the high dimensional data analysis. A variety of methods to address this problem have been implemented and these methods can be divided into two main categories: (1) Filtering based methods and (2) model-based or wrapper approaches (Wang *et al.*, 2005; Inza *et al.*, 2004). The filter method (Ben-Bassat, 1982) assesses the goodness of the proposed feature subset looking only at the intrinsic characteristics of the data, based on the relation of each single gene with the class label by the calculation of simple statistics computed from the empirical distribution. This approach is extensively used as a feature subset selection method in the microarray (Aris and Recce, 2002). While in the wrapper approach (Kohavi and John, 1997), which is a very powerful machine learning application, search is conducted in the space of genes, evaluating the goodness of each found gene subset by the estimation of the accuracy percentage of the specific classifier to be used.

One of the most important properties that should be considered for the biomarkers is the robustness. It is an important issue for the successful discovery of biomarkers, as it may greatly influence subsequent biological validations. In addition, a more robust set of markers may strengthen the confidence of an expert in the results of a selection method (Abeel *et al.*, 2010). Robustness, a property that allows a system to maintain its functions under certain external and internal perturbations, is a ubiquitously observed feature of biological systems (Kitano, 2004). Studying the relationship between the topology and robustness of

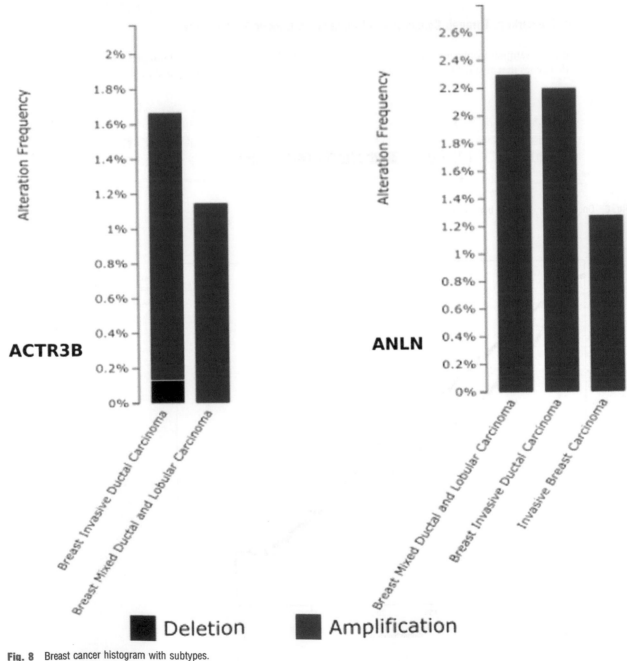

Fig. 8   Breast cancer histogram with subtypes.

metabolic networks may help to understand the functional organization principle of cells and could have important implications for disease studies (Schuster and Holzhütter, 1995) and drug target identifications (Bakker *et al.*, 2000).

The robustness of the metabolic network with respect to specific enzymes can be qualitatively estimated by the preservation or decay of the network after removal of the nodes or edges corresponding to these enzymes. The following topological features of metabolic networks may ensure the robustness of metabolism; these are (1) modularity, which contributes to the robustness of networks by decreasing the cross talk between different functional modules, detaining perturbations and damages to separable parts and preventing deleterious effects from spreading to the whole system (Stelling *et al.*, 2004); (2) bow-tie structure, which aids in forming a robust conserved core because it is the most tightly connected part of the network and there are multiple routes between any pair of nodes. Such connecting patterns provide an advantage in generating a coordinated response to various stimuli and increases the robustness of the whole system (Kitano, 2004); and (3) scale-free topology; the key feature of scale-free networks is the high-degree of error tolerance; that is, the ability of their nodes to communicate is unaffected by the failure of some randomly chosen nodes (Crucitti *et al.*, 2004). Thus the scale-free nature of metabolic networks indicates its high resistance towards random perturbations and thus could explain why some enzyme dysfunction at the metabolic level is without substantial phenotypic effect (Barabasi and Albert, 1999). The studies have shown that the scale-free networks are extremely vulnerable to attacks, i.e., the removal of a few hub nodes that play a crucial role in maintaining a network's connectivity will destroy the whole network (Crucitti *et al.*, 2004). Studies conducted by Mahadevan and Palsson showed that low-degree nodes are almost as likely to be critical to the overall network functions as high-degree nodes (Mahadevan and Palsson, 2005) by calculating the number of lethal reactions among all the reactions connected to every metabolite in the substrate graph of metabolic networks.

To show an example of analysis using biomarkers a dataset from (Pereira *et al.*, 2016) was used. It presents a somatic mutation profiling study of 2433 breast cancers, which approved the classification of the tumors into 10 integrative clusters (IntClusts).

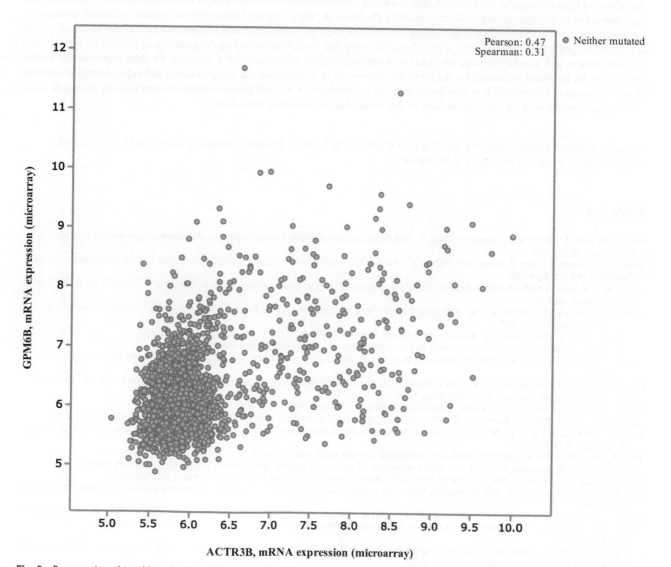

Fig. 9 Coexpression of two biomarkers, ACTR3B & GPM6B.

During this study (Pereira *et al.*, 2016) CNAs (copy number aberrations) were the main driver in an unsupervised clustering approach due to their influence on genes expression. The current analysis used the dataset above against the fifty genes found in PAM50 (**Table 2**). These genes served as a gene set for the cbioportal, so the mutations profiling could be performed. Figures below show different knowledges extracted, cancer types, and mutation happening along genes, genes with similar or exclusive expression, and finally survival estimation. Gene networks present an excellent input for models analysis using algorithmic methods such as Bayesian networks, leading to inferring and predicting the cancer evolution, trajectory, and progression (Caravagna *et al.*, 2016). **Fig. 5** shows the interaction of the PAM50 gene set where nodes are representing genes and edges (arrows) denote the interactions between them.

Thereby an oncoprint of four biomarkers (TMEM45B, TYMS, UBE2C, UBE2T) has been captured (**Fig. 6**) that shows the type of mutation occurring to the gene set.

After this, a survival study has been conducted (**Fig. 7**), which is performed for the p-value of 1.164e-5 and red color denotes the alteration in query gene while blue color shows the query gene without alteration. It has been noticed that the cases with alterations have higher survival rate than the nonaltered ones.

Then alteration frequency of ACTR3B and ANLN were determined through the histogram (**Fig. 8**) that denotes the alteration and the deletion frequency. Finally Pearson and Spearsman correlation coefficient induced shows the coexpression of the two biomarkers, that is, ACTR3B & GPM6B (**Fig. 9**).

Concluding Remarks

The advent of high-throughput technologies, and as a result, the generation of various kinds of omics data, has challenged both the experimental or computational scientific communities. Therefore an "omics cascade" came into the scenario where the genotype to the phenotype can be connected through various intermediate steps for better understanding the disease biology and their overall impact on the phenotypic observations at the physical or organism level. Understanding the genotype to phenotype scenario and its consequences will provide an edge towards better implementation of computational methods for their experimental validations. It will be an added advantage for the scientific community to amalgamate the computational and experimental procedures for the betterment of mankind. It is anticipated that this comprehensive text will provide systematic and ordered information on the metabolic world with its exact connection to the biomarker identification procedure.

See also: Biological Database Searching. Identification and Extraction of Biomarker Information. Integrative Analysis of Multi-Omics Data. Natural Language Processing Approaches in Bioinformatics

References

Abeel, T., Helleputte, T., Van De Peer, Y., Dupont, P., Saeys, Y., 2010. Robust biomarker identification for cancer diagnosis with ensemble feature selection methods. Bioinformatics 26, 392–398.

Antonov, A.V., Dietmann, S., Wong, P., Mewes, H.W., 2009. TICL – A web tool for network-based interpretation of compound lists inferred by high-throughput metabolomics. The FEBS Journal 276, 2084–2094.

Aris, V., Recce, M., 2002. A method to improve detection of disease using selectively expressed genes in microarray data. In: Proceedings of CAMDA'00, pp. 69–81. (S.M. Lin and K.F. Johnson, editors).

Bakker, B.M., Mensonides, F.I., Teusink, B., *et al.*, 2000. Compartmentation protects trypanosomes from the dangerous design of glycolysis. Proceedings of the National Academy of Sciences 97, 2087–2092.

Barabasi, A.L., Albert, R., 1999. Emergence of scaling in random networks. Science 286, 509–512.

Barabasi, A.L., Oltvai, Z.N., 2004. Network biology: Understanding the cell's functional organization. Nature Review Genetics 5, 101–113.

Bartel, J., Krumsiek, J., Theis, F.J., 2013. Statistical methods for the analysis of high-throughput metabolomics data. Computational and Structural Biotechnology Journal 4, e201301009.

Barupal, D.K., Haldiya, P.K., Wohlgemuth, G., *et al.*, 2012. MetaMapp: Mapping and visualizing metabolomic data by integrating information from biochemical pathways and chemical and mass spectral similarity. BMC Bioinformatics 13, 99.

Bates, J.T., Chivian, D., Arkin, A.P., 2011. GLAMM: Genome-Linked Application for Metabolic Maps. Nucleic Acids Research 39, W400–W405.

Baumgartner, C., Osl, M., Netzer, M., Baumgartner, D., 2011. Bioinformatic-driven search for metabolic biomarkers in disease. Journal of Clinical Bioinformatics 1, 2.

Beber, M.E., Fretter, C., Jain, S., *et al.*, 2012. Artefacts in statistical analyses of network motifs: General framework and application to metabolic networks. Journal of the Royal Society Interface 9, 3426–3435.

Ben-Bassat, M., 1982. Pattern recognition and reduction of dimensionality. Handbook of Statistics 2, 773–910.

Berkhout, J., Teusink, B., Bruggeman, F.J., 2013. Gene network requirements for regulation of metabolic gene expression to a desired state. Scientific Reports 3, 1417.

Boccaletti, S., Latora, V., Moreno, Y., Chavez, M., Hwang, D.-U., 2006. Complex networks: Structure and dynamics. Physics Reports 424, 175–308.

Booth, S.C., Weljie, A.M., Turner, R.J., 2013. Computational tools for the secondary analysis of metabolomics experiments. Computational and Structural Biotechnology Journal 4, e201301003.

Bourqui, R., Cottret, L., Lacroix, V., *et al.*, 2007. Metabolic network visualization eliminating node redundance and preserving metabolic pathways. BMC Systems Biology 1, 29.

Cakir, T., Khatibipour, M.J., 2014. Metabolic network discovery by top-down and bottom-up approaches and paths for reconciliation. Frontiers in Bioengineering and Biotechnology 2, 62.

Caravagna, G., Graudenzi, A., Ramazzotti, D., *et al.*, 2016. Algorithmic methods to infer the evolutionary trajectories in cancer progression. Proceedings of the National Academy of Sciences of the United States of America 113, E4025–E4034.

Chen, P.S., Su, J.L., Hung, M.C., 2012. Dysregulation of microRNAs in cancer. Journal of Biomedical Science 19, 90.

Cho, D.Y., Kim, Y.A., Przytycka, T.M., 2012. Chapter 5: Network biology approach to complex diseases. PLOS Computational Biology 8, e1002820.

Cooper, G.M., 2000. The central role of enzymes as biological catalysts. Sinauer Associates.

Crucitti, P., Latora, V., Marchiori, M., Rapisarda, A., 2004. Error and attack tolerance of complex networks. Physica A: Statistical Mechanics and its Applications 340, 388–394.

DeBerardinis, R.J., Thompson, C.B., 2012. Cellular metabolism and disease: What do metabolic outliers teach us? Cell 148, 1132–1144.

Degtyarenko, K., De Matos, P., Ennis, M., et al., 2007. ChEBI: A database and ontology for chemical entities of biological interest. Nucleic Acids Research 36, D344–D350.

Devoid, S., Overbeek, R., Dejongh, M., et al., 2013. Automated genome annotation and metabolic model reconstruction in the SEED and Model SEED. Systems Metabolic Engineering: Methods and Protocols. 17–45.

Downing, G., 2001. Biomarkers definitions working group. Biomarkers and surrogate endpoints. Clinical Pharmacology & Therapeutics 69, 89–95.

Droste, P., Nöh, K., Wiechert, W., 2013. Omix – A visualization tool for metabolic networks with highest usability and customizability in focus. Chemie Ingenieur Technik 85, 849–862.

Gao, J., Aksoy, B.A., Dogrusoz, U., et al., 2013. Integrative analysis of complex cancer genomics and clinical profiles using the cBioPortal. Science Signaling 6, pl1.

Heneghan, H., Miller, N., Lowery, A., Sweeney, K., Kerin, M., 2009. MicroRNAs as novel biomarkers for breast cancer. Journal of Oncology 2009.

Hergenhahn, M., Muhlemann, K., Hollstein, M., Kenzelmann, M., 2003. DNA microarrays: Perspectives for hypothesis-driven transcriptome research and for clinical applications. Current Genomics 4, 543–555.

Horai, H., Aranita, M., Nishioka, T., 2008. MassBank: Mass spectral database for metabolome analysis. In: Proceedings of the 56th ASMS Conference on Mass Spectrometry and Allied Topics, Denver, CO.

Hucka, M., Finney, A., Sauro, H.M., et al., 2003. The systems biology markup language (SBML): A medium for representation and exchange of biochemical network models. Bioinformatics 19, 524–531.

Hummel, J., Selbig, J., Walther, D., Kopka, J., 2007. The Golm Metabolome Database: A database for GC–MS based metabolite profiling. Metabolomics. 75–95.

Inza, I., Larranaga, P., Blanco, R., Cerrolaza, A.J., 2004. Filter versus wrapper gene selection approaches in DNA microarray domains. Artificial Intelligence in Medicine 31, 91–103.

Jeffrey, S.S., 2008. Cancer biomarker profiling with microRNAs. Nature Biotechnology 26, 400–401.

Jeong, H., Mason, S.P., Barabasi, A.L., Oltvai, Z.N., 2001. Lethality and centrality in protein networks. Nature 411, 41–42.

Joshi-Tope, G., Gillespie, M., Vastrik, I., et al., 2005. Reactome: A knowledgebase of biological pathways. Nucleic Acids Research 33, D428–D432.

Kanehisa, M., Goto, S., 2000. KEGG: Kyoto encyclopedia of genes and genomes. Nucleic Acids Research 28, 27–30.

Kankainen, M., Gopalacharyulu, P., Holm, L., Orešič, M., 2011. MPEA – Metabolite pathway enrichment analysis. Bioinformatics 27, 1878–1879.

Karp, P.D., Riley, M., Paley, S.M., Pellegrini-Toole, A., 2002. The metacyc database. Nucleic Acids Research 30, 59–61.

Karp, P.D., Weaver, D., Paley, S., et al., 2014. The EcoCyc database. EcoSal Plus 6.

Kitano, H., 2004. Biological robustness. Nature Reviews Genetics 5, 826–837.

Klamt, S., von Kamp, A., 2011. An application programming interface for CellNetAnalyzer. Biosystems 105, 162–168.

Kohavi, R., John, G.H., 1997. Wrappers for feature subset selection. Artificial intelligence 97, 273–324.

Le Du, F., Ueno, N.T., Gonzalez-Angulo, A.M., 2013. Breast Cancer Biomarkers: Utility in clinical practice. Current Breast Cancer Reports 5.

Lee, D.-S., Park, J., Kay, K., et al., 2008. The implications of human metabolic network topology for disease comorbidity. Proceedings of the National Academy of Sciences 105, 9880–9885.

Li, L., Jiang, H., Ching, W.-K., Vassiliadis, V.S., 2012. Metabolite biomarker discovery for metabolic diseases by flux analysis. In: Proceedings of the 2012 IEEE 6th International Conference on Systems Biology (ISB), pp. 1–5. IEEE.

Li, L., Jiang, H., Qiu, Y., Ching, W.K., Vassiliadis, V.S., 2013. Discovery of metabolite biomarkers: Flux analysis and reaction-reaction network approach. BMC Systems Biology 7 (Suppl. 2), S13.

Lindon, J.C., Nicholson, J.K., Holmes, E., 2011. The Handbook of Metabonomics and Metabolomics. Elsevier.

Lipid Maps, LIPID Metabolites And Pathways Strategy, Welcome Trust.

Madu, C.O., Lu, Y., 2010. Novel diagnostic biomarkers for prostate cancer. Journal of Cancer 1, 150–177.

Mahadevan, R., Palsson, B.O., 2005. Properties of metabolic networks: Structure versus function. Biophysical Journal 88, L07–L09.

Maudsley, S., Chadwick, W., Wang, L., et al., 2011. Bioinformatic approaches to metabolic pathways analysis. Methods in Molecular Biology 756, 99–130.

McDermott, J.E., Wang, J., Mitchell, H., et al., 2013. Challenges in biomarker discovery: Combining expert insights with statistical analysis of complex omics data. Expert Opinion on Medical Diagnostics 7, 37–51.

Melander, O., Newton-Cheh, C., Almgren, P., et al., 2009. Novel and conventional biomarkers for prediction of incident cardiovascular events in the community. JAMA 302, 49–57.

Mohney, R., Milburn, M., 2015. Providing insight into complex disease: Metabolomics links genetic loci to phenotype. The FASEB Journal 29, LB292.

Mueller, L.A., Zhang, P., Rhee, S.Y., 2003. AraCyc: A biochemical pathway database for Arabidopsis. Plant Physiology 132, 453–460.

Oliver, S.G., Winson, M.K., Kell, D.B., Baganz, F., 1998. Systematic functional analysis of the yeast genome. Trends in Biotechnology 16, 373–378.

Peleg, M., Rubin, D., Altman, R.B., 2005. Using Petri net tools to study properties and dynamics of biological systems. Journal of the American Medical Informatics Association 12, 181–199.

Pereira, B., Chin, S.-F., Rueda, O.M., et al., 2016. The somatic mutation profiles of 2,433 breast cancers refines their genomic and transcriptomic landscapes. Nature Communications 7.

Rohn, H., Junker, A., Hartmann, A., et al., 2012. VANTED v2: A framework for systems biology applications. BMC Systems Biology 6, 139.

Schellenberger, J., Park, J.O., Conrad, T.M., Palsson, B.O., 2010. BiGG: A biochemical genetic and genomic knowledgebase of large scale metabolic reconstructions. BMC Bioinformatics 11, 213.

Schlapfer, P., Zhang, P., Wang, C., et al., 2017. Genome-wide prediction of metabolic enzymes, pathways, and gene clusters in plants. Plant Physiology 173, 2041–2059.

Schuster, R., Holzhütter, H.G., 1995. Use of mathematical models for predicting the metabolic effect of large-scale enzyme activity alterations. The FEBS Journal 229, 403–418.

Sehgal, M., Gupta, R., Moussa, A., Singh, T.R., 2015. An integrative approach for mapping differentially expressed genes and network components using novel parameters to elucidate key regulatory genes in colorectal cancer. PLOS One 10, e0133901.

Shahzad, K., Loor, J.J., 2012. Application of top-down and bottom-up systems approaches in ruminant physiology and metabolism. Current Genomics 13, 379–394.

Shlomi, T., 2010. Metabolic network-based interpretation of gene expression data elucidates human cellular metabolism. Biotechnology & Genetic Engineering Reviews 26, 281–296.

Shukla, A., Singh, T.R., 2017. Computational network approaches and their applications for complex diseases. Translational Bioinformatics and its Application. Springer.

Smith, C.A., O'maille, G., Want, E.J., et al., 2005. METLIN: A metabolite mass spectral database. Therapeutic drug monitoring 27, 747–751.

Sridharan, G.V., Ullah, E., Hassoun, S., Lee, K., 2015. Discovery of substrate cycles in large scale metabolic networks using hierarchical modularity. BMC Systems Biology 9, 5.

Stelling, J., Sauer, U., Szallasi, Z, Doyle, F.J., Doyle, J., 2004. Robustness of cellular functions. Cell 118, 675–685.

Strimbu, K., Tavel, J.A., 2010. What are biomarkers? Current Opinion in HIV and AIDS 5, 463.

Suhre, K., Schmitt-Kopplin, P., 2008. MassTRIX: Mass translator into pathways. Nucleic Acids Research 36, W481–W484.

Sweeney, C., Bernard, P.S., Factor, R.E., et al., 2014. Intrinsic subtypes from PAM50 gene expression assay in a population-based breast cancer cohort: Differences by age, race, and tumor characteristics. Cancer Epidemiology, Biomarkers and Prevention 23, 714–724.

Vander Heiden, M.G., Cantley, L.C., Thompson, C.B., 2009. Understanding the Warburg effect: The metabolic requirements of cell proliferation. Science 324, 1029–1033.

Veeramani, B., Bader, J.S., 2010. Predicting functional associations from metabolism using bi-partite network algorithms. BMC Systems Biology 4, 95.

Villeger, A.C., Pettifer, S.R., Kell, D.B., 2010. Arcadia: A visualization tool for metabolic pathways. Bioinformatics, 26. . pp. 1470–1471.

Wang, J., Zuo, Y., Man, Y.G., et al., 2015. Pathway and network approaches for identification of cancer signature markers from omics data. Journal of Cancer 6, 54–65.

Wang, Y., Tetko, I.V., Hall, M.A., et al., 2005. Gene selection from microarray data for cancer classification – A machine learning approach. Computational Biology and Chemistry 29, 37–46.

Wang, Y., Xiao, J., Suzek, T.O., et al., 2009. PubChem: A public information system for analyzing bioactivities of small molecules. Nucleic Acids Research 37, W623–W633.

Wishart, D.S., Tzur, D., Knox, C., et al., 2007. HMDB: The human metabolome database. Nucleic Acids Research 35, D521–D526.

Xia, J., Wishart, D.S., 2010a. MetPA: A web-based metabolomics tool for pathway analysis and visualization. Bioinformatics 26, 2342–2344.

Xia, J., Wishart, D.S., 2010b. MSEA: A web-based tool to identify biologically meaningful patterns in quantitative metabolomic data. Nucleic Acids Research 38, W71–W77.

Xiong, M., Fang, X., Zhao, J., 2001. Biomarker identification by feature wrappers. Genome Research 11, 1878–1887.

Xu, C., Hu, S., Chen, X., 2016. Artificial cells: From basic science to applications. Material Today (Kidlington) 19, 516–532.

Yang, Q., Diamond, M.P., Al-Hendy, A., 2016. The emerging role of extracellular vesicle-derived miRNAs: Implication in cancer progression and stem cell related diseases. Journal of Clinical Epigenetics 2.

Young, R.A., 2000. Biomedical discovery with DNA arrays. Cell 102, 9–15.

Yousef, M., Najami, N., Abedallah, L., Khalifa, W., 2014. Computational approaches for biomarker discovery. Journal of Intelligent Learning Systems and Applications 6, 153.

Zhang, A., Sun, H., Wang, P., Han, Y., Wang, X., 2012. Modern analytical techniques in metabolomics analysis. Analyst 137, 293–300.

Zhu, X., Gerstein, M., Snyder, M., 2007. Getting connected: Analysis and principles of biological networks. Genes & Development 21, 1010–1024.

Investigating Metabolic Pathways and Networks

Md Altaf-Ul-Amin and Shigehiko Kanaya, Nara Institute of Science and Technology, Ikoma, Japan
Zeti-Azura Mohamed-Hussein, Universiti Kebangsaan Malaysia, Bangi, Selangor, Malaysia

Introduction

Living cells generate energy and produce building material for cell components and replenish enzymes by the process of metabolism. All organisms live and grow by receiving food and nutrients from the environment. The foods are processed through thousands of reactions. In cells chemical reactions take place round the clock constantly breaking and making chemical molecules and transferring ions and electrons and these reactions are called metabolic pathways. Therefore, the metabolites can be considered as the preliminary level molecules generated form food intakes which are gradually transformed into building blocks for producing proteins, RNAs and DNAs and other useful matter and energy for creating and maintaining cells and life.

Metabolic reactions follow the lows of physics and chemistry and thus modeling metabolic reactions require considering many physicochemical constraints (Palsson, 2006). Metabolic pathways are efficiently regulated to respond to external perturbations and internal needs and thus linked to signaling networks. Many severe human diseases are caused by metabolic imbalance e.g., diabetes, cancer, cardiovascular problems, obesity, gout, tyrosinemia are a few to name.

Metabolism is the general term for the following two kinds of reactions: (i) Catabolic reactions: Catabolism refers to chemical reactions that result in the breakdown of more complex organic molecules into simpler substances. Catabolic reactions usually release energy that is used to drive chemical reactions. In catabolism, large molecules such as polysaccharides, lipids, nucleic acids and proteins are broken down into smaller units such as monosaccharides, fatty acids, nucleotides, and amino acids. The energy of catabolic reactions is used to drive anabolic reactions. (ii) Anabolic reactions: Anabolism refers to chemical reactions in which simpler substances are combined to form more complex molecules. Anabolic reactions usually require energy. Anabolic reactions build new molecules and/or store energy. The energy for chemical reactions is stored in ATP.

The term metabolic network usually means a collection of metabolic reactions represented as networks where the metabolites are the nodes and two metabolites are connected if one of them is a substrate and the other is the product of a reaction. Genome scale reconstruction of a metabolic network involves thousands of metabolites and reactions. Metabolic reactions are catalyzed by enzymes. The enzymes are gene products or proteins in broader sense. Therefore, metabolic networks contain information about both metabolites and proteins where the metabolites are nodes and proteins/enzymes are edges. There are other ways of representing metabolic pathways such as Bipartite graphs and Petri nets (Koch *et al.*, 2004; Matsuno *et al.*, 2011). A Petri net is an attributed directed bipartite graph. A metabolic pathway can be represented as a bipartite graph by considering the metabolites as one set of nodes and the enzymes as another set of nodes and such representation can provide some overall preliminary information about the system. Other than the metabolic pathways, we can also construct different type of metabolic networks e.g., based on structural similarity or any other type of similarity between metabolites.

Some studies showed that the metabolic networks are scale free networks i.e., their degree distribution follows power law (Jeong *et al.*, 2000; Ma and Zeng, 2003). Above all metabolic networks can be regarded as small world networks for their power-law degree distribution, high clustering coefficient and low average path length and diameter (Strogatz, 2001; Fell and Wagner, 2000). High clustering coefficients imply the existence of modules in the networks. It has been proposed that the combined properties of power-law degree distribution and high clustering coefficient indicates that the modules in the networks are linked to one another in a hierarchical manner (Albert *et al.*, 2000).

Numerous and versatile researches have been conducted based on pathways and chemical structures of metabolites. In this book article, we focus somewhat detail on two research topics. In the first part of this article we discuss alkaloid synthesis pathways and in the second part of this article we discuss structural similarity based networks of metabolites and its usage in establishing structure activity relations.

Insight Into Alkaloid Synthesis Pathways

Metabolites can be broadly classified into two types, primary metabolites and secondary metabolites. Primary metabolites are involved in normal growth, development, and reproduction of an organism and are usually present in almost all organisms. On the other hand, secondary metabolites are not generally essential for the very survival of an organism but mainly have important ecological functions. Usually, secondary metabolites are present in taxonomically restricted groups of organisms such as plants, fungi, bacteria etc. The term 'secondary' was introduced in 1891 (Kossel, 1891) in the context of metabolites. The functions of secondary metabolites are acquired in evolution process involving pest and pathogen defense, UV-B-sunscreens (Dixon, 2001) etc. Secondary metabolites with known chemical structures are more than 3000 terpenoids, 9000 flavonoids, 1600 isoflavonoids and 12,000 alkaloids (Connolly and Hill, 1991; Ziegler and Facchini, 2008). Since 2004, we have been accumulating the relations between metabolites and producing species in KNApSAcK Core Database (DB, see "Relevant Websites section"), presently which are 102,005 species-metabolite relationships encompassing 20,741 species and 50,054 metabolites. It has been predicted based on current statistics of metabolites-species relations, that there are at least 1.06 million metabolites within all plants on this planet of which most are secondary metabolites (Afendi *et al.*, 2011).

The classification of secondary metabolites based on integrated information of chemical structure and metabolic pathways could provide important clues to activities of metabolites which lead to interpretation of function acquisition mechanisms of secondary metabolites in evolutional process. In this part of the article, we examine whether or not classification of alkaloids by ring skeletons can be related to metabolic pathways. Alkaloids are a large group of nitrogen-containing secondary metabolites. Almost every variety of organisms such as bacteria, fungi, plants, and animals produce alkaloids. Diverged polycyclic compounds including unsaturated and saturated bonds are produced by various organisms (**Fig. 1** shows some examples).

Systematic representation of alkaloid biosynthetic pathways has been established by Aniszewski based on ring skeletons. The skeleton nucleus of an alkaloid is the main criterion for alkaloid precursor determination in biosynthetic pathways. Skeletons for different alkaloid nuclei can be produced by L-lysine, for example, piperidine, indolizine, quinolizidine nuclei are respectively represented by skeletons C5N, C5NC3 and C5NC4 (Tadeusz, 2007). Here C5N means a skeleton with 6-membered ring including 1 nitrogen atom, C5NC3 means the heterocyclic ring skeleton composed by 6-membered ring including 1 nitrogen atom together with 5-meber ring including 1 nitrogen, and C5NC4 means the heterocyclic ring skeleton composed by 6-membered ring including 1 nitrogen atom together with 6-meber ring including 1 nitrogen. C5NC and C5NC4 contains common C-N bonds in two heterocyclic systems. As shown in **Fig. 1**, the synthetic pathways of quinolizine alkaloids from L-Lysine (L-Lys) to Lupanine (C2) and Multiflorine (C3) and to Lycodine (C6), three compounds C1, C2, and C3 have identical ring skeleton S1, whereas, C4 has the skeleton S2, and C5 and C6 have the skeleton S3. Here ring skeleton is defined as ring structures without saturated or unsaturated chemical bonds. Thus, classification of alkaloids based on ring skeletons can provide important information for systematic understanding of chemical structures and for predicting biosynthetic pathways. Here, we discuss structure-based classification of secondary metabolites as a multidisciplinary field combining chemo- and bio- informatics.

Data Set

Information of 478 polycyclic compounds were accumulated whose metabolic pathways were available in references. We collected pathway information from scientific literatures and constructed 32 pathway maps (Eguchi *et al.*, 2017). The summary of these 32 pathway maps is depicted in **Table 1**. We made alkaloid pathway maps considering starting compounds as amino acids, compounds related with amino acid biosynthesis (anthranilate, formyl anthranilate, indole-3-glycerol phosphate, O-methyl tyrosine) terpenes, compounds related with TCA cycle and fatty acids and nucleic acids because alkaloids are often divided into the true alkaloids which originate from amino acids and psuedoalkaloids that do not originate from amino acids, for example, terpene-like, steroid-like and purine-like alkaloids.

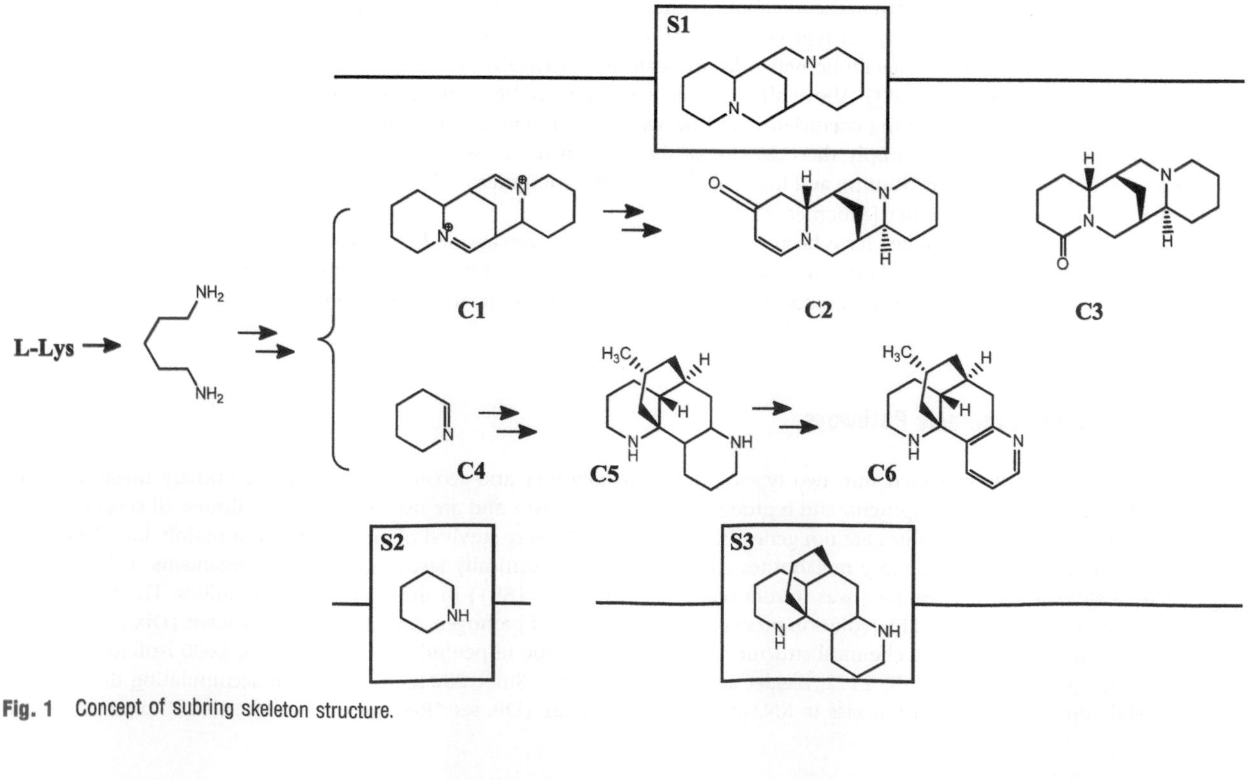

Fig. 1   Concept of subring skeleton structure.

Table 1   Summary of alkaloid metabolic pathways used in this study

Group of SS	3-phospho glycerate				Pyruvate				Phosphoenol pyruvate								Oxaloacetate		alpha-Ketoglutarate				Terpenes				TCA cycle		Fatty acid		Nucleic acids
Starting substance (SS)	Gly	L-Ser	D-Ser	L-Cys	L-Ala	D-Ala	L-Leu	L-Val	L-Trp	D-Trp	L-Tyr	L-Phe	Anthranilate	Formyl anthranilate	Indole-3-glycerol phosphate	O-Methyl tyrosine	L-Asp	L-Thr	L-Lys	L-Arg	L-His	L-Pro	L-Glu	IPP	DMAPP	Secologanin	GGPP	Cholesterol	Acetyl CoA	Oxaloacetate	Malonyl-CoA	Acetoacetyl CoA	Adenine

(Pathway Map ID, rows 1–30: dot matrix indicating presence of starting substances for each pathway map.)

Subring Skeleton Profiling

Fig. 2 shows the subring skeleton profiling with the example of benzoisoquinoline alkaloid biosynthetic pathway from L-Tyr to Sanguinarine (C13). Out of 7 compounds (C7-C13), C12 and C13 have the same ring skeleton S9 and the others have separate ring skeletons (S4-S8). Next, subring skeletons were produced for individual skeletons (S4-S9). For example, S4 corresponds to nine subring skeletons (SRSs) (A-I in Step 1 of **Fig. 2**). SRS matrix S was constructed by setting $s_{ij} = 1$ or 0 respectively depending on presence or absence of the jth SRS in the ith compound (Step 2). Here we used InChI (the IUPAC International Chemical Identifier) for isomorphism check for SRSs (Heller et al., 2015; Spjuth et al., 2013). In Step 3, hierarchical clustering of the compounds was performed using matrix S. There are several molecular fingerprint techniques such as PubChem (881 bits) (Bolton et al., 2008), CDK (1024 bits) (Steinbeck et al., 2003), Extended CDK (1024 bits) (Durant et al., 2002), MACCS (166 bits) (Klekota and Roth, 2008), Klekota-Roth (4860 bits) (PubChem Substructure Fingerprint, see "Relevant Websites section"), Substructure (307 bits) (Person VUE see "Relevant Websites section"), Estate (79 bits) (Minato, 1993), and atom pairs (780 bits) (Iwashita et al., 2012). Those molecular finger prints generally focuses on side-chain substructures of molecules. Alternatively, SRS profiling makes it possible to examine and compare compounds based on all possible SRS, so SRS profiling is useful for systematic understanding of the evolution process of rings systems of the compounds.

Subring Skeleton Profiling in Alkaloids

We extracted 2546 unique subring skeletons from 478 compounds. **Fig. 3** shows the distribution of the numbers of compounds along with the number of SRSs. It is interesting that there is no unique SRS in 478 compounds, that is, there is no SRS corresponding to only one compound.

Secondly, we represented each compound as a 2546 dimensional binary vector. Here, if ith substring skeleton is present in a target compound, the ith element was set to 1; otherwise, the ith element was set to 0. We applied ward clustering method to a matrix consisting of 478 compounds and 2546 unique SRSs and allocated 478 compounds into 29 clusters (Cluster ID = 1 to 29) as shown by the dendrogram in **Fig. 4**. All compounds were assigned to 187 ring skeletons which have been presented in Eguchi et al. (2017).

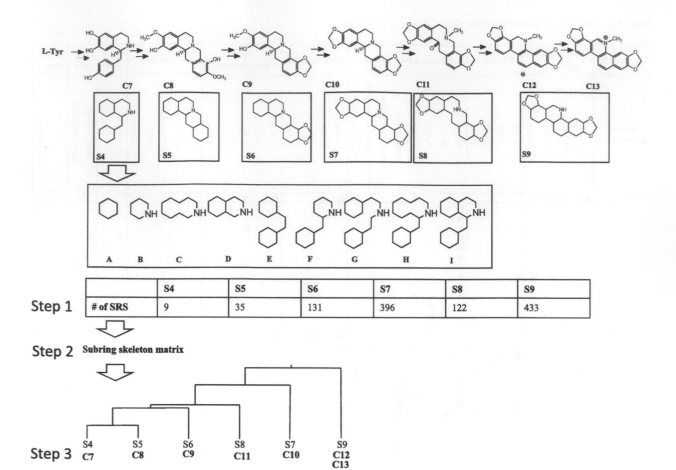

Fig. 2 Schematic diagram of subring skeleton (SRS) profiling.

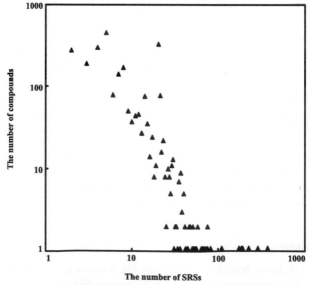

Fig. 3 Distribution of the number of SRSs along with number of compounds.

We divided the compounds into 6 major groups labelled as G1 (Clusters 1 and 2), G2 (Cluster 3), G3 (Cluster 4), G4 (Clusters 5–7), G5 (Clusters 8) and G6 (Cluster 9–29) as shown in **Fig. 4**; G1 and G2 are related with indole-diterpenes involving paxilline, terpendoles and lolitrems (G1) and strictosides (G2). These consist of polycyclic compounds comprised of six to nine rings characterized by 5–6 member rings and only one nitrogen; Compounds in G3 (Cluster 4) are related with steroidal alkaloids with

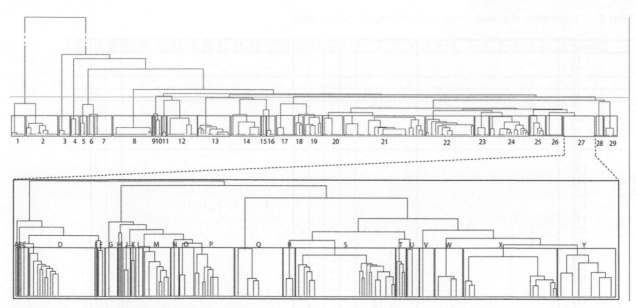

Fig. 4 Dendrogram of 478 compounds based on SRS profiling.

glucosides including alpha-solanine, alpha-chaconine, and alpha-tomatine and their skeletal chemical structures are assigned with steroidal alkaloids; compounds included in G4 (Clusters 5–7) are characterized by vindoline derivatives with greater than or equal to 2 nitrogen atoms; G5 corresponds to Ergot alkaloids. The other alkaloid compounds belong to G6 (Clusters 9–29) and also have very diverged ring skeletons. Clusters 9–20 can be characterized as follows; aglycones and glucosides of Tomatidines (Clusters 9 and 10, respectively), bis-isoquinolines (Cluster 11), morphinans (Cluster 12), quinazoline derivatives (Cluster 13), indolizidine derivatives (Cluster 14), polyneuridines (Cluster 15), Ajmalicines (Cluster16), Berberine and relatives (Clusters 17–19). Ipecac alkaloids (Cluster 20), isoquinolines including ring skeletons of glaudines (Cluster 21), beta-carbolines (Cluster22), chaetoglobosin (Cluster 23), ring skeletons roquefortines and acetylaszonaleins (Cluster 24), Emindoles (Cluster 25), quinolizidines (Cluster 26), iboganines (Cluster 28), and communesins (Cluster 29). Thus the 28 clusters except cluster 27 can be characterized by ring skeletons based on the sub-ring skeleton profiles proposed by Eguchi *et al.* (2017).

Almost half of the compounds (233 compounds) examined in this study belong to Cluster 27. So we further divide it into 25 sub-clusters to characterize ring skeletons as representatives of groups of compounds. The 25 sub-clusters in Cluster 27 are composed of relatively simple heterocyclic ring skeletons in comparison to other clusters. Five sub-clusters (A, B, C, D, E, F, and H) have indole type alkaloid structures based on ring skeletons, and especially characterized by brevianamides (A); cyclopiazonate derivates (B) and chanoclavin derivatives, that is, the former corresponds to a five-cyclic ergot alkaloids and the letter corresponds to tri-cyclic ergot alkaloids; chimonanthines (E); and iboga alkaloids (H). Furthermore, specific ring skeletons can be observed in individual sub- clusters such as, ergolines (B and C), cinchona alkaloids (G), iboga alkaloids (H and I), lycopodium alkaloids (J and K), isoquinolines (L), lupine alkaloids (M), quinolones (N), quinolones (O), acridines and quinolones (P), purine alkaloids (Q), and benzylisoquinoline alkaloids (T). In summary the conclusion is, alkaloid compounds can be classified and characterized according to generally defined ring systems based on subring skeleton profiles.

Relations Between Ring Structure and Pathways

We classified alkaloid compounds based on subring skeleton profiles and thus related general ring structures to groups of alkaloids. Next, we tried to find associations between modules in alkaloid metabolic pathways and ring structures. We mapped compounds onto 32 pathway maps and show in **Table 2** the summary of the relations between classification results and pathway maps. All but four clusters (Clusters 13, 22, 24, 25 and 27) correspond to single pathway maps (PMs). Thus, clusters expressed by the subring skeleton profiles are highly associated to alkaloid biosynthetic pathways. Such trends are also observed in case of the sub-clusters in Cluster 27 (10 out of 25 sub-clusters). Details of the relations between pathway maps and ring structures have been presented in Eguchi *et al.* (2017).

Structure Activity Relationship Based on Network of Metabolites

Organisms acquired selective functions through evolution to drive functional specialization together with retaining underlying enzymatic genes. Evolutionary pressures caused the appearance of different secondary metabolites and related pathways. These metabolites are important for healthy survival, e.g., pest and pathogen defense and UV-B sunscreens (Dixon, 2001). The aroma of black Périgord truffle, *T. melanosporum* is produced by secondary metabolism which is used to attract animals for sporulation (Islam *et al.*, 2013). Thus, plant

Table 2   Classification of alkaloid compounds in clusters with pathway maps

Cluster	1	2	3	4	5	6	7	8	9	10	11	12	13	14	15	16	17	18	19	20	21	22	23	24	25	26	27	28	29	30	31	32
1																														6		
2																														14		
3			5																													
4																															4	
5			3																													
6			3																													
7			3																													
8	17																															
9																															1	
10																															3	
11												2																				
12												13																				
13																			1			8	3	1	1							
14				13																												
15		2																														
16		4																														
17												8																				
18												4																				
19												8																				
20													9																			
21													12																			
22					13																											
23				5																												
24									1											6	1	3				1	4		1			
25																														1	5	
26															15																	
28			3																													
29				6																												
A				1																												
B								1																								
C		2			1																											
D			2		12		1	2		2	2						1													1		
E					1																											
F					2																									1		
G			5																													
H			1																													
I			1																													
J															3																	
K															2																	
L															8											3						
M															3																	
N																			1								2					
O																			4		2											
P															2				11								3					
Q	1																															16
R																			2		3											
S	4								3		16	2	1	2	5	1			3													
T											1	3																				
U											5																					
V	5																															
W	10																															
X	9										1				9		9	8														1
Y	18														3																	

secondary metabolites are compounds of diverse types of structures and serve as defense weapons used against bacteria, fungi, amoebae, plants, insects, and herbivorous animals and as agents of symbiosis between microbes and plants, nematodes, insects, and higher animals and also as pheromones and pollinators. Secondary metabolites help an organism maintain various interactions with the eco-systems, often adapting to match the environmental needs. Secondary metabolites of plants that color the plant or plant parts e.g., flowers are a good example of this, as the coloring of a flower can attract pollinators and also certain coloring of leaves or stems can defend against attack by animals. Volatile organic compounds (VOCs) are special type of metabolites. VOCs emitted by bacteria and fungi might have the potential to be alternatives to chemical pesticides to protect plants from pests and pathogens. Microbial VOCs are seen as biocontrol agents to control various phytopathogens and as biofertilizers for plant growth promotion. Furthermore, metabolites are deeply involved in human health care. The use of VOCs as biomarkers to detect human diseases is rapidly increasing. Plant metabolites are a major sources of drugs and they are widely used in pharmaceutical industries.

In order to systematize the relations between secondary metabolites and biological activities and to facilitate a comprehensive understanding of the relationships between the chemical structure of metabolites and their biological activities, we developed a metabolite-activity relation database known as the KNApSAcK Metabolite Activity DB (see "Relevant Websites section") (Nakamura et al., 2014). Here, we present a network-based approach to systematically understand the relationship between 3D-chemical structures of metabolites and their biological activities (Ohtana et al., 2014). We initially constructed a 3D-chemical structure similarity based network of secondary metabolites and then applied DPClusO (Altaf-Ul-Amin et al., 2006, 2012) algorithm to extract densely connected clusters (referred to as structure groups) of metabolites. We then statistically validated the relationship between the structure groups and biological activities and selected significant structure group-biological activity pairs using a threshold p-value. The p-value threshold was decided based on false discovery rate (FDR) to address the problems associated with multiple testing (Benjamini and Hochberg, 1995). Finally, we reconstructed a binary matrix consisting of selected structure groups and biological activities. Hierarchical clustering was then applied to the constructed matrix in order to detect global trends of relations between 3D structures and biological activities.

The Proposed Method to Assess Structure-Activity Relationships

The concept of the proposed method is depicted in **Fig. 5** and the details of the individual steps are described below.

In Step 1, a network was constructed where a node represents a metabolite and an edge represents high 3D structural similarity between metabolites. Fast heuristic graph match algorithm COMPLIG (Saito et al., 2012) was utilized to estimate structural similarity between metabolites at the 3D level. COMPLIG calculates structure similarity based on three factors namely, topology-distance, bond-order, and rotatable-bond and has been previously utilized for systematically classifying ligands in PDB (Saito et al., 2012). We estimated similarity score $S(A, B)$ between two metabolites A and B using the following equations:

$$S(A, B) = M(A, B) / \max\{N(A), N(B)\}$$

Here, $M(A, B)$ is the number of atoms and bonds matched between metabolites A and B, and $N(A)$ and $N(B)$ are the number of atoms and bonds in metabolites A and B, respectively. We considered 0.80 as the threshold similarity which was recommended by Saito et al. (2012). Thus, structurally similar metabolites were connected with each other to construct a network of metabolites.

In Step 2, we used a network-clustering algorithm DPClusO to classify metabolites into highly structurally similar groups. DPClusO generates clusters characterized by high density and separated by periphery in the networks (Altaf-Ul-Amin et al., 2006, 2012), and has been used in several big data analyses in molecular biology such as protein-protein interaction (Altaf-Ul-Amin et al., 2006), metabolomics (Takahashi et al., 2008) and prediction of functional relations between genes using gene expression (Altaf-Ul-Amin et al., 2014).

In Step 3, we annotated structure groups by biological activities using chi-square statistic χ^2 and an over-representation test statistic OV (Kanaya and Kudo, 1994) defined as follows:

$$\chi^2 = \frac{(c(x, k) - f(k) \cdot T)^2}{f(k) \cdot T} + \frac{(c(x, \overline{k}) - f(\overline{k}) \cdot T)^2}{f(\overline{k}) \cdot T}$$

$$OV = \frac{c(x, k) - f(k) \cdot T}{\sqrt{f(k) \cdot T}}$$

Here, $c(x,k)$ and $c(x, \overline{k})$ represent the number of metabolites with and without the kth activity in structure group x, $f(k)$ and $f(\overline{k})$ represent relative numbers of metabolites with and without the kth activity in the database, T represents the total number of metabolites in the structure group x. It is evident that the degree of freedom is 1 for the χ^2 value represented above.

A structure group can have significant p-values in χ^2-statistics either if it is overrepresented or underrepresented by metabolites of certain biological activity in the context of the ratio of the metabolites in the DB. However, our purpose is to relate a structure group to a biological activity if and only if the structure group is overrepresented by metabolites associated with that biological activity. Therefore, we first make sure that the OV statistic is positive for a structure group and then we evaluate its p-value.

In Step 4, we construct a data matrix based on the statistically significant relation between structure groups and biological activities, and carried out 2-dimensional hierarchical clustering for systematizing the relationship between metabolite structures and biological activities.

Selection of Statistically Significant Relationships Based on False Discovery Rate

We examined 3D-similarities among 2072 secondary metabolites by a fast heuristic graph-matching algorithm COMPLIG developed by Shirai and colleagues (Saito et al., 2012) and then 50,228 pairs of secondary metabolites having similarity score more than the threshold were selected to construct a network. Then structure groups were generated using the graph clustering algorithm DPClusO (Altaf-Ul-Amin et al., 2012) which was developed for overlapping clustering using the similar concepts of the DPClus algorithm (Altaf-Ul-Amin et al., 2006). DPClusO generated 671 densely connected clusters of secondary metabolites, which are called structure groups (SGs) in this study.

We searched for statistically significant relationships between 671 SGs and 140 biological activities (**Table 3**). The biological activities are of mainly two types: (i) Chemical ecology related activities indicated as E01–E48 in **Table 3** which are associated with metabolites involved in ecological interactions between species for survival and normal regulation of organisms, and (ii) human healthcare and medicine related activities indicated as M01–M92 which are associated to metabolites known as ingredients of healthy foods and medicines or biomarkers.

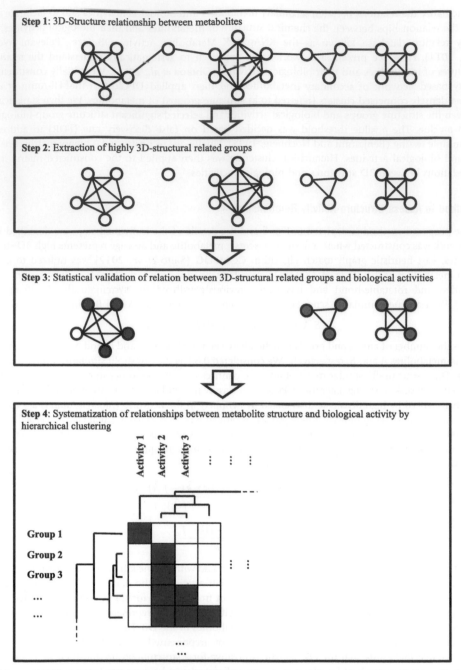

Fig. 5 Concept of the methodology: network construction based on 3D-structure similarity between metabolites. Nodes and edges represent metabolites and highly similar pairs of metabolites, respectively. Different colors in Step 3 represent different biological activities for individual metabolites. In Step 4, 2D-hierarchical clustering is carried out based on statistically significant relations between structure groups and biological activities. Red colors represent significant relation between corresponding structure group and biological activity.

We first selected 7650 structure group-biological activity pairs (SG-BA pairs) for which OV is positive to ensure over-representation of metabolites of the activity category in the associated cluster. We then examined FDR (cumulative q-values) using p-values calculated based on χ^2-statistics, and finally selected 983 SG-BA pairs which correspond to $p < 0.001$ and $q < 7.78 \times 10^{-3}$.

Relation Between Structure and Biological Activities

Multiple activities are generally reported for a metabolite, for example, (+)-catechin has been reported to have several biological activities in chemical ecology (e.g., E18, E20 and E32 in **Table 3**) and in human healthcare and medicine (e.g M29, M34, M39,

Table 3   Biological activities defined in the KNApSAcK Metabolite Activity DB

General description	Activity category
Plant growth regulator	Enhance germination (E01), Enhance stem growth (E02), Enhance root growth (E03), Enhance leaf growth(E04), Enhance flowering (E05), Enhance fruiting (E06), Enhance plant growth (E07), Inhibit seed germination (E08), Inhibit stem growth (E09), Inhibit root growth (E10), Inhibit leaf growth (E11), Inhibit flowering (E12), Inhibit fruiting (E13), Inhibit plant growth (E14), Allelopathic (E15), Phytoalexin (E16)
Attractant/repellent	Feeding attractant (E17), Feeding deterrent (E18), Pollinator attractant (E19), Oviposition attractant (E20), Oviposition deterrent (E21), Sex attractant (E22), Attractant (E23), Repellent (E24)
Selective toxicity	Phytotoxic (E25), Herbicidal (E26), Insecticidal (E27), Acaricidal (E28), Molluscicidal (E29), Piscicidal (E30), Nematocidal (E31)
Antimicrobial agent	Antibacterial (E32), Antituberculosis (E33), Antileprotic (E34), Antifungal (E35), Inhibit spore germination (E36), Antimicrobial (E37)
Antiviral agent	Antiviral (E38), Antihepatitic (E39), Anti-HIV (E40), Anti-HSV (E41)
Antiparasitic agent	Anthelmintic (E42), Antiprotozoal (E43), Antiamebic (E44), Antimalarial (E45), Antileishmanial (E46), Antitrypanosomal (E47), Pediculicide (E48)
Nervous system agent	Antipyretic (M01), Analgesic (M02), Antiarthritic (M03), Anesthetics (M04), Sedative (M05), Antispasmodic (M06), Anticonvulsant (M07), Antidementic (M08), Antidepressant (M09), CNS Stimulant (M10), Diaphoretic (M11), Emetic (M12), Antiemetic (M13), Antigout (M14), Antimigraine (M15), Antimyasthenic (M16), Antiparkinson (M17), Antipsychotic (M18), Muscle relaxant (M19)
Cardiovascular agent	Antidiabetic (M20), Hemostatic (M21), Antithrombotic (M22), Cardiotonic (M23), Antiarrhythmic (M24), Diuretic (M25), Antihypertensive (M26), Antihyperlipidemic (M27), Antianemic (M28), Other cardiovascular agent (M29)
Respiratory tract agent	Antitussive (M30), Expectorant (M31), Antiasthmatic (M32), Other respiratory tract agent (M33)
Digestive organ agent	Antidiarrheic (M34), Carminative (M35), Stomachic (M36), Laxative (M37), Choleretic (M38), Antihepatotoxic (M39), Other digestive organ agent (M40)
Genitourinary agent	Oxytocic (M41), Antifertility (M42), Abortifacient (M43), Other genitourinary agent (M44)
Anticancer agent	Antioxidant (M45), Anticancer (M46), Antitumor (M47), Antineoplastic (M48), Antimutagenic (M49)
Anti-inflammatory agent	Anti-inflammatory (M50), Antiallergic (M51), UV shield (M52), Antidermatitic (M53), Antiedemic (M54)
Immunological agent	Immunosuppressant (M55), Immunostimulant (M56), Immunomodulator (M57)
Nutrient	Nucleic acid (M58), Essential amino acid (M59), Nonessential amino acid (M60), Vitamin (M61), Nutrient (M62), Tonic (M63)
Nontherapeutic agent	Solvent (M64), Flavor (M65), Odor (M66), Pigment (M67), Emulsifying agent (M68), Antiseptic (M69)
Other health agent	Antiulcerogenic (M70), Depilatory (M71), Antidote (M72), Hormonal (M73), Dental (M74), Other health agent (M75)
Narcotic	Narcotic (M76)
Toxic	Phototoxic (M77), Neurotoxic (M78), Pneumotoxic (M79), Hepatotoxic (M80), Cytotoxic (M81), Toxic (M82)
Tumorigenic	Tumorigenic (M83), Mutagenic (M84), Genotoxic (M85), Teratogenic (M86)
Other disease-causing agent	Psychotomimetic (M87), Hemolytic (M88), Allergenic (M89), Irritant (M90), Dermatitic (M91), Edematous (M92)

M40, M45, M48, M70, M81, M82, M88 and M91 in **Table 3**) which are easily retrieved by entering "(+)-catechin" as Metabolite Name in the Metabolite Activity DB (Nakamura *et al.*, 2014). To systematically understand the relations between biological activities and structure groups, we constructed a 2-dimensional dendrogram, using a matrix showing relations among 488 structure groups and 139 activities.

Fig. 6 presents the relationship between SGs and biological activities in the perspective of hierarchical clustering. We tentatively distributed 139 biological activities into 13 clusters called BC1 to BC13. Relationships between major biological activities that are connected with 10 or more structure groups are listed in **Table 4**. It should be noted that activity categories in three clusters (BC1, BC2 and BC3) described as antimicrobial agent and plant growth regulator are related to ecology and six clusters (BC4, BC5, BC7, BC10, BC11 and BC13) are associated with human healthcare. On the other hand, three clusters (BC6, BC9 and BC12) are related to both ecology and healthcare activities.

To examine the relationship between chemical structures and biological activities, we selected SGs that are related to single activity category (**Table 3** shows the list of activity categories) and assigned chemical structural properties into individual SGs (SG-ID in **Tables 4** and **5**, SG-ID 389 is abbreviated as SG389 and so on in the following text). Three clusters of major metabolites namely isoflavonoids (BC1), flavones and isoflavones (BC2) and giberrellanes (BC3) were assigned as ecological activity agents. BC1 exhibits antifungal properties (E35) whereas BC2 contained phytoalexins (E16) and BC3 are characterized as plant growth regulators with properties such as stem growth enhancement (E02), plant growth enhancement (E07) and root growth inhibition (E10). BC6 mainly consists of phenolic substances with both ecological and healthcare activities, i.e. anthraquinones (SG113), coumarins (SG236 and SG237) flavones (SG147), phenylpropanoids (SG327 and SG404) as antibacterial agents (E32), and lignans (SG43, SG75, SG82, SG278 and SG376) as antitumor agents (M47), and stilbenoids (SG147) as antibacterial agents (E32). Flavonoids including isoflavonoids have diverse functions as both ecological and healthcare agents because most of the bioactivity groups (BC1, BC2, BC4, BC5, BC6, BC9 and BC12) include various structural derivatives and thus specific functions can be exerted by patterns of substitution groups in the chemical structures. Ecological activities of these metabolites are highly related with core chemical structures most likely because these metabolite groups characterize certain biosynthetic pathways. This leads to

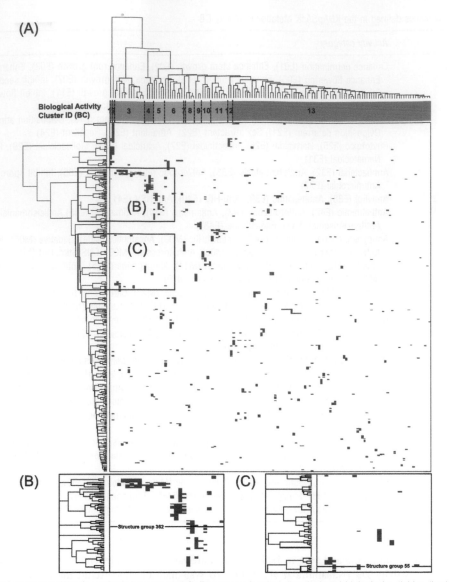

Fig. 6 2D-hierarchical clustering (Ward's method) between metabolite groups (vertical direction) and biological activities (horizontal direction). The whole map (A) and enlarged views (B) and (C). Index numbers in horizontal clustering represent cluster ID.

the explanation that the role of metabolites in plant physiological activities is highly related with evolution of biosynthetic pathways in plants.

SGs listed in the healthcare category of **Table 4** correspond to single activities but the extent of their effects in plants has not been fully understood. Efficacies in humans of many SGs consisting of alkaloids can be mentioned: BC5, isoquinoline alkaloids (SG217) as analgesic agents (M02), quinoline alkaloids (SG430) as sedatives (M05), terpene alkaloids (SG152 and SG220) as antihypertensivity agents (M26); BC6, indole alkaloids (SG651) with antitumor properties (M47); BC7, quinolizidine alkaloids (SG489) and terpene alkaloids (SG112 and SG267) with toxicity properties (M82); BC9, betalains (SG172, SG289, SG419, SG420, SG438, SG439 and SG497) as pigments (M67); BC11, steroid alkaloids (SG461) as laxatives (M37); BC13, pyrrolizidine alkaloids (SG320 and SG479) and quinolizidine alkaloids (SG429) as antidiabetic agents (M20), tropane alkaloids (SG578), and indole alkaloids (SG649) with hormonal properties (M73), quinoline alkaloids (SG261 and SG298) as phototoxic agents (M77), isoquinoline alkaloids (SG361, SG447 and SG644) and indole alkaloids (SG202 and SG317) with psychotomimetic properties (M87).

Alkaloids occur in 20% of all plants and the number of identified structures are more than 12,000 (Connolly and Hill, 1991; Ziegler and Facchini, 2008). Initially in the 1950s, most of these alkaloids were believed to be metabolic waste products (Wink *et al.*, 1998). Currently biological activities of alkaloids found in nature have been determined and the medical effects of alkaloids to humans are well known. Those include toxicity to animals, vertebrates and arthropods, effects of various metabolic systems in animals, inhibiting DNA synthesis and repair by intercalation with nucleic acids, and other reported effects on the nervous systems (Mithöfer and Boland, 2012). Specific healthcare activities can also be explained by class of metabolites,

Table 4 Related active categories in hierarchical clustering in **Fig. 4**

ID	Ecological activity			Healthcare		
	General description	Activity category	SG-ID	General description	Activity category	SG-ID
1	Antimicrobial agent	Antifungal (E35)	36, 68, 78, 250, 270, 389			
2	Plant growth regulator	Phytoalexin (E16)	7, 8, 11, 14, 16, 17, 22, 25, 27, 33, 49, 64, 70, 71, 85, 93, 115, 186, 269, 279			
3	Plant growth regulator	Enhance stem growth (E02)	392, 594			
		Enhance flowering (E05)				
		Enhance fruiting (E06)				
		Enhance plant growth (E07)	511			
		Inhibit root growth (E10)	510			
4				Nontherapeutic agent	Flavor (M65)	319, 349, 624
					Odor (M66)	409
				Other health agent	Antiseptic (M69)	97, 230
				Digestive organ agent	Carminative (M35)	469, 575
5				Cardiovascular agent	Antihypertensive (M26)	152, 220, 366
				Nervous system agent	Analgesic (M02)	217
					Sedative (M05)	430
				Narcotic	Narcotic (M76)	
6	Plant growth regulator	Allelopathic (E15)	331, 354, 460, 601	Anticancer agent	Antitumor (M47)	43, 75, 82, 278, 376, 651
	Selective toxicity	Antibacterial (E32)	113, 147, 236, 237, 327, 404			
7				Toxic	Toxic (M82)	112, 239, 267, 373, 411, 488, 489, 523
8	Attractant/ repellent		(no data)			(no data)
9		Oviposition attractant (E20)	145, 167	Nontherapeutic agent	Pigment (M67)	40, 172, 289, 419, 420, 438, 439, 497, 574
10				Nutrient	Essential amino acid (M59)	231, 294, 314, 546, 639, 640
				Genitourinary agent	Other genitourinary agent (M44)	387, 412
11				Digestive organ agent	Laxative (M37)	241, 252, 449, 461, 655
12	Attractant/ repellent	Feeding deterrent (E18)	104, 146, 183, 453	Anticancer agent	Antioxidant (M45)	2, 4, 9
13				Cardiovascular agent	Antidiabetic (M20)	320, 429, 479, 541, 578
				Other health agent	Hormonal (M73)	593, 622, 649
				Toxic	Phototoxic (M77)	98, 254, 261,276, 298
					Neurotoxic (M78)	357, 483, 583, 654
				Other disease-causing agent	Psychotomimetic (M87)	202, 317, 361, 447, 644

especially class of alkaloids listed in **Tables 4** and **5**. Comparative activity relationships between ecological and healthcare agents lead to systematization of meta-metabolomics combined with human and ecological metabolic pathways (Raes and Bork, 2008; Ibrahim and Anishetty, 2012). As an example the structure group 55 (**Fig. 7(A)**) is significantly related with multiple biological activities, that is, plant growth regulators such as enhancing stem growth (E02), enhancing leaf growth (E04), and enhancing plant growth (E07), and consists of 21 metabolites which are highly related with gibberellin and its relatives. Another example, structure group 362 (**Fig. 7(B)**) is associated with the following healthcare activities: sedative (M05), analgesic (M02), antispasmodic (M06) under the general description nervous system agent, antitussive (M30) under respiratory tract agent; narcotic (M76) under narcotic; and antidiarrheic (M34) under digestive organ agent. The core structure in group 362 can be identified as morphinoids.

Table 5   Structure properties for SGs in **Table 2**. The number of metabolites in SG is represented in parentheses

BC	Structure properties	SG-ID
1	Coumestrols	389(5)
	Isoflavonoids	36(30), 68(18), 78(16), 250(7), 270(7)
2	Anthraquinones	8(55), 16(47)
	Flavones	7(56), 8(55), 11(51), 14(50), 16(47), 17(46), 22(40), 25(37), 27(37), 49(24), 70(18), 186(9), 269(7)
	Flavanols	27(37)
	Flavanones	8(55), 85(16), 279(7)
	Flavonoids	33(33), 64(19)
	Isoflavanones	71(18), 115(13)
	Isoflavones	11(51), 16(47), 27(37), 71(18), 115(13)
	lignans	71(18), 115(13)
	Pterocarpanes	93(15)
3	Gibberellanes	392(5), 510(3), 594(3)
	Triholosides	511(3)
4	Biflavonoids	409(5)
	Cymenes	575(3)
	Furans	624(3)
	Glucosinolates	319(6)
	Nonalactones	349(5)
	Phenols	230(7)
	Phenylpropanoids	97(15), 469(4)
5	Coumarins	366(5)
	Isoquinoline alkaloids	217(8)
	Quinoline alkaloids	430(5)
	Terpene alkaloids	152(10), 220(8)
6	Anthraquinones	113(13)
	Coumarins	236(7), 237(7), 601(3)
	Sesquiterpenes	331(5), 354(5)
	Flavones	147(11)
	Indole alkaloids	651(5)
	Lignans	43(26), 75(17), 82(16), 278(7), 376(5)
	Phenylpropanoids	327(6), 404(5)
	Sesquiterpenes	460(4)
	Stilbenoids	147(11)
7	Cibarians	523(3)
	Cyanogenic glycosides	239(7), 373(5), 488(4)
	Heterodendrins	411(5)
	Quinolizidine alkaloids	489(4)
	Terpene alkaloids	112(13), 267(7)
9	Anthocyanins	574(3)
	Anthraquinones Betalains	40(27)
	Betalains	172(9), 289(6), 419(5), 420(5), 438(4), 439(4), 497(4)
	Flavanones	145(11), 167(10)
10	Amino acids	231(7), 294(6), 314(6), 546(3), 639(3), 640(3), 412(5)
	Lignans	387(5)
11	Anthraquinones	252(7)
	Carbazoles	449(4)
	Glycosides iridoids steroid Alkaloids	449(4)
	Iridoids	241(7), 655(3)
	Steroid alkaloids	461(4)
12	Flavanones	9(54), 104(14), 146(11), 183(9)
	Flavones	2(89), 4(75)
	Lycoricidines	453(4)
13	Amino acids	357(5)
	Benzofurans	254(7)
	Benzopyrans	276(7)
	Carboxylic acids	483(4)
	Indole alkaloids	202(8), 317(6), 649(3)
	Isoquinoline alkaloids	361(5), 447(4), 644(3)
	Monoterpenoids Phenylpropanoids	583(3)
	phenylpropanoids	98(15) 593(3), 622(3)

(Continued)

Table 5   Continued

BC	Structure properties	SG-ID
	Pyrrolizidine alkaloids	320(6), 479(4)
	Quinoline alkaloids	261(7), 298(6)
	Quinolizidine alkaloids	429(5)
	Skytanthines	541(3)
	Tropane alkaloids	578(3)
	Usambarensines	654(3)

(A) Structure group 55

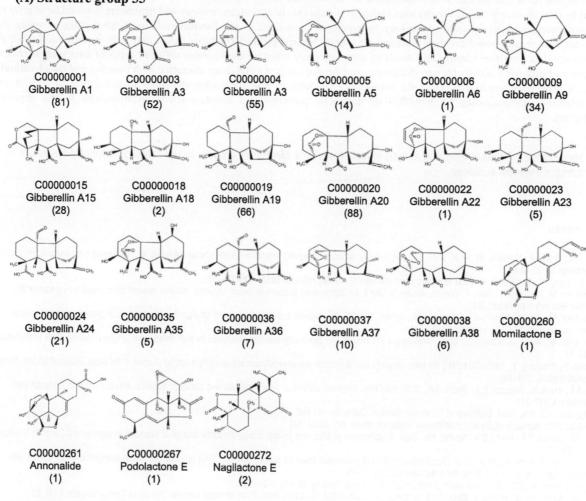

(B) Structure group 362

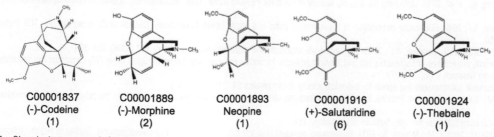

Fig. 7 Chemical structures belonging to structure groups. (A) Structure groups 55 and (B) 362. ID in KNApSAcK Core DB, name of the metabolite and the number of species reported in parentheses are described in this order.

Conclusions

Bioinformatics and Cheminformaitcs play important roles in interpretation and understanding chemical and biological data. Two of the major targets of Big Data science are to advance human health care and to understand ecosystems based on huge distributed data. Secondary metabolites are used by humans for various purposes and they play important roles in ecological relationships between species. The evolutionary history and broad functional spectrum of secondary metabolites is still not fully understood. In the present book article, we discuss two research topics, first is on alkaloid synthesis pathways and the other is on structure activity relationships of metabolites. In the first study we utilized the subring skeleton (SRS) profiles to systematize alkaloids into groups and to relate individual compounds and groups to metabolic pathways. Applying clustering method to SRS profiles, the variety of ring skeletons across 29 clusters and 25 subclusters was clearly understood. Systematization of core cyclic structure, biological activity and biosynthetic pathway of metabolites can provide new insight into interpretation of evolution process for active compounds in nature. The second topic is on a methodology for the integrated interpretation of the relationships between chemical structures and biological activities based on network clustering algorithm and taking into consideration statistics controlled by false discovery rate. Given the importance of metabolites in agriculture, ecology and healthcare it would be of great help to various sectors of science and technology to predict the functions of the function-unknown metabolites by using some computational means based on their chemical structures. Natural product chemistry associated with metabolomics will shift towards the data-intensive sciences and needs to simultaneously integrate and examine different types of data such as chemical structure and biological activity for new discoveries and development of novel drugs interacted with proteins and the identification of viable drug resources and other useful compounds. Techniques and approaches discussed in this article provide clues to comprehensive understanding of evolution of metabolic pathways and structure-activity relationships in the context of metabolites.

See also: Biological Pathways. Integrative Analysis of Multi-Omics Data. Metabolome Analysis. Natural Language Processing Approaches in Bioinformatics. Networks in Biology

References

Afendi, F.M., Okada, T., Yamazaki, M., *et al.*, 2011. KNApSAcK family databases: Integrated metabolite – Plant species databases for multifaceted plant research. Plant and Cell Physiology 53 (2), e1-e1.

Albert, R., Jeong, H., Barabási, A.-L., 2000. Error and attack tolerance of complex networks. Nature 406, 378–382.

Altaf-Ul-Amin, M., Katsuragi, T., Sato, T., Ono, N., Kanaya, S., 2014. An unsupervised approach to predict functional relations between genes based on expression data. BioMed Research International 2014.

Altaf-Ul-Amin, M., Shinbo, Y., Mihara, K., Kurokawa, K., Kanaya, S., 2006. Development and implementation of an algorithm for detection of protein complexes in large interaction networks. BMC Bioinformatics 7 (1), 207.

Altaf-Ul-Amin, M., Wada, M., Kanaya, S., 2012. Partitioning a PPI network into overlapping modules constrained by high-density and periphery tracking. ISRN Biomathematics 2012, 11.

Benjamini, Y., Hochberg, Y., 1995. Controlling the false discovery rate: A practical and powerful approach to multiple testing. Journal of the Royal Statistical Society. Series B (Methodological). 289–300.

Bolton, E.E., Wang, Y., Thiessen, P.A., Bryant, S.H., 2008. PubChem: Integrated platform of small molecules and biological activities. Annual Reports in Computational Chemistry 4, 217–241.

Connolly, J.D., Hill, R.A., 1991. Dictionary of Terpenoids. London: Champman and Hall.

Dixon, R.A., 2001. Natural products and plant disease resistance. Nature 411 (6839), 843.

Durant, J.L., Leland, B.A., Henry, D.R., Nourse, J.G., 2002. Reoptimization of MDL keys for use in drug discovery. Journal of Chemical Information and Computer Sciences 42 (6), 1273–1280.

Eguchi, R., Ono, N., Horai, H., *et al.*, 2017. Classification of alkaloid compounds based on Subring Skeleton (SRS) profiling: On finding relationship of compounds with metabolic pathways. Journal of Computer Aided Chemistry 18, 58–75.

Fell, D.A., Wagner, A., 2000. The small world of metabolism. Nature Biotechnology 18 (11), 1121–1122.

Heller, S.R., McNaught, A., Pletnev, I., Stein, S., Tchekhovskoi, D., 2015. InChl, the IUPAC international chemical identifier. Journal of Cheminformatics 7 (1), 23.

Ibrahim, M., Anishetty, S., 2012. A meta-metabolome network of carbohydrate metabolism: Interactions between gut microbiota and host. Biochemical and Biophysical Research Communications 428 (2), 278–284.

Islam, M.T., Mohamedali, A., Garg, G., *et al.*, 2013. Unlocking the puzzling biology of the black Périgord truffle Tuber melanosporum. Journal of Proteome Research 12 (12), 5349–5356.

Iwashita, H., Kawahara, J., Minato, S.I., 2012. ZDD-based computation of the number of paths in a graph. Hokkaido University, Division of Computer Science, TCS Technical Reports, vol. TCS-TR-A-10-60.

Jeong, H., Tombor, B., Albert, R., Oltvai, Z.N., Barabási, A.L., 2000. The large-scale organization of metabolic networks. Nature 407 (6804), 651–654.

Kanaya, S., Kudo, Y., 1994. Genome propensities of Escherichia coli and eleven coliphages for under- and over-abundances of sigma super (70)-consensus-like sequences. International Journal of Genome Research 1 (4), 261–277.

Klekota, J., Roth, F.P., 2008. Chemical substructures that enrich for biological activity. Bioinformatics 24 (21), 2518–2525.

Koch, I., Junker, B.H., Heiner, M., 2004. Application of Petri net theory for modelling and validation of the sucrose breakdown pathway in the potato tuber. Bioinformatics 21 (7), 1219–1226.

Kossel, A., 1891. On the chemical composition of the cell. Archives of Physiology 181.

Matsuno, H., Tanaka, Y., Aoshima, H., Matsui, M., Miyano, S., 2011. Biopathways representation and simulation on hybrid functional petri net. Studies in Health Technology and Informatics 162, 77–91.

Ma, H., Zeng, A.P., 2003. Reconstruction of metabolic networks from genome data and analysis of their global structure for various organisms. Bioinformatics 19 (2), 270–277.

Minato, S.I., 1993. Zero-suppressed BDDs for set manipulation in combinatorial problems. In: Proceedings of the 30th International Design Automation Conference, pp. 272–277. ACM.

Mithöfer, A., Boland, W., 2012. Plant defense against herbivores: Chemical aspects. Annual Review of Plant Biology 63, 431–450.

Nakamura, Y., Mochamad Afendi, F., Kawsar Parvin, A., et al., 2014. KNApSAcK metabolite activity database for retrieving the relationships between metabolites and biological activities. Plant and Cell Physiology 55 (1), e7.

Ohtana, Y., Abdullah, A.A., Altaf-Ul-Amin, M., et al., 2014. Clustering of 3D-structure similarity based network of secondary metabolites reveals their relationships with biological activities. Molecular Informatics 33 (11–12), 790–801.

Palsson, B.Ø., 2006. Systems Biology. Cambridge University Press.

Raes, J., Bork, P., 2008. Molecular eco-systems biology: Towards an understanding of community function. Nature Reviews Microbiology 6 (9), 693.

Saito, M., Takemura, N., Shirai, T., 2012. Classification of ligand molecules in PDB with fast heuristic graph match algorithm COMPLIG. Journal of Molecular Biology 424 (5), 379–390.

Spjuth, O., Berg, A., Adams, S., Willighagen, E.L., 2013. Applications of the InChI in cheminformatics with the CDK and Bioclipse. Journal of Cheminformatics 5 (1), 14.

Steinbeck, C., Han, Y., Kuhn, S., et al., 2003. The Chemistry Development Kit (CDK): An open-source Java library for chemo-and bioinformatics. Journal of Chemical Information and Computer Sciences 43 (2), 493–500.

Strogatz, S.H., 2001. Exploring complex networks. Nature 410 (6825), 268–276.

Tadeusz, A., 2007. Alkaloids – Secrets of life alkaloid chemistry. In: Biological Significance, Applications and Ecological Role. Elsevier.

Takahashi, H., Kai, K., Shinbo, Y., et al., 2008. Metabolomics approach for determining growth-specific metabolites based on Fourier transform ion cyclotron resonance mass spectrometry. Analytical and Bioanalytical Chemistry 391 (8), 2769.

Wink, M., Schmeller, T., Latz-Brüning, B., 1998. Modes of action of allelochemical alkaloids: Interaction with neuroreceptors, DNA, and other molecular targets. Journal of Chemical Ecology 24 (11), 1881–1937.

Ziegler, J., Facchini, P.J., 2008. Alkaloid biosynthesis: Metabolism and trafficking. Annual Review of Plant Biology 59, 735–769.

Relevant Websites

http://kanaya.naist.jp/knapsack_jsp/top.html
  KNApSAcK Core System.
http://kanaya.naist.jp/MetaboliteActivity/top.jsp
  Metabolite Activity.
http://www.pearsonvue.com/fl/realestate/fingerprint/
  Pearson VUE.
http://astro.temple.edu/~tua87106/list_fingerprints.pdf
  PubChem Substructure Fingerprint.

Biomolecular Structures: Prediction, Identification and Analyses

Prasun Kumar, University of Bristol, Bristol, United Kingdom
Swagata Halder and Manju Bansal, Indian Institute of Science, Bangalore, India

Glossary

Active site It is an asymmetric pocket, present on or near the surface of a biomolecule, that promotes chemical catalysis upon binding of appropriate substrate.

Alignment Method for comparing two or more sequences/structures to assess the overall similarity.

Base stacking Aromatic rings of DNA or RNA bases lie on top of each other.

Coiled-coils These structures are formed when two or more α-helices wind around each other to give a supercoil. The constituent helices may either run in the same (parallel) or in the opposite (anti-parallel) directions.

Domain A compact unit of protein structure that can fold on its own and have independent function.

Electrostatic interactions The non-covalent interaction between oppositely charged atoms or groups of atoms.

Homology modelling A computational method for modelling the structure of a biomolecule based on its sequence similarity to one or more biomolecules of known structure.

Motif It can be either sequence or structure motif. Sequence motifs have recognizable amino-acid sequences found in different proteins. Structural motifs are segments of protein 3D structure that is formed by the spatially close residues. These residues may or may not be adjacent in the sequence.

RNA-thermometer RNA-thermometer, also known as RNA-thermosensor, is a temperature sensitive non-coding RNA molecule that regulates gene expression.

Super-secondary structure Super-secondary structures are combination of secondary structures and can be considered as an intermediate between secondary and tertiary structures. α-hairpins, β-hairpins and β-α-β motifs are commonly found super-secondary structures.

Van der Waals interaction These are weak attractive forces between two atoms or groups of atoms that arise due to the fluctuations in electron distribution around the nuclei. Van der Waals forces are stronger between less electronegative atoms.

Central Dogma of Life

According to the classical view, also known as Crick's central dogma, "the coded genetic information hard-wired into DNA is transcribed into individual transportable cassettes, composed of messenger RNA (mRNA); each mRNA cassette contains the program for synthesis of a particular protein (or small number of proteins)" (Lodish *et al.*, 2000) (**Fig. 1**). Though all biological cells adhere to this rule, there are few notable exceptions as well (Birney *et al.*, 2007; Gerstein *et al.*, 2007). Over-simplification of this rule can allow us to make a statement: "DNA makes RNA and RNA makes proteins" and involves two distinct steps, namely transcription and translation. RNA polymerase along with transcription factors transfers the information coded in DNA to messenger RNA and the process is known as transcription. Translation process facilitates the sequence encoded in the RNA molecule to get decoded into an amino acid sequence which defines a protein. DNA must make identical copies of itself to pass on the genetic information from parent to offspring. DNA polymerase and its associated proteins make possible this phenomenon, known as replication. These events are highly dependent on the 3D structures of DNA/RNA as well as associated proteins. In this article, we will discuss various structural elements of DNA, RNA and proteins. We will also highlight different algorithms for their prediction, identification and analyses, with emphasis on more recent reports.

Base-Pairing and Double Helical Structure of DNA

The double helical structure of DNA, as proposed by Watson and Crick in 1953 (shown schematically in **Fig. 2(A)**), revolutionized our understanding of biology at the molecular level (Watson and Crick, 1953). The model had two strands entwining around a common helical axis and linked together by a specific Hydrogen-bond (H-bond) scheme (**Fig. 2(B)**) that plays a major role in stabilizing the nucleic acid structures. The canonical Watson-Crick DNA structure has right handed screw sense with the two chains in anti-parallel orientations and 10 nucleotides per turn. The separation among two consecutive bases in a chain is 3.4 Å along the helix axis (**Fig. 2(A)**). In general, there are two types of H-bonding in nucleic acid structures (1) Watson-Crick (WC) and (2) non-Watson-Crick (NWC). In the canonical Watson-Crick scheme two H-bonds occur between the Adenosine and the Thymine base-pairs (bps), while there are three such bonds between the Cytosine and the Guanine (**Fig. 2(B)**). The specificity of this base-pairing scheme is the key to conservative replication of DNA and the transmission of exact information from one generation to the next. However, the large number of nucleic acid structures determined by x-ray diffraction and available in various databases, such as Nucleic Acid Database (NDB; see Relevant Website section)

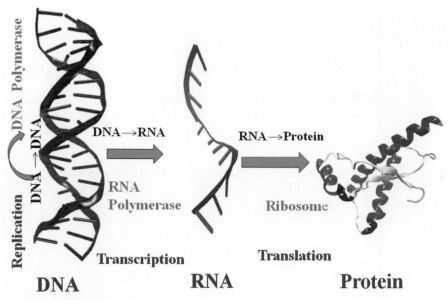

Fig. 1 Schematic representing the Central Dogma of Life.

(Coimbatore Narayanan *et al.*, 2014) and Protein Data Bank (PDB) (Berman *et al.*, 2000) has revealed a wide variety of structures and their conformational adaptability. In addition, a number of different types of non-WC base-pairing with two H-bonds have been observed (**Fig. 3**) (Lu and Olson, 2008).

DNA and RNA Can Adopt Different Structural Forms

Change in environment play a significant role on twisting, turning and stretching the structure of DNA leading to different forms of DNA (Bansal, 1999); described A-Z forms of DNA, with the exception of the letters F, Q, U, V and Y (Ghosh and Bansal, 2003). Among these helical forms, Watson-Crick model for B-DNA is the most commonly known. There are two other well-known type of helices: A-form and Z-form (**Table 1**). A-DNA was first observed by Franklin and Gosling in 1953 when they got the X-ray pattern recorded for fibres of the sodium salt of calf thymus DNA under low humidity (Franklin and Gosling, 1953). RNA double helices also have a structure similar to A-DNA (Rich and Davies, 1956). Z-DNA has two nucleotides in a repeating units and a left-handed screw sense. In general, it has alternating purine (Guanine) and pyrimidine (Cytosine) sequences with alternating sugar puckers as well as syn/anti conformations about the glycosyl bond (Wang *et al.*, 1979). Other forms of DNA are described elsewhere (Ghosh and Bansal, 2003).

Like DNA, each RNA strand contains nitrogenous bases covalently bound to a sugar-phosphate backbone. However, RNA is usually single-stranded and the sugar is ribose instead of deoxyribose as in DNA. It also contains Uracil in place of Thymine base. RNA molecules, usually, have a single-stranded structure that can fold over to form different secondary structures viz. hairpin loops, bulge loops, internal loops or multi loops. These loops are stabilized by intra-molecular H-bonds between complementary bases that are important for their functions as well as stability (Holley *et al.*, 1965). In general, RNA secondary structure can have four basic elements namely helices, loops, bulges, and junctions. Stem-loop or hairpin loop is the most common element of RNA secondary structure (Tinoco and Bustamante, 1999) and consists of a stem and a loop. Stem is formed when the RNA chain folds back to from a double helical tract and the unpaired nucleotides form a single stranded loop. Hairpins with loop length of four nucleotides are quite common and also known as tetraloops. Sequences of these tetraloops form three major clusters: UNCG, GNRA, and CUUG (N is one of the four nucleotides and R is a purine) with UNCG being the most stable (Hollyfield *et al.*, 1976). The unpaired nucleotides in one strand of a double helix produce bulge in that strand. However, if the bulge is present in both the strands, it is referred to as an internal loop (**Fig. 4**). Internal loops can be symmetric or asymmetric depending on the number of nucleotides in each bulge. Two hairpins or internal loops with single stranded RNA often interact with each other to produce pseudoknots, identified for the first time in the turnip yellow mosaic virus (Rietveld *et al.*, 1982). Pseudoknots are found to have catalytic activities (Staple and Butcher, 2005).

In the year 1960, the first experimental demonstration of DNA-RNA hybrid double helix paved the way for understanding the transfer of information from DNA to RNA (Rich, 1960). Currently, there are more than 100 DNA-RNA hybrid and chimera structures available in NDB.

Apart from double helices, DNA and RNA can form triplexes as well as quadruplexes. Triplexes are of two types namely (1) minor groove triplex and (2) major groove triplex. The minor groove triplex is found in almost all large RNAs (Devi *et al.*, 2015). The beet western yellow virus pseudoknot structure has a loop that forms a minor-groove triplex motif with a double

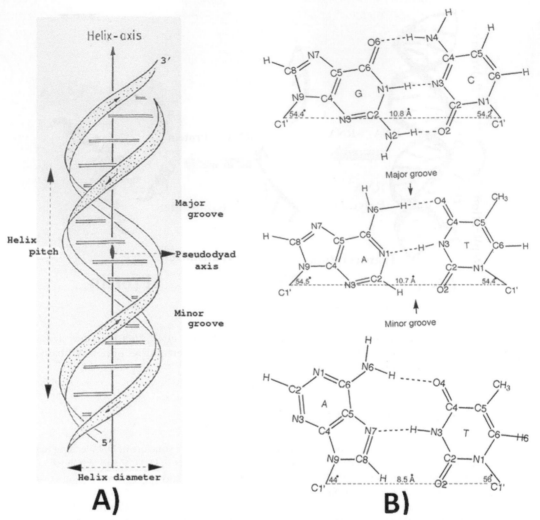

Fig. 2 (A) A schematic diagram of the Watson–Crick double helix. The base pairs are represented by horizontal bars and the sugar–phosphate backbones of the two chains, related by a twofold rotation axis perpendicular to the helix, are represented by ribbons running in opposite directions. The 5′ and 3′ ends are labelled for the ascending strand. The helix axis, its pitch and diameter and the major and the minor grooves have been identified. (B) Base pairs G·C and A·T with Watson–Crick and A·T with Hoogsteen hydrogen-bond schemes are shown as line diagrams. The base atoms are numbered according to the standard nomenclature and the hydrogen bonds between them are represented by dotted lines. The C1′–C1′ distance and the C1′–C1′–N1/N9 angles are indicated in each case. The minor-groove and major-groove sides of the Watson–Crick base pair is indicated in the case of the A·T base pair. Reproduced with permission of the International Union of Crystallography. Available at: https://journals.iucr.org/services/termsofuse.html.

helical stem via 2′-OH and triple-base interactions (Su *et al.*, 1999). Minor groove triplexes allow a stable packing of loop and helix that make them critical in the structure of large ribonucleotides including group I intron (Szewczak *et al.*, 1998), group II intron (Boudvillain *et al.*, 2000) and the ribosome. In RNAs, major groove triplexes are not as common as their minor groove counterparts as the major groove in RNA double helices is narrow. However, triplex in B-DNA is possible via the formation of Hoogsteen or reversed Hoogsteen H-bonds in the major groove (Jain *et al.*, 2008).

Quadruplexes are higher order nucleic acid structures that are generally formed by G-rich sequences (Gellert *et al.*, 1962). Hoogsteen type H-bonds allow four Guanine bases to associate and form a square planar structure, a Guanine quartet, that stack on top of each other to give a G-quadruplex. The presence of Alkali ions in the central channel between each pair of tetrads adds to their stability (Largy *et al.*, 2016). Eukaryotic telomeres which are characterized by periodically repeating G-tracts (Sundquist and Klug, 1989; Wright *et al.*, 1997), are associated with quadruplex structures. However, they are also found in non-telomeric genomic DNA. Quadruplexes can be formed from one, two or four separate strands of nucleic acid and depending on the number of strands they can have a wide range of topologies (Burge *et al.*, 2006; Rhodes and Lipps, 2015) (**Fig. 5**). Depending on the topology and number of constituent strands, there is a variation in the consensus sequence as well (Burge *et al.*, 2006). Quadruplexes can be formed by triplet repeats like GAA, CCG, or CAG (Khateb *et al.*, 2004; Matsugami *et al.*, 2003). A statistical survey of short sequences that can form quadruplex in the human genome have identified few commonly occurring sequences like CCTGTCA, CCTGTT, CCTGTC and CCTGTTA (Todd *et al.*, 2005). It has also been shown

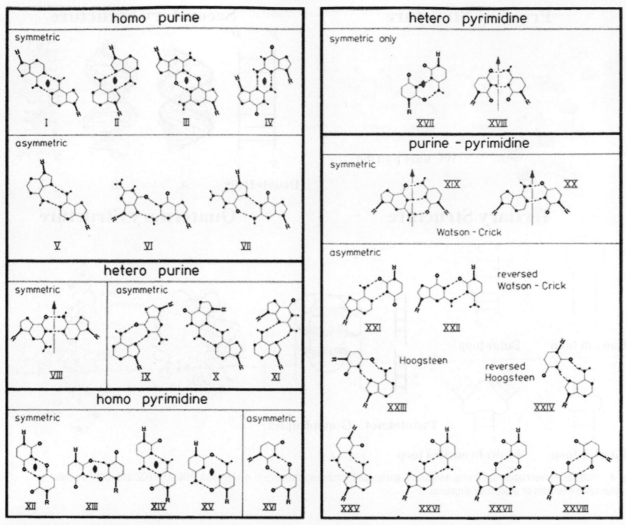

Fig. 3 Possible base pairing schemes between the bases. Adenine, Guanine, Uracil (Thymine), and Cytosine in their cononical (keto- and amino-) tautomeric forms and involving at least two H-bonds. A total of 28 base pairs including the two canonical WC pairs are possible. The reverse A·T/U and G·C WC pairs are asymmetric, and are numbered XXI and XXII respectively. Figure adopted from (with permission). Availabe at: http://x3dna.org/highlights/reverse-watson-crick-base-pairs.

Table 1   Comparison of various parameters of A-, B- and Z-DNA

Parameters	A-DNA	B-DNA	Z-DNA
Helix sense	Right-handed	Right-handed	Left-handed
Repeating unit	1 bp	1 bp	2 bp
Mean twist/bp (°)	+32.7	+36.0	−60/2
Mean number of bp/turn	11	10	12
Mean Rise/bp along axis (Å)	2.6	3.4	3.7
Pitch of helix (Å)	28.6	34.0	44.4
Major Groove	Narrow and deep	Wide and deep	Flat
Minor groove	Wide and shallow	Narrow and deep	Narrow and deep
Glycosyl torsion angle	Anti	Anti	Pyrimidine: anti, Purine: syn
Nucleotide phosphate to phosphate distance (Å)	5.9	7.0	Pyrimidine: 5.7, Purine: 6.1
Sugar ring pucker	C3'-endo	C2'-endo	Pyrimidine: C2'-endo, Purine: C3'-endo
Helix Diameter (Å)	23	20	18

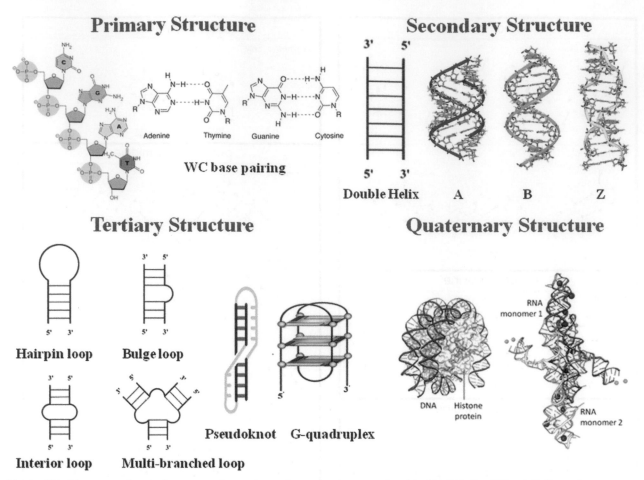

Fig. 4 Pictorial representation of primary, secondary, tertiary and quaternary structure of nucleic acid. PDB ID: 1EQZ and 4R4V are taken as representative examples of quaternary structures.

that the number of nucleotides in the loop, length of G-quartet and cations affect the formation and stability of duplex DNA vs quadruplexes (Cevec and Plavec, 2005; Risitano and Fox, 2004). In early 2001, quadruplexes were described as "structures in search of a function" (Simonsson, 2001). However, several experiments have now shown their functional importance (Maizels and Gray, 2013; Rhodes and Lipps, 2015). G-quadruplex-forming DNA motif has been reported to be important in predicting the position of DNA replication origins in human cells (Besnard *et al.*, 2012). G-quadruplexes are known to protect the ends of telomere as well as regulate their length (Rice and Skordalakes, 2016). Biological insights along with the bioinformatics analyses of quadruplexes has paved the path for the discovery of drugs targeting them (Fernando *et al.*, 2009; Hänsel-Hertsch *et al.*, 2017; Xu *et al.*, 2017).

Intercalated motifs or i-Motifs are another type of quadruplexes that are formed from Cytosine rich sequences by intercalation and hemi-protonated cytosine–cytosine base-pairing (Gehring *et al.*, 1993). These sequences were found to occur in gene promoter regions and that may allow them to play a pivotal role in gene transcription (Guéron and Leroy, 2000). Hence, targeting them with ligand can provide novel methods for targeting genetic diseases (Day *et al.*, 2014; Sheng *et al.*, 2017). These motifs are not observed in RNA as there will be a repulsion between 2'-OH of ribose sugar (Lacroix *et al.*, 1996). The experimental validation of the formation of i-motifs can be done by experimental methods like NMR studies, X-ray crystallography, UV molecular absorption, molecular fluorescence based techniques, fluorescence resonance energy transfer, fluorescence correlation spectroscopy, time-resolved transient absorption and emission spectroscopy (Benabou *et al.*, 2014). The property of these motifs to reversibly fold or unfold with the change in pH has been exploited in designing nano-machines (Liu and Balasubramanian, 2003; Son *et al.*, 2014; Wang *et al.*, 2010).

Predicting Nucleic Acids Secondary Structures

With the wealth of sequence information available due to the advancements in sequencing technologies, there is a steep increase in secondary structure prediction algorithms (Schroeder, 2009; Shapiro *et al.*, 2007). Realizing the importance of RNA secondary

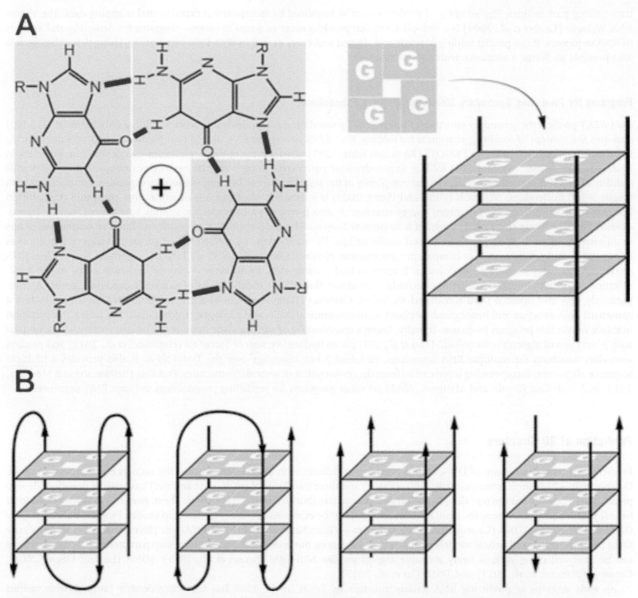

Fig. 5 Structure of G-quadruplexes. G-quadruplexes form in vitro in DNA or RNA sequences containing tracts of three to four guanine. (A) The building blocks of G-quadruplexes are G-quartets that arise from the association of four guanines into a cyclic arrangement stabilized by Hoogsten hydrogen bonding (N1–N6 and N2–N7). The planar G-quartets stack on top of one another, forming four-stranded helical structures. G-quadruplex formation is driven by monovalent cations such as Na$^+$ and K$^+$. (B) G-quadruplex structures are polymorphic and can be sub-grouped into different families, as for example parallel or antiparallel according to the orientation of the strands and can be inter- or intramolecular folded. Figure taken from Rhodes, D., Lipps, H.J., 2015. G-quadruplexes and their regulatory roles in biology. Nucleic Acids Research 43, 8627–8637.

structures, various algorithms and methods have been developed over the years (Schroeder, 2009). Accurate and reliable prediction of RNA secondary structure is a long but persisting challenge and predicting pseudoknots is even more challenging and hence some algorithms do not predict pseudoknots in the input RNA sequence. The various algorithms can be divided into two categories of software: (1) those that do not identify pseudoknots and (2) identify pseudoknots.

Programs for Predicting Secondary Structures Without the Pseudoknots

The *Unified Nucleic Acid Folding* or *UNAFold* (Markham and Zuker, 2008) constitutes a set of algorithms that simulate folding, hybridization and melting pathways for input nucleic acid sequence. *UNAFold* uses the Zuker algorithm (Zuker and Stiegler, 1981) for finding the minimum free-energy structure for a given sequence. Another software package *RNAstructure* can predict as well as analyze secondary structures in input DNA or RNA sequences (Bellaousov *et al.*, 2013; Reuter and Mathews, 2010) with various base-pairing probabilities. The accuracy of prediction can be improved by incorporating experimental mapping data. The *Vienna RNA Websuite* (Gruber *et al.*, 2008) is a web-platform that provides users an access to various programs for designing and analysis of RNA sequences. It can predict folding of single and aligned sequences as well as RNA-RNA interactions. Using this websuite, it is also possible to design a sequence with a given structure.

Programs for Predicting Secondary Structures With the Pseudoknots

RNA-STAR predicts the secondary structure of linear RNA by simulating a hypothetical process of folding (Abrahams *et al.*, 1990) and uses the concept of local trigger regions for folding. *RNA-STAR* allows the RNA to fold into pseudoknotted structures during the simulation. Another program *PKNOTS* (Rivas and Eddy, 1999) generates the optimal minimum energy structure for an input RNA sequence. It uses standard RNA folding thermodynamic parameters along with parameters describing the thermodynamic stability of pseudoknots. However, due to the complexity of the algorithm, it can be computationally expensive for sequences with length > 100 nucleotides. *NUPACK* (Dirks and Pierce, 2003) is a dynamic programming algorithm that computes the partition function and hence finds the minimum energy structure. It also provides probabilities for various base pairs (bps) in a pseudoknot. The *ILM* (Ruan *et al.*, 2004) program is an iterative loop matching algorithm that allows the addition or subtraction of bps in different iterations to form pseudoknots and maximize bps. This method can be applied for individual and aligned sequences as it may use both thermodynamic or comparative information. *HotKnots* (Ren *et al.*, 2005) is a heuristic algorithm that predicts RNA secondary structures including pseudoknots. It tends to find a stable stem by an iterative process and uses a free energy minimization algorithm for pseudoknot free secondary structures that allows identification of potential candidate stems. A comparatively new and updated semi-automated algorithm, *ConStruct* (Wilm *et al.*, 2008) aligns multiple RNA sequences to find a consensus RNA structure and hence combines both thermodynamic stability and phylogeny information. The interactive graphical interface makes this program more user-friendly. Using a combination of various algorithms, it can predict tertiary interactions as well. A very recent algorithm *TurboFold2* (Tan *et al.*, 2017) is an updated version of *TurboFold* (Harmanci *et al.*, 2011) and predicts secondary structures for multiple RNA homologs. *TurboFold* 2 has advantage over the *TurboFold* as it also provides a multiple sequence alignment, incorporating information from the conservation of secondary structures. *ProbKnot* (Bellaousov and Mathews, 2010) and *TurboKnot* (Seetin and Mathews, 2012) are other programs for predicting pseudoknots in input RNA sequences.

Prediction of 3D Structure

Prediction of tertiary structure of DNA/RNA is much more difficult with a wide gap between the sequence and structural space. Double helices have three rotational (tilt, roll and twist) and three translational (shift, slide and rise) base paired dinucleotide step parameters. These six parameters along with intra bp parameters (buckle, propeller, opening, shear, stretch and stagger) and local helical parameters (inclination, tip, displacement and rise) can be exploited to build a nucleic acid model. Programs like *NUCGEN* (Bansal *et al.*, 1995), 3DNA (Lu and Olson, 2008), *Curves* + (Blanchet *et al.*, 2011) and *RNAHelix* (Bhattacharyya *et al.*, 2017) use these parameters to build helical models with different sequences, but uniform or varying local step parameters. The 3D structures can be analyzed using various freely available algorithms like *NUPARM* (Bansal *et al.*, 1995), *3DNA* (Lu and Olson, 2008), *Curves* + (Blanchet *et al.*, 2011) and *DSSR* (Lu *et al.*, 2015).

An early attempt at predicting RNA tertiary structure by Levitt in the 1969 has seen considerable progress with various algorithms being now available. *ROSETTA* (Das and Baker, 2008), *MC-Sym* (Parisien and Major, 2008), *GARN2* (Boudard *et al.*, 2017) and *F-RAG* (Jain and Schlick, 2017) are few examples. *ROSETTA* uses the assembly of short fragments, taken from existing RNA crystal structures whose corresponding sequences match with a part of the target RNA. The generated models can be further refined to look more realistic. *MC-Sym* along with *MC-Fold* increases the accuracy of prediction of RNA 3D structure by using nucleotide cyclic motifs. *GARN2* samples 3D RNA structure at a coarse-grained model and takes the corresponding secondary structure as input. Among all possible structures, it extracts two best possible structures that are close to the native one. *F-RAG* is a graph-based fragment assembly method that generates atomic coordinates from coarse-grained RNA models.

The second component of central dogma includes a process of decoding protein sequence from RNA and the process is called translation. Apart from DNA and RNA, proteins are the other major macromolecules that are important for the sustenance of life.

Proteins–Building Blocks of Life

The term 'Proteins' was first coined by Gerardus Johannes Mulder in his article titled 'On the composition of some animal substances' (Mulder, 1839), where he proposed that animals rely on plants for most of their protein. Since then, proteins have been the subject of extensive studies. Proteins are polypeptides comprising of 20 standard L-amino acids and their derivatives. These amino acids are covalently bonded through peptide bonds formed between the carboxyl and amide group of adjacent amino acid residues. Proteins are essential for survival and normal functioning of living cells and viruses. Almost all biological processes in a cell or group of cells involve proteins.

Proteins can be classified into different categories using numerous criteria such as biological roles, chemical composition and structure. Based on their biological roles, proteins are categorized into contractile, defense, enzymes, nutrients/storage, regulatory, structural, transport and other functional proteins. Using their compositions, proteins can be classified into two categories namely (1) simple and (2) complex. Simple proteins consist only of amino acids. Whereas, complex proteins contain prosthetic groups along with the amino acids in their structure. Based on their shape, proteins can be divided into two sets: fibrous and globular. Fibrous proteins are insoluble in water and have primarily mechanical and structural functions that provide support to the cells as well as the whole organism. The presence of hydrophobic amino acids on their surface facilitates their packaging into very complex supramolecular structures. Fibroin, collagen, α-keratins and elastin are few examples of this class. On the other hand, globular proteins are generally soluble in water or aqueous media containing acids, bases, salts or alcohol and more complex than the fibrous proteins. They have a compact and spherical/ovoid shape. The concept of tertiary and quaternary structures is usually associated with globular proteins only. The complex confirmation of globular proteins gives rise to a large variety of biological functions and makes them more dynamic rather than static in their activities. Defining the functional roles of a protein is essential considering the widespread influence every protein has towards the survival of an organism.

The first step towards deciphering the function of a protein involves understanding the physico-chemical properties of constituent amino acid residues containing an amide group, carboxylic group and a side chain 'R' (except glycine where hydrogen is present instead of R). There are 20 standard amino acids, which serve as building blocks of proteins. Amino acids can be categorized into 5 subgroups using the polarity and charge of side-chains (Nelson *et al.*, 2008): (1) Nonpolar (aliphatic R group: Ala, Gly, Ile, Leu, Met, Pro and Val), (2) Polar (uncharged R group: Asn, Cys, Gln, Ser, Thr and Tyr), (3) Aromatic (Phe, Trp and Tyr), (4) basic (positively charged R group: Arg, His and Lys) and (5) acidic (negatively charged R group: Asp and Glu). A covalent link (-C(O)-NH) between the carboxylic acid group of one and the α-amino group of the other amino acid is known as a peptide bond. It has a partial double bond nature thereby restricting rotation about the bond and conferring planarity (Pauling, 1960). However, considerable freedom for rotation prevails around the N-C$^\alpha$ and C$^\alpha$-C bonds, giving rise to phi ((φ)) and psi (ψ) torsion angles (dihedral angles) respectively. In principle, (φ) and ψ can have any value between $-180°$ and $+180°$. However, certain values of (φ) and ψ are prohibited because they could result in steric clashes between atoms present in the polypeptide backbone as well as amino acid side chains. The polypeptide chain can take up the fully extended conformation with ((φ),ψ) being ($-180°, +180°$) resulting into the least steric hindrance. The peptide unit is most commonly characterized by *trans* conformation about the peptide bond in which the amide and carbonyl groups point in opposite directions. On the other hand, in *cis*-conformation, a less favorable conformation, both the amide and carbonyl groups in a peptide plane point in the same direction.

Using simple mechanized calculators, in 1963, G.N. Ramachandran and his coworkers predicted the possible allowed and disallowed combinations of the backbone dihedral angles ((φ),ψ) by assessing the conformations of the two-linked peptide units for the presence of short contacts between non-bonded atoms in a polypeptide chain (Ramachandran *et al.*, 1963; Ramachandran and Sasisekharan, 1968; Ramakrishnan and Ramachandran, 1965; Sasisekharan, 1962). The map is popularly referred as Ramachandran map (**Fig. 6**). The predictions were found to be corroborating with the experimentally determined protein structure of myoglobin in 1958 (Kendrew *et al.*, 1958). The Ramachandran plot has repeatedly been reconsidered and redrawn during its first half century of life (Bansal and Srinivasan, 2013; Carugo and Djinovic-Carugo, 2013). However, several differences have been observed among various studies depending on: (1) the amount of data used, (2) data quality and (3) the criteria implemented. In fact, it is important to note that the original map used only theoretical computations when none of

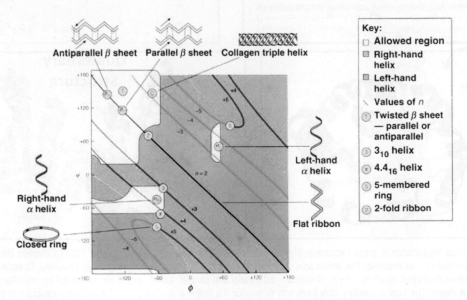

Fig. 6 Ramachandran map representing the sterically favorable regions in white. Various regular secondary structural elements are shown at location corresponding to their Φ and Ψ values. Figure is reproduced from text book Mathews, van Holde, and Ahren, Biochemistry, third edition, 2000.

the protein structures were available in public domain, whereas nowadays, authors make use of experimental observations also. Ramachandran map is used extensively to assess the stereochemical quality of 3D structures of proteins as a part of validation tools like PROCHECK (Laskowski *et al.*, 1993), Moleman2 (Kleywegt and Jones, 1996), and more recently MolProbity (Davis *et al.*, 2004; Williams *et al.*, 2017).

Hierarchical Organization and Classification of Proteins

Proteins are organized in a hierarchical manner and can be illustrated by four major levels defined as primary, secondary, tertiary and quaternary structures (**Fig. 7**). Such tiered organization of proteins facilitates better understanding and comprehension of their 3D structures. Primary structure can be defined as a linear sequence of constituent amino acids in a polypeptide chain without specifying their spatial arrangements. Secondary structures correspond to recurring arrangements of adjacent amino acids in a polypeptide chain. There are mainly three types of secondary structure elements (SSEs) namely (1) helix, (2) strand and (3) turns (connects two SSEs). Apart from these three regular SSEs, there also exist irregular secondary structures also known as 'random coils'. Higher than the level of secondary structure there exists 'super-secondary structure', a specific combination of secondary structures with explicit spatial arrangements such as α and β hairpins or β-α-β motif (Rao and Rossmann, 1973). SSEs organize themselves in 3D space to form the corresponding tertiary structure that is driven mainly by the non-specific hydrophobic interactions. The quaternary structure specifies the spatial relationships amongst the various polypeptides in a functional protein complex. The extensive growth of protein sequence and structure information has resulted in the creation of numerous classification resources for organizing proteins (Redfern *et al.*, 2005).

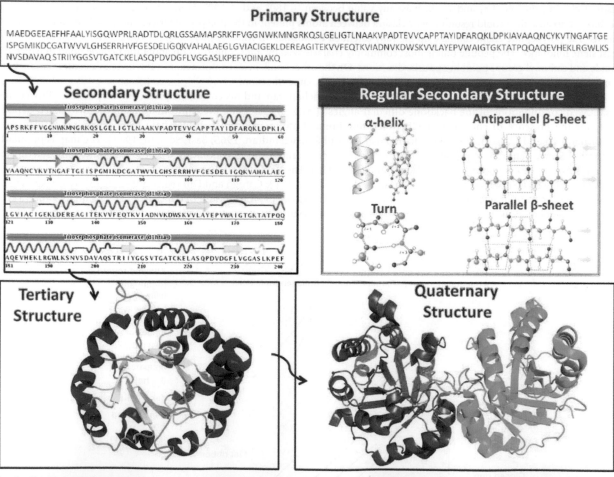

Fig. 7 The hierarchical organization in protein structure. Human triose phosphate isomerase (Uniprot code: P60174, Protein Data Bank (PDB) code: 1HTI) has been taken as an example. The amino acid sequence of a protein is considered as its primary structure. Stretches of amino acids adopt regular secondary structures (such as α-helix, β-sheets – antiparallel and parallel, turns), which are connected by irregular secondary structures, termed as loops. The local secondary structures fold to provide the native and usually functional tertiary structure of a protein. For many proteins, the tertiary structure represents the biologically functional form. For several proteins, assembly of tertiary structures gives rise to the quaternary structure, which is the biologically functional form of that protein.

Based on Structure

Two main structure-based classification databases, Structural Classification of Proteins (SCOP) (Andreeva *et al.*, 2014; Lo Conte *et al.*, 2000; Murzin *et al.*, 1995) and Class Architecture Topology and Homology (CATH) (Orengo *et al.*, 1997, 2003; Pearl *et al.*, 2003) combine sequence, structure and functional information to provide a hierarchical classification of known protein domains in the PDB. Fold classification based on Structure-Structure alignment of Proteins (FSSP) (Holm and Sander, 1996) classifies protein structures based on the pair-wise structural comparison using *DALI* program (Holm and Sander, 1996).

The focus of SCOP is to structurally characterize the proteins that are deposited in the PDB. SCOP considers evolutionary and structural domains of proteins and classifies them in a hierarchical manner. However, in the recently released version of SCOP, SCOP2 (Andreeva *et al.*, 2014), these relationships form a complex network of nodes representing a relationship of a particular type and is illustrated by a region of protein structure and sequence. Here we are describing the hierarchy of classification in SCOP database (**Fig. 8**).

i. Class (secondary structure composition and sequence/arrangement): members of different folds are placed under same class based on the extent of secondary structural content and order of occurrence of SSEs. Domains in globular proteins are usually classified under the following categories of 'Class'.

    a. All α class: members in this class are predominately composed of helices.
    b. All β class: members in this class are predominantly composed of β-sheets.
    c. α/β class: members comprise of interspersed helices and β strands in their structure.
    d. α + β class: members comprise of segregated helices and β strands in their structure.
    e. Multidomain class: a multidomain class comprises of members with domains of different folds.
    f. Small proteins: this class includes members corresponding to several disulfide rich and metal binding proteins with few or almost no regular secondary structures.
    g. Membrane proteins: this class includes membrane proteins.

ii. Fold (gross structural similarity): members in different superfamilies are grouped into one fold if the arrangement of major SSEs along with their topological connections is the same. Structural similarity among members in the same fold group arises from physicochemical properties favoring certain packing arrangements and chain topologies.

iii. Superfamily (probable evolutionary relationship): families showing overall structural similarity and in many cases gross functional similarity, thus indicating potential common evolutionary origin, are categorized into one Superfamily. Sometimes although the functions are not the same for the families within the superfamily, the nature of functions along with the topological and chemical equivalence of functional sites imply the potential evolutionary relationship between the families.

iv. Family (clear evolutionary relationship): family can be defined as a collection of related protein regions, which share high sequence identity and usually good functional and structural similarity. Most of the members of a family show more than 30% sequence identity with each other. However, there exist few examples of families in SCOP containing members with low sequence similarity to the globin family where sequence identity between members could be as low as 15%. However, all

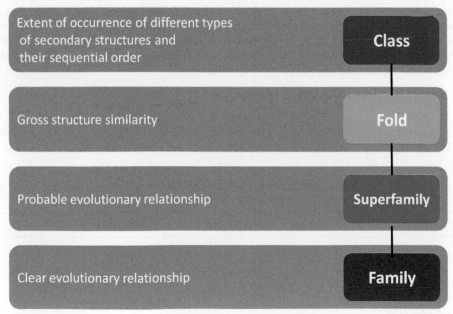

Fig. 8 Levels of classification in the database of Structural Classification of Proteins (SCOP).

members show the same overall structure and critical functional residues in topologically equivalent positions thus implying divergence from a common ancestor.

Based on Sequence Similarity

Protein sequences have been classified into different domain families based on sequence identity among sequences. Different databases which considers sequence identity as a major feature to classify proteins are Protein Family (Pfam) (Punta *et al.*, 2012), Simple Modular Architecture Research Tool (SMART) (Letunic *et al.*, 2015), InterPro (Mitchell *et al.*, 2015) and Protein Domain (ProDom) (Bru *et al.*, 2005). Homology searches in databases of sequence similarity based protein domain families are efficient and their coverage is higher than searches in structural databases as the number of sequences is higher than the number of structures.

Various Secondary Structural Elements in Proteins

The concept of repeating backbone torsion angles ((φ), ψ) or any other geometrical parameters along with the pattern of main chain-main chain (MM) N-H...O H-bonds defining a regular SSE in proteins is well established. The α-helices and extended β-strands, which are major regular SSEs found in proteins, were first predicted from theoretical studies (Pauling and Corey, 1951; Pauling *et al.*, 1951) and subsequently confirmed by X-ray diffraction analysis (Blake *et al.*, 1965; Perutz, 1951). Other SSEs like 3_{10}-helix (Donohue, 1953), π-helix (Low and Grenville-Wells, 1953), PolyProlineII (PPII)-helix (Cowan and McGavin, 1955) and left-handed α, 3_{10} and π-helices were also proposed from model building studies and found to occur occasionally (Ramachandran and Sasisekharan, 1968). **Table 2** enlists various parameters of these SSEs. They have found their importance in a number of structural biology applications, such as structure comparison (Gibrat *et al.*, 1996), visualization (Humphrey *et al.*, 1996; Sayle and Milner-White, 1995; Schrodinger, 2010) and classification (Murzin *et al.*, 1995; Orengo *et al.*, 1997). The formation of SSEs plays a major role in protein folding also (Murzin *et al.*, 1995; Orengo *et al.*, 1997).

α-Helices

Of all the postulated helices in proteins, α-helices are the most abundant and the first to be identified (Kendrew *et al.*, 1958; Pauling *et al.*, 1951). These helices have 3.6 residues per turn and 13 atoms in the ring formed by $NH_{(i+4)} \rightarrow O_i$ H-bonds (represented as 3.6_{13}) (Kendrew *et al.*, 1958; Pauling *et al.*, 1951). The model successfully explained the overall distribution of intensities in the fiber diffraction patterns for the fibrous proteins, recorded earlier by Astbury in early 1930s and for certain synthetic polypeptides. The helix was established as a familiar motif after the 3D structure of myoglobin using X-ray crystallography was solved (Kendrew *et al.*, 1958, 1960). The backbone dihedral angles ((φ),ψ) of residues in ideal right-handed α-helices are ($-57°$, $-47°$) that may vary for the constituent residues of the native α-helices. However, it appears that the sum of both dihedral angles (($\varphi)_i + \psi_{(i+1)}$) is approximately $-105°$. The amino acid side-chains protrude away from the helix axis and point roughly towards the N-terminus. This property has been used in preliminary, low resolution electron-density maps to determine the direction of the protein backbone (Terwilliger, 2010). The aggregate effect of the individual carbonyl groups (microdipoles) of the constituent residues, pointing along the helix axis, generates an overall dipole moment (Hol *et al.*, 1978). α-helix has attracted many world-renowned artists who have referred it explicitly in their work. The list of names includes Julie Newdoll in painting, Irving Geis in cartoon as well as Julian Voss-Andreae, Bathsheba Grossman, Byron Rubin and Mike Tyka in sculpture (**Fig. 9(A–B)**). Based on handedness of α-helix, it can be categorized into right-handed (clockwise) or left-handed (anticlockwise). Right-handed α-helices in protein structures outnumber their left-handed counterpart.

β-Strands

Besides α-helices, β-strands/sheets are another major SSE in globular proteins, which contain 20%–28% of all residues (Kabsch and Sander, 1983a,b). β-strands are the basic unit of a β-sheet, which can be considered as a helix with 2 residues/turn and

Table 2   Regular SSEs formed by polypeptide chains and their respective parameters. Plus and minus sign in 2nd column correspond to the right and left handed helices, respectively

Secondary structures	Residues per turn and chirality	Rise per residue (A°)	Radius of helix (A°)
α-helix	$+3.6$	1.5	2.3
π-helix	$+4.3$	1.1	2.8
310-helix	$+3.0$	2.0	1.9
Planar parallel sheet	$+2.0$	3.2	1.1
Planar anti-parallel sheet	$+2.0$	3.4	0.9
Twisted parallel or anti-parallel sheet	-2.3	3.3	1.0

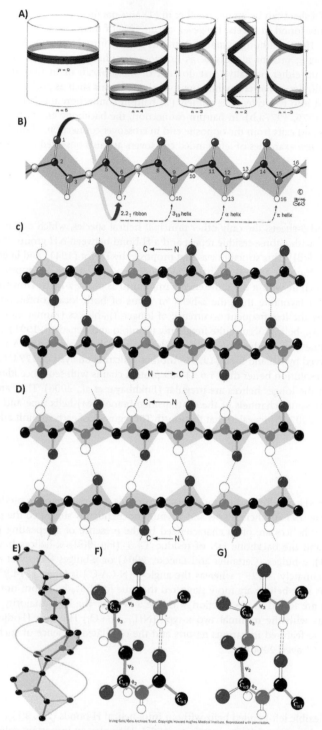

Fig. 9 Helices and their representative H-bond pattern. (A) Variation in the pitch (p) and radius of the cylinder with the change in the rise per residue. The pitch of a helix is defined as the translation during one complete turn, measured parallel to the helix- axis. It can be obtained by multiplying number of residues per turn and rise per residue. If p=0, the helix becomes a close ring and for number of residues per turn, n=2, the helix turns into a non-chiral ribbon and (B) Representative H-bond pattern in different type of helices and number of atoms involved in the closed ring formed by the N-H...O H-bond. (C) an anti-parallel β-sheet; (D) parallel β-sheet; (E) PPII-helix containing only Pro residues; Reverse turns () Type I and G) Type II in polypeptide chains. Dashed lines represent hydrogen bonds and amino acid Side chains are omitted for clarity. Used with permission from the Howard Hughes Medical Institute, Copyright 2015.

produce a translation of 3.2 to 3.4 Å/residue. They have fully extended conformation with $((\varphi),\psi)$ of the constituent residues falling within the energy minimum upper left quadrant of the Ramachandran map. The sequential neighboring C^α atoms are placed alternately above and below the plane of the sheet, giving it a pleated appearance and hence often termed as a β-pleated sheet. Two interacting strands of a sheet can be arranged either in (1) anti-parallel or (2) parallel to each other (**Fig. 9(C)** and (D)). Antiparallel strands are commonly found in sheets. However, about 20% of the β-sheets are observed to have both parallel and antiparallel strands (Richardson, 1977). Although parallel β-strands usually form large, moderately twisted sheets, occasionally it forms a cylinder with helices being present at outside as in triosephosphate isomerase structure. On the other hand, large antiparallel sheets, usually roll up either partially (first domain of thermolysin or in ribonuclease) or entirely to join edges facilitating the formation of a cylinder or barrel (membrane-spanning proteins such as porins). The connection between the two strands of a sheet can be divided into two categories namely (1) hairpin connection and (2) crossover connection (Richardson, 1981; Sternberg and Thornton, 1976, 1977a,b). In hairpin connection, the backbone enters and exits from the same end of the sheet, while the backbone enters and exits from the opposite end in crossover connection. Though right-handed crossovers are the rule in globular proteins, quite a few examples of left-handed crossovers are also observed (e.g., subtilisin and glucose phosphate isomerase).

3_{10}-Helices

Besides the classical α-helices and β-sheets, the only other principal helical species, which occurs to any great extent in globular protein structure, is the 3_{10}-helix with a three-residue repeat and a H-bond between NH group of residues '$i+3$' instead of '$i+4$' and CO group of ith residue (**Fig. 9(B)**). This structure was first proposed by Taylor (1941) and later discussed in detail by Huggins (1943), Bragg et al. (1950) and Donohue (1953). Its backbone conformational angles are approximately $(\varphi) = -49°$, $\psi = -26°$ (Ramachandran et al., 1966), which lie within the same energy minimum as of the α-helix. However, for a long periodic structure, the 3_{10}-helix is considerably less favorable than the α-helix in terms of both local conformational energy and geometry of H-bonds. The same is evident by the less frequent occurrence of longer 3_{10}-helices (Kumar and Bansal, 2015a,b). Though long 3_{10}-helices are very rare, shorter 3_{10}-helices occur quite frequently (Toniolo and Benedetti, 1991). A survey of 57 crystal structures, showed that 3.4% of total residues are involved in 3_{10}-helix (Barlow and Thornton, 1988). A total of 132, 3_{10}-helices with six amino acids or more were observed by Pal and Basu (1999). Another structural analysis of 1774 3_{10}-helices spanning five residues or more from highly resolved (resolution better than 1.6 Å) 689 protein chains with sequence identity being $\leq 20\%$ revealed that they occur quite frequently, but the longer helices are irregular (Enkhbayar et al., 2006). They are often found at the termini of α-helices. Structures of three potassium channels of the six transmembrane (TM) helix type and solved by x-ray crystallography (Clayton et al., 2008; Long et al., 2005a,b) revealed that the fourth TM segment of each subunit adopts a 3_{10}-helical conformation spanning 7–11 residues.

π-Helices

The discovery of α-helices triggered a race for finding various other possible helices. Donohue predicted the occurrence of 2.2_7, 3_{10}, 4.3_{14} and 4.4_{16} helices (Donohue, 1953), whereas Low and Baybutt independently suggested the possibility of the 4.4_{16} or π-helix (Low and Baybutt, 1952). The π-helices are often characterized by the presence of a repeating pattern of H-bond between the backbone C=O of residue 'i' and the backbone HN of residue '$i+5$' (**Fig. 9(B)**). π-helices have, therefore, been described as α-aneurisms (Keefe et al., 1993), α-bulges (Cartailler and Luecke, 2004) or π-bulges (Hardy et al., 2000). The sum of dihedral angles $((\varphi)_i + \psi_{(i+1)})$ is approximately $-125°$, whereas the angle τ (N-CA-C') is larger (114.9°) than the standard tetrahedral angle of 109.5°. The side chains in π-helices are more staggered than the ideal 3_{10}-helix, but not as well in the α-helix. Like 3_{10}-helices, a majority of π-helices are found in conjunction with the α-helices. The large majority of naturally occurring π-helices consist of five residue segments with the minimal two π-type (NH$_{(i+5)} \rightarrow$ O$_i$) H-bonds (Fodje and Al-Karadaghi, 2002). The functional roles of π-helices have featured in various reports and the correlated presence of such helices with the active sites in proteins (Medlock et al., 2007; Weaver, 2000).

PolyProlineII-helices

The PPII-helix is an extended, flexible left-handed helix without intra-helical H-bonds (**Fig. 9(E)**). The backbone dihedral angles of constituent residues are restricted to around $((\varphi) = -75°$, $\psi = 150°)$. They play an important role in structural proteins, unfolded states and as ligands for signaling proteins. The analysis of main chain conformations in proteins have shown that the left-handed PPII-helices are quite common in globular proteins (Adzhubei and Sternberg, 1993; Kumar and Bansal, 2016). Another survey of 274 non-homologous protein structures revealed that longer PPII-helices are rare, but at least one PPII-helix is present in the majority of proteins (Stapley and Creamer, 1999). Most PPII-helices are shorter than five residues. Though PPII-helices have a high preference for Pro residues, there is evidence for the presence of PPII conformations in helices containing non-Pro residues (Makarov et al., 1975; Tiffany and Krimm, 1968; Woody, 1992). A majority of the PPII-helices are solvent exposed and found to be frequently involved in protein-protein interactions (Berisio and Vitagliano, 2012). PPII-helix is observed to have a direct involvement in host-pathogen recognition for virus infections (Vermeire et al., 2011). These helices are also found to activate the phosphatidylinositol 3-kinase (PI3K)/Akt signaling pathway by the influenza-A virus (Hale et al., 2010). Recent advancements in identifying PPII-helices are well explained by Narwani et al. (2017).

Collagen Triple Helix

Collagen is a fibrous protein which is present in abundance in the human body, being a major constituent of skin, bones as well as various connective tissues. It helps in forming a scaffold to provide strength and structure. Collagens have a unique tripeptide repeat sequence with Glycine at every third position and the iminoacids Proline and Hydroxyproline often being present at the other two positions (Bowes and Kenten, 1948; Eastoe, 1955). The first triple helical structure of collagen had two inter chain H-bonds for every three residues (Ramachandran and Kartha, 1954, 1955). This was slightly modified to a one hydrogen-bonded structure (Rich and Crick, 1955). However a second water mediated hydrogen bond is also found to stabilize the triple helix (Ramachandran and Sasisekharan, 1961). Each helix in collagen has left handed screw sense and the major helix formed by three such helices is right handed. Each helix has 10 residues in 3 turns resulting in a pitch of 85.8 Å. The twist between two neighboring helices was found to be $-108.8°$ and rise of ~ 2.86 Å (Bhattacharjee and Bansal, 2005; Ramachandran and Kartha, 1955; Ramachandran and Sasisekharan, 1961). Molecular defects in biosynthesis of collagen can lead to many rare genetic diseases involving connective tissues like Ehlers-Danlos syndrome (De Paepe, 1998; Gaisl et al., 2017; Miyake et al., 2017; Prockop et al., 1979). Collagen has been shown to have wide range of applications in the medical and cosmetic field as it is biodegradable, biocompatible, easily available and weak antigenic (Cheng et al., 2017; Chvapil, 1977; Chvapil et al., 1973; Lee et al., 2001; Sheikh et al., 2017). In the field of tissue engineering, collagen based biomaterials are used to improve tissue functions (Parenteau-Bareil et al., 2010).

Turns

A turn is a region of the protein, which consists of four consecutive amino acids and allows the polypeptide chain in folding back on itself by nearly 180° **(Fig. 9(F–G))**. Venkatachalam (1968) explored all the plausible available conformations to a system of three linked peptide units consisting of four successive residues that can be stabilized by a backbone H-bond between the CO of residue 'i' and the NH of residue 'i + 3'. The resultant non-repetitive SSE, recognized from the theoretical conformational analysis, were termed as 'Turns'. He proposed three unique conformations based on $((\varphi),\psi)$ values (Turn I, II and III) along with their mirror images having $((\varphi),\psi)$ signs reversed (I′,II′ and III′). Lewis et al. (1973) analyzed the turns in a large dataset of 3D protein structures and proposed a more general definition using the distance (d) between the $C^{\alpha}(i)$ and the $C^{\alpha}(i + 3)$. The distance 'd' should be <7 Å to be a part of turn. Kuntz (1972) and Chou and Fasman (1977) have found 45% and 32% of protein chain in turns respectively. At the same time, considering only the central dipeptide, Zimmerman and Scheraga found 24% of the non-helical residues in turns (Zimmerman and Scheraga, 1977). Turns are also known as reverse turns, β-turns, β-bends, hairpin bends, 3_{10}-bends, kinks or widgets, among others. Helices and strands are often connected to each other by the tight turns. It has also been suggested that turns can direct the process of protein folding to the native conformation as they are best suited to provide the decisive long-range interactions that form tertiary structure (Lewis et al., 1971; Rose et al., 1976). Few proteins have been reported to have structure, which is heavily dependent on turns. For example, high-potential iron protein consists of 17 turns in 85 residues (Carter et al., 1974). Type-I and Type-II along with their mirror images I′ and II′ are most abundant types of turns.

Other SSEs

This class includes rarely occurring helices like 2.2_7-helices or left handed α, 3_{10} or π-helices. The repetitive C7 structure, the 2.2_7 helix or 2.2_7 ribbon, was first proposed for polypeptides by Donohue (1953) and later it was considered theoretically with $((\varphi) = -78.1°, \psi = 59.2°)$ (Ramachandran and Sasisekharan, 1968) for further studies. The 2.2_7–helix is a tight helix of 2.2 amino acids per turn and a 7 atom loop, closed by the H-bond between $NH_{(i+2)}$ and O_i. So far, this structure has not been reported in protein crystal structure.

The analysis of 31 verified left-handed helices from a set of 7284 proteins suggests that despite being rarely found in proteins, when they occur, they have structural or functional significance (Novotny and Kleywegt, 2005). Backbone dihedral angles (φ) and ψ of residues in left-handed helices are found to range from 30° to 130° and $-50°$ to 100° respectively, a mirror image of the residues in right-handed helices.

Computational Approaches for Identification of Secondary Structures in Proteins

SSEs define a protein motif and under physiological conditions almost all protein sequences have at least one 3D structure that determines their biological function. In this section, the computational methods developed for prediction/assignment of different SSEs from input sequence/protein structures are discussed.

Prediction of Secondary Structures Using Protein Sequences

One can find the root of protein secondary structure prediction in 1951, when the models for helix and sheet were proposed by Pauling and Corey (1951) and Pauling et al. (1951). Prediction of SSEs in bioinformatics aims to predict the local secondary structures of proteins based only on knowledge of their amino acid sequence. The prediction consists of classifying regions of the amino acid sequence into helices, β-strands or turns. Interest in developing the methods for predicting the secondary structures in protein started as soon as the first crystal structure was solved. These methods (Guzzo, 1965; Kotelchuck and Scheraga, 1969; Lewis *et al.*, 1970; Prothero, 1966; Schiffer and Edmundson, 1967) focused mainly on identifying regions, which are most likely to take α- helix conformation. With the increase in the number of solved protein structures, significantly improved algorithms were developed in 1970s. However, these methods attained the accuracy of 60%–65% and often under-predicted the strands (Mount, 2004). More than 20 different SSEs prediction methods have been reported till date. Some of them are shown in Fig. 10(A).

The first major breakthrough came with the development of Chou-Fasman method (Chou and Fasman, 1974), which relies predominantly on the probability parameters determined from relative frequencies of appearance of different amino acids in each

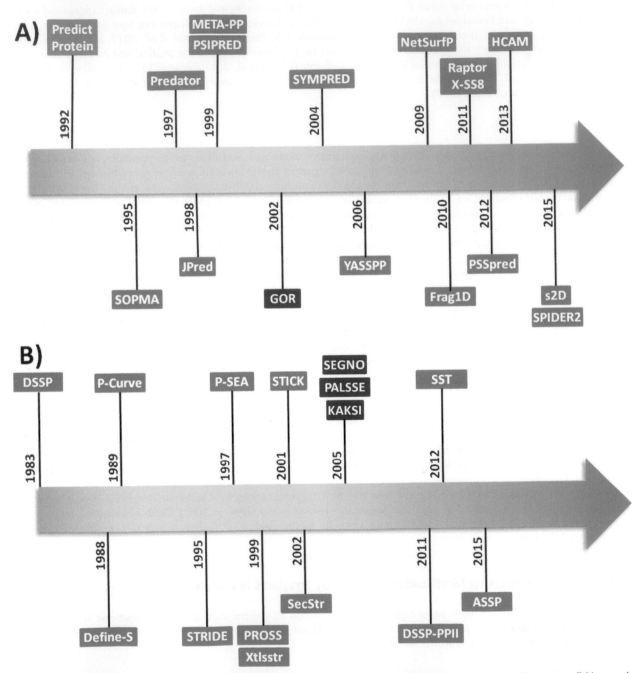

Fig. 10   (A) Timeline of protein secondary structure prediction algorithms. Boxes colored in blue indicate that the algorithms are available as web-server only, while those in green are available as standalone. GOR method, colored in red is available as a web-server as well as standalone program; (B) Timeline of protein secondary structure assignment algorithms. Boxes colored in blue suggest that the algorithm uses 3D geometry, while programs in green colored boxes use ((φ), ψ) and/ or H-bond patterns for SSE assignment. Algorithms in red colored box are hybrid methods.

type of major SSEs. This method is almost 50%–60% accurate in predicting SSEs (Kabsch and Sander, 1983a,b) that is significantly less than the modern machine learning-based techniques (Mount, 2004).

The GOR method (Garnier *et al.*, 1978), named after three scientists Garnier, Osguthorpe and Robson, is an information theory-based method and Bayesian in nature. The GOR method considers the probability of each amino acid having a secondary structure as well as the conditional probability of the amino acid in each structure given that its immediate neighbors have already formed that structure. The original GOR method predicted the secondary structures with roughly 65% accuracy. The original method is more successful in predicting α-helices than β-strands (Mount, 2004).

Methods like PSIPRED (Jones, 1999), SPINE (Dor and Zhou, 2007) and JPRED (Drozdetskiy *et al.*, 2015) are based on neural networks and predict the secondary structures with over 70% accuracy. SPINE-X (Faraggi *et al.*, 2009) algorithm can accurately predict the dihedral angles of the residues and hence improved the *ab-initio* structure prediction of proteins.

Apart from using only amino acid sequence, considering various other factors like effect of local environment (Zhong and Johnson, 1992), solvent accessibility of residues (Macdonald and Johnson, 2001) and protein structural class (Costantini *et al.*, 2006) can improve the SSE prediction as they also affect the SSEs in proteins (Adamczak *et al.*, 2005; Costantini *et al.*, 2007; Momen-Roknabadi *et al.*, 2008). Though the recent improvement produces a better prediction of SSEs and in particular β-strands, still the constraints to the prediction has not reached and continue to rise (Rost, 2001; Yang *et al.*, 2016).

Assigning SSEs to 3D Structures

Knowing the importance of secondary structures as well as the increase in the number of experimentally solved 3D structures, several methods have been proposed over the years to identify the SSEs from the given 3D structure of proteins. Secondary structures possess regularities in various geometric parameters like C^α distances, dihedral angles and specific patterns of H-bonds that can be utilized as criteria to define them. In general, most of the methods can correctly identify the location of the core of helices and strands in proteins. However, precise assignment of termini is still a problem as they are very often ill-defined and difficult to determine unambiguously. These methods can be broadly classified into three categories: (1) algorithms based on $((\varphi), \psi)$ and/ or H-bond patterns (2) algorithms based on 3D geometry and (3) hybrid methods, which use both (1) and (2). Programs like DSSP (Kabsch and Sander, 1983a,b; Touw *et al.*, 2015), STRIDE (Frishman and Argos, 1995) and PROSS (Srinivasan and Rose, 1999) fall into the first category, DEFINE (Richards and Kundrot, 1988), P-CURVE (Sklenar *et al.*, 1989), P-SEA (Labesse *et al.*, 1997), SST (Konagurthu *et al.*, 2012) and ASSP (Kumar and Bansal, 2015a,b) come under second category, whereas KAKSI (Martin *et al.*, 2005) and PALSSE (Majumdar *et al.*, 2005) fall under the third category. A few programs that specifically identify π (Fodje and Al-Karadaghi, 2002) and PPII (Cubellis *et al.*, 2005; King and Johnson, 1999; Mansiaux *et al.*, 2011; Srinivasan and Rose, 1999) -helices have also been developed.

The first ever automated method for SSE assignment was developed by Levitt and Greer (1977) who used distance and virtual torsion angle made by C^α atoms over a sliding window of four residues. Breakthrough in assigning SSEs came with the introduction of more comprehensive and widely used algorithm known as 'Dictionary of Secondary Structure of Proteins' (DSSP) (Kabsch and Sander, 1983a,b; Touw *et al.*, 2015) that is based on the detection of H-bond patterns defined by an electrostatic criterion. DSSP is considered as the gold standard for SSE assignment and used in number of software packages like Rasmol (Sayle and Milner-White, 1995) and GROMACS analysis tools (Berendsen *et al.*, 1995). DEFINE-S (Richards and Kundrot, 1988) uses only C^α coordinates, compares their distances with the distances in ideal SSEs and also provides information about the super-secondary structures. P-CURVE (Sklenar *et al.*, 1989) assigns SSEs based on the helicoidal parameters and global peptide axis for peptide units. Another widely used algorithm known as STRIDE (Frishman and Argos, 1995) uses $((\varphi), \psi)$ along with H-bond pattern. STRIDE has been implemented in a visualization tool VMD (Humphrey *et al.*, 1996) for assigning SSEs. P-SEA (Labesse *et al.*, 1997) uses a short C^α distance mask and two C^α dihedral angles to assigns SSEs, while PROSS (Srinivasan and Rose, 1999) is solely based on backbone dihedral angles. Another algorithm, Xtlsstr (King and Johnson, 1999) calculates backbone dihedral angles as well as distances and assigns SSEs that would be consistent with interactions of amide-amide groups observed from circular dichroism of a protein in the ultraviolet range. SECSTR (Fodje and Al-Karadaghi, 2002) is more sensitive to the π-helices. Using SECSTR, for the first time, authors reported the biasness of DSSP and STRIDE towards the α-helices. However the latest version of DSSP (Touw *et al.*, 2015) has addressed this problem and tried resolving it (Kumar and Bansal, 2015a,b). The algorithm PALSSE (Majumdar *et al.*, 2005) mainly uses distance and torsion angle constraints to identify core elements and later extends them to longer segments. Authors claim to assign SSEs up to 80% of the protein structure. KAKSI (Martin *et al.*, 2005) uses C^α distances and backbone dihedral angles to show the concordance with the assignments found in the PDB (Berman *et al.*, 2000) files. Another algorithm SST (Konagurthu *et al.*, 2012) uses minimum message length inference for the assignment of SSEs in protein structures. A comparatively new method 'Assignment of Secondary Structure in Proteins' (ASSP) uses only the path traversed by the C^α atoms of the consecutive residues (Kumar and Bansal, 2015a,b) and is an extension of HELANAL-Plus (Bansal *et al.*, 2000; Kumar and Bansal, 2012), a program for analysis of geometry of helices in proteins. The algorithm is based on the premise that a protein structure can be divided into uniform stretches that can be defined in terms of helical parameters and depending on their values, the stretches can be further classified into different SSEs, viz. α, 3_{10}, π, extended β-strands, PPII and other left-handed helices. Another, recently reported algorithm (Cao *et al.*, 2015) identifies α-helices along with 3_{10} and π-helices by dividing it into a minimization problem and a restraint satisfaction problem. It follows rigorously the geometry of helices. Brief description about various algorithms is tabulated in **Table 3** and **Fig. 10(B)**.

Table 3 Brief description of different secondary structure assignment algorithms

Sl. No.	Algorithm	Description	Reference
Category (i)			
1	DSSP	Detects the H-bond patterns using bond energy criterion	Kabsch and Sander (1983a,b)
2	STRIDE	Uses $((\varphi), \psi)$ along with H-bond pattern	Frishman and Argos (1995)
3	PROSS*	Uses only on the backbone dihedral angles $((\varphi), \psi)$	Srinivasan and Rose (1999)
4	SECSTR	Uses DSSP like H-bond definition and was developed to identify and analyze π-helices	Fodje and Al-Karadaghi (2002)
5	DSSP-PPII*	Identifies the PPII-helices in the region not assigned as a major SSE by DSSP and gives the output in the DSSP format	Mansiaux et al. (2011)
Category (ii)			
6	Levitt et al.	Uses distance and virtual torsion angle made by the C^α atoms over a sliding window of four residues	Levitt and Greer (1977)
7	DEFINE-S	Uses only C^α coordinates and compares the distance between various C^αs with the distances in ideal SSEs	Richards and Kundrot (1988)
8	P-CURVE	To start with, it chooses the successive repeating unit and does the analysis of mathematical analysis of protein curvature	Sklenar et al. (1989)
9	P-SEA	Solely based on the C^α atoms. Uses three distance, one angle and one dihedral angle	Labesse et al. (1997)
10	XTLSSTR*	Calculates two angles and three distances for assigning SSEs. The algorithm is driven by the concept of circular dichroism (CD) of a protein in the far ultraviolet range.	King and Johnson (1999)
11	STICK	Finds a set of best fit axes and later takes the average rise of the residues along each axis	Taylor (2001)
12	SST	Uses minimum message length inference for SSEs assignment	Konagurthu et al. (2012)
13	ASSP*	Use C^α atoms to identify the continuous stretches and later divides them into different SSEs	Kumar and Bansal (2015a,b)
Category (iii)			
13	KAKSI	Uses C^α distances and backbone dihedral angles to show the concordance with the assignments found in the Protein Data Bank	Martin et al. (2005)
14	PALSSE	Mainly uses distance and torsion angle constraints to identify core elements and later extends them to longer segments	Majumdar et al. (2005)
15	SEGNO*	The C^α atoms along with the backbone dihedral angles $((\varphi), \psi)$ and the angle-distance H-bond	Cubellis et al. (2005)

Source: Sklenar, H., Etchebest, C., Lavery, R., 1989. Describing protein structure: A general algorithm yielding complete helicoidal parameters and a unique overall axis. Proteins: Structure, Function, and Bioinformatics 6, 46–60.
The algorithms are divided according to the categories mentioned in the main text. Algorithms marked by '*' identify PPII-helices also along with other SSEs.

A comparative analysis of number of residues identified as being part of α-helices by different algorithms suggests that there is on an average $\sim 80\%$ agreement (Kumar and Bansal, 2015a,b). However, it has also been observed that many algorithms prefer α-helices over π- or 3_{10}-helices (Fodje and Al-Karadaghi, 2002; Kumar and Bansal, 2015a,b; Shelar et al., 2013). For example, residues Thr87-Leu134 of Oxidoreductase protein (PDB ID: 1SYY: A) have different residue-wise assignments by various algorithms. Surprisingly the program XTLSSTR assigned extended β-strand to the residues Glu120-Ala121, whereas the same segment remained unassigned by ASSP and DSSP (**Fig. 11**). Differences in the assignments by various algorithms suggest that one cannot have a single algorithm that works well for every protein structure and hence one should be careful in selecting an algorithm.

Experimental Approaches for Identification of Secondary Structures

Circular dichroism (CD): CD uses the differential absorption of left- and right-handed light by chromophores with intrinsic chirality or placed in a chiral environment. Proteins, in general, contain various chromophores that engender CD signals. CD spectroscopy can provide the information about the SSEs content, any conformational changes upon ligand binding or macromolecular interactions. The thermal stability of the biomolecule can also be studied (Kelly and Price, 2000). The CD spectrum obtained in the far UV region (260–190 nm) corresponding to the peptide bond absorption can delineate the content of SSEs like α-helix and β-sheet; whereas the spectrum in near UV region (320–260 nm) provides an information about the environment around the aromatic amino acids or chromophores and hence about the tertiary structure. Units used in CD are ellipticity (measured in millidegrees and represented as θ) or mean residue ellipticity (MRE and represented as $[\theta]$). Several web-servers use MRE values from the CD-spectrum to provide the percentage SSE content of the protein (Louis-Jeune et al., 2012; Micsonai et al., 2015; Perez-Iratxeta and Andrade-Navarro, 2008; Sreerama and Woody, 2000; Whitmore and Wallace, 2004; Wiedemann et al., 2013). Web-servers are also available to predict the CD

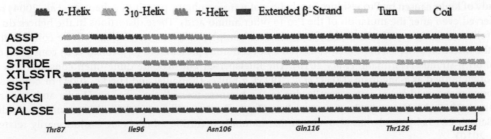

Fig. 11 Pictorial representation comparing the secondary structure assigned by different algorithms. Amino acid residues Thr87-Leu134 of Oxidoreductase protein (PDB ID: 1SYY; chain: A) is taken as an example.

spectrum of a modelled protein (Bulheller and Hirst, 2009; Mavridis and Janes, 2017). The updated version of CD is Synchrotron radiation circular dichroism (SRCD) spectroscopy that enhances the usage of conventional CD. The high light flux allows the collection of data at lower wavelengths, detection of spectra with higher signal-to-noise levels and measurements in the presence of strongly absorbing solvents also. Please refer to the reviews elsewhere (Kelly *et al.*, 2005; Kelly and Price, 2000; Miles and Wallace, 2006; Wallace, 2009) for better understanding and recent progresses in the field. CD and SRCD spectra as well as metadata can be deposited to open access data bank named PCDDB (Whitmore *et al.*, 2017).

Knowledge of the 3D structures of biomolecules helps in understanding their function. At the same time, they can also provide an information about the SSEs that may be more accurate than CD. X-ray crystallography, NMR or cryo-electron microscopy are the most commonly used methods for solving 3D structures.

X-ray crystallography: this field uses the fundamentals of X-ray diffraction and mathematical approaches to symmetry to solve the structure of a biomolecule. Since 1957, the year in which the first crystal structure of myoglobin (Kendrew *et al.*, 1958) was solved, the field has helped researchers to understand the cellular processes in more detail and facilitated the advancement of modern medicines as well. The field has attracted more than 25 Nobel Prizes, starting in 1915 with the Bragg father-and-son team. Though the work on DNA double helix fetched noble prize to Watson and Crick in 1953, the structure of a 12-base-pair palindromic DNA was finally solved in 1980 by the X-ray crystallography method (Wing *et al.*, 1980). As of now, 30th September 2017, almost 90% of the total deposited structures in PDB are solved by this method. Few recent reviews elsewhere (Garman, 2014; Ilari and Savino, 2008; Powell, 2016; Shi, 2014; Smyth and Martin, 2000) can be an interesting read.

Nuclear Magnetic Resonance (NMR): two independent studies laid the foundation for a new technique, NMR (Bloch, 1946; Purcell *et al.*, 1946). For this pioneer work, Edward Mills Purcell and Felix Bloch received the 1952 Nobel Prize in Physics. NMR exploits the magnetic properties of certain atomic nuclei and can provide detailed information about the structure, dynamics, reaction state, and chemical environment of molecules. As of 30th September 2017, almost 12,000 three-dimension structures solved by NMR have been deposited in PDB. For better understanding of NMR spectroscopy, one can refer to available books (Abraham, 1978; Callaghan, 1993; Hore, 2015).

Cryo-electron microscopy (Cryo-EM): use of electrons in place of X-rays has a lot of advantages as they can be scattered more strongly and can be accelerated by electric fields. 3D structures of large biological assemblies in solution or cell can be well studied using 3D electron microscopy (3DEM) (Frank, 2011). Application of EM in biological specimens has seen a steep rise in popularity since the first electron microscope was developed and bacteriophages were imaged by the Ruska brothers (Ruska, 1941; Ruska *et al.*, 1939). Cryo-EM imaging technique requires much less sample compare to NMR or X-ray crystallography and have fewer restrictions on sample purity. There are mainly three categories of cryo-EM namely (1) Cryo-electron tomography, (2) single-particle cryo-EM and (3) electron crystallography. These sub-disciplines are either used in isolation or combined with other techniques to analyze biological structures in different contexts. The recent advancements in direct electron detectors have improved the resolution of the structures solved by cryo-EM such that in atomic resolution is now achievable (Grigorieff, 2013; Ruskin *et al.*, 2013). The gain in popularity of this method can be gauged by the fact that many reviews detailing the methodological advances are published every year (Milne *et al.*, 2013). Currently there are almost 1750 structures, solved by EM that have been deposited in PDB.

Distortions in Regular SSEs

The departure from the ideal values of the geometric parameters for a given SSE is often called distortions and most of the SSEs in protein structure possess it. Occurrence of $(i + 4 \rightarrow i)$ NH...O H-bonds between the amino acids in the main-chain, makes the α-helices quite uniform in terms of geometric parameters. However, most helices in proteins are curved (Barlow and Thornton, 1988; Kumar and Bansal, 1998) and deviate from the ideal values of defining parameters that can be because of the solvent induced distortions (Blundell *et al.*, 1983), peptide bond distortions (Barlow and Thornton, 1988; Love *et al.*, 1972) or presence of Pro (Chakrabarti *et al.*, 1986; MacArthur and Thornton, 1996). Blundell and coworkers (Blundell *et al.*, 1983) did the first survey on the curvature of helices to conclude that the majority of the helices are curved. Distortions caused by Pro residues (Chakrabarti *et al.*, 1986; Chakrabarti and Chakrabarti, 1998; MacArthur and Thornton, 1996; Sankararamakrishnan and Vishveshwara, 1990, 1992), Ser and Thr residues (Ballesteros *et al.*, 2000; Deupi *et al.*, 2004) residues have also been studied. An interesting study of kinks caused by Pro residues in α-helices of transmembrane proteins (Yohannan *et al.*, 2004) reveals that the kinks are preserved even after the mutation of the Pro to other amino acids. These distortions in the helices do not allow the helix axis to follow a straight path. Recently, the analyses of simple insertions in α-helices of the coiled-coil structure has revealed that the insertion switches the coiled-coils into a novel fibrous protein fold (α/β coiled-coil) consisting of periodically interspersed short β-strands (Hartmann *et al.*, 2016). The interspersed π-helices are quite often considered as distortions in α-helices and often termed as α-aneurisms (Keefe *et al.*, 1993), α-bulges (Cartailler and Luecke, 2004) or π-bulges (Hardy *et al.*, 2000). The above mentioned belief was generally due to the biasness towards the α-helices (Fodje and Al-Karadaghi, 2002; Kumar and Bansal, 2015a,b). However, the presence of π or 3_{10}-helix distorts the entire helical segment by providing large bend (Kumar and Bansal, 2015a,b). Study has also shown that naturally occurring π-helices are evolutionarily related to α-helices (Cooley *et al.*, 2010).

Distortions in β-strands have also been reported (Blake and Oatley, 1977; Richardson *et al.*, 1978). One such distortion is a β-bulge that can be defined as a region between two consecutive β-type H-bonds that includes two residues on one strand and a single residue on the other strand (Richardson *et al.*, 1978). They occur very frequently in the coil regions, but are most easily visualized as local distortions in anti-parallel strands. Compared to parallel β-strands, it is generally believed that the anti-parallel strands are more stable as they can withstand greater twisting and other distortions like β-bulges and exposure to solvents. Only about 5% of the β-bulges were found between parallel strands (Richardson, 1981). Though β-bulges can be classified into several types, classic β-bulge occurs most frequently in the protein structures followed by 'G1', 'Wide' and 'parallel and GX' bulges. Classic β-bulge occurs between a narrow pair of H-bonds on anti-parallel strands and has the side chains of constituent residues in the same side of the β sheet, while G1 bulges can be defined as a classic bulge with Gly residue at the position 1. 'Wide type' β-bulges occur between a widely spaced pair of H-bonds on anti-parallel strands. GX bulges are the most unusual bulges and often contain Gly residue at position X. β-bulges affect the directionalities of the protein chain in the 3D structure, making them useful for determining the large features of β-sheet and/or extended hairpin loops.

A twist in the β-strands of a sheet can also be considered as a distortion as it introduces local conformational irregularities into the polypeptide backbone. Nevertheless, an extremely strong local twist helps to close the anti-parallel β-barrels containing five or six strands. Sheets with a right handed twist are more common and have a lower free energy than their straight or left-handed counterparts (Chothia, 1973).

Protein Structure and Sequence Repositories

PDB (Berman *et al.*, 2000) is the most comprehensive repository of structure data for biological macromolecules. The repository contains the primary structure and secondary structure information along with the atomic coordinates of a constituent atoms of biomolecule. It also contains corresponding experimental data. PDB101, an education portal of PDB provides detailed information about the PDB. As of 27th September 2017, PDB contains structure data for 133,920 Biological Macromolecular Structures (**Fig. 12**). On an average, the length of proteins ranges between 100 and 300 residues. However, there are big proteins containing 1000 or more residues as well as small proteins with at most 30 residues.

A dedicated data bank, EMDataBank (Lawson *et al.*, 2016), is also available online at EMDataBank (see Relevant Websites section) that is a unified global portal for deposition and retrieval of 3DEM density maps, atomic models, associated metadata and related stuffs. It has 5195 EMDB map entries, 1805 PDB coordinate entries as of 30th September 2017.

The 3D structures of experimentally-determined nucleic acids and complex assemblies can be deposited into a databank called nucleic acid database (NDB) (Coimbatore Narayanan *et al.*, 2014). The repository contains the sequences of the corresponding nucleic acid chain along with the derived geometric data, classifications of structures and motifs, standards for describing nucleic acid features. It is also linked to various software for the analyses. As of 27th September 2017, number of released structures in NDB is 9133.

Apart from PDB, NCBI (Geer *et al.*, 2010) and UniProt (Consortium, 2015) databases also provide comprehensive, high-quality and freely accessible resource of protein sequence and functional information. Another very important database, Pfam (Punta *et al.*, 2012), contains a large collection of protein families, each represented by multiple sequence alignments and Hidden Markov Models. The PDB ID of the members of each family is linked to the PDB database.

Several initiatives have been taken in the past to classify proteins into groups based on properties that are shared by all protein members of a group. Different properties such as structural similarity, sequence similarity and functional similarity have been employed to classify proteins. Classifying proteins in such a manner is especially useful in functional annotation of proteins which are newly discovered from genome sequence data. Also, it has been useful in predicting tentative structures for proteins with no 3D structural data.

Protein 3D Structure Prediction and Analyses

Protein structure prediction and engineering-design aim to fill the huge gap between the sequence and structure space. The protein structure prediction methods can be categorized into mainly three parts (1) *ab initio* methods (2) Threading (3) Homology modelling. The evolutionary information from the genomic sequences can be utilized efficiently to compute the protein 3D structures from their amino acid sequences (Marks *et al.*, 2012). The *ab initio (de-novo)* methods are based on the first

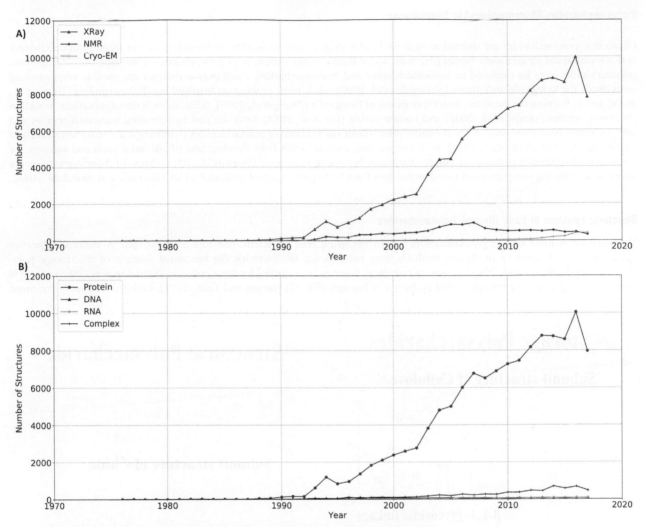

Fig. 12 Number of 3D structures deposited in the PDB on yearly basis as of 30th September 2017.

principle laws of physics as well as chemistry and based on the fact that the native structure of protein is always at energy minimum. Using this method, modelling a protein sequence of length >150 residues can be a challenge. However, the *de-novo* design of peptides using the computer-aided parameterization offers one solution. Even, the *de-novo* protein design can be used to create small stable proteins that can bind to any specific therapeutic targets (Chevalier *et al.*, 2017). Another method, threading or fold recognition searches the protein structure template in a library with lowest possible energy for the query sequence. Homology modelling or comparative modelling uses the protein sequence identity between the input protein sequence and sequence of the template structure to construct the 3D structure. Hence better identity between query and target sequence will fetch a better modelled structure.

Plethora of review articles are available on strategies and challenges to protein structure prediction (Bonneau and Baker, 2001; Dorn *et al.*, 2014; Floudas *et al.*, 2006; Kc, 2016; Petrey and Honig, 2005).

Once the structure is modelled, it is always advised to check its quality using PROCHECK (Laskowski *et al.*, 1993), MOL-PROBITY (Chen *et al.*, 2010), VERIFY_3D (Bowie *et al.*, 1991; Luthy *et al.*, 1992) and WHAT_CHECK (Hooft *et al.*, 1996). 3D structures of proteins open doors for various other structural analyses like functional annotation, interaction pathway analyses, target drug identification. Proteins in a cell cannot work alone and need interacting partners that can be a small molecule or biomolecule. Protein-protein interactions are mediated by hydrophobic interactions as well as H-bonds (De Las Rivas and Fontanillo, 2010). Understanding the importance of these interactions is vital in design and engineering of functional assemblies. The functional importance of the non-bonded interactions in assembly of biomolecular structures has been analyzed and firmly established through studies on DNA-protein (Mandel-Gutfreund *et al.*, 1998), RNA-protein (Wilson and Nierhaus, 2003), protein-protein (Singh *et al.*, 2003; Zondlo, 2010) and protein-ligand interactions (Panigrahi and Desiraju, 2007). Knowing the importance of these interactions, many algorithms have been developed over the years (Babu, 2003; Kumar *et al.*, 2014; Lindauer *et al.*, 1996; McDonald and Thornton, 1994; Tina *et al.*, 2007; Tiwari and Panigrahi, 2007).

Polysaccharides-Macromolecular Biopolymer

Classically, polysaccharides are defined as high molecular weight macromolecules composed of two or more monosaccharides that are connected by glycosidic bonds (Aspinall, 1985; Bochkov and Zaikov, 2016). Depending on the type of building units, polysaccharides may be classified as homosaccharides and heterosaccharides. Most polysaccharides are used as energy-storing units inside the living cells and tissues (Nonogaki et al., 2000), while some of them are involved in cellular signaling (Tincer et al., 2015) and in forming the protective outer membrane of living cells (Zhang et al., 2016). It has some in vitro applications as well in pharmacy, textiles (Sanghi et al., 2007) and nanomaterials (Lin et al., 2012). Over the past two decades, numerous reviews and symposia have been published on the structure, metabolism and function of polysaccharides (Ramberg et al., 2010; Srivastava and Kulshreshtha, 1989; Zong et al., 2012). With the growing interest in this field, development of advanced tools and software for prediction of secondary structure of polysaccharides is becoming imperative (Pérez et al., 2014). Most of these approaches are aimed at developing computational based techniques from NMR parameters of polysaccharides (Toukach and Ananikov, 2013).

Structural Features of Food Storage Polysaccharides

The three main food storage polysaccharides within the living cells are starch, cellulose and glycogen. A molecular genetics approach and 3D structure prediction methods have been chosen to determine the functional domain of the storage polysaccharides (Hostinová et al., 2003). Sequence homology has also been applied for these purposes (Svensson et al., 1989). Starch is formed when glucoses are linearly linked up by α 1–4 linkages (**Fig. 13**) (Brown and Kelly, 1993). Cellulose is mainly produced

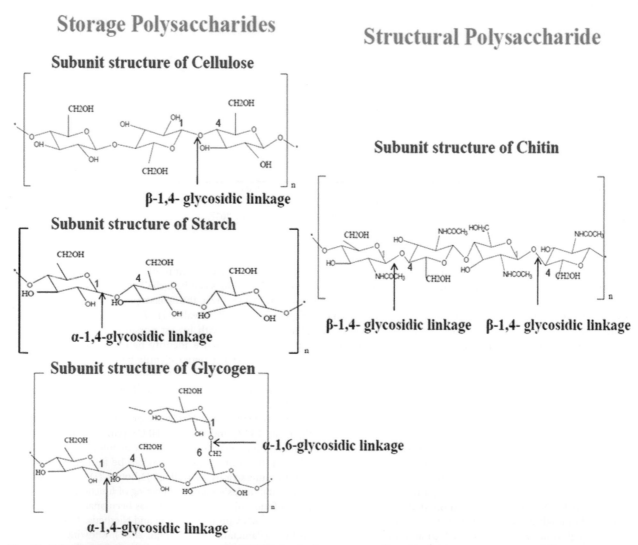

Fig. 13 Subunit structures of some common storage and structural polysaccharides. All structures are created by using ChemDraw Ultra software. Rhodes, D., Lipps, H.J., 2015. G-quadruplexes and their regulatory roles in biology. Nucleic Acids Research 43, 8627–8637.

from the hydrated form of some bacteria (e.g., Acetobactor Xylinum) (Ross *et al.*, 1987) containing thousands of beta-D-glucopyranose units.

Glycogen is the multi-branched polysaccharides of glucose. It serves as a form of energy storage in humans, animals, fungi, and bacteria (Arrese and Soulages, 2010). There are two types of linkages, mainly 1–4 linkages are found in the straight part where as 1–6 linkages are found in the branched part. The straight part is helically twisted in nature and containing six glucose units per turn.

Structural Features of Chitin Polysaccharides

Structural polysaccharides are mainly involved in forming cell walls of different plants and animals. Chitin and cellulose both are the examples of structural polysaccharides. Chitin is a naturally abundant mucopolysaccharide (Sekiguchi *et al.*, 1994), It consists of 2-acetamido-2-deoxy-β-D-glucose through a β $(1 \rightarrow 4)$ linkage (Muzzarelli, 1973).

Polysaccharide 3D Structure Prediction and Analyses

Polysaccharides and their glycol-conjugates play an important role in cell-cell adhesion (Gribova *et al.*, 2011), inflammation (Jiang *et al.*, 2010) and immune activity (Yang *et al.*, 2009; Yongxu and Jicheng, 2008). Therefore secondary structure predictions of polysaccharides become a crucial thing in understanding the biological phenomenon (Dwek, 1996). Secondary structures possess regularities in various geometric and conformational parameters like glycosidic angles and specific patterns of H-bonds. Several computational techniques have been developed for analyzing the conformations of polysaccharides *in vacuo* (Wormald *et al.*, 2002). Monte Carlo methods (Peters *et al.*, 1993) and genetic algorithms (Nahmany *et al.*, 2005) have also been used for these purpose. Molecular dynamics simulations were carried out using GROMACS software (Van Der Spoel *et al.*, 2005) with OPLS-AA force field (Jorgensen *et al.*, 1996). Carb-builder is one of the software that is used to build the molecular models of complex oligosaccharides or polysaccharides (Kuttel *et al.*, 2016). POLY 2.0 is another open source software (Engelsen *et al.*, 2014). It can generate complex branched carbohydrates and polysaccharides structures using data from their optimized building mono-saccharides and glycosidic linkages. SWEEt *also* serves the same purpose. It is a web-based software that quickly forms reliable three dimensional structures of polysaccharides from their preliminary sequence information (Bohne *et al.*, 1999). Advanced version of the SWEET only generates one of the conformations out of the manifold. Generated structure shows all the glycosidic linkages with reported variation of phi, psi and omega values. Sugar folding, a computer based tool is also used to predict the conformation of complex oligosaccharides in solution (Xia *et al.*, 2007). There is an effective software CASPER, used to determine the structure of the branched oligosaccharides and polysaccharides (Stenutz *et al.*, 1998). The CASPER program was developed for the analysis of the primary structures of oligosaccharides and for polysaccharides with repeating units. The approach is based mainly on NMR spectroscopy. Once the structure is modelled, we can visualize the secondary structures by SweetUnityMol, which is one of the specific computer graphics based software and can depict the complex interactions within polysaccharides (Pérez *et al.*, 2014).

Recent Advancement

A lot of polysaccharide structures have been elucidated from the crystallography in the last few years. Though the actual structure-function relationship is not yet established for many polysaccharides due to their diverse and complex structure. For the last three decades, besides the computer based tools, advanced NMR spectroscopy has also played an important role in determination of the structure of polysaccharides. A lot of advanced NMR techniques have been used, such as COSY (Lack *et al.*, 2007; Sinha *et al.*, 2010), NOESY (Fedonenko *et al.*, 2002; Larocque *et al.*, 2003; Linker *et al.*, 2001), TOCSY (Johnson and Pinto, 2002; Kjellberg *et al.*, 1998; Maciel *et al.*, 2008), HETCOR (Cescutti *et al.*, 1993) and NOE (Martin-Pastor and Bush, 1999; Michael *et al.*, 2002; Yamasaki and Bacon, 1991). Advancements in NMR methods with potential applications towards polysaccharide studies open a new area of research. Coarse grained molecular simulations (Bathe *et al.*, 2005; Wohlert and Berglund, 2011) can also provide some new insights in this field.

Closing Remarks: How Close Are We?

Lack of enough number of 3D structures and presence of more number of atoms that can interact to each other, make the SSE prediction and assignment difficult for nucleic acids. In contrast to di-peptide, di-nucleotide has got more flexibility as they have seven back bone torsion angles compared to only three in di-peptide. For example, there is an exponential increase in the number of possible structures with increase in the length of RNA (Zuker and Sankoff, 1984). A nucleic acid chain with 100 nucleotides has more than 10^{25} possible secondary structures (Mathews, 2006). Further, the discovery of RNA thermometers in 1989 (Altuvia *et al.*, 1989), made things more complicated as it was found that certain types of sequences can be very sensitive to change in temperature.

For a given protein structure, there is not a consensus in identifying SSEs. Especially, the termini of SSEs are not defined uniformly. In general, they have an agreement of about 80%. Many less frequently occurring SSEs like π-helices and PPII-helices are not defined in clear cut way. In fact, none of the available algorithms can identify 2.2_7-helices. Same holds true for the prediction of SSEs for any input sequence, but the accuracy of their prediction is improving with the increase in the number of 3D structures of proteins. Are we able to design a desired protein structure with natural amino acids? Answer is not a perfect yes. Are we able to incorporate the enzymatic activities in a designed peptides or proteins? Though the answer to this question can be yes, it will be with a caveat: the activity is far less than that in the native protein. A lot of work has been done, but there is still a long way to go. For example, information on which amino acids favour 3_{10} or π-helical conformations over α-helices, is still not clear. However, we are slowly and steadily reaching towards the goal and increasing number of 3D structures, as well as computational studies are playing a major role in understanding these features.

See also: *Ab initio* Protein Structure Prediction. Algorithms for Structure Comparison and Analysis: Docking. Algorithms for Structure Comparison and Analysis: Homology Modelling of Proteins. Algorithms for Structure Comparison and Analysis: Prediction of Tertiary Structures of Proteins. Biological Database Searching. Natural Language Processing Approaches in Bioinformatics. Sequence Analysis. Sequence Composition

References

Abraham, R.J., 1978. Nuclear Magnetic Resonance. Royal Society of Chemistry.

Abrahams, J.P., van den Berg, M., van Batenburg, E., Pleij, C., 1990. Prediction of RNA secondary structure, including pseudoknotting, by computer simulation. Nucleic Acids Research 18, 3035–3044.

Adamczak, R., Porollo, A., Meller, J., 2005. Combining prediction of secondary structure and solvent accessibility in proteins. Proteins 59, 467–475.

Adzhubei, A.A., Sternberg, M.J., 1993. Left-handed polyproline II helices commonly occur in globular proteins. Journal of Molecular Biology 229, 472–493.

Altuvia, S., Kornitzer, D., Teff, D., Oppenheim, A.B., 1989. Alternative mRNA structures of the cIII gene of bacteriophage lambda determine the rate of its translation initiation. Journal of Molecular Biology 210, 265–280.

Andreeva, A., Howorth, D., Chothia, C., *et al.*, 2014. SCOP2 prototype: A new approach to protein structure mining. Nucleic Acids Research 42, D310–D314.

Arrese, E.L., Soulages, J.L., 2010. Insect fat body: Energy, metabolism, and regulation. Annual Review of Entomology 55, 207–225.

Aspinall, G.O., 1985. The Polysaccharides, 3. Academic Press.

Babu, M.M., 2003. NCI: A server to identify non-canonical interactions in protein structures. Nucleic Acids Research 31, 3345–3348.

Ballesteros, J.A., Deupi, X., Olivella, M., *et al.*, 2000. Serine and threonine residues bend α-helices in the $\chi 1= g-$ conformation. Biophysical Journal 79, 2754–2760.

Bansal, M., 1999. D.N.A. structure: Yet another avatar? Current Science 76, 1178–1181.

Bansal, M., Bhattacharyya, D., Ravi, B., 1995. NUPARM and NUCGEN: Software for analysis and generation of sequence dependent nucleic acid structures. Computer Applications in the Biosciences: CABIOS 11, 281–287.

Bansal, M., Kumar, S., Velavan, R., 2000. HELANAL: A program to characterize helix geometry in proteins. Journal of Biomolecular Structure and Dynamics 17, 811–819.

Bansal, M., Srinivasan, N., 2013. Biomolecular Forms and Functions: A Celebration of 50 Years of the Ramachandran Map. World Scientific.

Barlow, D.J., Thornton, J.M., 1988. Helix geometry in proteins. Journal of Molecular Biology 201, 601–619.

Bathe, M., Rutledge, G.C., Grodzinsky, A.J., Tidor, B., 2005. A coarse-grained molecular model for glycosaminoglycans: Application to chondroitin, chondroitin sulfate, and hyaluronic acid. Biophysical Journal 88, 3870–3887.

Bellaousov, S., Mathews, D.H., 2010. ProbKnot: Fast prediction of RNA secondary structure including pseudoknots. RNA 16, 1870–1880.

Bellaousov, S., Reuter, J.S., Seetin, M.G., Mathews, D.H., 2013. RNAstructure: Web servers for RNA secondary structure prediction and analysis. Nucleic Acids Research 41, W471–W474.

Benabou, S., Avino, A., Eritja, R., *et al.*, 2014. Fundamental aspects of the nucleic acid i-motif structures. RSC Advances 4, 26956–26980.

Berendsen, H.J., van der Spoel, D., van Drunen, R., 1995. GROMACS: A message-passing parallel molecular dynamics implementation. Computer Physics Communications 91, 43–56.

Berisio, R., Vitagliano, L., 2012. Polyproline and triple helix motifs in host-pathogen recognition. Current Protein & Peptide Science 13, 855–865.

Berman, H.M., Westbrook, J., Feng, Z., *et al.*, 2000. The protein data bank. Nucleic Acids Research 28, 235–242.

Besnard, E., Babled, A., Lapasset, L., *et al.*, 2012. Unraveling cell type-specific and reprogrammable human replication origin signatures associated with G-quadruplex consensus motifs. Nature Structural & Molecular Biology 19, 837–844.

Bhattacharjee, A., Bansal, M., 2005. Collagen structure: The Madras triple helix and the current scenario. IUBMB Life 57, 161–172.

Bhattacharyya, D., Halder, S., Basu, S., *et al.*, 2017. RNAHelix: Computational modeling of nucleic acid structures with Watson–Crick and non-canonical base pairs. Journal of Computer-Aided Molecular Design 31, 219–235.

Birney, E., Stamatoyannopoulos, J.A., Dutta, A., *et al.*, 2007. Identification and analysis of functional elements in 1% of the human genome by the ENCODE pilot project. Nature 447, 799–816.

Blake, C.C.F., Oatley, S.J., 1977. Protein-DNA and protein-hormone interactions in prealbumin: A model of the thyroid hormone nuclear receptor? Nature 268, 115–120.

Blake, C.C., Koenig, D.F., Mair, G.A., *et al.*, 1965. Structure of hen egg-white lysozyme. A three-dimensional Fourier synthesis at 2 Angstrom resolution. Nature 206, 757–761.

Blanchet, C., Pasi, M., Zakrzewska, K., Lavery, R., 2011. CURVES + web server for analyzing the helical, backbone and groove parameters of nucleic acid structures. Nucleic Acids Research 39, W68–W73.

Bloch, F., 1946. Nuclear induction. Physical Review 70, 460.

Blundell, T., Barlow, D., Borkakoti, N., Thornton, J., 1983. Solvent-induced distortions and the curvature of alpha-helices. Nature 306, 281–283.

Bochkov, AFe, Zaikov, G.E., 2016. Chemistry of the O-Glycosidic Bond: Formation and Cleavage. Elsevier.

Bohne, A., Lang, E., von der Lieth, C.-W., 1999. SWEET-WWW-based rapid 3D construction of oligo-and polysaccharides. Bioinformatics (Oxford, England) 15, 767–768.

Bonneau, R., Baker, D., 2001. Ab initio protein structure prediction: Progress and prospects. Annual Review of Biophysics and Biomolecular Structure 30, 173–189.

Boudard, M., Barth, D., Bernauer, J., *et al.*, 2017. GARN2: Coarse-grained prediction of 3D structure of large RNA molecules by regret minimization. Bioinformatics. btx175.

Boudvillain, M., de Lencastre, A., Pyle, A.M., 2000. A tertiary interaction that links active-site domains to the 5′ splice site of a group II intron. Nature 406, 315–318.

Bowes, J.H., Kenten, R., 1948. The amino-acid composition and titration curve of collagen. Biochemical Journal 43, 358.

Bowie, J.U., Luthy, R., Eisenberg, D., 1991. A method to identify protein sequences that fold into a known three-dimensional structure. Science 253, 164–170.

Bragg, L., Kendrew, J.C., Perutz, M.F., 1950. Polypeptide chain configurations in crystalline proteins. Proceedings of the Royal Society of London A: Mathematical, Physical and Engineering Sciences 203, 321–357.

Brown, S.H., Kelly, R.M., 1993. Characterization of amylolytic enzymes, having both α-1, 4 and α-1, 6 hydrolytic activity, from the thermophilic archaea Pyrococcus furiosus and Thermococcus litoralis. Applied and Environmental Microbiology 59, 2614–2621.

Bru, C., Courcelle, E., Carrere, S., et al., 2005. The ProDom database of protein domain families: More emphasis on 3D. Nucleic Acids Research 33, D212–D215.

Bulheller, B.M., Hirst, J.D., 2009. DichroCalc – Circular and linear dichroism online. Bioinformatics 25, 539–540.

Burge, S., Parkinson, G.N., Hazel, P., et al., 2006. Quadruplex DNA: Sequence, topology and structure. Nucleic Acids Research 34, 5402–5415.

Callaghan, P.T., 1993. Principles of Nuclear Magnetic Resonance Microscopy. Oxford University Press on Demand.

Cao, C., Xu, S., Wang, L., 2015. An algorithm for protein helix assignment using helix geometry. PLOS ONE 10, e0129674.

Cartailler, J.P., Luecke, H., 2004. Structural and functional characterization of pi bulges and other short intrahelical deformations. Structure 12, 133–144.

Carter Jr., C.W., Kraut, J., Freer, S.T., et al., 1974. Two-Angstrom crystal structure of oxidized Chromatium high potential iron protein. The Journal of Biological Chemistry 249, 4212–4225.

Carugo, O., Djinovic-Carugo, K., 2013. Half a century of Ramachandran plots. Acta Crystallographica Section D 69, 1333–1341.

Cescutti, P., Toffanin, R., Kvam, B.J., et al., 1993. Structural determination of the capsular polysaccharide produced by Klebsiella pneumoniae serotype K40. FEBS Journal 213, 445–453.

Cevec, M., Plavec, J., 2005. Role of loop residues and cations on the formation and stability of dimeric DNA G-quadruplexes. Biochemistry 44, 15238–15246.

Chakrabarti, P., Bernard, M., Rees, D.C., 1986. Peptide-bond distortions and the curvature of alpha-helices. Biopolymers 25, 1087–1093.

Chakrabarti, P., Chakrabarti, S., 1998. C–H...O hydrogen bond involving proline residues in alpha-helices. Journal of Molecular Biology 284, 867–873.

Cheng, X., Shao, Z., Li, C., et al., 2017. Isolation, characterization and evaluation of collagen from jellyfish Rhopilema esculentum Kishinouye for use in hemostatic applications. PLOS ONE 12, e0169731.

Chen, V.B., Arendall III, W.B., Headd, J.J., et al., 2010. MolProbity: All-atom structure validation for macromolecular crystallography. Acta Crystallographica Section D 66, 12–21.

Chevalier, A., Silva, D.A., Rocklin, G.J., et al., 2017. Massively parallel de novo protein design for targeted therapeutics. Nature 550 (7674), 74–79.

Chothia, C., 1973. Conformation of twisted β-pleated sheets in proteins. Journal of Molecular Biology 75, 295–302.

Chou, P.Y., Fasman, G.D., 1974. Prediction of protein conformation. Biochemistry 13, 222–245.

Chou, P.Y., Fasman, G.D., 1977. Beta-turns in proteins. Journal of Molecular Biology 115, 135–175.

Chvapil, M., 1977. Collagen sponge: Theory and practice of medical applications. Journal of Biomedical Materials Research Part A 11, 721–741.

Chvapil, M., Kronenthal, R.L., van Winkle Jr, W., 1973. Medical and surgical applications of collagen. International Review of Connective Tissue Research 6.

Clayton, G.M., Altieri, S., Heginbotham, L., et al., 2008. Structure of the transmembrane regions of a bacterial cyclic nucleotide-regulated channel. Proceedings of the National Academy of Sciences of the United States of America 105, 1511–1515.

Coimbatore Narayanan, B., Westbrook, J., Ghosh, S., et al., 2014. The nucleic acid database: New features and capabilities. Nucleic Acids Research 42, D114–D122.

Consortium, T.U., 2015. UniProt: A hub for protein information. Nucleic Acids Research 43, D204–D212.

Cooley, R.B., Arp, D.J., Karplus, P.A., 2010. Evolutionary origin of a secondary structure: Pi-helices as cryptic but widespread insertional variations of alpha-helices that enhance protein functionality. Journal of Molecular Biology 404, 232–246.

Costantini, S., Colonna, G., Facchiano, A.M., 2006. Amino acid propensities for secondary structures are influenced by the protein structural class. Biochemical and Biophysical Research Communications 342, 441–451.

Costantini, S., Colonna, G., Facchiano, A.M., 2007. PreSSAPro: A software for the prediction of secondary structure by amino acid properties. Computational Biology and Chemistry 31, 389–392.

Cowan, P.M., McGavin, S., 1955. Structure of poly-L-proline. Nature 176, 501–503.

Cubellis, M.V., Cailliez, F., Lovell, S.C., 2005. Secondary structure assignment that accurately reflects physical and evolutionary characteristics. BMC Bioinformatics 6, S8.

Das, R., Baker, D., 2008. Macromolecular modeling with rosetta. Annual Review of Biochemistry 77, 363–382.

Davis, I.W., Murray, L.W., Richardson, J.S., Richardson, D.C., 2004. MOLPROBITY: Structure validation and all-atom contact analysis for nucleic acids and their complexes. Nucleic Acids Research 32, W615–W619.

Day, H.A., Pavlou, P., Waller, Z.A., 2014. i-Motif DNA: Structure, stability and targeting with ligands. Bioorganic & Medicinal Chemistry 22, 4407–4418.

De Las Rivas, J., Fontanillo, C., 2010. Protein-protein interactions essentials: Key concepts to building and analyzing interactome networks. PLOS Computational Biology 6, e1000807.

De Paepe, A., 1998. Heritable collagen disorders: From phenotype to genotype. Verh K Acad Geneeskd Belg 60, 463–482.

Deupi, X., Olivella, M., Govaerts, C., et al., 2004. Ser and Thr residues modulate the conformation of pro-kinked transmembrane alpha-helices. Biophysical Journal 86, 105–115.

Devi, G., Zhou, Y., Zhong, Z., et al., 2015. RNA triplexes: From structural principles to biological and biotech applications. Wiley Interdisciplinary Reviews: RNA 6, 111–128.

Dirks, R.M., Pierce, N.A., 2003. A partition function algorithm for nucleic acid secondary structure including pseudoknots. Journal of Computational Chemistry 24, 1664–1677.

Donohue, J., 1953. Hydrogen bonded helical configurations of the polypeptide chain. Proceedings of the National Academy of Sciences of the United States of America 39, 470–478.

Dorn, M., S, M.B.E., Buriol, L.S., Lamb, L.C., 2014. Three-dimensional protein structure prediction: Methods and computational strategies. Computational Biology and Chemistry 53PB, 251–276.

Dor, O., Zhou, Y., 2007. Achieving 80% ten-fold cross-validated accuracy for secondary structure prediction by large-scale training. Proteins 66, 838–845.

Drozdetskiy, A., Cole, C., Procter, J., Barton, G.J., 2015. JPred4: A protein secondary structure prediction server. Nucleic Acids Research 43, W389–W394.

Dwek, R.A., 1996. Glycobiology: Toward understanding the function of sugars. Chemical Reviews 96, 683–720.

Eastoe, J., 1955. The amino acid composition of mammalian collagen and gelatin. Biochemical Journal 61, 589.

Engelsen, S.B., Hansen, P.I., Perez, S., 2014. POLYS 2.0: An open source software package for building three-dimensional structures of polysaccharides. Biopolymers 101, 733–743.

Enkhbayar, P., Hikichi, K., Osaki, M., et al., 2006. 3(10)-helices in proteins are parahelices. Proteins 64, 691–699.

Faraggi, E., Yang, Y., Zhang, S., Zhou, Y., 2009. Predicting continuous local structure and the effect of its substitution for secondary structure in fragment-free protein structure prediction. Structure 17, 1515–1527.

Fedonenko, Y.P., Zatonsky, G.V., Konnova, S.A., et al., 2002. Structure of the O-specific polysaccharide of the lipopolysaccharide of Azospirillum brasilense Sp245. Carbohydrate Research 337, 869–872.

Fernando, H., Sewitz, S., Darot, J., et al., 2009. Genome-wide analysis of a G-quadruplex-specific single-chain antibody that regulates gene expression. Nucleic Acids Research 37, 6716–6722.

Floudas, C., Fung, H., McAllister, S., et al., 2006. Advances in protein structure prediction and de novo protein design: A review. Chemical Engineering Science 61, 966–988.

Fodje, M.N., Al-Karadaghi, S., 2002. Occurrence, conformational features and amino acid propensities for the pi-helix. Protein Engineering 15, 353–358.

Frank, J., 2011. Molecular Machines in Biology: Workshop of the Cell. Cambridge University Press.

Franklin, R.E., Gosling, R.G., 1953. The structure of sodium thymonucleate fibres. I. The influence of water content. Acta Crystallographica 6, 673–677.

Frishman, D., Argos, P., 1995. Knowledge-based protein secondary structure assignment. Proteins 23, 566–579.

Gaisl, T., Giunta, C., Bratton, D.J., et al., 2017. Obstructive sleep apnoea and quality of life in Ehlers-Danlos syndrome: A parallel cohort study. Thorax. [thoraxjnl-2016-209560].

Garman, E.F., 2014. Developments in x-ray crystallographic structure determination of biological macromolecules. Science 343, 1102–1108.

Garnier, J., Osguthorpe, D.J., Robson, B., 1978. Analysis of the accuracy and implications of simple methods for predicting the secondary structure of globular proteins. Journal of Molecular Biology 120, 97–120.

Geer, L.Y., Marchler-Bauer, A., Geer, R.C., *et al.*, 2010. The NCBI BioSystems database. Nucleic Acids Research 38, D492–D496.

Gehring, K., Leroy, J.-L., Guéron, M., 1993. A tetrameric DNA structure with protonated cytosine-cytosine base pairs. Nature 363, 561–565.

Gellert, M., Lipsett, M.N., Davies, D.R., 1962. Helix formation by guanylic acid. Proceedings of the National Academy of Sciences 48, 2013–2018.

Gerstein, M.B., Bruce, C., Rozowsky, J.S., *et al.*, 2007. What is a gene, post-ENCODE? History and updated definition. Genome Research 17, 669–681.

Ghosh, A., Bansal, M., 2003. A glossary of DNA structures from Λ to Z. Acta Crystallographica D Biological Crystallography 59, 620–626.

Gibrat, J.F., Madej, T., Bryant, S.H., 1996. Surprising similarities in structure comparison. Current Opinion in Structural Biology 6, 377–385.

Gribova, V., Auzely-Velty, R., Picart, C., 2011. Polyelectrolyte multilayer assemblies on materials surfaces: From cell adhesion to tissue engineering. Chemistry of Materials 24, 854–869.

Grigorieff, N., 2013. Structural biology: Direct detection pays off for electron cryo-microscopy. Elife 2, e00573.

Gruber, A.R., Lorenz, R., Bernhart, S.H., *et al.*, 2008. The Vienna RNA websuite. Nucleic Acids Research 36, W70–W74.

Guéron, M., Leroy, J.-L., 2000. The i-motif in nucleic acids. Current Opinion in Structural Biology 10, 326–331.

Guzzo, A.V., 1965. The influence of amino-acid sequence on protein structure. Biophysical Journal 5, 809–822.

Hale, B.G., Kerry, P.S., Jackson, D., *et al.*, 2010. Structural insights into phosphoinositide 3-kinase activation by the influenza A virus NS1 protein. Proceedings of the National Academy of Sciences of the United States of America 107, 1954–1959.

Hänsel-Hertsch, R., Di Antonio, M., Balasubramanian, S., 2017. DNA G-quadruplexes in the human genome: Detection, functions and therapeutic potential. Nature Reviews Molecular Cell Biology 18, 279–284.

Hardy, J.A., Walsh, S.T., Nelson, H.C., 2000. Role of an alpha-helical bulge in the yeast heat shock transcription factor. Journal of Molecular Biology 295, 393–409.

Harmanci, A.O., Sharma, G., Mathews, D.H., 2011. TurboFold: Iterative probabilistic estimation of secondary structures for multiple RNA sequences. BMC Bioinformatics 12, 108.

Hartmann, M.D., Mendler, C.T., Bassler, J., *et al.*, 2016. α/β coiled coils. eLife 5, e11861.

Holley, R.W., Apgar, J., Everett, G.A., *et al.*, 1965. Structure of a ribonucleic acid. Science. 1462–1465.

Hollyfield, J.G., Besharse, J.C., Rayborn, M.E., 1976. The effect of light on the quantity of phagosomes in the pigment epithelium. Experimental Eye Research 23, 623–635.

Holm, L., Sander, C., 1996. Mapping the protein universe. Science 273, 595–603.

Hol, W.G., van Duijnen, P.T., Berendsen, H.J., 1978. The alpha-helix dipole and the properties of proteins. Nature 273, 443–446.

Hooft, R.W., Vriend, G., Sander, C., Abola, E.E., 1996. Errors in protein structures. Nature 381, 272.

Hore, P.J., 2015. Nuclear Magnetic Resonance. USA: Oxford University Press.

Hostinová, E., Solovicová, A., Dvorský, R., Gašperík, J., 2003. Molecular cloning and 3D structure prediction of the first raw-starch-degrading glucoamylase without a separate starch-binding domain. Archives of Biochemistry and Biophysics 411, 189–1195.

Huggins, M.L., 1943. The structure of fibrous proteins. Chemical Reviews 32, 195–218.

Humphrey, W., Dalke, A., Schulten, K., 1996. VMD: Visual molecular dynamics. Journal of Molecular Graphics 14, 33–38.

Ilari, A., Savino, C., 2008. Protein structure determination by x-ray crystallography. Methods in Molecular Biology 452, 63–87.

Jiang, J.B., Qiu, J.D., Yang, L.H., *et al.*, 2010. Therapeutic effects of astragalus polysaccharides on inflammation and synovial apoptosis in rats with adjuvant-induced arthritis. International Journal of Rheumatic Diseases 13, 396–405.

Jain, A., Wang, G., Vasquez, K.M., 2008. DNA triple helices: Biological consequences and therapeutic potential. Biochimie 90, 1117–1130.

Jain, S., Schlick, T., 2017. F-RAG: Generating atomic coordinates from rna graphs by fragment assembly. Journal of Molecular Biology 429 (23), 3587–3605.

Johnson, M.A., Pinto, B.M., 2002. Saturation transfer difference 1D-TOCSY experiments to map the topography of oligosaccharides recognized by a monoclonal antibody directed against the cell-wall polysaccharide of group A Streptococcus. Journal of the American Chemical Society 124, 15368–15374.

Jones, D.T., 1999. Protein secondary structure prediction based on position-specific scoring matrices. Journal of Molecular Biology 292, 195–202.

Jorgensen, W.L., Maxwell, D.S., Tirado-Rives, J., 1996. Development and testing of the OPLS all-atom force field on conformational energetics and properties of organic liquids. Journal of the American Chemical Society 118, 11225–11236.

Kabsch, W., Sander, C., 1983a. Dictionary of protein secondary structure: Pattern recognition of hydrogen-bonded and geometrical features. Biopolymers 22, 2577–2637.

Kabsch, W., Sander, C., 1983b. How good are predictions of protein secondary structure? FEBS Letters 155, 179–182.

Kc, D.B., 2016. Recent advances in sequence-based protein structure prediction. Brief Bioinformatics 18 (6), 1021–1032.

Keefe, L.J., Sondek, J., Shortle, D., Lattman, E.E., 1993. The alpha aneurism: A structural motif revealed in an insertion mutant of staphylococcal nuclease. Proceedings of the National Academy of Sciences of the United States of America 90, 3275–3279.

Kelly, S.M., Jess, T.J., Price, N.C., 2005. How to study proteins by circular dichroism. Biochimica et Biophysica Acta (BBA)-Proteins and Proteomics 1751, 119–139.

Kelly, S.M., Price, N.C., 2000. The use of circular dichroism in the investigation of protein structure and function. Current Protein & Peptide Science 1, 349–384.

Kendrew, J.C., Bodo, G., Dintzis, H.M., *et al.*, 1958. A three-dimensional model of the myoglobin molecule obtained by x-ray analysis. Nature 181, 662–666.

Kendrew, J.C., Dickerson, R.E., Strandberg, B.E., *et al.*, 1960. Structure of myoglobin: A three-dimensional Fourier synthesis at 2 A. resolution. Nature 185, 422–427.

Khateb, S., Weisman-Shomer, P., Hershco, I., *et al.*, 2004. Destabilization of tetraplex structures of the fragile X repeat sequence (CGG) n is mediated by homolog-conserved domains in three members of the hnRNP family. Nucleic Acids Research 32, 4145–4154.

King, S.M., Johnson, W.C., 1999. Assigning secondary structure from protein coordinate data. Proteins 35, 313–320.

Kjellberg, A., Nishida, T., Weintraub, A., Widmalm, G., 1998. NMR spectroscopy of 13C-enriched polysaccharides: Application of 13C–13C TOCSY to sugars of different configuration. Magnetic Resonance in Chemistry 36, 128–131.

Kleywegt, G.J., Jones, T.A., 1996. Phi/psi-chology: Ramachandran revisited. Structure 4, 1395–1400.

Konagurthu, A.S., Lesk, A.M., Allison, L., 2012. Minimum message length inference of secondary structure from protein coordinate data. Bioinformatics 28, i97–i105.

Kotelchuck, D., Scheraga, H.A., 1969. The influence of short-range interactions on protein onformation. II. A model for predicting the alpha-helical regions of proteins. Proceedings of the National Academy of Sciences of the United States of America 62, 14–21.

Kumar, P., Bansal, M., 2012. HELANAL-Plus: A web server for analysis of helix geometry in protein structures. Journal of Biomolecular Structure and Dynamics 30, 773–783.

Kumar, P., Bansal, M., 2015a. Dissecting pi-helices: Sequence, structure and function. FEBS Journal 282, 4415–4432.

Kumar, P., Bansal, M., 2015b. Identification of local variations within secondary structures of proteins. Acta Crystallographica D Biological Crystallography 71, 1077–1086.

Kumar, P., Bansal, M., 2016. Structural and functional analyses of PolyProline-II helices in globular proteins. Journal of Structural Biology 196, 414–425.

Kumar, P., Kailasam, S., Chakraborty, S., Bansal, M., 2014. MolBridge: A program for identifying nonbonded interactions in small molecules and biomolecular structures. Journal of Applied Crystallography 47, 1772–1776.

Kumar, S., Bansal, M., 1998. Geometrical and sequence characteristics of alpha-helices in globular proteins. Biophysical Journal 75, 1935–1944.

Kuntz, I.D., 1972. Protein folding. Journal of the American Chemical Society 94, 4009–4012.

Kuttel, M.M., Ståhle, J., Widmalm, G., 2016. CarbBuilder: Software for building molecular models of complex oligo-and polysaccharide structures. Journal of Computational Chemistr 37, 2098–2105.

Labesse, G., Colloc'h, N., Pothier, J., Mornon, J.P., 1997. P-SEA: A new efficient assignment of secondary structure from C alpha trace of proteins. Computer Applications in the Biosciences: CABIOS 13, 291–295.

Lack, S., Dulong, V., Picton, L., *et al.*, 2007. High-resolution nuclear magnetic resonance spectroscopy studies of polysaccharides crosslinked by sodium trimetaphosphate: A proposal for the reaction mechanism. Carbohydrate Research 342, 943–953.

Lacroix, L., Mergny, J.-L., Leroy, J.-L., Hélène, C., 1996. Inability of RNA to form the i-motif: Implications for triplex formation. Biochemistry 35, 8715–8722.

Largy, E., Mergny, J.-L., Gabelica, V., 2016. Role of alkali metal ions in G-quadruplex nucleic acid structure and stability. The Alkali Metal Ions: Their Role for Life. pp. 203–258.

Larocque, S., Brisson, J.-R., Thérisod, H., et al., 2003. Structural characterization of the O-chain polysaccharide isolated from Bordetella avium ATCC 5086: Variation on a theme. FEBS Letters 535, 11–16.

Laskowski, R.A., MacArthur, M.W., Moss, D.S., Thornton, J.M., 1993. PROCHECK: A program to check the stereochemical quality of protein structures. Journal of Applied Crystallography 26, 283–291.

Lawson, C.L., Patwardhan, A., Baker, M.L., et al., 2016. EMDataBank unified data resource for 3DEM. Nucleic Acids Research 44, D396–D403.

Lee, C.H., Singla, A., Lee, Y., 2001. Biomedical applications of collagen. International Journal of Pharmaceutics 221, 1–22.

Letunic, I., Doerks, T., Bork, P., 2015. SMART: Recent updates, new developments and status in 2015. Nucleic Acids Research 43, D257–D260.

Levitt, M., Greer, J., 1977. Automatic identification of secondary structure in globular proteins. Journal of Molecular Biology 114, 181–239.

Lewis, P.N., Go, N., Go, M., et al., 1970. Helix probability profiles of denatured proteins and their correlation with native structures. Proceedings of the National Academy of Sciences of the United States of America 65, 810–815.

Lewis, P.N., Momany, F.A., Scheraga, H.A., 1971. Folding of polypeptide chains in proteins: A proposed mechanism for folding. Proceedings of the National Academy of Sciences of the United States of America 68, 2293–2297.

Lewis, P.N., Momany, F.A., Scheraga, H.A., 1973. Chain reversals in proteins. Biochimica et Biophysica Acta 303, 211–229.

Lindauer, K., Bendic, C., Sühnel, J., 1996. HBexplore – A new tool for identifying and analysing hydrogen bonding patterns in biological macromolecules. Computer Applications in the Biosciences: CABIOS 12, 281–289.

Linker, A., Evans, L.R., Impallomeni, G., 2001. The structure of a polysaccharide from infectious strains of Burkholderia cepacia. Carbohydrate Research 335, 45–54.

Lin, N., Huang, J., Dufresne, A., 2012. Preparation, properties and applications of polysaccharide nanocrystals in advanced functional nanomaterials: A review. Nanoscale 4, 3274–3294.

Liu, D., Balasubramanian, S., 2003. A Proton-fuelled DNA nanomachine. Angewandte Chemie International Edition 42, 5734–5736.

Lo Conte, L., Ailey, B., Hubbard, T.J., et al., 2000. SCOP: A structural classification of proteins database. Nucleic Acids Research 28, 257–259.

Lodish, H., Berk, A., Zipursky, S.L., et al., 2000. Molecular Cell Biology, fourth ed. National Center for Biotechnology InformationÕs Bookshelf.

Long, S.B., Campbell, E.B., Mackinnon, R., 2005a. Crystal structure of a mammalian voltage-dependent Shaker family K+ channel. Science 309, 897–903.

Long, S.B., Campbell, E.B., Mackinnon, R., 2005b. Voltage sensor of Kv1.2: Structural basis of electromechanical coupling. Science 309, 903–908.

Louis-Jeune, C., Andrade-Navarro, M.A., Perez-Iratxeta, C., 2012. Prediction of protein secondary structure from circular dichroism using theoretically derived spectra. Proteins 80, 374–381.

Love, W.E., Klock, P.A., Lattman, E.E., et al., 1972. The structures of lamprey and bloodworm hemoglobins in relation to their evolution and function. Cold Spring Harbor Symposia on Quantitative Biology. 349–357.

Low, B., Baybutt, R., 1952. The pi-helix – A hydrogen bonded configuration of the polypeptide chain. Journal of the American Chemical Society 74, 5806–5807.

Low, B.W., Grenville-Wells, H.J., 1953. Generalized mathematical relationships for polypeptide chain helices: The coordinates of the II helix. Proceedings of the National Academy of Sciences of the United States of America 39, 785–801.

Luthy, R., Bowie, J.U., Eisenberg, D., 1992. Assessment of protein models with three-dimensional profiles. Nature 356, 83–85.

Lu, X.-J., Bussemaker, H.J., Olson, W.K., 2015. DSSR: An integrated software tool for dissecting the spatial structure of RNA. Nucleic Acids Research 43, e142.

Lu, X.J., Olson, W.K., 2008. 3DNA: A versatile, integrated software system for the analysis, rebuilding and visualization of three-dimensional nucleic-acid structures. Nature Protocols 3, 1213–1227.

MacArthur, M.W., Thornton, J.M., 1996. Deviations from planarity of the peptide bond in peptides and proteins. Journal of Molecular Biology 264, 1180–1195.

Macdonald, J.R., Johnson Jr., W.C., 2001. Environmental features are important in determining protein secondary structure. Protein Science 10, 1172–1177.

Maciel, J.S., Chaves, L.S., Souza, B.W., et al., 2008. Structural characterization of cold extracted fraction of soluble sulfated polysaccharide from red seaweed Gracilaria birdiae. Carbohydrate Polymers 71, 559–565.

Maizels, N., Gray, L.T., 2013. The G4 genome. PLOS Genetics 9, e1003468.

Majumdar, I., Krishna, S.S., Grishin, N.V., 2005. PALSSE: A program to delineate linear secondary structural elements from protein structures. BMC Bioinformatics 6, 202.

Makarov, A.A., Esipova, N.G., Pankov, Y.A., et al., 1975. A Conformational study of beta-melanocyte-stimulation hormone. Biochemical and Biophysical Research Communications 67, 1378–1383.

Mandel-Gutfreund, Y., Margalit, H., Jernigan, R.L., Zhurkin, V.B., 1998. A role for CH... O interactions in protein-DNA recognition. Journal of Molecular Biology 277, 1129–1140.

Mansiaux, Y., Joseph, A.P., Gelly, J.C., de Brevern, A.G., 2011. Assignment of PolyProline II conformation and analysis of sequence–structure relationship. PLOS ONE 6, e18401.

Markham, N.R., Zuker, M., 2008. UNAFold: Software for nucleic acid folding and hybridization. Methods in Molecular Biology 453, 3–31.

Marks, D.S., Hopf, T.A., Sander, C., 2012. Protein structure prediction from sequence variation. Nature Biotechnology 30, 1072–1080.

Martin, J., Letellier, G., Marin, A., et al., 2005. Protein secondary structure assignment revisited: A detailed analysis of different assignment methods. BMC Structural Biology 5, 17.

Martin-Pastor, M., Bush, C.A., 1999. New strategy for the conformational analysis of carbohydrates based on NOE and ^{13}C NMR coupling constants. Application to the flexible polysaccharide of Streptococcus mitis J22. Biochemistry 38, 8045–8055.

Mathews, D.H., 2006. Revolutions in RNA secondary structure prediction. Journal of Molecular Biology 359, 526–532.

Matsugami, A., Okuizumi, T., Uesugi, S., Katahira, M., 2003. Intramolecular higher order packing of parallel quadruplexes comprising a G: g: G: g tetrad and a G (: a): G (: a): G (: a): G heptad of GGA triplet repeat DNA. Journal of Biological Chemistry 278, 28147–28153.

Mavridis, L., Janes, R.W., 2017. PDB2CD: A web-based application for the generation of circular dichroism spectra from protein atomic coordinates. Bioinformatics 33, 56–63.

McDonald, I.K., Thornton, J.M., 1994. Satisfying hydrogen bonding potential in proteins. Journal of Molecular Biology 238, 777–793.

Medlock, A.E., Dailey, T.A., Ross, T.A., et al., 2007. A pi-helix switch selective for porphyrin deprotonation and product release in human ferrochelatase. Journal of Molecular Biology 373, 1006–1016.

Michael, F.S., Szymanski, C.M., Li, J., et al., 2002. The structures of the lipooligosaccharide and capsule polysaccharide of Campylobacter jejuni genome sequenced strain NCTC 11168. FEBS Journal 269, 5119–5136.

Micsonai, A., Wien, F., Kernya, L., et al., 2015. Accurate secondary structure prediction and fold recognition for circular dichroism spectroscopy. Proceedings of the National Academy of Sciences of the United States of America 112, E3095–E3103.

Miles, A.J., Wallace, B.A., 2006. Synchrotron radiation circular dichroism spectroscopy of proteins and applications in structural and functional genomics. Chemical Society Reviews 35, 39–51.

Milne, J.L., Borgnia, M.J., Bartesaghi, A., et al., 2013. Cryo-electron microscopy – A primer for the non-microscopist. FEBS Journal 280, 28–45.

Mitchell, A., Chang, H.-Y., Daugherty, L., et al., 2015. The InterPro protein families database: The classification resource after 15 years. Nucleic Acids Research 43, D213–D221.

Miyake, M., Hori, S., Morizawa, Y., et al., 2017. Collagen type IV alpha 1 (COL4A1) and collagen type XIII alpha 1 (COL13A1) produced in cancer cells promote tumor budding at the invasion front in human urothelial carcinoma of the bladder. Oncotarget 8, 36099–36114.

Momen-Roknabadi, A., Sadeghi, M., Pezeshk, H., Marashi, S.A., 2008. Impact of residue accessible surface area on the prediction of protein secondary structures. BMC Bioinformatics 9, 357.

Mount, D.W., 2004. Bioinformatics: Sequence and Genome Analysis. New York: Cold Spring Harbor Laboratory Press.

Mulder, G.J., 1839. On the composition of some animal substances. Journal für Praktische Chemie 16, 15.

Murzin, A.G., Brenner, S.E., Hubbard, T., Chothia, C., 1995. SCOP: A structural classification of proteins database for the investigation of sequences and structures. Journal of Molecular Biology 247, 536–540.

Muzzarelli, R.A., 1973. Natural chelating polymers; alginic acid, chitin and chitosan. Natural Chelating Polymers; Alginic Acid, Chitin and Chitosan. Pergamon Press.

Nahmany, A., Strino, F., Rosen, J., et al., 2005. The use of a genetic algorithm search for molecular mechanics (MM3)-based conformational analysis of oligosaccharides. Carbohydrate Research 340, 1059–1064.

Narwani, T.J., Santuz, H., Shinada, N., et al., 2017. Recent advances on polyproline II. Amino Acids 49, 705–713.

Nelson, D.L., Lehninger, A.L., Cox, M.M., 2008. Lehninger Principles of Biochemistry. Macmillan.

Nonogaki, H., Gee, O.H., Bradford, K.J., 2000. A germination-specific endo-β-mannanase gene is expressed in the micropylar endosperm cap of tomato seeds. Plant Physiology 123, 1235–1246.

Novotny, M., Kleywegt, G.J., 2005. A survey of left-handed helices in protein structures. Journal of Molecular Biology 347, 231–241.

Orengo, C.A., Michie, A.D., Jones, S., et al., 1997. CATH – A hierarchic classification of protein domain structures. Structure 5, 1093–1108.

Orengo, C.A., Pearl, F.M., Thornton, J.M., 2003. The CATH domain structure database. Methods of Biochemical Analysis 44, 249–271.

Pal, L., Basu, G., 1999. Novel protein structural motifs containing two-turn and longer 3(10)-helices. Protein Engineering 12, 811–814.

Panigrahi, S.K., Desiraju, G.R., 2007. Strong and weak hydrogen bonds in the protein–ligand interface. Proteins: Structure, Function, and Bioinformatics 67, 128–141.

Parenteau-Bareil, R., Gauvin, R., Berthod, F., 2010. Collagen-based biomaterials for tissue engineering applications. Materials 3, 1863–1887.

Parisien, M., Major, F., 2008. The MC-Fold and MC-Sym pipeline infers RNA structure from sequence data. Nature 452, 51–55.

Pauling, L., 1960. The Nature of the Chemical Bond. Ithaca, NY: Cornell University Press.

Pauling, L., Corey, R.B., 1951. The pleated sheet, a new layer configuration of polypeptide chains. Proceedings of the National Academy of Sciences of the United States of America 37, 251–256.

Pauling, L., Corey, R.B., Branson, H.R., 1951. The structure of proteins; two hydrogen-bonded helical configurations of the polypeptide chain. Proceedings of the National Academy of Sciences of the United States of America 37, 205–211.

Pearl, F.M., Bennett, C.F., Bray, J.E., et al., 2003. The CATH database: An extended protein family resource for structural and functional genomics. Nucleic Acids Research 31, 452–455.

Perez-Iratxeta, C., Andrade-Navarro, M.A., 2008. K2D2: Estimation of protein secondary structure from circular dichroism spectra. BMC Structural Biology 8, 25.

Pérez, S., Tubiana, T., Imberty, A., Baaden, M., 2014. Three-dimensional representations of complex carbohydrates and polysaccharides–SweetUnityMol: A video game-based computer graphic software. Glycobiology 25, 483–491.

Perutz, M.F., 1951. New x-ray evidence on the configuration of polypeptide chains. Nature 167, 1053–1054.

Peters, T., Meyer, B., Stuike-Prill, R., et al., 1993. A Monte Carlo method for conformational analysis of saccharides. Carbohydrate Research 238, 49–73.

Petrey, D., Honig, B., 2005. Protein structure prediction: Inroads to biology. Molecular Cell 20, 811–819.

Powell, D.R., 2016. Review of X-Ray Crystallography. ACS Publications.

Prockop, D.J., Kivirikko, K.I., Tuderman, L., Guzman, N.A., 1979. The biosynthesis of collagen and its disorders. New England Journal of Medicine 301, 77–85.

Prothero, J.W., 1966. Correlation between the distribution of amino acids and alpha helices. Biophysical Journal 6, 367–370.

Punta, M., Coggill, P.C., Eberhardt, R.Y., et al., 2012. The Pfam protein families database. Nucleic Acids Research 40, D290–D301.

Purcell, E.M., Torrey, H.C., Pound, R.V., 1946. Resonance absorption by nuclear magnetic moments in a solid. Physical Review 69, 37.

Ramachandran, G.N., Kartha, G., 1954. Structure of collagen. Nature 174, 269–270.

Ramachandran, G.N., Kartha, G., 1955. Structure of collagen. Nature 176, 593–595.

Ramachandran, G.N., Ramakrishnan, C., Sasisekharan, V., 1963. Stereochemistry of polypeptide chain configurations. Journal of Molecular Biology 7, 95–99.

Ramachandran, G.N., Sasisekharan, V., 1961. Structure of collagen. Nature 190, 1004–1005.

Ramachandran, G.N., Sasisekharan, V., 1968. Conformation of polypeptides and proteins. Advances in Protein Chemistry 23, 283–438.

Ramachandran, G.N., Venkatachalam, C.M., Krimm, S., 1966. Stereochemical criteria for polypeptide and protein chain conformations. 3. Helical and hydrogen-bonded polypeptide chains. Biophysical Journal 6, 849–872.

Ramakrishnan, C., Ramachandran, G.N., 1965. Stereochemical criteria for polypeptide and protein chain conformations. II. Allowed conformations for a pair of peptide units. Biophysical Journal 5, 909–933.

Ramberg, J.E., Nelson, E.D., Sinnott, R.A., 2010. Immunomodulatory dietary polysaccharides: A systematic review of the literature. Nutrition Journal 9, 54.

Rao, S.T., Rossmann, M.G., 1973. Comparison of super-secondary structures in proteins. Journal of Molecular Biology 76, 241–256.

Redfern, O., Grant, A., Maibaum, M., Orengo, C., 2005. Survey of current protein family databases and their application in comparative, structural and functional genomics. Journal of Chromatography. B, Analytical Technologies in the Biomedical and Life Sciences 815, 97–107.

Ren, J., Rastegari, B., Condon, A., Hoos, H.H., 2005. HotKnots: Heuristic prediction of RNA secondary structures including pseudoknots. RNA 11, 1494–1504.

Reuter, J.S., Mathews, D.H., 2010. RNAstructure: Software for RNA secondary structure prediction and analysis. BMC Bioinformatics 11, 129.

Rhodes, D., Lipps, H.J., 2015. G-quadruplexes and their regulatory roles in biology. Nucleic Acids Research 43, 8627–8637.

Rice, C., Skordalakes, E., 2016. Structure and function of the telomeric CST complex. Computational and Structural Biotechnology Journal 14, 161–167.

Rich, A., 1960. A hybrid helix containing both deoxyribose and ribose polynucleotides and its relation to the transfer of information between the nucleic acids. Proceedings of the National Academy of Sciences 46, 1044–1053.

Rich, A., Crick, F.H., 1955. The structure of collagen. Nature 176, 915–916.

Rich, A., Davies, D.R., 1956. A new two stranded helical structure: Polyadenylic acid and polyuridylic acid. Journal of the American Chemical Society 78, 3548–3549.

Richards, F.M., Kundrot, C.E., 1988. Identification of structural motifs from protein coordinate data: Secondary structure and first-level supersecondary structure. Proteins 3, 71–84.

Richardson, J.S., 1977. beta-Sheet topology and the relatedness of proteins. Nature 268, 495–500.

Richardson, J.S., 1981. The anatomy and taxonomy of protein structure. Advances in Protein Chemistry 34, 167–339.

Richardson, J.S., Getzoff, E.D., Richardson, D.C., 1978. The beta bulge: A common small unit of nonrepetitive protein structure. Proceedings of the National Academy of Sciences of the United States of America 75, 2574–2578.

Rietveld, K., Van Poelgeest, R., Pleij, C.W., et al., 1982. The tRNA-Uke structure at the 3′ terminus of turnip yellow mosaic virus RNA. Differences and similarities with canonical tRNA. Nucleic Acids Research 10, 1929–1946.

Risitano, A., Fox, K.R., 2004. Influence of loop size on the stability of intramolecular DNA quadruplexes. Nucleic Acids Research 32, 2598–2606.

Rivas, E., Eddy, S.R., 1999. A dynamic programming algorithm for RNA structure prediction including pseudoknots. Journal of Molecular Biology 285, 2053–2068.

Rose, G.D., Winters, R.H., Wetlaufer, D.B., 1976. A testable model for protein folding. FEBS Letters 63, 10–16.

Ross, P., Weinhouse, H., Aloni, Y., et al., 1987. Regulation of cellulose synthesis in Acetobacter xylinum by cyclic diguanylic acid. Nature 325, 279–281.

Rost, B., 2001. Review: Protein secondary structure prediction continues to rise. Journal of Structural Biology 134, 204–218.

Ruan, J., Stormo, G.D., Zhang, W., 2004. An iterated loop matching approach to the prediction of RNA secondary structures with pseudoknots. Bioinformatics 20, 58–66.

Ruska, H., 1941. Über ein neues bei der bakteriophagen Lyse auftretendes Formelement. Naturwissenschaften 29, 367–368.

Ruska, H., Borries, B.V., Ruska, E., 1939. Die Bedeutung der übermikroskopie für die Virusforschung. Archives of Virology 1, 155–169.

Ruskin, R.S., Yu, Z., Grigorieff, N., 2013. Quantitative characterization of electron detectors for transmission electron microscopy. Journal of Structural Biology 184, 385–393.

Sanghi, R., Bhattacharya, B., Singh, V., 2007. Seed gum polysaccharides and their grafted co-polymers for the effective coagulation of textile dye solutions. Reactive and Functional Polymers 67, 495–502.

Sankararamakrishnan, R., Vishveshwara, S., 1990. Conformational studies on peptides with proline in the right-handed alpha-helical region. Biopolymers 30, 287–298.

Sankararamakrishnan, R., Vishveshwara, S., 1992. Geometry of proline-containing alpha-helices in proteins. International Journal of Peptide and Protein Research 39, 356–363.

Sasisekharan, V., 1962. Stereochemical criteria for polypeptide and protein structures. In: Ramanathan, N. (Ed.), Collagen. New York: Wiley & Sons, pp. 39–78.

Sayle, R.A., Milner-White, E.J., 1995. RASMOL: Biomolecular graphics for all. Trends in Biochemical Sciences 20, 374.

Schiffer, M., Edmundson, A.B., 1967. Use of helical wheels to represent the structures of proteins and to identify segments with helical potential. Biophysical Journal 7, 121–135.

Schrodinger, L.L.C., 2010. The PyMOL Molecular Graphics System, Version 1.3r1.

Schroeder, S.J., 2009. Advances in RNA structure prediction from sequence: New tools for generating hypotheses about viral RNA structure-function relationships. Journal of Virology 83, 6326–6334.

Seetin, M.G., Mathews, D.H., 2012. TurboKnot: Rapid prediction of conserved RNA secondary structures including pseudoknots. Bioinformatics 28, 792–798.

Sekiguchi, S., Miura, Y., Kaneko, H., et al., 1994. Molecular weight dependency of antimicrobial activity by chitosan oligomers. Food Hydrocolloids. 71–76.

Shapiro, B.A., Yingling, Y.G., Kasprzak, W., Bindewald, E., 2007. Bridging the gap in RNA structure prediction. Current Opinion in Structural Biology 17, 157–165.

Sheikh, Z., Qureshi, J., Alshahrani, A.M., et al., 2017. Collagen based barrier membranes for periodontal guided bone regeneration applications. Odontology 105, 1–12.

Shelar, A., Kumar, P., Bansal, M., 2013. Defining α-helix geometry by Cα atom trace vs ((φ)-ψ) torsion angles: A comparative analyses. In: Bansal, M., Srinivasan, N. (Eds.), Biomolecular Forms and Functions: A Celebration of 50 Years of the Ramachandran Map. Bengaluru: World Scientific, pp. 116–127.

Sheng, Q., Neaverson, J.C., Mahmoud, T., et al., 2017. Identification of new DNA i-motif binding ligands through a fluorescent intercalator displacement assay. Organic & Biomolecular Chemistry 15 (27), 5669–5673.

Shi, Y., 2014. A glimpse of structural biology through X-ray crystallography. Cell 159, 995–1014.

Simonsson, T., 2001. G-quadruplex DNA structures—variations on a theme. Biological Chemistry 382, 621–628.

Singh, S.K., Babu, M.M., Balaram, P., 2003. Registering α-helices and β-strands using backbone C-H... O interactions. Proteins: Structure, Function, and Bioinformatics 51, 167–171.

Sinha, S., Astani, A., Ghosh, T., et al., 2010. Polysaccharides from Sargassum tenerrimum: Structural features, chemical modification and anti-viral activity. Phytochemistry 71, 235–242.

Sklenar, H., Etchebest, C., Lavery, R., 1989. Describing protein structure: A general algorithm yielding complete helicoidal parameters and a unique overall axis. Proteins 6, 46–60.

Smyth, M.S., Martin, J.H., 2000. x ray crystallography. Molecular Pathology 53, 8–14.

Son, S., Nam, J., Kim, J., et al., 2014. i-motif-driven Au nanomachines in programmed siRNA delivery for gene-silencing and photothermal ablation. ACS Nano 8, 5574–5584.

Sreerama, N., Woody, R.W., 2000. Estimation of protein secondary structure from circular dichroism spectra: Comparison of CONTIN, SELCON, and CDSSTR methods with an expanded reference set. Analytical Biochemistry 287, 252–260.

Srinivasan, R., Rose, G.D., 1999. A physical basis for protein secondary structure. Proceedings of the National Academy of Sciences of the United States of America 96, 14258–14263.

Srivastava, R., Kulshreshtha, D.K., 1989. Bioactive polysaccharides from plants. Phytochemistry 28, 2877–2883.

Staple, D.W., Butcher, S.E., 2005. Pseudoknots: RNA structures with diverse functions. PLOS Biology 3, e213.

Stapley, B.J., Creamer, T.P., 1999. A survey of left-handed polyproline II helices. Protein Science 8, 587–595.

Stenutz, R., Jansson, P.-E., Widmalm, G., 1998. Computer-assisted structural analysis of oligo-and polysaccharides: An extension of CASPER to multibranched structures. Carbohydrate Research 306, 11–17.

Sternberg, M.J., Thornton, J.M., 1976. On the conformation of proteins: The handedness of the beta-strand-alpha-helix-beta-strand unit. Journal of Molecular Biology 105, 367–382.

Sternberg, M.J., Thornton, J.M., 1977a. On the conformation of proteins: An analysis of beta-pleated sheets. Journal of Molecular Biology 110, 285–296.

Sternberg, M.J., Thornton, J.M., 1977b. On the conformation of proteins: The handedness of the connection between parallel beta-strands. Journal of Molecular Biology 110, 269–283.

Su, L., Chen, L., Egli, M., et al., 1999. Minor groove RNA triplex in the crystal structure of a ribosomal frameshifting viral pseudoknot. Nature Structural & Molecular Biology 6, 285–292.

Sundquist, W.I., Klug, A., 1989. Telomeric DNA dimerizes by formation of guanine tetrads between hairpin loops. Nature 342, 825–829.

Svensson, B., Jespersen, H., Sierks, M., MacGregor, E., 1989. Sequence homology between putative raw-starch binding domains from different starch-degrading enzymes. Biochemical Journal 264, 309.

Szewczak, A.A., Ortoleva-Donnelly, L., Ryder, S.P., et al., 1998. A minor groove RNA triple helix within the catalytic core of a group I intron. Nature Structural & Molecular Biology 5, 1037–1042.

Tan, Z., Fu, Y., Sharma, G., Mathews, D.H., 2017. TurboFold II: RNA structural alignment and secondary structure prediction informed by multiple homologs. Nucleic Acids Research 45 (20), 11570–11581.

Taylor, H.S., 1941. Large molecules through atomic spectacles. Proceedings of the American Philosophical Society 85, 1–12.

Taylor, W.R., 2001. Defining linear segments in protein structure. Journal of Molecular Biology 310, 1135–1150.

Terwilliger, T.C., 2010. Rapid model building of alpha-helices in electron-density maps. Acta Crystallographica D Biological Crystallography 66, 268–275.

Tiffany, M.L., Krimm, S., 1968. New chain conformations of poly(glutamic acid) and polylysine. Biopolymers 6, 1379–1382.

Tina, K., Bhadra, R., Srinivasan, N., 2007. PIC: Protein interactions calculator. Nucleic Acids Research 35, W473–W476.

Tincer, G., Bayyurt, B., Arıca, Y., Gürsel, İ., 2015. Chitosan polysaccharide suppress toll like receptor dependent immune response [Çitosan polisakkaridi toll benzeri reseptöre bağlıbağışıklık yanıtını baskılar]. Turkish Journal of Immunology 3, 15–20.

Tinoco, I., Bustamante, C., 1999. How RNA folds. Journal of Molecular Biology 293, 271–281.

Tiwari, A., Panigrahi, S.K., 2007. HBAT: A complete package for analysing strong and weak hydrogen bonds in macromolecular crystal structures. In Silico Biology 7, 651–661.

Todd, A.K., Johnston, M., Neidle, S., 2005. Highly prevalent putative quadruplex sequence motifs in human DNA. Nucleic Acids Res 33, 2901–2907.

Toniolo, C., Benedetti, E., 1991. The polypeptide 310-helix. Trends in Biochemical Sciences 16, 350–353.

Toukach, F.V., Ananikov, V.P., 2013. Recent advances in computational predictions of NMR parameters for the structure elucidation of carbohydrates: Methods and limitations. Chemical Society Reviews 42, 8376–8415.

Touw, W.G., Baakman, C., Black, J., et al., 2015. A series of PDB-related databanks for everyday needs. Nucleic Acids Research 43, D364–D368.

Van Der Spoel, D., Lindahl, E., Hess, B., et al., 2005. GROMACS: Fast, flexible, and free. Journal of Computational Chemistry 26, 1701–1718.

Venkatachalam, C.M., 1968. Stereochemical criteria for polypeptides and proteins. V. Conformation of a system of three linked peptide units. Biopolymers 6, 1425–1436.

Vermeire, J., Vanbillemont, G., Witkowski, W., Verhasselt, B., 2011. The Nef-infectivity enigma: Mechanisms of enhanced lentiviral infection. Current HIV Research 9, 474–489.

Wallace, B.A., 2009. Protein characterisation by synchrotron radiation circular dichroism spectroscopy. Quarterly Reviews of Biophysics 42, 317–370.

Wang, A., Quigley, G.J., Kolpak, F.J., et al., 1979. Molecular structure of a left-handed double helical DNA fragment at atomic resolution. Nature 282, 680–686.

Wang, Z.-G., Elbaz, J., Willner, I., 2010. DNA machines: Bipedal walker and stepper. Nano Letters 11, 304–309.

Watson, J.D., Crick, F.H., 1953. Molecular structure of nucleic acids. Nature 171, 737–738.

Weaver, T.M., 2000. The pi-helix translates structure into function. Protein Science 9, 201–206.

Whitmore, L., Miles, A.J., Mavridis, L., et al., 2017. PCDDB: New developments at the protein circular dichroism data bank. Nucleic Acids Research 45, D303–D307.

Whitmore, L., Wallace, B.A., 2004. DICHROWEB, an online server for protein secondary structure analyses from circular dichroism spectroscopic data. Nucleic Acids Research 32, W668–W673.

Wiedemann, C., Bellstedt, P., Gorlach, M., 2013. CAPITO – A web server-based analysis and plotting tool for circular dichroism data. Bioinformatics 29, 1750–1757.

Williams, C.J., Headd, J.J., Moriarty, N.W., et al., 2017. MolProbity: More and better reference data for improved all-atom structure validation. Protein Science 27 (1), 293–315.

Wilm, A., Linnenbrink, K., Steger, G., 2008. ConStruct: Improved construction of RNA consensus structures. BMC Bioinformatics 9, 219.

Wilson, D.N., Nierhaus, K.H., 2003. The ribosome through the looking glass. Angewandte Chemie International Edition 42, 3464–3486.

Wing, R., Drew, H., Takano, T., et al., 1980. Crystal structure analysis of a complete turn of B-DNA. Nature 287, 755–758.

Wohlert, J., Berglund, L.A., 2011. A coarse-grained model for molecular dynamics simulations of native cellulose. Journal of Chemical Theory and Computation 7, 753–760.

Woody, R.W., 1992. Circular dichroism and conformation of unordered polypeptides. Advanced Biophysical Chemistry 2, 37–79.

Wormald, M.R., Petrescu, A.J., Pao, Y.-L., et al., 2002. Conformational studies of oligosaccharides and glycopeptides: Complementarity of NMR, X-ray crystallography, and molecular modelling. Chemical Reviews 102, 371–386.

Wright, W.E., Tesmer, V.M., Huffman, K.E., et al., 1997. Normal human chromosomes have long G-rich telomeric overhangs at one end. Genes & Development 11, 2801–2809.

Xia, J., Daly, R.P., Chuang, F.-C., et al., 2007. Sugar folding: A novel structural prediction tool for oligosaccharides and polysaccharides 2. Journal of Chemical Theory and Computation 3, 1629–1643.

Xu, H., Di Antonio, M., McKinney, S., et al., 2017. CX-5461 is a DNA G-quadruplex stabilizer with selective lethality in BRCA1/2 deficient tumours. Nature Communications 8, 14432.

Yamasaki, R., Bacon, B., 1991. Three-dimensional structural analysis of the group B polysaccharide of Neisseria meningitidis 6275 by two-dimensional NMR: The polysaccharide is suggested to exist in helical conformations in solution. Biochemistry 30, 851–857.

Yang, X.-M., Yu, W., Ou, Z.-P., et al., 2009. Antioxidant and immunity activity of water extract and crude polysaccharide from Ficus carica L. fruit. Plant Foods for Human Nutrition 64, 167–173.

Yang, Y., Gao, J., Wang, J., et al., 2016. Sixty-five years of the long march in protein secondary structure prediction: The final stretch? Brief Bioinformatics. doi:10.1093/bib/bbw129.

Yohannan, S., Faham, S., Yang, D., et al., 2004. The evolution of transmembrane helix kinks and the structural diversity of G protein-coupled receptors. Proceedings of the National Academy of Sciences of the United States of America 101, 959–963.

Yongxu, S., Jicheng, L., 2008. Structural characterization of a water-soluble polysaccharide from the roots of Codonopsis pilosula and its immunity activity. International Journal of Biological Macromolecules 43, 279–282.

Zhang, T., Zheng, Y., Cosgrove, D.J., 2016. Spatial organization of cellulose microfibrils and matrix polysaccharides in primary plant cell walls as imaged by multichannel atomic force microscopy. The Plant Journal 85, 179–192.

Zhong, L., Johnson Jr., W.C., 1992. Environment affects amino acid preference for secondary structure. Proceedings of the National Academy of Sciences of the United States of America 89, 4462–4465.

Zimmerman, S.S., Scheraga, H.A., 1977. Local interactions in bends of proteins. Proceedings of the National Academy of Sciences of the United States of America 74, 4126–4129.

Zondlo, N.J., 2010. Non-covalent interactions: Fold globally, bond locally. Nature Chemical Biology 6, 567–568.

Zong, A., Cao, H., Wang, F., 2012. Anticancer polysaccharides from natural resources: A review of recent research. Carbohydrate Polymers 90, 1395–1410.

Zuker, M., Stiegler, P., 1981. Optimal computer folding of large RNA sequences using thermodynamics and auxiliary information. Nucleic Acids Research 9, 133–148.

Zuker, M., Sankoff, D., 1984. RNA secondary structures and their prediction. Bulletin of Mathematical Biology 46, 591–621.

Further Reading

Almond, A., Sheehan, J.K., 2003. Predicting the molecular shape of polysaccharides from dynamic interactions with water. Glycobiology 13, 254–264.

Caffall, K.H., Mohnen, D., 2009. The structure, function, and biosynthesis of plant cell wall pectic polysaccharides. Carbohydrate Research 344, 1879–1900.

Cammas, A., Millevoi, S., 2017. RNA G-quadruplexes: Emerging mechanisms in disease. Nucleic Acids Research 45 (4), 1584–1595.

Hänsel-Hertsch, R., Di Antonio, M., Balasubramanian, S., 2017. DNA G-quadruplexes in the human genome: Detection, functions and therapeutic potential. Nature Reviews Molecular Cell Biology 18 (5), 279–284.

Jacobs, T.M., Williams, B., Williams, T., et al., 2016. Design of structurally distinct proteins using strategies inspired by evolution. Science 352 (6286), 687–690.

Jansson, P.E., Kenne, L., Widmalm, G., 1989. Computer-assisted structural analysis of polysaccharides with an extended version of CASPER using 1H- and 13C NMR data. Carbohydrate Research 188, 169–191.

Kelley, L.A., Sternberg, M.J., 2009. Protein structure prediction on the Web: A case study using the Phyre server. Nature Protocols 4 (3), 363–371.

Laing, C., Schlick, T., 2011. Computational approaches to RNA structure prediction, analysis, and design. Current Opinion in Structural Biology 21 (3), 306–318.

Lee, G., Nowsak, G., Jaroniec, J., Zhang, Q., Marszalec, P.E., 2004. Molecular dynamics simulations of forced conformational transitions in 1,6-linked polysaccharides. Biophysical Journal 87, 1456–1465.

Low, J.T., Weeks, K.M., 2010. SHAPE-directed RNA secondary structure prediction. Methods 52 (2), 150–158.

Mathews, D.H., Disney, M.D., Childs, J.L., 2004. Incorporating chemical modification constraints into a dynamic programming algorithm for prediction of RNA secondary structure. Proceedings of the National Academy of Sciences of the United States of America 101 (19), 7287–7292.

Miao, Z., Adamiak, R.W., Antczak, M., et al., 2017. RNA-Puzzles Round III: 3D RNA structure prediction of five riboswitches and one ribozyme. RNA 23 (5), 655–672.

Miao, Z., Westhof, E., 2017. RNA structure: Advances and assessment of 3D structure prediction. Annual Review of Biophysics 46, 483–503.

Moult, J., 2005. A decade of CASP: Progress, bottlenecks and prognosis in protein structure prediction. Current Opinion in Structural Biology 15 (3), 285–289.

Rohs, R., Jin, X., West, S.M., et al., 2010. Origins of specificity in protein-DNA recognition. Annual Review of Biochemistry 79, 233–269.

Sarkar, A., Perez, A., 2012. PolySac3BD: An annotated data base for 3 dimensional structures of polysaccharides. BMC Bioinformatics 13, 302.

Woolfson, D.N., 2017. Coiled-coil design: Updated and upgraded. In: Parry, D.A.D., Squire, J.M. (Eds.), Fibrous Proteins: Structures and Mechanisms. Springer International Publishing, pp. 35–61.

Relevant Websites

http://people.cryst.bbk.ac.uk/~ubcg25a/
  Bonnie Ann Wallace.
http://pfam.xfam.org/
  EMBL-EBI.
http://www.emdatabank.org/
  EMDataBank.
https://web.expasy.org/docs/swiss-prot_guideline.html
  Expasy.

http://www.glycam.com/
    GLYCAM Web.
https://rna.urmc.rochester.edu/index.html
    Mathews Lab.
http://nucleix.mbu.iisc.ernet.in/
    MBU.
http://ndbserver.rutgers.edu/
    ndb Nucleic Acid Database.
http://www.ebi.ac.uk/pdbe/pisa/
    Protein Data Bank.
http://kinemage.biochem.duke.edu/teaching/anatax/
    The Anatomy and Taxonomy of Protien Structure.
http://eddylab.org/
    The Eddy/Rivas Laboratory.
http://rna.tbi.univie.ac.at/
    ViennaRNA Web Services.
https://zhanglab.ccmb.med.umich.edu/
    Zhang Lab.

Biographical Sketch

Prasun Kumar received a Bachelor of Technology degree in Bioinformatics from SASTRA University. For his Ph.D. in molecular biophysics, he worked with Prof. Manju Bansal at Molecular Biophysics Unit, Indian Institute of Science. The main thrust of his graduate studies was to develop algorithms for the identification and analyses of various secondary structure elements in protein structures. His work on comprehensive *in-silico* analyses of commonly occurring, as well as less frequently observed helices like π and PolyProline-II helices in globular proteins provided more insights into the sequence-structure relationships. He has also worked on structural analyses of nucleic acids and contributed to the modifications of in-house programs NUPARM as well as NUC-GEN. Prasun is now a postdoctoral research associate in Prof. Derek N. Woolfson's group at University of Bristol, United Kingdom, where he is working on the development of algorithms and *de novo* design of coiled-coils with a focus on probing non-covalent interactions within these.

Swagata Halder, received a Master of Science degree in Chemistry from Bengal Engineering and Science University, Shibpur. She has done her Ph.D in Molecular Biophysics under the supervision of Prof. Chaitali Mukhopadhyay, Department of Chemistry in University of Calcutta. Her research work was based on "Effect of Glycosylation on the Protein Structure and Dynamics: Insights from Molecular Modelling". She has modelled and simulated various glycosylated proteins like legume lectin Soybean agglutinin (SBA) and some antifreeze proteins like Ocean Pout during her graduate research. The main focus of the study was to predict the atomistic details of protein-carbohydrate interactions which play important roles in molecular mechanism of some biologically relevant phenomenon. Swagata is now a postdoctoral fellow in Prof. Manju Bansal's research group at Indian Institute of Science, India. Her current research is on identification and characterization of RNA thermometers in bacteria by molecular dynamic simulations. She is also working on aggregation property of some disease related proteins in presence of DNA by Replica Exchange MD techniques.

Professor Manju Bansal carried out her doctoral research under the guidance of Prof G N Ramachandran at the Indian Institute of Science, Bangalore and worked on the triple helical structure of fibrous protein collagen. She received her PhD degree in 1977 and joined the faculty of IISc in 1982, where she is currently an INSA Senior Scientist and J.C. Bose National Fellow. She has been an Alexander von Humboldt Fellow at EMBL Heidelberg and Frei Univ Berlin, and a Senior Fulbright Fellow at UCSF, San Francisco. She was the founder-Director of the Institute of Bioinformatics and Applied Biotechnology, Bangalore and represents India on the Advisory Board of wwPDB. She has published more than 120 papers in International journals and mentored about 60 doctoral and graduate students. Dr. Bansal's research interests have primarily focused on relating protein and DNA sequences to their structures and function, by developing new concepts, computational algorithms and tools, particularly in the area of DNA promoter architecture. Lab URL: http://nucleix.iisc.ac.in/.

Engineering of Supramolecular RNA Structures

Effirul I Ramlan, Malaysia Genome Institute (MGI-NIBM), Kajang, Malaysia and University of Malaya, Kuala Lumpur, Malaysia
Mohd Firdaus-Raih, Universiti Kebangsaan Malaysia, Bangi, Malaysia

Supramolecular RNA Structures

Proteins are responsible for carrying out vital cellular functions achieved through the combination of self-assembly and conformational dynamics. The structural variability of protein (complex three-dimensional folded structures) underlies its ability in mediating almost all functions in living cells. With the discovery of small regulatory RNA (sRNAs) (Zamore and Haley, 2005) and the discovery of the catalytic ability of ribozymes (Altman, 1990), RNA emerges as a more versatile molecule than previously perceived. Similar to protein, RNA structure determines its function, but unlike protein, the secondary structure of RNA molecule provides more information regarding its tertiary folding; thus, promoting rational design of programmable and functional RNA supramolecular structures to be constructed (i.e., nanostructures of the size of 10 nm in dimension (Goodsell, 2004)).

The discovery of short RNAs' (which is 21–25 nt in length) role in regulating gene expression (Couzin, 2002) has sparked a strong interest in RNA molecules. In RNA interference, a short interfering RNA molecule (siRNA) forms base pair with a target region in mRNA, allowing a protein complex called RNA-induced silencing complex or (RISC) to attach and cleaves the target region (Hannon, 2002; Petersen et al., 2006). Another short RNAs called microRNA (miRNA), generated from an enzyme named Dicer that cleaved non-coding RNAs (i.e., RNA that do not code protein), binds imperfectly with the target region in mRNA (forming a bulge) to prevent the translation machinery from accessing this target region (Zamore and Haley, 2005). In addition to these short RNAs, another complex folded RNA domain called riboswitches also play a role in gene regulation. Riboswitches sense the presence of specific metabolites and harness their conformational switching to activate the gene-control mechanisms in preventing the production of protein (Mandal and Breaker, 2004; Nudler and Mironov, 2004).

RNA nanotechnology focuses on the engineering of functional and customizable supramolecular RNA structures as molecular devices utilizing the self-assembly principle of nucleic acids, reviewed in Jaeger and Chworos (2006); Guo (2010); Shu et al. (2014); Li et al. (2015); Jasinski et al. (2017). Advances in RNA nanotechnology have enabled the development of various RNA nanoparticles in nanomedicine, detailed explicitly in Jasinski et al. (2017). RNA nanoparticles have been developed as an alternate platform for targeted therapeutic delivery mechanism in the form of RNA aptamers (Esposito et al., 2011; Shigdar et al., 2011; Rockey et al., 2011; Guo et al., 2012; Thiel et al., 2012; Kang and Lee, 2012; Zhou et al., 2012; Sundaram et al., 2013), as Ribozymes-based therapeutic strategy (Mulhbacher et al., 2010; Shu et al., 2011), as gene expression regulator through utilization of various Riboswitches (Suess and Weigand, 2008; Serganov, 2009; Berens et al., 2015) and RNA interference therapy (Haque et al., 2012; Ye et al., 2012; Shu et al., 2015; Lee et al., 2015; Roh et al., 2016).

Instead of mimicking the methodologies commonly associated with synthetic DNA nanostructures (commonly known as "DNA Origami"), RNA nanostructures are able to follow a more natural suprastructures formation. This can be achieved through the multi-self-assemblies of natural occurring RNA motifs (i.e., optimization of kinetic foldings and thermodynamic requirement based on combination of existing RNA motifs). The conceptualization of the desired nanostructures is rather straight-forward since the design will be based on a dictionary (or database) of well-characterized RNA motifs. This tutorial highlights the various methodologies for constructing supra-molecular RNAs and presents a generic computational protocols to support the in-silico construction.

Properties of Ribonucleic Acids

Nucleic acids are macromolecules that play an important role as information carriers in cells. Two types occur, ribonucleic acids (RNA) and de-oxyribonucleic acids (DNA), which are named after the structure of a sugar component in these molecules. RNA and DNA are typically long linear polymers that consist of a large number of monomers taken from a set of four different nucleotides (C, G, A, and T or U for RNA). The sequential order in which these bases are interlinked in the nucleic acid molecule represents information. RNA has the task of transmitting information within the cell, while DNA transmits information from generation to generation. The genetic information is encoded in a dimer of two complementary nucleotide chains ('single-stranded' DNA or ssDNA) which upon self-assembly assumes the well known double-helical structure ('double-stranded' DNA or dsDNA). DNA is well suited as carrier of genetic information because of its energy degeneracy with respect to the sequential order of the nucleotides. The properties of RNA molecules are more dependent on the sequence of nucleotides and as a consequence RNA takes on additional roles in the cell aside from representing information.

Within the RNA hierarchical framework, stacking and Watson-Crick base pairing between complementary nucleotides (canonical base pairing) trigger folding and assembly of RNA primary sequences into secondary structures (hairpin loops, bulges, internal loops and multiloops) as depicted in **Fig. 1**. The hydroxyl group (-OH) at the 2′-carbon in ribose is not present in de-oxyribose (Berg et al., 2003). The consequence of this structural difference is twofold. DNA is considerably more stable against hydrolysis and forms more compact double strands, while RNA has more conformational flexibility (Bloomfield et al., 2000). The

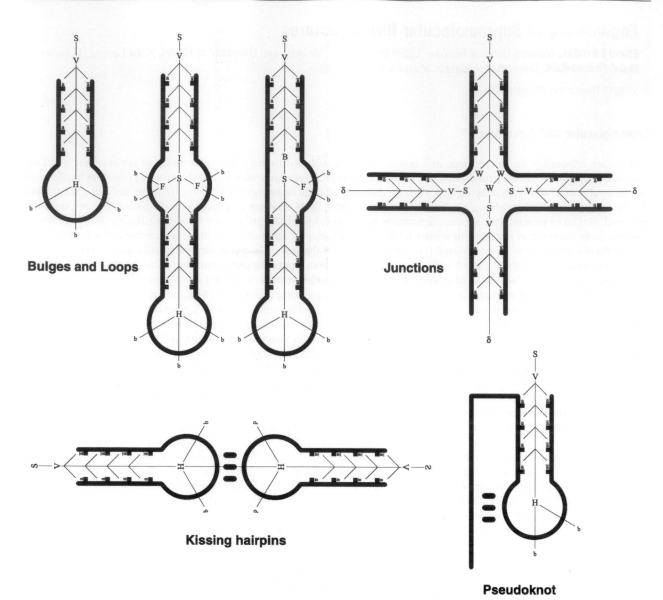

Bulges and Loops

Junctions

Kissing hairpins

Pseudoknot

Fig. 1 RNA Structural Motifs. The intra-molecular binding creates RNA motifs such as bulges, internal, and hairpin loops. RNA molecule can forms inter-molecular binding, which produces junctions. From 2-way or kink-turn, the commonly used 3-way or 3WJ in nanoparticles fabrication, four-way (shown here), and available up to 9 way junctions), kissing hairpins and pseudoknot. There are also GNRA-Loop Receptor, Triple helical scaffold and G-Quadruplex motifs that are common in RNA suprastructure constructions. Reproduced from Jasinski, D., Haque, F., Binzel, D.W., Guo, P., 2017. Advancement of the emerging field of RNA nanotechnology. ACS Nano 11 (2), 1142–1164.

2′-hydroxyl group locks the ribose sugar into a 3′-endo chair conformation. It is structurally favorable for the RNA double helix to adopt the A-form which is 20% shorter and wider than B-form DNA helices. The A-form RNA helices are thermodynamically more stable than the B-form DNA helices (SantaLucia-Jr, 1998). However, the 2′-hydroxyl group permits RNA to be susceptible to nuclease digestion which limits RNA stability in-vivo.

For a given RNA sequence, there is often a diverse set of secondary structures it can fold into. Which structure is favored will depend on the physico-chemical environment of the molecule, for example, the presence or absence of substrates or ions. In addition, the presence of non-canonical base pairs can contribute significantly to RNA folding. Affecting the rigidity and thermo-dynamic stability of RNA secondary structures (Mathews and Turner, 2006). Conversely, a diverse set of sequence configurations can yield a particular secondary structure (Draper, 1996; Zuker, 1989) through energy minimization model. Subsequently, interactions among secondary structure motifs lead to the formation of a tertiary structure which in some cases entails functionality (**Fig. 2**).

Compared to the folding of protein, the amount of energy released during the formation of RNA secondary structure is much larger than the energy required during the formation of its tertiary structure. On its own, RNA secondary structure is quite informative. Long helices that are present in the secondary phase are most likely preserved in its tertiary structure. This, therefore provide a reasonable prediction of the basic form and relative positioning for some elements in the tertiary structure (Higgs, 1995). Determining the secondary structures is an integral element of predicting the tertiary motifs.

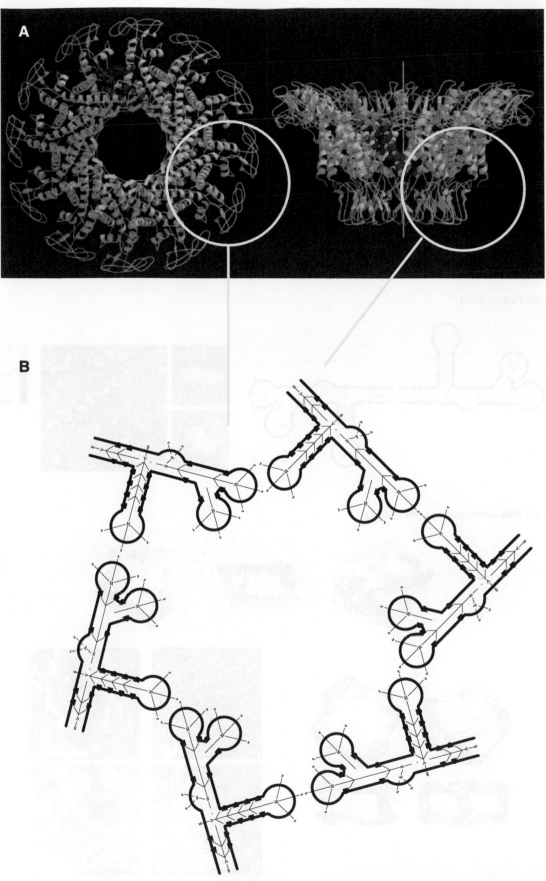

Fig. 2 The hierarchical folding of RNA molecule exemplified in the hexameric ring packaging RNA pRNA). A. The connector and structure ribbon diagrams of the Bacteriophage Φ 29 DNA packaging motor. Reproduced with permission from Simpson, A.A., Tao, Y., Leiman, P.G., *et al.*, 2000. Structure of the bacteriophage 29 DNA packaging motor. Nature 408, 745750. Copyright 2000 Nature Publishing Group. B. Conceptual representation of a pRNA hexamer assembled using the Hand-in-Hand strategy resembling the six packaging RNAs of Φ 29 DNA packaging motor.

A. via Hand-in-Hand

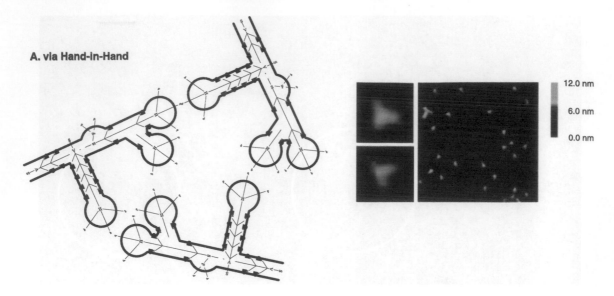

B. via Foot-to-Foot

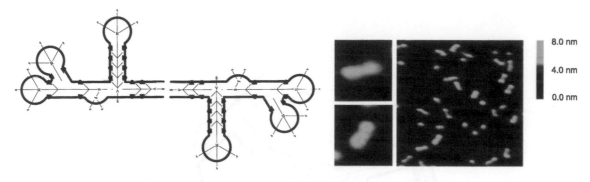

C. via RNA Architectonics (tectoRNA)

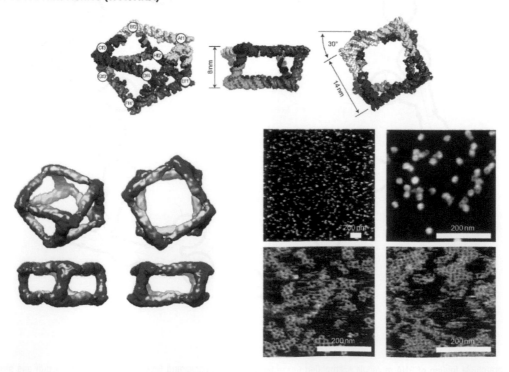

Natural occurring RNAs have been identified and characterized using NMR and crystallographic atomic structures (Leontis et al., 1995; Moore, 1999). Natural occurring RNAs provide a definitive blueprint in the design of supramolecular structures through the representation of the sequence to structure relationship (i.e., natural occurring structures are encoded in naturally conserved sequences). These natural motifs provide geometry information of helical elements, and mediate stereo-chemically precise and readily reversible tertiary and quaternary interactions (Jaeger and Chworos, 2006). This information allows RNA supra-structures to be engineered with relatively accurate approximation supplemented by the secondary structure prediction. In terms of engineering supra-molecular RNA structures, this hierarchical folding state has to be observed closely to avoid kinetically trapped misfolded states, which disrupt the formation of the intended structures.

Techniques for Constructing RNA Nanostructures

A variety of supramolecular RNA structures (also known as RNA nanopar-ticles) have been successfully fabricated using various self-assembly approaches. In depth reviews of these methodologies are available in Li et al. (2015); Jasinski et al. (2017). This section provides a description of these construction methodologies, and we strongly recommend readers to refer to the references that are supplemented in each method for further understanding of the self-assembly mechanisms.

Via Hand-In-Hand Interactions

The strategy utilizes RNA loop elements as inter-RNA mounting dovetails (Fig. 3(A)). Incorporating these internal RNA loops eliminates the need for external dovetail elements. The design principles are exemplified by the structural features of the packaging RNA (pRNA) derived from bacterio-phage phi29 (Guo et al., 1987). Through inter-locking loop interactions between different pRNAs, dimers, trimers, tetramers, pentamers, hexamers, and heptamers have been created (Guo et al., 1998; Shu et al., 2004, 2013a,b). Adaptation using non-covalent loop-loop contacts based on RNAI/IIi kissing-loop complex have been used to build RNA nanorings (Yingling et al., 2007; Grabow et al., 2011), which are thermostable, ribonuclease resistance and capable of delivering RNA interference modules.

Via Foot-to-Foot Interactions

Extending the 3'end of pRNA monomer with a single stranded palindrome sequence promotes self-assembly of two pRNA molecules. The complementarity of the palindrome sequence bridges the two foot orientations (i.e., foot-to-foot interaction) (as depicted Fig. 3 (B)) (Shu et al., 2004, 2013a,b). Construction of RNA hexamers, octamers, decamers, and dodecamers utilizing palindrome sequence to bridge RNA motifs, or scaffolds have been reported (Li et al., 2015). Combination of both hand-in-hand and foot-to-foot interactions has been reported to construct pRNA array (Shu et al., 2004). Fusions of sticky-end cohesion with foot-to-foot inter-actions were also reported to construct RNA nanoprisms in Hao et al. (2014) through the re-engineering of pRNA molecule.

Via Rational Design With Natural RNA Motifs

The discovery of natural occurring RNA molecules provides a definitive template in constructing RNA supramolecules, where precise structural information and structure to sequence relationship are defined through various RNA motifs. Rational design utilizing stable RNA motifs (e.g., kissing loops, dovetails, pseudoknots, kink turns, and multiway junctions) has produced exciting RNA supramolecule structures (Leontis et al., 1995; Leontis and Westhof, 2003; Petrov et al., 2013) Larger, more complex, and extraordinary stable natural motifs, such as phi29 motor of pRNA (Guo et al., 1998; Zhang et al., 2013), tRNA (Severcan et al., 2010), 5S RNA (Shu et al., 2011), and others (Grabow et al., 2011) have been used to form synthetic RNA supramolecules (Dibrov et al., 2011; Shu et al., 2013b; Jasinski et al., 2014; Khisamutdinov et al., 2014). A popular RNA motifs exploitation is the robust pRNA-3WJ motif. The extended work of hybrid strategy utilizing phi29 pRNA-3WJ motifs for nanostructures fabrication with precise size, 3D architecture and container, RNA Dendrimer and co-transcription and inter-cellularly multifunctional nanos-tructures have been reported (Jasinski et al., 2017).

Via RNA Architectonics (Tectorna)

RNA tectonics focuses on the modularity of RNA molecules (Jaeger and Chworos, 2006). The strategy exploited the ability of RNA structures to decomposed and reassembled into a new modular RNA structure (Ref. Fig. 3(C)). Through the inversion of the

---

Fig. 3 The fabrication of RNA supramolecular structures using various assembly strategies. A. The conceptual representation of the trimers formed between three monomers and B. The formation of dimer using the foot-to-foot strategy. Reproduced from Shu, D., Moll, W.-D., Deng, Z., Mao, C., Guo, P., 2004. Bottom-up assemblyof RNA arrays and superstructures as potential parts in nanotechnology. Nano Letters 4 (9), 1717–1723. Shu, Y., Haque, F., Shu, D., et al., 2013a. Fabrication of 14 different RNA nanoparticles for specific tumor targeting without accumulation in normal organs. RNA 19, 767–777. The AFM images for both are reproduced with permission from Shu, Y., Shu, D., Haque, F., Guo, P., 2013b. Fabrication of pRNA nanopar-ticles to deliver therapeutic RNAs and bioactive compounds into tumor cells. Nature Protocols 8, 1635–1659. Copyright 2013 Nature Publishing Group. C. A polyhedron construction using tRNAs. 3D model, cryo-EM and AFM images are reproduced with permission from Severcan, I., Geary, C., Chworos, A., et al., 2010. A polyhedron made of tRNAs. Nature Chemistry 2 (9), 772–779. Copyright 2010 Nature Publishing Group.

hierarchical folding (from tertiary to secondary structure to primary sequence), outline of the supramolecular RNA structures encompassing the tertiary motifs, secondary motifs, intra and inter-molecular interactions, and conserved sequences can be extracted. Thus, providing the geometry and self-assembly phases necessary to design the supramolecules. With the availability of Structural Classification of RNA (SCOR) (Klosterman *et al.*, 2004; Tamura *et al.*, 2004), nucleic acids databases (NDB) (Berman *et al.*, 1996), and the RNAjunction database (Bindewald *et al.*, 2008b), there exists a large number of candidate tectoRNA motifs. Readily configured as supramolecules through semi-rigid double helical bindings as exemplified in Westhof *et al.* (1996); Jaeger and Leontis (2000); Chworos *et al.* (2004); Shu *et al.* (2004); Nasalean *et al.* (2006); Dibrov *et al.* (2011); Ishikawa *et al.* (2013); Yu *et al.* (2015).

Via RNA Origami

The field of DNA nanotechnology leverages on the DNA complementarity self-assembly guided by the canonical Watson-Crick interactions (G-C and A-T base pairing), and structural rules (based on Holliday junction) to create DNA nanostructures (Lin *et al.*, 2006; Feldkamp and Niemeyer, 2006; Seeman, 2007, 2010; Lin *et al.*, 2009). These governing rules have resulted into various DNA nanoscaffolds (Brucale *et al.*, 2006; Erben *et al.*, 2007; Andersen *et al.*, 2008; Aldaye *et al.*, 2008; Zimmermann *et al.*, 2008; Bhatia *et al.*, 2009; Licata and Tkachenko, 2009) with extensive functionalities formed through self-assembly of DNA subunits called "DNA tiles". A different approach for DNA "origami" was presented in Rothemund (2006), where by a long stranded DNA is "stapled" into complex geometry using short complementary DNA strands. In this context, the less hierarchical and directed nature of DNA folding (i.e., double-stranded formation) are better suited for such approach, exemplified by the fabrication of various DNA supramolecules (Dietz *et al.*, 2009; Ke *et al.*, 2009; Douglas *et al.*, 2012; Zadegan *et al.*, 2012). The interpretation of RNA "origami" utilizing the short "stapled" approach is presented in Endo *et al.* (2014), where long ssRNAs are folded into rode-like structures using short RNA staples through in-vitro transcription of dsDNA scaffold and DNA staple templates. Further expansion of the "ssOrigami" method for single-stranded RNAs are discussed in Han *et al.* (2017).

Computational Methods of Constructing RNA Supramolecules

Despite the various strategies of constructing RNA supramolecules (as presented in Section "Techniques for Constructing RNA Nanostructures"), in actuality, the design and construction of these supramolecular structures relies heavily on manual assembly and fine tuning. Manual design has significant impact on the time and cost incurred to engineer these functional supramolecules, and taking into consideration the drive to produce more cost effective, and high demand for more complex structures, autonomous computational pipelines/protocols are a must. The general approach to RNA nanotechnology has now adapt to allow computational and folding prediction as one of the steps in the construction, immediately following the conceptualization as discussed in Guo (2010).

In contrast to protein, there exist well established computational tools that can aid in the secondary structure prediction and sequence design of RNA molecules. Tools such as *mfold* and *DINAMelt* (Zuker *et al.*, 1991; Zuker, 2003; Markham and Zuker, 2005), the *Vienna RNA Package* (Hofacker *et al.*, 1994), *RNAstructure* (Mathews *et al.*, 2004), *RNAsoft* (Andronescu *et al.*, 2003) and *RNAshapes* (Steffen *et al.*, 2006) are some of the most common and well-known in the prediction of RNA secondary structure. Secondary structure prediction is supplemented with sub-optimal prediction (Zuker, 1989; Wuchty *et al.*, 1999), which allows further determination of how well-defined the lowest free energy structure is, and at the same time highlight weak base-pairing positions that are present in a structure.

Secondary structure prediction has also been extended to includes interacting molecules (Andronescu, 2003; Dimitrov and Zuker, 2004; Muckstein *et al.*, 2006; Andronescu *et al.*, 2005; Bernhart *et al.*, 2006; Bindewald *et al.*, 2011). In the context of engineering RNA supramolecules, understanding the interactions between multiple RNA strands is essential in order to allow the evaluation of their binding compatibility to take place. The secondary structure prediction for interacting RNA molecules also quantifies the probability of homo-dimer formation (Dimitrov and Zuker, 2004). The relative probability of inter-molecular and intra-molecular binding is another critical aspect to consider. To arrive to the desired supramolecular structures, it is important that the base pairing within each molecule binds stronger than any possible intermolecular binding involving other molecules in the solution, or vice-versa depending on the intended function and structural constraints.

Although definitive sequence to structure mappings are available for natural occurring RNA motifs, the exploitation of multi-motifs self-assembly (following the previously discussed strategies) requires synthetic modification to the existing sequence. Therefore, consideration for the inverse folding prediction must be taken. The inverse folding problem involves designing RNA sequences that fold into a specified secondary structure (Schuster, 2006). By solving this problem, it allows for supramolecular structures to be artificially designed based on specific structural constraints and functionality. The three common inverse prediction tools are *RNAinverse* from the Vienna package (Hofacker *et al.*, 1994), *RNAdesigner* (Andronescu *et al.*, 2004) from the *RNAsoft* package (Andronescu *et al.*, 2003) and *INFO-RNA* (Busch and Backofen, 2006). In test cases of more than 150 nt artificially and naturally occurring RNA molecules, both these tools *RNAdesigner* and *INFO-RNA* produce encouraging results with both performs much better than RNAin-verse overall (Andronescu *et al.*, 2004; Busch and Backofen, 2006; Zadeh *et al.*, 2011).

Since, the characterization and categorization of known RNA motifs plays a major role in constructing RNA supramolecular structures, the curation of RNA motifs into searchable databases is a powerful tool for the computer aided design pipeline (Jaeger and Chworos, 2006; Bindewald *et al.*, 2008a,b). To facilitate the construction, information related to the conserved sequences and

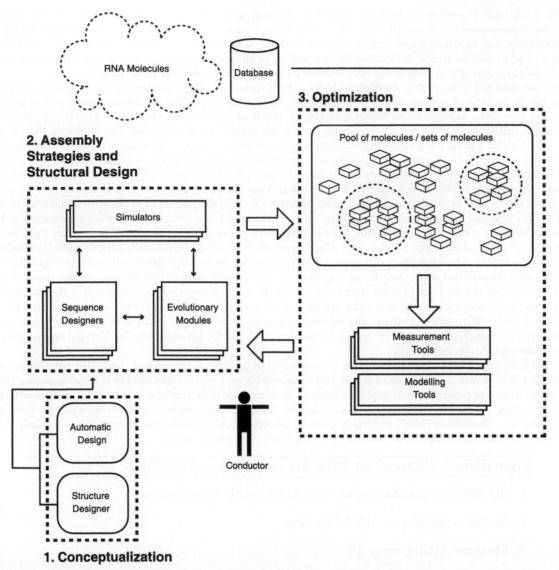

2. Assembly Strategies and Structural Design

RNA Molecules

Database

3. Optimization

Pool of molecules / sets of molecules

Simulators

Sequence Designers ↔ Evolutionary Modules

Measurement Tools

Modelling Tools

Automatic Design

Structure Designer

Conductor

1. Conceptualization

Fig. 4 The computational pipeline for engineering RNA supramolecular structures. The conceptualization produces hypothetical module of the structure that will undergo structural configuration and refinement before candidates are generated for lab verification.

structures mapping is key (i.e., to reduce the run time needed during inverse folding prediction and to ensure workability in the laboratory). This, determines the compatibility of multi-motifs self-assembly and other structural manipulations (Jaeger and Chworos, 2006). These databases classify RNA structures by function, tertiary interactions (geometry), as in the Structural Classification of RNA (SCOR) and nucleic acid database (NDB) (Berman et al., 1996; Klosterman et al., 2004; Tamura et al., 2004). One of the most commonly associated databases for RNA supramolecular construction is RNAJunction (Bindewald et al., 2008b). RNAJunction consists of approximately 13,000 junction motifs and kissing loops derived from the Protein Data Bank (PDB). These motifs are clustered into 2-way or 2WJ (bulge and internal loops) up to 9-way or 9WJ junctions. RNAJunction database also includes the basis of documented geometries and recurring base- and tertiary- interactions of these motifs.

In addition to the databases, there are various design tools that can aid the design of RNA supramolecular structures in three dimensional workspace (Bindewald et al., 2008a; Martinez et al., 2008; Jossinet et al., 2010; Xia et al., 2010). One such tool is NanoTiler (Bindewald et al., 2008a). NanoTiler generates candidate RNA motifs from the RNAJunction database or similar databases. These candidate motifs can be assemble through a variable length pre-defined RNA helices. The tool also allows sequence conservations, to ensure conformity of the tertiary foldings. NanoTiler can function similar to a design studio, where custom candidate motifs can be generated with various structural modifications subjected to the plausible characteristic of natural RNA folding principles, and it is also capable of producing RNA primary sequences to match these custom designed motifs. These sequences have good agreement to be realized in the laboratory as exemplified in the construction of RNA supramolecules depicted in Bindewald et al. (2008a).

In addition to NanoTiler, we have RNA2D3D (Martinez et al., 2008). RNA2D3D allows for rapid three dimensional modeling of the supramolecular structures using the primary sequence and secondary structure pairing information. It also provides adjustment tools for structural modification; to avoid steric clashes and optimize the thermodynamics. RNA2D3D capacity to integrate multiple motifs into a draft model of supramolecule structures (through default kissing-loop interactions) is essential in providing immediate feedback to the user. Alternatively, there are various general purpose molecular modeling packages, such as the Chimera (Pettersen *et al.*, 2004), and pyMol (Grell *et al.*, 2006), which are capable in modeling RNA supramolecular structures. However, due to its generic form, these tools lack the specific knowledge-based of RNA foldings; but offer flexibility for integration with other customizable pipelines.

Using the strategies (discussed in section "Techniques for Constructing RNA Nanostructures"), a generic computational pipeline can be established as depicted in **Fig. 4**. The implementation of the pipeline is subjected to the level of depth in the conceptualization phase as suggested in Afonin *et al.* (2014). This level can either be; whether (i) candidate motifs are already identified (or partially identified) or, (ii) a discovery to identify suitable motifs is needed. Key in the pipeline is the conceptualization phase. During this phase, the identification of the desired structures and functions are established. This includes consideration on the physico-chemical environment, size, complexity, geometry, restriction on sequences and relevant factors that should be based on extensive RNA folding knowledge base. The conceptualization will either produced constraints for immediate structural assembly and modification – For (i) (also referred as "Draft Secondary Structure" in Afonin *et al.* (2014)), or a set of criterion that can be used as search parameters in motif discovery - for (ii) (also referred as "Connectivity Rules" in Afonin *et al.* (2014)). Either way, both of these findings are essential and will be adapted as specification sheet during the construction phase.

Next, the selection of strategy for multi-motifs self-assembly. Although categorically different, these strategies are in-fact overlap (Afonin *et al.*, 2014). A closed design principle (i.e., where the self-assembly motifs are manually pre-determined) promotes a top-to-bottom optimization, where hypothetical supramolecular structures are decomposed into motifs with inter-molecular reactions reassembly components based on the "best-fit" strategy conforming to the selected motifs. In contrast, an open system, where only connectivity rules are defined (case (ii)), the bottom-up optimization is preferred. Combinatory search of the databases to find candidate motifs is executed and inter-molecular assembly recommendations would be made based on the "best-fit" strategy depending on the motif compatibility scores. During these process of optimizing the formation of structures, RNA 3D modeling programs such as NanoTiler and RNA2D3D are important. These tools provide immediate feedback on the compatibility of self-assembly between the suggested motifs.

Structural optimization follows next. The summary of the protocols are presented in Shapiro *et al.* (2008). The NanoTiler optimization protocol is described in Algo. 1. Interactions with NanoTiler are permissible via a graphical user interface or scripting language. NanoTiler allows optimization to be performed on motif placements and helix distortion to improve on the "best-fit" score. The bottom-up protocol is described in Algo. 2, and requires both RNA2D3D and NanoTiler. RNA2D3D allows interaction rules between multiple building blocks to be included (i.e., "Connectivity Rules") and rapidly generates the approximate supramolecular structure rendering. NanoTiler, in this instance acts as a refinement module to improve on the configuration of the selected motifs.

Algorithm 1 Protocol for RNA 3D Motifs using NanoTiler

1: 3D graph repsentation of structures $\leftarrow$ 3D coordinates

2: Motifs selection $\leftarrow$ RNAJunction

3: Measure fitting error (d)

4: **while** d **do**

5:     Identify $J \leftarrow$ junction

6:     Generate dsHelices (dsRNA) interpolating between fragments

7:     fn-mutate (J,dsRNA) $\leftarrow$ random chosen vertices

8:     Mesure d_1

9:     **if** $d_1 \leq d$ **then**

10:        replace J and dsRNA

11:    **end if**

12: **end while**

13: Optimize sequences for the model

14: Apply MM and MD for structural refinement

Algorithm 2 Protocol for RNA 2D Motifs using NanoTiler and RNA2D3D

1: 3D graph repsentation of structures ← 3D coordinates

2: Building Blocks ← Determine Secondary structure templates

3: Optimize sequences

4: Extract 3D coordinates ← Run RNA2D3D

5: Optimize sequences for the model

6: Apply MM and MD for structural refinement

As recommended by Shapiro *et al.* (2008), the designs are subjected to molecular mechanics and molecular dynamics inspection to ensure positive results in the laboratory. Output of the pipeline will then undergo the fabrication process. Two strategies for fabricating RNA supramolecular structure is discussed in Jaeger and Chworos (2006). The first approach is a single step assembly, in which all the sequences (i.e., primary sequence of the RNA motifs) are mixed together and assembled in a solution through a slow annealing process. The second strategy involves stepwise hierarchical self-assembly. Smaller sub-units are separately assembled before all these motifs are mixed together to form the supramoleculer structures. Conceptually similar to the hierarchical folding property of RNA molecule.

Conclusion

RNA supramolecule constructions involves intra/inter-molecular assembly of various RNA motifs. Understanding the folding of RNA motifs is essential in ensuring the conformity of the structure and functionality. The flexibility of RNA folding, allows variations (or meta-stable states) to exist within a small free energy value difference. This variability is further compounded when multiple motifs assembly are involved. Despite the presence of prediction tools to aid in the construction of RNA supramolecular structures, accurate prediction of tertiary and quarternary motifs remains a challenge. Prediction tools specific for tertiary structures are yet to be explored. Within this context, inverse folding involving multiple strands is necessary.

On the computational aspects, more enhancements are needed. For instance, the construction of supramolecule must consider a combination of an increased number of RNA motifs to improve on the demand for more complex multi-functional RNA structures. Accuracy in size, structural and function of these supramolecules are aspect that should be addressed during the design phase. Perhaps, a better combinatorial search with sufficient parameterization can help in identification of suitable RNA motifs, and a deep learning methodology can be incorporated in understanding the geometry and self-assembling mechanisms of complex natural occurring RNA supramolecule, thus, providing valuable insights into a better strategy of constructing RNA supramolecule. This will greatly benefit the field of RNA nanotechnology especially towards the design of a more complex and advanced supramolecule applicable towards the realization of nanomedicine.

See also: Biomolecular Structures: Prediction, Identification and Analyses. Natural Language Processing Approaches in Bioinformatics

---

References

Afonin, K.A., Kasprzak, W.K., Bindewald, E., *et al.*, 2014. In silico design and enzymatic synthesis of functional RNA nanoparticles. Accounts of Chemical Research 47 (6), 1731–1741.

Aldaye, F.A., Palmer, A.L., Sleiman, H.F., 2008. Assembling materials with dna as the guide. Science 321 (5897), 1795–1799.

Altman, S., 1990. Enzymatic cleavage of RNA by RNA (Nobel lecture). Ange-wandte Chemie International Edition 29, 749–758.

Andersen, F.F., Knudsen, B., Oliveira, C.L.P., *et al.*, 2008. Assembly and structural analysis of a covalently closed nano-scale dna cage. Nucleic Acids Research 36 (4), 1113–1119.

Andronescu, M., 2003. Algorithms for predicting the secondary structure of pairs and combinatorial sets of nucleic acid strands. Master's thesis, University of British Columbia, Vancouver.

Andronescu, M., Anguirre-Hernandez, R., Condon, A., Hoos, H.H., 2003. RNAsoft: A suite of RNA secondary structure prediction and design software tools. Nucleic Acids Research 31 (13), 3416–3422.

Andronescu, M., Fejes, A.P., Hutter, F., Condon, A., Hoos, H.H., 2004. A new algorithm for RNA secondary structure design. Journal of Molecular Biology 336 (3), 607–624.

Andronescu, M., Zhang, Z.C., Condon, A., 2005. Secondary structure prediction of interacting RNA molecules. Journal of Molecular Biology 345, 987–1001.

Shapiro, B.A., Bindewald, E., Kasprzak, W., Yingling, Y., 2008. Protocols for the in silico design of RNA nanostructures. In: Gazit E., N.R. (Ed.), Nanostructure Design. Methods in Molecular Biology, vol. 474. Humana Press, pp. 93–115.

Berens, C., Groher, F., Suess, B., 2015. RNA aptamers as genetic control devices: The potential of riboswitches as synthetic elements for regulating gene expression. Biotechnology Journal 10 (2), 246–257.

Berg, J.M., Tymoczko, J.L., Stryer, L., 2003. Biochemistry, fifth ed. New York: W. H. Freeman and Company.

Berman, H.M., Gelbin, A., Westbrook, J., 1996. Nucleic acid crystallography: A view from the nucleic acid database. Progress in Biophysics and Molecular Biology 66 (3), 255–288.

Bernhart, S.H., Tafer, H., Muckstein, U., et al., 2006. Partition function and base pairing probabilities of RNA heterodimers. Algorithms for Molecular Biology 1 (3), doi:10.1186/1748–7188 1–3.

Bhatia, D., Mehtab, S., Krishnan, R., et al., 2009. Icosahedral dna nanocapsules by modular assembly. Angewandte Chemie International Edition 48 (23), 4134–4137.

Bindewald, E., Afonin, K., Jaeger, L., Shapiro, B.A., 2011. Multistrand rna secondary structure prediction and nanostructure design including pseudoknots. ACS Nano 5 (12), 9542–9551.

Bindewald, E., Grunewald, C., Boyle, B., OConnor, M., Shapiro, B.A., 2008a. Computational strategies for the automated design of RNA nanoscale structures from building blocks using nanotiler. Journal of Molecular Graphics and Modelling 27 (3), 299–308.

Bindewald, E., Hayes, R., Yingling, Y.G., Kasprzak, W., Shapiro, B.A., 2008b. RNAJunction: A database of RNA junctions and kissing loops for three-dimensional structural analysis and nanodesign. Nucleic Acids Research 36, D392–D397.

Bloomfield, V.A., Crothers, D.M., Tinoco Jr., I., 2000. Nucleic Acids: Structures, Properties and Functions, first ed. California: University Science Books.

Brucale, M., Zuccheri, G., Rossi, L., et al., 2006. Characterization and modulation of the hierarchical self-assembly of nanostructured dna tiles into supramolecular polymers. Organic and Biomolecular Chemistry 4, 3427–3434.

Busch, A., Backofen, R., 2006. INFO-RNA – A fast approach to inverse RNA folding. Bioinformatics 22 (15), 1823–1831.

Chworos, A., Severcan, I., Koyfman, A.Y., et al., 2004. Building programmable jigsaw puzzles with RNA. Science 306 (5704), 2068–2072.

Couzin, J., 2002. Small RNAs make big splash. Science 298, 2296–2297.

Dibrov, S.M., McLean, J., Parsons, J., Hermann, T., 2011. Self-assembling RNA square. Proceedings of the National Academy of Sciences 108 (16), 6405–6408.

Dietz, H., Douglas, S.M., Shih, W.M., 2009. Folding dna into twisted and curved nanoscale shapes. Science 325 (5941), 725–730.

Dimitrov, R.A., Zuker, M., 2004. Prediction of hybridization and melting for double-stranded nucleic acids. Biophysical Journal 87, 215–226.

Douglas, S.M., Bachelet, I., Church, G.M., 2012. A logic-gated nanorobot for targeted transport of molecular payloads. Science 335 (6070), 831–834.

Draper, D.E., 1996. Strategies for RNA folding. Trends in biochemistry. Sciences 21, 145–149.

Endo, M., Takeuchi, Y., Emura, T., Hidaka, K., Sugiyama, H., 2014. Preparation of chemically modified RNA origami nanostructures. Chemistry A European Journal 20 (47), 15330–15333.

Erben, C.M., Goodman, R.P., Turberfield, A.J., 2007. A self-assembled dna bipyramid. Journal of the American Chemical Society 129 (22), 6992–6993.

Esposito, C.L., Passaro, D., Longobardo, I., et al., 2011. A neutralizing RNA aptamer against EGFR causes selective apoptotic cell death. PLOS ONE. e24071.

Feldkamp, U., Niemeyer, C.M., 2006. Rational design of dna nanoarchitectures. Angewandte Chemie International Edition 45 (12), 1856–1876.

Goodsell, D.S., 2004. Bionanotechnology: Lessons from Nature, first ed. Hoboken, New Jersey: Wiley-Liss.

Grabow, W.W., Zakrevsky, P., Afonin, K.A., et al., 2011. Self-assembling RNA nanorings based on RNAI/II inverse kissing complexes. Nano Letters 11 (2), 878–887.

Grell, L., Parkin, C., Slatest, L., Craig, P.A., 2006. Ez-viz, a tool for simplifying molecular viewing in pymol. Biochemistry and Molecular Biology Education 34 (6), 402–407.

Guo, P., 2010. The emerging field of RNA nanotechnology. Nature Nanotechnology 12 (5), 833–842.

Guo, P., Erickson, S., Anderson, D., 1987. A small viral RNA is required for in vitro packaging of bacteriophage phi29 DNA. Science 236 (4802), 690–694.

Guo, P., Haque, F., Hallahan, B., Reif, R., Li, H., 2012. Uniqueness, advantages, challenges, solutions, and perspectives in therapeutics applying RNA nanotechnology. Nucleic Acid Therapeutics 22 (4), 226–245.

Guo, P., Zhang, C., Chen, C., Garver, K., Trottier, M., 1998. Inter-RNA interaction of phage 29 pRNA to form a hexameric complex for viral DNA transportation. Molecular Cell 2 (1), 149–155.

Han, D., Qi, X., Myhrvold, C., et al., 2017. Single-stranded dna and rna origami. Science 358 (6369), Available at: http://science.sciencemag.org/content/358/6369/eaao2648.

Hannon, G.J., 2002. RNA interference. Nature 418, 244–251.

Hao, C., Li, X., Tian, C., et al., 2014. Construction of RNA nanocages by re-engineering the packaging RNA of Phi29 bacteriophage. Nature Communications 5, 3890.

Haque, F., Shu, D., Shu, Y., et al., 2012. Ultrastable synergistic tetravalent {RNA} nanopar-ticles for targeting to cancers. Nano Today 7 (4), 245–257.

Higgs, P.G., 1995. Thermodynamic properties of transfer RNA: A computational study. Journal of the Chemical Society, Faraday Transactions 9 (16), 2531–2540.

Hofacker, I.L., Fontana, W., Stadler, P.F., et al., 1994. Fast folding and comparison of RNA secondary structures. Chemical Monthly 125 (2), 167–188.

Ishikawa, J., Furuta, H., Ikawa, Y., 2013. RNA tectonics (tectoRNA) for RNA nanostructure design and its application in synthetic biology. Wiley Interdisciplinary Reviews: RNA 4 (6), 651–664.

Jaeger, L., Chworos, A., 2006. The architectonics of programmable RNA and DNA nanostructures. Current Opinion in Structural Biology 16 (4), 531–543.

Jaeger, L., Leontis, N.B., 2000. Tecto-RNA: One-dimensional self-assembly through tertiary interactions. Angewandte Chemie International Edition 39 (14), 2521–2524.

Jasinski, D., Haque, F., Binzel, D.W., Guo, P., 2017. Advancement of the emerging field of RNA nanotechnology. ACS Nano 11 (2), 1142–1164.

Jasinski, D.L., Khisamutdinov, E.F., Lyubchenko, Y.L., Guo, P., 2014. Physicochemically tunable polyfunctionalized RNA square architecture with fluorogenic and ribozymatic properties. ACS Nano 8 (8), 7620–7629.

Jossinet, F., Ludwig, T.E., Westhof, E., 2010. Assemble: An interactive graphical tool to analyze and build RNA architectures at the 2d and 3d levels. Bioinformatics 26 (16), 2057–2059.

Kang, K.-N., Lee, Y.-S., 2012. RNA aptamers: A review of recent trends and applications. In: Z.J., J. (Ed.), Future Trends in Biotechnology. Advances in Biochemical Engineering/Biotechnology. Berlin, Heidelberg: Springer, pp. 153–169.

Ke, Y., Sharma, J., Liu, M., et al., 2009. Scaffolded dna origami of a dna tetrahedron molecular container. Nano Letters 9 (6), 2445–2447.

Khisamutdinov, E.F., Jasinski, D.L., Guo, P., 2014. RNA as a boiling-resistant anionic polymer material to build robust structures with defined shape and stoichiometry. ACS Nano 8 (5), 4771–4781.

Klosterman, P.S., Hendrix, D.K., Tamura, M., Holbrook, S.R., Brenner, S.E., 2004. Three dimensional motifs from the scor, structural classification of RNA database: Extruded strands, base triples, tetraloops and uturns. Nucleic Acids Research 32 (8), 2342–2352.

Lee, T.J., Haque, F., Shu, D., et al., 2015. RNA nanoparticle as a vector for targeted siRNA delivery into glioblastoma mouse model. Oncotarget 6, 14766–14776.

Leontis, N.B., Lescoute, A., Westhof, E., 1995. The building blocks and motifs of RNA architecture. Current Opinion Structural Biology 16, 279287.

Leontis, N.B., Westhof, E., 2003. Analysis of RNA motifs. Current Opinion in Structural Biology 13 (3), 300–308.

Li, H., Lee, T., Dziubla, T., et al., 2015. RNA as a stable polymer to build controllable and defined nanostructures for material and biomedical application. Nano Today 10 (5), 631–655.

Licata, N.A., Tkachenko, A.V., 2009. Self-assembling dna-caged particles: Nanoblocks for hierarchical self-assembly. Physical Review E 79, 011404.

Lin, C., Liu, Y., Rinker, S., Yan, H., 2006. Dna tile based self-assembly: Building complex nanoarchitectures. ChemPhysChem 7 (8), 1641–1647.

Lin, C., Liu, Y., Yan, H., 2009. Designer dna nanoarchitectures. Biochemistry 48 (8), 1663–1674.

Mandal, M., Breaker, R.R., 2004. Gene regulation by riboswitches. Molecular cell biology 5, 451–463.

Markham, N.R., Zuker, M., 2005. DINAMelt web server for nucleic acid melting prediction. Nucleic Acid Research 33, W577–W581. doi:10.1093/nar/gki591.

Martinez, H.M., Jr, J.V.M., Shapiro, B.A., 2008. RNA2D3D: A program for generating, viewing, and comparing 3-dimensional models of RNA. Journal of Biomolecular Structure and Dynamics 25 (6), 669–683.

Mathews, D.H., Disney, M.D., Childs, J.L., *et al.*, 2004. Incorporating chemical modification constraints into a dynamic programming algorithm for prediction of RNA secondary structure. In: Proceedings of the National Academy of Sciencesvol. 101, pp. 7287–7292. USA.

Mathews, D.H., Turner, D.H., 2006. Prediction of RNA secondary structure by free energy minimization. Current Opinion in Structural Biology 16 (3), 270–278.

Moore, P.B., 1999. Structural motifs in RNA. Annual Review of Biochemistry 68, 287–300.

Muckstein, U., Tafer, H., Hackermuller, J., *et al.*, 2006. Thermodynamics of RNA-RNA binding. Bioinformatics 22 (10), 1177–1182.

Mulhbacher, J., St-Pierre, P., Lafontaine, D.A., 2010. Therapeutic applications of ribozymes and riboswitches. Current Opinion in Pharmacology 10 (5), 551–556.

Nasalean, L., Baudrey, S., Leontis, N.B., Jaeger, L., 2006. Controlling RNA self-assembly to form filaments. Nucleic Acids Research 34 (5), 1381–1392.

Nudler, E., Mironov, A.S., 2004. The riboswitch control of bacterial metabolism. Trends in biochemical sciences 29 (1), 11–17.

Petersen, C.P., Doench, J.G., Grishok, A., Sharp, P.A., 2006. The biology of short RNAs. In: Gesteland, R.F., Cech, T.R., Atkins, J.F. (Eds.), RNA World, third ed. New York: Cold Spring Harbor Laboratory Press, pp. 535–565.

Petrov, A.I., Zirbel, C.L., Leontis, N.B., 2013. Automated classification of RNA 3D motifs and the RNA 3D motif atlas. RNA 19 (10), 1327–1340.

Pettersen, E.F., Goddard, T.D., Huang, C.C., *et al.*, 2004. Ucsf chimera visualization system for exploratory research and analysis. Journal of Computational Chemistry 25 (13), 1605–1612.

Rockey, W.M., Hernandez, F.J., Huang, S.-Y., *et al.*, 2011. Rational truncation of an RNA aptamer to prostate-specific membrane antigen using computational structural modeling. Nucleic Acid Therapeutics 21 (5), 299–314.

Roh, Y.H., Deng, J.Z., Dreaden, E.C., *et al.*, 2016. A Multi-RNAi microsponge platform for simultaneous controlled delivery of multiple small interfering RNAs. Ange-wandte Chemie 128 (10), 3408–3412.

Rothemund, P.W.K., 2006. Folding dna to create nanoscale shapes and patterns. Nature 440, 297–302.

SantaLucia-Jr., J., 1998. A unified view of polymer, dumbbell, and oligonucleotide DNA nearest-neighbor thermodynamics. In: Proceedings of the National Academy of Sciences vol. 95, pp. 1460–1465. USA.

Schuster, P., 2006. Prediction of RNA secondary structures: From theory to models and real molecules. Reports on Progress in Physics 69, 1419–1477.

Seeman, N.C., 2007. An overview of structural dna nanotechnology. Molecular Biotechnology 37 (3), 246.

Seeman, N.C., 2010. Nanomaterials based on DNA. Annual Review of Biochemistry 79 (1), 65–87.

Serganov, A., 2009. The long and the short of riboswitches. Current Opinion in Structural Biology 19 (3), 251–259.

Severcan, I., Geary, C., Chworos, A., *et al.*, 2010. A polyhedron made of tRNAs. Nature Chemistry 2 (9), 772–779.

Shigdar, S., Lin, J., Yu, Y., *et al.*, 2011. RNA aptamer against a cancer stem cell marker epithelial cell adhesion molecule. Cancer Science 102 (5), 991–998.

Shu, D., Li, H., Shu, Y., *et al.*, 2015. Systemic delivery of Anti-miRNA for suppression of triple negative breast cancer utilizing RNA nanotechnology. ACS Nano 9 (10), 9731–9740.

Shu, D., Moll, W.-D., Deng, Z., Mao, C., Guo, P., 2004. Bottom-up assembly of RNA arrays and superstructures as potential parts in nanotechnology. Nano Letters 4 (9), 1717–1723.

Shu, D., Shu, Y., Haque, F., Abdelmawla, S., Guo, P., 2011. Thermody-namically stable RNA three-way junction for constructing multifunctional nanoparticles for delivery of therapeutics. Nature Nanotechnology 6, 658667.

Shu, Y., Haque, F., Shu, D., *et al.*, 2013a. Fabrication of 14 different RNA nanoparticles for specific tumor targeting without accumulation in normal organs. RNA 19, 767–777.

Shu, Y., Pi, F., Sharma, A., *et al.*, 2014. Stable RNA nanoparticles as potential new generation drugs for cancer therapy. Advanced Drug Delivery Reviews 66 (Suppl. C), 74–89.

Shu, Y., Shu, D., Haque, F., Guo, P., 2013b. Fabrication of pRNA nanopar-ticles to deliver therapeutic RNAs and bioactive compounds into tumor cells. Nature Protocols 8, 1635–1659.

Steffen, P., Voss, B., Rehmsmeier, M., Reeder, J., Giegerich, R., 2006. RNAshapes: An integrated RNA analysis package based on abstract shapes. Bioinformatics 22 (4), 500–503.

Suess, B., Weigand, J.E., 2008. Engineered riboswitches: Overview, problems and trends. RNA Biology 5 (1), 24–29.

Sundaram, P., Kurniawan, H., Byrne, M.E., Wower, J., 2013. Therapeutic RNA aptamers in clinical trials. European Journal of Pharmaceutical Sciences 48 (1), 259–271.

Tamura, M., Hendrix, D.K., Klosterman, P.S., *et al.*, 2004. Scor: Structural classification of rna, version 2.0. Nucleic Acids Research 32, D182–D184.

Thiel, K.W., Hernandez, L.I., Dassie, J.P., *et al.*, 2012. Delivery of chemo-sensitizing siRNAs to HER2 + -breast cancer cells using RNA aptamers. Nucleic Acids Research 40 (13), 6319–6337.

Westhof, E., Masquida, B., Jaeger, L., 1996. RNA tectonics: Towards RNA design. Folding and Design 1 (4), R78–R88.

Wuchty, S., Fontana, W., Hofacker, I.L., Schuster, P., 1999. Complete suboptimal folding of RNA and the stability of secondary structure. Biopolymers 49, 145–165.

Xia, Z., Gardner, D.P., Gutell, R.R., Ren, P., 2010. Coarse-grained model for simulation of RNA three dimensional structures. The Journal of Physical Chemistry B 114 (42), 13497–13506.

Ye, X., Hemida, M., Zhang, H.M., *et al.*, 2012. Current advances in Phi29 pRNA biology and its application in drug delivery. Wiley Interdisciplinary Reviews: RNA 3 (4), 469–481.

Yingling, G., Shapiro, Y., B., A., 2007. Computational design of an RNA hexagonal nanoring and an RNA nanotube. Nano Letters 7 (8), 2328–2334.

Yu, J., Liu, Z., Jiang, W., Wang, G., Mao, C., 2015. De novo design of an RNA tile that self-assembles into a homo-octameric nanoprism. Nature Communications 6, 5724.

Zadegan, R.M., Jepsen, M.D.E., Thomsen, K.E., *et al.*, 2012. Construction of a 4 zeptoliters switchable 3D DNA box origami. ACS Nano 6 (11), 10050–10053.

Zadeh, J.N., Steenberg, C.D., Bois, J.S., *et al.*, 2011. Nupack: Analysis and design of nucleic acid systems. Journal of Computational Chemistry 32 (1), 170–173.

Zamore, P.D., Haley, B., 2005. Ribo-gnome: The big world of small RNAs. Science 309, 1519–1524.

Zhang, H., Endrizzi, J.A., Shu, Y., *et al.*, 2013. Crystal structure of 3wj core revealing divalent ion-promoted thermostability and assembly of the phi29 hexameric motor pRNA. RNA 19, 1226–1237.

Zhou, J., Bobbin, M., Burnett, J., Rossi, J., 2012. Current progress of RNA aptamer-based therapeutics. Frontiers in Genetics 3, 234.

Zimmermann, J., Cebulla, M., Mnninghoff, S., vonKiedrowski, G., 2008. Self-assembly of a dna dodecahedron from 20 trisoligonucleotides with c3h linkers. Angewandte Chemie International Edition 47 (19), 3626–3630.

Zuker, M., 1989. On finding all suboptimal foldings of an RNA molecule. Science 244, 48–52.

Zuker, M., 2003. Mfold web server for nucleic acid folding and hybridization prediction. Nucleic Acids Research 31 (13), 3406–3415.

Zuker, M., Jaeger, J.A., Turner, D.H., 1991. A comparison of optimal and suboptimal RNA secondary structures predicted by free energy minimization with structures determined by phylogenetic comparison. Nucleic Acids Research 19 (10), 2707–2714.

Predicting RNA-RNA Interactions in Three-Dimensional Structures

Hazrina Y Hamdani, Universiti Sains Malaysia, Kepala Batas, Malaysia
Zatil H Yahaya and Mohd Firdaus-Raih, Universiti Kebangsaan Malaysia, Bangi, Malaysia

Introduction

Tertiary interactions, such as those mediated by hydrogen bonds, serve as stabilization elements of RNA 3D structure (Krasilnikov and Mondragón, 2003; Nissen et al., 2001). To date, numerous examples of tertiary interactions have been reported and these can easily be browsed via resources such as the RNA 3D Hub (Leontis and Zirbel, 2012), InterRNA (Appasamy et al., 2015), NCIR (Nagaswamy et al., 2002), SCOR (Tamura et al., 2004), RNAJunction (Bindewald et al., 2007), RNA 3D Motif Atlas (Parlea et al., 2016) and RNA Bricks (Chojnowski et al., 2014). Tertiary interactions that are highly conserved can be considered as 3D or tertiary motifs.

The capability to predict RNA-RNA interactions is of even more importance given recent depositions of large assemblies of the ribosomal subunits with reasonably high resolution (Prokhorova et al., 2017; Almutairi et al., 2017; Tereshchenkov et al., 2018). With high-resolution structures, the intricate atomic level interactions within the RNA's 3D structure can be adequate for structural analysis that can provide details of functional mechanisms (Koizumi et al., 2016). Tertiary interactions within the RNA structure are biologically significant from various aspects. In a recent study on viroid RNA, the 3D base motifs are important factors for function, viroid infection and viroid genome evolution (Wang et al., 2018). In addition, 3D structure of RNA has also shown to be conserved despite extensive sequence divergence (Capriotti and Marti-Renom, 2010). RNA tertiary motifs also provide specific transcriptional regulation together and may have therapeutic purposes in diseases (Huang et al., 2015). The 3D structure of messenger RNA (mRNA) is also crucial in regulating the production of encoded proteins in addition to controlling and modulating synthesis and function of proteins (Mauger et al., 2013).

There are variations as to what is defined as an RNA 3D motif. Here, we specifically discuss RNA base motifs that we define as a pattern of base arrangements that are annotated repeatedly in different locations either in the same RNA structure, or in different RNA molecules. Although there is a requirement for similarity in the 3D arrangement of the bases to be considered a motif, an alignment at the 1D sequence level is not required. In this article, we focus on computational methods that are able to identify base motifs and base-base interactions in the 3D structures of RNA.

RNA 3D motifs can be classified based on properties arising from the conformation of the RNA backbone and base pair interactions. Examples of conformational motifs include kink-turns, tetraloops, hook-turns, π turns, Ω turns and α loops (Klein et al., 2001; Woese et al., 1990; Szép et al., 2003; Wadley and Pyle, 2004). However, for base motifs or base-base interactions, the arrangement similarities of the bases in 3D space are used for classification.

Background

Hydrogen bonds play crucial roles in the structures of biological macromolecules. The role of the hydrogen bond in protein structures is well recognized – an excellent example of their contribution towards orderly maintenance of 3-D structure is their core structure stabilization contributions in protein secondary structures. For example, the amino group nitrogen in an alpha helix backbone is the donor atom for a carbonyl group. In DNA, the two hydrogen bond interactions for A-T and the three hydrogen bonds between G-C that hold together the two strands of DNA in a double helix conformation as first described by Watson and Crick (1953) have become canon. In RNA structures, the base components of the nucleotides are also able to hydrogen bond in the canonical Watson-Crick arrangement. Additionally, the more diverse conformations that an RNA structure is able to fold into allow for the bases to interact in a plethora of arrangements that in turn result in a diverse array of base pairing arrangements as reported by Tinoco et al. (1973) as RNA are generally single-stranded; hence, less restricted to double helical conformation compared to DNA.

The work of Tinoco et al. (1973) expanded the repertoire of possible base pairings by considering other base interaction interfaces additional to the Watson-Crick interface (such as the sugar and Hoogsteen edges) and different geometries (such as the reverse Watson-Crick base pair). These additional base pair arrangements were; thus, termed non-canonical interactions that did not conform to the AT GC hydrogen bonding rule described by Watson and Crick (1953) in addition to possibly deviating from the ratio of Chargaff's rules (Chargaff, 1951) which is applicable to DNA content.

It became clear that these non-canonical interactions were not mere rare exceptions to the rule through work, such as the NCIR database (Nagaswamy et al., 2002) by Fox and co-workers that catalogued a large number of non-canonical hydrogen bonded base interactions found in RNA structures reported in literature. Among the interactions in NCIR were arrangements that extended beyond simple base pairings to interactions consisting of three to five bases (see "Relevant Website section"). An extensive, manually curated literature sourced catalogue such as NCIR (Nagaswamy et al., 2002); although useful, would not be able to provide an overview or proper accounting of the breadth of interactions that can probably be found in the RNA structures currently available in the PDB (Berman, 2008).

The increasing number of RNA structures in the PDB signalled the requirement for accurate computational means of identifying base interactions and the motifs they partake in. The ability to identify such base interactions and their locations in the 3D structure can be an important contributor in the function prediction or determination process. The increase in the number of RNA structures in the PDB such as the more recently available entries for ribosomal subunits (e.g., PDB ID: 6CFK) , riboswitches (e.g., PDB ID: 6BFB), ribozymes (e.g., PDB ID: 5V3I), non-coding transcripts (e.g., PDB IDs: 5LYU, 5LSN) that are associated to human diseases ranging from cancer to infections are ripe targets for analysis of their base interactions in order to elucidate atomic level mechanistic details that can lead to potential therapeutic applications (Dasgupta *et al.*, 2017; Martinez-Zapien *et al.*, 2017; Podbevšek *et al.*, 2018; Rizvi *et al.*, 2018; Tereshchenkov *et al.*, 2018).

The computational analysis of RNA structures, specifically the interactions between and within RNA structures is not a new endeavor. However, due to the more recent availability of an increasing number of high resolution RNA structures, including very large complex assemblies, the computational analysis and comparisons of these structures in bulk is a nascent field that have the potential to be developed into pipelines to mine and develop RNA molecules as targets for therapeutic applications.

At this point, it must be made clear that an RNA base motif can consist of an arrangement of bases that are independent of their manner of hydrogen bonding. Nevertheless, using hydrogen bonds to define a motif is advantageous as there are clear definable parameters that can be calculated and these can also be used to differentiate different motifs that are otherwise visually similar.

The availability of high resolution RNA 3D structures enable the study of the basic interactions that stabilize the folded RNA molecule. In the early yeast tRNA structure, a network of hydrogen bond interactions was observed to run through most of the molecule with the exception of the exposed amino-acid and anticodon stems (Ladner *et al.*, 1975). Interaction networks in structured RNAs are therefore expected to feature prominently as a collective factor in stabilizing RNA structures. Among the interactions that can be found in such networks as listed by Lescoute and Westhof (2006) are: (i) phosphate-phosphate contacts mediated by water molecules or positively charged cations; (ii) phosphate-sugar hydrogen bonding usually mediated by the 2′-hydroxyl group; (iii) sugar-sugar hydrogen bonding interactions; (iv) base to phosphate or base to sugar hydrogen bonding; (v) base to phosphate or base to sugar stacking interactions; (vi) base to base hydrogen bonding interactions; (vii) base to base stacking interactions (Lescoute and Westhof, 2006).

Descriptions and Nomenclature of Base-Base Interactions

The base component of a nucleic acid can be divided into three edges: (i) the Watson-Crick face which is involved in the canonical Watson-Crick interactions, (ii) the sugar edge on the side of the glycosidic bond and (iii) the Hoogsteen edge (for purines) and CH edge (for pyrimidines) which are on the opposite side of the sugar face. Non-canonical base-base interactions therefore involve hydrogen bonding interfaced by one non-Watson-Crick base edge. Another type of non-canonical interaction may also occur which however involves the canonical Watson-Crick edges and was proposed by Francis Crick as the wobble-hypothesis (Crick, 1966). The orientation of bases to each other in RNA structures is not as easily described as can be done in DNA. The conformational diversity of RNA results in numerous other opportunities for bases to interact via non-canonical interactions as previously stated.

One method that can be used is to name the interactions based on the hydrogen bonding present. However, this is not as systematic nor does it provide an easy and immediate mental picture of the interaction. A nomenclature and classification system was proposed by Leontis and Westhof (2001) that enabled the diversity of possible base-base interactions to be better described. The basis of this nomenclature involved describing the base edges involved in the interaction in addition to the orientation of the glycosidic bond of one base to the other. We therefore propose that when descriptions of the arrangements are required, the Leontis and Westhof be used for uniformity and consistency.

Systems and/or Applications

Eleven servers that were found in the literature were compared for their utility in annotating base motifs or specific base-base interactions in RNA structures (**Tables 1** and **2**). The capacity of these different servers to find different types of base motifs and base-base interactions result in there being no single one stop solution for RNA structure annotation needs. These resources however complement each other in two ways – by using different methods for the searching and annotation and by covering different types of motifs that can be searched for and annotated. In general, all servers are able to accept as input either an existing PDB structure as a PDBID input or via an upload of the structure to be queried. Another feature shared by all the servers is the capability of providing visualization of the search output and making these output files available for downloads.

Analysis Approach and Utility of Base Arrangement Annotation

There are also a very limited set of tools that specifically annotates base arrangements or base-base interactions. In this analysis approach section, we compare and integrate these tools to those that take into account the folding of the RNA molecule into its substructure components, thus the services listed in **Tables 1** and **2** do not necessarily carry out base motif and base interaction

Table 1   A listing of the eleven web servers and their URLs that can be used for annotating 3D motifs in RNA structures

Web server	URL
NASSAM	http://mfrlab.org/grafss/nassam
WebFR3D	http://www.bgsu.edu/research/rna/web-applications/webfr3d.html
ARTS	http://bioinfo3d.cs.tau.ac.il/ARTS/
RCLICK	http://mspc.bii.a-star.edu.sg/minhn/rclick.html
R3D-BLAST	http://genome.cs.nthu.edu.tw/R3D-BLAST/
RAG-3D	http://www.biomath.nyu.edu/?q=RAG3D
COGNAC	http://mfrlab.org/grafss/cognac
FASTR3D	http://genome.cs.nthu.edu.tw/FASTR3D/
iPARTS2	http://genome.cs.nthu.edu.tw/iPARTS2/
SARA	http://structure.biofold.org/sara/
SETTER	http://setter.projekty.ms.mff.cuni.cz

annotation specifically. This enables expanding the discussion into how such tools can be used together to extract the most amount of information from an available RNA 3D structure.

In perhaps the majority of cases needing annotation of base arrangements in an RNA structure, the investigator starts with a newly solved structure, usually determined by X-ray diffraction. Tools that enable such structures to be annotated can thus provide a reference point for the investigator during analysis and visual inspection, especially for RNA structures that may involve complex interactions such as the ribosomal subunits. Unlike the redundancy often seen for sequence analysis programs, those that analyse at the structural level implement different approaches and were designed to find different targets thus resulting in the various servers being complementary to each other.

As an example, submitting a structure to the NASSAM server can provide a reference map for the investigator to identify known motifs. However, submitting the same structure to RAG-3D will retrieve a different set of results related to conserved topology that were not covered by NASSAM. The majority of these services annotate the RNA structure using a reference database thus limiting searches to known motifs and interactions.

In order to enable novel motif discovery, algorithms that are not dependent on a reference dataset need to be used. One method of discovering novel motifs would be to compare structures in order to look for unreported similar base arrangements or interactions present in multiple structures that may signal novelty. Such structure to structure annotations are possible by services such as ARTS and COGNAC, while some others actually require two or more structures as the input, such as RCLICK (see **Table 3**).

The use of hydrogen bonding patterns can also help differentiate between patterns. Subtle changes in the hydrogen bonding networks in the same structures that have undergone mutations or have been solved (crystallized) under different conditions can be used to identify structural shifts resulting from changes in the interactions between the bases. Furthermore, a highly hydrogen bonded grouping of bases that are repeated in different structures can imply that it may have functional or structural stabilization roles. Annotating such base interactions can thus be another means of identifying novel motifs.

Since most of these programs search and annotate an actual occurrence as opposed to being a prediction, what remains for the user to determine is how much the annotation conforms to the intended query. It is still possible to identify novel 3D motifs from such searches because the retrieved hits may deviate from the original query and may represent a yet unreported base arrangement. This was demonstrated by Firdaus-Raih et al. (2011) using the NASSAM program.

RNA structure annotation programs can also be used as a means of high-throughput structure annotation. The InterRNA database is an example of how the NASSAM and COGNAC algorithms were used to annotate high resolution RNA structures in the PDB (Appasamy et al., 2015). The RNA 3D Motif Atlas is the result of annotating a representative set of RNA 3D structures using FR3D (Sarver et al., 2008), which is available as the WebFR3D service. The DARTS database (Abraham et al., 2008) is derived from structural comparisons using the ARTS program.

Although structural genomics level approaches for RNA chain containing structures have never been attempted, these tools will allow for rapid and systematic annotation for the output of such projects. Due to the different but complementary nature of the available services, selection of the correct analysis program will depend on the objectives of the investigator.

Illustrative Example(s) or Case Studies

In order to demonstrate the RNA structure annotation process, specifically that of base motifs and base interactions, we have used the structure of a T box riboswitch (PDB ID 4MGN) (Grigg and Ke, 2013) as a query that was submitted to the services listed in **Table 1**. For services where a minimum of two structures needed to be submitted, the structure of another T box riboswitch (PDB ID 4LCK) (Zhang and Ferré-D'amaré, 2013) was also provided. The differences in the types of output and what each service is capable of presenting is provided in **Table 3**.

It is useful to note that novel motifs can also arise from a known or previously characterised arrangement in a different structural context. One such example is where a UAU Hoogsteen, Watson-Crick base triple, which is a known arrangement, was

Table 2 Comparison of web servers for RNA 3D motifs and substructures searching. A comparison of the eleven web servers for 3D motif searching in terms of their input, algorithm and output

Query	NASSAM	WebFR3D	ARTS	RCLICK	R3D-BLAST	RAG-3D	COGNAC	FASTR3D	iPARTS2	SARA	SETTER
Database											
PDB sourced structures	✓	✓	✓	✓	✓	✓	✓			✓	✓
Input query											
PDB ID or coordinate file of a complete RNA structure in PDB format	✓		✓	✓	✓	✓	✓	✓	✓	✓	✓
Multiple queries of PDB ID or PDB formatted coordinate files of RNA structures				✓			✓		✓	✓	✓
User-defined arrangement	✓	✓									
User-defined interaction	✓						✓				
User-defined secondary structure pattern							✓				
Sequence in FASTA format							✓				
Approaches											
Implements the base-centric geometric approach			✓								
Implement the hashing algorithm							✓				
Converts the 3D structure to sequence and runs alignments (BLAST)					✓						
Implement the phosphate atoms as the critical points			✓								
Implement 3D patterns of base arrangements are represented as the pseudo-atoms	✓										
Implements a graph theoretical search algorithm	✓										
Convert the structure into 3D graphs and classified based on the 2nd structure elements						✓					
Determine the base-base hydrogen bonds interactions and convert it into connection table	✓						✓				
Implement the cliques of three to seven residues				✓							
Local 3D structural alignment				✓							
Global 3D structural alignment									✓		
Implement suboptimal secondary structure								✓			
Implement hash table for speed up search								✓			
Convert the query pattern to sequence pattern, 2D pattern and 3D pattern to 2D structure								✓			
Implements a pairwise comparison method using the generalized secondary structure units											✓
Implements a unit-vector root-mean-square approach										✓	
Searches											
Search for the hydrogen bonds interactions	✓						✓				
Search for the 3D motifs with the specific nucleotides		✓					✓				
Search for the 3D motifs without specify the nucleotides	✓	✓					✓				
Search for the 3D patterns of base arrangements	✓										
Search for the similar substructure			✓	✓	✓			✓	✓	✓	✓
Searches for global structural similarity			✓	✓		✓			✓	✓	✓
Searches for local structural similarity			✓	✓		✓			✓		
Suggestion for the function for the substructure						✓				✓	
Output representation											
Structural visualization of searched motif/substructure	✓	✓	✓	✓	✓	✓	✓	✓	✓		✓
Downloadable output files	✓	✓	✓	✓	✓	✓	✓	✓	✓	✓	✓

Table 3 Comparison of the various results from the different tools for a T box riboswitch (PDB ID 4MGN) used as an input query. For services that require at least two input structure, the PDB entry for another T box riboswitch (PDB ID 4LCK) was also provided

Search	Server	
Motifs/substructures/ patterns	NASSAM	Returned one annotation of an A-minor motif and four annotations of base triple.
	WebFR3D	The server was unavailable for a period of time during this comparison due to repairs and upgrades.
	R3D-BLAST	The webserver searched one chain at a time; thus needing the search to be executed twice - once for each chain
		Chain A:
		Returned 12 hits of similar structures compared to 4MGN_A.
		Chain B:
		Returned 511 hits of similar structures compared to 4MGN_B.
	RAG-3D	Similar to the R3D-BLAST option, the RAG-3D searched only one chain at a time. Therefore, the search is done in two times by using Chain A and Chain B.
		Chain A (glyQS T box riboswitch):
		Returned 10 hits of similar structures compared to 4MGN_A and 90 hits of similar substructures compared to substructures of 4MGN_A. The similar substructures resulted from the nine subgraphs of the query topology (4MGN_A) that represented the input structure.
		Chain B (tRNA-glycine):
		Resulted 10 hits of similar structures compared to 4MGN_B and no substructure reported. The 10 hits from the 4MGN_B searched are different from the search of 4MGN_A.
	COGNAC	The webserver provides options to annotate the clusters of bases that are connected by hydrogen bonds in a structure or to annotate and compare two input structures. In this case study we annotate and compare two input structures which are 4MGN and 4LCK.
		COGNAC returned 15 annotations of base triples, six annotations of quadruple base Type 1, an annotation of quadruple base Type 2, two annotations of quintuple base Type 1, an annotation of quintuple base Type 2 and an annotation of sextuple base Type 1 for 4MGN.
		Compared to 4LCK, COGNAC returned 10 annotations of base triples and two annotations of quadruple base Type1. An annotation of base triples of 4MGN and 4LCK annotated at similar location in tRNA glycine's D-arm and variable loop.
	FASTR3D	No results returned – the 4MGN structure was not in the database used and no option to upload structures is available.
Alignment of RNA tertiary structures	ARTS	The webserver is temporary unstable.
	RCLICK	The server needs two input structures to execute the alignment. 4MGN is compared to 4LCK. The results of two structures are viewed using JSMol viewer.
		Rclick shows the alignment of RNA interactions between both input structures. Based on the results of the output, the value of the RMSD given is 2.07 Å. The hits of match residues for 4mgn when compared to 4LCK is 105 atoms. The server also returns with structure overlap of 33.55% and highlighted the aligned residues of the input structures using JSMol viewer.
	iPARTS2	The webserver requires the structures to be searched only one chain at the time and need two structures to be executed. Thus, the global alignment search is done between 4MGN and 4LCK with different chains.
		Chain IDs with T box riboswitch structure:
		Chain C of 4MGN is superimposed with chain C of 4LCK and returned with 84 hits of aligned residue pairs. The RMSD obtained from the alignment is 4.490 Å.
		Chain IDs with tRNA-glycine:
		Chain B of 4MGN is superimposed with chain B of 4LCK and returned with 68 hits of aligned residue pairs. The RMSD value resulted with 2.961 Å.
	SARA	Provides two options of search that are structure-based function assignment and pair-wise structure alignment. The case study search is done using the structure-based function assignment because it required an input of file in PDB format to be searched throughout the SCOR database with the parameter to also search against RNA structures that are larger than 1000 nucleotides.
		Returned 192 structures sorted based on the mean of the negative logarithm of the three P-values (MEANLN). The three P-values are negative logarithm of the P-value of the sequence alignment score (LNPID), negative logarithm of the P-value of the secondary structure alignment score (LNPSS) and negative logarithm of the P-value of the structure alignment score (LNPSI).
		(LNPSI).
	SETTER	The webserver provides options for the structures to be aligned as a whole structure or based on the selected chain. In this case study we aligned 4MGN and 4LCK for the whole structure and based on the selected chain (chain C) for both structures. The chain C represents the T-box riboswitch.
		The SETTER provides the alignment quality measures, which are RMSD, the percentage of structural identity (PSI), the percentage of sequence identity (PID), the number of aligned nucleotides and the number of exact base matches.
		The alignment quality for 4MGN and 4LCK are 2.209 for the RMSD, 0.060 for the PSI, 0.019 for the PID, 19 nucleotides were aligned and 6 bases matches.
		The alignment quality for the chain C for 4MGN and 4LCK are 1.794 for the RMSD, 0.233 for the PSI, 0.070 for the PID, 20 nucleotides were aligned and 6 bases matches.

found by the computer program NASSAM to be in a stacked arrangement on top of each other at a junction holding three subdomains of domain V in the prokaryotic 23S subunit and was found to be conserved in all available 23S subunit structures at the time it was reported (Firdaus-Raih *et al.*, 2011). In this particular case, annotation of the base triples led to the discovery that there were two of the same triples stacked together – such an arrangement may not be obvious even on close visual inspection due to the dense packing of nucleotides and the difficulty in discerning 3D motifs when visualizing these structures.

We further used the COGNAC service to compare and identify atomic level differences of base arrangements connected by hydrogen bonding interactions. This was demonstrated by using the structures of two mutant cyclic dinucleotide bis-(3'-5')-cyclic dimeric guanosine monophosphate (c-di-GMP-I) riboswitch that were bound to GpA (PDB ID 3UD4) and pGpA (PDB ID 3UD3) (Smith *et al.*, 2012). Due to space limitations, we selected only the base triple interactions to illustrate the differences between the structures. In 3UD4, six base triples interactions were annotated: U53.C55.G85, C17.C93.G14, G97.C13.G94, G94.C93.G14, G94. C93.G17 and C93.G94.C13; while in 3UD3, three base triple interactions were annotated: U53.C55.G85, C17.C93.G14, G97.C13. G94 (**Fig. 1**). Three of the base triples interactions in 3UD3 can be found in 3UD4, however a slight shift in the base arrangement between C93 and C94 in 3UD3 resulted in the loss of the hydrogen bonds between atom N4 of C93 and atom O6 of G94 (**Fig. 1**).

The differences in base interactions detected occurred on the opposite end to where the ribonucleoprotein interactions were occurring and closer to the sites of where pGpA and GpA binding occurred. This can imply those interactions differences observed may be due to the differences brought about by interactions with these two different molecules. However, as always, care must be taken when interpreting such data because they can also be experimental artifacts (i.e., crystallographic packing, X-ray resolution). Nevertheless, the differences can provide clues that can assist in forming hypotheses and thus lead towards experiments that can be more conclusive.

Discussion and Future Directions

There is a tendency to concentrate on descriptions and cataloguing with little reference to the relevance interactions in a functional context when computational means are deployed to annotate RNA structures. Perhaps this is not unexpected due to the need to first develop such capacity. However, the future direction of developments in this field should take into consideration more intensive integration of the mechanistic insights that can be gained from the annotation of structural motifs, particularly for base motifs and base interactions.

As larger and more complex structures, such as the ribosomal assemblies, are solved via crystallographic and Cryo-EM approaches, there is a clear need for computational approaches that can accurately annotate these structures and provide a means of comparison between them. In the case of NMR structures, the atomic level differences between the different models can be

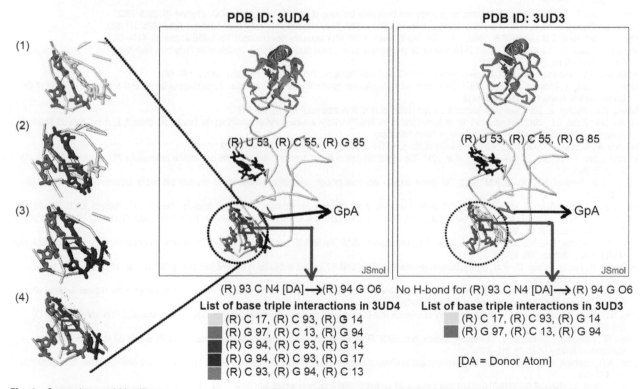

Fig. 1 Comparison and identification base arrangements arising from differences in the base-base hydrogen bonding interactions. The comparison and identification of the atomic level differences of base arrangements connected by hydrogen bonding interactions using the COGNAC service. This was demonstrated by using the structures of two mutant cyclic dinucleotide bis-(3'-5')-cyclic dimeric guanosine monophosphate (c-di-GMP-I) riboswitch that were bound to GpA (PDB ID 3UD4) and pGpA (PDB ID 3UD3).

quickly annotated and discerned. Such annotations can provide a useful mapping of the differences in base interactions and arrangements in the different models and correlated to biological or experimental context. Additionally, the ability to track the changes in the annotation, especially for NMR models, can be especially useful for tracking the dynamics of the RNA conformation with regard to the formation and/or deformation of base interactions and the effects these changes have on biological function.

Acknowledgement

MFR is funded by the Ministry of Science, Technology and Innovation grant 02-01-02-SF1278 and Universiti Kebangsaan Malaysia ICONIC-2013-007 and GUP-2014-008 grants.

See also: Biomolecular Structures: Prediction, Identification and Analyses. Characterizing and Functional Assignment of Noncoding RNAs. Engineering of Supramolecular RNA Structures. Natural Language Processing Approaches in Bioinformatics

References

Abraham, M., Dror, O., Nussinov, R., Wolfson, H.J., 2008. Analysis and classification of RNA tertiary structures. RNA 14 (11), 2274–2289.

Almutairi, M.M., Svetlov, M.S., Hansen, D.A., *et al.*, 2017. Co-produced natural ketolides methymycin and pikromycin inhibit bacterial growth by preventing synthesis of a limited number of proteins. Nucleic Acids Research 45, 9573–9582.

Appasamy, S.D., Hamdani, H.Y., Ramlan, E.I., Firdaus-Raih, M., 2015. InterRNA: A database of base interactions in RNA structures. Nucleic Acids Research 44, 266–271.

Berman, H.M., 2008. The Protein Data Bank: A historical perspective. Acta Crystallographica Section A: Foundations of Crystallography 64, 88–95.

Bindewald, E., Hayes, R., Yingling, Y.G., Kasprzak, W., Shapiro, B.A., 2007. RNAJunction: A database of RNA junctions and kissing loops for three-dimensional structural analysis and nanodesign. Nucleic Acids Research 36, 392–397.

Capriotti, E., Marti-Renom, M.A., 2010. Quantifying the relationship between sequence and three-dimensional structure conservation in RNA. BMC Bioinformatics 11, 322.

Chargaff, E., 1951. Structure and function of nucleic acids as cell constituents. Federation Proceedings. 654–659.

Chojnowski, G., Waleń, T., Bujnicki, J.M., 2014. RNA Bricks – a database of RNA 3D motifs and their interactions. Nucleic Acids Research 42, 123–131.

Crick, F.H., 1966. Codon – anticodon pairing: The wobble hypothesis. Journal of Molecular Biology 19, 548–555.

Dasgupta, S., Suslov, N.B., Piccirilli, J.A., 2017. Structural basis for substrate helix remodeling and cleavage loop activation in the Varkud satellite ribozyme. Journal of the American Chemical Society 139, 9591–9597.

Firdaus-Raih, M., Harrison, A.-M., Willett, P., Artymiuk, P.J., 2011. Novel base triples in RNA structures revealed by graph theoretical searching methods. BMC Bioinformatics 12 (Suppl. 13), S2.

Grigg, J.C., Ke, A., 2013. Structural determinants for geometry and Information Decoding of tRNA by T Box Leader RNA. Structure 21, 2025–2032.

Huang, W., Thomas, B., Flynn, R.A., *et al.*, 2015. DDX5 and its associated lncRNA Rmrp modulate Th17 cell effector functions. Nature 528, 517–522.

Klein, D.J., Schmeing, T.M., Moore, P.B., Steitz, T.A., 2001. The kink-turn: A new RNA secondary structure motif. The EMBO Journal 20, 4214–4221.

Koizumi, H., Suzuki, R., Tachibana, M., *et al.*, 2016. Importance of determination of Crystal Quality in Protein Crystals when Performing High-Resolution Structural Analysis. Crystal Growth & Design 16, 4905–4909.

Krasilnikov, A.S., Mondragón, A., 2003. On the occurrence of the T-loop RNA folding motif in large RNA molecules. RNA 9, 640–643.

Ladner, J.E., Jack, A., Robertus, J.D., *et al.*, 1975. Structure of yeast phenylalanine transfer-RNA at 2.5 A resolution. Proceedings of the National Academy of Sciences of the United States of America 72 (11), 4414–4418.

Leontis, N.B., Westhof, E., 2001. Geometric nomenclature and classification of RNA base pairs. RNA 7, 499–512.

Leontis, N.B., Zirbel, C.L., 2012. Nonredundant 3D Structure Datasets for RNA Knowledge extraction and benchmarking. In: Leontis, N., Westhof, E. (Eds.), RNA 3D Structure Analysis and Prediction. Berlin, Heidelberg: Springer Berlin Heidelberg.

Lescoute, A., Westhof, E., 2006. The interaction networks of structured RNAs. Nucleic Acids Research 34, 6587–6604.

Martinez-Zapien, D., Legrand, P., Mcewen, A.G., *et al.*, 2017. The crystal structure of the 5p′ functional domain of the transcription riboregulator 7SK. Nucleic Acids Research 45, 3568–3579.

Mauger, D.M., Siegfried, N.A., Weeks, K.M., 2013. The genetic code as expressed through relationships between mRNA structure and protein function. FEBS Letters 587 (8), 1180–1188.

Nagaswamy, U., Larios-Sanz, M., Hury, J., *et al.*, 2002. NCIR: A database of non-canonical interactions in known RNA structures. Nucleic Acids Research 30 (1), 395–397.

Nissen, P., Ippolito, J.A., Ban, N., Moore, P.B., Steitz, T.A., 2001. RNA tertiary interactions in the large ribosomal subunit: The A-minor motif. Proceedings of the National Academy of Sciences 98 (9), 4899–4903.

Parlea, L.G., Sweeney, B.A., Hosseini-Asanjan, M., Zirbel, C.L., Leontis, N.B., 2016. The RNA 3D Motif Atlas: Computational methods for extraction, organization and evaluation of RNA motifs. Methods 103, 99–119.

Podbevšek, P., Fasolo, F., Bon, C., *et al.*, 2018. Structural determinants of the SINE B2 element embedded in the long non-coding RNA activator of translation AS Uchl1. Scientific Reports 8, 3189.

Prokhorova, I., Altman, R.B., Djumagulov, M., *et al.*, 2017. Aminoglycoside interactions and impacts on the eukaryotic ribosome. Proceedings of the National Academy of Sciences of the United States of America 114, E10899–E10908.

Rizvi, N.F., Howe, J.A., Nahvi, A., *et al.*, 2018. Discovery of selective RNA-Binding small molecules by affinity-selection mass spectrometry. ACS Chemical Biology 13 (3), 820–831.

Sarver, M., Zirbel, C.L., Stombaugh, J., Mokdad, A., Leontis, N.B., 2008. FR3D: Finding local and composite recurrent structural motifs in RNA 3D structures. Journal of Mathematical Biology 56 (1–2), 215–252.

Smith, K.D., Lipchock, S.V., Strobel, S.A., 2012. Structural and biochemical characterization of linear dinucleotide analogs bound to the c-di-GMP-I aptamer. Biochemistry 51 (1), 425–432.

Szép, S., Wang, J., Moore, P.B., 2003. The crystal structure of a 26-nucleotide RNA containing a hook-turn. RNA 9, 44–51.

Tamura, M., Hendrix, D.K., Klosterman, P.S., *et al.*, 2004. SCOR: Structural Classification of RNA, version 2.0. Nucleic Acids Research 32, 182–184.

Tereshchenkov, A.G., Dobosz-Bartoszek, M., Osterman, I.A., *et al.*, 2018. Binding and action of amino acid analogs of chloramphenicol upon the bacterial ribosome. Journal of Molecular Biology 430 (6), 842–852.

Tinoco, I., Borer, P.N., Dengler, B., *et al.*, 1973. Improved estimation of secondary structure in ribonucleic acids. Nature 246, 40–41.

Wadley, L.M., Pyle, A.M., 2004. The identification of novel RNA structural motifs using COMPADRES: An automated approach to structural discovery. Nucleic Acids Research 32, 6650–6659.

Wang, Y., Zirbel, C.L., Leontis, N.B., Ding, B., 2018. RNA 3-dimensional structural motifs as a critical constraint of viroid RNA evolution. PLOS Pathogens 14, e1006801.

Watson, J.D., Crick, F.H.C., 1953. The structure of DNA. Cold Spring Harbor Symposia on Quantitative Biology 18, 123–131.

Woese, C.R., Winker, S., Gutell, R.R., 1990. Architecture of ribosomal RNA: Constraints on the sequence "tetra-loops". Proceedings of the National Academy of Sciences of the United States of America 87 (21), 8467–8471.

Zhang, J., Ferré-D'amaré, A.R., 2013. Cocrystal structure of a T-box riboswitch Stem I domain in complex with its cognate tRNA. Nature 500 (7462), 363–366.

Relevant Website

http://prion.bchs.uh.edu/bp_type/bp_structure.html
Department of Biology and Biochemistry, University of Houston, Texas, USA.

Applications of Ribosomal RNA Sequence and Structure Analysis for Extracting Evolutionary and Functional Insights

Chyan Leong Ng and Mohd Firdaus-Raih, Universiti Kebangsaan Malaysia, Bangi, Selangor, Malaysia

Introduction

RNA

The Central Dogma of Molecular Biology (Crick, 1958) has long recognized messenger RNA (mRNA) as an intermediary molecule for decoding genetic information to functional molecules. Along with transfer RNA (tRNA) and ribosomal RNA (rRNA), the roles of RNA molecules were primarily linked to protein synthesis. However, the current knowledge of RNA species has extended beyond mRNA, tRNA, and rRNA. Other RNA transcripts that are not translated to proteins (non-protein coding or ncRNA) such as microRNA (miRNA), small interfering RNA (siRNA), piwi-interacting RNA (piRNA) and long non-coding RNA (lncRNA). They partake in numerous other important cellular roles that include posttranscriptional modification and gene expression regulation. RNA molecules can be self-folded to form complex three-dimensional (3D) shapes that in turn allow them to perform functions similar to proteins such as catalysis. Examples of such RNA enzymes, termed ribozymes, were discovered in the 1980s (Guerrier-Takada et al., 1983; Kruger et al., 1982). Such independent catalytic capacity lends support to the RNA world hypothesis (Robertson and Joyce, 2012; Cech, 2012; Gilbert, 1986).

All RNA is transcribed through the complex machinery of RNA polymerase (RNAP). Bacteria uses a single type of RNAP for all RNA transcription while eukaryotic cells generally contain RNA polymerases I, II, and III. RNA polymerase I is responsible for the synthesis of ribosomal RNA (rRNAs) 28S, 18S, and 5.8S; RNA polymerase II transcribes mRNA, snRNA, and microRNA; RNA polymerase III is responsible for transcribing tRNA, 5S rRNA, and other small RNAs.

RNA Sequence and Structure Analysis

There are three levels of RNA structure – Primary, secondary, and tertiary. The primary structure can be obtained from the DNA sequence. However, the actual RNA polynucleotide may contain posttranscriptional modifications of the sugar moieties and nucleotide bases, as well as the results of splicing such as in the case of pre-mRNA (Batey et al., 1999) that are not present in the DNA sequence. A single-stranded RNA is able to form different types of secondary structure elements including stems, bulges, pseudoknots, hairpin loops, internal loops, and multiloops. These elements will then fold to form the 3D structures that are able to execute their intended biological functions. Similar to proteins, the sequence composition and resulting 3D structure of the folded RNA molecule dictate their biological functions. For example, although mRNA is generally regarded as a single-stranded sequence, its local sequence patterns are able to form secondary structures that have been shown to have important roles in regulating protein expression (Kudla et al., 2009; Hall et al., 1982).

Studies into the relationships of the sequences to the secondary and tertiary structure of tRNAs in the 1960s were important milestones that enabled RNA structure prediction. The tRNA molecules, which generally consist of ~76–90 nucleotides, were shown to form a conserved cloverleaf secondary structure with four helical segments that accommodate anticodon, acceptor, D, and T arms despite sharing low sequence identities (RajBhandary et al., 1967; Madison et al., 1966; Holley et al., 1965). These secondary structure predictions were confirmed with the determination of the three-dimensional (3D) structure of RNA for yeast alanine transfer RNA (Kim et al., 1974; Robertus et al., 1974; Kim et al., 1973; Holley et al., 1965).

The knowledge that RNA secondary structures can be evolutionarily conserved despite low sequence identity spurred the development of RNA secondary structure prediction methods. The advent of these methods led to the prediction of the secondary structures of the ribosomal RNAs - the 5S, 16S, and 23S subunits (Noller and Woese, 1981; Noller et al., 1981; Woese et al., 1980; Fox and Woese, 1975). The RNA secondary structure prediction algorithms were further improved by using a combination of sequence comparison analysis, thermodynamic parameters that quantified the minimum free energy of structure folds, chemical modification experiments, and pseudoknot predictions (Reuter and Mathews, 2010; Mathews et al., 2004, 1999, 1997; Lück et al., 1996; Zuker and Stiegler, 1981). Other parameters, including the implementation of the centroids Boltzmann-weighted ensemble model (Ding et al., 2008) and maximization of the expected base-pair accuracy (Lu et al., 2009), were able to further improve the secondary structure predictions. These algorithms have now been implemented as web accessible tools allowing for users to generate RNA secondary structures from sequence data – Examples of such tools are the Vienna RNA secondary structure server (see "Relevant Websites section") (Hofacker, 2003) and RNAstructure (see "Relevant Websites section") (Bellaousov et al., 2013).

Although the predicted secondary or tertiary structures of RNA can be confidently used to provide biological function information, experimentally determined RNA structures remain crucial in providing atomic level insights on the mechanisms of specific RNA molecules. The first crystal structure of tRNA that was determined in 1970s provided the evidence that allowed for the validation of the interactions predicted in the cloverleaf secondary structure model. The tRNA molecule was folded into an L-shaped molecule with the nucleotide components stabilized via hydrogen bonding and base stacking, thus further lending credence to the hypothesis that all tRNA may share a similar structure due to the specific position requirement of the anticodon loop and acceptor stem (Kim *et al.*, 1974; Robertus *et al.*, 1974; Kim *et al.*, 1973).

Since then, many 3D structures of RNA molecules such as the hammerhead ribozyme, group I ribozyme domain, hepatitis delta virus ribozyme, ribosomal RNAs, and small nuclear RNA (Nguyen *et al.*, 2016; Yan *et al.*, 2015; Ogle *et al.*, 2001; Ban *et al.*, 2000; Schluenzen *et al.*, 2000; Wimberly *et al.*, 2000; Ferré-D'Amaré *et al.*, 1998; Cate *et al.*, 1996; Scott *et al.*, 1995) have been determined. The availability of a wider set of experimentally determined 3D structures had also allowed for progress to be made in the development of methods for RNA fold and motif analysis (Butcher and Pyle, 2011; Klosterman *et al.*, 2002; Batey *et al.*, 1999; Ferré-D'Amaré and Doudna, 1999).

Due to the difficulty of experimentally acquiring high-resolution three-dimensional structures of RNA molecules using either nuclear magnetic resonance spectrometry (NMR), X-ray crystallography, or electron microscopy (Cryo-EM), computational methods that can predict RNA structural information and allow for their comparisons, are useful tools that can take advantage of the availability of the numerous genome sequences.

These computational approaches do share some similarity to 3D structure prediction of proteins in using approaches that include fragment assembly (including Monte-Carlo algorithms) such as for the programs FARNA, DMD, FARFAR (Das *et al.*, 2010; Ding *et al.*, 2008; Das and Baker, 2007), molecular dynamics simulations used in iFoldRNA (Sharma *et al.*, 2008); and the nucleotide cyclic motif employed by MC-Fold and MC-Sym (Parisien and Major, 2008). Many other 3D RNA structure prediction tools can be found in the "Relevant Websites section".

The key function of the ribosome to synthesize proteins is conserved in all domains of life including organelles. Due to this, the structure of the ribosome is also generally conserved despite variations in the nucleotide sequence (**Table 1**). This allows for the study of how these sequences evolved while maintaining the ultimate requirement of needing to preserve the end structure that can be formed. In this article, we explore the bioinformatics tools of varying utility that can be used to compare RNA sequences and structures to provide functional and evolutionary insights.

Background

Ribosomal rRNA

More than half of the cellular RNA content is rRNAs (Russell and Zomerdijk, 2006). The rRNAs form the main structural components of the ribosome's protein synthesis machinery. Generally, two-thirds of the ribosome consists of rRNA while the remainder is made up of ribosomal proteins; however, an opposite ratio exists for mammalian mitochondrial ribosomes (Sharma *et al.*, 2003). Ribosomes are assembled from two ribosomal subunits, the small ribosomal subunit (SSU), specifically the 30S for prokaryotic cells and 40S for eukaryotic cells, and the large ribosomal subunit (LSU), specifically 50S for prokaryotic cells and 60S for eukaryotic cells. The two ribosomal subunits form the 70s and 80s ribosomes in prokaryotes and eukaryotes, respectively, while mitochondrial organelles contain 55S ribosomes. Each subunit contains a number of ribosomal proteins and rRNAs as shown in **Table 1**. The rRNA molecules have extensive secondary structure that together with the ribosomal proteins assemble into the large RNA–protein complex that is the ribosome.

Table 1   General components of ribosome

	Bacteria[a]	Archaea[a]	Chloroplast[b, c]	Eukaryote[a]	Mitochondria	
					Mammalian[a]	Fungi[d]
Ribosome		70S		80S	55S	67S–74S
Molecular weight (MDa)		2.3–2.6		3.3–4.5	~2.7	3–3.3
Small subunit						
Sedimentation coefficient	30S		30–35S	40S	28S	37S
Molecular weight (MDa)	0.8		1–2	1.4	1.2	1.1
SSU rRNAs		16S		18S	12S	15S
Number of ribosomal protein		20–33		32	33	34
Large subunit						
Sedimentation coefficient (S)	50S			60S	39S	57S
Molecular weight (MDa)	1.6		2–3	2.6	2.4	1.9
LSU rRNAs	23S, 5S		23S, 5S, 4.5S	26S, 5.8S, 5S	16S	21S
Number of ribosomal protein		34–40		46	52	39

[a]Poehlsgaard and Douthwaite (2005).
[b]Hoober (2012).
[c]Olinares *et al.* (2010).
[d]Amunts *et al.* (2014).

Bioinformatics Tools in Ribosomal SSU rRNA Sequence and Structure Studies

The SSU rRNA is involved in decoding of mRNA (Carter et al., 2000; Clemons et al., 1999) while the large ribosomal subunit rRNA (LSU rRNA) is the site of the peptidyl transferase center (PTC) with ribozyme activity that catalyzes the formation of the peptide bond during protein synthesis (Ban et al., 2000; Noller et al., 1992).

SSU rRNA Sequence Studies

Sequence and phylogenetic studies of the SSU rRNAs have been intensively carried out for the past few decades (Cannone et al., 2002; Gutell et al., 1994; Woese, 1987; Gutell et al., 1985) with the first 16S rRNA completely sequenced for E. coli in 1978 (Brosius et al., 1978). The SSU rRNA sequence is particularly useful for phylogenetic studies because it is generally accepted that the SSU rRNA genetic material does not undergo horizontal gene transfer. Furthermore, each domain of life contains universally conserved sequences within a close phylogenetic distance while at the same time containing variable regions as a result of evolution that are significant enough to serve as molecular markers to distinguish eukarya, bacteria, and archaea or between species in the same domain of life (Woese et al., 1990). There are nine commonly known conserved regions (C1–C9) and nine variable regions (V1–V9) in SSU rRNA, although the variability for some of the variable regions differ between eukaryotes and prokaryotes (Hadziavdic et al., 2014; Neefs et al., 1993).

Considering that structural elements may play a role in evolution, analysis of evolutionary rates across the entire rRNA has shown that structural elements in the rRNA do evolve with different rates, and this rate also varies between the different domains of life. For instance, nucleotides at the conserved regions were found mainly unpaired while sequences that form stems in bacteria or loops in eukaryotes tend to evolve faster. At the 3D structure level, the regions that are important for protein synthesis including the decoding center of SSU rRNA and the PTC of LSU rRNA were consistently more conserved than the residues on the surface of the ribosome thus suggesting that the structurally dependent functional roles of these nucleotides are the reason for their conservation (Smit et al., 2007; Wuyts et al., 2001; Woese et al., 1980).

There are approximately 6 million SSU rRNA (16S/18S) sequences available in the high quality ribosomal RNA databases as of December 2017 in the SILVA Database (Quast et al., 2012) (see "Relevant Websites section"). The availability of such a vast number of rRNA sequences has permitted faster and more accurate analysis of rRNA using sequence alignment tools. For instance, one can apply BLASTN (Basic Local Alignment Search Tool) (Altschul et al., 1990) to find the species or closest homolog of a newly acquired rDNA sequence. If the analysis entails the comparison of several selected rRNA sequences from different species, multiple sequence alignment (MSA) programs such as Clustal W (Larkin et al., 2007; Thompson et al., 1994), T-Coffee (Tree-based Consistency Objective Function for alignment Evaluation) (Notredame et al., 2000), and MAFFT (Katoh and Standley, 2013; Katoh et al., 2002) can be used. A phylogenetic tree can then be constructed from the output of the MSA results. Nonetheless, these sequence alignment programs depend only on the primary sequence similarity of rRNA without considering any features of the evolutionarily conserved secondary structures.

Alignment programs that integrate covariation analysis and specifically intended for use with rRNA sequences that integrate covariation analysis have also been developed. For example, the Infernal (INFERence of RNA Alignment) program has been designed to align rRNA more accurately by applying a model-based approach using covariance models that can recognize covariations or patterns of conserved base pairs in the rRNA secondary structure (Nawrocki and Eddy, 2013; Eddy and Durbin, 1994). The concepts and methods associated with RNA comparative sequence analysis and structure prediction can also be obtained at http://www.rna.ccbb.utexas.edu/CAR/1D/ (Cannone et al., 2002) To deal with the high volume of rRNA sequences from the different species available, programs such as SINA (SILVA Incremental Aligner) (Pruesse et al., 2012) have been developed.

The available SSU rRNA sequences are an important resource for studying evolution that are housed in several high quality updated SSU rRNA databases that include SILVA (Quast et al., 2012), RDP (Cole et al., 2013), Greengenes (McDonald et al., 2012), and National Center for Biotechnology Information (NCBI) (Federhen, 2011). To ease the phylogenetic study of SSU rRNA sequences, including those that are newly sequenced from previously unstudied organisms, one can apply comprehensive software packages like SSU-ALIGN (Nawrocki, 2009) that contain tools to identify, analyze, perform secondary structure alignment, and visualize SSU rRNA. A rRNA sequence identified from a newly sequenced genome also can be annotated using programs such as RNammer (Lagesen et al., 2007) and HMMER 3.0 (Huang et al., 2009) or web-based tools such as EzCloud (see "Relevant Websites section") (Yoon et al., 2017).

SSU rRNA Secondary Structure Predictions

Pairwise and MSAs of SSU rRNA are not able to provide a structural level insight for the sequences being compared. However, secondary structure prediction is crucial for providing a higher level of understanding with regard to evolutionary and functional conservation of SSU rRNA. Unlike RNA folding algorithms that predict secondary and tertiary structures based on their global minimum energy or by using free energy minimization that involves thermodynamic parameters (Mathews et al., 1999; Zuker, 1989; Zuker and Stiegler, 1981), comparative analysis of rRNA secondary structures is based on the principle that RNA with different sequences are able to form similar structures (secondary and tertiary) and the unique structures with functional features will be evolutionarily conserved (Gutell et al., 2002; Woese et al., 1983, 1980; Noller et al., 1981). The free energy minimization approach was reported to be less accurate for generally long RNA secondary structure prediction including SSU rRNA (Doshi *et al.*, 2004). The accuracy of covariation based rRNA comparative analysis was further improved with the availability of a high number of rRNA sequences (Gutell *et al.*, 2002, 1986; Gutell, 1996).

In the 1980s, the secondary structures of 16S rRNA were predicted and described using comparative sequence analysis and combined to data of chemical modifications and enzymatic assays (Gutell *et al.*, 1985; Woese *et al.*, 1983, 1980). In general, a prokaryote 16S secondary structure that consists of about 1550 nucleotides can be arranged into several domains – including 5′ domain, central domain, 3′ major domain, and 3′ minor domain – which assemble into 50 helices for SSU rRNA. Comparisons of SSU rRNA secondary structures for prokaryotes, eukaryotes, and organelles have revealed core structural features that are conserved in all SSU rRNA, and in addition, unique structural features for each domain of life or organelles were also identified. For example, 18S rRNA is more complex with less regular helices and bigger loops compared to bacterial 16S rRNA (Woese *et al*, 1983). Integrating sequence alignments to secondary and tertiary structure analysis of SSU RNAs further revealed unique features of SSU rRNA conserved and variable regions that can be applied to distinguish a species at the molecular level and for categorization as eukarya, bacteria, or archaea (Woese *et al.*, 1990; Woese, 1987).

For instance, all bacterial SSU rRNAs were found to have a side bulge with six nucleotides at the hairpin loop (between nucleotide 500 and 545, *E. coli* numbering) that protrudes from the stalk of the rRNA structure. However, this same side bulge in archaea and eukarya were formed with seven nucleotides. Several of these distinct features were further identified to distinguish the rRNA of compared organisms, which can help in building a universal phylogenetic tree (Woese *et al.*, 1990, 1983; Gutell *et al.*, 1985). Furthermore, analysis of SSU rRNAs from organelles such as the 16S rRNA of chloroplast and the 12S rRNA of mitochondria also revealed substantial similarities of the primary sequences and at secondary structure level despite being of very different lengths thus suggesting that the core sequence and structure of rRNA is also conserved in the ribosomes of organelles (Zwieb *et al.*, 1981). In knowing that the secondary structures of SSU rRNA are more conserved than the sequence, differences in the secondary structures between SSU rRNAs have been extracted for taxonomic and evolutionary studies (Du *et al.*, 2017). Comparison of all SSU rRNA secondary structures when mapped across the three domains of life obtained from Comparative RNA Web (CRW) (Mears *et al.*, 2002) provides a valuable picture of phylogenetic conservation by allowing for the identification of nucleotides or structural regions that are either highly conserved or variable.

Secondary structure studies of SSU rRNAs before the atomic structure of the ribosome were determined to have contributed to the early functional understanding of the ribosome. For example, the highly conserved sequence and secondary structure of 530 loop region of the 16S rRNA, which consists of nucleotide G530, was predicted to form a pseudoknot that was of structural and functional importance in protein translation (Powers and Noller, 1991). When the atomic resolution structure of the 30S ribosome was solved, it was indeed revealed that the 530 loop is interacting with the anticodon stem-loop of tRNA that recognizes the mRNA codon at the ribosomal A site. The nucleotide G530 in the 530 loop together with bases A1492 and A1493 on helix 44 of SSU rRNA are now known to be crucial for correct codon–anticodon interaction during the decoding process (Ogle *et al.*, 2001).

Computer programs such as SSU-DRAW, which is part of the SSU-ALIGN package (Nawrocki, 2009), can generate secondary structures of newly identified SSU rRNAs with a high degree of confidence by using a template-based comparative analysis method. However, comparative analysis with covariation approach is still not able to reveal noncanonical base pairings that are often found in complex RNA structures such as rRNA. More recently available structure prediction approaches can integrate information on specific geometric and molecular interactions obtained from experimentally determined rRNA 3D structures that may thus improve secondary structure prediction (Petrov *et al.*, 2014).

SSU rRNA 3D Structure Studies

While sequences of SSU rRNA are now fairly easy to obtain via DNA sequencing and from there the secondary structure can also be predicted with high confidence, the accurate computational prediction of its 3D structure is still not possible. This is due to the generally long sequences that are in excess of 1000 nucleotides that also have interactions with ribosomal proteins in order to form the mega Dalton RNA–protein complex. Nonetheless, much effort is ongoing towards developing accurate tools for RNA 3D structure prediction. One initiative in this direction is RNA-Puzzles, a collective blind experiment to evaluate RNA prediction techniques (Cruz *et al.*, 2012).

At present, the 3D structure of SSU rRNA can only be acquired by determining the structure of the ribosome. X-ray crystallography and cryoelectron microscopy (cryo-EM) remain the only routes to experimentally obtain the ribosome's structure. The 3D coordinates of the rRNA chains can be extracted from the atomic resolution structures of the ribosome that have been deposited in the Protein Data Bank (PDB). Ribosomal RNA forms a stable ribosomal subunit when in complex with ribosomal proteins; this may explain why no independent structures of rRNA are available.

The 3D structure of rRNA can be analyzed and displayed with available molecular visualization software already being used for protein structures such as COOT (Emsley and Cowtan, 2004), Chimera (Pettersen *et al.*, 2004), PyMOL (Delano, 2002), and several others. Other programs such as Ribovision (Bernier *et al.*, 2014) were exclusively designed to visualize and analyze the primary sequences as well as secondary and three-dimensional structures of rRNA in a single platform. Selected bioinformatics tools that are available for sequence and structure analysis of SSU rRNA are listed in **Table 2**.

In 2000–2001, the high-resolution crystal structures were obtained for the 30S ribosomal subunits from thermophilic bacteria, *Thermus thermophilus* (Ogle *et al.*, 2001; Wimberly *et al.*, 2000; Schluenzen *et al.*, 2000) and the 50S subunit from the halophilic

Table 2   The list of programs and their applications in rRNA sequence and structure analysis

Function	Program/Server (URL)	Method/Content	URL
Sequence alignment	BLASTN	rDNA sequence alignment to rRNA sequence obtained from PDB database	https://blast.ncbi.nlm.nih.gov/Blast.cgi
	Clustal W	Multiple sequence alignment	https://www.ebi.ac.uk/Tools/msa/clustalw2/
	T-Coffee	Iterative alignment of DNA, RNA and protein sequences to get conserved residue/motif	http://tcoffee.crg.cat/apps/tcoffee/do:regular
	SINA	Quality checked and aligned ribosomal RNA sequence data	https://www.arb-silva.de/
	SSU-ALIGN	Structure based multiple sequences alignment of SSU ribosomal RNA sequences (16S & 18S) using covariance models	http://eddylab.org/software/ssu-align/
	Infernal ("INFERence of RNA Alignment")	rRNA alignment with model-based approach using covariance models (CM)	http://eddylab.org/infernal/
	CRWAlign	Template-based alignment	http://www.rna.icmb.utexas.edu/SAE/2F/CRWAlign/index.php
	MAFFT	Multiple ncRNA alignments	https://mafft.cbrc.jp/alignment/software/
Ribosomal RNA database	SILVA	A comprehensive online database for all ribosomal RNA including 16S/18S/23S/28S	https://www.arb-silva.de/
	RDP	Ribosomal Database Project	https://rdp.cme.msu.edu/
	Greengenes	16S rRNA gene database	http://greengenes.lbl.gov
Ribosomal RNA prediction	rmm_rRNA	Identification of rRNA sequences	http://weizhong-lab.ucsd.edu/metagenomic-analysis/server/hmm_rRNA/
	RNAmmer	Predict rRNAs from genome sequences	http://www.cbs.dtu.dk/services/RNAmmer/
	SSU-ALIGN	Identify, align, mask, and visualize SSU rRNA	http://eddylab.org/software/ssu-align/
Protein structure database	Protein Data Bank (PDB)	A database for the three-dimensional structural data of macromolecules including large complexes like ribosome	https://www.rcsb.org/
3D Structural display and analysis	COOT	Macromolecular model building, model completion and validation	https://www2.mrc-lmb.cam.ac.uk/personal/pemsley/coot/
	PyMOL	Molecular visualization system	https://pymol.org/2/
	Chimera	Structure visualization and analysis	https://www.cgl.ucsf.edu/chimera/
Ribosome information viewer	Ribovision	Open-source ribosome-information viewer website	http://apollo.chemistry.gatech.edu/RiboVision/Documentation/index.html

archaeon, *Haloarcula marismortui* (Ban *et al.*, 2000), which revealed in great depth the details of how the ribosome decodes mRNA and synthesizes the corresponding polypeptide en route to becoming a functional protein molecule. For the first time, the previously predicted secondary and tertiary structure of rRNAs could be compared and validated against experimentally determined examples. As a testament to the accuracy of the prediction tools, about 97%–98% of previously predicted rRNAs' base pairings were indeed found in the ribosomal crystal structures (Gutell *et al.*, 2002).

Advancements in cryo-EM and X-ray crystallography have resulted in several high-resolution ribosomal structures being determined for the ribosomes of eukaryotic species – human, protozoa, and yeast – (Zhang *et al.*, 2016; Khatter *et al.*, 2015; Wong *et al.*, 2014; Ben-Shem *et al.*, 2011; Rabl *et al.*, 2011) as well as the ribosome of organelles – mitochondria (human, pig, and yeast) and chloroplast (spinach) (Desai *et al.*, 2017; Amunts *et al.*, 2015; Greber *et al.*, 2015). Comparisons of SSU rRNA crystal structures for bacteria and eukaryotes have revealed that both domains of life share a similar structure at several of the hypervariable regions and help to provide information on secondary structure mappings that were not previously identified in 18S rRNA (Lee and Gutell, 2012).

Case Studies: Sequence Alignment Guided Structure Analysis of SSU rRNA From Prokaryotes, Eukaryotes, and Organelles

High-Resolution Ribosome Structures

Fourteen high-resolution (<4Å) structures of whole ribosomes available in the PDB were selected for this case study to demonstrate MSA guided structure analysis of SSU rRNA for two domains of life (prokaryote and eukaryote) and organelles (chloroplast and mitochondrial). The domain archaea was not included due to the lack of atomic structures for their 70S and 30S ribosomes. The selected target ribosomes include **prokaryotic 70S ribosomes**: Gram-negative bacteria *Escherichia coli* (PDB ID: 4YBB), and *Thermus thermophilus* (PDB ID: 4V51), Gram-positive bacteria *Bacillulus subtilis* (PDB ID: 3J9W) and *Staphylococcus aureus* (PDB ID: 5LI0); and *Mycobacterium tuberculosis* (PDB ID: 5V93) and *Mycobacterium smegmatis* (PDB ID: 5O61); **Eukaryotic 80S ribosomes**: *Saccharomyces cerevisiae* (PDB ID: 4V88), *Homo sapiens* (human) (PDB ID: 4UG0), *Leishmania donovani* (PDB ID: 5T2A) and *Plasmodium falciparum* (PDB ID: 3J7A); **Mitochondrial ribosomes**: *Saccharomyces cerevisiae* mitoribosome (PDB ID:

5MRC), *Sus scrofa* (Porcine) mitoribosome (PDB ID: 5AJ3) and *Homo sapiens* 55S mitoribosome (PDB iD: 3J9M); **Chloroplastid 70S ribosome**: *Spinacia oleracea* (spinach) chloroplast ribosome (PDB ID: 5MMM).

Multiple Sequence Alignment and Phylogenetic Tree Construction

The SSU rRNA sequences corresponding to the species of selected ribosomes including the SSU rRNA of *E. coli* (16S_E_coli), *T. thermophilus* (16S_T_thermophilus), *B. Subtilis* (16S_B_subtilis), *S. aureus* (16S_S_aureus), *M. smegmatis* (16S_M_smegmatis), *M. tuberculosis* (16S_M_tuberculosis), chloroplast of *S. oleracea* (16S_S_oleracea_Chloroplast), *S. cerevisae* (18S_S_cerevisae), *L. donovani*

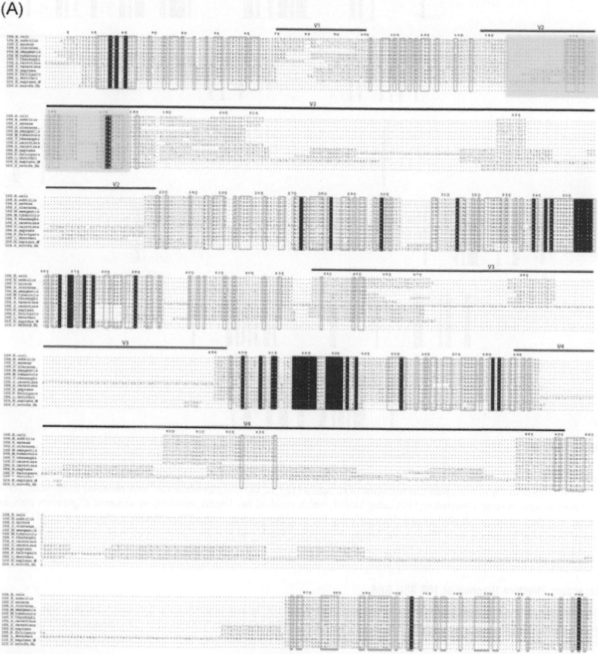

(A)

Fig. 1   Multiple sequence alignments for the SSU rRNA of 14 selected species with high-resolution (< 4 Å) ribosomal structures that were analyzed using fast Fourier transform and with the results subjected to phylogenetic tree construction using the neighbor-joining method with MAFFT (https://mafft.cbrc.jp/alignment/software/). (A) The MSA result in Clustal format as visualized using Espript program with the highly conserved regions highlighted in red (A). (B) The phylogenetic tree as visualized using Phylo.io. The variable regions (V1–V9) of *Escherichia coli* 16S SSU rRNA are indicated with horizontal black bars. The highlighted variable region of V2 (nucleotides 144–178) indicate the nucleotides that form helix h8 in bacterial 16S SSU rRNA, but form h3 and h4 of 12S mammalian mito-SSU rRNA.

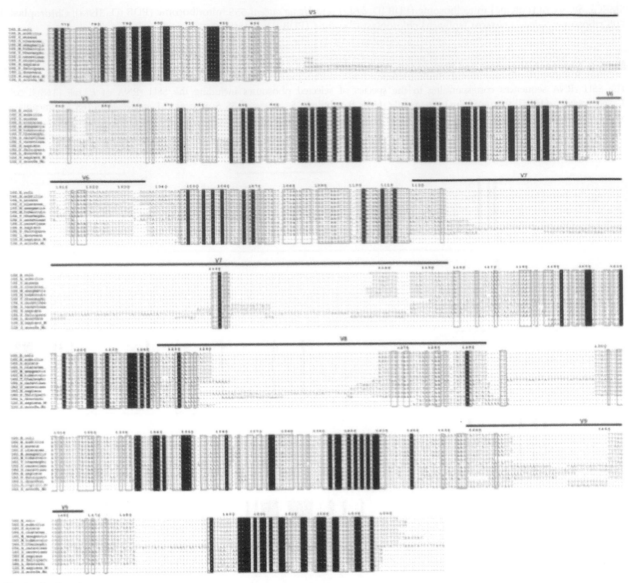

Fig. 1 Continued

(18S_L_donovani), *P. falciparum* (18S_P_falciparum), *H. sapiens* (18S_H_sapiens), mitochondrial ribosome of *S. cerevisae* (15S_S_cerevisae_Mitoribosome) and mitochondrial ribosome of *H. sapiens* (12S_H_sapiens_Mitoribosome) were obtained from NCBI. The FASTA formatted sequences were subjected to MSA using MAFFT, which employs fast Fourier transform in sequence alignments with an Auto setting, and then subjected to phylogenetic analysis using the neighbor-joining method (see "Relevant Websites section"). The phylogenetic trees were visualized with Phylo.io (Robinson *et al.*, 2016; Katoh and Standley, 2013; Katoh *et al.*, 2002). The MSA results in Clustal format were visualized with the ESPript program (Gouet *et al.*, 1999) to highlight the conserved regions.

Secondary Structure Diagram of 16S SSU RNA

The secondary structure diagrams of SSU rRNAs of human 18S, *E. coli* 16S, human mito ribosome 12S, and *S. cerevisae* mito ribosome 15S were obtained from the Comparative RNA Web server (see "Relevant Websites section"). Additionally, an overview of SSU rRNA conserved secondary structures across the three domains of life was also obtained from CRW (see "Relevant Websites section") (Mears *et al.*, 2002).

Comparison of 3D Structure of SSU rRNAs

The selected SSU rRNAs structure coordinates were obtained from the structures deposited in the PDB as listed in Section "SSU rRNA Sequence Studies." The 16S rRNA of *E. coli* (PDB ID: 4YBB) was used as a reference structure for 3D structure comparisons of human 18S rRNA (PDB ID: 4UG0), 15S rRNA of *S. cerevisiae* mito ribosome (PDB ID: 4V88), and 12S rRNA of

(B)

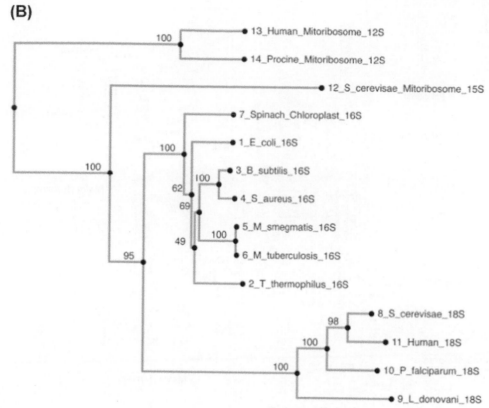

Fig. 1 Continued

human mito ribosome (PDB ID: 3J9M). The structure superposition was carried out using least-squares fitting in the COOT program (Emsley and Cowtan, 2004). The program PyMOL (DeLano, 2002) was used to visualize all the 3D structures that were analyzed in this case study.

Results and Discussion

The sequences of the 14 selected SSU rRNAs from prokaryote, eukaryote, and organelles with nucleotides lengths of 962–2205 were aligned. Despite the significant difference in length, the MSA showed that all the SSU rRNAs were generally well aligned, particularly at the previously identified conserved regions (Baker et al., 2003; Van de Peer et al., 1996) including helices h18, h27, h28, h30, h31, h44, and h45. In comparison to the mammalian cell's 12S mito ribosome, all the aligned 16S and 18S SSU rRNAs were found to have insertions mainly at the variable regions V1–V9 (**Fig. 1(A)**). Phylogenetic analysis based on the MSA results showed that bacteria, eukaryote, and mito ribosome SSU rRNAs were shown as different branches in the unrooted tree (**Fig. 1(B)**). The 16S rRNA of Gram-positive, Gram-negative bacteria, and mycobacterium are closely related to each other in one branch (**Fig. 1(B)**). In addition, chloroplast rRNA from spinach also clustered to prokaryote SSU rRNA despite having evolved to be an organelle that is important for photosynthetic plants and algae. The eukaryotic SSU rRNA for mammals, parasites, and yeasts was also shown to be more closely related to each other. Nonetheless, unlike the nuclear ribosome, the SSU rRNA of the mitochondrial ribosome in yeast is significantly deviated compared to the mammalian mito ribosome. The overall MSA and phylogenetic analysis can clearly distinguish sequences of SSU rRNA to the domain of life and organelle that it belongs to.

While the alignments are able to show that the nucleotide sequences are universally conserved across the SSU rRNA, especially at the conserved regions, such as the helices of h1 and h2 (nucleotide 11–23) and loop 530 region of helix h18 (nucleotide 515–536, all the nucleotide numberings used refer to those in E. coli SSU rRNA), there are limitations for the MSA results when it comes to demonstrating the conservation for the secondary structure. For example, the nucleotides 144–178 (V2 region) are known to form helix h8 in 16S rRNA, however similar residues of the mito ribosome were found to form helices h3 and h4 of 12S rRNA (**Fig. 1(A)** and **Fig. 2(A)**). The use of sequence comparisons alone is unable to provide a structural context to the RNA molecule. Comparisons of secondary structure are therefore necessary to further identify conservation in the RNA molecules from a structural perspective.

Based on the predicted secondary structures of the 12S, 15S, 16S, and 18S SSU rRNAs that were obtained from the Comparative RNA Web server (CRW) (see "Relevant Websites section") (Cannone et al., 2002) as shown in **Fig. 2**, all SSU rRNA secondary structure diagrams showed an overall similarity in containing the 3′ minor and major domains, 5′ major domains, and central domains (**Fig. 2**). The secondary structure regions that are formed with universally conserved nucleotides identified in the MSA (**Fig. 1(A)** and **Fig. 2(A)**) were found to be mostly conserved. Nonetheless, one can clearly identify the structural differences between

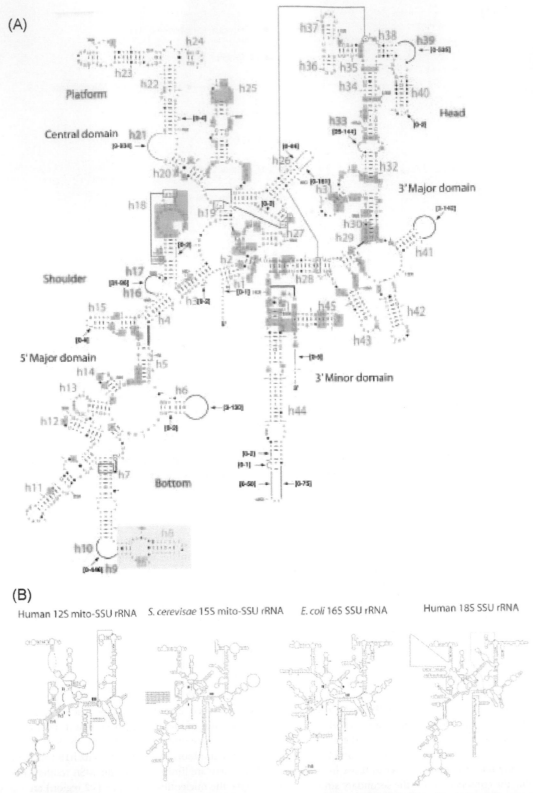

Fig. 2 The secondary structure of SSU rRNA. (A) The secondary structure of *Escherichia coli* 16S SSU rRNA with phylogenetic conservation superimposed across the three domains of life. This diagram was obtained from Comparative RNA Web (CRW) (http://www.rna.icmb.utexas.edu/SIM/4A/Minimal_Ribosome/) with slight modifications. Conserved nucleotide sequences are shown as ACGU: 98 + % conserve, acgu: 90%–98% conserved, •: 80%–90% conserved, and •: less than 80% conserved. Arcs represent the variable regions with the nucleotide number (lower and upper) known to exist. The nucleotides that were 100% conserved in the MSA shown in **Fig. 1** are highlighted in purple. The helices that are conserved in the three domains of life were labeled in green, while the helices in the variable regions are in blue. Helix h8 is highlighted in yellow. (B) The secondary structures of *Escherichia coli* 16S SSU rRNA, human 18S SSU rRNA, 15S yeast mito-SSU rRNA, and 12S human mito-SSU rRNA were obtained from CRW (http://www.rna.icmb.utexas.edu/SIM/4A/Minimal_Ribosome/) for comparison. Helices h3 and h4 of 12S human mito-SSU rRNA are highlighted in yellow.

the compared SSU rRNAs. For example, while the head region is highly similar, the bottom region was significantly deviated (**Fig. 2 (B)**). Such structural deviations will provide a better understanding of the evolutionary events that specific regions of the RNA molecule had undergone. Although the secondary structure is informative in revealing the general structure conservation of the RNA molecule that is missing in sequence alignments, it remains difficult to predict noncanonical base pairings and highly idiosyncratic RNA sequences – For example, a GC pairing can be assumed to conform to the Watson–Crick geometry but in reality, that GC pairing may actually be of the noncanonical reverse Watson–Crick arrangement. Recently, high-resolution structures have been used to aid in constructing a more complete and accurate secondary structure map of SSU rRNA (Petrov *et al.*, 2014).

The overall shape of SSU rRNAs in this case study, with the head, neck, beak, platform, body, shoulder, and spur features can be clearly discerned using molecular visualization (**Fig. 3**). The 12S mammalian mt-SSU rRNA was shown to have a contracted form in accordance to its shortest sequence length, while 15S, 16S, and 18S SSU rRNA have similar overall dimension (**Fig. 3(A)**). The contracted mammalian mt-SSU rRNA has been known to recruit more proteins in order to perform the specific synthesis of hydrophobic integral membrane proteins (Amunts *et al.*, 2015; O'brien, 2003). The yeast 15S mt-SSU rRNA had not undergone similar evolutionary events compared to its mammalian counterpart and thus maintains a size similar to bacterial 16S rRNA. The expansion segments of 18S human SSU rRNA compared to 16S SSU rRNA can also be identified (**Fig. 3(B)**). For detailed in depth discussion of the features for each SSU rRNA structure, please refer to the respective original publications. Overall, the 3D structures provide details that reveal universally conserved regions as well as structural features that show how rRNA have evolved specifically for a particular domain of life and organelles.

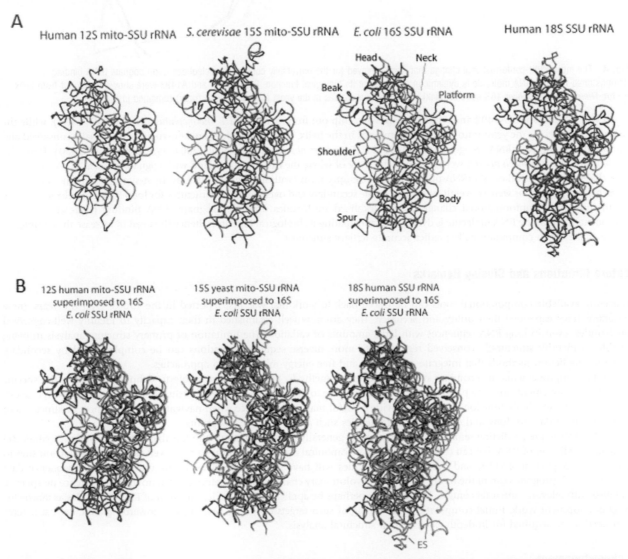

Fig. 3 The 3D structure of SSU rRNAs. (A) The 3D structure of SSU rRNAs were shown in same dimension by superimposed to the loop 530 nucleotides (cyan) of *Escherichia coli* 16S SSU rRNA. The nucleotides found to be 100% conserved in multiple sequence alignment of **Fig. 1(A)** are shown as pink in *E. coli* 16S SSU rRNA. The figure is generated by using the program PyMOL. (B) Comparison of SSU rRNA by superimposing of 12S human mito-SSU rRNA, 15S yeast mito-SSU rRNA, and 18S human SSU rRNA (gray) to 16S *E. coli* SSU rRNA (orange). ES indicates part of the expansion segments of 18S human SSU rRNA.

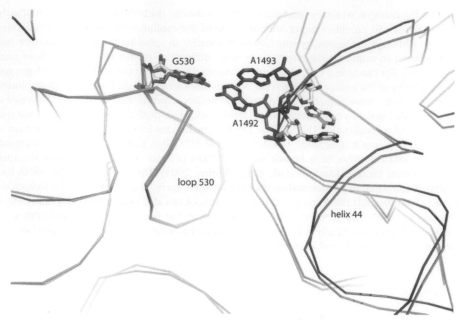

Fig. 4 The induced-fit conformational change that was employed for the universally conserved nucleotides upon cognate tRNA binding demonstrated that the RNA molecule is dynamic in carrying out its biological function. Both A1492 and A1493 were shown to flip out from helix 44 for *Thermus thermophiles* 16S subunit (pink). The same nucleotides in the yeast mito-SSU rRNA (gray) remained in the helix.

In **Fig. 4**, nucleotides A1492 and A1493 are shown to flip out from helix 44 of *T. thermophilus* 16S (PDB ID: 4V51), while the same nucleotides for the yeast mito-SSU rRNA remained in the helix. These nucleotides are known to be universally conserved and important for cognate tRNA recognition at the A site (Selmer *et al.*, 2006; Ogle *et al.*, 2001; Wimberly *et al.*, 2000). Here, the nucleotides in *T. thermophilus* 16S were shown at the stage of where the ribosome is bound with cognate tRNA at the A-site of 16S SSU rRNA, while 15S mito-SSU rRNA of yeast is in the empty form (without cognate tRNA at the A-site). Despite the universally conserved sequences, as well as overall agreement of the secondary and overall tertiary structures for loop 530 and helix 44, the use of an induced-fit conformational change on the localized nucleotides upon the cognate tRNA binding (Ogle *et al.*, 2001) demonstrating that the RNA molecule is dynamic in anticipating its biological functions, hence the need to increase the complexity of the challenge to computationally predict accurate tertiary structures.

Future Directions and Closing Remarks

Currently available computational tools can be traced back to work that was first reported in the 1960s. Over the years, these programs have expanded their utility and accuracy. They are now well established in their capacity to identify well-conserved nucleotides, even in long RNA sequences with large amounts of variation. The limitation of primary structure analysis in being unable to identify structurally conserved regions with more diverse sequence variations can be complemented by secondary structure prediction methods that integrate covariation and free energy minimization approaches.

Despite improvements in secondary structure prediction methods, they are still not able to definitively discern the specific molecular arrangements for base pairings and are thus not able to differentiate canonical versus noncanonical pairs. Nevertheless, such tools remain highly functional and can provide a useful map and guidance when navigating the sequences or structures of newly acquired data for long and complex RNA molecules such as the ribosomal subunits.

RNA 3D structure prediction remains a challenge and is generally limited to chains with less than 500 nucleotides. Accurate 3D structure prediction of RNA that can correctly differentiate canonical and noncanonical pairs, as well as identify interaction sites to metal ions, organic molecules, and other macromolecules will have great utility in using the vast amount of sequence data available. Such programs can in the future trace minor evolutionary changes that are relevant from not only a sequence perspective but also with relevant structural context. They can also perhaps be applicable for the identification of RNA molecules as targets for drug development work. Initial computational screening of such targets can direct investigators towards specific RNA structures that need to be acquired for in depth experimental structural analysis.

Acknowledgment

MFR is funded by the Ministry of Science, Technology and Innovation Malaysia grant 02-01-02-SF1278 and Universiti Kebangsaan Malaysia grant GP-K011849.

CLN is funded by the Universiti Kebangsaan Malaysia grant GP-K019584 and GUP-2017-070.

See also: Biomolecular Structures: Prediction, Identification and Analyses. Characterizing and Functional Assignment of Noncoding RNAs. Engineering of Supramolecular RNA Structures. Natural Language Processing Approaches in Bioinformatics. Predicting RNA-RNA Interactions in Three-Dimensional Structures. Prediction of Coding and Non-Coding RNA

References

Altschul, S.F., Gish, W., Miller, W., Myers, E.W., Lipman, D.J., 1990. Basic local alignment search tool. Journal of Molecular Biology 215, 403–410.

Amunts, A., Brown, A., Bai, X.C., *et al.*, 2014. Structure of the yeast mitochondrial large ribosomal subunit. Science 343 (6178), 1485–1489.

Amunts, A., Brown, A., Toots, J., Scheres, S.H., Ramakrishnan, V., 2015. The structure of the human mitochondrial ribosome. Science 348 (6230), 95–98.

Baker, G.C., Smith, J.J., Cowan, D.A., 2003. Review and re-analysis of domain-specific 16S primers. Journal of Microbiological Methods 55 (3), 541–555.

Ban, N., Nissen, P., Hansen, J., Moore, P.B., Steitz, T.A., 2000. The complete atomic structure of the large ribosomal subunit at 2.4 Å resolution. Science 289 (5481), 905–920.

Batey, R.T., Rambo, R.P., Doudna, J.A., 1999. Tertiary motifs in RNA structure and folding. Angewandte Chemie International Edition 38 (16), 2326–2343.

Bellaousov, S., Reuter, J.S., Seetin, M.G., Mathews, D.H., 2013. RNAstructure: Web servers for RNA secondary structure prediction and analysis. Nucleic Acids Research 41 (W1), W471–W474.

Ben-Shem, A., de Loubresse, N.G., Melnikov, S., *et al.*, 2011. The structure of the eukaryotic ribosome at 3.0 Å resolution. Science 334 (6062), 1524–1529.

Bernier, C.R., Petrov, A.S., Waterbury, C.C., *et al.*, 2014. RiboVision suite for visualization and analysis of ribosomes. Faraday Discussions 169, 195–207.

Brosius, J., Palmer, M.L., Kennedy, P.J., Noller, H.F., 1978. Complete nucleotide sequence of a 16S ribosomal RNA gene from Escherichia coli. Proceedings of the National Academy of Sciences 75 (10), 4801–4805.

Butcher, S.E., Pyle, A.M., 2011. The molecular interactions that stabilize RNA tertiary structure: RNA motifs, patterns, and networks. Accounts of Chemical Research 44 (12), 1302–1311.

Cannone, J.J., Subramanian, S., Schnare, M.N., *et al.*, 2002. The comparative RNA web (CRW) site: An online database of comparative sequence and structure information for ribosomal, intron, and other RNAs. BMC Bioinformatics 3 (1), 2.

Carter, A.P., Clemons, W.M., Brodersen, D.E., *et al.*, 2000. Functional insights from the structure of the 30S ribosomal subunit and its interactions with antibiotics. Nature 407 (6802), 340–348.

Cate, J.H., Gooding, A.R., Podell, E., *et al.*, 1996. Crystal structure of a group I ribozyme domain: Principles of RNA packing. Science 273 (5282), 1678–1685.

Cech, T.R., 2012. The RNA worlds in context. Cold Spring Harbor Perspectives in Biology 4 (7), a006742.

Clemons, W.M., May, J.L., Wimberly, B.T., *et al.*, 1999. Structure of a bacterial 30S ribosomal subunit at 5.5 Å resolution. Nature 400 (6747), 833–840.

Cole, J.R., Wang, Q., Fish, J.A., *et al.*, 2013. Ribosomal Database Project: Data and tools for high throughput rRNA analysis. Nucleic Acids Research 42 (D1), D633–D642.

Crick, F.H.C., 1958. On protein synthesis. Symposia of the Society for Experimental Biology 12, 138–163.

Cruz, J.A., Blanchet, M.F., Boniecki, M., *et al.*, 2012. RNA-Puzzles: A CASP-like evaluation of RNA three-dimensional structure prediction. RNA 18 (4), 610–625.

Das, R., Baker, D., 2007. Automated de novo prediction of native-like RNA tertiary structures. Proceedings of the National Academy of Sciences of the United States of America 104 (37), 14664–14669.

Das, R., Karanicolas, J., Baker, D., 2010. Atomic accuracy in predicting and designing noncanonical RNA structure. Nature Methods 7 (4), 291–294.

DeLano, W.L., 2002. The PyMOL molecular graphics system. Available at: http://pymol.org.

Desai, N., Brown, A., Amunts, A., Ramakrishnan, V., 2017. The structure of the yeast mitochondrial ribosome. Science 355 (6324), 528–531.

Ding, F., Sharma, S., Chalasani, P., *et al.*, 2008. Ab initio RNA folding by discrete molecular dynamics: From structure prediction to folding mechanisms. RNA 14 (6), 1164–1173.

Doshi, K.J., Cannone, J.J., Cobaugh, C.W., Gutell, R.R., 2004. Evaluation of the suitability of free-energy minimization using nearest-neighbor energy parameters for RNA secondary structure prediction. BMC Bioinformatics 5 (1), 105.

Du, Y.H., Zhao, Y.J., Tang, F.H., 2017. A new molecular approach based on the secondary structure of ribosomal RNA for phylogenetic analysis of mobilid ciliates. Current Microbiology. 1–9.

Eddy, S.R., Durbin, R., 1994. RNA sequence analysis using covariance models. Nucleic Acids Research 22 (11), 2079–2088.

Emsley, P., Cowtan, K., 2004. Coot: Model-building tools for molecular graphics. Acta Crystallographica Section D: Biological Crystallography 60 (12), 2126–2132.

Federhen, S., 2011. The NCBI taxonomy database. Nucleic Acids Research 40 (D1), D136–D143.

Ferré-D'Amaré, A.R., Doudna, J.A., 1999. RNA folds: Insights from recent crystal structures. Annual Review of Biophysics and Biomolecular Structure 28 (1), 57–73.

Ferré-D'Amaré, A.R., Zhou, K., Doudna, J.A., 1998. Crystal structure of a hepatitis delta virus ribozyme. Nature 395 (6702), 567–574.

Fox, G.E., Woese, C.R., 1975. 5S RNA secondary structure. Nature 256 (5517), 505–507.

Gilbert, W., 1986. Origin of life: The RNA world. Nature 319 (6055),

Gouet, P., Courcelle, E., Stuart, D.I., Métoz, F., 1999. ESPript: Analysis of multiple sequence alignments In PostScript. Bioinformatics (Oxford) 15 (4), 305–308.

Greber, B.J., Bieri, P., Leibundgut, M., *et al.*, 2015. The complete structure of the 55S mammalian mitochondrial ribosome. Science 348 (6232), 303–308.

Guerrier-Takada, C., Gardiner, K., Marsh, T., Pace, N., Altman, S., 1983. The RNA moiety of ribonuclease P is the catalytic subunit of the enzyme. Cell 35 (3), 849–857.

Gutell, R.R., 1996. Comparative sequence analysis and the structure of 16S and 23S rRNA. Ribosomal RNA: Structure, Evolution, Processing, and Function in Protein Biosynthesis. 111–128.

Gutell, R.R., Larsen, N., Woese, C.R., 1994. Lessons from an evolving rRNA: 16S and 23S rRNA structures from a comparative perspective. Microbiological Reviews 58 (1), 10–26.

Gutell, R.R., Lee, J.C., Cannone, J.J., 2002. The accuracy of ribosomal RNA comparative structure models. Current Opinion in Structural Biology 12 (3), 301–310.

Gutell, R.R., Noller, H.F., Woese, C.R., 1986. Higher order structure in ribosomal RNA. The EMBO Journal 5 (5), 1111.

Gutell, R.R., Weiser, B., Woese, C.R., Noller, H.F., 1985. Comparative anatomy of 16-S-like ribosomal RNA. Progress in Nucleic acid Research and Molecular Biology 32, 155–216.

Hadziavdic, K., Lekang, K., Lanzen, A., *et al.*, 2014. Characterization of the 18S rRNA gene for designing universal eukaryote specific primers. PLOS ONE 9 (2), e87624.

Hall, M.N., Gabay, J., Débarbouillé, M., Schwartz, M., 1982. A role for mRNA secondary structure in the control of translation initiation. Nature 295 (5850), 616–618.

Hofacker, I.L., 2003. Vienna RNA secondary structure server. Nucleic Acids Research 31 (13), 3429–3431.

Holley, R.W., Apgar, J., Everett, G.A., *et al.*, 1965. Structure of a ribonucleic acid. Science 1462–1465.

Hoober, J.K., 2012. Chloroplasts. Springer Science & Business Media. pp. 164–177.

Huang, Y., Gilna, P., Li, W., 2009. Identification of ribosomal RNA genes in metagenomic fragments. Bioinformatics 25 (10), 1338–1340.

Katoh, K., Standley, D.M., 2013. MAFFT multiple sequence alignment software version 7: Improvements in performance and usability. Molecular Biology and Evolution 30 (4), 772–780.

Katoh, K., Misawa, K., Kuma, K.I., Miyata, T., 2002. MAFFT: A novel method for rapid multiple sequence alignment based on fast Fourier transform. Nucleic Acids Research 30 (14), 3059–3066.

Khatter, H., Myasnikov, A.G., Natchiar, S.K., Klaholz, B.P., 2015. Structure of the human 80S ribosome. Nature 520 (7549), 640–645.

Kim, S.H., Quigley, G.J., Suddath, F.L., et al., 1973. Three-dimensional structure of yeast phenylalanine transfer RNA: Folding of the polynucleotide chain. Science 179 (4070), 285–288.

Kim, S.H., Suddath, F.L., Quigley, G.J., et al., 1974. Three-dimensional tertiary structure of yeast phenylalanine transfer RNA. Science 185 (4149), 435–440.

Klosterman, P.S., Tamura, M., Holbrook, S.R., Brenner, S.E., 2002. SCOR: A structural classification of RNA database. Nucleic Acids Research 30 (1), 392–394.

Kruger, K., Grabowski, P.J., Zaug, A.J., et al., 1982. Self-splicing RNA: Autoexcision and autocyclization of the ribosomal RNA intervening sequence of Tetrahymena. Cell 31 (1), 147–157.

Kudla, G., Murray, A.W., Tollervey, D., Plotkin, J.B., 2009. Coding-sequence determinants of gene expression in Escherichia coli. Science 324 (5924), 255–258.

Lagesen, K., Hallin, P., Rødland, E.A., et al., 2007. RNAmmer: Consistent and rapid annotation of ribosomal RNA genes. Nucleic Acids Research 35 (9), 3100–3108.

Larkin, M.A., Blackshields, G., Brown, N.P., et al., 2007. Clustal W and Clustal X version 2.0. Bioinformatics 23 (21), 2947–2948.

Lee, J.C., Gutell, R.R., 2012. A comparison of the crystal structures of eukaryotic and bacterial SSU ribosomal RNAs reveals common structural features in the hypervariable regions. PLOS ONE 7 (5), e38203.

Lu, Z.J., Gloor, J.W., Mathews, D.H., 2009. Improved RNA secondary structure prediction by maximizing expected pair accuracy. RNA 15 (10), 1805–1813.

Lück, R., Steger, G., Riesner, D., 1996. Thermodynamic prediction of conserved secondary structure: Application to the RRE element of HIV, the tRNA-like element of CMV and the mRNA of prion protein. Journal of Molecular Biology 258 (5), 813–826.

Madison, J.T., Everett, G.A., Kung, H., 1966. Nucleotide sequence of a yeast tyrosine transfer RNA. Science 153 (3735), 531–534.

Mathews, D.H., Banerjee, A.R., Luan, D.D., Eickbush, T.H., Turner, D.H., 1997. Secondary structure model of the RNA recognized by the reverse transcriptase from the R2 retrotransposable element. RNA 3 (1), 1–16.

Mathews, D.H., Disney, M.D., Childs, J.L., et al., 2004. Incorporating chemical modification constraints into a dynamic programming algorithm for prediction of RNA secondary structure. Proceedings of the National Academy of Sciences of the United States of America 101 (19), 7287–7292.

Mathews, D.H., Sabina, J., Zuker, M., Turner, D.H., 1999. Expanded sequence dependence of thermodynamic parameters improves prediction of RNA secondary structure. Journal of Molecular Biology 288 (5), 911–940.

McDonald, D., Price, M.N., Goodrich, J., et al., 2012. An improved Greengenes taxonomy with explicit ranks for ecological and evolutionary analyses of bacteria and archaea. The ISME Journal 6 (3), 610–618.

Mears, J.A., Cannone, J.J., Stagg, S.M., et al., 2002. Modeling a minimal ribosome based on comparative sequence analysis. Journal of Molecular Biology 321 (2), 215–234.

Nawrocki, E.P., 2009. Structural RNA Homology Search and Alignment Using Covariance Models. Washington University in St. Louis.

Nawrocki, E.P., Eddy, S.R., 2013. Infernal 1.1: 100-fold faster RNA homology searches. Bioinformatics 29 (22), 2933–2935.

Neefs, J.M., Van de Peer, Y., De Rijk, P., Chapelle, S., De Wachter, R., 1993. Compilation of small ribosomal subunit RNA structures. Nucleic Acids Research 21 (13), 3025–3049.

Nguyen, T.H.D., Galej, W.P., Bai, X.C., et al., 2016. Cryo-EM structure of the yeast U4/U6. U5 tri-snRNP at 3.7 Å resolution. Nature 530 (7590), 298–302.

Noller, H.F., Hoffarth, V., Zimmiak, L., 1992. Unusual resistance of peptidyl transferase to protein extraction. Science 265, 3587–3590.

Noller, H.F., Kop, J., Wheaton, V., et al., 1981. Secondary structure model for 23S ribosomal RNA. Nucleic Acids Research 9 (22), 6167–6189.

Noller, H.F., Woese, C.R., 1981. Secondary structure of 16S ribosomal RNA. Science 212 (4493), 403–411.

Notredame, C., Higgins, D.G., Heringa, J., 2000. T-Coffee: A novel method for fast and accurate multiple sequence alignment. Journal of Molecular Biology 302 (1), 205–217.

O'brien, T.W., 2003. Properties of human mitochondrial ribosomes. IUBMB Life 55 (9), 505–513.

Ogle, J.M., Brodersen, D.E., Clemons, W.M., et al., 2001. Recognition of cognate transfer RNA by the 30S ribosomal subunit. Science 292 (5518), 897–902.

Olinares, P.D.B., Ponnala, L., van Wijk, K.J., 2010. Megadalton complexes in the chloroplast stroma of Arabidopsis thaliana characterized by size exclusion chromatography, mass spectrometry, and hierarchical clustering. Molecular & Cellular Proteomics 9 (7), 1594–1615.

Parisien, M., Major, F., 2008. The MC-Fold and MC-Sym pipeline infers RNA structure from sequence data. Nature 452 (7183), 51–55.

Petrov, A.S., Bernier, C.R., Gulen, B., et al., 2014. Secondary structures of rRNAs from all three domains of life. PLOS ONE 9 (2), e88222.

Pettersen, E.F., Goddard, T.D., Huang, C.C., et al., 2004. UCSF Chimera – A visualization system for exploratory research and analysis. Journal of Computational Chemistry 25 (13), 1605–1612.

Poehlsgaard, J., Douthwaite, S., 2005. The bacterial ribosome as a target for antibiotics. Nature Reviews Microbiology 3 (11), 870–881.

Powers, T., Noller, H.F., 1991. A functional pseudoknot in 16S ribosomal RNA. The EMBO Journal 10 (8), 2203.

Pruesse, E., Peplies, J., Glöckner, F.O., 2012. SINA: Accurate high-throughput multiple sequence alignment of ribosomal RNA genes. Bioinformatics 28 (14), 1823–1829.

Quast, C., Pruesse, E., Yilmaz, P., et al., 2012. The SILVA ribosomal RNA gene database project: Improved data processing and web-based tools. Nucleic Acids Research 41 (D1), D590–D596.

Rabl, J., Leibundgut, M., Ataide, S.F., Haag, A., Ban, N., 2011. Crystal structure of the eukaryotic 40S ribosomal subunit in complex with initiation factor 1. Science 331 (6018), 730–736.

RajBhandary, U.L., Chang, S.H., Stuart, A., et al., 1967. Studies on polynucleotides, lxviii* the primary structure of yeast phenylalanine transfer RNA. Proceedings of the National Academy of Sciences of the United States of America 57 (3), 751–758.

Reuter, J.S., Mathews, D.H., 2010. RNAstructure: Software for RNA secondary structure prediction and analysis. BMC Bioinformatics 11 (1), 129.

Robertson, M.P., Joyce, G.F., 2012. The origins of the RNA world. Cold Spring Harbor Perspectives in Biology 4 (5), a003608.

Robertus, J.D., Ladner, J.E., Finch, J.T., et al., 1974. Structure of yeast phenylalanine tRNA at 3 Å resolution. Nature 250, 546–551.

Robinson, O., Dylus, D., Dessimoz, C., 2016. Phylo. io: Interactive viewing and comparison of large phylogenetic trees on the web. Molecular Biology and Evolution 33 (8), 2163–2166.

Russell, J., Zomerdijk, J.C., 2006. The RNA polymerase I transcription machinery. Biochemical Society Symposia. 73), 203–216.

Schluenzen, F., Tocilj, A., Zarivach, R., et al., 2000. Structure of functionally activated small ribosomal subunit at 3.3 Å resolution. Cell 102 (5), 615–623.

Scott, W.G., Finch, J.T., Klug, A., 1995. The crystal structure of an All-RNAhammerhead ribozyme: A proposed mechanism for RNA catalytic cleavage. Cell 81 (7), 991–1002.

Selmer, M., Dunham, C.M., Murphy, F.V., et al., 2006. Structure of the 70S ribosome complexed with mRNA and tRNA. Science 313 (5795), 1935–1942.

Sharma, M.R., Koc, E.C., Datta, P.P., et al., 2003. Structure of the mammalian mitochondrial ribosome reveals an expanded functional role for its component proteins. Cell 115 (1), 97–108.

Sharma, S., Ding, F., Dokholyan, N.V., 2008. iFoldRNA: Three-dimensional RNA structure prediction and folding. Bioinformatics 24 (17), 1951–1952.

Smit, S., Widmann, J., Knight, R., 2007. Evolutionary rates vary among rRNA structural elements. Nucleic Acids Research 35 (10), 3339–3354.

Thompson, J.D., Higgins, D.G., Gibson, T.J., 1994. CLUSTAL W: Improving the sensitivity of progressive multiple sequence alignment through sequence weighting, position-specific gap penalties and weight matrix choice. Nucleic Acids Research 22 (22), 4673–4680.

Van de Peer, Y., Chapelle, S., De Wachter, R., 1996. A quantitative map of nucleotide substitution rates in bacterial rRNA. Nucleic Acids Research 24 (17), 3381–3391.

Wimberly, B.T., Brodersen, D.E., Clemons, W.M., et al., 2000. Structure of the 30S ribosomal subunit. Nature 407 (6802), 327–339.

Woese, C.R., 1987. Bacterial evolution. Microbiological Reviews 51 (2), 221.

Woese, C.R., Gutell, R., Gupta, R., Noller, H.F., 1983. Detailed analysis of the higher-order structure of 16S-like ribosomal ribonucleic acids. Microbiological Reviews 47 (4), 621–629.

Woese, C.R., Kandler, O., Wheelis, M.L., 1990. Towards a natural system of organisms: Proposal for the domains Archaea, Bacteria, and Eucarya. Proceedings of the National Academy of Sciences of the United States of America 87 (12), 4576–4579.

Woese, C.R., Magrum, L.J., Gupta, R., *et al*., 1980. Secondary structure model for bacterial 16S ribosomal RNA: Phylogenetic, enzymatic and chemical evidence. Nucleic Acids Research 8 (10), 2275–2294.

Wong, W., Bai, X.C., Brown, A., *et al*., 2014. Cryo-EM structure of the Plasmodium falciparum 80S ribosome bound to the anti-protozoan drug emetine. eLife 3, e03080.

Wuyts, J., Van de Peer, Y., De Wachter, R., 2001. Distribution of substitution rates and location of insertion sites in the tertiary structure of ribosomal RNA. Nucleic Acids Research 29 (24), 5017–5028.

Yan, C., Hang, J., Wan, R., *et al*., 2015. Structure of a yeast spliceosome at 3.6-angstrom resolution. Science 349 (6253), 1182–1191.

Yoon, S.H., Ha, S.M., Kwon, S., *et al*., 2017. Introducing EzBioCloud: A taxonomically united database of 16S rRNA gene sequences and whole-genome assemblies. International journal of Systematic and Evolutionary Microbiology 67 (5), 1613–1617.

Zhang, X., Lai, M., Chang, W., *et al*., 2016. Structures and stabilization of kinetoplastid-specific split rRNAs revealed by comparing leishmanial and human ribosomes. Nature Communications 7, 13223.

Zuker, M., 1989. On finding all suboptimal foldings of an RNA molecule. Science 244, 48–52.

Zuker, M., Stiegler, P., 1981. Optimal computer folding of large RNA sequences using thermodynamics and auxiliary information. Nucleic Acids Research 9 (1), 133–148.

Zwieb, C., Glotz, C., Brimacombe, R., 1981. Secondary structure comparisons between small subunit ribosomal RNA molecules from six different species. Nucleic Acids Research 9 (15), 3621–3640.

Relevant Websites

http://www.rna.ccbb.utexas.edu/CAR/1D/
    1D. Methods: Structure Prediction with Comparative Sequence Analysis.
https://www.arb-silva.de
    Arb SILVA.
https://www.ezbiocloud.net
    EzBioCloud.net.
https://mafft.cbrc.jp/alignment/software/
    MAFFT – A multiple sequence alignment program – CBRC.
http://www.rna.icmb.utexas.edu/SIM/4A/Minimal_Ribosome/
    Modeling a Minimal Ribosome.
https://rna.urmc.rochester.edu/RNAstructureWeb/
    RNAstructure Webserver.
https://omictools.com/rna-structures-category
    RNA analysis – OMICtools.
http://www.rna.icmb.utexas.edu/DAT/3C/Structure/index.php
    Secondary Structure Diagram Retrieval – The Comparative RNA Web.
http://rna.tbi.univie.ac.at/
    ViennaRNA Web Services.

Computational Design and Experimental Implementation of Synthetic Riboswitches and Riboregulators

Munyati Othman and Siuk M Ng, Universiti Kebangsaan Malaysia, Bangi, Selangor, Malaysia
Mohd Firdaus-Raih, Universiti Kebangsaan Malaysia, Bangi, Malaysia

Introduction

Riboregulators consist of two basic components; an aptamer domain and an actuator (effector) domain. The aptamer domains are short single stranded DNA or RNA molecules made up of 20–100 nucleotides. These oligonucleotides adopt a variety of unique 3-dimensional (3D) structures that enable binding to specific ligands with high selectivity and specificity (Dunn *et al.*, 2017). The actuator domains are located downstream to the aptamer domain will undergo a conformational change upon ligand binding and is the effector that controls regulation of gene expression (Chang *et al.*, 2012). The modularity of the actuator domain allows it to effect control of gene expression through a variety of mechanisms including transcription, splicing, stability, RNA interference, and translation (Chang *et al.*, 2012; Liang *et al.*, 2011). The mixing and matching of RNA aptamers and actuator domains leads towards a functional synthetic riboregulator construct. Due to the sequence diversity and their high affinity for specific targets, aptamers are often used in riboregulator design.

Several strategies have been used to generate aptamers as candidates for riboregulators. One obvious strategy is to select from naturally occurring aptamers that are found in riboswitches. Naturally occurring aptamers such as the thiamine pyrophosphate (TPP) aptamer domain, have previously been reengineered to control the expression of green fluorescent protein (GFP) (Nomura and Yokobayashi, 2007). Aptamers can also be designed via computational approaches; for example, an aptamer that is able to interact with cytochrome P450 had been designed using molecular modelling methods (Shcherbinin *et al.*, 2015). Additionally, aptamers can also be derived from *de novo* selection of RNA binding elements via SELEX (Systematic Evolution of Ligands by Exponential enrichment), a method that has been used to identify synthetic aptamers that exhibit high affinity to specific ligands of interest (Tuerk and Gold, 1990). The first experiment deploying this method was for the detection of RNAs that are able to interact with T4 DNA polymerase (Tuerk and Gold, 1990). Since then, the targets for these SELEX sourced aptamers have greatly expanded to encompass a variety of molecules ranging from inorganic molecules to small organic molecules that include complex structures (Stoltenburg *et al.*, 2007), amino acids (Lozupone *et al.*, 2003), metal ions (Kawakami *et al.*, 2000), small organic compounds (Mann *et al.*, 2005), biological factors (Lauhon and Szostak, 1995), metabolites (Long *et al.*, 2016), proteins (Hassan *et al.*, 2017) and antibiotic (Berens *et al.*, 2001; Wallace and Schroeder, 1998).

A SELEX process starts with chemically synthesizing random oligonucleotide libraries consisting of 10^{13} to 10^{15} different sequence motifs that are then incubated directly with the target. The oligo-target complexes formed are subsequently partitioned from unbound and weakly bound oligonucleotides. The oligo-target complexes are eluted and amplified by PCR for DNA SELEX or subject to reverse transcription (RT)-PCR for RNA SELEX. The resulting bound oligo needs to be transformed into a new oligonucleotide pool. The new and enriched pool of selected oligonucleotides is used for the binding reaction with the target in the next SELEX round. Through iterative cycles of selection and amplification, the initial random oligonucleotide pool is reduced to relatively few sequence motifs with the highest affinity and specificity for the target.

High throughput sequencing (HTS) has revolutionized the SELEX technique (Nguyen Quang *et al.*, 2016) because after a series (> 15) of selection cycles, millions of aptamer sequences can be determined from HTS datasets. Programs such as Aptamotif, MPBind, AptaCluster, APTANI and AptaPLEX were developed to analyse the fast emerging data (Hoinka *et al.*, 2012, 2014; Jiang *et al.*, 2014; Caroli *et al.*, 2016; Hoinka and Przytycka, 2016). In this paper, the tools used to analyse SELEX data and for predicting the secondary structures of riboregulators are discussed.

Background

Riboregulator

RNAs are known to mediate gene expression in both prokaryotes and eukaryotes. In prokaryotes, riboregulators such as riboswitches and ribozymes control gene expression via *cis* or *trans* interactions with their targets (Winkler *et al.*, 2004; Mandal *et al.*, 2003). In eukaryotes, small RNAs act as microRNAs in order to control gene expression (Gottesman, 2002). The regulatory capacity of such RNAs have led to *in-vitro* and *in-silico* riboregulator design that impact transcription and translation in response to specific input.

Early studies of riboregulators were conducted by Isaac and co-workers (Isaacs *et al.*, 2004). The first type of engineered riboregulator consisted of complementary *cis* RNA sequence located upstream of the ribosome binding site (RBS) in a target gene. Upon transcription, the RNA transcript forms a stem-loop that interferes with ribosome binding. However, the subsequent binding of a cognate *trans*-acting RNA acts to promote and allow translation.

Another type of riboregulator, the toehold switch, is based on RNA-RNA interactions between the switch and the trigger RNAs (Green *et al.*, 2014). The switch RNA, also known as the transducer strand, contains the initial binding site for the trigger or *trans*-acting RNA strand, ribosome binding site (RBS), start codon, a 21nts linker sequence, followed by the coding sequence of the gene. The upstream of the coding sequence forms a hairpin that blocks translation. The complementary trigger RNA strand that binds to the initial binding site will expose the RBS and the start codon in order to initiate translation of the target gene (Green *et al.*, 2014).

Both riboregulators were rationally designed and comprised of a combination of aptamer and actuator domains. At present, secondary structure prediction is commonly used to assess the quality of the riboregulators (Wachsmuth *et al.*, 2013; Topp *et al.*, 2010).

Synthetic Riboswitches

Riboswitches have become an important tool in synthetic biology due to their ability to regulate gene expression and to integrate into a more complex genetic circuit (Topp and Gallivan, 2010). Synthetic riboswitches are widely used as riboregulators; for example, those that detect theophylline and antibiotics such as tetracycline and streptomycin, have been used to activate transcription, termination and protein translation by designing different actuator domains (Wachsmuth *et al.*, 2015; Desai and Gallivan, 2004; Domin *et al.*, 2017).

Systems and/or Applications

Computer programs can be used to filter SELEX or HT-SELEX data to discover new aptamers. The assembly of aptamer and actuator domains can then be analyzed using available webserver programs.

Input Formats

Most software accept FASTQ and FASTA formatted files as input. Secondary structure prediction via RNAfold, RNAstructure and Mfold accept a single RNA or DNA sequence in plain text or FASTA format as input.

Output and Average Time for Computations

Seven aptamer analysis software are discussed in this chapter. On average, these programs take up to several hours to run, depending on the size of the input data and the technical specifications of the computer being used. For secondary structure prediction, most tools take from only a few seconds to a few minutes to provide the predicted minimal free energy (MFE) secondary structure.

Analysis and Assessment

Aptamer Analysis

Seven programs were chosen to analyse aptamer sequences from available SELEX/HT-SELEX data. The programs selected were written in Python, Perl and C++. The general approach taken by all tools is summarized in **Table 1**.

Aptamotif, APTANI and AptaTRACE deploy principal sequence-structure analysis to filter for aptamers (Hoinka *et al.*, 2012; Caroli *et al.*, 2016; Dao *et al.*, 2016). APTANI builds on the Aptamotif algorithm and extends its usage to analyse both SELEX and

Table 1   List of tools for the analysis of SELEX/HT-SELEX. A list of aptamer analysis programs available and the approach used by each program in analyzing aptamers

Name (Language)	Input	Search approach	Reference
Aptamotif (Python)	FASTQ	Identify sequence-structure motifs	Hoinka *et al.* (2012)
MPBind (Python/R)	FASTA/FASTQ	Predict the binding potential combination of binding of all *n*-mers within a sequence	Jiang *et al.* (2014)
AptaCluster (C++)	FASTA/FASTQ	Cluster aptamers sequence based on k-mer counting	Hoinka *et al.* (2014)
FASTAptamer (Perl)	FASTQ	Compare population for sequence distribution, generates sequence cluster, calculater fold enrichment value and search for multiple sequence motifs	Alam *et al.* (2015)
APTANI (Python 3.3)	FASTQ	Identify aptamer motif from HT-SELEX and secondary structure information	Caroli *et al.* (2016)
AptaPLEX (C++)	FASTQ	Standalone demultiplexing software for HT-SELEX	Hoinka and Przytycka (2016)
AptaTRACE (C++, Java)	FASTQ	Identifying sequence structure motifs that show a signature of selection	Dao *et al.* (2016)

HT-SELEX data. Both tools use RNAsubopt to predict secondary structures in a specific energy range (Wuchty *et al.*, 1999; Backofen and Will, 2004). AptaTRACE requires Sfold or CapR for secondary structure prediction. The Sfold program needs to be installed, while CapR has been integrated into the program (Ding *et al.*, 2004; Fukunaga *et al.*, 2014). The AptaTrace process is divided into three parts: data processing, secondary structure profiling and motif extraction. The data processing involves selecting sequences as input based on user defined frequency thresholds. Then, AptaTRACER will select sequence motif(s) with the tendency of residing in a hairpin, bulge loop, inner loop, multiple loop, dangling end or being paired convergently into a specific structural context. The distribution of the k-mer's secondary structure contacts (K-context distribution was estimated using the relative entropy (KL-divergence). In Aptamotif and APTANI, four different types of secondary structure motifs are inspected, i.e. hairpin loop left, hairpin loop right, bulge loop and intra-strand loop. The AptaTRACE program identifies hairpins, bulge loops, inner loops, multibranch loops and dangling ends.

In contrast, MPBind predicts aptamers based on a statistical test (Jiang *et al.*, 2014). The aptamer sequences are assumed to consist of combination of *n*-mer. The combination of *n*-mer is given a score based on relative frequency change and relative abundance in the database. Then the potential binding aptamer is inferred from the combination of all *n*-mer within the sequence.

FASTAptamer is a multi-instruction tool starts by determining sequence frequency, multiplicity or copy number via FASTAptamer-Count. The output of the analysis can then be applied as input into downstream FASTAptamer scripts such as FASTAptamer-compared, FASTAptamer-cluster, FASTAptamer-enrich, FASTAaptamer-search, other FASTAptamer scripts or any program that accepts FASTAQ formatted files as input (**Fig. 1**). Using available scripts, the inputs are compared to the population for each sequence distribution, clusters are then generated for the sequences, the fold-enrichment of the sequences throughout the course of a selection are calculated and then the search for degenerate sequence motifs in the SELEX/HT-SELEX data is carried out (Alam *et al.*, 2015).

AptaCluster clusters SELEX/HT-SELEX data based on a calculated k-mer similarity measure (Hoinka *et al.*, 2014) that is executed in three steps. First, the data is compressed and filtered using Locality Sensitive Hashing (LSH). After filtration, the sequences with the same hash values will be in the same pool (Andoni *et al.*, 2013). Next, the clusters are extracted based on the high frequency of the sequence in the pool. Then the k-mer based on distance function is used to compute the distance between sequences and cluster them.

AptaPLEX is a standalone and independent demultiplexer specifically designed for HT-SELEX (Hoinka and Przytycka, 2016). The program can be used to analyse single or multiple HT-SELEX experiments at once. Aptaplex automatically recognizes and handles gzip compressed data and makes use of all available processing resources via its multi-threaded design while minimizing memory usage.

Secondary Structure Prediction

The stability and biochemical properties of a RNA molecule is largely determined by the base pairing interactions. After the aptamer couples with the actuator domain, secondary structure prediction is carried out. This step is important to visualise the folding of the aptamer domain, the interaction between the aptamer domain and actuator domain, or to determine the stability of the folding via its minimum free energy. Several webservers are available for secondary structure prediction - RNAstructure, RNAfold and Mfold are three of the software discussed here (Reuter and Mathews, 2010; Gruber *et al.*, 2008; Zuker, 2003).

RNAstructure uses thermodynamics and utilizes parameters from the Turner group to predict secondary structure (Reuter and Mathews, 2010). This webserver can also predict base pair probabilities using a partition function, in addition to bimolecular secondary structure and common secondary structure prediction for two or more sequences. The bimolecular secondary structure prediction folds two sequences into their lowest hybrid free energy conformation. The server combines the capabilities of bimolecular folding and duplex folding to create two distinct sets of possible bimolecular structures. To predict the common secondary structure for two or more sequences, the server combines the capabilities of Multilign and TurboFold to create distinct sets of possible structures for multiple sequences.

RNAfold is a secondary structure prediction program that is built based on algorithms proposed by Zuker and Stiegler, and John McCaskill (Gruber *et al.*, 2008). Zuker and Stiegler proposed a dynamic programming algorithm to predict the minimum free energy (MFE) of a sequence, while John McCaskill calculated the equilibrium base pairing probability of secondary structures

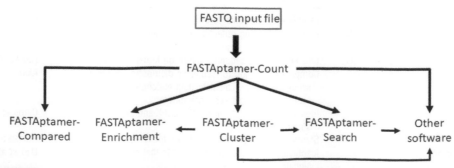

Fig. 1   Flow chart of FASTAptamer tools. FASTAptamer consist of multiple tools to analyse data from SELEX or HT-SELEX.

through a partition function (PF) algorithm (Zuker and Stiegler, 1981; McCaskill, 1990). However, it is also suggested that the predicted structures can be further augmented with reliability information to get more accurate structures.

Mfold is used to predict the secondary structures of RNA or DNA sequences (Zuker, 2003). Depending on the input sequence, mfold predicts a minimum free energy, ΔG, as well as the minimum free energies for all potential foldings. Over the years, new functions have been implemented such as the prediction of two state melting temperature and hybridization of two RNA or DNA strands.

Illustrative Examples and Case Studies

Previous experiments have demonstrated that the combination of SELEX, high throughput sequencing and bioinformatics can successfully identify aptamers for specific ligands such as LAG3 and TIM3 (Soldevilla et al., 2017; Hervas-Stubbs et al., 2016; Pei et al., 2017; Eaton et al., 2015). However, these identified aptamers were not reported to be riboregulators. The reason why the identified aptamers were not used as riboregulators because they are cytotoxic, insoluble, highly reactive and impermeable to cell membranes.

There are three aptamers identified via SELEX that have been reported as riboregulators namely the theophylline, tetracycline and streptomycin aptamers. The theophylline aptamer, can bind to theophylline with high affinity compared to other ligands and is the most prominent aptamer that can be manipulated as a riboregulator (Berens et al., 2001; Wallace and Schroeder, 1998; Jenison et al., 1994). The theophylline aptamer has been exploited to trigger expression via translation and transcription depending on the actuator domain (Wachsmuth et al., 2013, 2015; Desai and Gallivan, 2004; Suess et al., 2004). In 2004, a translational control element was carried out by cloning a theophylline aptamer upstream of the ribosome binding site of the reporter gene (Desai and Gallivan, 2004; Suess et al., 2004). In 2013, the theophylline aptamer was fused to an intrinsic terminator thus creating a transcriptional riboregulator (Wachsmuth et al., 2013). The secondary structure combination of the aptamer and actuator domains were analysed using the RNAfold program of the Vienna RNA package. The RNAfold program was used to calculate the free energy value and predict the secondary structure. The conformation of this aptamer has been studied extensively and shows a similar structure to the minimum free energy (MFE) predicted by RNAfold. The construct was able to terminate the expression of a reporter gene in the absence of theophylline. The same approach was used to design riboregulators using tetracycline and streptomycin as ligands (Domin et al., 2017). The tetracycline and streptomycin aptamers were cloned into the 5′ untranslated region of the bgaB reporter. The aptamer responded to tetracycline and showed β-galactosidase activity.

Discussions and Future Directions

In the early 2000s, aptamers present in riboregulators were isolated in vitro and none of them were identified using SELEX/HT-SELEX analysis programs (Berens et al., 2001; Wallace and Schroeder, 1998; Jenison et al., 1994). The development of SELEX/HT-SELEX analysis programs had only started in early 2010 although the search for aptamers started 20 years ago. The programs can

Table 2 Characteristic of tools for the analysis of SELEX and HT-SELEX data. Characteristic differences of tools for the analysis of SELEX and HT-SELEX data

	Aptamotif	APTANI	Aptatrace	MPBind	AptaCluster	FASTAptamer	AptaPLEX
SELEX	✓	✓	✓	✓	✓	✓	
HT-SELEX		✓	✓		✓	✓	✓
Program language	Phython	Python 3.3	C++	Python 2.7	C++	Perl	C++
Strategies							
Motif structure prediction	✓ Mfold	✓ RNAsubopt	✓				
MFE	✓	✓					
Secondary structure Motif	✓	✓		✓			
Loop structure investigation	✓	✓	✓				
Cluster investigation		✓ Cluster Omega			✓ Hamming edit distance	✓ Levenshtein edit distance	
Statistical test				✓			
Secondary structure	Mfold			RNAfold			
Minimum free energy	✓			✓			
Other dependencies		Cluster Omega, RNAsubopt	Sfold, CapR, CMAKE	None	Boost libraries, MySQL database	None	Boost libraries
License		None				GNU general public License V3	GLP v.2
Output can be used as input for other analysis						✓	✓
Equilibrium base pairing probability				✓			

be group into four strategies; i. sequence-structure motifs ii. statistical analysis iii. clustering and iv. multiplexer. The differences and similarities of each SELEX/ HT-SELEX analysis program are summarized in **Table 2**.

In order to use these programs, they need to be installed together with their software dependencies. Fastaaptamer and MpBind are the only programs that do not require any additional software to be installed. Among these programs, FASTAaptamer is the most user friendly program. It requires only a basic knowledge of command line operations and the user's manual include the command line options. Advanced users can opt to integrate the analysis into a customized workflow or an existing sequence analysis pipeline (Alam *et al.*, 2015).

However, to our knowledge, there are no known assessments that compare the efficiency, accuracy and speed of each program in analyzing SELEX or HT-SELX data. It is necessary to examine more sensitive aptamers to a simple ligand so that they can be explored for eventual application riboregulator. The information obtained can be analyzed using the existing program. However, existing programs can be improved to make it easier to use and analyse data more accurately for shorter time.

Riboregulators generated from the mixing and matching of aptamer and actuator domains can work well with their specific ligands. To avoid false positives, a rationally designed riboregulator is evaluated through iterative design-build-test cycles. This is followed by global modelling of the RNA structure. As RNA sequence folds into secondary structure during transcription and this process is difficult to mimic *in vitro*, it is important to carry out the secondary structure prediction prior to actual synthesis of the candidates.

In the case of riboregulator design, it is suggested to use stochastic kinetic folding simulation approach (Endoh and Sugimoto, 2015; Thimmaiah *et al.*, 2015; Carothers *et al.*, 2011). In addition, an *in-silico* prediction method that can perform direct comparisons to *in-vivo* gene regulation activities through parallel assays should be developed (Geertz *et al.*, 2012).

Closing Remarks

The construction of riboregulators via rational design can be a future conventional approach to analyse RNA sequences engaged in gene regulation. As more RNA data are made available, computational design of synthethic riboregulators provides a fast and cost-effective way to discover their potential applications in the organism of interest. However, the computational approaches should ideally be combined with laboratory evidence in order to best evaluate the versatility and functionality of the design.

Acknowledgement

MFR is funded by the Ministry of Science, Technology and Innovation grant 02-01-02-SF1278 and the Universiti Kebangsaan Malaysia grant DIP-2017-013.

See also: Applications of Ribosomal RNA Sequence and Structure Analysis for Extracting Evolutionary and Functional Insights. Biomolecular Structures: Prediction, Identification and Analyses. Natural Language Processing Approaches in Bioinformatics. Predicting RNA-RNA Interactions in Three-Dimensional Structures. Sequence Analysis. Sequence Composition

References

Alam, K.K., Chang, J.L., Burke, D.H., 2015. FASTAptamer: A bioinformatic toolkit for high-throughput sequence analysis of combinatorial selections. Molecular Therapy- Nucleic Acids 4, e230.
Andoni, A., Indyk, P., 2013. In: Conference Proceedings, 2006 IEEE 54th Annual Symposium on Foundations of Computer Science, pp. 459–468. Berkeley, Calfornia: IEEE.
Backofen, R., Will, S., 2004. Local sequence-structure motifs in RNA. Journal of Bioinformatics and Computational Biology 2, 681–698.
Berens, C., Thain, A., Schroeder, R., 2001. A tetracycline-binding RNA aptamer. Bioorganic & Medicinal Chemistry 9, 2549–2556.
Caroli, J., Taccioli, C., De La Fuente, A., *et al.*, 2016. APTANI: A computational tool to select aptamers through sequence-structure motif analysis of HT-SELEX data. Bioinformatics 32, 161–164.
Carothers, J.M., Goler, J.A., Juminaga, D., Keasling, J.D., 2011. Model-driven engineering of RNA devices to quantitatively program gene expression. Science 334, 1716–1719.
Chang, A.L., Wolf, J.J., Smolke, C.D., 2012. Synthetic RNA switches as a tool for temporal and spatial control over gene expression. Current Opinion in Biotechnology 23, 679–688.
Dao, P., Hoinka, J., Takahashi, M., *et al.*, 2016. AptaTRACE elucidates RNA sequence-structure motifs from selection trends in HT-SELEX experiments. Cell Systems 3, 62–70.
Desai, S.K., Gallivan, J.P., 2004. Genetic screens and selections for small molecules based on a synthetic riboswitch that activates protein translation. Journal of the American Chemical Society 126, 13247–13254.
Ding, Y., Chan, C.Y., Lawrence, C.E., 2004. Sfold web server for statistical folding and rational design of nucleic acids. Nucleic Acids Research 32, W135–W141.
Domin, G., Findeiß, S., Wachsmuth, M., *et al.*, 2017. Applicability of a computational design approach for synthetic riboswitches. Nucleic Acids Research 45, 4108–4119.
Dunn, M.R., Jimenez, R.M., Chaput, J.C., 2017. Analysis of aptamer discovery and technology. Nature Reviews Chemistry 1, 0076.
Eaton, R.M., Shallcross, J.A., Mael, L.E., *et al.*, 2015. Selection of DNA aptamers for ovarian cancer biomarker HE4 using CE-SELEX and high-throughput sequencing. Analytical and Bioanalytical Chemistry 407, 6965–6973.
Endoh, T., Sugimoto, N., 2015. Rational design and tuning of functional RNA switch to control an allosteric intermolecular interaction. Analytical Chemistry 87, 7628–7635.
Fukunaga, T., Ozaki, H., Terai, G., *et al.*, 2014. CapR: Revealing structural specificities of RNA-binding protein target recognition using CLIP-seq data. Genome Biology 15, R16.

Geertz, M., Shore, D., Maerkl, S.J., 2012. Massively parallel measurements of molecular interaction kinetics on a microfluidic platform. Proceedings of the National Academy of Sciences 109, 16540–16545.

Gottesman, S., 2002. Stealth regulation: Biological circuits with small RNA switches. Genes & Development 16, 2829–2842.

Green, A.A., Silver, P.A., Collins, J.J., Yin, P., 2014. Toehold switches: De-novo designed regulators of gene expression. Cell 159, 925–939.

Gruber, A.R., Lorenz, R., Bernhart, S.H., et al., 2008. The Vienna RNA websuite. Nucleic Acids Research 36, W70–W74.

Hassan, E.M., Willmore, W.G., McKay, B.C., DeRosa, M.C., 2017. In vitro selections of mammaglobin A and mammaglobin B aptamers for the recognition of circulating breast tumor cells. Scientific Reports 7, 14487.

Hervas-Stubbs, S., Soldevilla, M.M., Villanueva, H., et al., 2016. Identification of TIM3 2′-fluoro oligonucleotide aptamer by HT-SELEX for cancer immunotherapy. Oncotarget 7, 4522–4530.

Hoinka, J., Berezhnoy, A., Sauna, Z.E., et al., 2014. AptaCluster – A method to cluster HT-SELEX aptamer pools and lessons from its application. Research in Computational Molecular Biology 8394, 115–128.

Hoinka, J., Przytycka, T., 2016. AptaPLEX – A dedicated, multithreaded demultiplexer for HT-SELEX data. Methods 106, 82–85.

Hoinka, J., Zotenko, E., Friedman, A., et al., 2012. Identification of sequence–structure RNA binding motifs for SELEX-derived aptamers. Bioinformatics 28, i215–i223.

Isaacs, F.J., Dwyer, D.J., Ding, C., et al., 2004. Engineered riboregulators enable post-transcriptional control of gene expression. Nature Biotechnology 22, 841–847.

Jenison, R.D., Gill, S.C., Pardi, A., Polisky, B., 1994. High-resolution molecular discrimination by RNA. Science 263, 1425.

Jiang, P., Meyer, S., Hou, Z., et al., 2014. MPBind: A meta-motif-based statistical framework and pipeline to predict binding potential of SELEX-derived aptamers. Bioinformatics 30, 2665–2667.

Kawakami, J., Imanaka, H., Yokota, Y., Sugimoto, N., 2000. In vitro selection of aptamers that act with Zn2+. Journal of Inorganic Biochemistry 82, 197–206.

Lauhon, C.T., Szostak, J.W., 1995. RNA aptamers that bind flavin and nicotinamide redox cofactors. Journal of the American Chemical Society 117, 1246–1257.

Liang, J.C., Bloom, R.J., Smolke, C.D., 2011. Engineering biological systems with synthetic RNA molecules. Molecular Cell 43, 915–926.

Long, Y., Pfeiffer, F., Mayer, G., et al., 2016. Selection of aptamers for metabolite sensing and construction of optical nanosensors. In: Mayer, G. (Ed.), Nucleic Acid Aptamers: Selection, Characterization, and Application. New York, NY: Springer New York, pp. 3–19.

Lozupone, C., Changayil, S., Majerfeld, I., Yarus, M., 2003. Selection of the simplest RNA that binds isoleucine. RNA 9, 1315–1322.

Mandal, M., Boese, B., Barrick, J.E., et al., 2003. Riboswitches control fundamental biochemical pathways in Bacillus subtilis and other bacteria. Cell 113, 577–586.

Mann, D., Reinemann, C., Stoltenburg, R., Strehlitz, B., 2005. In vitro selection of DNA aptamers binding ethanolamine. Biochemical and Biophysical Research Communications 338, 1928–1934.

McCaskill, J.S., 1990. The equilibrium partition function and base pair binding probabilities for RNA secondary structure. Biopolymers 29, 1105–1119.

Nguyen Quang, N., Perret, G., Duconge, F., 2016. Applications of high-throughput sequencing for in vitro selection and characterization of aptamers. Pharmaceuticals 9, 76.

Nomura, Y., Yokobayashi, Y., 2007. Reengineering a natural riboswitch by dual genetic selection. Journal of the American Chemical Society 129, 13814–13815.

Pei, S., Slinger, B.L., Meyer, M.M., 2017. Recognizing RNA structural motifs in HT-SELEX data for ribosomal protein S15. BMC Bioinformatics 18, 298.

Reuter, J.S., Mathews, D.H., 2010. RNAstructure: Software for RNA secondary structure prediction and analysis. BMC Bioinformatics 11, 129.

Shcherbinin, D.S., Gnedenko, O.V., Khmeleva, S.A., et al., 2015. Computer-aided design of aptamers for cytochrome p450. Journal of Structural Biology 191, 112–119.

Soldevilla, M.M., Hervas, S., Villanueva, H., et al., 2017. Identification of LAG3 high affinity aptamers by HT-SELEX and Conserved Motif Accumulation (CMA). PLOS ONE 12, e0185169.

Stoltenburg, R., Reinemann, C., Strehlitz, B., 2007. SELEX- A (r)evolutionary method to generate high-affinity nucleic acid ligands. Biomolecular Engineering 24, 381–403.

Suess, B., Fink, B., Berens, C., et al., 2004. A theophylline responsive riboswitch based on helix slipping controls gene expression in vivo. Nucleic Acids Research 32, 1610–1614.

Thimmaiah, T., Voje, W.E., Carothers, J.M., 2015. Computational design of RNA parts, devices, and transcripts with kinetic folding algorithms implemented on multiprocessor clusters. In: Marchisio, M.A. (Ed.), Computational Methods in Synthetic Biology. New York, NY: Springer New York, pp. 45–61.

Topp, S., Gallivan, J.P., 2010. Emerging applications of riboswitches in chemical biology. ACS Chemical Biology 5, 139–148.

Topp, S., Reynoso, C.M.K., Seeliger, J.C., et al., 2010. Synthetic riboswitches that induce gene expression in diverse bacterial species. Applied and Environmental Microbiology 76, 7881–7884.

Tuerk, C., Gold, L., 1990. Systematic evolution of ligands by exponential enrichment: RNA ligands to bacteriophage T4 DNA polymerase. Science 249, 505–510.

Wachsmuth, M., Domin, G., Lorenz, R., et al., 2015. Design criteria for synthetic riboswitches acting on transcription. RNA Biology 12, 221–231.

Wachsmuth, M., Findeiß, S., Weissheimer, N., et al., 2013. De novo design of a synthetic riboswitch that regulates transcription termination. Nucleic Acids Research 41, 2541–2551.

Wallace, S.T., Schroeder, R., 1998. In vitro selection and characterization of streptomycin-binding RNAs: Recognition discrimination between antibiotics. RNA 4, 112–123.

Winkler, W.C., Nahvi, A., Roth, A., et al., 2004. Control of gene expression by a natural metabolite-responsive ribozyme. Nature 428, 281.

Wuchty, S., Fontana, W., Hofacker, I.L., Schuster, P., 1999. Complete suboptimal folding of RNA and the stability of secondary structures. Biopolymers 49, 145–165.

Zuker, M., 2003. Mfold web server for nucleic acid folding and hybridization prediction. Nucleic Acids Research 31, 3406–3415.

Zuker, M., Stiegler, P., 1981. Optimal computer folding of large RNA sequences using thermodynamics and auxiliary information. Nucleic Acids Research 9, 133–148.

Genome-Wide Probing of RNA Structure

Xiaojing Huo, Jeremy Ng, Mingchen Tan, and Greg Tucker-Kellogg, National University of Singapore, Singapore

Introduction

RNA is among the most versatile molecules in biology. While the information-encoding role of RNA has been known since the discovery of messenger RNA, research over the last three decades has uncovered functional roles for RNA in a vast range of processes (Cech and Steitz, 2014), including regulation of transcription, RNA splicing and editing, catalysis of protein synthesis (Nissen et al., 2000), and control of chromatin structure (Khalil et al., 2009; Nájzer and Lei, 2014). To carry out its functions RNA must form secondary structures and fold into tertiary structures to bind small molecules and proteins, as well as to respond to environmental cues (Cruz and Westhof, 2009; Tinoco and Bustamante, 1999). Understanding these structures and how they form is essential for understanding how RNA performs its functions.

While the proper folding of RNA is crucial for its normal functions, RNA misfolding often leads to dysregulation and contributes to disease. For example, a large number of pathogenic RNA structures have been found in neurological diseases, including APP for Alzheimer's disease and -synuclein for Parkinson's disease with the formation of internal ribosome entry sites in mRNAs (Bernat and Disney, 2015). The motor neuron disease-associated RNA-binding proteins TDP-43 and FUS have been reported to function as RNA chaperones to ensure proper folding of repeat-associated RNAs for translation (Ishiguro et al., 2017). Outside of neuroscience, a semiglobular ribozyme RNA can misfold into a dimer and activate the innate immune response protein, Protein Kinase R (PKR), providing a potential link between RNA misfolding and disease via innate immunity (Heinicke and Bevilacqua, 2012).

Here we consider RNA secondary structure to comprise regions of RNA base pairing, loops, and hairpins that form a hierarchical architecture (Cruz and Westhof, 2009), and tertiary structure to comprise the (often divalent cation-dependent) interactions between secondary structural units. Some recurrent structural features such as pseudoknots may be considered secondary structures despite not being strictly hierarchical, while loop-loop interactions involving Watson-Crick base pairing (Lee and Crothers, 1998) are usually considered tertiary structures.

X-ray crystallography and NMR spectroscopy have been used to determine numerous high resolution three-dimensional structures for both RNA and ribonucleoprotein complexes (Feigon, 2015; Westhof, 2015). Many now classic secondary structural patterns in RNA, such as the cloverleaf base pairing structures of tRNA (Kim et al., 1974) and ultra-stable RNA stem loops (Cheong et al., 1990) have been defined in three dimensions, while important new tertiary structural motifs have been identified and characterized (Devi et al., 2015; Nissen et al., 2001). Structure determination studies have also been used to dissect the detailed structural features of catalytic RNA function, such as the basis of polypeptide bond formation in protein synthesis (Nissen et al., 2000) and the nuclease function of RNAse P (Reiter et al., 2010).

The size and flexibility of many RNA molecules, however, make determination of their full three dimensional structures impossible. RNA molecules undergo dynamic changes in structure over an enormous range of timescales, and large RNA molecules are often best described as an ensemble of structures (Mustoe et al., 2014). Refolding of RNA molecules in vitro is highly dependent on experimental conditions and at best can represent only a subset of the dynamic conformations assumed by RNA in the cell. In addition, RNA functions are both so widespread and so dynamic that they need to be understood in concert across the genome in addition to being determined one structure at a time.

Secondary structure prediction applications are discussed elsewhere in this volume need cross-reference and have been greatly aided by improved thermodynamic rules from experimental studies as well as algorithms to enumerate multiple structures from a thermodynamic ensemble (Mathews and Turner, 2006). Free energy minimization of secondary structure from sequence, however, is far from perfect, and is greatly improved by structural constraints provided by experimental data (Hajdin et al., 2013; Mathews et al., 2004).

A widely used and powerful approach for interrogating RNA structure is to challenge RNA molecules in solution with structure-dependent chemical or enzymatic probes. Structural probing experiments can identify regions of sequence that are accessible to cleavage or modification, and thus infer which nucleotides are more likely to be double stranded, single stranded, flexible, constrained, or involved in tertiary interactions. The traditional approach is a form of footprinting experiment: treating an RNA with a reagent to induce modification or cleavage, and then detecting termination of reverse transcription (RT) products on a polyacrylamide gel. A simple interpretation is for the footprints (indicating termination of RT) to be evenly distributed and more prevalent along the unfolded stretches of sequence. The termination positions are determined by polyacrylamide gel electrophoresis and quantitative analysis from the changes of footprint on, say, unfolding. Thus, it is possible to detect location of the secondary and tertiary structure of RNA (Peattie and Gilbert, 1980).

While powerful, conventional RNA structure probing approaches have also suffered from severe limitations. Enzymatic probes and many chemical probes cannot be employed for in vivo studies, and traditional chemical probes are dependent on the RNA sequence as well as structure. RNA molecules are interrogated one species at a time. Using conventional polyacrylamide gels to analyze RT termination severely restricts the size of RNA fragments that can be analyzed, and interrogates only the first modified position of any RNA molecule. Finally, traditional probing methods examine structure features at individual sequence positions, but are unable to directly interrogate long range interactions, which form the vast majority of RNA secondary and tertiary structure.

Advances over the last decade are removing all of these limitations. Selective 2'-hydroxyl acylation and primer extension (SHAPE) chemistry makes it possible to probe RNA flexibility at single nucleotide resolution independent of nucleotide identity (Merino et al., 2005). Capillary electrophoresis increases the size and throughput of structure probing experiments over conventional gels (Mitra et al., 2008; Wilkinson et al., 2008). Conditions that convert adducts to mutations during reverse transcription allow measurement of correlated modifications at multiple positions (Siegfried et al., 2014; Zubradt et al., 2016). High throughput sequencing technology makes it possible to simultaneously interrogate large numbers of RNAs, even whole transcriptomes, in a single experiment (Kwok, 2016). Finally, direct chemical probes of base pairing make it possible to interrogate long range interactions in vitro and in vivo (Aw et al., 2016; Lu et al., 2016; Sharma et al., 2016).

Computational innovations have accompanied each new experimental advance. New computational methods and bioinformatics resources not only help researchers interpret high throughput data from new experimental technologies, but also help to improve predictions of RNA folding using both hard and soft constraints supplied from experiments. One happy result is that databases have arisen to store and organize the increasing output of RNA structure probing studies, and now make structure probing results openly available to researchers. The vast increase in structural data is creating new opportunities to understand the rules of RNA folding.

Background

Chemical and Enzymatic Structure Probing of RNA

Both chemical reagents and nucleases can be used as structure-dependent probes by cleaving RNA or creating covalent modifications that can be detected by subsequent cleavage and direct labeling or primer extension (Ziehler and Engelke, 2001). Chemical probes of RNA structure have been used for RNA footprinting studies since 1980 (Peattie and Gilbert, 1980). The widely used chemical probe dimethyl sulfate (DMS), for example, methylates the N1 of adenine, the N7 of guanine, and the N3 of cytidine. When a reverse transcriptase is used to generate a cDNA from a DMS-modified RNA, the primer extension halts opposite modified A and C nucleotides; the first modified position is identified via polyacrylamide gel electrophoresis. Since the positions methylated by DMS are directly involved in double stranded base pairing, accessibility to DMS modification is a surrogate measure of single-stranded A and C positions (Tijerina et al., 2007).

A number of other base-specific probes are used besides DMS to interrogate RNA secondary structure. For example, kethoxal modifies guanines and CMCT can modify U or G; these modifications only occur at single-stranded regions and so can be used as probes of secondary structure (Brow and Noller, 1983; Ho and Gilham, 1971). When multiple chemical probes with different specificities are used in a combination of experiments, base-specific chemical probes can interrogate every position of an RNA molecule, but individual probes that modify base moieties are inherently sequence-dependent.

For many years the only sequence-independent chemical probe in widespread use was hydroxyl radical (Tullius and Greenbaum, 2005), which leads to RNA cleavage at positions where the RNA backbone is accessible to solvent. In 2005, Kevin Weeks' team introduced a new structure probing chemistry called SHAPE that modifies the ribose moiety of an RNA molecule (Merino et al., 2005). A SHAPE reagent probes nucleotide flexibility by esterifying the 2' position of a nucleotide; the reaction is inhibited by a conformationally constrained 3' phosphodiester, and so SHAPE serves as a conformational probe of RNA. Much like DMS modifications at A and C nucleotides, SHAPE modifications halt reverse transcription so that termination products can be detected on polyacrylamide gels, but unlike DMS, SHAPE can interrogate every position of an RNA sequence. DMS and SHAPE reagents are the two most widely used chemical probes of RNA structure.

While the examples above are chemical, nucleases can also function as probes of single-stranded or double-stranded RNA. Many RNAses uses for such experiments are base-specific (Knapp, 1989), but some more recently used endonucleases show little base specificity in vitro (Daou-Chabo and Condon, 2009). It should be noted that depending on enzymatic reactions for RNA structure may introduce additional dependencies such as steric accessibility of enzyme-substrate interactions.

High-Throughput Structure Probing and Automation

The throughput of RNA footprinting was dramatically improved by combining DMS and SHAPE probes with capillary electrophoresis (CE) (Mitra et al., 2008; Wilkinson et al., 2008), and developing automated algorithms to process and quantify chemical reactivities at single-nucleotide resolution (Mitra et al., 2008; Vasa et al., 2008). Capillary electrophoresis also greatly increased the size of individual RNA molecules that could be analyzed by structure probing experiments, limited by the capillary electrophoresis itself and the software's ability to align the electrophoretic signal to sequence, correct for drop-off over the length of sequence, and convert to per-nucleotide reactivities. The underlying methods are not only applicable to RNA structure studies, but for footprinting protein binding sites to RNA.

The increased throughput of capillary electrophoresis and automation applied to RNA structure probing provided a major step towards genome-scale probing of RNA structure. In addition to the technology development and invention of CE-SHAPE, Wilkinson et al. (2008) identified structural properties of the HIV genome that would later be recapitulated and extended in later

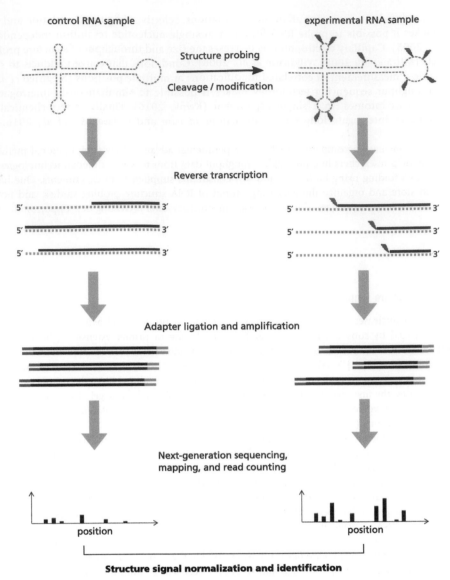

Fig. 1 .Schematic diagram of NGS-based genome-wide probing of RNA structure. The sample of an RNA population with secondary structure is split evenly into control and experiment. In experimental RNA sample, the particular structured nucleotides (double stranded or single stranded) are probed through enzymatic cleavage or chemical modification. These probing nucleotides terminate RT or introduce point mutations at the probing sites. Both control and experimental samples are processed for cDNA library preparation and NGS. The RT stops or mutations are counted on each nucleotide in experimental sample and normalized against the control. By identifying the probing signals (RT stops or mutations), the structure of each nucleotide is determined.

genome wide studies, such as the conservation of structural domains across different biological states, quantitative differences in structure between coding and non-coding regions, high levels of structure in regulatory RNA sequences, and identification of RNA recognition motifs for protein binding in intact biological systems. CE-SHAPE was also essential for the first whole-genome RNA structure studies of retroviruses such as the HIV genome (Watts *et al.*, 2009), which identified not only the secondary structure of HIV but important links between RNA structure and protein coding.

RNA Structure Probing With Deep Sequencing

Both conventional and capillary electrophoresis-based structure probing extend primers from defined sites, often combined with a structure "cassette" to ensure processivity of the reverse transcriptase. Next-generation sequencing (NGS) technology dramatically increased the potential for whole-genome studies (Aviran *et al.*, 2011; Kertesz *et al.*, 2010; Lucks *et al.*, 2011; Underwood *et al.*, 2010) of RNA structure by allowing simultaneous measurement of hundreds or thousands of RNA molecules. Rather than using labeled primers as in capillary electrophoresis, double stranded cDNA libraries are prepared after enzymatic or chemical

Table 1 Methodological advances towards genome-wide probing of RNA structure

Method	Probe	Structural specificity	Sequence specificity	Detection of probing site	RNA status	Milestone	Reference
PARS	Nuclease S1	ssRNA	None	RT stop	In vitro; native deproteinized	Detection of both ss and ds RNA; genome-wide	Kertesz et al. (2010)
	RNAse V1	dsRNA				Structure probing with enzymatic probe	Wan et al. (2012), Wan et al. (2013, 2014)
FragSeq	Nuclease P1	ssRNA	None	RT stop	In vitro	Genome-wide structure probing with enzymatic probe	Underwood et al. (2010)
dsRNA-seq	RNase I	ssRNA	None	RT stop	In vitro; native deproteinized	Genome-wide structure probing with enzymatic probe	Zheng et al. (2010), Li et al. (2012)
ssRNA-Seq SHAPE-seq; Shape-seq 2.0	RNAse V1	dsRNA					
	NMIA; 1M7	ssRNA	None	RT stop	In vitro	NGS combined with SHAPE probing; rigorous model for intensity drop-off	Lucks et al. (2011), Loughrey et al. (2014)
DMS-seq	DMS	ssRNA	A, C	RT stop	In vitro; in vitro, denatured	Genome-wide in vitro structure probing; Circularization libraries	Rouskin et al. (2014)
Structure-seq	DMS	ssRNA	A, C	RT stop	In vitro; in vitro	Genome-wide in vitro structure probing	Ding et al. (2015)
DMS-MaPseq	DMS	ssRNA	A, C	mutation	In vitro	Genome-wide RNA structure mutational profiling in vivo; circularization libraries	Zubradt et al. (2016)
RING-MAP	DMS	ssRNA	A, C	mutation	In vitro	Detection of long-range interactions and correlations reflecting distinct conformations	Homan et al. (2014)
Mod-seq	DMS	ssRNA	A, C	RT stop	In vitro	High-throughput sequencing for structure probing with long RNAs	Talkish et al. (2014)
CIRS-seq	DMS; CMCT	ssRNA	A, C; G, U	RT stop	Native deproteinized	two probes cover all four nucleotides	Incarnato et al. (2014, 2015)
SHAPE-MaP	NMIA; 1M7	ssRNA	None	mutation	In vitro	Enable the detection of low-abundance RNAs	Siegfried et al. (2014)
icSHAPE	NAI-N3	ssRNA	None	RT stop	In vitro; in vitro	Modified SHAPE reagent to penetrate cell; Use biotin conjugation on probes to enrich probed RNAs	Spitale et al. (2015)
PARIS	AMT (psoralen)	dsRNA	None	Cross-links	In vitro	Use psoralen derivative to penetrate cell and cross-link dsRNA	Lu et al. (2016)
LIGR-seq	AMT (psoralen)	dsRNA	None	Cross-links	In vitro	Ligation after cross-link to study RNA-RNA interactions	Sharma et al. (2016)
SPLASH	biopsoralen crosslinking	RNA-RNA interactions	None	Cross-links	In vitro	Enrichment on streptavidin beads	Aw et al. (2016)

modification with adapter sequences added at both ends for paired end deep sequencing (**Fig. 1**). The additional steps, such as conversion of the modified RNA to cDNA and preparation of the library with adapters for sequencing, add additional sources of bias and variation to the resulting signal that need to be addressed by some combination of experiment and analysis. A summary of advances is shown in **Table 1**.

Genome-Wide Enzymatic Probing Methods

Enzymatic probes were first used for genome-wide next-generation RNA structure probing in 2010. The methods differ in a variety of ways, as well as in their applications, but all share a common outline of *in vitro* RNA isolation, cleavage with structure-specific enzymes, adapter ligation and library preparation, and paired end sequencing.

In the development of FragSeq, Underwood *et al.* (2010) used endonuclease P1 from *Penicillium citrinum* to cut RNA preferentially at single stranded regions. RNAase P1 cleaves RNA to leave a 5′ phosphate and 3′ hydroxyl, features which were exploited in the adapter ligation steps of the method. True RNAse P1 digestion products were distinguished from both endogenous 5′ phosphate-containing RNAs and endogenous breaks by comparing experimental libraries to control libraries prepared from undigested RNA or RNA treated with polynucleotide kinase + ATP, respectively. The authors developed a "cutting score" to interpret FragSeq data, and while they initially validated and calibrated the method on *in vitro* RNA molecules with known secondary structure, they also applied it to the entire mouse nuclear transcriptome.

In dsRNA-seq, Zheng *et al.* (2010) focused on double stranded regions of RNA from *Arabidopsis* in order to identify novel substrates of the RNA-dependent RNA polymerase 6 (RDR6), which synthesizes dsRNA during small RNA biogenesis. Unlike the other methods described here, the dsRNA-seq approach does not interrogate individual nucleotides for their structure-specific cleavage, but isolates and sequences fragmented double-stranded RNA after enzymatic depletion single stranded RNA regions.

In PARS, Kertesz *et al.* (2010) used two different enzymes with different structural specificities: RNAse VI cleaves 3′ of double stranded nucleotides and endonuclease S1 specific for single stranded regions. Like FragSeq, the cleavage products contain 5′ phosphates at the cleavage site and so adapter ligation is specific to this expectation. A "PARS score" is set as the log ratio of sequence reads for each nucleotide after V1 and S1 cleavage, and thus a high PARS score reflects a higher likelihood of being double stranded. The original PARS study was applied to the entire yeast transcriptome, validating known structures and characterizing previously unknown structures. Interestingly, coding regions of mRNA were more structured on average than flanking UTR sequences.

Rigorous Computational Models of High-Throughput Structure Probing Data

SHAPE provides nucleotide flexibility information at single-nucleotide resolution. The heuristic models of reverse transcriptase drop-off used for SHAPE-CE are insufficient for comprehensive analysis of next generation sequencing platform data, so for SHAPE-seq (Lucks *et al.*, 2011). Aviran *et al.* (2011) developed a rigorous maximum likelihood model for the experimental process of chemical probing followed by paired end deep sequencing. The SHAPE-seq model includes parameter estimates for the natural drop-off propensity at each nucleotide in a transcript, which is itself a property of local structure and so varies along the sequence. The chemical modification model represents the number of exposures of an RNA to an electrophile as a Poisson process. The conditions of RNA structure probing experiments are generally designed to favor single-hit kinetics, corresponding to a Poisson rate process $c \approx 1$, but under such conditions many molecules are not exposed to electrophiles at all and a significant proportion will experience multiple modifications. By incorporating the ML estimate of the natural drop-off and developing an efficient optimization procedure for the model parameters, the authors were able to obtain per-nucleotide reactivity estimates that both supported the use of deep sequencing technology for highly parallel structure probing and provided a theoretical framework to improve existing methods.

In Vivo Chemical Probing of RNA

Enzymatic probing approaches are largely limited to *in vitro* studies of RNA structure, which does not directly interrogate the state of RNA in the cell. *In vitro* probing studies also require additional preparation steps that can alter RNA structure or intentionally re-fold RNA molecules prior to interrogation. Chemical probes have the potential to penetrate the cell for *in vivo* measurements. DMS has been used to probe RNA in cells since at least 1998 (Luo *et al.*, 1998). The original SHAPE reagents react with the hydroxyl group of water, which obviates the need to quench the reaction, but relatively long reaction times prevents the SHAPE reagent NMIA from being used in intact cells. Two SHAPE reagents designed for use *in vivo* studies (NAI and FAI) were developed (Spitale *et al.*, 2013) with high solubility and reactivity; along with some use of 1M7, these reagents make *in vivo* SHAPE experiments more accessible.

Whole transcriptome *in vivo* chemical probing was further advanced with the development of icSHAPE (Flynn *et al.*, 2016), in which the NAI reagent designed for *in vivo* SHAPE was further modified by addition of an azide (NAI-N$_3$). Any genome wide *in vivo* profiling of RNA structure must contend with the overwhelming proportion of unmodified RNA sequence; the azido moiety on NAI-N$_3$ is used in a 'click' reaction to attach biotin at the modified nucleotide, and thus enrich the RNA for modifications by isolation on streptavidin beads.

Beyond One Modification Per RNA Molecule

Mutational profiling (MaP)

Identifying modification sites by truncation of reverse transcription identifies the first modified nucleotide encountered by reverse transcriptase, and necessitates conditions of one-hit kinetics. This limitation prevents the detection of correlated modifications in single RNA molecules which would give insights into alternative structures and long range interactions. To overcome this limitation, conditions of reverse transcription have been developed that allow SHAPE modifications to be read through and converted into mutations (Smola et al., 2015). The result is a mutational profile, or MaP, that encodes chemical modification in sequence, thereby simplifying the library preparation steps for highly parallel sequencing, gaining accuracy for low abundance RNAs, and allowing in principle the measurement of multiple modifications in single molecules.

Multiple types of mutations are created in SHAPE-MaP experiments, so the interpretations of data is handled differently from traditional CE-SHAPE or SHAPE-seq. Software for interpreting SHAPE-MaP data (Busan and Weeks, 2018) is designed to account for the different types of mutations, including possibly ambiguous reads, in order to estimate reactivities for each nucleotide with more precision than conventional SHAPE.

Mutational profiling can be performed with DMS as well as with SHAPE reagents (Homan et al., 2014; Zubradt et al., 2016). Homan et al. (2014) used a DMS-MaP approach with conditions optimised to produce multiple modifications per RNA molecule and identify RNA interactions groups, or RINGs. The interacting groups are observed as correlated mutations from either dynamic "breathing" of RNA structures (thus identifying through-space interactions) or multiple distinct structures taken by a molecule. To identify the underlying structures, the correlated reactivities can be subjected to spectral decomposition into distinct clusters; each cluster can be modeled as arising from a distinct structural form. Interestingly, the RING-MaP approach makes it possible to characterize ligand-dependent conformational changes in riboswitches, as well as underlying structures in ensembles more generally.

Combining systematic mutation with chemical probing

An alternative approach to long range interactions is to combine structural probing with systematic mutation of a target RNA molecule. Since mutations at base paired nucleotides are likely to increase the flexibility of it's normal pairing partner, a two-dimensional "mutate-and-map" strategy can identify base pairs with high precision (Kladwang and Das, 2010; Kladwang et al., 2011). The systematic mutation approach of mutate-and-map adds precision to DMS and SHAPE profiling experiments, and can be used to infer long range interactions (Tian et al., 2014).

Direct determination of long-range interactions

RING-MaP and mutate-and-map data provide important indirect inference of long range interactions from structure probing experiments. In 2016, three groups simultaneously developed methods for in vivo profiling of long range RNA interactions using variations of psoralen crosslinking (Aw et al., 2016; Lu et al., 2016; Sharma et al., 2016). Derivatives of the small molecule psoralen have long been used to cross-link RNA. For in vivo cross-linking, psoralen has favorable properties: psoralen intercalates at base-paired nucleotides, some derivatives readily enter cells, and psoralen forms reversible cross-links across double-stranded RNA after illumination at 365 nm.

In LIGR-seq, Sharma et al. (2016) used AMT, psoralen variant that readily penetrates cells, to cross-link RNA followed by endonuclease digestion and proximity ligation to identify interactions by paired end sequencing. They applied LIGR-seq to HEK-293 cells and were able to identify both known and novel interactions involving non-coding RNAs, and highlighted a surprising number of interactions for the orphan snoRNA SNORD83B. In PARIS, Lu et al. (2016) also used AMT for cross-linking, but enriched the cross-linked regions with 2D gel electrophoresis. The results are discussed below as one of the case studies of genome-wide RNA structure probing. In SPLASH, Aw et al. (2016) used a biotinylated psoralen for cross-linking. The use of biotinylated psoralen required a mild detergent to increase cellular update in mammalian cells and in yeast, but enabled enrichment of crosslinked regions using streptavidin beads. The SPLASH study identified a number of clear structural properties of classes of RNA, such as the long ranger intramolecular interactions within UTRs of mRNAs, and newly identified interactions between snoRNAs and rRNA.

Direct detection of RNA interaction in helices is a major step forward for genome-wide RNA structure studies. Each of the methods described above uses proximity ligation and high-throughput paired end sequencing to determine gapped reads that represent long range interactions through base pairing. While most of the mapped reads are ungapped, possibly due to limitations of the proximity ligation, the sensitivity and power of direct interaction methods dramatically increase the capabilities of RNA structure probing methods.

Example Applications

Genome wide profiling RNA structure profiling applications are expanding rapidly. Here we briefly review two studies that provide some indication of how much insight these experiments can provide.

Genome Wide Measurement of RNA Unfolding

The melting temperature of a double stranded RNA molecule has long been used as a measure of folding stability. RNA unfolding is conventionally measured by change in UV absorbance. Wilkinson *et al.* (2005) first combined RNA structure probing with temperature-driven unfolding to determine the temperature dependence of structural interactions in the unfolding of a tRNA^{Asp} transcript. Wan *et al.* (2012) used the PARS approach with RNAse V1 to determine the melting temperature per base across the yeast genome by a method they termed Parallel Analysis of RNA structures with Temperature Elevation (PARTE). PARS had already been used for genome-wide analysis of the yeast transcriptome, and RNAse V1 was shown to retain its specificity for double stranded RNA up to 75°C, so it was possible to develop conditions for single-hit kinetics with PARS over a range of temperatures after *in vitro* RNA refolding.

A computational method for estimating Tm values for individual nucleotides was developed along with PARTE and used to estimate the Tm values for over 350,000 bases in the yeast transcriptome. When these Tm values were averaged per gene to generate an estimated melting temperature (eTm) per gene, the eTm values were moderately concordant with UV-measured Tm values of randomly chosen short transcripts, and more highly concordant for those transcripts with the most read coverage. The eTm values were also correlated with Tm values predicted using RNAfold, but showed marked deviations for some molecules, suggesting that experimental temperature-dependent structure probing data could be used to improve RNA unfolding predictions much like ordinary structure probing data are used to constrain predicted RNA secondary structures.

The PARTE analysis made it possible to associate RNA folding energy with RNA feature annotations. Noncoding RNAs, for example, showed both more highly stable bases (Tm > 75°C) and higher eTm values than mRNAs. Among mRNA transcripts, the coding sequence (CDS) appears to be more structured than the 5'-UTR and 3'-UTR regions, as had been shown earlier (Kertesz *et al.*, 2010). However, the PARTE analysis also identified a polarity of structural features (local eTm) within mRNAs that demarcated the CDS and could not be explained by GC content alone: the most meltable region of mRNA is −3 to +3 nucleotides around the start codon and the most stable paired region is 20 nucleotides immediately upstream and 10 nucleotides immediately downstream of the stop codon. Interestingly, structural stability at the start of the CDS showed a weak inverse correlation with translation rate.

The PARTE analysis identified known and putative RNA functional elements by virtue of their structural stability. Very stable structures in 3'-UTRs, for example, included known structures directly involved in heat shock response, while 5'-UTRs were enriched in structures with lower eTm (30–37°C) and highly enriched for genes whose expression decreased in heat shock transcriptional profiling experiments, suggesting that these low eTm structures may function as RNA thermometers. Indeed, when RNAs were binned by eTm values, the least stable RNAs (with eTm 26–40°C) were predictive of the pattern of heat shock-induced *in vivo* RNA decay. The authors propose, and show data to support, that these less structured RNA regions may function as RNA thermometers of RNA decay by blocking exosome processing at low temperature. Increasingly stable RNA structures progressively blocked exosome processing, indicating the exosome recognizes unpaired bases to degrade RNAs that unfold during heat shock.

Phylogenetic Conservation of Directly Observed Duplexes

DMS-seq, structure-seq and icSHAPE have all been used to identify single-stranded regions of RNA *in vivo* by chemical probing of flexible or unpaired bases (Ding *et al.*, 2014; Rouskin *et al.*, 2014; Spitale *et al.*, 2015). However, while these methods provide constraints on the structure at individual nucleotide positions, they do not provide any direct information about long range interactions. Lu *et al.* (2016) used psoralen probing of RNA duplex in living cells, termed PARIS (psoralen analysis of RNA interactions and structures) to identify long range interactions directly via paired end sequencing (see Section "Direct Determination of Long-Range Interactions" for a discussion of the method itself).

Conservation and covariation of duplex structures

Lu *et al.* (2016) performed PARIS in two human cell lines (HeLa and HEK293T) and in mouse embryonic stem (mES) cells, and identified duplex groups (DGs) from gapped reads. A substantial proportion DGs spanned much larger regions of sequence (> 1000 bp) than normally identifiable or predictable, which offers new opportunities to investigate structure conservation and covariation (Smith *et al.*, 2013). By directly pairing the helices observed in DGs for human and mouse data, Lu *et al.* (2016) were able to perform covariation analysis on structures conserved between human and mouse, and use the PARIS-identified helices along with icSHAPE data to guide a much broader phylogenetic analysis of conserved structures.

Long range interactions are typically ignored in such structure covariation analysis because of the computational complexity of an unconstrained search; the PARIS constraints make it possible to focus directly on covariation at observed structural interactions, regardless of the distance between the paired sequence arms. In addition, PARIS data make it possible to avoid incorrectly assigned covariation searches that naturally become the focus of an unconstrained analysis.

Distinguishing between alternative RNA structures

As discussed in Section "Beyond One Modification Per RNA Molecule", one-dimensional structure probing data using single-hit kinetics infers only an average reactivity, even if multiple alternative RNA structures exist. Mutational profiling, correlation methods, and mutate-and-map strategies provide information about dynamics and alternative structures important for RNA structure-function relationships. PARIS also provides precise information about alternative structures, which can be directly detected as duplexes that are mutually incompatible. The authors analyzed the 50 mRNAs with the most detected helices as candidates for alternative structures: about 20%–50% of DGs from these mRNAs were found involved in at least one pair of alternative structures, suggesting that alternative structures are pervasive. The result also suggests that direct duplex detection can be used to identify functional RNA conformational switches such as riboswitches and RNA thermometers.

Higher order structure of XIST lncRNA in epigenetic silencing

PARIS, icSHAPE and phylogenetic conservation were combined to determine the higher order structure of XIST, a 19kb lncRNA essential for X chromosome inactivation, but whose structure has been contested. Global PARIS data revealed both local duplexes and multiple long-range interactions in the XIST lncRNA in what appear to be four structural domains. Phylogenetic analysis showed conservation of a subset of PARIS-determined helical structures, consistent with a functional role for three of the four domains.

An intriguing feature of XIST is the A-repeat, a spaced multicopy conserved sequence at the 5′end of the XIST RNA. Previous data had shown that the A-repeat is not required for XIST to coat the X chromosome in mouse, but is required for epigenetic silencing. The A-repeat had also been shown to be required for XIST RNA binding to the Spen protein, which provides an appealing link to epigenetic silencing. The A-repeat structure was difficult to determine, however, in part because of its repetition, and in part because of the limitations of conventional structure probing data and associated computational predictions.

The PARIS data indicate that the A-repeat region forms an isolated domain with extensive inter-repeat interactions, between the first halves of repeats, and mostly between neighboring repeats. The structure of inter-repeat units from PARIS is consistent with the icSHAPE data, and suggest that the A-repeats in XIST form a higher order structure. Since previous data had shown that Spen did not show any preference for single A-repeat units (Monfort *et al.*, 2015), it was possible that higher order structure was required for Spen RNA binding. Lu *et al.* (2016) performed iCLIP experiments to test this and found that Spen interacted virtually exclusively with the single stranded spacer regions between A-repeat units, suggesting that the A-repeat domain RNA architecture facilitates Spen binding.

Challenges and Future Directions

In this article, we have discussed the experimental and computational approaches for genome wide, next-generation sequencing-based RNA structure probing. The expanding repertoire of experimental RNA probing studies, now able to interrogate long range interactions as well as individual nucleotide positions, provide data for constraint based RNA folding algorithms that greatly exceed the performance of unconstrained folding predictions. Scientists in the field are taking advantage of these emerging technologies to provide tools and resources for the broader scientific community.

Many of the individual labs cited in this article have developed software for processing chemical probing data and producing reactivities or predictions as described in their papers. The full list is too numerous to describe here, but the citations above and the summary of **Table 1** are meant to provide a brief guide.

Constraints and Databases

RNA folding and prediction models that include constraint from experimental probing data are rapidly improving. The power of such constraints has been recognized for some time (Deigan *et al.*, 2008; Low and Weeks, 2010; Weeks, 2010), but techniques such as mutate-and-map (Kladwang *et al.*, 2011) SHAPE-MaP (Smola *et al.*, 2015), and direct duplex probing methods add a great deal of power to the available constraints. Computational methods for incorporating those constraints into folding prediction continue to advance (Lorenz *et al.*, 2016; Rice *et al.*, 2014), including recent extension to homologous sequences (Tan *et al.*, 2017).

Making use of such data requires it to be organized and accessible. The FoldAtlas database (Norris *et al.*, 2017) and Structure Surfer (Berkowitz *et al.*, 2016) are intended as a comprehensive archive of RNA structure probing data. FoldAtlas includes a focus on mutate-and-map studies.

The combination of high-throughput sequencing, innovative library preparation, and rigorous computational models is rapidly creating a new understanding of RNA structure *in vitro* and *in vivo*. The development of *in vivo* probing methods is exciting for many reasons, not least because it has suggested that RNA may be less structured in the cell than often observed in the tube. It is tempting to think that whole genome RNA probing technology may obviate the need for more focused structure probing studies, but this is unlikely to be the case: focused methods such as mutate-and-map interrogate target RNAs in depth and provide unique insight into sequence-structure relationships.

Emergence of Single-Molecule Sequencing Technologies

Virtually all of the recent sequencing studies for RNA structure probing have utilized "next-generation sequencing" that provide tens of millions of relatively short paired end reads. Using this high-throughput sequencing technology for RNA structure studies has required development of innovative library generation protocols; the protocols can be complex, but are a basic requirement of the sequencing technology. Furthermore, termination-based structure profiling is limited to one modification per molecule. While mutational profiling (MaP) approaches can read multiple modifications of a single molecule they are still limited by the underlying sequencing technology and library preparation requirements.

Recently developed single molecule sequencing technologies have been reported to read extremely long DNA and RNA sequences (Garalde *et al.*, 2018; Jain *et al.*, 2018), and can in principle directly detect covalent modifications of individual nucleotides (Vilfan *et al.*, 2013). This exciting capability has the potential to eliminate the library preparation requirements of current structure probing methods. Indeed, it seems inevitable that the next era of RNA structure probing studies will use single molecule direct sequencing of chemically modified RNAs to combine the best features of chemical probing and mutational profiling, detecting numerous modifications of single RNA molecules read across their entire lengths.

Acknowledgements

This work is supported by Singapore MOE AcRF T2 grant R154-000-A24-112 to Greg Tucker-Kellogg.

See also: Applications of Ribosomal RNA Sequence and Structure Analysis for Extracting Evolutionary and Functional Insights. Biomolecular Structures: Prediction, Identification and Analyses. Characterizing and Functional Assignment of Noncoding RNAs. Computational Design and Experimental Implementation of Synthetic Riboswitches and Riboregulators. Engineering of Supramolecular RNA Structures. Exome Sequencing Data Analysis. Functional Enrichment Analysis. Natural Language Processing Approaches in Bioinformatics. Next Generation Sequencing Data Analysis. Predicting RNA-RNA Interactions in Three-Dimensional Structures. Prediction of Coding and Non-Coding RNA. Whole Genome Sequencing Analysis

---

References

Aviran, S., Trapnell, C., Lucks, J.B., *et al.*, 2011. Modeling and automation of sequencing-based characterization of RNA structure. Proceedings of the National Academy of Sciences of the United States of America 108, 11069–11074. Available at: https://doi.org/10.1073/pnas.1106541108.

Aw, J.G., Shen, Y., Wilm, A., *et al.*, 2016. In vivo mapping of eukaryotic RNA interactomes reveals principles of higher-order organization and regulation. Molecular Cell 62, 603–617. Available at: https://doi.org/10.1016/j.molcel.2016.04.028.

Berkowitz, N.D., Silverman, I.M., Childress, D.M., *et al.*, 2016. A comprehensive database of high-throughput sequencing-based RNA secondary structure probing data (Structure Surfer). BMC Bioinformatics 17, 1–9. Available at: https://doi.org/10.1186/s12859-016-1071-0.

Bernat, V., Disney, M.D., 2015. RNA structures as mediators of neurological diseases and as drug targets. Neuron 87, 28–46. Available at: https://doi.org/10.1016/j.neuron.2015.06.012.

Brow, D.A., Noller, H.F., 1983. Protection of ribosomal RNA from kethoxal in polyribosomes. Implication of specific sites in ribosome function. Journal of Molecular Biology 163, 27–46. Available at: https://doi.org/10.1016/0022-2836(83)90028-1.

Busan, S., Weeks, K.M., 2018. Accurate detection of chemical modifications in RNA by mutational profiling (MaP) with ShapeMapper 2. RNA 24, 143–148. Available at: https://doi.org/10.1261/rna.061945.117.

Cech, T.R., Steitz, J.A., 2014. The noncoding RNA revolution – Trashing old rules to forge new ones. Cell 157, 77–94. Available at: https://doi.org/10.1016/j.cell.2014.03.008.

Cheong, C., Varani, G., Tinoco, I., 1990. Solution structure of an unusually stable RNA hairpin, 5′GGAC(UUCG)GUCC. Nature 346, 680–682. Available at: https://doi.org/10.1038/346680a0.

Cruz, J.A., Westhof, E., 2009. The dynamic landscapes of RNA architecture. Cell 136, 604–609. Available at: https://doi.org/10.1016/j.cell.2009.02.003.

Daou-Chabo, R., Condon, C., 2009. RNase J1 endonuclease activity as a probe of RNA secondary structure. RNA 15, 1417–1425. Available at: https://doi.org/10.1261/rna.1574309.

Deigan, K.E., Li, T.W., Mathews, D.H., Weeks, K.M., 2008. Accurate SHAPE-directed RNA structure determination. Proceedings of the National Academy of Sciences of the United States of America 2008, 97–102. Available at: https://doi.org/10.1073/pnas.0806929106.

Devi, G., Zhou, Y., Zhong, Z., Toh, D.F.K., Chen, G., 2015. RNA triplexes: From structural principles to biological and biotech applications. Wiley Interdisciplinary Reviews: RNA 6, 111–128. Available at: https://doi.org/10.1002/wrna.1261.

Ding, Y., Kwok, C.K., Tang, Y., Bevilacqua, P.C., Assmann, S.M., 2015. Genome- wide profiling of in vivo RNA structure at single-nucleotide resolution using structure-seq. Nature Protocols 10, 1050–1066 https://doi.org/10.1038/nprot.2015.064

Ding, Y., Tang, Y., Kwok, C.K., Zhang, Y., Bevilacqua, P.C., Assmann, S.M., 2014. In vivo genome-wide profiling of RNA secondary structure reveals novel regulatoryfeatures. Nature 505, 696–700https://doi.org/10.1038/nature12756

Feigon, J., 2015. Back to the future of RNA structure. RNA 21, 611–612. Available at: https://doi.org/10.1261/rna.050716.115.

Flynn, R.A., Zhang, Q.C., Spitale, R.C., *et al.*, 2016. Transcriptome-wide interrogation of RNA secondary structure in living cells with icSHAPE. Nature Protocols 11, 273–290. Available at: https://doi.org/10.1038/nprot.2016.011.

Garalde, D.R., Snell, E.A., Jachimowicz, D., *et al.*, 2018. Highly parallel direct RNA sequencing on an array of nanopores. Nature Methods 15, 201–206. Available at: https://doi.org/10.1038/nmeth.4577.

Hajdin, C.E., Bellaousov, S., Huggins, W., *et al.*, 2013. Accurate SHAPE-directed RNA secondary structure modeling, including pseudoknots. Proceedings of the National Academy of Sciences of the United States of America 110, 5498–5503. Available at: https://doi.org/10.1073/pnas.1219988110.

Heinicke, L.A., Bevilacqua, P.C., 2012. Activation of PKR by RNA misfolding: HDV ribozyme dimers activate PKR. RNA 18, 2157–2165. Available at: https://doi.org/10.1261/rna.034744.112.

Ho, N.W., Gilham, P.T., 1971. Reaction of pseudouridine and inosine with N-cyclohexyl-N′-beta-(4-methylmorpholinium)ethylcarbodiimide. Biochemistry 10, 3651–3657.

Homan, P.J., Favorov, O.V., Lavender, C.A., *et al.*, 2014. Single-molecule correlated chemical probing of RNA. Proceedings of the National Academy of Sciences of the United States of America 111, 13858–13863. Available at: https://doi.org/10.1073/pnas.1407306111.

Incarnato, D., Neri, F., Anselmi, F., Oliviero, S., 2014. Genome-wide profiling of mouse RNA secondary structures reveals key features of the mammalian transcriptome. Genome Biology 15, 491 https://doi.org/10.1186/s13059-014-0491-2

Incarnato, D., Neri, F., Anselmi, F., Oliviero, S., 2015. RNA structure framework:Automated transcriptome-wide reconstruction of RNA secondary structures fromhigh-throughput structure probing data. Bioinformatics 32, 459–461 https://doi.org/10.1093/bioinformatics/btv571

Ishiguro, T., Sato, N., Ueyama, M., et al., 2017. Regulatory role of RNA chaperone TDP-43 for RNA misfolding and repeat-associated translation in SCA31. Neuron 94, 108–124.e7. Available at: https://doi.org/10.1016/j.neuron.2017.02.046.

Jain, M., Olsen, H.E., Turner, D.J., et al., 2018. Linear assembly of a human centromere on the Y chromosome. Nature Biotechnology 36, 321–323. Available at: https://doi.org/10.1038/nbt.4109.

Kertesz, M., Wan, Y., Mazor, E., et al., 2010. Genome-wide measurement of RNA secondary structure in yeast. Nature 467, 103–107. Available at: https://doi.org/10.1038/nature09322.

Khalil, A.M., Guttman, M., Huarte, M., et al., 2009. Many human large intergenic noncoding RNAs associate with chromatin-modifying complexes and affect gene expression. Proceedings of the National Academy of Sciences of the United States of America 106, 11667–11672. Available at: https://doi.org/10.1073/pnas.0904715106.

Kim, S.H., Suddath, F.L., Quigley, G.J., et al., 1974. Three-dimensional tertiary structure of yeast phenylalanine transfer RNA. Science 185, 435–440. Available at: https://doi.org/10.1126/science.185.4149.435.

Kladwang, W., Das, R., 2010. A mutate-and-map strategy for inferring base pairs in structured nucleic acids: Proof of concept on a DNA/RNA helix. Biochemistry 49, 7414–7416. Available at: https://doi.org/10.1021/bi101123g.

Kladwang, W., VanLang, C.C., Cordero, P., Das, R., 2011. A two-dimensional mutate-and-map strategy for non-coding RNA structure. Nature Chemistry 3, 954–962. Available at: https://doi.org/10.1038/nchem.1176.

Knapp, G., 1989. Enzymatic approaches to probing of RNA secondary and tertiary structure. Methods in Enzymology 180, 192–212. Available at: https://doi.org/10.1016/0076-6879(89)80102-8.

Kwok, C.K., 2016. Dawn of the in vivo RNA structurome and interactome. Biochemical Society Transactions 44, 1395–1410. Available at: https://doi.org/10.1042/BST20160075.

Lee, A.J., Crothers, D.M., 1998. The solution structure of an RNA loop-loop complex: The ColE1 inverted loop sequence. Structure 6, 993–1005. Available at: https://doi.org/10.1016/S0969-2126(98)00101-4.

Li, F., Zheng, Q., Ryvkin, P., Dragomir, I., Desai, Y., Aiyer, S., Valladares, O., Yang, J., Bambina, S., Sabin, L.R., Murray, J.I., Lamitina, T., Raj, A., Cherry, S., Wang, L.S., Gregory, B.D., 2012. Global Analysis of RNA Secondary Structure in Two Metazoans. Cell Reports 1, 69–82 https://doi.org/10.1016/j.celrep.2011.10.002

Lorenz, R., Wolfinger, M.T., Tanzer, A., Hofacker, I.L., 2016. Predicting RNA secondary structures from sequence and probing data. Methods 103, 86–98. Available at: https://doi.org/10.1016/j.ymeth.2016.04.004.

Loughrey, D., Watters, K.E., Settle, A.H., Lucks, J.B., 2014. SHAPE-Seq 2.0: Sys- tematic optimization and extension of high-throughput chemical probing of RNA secondary structure with next generation sequencing. Nucleic Acids Research 42, e165–e165. https://doi.org/10.1093/nar/gku909

Low, J.T., Weeks, K.M., 2010. SHAPE-directed RNA secondary structure prediction. Methods 52, 150–158. Available at: https://doi.org/10.1016/j.ymeth.2010.06.007.

Lu, Z., Zhang, Q.C., Lee, B., et al., 2016. RNA duplex map in living cells reveals higher-order transcriptome structure. Cell 165, 1267–1279. Available at: https://doi.org/10.1016/j.cell.2016.04.028.

Lucks, J.B., Mortimer, S.A., Trapnell, C., et al., 2011. Multiplexed RNA structure characterization with selective 2′-hydroxyl acylation analyzed by primer extension sequencing (SHAPE-Seq). Proceedings of the National Academy of Sciences 108, 11063–11068. Available at: https://doi.org/10.1073/pnas.1106501108.

Luo, D., Condon, C., Grunberg-Manago, M., Putzer, H., 1998. In vitro and in vivo secondary structure probing of the thrS leader in Bacillus subtilis. Nucleic Acids Research 26, 5379–5387.

Mathews, D.H., Disney, M.D., Childs, J.L., et al., 2004. Incorporating chemical modification constraints into a dynamic programming algorithm for prediction of RNA secondary structure. Proceedings of the National Academy of Sciences of the United States of America 101, 7287–7292. Available at: https://doi.org/10.1073/pnas.0401799101.

Mathews, D.H., Turner, D.H., 2006. Prediction of RNA secondary structure by free energy minimization. Current Opinion in Structural Biology 16, 270–278. Available at: https://doi.org/10.1016/j.sbi.2006.05.010.

Merino, E.J., Wilkinson, K.A., Coughlan, J.L., Weeks, K.M., 2005. RNA structure analysis at single nucleotide resolution by selective 2′-hydroxyl acylation and primer extension (SHAPE). Journal of the American Chemical Society 127, 4223–4231. Available at: https://doi.org/10.1021/ja043822v.

Mitra, S., Shcherbakova, I.V., Altman, R.B., Brenowitz, M., Laederach, A., 2008. High-throughput single-nucleotide structural mapping by capillary automated footprinting analysis. Nucleic Acids Research 36, 1–10. Available at: https://doi.org/10.1093/nar/gkn267.

Monfort, A., Di Minin, G., Postlmayr, A., et al., 2015. Identification of Spen as a crucial factor for Xist function through forward genetic screening in haploid embryonic stem cells. Cell Reports 12, 554–561. Available at: https://doi.org/10.1016/j.celrep.2015.06.067.

Mustoe, A.M., Brooks, C.L., Al-Hashimi, H.M., 2014. Hierarchy of RNA functional dynamics. Annual Review of Biochemistry 83, 441–466. Available at: https://doi.org/10.1146/annurev-biochem-060713-035524.

Nájzer, E., Lei, E.P., 2014. Modulation of chromatin modifying complexes by noncoding RNAs in trans. Current Opinion in Genetics & Development 25, 68–73. Available at: https://doi.org/10.1016/j.gde.2013.11.019.

Nissen, P., Hansen, J., Ban, N., Moore, P.B., Steitz, T.A., 2000. The structural basis of ribosome activity in peptide bond synthesis. Science 289, 920–930.

Nissen, P., Ippolito, J.A., Ban, N., Moore, P.B., Steitz, T.A., 2001. RNA tertiary interactions in the large ribosomal subunit: The A-minor motif. Proceedings of the National Academy of Sciences of the United States of America 98, 4899–4903. Available at: https://doi.org/10.1073/pnas.081082398.

Norris, M., Kwok, C.K., Cheema, J., et al., 2017. FoldAtlas: A repository for genome-wide RNA structure probing data. Bioinformatics 33, 306–308. Available at: https://doi.org/10.1093/bioinformatics/btw611.

Peattie, D.A., Gilbert, W., 1980. Chemical probes for higher-order structure in RNA. Proceedings of the National Academy of Sciences of the United States of America 77, 4679–4682. Available at: https://doi.org/10.1073/pnas.77.8.4679.

Reiter, N.J., Osterman, A., Torres-Larios, A., et al., 2010. Structure of a bacterial ribonuclease P holoenzyme in complex with tRNA. Nature 468, 784–789. Available at: https://doi.org/10.1038/nature09516.

Rice, G.M., Leonard, C.W., Weeks, K.M., 2014. RNA secondary structure modeling at consistent high accuracy using differential SHAPE. RNA 20, 846–854. Available at: https://doi.org/10.1261/rna.043323.113.

Rouskin, S., Zubradt, M., Washietl, S., Kellis, M., Weissman, J.S., 2014. Genome-wide probing of RNA structure reveals active unfolding of mRNA structures in vivo. Nature 505, 701–705. Available at: https://doi.org/10.1038/nature12894.

Sharma, E., Sterne-Weiler, T., O'Hanlon, D., Blencowe, B.J., 2016. Global mapping of human RNA-RNA interactions. Molecular Cell 62, 618–626. Available at: https://doi.org/10.1016/j.molcel.2016.04.030.

Siegfried, N.A., Busan, S., Rice, G.M., Nelson, J.A.E., Weeks, K.M., 2014. RNA motif discovery by SHAPE and mutational profiling (SHAPE-MaP). Nature Methods 11, 959–965.

Smith, M.A., Gesell, T., Stadler, P.F., Mattick, J.S., 2013. Widespread purifying selection on RNA structure in mammals. Nucleic Acids Research 41, 8220–8236. Available at: https://doi.org/10.1093/nar/gkt596.

Smola, M.J., Rice, G.M., Busan, S., Siegfried, N.A., Weeks, K.M., 2015. Selective 2′-hydroxyl acylation analyzed by primer extension and mutational profiling (SHAPE-MaP) for direct, versatile and accurate RNA structure analysis. Nature Protocols 10, 1643–1669. Available at: https://doi.org/10.1038/nprot.2015.103.

Spitale, R.C., Crisalli, P., Flynn, R.A., et al., 2013. RNA SHAPE analysis in living cells. Nature Chemical Biology 9, 18–20. Available at: https://doi.org/10.1038/nchembio.1131.

Spitale, R.C., Flynn, R.A., Zhang, Q.C., et al., 2015. Structural imprints in vivo decode RNA regulatory mechanisms. Nature 519, 486–490. Available at: https://doi.org/10.1038/nature14263.

Talkish, J., May, G., Lin, Y., Woolford, J.L., McManus, C.J., 2014. Mod-seq: High- throughput sequencing for chemical probing of RNA structure. Rna 20, 713–720 https://doi.org/10.1261/rna.042218.113

Tan, Z., Sharma, G., Mathews, D.H., 2017. Modeling RNA secondary structure with sequence comparison and experimental mapping data. Biophysical Journal 113, 330–338. Available at: https://doi.org/10.1016/j.bpj.2017.06.039.

Tian, S., Cordero, P., Kladwang, W., Das, R., 2014. High-throughput mutate-map-rescue evaluates SHAPE-directed RNA structure and uncovers excited states. RNA 20, 1815–1826. Available at: https://doi.org/10.1261/rna.044321.114.

Tijerina, P., Mohr, S., Russell, R., 2007. DMS footprinting of structured rnas and rna-protein complexes. Nature Protocols 2, 2608–2623. Available at: https://doi.org/10.1038/nprot.2007.380.

Tinoco, I., Bustamante, C., 1999. How RNA folds. Journal of Molecular Biology 293, 271–281. Available at: https://doi.org/10.1006/jmbi.1999.3001.

Tullius, T.D., Greenbaum, J.A., 2005. Mapping nucleic acid structure by hydroxyl radical cleavage. Current Opinion in Chemical Biology 9, 127–134. Available at: https://doi.org/10.1016/j.cbpa.2005.02.009.

Underwood, J.G., Uzilov, A.V., Katzman, S., et al., 2010. FragSeq: Transcriptome-wide RNA structure probing using high-throughput sequencing. Nature Methods 7, 995–1001. Available at: https://doi.org/10.1038/nmeth.1529.

Vasa, S.M., Guex, N., Wilkinson, K.A., Weeks, K.M., Giddings, M.C., 2008. ShapeFinder: A software system for high-throughput quantitative analysis of nucleic acid reactivity information resolved by capillary electrophoresis. RNA 14, 1979–1990. Available at: https://doi.org/10.1261/rna.1166808.

Vilfan, I.D., Tsai, Y.C., Clark, T.A., et al., 2013. Analysis of RNA base modification and structural rearrangement by single-molecule real-time detection of reverse transcription. Journal of Nanobiotechnology 11, 1–11. Available at: https://doi.org/10.1186/1477-3155-11-8.

Wan, Y., Qu, K., Ouyang, Z., Chang, H.Y., 2013. Genome-wide mapping of RNA structure using nuclease digestion and high-throughput sequencing. Nature Protocols 8, 849–869 https://doi.org/10.1038/nprot.2013.045

Wan, Y., Qu, K., Ouyang, Z., et al., 2012. Genome-wide measurement of RNA folding energies. Molecular Cell 48, 169–181. Available at: https://doi.org/10.1016/j.molcel.2012.08.008.

Wan, Y., Qu, K., Zhang, Q.C., Flynn, R.A., Manor, O., Ouyang, Z., Zhang, J., Spitale, R.C., Snyder, M.P., Segal, E., Chang, H.Y., 2014. Landscape and variation of RNA secondary structure across the human transcriptome. Nature 505, 706–709 https://doi.org/10.1038/nature12946

Watts, J.M., Dang, K.K., Gorelick, R.J., et al., 2009. Architecture and secondary structure of an entire HIV-1 RNA genome. Nature 460, 711–716. Available at: https://doi.org/10.1038/nature08237.

Weeks, K.M., 2010. Advances in RNA structure analysis by chemical probing. Current Opinion in Structural Biology 20, 295–304. Available at: https://doi.org/10.1016/j.sbi.2010.04.001.

Westhof, E., 2015. Twenty years of RNA crystallography. RNA 21, 486–487. Available at: https://doi.org/10.1261/rna.049726.115.

Wilkinson, K.A., Gorelick, R.J., Vasa, S.M., et al., 2008. High-throughput SHAPE analysis reveals structures in HIV-1 genomic RNA strongly conserved across distinct biological states. PLOS Biology 6, e96. Available at: https://doi.org/10.1371/journal.pbio.0060096.

Wilkinson, K.A., Merino, E.J., Weeks, K.M., 2005. RNA SHAPE chemistry reveals nonhierarchical interactions dominate equilibrium structural transitions in tRNAAsp transcripts. Journal of the American Chemical Society 127, 4659–4667. Available at: https://doi.org/10.1021/ja0436749.

Zheng, Q., Ryvkin, P., Li, F., et al., 2010. Genome-wide double-stranded RNA sequencing reveals the functional significance of base-paired RNAs in arabidopsis. PLOS Genetics 6, e1001141. Available at: https://doi.org/10.1371/journal.pgen.1001141.

Ziehler, W.A., Engelke, D.R., 2001. Probing RNA structure with chemical reagents and enzymes. In: Current Protocols in Nucleic Acid Chemistry. Hoboken, NJ: John Wiley & Sons, Inc., pp. 6.1.1–6.1.21. Available at: https://doi.org/10.1002/0471142700.nc0601s00.

Zubradt, M., Gupta, P., Persad, S., et al., 2016. DMS-MaPseq for genome-wide or targeted RNA structure probing in vivo. Nature Methods 14, 75–82. Available at: https://doi.org/10.1038/nmeth.4057.

Biographical Sketch

Xiaojing Huo is a postdoctoral research fellow in Prof. Greg Tucker-Kellogg's at the National University of Singapore. She did her PhD training in functional genomics and RNA-seq studies of tumorigenesis models in zebrafish. Her current research interest is on dissection of TGFβ signaling in models of human cancers.

Jeremy Ng is a graduate student in computational and molecular biology at the National University of Singapore. His research interest is the regulation of TGFβ signaling axis decisions following ligand exposure.

Tan Mingchen is a PhD candidate in computational biology at National University of Singapore. His research a Prize Collecting Steiner system to dissect regulatory networks from heterogeneous genomic data.

Greg Tucker-Kellogg is Professor in Practice in the Department of Biological Sciences and Director of the Faculty of Science Computational Biology Program at the National University of Singapore. He received his PhD in from Yale University under Peter Moore, and was a Jane Coffin Childs Postdoctoral Fellow at Harvard Medical School with Christopher T. Walsh. Prior to joining the NUS faculty, he spent nearly 15 years in the biotech and pharmaceutical industries. His laboratory is developing tools for both optogenetic regulation of cancer signaling pathways and for measurement of single-cell chromatin dynamics.

Assessment of Structure Quality (RNA and Protein)

Nicolas Palopoli, Universidad Nacional de Quilmes & CONICET, Bernal, Buenos Aires, Argentina

Introduction

Knowledge of the three-dimensional structure of biological molecules has been a permanent goal and often a breakthrough achievement in modern science. Structural (molecular) biology has developed since the late 1950s and now constitutes one of the major forces of scientific progress; for an exciting account on the history of the field by some of its key players, see Nature Structural and Molecular Biology (2011). Among these were Kendrew et al. (1958), who first published the structure of myoglobin by X-ray analysis. The application of this technique to determine the tertiary structure of proteins as rigid solids has brought about a revolution in structural biology. Ever since, more than 130,000 protein structures have been resolved at atomic resolution by different techniques and deposited in the publicly available Protein Data Bank (PDB) (Berman et al., 2000). Nuclear magnetic resonance (NMR) spectroscopy has allowed the determination of dynamic protein structures in solution or in membranes since the late 1970s (Wüthrich, 2001). Small angle scattering of neutrons (SANS) and X-rays (SAXS) provide means to study the size and shape of proteins (Mertens and Svergun, 2010). These techniques can be applied jointly with X-ray crystallography (Tsutakawa et al., 2007; Wang and Wang, 2017) or NMR (Hennig and Sattler, 2014) to analyze tertiary structures, including those of flexible proteins or large complexes. More recently, cryo-electron microscopy (cryo-EM or simply EM) has been successfully applied to reveal the structures of proteins that could not be determined by other means, although generally at a lower resolution (Bai et al., 2015). Despite the valuable advances in the field, protein structure determination remains a challenging endeavour, due to high associated costs, experimental constraints like the need for overexpression and purification of the sample and certain properties of some proteins such as highly flexible disordered regions.

The methodologies for high-quality, atomic-resolution RNA structure determination are similar to those applied for proteins (Felden, 2007). X-ray crystallography and NMR spectroscopy can provide detailed information about RNA in solid phase or in solution, respectively, with cryo-EM still offering lower resolution structures. However, general interest in RNA biology developed later than for proteins and our knowledge of the field is comparatively restricted. To date, the Protein Data Bank (Berman et al., 2000) lists 1297 RNA-only structures and 2067 RNA-protein complexes, most of them also linked in the Nucleic Acid Database (Coimbatore Narayanan et al., 2014). These represent barely 2,5% of the total PDB entries as of September 2017, with a steady pace of 30–81 new structures deposited per year in the last two decades. This scarcity must also be related with intrinsic experimental difficulties such as dealing with a vast RNA backbone conformational space (Murray et al., 2003). Besides the possibility of determining the position of its atoms, low-resolution RNA structure analysis can be performed by other experimental methods such as different in vivo and in vitro structure-specific chemical and enzymatic probes of base pairing and interactions (Kubota et al., 2015), or the selective 2'-hydroxyl acylation analyzed by primer extension (SHAPE) (Weeks and Mauger, 2011) for detecting unconstrained, flexible positions.

Experimental procedures for the determination of protein or RNA three-dimensional structure include a final step of quality control and model refinement. The worldwide Protein Data Bank (wwPDB) has provided in-house tools for deposition and annotation of protein and nucleic acid structures (Dutta et al., 2009), including the PDB Validation Suite (Westbrook et al., 2003) for curation and validation of submissions, that recently converged in the unified OneDep system (Young et al., 2017). The agreement between diffraction data and the atomic coordinates of the final model is typically measured by the R-value criterion of accuracy and by the less biased and more reliable R_{free} cross-validation statistical (Brünger, 1992). Model-to-data quality of fit, plus the geometric and stereochemical properties of solved structures, can also be evaluated with external, standalone tools such as the PHENIX crystallographic software (Adams et al., 2010) and PROSESS (Protein Structure Evaluation Suite & Server) (Berjanskii et al., 2010). Moreover, PROCHECK (Laskowski et al., 1993), WHAT_CHECK (Hooft et al., 1996) and MolProbity (Chen et al., 2010), among others, seek to assess how far the properties of experimental or computational structures are from those observed in known structures. Even after quality checks and improvements, many solved structures are neither complete nor free from errors, and although X-ray crystallography models are generally acceptable, there is still inconsistency in terms of resolution and quality measures in the PDB (Domagalski et al., 2014).

Regardless of the methodology and despite the many advances in the field, experimental structure determination remains a challenging task for many reasons, including high associated costs in materials and manpower, experimental constraints like sample size needed or the difficulty to obtain good crystals, and intrinsic properties of biomolecules such as large molecular weights and high flexibility. In this context, computational prediction of three-dimensional structures has lately become a readily applicable approach to generate structural data when no further evidence is available. Enough computational power is now accessible and affordable, and modern methods, although still far from perfect, can provide sufficiently reliable and useful structure models.

Several methods exist that can predict one or more likely conformations of the target molecule that might resemble its native conformers. Historically, the most successful methods have been those that try to derive three-dimensional information from close homologues of known structure. This comparative modeling approach is better suited for globular proteins of identifiable folds, where a suitable template should be easy to retrieve. When no homologous structure is available, or when trying to reconstruct hard targets such as membrane proteins or intrinsically disordered regions, template-free methods can derive hundreds or thousands of structures from first principles, aiming to include a sample of several native-like conformations among them. Similarly, RNA structure prediction can be performed *ab initio* or based on secondary structure elements and long-range tertiary contacts (Laing and Schlick, 2011). RNA molecules can be represented as highly simplified, coarse-grained models that work better for long RNAs, or detailed all-atom simulations most suitable for small RNAs (Laing and Schlick, 2010, 2011). Overall, nevertheless, modeling of RNA tertiary structure still suffers from our relatively limited knowledge of RNA native structures.

The struggle for better structural modeling techniques led to the establishment of several efforts for the large-scale evaluation of protein structure prediction methods. Although now deprecated, LiveBench (Bujnicki *et al.*, 2001) and EVA (Eyrich *et al.*, 2001; Koh *et al.*, 2003) were the first to offer an automated benchmark of several public methods. The Critical Assessment of protein Structure Prediction (CASP) experiments (Moult *et al.*, 2017) are the longest-running and quite possibly most productive of these initiatives. Every two years since 1994 (Moult *et al.*, 1995), the organizers of CASP propose several target proteins which structures remain unknown to the participants but have already been solved experimentally by external collaborators. Developers of manual and automatic programs for protein structure modeling submit their predictions on these targets, for the assessment of the structural similarity between target and model structures and the overall quality of the prediction methods employed. The last published results continue to show a steady progress in modeling performance, with yet much room for improvement (Moult *et al.*, 2016). Although template-free modeling techniques (for the rare cases where no structure with detectable similarity to the target is available) has proven to successfully predict large proteins (Ovchinnikov *et al.*, 2016), this area remains particularly challenging (Kinch *et al.*, 2016). Thus, CASP ROLL (Moult *et al.*, 2014) has been introduced to provide a continuous and equally blind assessment of *de novo* structure prediction. Similarly, and recognizing the constant need for better quality assessment methods, the Continuous Automated Model EvaluatiOn (CAMEO) (Haas *et al.*, 2013) provides an ongoing evaluation of protein structure prediction servers by comparison to novel experimental structures released by the PDB (Berman *et al.*, 2000). A similar effort has been set up more recently by the RNA structure modeling community. Named RNA-Puzzles (Cruz *et al.*, 2012), it provides a blind evaluation of prediction methods on a wide diversity of functional RNA molecules, including large RNA structures (Miao *et al.*, 2015), riboswitches and more (Miao *et al.*, 2017).

This article discusses the Model Quality Assessment Programs, or MQAPs for short, which aim to predict the quality of three-dimensional structure models of biomolecules by applying computational methods that produce global and/or local scores. The field of Model Quality Assessment (MQA) was introduced as a CASP category in CASP7 (2007) (Cozzetto *et al.*, 2007), when participants were assessed on their ability to determine a priori the quality of models built by prediction servers for CASP targets. Since 'quality' is hard to define, and thus cannot be assessed confidently, Estimation of Model Accuracy (EMA) was recently proposed as a more descriptive definition of the task (Kryshtafovych *et al.*, 2016). Although this is a fair concern, the terms MQA and MQAP have been extensively used in the community and are preferred for this work.

Many programs allow scoring and ranking of structural models, or decoys, based on their intrinsic properties and regardless of the availability of an observed structure. Several other protocols can be used for benchmarking models by comparing them to known experimental structures. Some programs propose a mixed approach that relies on the comparison of the model under evaluation with a set of alternative decoys, built for the occasion, to identify conserved structural features. Although these approaches can be collectively referred to as MQAPs, they serve different goals and thus will be treated as separate categories. This article tries to avoid outdated and conflicting resources. For example, different energy functions have been used as single scores for the determination of the top-ranked models and may qualify (perhaps incorrectly) as MQAPs, but they are not covered extensively here. This article is also not intended as a comprehensive catalogue of all available methods for structure quality assessment. Instead, it recalls those methods which have had an impact on the field and highlights other established alternatives that are part of the current state-of-the-art. Also, it is not focused on the algorithms and parameters of the methods, but rather presents their foundations and comments on their applicability.

Background/Fundamentals

The biomolecular modeling community has reached a point of maturity in which the generation of structural models appears straightforward. However, their quality would be largely dependent on the properties of the target molecule, the capabilities of the program employed and the knowledge and experience of the researcher for selecting the right tools and options. Given this complexity, it is hard to ensure in advance the adequacy and utility of models that are generally derived from approximate methods. Most programs rely on finding the most efficient paths towards native-like models, even if these are not optimal. To cope with this limitation, a usual choice is to output a varying number of possible models, expecting that they will provide enough good options. Therefore, regardless of the modeling procedure, a crucial step is the ability to score, rank and select among the many models proposed (Kihara *et al.*, 2009). This is generally attempted by a large-scale computational assessment of structure quality, possibly followed by human evaluation of outstanding candidates. Both protein and RNA structures can be assessed in relationship to a reference structure or by analysing their characteristic structural features. Proteins are organized hierarchically, from local geometric arrangements and bonding patterns that define secondary structures, drive the adoption of conserved tertiary folds and favour interchain contacts to form functional complexes. RNAs are defined by specific base pairing and stacking patterns which result in local structure motifs like bulges, stems or hairpin loops, linked by long-range interactions that determine the tertiary structure. These features, like many others, can be extracted from high-confidence existing structures and processed in different ways to generate a knowledge-based predictor of model quality.

Energy functions have been used for a relative estimation of model accuracy since the first attempts in structural modeling. Early studies on incorrectly folded protein models demonstrated that wrong models can have comparable energy values to acceptable structures, even if their interactions, side-chain packing, or solvent accessibility are distorted (Novotný *et al.*, 1984, 1988). Further developments led to more comprehensive and specific formulations to estimate the total free energy of structural models. For example, MODELLER (Sali and Blundell, 1993) applies internal scoring functions to assess its protein homology models, including the empirical and distant-dependent Discrete Optimized Protein Energy statistical potential (DOPE) (Shen and Sali, 2006). The ROSETTA suite for ab initio structure modeling (Leaver-Fay *et al.*, 2011) combines a statistical potential with a physical energy function for the scoring of ab initio protein and RNA models. Unfortunately, energy-based scores such as these are limited in their approach. Given the enormous diversity and changing nature of biomolecules, it is difficult to determine empirically and model reliably the expected energy of each native structure. An evaluation based in energy properties may oversee other conflicting characteristics of the models; plus, it would not be possible to draw a line between good and bad predictions based on their energies alone. With programs applying different definitions and optimizations of the energy calculation, their scores may not be directly comparable among structures. Therefore, they could only be used for relative rankings of models obtained by individual programs, which may generally not converge to the same answer. To deal with these issues, a whole set of criteria for testing the quality of structure models have matured over the last decades, implemented through many programs specifically designed for the task.

A common approach to determine the quality of structure models has been the evaluation of their stereochemical properties. Both PROCHECK (Laskowski *et al.*, 1993) and WHATCHECK (Hooft *et al.*, 1996) quantify the deviation in several structural measures between the models and known protein structures. These methods oversee that both native and non-native models can be stereochemically correct. To differentiate among these, several programs incorporate energy functions or statistical potentials derived from the analysis of known structures. Two highly popular approaches have been PROSA II (Sippl, 1993), with a knowledge-based energy function built from inter-residue distance probabilities, and VERIFY3D (Eisenberg *et al.*, 1997), which evaluates the compatibility of the primary and tertiary structures of a model according to a 3D profile of the structural environments observed in real structures. All the previous methods have enjoyed the greatest relevance in the first years of model quality assessment, and although other approaches have proved to be more effective (many of them covered in Section "Model Quality Assessment of Protein Structures"), usage of these methods can still be found in new publications.

Model quality assessment programs can be organized into different categories depending on their general approach to model evaluation. Single-model programs estimate global accuracy by assigning an absolute score to each model based on their geometrical or energetic properties alone. Their performance would depend on a good correlation of the scoring function with actual model quality. Global consensus-based methods (also called clustering methods), while may still calculate absolute scores, would also aim at providing a reliable ranking of a set of models by performing all-against-all comparisons, recognizing the best one(s) and ideally drawing a line between good and bad structures. A mixed type are the quasi-single-model MQAPs. These methods take as input a single model and expands it into an extensive set of decoys, which could be built *ad hoc* with local or external methods. They assess the quality of every model by pairwise comparisons against a subset of high-quality models, taken as reference from the dataset via single-model methods. A special category could be the meta-methods, which combine predictions from different MQAPs into a single quality score. It can be argued that these methods are single-model or consensus-based approaches depending on the nature of the scores they combine; thus, for simplicity, meta-methods are not treated separately in this manuscript. The methods described above may evaluate model accuracy at different levels. Local predictors would seek a per-residue evaluation, while others would provide a unique descriptor of the global quality of the model, either by combining local scores or by analysing the structure as a whole. Also, they can be implemented as automatic, semi-automatic or manual methods, requiring varying levels of human intervention to run the programs and translate raw evaluation results into meaningful information.

Applications

The following subsections present a selection of current relevant options for model quality assessment. The information is organized for protein and RNA structures separately, although some methods can be applied to both types of macromolecules. MQAPs are also classified based on their general approach to assessment, with methods measuring similarity to a reference structure, predicting the quality of single models alone, or by a consensus analysis of multiple decoys. A summary of the classification, characteristics and online availability of these methods is provided in **Table 1**.

Model Quality Assessment of Protein Structures

Validation against reference structure

Programs to calculate root mean square deviation (RMSD)

RMSD (Nishikawa and Ooi, 1972; Levitt, 1976) is a measure of the average Euclidean distance between equivalent atoms of two biomolecular structures, computed as

$$RMSD = \sqrt{\frac{1}{N}\sum_{i=1}^{N} d_i^2}$$

Table 1 Classification and availability of model quality assessment programs (MQAPs) described in Section "Applications"

Program	Target	Category	Type	Description	Webserver	Download
MAMMOTH	Proteins	Similarity	Global	Pairwise, rigid-body structure alignment. Similarity assessment by RMSD, p-value. Multiple alignment version available (MAMMOTH-mult).	https://ub.cbm.uam.es/software/online/mammoth.php	https://ub.cbm.uam.es/software/mammoth.php
SuperPose	Proteins	Similarity	Local/global	Pairwise and multiple structure alignment. Similarity assessment by RMSD at residue resolution.	http://wishart.biology.ualberta.ca/SuperPose/	No
ProFit	Proteins	Similarity	Local/global	Pairwise structure alignment. Similarity assessment by RMSD at residue resolution.	http://www.bioinf.org.uk/profit/	http://www.bioinf.org.uk/software/swreg.html
TopMatch	Proteins	Similarity	Local/global	Pairwise fuzzy/precise structure alignment. Similarity assessment by RMSD and Gaussian function.	https://topmatch.services.came.sbg.ac.at	https://www.came.sbg.ac.at/downloads.php
CE	Proteins	Similarity	Global	Pairwise, rigid-body structure alignment. Similarity assessment by RMSD.	http://source.rcsb.org/	http://source.rcsb.org/download.jsp
FatCat	Proteins	Similarity	Global	Pairwise, flexible and rigid-body structure alignment. Similarity assessment by RMSD.	http://source.rcsb.org/	http://source.rcsb.org/download.jsp
MaxSub	Proteins	Similarity	Local/global	Pairwise, rigid-body structure alignment. Similarity assessment by RMSD and normalized S-score.	https://www.cs.bgu.ac.il/~dfischer/MaxSub/query.html	http://fischerlab.cse.buffalo.edu/maxsub
TM-score	Proteins, RNA	Similarity	Local/global	Pairwise, rigid-body structure alignment. Similarity assessment by RMSD and TM-score.	https://zhanglab.ccmb.med.umich.edu/TM-score/	https://zhanglab.ccmb.med.umich.edu/TM-score/
LGA	Proteins	Similarity	Local/global	Pairwise, rigid-body structure alignment. Similarity assessment by RMSD and a combination of Longest Continuous Segments (LCS) and Global Distance Test (GDT) scores.	http://proteinmodel.org/AS2TS/LGA/lga.html	http://proteinmodel.org/AS2TS/download_area/
Dali	Proteins	Similarity	Global	Pairwise, rigid-body structure alignment by search of largest common substructure. Similarity assessment by Z-score.	http://ekhidna2.biocenter.helsinki.fi/dali/	No
local Distance Difference Test (lDDT)	Proteins	Similarity	Local/global	Pairwise and multiple superposition-free structure alignment. Similarity assessment on different distance cutoffs.	https://swissmodel.expasy.org/lddt	https://swissmodel.expasy.org/lddt/downloads/
CAD-score	Proteins, RNA	Similarity	Local/global	Pairwise structure alignment based on Voronoi tessellations. Similarity assessment on all-atom, main-chain only and side-chain only contacts.	http://bioinformatics.ibt.lt/cad-score/	https://bitbucket.org/kliment/cadscore/downloads/
MolProbity	Proteins, RNA	Single-model	Local/global	Allows calculation of steric clashes, incorrect bonds and wrong bond lengths and angles. Other protein-specific validations are available.	http://molprobity.biochem.duke.edu/	https://github.com/rlabduke/MolProbity
ProQ	Proteins	Single-model	Local/global	Neural network-based assessment of structural similarity to hypothetical reference via LG-score and MaxSub scores. Local prediction version developed as ProQres.	https://proq.bioinfo.se/cgi-bin/ProQ/ProQ.cgi	http://proq.bioinfo.se/ProQ/ProQ.html

(Continued)

Table 1   Continued

Program	Target	Category	Type	Description	Webserver	Download
ProQ2	Proteins	Single-model	Local/global	Similar to ProQ, with individual residue weighting based on evolutionary profiles.	http://duffman.it.liu.se/ProQ2	https://github.com/bjornwallner/ProQ_scripts
ProQ3	Proteins	Single-model	Local/global	Similar to ProQ but using Support Vector Machines.	http://proq3.bioinfo.se/	https://bitbucket.org/ElofssonLab/proq3/downloads/
ProQ3D	Proteins	Single-model	Local/global	Similar to ProQ but using deep neural networks.	http://proq3.bioinfo.se/	https://bitbucket.org/ElofssonLab/proq3/downloads/
MESHI-Score	Proteins	Single-model	Global	Machine learning-based assessment of structural quality aiming to predict real GDT_TS. MESHI-Score is a combination of scores from multiple predictors of structure and energy features.	No	http://meshi1.cs.bgu.ac.il/meshi_score/
SVMQA	Proteins	Single-model	Global	Assessment of structural quality based on Support Vector Machines to predict TM-score and GDT_TS. Uses statistical potential and structural features.	No	http://lee.kias.re.kr/~protein/wiki/doku.php
ModFOLD	Proteins	Single-model (original), quasi-single-model (from v3)	Local/global	Assessment of structural quality based on artificial neural networks. Combines outputs from different single- and quasi-single-model methods.	http://www.reading.ac.uk/bioinf/ModFOLD/	http://www.reading.ac.uk/bioinf/downloads/
QMEAN	Proteins	Single-model	Local/global	Assessment based on combination of statistical potentials with structure descriptors, given as Z-scores. Consensus version QMEANclust is available.	http://swissmodel.expasy.org/qmean	No
Qprob/MULTICOM-NOVEL	Proteins	Single-model	Global	Assessment based on probability density functions to infer errors in predicted structural and physico-chemical properties.	http://calla.rnet.missouri.edu/qprob/	http://calla.rnet.missouri.edu/qprob/
MetaMQAP	Proteins	Single-model	Local/global	Machine learning-based approach to predict deviation of structural features against expected real structure.	https://genesilico.pl/toolkit/unimod?method=MetaMQAPII	No
VoroMQA	Proteins	Single-model	Local/global	Assessment based on statistical potentials considering intra-protein and protein-solvent interatomic areas.	http://bioinformatics.ibt.lt/wtsam/voromqa	https://bitbucket.org/kliment/voronota/downloads
Pcons	Proteins	Consensus	Local/global	Neural network approach to predict and rank ProQ score by comparison with decoys obtained from public fold recognition servers.	http://pcons.net	http://pcons.net/index.php?about=download
ModFOLDclust	Proteins	Consensus	Local/global	Consensus-based assessment using ModFOLD scores.	http://www.reading.ac.uk/bioinf/ModFOLD/	http://www.reading.ac.uk/bioinf/downloads/
Pcomb	Proteins	Consensus	Local/global	Score based on linear combination of ProQ2 or ProQ3 and Pcons.	No	https://github.com/ElofssonLab/Pcomb3_CASP12
iFoldRNA	RNA	Similarity	Global	Pairwise, global structure alignment. Similarity assessment by RMSD, p-value.	http://redshift.med.unc.edu/ifoldrna	http://redshift.med.unc.edu/ifoldrna/

Name	Type	Category	Scope	Description	Standalone	Web server
RNAlyzer	RNA	Similarity	Local/global	Pairwise, global/local structure alignment. Similarity assessment by RMSD on different distance cutoffs.	http://rnalyzer.cs.put.poznan.pl/	No
RNAssess	RNA	Similarity	Local/global	Based on RNAlyzer but similarity also measured by Deformation Index and Deformation Profile.	No	http://massess.cs.put.poznan.pl/
MCQ4Structures	RNA	Similarity	Local/global	Pairwise and multiple superposition-free structure comparison in torsional angle space.	http://www.cs.put.poznan.pl/tzok/wiki/index.php?n=Projects.MCQ4Structures	No
Rclick	RNA	Similarity	Global	Pairwise structure alignment based on graph theory and least-squares fitting. Similarity assessment by global RMSD, Fragment Score and Topology Score.	No	http://mspc.bii.a-star.edu.sg/minhn/rclick.html
FARFAR	RNA	Consensus	Global	Comparison against dataset of de novo generated decoy sets with heavy-atom RMSD calculation. Standalone version requires Rosetta.	https://www.rosettacommons.org/docs/latest/application_documentation/rna/rna-denovo	http://rosie.rosettacommons.org/rna_denovo/submit
WebRASP	RNA	Consensus	Local/global	Assessment based on energy scores calculated with distance-dependent empirical contact potential. Requires manual comparison of decoy scores.	http://melolab.org/webrasp/download.php	http://melolab.org/webrasp/home.php
3dRNAscore	RNA	Consensus	Local/global	Assessment based on energy scores from contact potential including base-stacking and torsion angle contribution.	http://biophy.hust.edu.cn/3dRNAscore.html	http://biophy.hust.edu.cn/3dRNAscore

where d_i is the Euclidean distance between the i-th pair of atoms, one from each structure, and N is the total number of pairs being considered. RMSD is expressed in units of length, with Ångstrom (Å, equal to 10^{-10}m) being the most common. Calculation of RMSD requires a good (and fast) or optimal superposition of the structures to minimize the distances (Kabsch, 1976; Coutsias *et al.*, 2004).

RMSD is a simple and yet useful measure that has been so widely adopted for the last three decades that it is pointless trying to enumerate all implementations available. It is currently possible to calculate RMSD using standalone tools (such as MAMMOTH (Ortiz *et al.*, 2002)), web servers (e.g., SuperPose (Maiti *et al.*, 2004)) and bioinformatics software libraries (including BioPython (Cock *et al.*, 2009), BioJava (Holland *et al.*, 2008) and other extensions to popular programming languages). Although RMSD has been widely applied as a measure of global similarity, programs such as ProFit, which implements a special least squares fitting algorithm (McLachlan, 1982), provide local RMSD values to compare specific regions or even individual residues. Some programs, like TopMatch (Sippl and Wiederstein, 2012), would not limit the comparison to RMSD values but extend the output with additional descriptors of structural similarity. Each program may introduce small variations to the calculation to suit different goals. For example, RMSD is often computed from distances between Cα atoms only, but Cβ and other sidechain carbons can also be incorporated. RMSD relies on a superposition of the structures that could treat them as rigid bodies, as in the Combinatorial Extension (CE) algorithm (Shindyalov and Bourne, 1998) or allow some flexibility for more accurate alignments (e.g., in FatCat (Ye and Godzik, 2004)).

Levitt-Gerstein score (LG-score)

LG-score (Levitt and Gerstein, 1998) was designed to tolerate local fluctuations in order to gain sensitivity for the similarity in global topology. It was first developed as a standalone application but, since the early 2000s, it has been adopted and modified for the development of several other similarity measures, as exposed in the following sections.

Superposition of two structures is performed by first calculating all pairwise distances between every atom in each structure, which are then used for an iterative process of least-squares fitting of one structure onto the other. Prioritization of global similarities is achieved by setting an empirically derived distance cutoff (typically 5 Å) to downweigh equivalent residues far from each other, such as those that can be found in flexible local regions. This is directly incorporated into the original LG-score formulation:

$$LG = M\left(\sum \frac{1}{1 + (d_{ij}/d_0)^2} - \frac{N_{gap}}{2}\right)$$

Here $M = 20$, d_{ij} is the distance between equivalent residues i and j *(the summation is performed over all pairs)*, d_0 is the distance cutoff (5 Å) and N_{gap} is the total number of internal gaps in the alignment. Thus, the LG-score represents the score of the best alignment found by the algorithm. The LG-score can be transformed into a statistical significance score or P-value, independent of protein size, by comparison to a distribution of scores from random alignments of unrelated proteins.

MaxSub

MaxSub (Siew *et al.*, 2000) identifies the largest subset of Cα atoms of a protein structure model that can be superposed correctly on the equivalent atoms of a reference structure. Given the complexity of the process, the maximal superposition needs to be found by an heuristical algorithm. MaxSub uses a sliding window of a certain size (usually 4 residues) to compare equivalent residues in an initial residue-based alignment. In each comparison step, the algorithm adds the residues that are within a distance threshold of each other (3.5 Å by default) to the largest subset found so far, recalculating the superposition of this set and removing those residues that exceed the threshold afterwards. When the algorithm converges to a global alignment, a single, normalized score S is calculated as:

$$S = \left(\sum_i^N \frac{1}{1 + \left(\frac{d_i}{d}\right)^2}\right)/q$$

Here d_i is the distance between the i-th equivalent Cα atoms and d is the distance threshold for the comparison; the sum is performed over all residues i in the largest aligned subset and normalized by q, the number of Cα in the reference structure. The MaxSub S score ranges from 0 when no superimposable atoms are found to 1 when the structures are identical.

Template Modeling score (TM-score)

TM-score (Zhang and Skolnick, 2004) was designed as a size-independent, normalized and alignment-based variation of the LG-score. After optimal superposition of the model and reference structures, the TM-score is calculated almost identically to the MaxSub S score, but with the threshold d replaced by a d_0 scale factor. Therefore, the distances between all residues aligned to the reference structure are considered (instead of only those with $d_i < d$ as in MaxSub), giving stronger weights to close contacts. TM-scores are within the range (0,1] with higher scores indicating more similarity. It was found empirically that TM-scores < 0.20 correspond to random alignments, while TM-scores > 0.50 indicate a conserved fold.

Local-Global alignment (LGA)

LGA (Zemla, 2003) was designed to provide the best global superposition between two structures while simultaneously finding their regions of local similarity, either with or without the use of an alignment to define equivalent residues. LGA applies two complementary algorithms, LCS and GDT (see below), to identify continuous segments of superimposable residues and to provide the largest superimposable sets of residues, respectively. Their similarity scores are linearly combined in the scoring function LGA_S, which allows selection and ranking of similar regions and helps in evaluating the total level of structural similarity.

Longest continuous segments (LCS)

LCS Identifies the longest fragment of connected residues within the predicted model for which the RMSD against the target is below certain thresholds (1 Å, 2 Å and 5 Å are generally selected). The use of several RMSD cutoffs allows detailed inspection of local similarities that may go unnoticed under a unique value.

Global distance test (GDT)

Given two structures, GDT finds the largest set of residues in common that fit under a predefined distance threshold. Since the residues do not need to be connected to each other, this is a measure of whole structure similarity. The algorithm starts by obtaining the RMSD and a superposition of all continuous segments identified by LCS, plus all possible segments of three, five or seven residues. Then, it iteratively extends the list of equivalent residues by adding all those that fit under the chosen thresholds. Typical values are in the range of 0.5–10.0 Å, with a step of 0.5 Å. Many variants of the GDT score can be applied. To provide a single-value description of structural similarity, the Global Distance Test Total Score (GDT_TS) (Cristobal *et al.*, 2001) was defined as the average of GDT calculations at 1 Å, 2 Å, 4 Å and 8 Å cutoffs:

$$GDT_TS = (GDT_{1Å} + GDT_{2Å} + GDT_{4Å}GDT_{8Å})/4Å$$

Therefore, GDT_TS represents the average coverage of the reference structure by all common substructures. It has become the *de facto* version of GDT, although a stricter High Accuracy variant (GDT_HA), where the cutoffs are reduced in half, is also frequently observed. It also provides a standard of quality in CASP, where the correlation to the GDT_TS has been used to evaluate model quality assessment methods.

Dali

Dali (Holm and Laakso, 2016) has been a reference method for protein structure comparison for the last two decades (Holm and Sander, 1993). The program and its web server version search for the largest common substructure between two structures (e.g., a model and a reference conformation) to calculate a suboptimal alignment. This is built by comparing the distance matrices of all-versus-all Cα contacts in each structure, building up from elementary patterns such as hexapeptides. The significance of the structural similarity between two structures A and B is measured by a unique quantity, called Z-score, defined as

$$Z = \frac{S(A, B) - \mu(N)}{\sigma(N)}$$

Here, $S(A,B)$ is the sum over all pairs of residues in the common substructure of A and B, of a custom pairwise similarity score that accounts for the distance between residues (see Supplementary material in Holm and Rosenström (2010) for more details). $\mu(N)$ and $\sigma(N)$ represent the mean and standard deviation of the S scores, respectively, averaged for different protein lengths. A structural alignment is considered significantly different from a random alignment when $Z > 2$. Therefore, the Z-score represents a relative measure of structural similarity that, while not directly useful to compare unrelated structures, can be taken as a quantitative indicator of the 'native-likeness' of a protein model with respect to a native structure.

local distance difference test (lDDT)

lDDT (Mariani *et al.*, 2013) provides a score of local distance differences between a model and one (or many) reference structures, without the need of superposing the structures in advance. To achieve this, lDDT calculates all pairwise interatomic distances between residues that are found below a certain threshold in each structure. The final lDDT score is the average fraction of conserved interatomic distances at thresholds 0.5 Å, 1 Å, 2 Å and 4 Å. Since the distances are evaluated per atom, both local (residue-based) and global scores can be determined.

CAD-score

CAD-score (Olechnovič *et al.*, 2013) evaluates atomic-level contact area differences (CAD) in physical contacts between a model and a reference structure of a macromolecule, including proteins and nucleic acids. Each of the contact areas, modelled from a Voronoi tessellation of the structure, contain a Cα and all points of the protein surface closer to this than to any other Cα. The analysis can comprise the whole structure or just an interface. Both local and global scores are provided and allow all pairwise comparisons between all-atom contacts, contacts of atoms in side chains or contacts involving main chain atoms only.

Single-model and quasi-single-model MQAP

MolProbity

MolProbity (Davis *et al.*, 2004) is a web-server and standalone suite of programs for local and global validation of both protein and nucleic acid structures. Its signature feature is the calculation of the number of steric clashes, defined by overlaps ≥ 0.4 Å, and its proportion per thousand residues (the "clash score") (Word *et al.*, 1999). It can be used to identify weak or missing hydrogen bonds where expected, unusual van der Waals contacts leading to under- or over-packing and deviations of covalent bond lengths and angles in any 3D structure. It provides additional protein-specific validations like Ramachandran analysis, assessment of peptide bond angles and cis-peptides and identification of unexpected beta-carbon geometries and side-chain rotamers. Some of these scores have been incorporated into the Structure Validation Reports, available for the structures deposited at the worldwide Protein Data Bank websites (Read *et al.*, 2011).

ProQ

ProQ (Wallner and Elofsson, 2003) and several of its variants have been among the top performers in many of the CASP competitions. The original method introduced the ability to predict the quality of a protein structure model, aiming to separate correct models among many incorrect alternatives. ProQ trains a neural network to estimate the values of typical structural similarity measures that would be achieved by a protein model if it were compared with a reference structure. In particular, ProQ informs the expected values of the LG-score and the MaxSub score. Training is based on several structural features that can be calculated from any single protein structure, both at local level (interatomic and residue contacts) and more globally (solvent accessibility, secondary structure, overall shape). Although ProQ provides a global quality score, it was later extended for local prediction with the ProQres method (Wallner and Elofsson, 2006).

ProQ2 (Ray *et al.*, 2012) is based on the same ideas of ProQ, but successfully improved to be the top performing method in different benchmarks (Uziela and Wallner, 2016). In ProQ2, an update and extension of sequence and structure features was combined with individual weighting of all residues based on evolutionary profiles obtained from sequence alignments. This enables a local prediction of quality represented by the *S*-score, originally by Levitt and Gerstein, but calculated here for each residue i with a distance cutoff $d_i = 3$ Å, as follows:

$$S_i = \frac{1}{1 + (d_i/d_0)^2}$$

The local scores for all residues are averaged to yield a global quality measure of correctness in the range [0,1].

The latest versions of ProQ achieve a better assessment of model quality by incorporating methods of machine learning based on deep learning from input parameters. Different approaches have been developed, with ProQ3 (Uziela *et al.*, 2016) using Support Vector Machines (SVMs) and ProQ3D (Uziela *et al.*, 2017) applying a deep neural network. Both ProQ3 and ProQ3D combine the input features used in ProQ2 with two energy potentials taken from the Rosetta ab initio modeling suite (Leaver-Fay *et al.*, 2011): one potential is based on all atoms for greater accuracy, while the other only considers simplified side-chain representations to account for incomplete models.

MESHI-Score

MESHI-Score (Mirzaei *et al.*, 2016) is a machine learning method that aims to predict the real GDT_TS score of a protein model, based on the combination of estimates of numerous structural features made by an extensive number of predictors. ~80,000 decoys from the latest CASP experiments were used to train more than a thousand prediction functions. Each predictor was trained on a non-linear combination of 15 features selected at random from pairwise energy potentials, bond lengths and angles, solvation, radius of gyration, protein frustration, compatibility of predicted and observed secondary structure and solvent accessibility, etc. To predict the quality of a decoy, it is first regularized to correct structure or energy inconsistencies, and their structural features are then fed to the predictors for determination of the individual scores. The weighted median of these scores constitute the MESHI-Score global assessment of quality.

SVMQA

SVMQA (Manavalan and Lee, 2017) is a single-model global quality assessment program based on support vector machines. These have been trained on target domain from previous CASP experiments to predict TM-score and GDT_TS. The prediction is performed through a combination of 8 statistical potential energy terms and an estimation of the compatibility between 11 structural features predicted from sequence and observed in the model. If a set of alternative models is provided, SVMQA can both rank the models and select the best from a given subset.

ModFOLD

ModFOLD (McGuffin, 2007) was originally developed as a single-model quality assessment method. The evaluation was performed with an artificial neural network trained to predict TM-score as a measure of quality, using a combination of outputs from ProQ, the ModCHECK method for assessing sequence-structure compatibility using threading potentials (Pettitt *et al.*, 2005) and the ModSSEA method based on the alignment of secondary structure elements that were predicted in the target and observed in the model (McGuffin, 2007). After further improvements (McGuffin, 2009), ModFOLD3 (Roche *et al.*, 2014) pioneered the development of quasi-single MQAPs for local and global validation, using ModFOLDclust2 to compare the structure of interest with alternative models generated ad hoc. The ModFOLD3 web server has been consistently ranked among the top methods for quality assessment in recent CASP editions (Kryshtafovych *et al.*, 2014; Kryshtafovych *et al.*, 2016).

ModFOLD6 (Maghrabi and McGuffin, 2017) is the latest version of the method. Although it now works under a hybrid approach, it is still among the best performers in CASP. The neural network is now trained and applied with scores from three single-model methods (ProQ2 and the newly developed Secondary Structure Agreement, SSA, and Contact Distance Agreement,

CDA) plus three quasi-single model scoring methods (Disorder B-factor Agreement, DBA, and residue-specific versions of the ModFOLD5 and ModFOLDclust algorithms). For each model, the output is a set of improved per-residue quality scores, together with their mean value as an indicator of global quality. Two variants of ModFOLD6 were presented that differ in the criterium used for global model ranking. ModFOLD6_rank (the default option in the ModFOLD web server) optimizes the selection of models with best quality, even if their predicted scores do not resemble the observed. Instead, ModFOLD6_cor optimizes the correlation between predicted and observed global scores.

Qualitative model energy analysis (QMEAN)

The QMEAN scoring function (Benkert et al., 2008) is used to derive local and global quality assessments for single structure models. It is formulated as a linear combination of four statistical potentials covering the local geometry and interactions within the model, with two terms describing the agreement of predicted and observed secondary structure and solvent accessibility. The global scores are expressed in the range [0,1] (with higher scores for better models). However, the QMEAN web server transforms them into statistically valid Z-scores by comparison with the expectations from a dataset of high-resolution X-ray crystallography structures. Local scores are color-coded within the same range and mapped onto each position of the sequence.

The hybrid version QMEANclust (Benkert et al., 2009) allowed the evaluation of an ensemble of alternative models via an all-against-all comparison of single-model QMEAN scores. QMEANclust calculates QMEAN scores of all models to identify the subset of highest-scoring candidates. Their pairwise distances are calculated as GDT_TS scores and then converted to global QMEANclust scores (the median of a model's GDT_TS to all others). The best models are taken again for the calculation of local consensus scores, but as the selection is now based on their QMEANclust scores, this increases the probability of analysing locally correct conformations.

Qprob/MULTICOM-NOVEL

Qprob (Cao et al., 2016a) is a novel method for quality assessment based on a statistical analysis of estimated errors in the prediction of model structure features. Besides being a standalone tool, Qprob is part of the MULTICOM suite, thus sometimes referred to as MULTICOM-NOVEL (Cao and Cheng, 2016). For each model, Qprob calculates the scores for several descriptors of secondary structure, compactness and solvent accessibility and four different energy scores, all normalized in the range [0,1] when needed. Each of these feature scores is compared with a probability density function (p.d.f.) to predict a feature-exclusive global quality score. This p.d.f. needs to be calculated from a reference set of structures. Here, the same features were extracted from many CASP9 decoy sets and contrasted with the real GDT_TS score against the target structure. Assuming a normal distribution of the differences between predicted and observed scores, their mean and standard deviation are obtained and used for the calculation of the p.d.f. Finally, a weighted combination of the predicted scores for all 11 features provides a single score taken as global estimator of model quality.

A mixed approach (Cao et al., 2014a) was also designed to improve the selection of good models by identifying them with a comprehensive selection of quality assessment methods, combined with a clustering procedure to ensure diversity among the selected models. Decoys were scored by combining 14 single-model quality assessment methods such as ProQ2 and Qprob/MULTICOM-NOVEL, plus clustering methods like Pcons and ModFOLDclust. The average scores from all MQAPs and from six selected methods are used together with a clustering procedure to select the top five and sufficiently diverse models.

MetaMQAP

MetaMQAP (Pawlowski et al., 2008) is a meta-server that predicts the local and global structural deviation of a model against the real (and possibly unknown) structure. It uses a machine learning approach, based on a multivariate linear regression model originally trained on CASP5 and CASP6 datasets, to combine the output of several MQAPs and local structure descriptors. The regression model is applied on selected residues to avoid prediction biases from trivial features like accessibility, hydrophobicity, secondary structure, etc. MetaMQAPII, the latest version of this program, reports a score that predicts the absolute deviation of each Cα atom against the equivalent atom in the putative reference structure.

VoroMQA

VoroMQA (Olechnovič and Venclovas, 2017) is an all-atom statistical potential-based MQAP built on the same principles than the CAD-score, but without the need for a reference structure. Observed interactions within the protein and inferred contacts with solvent atoms are described by contact areas instead of the commonly used atom distances. VoroMQA provides a normalized score at the atomic, residue and global levels.

Consensus MQAP

Pcons

Pcons (Lundström et al., 2001; Wallner and Elofsson, 2007) was the first automated consensus method in CASP. Given a structure of interest, a set of alternative models is obtained from several public servers for fold recognition. Models from different servers are collectively compared to identify common structural patterns which would be more likely to be correct. In this regard, it is similar to the once popular but now discontinued 3D-Jury method (Ginalski et al., 2003), but the structural superposition is performed in Pcons using the Levitt-Gerstein algorithm. The models are ranked using a neural network approach that predicts the residue-based S-score of model quality and its global average, as in Section ProQ.

ModFOLDclust

When many models of a target protein are available, ideally built with several alternative modeling methods, ModFOLDclust (McGuffin and Roche, 2010) would probably offer the most accurate local and global quality assessment results among all the ModFOLD-derived methods. The original ModFOLDclust algorithm adapted the 3D Jury method (Ginalski *et al.*, 2003), just like Pcons, and later incorporated per-residue quality scores. ModFOLDclust2 is the faster and still accurate current version of the method. It combines (by averaging) the scores from ModFOLDclust with the scores provided by ModFOLDclustQ, a variant that uses the Q estimate of structural similarity based on internal residue distances (McGuffin and Roche, 2010). The high speed of the latter algorithm allows clustering of many thousands of alternative models without compromising accuracy. It is now developed as part of ModFOLD.

Pcomb

Pcomb (Larsson *et al.*, 2009) (called Wallner in CASP11) is a consensus approach for local and global quality assessment. The Pcomb score is derived from a linear combination of the scores from a single-model ProQ method (originally ProQ2, now using ProQ3) and the consensus-based predictor (ProQ and Pcons, respectively), optimized with a four-fold higher weight to the former. Pcomb-domain (Elofsson *et al.*, 2017), a slightly modified version that uses an initial definition of domains, was also developed to identify good models of individual domains that are not among the best for the whole structure.

Model Quality Assessment of RNA Structures

Validation against reference structure

Programs to calculate RMSD and other traditional measures in proteins

Like in protein quality assessment, RNA structure models can be evaluated by comparison to a reference structure taken as gold standard of native-likeness. Structural distance is usually determined by typical scores for protein comparisons, most commonly Root Mean Square Deviation (RMSD), TM-score, GDT_TS and CAD-score. However, as presented in the following subsections, new programs and scoring functions were developed that not only calculate these measures, but also account for RNA-specific features like base pairing constraints. Many model-reference comparisons are alignment-based, and some programs, besides identifying equivalent residues, provide different similarity measures that help to assess the quality of the predicted models (see for example Rclick).

iFoldRNA

Besides its main goal of providing RNA folding simulations, the iFoldRNA web server (Hajdin *et al.*, 2010) can be used to estimate the statistical significance of an RMSD value. This is achieved by computing the RMSD *P*-value against a pre-calculated distribution of RMSDs obtained from conformational space sampling of RNA molecules using replica-exchange discrete molecular dynamics. These RMSD are normally distributed, with a mean dependent on the length of the molecule and whether base pairing constraints were considered or not. *P*-values > 0.01 can be taken as successful predictions in which RNA models are better than those expected by chance.

RNAlyzer

RNAlyzer (Lukasiak *et al.*, 2013) is a standalone application that facilitates a quantitative and visual evaluation of RNA structure models by contrast to a reference structure. For every nucleotide of the reference structure, the program defines the set of atoms in the whole structure that are located inside a sphere of a certain radius and centered on a user-selected atom (either P, C1′, O5′ or O3′). These are superposed with their equivalent atoms from the model and the RMSD between them is determined. The comparison can be based on all atoms or restricted to a selected type.

RNAlyzer uses increasing sphere radii to simultaneously plot the structural distance between multiple models and the reference structure at different accuracy levels, thus describing the change in prediction quality from local environments to the whole structure. Multiple-model plots allow visual ranking of the predicted models, while detailed individual representations are available for nucleotide-specific inspection of prediction quality. RNAlyzer remains one of the few methods for local evaluation of RNA structure models.

RNAssess

RNAssess (Lukasiak *et al.*, 2015) is a web server built on the RNAlyzer framework by the same authors, adding the convenience of an online resource. Like RNALyzer, it provides a continuous comparison of predicted and known structures from local to global environments, with multi-model and single-model plots available for a detailed quality assessment. A defining feature of RNAssess is that several metrics can be applied for a tailored comparison against the reference structure. In particular, it provides direct access to Deformation Index and Deformation Profile, two useful similarity metrics designed specifically for RNA structures that have been adopted for the official ranking of models submitted to RNA-Puzzles (Miao *et al.*, 2017).

Deformation index (DI)

The Deformation Index (Parisien *et al.*, 2009) is a normalization of the RMSD by the base Interaction Network Fidelity (INF), which accounts for the accuracy in predicted base-pair and base-stacking interactions:

$$DI = \frac{RMSD}{INF}$$

The complete sets of interactions between nucleotides in each of the structures are compared by set theory operations to build a confusion matrix of True and False predictions. This is used to compute INF as the Matthews Correlation Coefficient (MCC), a measure of quality for binary classifications that equals 1 when the model reproduces the exact base interactions found in the reference (and consequently, $DI = RMSD$) and approaches 0 (with DI tending to infinite) as the number of shared interactions diminishes.

Deformation profile (DP)

The Deformation Profile (Parisien *et al.*, 2009) consists of a distance matrix of size $N \times M$, where N and M are the lengths of the model and reference structures, respectively. Taken in turns, each pair of equivalent nucleotides is optimally superposed, affecting the relative positioning of all other nucleotides. In each step, the average distances between all corresponding nucleotides are calculated. The resulting RMSD values are stored as one row of the matrix; its average value would be indicative of local similarity around the nucleotide. Similarly, average values of each column would suggest if the distance between the pair of nucleotides is highly dependent on the prediction quality of all other nucleotides. The main diagonal stores the average atomic distance of each nucleotide. Defined this way, DP values can simultaneously suggest similarity at different scales, with the global DP score simply computed as the average distance between a model and the reference structure.

Mean of circular quantities (MCQ4Structures)

MCQ4Structures (Zok *et al.*, 2014) implements the Mean of Circular Quantities (MCQ) algorithm. It was designed to assess similarity based on a reduced trigonometric depiction of RNA structure where every nucleotide is only represented by eight torsion angles. MCQ shows the dissimilarity between two RNA structures, computed from the distances between each pair of equivalent torsion angles (see extended definition and formula in Zok *et al.* (2014)). Thus, MCQ is a distance measure, with greater MCQ values showing more structural differences.

Longest Continuous Segments in Torsion Angle space (LCS-TA) (Wiedemann *et al.*, 2017) is an extension of the MCQ algorithm that allows identification of the longest contiguous segment with significant local similarity between two structures. For any pair of segments compared, a certain MCQ maximum threshold should be defined by the user to address if their sets of torsion angles are similar. LCS-TA informs the MCQ score of the longest segment under this threshold, its location within both structures and its length (called LCS) serving as a measure of local similarity. LCS-TA has been implemented as part of the MCQ4 Structures application by the same group.

Rclick

Rclick (Nguyen and Verma, 2015; Nguyen *et al.*, 2017) extends the CLICK algorithm (Nguyen *et al.*, 2011; Nguyen and Madhusudhan, 2011), designed for optimal protein structure superposition, to the alignment of pairs of RNA structures. It can be used to provide a set of alignment-based statistics representing the RNA model-reference structural similarity. Rclick reduces the structures to sets of three to seven nucleotide residues, each represented by one or more points in space, and in which all possible interconnections are considered. These sets, or cliques (a term borrowed from graph theory), are subjected to a least squares fit to identify and superpose equivalent residues between the structures. Since the connectivity between residues is not relevant for clique matching, Rclick works as a topology-independent alignment program. The output of the Rclick server informs the RMSD and structure overlap (number of equivalent positions within 4 Å) between the optimally aligned structures. These are common structural similarity measures that are also presented by other RNA structure alignment tools such as SETTER (Cech *et al.*, 2012). More importantly, Rclick calculates a Fragment Score, which becomes maximum when all equivalent fragments are contiguous in both sequences, plus a Topology Score that is maximized when the matched fragments have the same directionality.

Single-model and Quasi-single-model MQAP

MolProbity

MolProbity (Davis *et al.*, 2007) provides several automatic analyses of local and global quality for different types of biological structures. It was already covered before for the assessment of protein structure models. Besides general assessments for both proteins and nucleic acids, evaluation of backbone conformations and incorrectly modelled ribose sugar puckers is also available for single RNA structures.

Consensus MQAP

Fragment assembly of RNA with full-atom refinement (FARFAR)

FARFAR (Das *et al.*, 2010) is an extension of the original FARNA protocol (Das and Baker, 2007) based on the Rosetta methodology for ab initio modeling (Leaver-Fay *et al.*, 2011). It includes a novel and more descriptive force field which allows prediction and assessment of RNA 3D models of multiple sizes, from small motifs to complex folds. FARFAR, like many others, generates sets of decoys that can be clustered according to fold similarity to select groups of native-like models. A clustering procedure was developed to select the largest cluster of lowest-energy structures with less structural divergence among them (Cheng *et al.*, 2015). By setting an appropriate RMSD threshold within each cluster it is possible to control the allowed variability of the modeling procedure and thus estimate its predictive accuracy.

WebRASP

WebRASP (Norambuena *et al.*, 2013) is an online implementation of the standalone Ribonucleic Acids Statistical Potential (RASP), a knowledge-based, distance-dependent pairwise contact potential for RNA structures (Capriotti *et al.*, 2011). The

WebRASP server calculates the total energy score, the normalized energy per contact and the energy profile per site for a single RNA structure. Its output allows visual mapping of energy scores, coded by color gradients, onto the RNA structure. Since the energy scores do not have a direct correlation with prediction quality, it works as a consensus-based MQAP in which all models under scrutiny should be run and later ranked manually for a comparative determination of the best predictions.

3dRNAscore

3dRNAscore (Wang et al., 2015) is an empirical potential for RNA structure evaluation. Its contact potential adds the contribution of RNA base-stacking between adjacent nucleotide residues to total energy calculations. Moreover, it also contemplates the stability effect of backbone torsion dihedral angles, which are directly related with RNA structure flexibility.

The latest version of the 3dRNA web server (Wang et al., 2017) implements 3dRNAscore for a consensus assessment and ranking of its own predicted RNA models. The models are built from their secondary structure elements, selecting from a template library of helices and loop conformations which are later assembled into a complete tertiary structure. Further refinement by simulated annealing is performed, including the use of co-evolutionary information by Direct Coupling Analysis (DCA) (Morcos et al., 2011; Weinreb et al., 2016) to contemplate direct interactions between nucleotides. The final models are clustered by the density-based DBSCAN method (Ester et al., 1996) that groups close structures together. 3dRNAscan is applied to all models in the five most populated clusters to select the best model from each of them.

Analysis and Assessment

Validation against Reference Structure

RMSD has been commonly used to quantify dissimilarity between two or more biomolecular structures, and therefore, it also became a method of choice for validation of protein and RNA models when the reference structure is known. Despite its simplicity and convenience, it is hardly the best option, with many known flaws such as the dependence on protein length and structure resolution (Carugo, 2007). Recognizing these limitations, the community has developed alternative and improved measures (which, unfortunately, still lack the wide adoption of the traditional RMSD, especially outside the community of experts in structural bioinformatics.) Among these is the RMSD_100, a normalization of the RMSD to reflect the expected value if the structures under comparison were 100 residues (Carugo and Pongor, 2001). In the last years, the more accurate GDT_TS score is becoming commonplace, being used as the default measure to quantify the performance in prediction of CASP participants since its third edition. Like many of the novel approaches, it was designed to find the most conserved substructure. LG-score was probably the first measure of structural similarity specifically proposed to overcome known drawbacks of traditional distances measures like the RMSD. It has had a great impact on the field, being incorporated with modifications into several other popular MQAPs like MaxSub and LGA. TM-score was first proposed as a method to evaluate structural templates for comparative modeling, under the premise that template correctness would be correlated with the measured quality of final full-length models. This role has been surpassed and TM-score is now a standard method to quantify global pairwise structural similarity.

These better methods are not without known flaws. Despite being the official measure in CASP for the last two decades, the uncertainty of GDT_TS calculations has only been estimated very recently (Li et al., 2016). Also, although they are less biased than the RMSD, both the similarity scores GDT and MaxSub still show some dependency on protein length (Zhang and Skolnick, 2004). In fact, MaxSub is more likely to give a good score when the reference structure is short, while the LG-score would tend to be good for comparisons against long structures (Wallner and Elofsson, 2003). (These contrasting behaviours were cleverly combined in the development of the single-model method ProQ, with its different versions being among the best performers in many CASP editions.) A common limitation of all these methods is the need for a subjective distance threshold for selecting pairs of residues to compare, which are hard to justify and customize sensibly.

Many methods for comparison against a reference structure aim to identify the number of equivalent residues and the deviation between the superposed structures. These two scores are hard to optimize simultaneously. The assessment has often been done on Cα differences alone, to account for conserved folds, but leaving non-Cα out of the comparison oversees differences in almost 90% of the atoms that constitute a protein model (Keedy et al., 2009). It is expected that in good models, the overall fold similarity would compensate for highly flexible regions. Superposition-based scores like RMSD and GDT may not provide adequate measurements of quality for good models that are only partly correct. A unique global score would tend to average the comparison and miss atomic-level discrepancies, but at the same time, local structural differences would inflate the global dissimilarity score. Given the case of multi-domain proteins, treating the structures as rigid bodies does not allow consideration of changes in the relative orientation of domains, affecting the reliability of global scores. Flexible superpositions can overcome this limitation, but would only be able to provide good local or domain-based scores of long superposed substructures. Applying non-rigid-body scoring schemes would be a sensible option in those cases, and for that reason lDDT, CAD and SphereGrinder (Antczak et al., 2015) have been incorporated as novel reference measures for evaluation of MQAPs from CASP11 (Kryshtafovych et al., 2016). lDDT has also been the default measure in the CAMEO project (Haas et al., 2017), since an automated and continuous quality assessment protocol should be robust under different scenarios. Besides, DALI and CE can provide an alternative to superposition by comparing intra-structure residue-residue distances.

The previous methods are based on comparisons of general properties against a reference structure. They can be tailored to evaluate similarity between pairs of structures of most biomolecules, including RNA models that are usually assessed by RMSD, GDT or CAD-score. RNA-specific methods are designed to contemplate special features of RNA structure that allow a more meaningful discrimination, even among models showing similar RMSD to a reference structure. For example, the Deformation Index incorporates the evaluation of nucleotide residue interactions commonly observed in RNA structures. Organizers of the RNA-Puzzles experiments recognized the outstanding need to develop new criteria for the comparative assessment of RNA structure models at different levels, from local to global, while considering the structural topology, torsion angles, and bond angles and lengths (Miao et al., 2017). There are methods such as RNAlyzer that use RMSD to evaluate the global quality of structure models but also offers details on local environments. These could be of great importance for functional RNAs like riboswitches or ribozymes where an accurate modeling of binding or active sites is particularly wanted (Lukasiak et al., 2013).

Single-model and quasi-single-model MQAP

In comparison with reference-based measures, there have been less alternatives for evaluating the quality of a model based on intrinsic properties of the model alone. This is still critical in the assessment of RNA structure models, where MolProbity is one of the few, if not the only available pure method for the analysis of individual structures. Although its clash score evaluation (Chen et al., 2010) is widely used, it is limited to the assessment of atomic distances only. Protein-based single-model methods were also uncommon, with only 5 participants in this category in CASP10 (Kryshtafovych et al., 2014). Perhaps due to this limited development, single-model MQAPs were a step behind consensus MQAPs in ranking a set of alternative models for CASP targets. This changed lately, as 22 single-model methods took part in the latest edition of CASP and brought an evident increase in performance (Kryshtafovych et al., 2017). Single-model methods are now competitive for many tasks, thanks to the use of improved energy functions and recent developments in machine learning approaches (Moult et al., 2017).

ProQ2 was among the top-ranked methods in CASP11 for the identification of the best model in a dataset, and it was also a good choice for identifying correct local features (Kryshtafovych et al., 2016). The performance of ProQ2 was improved by its newest version ProQ3 in CASP12, which saw single-model methods as the top alternatives for many analyses. The best among these surpassed top CASP11 predictors in selecting the best models out of each decoy dataset (Elofsson et al., 2017). ProQ3, together with single-model methods SVMQA and MESHI-score, have been the top performers overall in CASP12 for this task (Kryshtafovych et al., 2017). In fact, GDT-based measures recognized SVMQA as a top method for identifying good-quality models, regardless of the general approach (Manavalan and Lee, 2017). While distinguishing good from bad models is still better with consensus or quasi-single methods, the best among these use single-model approaches to derive their scores (Elofsson et al., 2017). The benefits of single-model methods are not only recognized by the systematic assessment of CASP. For example, MolProbity, which can evaluate the stereochemical properties of both protein and nucleic acids structures, is a convenient single-model method that has been recommended for the evaluation of side-chain rotamers in X-ray structures by the PDB Validation Task Force team (Read et al., 2011).

Single-model approaches are still behind quasi-single-model methods that, if dataset requirements are met, can often match the performance of consensus-based approaches. When many models are available and show a wide range of accuracy values, and they are prone to be partitioned into good and bad models, quasi-single methods can compete with consensus approaches (Kryshtafovych et al., 2014). In CASP12, estimation of the absolute global correctness of a model (measured as the difference against four reference evaluation scores such as GDT_TS) showed the quasi-single-model approach of ModFOLD6 as the best, followed closely by ProQ3 and a single-model version of MULTICOM (Kryshtafovych et al., 2017). In general, if a reliable set of multiple models is not available for consensus approaches, quasi-single model methods like ModFOLD6 could be a good choice (Kryshtafovych et al., 2017).

It should be noted that the choice of accuracy measure has a crucial impact on the comparative evaluation of the different approaches. It was seen in CASP11 that single-model methods could rank even higher if assessed by measures that consider local similarity, probably because many are built on local descriptions of geometries and energies (Kryshtafovych et al., 2016). Indeed, while GDT_TS shows a clear advantage of consensus and quasi-single based methods in model ranking, other measures like lDDT (based on local distance similarity) and CAD (which compares contact areas) highlight that model accuracy correlates best with the scores from ProQ3 and other single-based methods (Elofsson et al., 2017).

Consensus MQAP

Consensus-based MQAPs usually perform better than single-model methods and up until CASP11, the organizers reported best performances from consensus-based approaches in all categories. ModFOLDclust outperformed all other methods in predicting both global and residue-based quality in CASP8 and was also among the best in CASP9 and CASP10 (Kryshtafovych et al., 2014). QMEANclust was best ranked overall in CASP9 (Kryshtafovych et al., 2011), and other consensus-based methods like MULTICOM, QMEANClust and MetaMQAPclust achieved the top eight spots, with statistically equal performances on a per-target analysis. In CASP11, the top performance of the improved single-model method ProQ2 in selecting the best model available was matched by the clustering-based programs Pcomb and Pcons (Kryshtafovych et al., 2016). Consensus-based methods were still better than other approaches in separating correct and incorrect models in CASP12 (Elofsson et al., 2017). Pcomb showed a statistically better performance than most other methods, followed closely by other consensus-based alternatives. In CASP11 and CASP12, local accuracy was generally better predicted by consensus-based approaches, such as Pcons and ModFOLDclust (Kryshtafovych et al., 2016; Elofsson et al., 2017), which were also significantly better than all other methods in assigning per-residue error estimates. Together with Pcomb, they were the top ranked methods for separating good from bad regions of the models (Kryshtafovych et al., 2017).

The scarcity of non-comparative methods for RNA model quality assessment affects the progress of the field and our understanding of its strengths and limitations. Although no comprehensive analysis has been performed, organizers of the RNA-Puzzles experiments highlighted the advantages of applying a set of metrics that evaluate different structural characteristics for a broader assessment of RNA models (Miao et al., 2017). Following this path, it is expected that integrative consensus-based approaches such as the implemented in the 3DRNA web server could provide the best assessments in the near future.

It is clear from the previous paragraphs that consensus-based methods are generally a good choice for model assessment, but they should not be applied lightly. There are certain caveats associated with their design or performance that may lead to the adoption of other methods better suited for the task at hand. Most consensus-based methods are not intended to assess multi-domain protein models, as they would systematically give higher scores to suboptimal models of the complete structure than to better structures of individual domains. This could become a major issue as modeling methods are now more capable of predicting structures in complex, which are particularly difficult for experimental determination.

An independent assessment by MULTICOM authors showed consensus-based approaches could fail when low-quality models dominate the dataset, especially if many of them are similar to each other (Cao et al., 2014a). In such a scenario it is expected to find a high proportion of bad models, generally within a broad distribution of quality scores, and clustering methods would perform badly since most structures would resemble a low-quality consensus (Moult et al., 2017). The performance of consensus methods (and quasi-single methods too) seems to depend on the existence of best models which scores are much better than the rest (Kryshtafovych et al., 2016). This may all explain why single-model method like SVMQA gave a top performance in CASP12, in which many of the protein targets were difficult to predict (Manavalan and Lee, 2017). Limiting the analysis to hard targets from CASP7 and CASP8 also showed their behaviour was relatively on par with that of single-model methods (Cozzetto et al., 2009).

On the practical side, consensus-based methods would become much slower than single-model methods as the number of models in the dataset grows (Cao et al., 2016a). Although just 20 models were found sufficient for the top performance of consensus-based methods in CASP8 (Cozzetto et al., 2009), the end user may need to generate many more models to achieve a wide spread of quality values (Kryshtafovych et al., 2014). Therefore, consensus-based methods may not be the best available option for researchers that need to assess the global or local quality of a single model to allow its functional analysis.

Discussion

The field of quality assessment of protein and RNA structure models has been making steady progress for more than three decades. Some well-performing MQAPs are now unavailable, like the promising methods MQAPsingle (quasi-single) (Pawlowski et al., 2016) and MetaMQAPclust (consensus-based) (Pawlowski and Bujnicki, 2012), and the clustering methods MUFOLD-QA and MUFOLD-WQA (Zhang et al., 2011) that were among the best in CASP9 (Kryshtafovych et al., 2011). Fortunately, and although with varying levels of success, current MQAPs still comprise several useful methodologies and approaches.

Model assessment is usually performed by comparison against a reference. It is important to recall that experimentally solved structures are also scientific models, based on the interpretation of empirical data, and thus they are not necessarily a faithful representation of reality (Mackay et al., 2017). Quality assessment protocols that rely on comparisons with a reference structure should be taken cautiously. As most similarity measures (like GDT_TS or TM-score) may not have a direct relationship with native-likeness, the best models ranked by such measures might not necessarily resemble real structures.

Typical tools for the analysis of individual structures like Verify3D and Prosa, which have long been used for the evaluation of structures obtained from experimental techniques, have now been outperformed by some of the best modern MQAPs like ModFOLD and ProQ, according to certain analyses (Haas et al., 2017). Both single- or multi-model methods could provide the best assessment of structural models depending on the task at hand, although no method is ideal. Many MQAPs have been developed to distinguish between native and non-native structures, but as mentioned above, structural modeling could be such a hard task that even the best models may fail to describe the native state. Other MQAP have been designed to find the best available models even in these complicated scenarios. The CASP experiments demonstrated that regardless of the approach, not even the best MQAPs could consistently perform well for every protein (Kryshtafovych and Fidelis, 2009). While some methods could succeed in picking the best available structures, they may perform poorly in ranking all models in a decoy set, or vice versa (Kryshtafovych et al., 2014).

As a cautionary note, it should be highlighted that scores derived from MQAPs must behave as a true metric to allow a fair and predictable comparison of alternative models. This has often not been respected, as illustrated by a well-established method such as the Z-score provided by Dali (Adams and Naylor, 2003). Its formulation is such that two independent pairs of identical structures could receive different Z-scores, violating a basic premise of a similarity metric.

Future Directions

The field of model quality assessment is heading to improved and more capable methods. Several metrics based on GDT_TS were already proposed to capture differences beyond Cα atoms (Keedy et al., 2009) and we could expect others to integrate independent assessments of both local and global similarity. Some of the new MQAP may revisit typical assets in structural analysis like evolutionary information. It has only been incorporated into MQAPs as site-specific residue conservation data extracted from sequence databases. ConQuass (Kalman and Ben-Tal, 2010), now deprecated, tried to determine the correlation between the observed amino acids at each site with the model structure. We developed the BeEP server (Palopoli *et al.*, 2013), an MQAP that estimates the correspondence between the substitution pattern simulated under the structural constraints imposed by a protein model and its observed evolutionary history. We expect the explicit use of evolutionary information, as implemented in BeEP, as a clear path towards the advancement of existing programs.

Novel methods should be able to handle special cases of biomolecules like membrane proteins or small RNAs. MQAPs are crucial here since computational models of these structures are usually difficult to obtain with confidence. Unfortunately, these models are still hard to assess by common methods which are not parameterized for their unique characteristics. Advances are being made, as in ProQM-resample (Wallner, 2014) and QMEANBrane (Studer *et al.*, 2014) which allow for the specific assessment of transmembrane protein models.

The last years have seen the development of methods that depart from traditional approaches. The current advancement of deep learning techniques promises a substantial improvement in computational methods for biological research. Model quality assessment programs are not exempt from this trend, with new methods like SMOQ (Cao *et al.*, 2014b), DeepQA (Cao *et al.*, 2016b) and QACon (Cao *et al.*, 2017) already matching state-of-the-art performances. Other modern approaches are also performing well and are likely to be further explored soon. Among these are the graph-based methods implemented in GMQ (Shin *et al.*, 2017), and the addition of information from homologous structures to existing quality scores by machine learning, used by the yet unpublished QMEANDisCo method that performed among the best in the latest CAMEO report (Haas *et al.*, 2017).

As the native state is better described by an ensemble of conformers, an important upcoming challenge is to account for the identification of models integrating this ensemble. They could involve from large conformational changes such as the relative rigid-body movements of large domains (Gerstein and Echols, 2004) to tiny rearrangements as derived from rotations of residues to open, close or enlarge tunnels and cavities (Gora *et al.*, 2013). Discrimination of models with such structural differences should require the development of more sophisticated methods in order to provide functional and reliable 3D models (Palopoli *et al.*, 2016; Monzon *et al.*, 2017). Although some efforts on this direction have been taken, such as with the lDDT score (Mariani *et al.*, 2013) that can take an ensemble of equivalent conformers as reference, the community still needs to widely adopt conformational diversity as a central element in quality evaluation.

Closing Remarks

Current state-of-the-art model quality assessment programs can be useful to assess structural models in real-life study cases. Although consensus-based and quasi-single methods used to perform best than pure single-model MQAPs, and they may still be preferred for local and absolute quality estimations, progress in the latter means they could now be equally or even more effective in ranking models and selecting the best ones. There is still no optimal and universal solution, however, and there's a need for novel protocols for model quality assessment that can achieve a high level of discrimination in complicated scenarios. Within this active field, we expect the strengths and weaknesses shared by successful current programs will lead to improved performances of the upcoming methods.

Acknowledgements

The author would like to thank Dr. Gustavo Parisi for his insights on this manuscript, and both him and Dr. Cristina Marino-Buslje for allowing the time to work in it. The author is Researcher of the National Scientific and Technical Research Council (CONICET) in Argentina.

See also: Applications of Ribosomal RNA Sequence and Structure Analysis for Extracting Evolutionary and Functional Insights. Biomolecular Structures: Prediction, Identification and Analyses. Engineering of Supramolecular RNA Structures. Genome-Wide Probing of RNA Structure. Natural Language Processing Approaches in Bioinformatics. Predicting RNA-RNA Interactions in Three-Dimensional Structures

References

Adams, D.C., Naylor, G.J.P., 2003. A comparison of methods for assessing the structural similarity of proteins. In: Guerra, C., Istrail, S. (Eds.), Mathematical Methods for Protein Structure Analysis and Design, Lecture Notes in Computer Science. Berlin, Heidelberg: Springer Berlin Heidelberg, pp. 109–115.

Adams, P.D., Afonine, P.V., Bunkóczi, G., *et al.*, 2010. PHENIX: A comprehensive Python-based system for macromolecular structure solution. Acta Crystallogr. D Biol. Crystallogr. 66, 213–221.

Antczak, P.L.M., Ratajczak, T., Lukasiak, P., Blazewicz, J., 2015. SphereGrinder – Reference structure-based tool for quality assessment of protein structural models. In: Proceedings of the 2015 IEEE International Conference on Bioinformatics and Biomedicine (BIBM), IEEE, pp. 665–668.

Bai, X., McMullan, G., Scheres, S.H.W., 2015. How cryo-EM is revolutionizing structural biology. Trends Biochem. Sci. 40, 49–57.

Benkert, P., Schwede, T., Tosatto, S.C., 2009. QMEANclust: Estimation of protein model quality by combining a composite scoring function with structural density information. BMC Struct. Biol. 9, 35.

Benkert, P., Tosatto, S.C.E., Schomburg, D., 2008. QMEAN: A comprehensive scoring function for model quality assessment. Proteins 71, 261–277.

Berjanskii, M., Liang, Y., Zhou, J., et al., 2010. PROSESS: A protein structure evaluation suite and server. Nucleic Acids Res. 38, W633–W640.

Berman, H.M., Westbrook, J., Feng, Z., et al., 2000. The protein data bank. Nucleic Acids Res. 28, 235–242.

Brünger, A.T., 1992. Free R value: A novel statistical quantity for assessing the accuracy of crystal structures. Nature 355, 472–475.

Bujnicki, J.M., Elofsson, A., Fischer, D., Rychlewski, L., 2001. LiveBench-1: Continuous benchmarking of protein structure prediction servers. Protein Sci. 10, 352–361.

Cao, R., Adhikari, B., Bhattacharya, D., et al., 2017. QAcon: Single model quality assessment using protein structural and contact information with machine learning techniques. Bioinformatics 33, 586–588.

Cao, R., Bhattacharya, D., Adhikari, B., Li, J., Cheng, J., 2016a. Massive integration of diverse protein quality assessment methods to improve template based modeling in CASP11. Proteins 84 (Suppl. 1), S247–S259.

Cao, R., Bhattacharya, D., Hou, J., Cheng, J., 2016b. DeepQA: Improving the estimation of single protein model quality with deep belief networks. BMC Bioinform. 17, 495.

Cao, R., Cheng, J., 2016. Protein single-model quality assessment by feature-based probability density functions. Sci. Rep. 6, 23990.

Cao, R., Wang, Z., Cheng, J., 2014a. Designing and evaluating the MULTICOM protein local and global model quality prediction methods in the CASP10 experiment. BMC Struct. Biol. 14, 13.

Cao, R., Wang, Z., Wang, Y., Cheng, J., 2014b. SMOQ: A tool for predicting the absolute residue-specific quality of a single protein model with support vector machines. BMC Bioinform. 15, 120.

Capriotti, E., Norambuena, T., Marti-Renom, M.A., Melo, F., 2011. All-atom knowledge-based potential for RNA structure prediction and assessment. Bioinformatics 27, 1086–1093.

Carugo, O., 2007. Statistical validation of the root-mean-square-distance, a measure of protein structural proximity. Protein Eng. Des. Sel. 20, 33–37.

Carugo, O., Pongor, S., 2001. A normalized root-mean-square distance for comparing protein three-dimensional structures. Protein Sci. 10, 1470–1473.

Cech, P., Svozil, D., Hoksza, D., 2012. SETTER: Web server for RNA structure comparison. Nucleic Acids Res. 40, W42–W48.

Chen, V.B., Arendall, W.B., Headd, J.J., et al., 2010. MolProbity: All-atom structure validation for macromolecular crystallography. Acta Crystallogr. D Biol. Crystallogr. 66, 12–21.

Cheng, C.Y., Chou, F.-C., Das, R., 2015. Modeling complex RNA tertiary folds with Rosetta. Methods Enzymol. 553, 35–64.

Cock, P.J.A., Antao, T., Chang, J.T., et al., 2009. Biopython: Freely available Python tools for computational molecular biology and bioinformatics. Bioinformatics 25, 1422–1423.

Coimbatore Narayanan, B., Westbrook, J., Ghosh, S., et al., 2014. The nucleic acid database: New features and capabilities. Nucleic Acids Res. 42, D114–D122.

Coutsias, E.A., Seok, C., Dill, K.A., 2004. Using quaternions to calculate RMSD. J. Comput. Chem. 25, 1849–1857.

Cozzetto, D., Kryshtafovych, A., Ceriani, M., Tramontano, A., 2007. Assessment of predictions in the model quality assessment category. Proteins 69 (Suppl. 8), S175–S183.

Cozzetto, D., Kryshtafovych, A., Tramontano, A., 2009. Evaluation of CASP8 model quality predictions. Proteins 77 (Suppl. 9), S157–S166.

Cristobal, S., Zemla, A., Fischer, D., Rychlewski, L., Elofsson, A., 2001. A study of quality measures for protein threading models. BMC Bioinform. 2, 5.

Cruz, J.A., Blanchet, M.-F., Boniecki, M., et al., 2012. RNA-Puzzles: A CASP-like evaluation of RNA three-dimensional structure prediction. RNA 18, 610–625.

Das, R., Baker, D., 2007. Automated de novo prediction of native-like RNA tertiary structures. Proc. Natl. Acad. Sci. USA 104, 14664–14669.

Das, R., Karanicolas, J., Baker, D., 2010. Atomic accuracy in predicting and designing noncanonical RNA structure. Nat. Methods 7, 291–294.

Davis, I.W., Leaver-Fay, A., Chen, V.B., et al., 2007. MolProbity: All-atom contacts and structure validation for proteins and nucleic acids. Nucleic Acids Res. 35, W375–W383.

Davis, I.W., Murray, L.W., Richardson, J.S., Richardson, D.C., 2004. MOLPROBITY: Structure validation and all-atom contact analysis for nucleic acids and their complexes. Nucleic Acids Res. 32, W615–W619.

Domagalski, M.J., Zheng, H., Zimmerman, M.D., et al., 2014. The quality and validation of structures from structural genomics. Methods Mol. Biol. 1091, 297–314.

Dutta, S., Burkhardt, K., Young, J., et al., 2009. Data deposition and annotation at the worldwide protein data bank. Mol. Biotechnol. 42, 1–13.

Eisenberg, D., Lüthy, R., Bowie, J.U., 1997. VERIFY3D: Assessment of protein models with three-dimensional profiles. In: Carter Jr., C., Sweet, R. (Eds.), Macromolecular Crystallography Part B, Methods in Enzymology. Elsevier, pp. 396–404.

Elofsson, A., Joo, K., Keasar, C., et al., 2017. Methods for estimation of model accuracy in CASP12. Proteins 86, 361–373.

Ester, M., Kriegel, H.-P., Sander, J., et al., 1996. A density-based algorithm for discovering clusters in large spatial databases with noise. In: Proceedings of the Second International Conference on Knowledge Discovery and Data Mining (KDD-96), pp. 226–231.

Eyrich, V.A., Martí-Renom, M.A., Przybylski, D., et al., 2001. EVA: Continuous automatic evaluation of protein structure prediction servers. Bioinformatics 17, 1242–1243.

Felden, B., 2007. RNA structure: Experimental analysis. Curr. Opin. Microbiol. 10, 286–291.

Gerstein, M., Echols, N., 2004. Exploring the range of protein flexibility, from a structural proteomics perspective. Curr. Opin. Chem. Biol. 8, 14–19.

Ginalski, K., Elofsson, A., Fischer, D., Rychlewski, L., 2003. 3D-Jury: A simple approach to improve protein structure predictions. Bioinformatics 19, 1015–1018.

Gora, A., Brezovsky, J., Damborsky, J., 2013. Gates of enzymes. Chem. Rev. 113, 5871–5923.

Haas, J., Barbato, A., Behringer, D., et al., 2017. Continuous automated model evaluation (CAMEO) complementing the critical assessment of structure prediction in CASP12. Proteins 86, 387–398.

Haas, J., Roth, S., Arnold, K., et al., 2013. The protein model portal – A comprehensive resource for protein structure and model information. Database 2013, bat031.

Hajdin, C.E., Ding, F., Dokholyan, N.V., Weeks, K.M., 2010. On the significance of an RNA tertiary structure prediction. RNA 16, 1340–1349.

Hennig, J., Sattler, M., 2014. The dynamic duo: Combining NMR and small angle scattering in structural biology. Protein Sci. 23, 669–682.

Holland, R.C.G., Down, T.A., Pocock, M., et al., 2008. BioJava: An open-source framework for bioinformatics. Bioinformatics 24, 2096–2097.

Holm, L., Laakso, L.M., 2016. Dali server update. Nucleic Acids Res. 44, W351–W355.

Holm, L., Rosenström, P., 2010. Dali server: Conservation mapping in 3D. Nucleic Acids Res. 38, W545–W549.

Holm, L., Sander, C., 1993. Protein structure comparison by alignment of distance matrices. J. Mol. Biol. 233, 123–138.

Hooft, R.W., Vriend, G., Sander, C., Abola, E.E., 1996. Errors in protein structures. Nature 381, 272.

Kabsch, W., 1976. A solution for the best rotation to relate two sets of vectors. Acta Cryst. A 32, 922–923.

Kalman, M., Ben-Tal, N., 2010. Quality assessment of protein model-structures using evolutionary conservation. Bioinformatics 26, 1299–1307.

Keedy, D.A., Williams, C.J., Headd, J.J., et al., 2009. The other 90% of the protein: Assessment beyond the Calphas for CASP8 template-based and high-accuracy models. Proteins 77 (Suppl. 9), S29–S49.

Kendrew, J., Bodo, G., Dintzis, H., et al., 1958. A three-dimensional model of the myoglobin molecule obtained by X-ray analysis. Nature 181, 662–666.

Kihara, D., Chen, H., Yang, Y.D., 2009. Quality assessment of protein structure models. Curr. Protein Pept. Sci. 10, 216–228.

Kinch, L.N., Li, W., Monastyrskyy, B., Kryshtafovych, A., Grishin, N.V., 2016. Evaluation of free modeling targets in CASP11 and ROLL. Proteins 84 (Suppl. 1), S51–S66.

Koh, I.Y.Y., Eyrich, V.A., Marti-Renom, M.A., et al., 2003. EVA: Evaluation of protein structure prediction servers. Nucleic Acids Res. 31, 3311–3315.

Kryshtafovych, A., Barbato, A., Fidelis, K., et al., 2014. Assessment of the assessment: Evaluation of the model quality estimates in CASP10. Proteins 82 (Suppl. 2), S112–S126.

Kryshtafovych, A., Barbato, A., Monastyrskyy, B., et al., 2016. Methods of model accuracy estimation can help selecting the best models from decoy sets: Assessment of model accuracy estimations in CASP11. Proteins 84 (Suppl. 1), S349–S369.

Kryshtafovych, A., Fidelis, K., 2009. Protein structure prediction and model quality assessment. Drug Discov. Today 14, 386–393.

Kryshtafovych, A., Fidelis, K., Tramontano, A., 2011. Evaluation of model quality predictions in CASP9. Proteins 79 (Suppl. 10), S91–S106.

Kryshtafovych, A., Monastyrskyy, B., Fidelis, K., Schwede, T., Tramontano, A., 2017. Assessment of model accuracy estimations in CASP12. Proteins 86, 345–360.

Kubota, M., Tran, C., Spitale, R.C., 2015. Progress and challenges for chemical probing of RNA structure inside living cells. Nat. Chem. Biol. 11, 933–941.

Laing, C., Schlick, T., 2010. Computational approaches to 3D modeling of RNA. J. Phys. Condens. Matter 22, 283101.

Laing, C., Schlick, T., 2011. Computational approaches to RNA structure prediction, analysis, and design. Curr. Opin. Struct. Biol. 21, 306–318.

Larsson, P., Skwark, M.J., Wallner, B., Elofsson, A., 2009. Assessment of global and local model quality in CASP8 using Pcons and ProQ. Proteins 77 (Suppl. 9), S167–S172.

Laskowski, R.A., MacArthur, M.W., Moss, D.S., Thornton, J.M., 1993. PROCHECK: A program to check the stereochemical quality of protein structures. J. Appl. Crystallogr. 26, 283–291.

Leaver-Fay, A., Tyka, M., Lewis, S.M., et al., 2011. ROSETTA3: An object-oriented software suite for the simulation and design of macromolecules. Methods Enzymol. 487, 545–574.

Levitt, M., 1976. A simplified representation of protein conformations for rapid simulation of protein folding. J. Mol. Biol. 104, 59–107.

Levitt, M., Gerstein, M., 1998. A unified statistical framework for sequence comparison and structure comparison. Proc. Natl. Acad. Sci. USA 95, 5913–5920.

Li, W., Schaeffer, R.D., Otwinowski, Z., Grishin, N.V., 2016. Estimation of uncertainties in the global distance test (GDT_TS) for CASP models. PLOS ONE 11, e0154786.

Lukasiak, P., Antczak, M., Ratajczak, T., et al., 2013. RNAlyzer – Novel approach for quality analysis of RNA structural models. Nucleic Acids Res. 41, 5978–5990.

Lukasiak, P., Antczak, M., Ratajczak, T., et al., 2015. RNAssess – A web server for quality assessment of RNA 3D structures. Nucleic Acids Res. 43, W502–W506.

Lundström, J., Rychlewski, L., Bujnicki, J., Elofsson, A., 2001. Pcons: A neural-network-based consensus predictor that improves fold recognition. Protein Sci. 10, 2354–2362.

Mackay, J.P., Landsberg, M.J., Whitten, A.E., Bond, C.S., 2017. Whaddaya know: A guide to uncertainty and subjectivity in structural biology. Trends Biochem. Sci. 42, 155–167.

Maghrabi, A.H.A., McGuffin, L.J., 2017. ModFOLD6: An accurate web server for the global and local quality estimation of 3D protein models. Nucleic Acids Res.. 45.

Maiti, R., Van Domselaar, G.H., Zhang, H., Wishart, D.S., 2004. SuperPose: A simple server for sophisticated structural superposition. Nucleic Acids Res. 32, W590–W594.

Manavalan, B., Lee, J., 2017. SVMQA: Support-vector-machine-based protein single-model quality assessment. Bioinformatics 33, 2496–2503.

Mariani, V., Biasini, M., Barbato, A., Schwede, T., 2013. lDDT: A local superposition-free score for comparing protein structures and models using distance difference tests. Bioinformatics 29, 2722–2728.

McGuffin, L.J., 2007. Benchmarking consensus model quality assessment for protein fold recognition. BMC Bioinform. 8, 345.

McGuffin, L.J., 2009. Prediction of global and local model quality in CASP8 using the ModFOLD server. Proteins 77 (Suppl. 9), S185–S190.

McGuffin, L.J., Roche, D.B., 2010. Rapid model quality assessment for protein structure predictions using the comparison of multiple models without structural alignments. Bioinformatics 26, 182–188.

McLachlan, A.D., 1982. Rapid comparison of protein structures. Acta Cryst. A 38, 871–873.

Mertens, H.D.T., Svergun, D.I., 2010. Structural characterization of proteins and complexes using small-angle X-ray solution scattering. J. Struct. Biol. 172, 128–141.

Miao, Z., Adamiak, R.W., Antczak, M., et al., 2017. RNA-puzzles Round III: 3D RNA structure prediction of five riboswitches and one ribozyme. RNA 23, 655–672.

Miao, Z., Adamiak, R.W., Blanchet, M.-F., et al., 2015. RNA-puzzles Round II: Assessment of RNA structure prediction programs applied to three large RNA structures. RNA 21, 1066–1084.

Mirzaei, S., Sidi, T., Keasar, C., Crivelli, S., 2016. Purely structural protein scoring functions using support vector machine and ensemble learning. IEEE/ACM Trans. Comput. Biol. Bioinform..

Monzon, A.M., Zea, D.J., Marino-Buslje, C., Parisi, G., 2017. Homology modeling in a dynamical world. Protein Sci. 26, 2195–2206.

Morcos, F., Pagnani, A., Lunt, B., et al., 2011. Direct-coupling analysis of residue coevolution captures native contacts across many protein families. Proc. Natl. Acad. Sci. USA 108, E1293–E1301.

Moult, J., Fidelis, K., Kryshtafovych, A., Schwede, T., Tramontano, A., 2014. Critical assessment of methods of protein structure prediction (CASP) – Round X. Proteins 82 (Suppl. 2), S1–S6.

Moult, J., Fidelis, K., Kryshtafovych, A., Schwede, T., Tramontano, A., 2016. Critical assessment of methods of protein structure prediction: Progress and new directions in Round XI. Proteins 84 (Suppl. 1), S4–S14.

Moult, J., Fidelis, K., Kryshtafovych, A., Schwede, T., Tramontano, A., 2017. Critical assessment of methods of protein structure prediction (CASP)-Round XII. Proteins 86, 7–15.

Moult, J., Pedersen, J.T., Judson, R., Fidelis, K., 1995. A large-scale experiment to assess protein structure prediction methods. Proteins 23, ii–v.

Murray, L.J.W., Arendall, W.B., Richardson, D.C., Richardson, J.S., 2003. RNA backbone is rotameric. Proc. Natl. Acad. Sci. USA 100, 13904–13909.

2011.Celebrating structural biology. Nat. Struct. Mol. Biol. 18, 1304–1316.

Nguyen, M.N., Madhusudhan, M.S., 2011. Biological insights from topology independent comparison of protein 3D structures. Nucleic Acids Res. 39, e94.

Nguyen, M.N., Sim, A.Y.L., Wan, Y., Madhusudhan, M.S., Verma, C., 2017. Topology independent comparison of RNA 3D structures using the CLICK algorithm. Nucleic Acids Res. 45, e5.

Nguyen, M.N., Tan, K.P., Madhusudhan, M.S., 2011. CLICK – Topology-independent comparison of biomolecular 3D structures. Nucleic Acids Res. 39, W24–W28.

Nguyen, M.N., Verma, C., 2015. Rclick: A web server for comparison of RNA 3D structures. Bioinformatics 31, 966–968.

Nishikawa, K., Ooi, T., 1972. Tertiary structure of proteins. II. Freedom of dihedral angles and energy calculation. J. Phys. Soc. Jpn. 32, 1338–1347.

Norambuena, T., Cares, J.F., Capriotti, E., Melo, F., 2013. WebRASP: A server for computing energy scores to assess the accuracy and stability of RNA 3D structures. Bioinformatics 29, 2649–2650.

Novotný, J., Bruccoleri, R., Karplus, M., 1984. An analysis of incorrectly folded protein models. J. Mol. Biol. 177, 787–818.

Novotný, J., Rashin, A.A., Bruccoleri, R.E., 1988. Criteria that discriminate between native proteins and incorrectly folded models. Proteins 4, 19–30.

Olechnovič, K., Kulberkytė, E., Venclovas, Č., 2013. CAD-score: A new contact area difference-based function for evaluation of protein structural models. Proteins 81, 149–162.

Olechnovič, K., Venclovas, Č., 2017. VoroMQA: Assessment of protein structure quality using interatomic contact areas. Proteins 85, 1131–1145.

Ortiz, A.R., Strauss, C.E.M., Olmea, O., 2002. MAMMOTH (matching molecular models obtained from theory): An automated method for model comparison. Protein Sci. 11, 2606–2621.

Ovchinnikov, S., Kim, D.E., Wang, R.Y.-R., et al., 2016. Improved de novo structure prediction in CASP11 by incorporating coevolution information into Rosetta. Proteins 84 (Suppl. 1), S67–S75.

Palopoli, N., Lanzarotti, E., Parisi, G., 2013. BeEP Server: Using evolutionary information for quality assessment of protein structure models. Nucleic Acids Res. 41, W398–W405.

Palopoli, N., Monzon, A.M., Parisi, G., Fornasari, M.S., 2016. Addressing the role of conformational diversity in protein structure prediction. PLOS ONE 11, e0154923.

Parisien, M., Cruz, J.A., Westhof, E., Major, F., 2009. New metrics for comparing and assessing discrepancies between RNA 3D structures and models. RNA 15, 1875–1885.

Pawlowski, M., Bujnicki, J.M., 2012. The utility of comparative models and the local model quality for protein crystal structure determination by molecular replacement. BMC Bioinform. 13, 289.

Pawlowski, M., Gajda, M.J., Matlak, R., Bujnicki, J.M., 2008. MetaMQAP: A meta-server for the quality assessment of protein models. BMC Bioinform. 9, 403.

Pawlowski, M., Kozlowski, L., Kloczkowski, A., 2016. MQAPsingle: A quasi single-model approach for estimation of the quality of individual protein structure models. Proteins 84, 1021–1028.

Pettitt, C.S., McGuffin, L.J., Jones, D.T., 2005. Improving sequence-based fold recognition by using 3D model quality assessment. Bioinformatics 21, 3509–3515.

Ray, A., Lindahl, E., Wallner, B., 2012. Improved model quality assessment using ProQ2. BMC Bioinform. 13, 224.

Read, R.J., Adams, P.D., Arendall, W.B., et al., 2011. A new generation of crystallographic validation tools for the protein data bank. Structure 19, 1395–1412.

Roche, D.B., Buenavista, M.T., McGuffin, L.J., 2014. Assessing the quality of modelled 3D protein structures using the ModFOLD server. Methods Mol. Biol. 1137, 83–103.

Sali, A., Blundell, T.L., 1993. Comparative protein modelling by satisfaction of spatial restraints. J. Mol. Biol. 234, 779–815.

Shen, M.-Y., Sali, A., 2006. Statistical potential for assessment and prediction of protein structures. Protein Sci. 15, 2507–2524.

Shin, W.-H., Kang, X., Zhang, J., Kihara, D., 2017. Prediction of local quality of protein structure models considering spatial neighbors in graphical models. Sci. Rep. 7, 40629.

Shindyalov, I.N., Bourne, P.E., 1998. Protein structure alignment by incremental combinatorial extension (CE) of the optimal path. Protein Eng. Des. Sel. 11, 739–747.

Siew, N., Elofsson, A., Rychlewski, L., Fischer, D., 2000. MaxSub: An automated measure for the assessment of protein structure prediction quality. Bioinformatics 16, 776–785.

Sippl, M.J., 1993. Recognition of errors in three-dimensional structures of proteins. Proteins 17, 355–362.

Sippl, M.J., Wiederstein, M., 2012. Detection of spatial correlations in protein structures and molecular complexes. Structure 20, 718–728.

Studer, G., Biasini, M., Schwede, T., 2014. Assessing the local structural quality of transmembrane protein models using statistical potentials (QMEANBrane). Bioinformatics 30, i505–i511.

Tsutakawa, S.E., Hura, G.L., Frankel, K.A., Cooper, P.K., Tainer, J.A., 2007. Structural analysis of flexible proteins in solution by small angle X-ray scattering combined with crystallography. J. Struct. Biol. 158, 214–223.

Uziela, K., Menéndez Hurtado, D., Shu, N., Wallner, B., Elofsson, A., 2017. ProQ3D: Improved model quality assessments using deep learning. Bioinformatics 33, 1578–1580.

Uziela, K., Shu, N., Wallner, B., Elofsson, A., 2016. ProQ3: Improved model quality assessments using Rosetta energy terms. Sci. Rep. 6, 33509.

Uziela, K., Wallner, B., 2016. ProQ2: Estimation of model accuracy implemented in Rosetta. Bioinformatics 32, 1411–1413.

Wallner, B., 2014. ProQM-resample: Improved model quality assessment for membrane proteins by limited conformational sampling. Bioinformatics 30, 2221–2223.

Wallner, B., Elofsson, A., 2003. Can correct protein models be identified? Protein Sci. 12, 1073–1086.

Wallner, B., Elofsson, A., 2006. Identification of correct regions in protein models using structural, alignment, and consensus information. Protein Sci. 15, 900–913.

Wallner, B., Elofsson, A., 2007. Prediction of global and local model quality in CASP7 using Pcons and ProQ. Proteins 69 (Suppl. 8), S184–S193.

Wang, H.-W., Wang, J.-W., 2017. How cryo-electron microscopy and X-ray crystallography complement each other. Protein Sci. 26, 32–39.

Wang, J., Mao, K., Zhao, Y., et al., 2017. Optimization of RNA 3D structure prediction using evolutionary restraints of nucleotide-nucleotide interactions from direct coupling analysis. Nucleic Acids Res. 45, 6299–6309.

Wang, J., Zhao, Y., Zhu, C., Xiao, Y., 2015. 3dRNAscore: A distance and torsion angle dependent evaluation function of 3D RNA structures. Nucleic Acids Res. 43, e63.

Weeks, K.M., Mauger, D.M., 2011. Exploring RNA structural codes with SHAPE chemistry. Acc. Chem. Res. 44, 1280–1291.

Weinreb, C., Riesselman, A.J., Ingraham, J.B., et al., 2016. 3D RNA and functional interactions from evolutionary couplings. Cell 165, 963–975.

Westbrook, J., Feng, Z., Burkhardt, K., Berman, H.M., 2003. Validation of protein structures for protein data bank. In: Carter, C.W., Sweet, R.M. (Eds.), Macromolecular Crystallography, Part D, Methods in Enzymology. Elsevier, pp. 370–385.

Wiedemann, J., Zok, T., Milostan, M., Szachniuk, M., 2017. LCS-TA to identify similar fragments in RNA 3D structures. BMC Bioinform. 18, 456.

Word, J.M., Lovell, S.C., LaBean, T.H., et al., 1999. Visualizing and quantifying molecular goodness-of-fit. Small-probe contact dots with explicit hydrogen atoms. J. Mol. Biol. 285, 1711–1733.

Wüthrich, K., 2001. The way to NMR structures of proteins. Nat. Struct. Biol. 8, 923–925.

Ye, Y., Godzik, A., 2004. FATCAT: A web server for flexible structure comparison and structure similarity searching. Nucleic Acids Res. 32, W582–W585.

Young, J.Y., Westbrook, J.D., Feng, Z., et al., 2017. OneDep: Unified wwPDB system for deposition, biocuration, and validation of macromolecular structures in the PDB archive. Structure 25, 536–545.

Zemla, A., 2003. LGA: A method for finding 3D similarities in protein structures. Nucleic Acids Res. 31, 3370–3374.

Zhang, J., Wang, Q., Vantasin, K., et al., 2011. A multilayer evaluation approach for protein structure prediction and model quality assessment. Proteins 79 (Suppl. 10), S172–S184.

Zhang, Y., Skolnick, J., 2004. Scoring function for automated assessment of protein structure template quality. Proteins 57, 702–710.

Zok, T., Popenda, M., Szachniuk, M., 2014. MCQ4Structures to compute similarity of molecule structures. Cent. Eur. J. Oper. Res. 22, 457–473.

Further Reading

Jain, S., Richardson, D.C., Richardson, J.S., 2015. Computational methods for RNA structure validation and improvement. Methods Enzymol. 558, 181–212. doi:10.1016/bs.mie.2015.01.007.

Kufareva, I., Abagyan, R., 2012. Methods of protein structure comparison. Methods Mol. Biol. 857, 231–257. doi:10.1007/978-1-61779-588-6_10.

McGuffin, L.J., 2010. Model quality prediction (Chapter 15). In: Rangwala, H., Karypis, G. (Eds.), Introduction to Protein Structure Prediction. Hoboken, New Jersey, USA: Published by John Wiley & Sons, Inc.

Miao, Z., Westhof, E., 2017. RNA structure: Advances and assessment of 3D structure prediction. Annu. Rev. Biophys. 46, 483–503. doi:10.1146/annurev-biophys-070816-034125.

Sierk, M.L., Kleywegt, G.J., 2004. Déjà Vu all over again: Finding and analyzing protein structure similarities. Structure 12, 2103–2111. doi:10.1016/j.str.2004.09.016.

Wallner, B., Elofsson, A., 2008. Quality assessment of protein models. In: Bujnicki, J.M. (Ed.), Prediction of Protein Structures, Functions, and Interactions. Chichester, UK: John Wiley & Sons, Ltd. Available at: http://dx.doi.org/10.1002/9780470741894.ch6.

Relevant Websites

http://predictioncenter.org/
CASP Protein Structure Prediction Center.
http://psvs-1_5-dev.nesg.org/
Protein Structure Validation Software suite.
http://services.mbi.ucla.edu/SAVES/
The Structure Analysis and Verification Server.
http://www.wwpdb.org/validation/validation-reports
wwPDB Validation Reports: User Guide.

Biographical Sketch

Nicolás Palopoli has been computational biologist since 2005. He studied Biotechnology at *Universidad Nacional de Quilmes* (UNQ) in Buenos Aires, Argentina, where he also got his PhD title in Basic and Applied Sciences. He was a postdoctoral research fellow at *Universidad de Buenos Aires*, Argentina and University of Southampton, UK. He recently returned to the Structural Bioinformatics Group (UNQ) as Assistant Researcher from the National Scientific and Technical Research Council of Argentina (CONICET). He is always interested in understanding the structural properties, biological function and evolutionary relationships of proteins. His current research projects involve protein-protein interactions mediated by Short Linear Motifs (SLiMs) and the special features associated with protein intrinsic disorder. He is also a patient lecturer, respectful colleague and proud husband and dad.

Study of the Variability of the Native Protein Structure

Xusi Han, Woong-Hee Shin, Charles W Christoffer, Genki Terashi, Lyman Monroe, and Daisuke Kihara, Purdue University, West Lafayette, IN, United States

Introduction

Proteins are flexible molecules. After being translated from a messenger RNA by a ribosome, a protein folds into its native structure (the structure of lowest free energy), which is suitable for carrying out its biological function. Although the native structure of a protein is stabilized by physical interactions of atoms including hydrogen bonds, disulfide bonds between cysteine residues, van der Waals interactions, electrostatic interactions, and solvation (interactions with solvent), the structure still admits flexible motions. Motions include those of side-chains, and some parts of main-chains, especially regions that do not form the secondary structures, which are often called loop regions. In many cases, the flexibility of proteins plays an important or essential role in the biological functions of the proteins. For example, for some enzymes, such as triosephosphate isomerase (Derreumaux and Schlick, 1998), loop regions that exist in vicinity of active (i.e., enzymatic reaction) sites, takes part in binding and holding a ligand molecule. Transporters, such as maltose transporter (Chen, 2013), are known to make large open-close motions to transfer ligand molecules across the cellular membrane. For many motor proteins, such as myosin V that "walk" along actin filament as observed in muscle contraction (Kodera and Ando, 2014), flexibility is the central for their functions.

Reflecting such intrinsic flexibility of protein structures, differences are observed in protein tertiary structures determined by experimental methods such as X-ray crystallography, nuclear magnetic resonance (NMR) when they are solved under different conditions. In this article, we start by introducing two studies that surveyed such structural differences of the same proteins found in the public repository of protein structures, Protein Data Bank (PDB) (Berman *et al.*, 2000), which contains over 136,000 entries at the time of writing this article (December 2017). Thus, structural variability of a protein can be observed by comparing static structures determined under different conditions. Experimentally, conformational variability can be measured by NMR and other spectroscopic techniques (Greenleaf *et al.*, 2007; Parak, 2003; Hinterdorfer and Dufrene, 2006). Alternatively, structural changes, i.e., flexibility, can be observed for a single protein structure by performing computational simulations or predictions of dynamics of the protein structure. Computational methods for elucidating protein structure flexibility are also useful for estimating the free energy of molecular interactions as well as structure refinement needed when determining protein tertiary structures. In this article we overview such computational tools with some examples of application.

Discussion in this article is focused on protein structures that have overall stable fixed structures (with some flexibility in side-chains and parts of the main-chain, e.g., loops). However, note that there is a different class of proteins that do not form stable structures at all under physiological conditions. Such proteins are called intrinsically disordered proteins (IDPs) (Dunker *et al.*, 2008). IDPs were not paid much attention for a long time since their structures cannot be determined by regular experimental structural biology methods, such as X-ray crystallography or NMR, due to their intrinsic flexibility. But from around 2000, IDPs attracted large attention as long-neglected protein structures, and have been studied extensively since then. IDPs have characteristic amino acid sequence patterns, from which IDPs can be predicted from their amino acid sequences (Ferron *et al.*, 2006). It is estimated that about 5%–30% of amino acid sequences in an organism's proteome are intrinsically disordered (Oates *et al.*, 2013). It was found that disordered regions are often responsible for establishing protein-protein interactions, especially for proteins that interact with multiple proteins. The D2P2 database (Oates *et al.*, 2013) provides predicted IDPs in over 1700 genomes by many existing IDP prediction methods.

Fundamentals

Conformational Transitions Observed in Experimentally Determined Structures

Structural variability of proteins can be observed by comparing structures that are experimentally determined in different conditions. Kosloff and Kolodny (2008) performed a systematic study on protein structure variability relative to the sequence identity including cases that two structures are 100% identical in their sequences. The dataset was comprised of 19,295 protein chains taken from the April 2005 PDB, which are longer than 35 residues and were determined at a resolution of 2.5 Å or higher using X-ray crystallography. To eliminate redundant protein chains in the dataset, no pairs have 100% sequence identity and less than 1 Å root-mean square deviation (RMSD) between each other. Out of the 1941 chain pairs with 100% sequence identity in this dataset, there were 444 (22.9%) pairs with an RMSD of 3 Å or larger and 158 (8.1%) pairs with an RMSD over 6 Å. Such cases included chain pairs that have very different structures of over a 10 Å RMSD. They classified the sources of structural dissimilarity, which included different quaternary protein-protein interactions, protein-ligand and protein-DNA/RNA interactions, different crystallization conditions such as pH or salt conditions, and alternative crystallographic conformations of the same proteins. Thus, as is also discussed in other studies (Goh *et al.*, 2004; Boehr *et al.*, 2009), one of the main reasons for the existence of alternative conformations is due to physical interactions with other molecules. Most large conformational changes observed in protein structures are inherent to their biological functions, as Gan *et al.* (2002) pointed out in their work.

 Encyclopedia of Bioinformatics and Computational Biology, Volume 3   doi:10.1016/B978-0-12-809633-8.20148-9

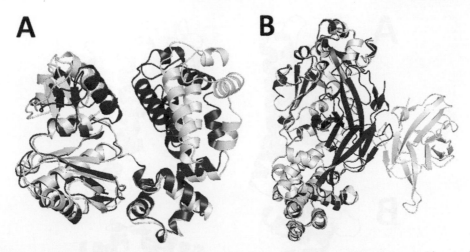

Fig. 1 Superimpositions of protein structures with a large conformational change. (A) Structure of DNA polymerase β in open (PDB ID: 9ICX, chain A, colored in light grey) and closed (PDB: 1BPY, chain A, colored in black) conformations. DNA in the crystal structures are omitted in the figure. (B) Structure of diphtheria toxin in open (PDB: 1DDT, chain A, colored in light grey) and closed (PDB: 1MDT, chain A, colored in black) conformations.

We show several examples of large conformational change of proteins. The first example is human DNA polymerase β in open and closed conformations (**Fig. 1(A)**) (Pelletier *et al.*, 1996; Sawaya *et al.*, 1997). The RMSD between the two structures is 5.3 Å. This conformational change is needed for its biological function, catalytic polymerization of nucleotides as well as binding and releasing DNA. The second example is diphtheria toxin in open and closed conformations (**Fig. 1(B)**). The RMSD is 11.0 Å (Bennett and Eisenberg, 1994). This protein has three domains, the catalytic domain, the transmembrane domain, and the C-terminus receptor binding domain. In the two structures superimposed in **Fig. 1(B)**, the arrangement of these three domains is very different. Particularly, the receptor domain shown on the right side of the figure is distant from the rest of the structure in the open conformation. This drastic conformational change is speculated to be essential for penetrating the host cell membrane, a critical step for intoxication.

Fig. 2 shows three more examples where binding with other molecule is involved in the conformational change. **Fig. 2(A)** shows structure of export chaperone FliS in *Aquifex aeolicus* (Evdokimov *et al.*, 2003). FliS acts as a flagellar export chaperone, which binds specifically to FliC to regulate its export and assembly process. The structure of unbound FliS is an antiparallel four-helix bundle (**Fig. 2(A)**, Left). The N-terminal cap blocks the hydrophobic binding site in FliS when FliC is absent. Upon complex formation with FliC, there is a substantial conformation change in FliS (**Fig. 2(A)**, Right), where the N-terminus in FliS displaces to form a short helix on one side of the bundle (on the right side of the panel), interacting with one helical segment in FliC. The RMSD between the two conformation is 6.4 Å. The next one is a textbook example, calmodulin (**Fig. 2(B)**). Calmodulin undergoes a large conformational change between the apo (i.e., non-ligand binding) state and the calcium-binding state (Yamniuk and Vogel, 2004). In calcium-free calmodulin, each globular domain is made up of four helices running in parallel/antiparallel orientations to each other (**Fig. 2(B)**, Left). In the calcium-bound form, the interdomain region forms a long α-helix (the right panel) instead of two short α-helices in the apo form. This helical rearrangement exposes hydrophobic binding patches on the surface of each domain, which binds to peptide sequences in target enzymes. The RMSD between the two structures is 12.9 Å. The last example in **Fig. 2** is RfaH, a member of a universally conserved family of transcription factors (**Fig. 2(C)**). In its closed form, RfaH C-terminal domain (CTD) forms an α hairpin that masks an RNA Polymerase binding site in RfaH N-terminal domain (NTD) (Belogurov *et al.*, 2007) (**Fig. 2(C)**, Left, the light grey region). But upon release from RfaH-NTD, RfaH-CTD refolds into a β barrel that binds to the ribosome to activate translation (the right panel) (Burmann *et al.*, 2012). The RMSD between the two structures of the RfaH-CTD is 14.0 Å. The dramatic switch from α helix to β barrel transforms the function of RfaH from transcription factor to translation factor.

Molecular Dynamics

From this subsection, we introduce several computational methods that can simulate or model structural variability of proteins.

Molecular dynamics (MD) simulation is a computer simulation technique to investigate the movement of atoms and molecules based on the principles of physics. Since its first application for biomolecules published 40 years ago (Mccammon *et al.*, 1977), it has become a popular and standard tool for studying biomolecular motion. The basic concepts of MD are (1) to divide time into discrete time steps (1 or 2 fs, generally) and (2) to solve Newton's equations of motion (Eq. (1)) at every time step:

$$F(\mathbf{x}) = -\nabla U(\mathbf{x}) = m\frac{d^2\mathbf{x}}{dt^2} \tag{1}$$

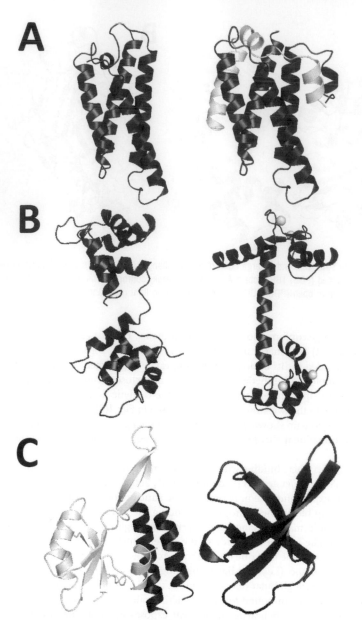

Fig. 2 Conformational transitions upon protein-ligand interactions. (A) Structure of FliS in unbound state (PDB: 1ORJ, chain A, left panel) and bound state (PDB :1ORY, right panel). FliC is colored in light grey in the FliS-FliC complex. (B) Structure of calmodulin in the unbound state (PDB: 1DMO, chain A) and the calcium-binding state (PDB: 1CLL, chain A). Calcium ions in the crystal structure are shown as spheres colored in light grey on the right panel. (C) Structure of full-length RfaH in closed form (PDB: 2OUG, chain A) and RfaH C terminal domain in open form (PDB 2LCL, chain A). RfaH N terminal domain is colored in light grey in the closed state (left).

$F(\mathbf{x})$, $U(\mathbf{x})$, $\mathbf{x}$, and m are a force, a potential energy, a coordinate of an atom, and a mass of an atom, respectively. Since the system is composed of a number of atoms, Eq. (1) cannot be solved analytically. Therefore, the trajectory of an atom can be obtained by integrating the potential energy at every time step numerically. The most famous algorithm for the numerical integration is Verlet algorithm (Verlet, 1967). A potential energy acting on an atom, $U(\mathbf{x})$, is calculated by a force field, which is composed of a functional form representing each force terms. Basically, the force field is composed of bonded and nonbonded terms (Eq. (2)).

$$U_{total} = U_{Bonded} + U_{Nonbonded} \qquad\qquad (2)$$

A bonded term is a pairwise interaction energy of atoms that are connected by covalent bonds. It is composed of four terms; bond, angle, torsion, and improper torsion (**Fig. 3**, Eq. (3)). Different from the previous three terms that work on all atoms, improper torsion term only acts on special sets of atoms such as a peptide bond and benzene and prevents a deviation from planarity of the atom sets.

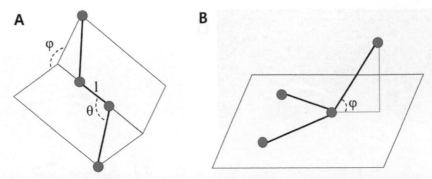

Fig. 3 Definitions of angles in the force field. (A) The bond length *l*, bond angle θ and the torsion angle, (φ). (B) Improper torsion.

$$U_{Bonded} = U_{Bond} + U_{angle} + U_{Torsion} + U_{Improper}$$

$$= \sum_{Bonds} \frac{k_{bi}}{2}\left(1 - l_{i,eq}\right)^2 + \sum_{Angles} \frac{k_{\theta i}}{2}\left(\theta_i - \theta_{i,eq}\right)^2 + \sum_{Torsions} \sum_{n} \frac{V_{n,i}}{2}\left[1 + cos\left(n(\varphi)_i - (\varphi)_{i,0}\right)\right] + \sum_{Improper} \frac{k_{(\varphi)i}}{2}\left((\varphi)_i - (\varphi)_{i,eq}\right)^2 \qquad (3)$$

The bond and the angle terms reflect vibration of bond lengths and angles along with covalent bonds. l and θ are the bond length and bond angle at the current state (**Fig. 3(A)**). The parameters, k_b, l_{eq}, k_θ, and θ_{eq}, are force constants and values of a bond in the equilibrium state. They are derived from gas phase spectroscopy and/or crystal structures of small molecules. The functional forms of the terms are approximated as harmonic oscillators. The torsion term calculates bond energies associated with proper torsion angles, (φ) in **Fig. 3(A)**. Since it is periodic, it has a cosine functional form, and the parameters, V_n and (φ)$_0$ are obtained from quantum mechanics calculation. The improper torsion has a functional form of a harmonic oscillator (**Fig. 3(B)**).

A nonbonded term describes the long-range interaction of atoms, which consists of van der Waals and Coulomb potentials:

$$U_{Nonbonded} = U_{van\ der\ Waals} + U_{Coulomb} = \sum_{i=1}^{N}\sum_{j=i+1}^{N}\left\{4\varepsilon_{ij}\left[\left(\frac{\sigma_{ij}}{r_{ij}}\right)^{12} - \left(\frac{\sigma_{ij}}{r_{ij}}\right)^6\right] + \frac{q_i q_j}{4\pi\varepsilon r_{ij}}\right\} \qquad (4)$$

In the van der Waals term, σ_{ij} and r_{ij} are the radius and well depth, respectively. They are calculated by taking the arithmetic mean ($\sigma_{ij} = (\sigma_{ii} + \sigma_{jj})/2$) and the geometric mean ($\varepsilon_{ij} = \sqrt{\varepsilon_{ii}\varepsilon_{jj}}$) of parameters of the di-atomic system. For the Coulomb term, q_i is an atomic charge of atom i, and ε is a dielectric constant that reflects a solvent polarity (e.g., $\varepsilon = 1$ for vacuum, $\varepsilon = 4$ for protein, and $\varepsilon = 80$ for water in implicit solvent model).

Most biological reactions take place in a cell, surrounded by water molecules; thus it is important to consider the effects of water. In MD and other simulation methods, water molecules can be treated in two ways; an implicit solvation and an explicit solvation model. An implicit solvation model (**Fig. 4(A)**), which is also called continuum solvent, considers solvent as a continuous isotropic medium. It approximates solvent molecules as a homogeneously polarizable, averaged medium (Skyner *et al.*, 2015). The main parameter for the continuum model is a dielectric constant ε, and supplementary parameters are used to describe solvent properties such as surface tension. Atoms in solution are represented as spherical cavities with atomic charges embedded in homogeneously polarizable solvent (**Fig. 4(A)**). An explicit solvation model (**Fig. 4(B)**) treats water molecules explicitly. This is a more realistic model than the implicit solvation model, since physical interaction between a solute and solvent molecules can be directly calculated from the same functional form of the force field. However, the number of atoms in the system is increased drastically in an explicit solvation model; therefore, it takes much more time to calculate potential energy of the solute atoms and trajectory of them. The most famous model of explicit water is TIP3P (Jorgensen *et al.*, 1983).

Coarse-Grained Protein Structure Models

If the size of a protein to simulate is very large, a MD simulation for a biologically relevant time span with an atomistic representation may be computationally infeasible. One way to solve this issue is to represent a protein structure with a simplified (coarse-grained, CG) model. In a coarse-grained model, the complexity of the system is reduced by grouping atoms together into pseudo particles (Barnoud and Monticelli, 2015). Reducing the number of particles decreases the number of interactions to calculate and makes the energy landscape smoother, both of which contribute to shortening the computational time for simulation compared to an atomistic model. The functional form of a CG force field is similar to that for an atomistic force field. The parameters of a CG force field are determined to be able to produce similar trajectories as atomistic MD simulation.

One of the well-known CG force fields is MARTINI (Marrink *et al.*, 2007). Generally, the MARTINI force field maps a group of four heavy atoms to one interaction site (bead). The beads of amino acids are mainly classified into four; polar, nonpolar, apolar, and charged. These are further categorized into subclasses based on hydrogen-bonding capabilities and polarity, resulting in 18 types of beads. Comparing to an atomistic simulation, the MARTINI force field yields a speed-up of 2–3 orders of magnitude. Other CG protein models include UNRES (United RESidues) (Liwo *et al.*, 2004, 2005) and CABS (C-Alpha, c-Beta, Side-chain)

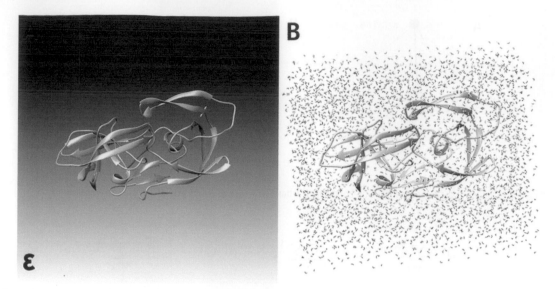

Fig. 4 Two solvent models. (A) The implicit solvent model, where solvent is represented as a dielectric constant of ε. (B) The explicit solvent model. A water molecule is represented as a bent line with oxygen and hydrogen atoms colored in red and white, respectively. Interactions between atoms in water molecules and proteins are computed in the same way using the equations of the force field used.

(Kolinski, 2004). In the UNRES model, each amino acid residue is represented by only two interaction sites, an ellipsoid at the side-chain centroid and another one at the center of Cα-Cα bond. The force field of UNRES is derived as a restricted free energy function, which considers averaging the all-atom energy over the degrees of freedom that are neglected in the UNRES model. Thus, UNIRES is a physics-based united residue force field. In the CABS model, each amino acid residue is represented by four interaction centers; the Cα atom, the center of Cα-Cα bond, the Cβ atom, and the center of mass of the side-group. To facilitate faster simulations, Cα atoms in the CABS model are projected onto a cubic lattice with 0.61 Å spacing. The force field of CABS is based on statistical potentials that mimic averaged interactions observed in globular protein structures in PDB.

Elastic Network Models

As discussed in Section "Coarse-Grained Protein Structure Models", coarse-grained models of protein dynamics are used to reduce the computational cost of analysis. Some of the simplest such models are elastic network models (ENMs). In an ENM, pairwise interactions in a structure are modelled as Hookean springs at equilibrium, i.e., a model where beads representing interaction centers (e.g., amino acid residues) are connected by springs. In other words, the potential energy function has the form $\sum \frac{1}{2}\gamma_{ij}\left(r_{ij} - r_{ij}^0\right)$, where γ_{ij} are positive constants characterizing the stiffness of the interaction and r_{ij}^0 is the initial distance between atoms i and j; in contrast to the general form of MD potentials given in Section "Coarse-Grained Protein Structure Models", ENMs effectively model all interactions as bonds. Tirion considered an all-atom elastic network model with all γ_{ij} identical and atom pairs interacting if their distance was less than the sum of their van der Waals radii and an arbitrary cutoff (Tirion, 1996). That study established that normal mode analysis (NMA), which decomposes the general motion of a system into linearly independent modes of harmonic motion, of such potentials could reproduce the density of slow normal modes of more complicated and costly potentials. Hinsen showed that the slow modes of ENMs can in fact reproduce large-scale deformation, even when only α carbons were considered (Hinsen, 1998). Such coarse ENMs with a single point mass per residue have become popular; in the following sections, we discuss two such models.

Anisotropic network model

Although not chronologically the first residue-level ENM, the anisotropic network model (ANM) is the more general of the two we discuss here. Introduced by Doruker et al. (2000) and expounded by Atilgan et al. (2001) and Eyal et al. (2006), the ANM potential has all γ_{ij} identical and all interaction cutoffs identical (e.g., 7 Å). Here, the NMA is performed with respect to the Cartesian coordinates of each α carbon; i.e., the Hessian of the potential has the block matrix form

$$H = \begin{bmatrix} H_{ii} & \cdots & H_{ij} \\ \vdots & \ddots & \vdots \\ H_{ji} & \cdots & H_{jj} \end{bmatrix} \tag{5}$$

where each block expands to

$$H_{ij} = \begin{bmatrix} \dfrac{\partial^2 U_{ij}}{\partial x_i \partial x_j} & \dfrac{\partial^2 U_{ij}}{\partial x_i \partial y_j} & \dfrac{\partial^2 U_{ij}}{\partial x_i \partial z_j} \\[2mm] \dfrac{\partial^2 U_{ij}}{\partial y_i \partial x_j} & \dfrac{\partial^2 U_{ij}}{\partial y_i \partial y_j} & \dfrac{\partial^2 U_{ij}}{\partial y_i \partial z_j} \\[2mm] \dfrac{\partial^2 U_{ij}}{\partial z_i \partial x_j} & \dfrac{\partial^2 U_{ij}}{\partial z_i \partial y_j} & \dfrac{\partial^2 U_{ij}}{\partial z_i \partial z_j} \end{bmatrix} \tag{6}$$

Computing the eigenpairs of H yields $3N - 6$ eigenpairs corresponding to internal modes. The eigenvalues λ_k and frequencies ω_k of the modes are related by

$$\omega_k^2 = \gamma \lambda_k \tag{7}$$

Although H is not invertible, we can construct a pseudo-inverse

$$H^{-1} = \sum_{k-7}^{3N} \frac{u_k u_k^T}{\lambda_k} \tag{8}$$

where u_k are eigenvectors and eigenpairs are in increasing order by eigenvalue magnitude. Cross-correlations between the equilibrium fluctuations of residues i and j are then given by

$$C_{ij} = \frac{tr\left(H_{ij}^{-1}\right)}{\sqrt{tr\left(H_{ii}^{-1}\right) tr\left(H_{jj}^{-1}\right)}} \tag{9}$$

where H_{ij}^{-1} is the (i,j)th 3×3 block of H^{-1}. The B-factor of atom i, defined as $8\pi^2$ times the mean squared displacement of atom i,

$$B_i = \frac{8\pi^2 k_B T}{3\gamma} tr\left(H_{ii}^{-1}\right) \tag{10}$$

where k_B is the Boltzmann constant and T is the temperature.

ANM has been used to study the dynamics of biomolecules that are related to their biological functions (Navizet et al., 2004; Keskin et al., 2002).

Gaussian network model

Compared to ANM, which can evaluate directional preferences of vibrational dynamics of proteins, Gaussian Network Model (GNM) only provides displacements and correlations between displacements of amino acid residues (Bahar et al., 1997). Mathematically, any information obtained from GNM can also be obtained from ANM; however, if only isotropic information is needed, GNM is computationally cheaper. To calculate the isotropic cross-correlations and B-factors under a GNM, we start from the graph Laplacian Γ of the graph where vertices correspond to atoms and edges correspond to interactions. Then, the cross-correlations are given by

$$C_{ij} = \frac{\Gamma_{ij}^{-1}}{\sqrt{\Gamma_{ii}^{-1} \Gamma_{jj}^{-1}}} \tag{10}$$

where Γ^{-1} is a pseudoinverse as in Section "Anisotropic network model", and the B-factors are given by

$$B_i = \frac{8\pi^2 k_B T}{3\gamma} \Gamma_{ii}^{-1} \tag{11}$$

Residue fluctuations computed from GNM have been shown to agree with the X-ray crystallographic B-factor, which reflects fluctuation of each atom at its position in the crystal structure (Bahar et al., 1998). GNM has also been used for characterizing functional motions of proteins (Yang and Bahar, 2005) and macromolecules, such as ribosome (Wang et al., 2004).

Flexpred

Variability of positions of residues in a protein structure can be also predicted from structural features of amino acids. Jamroz et al. (2012) developed FlexPred, which uses support vector regression (SVR) to predict residue fluctuations observed in 10 ns MD simulations, with a mean error in tests of 1.1 Å. Fluctuation is defined as

$$\sqrt{\langle (\Delta R_i)^2 \rangle}^{\text{ref}} = \sqrt{\frac{1}{T} \sum_{t_j = 1}^{T} \left(x_i(t_j) - x_i^{\text{ref}}\right)^2} \tag{12}$$

where T is the number of frames in the MD trajectory, $x_i(t_j)$ is the position of the α carbon of residue i at time t_j, and x_i^{ref} is the position of the α carbon of residue i in the protein structure. Structural features for each α carbon/residue that were found to be useful as input to SVR include distance to the structure's center of mass, the number of surrounding residues that are in contact, the number of hydrophobic/hydrophilic contacts, solvent-accessible surface area, residue depth (the distance of the residue from protein surface), and secondary structure type.

Application and Case Studies

In this section we provide available software for analysing protein structure variability with some example applications.

Examples of Structural Variability in Protein Families

Structural variation of a protein can be quantified by superimposing the structures. Structure superimposition can help us reveal conserved regions among the structures which may be of functional importance as well as structure divergence and flexibility.

There have been a variety of multiple structure alignment methods developed over the years, which employ different scoring functions and different heuristics. Two examples are MAMMOTH-mult (Lupyan *et al.*, 2005) (see "Relevant Websites section") and POSA (Ye and Godzik, 2005) (see "Relevant Websites section"). Both methods first conducts all pairwise structure alignments and constructs a dendrogram from pairwise similarity scores. Then, following the dendrogram, pairwise structure alignment is performed from leaf nodes, and finally all the structures are superimposed. This superimposition then undergoes an iterative refinement process (progressive alignment).

Multiple structure alignment is useful for understanding structural variability of single protein as well as structures of a protein family. **Fig. 5** shows such an example, an alignment of three lectins, which have the legume lectin-like fold. Lectins are a group of carbohydrate binding proteins with large variation in size and structure. Characteristics of the lectin fold is the presence of a two

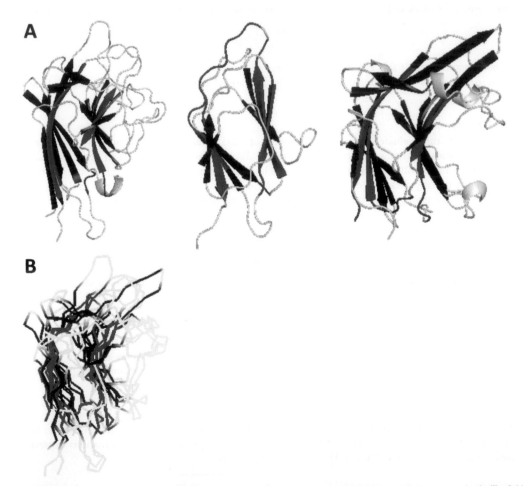

Fig. 5 Structure variation of proteins containing lectin fold. (A) Ribbon diagrams of three structures containing legume lectin-like fold. From left to right: Peanut lectin (PDB: 2PEL, chain A), Spermadhesin (PDB: 1SPP, chain A), Glucanase (PDB: 2AYH, chain A). All structures all shown in the same orientation. Common core identified in the POSA alignment are colored in red. Residues in common core are: residues 44–48, 51–53, 64–69, 200–209, 217–228 in 2pel-A; residues 28–35, 44–49, 85, 87–95, 97–108 in 1spp-A; residues 62–66, 69–77, 175–184, 203–214 in 2ayh-A. Beta sheets are colored in black. Helices and loops are colored in grey. (B) Superimposition of all structures. Structure alignments were produced using POSA.

Table 1   Popular molecular dynamics software

Name	Website
Amber	ambermd.org
CHARMM	www.charmm.org
GROMACS	gromacs.org
NAMD	www.ks.uiuc.edu/Research/namd
Desmond	www.deshawresearch.com/resources_desmond.html

β-sheets positioned almost in parallel (Chandra et al., 2001). Although all structures with lectin fold possess the β-sheets with the particular geometry, curvature of a sheet and the presence of binding site loops and hydrophobic cores vary among those structures (**Fig. 5(A)**). The multiple structure alignment by POSA overlays β-sheets of the three proteins and particularly reveals that all three proteins possess a common core of 36 amino acids, three β strands shown in red in **Fig. 5(B)**. The average RMSD between three structure pairs is 3.0 Å. Compared with peanut lectin (Left in **Fig. 5(A)**), spermadhesin (Middle) and glucanase (Right) have an RMSD of 2.88 Å (for aligned 80 residues) and an RMSD of 3.02 Å (for aligned 172 residues), respectively.

Software for Molecular Dynamics Simulations

MD can be performed using several program packages to simulate protein flexibility. **Table 1** lists popular MD simulation programs. All of the programs are free for academic users. The first MD package, Amber (Assisted Model Building with Energy Refinement) (Case et al., 2005), was originally developed for refining NMR structures. The name 'Amber' refers to both force fields for the simulation of biomolecules and the MD program package. The most widely used force field versions are Amber94, Amber99SB, and Amber03. The next one, CHARMM (Chemistry at HARvard Macromolecular Mechanics) (Brooks et al., 2009), also refers to both force fields and the program package. It was originally developed by Martin Karplus of Harvard University, USA. It is the oldest biomolecular MD package listed in **Table 1**. CHARMM-GUI (see "Relevant Website section") provides a web-based graphical tools for setting up input files for the simulation. GROMACS (GROningen MAchine for Chemical Simulations) (Pronk et al., 2013) typically runs 3–10 times faster than other MD programs. Unlike Amber and CHARMM, GROMACS does not have its own force field. Instead, it can import Amber, CHARMM, GROMOS, and the OPLS force field to run MD simulation. The unique feature of the program is that it is an open-source software released under the GPL license. NAMD (NAnoscale Molecular Dynamics) is developed by the Theoretical and Computational Biophysics Group at the University of Illinois, Urbana-Champaign, USA (Phillips et al., 2005). It is designed to efficiently run on parallel machines for simulating large molecules. The program has high compatibility with other MD programs such as CHARMM, since NAMD has same input, output, and force field formats as CHARMM.

Desmond is developed by D.E. Shaw Research (Bowers et al., 2006). The program uses its novel parallel algorithms and numerical methods to achieve high computing performance. Desmond can import AMBER, CHARMM, and the OPLS force field to run MD simulation.

MD-Based Protein Structure Model Refinement

From Sections "MD-Based Protein Structure Model Refinement", "Refinement of Structures from Electron Microscopy Data", "Protein Folding" and "Free Energy Calculation" we will discuss notable applications of MD simulation for addressing protein structure variability. The first one is structure refinement for computationally modelled protein structure models. Protein structures can be computationally modelled with a reasonable accuracy if a structure of a related protein is already solved and available in PDB. The protein structure modelling technique that uses known structures as a template is called homology modelling or comparative modelling (Fiser, 2010). However, structure models usually still have deviation from the correct (native) structure of the protein, which may be as subtle as side-chain orientations to as large as a domain or loop motion relative to the native structure. The basic assumption of using MD for refining a structure model is that the conformational ensemble generated by MD simulation from the model contains a better structure that is closer to the native structure. The approach can also be applied to structure models built from low-resolution experimental data such as low-resolution X-ray crystallography (Mcgreevy et al., 2014) and cryo-electron microscopy (cryo-EM) density maps (Singharoy et al., 2016).

In the field of protein structure prediction, It has been recognized that running MD simulations for a structure model does not improve a model consistently, but rather drifts the structure away from the native structure because the conformational space is very large. However, the situation has changed in 2012, when MD-based methods were developed that refined models consistently in a protein structure prediction contest, the Critical Assessment of Techniques for Protein Structure Prediction (CASP) (Nugent et al., 2014). Since then several MD-based structure refinement methods have been developed. These methods typically run MD with constraints so that the overall structure does not change drastically. Also the methods combine a structural averaging step and cross-check structures with additional structure evaluation scores (Mirjalili and Feig, 2013; Lee et al., 2018; Terashi and Kihara, 2018). A drawback of the current methods is that the structure improvement they can achieve is small due to the constraints applied in the simulation, which do not allow large conformational changes in the model.

Refinement of Structures From Electron Microscopy Data

MD is also used for refining protein structures derived from low-resolution experimental data. The experimental data referred to here is the three-dimensional reconstruction of electron microscopy (EM) data, commonly referred to as EM maps. The fundamental methodology for combining MD approaches and experimental data is to perform the MD with an additional metric meant to measure the quality of fit between the atomic model and the EM map.

One method for measuring quality of fit is to convert the EM map data into a potential energy landscape. In this methodology, high density regions of the EM map will have low energy penalties for atoms to occupy that space, while low density regions will have higher energy penalties for atoms to occupy that space. The energy term is then added to the rest of the terms in an MD simulation (Eq. (3)). The most popular method which applies a quality-of-fit metric in this way is Molecular Dynamics Flexible Fitting (MDFF) (Singharoy et al., 2016). An alternative metric for fit quality is cross correlation. The cross correlation between an atomic model and an EM map is determined by generating a simulated density map from the atomic model and determining the similarity of the simulated and experimental maps. A popular method which implements this kind of quality of fit metric is ROSETTA (Dimaio et al., 2015). It is important when implementing these kinds of refinement techniques to remember that the refinement can only be as good as the experimental data allows. As the resolution of EM maps decreases, the extent to which multiple refinement techniques agree with each other will tend to decrease (Monroe et al., 2017).

Protein Folding

Many proteins fold over a time scale on the order of millisecond or longer. Some proteins in the low millisecond range are Trp cage and Villin headpiece with sizes of 20 and 35 residues, respectively. These two α-helical proteins have successfully been simulated from unfolded states to folded states in simulations lasting 10 ns to 1 ms (Simmerling et al., 2002; Duan and Kollman, 1998), and achieving Cα RMSDs of 0.97 and 3.0 Å, respectively. On an even larger scale, the folding and unfolding of ubiquitin, a 76 residue $\alpha\beta$ protein, has been studied through high temperature, 1 ms simulations to an RMSD of 0.5 Å to the crystal structure of the protein (Piana et al., 2013).

Free Energy Calculation

One of the most interesting applications of MD simulation is free energy calculation of a system. From a statistical thermodynamics point of view, free energy calculation is based on the ergodicity hypothesis, which claims that all possible microstates in the phase space can be covered by a trajectory of a system in a long time. With this hypothesis, we can assume that the average of an observable, such as enthalpy, over time is the same as its statistical ensemble. One of the classical example of this application is a protein folding energy landscape (Lei et al., 2007).

Another useful application of free energy calculation is protein-ligand binding free energy (ΔG_{bind}) using The Molecular Mechanics energies combined with the Poisson–Boltzmann and Surface Area continuum solvation (MM/PBSA) method (Genheden and Ryde, 2015). MM/PBSA starts by generating MD trajectories of a protein-ligand complex, a protein, and a ligand. From the trajectories, snapshots of the system are picked up with a certain time interval. The Gibbs free energy of a molecule at a snapshot is calculated as:

$$G = E_{Bond} + E_{vdW} + E_{Coul} + G_{pol} + G_{np} - TS \tag{13}$$

E_{Bond}, E_{vdW}, and E_{Coul} are bonded term, van der Waals, and Coulomb force of a molecule, respectively. The three terms are calculated by the molecular mechanics force field (MM). G_{pol} and G_{np} are solvation energies of polar and nonpolar atoms of a molecule, obtained by solving the Poisson-Boltzmann equation for polar atoms and is proportional to surface area for nonpolar atoms. Although the MD trajectory is obtained from explicit solvent condition, the solvation energy is calculated with implicit solvation (PBSA). The last term, TS in Eq. (13) is entropy, calculated from normal mode analysis, multiplied by absolute temperature.

By taking average of Gibbs free energy across snapshots, binding free energy is calculated as follows:

$$\Delta G_{bind} = \langle G_{Protein-Ligand} \rangle - \langle G_{Protein} \rangle - \langle G_{Ligand} \rangle \tag{14}$$

$\langle G_i \rangle$ is an average of Gibbs free energy of a molecule i. The MM/PBSA has been successfully applied to estimating binding free energies of drugs (Zoete et al., 2003; Pearlman, 2005).

Protein Flexibility Prediction With Flexpred

As discussed in Section "FlexPred", flexibility of a protein structure can be predicted from structural features of amino acids in the structure. The method, FlexPred is available as a web server (see "Relevant Websites section") and downloadable software (Peterson et al., 2017). Fig. 6 shows an example of prediction for bovine angiogenin (PDB: 1AGI, 125 residues long). The plot shows flexibility, how far in Euclidean distance (Å) each amino acid moves on average (in 10 ns MD simulation) along the protein chain (Eq. (12)). At the bottom of the page, there are links to download the fluctuation predictions in CSV form and in the B-factor field of a PDB file. In this example, the predicted fluctuations and crystallographic B-factors correlate with correlation coefficient 0.82. Fig. 6(B) shows a side-by-side comparison of the predicted fluctuations (Left) and the B-factors (Right).

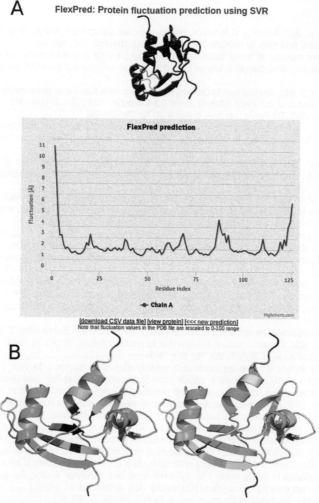

Fig. 6 Example of protein structure flexibility prediction. FlexPred was used. (A) Predicted fluctuation of residues of bovine angiogenin (PDB ID: 1AGI). The y-axis shows the fluctuation (Eq. (12)) of each residue. (B) Predicted fluctuation mapped on residues in the PDB file. Values are stored in the B-factor field of the PDB file. Left, prediction; Right, structure colored by crystallographic B-factor of 1AGI.

Conclusion

Proteins are flexible molecules. Some motions are important for biological function of proteins. How the structure of a protein varies can be obtained if the protein structure is solved under different conditions by experimental methods. Variability of a structure can be also experimentally measured by using NMR or spectroscopic techniques. Computationally, structure variability can be simulated by atomistic MD or coarse-grained models, and can also be predicted from the structure. Applications of MDs, multiple structure alignment, and flexibility prediction are shown.

Acknowledgement

This work was partly supported by the National Institutes of Health (R01GM123055) and the National Science Foundation (IIS1319551, IOS1127027, DMS1614777).

See also: Biological Database Searching. Biomolecular Structures: Prediction, Identification and Analyses. Natural Language Processing Approaches in Bioinformatics

References

Atilgan, A.R., Durell, S.R., Jernigan, R.L., et al., 2001. Anisotropy of fluctuation dynamics of proteins with an elastic network model. Biophys. J. 80, 505–515.

Barnoud, J., Monticelli, L., 2015. Coarse-grained force fields for molecular simulations. Methods Mol. Biol. 1215, 125–149.

Bahar, I., Atilgan, A.R., Erman, B., 1997. Direct evaluation of thermal fluctuations in proteins using a single-parameter harmonic potential. Fold. Des. 2, 173–181.

Bahar, I., Wallqvist, A., Covell, D.G., Jernigan, R.L., 1998. Correlation between native-state hydrogen exchange and cooperative residue fluctuations from a simple model. Biochemistry 37, 1067–1075.

Belogurov, G.A., Vassylyeva, M.N., Svetlov, V., et al., 2007. Structural basis for converting a general transcription factor into an operon-specific virulence regulator. Mol. Cell 26, 117–129.

Bennett, M.J., Eisenberg, D., 1994. Refined structure of monomeric diphtheria toxin at 2.3 A resolution. Protein Sci. 3, 1464–1475.

Berman, H.M., Westbrook, J., Feng, Z., et al., 2000. The Protein Data Bank. Nucleic Acids Res. 28, 235–242.

Boehr, D.D., Nussinov, R., Wright, P.E., 2009. The role of dynamic conformational ensembles in biomolecular recognition. Nat. Chem. Biol. 5, 789–796.

Bowers, K.J., Chow, E., Xu, H., et al., 2006. Scalable algorithms for molecular dynamics simulations on commodity clusters. In: Proceedings of the ACM/IEEE Conference on Supercomputing (SC06). Tampa, Florida.

Brooks, B.R., Brooks, C.L., Mackerell 3rd, A.D., et al., 2009. CHARMM: The biomolecular simulation program. J. Comput. Chem. 30, 1545–1614.

Burmann, B.M., Knauer, S.H., Sevostyanova, A., et al., 2012. An alpha helix to beta barrel domain switch transforms the transcription factor RfaH into a translation factor. Cell 150, 291–303.

Case, D.A., Cheatham, T.E., Darden 3rd, T., et al., 2005. The Amber biomolecular simulation programs. J. Comput. Chem. 26, 1668–1688.

Chandra, N.R., Prabu, M.M., Suguna, K., Vijayan, M., 2001. Structural similarity and functional diversity in proteins containing the legume lectin fold. Protein Eng. 14, 857–866.

Chen, J., 2013. Molecular mechanism of the Escherichia coli maltose transporter. Curr. Opin. Struct. Biol. 23, 492–498.

Derreumaux, P., Schlick, T., 1998. The loop opening/closing motion of the enzyme triosephosphate isomerase. Biophys. J. 74, 72–81.

Dimaio, F., Song, Y., Li, X., et al., 2015. Atomic-accuracy models from 4.5-A cryo-electron microscopy data with density-guided iterative local refinement. Nat. Methods 12, 361–365.

Doruker, P., Atilgan, A.R., Bahar, I., 2000. Dynamics of proteins predicted by molecular dynamics simulations and analytical approaches: Application to alpha-amylase inhibitor. Proteins Struct. Funct. Genet. 40, 512–524.

Duan, Y., Kollman, P.A., 1998. Pathways to a protein folding intermediate observed in a 1-microsecond simulation in aqueous solution. Science 282, 740–744.

Dunker, A.K., Silman, I., Uversky, V.N., Sussman, J.L., 2008. Function and structure of inherently disordered proteins. Curr. Opin. Struct. Biol. 18, 756–764.

Evdokimov, A.G., Phan, J., Tropea, J.E., et al., 2003. Similar modes of polypeptide recognition by export chaperones in flagellar biosynthesis and type III secretion. Nat. Struct. Biol. 10, 789–793.

Eyal, E., Yang, L.W., Bahar, I., 2006. Anisotropic network model: Systematic evaluation and a new web interface. Bioinformatics 22, 2619–2627.

Ferron, F., Longhi, S., Canard, B., Karlin, D., 2006. A practical overview of protein disorder prediction methods. Proteins 65, 1–14.

Fiser, A., 2010. Template-based protein structure modeling. Methods Mol. Biol. 673, 73–94.

Gan, H.H., Perlow, R.A., Roy, S., et al., 2002. Analysis of protein sequence/structure similarity relationships. Biophys. J. 83, 2781–2791.

Genheden, S., Ryde, U., 2015. The MM/PBSA and MM/GBSA methods to estimate ligand-binding affinities. Expert Opin. Drug Discov. 10, 449–461.

Goh, C.S., Milburn, D., Gerstein, M., 2004. Conformational changes associated with protein-protein interactions. Curr. Opin. Struct. Biol. 14, 104–109.

Greenleaf, W.J., Woodside, M.T., Block, S.M., 2007. High-resolution, single-molecule measurements of biomolecular motion. Annu. Rev. Biophys. Biomol. Struct. 36, 171–190.

Hinsen, K., 1998. Analysis of domain motions by approximate normal mode calculations. Proteins Struct. Funct. Genet. 33, 417–429.

Hinterdorfer, P., Dufrene, Y.F., 2006. Detection and localization of single molecular recognition events using atomic force microscopy. Nat. Methods 3, 347–355.

Jamroz, M., Kolinski, A., Kihara, D., 2012. Structural features that predict real-value fluctuations of globular proteins. Proteins 80, 1425–1435.

Jorgensen, W.L., Chandrasekhar, J., Madura, J.D., Impey, R.W., Klein, M.L., 1983. Comparison of simple potential functions for simulating liquid water. J. Chem. Phys. 79, 926–935.

Keskin, O., Durell, S.R., Bahar, I., Jernigan, R.L., Covell, D.G., 2002. Relating molecular flexibility to function: A case study of tubulin. Biophys. J. 83, 663–680.

Kodera, N., Ando, T., 2014. The path to visualization of walking myosin V by high-speed atomic force microscopy. Biophys. Rev. 6, 237–260.

Kolinski, A., 2004. Protein modeling and structure prediction with a reduced representation. Acta Biochim. Pol. 51, 349–371.

Kosloff, M., Kolodny, R., 2008. Sequence-similar, structure-dissimilar protein pairs in the PDB. Proteins 71, 891–902.

Lee, G.R., Heo, L., Seok, C., 2017. Simultaneous refinement of inaccurate local regions and overall structure in the CASP12 protein model refinement experiment. Proteins 86 (Suppl. 1), S168–S176.

Lei, H., Wu, C., Liu, H., Duan, Y., 2007. Folding free-energy landscape of villin headpiece subdomain from molecular dynamics simulations. Proc. Natl. Acad. Sci. USA 104, 4925–4930.

Liwo, A., Khalili, M., Scheraga, H.A., 2005. Ab initio simulations of protein-folding pathways by molecular dynamics with the united-residue model of polypeptide chains. Proc. Natl. Acad. Sci. USA 102, 2362–2367.

Liwo, A., Oldziej, S., Czaplewski, C., Kozlowska, U., Scheraga, H.A., 2004. Parameterization of backbone-electrostatic and multibody contributions to the UNRES force field for protein-structure prediction from ab initio energy surfaces of model systems. J. Phys. Chem. B 108, 9421–9438.

Lupyan, D., Leo-Macias, A., Ortiz, A.R., 2005. A new progressive-iterative algorithm for multiple structure alignment. Bioinformatics 21, 3255–3263.

Marrink, S.J., Risselada, H.J., Yefimov, S., Tieleman, D.P., De Vries, A.H., 2007. The MARTINI force field: Coarse grained model for biomolecular simulations. J. Phys. Chem. B 111, 7812–7824.

Mccammon, J.A., Gelin, B.R., Karplus, M., 1977. Dynamics of folded proteins. Nature 267, 585–590.

Mcgreevy, R., Singharoy, A., Li, Q., et al., 2014. xMDFF: Molecular dynamics flexible fitting of low-resolution X-ray structures. Acta Crystallogr. D Biol. Crystallogr. 70, 2344–2355.

Mirjalili, V., Feig, M., 2013. Protein structure refinement through structure selection and averaging from molecular dynamics ensembles. J. Chem. Theory Comput. 9, 1294–1303.

Monroe, L., Terashi, G., Kihara, D., 2017. Variability of protein structure models from electron microscopy. Structure 25, 592–602. e2.

Navizet, I., Lavery, R., Jernigan, R.L., 2004. Myosin flexibility: Structural domains and collective vibrations. Proteins 54, 384–393.

Nugent, T., Cozzetto, D., Jones, D.T., 2014. Evaluation of predictions in the CASP10 model refinement category. Proteins 82 (Suppl. 2), S98–S111.

Oates, M.E., Romero, P., Ishida, T., et al., 2013. D(2)P(2): Database of disordered protein predictions. Nucleic Acids Res. 41, D508–D516.

Parak, F.G., 2003. Proteins in action: The physics of structural fluctuations and conformational changes. Curr. Opin. Struct. Biol. 13, 552–557.

Pearlman, D.A., 2005. Evaluating the molecular mechanics poisson-boltzmann surface area free energy method using a congeneric series of ligands to p38 MAP kinase. J. Med. Chem. 48, 7796–7807.

Pelletier, H., Sawaya, M.R., Wolfle, W., Wilson, S.H., Kraut, J., 1996. Crystal structures of human DNA polymerase beta complexed with DNA: Implications for catalytic mechanism, processivity, and fidelity. Biochemistry 35, 12742–12761.

Peterson, L., Jamroz, M., Kolinski, A., Kihara, D., 2017. Predicting real-valued protein residue fluctuation using FlexPred. Methods Mol. Biol. 1484, 175–186.

Phillips, J.C., Braun, R., Wang, W., et al., 2005. Scalable molecular dynamics with NAMD. J. Comput. Chem. 26, 1781–1802.

Piana, S., Lindorff-Larsen, K., Shaw, D.E., 2013. Atomic-level description of ubiquitin folding. Proc. Natl. Acad. Sci. USA 110, 5915–5920.

Pronk, S., Pall, S., Schulz, R., et al., 2013. GROMACS 4.5: A high-throughput and highly parallel open source molecular simulation toolkit. Bioinformatics 29, 845–854.

Sawaya, M.R., Prasad, R., Wilson, S.H., Kraut, J., Pelletier, H., 1997. Crystal structures of human DNA polymerase beta complexed with gapped and nicked DNA: Evidence for an induced fit mechanism. Biochemistry 36, 11205–11215.

Simmerling, C., Strockbine, B., Roitberg, A.E., 2002. All-atom structure prediction and folding simulations of a stable protein. J. Am. Chem. Soc. 124, 11258–11259.

Singharoy, A., Teo, I., Mcgreevy, R., et al., 2016. Molecular dynamics-based refinement and validation for sub-5 A cryo-electron microscopy maps. eLife. 5.

Skyner, R.E., Mcdonagh, J.L., Groom, C.R., Van Mourik, T., Mitchell, J.B.O., 2015. A review of methods for the calculation of solution free energies and the modelling of systems in solution. Phys. Chem. Chem. Phys. 17, 6174–6191.

Terashi, G., Kihara, D., 2018. Protein structure model refinement in CASP12 using short and long molecular dynamics simulations in implicit solvent. Proteins 86 (Suppl. 1), S189–S201.

Tirion, M.M., 1996. Large amplitude elastic motions in proteins from a single-parameter, atomic analysis. Phys. Rev. Lett. 77, 1905–1908.

Verlet, L., 1967. Computer experiments on classical fluids. I. Thermodynamical properties of Lennard-Jones molecules. Phys. Rev. 159, 98.

Wang, Y., Rader, A.J., Bahar, I., Jernigan, R.L., 2004. Global ribosome motions revealed with elastic network model. J. Struct. Biol. 147, 302–314.

Yamniuk, A.P., Vogel, H.J., 2004. Calmodulin's flexibility allows for promiscuity in its interactions with target proteins and peptides. Mol. Biotechnol. 27, 33–57.

Yang, L.W., Bahar, I., 2005. Coupling between catalytic site and collective dynamics: A requirement for mechanochemical activity of enzymes. Structure 13, 893–904.

Ye, Y., Godzik, A., 2005. Multiple flexible structure alignment using partial order graphs. Bioinformatics 21, 2362–2369.

Zoete, V., Michielin, O., Karplus, M., 2003. Protein-ligand binding free energy estimation using molecular mechanics and continuum electrostatics. Application to HIV-1 protease inhibitors. J. Comput. Aided Mol. Des. 17, 861–880.

Relevant Websites

http://www.charmm-gui.org
Charmm-Gui.
http://kiharalab.org/flexPred/
FlexPred Server - Kihara Lab.
https://ub.cbm.uam.es/software/online/mamothmult.php
MAMMOTH-Mult - Unidad de Bioinformatica CBMSO.
http://posa.sanfordburnham.org/
POSA Home - Sanford Burnham Prebys Medical Discovery Institute.

Biographical Sketch

Xusi Han is currently a PhD candidate in Department of Biological Sciences at Purdue University, West Lafayette, Indiana, USA. She is also pursuing toward the M.S. degree in Applied Statistics at Purdue University. She received the B.S. degree from Minzu University of China, Beijing, China, in 2009. Her current research interests include protein global structure comparison, protein structure classification, and graph analysis for electron microscopy density maps.

Woong-Hee Shin is currently a postdoctoral researcher of the Kihara Lab in the Department of Biological Sciences at Purdue University. He received the B.Sc. in chemistry from Seoul National University, South Korea in 2008. He also received the PhD degree in chemistry in 2014 from Seoul National University. During his PhD research, he developed a flexible-receptor ligand docking program, GalaxyDock, and performed virtual ligand library screening to find active molecules of nuclear receptors. After receiving his PhD, he joined the Kihara lab in August 2014. His current research interests are development and application of computational drug discovery programs.

Charles Christoffer is currently a graduate member of the Kihara Lab at Purdue University, West Lafayette, Indiana, USA. He received the B.S. degree in Computer Science and Applied Mathematics from Purdue University in 2015. He is currently pursuing the PhD degree with the Department of Computer Science at Purdue University. His research interests include geometric data structures, computer vision, and image processing, especially their application to structural bioinformatics. Within structural bioinformatics, he is particularly interested in protein docking and structure database search.

Genki Terashi is currently a postdoctoral researcher of the Kihara Lab in the Department of Biological Sciences at Purdue University, West Lafayette, Indiana, USA. He received the B.S., M.S., and PhD degrees in Pharmaceutical Sciences from Kitasato University, Tokyo, Japan, in 2002, 2004 and 2008, respectively. His current research interests include protein structure model refinement, protein structure modelling and comparison, and protein-protein docking. Application of Machine Learning method to the structural biology is also his research interest.

Lyman Monroe is a PhD candidate in the Department of Biological Sciences at Purdue University, West Lafayette, Indiana, USA. He received the B.S. degree in Physics from Purdue University in 2012, as well as a second B.S. degree in Chemistry from Purdue University in 2013. His projects include protein structure modelling and refinement using molecular dynamics simulation.

Daisuke Kihara is a full professor in the Department of Biological Sciences and the Department of Computer Science at Purdue University, West Lafayette, Indiana, USA. He received the B.S. degree in Biochemistry from the University of Tokyo, Japan in 1994, and the M.S. and PhD degrees from Kyoto University, Japan in 1996 and 1999, respectively. He was a postdoctoral researcher with Prof. Jeffrey Skolnick at the Danforth Plant Science Center, St. Louis and at SUNY Buffalo from 1999 to 2003. He joined Purdue University as an assistant professor in 2003 and was promoted to associate professor in 2009 and to full professor in 2014. His research field is bioinformatics. His research projects include protein docking, protein tertiary structure prediction, structure- and sequence-based protein function prediction, and computational drug design. He has published over 140 research papers and book chapters. His research projects have been supported by funding from the National Institutes of Health, the National Science Foundation, the Office of the Director of National Intelligence, and industry. In 2013, he was named a University Faculty Scholar by Purdue University.

Identifying Functional Relationships Via the Annotation and Comparison of Three-Dimensional Amino Acid Arrangements in Protein Structures

Mohd Firdaus-Raih and Nur Syatila Abdul Ghani, Universiti Kebangsaan Malaysia, Bangi, Malaysia

Introduction

The primary computational approach used for assigning biological function to protein sequences is dependent on the extrapolation of function based on sequence level similarities. Although the increase in the number of sequences with annotated functions has made sequence alignment based tools highly accurate and adequate, there remains a subset of proteins that have yet to be characterized for function. In the numerous genome sequences being generated at present, many of these sequences are annotated as hypothetical proteins based on the prediction that their open reading frames can hypothetically code for a protein. Many such hypothetical proteins have been expressed, purified and had their structures determined by crystallographic methods via structural genomics approaches. This is evident in the number of proteins with uncharacterized functions that are being deposited in the Protein Data Bank (PDB) (Rose et al., 2017). It is known that at levels where sequence similarity is no longer detectable, fold similarity may still exist and hence still result in similar functions. Therefore, considerable efforts have been made to determine the functions of such hypothetical proteins by characterizing their three-dimensional (3D) structures.

Although the molecular structure of a protein can be expected to reveal potential fold similarities to structures with characterized function, there are still protein structures in the PDB that do not have any fold similarities to any other characterized examples (Nadzirin and Firdaus-Raih, 2012). As a result, these proteins are still classified as having uncharacterized function despite having lost the hypothetical protein label. One approach towards identifying the potential function of such proteins would be to investigate the potential for specific arrangements of amino acids to carry out a particular chemical reaction or biological function. A common example can be seen where convergent evolution leads toward the formation of catalytic triads that share no common evolutionary history and in such cases the resultant 3D arrangement to form the triad is a requirement for catalysis to occur. In order to execute the analysis of 3D structures for such arrangements, the tools employed will have to extend beyond sequence and fold level comparisons to the level of specific 3D formations of the amino acid residues.

The availability of information regarding specific interacting residues for different modes of protein functions and interactions such as catalytic sites (Porter et al., 2004), protein-DNA (Luscombe et al., 2001; Selvaraj et al., 2002; Angarica et al., 2008; Contreras-Moreira, 2010), protein-RNA (Jones et al., 2001), protein-protein (Raih et al., 2005; Kinjo and Nakamura, 2010), protein-carbohydrate (Malik et al., 2010) as well as other protein-ligand interactions and sites that are potential interaction surfaces such as clefts (Laskowski et al., 1996), can be utilized as a database of known motifs to search against. The SIFTS database is an excellent example of a resource containing cross-referenced datasets that include residue level mappings which can in turn be deployed for use as a motifs database (Velankar et al., 2013).

By integrating computational tools that are able to search at the sub-structure level or for specific residue arrangements with the prior knowledge on the function of similarly arranged residues, the user of such tools may be able to pin-point a possible line of enquiry for further investigation that may lead towards successful functional characterization of a protein of unknown function. In this article, computational methods of searching or comparing 3D level arrangements of amino acids are compared, and the approaches as well as general strategies for their use are discussed.

Background

Fold Comparisons Versus Amino Acid 3D Motif Searching

It is well known that in homologous proteins, divergence of sequence identity to even less than 30% can still result in the maintenance of a similar general fold (Chothia and Lesk, 1986). This has led to the development of numerous methods and databases specifically aimed at classifying and comparing the similarities in folding for protein 3D structures. Methods that perform structural alignments such as DALI (Holm et al., 2006), FATCAT (Ye and Godzik, 2004) and VAST (Gibrat et al., 1996) have long been frontline tools for the annotation of protein structures. Such fold comparison methods have proven useful even in the absence of any significant sequence similarity as demonstrated by Artymiuk et al. (1997) who reported that the domain folding of a then recently solved structure of adenylyl cyclase resembled the 'palm' domain of the polymerase I family of prokaryotic DNA polymerases.

However, in cases of convergent evolution, the absence of not only detectable sequence similarity, but also fold similarity, can be observed in proteins that execute generally similar mechanisms in order to carry out their functions. For proteins that have sites sharing a similar mechanistic function with others, but are unrelated in other parts of the structure, there may exist clusters of amino acids that are similarly arranged despite undetectable sequence similarity and different folding. Such similarity in 3D arrangements of amino acids in evolutionarily unrelated proteins can result in similar chemical activity or molecular function such as catalytic sites, ligand binding sites and various nucleic acid binding sites. In order to enable a structure to be annotated or compared for such similar 3D amino acid constellations, the methods need to be able to accept a query that can be compared against 3D structure data such as those in the PDB. By developing methods that can search for such similarities, we would then be able to associate hypothetical proteins to characterized proteins as well as generate an inventory of conserved side chain arrangements and the functions that they serve.

In general, there are two approaches that can be taken to carry out searches for such tertiary motifs. One approach would be to enable the search engine or comparison program to accept an input file containing 3D structural information such as a PDB coordinate file and using that input as a query to search against a database of 3D motifs or a database of 3D structures. Another approach would be to allow a user to define or design the query that is representative of a 3D motif and using that input as a query to search against a database of 3D structures. There are now a number of programs that are able to carry out such searches and although they subscribe to the two general approaches mentioned above, the implemented algorithms between these available programs differ. In many cases, the different programs available complement each other by filling in the gaps in terms of search methodology, coverage and computational capacity. In this paper, only computer programs that carry out these types of 3D motif searches that are also available as web services and using PDB associated data are discussed (**Table 1**).

Fold and Sequence Independent Motifs in Protein Structures

Advances in macromolecular crystallography and high throughput molecular biology have led to numerous structural genomics projects. In Chothia (1992) reported that the number of different families was finite and may be as limited as one thousand distinct protein shapes. Therefore, as the PDB expands, it is most likely that the number of novel folds reported will not increase dramatically despite the contributions by the depositions from the structural genomics initiatives. This slow-down in the rate of growth for novel protein structural data in the PDB had been reported by Levitt (2007). As a result of the structural genomics contributions and the decrease in novel folds being discovered, concerted efforts are now being directed by many structural biology groups to target the solution of structures for proteins with unknown functions, specifically proteins that were annotated

Table 1   List of computational programs for 3D motif search

Input format	Query type	Program/service	Search approach
Input file format: PDB	Complete protein structure	COFACTOR	Identify proteins of similar fold and functional sites though global and local structural similarities (Roy et al., 2012).
		eF-Seek	Search for similar binding sites in PDB based on molecular surfaces and calculation of electrostatic potentials (Kinoshita et al., 2007).
		GIRAF	Identification of ligand binding sites in the PDB that are structurally similar to substructures of the query (Kinjo and Nakamura, 2007).
		MetaPocket 2.0	Identification of binding cavities using multiple computational platforms (Zhang et al., 2011).
		MultiBind	Recognize common spatial patterns through multiple structural alignment of binding sites from a set of bound structures (Shulman-Peleg et al., 2008).
		ProFunc	Identification of probable active sites and possible homologues in the PDB (Laskowski et al., 2005).
		SPRITE	Convert a protein structure into representative pseudo-atom vectors for searching against a database of pseudo-atom vectors representing known 3D motifs and sites(Nadzirin et al., 2012).
		ProBis	Compare protein surfaces and recognizes geometrically similar regions (Konc and Janezic, 2010).
		SA-Mot	Identification of structural motif from protein loop structures using structural alphabet HMM-SA (Regad et al., 2010).
	Complete protein structure/ 3D motif	SuMo	Find similarity in 3D structure or substructures of proteins against ligand binding site in PDB through heuristic search of chemical group triplets (Jambon et al., 2005).
		PINTS	Find recurring three-dimensional patterns of amino acids common to two sets structures by measuring the inter-residue distances (Stark et al., 2003).
	3D motif	ASSAM	Convert a PDB coordinate file representing a 3D motif or arrangement into representative pseudo-atom vectors for searching against a database of pseudo-atom vectors representing structures in the PDB (Nadzirin et al., 2012).
		RASMOT-3D PRO	Search a PDB file for secondary structure independent patterns or larger super secondary structure residue arrangements(Debret et al., 2009).
Other	Other	IMAAAGINE	Search a user provided residue arrangement based on the distances between residues or residue types (Nadzirin et al., 2013).
		PDBeMotif	Search possible binding sites and structural motifs of a protein structure, or all instances of residue pattern in the PDB (Golovin and Henrick, 2008).

Note: A listing of the fifteen web servers discussed that can search for specific 3D arrangements of amino acid residues.

as hypothetically encoding a protein that bears no sequence similarity to any proteins of known or characterized function (Eisenstein *et al.*, 2000; Cruz-Migoni *et al.*, 2011).

Once the structures of such proteins have been solved, they are typically subjected to fold similarity searching in order to determine whether the fold is already existent in the PDB. In cases where fold similarity can be attributed, there may likely be significant insights gleaned from the structure to influence the direction of further study. Nevertheless, there are numerous other protein structures that remain annotated as 'uncharacterized' in the PDB. A survey of the proteins annotated as 'uncharacterized' in the PDB revealed that there were 1084 proteins that had no similarity to any known sequence or folds at the time of the analysis as of May 2012 (Nadzirin and Firdaus-Raih, 2012). When both sequence and fold similarity options have been ruled out for inferring homologous function for a newly solved structure, an alternative option would be to investigate whether conserved 3D motifs that constitute catalytic and binding sites could be identified despite the absence of detectable sequence and fold similarity. The programs ProFunc (Laskowski *et al.*, 2005), GIRAF (Kinjo and Nakamura, 2009), PINTS (Stark *et al.*, 2003), SA-Mot (Regad *et al.*, 2010) and SPRITE (Nadzirin *et al.*, 2012) (**Table 1**) are capable of identifying such 3D motifs. These programs approach a search using different methodologies and at present there is no single all capable program. Instead, they can be used collectively to complement each other where a gap in the capacity of one program is taken up by other programs. Another factor for consideration is the fact that these programs search different databases. As a result, a user may need to run multiple searches to attain coverage of all the relevant databases used and thus increasing the possibility of retrieving a significant hit.

Systems and/or Applications

In this article, we assess and compare the utility of fifteen different computer programs for structural analysis (**Table 1**), particularly those that can identify specific 3D arrangements of the amino acid residues and are also accessible to users as a web service. We also evaluate their accuracy in different scenarios and present a strategy for the users on how to potentially analyse structures with uncharacterized functions via these tools. Undoubtedly, some programs may even perform better than the ones we have evaluated here, however, if they are not freely available and accessible via a web interface, they were not incorporated into this article.

Input Formats

With the exception of the IMAAAGINE server, all the other services accept a PDB formatted coordinate file as input. Both the IMAAAGINE and PDBeMotif servers allow for a user-defined pattern of amino acids provided as input via the web interface. The IMAAAGINE server requires that the user conceptualize an amino acid arrangement that is defined by distances between the residues in the pattern. The PDBeMotif server additionally provides comprehensive analyses of sequence, 3D motifs, and the ligand environment that can be provided as input via the web interface.

Output and Average Time for Computations

The fifteen servers assessed typically take from approximately a minute up to several hours for a calculation involving a protein structure that we had used as a test input. However, this rather large variation was expected due to the calculation times depending on factors that include, but are not limited to input size, the number of jobs being computed or queued on the servers and the different algorithms employed by the services. Most servers returned a tabulated summary of hits ranked by local structural similarity scores and downloadable results, while some servers also facilitated or allowed for the visualization of matched 3D arrangements (**Table 2**).

Analysis and Assessment

Searching Motifs/Sites Databases With a Structure Query

In the case of many protein structures that have no detectable sequence similarity, a fold similarity search using DALI may be sufficient for identifying structural homology. However, even in such cases, comparing specific clusters of amino acids within the structure can yield further insights regarding the specific activity or interaction partners of the protein. A simple step by step strategy that can be adopted after an initial fold level similarity search would be to submit the structure of interest to either selected or all of the services listed in **Table 1** that are able to process a complete PDB structure as a search query. In selecting specific services, one should consider the capacities and database scope for the programs used. For example, the database attached to SPRITE is drawn from motifs in the catalytic site atlas (CSA) (Porter *et al.*, 2004), the ProCarb dataset (Malik *et al.*, 2010), the 3D-Footprint dataset and those manually extracted from literature. The ProBis service works by comparing protein surfaces and identifying geometrically similar regions thus making it less dependent on requiring prior knowledge regarding a motif such as SPRITE (Konc and Janezic, 2010) (**Table 3**).

When using predictive and/or computational methods, it is generally prudent to use several programs that employ different approaches by selecting representatives or highly used programs from each methodology class. The results from these various programs can then be compared and in cases where there is a clear agreement, those particular results can be further investigated. Nevertheless, the problem

Table 2 Comparison of different computational programs for detection of 3D motif

Program/service name	COFACTOR	E²-Seek	GIRAF	MetaPocket	MultiBind	ProFunc	SPRITE	ProBis	SA-Mot	SuMo	PINTS	ASSAM	RASMOT-3D Pro	IMAAAGINE	PDBeMotif
Input query															
PDB ID or coordinate file of a complete protein structure in PDB format	✓	✓				✓	✓		✓	✓	✓		✓		✓
Coordinate file of 3D pattern consists of several amino acids in PDB format		✓	✓		✓	✓	✓	✓		✓	✓	✓	✓	✓	✓
A set of PDB IDs or coordinate files of bound protein structures in PDB format					✓			✓							
User-defined template of residue arrangement or combination of multiple queries						✓	✓				✓	✓		✓	
Approaches															
Implements sequence and fold-dependent methods	✓														
Implements structure-based methods	✓	✓	✓	✓	✓	✓	✓	✓	✓	✓	✓	✓	✓	✓	✓
Searches for global structural similarity	✓	✓				✓		✓							
Searches for local structural similarity		✓	✓	✓	✓	✓	✓	✓	✓	✓	✓	✓	✓	✓	✓
Searches for pairwise structural similarity					✓	✓		✓			✓				
Searches/predicts for:															
Homologous structures	✓	✓				✓		✓							
Catalytic sites	✓	✓	✓			✓	✓		✓	✓	✓	✓	✓	✓	✓
Ligand binding sites	✓	✓	✓	✓	✓	✓	✓	✓		✓	✓				✓
DNA/RNA-binding sites			✓			✓		✓							
Protein–protein interfaces			✓		✓	✓		✓							
Pocket sites on protein surfaces	✓	✓		✓		✓		✓							
3D motifs	✓	✓	✓	✓	✓	✓	✓	✓	✓	✓	✓	✓	✓	✓	✓
Output type/format															
List of predicted 3D motifs ranked by structural similarity scores	✓	✓	✓	✓	✓	✓	✓	✓	✓	✓	✓	✓	✓		✓
Direct molecular visualization of predicted 3D motifs enabled	✓	✓		✓		✓		✓							
Downloadable output files	✓	✓	✓	✓	✓	✓	✓	✓	✓	✓	✓	✓	✓	✓	✓

Note: A comparison of the fifteen web servers for 3D motif searching in terms of their input, algorithm and output.

Table 3   Relevant hits for query of BPSL1549 protein

Prediction	Server	Results
Homologs	COFACTOR	Returned 10 chain homologs from fold comparison, which includes CNF1-C, and several uncharacterized proteins. Gene Ontology (GO) term prediction for Biological Process (BP) resulted with 'arginine biosynthesic process'.
	ProFunc	Returned 10 PDB chains with similar fold, including chemotaxis deamidase and several uncharacterized proteins. The server predicts possible function of BPSL1549 in the regulation of helicase activity and molecular function, based on GO prediction for Biological Process (BP).
3D motif	MetaPocket 2.0	Resulted with top 3 pocket sites clustered from sites generated by 8 prediction tools, where each consists of large number of residues.
	ProBis	Returned 100 similar proteins with aligned residues from structural superposition, which include a putative ABC transporter (PDB chain: 4pe6A) with 11 aligned residues. The server predicted putative ligands of BPSL1549 protein for small molecules, proteins and ions. The server also predicted a binding site for Bromide ion, similarly reported by PDBeMotif.
	COFACTOR	Predicted PDB chains with similar binding sites for adenosine monophosphate, cerulenin, magnesium and sodium ions.
	GIRAF	Returned 100 structures with similar 3D templates, ranked by normalized GIRAF score, where top five hits consist of more than 10 aligned residues from structural superposition.
	PDBeMotif	The server reported matched small 3D motifs and a binding site for bromide ions within 5.0Å to the ligand.
	ProFunc	The server returned several hits from reverse template search that mapped to auto-generated templates from BPSL1549 protein itself, which include templates from several keap proteins.
	Ef-seek	Returned predicted ligand binding sites from matched PDB structures ranked by Z-score, which include binding sites for PDB ligand code of PEF, BCR, STE, and LIL.
	SA-mot	Predicted a functional candidate motif consisting of a fragment of seven residues that are continuous in sequence.
	SPRITE	Returned proteins with similar 3D template as BPSL1549 ranked by RMSD value. The hits include a chemotaxis methylation protein (2f9zD) where a residue arrangement of Thr88, Cys94, and His106 from BPSL1549 protein matches Thr21, Cys27, and His44 residues from the chemotaxis methylation protein.
	SuMo	Returned matching ligand binding sites sorted by site volume, which include binding sites for PDB ligand codes of ACT, PO4, MLI, SF4, and GLC.

Note: A listing of the results returned by the different services when the BPSL1549/3tu8 protein structure was used as a query to identify 3D motifs present in the structure.

should not be approached using a one size fits all solution and as such, other results may also warrant further investigation. For example, if two seemingly non-homologous structures that share no detectable sequence identity were to have 3D motifs that could be superimposed after using a 3D site search program such as SPRITE, PROBis and PINTS, their sequences can be manually aligned using the superposed arrangement as a reference point. The decision to proceed further with a particular motif can take into account a number of factors that are determined by the user depending on their own interests and motivation. The residues that match to sites from a database can be further extracted and submitted as a query for searching against a database of PDB structures. Computer programs such as RASMOT-3D Pro (Debret et al., 2009) and ASSAM (Nadzirin et al., 2012) are able to execute such queries.

Searching a Structure Database Using a 3D Motif Query

The obvious limitation of using a complete structure to query a motif database is the requirement of prior knowledge for the motifs while the clear advantage would be that such motifs would probably be well characterized with perhaps attached experimental annotations. Although it would be useful to be able to annotate a newly solved protein structure for known sites, there are situations where no prior knowledge exists of a motif that can be found for that query. In such a scenario, a visual examination or surface analysis of the structure may provide incipient information on potentially functional residues. Once the residues of interest have been identified, they can then be provided as queries to search for structures where similar arrangements occur. This approach does not require these sites to have been previously identified or annotated. If similar arrangements are found, contextual references and comparisons can then be made for the structures where the arrangements are present. In comparison to methods that use a whole structure input, there are fewer programs that are able to receive a pattern input for searching against a database of 3D structures. Two such services that are available on the web are ASSAM (Nadzirin et al., 2012) and RASMOT-3D Pro (Debret et al., 2009).

Although the RASMOT-3D Pro (Debret et al., 2009) and ASSAM (Nadzirin et al., 2012) programs essentially carry out the same type of search, where a motif in PDB format can be submitted as a query, the representation system used for the amino acids in 3D space are different. In the RASMOT-3D Pro program, the Cα and Cβ positions are used to represent a residue (Debret et al., 2009); while in ASSAM, the side chain positions are represented using pseudo-atom vectors (Nadzirin et al., 2012). This has been demonstrated to result in a different retrieval list because an overlapping side chain position may have extended from Cα atoms

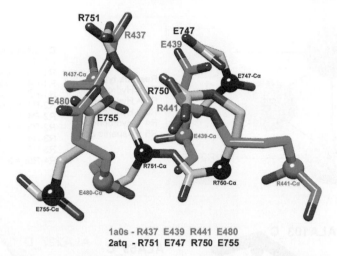

1a0s - R437 E439 R441 E480
2atq - R751 E747 R750 E755

Fig. 1 Superposition of Arg-Glu-Arg-Glu patterns found in two different protein structures. The superposition of an Arg-Glu-Arg-Glu pattern consisting of two arginine and two glutamic acid from a sucrose-specific porin (PDBID: 1a0s) (green) and a DNA polymerase (PDBID: 2atq) (blue) where the side chains overlap although the Cα atoms do not. The atoms are shown in ball-and-stick representation, Cα atoms as spheres, and all other atoms in stick representation.

that do not overlap (Nadzirin *et al.*, 2012) (**Fig. 1**). Therefore, a side chain based representation can be useful in cases of convergent evolution where the positions of the side chains remain conserved in 3D space in order to effect a specific chemical outcome such as catalysis. RASMOT-3D Pro offers the user an option of searching for the query motif in a set of up to 10 user provided structures; ASSAM only allows for pre-set database options.

Discovery of Novel Motifs Present Only in a Structural Context

With the exception of PDBeMotif (Golovin and Henrick, 2008) and IMAAAGINE (Nadzirin *et al.*, 2013), other programs listed in **Table 1** have a limitation where they require prior knowledge of the 3D motifs available for searching against, or the coordinates of a specific 3D arrangement to be provided as a search query. PDBeMotif and IMAAAGINE can carry out PDB searches using a query where the user can determine the type of amino acid and specify the distances between them without knowing how they are exactly arranged in 3D space. This overcomes the need for the user to define a specific pattern such as for several of the other previously listed programs in **Table 1**. Due to the use of pre-computed distance information within each single protein chain in a PDB file for its database, PDBeMotif only finds sub-structures if all the amino acids are in the same chain.

The IMAAAGINE program was engineered to carry out searches for a query that was designed by the user although it does not provide extensive key word querying capabilities such as in PDBeMotif. The IMAAAGINE queries can be very generic in nature such as: "are there arrangements where the side chain of an aspartic acid is surrounded by four hydrophobic residues?" (**Fig. 2**). The advantages of such a search capability are: (i) the ability to search for conserved 3D arrangements that are novel; and (ii) the ability to identify motifs present only in a structural context that are not detectable at the sequence level. This differs from the capability provided by other programs, such as RASMOT-3D Pro, ASSAM and SPRITE, that search a database of PDB structures for motifs. In these programs, prior knowledge of the motif is required to be provided as a PDB formatted input. However, in the case of IMAAAGINE, the user can approach a query based on a biochemical understanding of how a cluster of amino acids can be theoretically arranged in order to achieve a certain function. Since no prior knowledge is required regarding an exact arrangement of the amino acids to be used as a query, this allows for a broader search that may in turn retrieve hits that were not originally intended by the user.

Due to its flexible query input, the IMAAAGINE program has the capacity to retrieve highly conserved arrangements that may have been below the radar of standard structural analysis and annotation approaches. Furthermore, an IMAAAGINE search is not restricted by the location of residues to a particular chain or monomer in a multimeric assembly since it considers only the relative positions of a side chain representation to others based on calculated distances. The results of an IMAAAGINE search can therefore uncover arrangements, that if found to be highly conserved, can then be considered a novel 3D motif. Such motifs may prove to be functionally relevant although its conservation is identifiable only from a structural context and can therefore be not obvious from a purely sequence analysis approach. In the next section, case studies are presented that compare and illustrate the differences of the webservers discussed.

Illustrative Examples and Case Studies

Detection of 3D Motif in Protein Structure – Possible Functional Annotation of a Hypothetical Protein

The protein sequence encoded by the ORF *bpsl1549*, from the genome of the pathogen *Burkholderia pseudomallei*, was originally annotated as a hypothetical protein (Holden *et al.*, 2004) with no detectable sequence similarity to any sequences other than

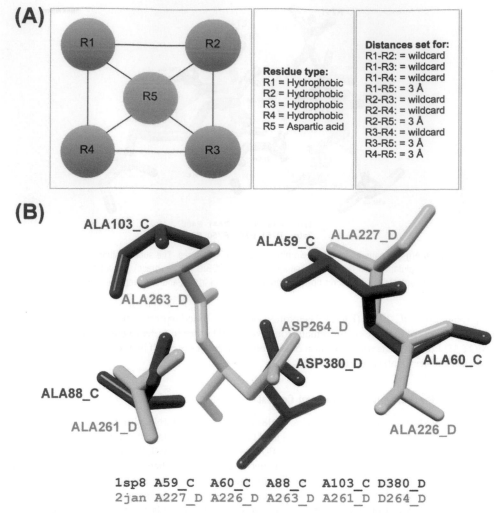

Fig. 2 An example of an IMAAAGINE query for a user-defined arrangement of amino acids. (A) This IMAAAGINE input example shows a search for an aspartic acid (R5) surrounded by four hydrophobic residues within the distance of 3.0 Å (R1-R4). (B) The retrieved overlapping side chains for the search is shown from the superposition of 3D patterns consisting of four alanine surrounding an aspartic acid from a 4-hydroxyphenylpyruvate dioxygenase (PDBID: 1sp8) and a tyrosyl-tRNA synthetase (PDBID: 2jan).

obvious homologs of itself within the Burkholderia genus. The crystallographic structure for BPSL1549 was then acquired (Cruz-Migoni *et al.*, 2011) (**Fig. 3(A)**) and fold comparisons using DALI revealed fold similarity to the catalytic domain of cytotoxic necrotizing factor 1 (CNF1-C) from *Escherichia coli* (PDB ID: 1hq0), with a Z-score of 9.5 and a chemotaxis deamidase from *Thermotoga maritima* (PDB ID: 2f9z) with a Z-score of 5.9 (**Fig. 3(B)**).

The structure of BPSL1549 (PDB ID: 3tu8) consists of a beta-sandwich fold surrounded by α-helices and loops (**Fig. 3(A)**) as similarly observed in the catalytic domain of CNF1-C (Cruz-Migoni *et al.*, 2011), an enzyme catalyzing glutamine deamidation that results in the alteration of the host cell actin cytoskeleton. This provided a clue that BPSL1549 may be involved in a similar activity and was compounded by the fact that a SPRITE search identified similarly arranged residues consisting Thr88, Cys94 and His106 in BPSL1549 that matched the CNF1-C catalytic triad consisting of Val833, Cys866 and His881, where the cysteine and histidine are conserved among such toxins and required for deamidation of glutamine (Buetow *et al.*, 2001; Cruz-Migoni *et al.*, 2011) (**Fig. 3(C)**). The SPRITE search also returned a similar arrangement of Thr-Cys-His shared with a chemotaxis deamidase from *T. maritima* (PDB ID: 2f9z) at an RMSD value of 0.49, thus signifying the possible role of BPSL1549 and the importance of such arrangement in glutamine deamidation. A search on SuMo web server on the other hand, returned a similar arrangement of Thr-His-Val shared between BLF1 and D-xylose isomerase from *Streptomyces rubiginosus* (PDB IDs: 3kbn and 1xic) (Kovalevsky *et al.*, 2011; Carrell *et al.*, 1994).

COFACTOR and ProFunc were used to search for possible homologs of BPSL1549 and both servers returned a different set of similar structures and GO terms prediction. The COFACTOR server proposed a possible role for BPSL1549 in glutamate N-acetyltransferase activity for Molecular Function (MF) and arginine biosynthesis for Biological Process (BP) prediction, while ProFunc predicted the function of BLF1 to be involved in regulation of helicase activity and molecular function for Biological Process (BP) prediction. The information from different servers can prove useful collectively (**Fig. 3(D)**) as it was ultimately proven that BPSL1549 is a deamidase that converts Gln to Glu on its target molecule, the translation initiation factor eIF4A which has a

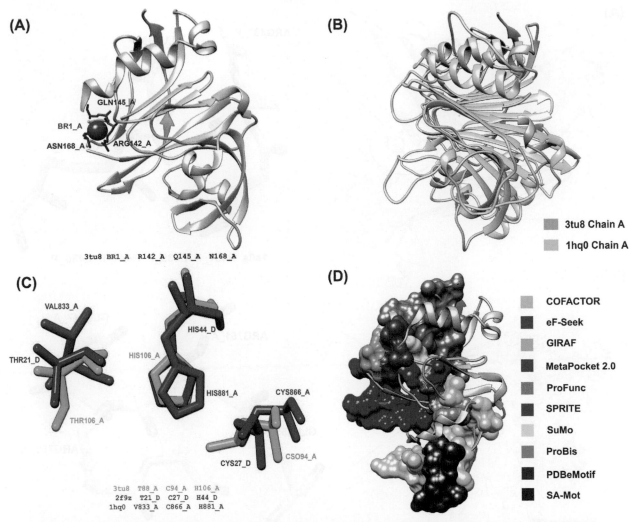

Fig. 3 Detection of 3D motif using various 3D motif searching methods. (A) Ribbon representation of a crystal structure of BPSL1549 from *Burkhodleria pseudomallei* (PDBID: 3tu8). The residues binding the bromide ion (in red) are displayed as blue sticks. (B) The BPSL1549 (PDBID: 3tu8) in tan color and the CNF1-C (PDBID: 1hq0) in light blue color are shown in ribbon representation, after the superposition. (C) Superposition of catalytic triad residues from chemotaxis deamidase (PDBID: 2f9z) (red) and CNF1-C (PDBID: 1hq0) (magenta) to BPSL1549 (PDBID: 3tu8) (cyan). (D) A graphical representation displaying the BPSL1549/3tu8 structure with the output from various webservers (in different colors) mapped onto it in molecular surface representation.

helicase function (Cruz-Migoni *et al.*, 2011). This resulted in the renaming of BPSL1549 to Burkholderia lethal factor 1 (BLF1) due to it being the first confirmed toxin for *B. pseudomallei*. Similar residues for the bromine ligand binding site was detected by ProBis and PDBeMotif – Gln145, Arg142, and Asn168 with no other protein sharing a similar residue arrangement. **Table 2** summarizes the findings when BLF1 (PDB ID: 3tu8) was used a the search query.

Detection of Arg-Glu-Arg-Glu Query Motif in Database of PDB Structures

It is also a common approach to visualize a structure using the various molecular graphics software available in order to glean some insights into the function of a newly solved structure. Through such visual inspections, specific residue arrangements of interest can be identified – for example arrangements that may have potential as a catalytic site or ligand binding site. It then becomes useful to identify whether such similar residue arrangements exist in other structures and whether there are known functions associated with them. To demonstrate this, a four residue arrangement consisting of Arg, Glu, Arg, Glu (RERE – **Fig. 4(A)**) from a *Salmonella typhimurium* sucrose-specific porin (PDB ID: 1a0s) was extracted from the main PDB file and submitted as an ASSAM search. The 1a0s structure was classified as a LamB porin domain (PFAM accession: PF02264) in PFAM and contains 16 antiparallel strands with several binding sites for glycosyl groups along the channel involved in sugar transport (Forst *et al.*, 1998) **(Fig. 4(A))**.

The ASSAM search retrieved a RERE arrangement in a fusion protein consisting of a DNA polymerase with a single-stranded DNA binding protein (PDB ID: 2atq; **Fig. 4(B)**). The R437, E439, R441, E480 side-chains from 1a0s are similarly arranged spatially with R751, E747, R750 E755 from 2atq **(Fig. 4)**. The 2atq structure consists of an N-terminal domain that allows binding of T4/

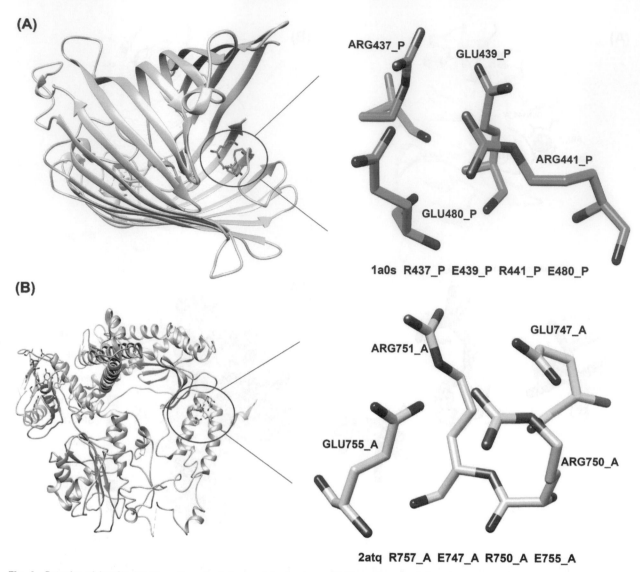

Fig. 4 Detection of Arg-Glu-Arg-Glu patterns in distinct protein structures. (A) The pattern consisting of two arginine and two glutamic acid (RERE) in a sucrose-specific porin (PDBID: 1a0s) is depicted as sticks (green) and magnified on the right panel. (B) The same RERE arrangement in a DNA-polymerase (PDBID: 2atq) depicted as sticks (light blue) and magnified in the right panel.

RB69 single-stranded DNA binding protein to single-stranded DNA, a C-terminal domain that mediates the interaction with accessory proteins and a DNA-binding domain that binds to single-stranded DNA (Sun *et al.*, 2006) (**Fig. 4(B)**). It is clear that the two structures do not share any similar sequence or fold despite the fact that these four side-chains form a restricted spatial arrangement present in both structures that can be 3-dimensionally superimposed (**Fig. 1**). From the superpositions, it is evident that the overlap occurs at the side-chain positions and not at the alpha-carbon positions thus making them potentially significant in terms of the functional chemistry for both molecules. However, in cases when conservation is at the core back-bone level with variations in the spatial arrangements of the side-chain leading to slightly different chemistry – such as different target ligands for the site, then the RASMOT-3D Pro server would be a more suitable option to search with.

Discussions and Future Directions

The capacity to infer function by associating the chemical capacity or functional potential of 3D motifs is an important step towards the computational annotation and ultimate functional characterization of the many structures of proteins with uncharacterized functions. Nevertheless, most computational function annotation is still carried out at the primary structure or amino acid sequence level. While many of the programs discussed in this article may be able to make associations between conserved 3D amino acid arrangements in proteins of unrelated sequences and folds, there is still a need for novel 3D motifs to be identified using mainstream sequence analysis, especially 3D motifs that are functionally relevant only in a structural context.

As an example, a 3D interface between three chains of the same sequence that consists of a single residue, each at the interface, such as histidine, can be considered a three histidine tertiary motif. However, such a 3D motif will only be represented by a single residue and position in the sequence. This therefore necessitates the development of programs that are able to bridge the gap and identify such single residue motifs perhaps via machine learning approaches using the physico-chemical profiles of the surrounding residues once they are identified as structurally contextual motifs. The information from such investigations can therefore be incorporated back into sequence level analysis thus allowing for accurate identification of motifs that are relevant only in a structural context.

Closing Remarks

The ability to search for similar 3D arrangements of amino acids is of great utility in the post-genomics era, especially in light of the many structural genomics initiatives. However, there is no clear one-stop service or one size fits all solution at present. Despite this, expert use of the available tools and services have been proven as useful means of providing insights towards a line of enquiry that can ultimately enable the functions of uncharacterized proteins to be successfully determined.

Acknowledgement

MFR is funded by the Ministry of Science, Technology and Innovation grant 02-01-02-SF1278.

See also: Biomolecular Structures: Prediction, Identification and Analyses. Natural Language Processing Approaches in Bioinformatics. Study of The Variability of The Native Protein Structure

References

Angarica, V., Perez, A., Vasconcelos, A., Collado-Vides, J., Contreras-Moreira, B., 2008. Prediction of TF target sites based on atomistic models of protein-DNA complexes. BMC Bioinform. 9, 436.

Artymiuk, P.J., Poirrette, A.R., Rice, D.W., Willett, P., 1997. A polymerase I palm in adenylyl cyclase? Nature 388, 33–34.

Buetow, L., Flatau, G., Chiu, K., Boquet, P., Ghosh, P., 2001. Structure of the Rho-activating domain of Escherichia coli cytotoxic necrotizing factor 1. Nat. Struct. Mol. Biol. 8, 584–588.

Carrell, H.L., Hoier, H., Glusker, J.P., 1994. Modes of binding substrates and their analogues to the enzyme D-xylose isomerase. Acta Crystallogr. D Biol. Crystallogr. 50, 113–123.

Chothia, C., 1992. Proteins. One thousand families for the molecular biologist. Nature 357, 543–544.

Chothia, C., Lesk, A.M., 1986. The relation between the divergence of sequence and structure in proteins. EMBO J. 5, 823–826.

Contreras-Moreira, B., 2010. 3D-footprint: A database for the structural analysis of protein – DNA complexes. Nucleic Acids Res. 38, D91–D97.

Cruz-Migoni, A., Hautbergue, G.M., Artymiuk, P.J., et al., 2011. A Burkholderia pseudomallei toxin inhibits helicase activity of translation factor eIF4A. Science 334, 821–824.

Debret, G., Martel, A., Cuniasse, P., 2009. RASMOT-3D PRO: A 3D motif search webserver. Nucleic Acids Res. 37, W459–W464.

Eisenstein, E., Gilliland, G.L., Herzberg, O., et al., 2000. Biological function made crystal clear – Annotation of hypothetical proteins via structural genomics. Curr. Opin. Biotechnol. 11, 25–30.

Forst, D., Welte, W., Wacker, T., Diederichs, K., 1998. Structure of the sucrose-specific porin ScrY from Salmonella typhimurium and its complex with sucrose. Nat. Struct. Mol. Biol. 5, 37–46.

Gibrat, J.-F., Madej, T., Bryant, S.H., 1996. Surprising similarities in structure comparison. Curr. Opin. Struct. Biol. 6, 377–385.

Golovin, A., Henrick, K., 2008. MSDmotif: Exploring protein sites and motifs. BMC Bioinform. 9, 312.

Holden, M.T., Titball, R.W., Peacock, S.J., et al., 2004. Genomic plasticity of the causative agent of melioidosis, Burkholderia pseudomallei. Proc. Natl. Acad. Sci. USA 101, 14240–14245.

Holm, L., Kaariainen, S., Wilton, C., Plewczynski, D., 2006. Using Dali for structural comparison of proteins. Curr. Protoc. Bioinform. (Chapter 55.5.1–5.5.24).

Jambon, M., Andrieu, O., Combet, C., et al., 2005. The SuMo server: 3D search for protein functional sites. Bioinformatics 21, 3929–3930.

Jones, S., Daley, D.T.A., Luscombe, N.M., Berman, H.M., Thornton, J.M., 2001. Protein – RNA interactions: A structural analysis. Nucleic Acids Res. 29, 943–954.

Kinjo, A.R., Nakamura, H., 2007. Similarity search for local protein structures at atomic resolution by exploiting a database management system. Biophysics (Nagoya-shi) 3, 75–84.

Kinjo, A.R., Nakamura, H., 2009. Comprehensive structural classification of ligand-binding motifs in proteins. Structure 17, 234–246.

Kinjo, A.R., Nakamura, H., 2010. Geometric similarities of protein–protein interfaces at atomic resolution are only observed within homologous families: An exhaustive structural classification study. J. Mol. Biol. 399, 526–540.

Kinoshita, K., Murakami, Y., Nakamura, H., 2007. eF-seek: Prediction of the functional sites of proteins by searching for similar electrostatic potential and molecular surface shape. Nucleic Acids Res 35, W398–W402.

Konc, J., Janezic, D., 2010. ProBiS algorithm for detection of structurally similar protein binding sites by local structural alignment. Bioinformatics 26, 1160–1168.

Kovalevsky, A.Y., Hanson, L., Fisher, S.Z., et al., 2011. Metal ion roles and the movement of hydrogen during the reaction catalyzed by D-xylose isomerase: A joint X-ray and neutron diffraction study. Structure 18, 688–699.

Laskowski, R.A., Luscombe, N.M., Swindells, M.B., Thornton, J.M., 1996. Protein clefts in molecular recognition and function. Protein Sci. 5, 2438–2452.

Laskowski, R.A., Watson, J.D., Thornton, J.M., 2005. ProFunc: A server for predicting protein function from 3D structure. Nucleic Acids Res. 33, W89–W93.

Levitt, M., 2007. Growth of novel protein structural data. Proc. Natl. Acad. Sci. USA 104, 3183–3188.

Luscombe, N.M., Laskowski, R.A., Thornton, J.M., 2001. Amino acid–base interactions: A three-dimensional analysis of protein–DNA interactions at an atomic level. Nucleic Acids Res. 29, 2860–2874.

Malik, A., Firoz, A., Jha, V., Ahmad, S., 2010. PROCARB: A database of known and modelled carbohydrate-binding protein structures with sequence-based prediction tools. Adv. Bioinform. 436036.

Nadzirin, N., Firdaus-Raih, M., 2012. Proteins of unknown function in the Protein Data Bank (PDB): An inventory of true uncharacterized proteins and computational tools for their analysis. Int. J. Mol. Sci. 13, 12761–12772.

Nadzirin, N., Gardiner, E.J., Willett, P., Artymiuk, P.J., Firdaus-Raih, M., 2012. SPRITE and ASSAM: Web servers for side chain 3D-motif searching in protein structures. Nucleic Acids Res. 40, W380–W386.

Nadzirin, N., Willett, P., Artymiuk, P.J., Firdaus-Raih, M., 2013. IMAAAGINE: A webserver for searching hypothetical 3D amino acid side chain arrangements in the protein data bank. Nucleic Acids Res. 41, W432–W440.

Porter, C.T., Bartlett, G.J., Thornton, J.M., 2004. The Catalytic Site Atlas: A resource of catalytic sites and residues identified in enzymes using structural data. Nucleic Acids Res. 32, D129–D133.

Raih, M.F., Ahmad, S., Zheng, R., Mohamed, R., 2005. Solvent accessibility in native and isolated domain environments: General features and implications to interface predictability. Biophys. Chem. 114, 63–69.

Regad, L., Martin, J., Nuel, G., Camproux, A.-C., 2010. Mining protein loops using a structural alphabet and statistical exceptionality. BMC Bioinform. 11, 75.

Rose, P.W., Prlic, A., Altunkaya, A., et al., 2017. The RCSB protein data bank: Integrative view of protein, gene and 3D structural information. Nucleic Acids Res. 45, D271–D281.

Roy, A., Yang, J., Zhang, Y., 2012. COFACTOR: An accurate comparative algorithm for structure-based protein function annotation. Nucleic Acids Res. 40, W471–W477.

Selvaraj, S., Kono, H., Sarai, A., 2002. Specificity of Protein – DNA Recognition Revealed by Structure-based Potentials: Symmetric/asymmetric and Cognate/Non-cognate Binding. J. Mol. Biol. 322, 907–915.

Shulman-Peleg, A., Shatsky, M., Nussinov, R., Wolfson, H.J., 2008. MultiBind and MAPPIS: Webservers for multiple alignment of protein 3D-binding sites and their interactions. Nucleic Acids Res. 36, W260–W264.

Stark, A., Sunyaev, S., Russell, R.B., 2003. A model for statistical significance of local similarities in structure. J. Mol. Biol. 326, 1307–1316.

Sun, S., Geng, L., Shamoo, Y., 2006. Structure and enzymatic properties of a chimeric bacteriophage RB69 DNA polymerase and single-stranded DNA binding protein with increased processivity. Proteins 65, 231–238.

Velankar, S., Dana, J.M., Jacobsen, J., et al., 2013. SIFTS: Structure integration with function, taxonomy and sequences resource. Nucleic Acids Res. 41, D483–D489.

Ye, Y., Godzik, A., 2004. FATCAT: A web server for flexible structure comparison and structure similarity searching. Nucleic Acids Res. 32, W582–W585.

Zhang, Z., Li, Y., Lin, B., Schroeder, M., Huang, B., 2011. Identification of cavities on protein surface using multiple computational approaches for drug binding site prediction. Bioinformatics. 27, 2083–2088.

Computational Protein Engineering Approaches for Effective Design of New Molecules

Jaspreet Kaur Dhanjal, Vidhi Malik, Navaneethan Radhakrishnan, Moolchand Sigar, Anjani Kumari, and Durai Sundar,
DBT-AIST International Laboratory for Advanced Biomedicine (DAILAB), Indian Institute of Technology Delhi, New Delhi, India

Introduction

Proteins are one of the most important building blocks of the body, and are comprised of 20 different amino acids. They display a wide variety of functions including structural, catalytic, sensory, motility, immune response, transport, and many more. Owing to such diverse functions, proteins have attracted a lot of attention in the fields of agriculture, therapeutics, and industry. Protein engineering, in general, involves either synthesis of new proteins or alteration of existing protein structure and sequence in order to achieve desired functions. It aims at improving catalytic properties, stability (thermal, pH, solvent), specificity, and yield of proteins, and finds wide applications in the fields of medicine, nanotechnology, biopolymer production, detergent, and food industry.

In the early 1980s, the advancement in the field of recombinant DNA technology enabled the engineering of proteins that was mediated via changes in the proteins' amino acid sequence (Ulmer, 1983). Subsequently several other methods were developed for engineering proteins including random mutagenesis, site directed mutagenesis, evolutionary methods, domain shuffling, and others. Subtilisins in detergent industry; tissue plasminogen activator (tPA) in heart attack and stroke treatment; Humalog, Novolog, and Apidra (engineered insulin) for diabetes treatment; and engineered amylases and lipases used in food industry are some of the examples of commercially available engineered proteins (Walsh, 2007; Turanli-Yildiz et al., 2012). Despite being so promising, widespread application of protein engineering techniques was limited owing to labor-intensive and time-consuming protocols, and use of large amount of resources.

In the past few decades, a tremendous revolution in computational protein engineering has helped protein manipulation in overcoming the above mentioned barriers. Novel protein design algorithms, advancement in structural bioinformatics, molecular force fields, and availability of immense information regarding 3D protein structure in databases like Protein Data Bank have revolutionized the field of computational protein engineering. Computational protein designing broadly focuses on (1) generation of *de novo* amino acid sequences that can adopt stable 3D structure, or modification of the existing scaffold to improve the stability of the protein in non-native environment, and (2) evolving newer functions in proteins by harnessing information from known crystal structures (Alvizo and Mayo, 2008). A schematic representation of common computational protein engineering approaches is illustrated in **Fig. 1**. These include (1) *de novo* protein modeling, (2) rational designing of proteins based on existing structural templates, and (3) statistical modeling. *De novo* protein structure prediction methods make use of general protein folding principles and energetics (deduced from native structures) to assign tertiary structures to the sequence of amino acids. It is generally used for the sequences with no close homologs with experimentally solved structures. *De novo* methods involve vast computations and hence are so far limited to small proteins only. In rational designing approach, rather than attempting to start from scratch, the experimentally known protein structures can be utilized as templates to build on. This approach at least ensures the *in vivo* stability of the engineered proteins. Here, the rationale is to look for the part of protein that is less important for proper folding, and remodel it to introduce new functionality. Statistical modeling or the data-driven approaches are used to infer relationships between protein sequence, structure, and function from experimental data. These learning algorithms are based on the fact that the amino acids comprising the proteins encode their chemical properties and govern their biological functions. These statistical models are capable of capturing the global behavior of proteins, are not biased, and therefore can be used to make predictions for novel sequences.

Some of the commonly used computational algorithms and approaches for aiding in protein engineering include dead-end elimination (DEE), molecular dynamics simulations, Monte Carlo simulated annealing, and genetic algorithms (Park et al., 2004; Floudas et al., 2006). Many tools are available to computationally evaluate the effect of changes made in the protein structure. For example, *SCHEMA* is a tool that calculates DNA recombination mediated disruption in terms of the *E* value (where *E* is the average disruption of residue contact). The engineered protein with low *E* value is taken further to achieve functionally active modified protein that is less identical to the parent protein (Meyer et al., 2003). Protein Sequence Activity Relationships (ProSAR) is another tool that can sort diverse mutations by predicting their effect on desired protein activity and thus providing mutants that are highly improved in comparison to the wild-type protein (Fox et al., 2007). *Rosseta*, the most commonly used computational method, aims at creating new biocatalysts from existing template structure, taking into account an active site's quantum mechanical parameters and carrying out design around the reaction's transition state (Rothlisberger et al., 2008; Der et al., 2013). A few other computational protein design tools include FoldX, FlexPreD, and Iterative Protein Redesign and Optimization (IPRO) (Li et al., 2012; Verma et al., 2012; Saraf et al., 2006). **Table 1** lists some of these commonly used tools with their brief description.

A large number of successful stories of protein engineering are reported in the literature. The structures predicted by computational methods have been shown to have atomic level accuracy with respect to NMR structure of protein (Murphy et al., 2015). Recently, a peptide design was reported that mimicked the N-trimer region of the GP2 fusion protein of the Ebola virus, which is a potential target for drugs (Clinton et al., 2015).

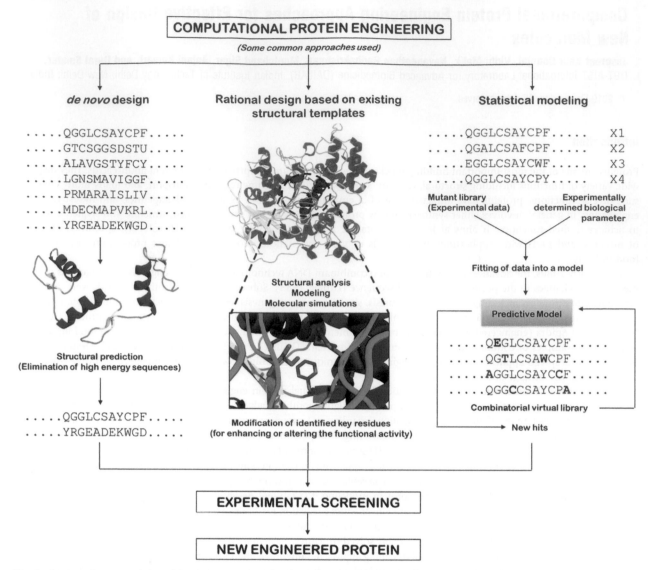

Fig. 1 A schematic representation of the common computational protein engineering approaches: *de novo* designing, protein engineering based on the existing templates, and statistical modeling.

The available computational methods are robust and help in decoding the information hidden in the sequences for protein engineering. Most of the biochemical processes depend upon the specificity of interacting proteins in a crowded cellular environment. Also the stability of the structured proteins influences the formation of functional complexes to initiate the biological response. Thus, the efficiency of any such interaction is primarily governed by two factors: stability and specificity. So, rational re-engineering of proteins must involve improvement in stability, and reduction in affinity for competing binders. Maintaining a balance between the stability and specificity has always remained a challenging task and holds potential implications for the development of newer tools based on existing biological systems for varied applications. Here, successful stories of proteins that have been engineered using various computational approaches have been discussed, with a focus on three important aspects: protein specificity, stability, and novel functionality.

Applications of Computational Protein Engineering

Alteration in the *Specificity* of Macromolecules by Structural Modifications

The function of nearly all proteins depends on their ability to bind other molecules, or ligands, with a high degree of specificity. High specificity in proteins makes them important players for many industrial and therapeutic applications. Specificity, in simple words, can be described as the ability of a protein to bind one molecule in preference to other molecules. In this section, we have

Table 1 Computational tools for engineering of proteins

Protein engineering approach	Resource	Description
De novo designing	PyRosetta Toolkit (Adolf-Bryfogle and Dunbrack, 2013)	Graphical user interface for de novo designing of proteins using Rosetta toolkit
	EvoDesign (Mitra et al., 2013)	Structure and evolutionary profile based search to design proteins
	ORBIT (Dahiyat and Mayo, 1996)	Uses rotamer description of side chains to predict the most optimal geometry for any amino acid sequence from vast number of possible solutions
	POCKETOPTIMIZER (Stiel et al., 2016)	Optimizes protein-binding site for new ligand
	SABER (Nosrati and Houk, 2012)	Selection of active/binding sites for enzyme redesign (SABER). Designs new active/binding site by identifying protein active sites with similar arrangement of catalytic residues from PDB
	DEEPer (Hallen et al., 2013)	Algorithm for protein engineering through generation of ensemble of protein backbone and side chain flexibility
Structure or template based designing	DEZYMER (Hellinga and Richards, 1991)	Utilizes backbone information to identify positions of residues to be modified for incorporation of new binding site
	CAVER (Chovancova et al., 2012)	Uses molecular dynamics simulation trajectories to identify tunnel and channel characteristics from large ensemble of protein conformations. This information can be utilized to engineer phenomena of molecular transport, enzymatic catalysis, and molecular recognition
	Metal Search (Clarke and Yuan, 1995)	Uses backbone coordinates to identify cluster of residues that can form tetrahedral metal binding site upon replacement with Cys or His
	FlexPred (Kuznetsov and Mcduffie, 2008)	Web server to predict protein flexibility by recognizing residues involved in conformational switches
Statistical modeling	FoldX (Schymkowitz et al., 2005)	An empirical force-field based method designed to check the effect of mutations on stability and folding dynamics of proteins
	AUTO-MUTE (Masso and Vaisman, 2010)	Web server based on machine learning algorithms designed for predicting effect of mutations on stability of proteins
	iPTREE-STAB (Huang et al., 2007)	Utilizes decision tree algorithm to discriminate between stabilizing and destabilizing mutations; employs regression and classification tree algorithm for prediction of effect of mutations on protein stability
	MuD (Wainreb et al., 2010)	Mutation Detector (MuD): utilizes Random Forest based algorithm to discriminate between functionally neutral and non-neutral mutations. It utilizes structure and sequence information to predict the effect of mutations on protein function
	PEAT-SA (Johnston et al., 2011)	Empirical based method to predict the effect of mutation on ligand affinity, pKa values and stability of protein

discussed some examples where computational approaches have been used to enhance the specificity of the proteins for their successful diverse applications.

Computational design of zinc finger proteins for specific binding to DNA sequences

Zinc finger nucleases (ZFNs) are promising genome engineering tools having the potential to edit DNA at the molecular level, thereby paving the way for many biological applications. These chimeric proteins are made up of two domains, one that recognizes specific DNA sequence within the complete genome and the other is a non-specific endonuclease domain that helps in introducing a double stranded break in the target sequence. The versatility of the ZFNs in the field of targeted genome editing is attributed to its DNA binding domain, which is made up of three zinc finger (ZF) motifs linked using short spacer sequences (Urnov et al., 2005).

These ZF proteins comprise the largest family of transcription factors in eukaryotes. Each ZF motif contains amino acids folded into a $\beta\beta\alpha$-structure. Extensive structural studies revealed that the modular structure remains highly conserved and the specificity of these factors toward their target DNA relies only on four amino acids, positioned at $-1, 2, 3,$ and 6 residues with respect to the start of alpha helix (Elrod-Erickson et al., 1998; Wolfe et al., 2000; Pabo et al., 2001). Soon, it was realized that these positions can be altered artificially for changing the binding specificity of these motifs toward some other sequences. Knowledge of ZF motifs with the ability to recognize all possible DNA codons thus became a prime objective of the scientific community to gain the power for constructing artificial ZFPs for the purpose of genome manipulation for therapeutic advantages.

Experimental techniques for engineering ZF proteins by rational designing or selection from large libraries, despite being useful, were time consuming, expensive, laborious, and not accessible in academic settings (Beerli and Barbas, 2002; Greisman and Pabo, 1997). Also, randomization of all 20 amino acids at essential DNA contact positions even in three finger ZF proteins can result in an enormously huge number of possibilities that become impossible to handle experimentally. Therefore, only partial libraries could be constructed by restricting the substitution at variable sites with some key amino acid residues. Thus, one possible solution was to computationally design ZF proteins using screening or prediction algorithms.

Construction of the first non-natural ZF motif using computational approach was first reported in 1997 (Dahiyat and Mayo, 1997). A virtual combinatorial library consisting of 1.9×10^{27} amino acid sequences was constructed. This library size was reported to be 15 times larger than the random libraries obtained by experimental approaches. The size of possibilities further increased to 1.1×10^{62} by explicitly considering the rotamers of each possible amino acid at each possible position. DEE algorithm was used to find globally optimal sequences in their optimal conformations. The library was screened using an algorithm designed on the basis of physiochemical potential functions and stereochemical constraints. The structure of top ranking sequence hit was solved using nuclear magnetic resonance spectroscopy and was found to be well-ordered and in agreement with the design target structure, Zif-268. This study demonstrated the potential of computational techniques for searching huge combinatorial libraries, essential for designing novel proteins with high specificity (Dahiyat and Mayo, 1997).

Consequently, many prediction tools were developed based on the knowledge gained from the growing structural information on ZF proteins. These tools can basically be divided into two categories: (1) tools developed using experimental sequence- or structure-based data, and (2) tools simulating the biochemical interactions between ZF protein and its target DNA and estimating the specificity of binding (Grover et al., 2010). Here, we briefly discuss a few tools to give an insight to the approach these tools use for computational design of ZF proteins. *Zinc Finger Tools* is a web-based utility that makes use of 49 different helices that can recognize 16 GNN, 15 ANN, 15 CNN, and 3 TNN DNA triplets. The search tool looks for all possible target sites (adjacent or interspaced) formed by any of these DNA triplets on either strand. It also reports the specificity of the ZF protein predicted using these domains from the results of a multi-target ELISA specificity assay carried out for individual ZF. Apart from predicting ZF proteins for a given sequence, the tool can also predict the probable binding site for a given ZF protein (Mandell and Barbas, 2006). Further, along with the information of the binders (i.e., known examples of high affinity ZFs and their corresponding targets), weak and non-binders were used in the development of another tool. This predicts the most optimal ZF proteins for a given DNA sequence using support vector machines (Persikov et al., 2009). *Zif-Predict* is a sequence-based tool employing artificial neural networks for prediction of ZF proteins for the input nucleotide sequence. An advantage of this tool is that it takes into account the binding preference of one amino acid in the presence of another in its neighborhood, called the synergistic mode of binding (Molparia et al., 2010). Another addition to this league is Zif-Predict Interfacial Hydrogen Bond Energy (IHBE) that uses hydrogen bond energies between amino acid residues and nucleotides to predict the highest affinity ZF proteins for the user-input DNA. This is carried out by using energies calculated for all possible combinations of triplets and ZFs with different amino acids at 4 crucial positions $(-1, +2, +3, +6)$, thus covering the complete interaction sample set (Dutta et al., 2016b). *ZifNN* is a tool different from the ones mentioned above. It does not depend upon the experimental data, rather uses an *in silico* derived data set of 50 three-dimensional ZF protein-DNA complexes and the estimation of hydrogen bond energies. The predictions are made using neural network models (Dutta et al., 2016a). In addition to this, attempts were also made to improve the *in silico* modeling of ZF protein-DNA docked complexes using HADDOCK (Chou et al., 2010). The number of sequences that can be targeted using engineered ZF proteins can be tremendously increased by designing ZF motifs for nearby but not contiguous regions in DNA. For this, a linker with appropriate length that can help in skipping the nucleotides not to be targeted while helping the next motif to correctly align with the DNA triplet is designed. A computational model has been developed for structure-based design of protein linkers for ZFNs that can skip up to 10 bp between adjacent ZF, recognized DNA triplet in the target genomic sequence (Anand et al., 2013). All these efforts have taken the computational design of ZF proteins to the next level.

Structure-based computational engineering of a therapeutic antibody for improving its binding affinity

High specificity and affinity of antibodies are routinely being exploited for therapeutic and industrial purposes. These molecules are an excellent choice for fabricating diagnostic kits and biosensors.

Antibody–antigen complexes display an intense network of interactions involving multiple non-covalent bonds, making it difficult to quantify these interactions at the molecular and atomic levels. However, advancement in computational power and understanding of biological systems has led to the development of force-field parameters that can help in simulating these systems *in silico* (Barderas et al., 2008; Park and Jeon, 2011). Here, we have discussed a recent report where structure-based computational techniques have been used to improve the biotherapeutic potential of 11K2 antibody (Kiyoshi et al., 2014). The main objective of the study was to increase the binding affinity of 11K2 for its target antigen, monocyte chemotactic protein-1 (MCP-1). MCP-1 is a key player in many inflammatory diseases like arteriosclerosis, allergy, and rheumatoid arthritis. Knowledge gained from the crystal structure of K2-MCP-1 complex (PDB ID: 2BDN) suggested that the binding affinity of the antibody can further be increased by optimizing the complementarity determining region (CDR) of the variable domain of the light chain (VL). The interaction surface between the CDR of the VL and MCP-1 was found to be much smaller than that of the CDR of the variable domain of the heavy chain (VH) (Kiyoshi et al., 2014).

Firstly, the 62 amino acids forming the CDR of 11K2 were mutated *in silico* with another 19 possible amino acids to generate a virtual library of 1178 mutants of 11K2. For each mutation, 100 randomized models were generated using MODELLER, Discovery

Studio Suite. Each model was further optimized by using a combination of simulated annealing and molecular mechanics minimization. Similarly, 1000 structures for the wild-type Ab were also generated to be considered as reference. The mutants with more favorable energy of interaction than the wild-type 11K2 were then selected for *in vitro* examination. It was observed that the selected candidates were the ones with substitution by a charged residue (Arg, Lys, Glu, or Asp). The technique of surface plasmon resonance spectroscopy was then used to calculate the kinetic rate constants of the binding of wild-type 11K2 and engineered single-mutants to immobilized MCP-1. The enhanced affinity of the new models was attributed to slower dissociation rate constants rather than faster association rate constants (Kiyoshi *et al.*, 2014). This structure based computational engineering of therapeutic antibody led to approximately 5-fold increase in affinity of Ab for its target antigen and hence strongly reflects upon the potential of computational protein engineering in the coming era (Kiyoshi *et al.*, 2014).

Computational approaches for studying the dynamics of CRISPR-Cas9 system and predicting their binding specificity

CRISPR (Clustered Regularly Interspaced Short Palindromic Repeats) system has become a sensational genome editing technology in recent days. This system consists of two components: a guide RNA and a Cas9 (CRISPR associated protein 9) nuclease. The 5′ end of guide RNA contains the 20-nucleotide stretch complementary to the region of interest in genome followed by a protospacer adjacent motif. This CRISPR RNA drives the Cas9 nuclease to this complementary site in DNA and guides it to introduce a double strand break (DSB) in that region. Hence, Cas9 can be directed to produce DSB in any region in the genomic DNA that is of the form N(20)-NGG by designing guide RNA with the complementary sequence of target (Hsu *et al.*, 2014; Doudna and Charpentier, 2014; Ran *et al.*, 2013b). Designing the experiment using CRISPR is simple and promising; however the major drawback that is limiting its widespread use for industrial and therapeutic purposes is its off-target activity (Tsai *et al.*, 2015). The guide RNA-Cas9 complex can bind and cleave other unintended regions in the genome having sequence similarity with the target region. A major part of published studies in CRISPR is thus aimed at understanding the factors governing and improving the specificity of the system (Doudna and Charpentier, 2014; Hsu *et al.*, 2014; Chéron *et al.*, 2017; Ran *et al.*, 2013b).

Modifications to the actual system were designed to tackle this problem of off-target activity. The strategy of paired nickases was developed, which reduces the off-target activity by 50–1500 without affecting the on-target activity (Shen *et al.*, 2014; Ran *et al.*, 2013a). fCas9 is another strategy similar to paired nickases produced by fusing inactive dCas9 (Cas9 that lacks endonuclease activity) with one of the two monomers of *FokI* endonuclease. Hence, to make a DSB, fusion of two fCas9 monomers is required. Each monomer is complexed with a guide RNA that binds to targets 15–25 base pairs apart in the region of interest to make a DSB (Guilinger *et al.*, 2014). It has also been shown that usage of truncated guide RNAs (17 nt) led to decreased off-target activity (Fu *et al.*, 2014). Despite these efforts, off-target activity could not be avoided. Checking for potential sites similar to the target DNA locus therefore becomes a prerequisite to prevent wastage of time and resources.

A number of computational tools have been developed and are available online for selecting a potential target within the region of interest in the genome with least or no off-target activity. *CHOPCHOP, CCTop, E-CRISP, Cas-OFFinder, GT-Scan, sgRNAcas9,* and *MIT CRISPR Design* are some of the popular tools among them (Xie *et al.*, 2014; O'brien and Bailey, 2014; Heigwer *et al.*, 2014; Montague *et al.*, 2014; Labun *et al.*, 2016; Stemmer *et al.*, 2015; Bae *et al.*, 2014; Ran *et al.*, 2013b). These tools generally use similarity search methods to find off-target sites for each target and rank them. However, theoretically there is no single tool that accurately predicts all possible off-target mutations for a target site.

Another approach to improve specificity of Cas9 was engineering it through structure-guided protein engineering techniques. This method was based on studying the available crystal structure of Cas9 complexed with guide RNA and DNA and hypothesizing mutations that improve specificity. The detailed investigation of the system can be done using computational approaches. It was found from the structure that non-target strand of DNA was stabilized by a charged groove in Cas9 located in between HNH, RuvC, and PAM recognition domain. It was hypothesized that if the positively charged residues in this non-target charged groove is neutralized, it might encourage rehybridization of the DNA thereby reducing the mismatch tolerance in RNA–DNA binding. Hence mutants with individual substitutions in the 31 residues in the non-target groove were generated and their specificity was studied. Five of the 31 mutants showed decreased off-target activity by a factor of 10 compared to the wild type. After performing combinatorial mutagenesis studies using top performing mutants from previous screening, three were identified to be efficient. They were (1) SpCas9 (K855A), (2) mSpCas9 (K810A/K1003A/R1060A) or eSpCas9(1.0), and (3) SpCas9 (K848A/K1003A/R1060A) or eSpCas9(1.1). All three were assessed for specificity and their off-target activity was found to be significantly lower than that of wild type (Slaymaker *et al.*, 2016; Doudna and Charpentier, 2014; Ran *et al.*, 2013b).

Recently, researchers have started using molecular dynamics simulations to study the activity of Cas9-guide RNA complex. Conformational dynamics studies during cleavage have shown the plasticity of HNH domain and role played by non-target DNA in activation of HNH nuclease domain (Palermo *et al.*, 2016). Simulation revealed that Cas9 cleavage results in one base pair staggered end with overhangs and not blunt end in DNA (Zuo and Liu, 2016). Further studies on guide RNA-Cas9 mediated DSB mechanism may aid in designing more specific complexes without any off-target activity.

Re-engineering of Proteins to Make Their Structure More *Stable*

The feasibility of biological processes is initially dependent on the stability of the proteins involved. One of the main challenges faced while enhancing the stability is to not affect the activity of the target protein. Protein stability in general implies minimizing the total potential energy stored within a protein. Efficient functioning of any molecule requires it to be stable, which is generally maintained by various interactions. In this section, we discuss various computational approaches available to analyze and predict structural changes that can be incorporated into the protein to enhance its stability.

In silico *approach to enhance the stability of TEV protease*

The tobacco etch virus (TEV) protein is a nuclear inclusion protease weighing 27 kDa (Allison et al., 1986). The protease is involved during TEV biogenesis for the formation of single proteins after proteolytic degradation of the viral polyprotein (Adams et al., 2005). Its stringent specificity and robustness make it ideal for *in vitro* protein purification and *in vivo* testing of protein–protein interactions (Wehr et al., 2006). The canonical recognition sequence targeted by the protease is ENLYFQ-G/S (Adams et al., 2005).

Here, *in silico* engineering of protease was carried out to enhance its stability and solubility (Cabrita et al., 2007). Being a popular protein for removal of tags from recombinant proteins, its production and storage presented major challenges. The drawbacks were overcome by performing a rational search of point mutations that could be introduced in the protein for improvement of its stability and solubility than its native-state. With the aim of selecting the variants with better results, potential single-site mutations were introduced using PoPMuSiC algorithm (Kwasigroch et al., 2002). The program PoPMuSiC predicts changes in the free energy of protein folding. The predicted changes were based on database-derived potentials (Gilis and Rooman, 1996). The features of TEV were improved in such a manner that (a) the structural integrity as well as the activity is sustained, and (b) the solubility remained even at higher concentrations.

The analysis of calculated potentials predicted five variants to be more stable. The calculations of potentials were obtained by linear combination of the interactions involved and the propensity of the interacting residues. Experimental characterization of the five variants was done by using assays like solubility assay, enzyme kinetics, and equilibrium unfolding analysis. Thus, the goal of designing a completely active TEV variant having better stability and more solubility was successful. Similar rational approach combining different techniques can be applied to any protein structure. Such an accomplishment becomes a powerful tool in the field of biotechnology.

Computational designing of β-sheet surfaces to boost protein stability

β-strands constitute β-sandwich or β-barrel in approximately one quarter of all known protein structures (Gerstein, 1998). In such conformations, one face of the sheet points toward the hydrophobic core of the protein, while the other face aims toward the solvent. The residues facing toward the core are vital in determining the stability of the protein by forming strong bonding interactions. However, the stability can also be detected through the solvent-facing residues. Hence, a significant amount of effort has been made to understand the structural features contributing to β-sheet stability (Lassila et al., 2002; Der et al., 2013; Lawrence et al., 2007).

A study was conducted to redesign the β-sheet surfaces of the fibronectin type III domain of the protein tenascin (TNfn3) using the molecular modeling program Rosetta (Gerstein, 1998). TNfn3 has been a model system to extensively study protein folding and stability. Mutational changes to improve these features have already been demonstrated by many reports. The mutations stabilizing the protein structure have mostly been located in the protein core (Gilbreth et al., 2014; Jacobs et al., 2012).

In silico experiments conducted for this study used the all-atom energy function in Rosetta to achieve the objective. This module was parameterized with a diverse set of sequence design and structure prediction tests. In addition, an attempt was made to validate an empirical approach to achieve the protein stability. The number of salt bridges (glutamate or aspartate paired with lysine or arginine) was increased on the surface of the β-sheets. A significant challenge faced while designing β-sheet proteins was to specify the pairing. The problem was created during tertiary folding of proteins because strands that are distant in primary sequence tend to be paired in the final structure.

Interestingly, the charged residues on TNfn3 could be placed on the strands based on opposite charging through mutational studies. Also, it was ensured that β-strands that are close in primary sequence are not paired in the final protein structure. The rationale for this arrangement was that the charges would favor the folding and stability of the protein due to favorable electrostatic interactions in the folded structural state. Simultaneously, disfavoring of kinetically accessible misfolded states would occur.

Thus, dramatic increase in protein stability was achieved by optimizing interactions on the surfaces of small β-sheet proteins. Two variants of the β-sandwich protein from tenascin were obtained after designing. They were carrying seven and 14 mutations respectively on their β-sheet surfaces. Due to these changes, the thermal midpoint for unfolding was increased. Additionally, the approach based on increasing the number of potential salt bridges on the surfaces of the β-sheets was not found to be a robust strategy.

Computational Protein Engineering for *Addition of Novel Function* to Existing Proteins

The previous sections detailed the potential of computational protein engineering techniques in improving the specificity and stability of the target protein. Similar approaches can also be utilized to add a completely new function to a protein, such as addition of substrate binding site, metal binding site, and catalytic site. The following section describes some successful studies.

Study of adaptability of periplasmic binding proteins: Computational modification of ligand-binding site for different substrates and their application as biosensors

Biosensors are based on the general principle of detection of protein–ligand interaction and transmission of this interaction into the signal detection mechanism. Application of protein as a biosensor requires a well-defined change in confirmation of its structure upon binding with ligand molecule. This change in confirmation can be coupled with fluorescent detection by incorporating fluorophores at the allosteric site of protein that can detect change induced by ligand binding (Hellinga and Marvin, 1998; Dwyer and Hellinga, 2004). Emerging protein engineering techniques allow the integration of signal transducing functional groups into the protein molecule itself that can bring electrostatic or optical changes upon interaction with ligands (Hellinga and Marvin, 1998). Moreover, specificity of protein for ligands can be altered using these techniques (Hellinga and Marvin, 1998; Reimer *et al.*, 2014).

Periplasmic binding proteins (PBPs) from *E. coli* are a widely studied superfamily of proteins for changing their ligand specificities. PBPs are periplasmic protein receptors involved in chemotaxis and nutrient uptake with wide variety of substrate specificities, including amino acids, carbohydrates, oligopeptides, metal ions, and anions (Dwyer and Hellinga, 2004). The PBPs superfamily is characterized by high sequence diversity with conserved structural domain (Hellinga and Marvin, 1998). It consists of two globular domains with ligand-binding site at the interface, connected by two- or three-stranded hinge region (Quiocho and Ledvina, 1996; Hellinga and Marvin, 1998; Dwyer and Hellinga, 2004). Ligand binding at the interface changes the confirmation of protein from open ligand-free form to closed ligand-bound form by induction of large bending at the hinge region. This ligand-based conformational change of PBPs provides a great advantage in coupling it to physical detectable signal. Allosteric coupling of reporter group with ligand-induced conformational change of PBPs was successfully implemented to create allosterically regulated biosensors for trinitrotoluene (TNT), L-lactate, serotonin, and Zn(II), (Marvin and Hellinga, 2001; Looger *et al.*, 2003; Dwyer and Hellinga, 2004). Here, we have discussed a few case studies as an example for application of protein engineering in creating biosensors for TNT and metal ion Zn(II) by incorporation of metal binding site.

Modification of PBPs ligand-binding site by adding sensory function for TNT: TNT is not a natural molecule, has carcinogenic properties, and is a potent contaminant of soil and water. Development of strategies to design cost-effective sensors for detection of level of TNT in soil and water was required. Manipulation of PBPs for binding with chemical threats and pollutants like TNT might provide the advantage of designing specific cell-based detectors for these pollutants (Looger *et al.*, 2003). The ligand-binding site of three members of the PBPs superfamily of *E. coli* was engineered for binding of TNT in place of their wild-type ligand (Looger *et al.*, 2003). Three PBPs under study were arabinose-binding protein (ABP), ribose-binding protein (RBP), and histidine-binding protein (HBP). High-resolution three-dimensional structures of proteins in association with their respective ligands were obtained from databases. First, interaction studies of protein with wild-type ligands were performed to identify the amino acid residues involved in protein–ligand interactions. This step was followed by repeated combination of protein-target docking and mutation of identified amino acids residues; that resulted into 10^{45}–10^{68} mutant structures for 12–18 amino acid residues. Resulting combinatorial mutant structures were resolved based on DEE theorem. Identification of global minimum of a semiempirical potential function was determined for system's molecular interactions. This yielded a complementary surface design for TNT in ABP, RBP, and HBP by exploring essential parameters for recognition of molecule, comprising of molecular shape, size, functional groups, chirality, charge, water solubility, internal flexibility, and molecular surface. The designed surface for TNT was electrically neutral, satisfied hydrogen bonding potential of TNT's functional groups, and hydrophobic residues of TNT were interacting with aliphatic amino acid's side chain. Interactions with aromatic side chain were also noticed in one of the design for ABP and HBP, TNT.A1, and TNT.H1, respectively.

The structures of six receptors were selected with binding specificity for TNT (with mutations ranging from 5 to 17 amino acid residues) for experimental validation. Mutant proteins were designed, overexpressed, purified, and altered by incorporation of fluorescent dye, that is thiol-reactive styryl dye conjugated to cys residue, at the site that responds to the confirmation change at the hinge region upon binding of TNT. Ligand dependent changes in fluorescence were monitored for wild-type ligand, TNT, and closely related decoy structures of TNT by titration. All six receptors showed detectable binding affinity for TNT and no binding affinity with wild-type ligand was observed. Also when their binding affinity with related decoy structures was analyzed, specifically 2,4- and 2,6-dinitotoluene (2,4-DNT and 2,6-DNT) and trinitrobenzene (TNB), it was observed that all six receptors can distinguish between TNT and their related decoy compounds with exception of ABP design, which could not recognize the absence of single methyl group in TNB. Out of the three TNT designs of RBP, affinities of two of them were comparable to the affinity of wild-type protein, that is, 0.1–1.5 mM. Affinity of TNT to nanomolar level was observed for one of the TNT designs of RBP receptor, TNT.R3, which was used for the first time to develop a biosensor for detection of underwater level of TNT into the sea using robotic vehicles for tracing underwater plumes (Mead, 2002).

Modification of Periplasmic binding proteins ligand-binding site by adding sensory function for Zn(II): Modification of maltose-binding protein (MBP) to add zinc binding site near or within maltose-binding interface will be discussed in this section (Marvin and Hellinga, 2001). *DEZYMER* was used to generate 20 initial designs for zinc binding site consisting of three histidine residues and one water molecule. Four of these were structurally constructed, two of them were designed to replace three maltose-binding residues (that is A1: A63$_{II}$H, R66$_{II}$H, W340$_I$H; A2: A63$_{II}$H, R66$_{II}$H, Y155$_I$H), and the others were located near the maltose-binding site; additional mutations were also introduced to prohibit steric clashes (this site was named as B site, B1: K42$_{II}$H, E44$_{II}$H, Y34$_{11}$H, E45$_{II}$A, R344$_{II}$A; B2: P48$_{II}$H, G69$_{II}$H, S337$_I$H, R66$_{II}$S, Y70$_{II}$A). Both A and B sites showed the same degree of fluorescence change in presence of the ligand and were able to bind the zinc molecule, while only A site could form zinc mediated formation of closed state. This suggested the need of iterative design strategy for increasing zinc binding affinity, optimization of target site, and elimination of vestigial interactions. Three strategies were used for an iterative progressive design cycle to improve binding affinity for zinc:

1. *Combination of zinc binding sites*: Out of all possible combinations of A1, A2 and B1, B2, only A2B1 combination was sterically feasible. A2B1 showed sigmoidal zinc binding; hill coefficient of 2.0 indicated cooperative interaction between two sites and upon zinc binding fluorescence level was increased by 17.7 fold. This showed that A2B1 mutant resulted in improved zinc bound closed state of protein with increased fluorescence detection signal.

2. *Primary coordination sphere optimization*: Primary coordination sphere was optimized instead of His$_3$Zn sites as designed in previous steps. Alanine mutagenesis screening of "A" sites was performed by mutating its each residue to alanine. H63$_{II}$ site was common to both A1 and A2 site and its mutation to H63$_{II}$A partly destroyed zinc binding. Other non-overlapping residue mutations were also vital but the mutation in nearby residues, D65$_{II}$, demonstrates its importance in coordinating zinc ion. Molecular modeling studies were carried out that suggested the placement of forth residue at Y155$_I$ in A1 and W340$_I$ in A2 for optimization of coordination sphere. Mutation studies for these positions led to selection of Y155$_I$E and W340$_I$E mutants that showed higher binding affinity for zinc than their original counterparts A1 and A2, respectively. New site was designed by fusion of vertices, from His$_2$Glu$_2$ vertices of A1 and A2, to form A* site (H63$_{II}$, H66$_{II}$, E155$_I$, E340$_I$) with zinc binding affinity increased to K$_d$ value of 5.1 μM.

3. *Exploitation of conformational equilibrium*: Overall zinc binding affinity is the sum of intrinsic affinity for closed state for zinc and intrinsic equilibrium of open and closed state in absence of zinc. Therefore, zinc binding affinity can be improved by manipulation of these factors. Two strategies were employed for manipulation of intrinsic equilibrium between open and closed state:

   a. Vestigial maltose binding residues, E111$_I$ and K15$_{II}$, single and double mutants were created by replacing them with Met and Ala, respectively in A* design. These mutants resulted in enhanced binding efficiency of zinc.
   b. Mutations were made in protoallosteric site in hinge region that is conformationally different in two states. I329 was tightly packed in open state but binding of ligand changed its compact packing in closed state. Its mutation to I329F was studied to destabilize its open state, which led to increased zinc binding affinity for A* design, with K$_d$ value of 350 nM.

It can be concluded from the above study that this kind of iterative progressive design approach can be utilized to convert proteins like MBP into biosensors for metal through addition of metal binding sites within the binding site of its substrate.

Computational modification of periplasmic binding proteins by addition of catalytic function for design of biologically active enzyme

PBPs structures were also tested for addition of new catalytic function, by creating catalytic site for triose phosphate isomerase (TIM) in RBP and the mutated RBP was found to be a biologically active enzyme that can support the growth of *E. coli* in gluconeogenic conditions (Dwyer *et al.*, 2004). TIM is a glycolytic pathway enzyme that interconverts dihydroxyacetone phosphate (DHAP) and glyceraldehyde 3-phosphate (GAP). This isomerization reaction requires successive transfer of two protons with enediol(ate) as intermediate and requires three catalytic residues, i.e., glutamate, histidine, and lysine. Introduction of TIM catalytic site into RBP was accomplished by mutating ligand-binding interface residues in a step-by step manner. Firstly, RBP was modified to add substrate binding site for DHAP and GAP irrespective of catalytic activity. This was accomplished using similar methods as mentioned in the case study describing addition of binding site of TNT in PBPs. Secondly, the catalytic site residues were introduced into the modified substrate binding site by specifying geometrical constraints of the active site that should be compatible with bond formation with substrates, enediol(ate) intermediate and transition state. The whole process was executed in three steps:

1. First geometrical constraints critical for interactions required for catalysis were designed.
2. Combinatorial search algorithm was employed to generate geometric constraints that satisfy constraints for both substrate specificity and catalysis simultaneously.
3. Receptor design algorithms were used to place generated complementary surface around bound substrate.

The catalytic design site obtained in this step was distinct from the designs generated for substrate binding in the first step. Fourteen (14) designs were selected for testing, out of which one design, NovoTim1.0, showed increased activity and was competitively inhibited by a known inhibitor of TIM, i.e., phosphoglycolate. NovoTim1.0 was found to be less thermostable in comparison to TIM; therefore further modification of residues surrounding binding surfaces of substrates was carried out. These modifications provided variants of NovoTim1.0, namely NovoTim1.2, which showed increased stability of protein by 15°C and increased k_{cat} (rate of reaction) and K_M (Michaelis constant) by twofold. NovoTim1.2 was formed by mutation and redesign of nine interfacial and nine binding residues of NovoTim1.0, its parent molecule. NovoTims1.0 and 1.2 were further tested by their expression in TIM deficient strains of *E. coli* for growth of bacteria on gluconeogenic substrates, glycerol and lactate, in presence and absence of inducer IPTG (isopropyl β-D-1-thiogalactopyranoside). Both versions supported growth of bacteria on lactate medium but could not utilize glycerol as a substrate for growth. Therefore, further mutants were created to design a mutant that, when transformed into bacteria, can aid bacteria to utilize glycerol as a medium for growth. NovoTims1.2.1 to 1.2.4 versions were obtained with mutations of protein surface residues and increased *k*cat and *k*cat/*KM* values by two-fold and three-fold, respectively.

In this study, the authors clearly demonstrated how combination of computational and experimental procedures can convert non-catalytic protein into a biologically active enzyme that can aid bacteria to utilize gluconeogenic substrate for growth. This approach can be generalized to create various types of enzymes by either utilizing PBPs or any other protein.

Future Challenges of Computational Protein Engineering

With rapidly advancing computational power, *in silico* protein engineering methods have become more common and many successful applications have been reported. But some challenges still remain to be addressed in the field of computational protein engineering to have reliable and successful *in silico* protein designs. Some of the challenges are discussed here.

Initially, to lower the complexity and to decrease the computational time, the protein backbone is kept fixed and its degrees of freedom are eliminated in the protein engineering methods. Hence, residual combinations that require slight changes in backbone become unattainable. Also, these backbone methods cannot be applied to design *de novo* backbone structures. Owing to the drawbacks of fixed backbone methods, flexible backbone protein design methods like parameterization of structures, ensemble approach, and simultaneous optimization have been developed that have their own challenges. Parameterization of structures is a method that allows flexibility while modeling backbone, but decreases the degrees of freedom. Yet there are some successful studies reported using this method (Harbury *et al.*, 1995, 1998). The drawback in this method is that it does not allow explicit flexibility of backbone. In the ensemble approach, an ensemble of protein backbone structures is used to achieve flexibility and then the fixed backbone method is applied to each structure in the ensemble. The limitation in this method is that only a limited number of backbone structures can be studied. In the simultaneous optimization method, flexibility is allowed to backbone and side chains simultaneously. Although different flexibility backbone methods are established, there is an absence of good correlation between stabilities of a protein determined experimentally and computationally (Choi *et al.*, 2009). Allowing backbone flexibility thus still remains a challenge in protein engineering.

Negative design is a method to ensure specificity. Positive design involves engineering of protein to have a desired function, whereas negative design is for preventing undesired functions. In negative design, a sequence is interrogated against multiple structures so that it does not form alternate conformations. It helps in selecting sequences that form a unique structure. Prior knowledge about target structure and undesired complexes is needed in order to avoid sequences that can form undesired structures. Different negative design approaches have been reported in literature. Of these, multi-state design is a potential approach for designing proteins with specificity. Combinatorial engineering is another useful method to attain high specificity. Combining the power of computational negative design tools along with high throughput assays poses a challenge. Protein folding is a longstanding issue in protein science. Incorporating negative design to destabilize alternate structures is a challenging task (Choi *et al.*, 2009).

Another daunting task in the protein engineering pipeline is high throughput sampling of predicted structures. After computational design, all the successful designs have to be cloned in a vector, expressed in a cell, and purified for characterization. Repeating this for all successful designs one after another will be expensive, time consuming, and laborious. Hence, in future, any high throughput protein fabrication method to be developed should have automation in all the aforementioned tasks. Another approach can be constructing a gene library that represents the ensemble of proteins and expressing them simultaneously. Screening can be applied to select the protein with the desired property. So far, the selection methods applied on these libraries have been of low resolution without atomistic level sequence interrogations (Choi *et al.*, 2009).

We have discussed here some successful computational approaches that have been used to engineer proteins with better specificity, stability, and newer functionality. These examples reflect the advantages of using computational tools to mine the information embedded within the sequence and structure of native proteins, and redefine it for our interests. Though computational protein engineering methods are evolving to be imperative tools in the tedious and complex process of engineering proteins, some associated challenges still leave the scope for further innovation and improvement.

See also: Biomolecular Structures: Prediction, Identification and Analyses. Identifying Functional Relationships Via the Annotation and Comparison of Three-Dimensional Amino Acid Arrangements in Protein Structures. Natural Language Processing Approaches in Bioinformatics. Sequence Analysis. Sequence Composition. Study of The Variability of The Native Protein Structure

References

Adams, M.J., Antoniw, J.F., Beaudoin, F., 2005. Overview and analysis of the polyprotein cleavage sites in the family Potyviridae. Molecular Plant Pathology 6, 471–487.

Adolf-Bryfogle, J., Dunbrack Jr, R.L., 2013. The PyRosetta Toolkit: A graphical user interface for the Rosetta software suite. PLOS ONE 8, e66856.

Allison, R., Johnston, R.E., Dougherty, W.G., 1986. The nucleotide sequence of the coding region of tobacco etch virus genomic RNA: Evidence for the synthesis of a single polyprotein. Virology 154, 9–20.

Alvizo, O., Mayo, S.L., 2008. Evaluating and optimizing computational protein design force fields using fixed composition-based negative design. Proceedings of the National Academy of Science of the United States of America 105, 12242–12247.

Anand, P., Schug, A., Wenzel, W., 2013. Structure based design of protein linkers for zinc finger nuclease. FEBS Letters 587, 3231–3235.

Bae, S., Park, J., Kim, J.-S., 2014. Cas-OFFinder: A fast and versatile algorithm that searches for potential off-target sites of Cas9 RNA-guided endonucleases. Bioinformatics. btu048.

Barderas, R., Desmet, J., Timmerman, P., Meloen, R., Casal, J.I., 2008. Affinity maturation of antibodies assisted by in silico modeling. Proceedings of the National Academy of Sciences 105, 9029–9034.

Beerli, R.R., Barbas, C.F., 2002. Engineering polydactyl zinc-finger transcription factors. Nature Biotechnology 20, 135–141.

Cabrita, L.D., Gilis, D., Robertson, A.L., *et al.*, 2007. Enhancing the stability and solubility of TEV protease using in silico design. Protein Science 16, 2360–2367.

Chéron, J.-B., Casciuc, I., Golebiowski, J., Antonczak, S., Fiorucci, S., 2017. Sweetness prediction of natural compounds. Food Chemistry 221, 1421–1425.

Choi, E.J., Guntas, G., Kuhlman, B., 2009. 18 future challenges of computational protein design. Protein Engineering and Design 75, 367.

Chou, C.-C., Rajasekaran, M., Chen, C., 2010. An effective approach for generating a three-Cys 2 His 2 zinc-finger-DNA complex model by docking. BMC Bioinformatics 11, 334.

Chovancova, E., Pavelka, A., Benes, P., *et al.*, 2012. CAVER 3.0: A tool for the analysis of transport pathways in dynamic protein structures. PLOS Computational Biology 8, e1002708.

Clarke, N.D., Yuan, S.M., 1995. Metal search: A computer program that helps design tetrahedral metal-binding sites. Proteins: Structure, Function, and Bioinformatics 23, 256–263.

Clinton, T.R., Weinstock, M.T., Jacobsen, M.T., *et al.*, 2015. Design and characterization of ebolavirus GP prehairpin intermediate mimics as drug targets. Protein Science 24, 446–463.

Dahiyat, B.I., Mayo, S.L., 1996. Protein design automation. Protein Science 5, 895–903.

Dahiyat, B.I., Mayo, S.L., 1997. De novo protein design: Fully automated sequence selection. Science 278, 82–87.

Der, B.S., Kluwe, C., Miklos, A.E., *et al.*, 2013. Alternative computational protocols for supercharging protein surfaces for reversible unfolding and retention of stability. PLOS ONE 8, e64363.

Doudna, J.A., Charpentier, E., 2014. The new frontier of genome engineering with CRISPR-Cas9. Science 346, 1258096.

Dutta, S., Madan, S., Parikh, H., Sundar, D., 2016a. An ensemble micro neural network approach for elucidating interactions between zinc finger proteins and their target DNA. BMC Genomics 17, 97.

Dutta, S., Madan, S., Sundar, D., 2016b. Exploiting the recognition code for elucidating the mechanism of zinc finger protein-DNA interactions. BMC Genomics 17, 109.

Dwyer, M.A., Hellinga, H.W., 2004. Periplasmic binding proteins: A versatile superfamily for protein engineering. Current Opinion in Structural Biology 14, 495–504.

Dwyer, M.A., Looger, L.L., Hellinga, H.W., 2004. Computational design of a biologically active enzyme. Science 304, 1967–1971.

Elrod-Erickson, M., Benson, T.E., Pabo, C.O., 1998. High-resolution structures of variant Zif268–DNA complexes: Implications for understanding zinc finger–DNA recognition. Structure 6, 451–464.

Floudas, C.A., Fung, H.K., Mcallister, S.R., Mönnigmann, M., Rajgaria, R., 2006. Advances in protein structure prediction and de novo protein design: A review. Chemical Engineering Science 61, 966–988.

Fox, R.J., Davis, S.C., Mundorff, E.C., *et al.*, 2007. Improving catalytic function by ProSAR-driven enzyme evolution. Nature Biotechnology 25, 338–344.

Fu, Y., Sander, J.D., Reyon, D., Cascio, V.M., Joung, J.K., 2014. Improving CRISPR-Cas nuclease specificity using truncated guide RNAs. Nature Biotechnology 32, 279–284.

Gerstein, M., 1998. How representative are the known structures of the proteins in a complete genome? A comprehensive structural census. Folding and Design 3, 497–512.

Gilbreth, R., Chacko, B., Grinberg, L., Swers, J., Baca, M., 2014. Stabilization of the third fibronectin type III domain of human tenascin-C through minimal mutation and rational design. Protein Engineering Design and Selection 27, 411–418.

Gilis, D., Rooman, M., 1996. Stability changes upon mutation of solvent-accessible residues in proteins evaluated by database-derived potentials. Journal of Molecular Biology 257, 1112–1126.

Greisman, H.A., Pabo, C.O., 1997. A general strategy for selecting high-affinity zinc finger proteins for diverse DNA target sites. Science 275, 657–661.

Grover, A., Pande, A., Choudhary, K., Gupta, K., Sundar, D., 2010. Re-programming DNA-binding specificity in zinc finger proteins for targeting unique address in a genome. Systems and Synthetic Biology 4, 323–329.

Guilinger, J.P., Thompson, D.B., Liu, D.R., 2014. Fusion of catalytically inactive Cas9 to FokI nuclease improves the specificity of genome modification. Nature Biotechnology 32, 577–582.

Hallen, M.A., Keedy, D.A., Donald, B.R., 2013. Dead-end elimination with perturbations (DEEPer): A provable protein design algorithm with continuous sidechain and backbone flexibility. Proteins: Structure, Function, and Bioinformatics 81, 18–39.

Harbury, P.B., Plecs, J.J., Tidor, B., Alber, T., Kim, P.S., 1998. High-resolution protein design with backbone freedom. Science 282, 1462–1467.

Harbury, P.B., Tidor, B., Kim, P.S., 1995. Repacking protein cores with backbone freedom: Structure prediction for coiled coils. Proceedings of the National Academy of Sciences 92, 8408–8412.

Heigwer, F., Kerr, G., Boutros, M., 2014. E-CRISP: Fast CRISPR target site identification. Nature Methods 11, 122–123.

Hellinga, H.W., Marvin, J.S., 1998. Protein engineering and the development of generic biosensors. Trends in Biotechnology 16, 183–189.

Hellinga, H.W., Richards, F.M., 1991. Construction of new ligand binding sites in proteins of known structure: I. Computer-aided modeling of sites with pre-defined geometry. Journal of Molecular Biology 222, 763–785.

Hsu, P.D., Lander, E.S., Zhang, F., 2014. Development and applications of CRISPR-Cas9 for genome engineering. Cell 157, 1262–1278.

Huang, L.-T., Gromiha, M.M., Ho, S.-Y., 2007. iPTREE-STAB: Interpretable decision tree based method for predicting protein stability changes upon mutations. Bioinformatics 23, 1292–1293.

Jacobs, S.A., Diem, M.D., Luo, J., *et al.*, 2012. Design of novel FN3 domains with high stability by a consensus sequence approach. Protein Engineering Design and Selection 25, 107–117.

Johnston, M.A., Søndergaard, C.R., Nielsen, J.E., 2011. Integrated prediction of the effect of mutations on multiple protein characteristics. Proteins: Structure, Function, and Bioinformatics 79, 165–178.

Kiyoshi, M., Caaveiro, J.M., Miura, E., *et al.*, 2014. Affinity improvement of a therapeutic antibody by structure-based computational design: Generation of electrostatic interactions in the transition state stabilizes the antibody-antigen complex. PLOS ONE 9, e87099.

Kuznetsov, I.B., Mcduffie, M., 2008. FlexPred: A web-server for predicting residue positions involved in conformational switches in proteins. Bioinformation 3, 134.

Kwasigroch, J.M., Gilis, D., Dehouck, Y., Rooman, M., 2002. PoPMuSiC, rationally designing point mutations in protein structures. Bioinformatics 18, 1701–1702.

Labun, K., Montague, T.G., Gagnon, J.A., Thyme, S.B., Valen, E., 2016. CHOPCHOP v2: A web tool for the next generation of CRISPR genome engineering. Nucleic Acids Research. gkw398.

Lassila, K.S., Datta, D., Mayo, S.L., 2002. Evaluation of the energetic contribution of an ionic network to beta-sheet stability. Protein Science 11, 688–690.

Lawrence, M.S., Phillips, K.J., Liu, D.R., 2007. Supercharging proteins can impart unusual resilience. Journal of the American Chemical Society 129, 10110–10112.

Li, X., Zhang, Z., Song, J., 2012. Computational enzyme design approaches with significant biological outcomes: Progress and challenges. Computational and Structural Biotechnology Journal 2, e201209007.

Looger, L.L., Dwyer, M.A., Smith, J.J., Hellinga, H.W., 2003. Computational design of receptor and sensor proteins with novel functions. Nature 423, 185–190.

Mandell, J.G., Barbas, C.F., 2006. Zinc Finger Tools: Custom DNA-binding domains for transcription factors and nucleases. Nucleic Acids Research 34, W516–W523.

Marvin, J.S., Hellinga, H.W., 2001. Conversion of a maltose receptor into a zinc biosensor by computational design. Proceedings of the National Academy of Sciences 98, 4955–4960.

Masso, M., Vaisman, I.I., 2010. AUTO-MUTE: Web-based tools for predicting stability changes in proteins due to single amino acid replacements. Protein Engineering, Design & Selection 23, 683–687.

Mead, K.S., 2002. Using lobster noses to inspire robot sensor design. Trends in Biotechnology 20, 276–277.

Meyer, M.M., Silberg, J.J., Voigt, C.A., *et al.*, 2003. Library analysis of SCHEMA-guided protein recombination. Protein Science 12, 1686–1693.

Mitra, P., Shultis, D., Zhang, Y., 2013. EvoDesign: De novo protein design based on structural and evolutionary profiles. Nucleic Acids Research 41, W273–W280.

Molparia, B., Goyal, K., Sarkar, A., Kumar, S., Sundar, D., 2010. ZiF-Predict: A web tool for predicting DNA-binding specificity in C2H2 zinc finger proteins. Genomics, Proteomics & Bioinformatics 8, 122–126.

Montague, T.G., Cruz, J.M., Gagnon, J.A., Church, G.M., Valen, E., 2014. CHOPCHOP: A CRISPR/Cas9 and TALEN web tool for genome editing. Nucleic Acids Research 42, W401–W407.

Murphy, G.S., Sathyamoorthy, B., Der, B.S., *et al.*, 2015. Computational de novo design of a four-helix bundle protein–DND_4HB. Protein Science 24, 434–445.

Nosrati, G.R., Houk, K., 2012. SABER: A computational method for identifying active sites for new reactions. Protein Science 21, 697–706.

O'brien, A., Bailey, T.L., 2014. GT-Scan: Identifying unique genomic targets. Bioinformatics. btu354.

Pabo, C.O., Peisach, E., Grant, R.A., 2001. Design and selection of novel Cys2His2 zinc finger proteins. Annual Review of Biochemistry 70, 313–340.

Palermo, G., Miao, Y., Walker, R.C., Jinek, M., Mccammon, J.A., 2016. Striking plasticity of CRISPR-Cas9 and key role of non-target DNA, as revealed by molecular simulations. ACS Central Science 2, 756–763.

Park, H., Jeon, Y.H., 2011. Free energy perturbation approach for the rational engineering of the antibody for human hepatitis B virus. Journal of Molecular Graphics and Modelling 29, 643–649.

Park, S., Yang, X., Saven, J.G., 2004. Advances in computational protein design. Current Opinion in Structural Biology 14, 487–494.

Persikov, A.V., Osada, R., Singh, M., 2009. Predicting DNA recognition by Cys2His2 zinc finger proteins. Bioinformatics 25, 22–29.

Quiocho, F.A., Ledvina, P.S., 1996. Atomic structure and specificity of bacterial periplasmic receptors for active transport and chemotaxis: Variation of common themes. Molecular Microbiology 20, 17–25.

Ran, F.A., Hsu, P.D., Lin, C.-Y., *et al.*, 2013a. Double nicking by RNA-guided CRISPR Cas9 for enhanced genome editing specificity. Cell 154, 1380–1389.

Ran, F.A., Hsu, P.D., Wright, J., *et al.*, 2013b. Genome engineering using the CRISPR-Cas9 system. Nature Protocols 8, 2281–2308.

Reimer, A., Yagur-Kroll, S., Belkin, S., Roy, S., Van Der Meer, J.R., 2014. *Escherichia coli* ribose binding protein based bioreporters revisited. Scientific Reports 4, 5626.

Rothlisberger, D., Khersonsky, O., Wollacott, A.M., *et al.*, 2008. Kemp elimination catalysts by computational enzyme design. Nature 453, 190–195.

Saraf, M.C., Moore, G.L., Goodey, N.M., *et al.*, 2006. IPRO: An iterative computational protein library redesign and optimization procedure. Biophysics Journal 90, 4167–4180.

Schymkowitz, J., Borg, J., Stricher, F., *et al.*, 2005. The FoldX web server: An online force field. Nucleic Acids Research 33, W382–W388.

Shen, B., Zhang, W., Zhang, J., *et al.*, 2014. Efficient genome modification by CRISPR-Cas9 nickase with minimal off-target effects. Nature Methods 11, 399–402.

Slaymaker, I.M., Gao, L., Zetsche, B., *et al.*, 2016. Rationally engineered Cas9 nucleases with improved specificity. Science 351, 84–88.

Stemmer, M., Thumberger, T., Del Sol Keyer, M., Wittbrodt, J., Mateo, J.L., 2015. CCTop: An intuitive, flexible and reliable CRISPR/Cas9 target prediction tool. PLOS ONE 10, e0124633.

Stiel, A.C., Nellen, M., Höcker, B., 2016. Pocket optimizer and the design of ligand binding sites. Computational Design of Ligand Binding Proteins. 63–75.

Tsai, S.Q., Zheng, Z., Nguyen, N.T., *et al.*, 2015. GUIDE-seq enables genome-wide profiling of off-target cleavage by CRISPR-Cas nucleases. Nature Biotechnology 33, 187–197.

Turanli-Yildiz, B., Alkim, C., Cakar, Z.P., 2012. Protein Engineering Methods and Applications. Rijeka, Croatia: INTECH Open Access Publisher.

Ulmer, K.M., 1983. Protein engineering. Science 219, 666–671.

Urnov, F.D., Miller, J.C., Lee, Y.-L., *et al.*, 2005. Highly efficient endogenous human gene correction using designed zinc-finger nucleases. Nature 435, 646–651.

Verma, R., Schwaneberg, U., Roccatano, D., 2012. Computer-aided protein directed evolution: A review of web servers, databases and other computational tools for protein engineering. Computational and Structural Biotechnology Journal 2, e201209008.

Wainreb, G., Ashkenazy, H., Bromberg, Y., *et al.*, 2010. MuD: An interactive web server for the prediction of non-neutral substitutions using protein structural data. Nucleic Acids Research 38, W523–W528.

Walsh, G., 2007. Protein engineering: Case studies of commercialized engineered products. Biochemistry and Molecular Biology Education 35, 2–8.

Wehr, M.C., Laage, R., Bolz, U., *et al.*, 2006. Monitoring regulated protein-protein interactions using split TEV. Nature Methods 3, 985–993.

Wolfe, S.A., Nekludova, L., Pabo, C.O., 2000. DNA recognition by Cys2His2 zinc finger proteins. Annual Review of Biophysics and Biomolecular Structure 29, 183–212.

Xie, S., Shen, B., Zhang, C., Huang, X., Zhang, Y., 2014. sgRNAcas9: A software package for designing CRISPR sgRNA and evaluating potential off-target cleavage sites. PLOS ONE 9, e100448.

Zuo, Z., Liu, J., 2016. Cas9-catalyzed DNA cleavage generates staggered ends: Evidence from molecular dynamics simulations. Scientific Reports 5.

Biographical Sketch

Jaspreet Kaur received her M.Tech. in Bioinformatics from Delhi Technological University, India in 2013, and B.Tech. in Biotechnology from Amity University, India (2011). She joined the Indian Institute of Technology, Delhi, India in 2014 for her PhD program. She works in the field of computer-aided drug design and is devising computational approaches for aiding in targeted genome editing.

Vidhi Malik received her M.Tech. in Bioinformatics from Delhi Technological University, India in 2013 and B.Tech. in Biotechnology from Sardar Vallabhbhai Patel University of Agriculture and Technology, India in 2011. She joined the Indian Institute of Technology, Delhi, India in 2015 for her PhD program. Her research interest lies in next generation sequence (NGS) data analysis and computer-aided drug design.

Navaneethan Radhakrishnan received his B.Tech. in Bioinformatics from Tamil Nadu Agricultural University, India in 2016. He joined the Indian Institute of Technology Delhi, India in 2016 as Junior Research Fellow in the Department of Biochemical Engineering and Biotechnology. His research interest lies in understanding the biological systems using computational approaches.

Moolchand Sigar received his M.Sc. in Biochemistry from University of Hyderabad, India in 2011, and B.Sc. in Biotechnology from University of Bikaner, India (2008). He joined Indian Institute of Technology, Delhi, India in 2012 for his PhD program. His research interest lies in engineering and production of therapeutic proteins.

Anjani Kumari received her B.Tech. in Biotechnology from Amity University, India in 2015. She completed her M.S. (Research) program in Biochemical Engineering and Biotechnology at IIT Delhi in 2017. Her research interest lies in computer-aided drug discovery.

Durai Sundar is a DuPont Young Professor in the Department of Biochemical Engineering and Biotechnology at Indian Institute of Technology, Delhi. He obtained his education from Pondicherry University and Johns Hopkins University, Baltimore, USA. He is a specialist in molecular and computational biology and his current research interests are in rational design of genome editing tools and in the biological activity of natural drugs.

Protein Design

Ragothaman M Yennamalli, Jaypee University of Information Technology, Waknaghat, Himachal Pradesh, India

Introduction

A cursory search of the Protein Data Bank (PDB) with the keyword "*de novo*" returns 962 entries, while for the keyword "designed", 6225 entries were returned [as of August 2017]. Although these numbers (*de novo* or designed structures) are 1000 times lesser in magnitude (compared to the total number of structures the PDB holds, which is close to 135,000 structures), these ~7000 structures indicate how far the field of protein design has advanced, since 1950s. Protein designing projects are ambitious in their goal due to the simple yet complex problem of protein folding. Much has been learned about how a protein folds, and these fundamental knowledge have helped further the area of protein design to conceive proteins with imaginative structures (Richardson and Richardson, 1989; Bowie *et al.*, 1991).

The impetus for protein design is two-fold: (i) assumption that we can design a complex natural system from first principles, and (ii) the "made to order" macromolecules that can solve important biochemical hurdles. The basic or fundamental problem with protein design in achieving a three dimensional, stable, and functional macromolecule is to cross the conformational entropy from the primary to the tertiary structure (Bowie *et al.*, 1991; Dahiyat and Mayo, 1997). There are many methods that can be used to reduce the conformational entropy (Baxa *et al.*, 2014). These include covalent cross-links and other artificial constraints that limit the conformational possibilities of the designed molecule (Leitner *et al.*, 2010; Sinz *et al.*, 2015).

There have been two basic design principles employed in designing proteins *de novo*: positive design and negative design (DeGrado *et al.*, 1989). Positive design of protein structures is the idea to design a protein with the desired structure as the goal, and rationally add/remove residues to achieve that structure. In contrast, negative design involves designing a structure along with ways to reduce formation of or competition from alternative conformations that may arise. While both methods involve rational design, there are advantages of using one over the other. Nevertheless, *de novo* design of protein structures using both methods has been successful to a varying degree. **Fig. 1** shows a representative set of structures that have been successfully designed and have advanced the field of protein design.

Since 1950s, designing alpha helices took precedence than the beta sheets, due to:

a) The stabilizing hydrogen bond network (**Fig. 2**).
b) The observation of isolated helices being stable in solution (Brown and Klee, 1971; Kim and Baldwin, 1984; Marqusee and Baldwin, 1987; Shoemaker *et al.*, 1987; Marqusee *et al.*, 1989).
c) Its oligomerization property observed by Crick, Pauling and Corey in supercoiled helices that when two helices twist around each other there are 3.5 residues per turn, which is less than the ideal 3.6 residues per turn rule, thereby leading to a repetition of the entire structure at every seven residues (Crick, 1953; Pauling and Corey, 1953).
d) The possibility of designing the minimal sequence, which can be repeated to construct a four- or six-bundle helices that can either self assemble or assemble in the presence of an external assembly inducer (Schafmeister *et al.*, 1997).

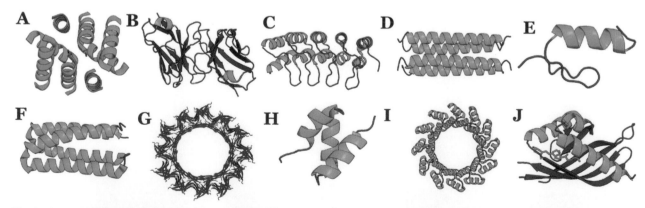

Fig. 1 A representative set of structures that have been designed *de novo*, where they are shown in cartoon representation with helices colored cyan, β-strands colored red, and loops colored magenta. (A) Octameric *de novo* Designed Peptide (pdb id:1l4x), (B) *de novo* Design of an Antibody Combining Site (pdb id:1ivl), (C) Self-Assembling Cyclic Protein Homo-Oligomer (pdb id:4hb5), (D) Right-Handed Coiled Coil Tetramer (pdb id:1rh4), (E) Beta Beta Alpha Protein Motif (pdb id:1fsv), (F) *de novo* Design of a Hyperstable Non-Natural Protein-Ligand Complex (pdb id:5tgw), (G) Giant Double-Walled Peptide Nanotube (pdb id:5vf1), (H) *de novo* Designed Mini Protein Hhh_Rd1_0142 (pdb id:5uoi), (I) Computationally Designed Left-Handed Alpha/Alpha Toroid With 12 Repeats (pdb id:5byo), and (J) Computationally Designed Vitamin-D3 Binder (pdb id:5iep).

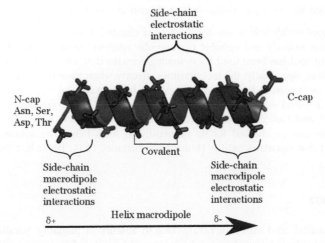

Fig. 2 Helix stabilizing properties. Schematic representation of an ideal helix indicating the various properties that stabilize the helix. Adapted from Bryson, J.W., *et al.*, 1995. Protein design: A hierarchic approach. Science (New York, NY) 270 (5238), 935–941.

Fundamentals

Before taking a sequence and designing it into a novel structure (α-helical or β-sheets or mixed), few pointers need to be kept in mind:

1. Similar stretch of residues can form different secondary structure.
   It has been observed that the same residue stretch of up to five amino acids can form different conformations, such as α-helix, β-strand, and loop. This indicates that a sequence forming a structure is dependent on its local environment.
2. There are only so many folds present.
   The relatively limited number of folds in the protein universe can be considered as a double edged sword. The 1000 odd folds we know today indicate that proteins tend to fold in one of the restricted ways. It also suggests the possibility of creating new folds using computational tools. The former has led to the reverse folding problem, called threading, where a sequence is checked for its compatibility to fold into one of the known folds.
3. Reducing the entropy of protein by introducing disulfide bonds (Wetzel, 1987).
4. Glycine introduces relatively more conformational freedom than the other 19 amino acids.
5. In contrast, Proline introduces less conformational freedom due to its covalent bond with the main chain.
6. It is known that the residues at the end of a helix are positively (at the C-terminus) and negatively (at the N-terminus) charged, which help in stabilizing the helix by balancing the helix dipole charge. Thus, changing the helix stabilizing residues influences the stability of a protein (Nicholson *et al.*, 1988; Richardson and Richardson, 1988).
7. If a core of a protein has a cavity, filling the cavity makes the protein destabilize it.

Designing an α-Helical Structure

Historically, alpha helical peptides and all-α proteins were relatively easier to design. In order to design alpha helical proteins, the sequence under consideration should be scrutinized with the following guidelines.

1. The sequence should be able to form amphiphilic secondary structures, where there is a periodicity of polar and nonpolar residues. For example, every third or fourth position being nonpolar.
2. A general rule of thumb is that the sequence should have residues that are highly likely to be part of a helix (Ala, Glu, Leu, and Met) (Richardson, 1981). Specifically, multiple alanine residues stabilize the helix. However, if the nonpolar periodicity of 3 or 4 is not maintained, then there is a lower preference to form a helical structure (Xiong *et al.*, 1995).
3. Introduction of salt-bridges and hydrogen bonds between side chains of residues that are one helical turn away (Marqusee *et al.*, 1989; Lyu *et al.*, 1990; Huyghues-Despointes *et al.*, 1993; Park *et al.*, 1993; Scholtz *et al.*, 1993).
4. A charged residue can be introduced at the N or C terminus of the α-helix, creating a macrodipole (**Fig. 2**).
5. Capping the helix ends with Asn, Ser, Asp, or Thr to satisfy the hydrogen-bond donors and acceptors.
6. Adding hydrogen bond(s) between side chains of residues that are one helical turn away.
7. In the case of Ser, Thr, and other amino acids that can be phosphorylated, their location in the interior of the helix may lead to destabilization. However, the N-terminus capping of a phosphorylated residue leads to stabilization of the helix. This is due to the electronic interaction of the phosphorylated residue with the peptide backbone.

Certain tools that can be used specifically to design helices are helical wheel and predicting helicity.

Helical wheel is a simple tool to identify if the distribution of charged residues and hydrophobic residues would lead to aggregation. When the helix has majorly hydrophobic or nonpolar residues on one side, there is a high chance of protein aggregation. This highly efficient tool has been used for designing proteins that are primarily coiled coil, and for helix bundles comprised of 3, 4, 5, and 6 helices. Specifically, the tool becomes effective when these helices are linked by loops or turns and to check if the "ridges in groove" or "knobs in holes" packing needs to be checked.

Some of the tools that plot a helical wheel for a given sequence are: DrawCoil 1.0 (see Relevant Websites Section), Pepwheel (see Relevant Websites Section), and Helical Wheel Projection (see Relevant Websites Section).

Also, the designed sequence can be checked for its propensity to form helices by submitting the sequence to AGADIR (see Relevant Websites Section) that calculates helicity (Munoz and Serrano, 1994, 1995a,b, 1997; Lacroix et al., 1998).

Designing a β-Sheet Structure

β-sheets can be parallel, antiparallel, and mixed in nature. Due to absence of planarity, parallel β-sheets are less stable than antiparallel sheets. This is due to the relative absence of inter-strand hydrogen bonds in parallel β-sheets, which provide for stronger interaction. Fig. 1(B), (G), and (J) highlight the successful design of a β-strand rich proteins.

In 1996, the design of a decapeptide adopting a β-hairpin structure involving a β-bulge and three other dodecapeptides adopting a type I' β-turn made the protein design possible for β-rich proteins (de Alba et al., 1996; Ramirez-Alvarado et al., 1996; Stanger and Gellman, 1998). These reports fueled enthusiasm in four different groups to design a three stranded antiparallel β-sheet proteins (each differing in residue length) (Kortemme et al., 1998; Schenck and Gellman, 1998; Sharman and Searle, 1998; de Alba et al., 1999). Irrespective of the method they employed, some of the criteria that were included in all the above mentioned β-sheet proteins are:

1. Residues that have higher β-strand propensities were included in the sequence.
2. Inter-strand pairs were selected that have higher preference to make a stable bond.
3. Involving positively charged residues (2 to 5 residues, at least) so that aggregation of proteins is eliminated, and increases solubility.

Positive charge distribution is essential in designing β-sheet proteins, because when they are distributed on both sides of the sheet, aggregation of proteins is reduced to a large extent. Another method to design a β-sheet protein with a stable hydrophobic core involves adding a type I' β-turn to the designed β-hairpin protein by using residues, such as Phe, Trp, Asn, and Gly, so that the side chains face the other strand's hydrophobic residues' side chains (Tyr and Val) (Griffiths-Jones and Searle, 2000).

Similar to α-helices, some of the guidelines to be used while designing β-sheet proteins are as follows:

1. The role of a β-turn is crucial, as it dictates the β-strand. This is a necessary but not a sufficient condition while designing β-sheet proteins. For example, the D form of Pro in the turn stabilizes the β-hairpin structure, compared to the L form.
2. Residues that have high propensity to form β-sheet should be used. For example, Val, Ile, Phe, Trp, Tyr, Leu, and Thr.
3. Gly should be avoided, as its incorporation leads to destabilization.
4. Including salt-bridge forming residues in inter-strands stabilize the β-sheet protein. For example, a salt-bridge formed between Glu and Lys residues. On the same note, salt-bridges at the ends of β-hairpin are more stabilizing.
5. Presence of interactions between hydrophobic residues, such as Ile-Trp, Ser-Thr, and Trp/Val-Tyr/Phe stabilize the protein as their contributions are larger.
6. Side chain-side chain interactions from diagonal directions between two strands also contribute towards stability. For example, Tyr-Lys, Phe/Trp-Lys/Arg interactions.
7. Presence of a right-handed β-sheet twist.
8. The hydrophobic cluster between the strands contributed by Trp, Val, Phe, and Tyr residues vastly stabilize the β-sheet proteins.
9. As a general rule of thumb, incorporating disulfide bonds stabilize the protein with β-hairpin structures.

Relatively speaking, there are fewer examples of β-sheet proteins designed de novo. However, α/β mixed structures have been designed with great success (Struthers et al., 1996). For example, Top7 by David Baker group and a $\beta\beta\alpha$ motif structure that is similar to a zinc-finger, which has a β-hairpin structure (Kuhlman et al., 2003).

Tools Currently Available for Protein de novo Design

Irrespective of topology of the intended protein to be designed, some tools are listed below that are routinely used for de novo protein design, and also keeping in mind the ease of use from user's perspective.

Rosetta and Rosetta Design

Among the tools that are currently available, Rosetta (Simons *et al.*, 1999), developed by David Baker group at University of Washington, has been the most popular and widely used (Jiang *et al.*, 2008; Siegel *et al.*, 2010; Damborsky and Brezovsky, 2014). The suite of software (see Relevant Websites Section) has sped the design of protein structures. Details of Rosetta's design algorithm and specifics are discussed in Simons *et al.* (1997, 1999), Raveh *et al.* (2010) and DiMaio *et al.*, (2011) and they have been reviewed elsewhere (Mandell and Kortemme, 2009; Der and Kuhlman, 2011). Specifically, Rosetta Design (see Relevant Websites Section) can be accessed via the command line interface of Rosetta or via webserver (Lyskov *et al.*, 2013).

Evodesign

Evodesign (see Relevant Websites Section) developed by Zhang group at University of Michigan is a web based server to design protein sequences using a scaffold as an input. The scaffold is searched against the known protein families and the resulting conformation takes into consideration local environmental factors, such as solvent accessibility, packing, and secondary structure (Mitra *et al.*, 2013).

Protein WISDOM

Protein Wisdom (see Relevant Websites Section) is a web server tool for designing proteins from sequence information. The design and validation involves two steps: using either a rigid or flexible scaffold (or template), a sequence is selected from a pool of candidate sequences; and validation is done by fitting the sequence into known folds to calculate the "fold specificity" (Smadbeck *et al.*, 2013).

OSPREY

Open Source Protein REdesign for You (OSPREY) (see Relevant Websites Section) like Rosetta is a suite of programs developed by Donald group at Duke University. While Rosetta is licensed free for academics, OSPREY is open-source and freely available to download and use. OSPREY uses protein flexibility to create low-energy corpus of structures to identify the globally optimal structure. From the user's perspective, OSPREY runs as a standalone tool and is not available as a web-server (Gainza *et al.*, 2013).

ISAMBARD

Intelligent System for Analysis, Model Building And Rational Design (ISAMBARD) (see Relevant Websites Section) is another open-source suite of software for designing proteins developed by Woflsoon group at University of Bristol. Keeping with the popularity of Python, ISAMBARD uses predefined python object based method to design protein structures. Those with a basic python skill will be able to use this modular and scalable software to design protein structures (Wood *et al.*, 2017).

FireProt

Rather than a general protein design tool, FireProt (see Relevant Websites Section) is a specific protein design tool for designing multiple-point mutant proteins that are likely to be thermostable (Musil *et al.*, 2017).

iRDP

Similar to FireProt, in-silico Rational Design of Proteins (iRDP) (see Relevant Websites Section) is a webserver that uses a four-step approach to rationally design proteins. Specifically, from the input it compares existing protein structures for structural stability factors, followed by mutational analysis, and their impact to local environmental changes, and identifying the optimal structure that would have a higher thermostability than the previous structure (Panigrahi *et al.*, 2015).

IPRO

Iterative Protein Redesign and Optimization procedure (IPRO) (see Relevant Websites Section) from the Maranas group at Pennsylvania State University, uses a combinatorial approach to redesign a protein library using energy based scoring functions. As claimed by the developers, it uses a iterative process to make additive mutations that improve the designed protein's substrate specificity (Saraf *et al.*, 2006; Fazelinia *et al.*, 2007).

Scaffold Selection

Keeping in view that new protein can be designed from pre-existing structures; ScaffoldSelection (see Relevant Websites Section) is a tool that scans large sets of structures for a particular reaction scaffold (Malisi *et al.*, 2009). For the user, the tool can be downloaded as binaries for Linux, Mac, and Windows operating systems and run as a standalone software/tool.

Pocketoptimizer

Pocketoptimizer (see Relevant Websites Section) is an allied tool that can be used to design active site region, either to improve or modify ligand/substrate binding (Stiel *et al.*, 2016).

Conclusions

Protein design is an active, exciting area of research that has wide applications in drug design, medicine, and advancing the study of protein folding. When designing protein structures, one has to ask few questions and these questions drive or direct the use of tools to answer those questions.

1. Is the aim to engineer a protein's function/activity or designing a structure *de novo*?
2. Is the design fitting with the already known do's and don't's?
3. Is there another variable that is specific for the protein and its intended use?

There can be more additional questions added and the framework/checklist can act as a guide to the specific task in hand.

While, there are many success stories in *de novo* protein design, there are some challenges for the road ahead. Some of the challenges that have been discussed (Kuhlman *et al.*, 2009) are:

1. Sampling the conformational space of the backbone to move towards a completely flexible backbone based design. Currently, majority of the *de novo* designed proteins are on the basis of having a rigid scaffold or frame throughout the design pipeline.
2. To reduce the presence of alternate conformations from the desired/designed conformation.
3. Designing specific protein-protein interactions using a much easier and faster method.

Recently, Rocklin *et al.* from David baker's lab have used minimal proteins (proteins having a residue length below 50 amino acids) to understand the factors that determine protein folding. Specifically, they used computationally driven approach, where four topologies ($\alpha\alpha\alpha$, $\beta\alpha\beta\beta$, $\alpha\beta\beta\alpha$, and $\beta\beta\alpha\beta\beta$) were designed using 5000–40,000 sequences for each topology. Using yeast based proteolysis assay, a stability score was given to each designed protein, which enabled them to identify 2788 stable proteins. Such "massively-parallel" design has indeed pushed the limits of high-throughput design and the method can be applied to proteins of more than 50 amino acids in length (Rocklin *et al.*, 2017).

Acknowledgement

RMY acknowledges the infrastructural support given by Jaypee University of Information Technology, Waknaghat for completing this manuscript. Authorship was decided using a tic-tac-toe game with self. He also acknowledges Pulkit Anupam Srivastava for critical reading of the manuscript.

See also: Biomolecular Structures: Prediction, Identification and Analyses. Computational Protein Engineering Approaches for Effective Design of New Molecules. Identifying Functional Relationships Via the Annotation and Comparison of Three-Dimensional Amino Acid Arrangements in Protein Structures. Natural Language Processing Approaches in Bioinformatics. Sequence Analysis. Sequence Composition. Study of The Variability of The Native Protein Structure

---

References

Baxa, M., Haddadian, E., Jumper, J., Freed, K., Sosnick, T., 2014. Loss of conformational entropy in protein folding calculated using realistic ensembles and its implications for NMR-based calculations. Proceedings of the National Academy of Sciences 111 (43), 15396–15401.

Bowie, J.U., Luthy, R., Eisenberg, D., 1991. A method to identify protein sequences that fold into a known three-dimensional structure. Science (New York, NY) 253 (5016), 164–170.

Brown, J.E., Klee, W.A., 1971. Helix-coil transition of the isolated amino terminus of ribonuclease. Biochemistry 10 (3), 470–476.

Crick, F.H.C., 1953. The packing of {α}-helices: Simple coiled-coils. Acta Crystallographica 6 (8–9), 689–697. doi:10.1107/S0365110X53001964.

Dahiyat, B.I., Mayo, S.L., 1997. De novo protein design: Fully automated sequence selection. Science (New York, NY) 278 (5335), 82–87.

Damborsky, J., Brezovsky, J., 2014. Computational tools for designing and engineering enzymes. Current Opinion in Chemical Biology 19, 8–16. doi:10.1016/j.cbpa.2013.12.003.

de Alba, E., *et al.*, 1996. Conformational investigation of designed short linear peptides able to fold into beta-hairpin structures in aqueous solution. Folding & Design 1 (2), 133–144.

de Alba, E., *et al.*, 1999. De novo design of a monomeric three-stranded antiparallel beta-sheet. Protein Science : A Publication of the Protein Society 8 (4), 854–865. doi:10.1110/ps.8.4.854.

DeGrado, W.F., Wasserman, Z.R., Lear, J.D., 1989. Protein design, a minimalist approach. Science (New York, NY) 243 (4891), 622–628.

Der, B.S., Kuhlman, B., 2011. Biochemistry. From computational design to a protein that binds. Science (New York, NY) 332 (6031), 801–802. doi:10.1126/science.1207082.

DiMaio, F., et al., 2011. Modeling symmetric macromolecular structures in Rosetta3. PLOS ONE 6 (6), e20450. doi:10.1371/journal.pone.0020450.

Fazelinia, H., Cirino, P.C., Maranas, C.D., 2007. Extending Iterative Protein Redesign and Optimization (IPRO) in protein library design for ligand specificity. Biophysical Journal 92 (6), 2120–2130. doi:10.1529/biophysj.106.096016.

Gainza, P., et al., 2013. OSPREY: Protein design with ensembles, flexibility, and provable algorithms. Methods in Enzymology 523, 87–107. doi:10.1016/B978-0-12-394292-0.00005-9.

Griffiths-Jones, S.R., Searle, M.S., 2000. Structure, folding, and energetics of cooperative interactions between the β-Strands of a de novo designed three-stranded antiparallel β-sheet peptide. Journal of the American Chemical Society 122 (35), 8350–8356. doi:10.1021/ja000787t.

Huyghues-Despointes, B.M., Scholtz, J.M., Baldwin, R.L., 1993. Effect of a single aspartate on helix stability at different positions in a neutral alanine-based peptide. Protein Science: A Publication of the Protein Society 2 (10), 1604–1611. doi:10.1002/pro.5560021006.

Jiang, L., et al., 2008. De novo computational design of retro-aldol enzymes. Science (New York, NY) 319 (5868), 1387–1391. doi:10.1126/science.1152692.

Kim, P.S., Baldwin, R.L., 1984. A helix stop signal in the isolated S-peptide of ribonuclease A. Nature 307 (5949), 329–334.

Kortemme, T., Ramirez-Alvarado, M., Serrano, L., 1998. Design of a 20-amino acid, three-stranded beta-sheet protein. Science (New York, NY) 281 (5374), 253–256.

Kuhlman, B., et al., 2003. Design of a novel globular protein fold with atomic-level accuracy. Science (New York, NY) 302 (5649), 1364–1368. doi:10.1126/science.10894270.

Kuhlman, B., Jung Choi, E., Guntas, G., 2009. Future challenges of computational protein design. In: Protein Engineering and Design, CRC Press. Available at: http://dx.doi.org/10.1201/9781420076592.ch18.

Lacroix, E., Viguera, A.R., Serrano, L., 1998. Elucidating the folding problem of alpha-helices: Local motifs, long-range electrostatics, ionic-strength dependence and prediction of NMR parameters. Journal of Molecular Biology 284 (1), 173–191. doi:10.1006/jmbi.1998.2145.

Leitner, A., Walzthoeni, T., Kahraman, A., et al., 2010. Probing native protein structures by chemical cross-linking, mass spectrometry, and bioinformatics. Molecular & Cellular Proteomics 9 (8), 1634–1649.

Lyskov, S., et al., 2013. Serverification of molecular modeling applications: The rosetta online server that includes everyone (ROSIE). PLOS ONE 8 (5), e63906. doi:10.1371/journal.pone.0063906.

Lyu, P.C., et al., 1990. Side chain contributions to the stability of alpha-helical structure in peptides. Science (New York, NY) 250 (4981), 669–673.

Malisi, C., Kohlbacher, O., Hocker, B., 2009. Automated scaffold selection for enzyme design. Proteins 77 (1), 74–83. doi:10.1002/prot.22418.

Mandell, D.J., Kortemme, T., 2009. Backbone flexibility in computational protein design. Current Opinion in Biotechnology 20 (4), 420–428. doi:10.1016/j.copbio.2009.07.006.

Marqusee, S., Baldwin, R.L., 1987. Helix stabilization by Glu-·Lys+ salt bridges in short peptides of de novo design. Proceedings of the National Academy of Sciences of the United States of America. 8898–8902.

Marqusee, S., Robbins, V.H., Baldwin, R.L., 1989. Unusually stable helix formation in short alanine-based peptides. Proceedings of the National Academy of Sciences of the United States of America 86 (14), 5286–5290.

Mitra, P., Shultis, D., Zhang, Y., 2013. EvoDesign: de novo protein design based on structural and evolutionary profiles. Nucleic Acids Research 41, W273–W280. doi:10.1093/nar/gkt384.

Munoz, V., Serrano, L., 1994. Elucidating the folding problem of helical peptides using empirical parameters. Nature Structural Biology 1 (6), 399–409.

Munoz, V., Serrano, L., 1995a. Elucidating the folding problem of helical peptides using empirical parameters. II. Helix macrodipole effects and rational modification of the helical content of natural peptides. Journal of Molecular Biology 245 (3), 275–296.

Munoz, V., Serrano, L., 1995b. Elucidating the folding problem of helical peptides using empirical parameters. III. Temperature and pH dependence. Journal of Molecular Biology 245 (3), 297–308. doi:10.1006/jmbi.1994.0024.

Munoz, V., Serrano, L., 1997. Development of the multiple sequence approximation within the AGADIR model of alpha-helix formation: Comparison with Zimm-Bragg and Lifson-Roig formalisms. Biopolymers 41 (5), 495–509. doi:10.1002/(SICI)1097-0282(19970415)41:5<495::AID-BIP2>3.0.CO;2-H.

Musil, M., et al., 2017. FireProt: Web server for automated design of thermostable proteins. Nucleic Acids Research. doi:10.1093/nar/gkx285.

Nicholson, H., Becktel, W.J., Matthews, B.W., 1988. Enhanced protein thermostability from designed mutations that interact with alpha-helix dipoles. Nature 336 (6200), 651–656. doi:10.1038/336651a0.

Panigrahi, P., et al., 2015. Engineering proteins for thermostability with iRDP web server. PLOS ONE 10 (10), e0139486. doi:10.1371/journal.pone.0139486.

Park, S.H., Shalongo, W., Stellwagen, E., 1993. Residue helix parameters obtained from dichroic analysis of peptides of defined sequence. Biochemistry 32 (27), 7048–7053.

Pauling, L., Corey, R.B., 1953. Compound helical configurations of polypeptide chains: Structure of proteins of the alpha-keratin type. Nature 171 (4341), 59–61.

Ramirez-Alvarado, M., Blanco, F.J., Serrano, L., 1996. De novo design and structural analysis of a model beta-hairpin peptide system. Nature Structural Biology 3 (7), 604–612.

Raveh, B., London, N., Schueler-Furman, O., 2010. Sub-angstrom modeling of complexes between flexible peptides and globular proteins. Proteins 78 (9), 2029–2040. doi:10.1002/prot.22716.

Richardson, J.S., 1981. The anatomy and taxonomy of protein structure. Advances in Protein Chemistry 34, 167–339.

Richardson, J.S., Richardson, D.C., 1988. Amino acid preferences for specific locations at the ends of alpha helices. Science (New York, NY) 240 (4859), 1648–1652.

Richardson, J.S., Richardson, D.C., 1989. The de novo design of protein structures. Trends in Biochemical Sciences 14 (7), 304–309.

Rocklin, G.J., et al., 2017. Global analysis of protein folding using massively parallel design, synthesis, and testing. Science (New York, NY) 357 (6347), 168–175. doi:10.1126/science.aan0693.

Saraf, M.C., et al., 2006. IPRO: An iterative computational protein library redesign and optimization procedure. Biophysical Journal 90 (11), 4167–4180. doi:10.1529/biophysj.105.079277.

Schafmeister, C.E., et al., 1997. A designed four helix bundle protein with native-like structure. Nature Structural Biology 4 (12), 1039–1046.

Schenck, H.L., Gellman, S.H., 1998. Use of a designed triple-stranded antiparallel beta-Sheet to probe beta-sheet cooperativity in aqueous solution. Journal of the American Chemical Society 120 (11), 4869–4870. doi:10.1021/ja973984+.

Scholtz, J.M., et al., 1993. The energetics of ion-pair and hydrogen-bonding interactions in a helical peptide. Biochemistry 32 (37), 9668–9676.

Sharman, G.J., Searle, M.S., 1998. Cooperative interaction between the three strands of a designed antiparallel β-sheet. Journal of the American Chemical Society 120 (21), 5291–5300. doi:10.1021/ja9705405.

Shoemaker, K.R., et al., 1987. Tests of the helix dipole model for stabilization of alpha-helices. Nature 326 (6113), 563–567. doi:10.1038/326563a0.

Siegel, J.B., et al., 2010. Computational design of an enzyme catalyst for a stereoselective bimolecular Diels-Alder reaction. Science (New York, NY) 329 (5989), 309–313. doi:10.1126/science.1190239.

Simons, K.T., et al., 1997. Assembly of protein tertiary structures from fragments with similar local sequences using simulated annealing and Bayesian scoring functions. Journal of Molecular Biology 268 (1), 209–225. doi:10.1006/jmbi.1997.0959.

Simons, K.T., et al., 1999. Improved recognition of native-like protein structures using a combination of sequence-dependent and sequence-independent features of proteins. Proteins 34 (1), 82–95.

Sinz, A., Arlt, C., Chorev, D., Sharon, M., 2015. Chemical cross-linking and native mass spectrometry: A fruitful combination for structural biology. Protein Science 24 (8), 1193–1209.

Smadbeck, J., et al., 2013. Protein WISDOM: A workbench for in silico de novo design of biomolecules. Journal of Visualized Experiments: JoVE. 77. doi:10.3791/50476.

Stanger, H.E., Gellman, S.H., 1998. Rules for antiparallel β-sheet design: D-pro-gly is superior to L-Asn-Gly for β-hairpin nucleation. Journal of the American Chemical Society 120 (17), 4236–4237. doi:10.1021/JA973704Q.

Stiel, A.C., Nellen, M., Hocker, B., 2016. PocketOptimizer and the design of ligand binding sites. Methods in Molecular Biology Clifton NJ 1414, 63–75. doi:10.1007/978-1-4939-3569-7_5.

Struthers, M.D., Cheng, R.P., Imperiali, B., 1996. Design of a monomeric 23-residue polypeptide with defined tertiary structure. Science (New York, NY) 271 (5247), 342–345.

Wetzel, R., 1987. Harnessing disulfide bonds using protein engineering. Trends in Biochemical Sciences 12 (Suppl.), 478–482. Available at: https://doi.org/10.1016/0968-0004(87)90234-9.

Wood, C.W., et al., 2017. ISAMBARD: An open-source computational environment for biomolecular analysis, modelling and design. Bioinformatics (Oxford). doi:10.1093/bioinformatics/btx352.

Xiong, H., et al., 1995. Periodicity of polar and nonpolar amino acids is the major determinant of secondary structure in self-assembling oligomeric peptides. Proceedings of the National Academy of Sciences of the United States of America 92 (14), 6349–6353.

Further Reading

Baldwin, R.L., 1995. Alpha-helix formation by peptides of defined sequence. Biophysical Chemistry 55 (1–2), 127–135.

Barlow, D.J., Thornton, J.M., 1988. Helix geometry in proteins. Journal of Molecular Biology 201 (3), 601–619.

Blanco, F., Ramirez-Alvarado, M., Serrano, L., 1998. Formation and stability of beta-hairpin structures in polypeptides. Current Opinion in Structural Biology 8 (1), 107–111.

Carey, P., 2008. Protein Engineering and Design. San Diego, CA: Academic Press.

Chakrabartty, A., Baldwin, R.L., 1995. Stability of alpha-helices. Advances in Protein Chemistry 46, 141–176.

Fisk, J.D., Gellman, S.H., 2001. A parallel beta-sheet model system that folds in water. Journal of the American Chemical Society. 343–344.

Guerois, R., De la Paz, M., 2006. Protein Design Methods in Molecular Biology, 340. Springer.

Jensen, K., 2010. Peptide and Protein Design for Biopharmaceutical Applications. Chichester: Wiley.

Lacroix, E., et al., 1999. The design of linear peptides that fold as monomeric beta-sheet structures. Current Opinion in Structural 9 (4), 487–493.

Nowick, J.S., Cary, J.M., Tsai, J.H., 2001. A triply templated artificial beta-sheet. Journal of the American Chemical Society 123 (22), 5176–5180.

Park, S., Cochran, J., 2010. Protein Engineering and Design. Boca Raton: CRC Press.

Presta, L.G., Rose, G.D., 1988. Helix signals in proteins. Science (New York, NY) 240 (4859), 1632–1641.

Richardson, J.S., Richardson, D.C., 1988. Amino acid preferences for specific locations at the ends of alpha helices. Science New York, NY) 240 (4859), 1648–1652.

Rohl, C.A., Baldwin, R.L., 1998. Deciphering rules of helix stability in peptides. Methods in Enzymology 295, 1–26.

Scholtz, J.M., Baldwin, R.L., 1992. The mechanism of alpha-helix formation by peptides. Annual Review of Biophysics and Biomolecular Structure 21, 95–118. doi:10.1146/annurev.bb.21.060192.000523.

Searle, M.S., Ciani, B., 2004. Design of beta-sheet systems for understanding the thermodynamics and kinetics of protein folding. Current Opinion in Structural Biology 14 (4), 458–464. doi:10.1016/j.sbi.2004.06.001.

Serrano, L., 2000. The relationship between sequence and structure in elementary folding units. Advances in Protein Chemistry 53, 49–85.

Venkatraman, J., Shankaramma, S.C., Balaram, P., 2001. Design of folded peptides. Chemical Reviews 101 (10), 3131–3152.

Relevant Websites

http://agadir.crg.es/
   Adagir.
http://www.cs.duke.edu/donaldlab/osprey.php
   Donald lab.
http://www.grigoryanlab.org/drawcoil
   Drawcoil 1.0.
http://rzlab.ucr.edu/scripts/wheel/wheel.cgi
   Helical Wheel Projections - RZLab.
http://irdp.ncl.res.in
   iRDP.
https://loschmidt.chemi.muni.cz/fireprot
   LOSCHMIDT laboratories.
http://www.eb.tuebingen.mpg.de/research/research-groups/birte-hoecker/algorithms-and-software/pocketoptimizer.html
   Max Planck Institute for Developmental Biology.
http://www.eb.tuebingen.mpg.de/research/research-groups/birte-hoecker/algorithms-and-software/scaffoldselection.html
   Max Planck Institute for Developmental Biology.
http://maranas.che.psu.edu/submission/IPRO_2.htm
   PENNSTATE.
http://emboss.bioinformatics.nl/cgi-bin/emboss/pepwheel
   Pepwheel.
http://atlas.princeton.edu/proteinwisdom
   Protein WISDOM.
https://pypi.python.org/pypi/isambard
   Python.
https://www.rosettacommons.org/
   Rosetta commons.
http://rosettadesign.med.unc.edu
   Rosetta commons.
http://rosie.rosettacommons.org/
   Rosetta commons.
https://zhanglab.ccmb.med.umich.edu/EvoDesign
   Zhang lab.

Biographical Sketch

Ragothaman Yennamalli is an Assistant Professor at Jaypee University of Information Technology, Waknaghat, Himachal Pradesh, India. He completed his PhD in Computational Biology and Bioinformatics from Jawaharlal Nehru University, New Delhi. He conducted postdoctoral research at Jawaharlal Nehru University in India and at Iowa State University (2009–2011), University of Wisconsin-Madison (2011–2012), and Rice University (2012–2014) in USA. He is a structural and computational biologist with more than a decade of experience in predictive modelling and biomolecular simulation projects. Dr. Yennamalli's skills involve molecular docking, molecular dynamics simulation, coarse grained modelling, machine learning, data mining, data analytics, and molecular modelling. Website: http://bit.ly/raghu_juit.

Molecular Dynamics Simulations in Drug Discovery

Sy-Bing Choi, Beow Keat Yap, Yee Siew Choong, and Habibah Wahab, Universiti Sains Malaysia, Pulau Pinang, Malaysia

Background

The need for reduction of cost and time had led to the emergence of computer-aided drug design technology in drug discovery pipeline. While molecular docking and other high throughput virtual screening have played significant roles in screening large libraries of compounds, atomistic Molecular Dynamics (MD) simulation, is increasingly gaining trust in guiding the prediction of comprehensive drug-target binding interactions with the cognate protein receptors, which are important in successful hit discovery and optimisation. The classical 'lock-and-key' theory of ligand binding where the lock is a rigid protein receptor complemented by small molecules which act as keys, is no longer able to account for the drug binding event, as conformational changes upon ligand binding to receptor proteins are well known. These conformational changes range from modest loop motion to hinge bending Jorgensen, 1991). Most docking programmes can only give a static picture ('lock-and-key') of what is happening during drug binding. Thus, MD simulations are the method of choice, to study drug-target binding allowing conformational changes to be investigated further (De Vivo *et al.*, 2016).

In a typical all-atom MD simulation, the movements of all the atoms of a drug and its target protein (or other macromolecule) in physiological solvent environment are simulated over time (lasting for hundreds of nanoseconds or longer) in a series of discrete short time steps (e.g., 2 fs). At each time step, the forces on each atom are computed (based on force field method) from the atomic position and velocity according to Newton's Laws of Motions. The trajectories obtained will be used to study the dynamics and behaviours of the system as well as making prediction on the binding affinity of the ligands to the receptor. The use of molecular dynamics (MD) simulation along with the current advancement in computational technology allows such valuable prediction to be obtained with reasonable cost and time. The applications of MD simulation in drug discovery is wide ranging, from the investigation of protein-ligand binding and unbinding to mutation effects for this binding and computing the free energy of binding. The application of molecular dynamics in relation to drug discovery in general have been reviewed previously (De Vivo *et al.*, 2016; Durrant and McCammon, 2011; Borhani and Shaw, 2012). In this review, we focus specifically on the contribution of MD simulations in the attempt to battle tuberculosis (TB), one of the ancient deadly diseases that still persist today.

Mycobacterium tuberculosis (MTB), the causative agent of human tuberculosis (TB), is a bacterial pathogen, listed as one of the top ten causes of death worldwide. Currently, it is the leading cause of death from a single infectious agent surpassing even human immunodeficiency virus (HIV) with 1.4 million people killed per year and an estimated 2 billion people are latently infected worldwide. In 2016, an estimated 10.4 million people developed active TB (WHO, 2017). MTB (**Fig. 1**) has been known to infect human from thousands of years. In general, there are two phases in MTB life cycle, i.e., the replication phase (active TB) and the dormant phase (inactive TB) (**Fig. 2**). Both phases involve different metabolic pathways, with carbohydrate as the main source in active TB phase, and lipid as sole carbon source in dormant phase. To date, most drugs available for MTB infection are only targeting the replication phase of the MTB infection. However, there is an imminent need for finding effective drugs that can target MTB in the dormant phase, as 95% of current MTB infection is becoming latent.

MTB has a remarkable ability to avoid the attacks of host's immune system and has developed sophisticated strategies for successful infection that make it challenging to treat the disease. The current MTB therapy is a two-month intensive phase of a four-drug combinations of isoniazid (INH), rifampicin (RIF), pyrazinamide (PZA) and ethambutol (EMB) followed by a longer continuation phase of INH and RIF to eradicate the remaining bacilli that have entered a dormant, slowly-replicating latent phase.

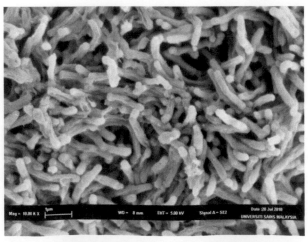

Fig. 1 Scanning electron microscope (SEM) image of H37Rv strain (ATCC 25618) of *Mycobacterium tuberculosis.*

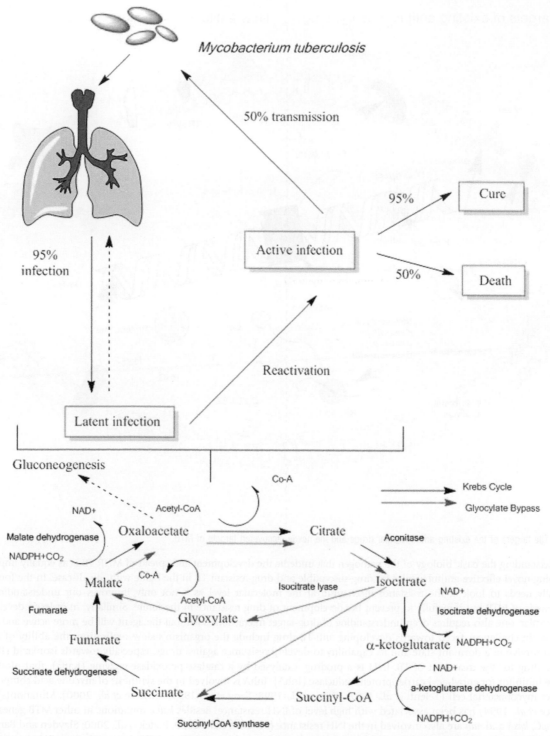

Fig. 2 Stages of transmission and progression of MTB infections. Two different metabolic pathways used by MTB in replication and dormant phase of MTB infection are shown.

Fig. 3 shows the targets of these drugs in MTB. The emergence of multidrug-resistant MDR-TB strains (resistance to RIF and INH) complicates the therapy as the treatment can extend up to 2 years and requires more toxic, less efficacious second- or third-line agents such as fluoroquinolone and kanamycin. The appearance of the extensively drug-resistant tuberculosis (XDR-TB) and totally drug-resistant tuberculosis (TDR-TB) have made the treatment even more difficult (Hoagland et al., 2016) and expensive. The average cost of treating a TB patient increases with resistance; from $18,000 to treat drug-susceptible TB to $513,000 to treat the most drug-resistant form of the disease (XDR TB). The therapy takes a long time to complete, disrupts lives, and has potentially serious and side effects such as depression or psychosis, hearing loss, hepatitis, and kidney impairment (CDC, 2017).

Targets of existing antituberculosis drug | New antituberculosis targets

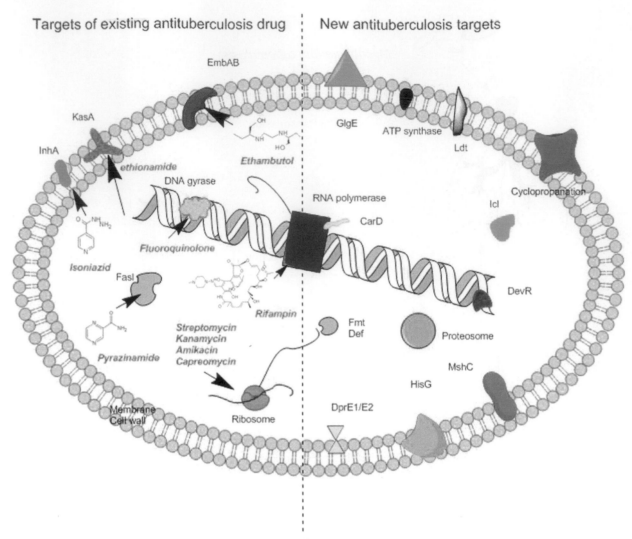

Fig. 3 The targets of the existing antitubercular drugs and the newly discovered targets of MTB.

Understanding the basic biology of the pathogen that underlie the development and spread of MDR TB is as equally important as developing novel effective antitubercular for drug-susceptible and drug-resistant TB in the battle with this disease. In the former case, one really needs to look at the resistance mechanism at the molecular level as it not only improves our understanding of the pathogenesis of MTB but hopefully to prevent the development of drug resistance in the future. Similarly, in order to develop novel antitubercular, one also requires deep understanding of drug-target interactions such that the agent will be more active and selective.

The main challenges faced towards developing anti-TB drug include the organism's slow replication, the ability of *M. tuberculosis* to survive in a dormant state and its capability to develop resistance against drugs, especially towards isoniazid (INH), the first line drug for the treatment of TB. INH is a prodrug, catalysed by a catalase peroxidase enzyme (KatG), that produces the ultimate inhibitor for enoyl-acyl carrier protein reductase (InhA). InhA is involved in the synthesis of mycolic acid components of the outer mycobacterial cell (Telenti *et al.*, 1997; Wang *et al.*, 1998; Fang *et al.*, 1999; Vilcheze *et al.*, 2000). Mutation(s) in *katG* (Banerjee *et al.*, 1994) has been associated with high level of INH resistance. Besides *katG*, mutations in other MTB genes, such as *inhA*, *ahpC*, *kasA* and *ndh* are also involved in the INH resistance (Vilcheze *et al.*, 2000; Piatek *et al.*, 2000; Slayden and Barry, 2000; Torres *et al.*, 2000) with the mutations within *inhA* have been reported up to 32% in INH-resistant isolates (Heym *et al.*, 1995; Morris *et al.*, 1995; Lee *et al.*, 1999; Kiepiela *et al.*, 2000). Beside INH, MTB has been shown to develop resistance towards other TB drugs. **Table 1** lists some examples of current tuberculosis drugs and their targets as well as genes associated with their resistance (Telenti, 1998; Zhang *et al.*, 2006; Hards *et al.*, 2015; Lewis and Sloan, 2015).

To date, in the quest for developing new active antitubercular, there have been many new drug targets identified alongside the well established targets for MTB and these numbers are increasing as new technologies emerged. Recent reviews (Wellington and Hung, 2018; Ferraris *et al.*, 2018; Hoagland *et al.*, 2016) have provided interesting snapshots of some of these molecular targets which are involved in vital cellular biological processes such as cell wall synthesis, energy metabolism, protein synthesis, phosphate transport and the metabolism of key molecules and cofactors. Here, we aim to provide dynamic snapshots of these molecular targets using MD simulations to further improve our understanding of the action and resistance mechanisms of various

Table 1   Current tuberculosis drugs, their molecular targets and gene(s) associated with their resistance

Drug	Mechanism of action	Target	Gene(s) involved in resistance
Isoniazid	Inhibition of cell wall mycolic acid synthesis	Enoyl acyl carrier protein reductase (InhA)	katG, inhA,
Rifampicin	Inhibition of RNA synthesis	RNA polymerase, subunit B (rpoB)	rpoB
Pyrazinamide	Depletion of membrane energy	Membrane energy metabolism, precise target still debatable	pncA, panD, rpsA
Ethambutol	Inhibition of cell wall synthesis	Arabisonyl transferase	embCAB
Streptomycin	Inhibition of protein synthesis	Ribosomal S12 protein and 16SrRNA	rpsL, rrs
Kanamycin	Inhibition of protein synthesis	16SrRNA	Rrs
Capreomycin	Inhibition of protein synthesis	16SrRNA, 50Sribosome, rNA methyltransferase (TlyA)	Rrs, tlyA
Fluoroquinolones	Inhibition of DNA synthesis	DNA gyrase	gyrA, gyrB
Ethionamide	Inhibition of mycolic acid synthesis	Acyl carrier protein reductase (InhA)	inhA, etaA/ethA
Para-amino salicylic acid	Inhibition of folate pathway	Dihydrofolate reductase, dfrA	thyA, dfrA
Bedaquiline	Inhibition of ATP synthase	The proton pump of mycobacterial ATP (adenosine 5′-triphosphate) synthase	atpE
Delamanid	Inhibition of mycobacterial cell wall components, methoxy mycolic acid and ketomycolic acid synthesis	Deazaflavin dependent nitroreductase	fgd, Rv3547, fbiA, fbiB, and fbiC

Note: Reproduced from Telenti, A., 1998. Genetics of drug resistant tuberculosis. Thorax 53, 793–797. Zhang, Y., Post-Martens, K., Denkin, S., 2006. New drug candidates and therapeutic targets for tuberculosis therapy. Drug Discov. Today 11, 21–27. Hards, K., Robson, J.R., Berney, M., et al., 2015. Bactericidal mode of action of bedaquiline. J. Antimicrob. Chemother. 70, 2028–2037. Lewis, J.M., Sloan, D.J., 2015. The role of delamanid in the treatment of drug-resistant tuberculosis. Ther. Clin. Risk Manag. 11, 779–791.

drugs towards their corresponding TB targets and how the results have been instrumental in the optimisation stage of drug discovery against existing and newly discovered targets.

Applications and Case Studies

MD simulations have been applied to investigate the structural dynamics of various drug targets and to unravel mechanistic information. Such information includes the effects of mutations, role of waters on the ligand binding as well as the prediction of potentially new ligand binding site. The methodology has also been used in *in silico* drug discovery campaign, from preparation of protein structure for structure-based drug design and discovery studies, to evaluation of the binding interactions, stability and free binding energies of protein-ligand complexes (**Fig. 4**). These applications in battling tuberculosis are discussed in greater detail below.

Elucidating the Structural Dynamics and Mechanisms of MTB Targets

The static models provided by docking simulations give valuable insights into macromolecular structure, but drug binding is a dynamic event. At physiological condition, macromolecules (targets) are in constant motion surrounded by solvents. Drug binding to the target typically results in the target's conformational shifts that is usually different in the absence of drug binding. This binding event, is governed by enthalpic contribution which stabilizes the interactions through the formation of hydrogen bonds, salt bridges and/or van der Waals interactions; as well as the entropic penalties from the loss of conformational freedom of the target and drug. Amino acid mutations occurring in many MTB drug targets, which have contributed to many clinically drug-resistant strains, may disrupt shape complementarity as well as physicochemical compatibility that affect the binding of drug to the target (Lahti *et al.*, 2012). All these dynamic events, can easily be studied using MD simulations.

The understanding of conformational changes of selected MTB targets is crucial in designing effective molecules for drug discovery. For this reason, *in silico* site-directed mutagenesis has been performed to understand how the functionally important binding site residues in targeted MTB enzymes affect the conformational changes as well as the binding of potential inhibitors. To illustrate, studies on an enzyme involves in glyoxylate pathway is chosen as an example. As dormant phase MTB is in non-replicating mode, MTB shifts its metabolism pathway to utilise fatty acids or lipids as the carbon source to survive in the macrophage. Therefore, the energy of MTB is produced via glyoxylate pathway to bypass the oxygen-dependent tricarboxylic acid cycle (also known as Krebs cycle). Shukla and co-workers revealed that H46A, L418A and F345A mutations in isocitrate lyase, an enzyme in the glyoxylate shunt, resulted in the loss of activity due to geometry alteration in the binding site. The altered active site geometry disturbed the enzyme transition state, rendering the enzyme inactive (Shukla *et al.*, 2018, 2017a,b; **Fig. 5**). A similar approach has also been used against different MTB targets such as pantothenate synthase (Pandey *et al.*, 2018), catalase peroxidase (Singh *et al.*, 2018; Srivastava *et al.*, 2017; Pimentel *et al.*, 2017; Unissa *et al.*, 2017), pyrazinamidase (Aggarwal *et al.*, 2018), RecA *Mtu* Intein (Zwarycz *et al.*, 2017), RNA polymerase (Singh *et al.*, 2017), RpoB protein (Nusrath Unissa *et al.*, 2016), where conformational stability as well as shrinking or enlarging the binding site cavity caused by mutations were studied with respect to their effect on individual functionality of MTB drug targets.

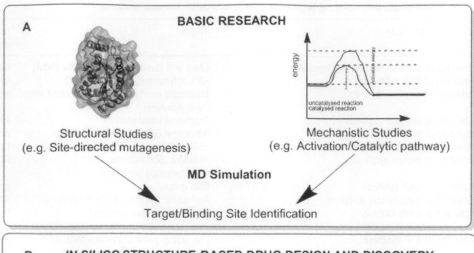

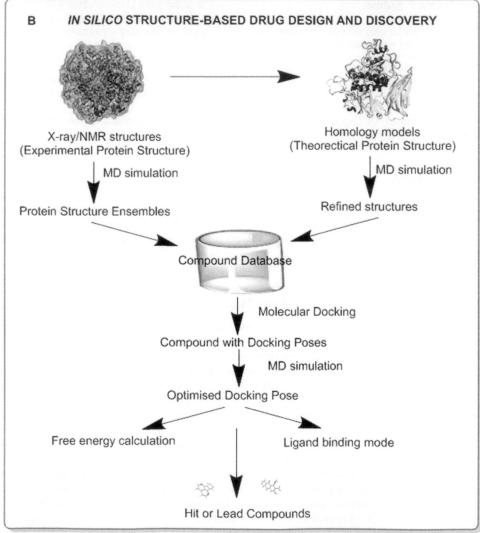

Fig. 4 General applications of MD simulations in (A) basic research and (B) *in silico* structure-based drug design and discovery.

Apart from studying the conformational changes upon mutation, MD has also been used to understand the functional behaviour of drug target in its different subunit form. To illustrate, Parker and co-workers revealed that disruption of the tetrameric conformation of 3-deoxy-D-*arabino*-heptulosonate 7-phosphate synthase (DAH7PS) by substitution of G232P to dimer resulted in changes in conformation as well as the polar and solvation properties by MD analysis. This ultimately resulted in the reduction of catalytic efficiency and the loss of allosteric response, suggesting the importance of maintaining

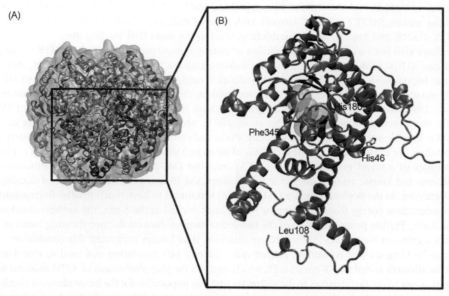

Fig. 5 (A) ICL In its tetrameric form (PDB ID: 1F8I). (B) Point mutations H46A, H180A, F345A and L108A constructed by Shukla *et al.* (2015, 2017a,b, 2018). L108 and H46 are distant from the ICL binding site (in surface representation).

the quaternary structure (i.e., the tetrameric form) for its function. This was further validated experimentally with enzyme kinetics study (Jiao *et al.*, 2017).

2-*trans-enoyl*-ACP (CoA) reductase (InhA) is involved in the biosynthesis of mycolic acid, an essential unique component of the MTB cell wall. This enzyme is the primary target of isoniazid (the first-line antituberculosis drug). Therefore, inhibition of InhA by isoniazid will hinder the synthesis of the MTB cell wall. MD simulations have also been used by Basso's group to investigate the crowding effect on 2-*trans*-enoyl-ACP (CoA) reductase (InhA) enzyme from MTB (Rotta *et al.*, 2017). As crowding effect is impossible to mimic in *in vitro* experiment, investigation of the crowding effect on the respective protein was performed *in silico*, by mimicking the cellular crowd (Ferreira *et al.*, 2016). Briefly, the behaviour of InhA in different solutions such as sucrose, glucose and PEG at different concentration is compared. Their study suggested that the flexibility of InhA and the variation in the volume of the active site is strongly related to the concentrations of the sucrose and glucose solutions used, with high rigidity and compactness of InhA shown on the B-factor interpretation in highly concentrated sucrose and glucose solutions mimicking the cellular environment. Based on these observations, Basso and co-workers suggested that the active site packing of InhA could interfere with processes such as substrate entrance and/or product release. The findings from this study also serve as a surrogate of *in vivo* intracellular medium for anti-tuberculosis drug screening campaigns (Rotta *et al.*, 2017).

In combination with QM/MM (hybrid quantum mechanics/molecular mechanics), MD simulation is also able to provide in-depth details of a chemical reaction. Yao *et al.* (2017) utilised QM/MM approach to study the catalytic mechanism and the nature of the rate-limiting step involving the shikimate kinase enzyme in the shikimate pathway which has recently been recognised as an antimicrobial drug target for MTB. The shikimate kinase pathway is used by plants and bacteria to synthesize shikimate, which is a common precursor in the synthesis of aromatic amino acids and secondary metabolites. Their results were found to correlate well with the experimental data where the phosphorylation transfer process, which is the rate-limiting step of SK-catalysed phosphorylation of shikimic acid (SKM), is a concerted one step reaction proceeding through a loose transition state.

Prediction of a New Ligand-Binding Site in MTB Targets

Predicting a new ligand binding sites on receptor structures, which are obtained either from experimental or computational methods, is a useful first step in structure-based drug design (Jian *et al.*, 2016). MD simulations have also been used to predict the binding site of isoniazid (INH) in MTB's KatG protein, in which its S315T mutation has been associated with INH resistance, presumably due to its reduced affinity (Yu *et al.*, 2003). INH is a prodrug which needs activation by the KatG protein to exert its action. Although the exact binding site of INH to KatG is unknown, it has been previously proposed that there are three potential binding sites of INH on KatG, close to the heme site, referred to as Site-1, Site-2 and Site-3 (Kamachi *et al.*, 2015a,b; Vidossich *et al.*, 2014). To pinpoint the exact binding site, a 100 ns MD simulations for each of the docked complex of INH at the three potential binding sites of the wild-type and S315T mutant KatG were carried out (Srivastava *et al.*, 2017). Interestingly, only Site-1 bound INH resulted in conformational change to the important heme group of KatG, suggesting that Site-1 is the main INH binding site. Moreover, further MD trajectories analysis revealed no significant change to RMSD, RMSF, Rg, hydrogen bond occupancy and solvent-accessible surface area (SASA) for both wild-type and mutant systems of all but Site-1 bound INH systems. In addition, subsequent estimation of INH binding energy with MM-PBSA from the stable MD trajectories of the complex revealed a strong binding energy for Site-1 bound INH (wild-type) with a value of

− 44.201 kJ/mol versus − 0.090 kJ/mol and − 3.805 kJ/mol in Site-2 and Site 3, respectively. A comparatively weaker binding affinity of INH in Site-1 of the mutant S315T (− 35.307 kJ/mol), with reduced hydrogen bond occupancy involving key residues for INH activation, i.e., Tyr229, His108 and Arg104, further establishing Site-1 as the main INH binding site.

MD simulations have also been used to assist prediction of potential allosteric sites of various MTB targets, such as the UDP-Galactopyranose Mutase (UGM) (Shi et al., 2016) and the shikimate kinase (SK) enzymes (Mehra et al., 2016a). UGM plays an important role in the biosynthesis of mycobacterial cell wall, as it catalyses the reversible conversion of UDP-galactopyranose (UDP-Galp) to UDP-galactofuranose (UDP-Galf), which is required for the building of arabinogalactan chain in the mycobacterial cell wall (Besra et al., 1995; Nassau et al., 1996). UGM gene knockout was found to inhibit the growth of MTB, indicating that UGM is essential for the growth of mycobacteria (Pan et al., 2001). Moreover, both UGM and Galf are not found in human, suggesting that UGM is a viable anti-TB drug target. Recently, Pinto and colleagues (Shi et al., 2016) have successfully discovered a second druggable binding site in UGM based on the analysis of 80 ns MD simulations (RMSF, number of contacts and interaction energies) of the complex of a novel non-substrate-like UGM inhibitor (MS-208, identified from saturation transfer difference (STD) NMR experiments and kinetic assays), docked at the allosteric site (A-site, predicted from blind docking) or the active site (S-site) of the UGM enzyme. As the docked complex (at the A-site) was found to have much smaller fluctuations, larger number of contacts, and larger interaction energy than the complex of inhibitor docked at the S-site, the authors concluded that MS-208 is likely to bind to the A-site. Further point mutation of the two interacting residues on the two flanking loops of A-site (Y253A and D322A) resulted in a significant loss in MS-208 inhibitory activities, thus further supported this conclusion.

In a separate study by Nargotra and co-workers (Mehra et al., 2016a), MD simulation was used to elucidate the probability of inhibitor binding at the allosteric site of the SK enzyme. SK, which catalyses the phosphorylation of 3-OH-shikimic acid (in the presence of ATP as co-substrate), is one of the key enzymes in the shikimate pathway responsible for the biosynthesis of chorismate, an important precursor for the subsequent biosynthesis of common aromatic amino acid residues (Phe, Trp, Tyr) and secondary metabolites essential for the MTB survival (Herrmann and Weaver, 1999; Parish and Stoker, 2002). As the best SK inhibitor, 5489375 showed uncompetitive inhibition for SK and noncompetitive inhibition for ATP in in vitro experiments. Thus, it is suggested that the inhibitor may have potentially bound at another binding site. To investigate this, the inhibitor was docked to the common allosteric site of three different protein complexes, i.e., the Michaelis complex, complex A and the product complex, as predicted by SiteMap, and each complexes was subjected to a 10 ns MD simulation. Interestingly, the inhibitor was found to be displaced out of the initial binding cavity of the Michaelis complex and complex A to the surface of the protein after about 4 ns and 1 ns of simulations, respectively. Whilst the inhibitor remained in the initial binding cavity of the product complex throughout the simulation, with low ligand RMSD (∼ 5 Å) and RMSF values (< 3.5 Å). This suggests that the inhibitor is likely to bind to the allosteric site only after the reaction products are formed. Additionally, further MD analysis demonstrated that hydrogen bond and hydrophobic contacts formed between residues Arg43, Ile45 and Phe57 of the enzyme and the inhibitor for at least 23% of the simulation time, suggesting that the binding of the inhibitor at the allosteric site of the SK enzyme is stabilised by these residues.

Preparation of Target Structure for Structure-Based Drug Design and Discovery Studies

A protein undergoes continual conformational changes under physiological conditions while maintaining its overall fold, i.e., 3D structure. A snapshot of a protein typically provided by the X-ray crystal structure would not be able to account for the continual conformational changes although the overall topology of the folded state remains conserved. During docking using a protein's crystal structure, a slightly different orientation of even a single side chain in the binding site of the protein can significantly influence docking results (Zhao and Caflisch, 2015). To address this issue, MD simulations have been used to generate multiple conformers of target proteins, where ensembles of snapshots from MD simulations of target proteins such as InhA enzymes from wild-type and 116T and 121V mutants, were selected for docking with inhibitors (Cohen et al., 2011; Khan et al., 2017). The idea is to model the explicit flexibility of the target proteins, which is postulated to be more accurate and realistic than rigid crystal structure for docking. Not surprisingly, the mode of ligand binding, the number of interacting residues and the ligand binding affinity in this models varied significantly from the docked ligand on the crystal structure, with more interacting residues observed for the ensembles. For example, Ser94 and Gly96 residues are also found to be crucial for strong drug-InhA interactions, in addition to the Lys165 and Ile194 residues, but these interactions (involving Ser94 and Gly96) were not observed in the crystal structure (PDB: 2NSD) (Khan et al., 2017; He et al., 2007).

Generation of ensembles of target proteins with MD simulations for docking, however, is not possible when no 3D structure is available. This is especially true for novel targets where the experimental 3D structures are usually yet to be determined. In TB, this include enzymes involved in the biochemical pathways for the biosynthesis of peptidoglycan, a key component of the MTB cell wall, such as the enzymes for the formation of UDP-GlcNAc from D-fructose-6-phosphate (GlmS, GlmM, GlmU), UDP-MurNAc from UDP-GlcNAc (MurA, MurB), UDP-MurNAc-tetrapeptide from UDP-MurNAc, and UDP-MurNAc-pentapeptide from UDP-MurNGlyc (MurC-MurF) (Alderwick et al., 2015). Although these enzymes have long been characterised biochemically, not much work has been done on them until recently when the incidence of multi-drug resistant TB is getting more rampant. As such, homology models of the target enzymes such as MurA (Babajan et al., 2011), MurC (Anuradha et al., 2010), MurD (Arvind et al., 2012), MurG (Fakhar et al., 2016), MurI, MraY, DapE, DapA, Alr and Ddl (Fakhar et al., 2016) were built based on the 3D structure of the template proteins in the PDB database with high sequence similarities to the target. Homology models, however, generally require further refinement, and this is usually performed by MD simulations on a 10–100 ns timescale on explicit environment (Fan and Mark, 2004). In these models, 5–20 ns of MD simulations were performed for refinement, and root mean square deviation (RMSD) and radius of gyration (Rg) were calculated and compared to their corresponding templates or previous states to confirm the stability of these models. Subsequent use of these models for docking highlighted certain important residues for ligand and substrate binding and selectivity (e.g., Gly125, Lys126, Arg331 and Arg332 in MurC; His192, Arg382, Ser463 and Tyr470 in MurD) (Anuradha et al., 2010; Arvind et al., 2012). In addition, 10 potential inhibitors for MurG have been identified from the MD-refined model (Saxena et al., 2017), although none of these observations have been validated by in vitro experiments.

Evaluation of the Binding Interactions, Stability and Free Binding Energies of Protein-Ligand Complexes

Apart from preparing protein structures for structure-based studies, MD simulations are also often used in tandem with docking studies to further optimise the docking poses of anti-TB drug candidate as well as identified hits from virtual screening or in vitro assays. One example is a study by de Jonge and colleagues, who have used energy minimisation (EM) – MD simulation cycles (60 cycles of alternate 1500 EM iterations and 1500 MD iterations of 0.2 fs) to optimise docking pose for each stereoisomer of the lead inhibitor of MTB ATPase, R207910 (de Jonge et al., 2007). Computed interaction energies of the optimised docking poses showed that the RS stereoisomer bound more strongly to MTB ATPase than the SR, RR and SS stereoisomers, which are in agreement with the observed antimicrobial activity.

MD simulations are also commonly used to explore stability of ligand binding modes to various TB protein targets such as GyrB (Maharaj and Soliman, 2013; Islam and Pillay, 2017), GlgE (Sengupta et al., 2015), MurG (Saxena et al., 2017), GlmU (Mehra et al., 2016b; Soni et al., 2015), LipU (Kaur et al., 2018), MtbA (Maganti et al., 2015), MbtI (Maganti et al., 2016), sHSP16.3 (Jee et al., 2017), ASADH (Kumar et al., 2015), AAC (Prabu et al., 2015), PknG (Singh et al., 2015), Folylpolyglutamate synthetase (Hung et al., 2014) and α subunit Trp synthase (Naz et al., 2018). Generally, as low as 2 ns (Maharaj and Soliman, 2013) and as high as 60 ns (Jee et al., 2017) of MD simulations have been performed for this purpose, although 10 ns simulations are also seen being carried out for most protein-ligand complexes. To evaluate the stability of the protein-ligand complexes, convergence of RMSD and root mean square fluctuation (RMSF) plots of the protein backbone (e.g., Cα atoms) and ligands' non-hydrogen atom are monitored. In some studies, radius of gyration was also calculated to determine the changes in protein compactness and conformation upon ligand binding (Islam and Pillay, 2017; Kaur et al., 2018). Less commonly, variability in potential energies and important ligand/residue distances were measured in order to evaluate the stability of the docked complex (Maharaj and Soliman, 2013; Kumar et al., 2015).

A stable ligand-protein complex observed from MD simulations is important as it allows a better prediction of a ligand binding mode on the target protein which are dynamic in nature. More importantly, this information allows the identification of moieties critical for ligand-protein interaction. Generally, there are two common approaches that have been used to extract such information from stable trajectories of MD simulations involving TB protein target-inhibitor complexes. In the first approach, an average structure from the stable trajectories is calculated followed by visualisation of the protein-ligand interactions via a molecular visualisation software. This approach is illustrated in a study by Saxena and colleagues who compared the protein-ligand interactions of the average structure from stable MD simulations (20–25 ns) to the initial docked pose, and identified two of the seven residues (i.e., Leu290 and Met310) at the binding site of MurG that retained close interactions with the lead molecules as key residues important for MurG inhibition (Saxena et al., 2017).

The second approach is by calculating the hydrogen bond occupancy involving the active site residues of the protein target and the ligand throughout the MD simulations. For examples, Kumar and colleagues discovered that the hydrogen bond occupancy for β-AFP ligand and inhibitor, NSC4862 on MTB-ASADH during whole MD simulation are 81.4% and 54.3% with Arg99 and 43.8%; and 30.3% with Arg249, respectively; suggesting that these highly conserved active site residues are critical for ASADH inhibition (Kumar et al., 2015). Similarly, Mehra and colleagues revealed that Ser320, Thr321 and Asp424 of MTB Proteasome involved in hydrogen bond interactions with G7650246 in more than 25% of the simulation times, while residues Ala434, Arg439, Ala451 and Lys464 of GlmU have at least 20% hydrogen bond occupancy with inhibitor 5810599, suggesting that these residues are important for Proteasome and GlmU inhibitions, respectively (Mehra et al., 2015, 2016b).

In addition to obtaining protein-ligand stability and interaction information, MD simulations are also being used for free energy calculation and free energy decomposition analysis of various anti-TB inhibitors. These are performed on stable MD trajectories of ligand-receptor complex, using Molecular Mechanics Poisson-Boltzmann Surface Area (MM-PBSA), Molecular Mechanics Generalised Born Surface Area (MM-GBSA) or Linear Interaction Energy (LIE) approximation approaches. The use of MM-PBSA and MM-GBSA to estimate ligand-binding affinities are not new (Genheden and Ryde, 2015). For instance, Kamsri and colleagues calculated the binding free energies of diphenyl ether inhibitors (compounds 17, 18, 19 and 29) in InhA using MM-PBSA method based on 125 snapshots from last 1 ns of MD trajectory; this calculated energies were found to agree well with the experimentally determined ΔG (Kamsri et al., 2014b). Similarly, Kumar and colleagues used MM-GBSA to calculate binding free energy from 200 frames of the last 20 ns of 100 ns production run and successfully identified two InhA inhibitors (TB2, TB10) with better energies than the control ligand, (5-hexyl-2-(2-methylphenoxy)) phenol ($IC_{50} = 5$ nM). These compounds were found to give >90% inhibition of H37Rv strain of MTB in BACTEC assay (Kumar et al., 2017). On the other hand, Timmers and colleagues demonstrated that calculation of free energy binding from MD trajectories with LIE method (which is a semi-empirical approach that combines advantages of free energy perturbation and thermodynamics integration) is as accurate as MM-PBSA or MM-GBSA methods, with only 0.7 kcal/mol difference in the calculated binding energy of an inhibitor (compound 9) on cytidine deaminase (MtCDA) compared to the experimental value ($IC_{50} = 151.74$ µM, $\Delta G_{exp} = -5.2$ kcal/mol, $\Delta G_{LIE} = -5.9$ kcal/mol) (Timmers et al., 2012).

MD simulations have also been used to build quantitative models to predict binding affinities of e.g., aryl acid-AMP bisubstrate inhibitors of MbtA (Labello *et al.*, 2008). The model was constructed based on correlation between the LIE-estimated free energy binding from MD trajectories and the experimental indicator of binding affinity. Interestingly, this model was able to predict the binding affinity of an unknown related compound, N-6-cyclopropyl-2-phenyl-Sal-AMS, with predicted binding affinity = 1.6 nM versus experimental Ki of 0.7 nM. In a separate study, snapshots from MD trajectories have been used to generate structure-based e-pharmacophore model of CmaA1 based on the interactions of the active site residues with the natural ligands SAM and SAHC (Choudhury *et al.*, 2015). These models were found to be able to correctly identify up to 17 out of 23 reference compounds screened compared to only one for model generated from crystal structure.

Example of Successful MD Study

MD simulation has been used to understand the mechanism of resistance of INH towards its target, i.e., InhA. Wahab and co-workers had investigated the mechanism of mycobacterial resistance against isoniazid, focusing on the active site of MTB InhA (Wahab *et al.*, 2009) (**Fig. 6(A)**). This work was initiated with molecular docking simulation of isonicotinic acyl-NADH (INADH; the active form of isoniazid) in both the wild-type and resistant-type (S94A) of InhA (**Fig. 5(B)**), followed by MD simulation to further investigate the dynamics behaviour of INADH in InhA. Interestingly, higher flexibility at the binding site was observed for resistant-type InhA compared to the wild-type, as reflected by the disruption of hydrogen bond network, and lesser hydrophobic, van der Waals and electrostatics interactions in the former. The smaller free energy binding, ΔG in resistant-type also correlates well with the interactions analysis where higher fluctuation caused by INADH was observed. In addition, the existence of water-mediated hydrogen bond network with INADH in the wild-type further supports the hypothesis that the conversion of prodrug isoniazid into its active form, INADH, is mediated by KatG on InhA. Further study (Choong and Wahab, 2011) on the dynamics of INADH in other reported single point mutations of InhA (I16T, I21T, I21V, I47T, V78 and I95P) (**Fig. 6(B)**; Rouse *et al.*, 1995; Milano *et al.*, 1996; Miesel *et al.*, 1998), showed that the reduced side chain volume in all InhA mutants has provided more rooms for structural fluctuations in both INADH and mutated InhA residues, thus decreasing the INADH binding affinity, in agreement with the experimental findings on low-level isoniazid resistance for InhA mutants (**Fig. 6**). Although the resistance to isoniazid has been known for 70 years, there are still rooms to improve our understanding to this phenomena by using MD simulations in combination of other physical methods such as ultrafast two-dimensional infrared spectroscopy as presented recently by Hunt and co-workers (Shaw *et al.*, 2017) and the knowledge from the simulations could be exploited further in searching for potential inhibitors as alternative to isoniazid.

Using MD to understand the underlying INH mechanism of action, has allowed Venugopala and co-workers to venture into discovering InhA inhibitors by combining this technique with docking calculation (Khedr *et al.*, 2017). *In silico* docking trisubstituted indolizine analogues along with resazurin microplate assay screening were conducted to screen on the

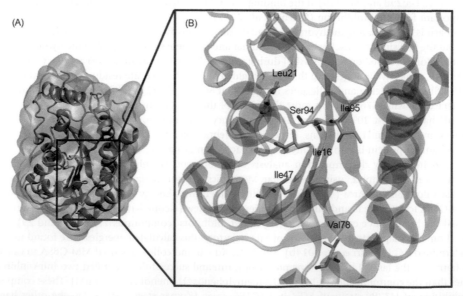

Fig. 6 (A) Crystal structure of MTB enoyl-acyl carrier protein reductase 9PDB ID: 1ZID. Reproduced from Rozwarski, D.A., Grant, G.A., Barton, D. H., Jacobs, W.R., Jr., Sacchettini, J.C., 1998. Modification of the NADH of the isoniazid target (InhA) from Mycobacterium tuberculosis. Science 279, 98–102. (B) Point mutations S94A, I16T, I21T, I21V, I47T, V78 and I95P constructed by Choong and Habibah. Reproduced from Choong, Y. S., Wahab, H., 2011. Effects of enoyl-acyl protein carrier reductase mutations on physiochemical interactions with isoniazid: Molecular dynamics simulation. Wahab, H.A., Choong, Y.S., Ibrahim, P., Sadikun, A., Scior, T., 2009. Elucidating isoniazid resistance using molecular modeling. J. Chem. Inf. Model. 49, 97–107.

indolizine analogues. 50 ns MD simulation was conducted on the top selected hit from docking and assay results. Their assay results had shown that by substitution of ethyl group at second position of indolizine nucleus, it exhibited activity against susceptible and multidrug-resistant strains of MTB at concentration of 5.5 and 11.3 μg/mL, respectively. Correlation was found for compound with ethyl substitution at second position of indolizine nucleus on the docking data with highest free binding energy of ΔG − 24.11 (kcal/mol). With MD simulation, MM-PB/GBSA results had also indicated well correlation with docking as well as the experimental data. Besides, Pongpo and co-workers had also adopted MD simulation (Kamsri *et al.*, 2014a) that further extended the work with 3D-QSAR to understand the structural basis of diphenyl ether derivatives on InhA (Kamsri *et al.*, 2014b). The volume of the binding cavity and the surface area of the compounds were correlated with the inhibitory activity. Their results indicated that smaller binding site cavity with higher surface area of the compound served to increase the inhibitory activity. Larger binding site cavity may imply less fitting of the compound to the binding site and thus leading to the loss of activity. Besides, energy decomposition of important residues such as Phe149, Tyr158, Met161, Met199, Val203 were analysed using MM-PBSA method. In their work later Kamsri *et al.* (2014b), 3D-QSAR approach was used to identify the key features of diphenyl ether derivatives for InhA inhibition were and again MD was used to study the binding energy using MM-PBSA calculation.

As a prodrug, isoniazid needs to be activated by KatG enzyme of which the mutations, has also been correlated with the INH resistance. To date, there is no crystal structure of isoniazid bound to KatG MTB. Using molecular docking of INH on KatG followed by 100ns MD simulation has allowed the identification of INH binding site on MtKatG whereby only one site (Site-1) resulted in conformational change when INH bound to it suggesting it as the main INH binding site (Srivastava *et al.*, 2017). This information is crucial such that future INH targeting inhibitors should avoid being metabolised by KatG enzyme. Theoretically, MD can be used to assess whether or not a new potential inhibitor of InhA can be metabolised by KatG from the prediction of the binding interaction of the molecule with the enzyme. Avoiding being metabolised by KatG enzyme will prevent drug resistance due to mutation or deletion of this enzyme in MTB.

The ability of MTB to go into a dormant state has caused a treatment nightmare as such targeting an enzyme important to the survival of MTB in the dormant state is a good alternative in finding potential TB drugs. Isocitrate lyase (ICL), is one of the key (**Fig. 4(A)**) enzymes involved in energy generation in MTB via glycoxylate shunt. It is one of the important targets in dormant phase MTB. Research on ICL especially on structure based drug design is still popular and ongoing. However, due to its small polar active site, only moderate ICL inhibitors have been reported (Mdluli *et al.*, 2014), thus opportunities to understand the structure, dynamics and stability of this enzyme for drug design cannot be understated.

To date, both *apo-* and *holo-* forms of ICL have been reported (PDB ID: 1F61; 1F8I; 1F8M; 5DQL). To understand the functional behaviour of ICL in its different subunit forms, MD simulations of ICL have been carried out (Lee *et al.*, 2017). Briefly, ICL in its dimer form was studied in three different conditions, i.e., one apo and two complex forms in order to investigate the open and close conformation of both bound and unbound states with its substrate. Analysis from the MD trajectories suggested that the open–close behaviour of the entrance of ICL active site is highly dependent on the type of ligands as free energy calculations showed a stronger binding affinity for isocitrate (gate-opening) than glycoxylate or succinate (gate-closing) (**Fig. 7(A–D)**). A total of four residues were suggested to be the possible points for cleavage of isocitrate at the C2–C3 bond by nucleophilic attack.

Investigation on ICL is also the centre of attention for Shukla and co-workers who were interested to understand the effects of mutation of this enzyme (Shukla *et al.*, 2015) using MD approach. The effect of flexibility of ICL on the functionality of this enzyme was first investigated by a single point mutation of His180 (**Fig. 4(B)**). Observations on the dynamic changes of ICL revealed a disrupted interaction between His180 and Tyr89, which affects the tetrameric assembly important for the enzymatic activities. Subsequent site-directed mutagenesis work on a different binding site residue, Phe345 (Shukla *et al.*, 2017a; **Fig. 4(B)**), discovered that the flexibility of the enzyme in the binding site was increased for the mutant type, resulting in the decreased stability of the whole enzyme.

Point mutation on H46A (Shukla *et al.*, 2018) using MD were also conducted. Interestingly, although the point mutation site (H46A) is far away from the binding site of ICL, they found that the conformation at the binding site and the volume of binding site cavity were altered, and the loss of enzyme activity was observed. They predicted that this could be due to the loss in structural plasticity and collective motion. This postulation is reflected by the time-dependent secondary structure analysis. In their extensive MD simulation on both wild-type and mutant-type (H46A), significant secondary structure changes were observed where the catalytic cleft of the wild-type was found to adopt a higher numbers of turn and bend with the formation of 3-helices. The number of these loops, turns and 3-helices structures were significantly lower in the mutant-type, indicating a more rigid structure in the mutant. In addition, with H46A mutation, the residue interaction network at the active site was also found to lead to the changes in the active site environment. These observations suggest that apart from the active site residues, His46, which is distance away from the active site cleft, can also affects the ICL functionality, and thus is also a promising site to be exploited (other than the active site) in discovery of novel ICL inhibitors.

Again, the information generated by MD simulations have been used in *in silico* identification of potential inhibitor of ICL from the ZINC database (Shukla *et al.*, 2017c). To compare the dynamics of the protein upon ligand binding, MD simulations were performed, and principle component analysis (PCA) was calculated for the stable trajectories (last 20 ns) to predict large concerted motions during ligand binding to ICL. Values for the first few eigenvectors of apo-ICL were found to be higher than the ICL-ligand complexes, suggesting that the apo-ICL has more correlated motions, and thus less stable than the ICL-ligand complexes. In other words, ligand binding stabilised the complex. Additionally, 2D projection of the trajectories for PC1 and PC2 for ICL-

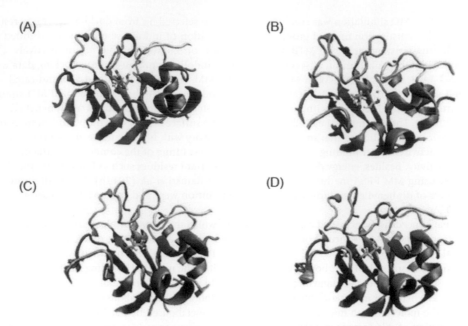

Fig. 7 Enzyme active site views of holo ICL dimer at 30 ns MD simulation. (A) Complex_ICL (with the presence of glycoxylate and succinate) active site 1, (B) Complex_ICL (with the presence of glycoxylate and succinate) active site 2, (C) Complex_ICL (with the presence of isocitrate only) active site 1 and (D) Complex_ICL (with the presence of isocitrate only) active site 2. Loops were highlighted in colours with respective active site 1/active site 2 residue number. Red: residues 91–93/518–520; Yellow: residues 104–114/531–541; Green: residues 154–159/581–585; Pink: residues 185–196/612–623; Cyan: residues 230–234/657–661; Purple: residues 285–289/712–716; Ice-blue: residues 314–319/741–746.

ZINC2111081 complex revealed that it occupied less space in the phase space than other compounds, with well-defined cluster, suggesting that ZINC2111081 formed more stable complex with ICL.

The above scenarios although limited to two enzymes can easily be extended to other MTB drug targets of which some of them have been covered in the previous section. Clearly, the application of MD in drug design is of immense importance, however, it should be noted that the potency of inhibitors is only the first step in drug discovery. Other aspects of drug development such as toxicity, pharmacokinetics and pharmacodynamics are also important determinants for the inhibitors to succeed in clinical trials. Limitations of MD must also be taken into consideration. Improvement of force fields, length of the simulations, enhanced sampling, inclusion of entropy effects, allosteric modulation and solvation effects should also be given special emphasis in the MD study relating to drug discovery.

Concluding Remarks

From the evaluation of the fundamental understanding of conformation alteration, functionally significant interaction as well as mechanism of action of lead compound on potential drug targets in MTB, MD simulation no doubt is one of the most time and cost-effective tools to be used. Moreover, it is also able to enhance the drug-receptor binding mode, as well as predicting drug binding affinity at better accuracy, which is important in understanding the structure-activity relationship in drug discovery. Additionally, combining molecular insights from MD simulation with other *in silico* approaches such as high-throughput screening of potential hit, in-depth atomic interaction studies using QM/MM as well as further validation by conventional experiments would certainly help to further enhance the efficiency in discovery of new anti-TB drugs for the benefits of the mankind.

Acknowledgement

We thank Dr Thaigarajan Parumasivam for his generosity in providing the SEM image of the H37Rv strain (ATCC 25618) of *Mycobacterium tuberculosis*. Special thanks to Dr Lee Yie Vern for her permission to reuse and readapt the ICL MD trajectories. Choong YS would like to acknowledge Universiti Sains Malaysia Bridging Grant (304/CIPPM/6316018).

See also: Biological Database Searching. Biomolecular Structures: Prediction, Identification and Analyses. Cloud-Based Molecular Modeling Systems. Comparative Epigenomics. Identifying Functional Relationships Via the Annotation and Comparison of Three-Dimensional Amino Acid Arrangements in Protein Structures. Natural Language Processing Approaches in Bioinformatics. Structure-Based Drug Design Workflow

References

Aggarwal, M., Singh, A., Grover, S., et al., 2018. Role of pncA gene mutations W68R and W68G in pyrazinamide resistance. J. Cell .Biochem. 119, 2567–2578.

Alderwick, L.J., Harrison, J., Lloyd, G.S., Birch, H.L., 2015. The mycobacterial cell wall–peptidoglycan and arabinogalactan. Cold Spring Harb.Perspect. Med. 5, a021113.

Anuradha, C.M., Mulakayala, C., Babajan, B., et al., 2010. Probing ligand binding modes of Mycobacterium tuberculosis MurC ligase by molecular modeling, dynamics simulation and docking. J. Mol. Model. 16 (1), 77–85.

Arvind, A., Kumar, V., Saravanan, P., Mohan, C.G., 2012. Homology modeling, molecular dynamics and inhibitor binding study on MurD ligase of Mycobacterium tuberculosis. Interdiscip. Sci. 4, 223–238.

Babajan, B., Chaitanya, M., Rajsekhar, C., et al., 2011. Comprehensive structural and functional characterization of Mycobacterium tuberculosis UDP-NAG enolpyruvyl transferase (Mtb-MurA) and prediction of its accurate binding affinities with inhibitors. Interdiscip. Sci. 3, 204–216.

Banerjee, A., Dubnau, E., Quemard, A., et al., 1994. inhA, a gene encoding a target for isoniazid and ethionamide in Mycobacterium tuberculosis. Science 263, 227–230.

Besra, G.S., Khoo, K.H., Mcneil, M.R., et al., 1995. A new interpretation of the structure of the mycolyl-arabinogalactan complex of Mycobacterium tuberculosis as revealed through characterization of oligoglycosylalditol fragments by fast-atom bombardment mass spectrometry and 1H nuclear magnetic resonance spectroscopy. Biochemistry 34, 4257–4266.

Borhani, D.W., Shaw, D.E., 2012. The future of molecular dynamics simulations in drug discovery. J. Comput. Aided Mol. Des. 26, 15–26.

CDC, 2017. Economic toll of drug resistant TB [Online]. Available at: https://www.cdc.gov/tb/topic/drtb/default.htm (accessed 31.03.18).

Choong, Y.S., Wahab, H., 2011. Effects of Enoyl-Acyl protein carrier reductase mutations on physiochemical interactions with isoniazid: Molecular dynamics simulation.

Choudhury, C., Priyakumar, U.D., Sastry, G.N., 2015. Dynamics based pharmacophore models for screening potential inhibitors of mycobacterial cyclopropane synthase. J. Chem. Inf. Model 55, 848–860.

Cohen, E.M., Machado, K.S., Cohen, M., D.E. Souza, O.N., 2011. Effect of the explicit flexibility of the InhA enzyme from Mycobacterium tuberculosis in molecular docking simulations. BMC Genom. 12 (Suppl. 4), S7.

Durrant, J.D., McCammon, J.A., 2011. Molecular dynamics simulations and drug discovery. BMC Biol. 9, 71.

Fakhar, Z., Naiker, S., Alves, C.N., et al., 2016. A comparative modeling and molecular docking study on Mycobacterium tuberculosis targets involved in peptidoglycan biosynthesis. J. Biomol. Struct. Dyn. 34, 2399–2417.

Fang, Z., Doig, C., Rayner, A., et al., 1999. Molecular evidence for heterogeneity of the multiple-drug-resistant Mycobacterium tuberculosis population in Scotland (1990 to 1997). J. Clin. Microbiol. 37, 998–1003.

Fan, H., Mark, A.E., 2004. Refinement of homology-based protein structures by molecular dynamics simulation techniques. Protein Sci. 13, 211–220.

Ferraris, D., Miggiano, R., Rossi, F., Rizzi, M., 2018. Mycobacterium tuberculosis molecular determinants of infection, survival strategies, and vulnerable targets. Pathogens 7, 17.

Ferreira, L.A., Madeira, P.P., Breydo, L., et al., 2016. Role of solvent properties of aqueous media in macromolecular crowding effects. J. Biomol. Struct. Dyn. 34, 92–103.

Genheden, S., Ryde, U., 2015. The MM/PBSA and MM/GBSA methods to estimate ligand-binding affinities. Expert Opin. Drug Discov. 10, 449–461.

Hards, K., Robson, J.R., Berney, M., et al., 2015. Bactericidal mode of action of bedaquiline. J. Antimicrob. Chemother. 70, 2028–2037.

Herrmann, K.M., Weaver, L.M., 1999. The shikimate pathway. Annu. Rev. Plant Physiol. Plant Mol. Biol. 50, 473–503.

Heym, B., Alzari, P.M., Honore, N., Cole, S.T., 1995. Missense mutations in the catalase-peroxidase gene, katG, are associated with isoniazid resistance in Mycobacterium tuberculosis. Mol. Microbiol. 15, 235–245.

He, X., Alian, A., Ortiz De Montellano, P.R., 2007. Inhibition of the Mycobacterium tuberculosis enoyl acyl carrier protein reductase InhA by arylamides. Bioorg. Med. Chem. 15, 6649–6658.

Hoagland, D., Liu, J., Lee, R.B., Lee, R.E., 2016. New agents for the treatment of drug-resistant Mycobacterium tuberculosis. Advanced Drug Deliv. Rev. 102, 55–72.

Hung, T.C., Chen, K.B., Lee, W.Y., Chen, C.Y., 2014. The inhibition of folylpolyglutamate synthetase (folC) in the prevention of drug resistance in Mycobacterium tuberculosis by traditional Chinese medicine. Biomed. Res. Int. 2014, 635152.

Islam, M.A., Pillay, T.S., 2017. Identification of promising DNA GyrB inhibitors for Tuberculosis using pharmacophore-based virtual screening, molecular docking and molecular dynamics studies. Chem. Biol. Drug. Des. 90, 282–296.

Jee, B., Kumar, S., Yadav, R., et al., 2017. Ursolic acid and carvacrol may be potential inhibitors of dormancy protein small heat shock protein16.3 of Mycobacterium tuberculosis. J. Biomol. Struct. Dyn. 1–10.

Jian, J.-W., Elumalai, P., Pitti, T., et al., 2016. Predicting ligand binding sites on protein surfaces by 3-dimensional probability density distributions of interacting atoms. PLOS ONE 11, e0160315.

Jiao, W., Blackmore, N.J., Nazmi, A.R., Parker, E.J., 2017. Quaternary structure is an essential component that contributes to the sophisticated allosteric regulation mechanism in a key enzyme from Mycobacterium tuberculosis. PLOS ONE 12, e0180052.

de Jonge, M.R., Koymans, L.H., Guillemont, J.E., Koul, A., Andries, K., 2007. A computational model of the inhibition of Mycobacterium tuberculosis ATPase by a new drug candidate R207910. Proteins 67, 971–980.

Jorgensen, W.L., 1991. Rusting of the lock and key model for protein-ligand binding. Science 254, 954.

Kamsri, P., Koohatammakun, N., Srisupan, A., et al., 2014a. Rational design of InhA inhibitors in the class of diphenyl ether derivatives as potential anti-tubercular agents using molecular dynamics simulations. SAR QSAR Environ. Res. 25, 473–488.

Kamsri, P., Punkvang, A., Saparpakorn, P., et al., 2014b. Elucidating the structural basis of diphenyl ether derivatives as highly potent enoyl-ACP reductase inhibitors through molecular dynamics simulations and 3D-QSAR study. J. Mol. Model. 20, 2319.

Kamachi, S., Hirabayashi, K., Tamoi, M., et al., 2015a. The crystal structure of isoniazid-bound KatG catalase-peroxidase from Synechococcus elongatus PCC7942. FEBS J. 282, 54–64.

Kamachi, S., Hirabayashi, K., Tamoi, M., et al., 2015b. Crystal structure of the catalase-peroxidase KatG W78F mutant from Synechococcus elongatus PCC7942 in complex with the antitubercular pro-drug isoniazid. FEBS Lett 589, 131–137.

Kaur, G., Pandey, B., Kumar, A., et al., 2018. Drug targeted virtual screening and molecular dynamics of LipU protein of Mycobacterium tuberculosis and Mycobacterium leprae. J. Biomol. Struct. Dyn. 1–38.

Khan, A.M., Shawon, J., Halim, M.A., 2017. Multiple receptor conformers based molecular docking study of fluorine enhanced ethionamide with mycobacterium enoyl ACP reductase (InhA). J. Mol. Graph. Model. 77, 386–398.

Khedr, M.A., Pillay, M., Chandrashekharappa, S., et al., 2017. Molecular modeling studies and anti-TB activity of trisubstituted indolizine analogues; molecular docking and dynamic inputs. J. Biomol. Struct. Dyn. 1–16.

Kiepiela, P., Bishop, K.S., Smith, A.N., Roux, L., York, D.F., 2000. Genomic mutations in the katG, inhA and aphC genes are useful for the prediction of isoniazid resistance in Mycobacterium tuberculosis isolates from Kwazulu Natal, South Africa. Tuber. Lung Dis. 80, 47–56.

Kumar, R., Garg, P., Bharatam, P.V., 2015. Shape-based virtual screening, docking, and molecular dynamics simulations to identify Mtb-ASADH inhibitors. J. Biomol. Struct. Dyn. 33, 1082–1093.

Kumar, V., Jhamb, S.S., Sobhia, M.E., 2017. Cell wall permeability assisted virtual screening to identify potential direct InhA inhibitors of Mycobacterium tuberculosis and their biological evaluation. J. Biomol. Struct. Dyn. 1–17.

Labello, N.P., Bennett, E.M., Ferguson, D.M., Aldrich, C.C., 2008. Quantitative three dimensional structure linear interaction energy model of 5'-O-[N-(salicyl)sulfamoyl] adenosine and the aryl acid adenylating enzyme MbtA. J. Med. Chem. 51, 7154–7160.

Lahti, J.L., Tang, G.W., Capriotti, E., Liu, T., Altman, R.B., 2012. Bioinformatics and variability in drug response: A protein structural perspective. J. R. Soc. Interface 9, 1409–1437.

Lee, Y.V., Choi, S.B., Wahab, H.A., Choong, Y.S., 2017. Active site flexibility of Mycobacterium tuberculosis isocitrate lyase in dimer form. J. Chem. Inf. Model. 57, 2351–2357.

Lee, A.S., Lim, I.H., Tang, L.L., Telenti, A., Wong, S.Y., 1999. Contribution of kasA analysis to detection of isoniazid-resistant Mycobacterium tuberculosis in Singapore. Antimicrob. Agents Chemother. 43, 2087–2089.

Lewis, J.M., Sloan, D.J., 2015. The role of delamanid in the treatment of drug-resistant tuberculosis. Ther. Clin. Risk Manag. 11, 779–791.

Maganti, L., Consortium, O., Ghoshal, N., 2015. 3D-QSAR studies and shape based virtual screening for identification of novel hits to inhibit MbtA in Mycobacterium tuberculosis. J Biomol. Struct. Dyn. 33, 344–364.

Maganti, L., Grandhi, P., Ghoshal, N., 2016. Integration of ligand and structure based approaches for identification of novel Mbtl inhibitors in Mycobacterium tuberculosis and molecular dynamics simulation studies. J. Mol. Graph. Model. 70, 14–22.

Maharaj, Y., Soliman, M.E., 2013. Identification of novel gyrase B inhibitors as potential anti-TB drugs: Homology modelling, hybrid virtual screening and molecular dynamics simulations. Chem. Biol. Drug. Des. 82, 205–215.

Mdluli, K., Kaneko, T., Upton, A., 2014. Tuberculosis drug discovery and emerging targets. Ann. N. Y. Acad. Sci. 1323, 56–75.

Mehra, R., Chib, R., Munagala, G., et al., 2015. Discovery of new Mycobacterium tuberculosis proteasome inhibitors using a knowledge-based computational screening approach. Mol. Divers 19, 1003–1019.

Mehra, R., Rajput, V.S., Gupta, M., et al., 2016a. Benzothiazole derivative as a novel Mycobacterium tuberculosis shikimate kinase inhibitor: Identification and elucidation of its allosteric mode of inhibition. J. Chem. Inf. Model. 56, 930–940.

Mehra, R., Rani, C., Mahajan, P., et al., 2016b. Computationally guided identification of novel Mycobacterium tuberculosis GlmU inhibitory leads, their optimization, and in vitro validation. ACS Comb. Sci. 18, 100–116.

Miesel, L., Weisbrod, T.R., Marcinkeviciene, J.A., Bittman, R., Jacobs Jr., W.R., 1998. NADH dehydrogenase defects confer isoniazid resistance and conditional lethality in Mycobacterium smegmatis. J. Bacteriol. 180, 2459–2467.

Milano, A., de Rossi, E., Gusberti, L., et al., 1996. The katE gene, which encodes the catalase HPII of Mycobacterium avium. Mol. Microbiol. 19, 113–123.

Morris, S., Bai, G.H., Suffys, P., et al., 1995. Molecular mechanisms of multiple drug resistance in clinical isolates of Mycobacterium tuberculosis. J. Infect. Dis. 171, 954–960.

Nassau, P.M., Martin, S.L., Brown, R.E., et al., 1996. Galactofuranose biosynthesis in Escherichia coli K-12: Identification and cloning of UDP-galactopyranose mutase. J. Bacteriol. 178, 1047–1052.

Naz, S., Farooq, U., Ali, S., et al., 2018. Identification of new benzamide inhibitor against alpha-subunit of tryptophan synthase from Mycobacterium tuberculosis through structure-based virtual screening, anti-tuberculosis activity and molecular dynamics simulations. J. Biomol. Struct. Dyn. 1–11.

Nusrath Unissa, A., Hassan, S., Indira Kumari, V., Revathy, R., Hanna, L.E., 2016. Insights into RpoB clinical mutants in mediating rifampicin resistance in Mycobacterium tuberculosis. J. Mol. Graph. Model. 67, 20–32.

Pandey, B., Grover, S., Goyal, S., et al., 2018. Alanine mutation of the catalytic sites of Pantothenate Synthetase causes distinct conformational changes in the ATP binding region. Sci. Rep. 8, 903.

Pan, F., Jackson, M., Ma, Y., Mcneil, M., 2001. Cell wall core galactofuran synthesis is essential for growth of mycobacteria. J. Bacteriol. 183, 3991–3998.

Parish, T., Stoker, N.G., 2002. The common aromatic amino acid biosynthesis pathway is essential in Mycobacterium tuberculosis. Microbiology 148, 3069–3077.

Piatek, A.S., Telenti, A., Murray, M.R., et al., 2000. Genotypic analysis of Mycobacterium tuberculosis in two distinct populations using molecular beacons: Implications for rapid susceptibility testing. Antimicrob. Agents Chemother. 44, 103–110.

Pimentel, A.L., de Lima Scodro, R.B., Caleffi-Ferracioli, K.R., et al., 2017. Mutations in catalase-peroxidase KatG from isoniazid resistant Mycobacterium tuberculosis clinical isolates: Insights from molecular dynamics simulations. J. Mol. Model. 23, 121.

Prabu, A., Hassan, S., Prabuseenivasan, Shainaba, A.S., Hanna, L.E., Kumar, V., 2015. Andrographolide: A potent antituberculosis compound that targets aminoglycoside 2'-N-acetyltransferase in Mycobacterium tuberculosis. J. Mol. Graph. Model. 61, 133–140.

Rotta, M., Timmers, L., Sequeiros-Borja, C., et al., 2017. Observed crowding effects on Mycobacterium tuberculosis 2-trans-enoyl-ACP (CoA) reductase enzyme activity are not due to excluded volume only. Sci. Rep. 7, 6826.

Rouse, D.A., Li, Z., Bai, G.H., Morris, S.L., 1995. Characterization of the katG and inhA genes of isoniazid-resistant clinical isolates of Mycobacterium tuberculosis. Antimicrob. Agents Chemother. 39, 2472–2477.

Saxena, S., Abdullah, M., Sriram, D., Guruprasad, L., 2017. Discovery of novel inhibitors of Mycobacterium tuberculosis MurG: Homology modelling, structure based pharmacophore, molecular docking, and molecular dynamics simulations. J. Biomol. Struct. Dyn. 1–15.

Sengupta, S., Roy, D., Bandyopadhyay, S., 2015. Structural insight into Mycobacterium tuberculosis maltosyl transferase inhibitors: Pharmacophore-based virtual screening, docking, and molecular dynamics simulations. J. Biomol. Struct. Dyn. 33, 2655–2666.

Shaw, D.J., Hill, R.E., Simpson, N., et al., 2017. Examining the role of protein structural dynamics in drug resistance in Mycobacterium tuberculosis. Chem. Sci. 8, 8384–8399.

Shi, Y., Colombo, C., Kuttiyatveetil, J.R., et al., 2016. A Second, druggable binding site in UDP-Galactopyranose mutase from Mycobacterium tuberculosis? Chembiochem 17, 2264–2273.

Shukla, H., Kumar, V., Singh, A.K., et al., 2015. Insight into the structural flexibility and function of Mycobacterium tuberculosis isocitrate lyase. Biochimie 110, 73–80.

Shukla, H., Shukla, R., Sonkar, A., Pandey, T., Tripathi, T., 2017a. Distant Phe345 mutation compromises the stability and activity of Mycobacterium tuberculosis isocitrate lyase by modulating its structural flexibility. Sci. Rep. 7, 1058.

Shukla, H., Shukla, H., Sonkar, A., Pandey, T., Tripathi, T., 2017c. Structure-based screening and molecular dynamics simulations offer novel natural compounds as potential inhibitors of Mycobacterium tuberculosis isocitrate lyase. J. Biomol. Struct. Dyn. 1–13.

Shukla, H., Shukla, R., Sonkar, A., Tripathi, T., 2017b. Alterations in conformational topology and interaction dynamics caused by L418A mutation leads to activity loss of Mycobacterium tuberculosis isocitrate lyase. Biochem. Biophys. Res. Commun. 490, 276–282.

Shukla, R., Shukla, H., Tripathi, T., 2018. Activity loss by H46A mutation in Mycobacterium tuberculosis isocitrate lyase is due to decrease in structural plasticity and collective motions of the active site. Tuberculosis 108, 143–150.

Shi, Y., Colombo, C., Kuttiyatveetil, J.R., et al., 2016. A Second, Druggable Binding Site in UDP-Galactopyranose Mutase from Mycobacterium tuberculosis? Chembiochem 17, 2264–2273.

Singh, A., Grover, S., Pandey, B., Kumari, A., Grover, A., 2018. Wild-type catalase peroxidase vs G279D mutant type: Molecular basis of Isoniazid drug resistance in Mycobacterium tuberculosis. Gene 641, 226–234.

Singh, A., Grover, S., Sinha, S., et al., 2017. Mechanistic principles behind molecular mechanism of rifampicin resistance in mutant rna polymerase beta subunit of mycobacterium tuberculosis. J. Cell Biochem. 118, 4594–4606.

Singh, N., Tiwari, S., Srivastava, K.K., Siddiqi, M.I., 2015. Identification of novel inhibitors of mycobacterium tuberculosis pknG using pharmacophore based virtual screening, docking, molecular dynamics simulation, and their biological evaluation. J. Chem. Inf. Model. 55, 1120–1129.

Slayden, R.A., Barry 3rd, C.E., 2000. The genetics and biochemistry of isoniazid resistance in Mycobacterium tuberculosis. Microbes. Infect. 2, 659–669.

Soni, V., Suryadevara, P., Sriram, D., et al., 2015. Structure-based design of diverse inhibitors of Mycobacterium tuberculosis N-acetylglucosamine-1-phosphate uridyltransferase: Combined molecular docking, dynamic simulation, and biological activity. J. Mol. Model. 21, 174.

Srivastava, G., Tripathi, S., Kumar, A., Sharma, A., 2017. Molecular investigation of active binding site of isoniazid (INH) and insight into resistance mechanism of S315T-MtKatG in Mycobacterium tuberculosis. Tuberculosis 105, 18–27.

Telenti, A., 1998. Genetics of drug resistant tuberculosis. Thorax 53, 793–797.

Telenti, A., Honore, N., Bernasconi, C., et al., 1997. Genotypic assessment of isoniazid and rifampin resistance in Mycobacterium tuberculosis: A blind study at reference laboratory level. J. Clin. Microbiol. 35, 719–723.

Timmers, L.F., Ducati, R.G., Sanchez-Quitian, Z.A., et al., 2012. Combining molecular dynamics and docking simulations of the cytidine deaminase from Mycobacterium tuberculosis H37Rv. J. Mol. Model. 18, 467–479.

Torres, M.J., Criado, A., Palomares, J.C., Aznar, J., 2000. Use of real-time PCR and fluorimetry for rapid detection of rifampin and isoniazid resistance-associated mutations in Mycobacterium tuberculosis. J. Clin. Microbiol. 38, 3194–3199.

Unissa, A.N., Doss, C.G., Kumar, T., et al., 2017. Analysis of interactions of clinical mutants of catalase-peroxidase (KatG) responsible for isoniazid resistance in Mycobacterium tuberculosis with derivatives of isoniazid. J. Glob. Antimicrob. Resist. 11, 57–67.

Vilcheze, C., Morbidoni, H.R., Weisbrod, T.R., et al., 2000. Inactivation of the inhA-encoded fatty acid synthase II (FASII) enoyl-acyl carrier protein reductase induces accumulation of the FASI end products and cell lysis of Mycobacterium smegmatis. J. Bacteriol. 182, 4059–4067.

Vidossich, P., Loewen, P.C., Carpena, X., et al., 2014. Binding of the antitubercular pro-drug isoniazid in the heme access channel of catalase-peroxidase (KatG). A combined structural and metadynamics investigation. J Phys Chem B 118, 2924–2931.

De Vivo, M., Masetti, M., Bottegoni, G., Cavalli, A., 2016. Role of molecular dynamics and related methods in drug discovery. J. Med. Chem. 59, 4035–4061.

Wahab, H.A., Choong, Y.S., Ibrahim, P., Sadikun, A., Scior, T., 2009. Elucidating isoniazid resistance using molecular modeling. J. Chem. Inf. Model. 49, 97–107.

Wang, J.Y., Burger, R.M., Drlica, K., 1998. Role of superoxide in catalase-peroxidase-mediated isoniazid action against mycobacteria. Antimicrob. Agents Chemother. 42, 709–711.

Wellington, S., Hung, D.T., 2018. The expanding diversity of Mycobacterium tuberculosis drug targets. ACS Infect. Dis.

WHO, 2017. Global tuberculosis report 2017.

Yao, J., Wang, X., Luo, H., Gu, P., 2017. Understanding the catalytic mechanism and the nature of the transition state of an attractive drug-target enzyme (Shikimate Kinase) by quantum mechanical/molecular mechanical (QM/MM) studies. Chemistry 23, 16380–16387.

Yu, S., Girotto, S., Lee, C., Magliozzo, R.S., 2003. Reduced affinity for Isoniazid in the S315T mutant of Mycobacterium tuberculosis KatG is a key factor in antibiotic resistance. J. Biol. Chem. 278, 14769–14775.

Zhang, Y., Post-Martens, K., Denkin, S., 2006. New drug candidates and therapeutic targets for tuberculosis therapy. Drug Discov. Today 11, 21–27.

Zhao, H., Caflisch, A., 2015. Molecular dynamics in drug design. Eur. J. Med. Chem. 91, 4–14.

Zwarycz, A.S., Fossat, M., Akanyeti, O., et al., 2017. V67L mutation fills an internal cavity to stabilize reca mtu intein. Biochemistry 56, 2715–2722.

Protein-Carbohydrate Interactions

Adeel Malik, Chungnam National University, Daejeon, South Korea
Mohammad H Baig, Yeungnam University Gyeongsan, Gyeongbuk, South Korea
Balachandran Manavalan, Ajou University School of Medicine, Suwon, Republic of Korea

Introduction

Carbohydrates (also known as sugars or glycans) provide the primary source of energy for living organisms, are used as structural elements, and are the essential components of cofactors (such as ATP, NADPH, etc), glycoproteins and polynucleotides (Quiocho, 1989). These carbohydrates interact with diverse types of proteins and are the basis of many biological processes, both normal and pathological ones including fertilization, immune response, cancer, etc. These interactions also play key roles in several cell adhesion phenomena, among them the attachment of parasites, fungi, bacteria, and viruses to host cells; an indispensable step for the infection (Karlsson, 1991; Ofek et al., 2003). In numerous cases, the protein-carbohydrate interaction may not be a straightforward event but only an initial step that may trigger complex signaling cascades (De Schutter and Van Damme, 2015). Carbohydrates can play so many different roles in molecular recognition due to their ability to generate a broad range of structurally diverse moieties from few monosaccharides that are connected by various linkage types (Audette et al., 2003). Additionally, these carbohydrates can be extremely branched, therefore allowing oligosaccharides to offer nearly a limitless diversity of structural variations.

The significance of protein–carbohydrate interactions in regulating several physiological processes has been acknowledged since decades now. However, the molecular basis underlying such interactions has emerged in recent times. Application of X-ray crystallography to study protein-carbohydrate interactions is the main technique involved, but carbohydrates are quite challenging to crystallize because their inherent flexibility may not be compliant to structural analysis. They may even avert crystallographic studies if this flexible nature on the protein surface hampers the arrangement of crystal contacts, which normally prompts their enzymatic elimination as part of the sample preparation for crystallization (Agirre et al., 2017). Therefore, to get the conformational and dynamical information; the application of NMR spectroscopy was utilized. Because of the typical features of carbohydrates, it is established that relaxation NMR parameters should be integrated with computational methods in order to define the structural characteristics of carbohydrates in an explicit manner. Therefore, to better understand the structure/activity relationships of protein-carbohydrate interactions, interdisciplinary approaches are probably the best options that can be applied to study these complexes (Jiménez-Barbero et al., 1999).

Other traditional approaches, including the hemagglutination inhibition assay (Lis and Sharon, 1972), enzyme-linked lectin assay (McCoy et al., 1983), surface plasmon resonance (Duverger et al., 2003) and isothermal titration calorimetry (Dam and Brewer, 2002), have been used to investigate carbohydrate recognition by proteins. Regardless of their successful application to elucidate the details of protein-carbohydrate interactions, such techniques are labor-intensive and may have certain restrains in terms of requirements of large amounts of pure carbohydrate samples, protein size, solubility, or ease of crystallization, besides the cost (Zhang et al., 2016). Because of these shortcomings the conventional methods seem inapplicable as high-throughput analytic methods (Park et al., 2007). With the introduction of carbohydrate microarrays in 2002 (Wang et al., 2002; Fukui et al., 2002) the limitations of the requirements for low sample quantities and attaining high-throughput parallel screening were overcome (Puvirajesinghe and Turnbull, 2016). However, limited number of efficient analysis tools to extract relevant information limits the use of glycan microarray data (Malik et al., 2014). Rapid advances in the method, in addition to its application in investigation of protein-carbohydrate interactions, it is now possible to successfully discriminate the selective interactions of carbohydrates with bacteria, viruses and eukaryotic as well as live cell responses to immobilized glycans (Puvirajesinghe and Turnbull, 2016). Recently, hydrogen/deuterium exchange mass spectrometry (HDX-MS) was applied to investigate the sites for ligand binding within carbohydrate-binding proteins (Zhang et al., 2016). No doubt these experimental methods are indispensable to fully understand protein-carbohydrate interactions; however, they have certain challenges associated with them such as weak binding affinity and synthetic complexity of specific carbohydrates (Ng et al., 2015). Additionally, other limiting factors that hinder these studies include cost, time and labor. To overcome these challenges, several computational methods to study these types of interactions have been proposed and applied to identify carbohydrate binding sites in proteins.

These computational methods can be divided into three categories: (i) knowledge- or empirical-based methods; (ii) machine-learning based methods; and (iii) molecular dynamics based methods. Here, we discuss these methods that have been applied to study protein carbohydrate interactions.

Knowledge- or Empirical-Based Methods

A three-dimensional (3D) structure of a protein-carbohydrate complex obtained *via* X-ray crystallographic or NMR based methods is desirable to understand the interactions involved. Because of the limitations of these experimental methods to determine such complexes, knowledge-, empirical-, and structure-based methods have been developed for the prediction of glycan interacting residues from the 3D structures. (Taroni *et al.*, 2000) calculated six parameters [relative accessible surface area (RSA), residue propensity, solvation potential, planarity, hydrophobicity, and protrusion] of glycan binding sites on a set of 19 non-homologous carbohydrate binding proteins using PATCH program (Taroni *et al.*, 2000). These parameters were then utilized to resolve if the surface patch under scrutiny is a carbohydrate-binding site. This analysis revealed that RSA, protrusion index and residue propensity were the three best parameters that differentiate the carbohydrate binding sites from other surfaces. Evaluation of this method on two independent datasets (Test set1, which does not show any homology to the main dataset, and, Test set2 which consists of structures homologous to either the main data set or the Test set1) showed the overall prediction accuracy of 65%, which was a higher success rate for enzymes as compared to lectins.

In another work, empirical rules of the spatial distribution of protein atoms around carbohydrate-binding sites were used for prediction (Shionyu-Mitsuyama *et al.*, 2003). This method also requires a known 3D structure of a protein-carbohydrate complex to construct the empirical rules, and subsequently, these rules were utilized to search the carbohydrate binding sites on the target protein. The empirical rules were constructed using a non-redundant data set of 80 protein-carbohydrate complexes and the prediction system was tested on an independent dataset of 50 experimentally derived complexes. This method worked better for Galactose, Glucose and *N*-Acetylglucosamine binding sites as compared to Mannose binding sites. The attributes or properties used between the above-mentioned two methods is different in a sense that the former method (Taroni *et al.*, 2000) uses amino acid propensity whereas the latter system employs the spatial distribution of amino acid residues at the glycan-binding sites (Shionyu-Mitsuyama *et al.*, 2003).

Sujatha and Balaji (2004) developed a program called COTRAN to search for the potential galactose-interacting sites in proteins. They utilized 18 protein-galactose complexes belonging to 7 non-homologous families and investigated the galactose-binding sites. This method utilizes a combination of the inferred geometrical characteristics in addition to structural features [for example, accessible surface area (ASA) and secondary structure] to detect a possible galactose-binding site signature with very high accuracy.

Recently, Zhao *et al.* (2014) developed a structure-based function-prediction method called SPOT-Struc that recognizes carbohydrate-binding proteins (Zhao *et al.*, 2014). This method predicts interacting residues by structural alignment program SPalign (Yang *et al.*, 2012) and knowledge-based statistical potential [distance-scaled finite-ideal gas reference state (DFIRE)] is used for predicting the binding affinity scoring. In this method, a template library of 523 (T523) carbohydrate binding proteins (CBPs) was derived from PROCARB (Malik *et al.*, 2010) database. Additionally, a positive binding domain dataset consisting of 113 CBPs (BD113) and a negative dataset of 3442 non-CBPs (NB3442) were constructed at 30% sequence identity cutoff. The prediction system works by first aligning the target structure against the templates (T523 dataset) by structural alignment tool SPalign, where the structural similarity score is calculated by a scoring function called SP-score (Yang *et al.*, 2012). In case the SP-score is larger than a given threshold, the model for the complex structure between the query protein and template carbohydrate is generated by substituting template protein structure with the query structure in the template complex structure. The model complex structure is further used to calculate the binding affinity by the DFIRE (Zhou and Zhou, 2002; Yang and Zhou, 2008). The query is predicted as a CBP if the binding affinity is above a certain threshold; else non-CBP. Finally, the predicted structures from SPOT-Struc are utilized for the prediction of interacting residues. If any heavy atom of an amino acid is within a contact distance of <4.5 Å from any heavy atom of the carbohydrate was defined as a binding site. A leave-one-out cross-validation (LOOCV) method on BD113 and NB3442 datasets achieved the MCC of 0.63 and 0.58 for the prediction of CBPs and carbohydrate-interacting residues, respectively at 52% sensitivity and 79% positive predictive value (PPV) of CBP prediction. A comparable level of accuracy was observed for two additional datasets of bound (HOLO) and unbound (APO) structures of CBP.

An approach based on the energy function for identifying the carbohydrate binding sites has also been proposed (Gromiha *et al.*, 2014) that uses AMBER force field with GLYCAM06 (Kirschner *et al.*, 2008) parameters for calculating the interaction energy between the atoms in a protein and the bound carbohydrate. The residues that are involved in interactions with carbohydrates have been analyzed in terms of binding segments which is based on the number of sequential binding residues in protein sequences. For instance, a 4-residue binding segment has a region of four back-to-back binding residues. This study generated several statistics, including incidence of amino acid residues at different interaction energies, binding propensity scores of amino acid residues in protein-carbohydrate complexes, contribution of various atom types in these types of interactions, inclination of dipeptides and tripeptides around the binding sites, highlighting the significance of stronger atomic level contributions from carbohydrates as compared to proteins.

Machine Learning (ML)-Based Methods

ML-based methods have been successfully applied in both sequence- and structure-based methods. Although, ML-based approach is the same but the input features or attributes are different between sequence- and structure-based methods (**Fig. 1**). In general, different features are extracted from the protein sequences or structures (including knowledge-based information) and are used as inputs for ML methods, and the binding site is obtained from them. Extensive use of ML has been applied to address various biological questions. The biggest advantages of ML is that it can deal with multiple features or attributes at the same time and capture the hidden relationships among them, which are otherwise challenging to derive with knowledge- or empirical-based methods (Manavalan *et al.*, 2014; Manavalan and Lee 2014a; Manavalan *et al.*, 2017b,c. Alpaydin, 2014; Bastanlar and Ozuysal, 2014; Nilsson, 1996). In the following subsections, we discuss sequence- and structure-based methods in which ML has been applied to study protein-carbohydrate interactions.

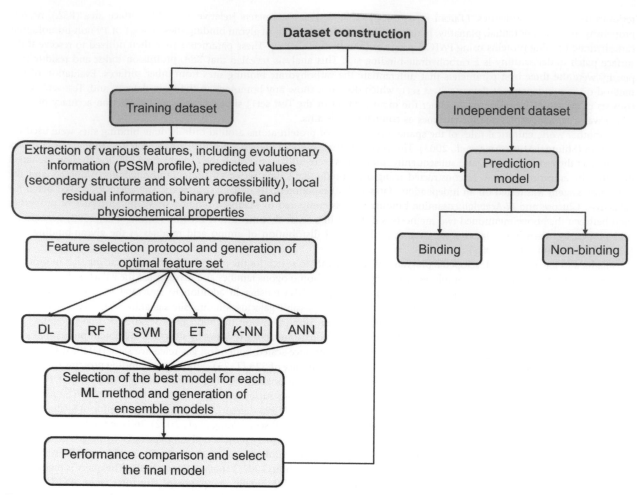

Fig. 1 An overview of ML-based prediction framework. It involves four different stages: (i) construction of the datasets; (ii) extraction of features from the sequence or structures and the selection of important features; (iii) development of the prediction models using various ML methods; (iv) final model selection based on their performances in training dataset and independent dataset.

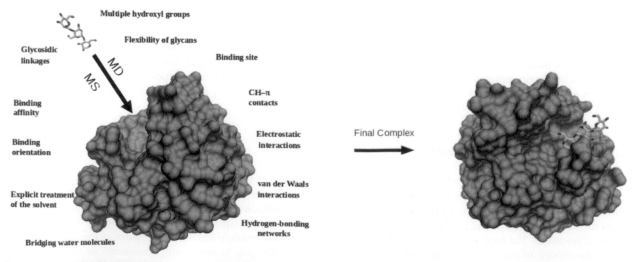

Fig. 2 A summary of important Molecular simulations (MS) and Molecular docking (MD) parameters that need to be considered while studying protein-carbohydrate interactions by using molecular dynamics methods. The coordinates of PDB ID 3MAN was used to generate the figure by using VMD (Humphrey *et al.*, 1996).

Structure-Based Prediction Methods

The first structure-based method using ML was proposed in 2009, where they applied support vector machine (SVM) to predict the glucose binding sites (Nassif et al., 2009), whose optimal features were identified using random forest (RF) algorithm. This study revealed that in addition to carboxylate residues, the significance of ordered water molecules and ions might participate in deciphering glucose-binding specificity. Additionally, the relevance of high concentration of negatively charged atoms that make direct contacts with the glucose was highlighted. Using LOOCV, this method achieved 8.11% error, 89.66% sensitivity and 93.33% specificity with a dataset of 43 glucose- and 68 non-glucose-binding sites. Similarly, mannose binding sites were also predicted by using RF by extracting at least 15 features (e.g., charge, hydrophobicity, hydrogen bonding, etc.) both at the atomic as well as residue level (Khare et al., 2012). This method achieved an accuracy of 96% and 94% with respect to individual feature and combined features, respectively. However, the applicability of this prediction model remains to be determined because a very small dataset (only 11 protein-mannose complexes) was used for the prediction model development. The common feature of two structure-based methods and the knowledge-based method by Sujatha and Balaji is their specificity for a particular type of sugar (e. g., glucose, mannose or galactose).

ML algorithms have also been applied to predict non-specific carbohydrate binding sites in proteins. A method called InCa-SiteFinder, which utilizes the amino acid propensities and van der Waals energy of a protein–probe interaction for searching or predicting the non-covalent inositol and non-specific glycan binding sites on the protein structures (Kulharia et al., 2009). This method used a dataset of 375 protein–carbohydrate complexes (which is larger compared to the earlier studies) to derive amino acid propensities. InCa-SiteFinder uses a two-step procedure to predict the carbohydrate binding sites. The first step employs an energetic grid-based approach (Laurie and Jackson, 2005) to detect potential sites on the protein with a higher possibility of being a binding site, whereas in the next step it uses potential sites information along with the amino acid propensities to predict the region of carbohydrate binding sites. The performance of InCa-SiteFinder was assessed by a single parameter, tau (τ) which in turn is a product of two individual parameters, precision (P) and coverage (C) (i.e., $\tau = P^*C$). This method performed reasonably well when tested on 80 protein–ligand complexes. Furthermore, this method achieved 98% specificity and 73% sensitivity with an overall error rate of 12%, when tested on dataset of 40 known drug-like compound binders as well as 40 known carbohydrate binders to predict the carbohydrate binding site locations and to further distinguish both the types from one another.

Another method was developed which was different as compared to earlier described methods in a sense that it utilizes a unique encoding scheme of the 3D probability density maps representing the distributions of 36 non-covalent interacting atom types around protein surfaces (Tsai et al., 2012). The 36 atoms represent 30 atom types from proteins, 5 from carbohydrate ligands, and 1 from the water. A ML model was trained for all the 30 types of protein atoms. In ML models, each attribute is representing the normalized distance-weighted sum of the 3D probability density for the one interacting atom type (out of 36) on the protein surface. Three types of ML algorithms were used to predict the carbohydrate binding sites: (a) Artificial neural network (ANN), (b) SVM, and (c) ANN with bootstrap aggregation (ANN_BAGGING). For training as well as testing, only atoms on protein surfaces that have solvent accessible area of larger than 0 were included. These ML models were trained to learn the patterns of the attributes to discriminate between binding- and non-binding site atoms. Furthermore, the probability of each amino acid atom assumed to be within a glycan binding site was scaled into a prediction confidence level between 0 and 1. Surface atoms of protein with greater certainty levels from the predictors were grouped to output provisional glycan-binding patches. The predictors were validated on a non-redundant dataset of 497 proteins with known binding sites for carbohydrate by a 10-fold cross-validation, and additionally tested on an independent dataset of 108 proteins. ANN_BAGGING method produced the best result with an average Matthews correlation coefficient (MCC), sensitivity, and specificity of 0.45, 0.49, and 0.97 respectively, when compared to other two methods.

In general, the above methods are dependent on the protein's local structural descriptors and hence are of little significance in case of the unavailability of their 3D structures.

Sequence-Based Prediction Methods

It is well known that the frequency of mutations at functional sites during evolution is much lesser as compared to the other parts of a protein (Livingstone and Barton, 1993; Zvelebil et al., 1987). The difference in amino acids at these functional sites can be represented in the form of sequence conservation patterns by using matrices of position-specific variations, known as profiles (Gribskov et al., 1990), or by statistical methods, such as Hidden Markov Models (HMMs) (Krogh et al., 1994; Eddy, 1998). Sequence homologies (local as well as global) can be detected by these methods or by more sensitive approaches such as Position Specific Iterative (PSI) blast program (Altschul et al., 1997) search, thereby implying putative functions and functional sites, by comparison. Sequence-based methods exploiting ML have become indispensable to the functional annotation of proteins since decades (Kneller et al., 1990; Ahmad and Sarai, 2005; Liu and Rost, 2004; Firoz et al., 2011). In addition to many other disciplines of bioinformatics, ML methods have been extensively employed in the prediction of interaction sites between two biomacromolecules. In general, ML refers to the modifications in systems that carry out tasks such as recognition, diagnosis, planning, robot control, prediction, etc., which are linked with artificial intelligence (AI) (Nilsson, 1996). The main objective of ML is to program computers to use model data or previous experience to resolve a problem at hand (Alpaydin, 2014). The rapid upsurge in biological data as well as the processing potential and storage capacity of computers has led to enhanced developments in the field of ML (Bastanlar and Ozuysal, 2014). Given a protein sequence which is expected to interact with another molecule (DNA, RNA, carbohydrates, ligands, etc.) the challenge of ML is to guess which amino acid residues might be involved in the interactions (Wang and Brown, 2006).

In sequence-based methods, there are two types of approaches that can be used to encode input protein sequences (Hwang et al., 2007): (a) Single sequence approach – Each amino acid residue is converted into a 20 bit vector and propagated through a ML model along with its neighboring residues (Gallet et al., 2000; Ofran and Rost, 2007) as well as combining additional structural information (Ahmad and Sarai, 2005). (b) Evolutionary information (EI) – This approach utilizes residue conservation and EI (position specific scoring matrices (PSSMs)) by using PSI-BLAST (Altschul et al., 1997). In this method, the target sequence is searched for homology against a protein database and generates a profile for the input sequence in the form of scoring matrices, which is then supplied to a ML algorithm such as neural networks or SVM for prediction. Sequence profiles of neighboring residues and structural information have increased the prediction accuracy (Hwang et al., 2007; Wang and Brown, 2006; Zhou and Shan, 2001; Kuznetsov et al., 2006).

Several developments have been made for the prediction of protein-protein interaction sites (Zhou and Shan, 2001; Ofran and Rost, 2007; Li et al., 2012; Fariselli et al., 2002), prediction of DNA (Ahmad and Sarai, 2005; Carson et al., 2010; Ofran et al., 2007) and ligand binding sites in proteins (Passerini et al., 2006; Shu et al., 2008; Chen et al., 2014; Suresh et al., 2015). Recognizing the significance of protein-carbohydrate interactions, Malik and Ahmad (2007) developed the first sequence-based method using ANNs to predict carbohydrate binding sites in proteins (Malik and Ahmad, 2007). They trained two separate neural network architectures using evolutionary profiles of protein sequences and information from single sequences to predict carbohydrate binding sites. The network using EI achieved 87% sensitivity of prediction at 23% specificity whereas with the single sequences, 68% sensitivity and 55% specificity for all carbohydrate-binding sites was obtained. The authors proposed that the prediction accuracy can be improved further when their method trained with the larger size of the dataset in the future. Although, this method was developed using the dataset of 40 protein-carbohydrate complexes, it showed an improved performance when tested on a dataset generated by Sujatha and Balaji (2004). The method was later implemented in the form of a web server, CBS-Pred (Malik et al., 2010) and can be accessed at see "Relevant Websites section". The work triggered interest within the scientific community which resulted in the development of new sequence-based methods to predict carbohydrate binding sites by employing ML. Most of these methods focused on a specific type of sugar. For example, SVM based classifiers were developed to predict mannose interacting residues (MIRs) from the primary sequences of mannose binding proteins (MBPs) (Agarwal et al., 2011). The method employs several modules such as similarity-based module, SVM based module which uses binary profile of patterns, SVM module using EI, and a module on the basis of composition profile of patterns (CPP) or local composition for predicting mannose binding residues in proteins. Among these different modules, the CPP based SVM method outperformed other modules by achieving a maximum MCC of 0.61. A method called MOWGLI was also developed to predict MIRs that uses an ensemble of base classifiers using PSSM (Pai and Mondal, 2016). In this method, the base classification algorithm was developed by exploring RF and SVM trained by various subsets of training data set of 128 mannose binding proteins using 10-fold cross-validation. The performance of the method was measured on a separate test dataset of 29 mannose binding proteins and achieved an accuracy of 92%. A standalone version of this method is available at see "Relevant Websites section". With the exception of CBS-Pred (Malik et al., 2010), the type of interacting carbohydrate is known in all of the above-mentioned methods. However, it becomes more difficult when such information is unknown well in advance. Another sequence-based method that integrates sequence and predicted structural features for the prediction of nonspecific carbohydrate binding sites was developed (Taherzadeh et al., 2016). The method in addition to EI, uses sequence derived structural information (such as solvent accessibility and secondary structure), seven physico-chemical features (volume, steric parameter, isoelectric point, hydrophobicity, polarizability, alpha-helix and beta-sheet probability) of amino acids, information about the disordered residues, and the protein length as the input features. The most effective features were selected to build a classifier based on SVMs and the method achieved an area under receiver operating characteristic curve (AUC) of 0.78 and 0.77 for 10-fold cross-validation and independent test.

Recently, a method was developed which classifies sugars into acidic and non-acidic sugars and discriminates between their amino acid composition at the binding sites (Banno et al., 2017). These characteristics were then used to design two predictors viz, an acid sugar binding predictor and a non-acidic sugar binding predictor. Additionally, a third predictor was developed that combined the output of the two above mentioned predictors. The dataset used to develop this method consists of 369 sugar-binding proteins, 136 acidic sugar-, and 270 non-acidic-sugar-binding proteins. A PSSM profile of sugar-interacting sites and their neighboring residues were employed to predict the sugar binding sites by using SVM. The method achieved an AUC of 0.787 and 0.752 for the acidic and non-acidic sugar binding predictors, respectively, on the basis of a 5-fold cross-validation. In case, the characteristic nature of sugar was unknown or is known to be non-acidic, the combined predictor performed best with AUC of 0.760. The method is freely available for download as a standalone program (see "Relevant Websites section").

To date, there are three structure-based methods and five sequence-based methods publicly available for the prediction of carbohydrate binding sites. The web server link and other details are provided in **Table 1**.

Advantages of sequence-based methods over structure-based methods

Due to the advancement in sequencing technology, the number of sequences deposited in the protein sequence database is growing exponentially, which has outpaced the experimental determination of protein structures. This has created a big void between the number of protein sequence entries and their experimentally determined 3D structures. This sequence-structure gap is expected to increase further in the future. As a result, sequence-based bioinformatics tools have become indispensable for researchers as they are not dependent on a costly and time-consuming procedure of experimental determination of protein structures (Hwang et al., 2007). Moreover, sequence-based tools have attractive leverage in managing high-throughput data generated in the fast-growing proteomics field. Although, sequence-based methods have several advantages, the prediction accuracy is slightly lower than the structure-based methods. Their accuracy may become better once the key question to identify the best features that may help in improving the prediction of these binding sites is addressed.

Table 1   List of available methods to predict carbohydrate-binding sites in proteins. The methods highlighted in bold font and normal fonts respectively denote the structure- and sequence-based methods

Method	Link	Carbohydrate specificity	Status (As of 12th Oct 2017)	Reference
InCa-SiteFinder	http://www.modeling.leeds.ac.uk/InCaSiteFinder/	Non-specific	In active	Kulharia et al. (2009)
ISMBLab_PCA	http://ismblab.genomics.sinica.edu.tw/	Non-specific	Active	Tsai et al. (2012)
SPOT-CBP	http://sparks-lab.org/yueyang/server/SPOT-CBP/	Non-specific	Active	Zhao et al. (2014)
CBS-Pred	http://www.procarb.org/procarbdb/cbs-pred.html	Non-specific	Active	Malik et al. (2010)
PreMieR	http://crdd.osdd.net/raghava//premier/	Mannose	Active	Agarwal et al. (2011)
MOWGLI	https://sites.google.com/site/sukantamondal/software	Mannose	Active	Pai and Mondal (2016)
SPRINT-CBH	http://sparks-lab.org/server/SPRINT-CBH/	Non-specific	Active	Taherzadeh et al. (2016)
SBRP	https://zenodo.org/record/61513#.WcB-4hdLeis	Acidic and non-acidic sugars	Active	Banno et al. (2017)

Table 2   Summary of the parameterization protocols for some of the well known force-fields dedicated to carbohydrates and an example application of these force fields in simulating the protein-carbohydrate complexes

Force field	Parameterization protocol used for the development					Example application
	Vdw terms	Torsion terms	1,4-Scaling (Elec/vdW)	Unique atom types for α- and β-anomers	Unique charge sets for a- and b-anomers	
GLYCAM	AMBER PARM94	Fit to QM rotationalm energy curves	X	x	√	Mishra et al. (2014)
CHARMM	CHARMM22		X	√	x	Mallajosyula et al. (2015)
OLPS-AA-SEI	OPLS-AA		√	√	√	Kony et al. (2002)
GROMOS	GROMOS-45A4		X	√	√	Vital De Oliveira (2014)

Note: For detailed review of these force fields, interested readers are referred to Fadda, E., Woods, R.J., 2010. Molecular simulations of carbohydrates and protein-carbohydrate interactions: Motivation, issues and prospects. Drug Discov. Today 15, 596–609 and Xiong, X., Chen, Z., Cossins, B.P., et al., 2015. Force fields and scoring functions for carbohydrate simulation. Carbohydr. Res. 401, 73–81 of the reference section.

In general, structure-based methods always perform better than the sequence-based methods. This is mainly due to the following reasons: (*i*) structure-based methods contain features derived from both the sequences as well as from the structures. Basically, it includes a sequence-based method and improving the corresponding algorithm by adding the structural information (*ii*) the information/features derived from the structures is more accurate when compared to the sequences. However, this method requires a 3D structure as an input, but again solving a 3D structure is not simple, and requires lot of time and effort. As a result, sequence-based methods are preferred.

Molecular Dynamics Based Methods

Force Fields

Molecular dynamic simulation studies are performed to gain a possible observation of the progression of motions in the molecular systems at atomic level (Hansson et al., 2002). These are based on the deterministic propagation of various forces interim on a molecular system. These computer simulation processes have provided us with powerful tools to deeply investigate the detailed molecular interactions. For a successful simulation, we need an accurate force field which could provide a realistic portrayal of the systems. The development of accurate force-fields for protein-carbohydrate interactions has been an area of active research. It is a very laborious task to develop an accurate force field compatible to deal with the carbohydrates (Xiong et al., 2015). Over the last couple of decades a large number of force fields capable of dealing with carbohydrates were developed. These force fields were developed by outspreading the classic force fields making them to deal with different carbohydrates.

Here we are listing some of the major force fields specifically developed to handle carbohydrates. These force fields are either dedicated ones for carbohydrates or they are an extension of the previously used force fields with changes implemented. GLY-CAM06, CHARMM36, 53A6GLYC, GROMOS and OPLS-AA-SEI (Scaling Electrostatic Interaction), are some of the major carbohydrate force fields (**Table 2**). These force fields were developed for better consistency for simulating the larger systems including nucleic acids, proteins, and lipids.

GLYCAM06

This force field is compatible for a large group of carbohydrates, in addition to acetylated amino sugars, neuraminic acid, and iduronic acid (Kirschner et al., 2008). This force field is widely used for modeling the protein–carbohydrate complexes in addition to the modeling of carbohydrates, glycolipids and glycoproteins (Tessier *et al.*, 2008; DeMarco and Woods, 2008). GLYCAM06 is compatible with the AMBER force field (Fadda and Woods, 2010) and comprises of parameters appropriate for the simulation of carbohydrates (Kirschner *et al.*, 2008). These parameters of GLYCAM06 can be effectively used for simulating carbohydrates of different conformations and ring sizes (both oligosaccharides and monosaccharides). Using appropriate file-conversion tools, GLYCAM06 is fit for use in other simulation packages (Dejoux *et al.*, 2001). Additionally, GLYCAM06 is loaded with parameters developed by considering a test set of 100 molecules from different chemical families, like carboxylates, alcohols, amides, esters, hydrocarbons, ethers and other molecules of diverse functional groups which have been fitted to quantum-mechanical data (Perez and Tvaroska, 2014). Several stereoelectronic effects influencing the bond and angle variations at the anomeric carbon atom have been parametrized in this force field (Biarnës *et al.*, 2010). These features allow it for mimicking the ring inversion observed in glycosidic monomers during several catalytic events. The comparison of the GLYCAM06 derived results with experimental findings suggested that this force field correctly reproduces the rotational energies and carbohydrate features (Guvench *et al.*, 2009).

CHARMM36

The force field for handling carbohydrates is one of the modifications added to CHARMM all-atom biomolecular force fields (Hatcher *et al.*, 2009; Guvench *et al.*, 2008; Guvench *et al.*, 2009; MacKerell *et al.*, 1998, 2004). This updated force field is embedded with parameters allowing the simulation of unsubstituted oligosaccharides as well as monosaccharides. A large number of revisions for handling carbohydrates have been implemented in the upgraded version of this force field. These updates extend the capability of this force field for handling the five-membered sugar rings and oligosaccharides. The same hierarchical parameterization process and handling of 1,4 nonbonded interactions are exploited to guarantee complete compatibility with other CHARMM biomolecular force fields (MacKerell *et al.*, 1998). The current parameterization of CHARMM makes it compatible for simulating the monosaccharides (i.e., glucopyranoses and diastereoisomers (Guvench *et al.*, 2008) and aldo- and fructofuranoses (Hatcher *et al.*, 2009) and for unsubstituted oligosaccharides (Guvench *et al.*, 2008).

OPLS-AA-SEI

OPLS-AA Scaling of Electrostatic Interactions also known as OPLS-AA-SEI, an upgraded version of OPLS-AA biomolecular force field with parameters for carbohydrates for the improved prediction of its conformational changes (mainly Φ and Ψ angles) (Kony *et al.*, 2002). In comparison to OPLS-AA, OPLS-AA-SEI has been reported to be more accurate in terms of reproducing quantum mechanics (QM) relative energies.

GROMOS

Two different versions for dealing with carbohydrates have been developed. The first one is the classic GROMOS 45A4 and the advanced one is GROMOS 53A6GLYC. The GROMOS 45A4 is compatible for dealing with mono-, di-, oligo-, or polysaccharides (Lins and Hunenberger, 2005) and comprises of advance and better parameters designed specifically for carbohydrates. It also consists of parameters for handling mono- and oligosaccharides on the basis of pyranosides. GROMOS 53A6GLYC is another improved version with more advanced features set for simulating the carbohydrates in explicit-solvent. This version allowed appropriate depiction of the best possible conformation out of all 16 aldohexopyranose-based monosaccharides (Pol-Fachin, 2017).

Molecular Docking

As compared to protein-ligands, the interaction of a protein and a carbohydrate is more dynamic (Fadda and Woods, 2010). The affinities of these interactions are more likely dependent on several relatively weak interactions. In protein-carbohydrate--interactions, CH–π interactions and hydrogen bonds are the main types of interactions (Spiwok *et al.*, 2005). Molecular docking of proteins and their interacting carbohydrates is still a challenge, due to the inaccuracy of scoring functions for accurate prediction of their interaction. At present, very limited number of carbohydrate specific scoring functions have been developed and reported. It is a great need to develop a scoring function capable of accurately predicting the correct binding pose, along with binding free energy of the complex.

Some major docking tools like AutoDock (Morris *et al.*, 2008), Glide (Friesner *et al.*, 2004), GOLD (Verdonk *et al.*, 2003), and FlexX (Cross, 2005) are in use for studying protein-carbohydrate interactions. In a recent study the ability of these docking tools were compared and assessed. The top ranked poses generated by each of these tools was compared to its already known crystal counterpart. This comparison highlighted the weakness and strength of each tool. The findings of this study revealed the best results were obtained by GLIDE (Agostino *et al.*, 2009). Though the finding of this study shows the RMSD of the predicted results were in range with the experimentally determined structures, however, the best predicted results do not correspond to the experimental data.

The findings of several studies conducted on protein-carbohydrate interactions gives an impression that it is still extremely challenging to develop accurate and efficient methods for calculating the binding affinity of such complexes (DeMarco and Woods, 2008). In the last decade, a significant increase in the application of molecular docking methods for studying protein--carbohydrate interactions was observed (Reina *et al.*, 2008; Takaoka *et al.*, 2007; De Geus *et al.*, 2009; Chen and Shoichet, 2009; Gomez *et al.*, 2016; Bakkers *et al.*, 2016; Mompean *et al.*, 2017; Walker *et al.*, 2017). For a successful docking, an efficient searching algorithm along with a robust scoring function is critically required (Hill and Reilly, 2008). In case of protein-carbohydrate interactions the bridging water molecules and CH–π interactions are also key role players (Raju *et al.*, 2009; Spiwok *et al.*, 2005; Vandenbussche *et al.*, 2008). The more commonly used molecular docking programs had certain limitations in dealing with these important factors involved in the interaction of carbohydrates to proteins.

Limitations of traditional molecular docking tools

It is very challenging for the regularly used docking programs to identify the shallow carbohydrate binding sites. In addition, compared to other organic molecules, carbohydrates are significantly more flexible (Kerzmann *et al.*, 2008; Imberty, 1997). These widely used molecular docking programs are mainly developed for analyzing the binding of small molecules. The use of these traditional docking methods is not capable to accurately predict the orientation of carbohydrate within the binding site and the relative binding affinity of this conformational pose (interaction energy). There are several factors which are responsible for their inability to deal with the carbohydrates. Unlike small ligands, carbohydrates are extremely flexible, and consist of several hydroxyl groups (DeMarco and Woods, 2008). The presence of wide hydrogen-bonding networks along with the formation of CH–π contacts are the major reasons which restrict these traditional docking tools from accurately predicting carbohydrate-protein complexes (Spiwok, 2017; Grant and Woods, 2014).

Moreover, the explicit treatment of the solvent is required for capturing the hydrogen bonds between carbohydrates with water (Nivedha *et al.*, 2016, 2014; Kirschner and Woods, 2001). Some of the essential parameters required for the efficient docking of protein-carbohydrate interactions are summarized in **Fig. 2**. Due to these major challenges, it is difficult to correctly predict the carbohydrate binding sites and their affinities using traditional docking methods.

Advancement towards designing computational methods for protein-carbohydrate docking

Several approaches were made towards preparing a better method for accurate prediction of protein-carbohydrate interactions. Studies performed on carbohydrate docking used the scoring functions which were customized either by recalibrating the existing terms (Laederach and Reilly, 2003) or by including few more additional functions capable of modeling some of the specific features of protein–carbohydrate interactions (Kerzmann *et al.*, 2006). Kerzmann *et al.* (2006) specifically designed a scoring and an energy function termed as Sugar-Lectin Interactions and DoCKing (SLICK), for predicting the binding poses and free energy calculations for carbohydrates to proteins. This scoring function accounts for CH–π interactions, solvation effects, hydrogen bonds, van der Waals interactions and electrostatics. The binding free energies predicted using SLICK showed high accuracy when compared to the experimental binding energies. This is due to the calibration of the parameters for the empirical energy function. This function is available in the molecular modeling package of BALLDock (see "Relevant Websites section") (Gauto *et al.*, 2013). The glycosidic linkages within oligosaccharides are the critical source of flexibility. In previous studies, scoring functions were customized for carbohydrate docking. This customization was done by either recalibration of existing terms or the annexation of supplementary functions capable of modeling the protein–carbohydrate interactions. The SLICK scoring function comprises of an energy term for CH–π stacking interactions and was calibrated by using a set of lectin-carbohydrate complexes (Kerzmann *et al.*, 2006). Later it was found that incorporating the explicit water molecules during the docking of carbohydrates (Samsonov *et al.*, 2011) as well as inclusion of the placement of hydroxyl groups of carbohydrates in water site positions (Gauto *et al.*, 2013) leads to improvements in docking accuracy. Inclusion of the conformational preferences of oligosaccharides within a scoring function additionally enhances the accuracy and efficiency of carbohydrate docking. Recently, Carbohydrate Intrinsic (CHI) energy functions assign relative energies to the torsion angles of the glycosidic linkages. The distribution of glycosidic torsion angles in protein–carbohydrate complexes obtained by CHI-energy profiles resembled with those obtained from the Protein Data Bank (PDB) (Nivedha *et al.*, 2014).

Reports also suggest the inclusion of Carbohydrate Intrinsic (CHI) energy functions in carbohydrate docking algorithms would be beneficial (Nivedha *et al.*, 2014). The CHI-energy function was incorporated into the AutoDock Vina (ADV), and was termed Vina-Carb (VC) (Trott and Olson, 2010; Nivedha *et al.*, 2016). For the development of Vina-Carb, a dataset consisting of 29 apoprotein structures and 101 protein–carbohydrate complexes were used. Findings show that the addition of CHI-energy function within the Vina-Carb increases its success rate from 55% to 74% (Nivedha *et al.*, 2016). However, while dealing with the ligands that partially extend into solution, Vina-Carb was unable to reproduce the experimental findings (Nivedha *et al.*, 2016). This is an issue which needs to be addressed for a successful development of scoring function for accurately describing the protein-carbohydrate interactions. Recently, RosettaCarbohydrate Framework was developed for the modeling and docking of oligomeric and polymeric carbohydrate ligands and glycoconjugates (Labonte *et al.*, 2017). The framework can handle the sampling of glycosidic bonds, side-chain conformations, and ring forms, and it can also use a glycan-specific term within its scoring function.

Applications

Among the currently available methods for the prediction of carbohydrate binding sites, two each from the sequence- and structure-based methods have been presented here (**Table 3**). Briefly, CBS-Pred has been used in three such studies and predicted three aromatic residues involved in polysaccharide binding (Park *et al.*, 2014), lipopolysaccharide binding amino acids in several peptides (Brzozowska *et al.*, 2015), and mannose interacting residues in CrataBL glycoprotein (Pol-Fachin, 2017). SPRINT-CBH was also used to predict the mannose interacting residues of CrataBL, and a carbohydrate binding tyrosine residue of an unknown gene PA5359 from *Pseudomonas aeruginosa* (Gunasekera *et al.*, 2017). In case of structure-based methods, ISMBLab_PCA has been used most commonly. For example, it was used for the prediction of carbohydrate binding sites in a toxin, pneumolysin

Table 3   Application of different carbohydrate binding site prediction methods. The methods highlighted in bold are structure-based and require a 3D structure of a protein for prediction

Method	Types of carbohydrates under investigation	Reference
CBS-Pred	Polysaccharide	Park *et al.* (2014)
	Monosaccharide	Pol-Fachin (2017)
	Lipopolysaccharide	Brzozowska *et al.* (2015)
SPRINT-CBH	Carbohydrate binding	Gunasekera *et al.* (2017)
	Monosaccharide	Pol-Fachin (2017)
InCa-SiteFinder	Druggable pocket	Dharra *et al.* (2017)
ISMBLab_PCA	Monosaccharide	Pol-Fachin (2017)
	Sialyl Lewis X, Lewis B and mannose	Lawrence *et al.* (2015)
	LewisX and Sialyl LewisX	Shewell *et al.* (2014)

(Shewell *et al.*, 2014; Lawrence *et al.*, 2015). In addition to the sequence-based prediction, the mannose binding sites of CrataBL (Pol-Fachin, 2017) were also predicted by using ISMBLab_PCA.

In the case of docking, over the past two decades various attempts have been made to dock carbohydrates to their protein partners (Imberty, 1997; Bitomsky and Wade, 1999; Mulakala and Reilly, 2005; Gohier *et al.*, 1996). The docking ability of several softwares was also compared to calculate the binding affinity of *Ralstonia solanacearum* lectin (RSL) (Mishra *et al.*, 2012). More recent docking methods have also been applied to investigate the interactions of carbohydrates and their interacting proteins. Being published in 2016, a limited number of studies highlighting the application of Vina-Carb are available. For example, a recent a study by Gómez *et al.* (2016) demonstrated the use of Vina-Carb for docking of hexasaccharide into the endo-β-1,4-xylanase (*Xyl2*) active site. Since the methods for specifically docking the carbohydrates are just beginning to appear, it will be a while before their accuracy could be tested for a wide range of carbohydrates.

Future Directions

The information about the factors, which direct or inhibit the binding of a carbohydrate to an amino acid, is believed to exist in the evolutionary profile of the sequence as well as the identity and structure of amino acid residues in the neighboring environments of potential carbohydrate binding sites (Malik and Ahmad, 2007). Although several computational methods have been developed for the protein-carbohydrate interactions, yet none of these methods can offer satisfactory predictions given the diversity of carbohydrates. Methods dealing with specific types of carbohydrates might be promising but they have a limited practical application, whereas the predictors for non-specific carbohydrates may have a broader application, however, at the cost of accuracy. Another issue with the existing methods is that there is no consensus definition for a binding site. The binding and non-binding residues are defined based on a certain distance cut-off. Therefore, it is necessary to optimize the distance cut-off threshold because the introduction of higher cut-off may introduce many false positive and false negative in the dataset (Ding *et al.*, 2010). Currently, the existing sequence-based methods use similar features, small datasets for their prediction model development, no systematic feature selection protocol was employed to quantify the important features, and none of the methods explored different ML methods using the same dataset to identify the most appropriate one for this problem. The key question, however remains to derive or develop a novel feature beyond the PSSM profile, predicted secondary structure and solvent accessibility, along with the exploration of ML-based methods and systematic feature selection protocol, which will be helpful to improve the prediction accuracy and stimulate further development in this field. Additionally, the carbohydrate binding residues predicted from ML-based methods could be utilized to design molecular dynamics based studies. Similar approaches were suggested for studying protein–DNA interactions (Kaufman and Karypis, 2012). Such approaches may help to increase the overall carbohydrate-binding sites prediction performance.

Conclusion

Experimental identification of protein-carbohydrate complex is very difficult, expensive and often time-consuming, and, therefore, the development of computational methods is necessary to predict the carbohydrate-binding sites from the given uncharacterized protein sequence. The expeditious increase of the structure databases offers an opportunity to apply knowledge-based or molecular dynamics based approaches for prediction, but these methods offer limited utility and cannot be used if the 3D structures of proteins are unavailable. Therefore, the development of more accurate sequence-based predictors is the need of the hour.

See also: Biomolecular Structures: Prediction, Identification and Analyses. Natural Language Processing Approaches in Bioinformatics. Protein–Protein Interaction Databases

References

Agarwal, S., Mishra, N.K., Singh, H., Raghava, G.P., 2011. Identification of mannose interacting residues using local composition. PLOS ONE 6, e24039.

Agirre, J., Davies, G.J., Wilson, K.S., Cowtan, K.D., 2017. Carbohydrate structure: The rocky road to automation. Curr. Opin. Struct. Biol. 44, 39–47.

Agostino, M., Jene, C., Boyle, T., Ramsland, P.A., Yuriev, E., 2009. Molecular docking of carbohydrate ligands to antibodies: Structural validation against crystal structures. J. Chem. Inf. Model. 49, 2749–2760.

Ahmad, S., Sarai, A., 2005. PSSM-based prediction of DNA binding sites in proteins. BMC Bioinform. 6, 33.

Alpaydin, E., 2014. Introduction to Machine Learning. MIT press.

Altschul, S.F., Madden, T.L., Schæffer, A.A., et al., 1997. Gapped BLAST and PSI-BLAST: A new generation of protein database search programs. Nucleic Acids Res. 25, 3389–3402.

Audette, G.F., Delbaere, L.T., Xiang, J., 2003. Mapping protein: Carbohydrate interactions. Curr. Protein Pept. Sci. 4, 11–20.

Bakkers, M.J., Zeng, Q., Feitsma, L.J., et al., 2016. Coronavirus receptor switch explained from the stereochemistry of protein-carbohydrate interactions and a single mutation. Proc. Natl. Acad. Sci. USA 113, E3111–E3119.

Banno, M., Komiyama, Y., Cao, W., et al., 2017. Development of a sugar-binding residue prediction system from protein sequences using support vector machine. Comput. Biol. Chem. 66, 36–43.

Bastanlar, Y., Ozuysal, M., 2014. Introduction to machine learning. Methods Mol. Biol. 1107, 105–128.

Biarnës, X., Ardëvol, A., Planas, A., Rovira, C., 2010. Substrate conformational changes in glycoside hydrolase catalysis. A first-principles molecular dynamics study. Biocatal. Biotransform. 28, 33–40.

Bitomsky, W., Wade, R.C., 1999. Docking of glycosaminoglycans to heparin-binding proteins: Validation for aFGF, bFGF, and antithrombin and application to IL-8. J. Am. Chem. Soc. 121, 3004–3013.

Brzozowska, E., Pyra, A., Miśków, M., Górska, S., Gamian, A. 2015. C-terminal sequence determinants of T4 bacteriophage tail fiber adhesin for specific lipopolysaccharide recognition.

Carson, M.B., Langlois, R., Lu, H., 2010. NAPS: A residue-level nucleic acid-binding prediction server. Nucleic Acids Res. 38, W431–W435.

Chen, P., Huang, J.Z., Gao, X., 2014. LigandRFs: Random forest ensemble to identify ligand-binding residues from sequence information alone. BMC Bioinform. 15 (Suppl. 15), S4.

Chen, Y., Shoichet, B.K., 2009. Molecular docking and ligand specificity in fragment-based inhibitor discovery. Nat. Chem. Biol. 5, 358–364.

Cross, S.S., 2005. Improved FlexX docking using FlexS-determined base fragment placement. J. Chem. Inf. Model. 45, 993–1001.

Dam, T.K., Brewer, C.F., 2002. Thermodynamic studies of lectin-carbohydrate interactions by isothermal titration calorimetry. Chem. Rev. 102, 387–430.

De Geus, D.C., Van Roon, A.M., Thomassen, E.A., et al., 2009. Characterization of a diagnostic Fab fragment binding trimeric Lewis X. Proteins 76, 439–447.

De Schutter, K., Van Damme, E.J., 2015. Protein-carbohydrate interactions, and beyond. Multidisciplinary Digital Publishing Institute.

Dejoux, A., Cieplak, P., Hannick, N., Moyna, G., Dupradeau, F.-Y., 2001. AmberFFC, a flexible program to convert AMBER and GLYCAM force fields for use with commercial molecular modeling packages. J. Mol. Model. 7, 422–432.

DeMarco, M.L., Woods, R.J., 2008. Structural glycobiology: A game of snakes and ladders. Glycobiology 18, 426–440.

Dharra, R., Talwar, S., Singh, Y., Gupta, R., et al., 2017. Rational design of drug-like compounds targeting Mycobacterium marinum MelF protein. PLoS ONE 12, e0183060.

Ding, X.M., Pan, X.Y., Xu, C., Shen, H.B., 2010. Computational prediction of DNA-protein interactions: A review. Curr. Comput. Aided Drug Des. 6, 197–206.

Duverger, E., Frison, N., Roche, A.-C., Monsigny, M., 2003. Carbohydrate-lectin interactions assessed by surface plasmon resonance. Biochimie 85, 167–179.

Eddy, S.R., 1998. Profile hidden Markov models. Bioinformatics (Oxford) 14, 755–763.

Fadda, E., Woods, R.J., 2010. Molecular simulations of carbohydrates and protein-carbohydrate interactions: Motivation, issues and prospects. Drug Discov. Today 15, 596–609.

Fariselli, P., Pazos, F., Valencia, A., Casadio, R., 2002. Prediction of protein–protein interaction sites in heterocomplexes with neural networks. Eur. J. Biochem. 269, 1356–1361.

Firoz, A., Malik, A., Joplin, K.H., et al., 2011. Residue propensities, discrimination and binding site prediction of adenine and guanine phosphates. BMC Biochem. 13 (12), 20.

Friesner, R.A., Banks, J.L., Murphy, R.B., et al., 2004. Glide: A new approach for rapid, accurate docking and scoring. 1. Method and assessment of docking accuracy. J. Med. Chem. 47, 1739–1749.

Fukui, S., Feizi, T., Galustian, C., Lawson, A.M., Chai, W., 2002. Oligosaccharide microarrays for high-throughput detection and specificity assignments of carbohydrate-protein interactions. Nature Biotechnol. 20, 1011–1017.

Gallet, X., Charloteaux, B., Thomas, A., Brasseur, R., 2000. A fast method to predict protein interaction sites from sequences. J. Mol. Biol. 302, 917–926.

Gauto, D.F., Petruk, A.A., Modenutti, C.P., et al., 2013. Solvent structure improves docking prediction in lectin-carbohydrate complexes. Glycobiology 23, 241–258.

Gohier, A., Espinosa, J.F., Jimenez-Barbero, J., et al., 1996. Knowledge-based modeling of a legume lectin and docking of the carbohydrate ligand: The Ulex europaeus lectin I and its interaction with fucose. J. Mol. Graph. 14, 363–364.

Gomez, S., Payne, A.M., Savko, M., et al., 2016. Structural and functional characterization of a highly stable endo-beta-1,4-xylanase from Fusarium oxysporum and its development as an efficient immobilized biocatalyst. Biotechnol. Biofuels 9, 191.

Grant, O.C., Woods, R.J., 2014. Recent advances in employing molecular modelling to determine the specificity of glycan-binding proteins. Curr. Opin. Struct. Biol. 28, 47–55.

Gribskov, M., Lothy, R., Eisenberg, D., 1990. Profile analysis. Methods Enzymol. 183, 146–159.

Gromiha, M.M., Veluraja, K., Fukui, K., 2014. Identification and analysis of binding site residues in protein-carbohydrate complexes using energy based approach. Protein Pept. Lett. 21, 799–807.

Gunasekera, T.S., Bowen, L.L., Zhou, C.E., et al., 2017. Transcriptomic analyses elucidate adaptive differences of closely related strains of pseudomonas aeruginosa in fuel. Appl. Environ. Microbiol. 83.

Guvench, O., Greene, S.N., Kamath, G., et al., 2008. Additive empirical force field for hexopyranose monosaccharides. J. Comput. Chem. 29, 2543–2564.

Guvench, O., Hatcher, E.R., Venable, R.M., Pastor, R.W., Mackerell, A.D., 2009. CHARMM additive all-atom force field for glycosidic linkages between hexopyranoses. J. Chem. Theory Comput. 5, 2353–2370.

Hansson, T., Oostenbrink, C., Van Gunsteren, W., 2002. Molecular dynamics simulations. Curr. Opin. Struct. Biol. 12, 190–196.

Hatcher, E., Guvench, O., Mackerell, A.D., 2009. CHARMM additive all-atom force field for aldopentofuranoses, methyl-aldopentofuranosides, and fructofuranose. J. Phys. Chem. B 113, 12466–12476.

Hill, A.D., Reilly, P.J., 2008. A Gibbs free energy correlation for automated docking of carbohydrates. J. Comput. Chem. 29, 1131–1141.

Hwang, S., Gou, Z., Kuznetsov, I.B., 2007. DP-Bind: A web server for sequence-based prediction of DNA-binding residues in DNA-binding proteins. Bioinformatics 23, 634–636.

Humphrey, W., Dalke, A., Schulten, K., 1996. VMD: Visual molecular dynamics. J. Mol. Graph. 14 (33–38), 27–28.

Imberty, A., 1997. Oligosaccharide structures: Theory versus experiment. Curr. Opin. Struct. Biol. 7, 617–623.

Jimënez-Barbero, J., Asensio, J.L., Caóada, F.J., Poveda, A., 1999. Free and protein-bound carbohydrate structures. Curr. Opin. Struct. Biol. 9, 549–555.

Karlsson, K.-A., 1991. Glycobiology: A growing field for drug design. Trends Pharmacol. Sci. 12, 265–272.

Kaufman, C., Karypis, G., 2012. Computational tools for protein–DNA interactions. WIREs Data Mining Knowl. Discov. 2, 14–28.

Kerzmann, A., Fuhrmann, J., Kohlbacher, O., Neumann, D., 2008. BALLDock/SLICK: A new method for protein-carbohydrate docking. J. Chem. Inf. Model. 48, 1616–1625.

Kerzmann, A., Neumann, D., Kohlbacher, O., 2006. SLICK – Scoring and energy functions for protein-carbohydrate interactions. J. Chem. Inf. Model. 46, 1635–1642.

Khare, H., Ratnaparkhi, V., Chavan, S., Jayraman, V., 2012. Prediction of protein-mannose binding sites using random forest. Bioinformation 8, 1202–1205.

Kirschner, K.N., Woods, R.J., 2001. Solvent interactions determine carbohydrate conformation. Proc. Natl. Acad. Sci. USA 98, 10541–10545.

Kirschner, K.N., Yongye, A.B., Tschampel, S.M., et al., 2008. GLYCAM06: A generalizable biomolecular force field. Carbohydrates. J. Comput. Chem. 29, 622–655.

Kneller, D.G., Cohen, F.E., Langridge, R., 1990. Improvements in protein secondary structure prediction by an enhanced neural network. J. Mol. Biol. 214, 171–182.

Kony, D., Damm, W., Stoll, S., Van Gunsteren, W.F., 2002. An improved OPLS-AA force field for carbohydrates. J. Comput. Chem. 23, 1416–1429.

Krogh, A., Mian, I.S., Haussler, D., 1994. A hidden Markov model that finds genes in E. coli DNA. Nucleic Acids Res. 22, 4768–4778.

Kulharia, M., Bridgett, S.J., Goody, R.S., Jackson, R.M., 2009. InCa-SiteFinder: A method for structure-based prediction of inositol and carbohydrate binding sites on proteins. J. Mol. Graph. Model. 28, 297–303.

Kuznetsov, I.B., Gou, Z., Li, R., Hwang, S., 2006. Using evolutionary and structural information to predict DNA-binding sites on DNA-binding proteins. Proteins 64, 19–27.

Labonte, J.W., Adolf-Bryfogle, J., Schief, W.R., Gray, J.J., 2017. Residue-centric modeling and design of saccharide and glycoconjugate structures. J. Comput. Chem. 38, 276–287.

Laederach, A., Reilly, P.J., 2003. Specific empirical free energy function for automated docking of carbohydrates to proteins. J. Comput. Chem. 24, 1748–1757.

Laurie, A.T., Jackson, R.M., 2005. Q-SiteFinder: An energy-based method for the prediction of protein-ligand binding sites. Bioinformatics 21, 1908–1916.

Lawrence, S.L., Feil, S.C., Morton, C.J., et al., 2015. Crystal structure of Streptococcus pneumoniae pneumolysin provides key insights into early steps of pore formation. Sci. Rep. 5, 14352.

Li, B.Q., Feng, K.Y., Chen, L., Huang, T., Cai, Y.D., 2012. Prediction of protein-protein interaction sites by random forest algorithm with mRMR and IFS. PLOS ONE 7, e43927.

Lins, R.D., Hunenberger, P.H., 2005. A new GROMOS force field for hexopyranose-based carbohydrates. J. Comput. Chem. 26, 1400–1412.

Lis, H., Sharon, N., 1972. Soy bean (Glycine max) agglutinin. Methods Enzymol. 28, 360–365.

Liu, J., Rost, B., 2004. Sequence-based prediction of protein domains. Nucleic Acids Res. 32, 3522–3530.

Livingstone, C.D., Barton, G.J., 1993. Protein sequence alignments: A strategy for the hierarchical analysis of residue conservation. Bioinformatics 9, 745–756.

MacKerell, A.D., Bashford, D., Bellott, M., et al., 1998. All-atom empirical potential for molecular modeling and dynamics studies of proteins. J. Phys. Chem. B 102, 3586–3616.

MacKerell Jr., A.D., Feig, M., Brooks 3rd, C.L., 2004. Extending the treatment of backbone energetics in protein force fields: Limitations of gas-phase quantum mechanics in reproducing protein conformational distributions in molecular dynamics simulations. J. Comput. Chem. 25, 1400–1415.

Malik, A., Ahmad, S., 2007. Sequence and structural features of carbohydrate binding in proteins and assessment of predictability using a neural network. BMC Struct. Biol. 7, 1.

Malik, A., Firoz, A., Jha, V., Ahmad, S., 2010. PROCARB: A database of known and modelled carbohydrate-binding protein structures with sequence-based prediction tools. Adv. Bioinform. 436036.

Malik, A., Lee, J., Lee, J., 2014. Community-based network study of protein-carbohydrate interactions in plant lectins using glycan array data. PLOS ONE 9, e95480.

Mallajosyula, S.S., Jo, S., Im, W., Mackerell Jr., A.D., 2015. Molecular dynamics simulations of glycoproteins using CHARMM. Methods Mol. Biol. 1273, 407–429.

Manavalan, B., Basith, S., Shin, T.H., et al., 2017b. MLACP: Machine-learning-based prediction of anticancer peptides. Oncotarget 8 (44), 77121–77136.

Manavalan, B., Lee, J., 2017a. SVMQA: Support-vector-machine-based protein single-model quality assessment. Bioinformatics 33, 2496–2503.

Manavalan, B., Lee, J., Lee, J., 2014. Random forest-based protein model quality assessment (RFMQA) using structural features and potential energy terms. PLOS ONE 9, e106542.

Manavalan, B., Shin, T.H., Lee, G., 2017c. DHSpred: Support-vector-machine-based human DNase I hypersensitive sites prediction using the optimal features selected by random forest. Oncotarget.

McCoy, J.P., Varani, J., Goldstein, I.J., 1983. Enzyme-linked lectin assay (ELLA): Use of alkaline phosphatase-conjugated Griffonia simplicifolia B4 isolectin for the detection of α-D-galactopyranosyl end groups. Anal. Biochem. 130, 437–444.

Mishra, S.K., Adam, J., Wimmerova, M., Koca, J., 2012. In silico mutagenesis and docking study of Ralstonia solanacearum RSL lectin: Performance of docking software to predict saccharide binding. J. Chem. Inf. Model. 52, 1250–1261.

Mishra, S.K., Kara, M., Zacharias, M., Koca, J., 2014. Enhanced conformational sampling of carbohydrates by Hamiltonian replica-exchange simulation. Glycobiology 24, 70–84.

Mompean, M., Villalba, M., Bruix, M., Zamora-Carreras, H., 2017. Insights into protein-carbohydrate recognition: A novel binding mechanism for CBM family 43. J. Mol. Graph. Model. 73, 152–156.

Morris, G.M., Huey, R., Olson, A.J., 2008. Using AutoDock for ligand-receptor docking. Curr. Protoc. Bioinform. (Chapter 8, Unit 8 14).

Mulakala, C., Reilly, P.J., 2005. Force calculations in automated docking: Enzyme-substrate interactions in Fusarium oxysporum Cel7B. Proteins 61, 590–596.

Nassif, H., Al-Ali, H., Khuri, S., Keirouz, W., 2009. Prediction of protein-glucose binding sites using support vector machines. Proteins: Struct. Funct. Bioinform. 77, 121–132.

Ng, S., Lin, E., Kitov, P.I., et al., 2015. Genetically encoded fragment-based discovery of glycopeptide ligands for carbohydrate-binding proteins. J. Am. Chem. Soc. 137, 5248–5251.

Nilsson, N.J., 1996. Introduction to Machine Learning. An Early Draft of a Proposed Textbook.

Nivedha, A.K., Makeneni, S., Foley, B.L., Tessier, M.B., Woods, R.J., 2014. Importance of ligand conformational energies in carbohydrate docking: Sorting the wheat from the chaff. J. Comput. Chem. 35, 526–539.

Nivedha, A.K., Thieker, D.F., Makeneni, S., Hu, H., Woods, R.J., 2016. Vina-Carb: Improving glycosidic angles during carbohydrate docking. J. Chem. Theory Comput. 12, 892–901.

Ofek, I., Hasty, D.L., Sharon, N., 2003. Anti-adhesion therapy of bacterial diseases: Prospects and problems. FEMS Immunol. Med. Microbiol. 38, 181–191.

Ofran, Y., Mysore, V., Rost, B., 2007. Prediction of DNA-binding residues from sequence. Bioinformatics 23, i347–i353.

Ofran, Y., Rost, B., 2007. Protein-protein interaction hotspots carved into sequences. PLOS Comput. Biol. 3, e119.

Pai, P.P., Mondal, S., 2016. MOWGLI: Prediction of protein-Mannose interacting residues with ensemble classifiers using evolutionary information. J. Biomol. Struct. Dyn. 34, 2069–2083.

Park, S., Lee, M.R., Shin, I., 2007. Fabrication of carbohydrate chips and their use to probe protein-carbohydrate interactions. Nat. Protoc. 2, 2747–2758.

Park, Y.D., Shin, S., Panepinto, J., et al., 2014. A role for LHC1 in higher order structure and complement binding of the Cryptococcus neoformans capsule. PLOS Pathog. 10, e1004037.

Passerini, A., Punta, M., Ceroni, A., Rost, B., Frasconi, P., 2006. Identifying cysteines and histidines in transition-metal-binding sites using support vector machines and neural networks. Proteins 65, 305–316.

Perez, S., Tvaroska, I., 2014. Carbohydrate-protein interactions: Molecular modeling insights. Adv. Carbohydr. Chem. Biochem. 71, 9–136.

Pol-Fachin, L., 2017. Insights into the effects of glycosylation and the monosaccharide-binding activity of the plant lectin CrataBL. Glycoconj. J. 34, 515–522.

Puvirajesinghe, T.M., Turnbull, J.E., 2016. Glycoarray technologies: Deciphering interactions from proteins to live cell responses. Microarrays (Basel) 5.

Quiocho, F.A., 1989. Protein-carbohydrate interactions: Basic molecular features. Pure Appl. Chem. 61, 1293–1306.

Raju, R.K., Ramraj, A., Hillier, I.H., Vincent, M.A., Burton, N.A., 2009. Carbohydrate-aromatic pi interactions: A test of density functionals and the DFT-D method. Phys. Chem. Chem. Phys. 11, 3411–3416.

Reina, J.J., Diaz, I., Nieto, P.M., et al., 2008. Docking, synthesis, and NMR studies of mannosyl trisaccharide ligands for DC-SIGN lectin. Org. Biomol. Chem. 6, 2743–2754.

Samsonov, S.A., Teyra, J., Pisabarro, M.T., 2011. Docking glycosaminoglycans to proteins: Analysis of solvent inclusion. J. Comput. Aided Mol. Des. 25, 477–489.

Shewell, L.K., Harvey, R.M., Higgins, M.A., et al., 2014. The cholesterol-dependent cytolysins pneumolysin and streptolysin O require binding to red blood cell glycans for hemolytic activity. Proc. Natl. Acad. Sci. USA 111, E5312–E5320.

Shionyu-Mitsuyama, C., Shirai, T., Ishida, H., Yamane, T., 2003. An empirical approach for structure-based prediction of carbohydrate-binding sites on proteins. Protein Eng. 16, 467–478.

Shu, N., Zhou, T., Hovmoller, S., 2008. Prediction of zinc-binding sites in proteins from sequence. Bioinformatics 24, 775–782.

Spiwok, V., Lipovova, P., Skalova, T., et al., 2005. Modelling of carbohydrate-aromatic interactions: Ab initio energetics and force field performance. J. Comput. Aided Mol. Des. 19, 887–901.

Spiwok, V., 2017. CH/pi interactions in carbohydrate recognition. Molecules 22.

Sujatha, M.S., Balaji, P.V., 2004. Identification of common structural features of binding sites in galactose-specific proteins. Proteins 55, 44–65.

Suresh, M.X., Gromiha, M.M., Suwa, M., 2015. Development of a machine learning method to predict membrane protein-ligand binding residues using basic sequence information. Adv. Bioinform. 2015, 843030.

Taherzadeh, G., Zhou, Y., Liew, A.W., Yang, Y., 2016. Sequence-based prediction of protein-carbohydrate binding sites using support vector machines. J. Chem. Inf. Model. 56, 2115–2122.

Takaoka, T., Mori, K., Okimoto, N., Neya, S., Hoshino, T., 2007. Prediction of the structure of complexes comprised of proteins and glycosaminoglycans using docking simulation and cluster analysis. J. Chem. Theory Comput. 3, 2347–2356.

Taroni, C., Jones, S., Thornton, J.M., 2000. Analysis and prediction of carbohydrate binding sites. Protein Eng. 13, 89–98.

Tessier, M.B., Demarco, M.L., Yongye, A.B., Woods, R.J., 2008. Extension of the GLYCAM06 biomolecular force field to lipids, lipid bilayers and glycolipids. Mol. Simul. 34, 349–363.

Trott, O., Olson, A.J., 2010. AutoDock Vina: Improving the speed and accuracy of docking with a new scoring function, efficient optimization, and multithreading. J. Comput. Chem. 31, 455–461.

Tsai, K.C., Jian, J.W., Yang, E.W., et al., 2012. Prediction of carbohydrate binding sites on protein surfaces with 3-dimensional probability density distributions of interacting atoms. PLOS ONE 7, e40846.

Vandenbussche, S., Diaz, D., Fernandez-Alonso, M.C., et al., 2008. Aromatic-carbohydrate interactions: An NMR and computational study of model systems. Chemistry 14, 7570–7578.

Verdonk, M.L., Cole, J.C., Hartshorn, M.J., Murray, C.W., Taylor, R.D., 2003. Improved protein-ligand docking using GOLD. Proteins 52, 609–623.

Vital De Oliveira, O., 2014. Molecular dynamics and metadynamics simulations of the cellulase Cel48F. Enzyme Res. 2014, 692738.

Walker, A.R., Bonomi, R., Popov, V., Gelovani, J.G., Andres Cisneros, G., 2017. Investigating carbohydrate based ligands for galectin-3 with docking and molecular dynamics studies. J. Mol. Graph. Model. 71, 211–217.

Wang, D., Liu, S., Trummer, B.J., Deng, C., Wang, A., 2002. Carbohydrate microarrays for the recognition of cross-reactive molecular markers of microbes and host cells. Nat. Biotechnol. 20, 275–281.

Wang, L., Brown, S.J., 2006. BindN: A web-based tool for efficient prediction of DNA and RNA binding sites in amino acid sequences. Nucleic Acids Res. 34, W243–W248.

Xiong, X., Chen, Z., Cossins, B.P., et al., 2015. Force fields and scoring functions for carbohydrate simulation. Carbohydr. Res. 401, 73–81.

Yang, Y., Zhan, J., Zhao, H., Zhou, Y., 2012. A new size-independent score for pairwise protein structure alignment and its application to structure classification and nucleic-acid binding prediction. Proteins 80, 2080–2088.

Yang, Y., Zhou, Y., 2008. Ab initio folding of terminal segments with secondary structures reveals the fine difference between two closely related all-atom statistical energy functions. Protein Sci. 17, 1212–1219.

Zhang, J., Kitova, E.N., Li, J., et al., 2016. Localizing carbohydrate binding sites in proteins using hydrogen/deuterium exchange mass spectrometry. J. Am. Soc. Mass Spectrom. 27, 83–90.

Zhao, H., Yang, Y., Von Itzstein, M., Zhou, Y., 2014. Carbohydrate-binding protein identification by coupling structural similarity searching with binding affinity prediction. J. Comput. Chem. 35, 2177–2183.

Zhou, H., Zhou, Y., 2002. Distance-scaled, finite ideal-gas reference state improves structure-derived potentials of mean force for structure selection and stability prediction. Protein Sci. 11, 2714–2726.

Zhou, H.X., Shan, Y., 2001. Prediction of protein interaction sites from sequence profile and residue neighbor list. Proteins 44, 336–343.

Zvelebil, M.J., Barton, G.J., Taylor, W.R., Sternberg, M.J., 1987. Prediction of protein secondary structure and active sites using the alignment of homologous sequences. J. Mol. Biol. 195, 957–961.

Relevant Websites

www.ball-project.org
   BALL Project.

http://www.procarb.org/procarbdb/
   PROCARB HOME.

https://zenodo.org/record/61513#.WcB-4hdLeis
   SBRP: sbrp I Zenodo.

https://sites.google.com/site/sukantamondal/software
   Software – Sukanta MONDAL– Google Sites.

Computational Prediction of Nucleic Acid Binding Residues From Sequence

Nur SA Ghani and Mohd Firdaus-Raih, Universiti Kebangsaan Malaysia, Bangi, Malaysia
Shandar Ahmad, Jawaharlal Nehru University, New Delhi, India

Introduction and Background

Protein–nucleic acid interactions play key roles in many biological processes. In a large group of such events, the binding of the proteins to their respective nucleic acid counterpart affects some regulatory outcome such as transcriptional and translational regulation and protein synthesis. Activation of an immune system in response to pathogen invasion is another example in which specific nucleic acid compositions of pathogens are recognized as the first step in a complex biological pathway. Approximately 21% of proteins are denoted as nucleic acid binding, based on UniprotKB/SwissProt database (Boutet *et al.*, 2007). Nucleic acid binding proteins are mostly composed of at least one DNA/RNA-binding domain where the interfacing with amino acids take place in specific or nonspecific manner.

DNA-binding proteins (DBPs), such as transcription factors, DNA polymerases, DNA ligases, some Toll like receptors, and methyltransferases can be represented by various DNA-binding domains carrying different molecular functions. Common DNA-binding domains include the zinc finger, helix-turn-helix, leucine zipper, and helix-loop-helix domains. On the other hand, many RNA-binding proteins are important for posttranscriptional regulation (Glisovic *et al.*, 2008) and the regulation of gene expression (Ray *et al.*, 2013). One or more RNA-binding domains facilitate the formation of protein–RNA interfaces. This includes RNA recognition motifs such as the K Homology motif, RGG box motif, and DEAD/DEAH box domain (Lunde *et al.*, 2007).

While proteins adopt different mechanisms for both DNA- and RNA-binding activity, general methods of detecting binding residues, before the crystal structure of a complex is solved, are useful to comprehend the molecular recognition capacity and interface mechanics and hence designing molecular interventions. Experimental methods like X-ray crystallography and nuclear magnetic resonance have been used to determine the structures of numerous protein–nucleic acid complexes and these structures have greatly contributed to the understanding of what constitutes as protein–nucleic acid interfaces and favorable modes of interactions in the structural context.

Such experimental methods lead to the steady growth in the numbers of protein–nucleic acid complexes deposited into the Protein Data Bank (Rose *et al.*, 2017). As of September 2017, the database contains entries for 4317 and 2290 protein–DNA and protein–RNA complexes, respectively. Experimental methods of determining protein–nucleic acid interactions are time-consuming and expensive. Furthermore, experimental approaches will not be able to cope with the ever-increasing number of protein sequences requiring annotation for their potential nucleic acid binding ability. It is also not possible to solve the crystal structure of every homolog for every NA-binding protein, even though small sequence-level changes may significantly alter the interaction dynamics. Hence, computational platforms for prediction of nucleic acid binding sites from sequence can provide an alternative that can be just as reliable to analyze protein–nucleic acid interactions.

Over the years, a number of computational tools have been developed for the prediction of DNA/RNA-binding residues in sequence data. Here, we survey a selection of such tools that are available as web services. Our focus in this article is to compare web servers in terms of: (i) the data they use as the input during training and subsequent use by researchers; (ii) the engine that drives their predictions: (iii) the kind of output they generate; and (iv) the performance levels claimed during their publications, some of which we have benchmarked for a quick estimate of their relative advantage. Such reviews are also available in the literature as part of other studies but with a growing number of new tools and perspectives that can be developed, we feel that an overview in a nutshell for reference purposes is needed. We have structured our discussion into four parts. First, we take a look at the user interaction of the tools for binding site predictions. Particularly, we discuss the user inputs and output formats in each of the available tools. Subsequently, we look at the techniques used in developing these prediction methods, including the datasets and the features for data driven models. Then, we describe the performance scores and evaluation strategies of binding site prediction tools and discuss the challenges therein. Finally, we present some case studies and discuss how users can get the best out of multiple prediction tools available over the web.

Computational Tools for Nucleic Acid Binding Prediction: The User Perspective

Detection of amino acids that interact with nucleic acids from protein sequence can be most useful as well as challenging when no structural information is available. A number of computational platforms have been developed for predicting DNA-binding residues from sequence, such as DP-Bind (Hwang *et al.*, 2007), DQPred-DBR (Chai *et al.*, 2016), TargetDNA (Hu *et al.*, 2016), and DRNAPred (Yan and Kurgan, 2017). Some of the methods to predict RNA-binding site/residues from protein sequence include DRNAPred (Yan and Kurgan, 2017), AaRNA (Li *et al.*, 2014), PRIdictor (Tuvshinjargal *et al.*, 2016), RNABindRPlus (Walia *et al.*, 2014), RNABindR (Walia *et al.*, 2012), and SRCPred (Fernandez *et al.*, 2011). AaRNA and SRCPred are also able to predict dinucleotide contacts. These methods allow for the rapid detection of amino acids that are thought to be interacting with nucleic acids. In some cases, users are interested in specific DNA or RNA-binding predictions and the use of different tools may provide overlapping predictions. Some tools are developed with this deconvolutionary objective in mind. **Table 1** summarizes the list of selected tools for the prediction together with their descriptions while **Table 2** provides a comparison of the features and capability of each service.

Server Inputs and Formats

Most prediction methods require a protein sequence in the FASTA format or single code amino acid sequence as the query by either pasting them or uploading the file(s). The ability of several programs – DRNAPred, RNABindRPlus and RNABindR to rapidly predict DNA-binding residues for a batch of protein sequences provide them an advantage in contrast with other prediction methods. Amino acid sequences of desired proteins can be culled from protein chains in the Protein Data Bank (Rose *et al.*, 2017) or protein sequence databases like NCBI RefSeq (Pruitt *et al.*, 2007) and SwissProt (Bairoch and Apweiler, 2000). In an unlikely scenario, when users only have a PDB-formatted protein structure, various programming scripts and PDB-related web servers can be used to extract amino acid sequence from SEQRES records found in the PDB file, such as ccPDB (Singh *et al.*, 2012), PDBFINDER (Touw *et al.*, 2015) and PISCES (Wang and Dunbrack, 2003) web servers.

Output and Average Time for Computations

The time for the computation to be completed is often influenced by the list of queries submitted to the server at a given time. A prediction conducted for a single protein sequence could take a few minutes on average to be completed, where the output is either submitted to an email address or displayed on the web server directly upon job completion. The predictions conducted by these web servers mostly return binding propensities, with the predicted probability values and binary label for each amino acid in the sequence, commonly termed as "0" for nonbinding or "1" for binding.

Methodologies Behind Binding Site Prediction Tools

Training Datasets

Protein–nucleic acid contact data

Protein structure datasets play a crucial role in the development of prediction methods for protein–nucleic acid interfaces. Methods that predict nucleic acid binding residues are commonly trained and tested upon a set of nucleic acid binding residues with a distinct definition of contacts. The contact data are derived from proteins known to bind to nucleic acids, either from protein–nucleic acid complexes or annotated DNA/RNA-binding proteins. Protein structures are retrieved from the Protein Data Bank (Rose *et al.*, 2017) and certain filters are applied before training them. In most cases, refinements are carried out based on (1) structure quality, that is, X-ray crystallography determined structures at high resolution; and (2) sequence identity with distinct cutoff values to generate nonredundant structures/folds. The datasets generated by each prediction tool might also differ from one another according to different exclusion criteria such as exclusion of proteins with inadequate residue lengths (Li *et al.*, 2014; Walia *et al.*, 2012), and the removal of residues with missing coordinates (Hwang *et al.*, 2007; Yan and Kurgan, 2017).

Different annotations of protein–nucleic acid interactions at the residue level have been used to generate a sample pool containing binding residues for the training of prediction methods. The binding interfaces are defined by the maximal distance between amino acids to any atom from the nucleic acid. One often-used definition for a binding residue is that any amino acid

Table 1   Computational programs for sequence-based DNA/RNA-binding residue prediction

Prediction	Service/ program	Description
DBR	DP-Bind	A sequence-based prediction method using three different machine learning methods to generate a consensus prediction of DNA-binding residues (Hwang *et al.*, 2007); (http://lcg.rit.albany.edu/dp-bind/)
	DQPred-DBR	An evolution-based prediction method using dynamic model to detect DNA-binding residues (Chai *et al.*, 2016) (http://www.inforstation.com/webservers/DQPred-DBR/predict.html)
	TargetDNA	A SVM-based method using weighted evolutionary profiles to target protein–DNA binding residues (Hu *et al.*, 2016) (http://csbio.njust.edu.cn:8080/TargetDNA/)
DBR/RBR	DRNAPred	A combined prediction method for DNA- and RNA-binding residues using sequence and structural features based on protein sequence (Yan and Kurgan, 2017) (http://biomine.cs.vcu.edu/servers/DRNApred/)
RBR	AaRNA	A sequence and structure-based prediction method for RNA-binding propensity using homology modeling and neural networks (Li *et al.*, 2004) (https://sysimm.ifrec.osaka-u.ac.jp/aarna/)
	PRIdictor	A sequence-based method to predict protein–RNA interfaces from RNA and protein sequences according to global and local features (Tuvshinjargal *et al.*, 2016) (http://bclab.inha.ac.kr/pridictor/pridictor.html)
	RNABindRPlus	A combined homology and SVM-based prediction method using evolutionary profile to locate RNA-binding residues (Walia *et al.*, 2014) (http://ailab1.ist.psu.edu/RNABindRPlus/)
	RNABindR	A protein–RNA interface prediction tool that combine naïve Bayes and SVM methods using both sequence and structural features from protein sequence (Walia *et al.*, 2012) (http://ailab1.ist.psu.edu/RNABindR/)
	SRCPred	A PSSM-based prediction tool for RNA dinucleotide contacts in protein sequence using neural networks (Fernandez *et al.*, 2011) (http://ccbb.jnu.ac.in/shandar/servers/srcpred/)

Source: A listing of nine web servers aimed for the prediction of nucleic acid binding residue using sequence-based methods.

Table 2　Comparison of different computational programs for prediction of nucleic acid binding residues

	Program/service name								SRCpred
	DP-Bind	DQPred-DBR	TargetDNA	DRNAPred	AaRNA	PRIdictor	RNABindPlus	RNABindR	
Input query									
FASTA-formatted/one letter code protein sequence	✓	✓	✓	✓	✓	✓	✓	✓	✓
Nucleic acid sequence						✓			
Allows multiple sequences				✓			✓	✓	
PDB structure					✓				
User-defined method/threshold value	✓	✓	✓						
Prediction approach									
Dynamic model		✓							
Support vector machine (SVM)	✓	✓	✓			✓	✓	✓	
Logistic regression				✓			✓		
Naïve Bayes								✓	
Neural networks					✓				✓
Hidden Markov model				✓	✓				
Homology-based method		✓					✓		
Training datasets									
Protein Data Bank (PDB)	✓	✓	✓	✓	✓	✓	✓	✓	✓
Protein sequences	✓			✓					
Type of sequence-based prediction									
Predict DBS/DBR	✓	✓	✓	✓					
Predict RBS/RBR				✓	✓	✓	✓	✓	✓
Dinucleotide contacts					✓				✓
Use sequence features	✓	✓		✓	✓	✓	✓	✓	✓
Use structural features	✓			✓		✓		✓	✓
Sequence-derived features									
Sequence features									
PSSM-based evolutionary conservation score	✓	✓	✓				✓	✓	✓
Non-PSSM-based evolutionary conservation score	✓			✓	✓		✓	✓	
Sequence neighborhood				✓	✓			✓	✓
Physicochemical and biochemical properties				✓	✓	✓			✓
Structural features									
Spatial neighborhood	✓							✓	
Interaction propensity						✓			
Solvent accessibility	✓		✓	✓		✓			✓
Predicted secondary structure	✓			✓					
Predicted intrinsic disorder				✓					
Performance measures									
Accuracy	✓	✓	✓			✓			
Area under the ROC curve (AUC)		✓		✓	✓				✓
F-measure					✓		✓	✓	
Matthews correlation coefficient (MCC)		✓	✓	✓	✓	✓	✓	✓	
Precision			✓		✓				
Sensitivity	✓	✓	✓	✓	✓	✓	✓	✓	✓
Specificity	✓	✓	✓	✓	✓	✓	✓	✓	✓
Output									
Prediction score	✓	✓	✓	✓	✓	✓	✓	✓	✓
Binary labeled amino acid	✓	✓	✓	✓	✓	✓	✓	✓	✓
A set of homologous proteins						✓	✓		
Downloadable output file	✓	✓	✓	✓	✓	✓	✓	✓	✓

Source: A comparison of nine web servers for nucleic acid binding residue prediction in terms of their input, prediction approach, data set, and output.

residue with a distance of less than 3.5 Å to any nucleic acid atom is treated to be in the interface. This definition has been used by DBSPred, SDCPred, DBS-PSSM, DRNAPred, AaRNA, and SRCPred web servers (Ahmad et al., 2004; Andrabi et al., 2009; Ahmad and Sarai, 2005; Yan and Kurgan, 2017; Li et al., 2014; Fernandez et al., 2011) with Fernandez et al. (2011) additionally integrating the annotation of RNA-binding motifs retrieved from the SCOR database (Hubbard and Thornton, 1993). Tuvshinjargal et al. (2016) (PRIdictor), on the other hand, defined protein–nucleic acid interaction in a more specific way that involved three different types of intermolecular forces including hydrogen bonds, hydrophobic forces and water-mediated contacts – As retrieved from Nucleic acid–Protein Interaction Database (Kirsanov et al., 2013).

Protein sequences

Most prediction methods rely on experimentally determined crystal structures of protein–nucleic acid complexes. Such high resolution datasets provide binding or nonbinding information at a single residue level. On the other hand long stretches of amino acids are annotated as NA-binding in sequence datasets, which is useful in discriminating binding domains. Some NA-binding site prediction methods have also used such annotations to evaluate the prediction at the proteome scale. Examples of this are the use of nonredundant protein sequences from NCBI in the work of Hwang et al. (2007) and human protein sequences from UniProt database and several curated databases as adopted by Yan and Kurgan (2017). Programs that implement a homology-based method like DQPred-DBR and RNABindPlus generate their training sets of known binding residues obtained from sequence homologs of the query proteins searched against the Protein–RNA Interface Database (PRIDB) (Lewis et al., 2011) and SwissProt (Bairoch and Apweiler, 2000), respectively.

Prediction Algorithms

Machine learning methods

Machine learning methods are commonly employed on other problems of sequence-based structure and function predictions in proteins (Al-Shahib et al., 2007), for example, secondary structure prediction (Wang et al., 2016) and prediction of interfaces for protein–protein complexes (Sun et al., 2017). These methods have also been adapted to predict protein–nucleic acid interactions (Hwang et al., 2007; Chai et al., 2016; Hu et al., 2016). Prediction models based on these machine learning methods are trained and tested with benchmark datasets of known class labels (binding or nonbinding) and a variety of prediction features usually derived from sliding windows over the whole sequence. These methods include neural networks (Li et al., 2014; Ahmad and Sarai, 2005; Ahmad et al., 2004; Fernandez et al., 2011), support vector machines (SVMs) (Hwang et al., 2007; Chai et al., 2016; Hu et al., 2016; Tuvshinjargal et al., 2016; Walia et al., 2014, 2012), naïve Bayes (Walia et al., 2012); random forest (Ma et al., 2011), logistic regression models (Yan and Kurgan, 2017; Walia et al., 2014), and hidden Markov models (Yan and Kurgan, 2017; Li et al., 2014).

Artificial neural network (ANN) models typically contain three *layers*- the input, hidden, and output layers - where each layer is made up of a designed number of *nodes* according to the features used for prediction (Lancashire et al., 2009). SVM is another popular technique adopted to predict nucleic acid binding residues, where it was shown to outperform other machine learning methods apparently due to its ability to develop more robust models. An SVM-based prediction model is based on trained parameters of a kernel, which assigns class labels to new data. In the case of binding residue prediction, the prediction model is trained and tested with sets of annotated binding residues (positive class samples) and/or nonbinding residues (negative class samples), where they learn to classify objects from known data and compare with expected output in a supervised manner.

Most prediction methods on the web receive a set of amino acids in the form of a vector as the input, yield a binding propensity for individual residue in the sequence that indicates probability of target residue to be in a particular class, and at given thresholds generate a binary label for each residue.

Alignment-based methods

Alignment-based methods can be useful to predict protein–nucleic acid interactions when similar NA-binding sequences are available for the query sequence, since binding residues are often conserved among similar proteins. As an example of such approaches, Walia et al. (2014) combined HomPRIP, a homology-based method and SVM to predict RNA-binding residues in protein sequences. They defined the conservation of residues as an interface conservation (IC) score, that is, the degree of conservation of residues in the query protein as compared to its sequence homologs. These scores were derived from pairwise sequence alignments. The program first searches for sequence homologs using BLAST against PRIDB, calculates an IC score for each sequence homolog, and later assigns putative binding residues based on the known binding residues annotated in homologs. Another prediction program, DQPred-DBR, generates a dynamic sample to train the SVM-based prediction model, which includes a set of binding residues derived from sequence homologs of the query protein, searched against the SwissProt database. Alignment-based methods are intuitive and powerful but are greatly dependent on similarity thresholds. Lower similarity thresholds result in a lesser number of initial samples for prediction. When no homologs can be detected for the query protein, there is no choice but to use a method developed using a sliding window approach, employed in almost all the other methods described in this article.

Discriminative Features in Data Driven Models

A combination of features obtained from protein sequences are used to train and evaluate the performance of prediction models. These features include evolutionary information, sequence features within a window, structural features, and physical or biochemical features. Commonly used features for protein–nucleic acid interactions that are extracted from sequence only information include evolutionary information from PSSM, neighboring residues, accessible surface area (ASA), and secondary structure prediction.

Sequence features
Evolutionary conservation
Evolutionary conservation in the form of position specific scoring matrices (PSSMs) essentially indicates the probability of each residue to be conserved in a specific position of the sequence (Ahmad and Sarai, 2005). However, it goes beyond simple conservation as it also accounts for specific substitution patterns, which provides it with clues to characterize each position. These features have been used with the assumption that most binding sites are conserved to some extent. The substitution profiles of specific NA-binding residues should reflect a particular trend so as not to lose the binding capacity and this pattern can be captured by a machine learning model such as a neural network. Thus, PSSM is perhaps the most popular representation of sequence information for predicting binding sites. A large number of prediction programs use evolutionary information in the form of PSSM, including DP-Bind, DQPred-DBR, TargetDNA, RNABindPlus, RNABindR, and SRCPred.

PSSM profiles are generally obtained from PSI-BLAST searches of the query protein against a sequence database and a Nx20 matrix is obtained representing the substitution probability of individual residues to all other amino acid types in a given length of the sequence. Ahmad and Sarai (2005) proved that evolutionary information from PSSM is a powerful feature to discriminate binding and nonbinding residues and this was similarly suggested by Hwang *et al.* (2007) where the accuracy of prediction increased when using PSSM profiles alone or when combined with structural features.

Sequence neighborhood
Residue nearest neighbors can influence prediction, with the assumption that a network of residues is required for the protein to bind to nucleic acid residues (Yan and Kurgan, 2017; Miao and Westhof, 2015). Thus, residues with high propensity sequence neighbors would be more likely to bind to nucleic acids. Some prediction methods include sequential neighbors of target residues as one of the features for prediction using sliding windows of size $2N + 1$ where N represents nearest neighbors on either side (Walia *et al.*, 2012). Yan and Kurgan (2017) defined nearest neighbors using a sliding window of size 3 (one neighbor on each side); Li *et al.* (2014) used a sliding window of size 5 (2 contiguous residues on each side); Walia *et al.* (2012) used a sliding window of 25 for 12 sequential residues on each side; and Fernandez *et al.* (2011) used varying sizes of sliding windows for 1–8 sequence neighbors.

Structural features
The use of structural features such as solvent accessibility and secondary structure can also assist in the prediction of protein––nucleic acid interactions. Such low resolution structure information can either be derived from a solved protein structure or taken from another sequence-based prediction program, as discussed below.

(1) *Solvent accessibility*
  A protein's binding activities typically occur via their exposed surfaces. Binding residues are more likely to reside in the exposed area, rather than in buried regions. Some methods include predicted solvent accessibility as one of the features used in the prediction (Yan and Kurgan, 2017; Hwang *et al.*, 2007; Tuvshinjargal *et al.*, 2016; Hu *et al.*, 2016). TargetDNA uses SANN (Joo *et al.*, 2012) to predict solvent accessibility using sequence neighborhood and classify each residue into three classes – Buried, intermediate, and exposed residue; DPbind uses information on accessible surface area derived from a DSSP profile (Kabsch and Sander, 1983) in which higher ASA values represent a higher degree of exposure for target residues, and residues below a defined threshold value are annotated as "surface accessible residue"; SRCPred uses ASA information from NACCESS (Hubbard and Thornton, 1993); DRNApred combines several prediction tools to predict solvent accessibility from sequence using PROFphd (Rost and Sander, 1994), NETASA (Ahmad and Gromiha, 2002), and RVP-net (Ahmad *et al.*, 2003).

(2) *Secondary structure*
  Secondary structure preferences for DNA/RNA-binding sites may also influence the prediction. The DSSP program is able to calculate hydrogen bonds and label predicted secondary structure elements for each residue, including beta sheets, alpha helices, and turns. A PSI-blast based secondary structure prediction method, PSIPRED (McGuffin *et al.*, 2000), is used by DRNApred to assist the prediction. The program adopts neural networks to predict secondary structure from protein sequence based on the evolutionary conservation profile.

Evaluating Confidence Levels of Predictions

Accuracy, Sensitivity, and Specificity

A number of measures, such as accuracy, specificity, F-measure, MCC, receiving operating characteristics (ROC) curve, and the area under the ROC curve (AUROC) have been used to evaluate the performance of prediction models for making correct classification of unseen data during testing (**Table 3**). The raw data generated from predictions are presented in the confusion matrix (Sokolova *et al.*, 2006), which also encode values for true positive (TP), true negative (TN), false positive (FP), and false negative (FN). Values in the confusion matrix are used to calculate the performance measures like accuracy, sensitivity, and specificity, which are some good measures used to evaluate the correctness of the prediction, whether binding residue is correctly identified as such. Accuracy measures the proportion of correctly classified samples against all samples. This is generally not a good measure if the class labels are not equally distributed as in the NA-binding site data. A high accuracy may simply indicate that more residues are labeled in the more populated class (nonbinding). Sensitivity ($TP/(TP + FN)$) measures the true positive rate by calculating true positive samples against the total number of false negative and true positive samples, that is, the proportion of binding residues that are correctly identified. A highly sensitive model for NA-binding sites leads to many residues wrongly labeled to be binding. Specificity, on the other hand, measures the true negative rate by calculating true negative against the total number of true negative and false positive samples that is, the proportion of nonbinding residues that are predicted as such. The F-measure is a harmonic mean of sensitivity and specificity, and MCC can provide a more balanced performance estimate of a prediction model. A comparison of the prediction capability of each tool in **Table 1** is provided in **Table 3**.

Area Under the ROC Curve

Sensitivity and specificity of prediction models can typically be adjusted by a threshold as the predictions are usually on a continuous scale between 0 and 1. To gain a model performance estimate over its full range of predicted scores, the ROC is used. ROC curves can be built between various combinations such as precision recall (P-R curve) or as a plot of true positive rate (sensitivity) represented on the y-axis and true negative rate (1-specificity) on the x-axis, indicating sensitivity/specificity pairs at different threshold values (Sokolova *et al.*, 2006; Fawcett, 2006). AUROC curve can be used to measure accuracy based on a ROC curve. AUROC quantifies to what extent a classifier can make accurate estimates of data labels at various thresholds (Fawcett, 2006).

It may be noted that the prediction scores from different methods may not be directly comparable to each other due to distinct datasets and cross-validation strategies used by individual methods. Therefore, when choosing a method for a new dataset, careful understanding of reported performance levels may be needed.

Illustrative Example(s) or Case Studies

To demonstrate the utility of web servers in identifying DNA- and RNA-binding residues, we have tested a selection of them using individual query sequences derived from protein–nucleic acid complexes – A human transcription factor in complex with double-stranded DNA (PDBID: 5fd3, Chain B) (Marceau *et al.*, 2016) and a human E3 ubiquitin ligase bound to an RNA molecule (PDBID: 5www, Chain A) (Yang *et al.*, 2017). It is clear that most prediction servers can estimate the interface residues in the test protein sequences with high accuracy with small differences in performance.

Prediction of DNA-Binding Residues

The crystal structure of DNA-binding protein Lin54 bound to its DNA promoter (PDBID: 5fd3) was solved with the residues involved in DNA recognition for the cell cycle genes homology region sequence clearly characterized (Marceau *et al.*, 2016). A

Table 3   Evaluation of the prediction of binding residues using different prediction methods

Prediction	TP	FP	TN	FN	SN	SP	ACC	F-m	MCC
DNA-binding residue prediction									
DP-Bind	12	23	115	4	0.75	0.83	0.83	0.47	0.42
TargetDNA	11	8	111	5	0.69	**0.93**	**0.90**	**0.63**	**0.58**
DRNAPred	14	36	83	2	**0.88**	0.70	0.72	0.42	0.38
DQPred-DBR	14	32	87	2	0.88	0.73	0.75	0.45	0.41
RNA-binding residue prediction									
AaRNA	5	1	73	15	0.25	**0.99**	**0.83**	**0.38**	**0.40**
DRNAPred	3	15	59	17	0.15	0.80	0.66	0.16	−0.05
PRIdictor	2	2	72	18	0.10	0.97	0.79	0.17	0.15
RNABindR	8	36	38	12	**0.40**	0.51	0.49	0.25	−0.07
RNABindRPlus	3	3	71	17	0.15	0.96	0.79	0.23	0.18
SRCPred	7	21	53	13	0.35	0.72	0.64	0.29	0.06

Source: Prediction of DNA- and RNA-binding residue using different prediction methods – DP-Bind (annotation propensities of ≥ 0.5 for major consensus prediction); TargetDNA (FPR $\approx$ 5%, annotation propensities of ≥ 0.05); DRNAPred (propensities > 0.4727 and > 0.1493 for DNA- and RNA-binding residue annotation); DQPred-DBR (similarity threshold of 0.7 and prediction threshold of 0.5, annotation propensities of ≥ 0.5); AaRNA (annotation propensities of ≥ 0.5); PRIdictor (annotation propensities of ≥ 0.5); RNABindR (annotation propensities of ≥ 0.5); RNABindRPlus (annotation propensities of ≥ 0.5); and SRCPred (annotation propensities of ≥ 0.05 for at least one dinucleotide contact). TP = True Positive, FP = False Positive, TN = True Negative, FN = False Negative, SN = Sensitivity, SP = Specificity, ACC = Accuracy, F-m = F-measure, MCC = Matthews Correlation Coefficient. Highest value for each column is highlighted in bold.

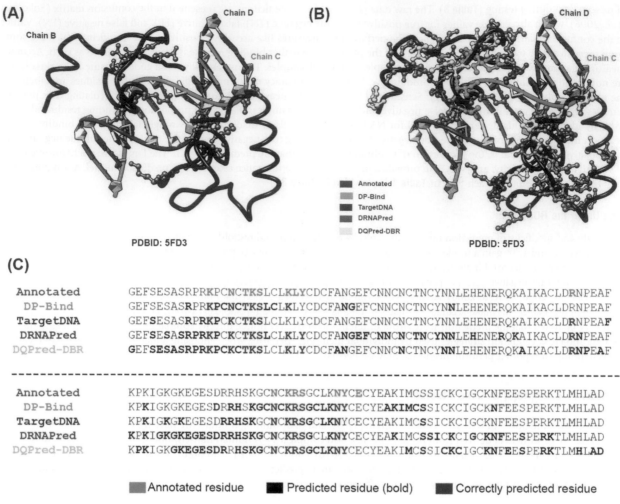

Fig. 1 Prediction of DNA-binding residues for a human transcription factor sequence. (A) A crystal structure of Lin54 protein containing tesmin domain (Chain B) bound to double-stranded DNA (Chain C and D) (PDBID: 5FD3), with annotated binding residues highlighted in orange color. (B) Predicted binding residues from different prediction tools depicted in the structure. Binding residues are shown in ball and stick representation. (C) Prediction of binding residues from the query sequence containing 134 amino acids. Annotated binding residues is colored in green, predicted binding residue in bold letter, and residue that is correctly predicted as binding is colored in red.

BLAST search against the PDB yielded no other structure with a similar sequence, while searching against the UniProtKB/SwissProt database retrieved similarities to tesmin and cysteine-rich (CXC) domain-containing proteins. Sixteen of the 135 residues in Lin54 are involved in protein–DNA contacts through hydrogen bonds and van der Waals interactions. All tested prediction tools correctly predicted at least 10 residues out of the 16 annotated binding residues (**Fig. 1**).

Prediction of RNA-Binding Residues

KH domains are known to bind RNA and are important for posttranscriptional activities. The KH-RNA binding interfaces could be observed in the structure of a KH1 domain of human RNA-binding E3 ubiquitin-protein ligase MEX-3C complex with RNA (PDB ID: 5www). **Fig. 2** illustrates the annotations derived from the experimental data (**Fig. 2(B)**) and the comparison between predicted binding residues from different prediction tools (**Fig. 2(C–H)**). Results indicate lower performance of most prediction methods for RNA-binding residue prediction compared to methods for DNA-binding residue prediction. All methods correctly predicted at least two binding residues from 20 annotated binding residues.

NA-binding residues are usually conserved among homologous proteins. Most prediction methods include annotations from representative protein–nucleic acid complexes in the training sets. Querying for a protein sequence with adequate sequence similarity (sequence identity of more than 30%) to any of the proteins in training datasets would more likely infer binding residues similarly as that of its homologs. Protein sequences used for both case studies however lack such sequence similarities to protein–nucleic acid complexes in the PDB. In both cases, all prediction methods successfully discriminate binding and non-binding residues, regardless of their extent of correctly predicting real binding residues. In such a scenario, the use of PSSM profiles

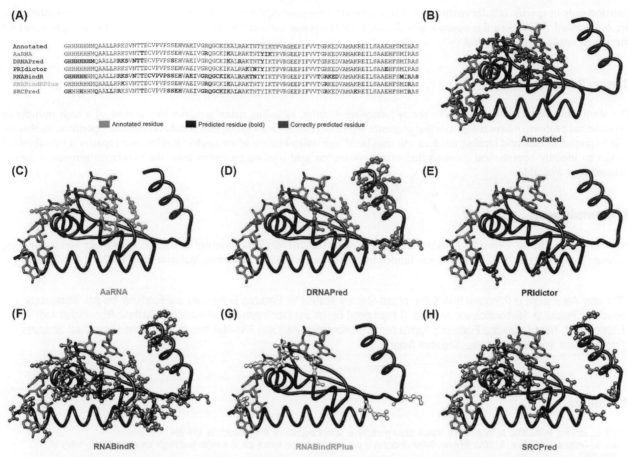

Fig. 2 Protein–RNA interactions in a KH domain protein predicted by different prediction tools. (A) A comparison of binding residues predicted from the query sequence containing 94 amino acids. Annotated binding residues is colored in green, predicted binding residue in bold letter, and residue that is correctly predicted as binding is colored in red. (B) A crystal structure of KH domain from human E3 ubiquitin ligase, with annotated RNA-binding residues colored in orange. (C–H) Predicted binding residues for RNA sequence annotated from different prediction web servers are shown in the structural context, in order, AaRNA, DRNAPred, PRIdictor, RNABindR, RNABindRPlus, and SRCPred. Binding residues are indicated in ball and stick atom representation.

could improve predictions, as similarly suggested by Walia *et al.* (2012), since evolutionary information for the query protein is retrieved from a larger number of protein sequences compared to the amount of annotated protein structures. Other than that, the definition of contacts used by individual methods could contribute to the performance variations observed. For example, DP-Bind uses a larger cut-off value of 4.5 Å compared to typical distance cut-off value of 3.5 Å adopted by several methods like AaRNA, DQPred, and DRNAPred, thus creating a larger pool of positive samples.

Discussion and Future Directions

Most of the prediction methods highlighted in this article were intended to determine putative residues important for protein––nucleic acid interaction from protein sequence in the absence of prior annotation for nucleic acid binding or sequence homology. Most prediction methods have been designed with a broad selection of features that include evolutionary conservation, amino acid composition, sequence neighborhood, solvent accessibility, and secondary structure, that have been incorporated into well-established prediction models like neural networks and SVMs. Despite the dependence of these methods on the smaller pool of experimental protein structures, they perform reliable discrimination of binding and nonbinding residues with the assumption that nucleic acid binding interfaces can be similar among proteins of the same group. These methods may potentially be useful to determine novel nucleic acid binding proteins on a proteome level, especially in the case of proteins of unknown function, or proteins for which their ability to bind to nucleic acids has yet to be characterized. Another potential application would be to identify residues for docking simulations to visualize the interactions between proposed binding residues for predicted protein structures or structures believed to be DNA/RNA-binding but solved without the nucleic acid partner present. One perspective that could be of great interest for research in this area is the context dependent functional annotations. In this direction, a breakthrough of sorts has recently appeared in the works of Ahmad *et al.* (2017) in which they have argued that some DBPs might acquire their function only in specific cellular environments represented by the gene expression levels of their source gene and also others that are coexpressed. We believe this opens a new direction for functional annotations not only for nucleic acid binding but also for functional annotations in general.

Closing Remarks

The abundance of protein sequences in the sequence repositories, including many genomes that consist of a high number of hypothetical proteins, makes computational sequence level tools useful for assigning functional annotations. Specific tools that are able to predict nucleic acid binding residues will thus be of high utility in cases where nucleic acid binding capacity is hypothesized and/or to identify hypothetical proteins that may have nucleic acid binding capability from the numerous genome sequence datasets now available.

Acknowledgments

MFR was funded by the Universiti Kebangsaan Malaysia grant DIP-2017-013 and Ministry of Science, Technology and Innovation, Malaysia grant 02-01-02-SF1278; NSAG was funded by the Ministry of Higher Education, Malaysia grant LEP2.0/14/UKM/BT/02/2.

See also: Applications of Ribosomal RNA Sequence and Structure Analysis for Extracting Evolutionary and Functional Insights. Biomolecular Structures: Prediction, Identification and Analyses. Computational Design and Experimental Implementation of Synthetic Riboswitches and Riboregulators. Natural Language Processing Approaches in Bioinformatics. Predicting RNA-RNA Interactions in Three-Dimensional Structures. Protein–Protein Interaction Databases. Sequence Analysis

---

References

Ahmad, S., Gromiha, M.M., 2002. NETASA: Neural network based prediction of solvent accessibility. Bioinformatics 18, 819–824.

Ahmad, S., Gromiha, M.M., Sarai, A., 2003. RVP-net: Online prediction of real valued accessible surface area of proteins from single sequences. Bioinformatics 19, 1849–1851.

Ahmad, S., Gromiha, M.M., Sarai, A., 2004. Analysis and prediction of DNA-binding proteins and their binding residues based on composition, sequence and structural information. Bioinformatics 20, 477–486.

Ahmad, S., Prathipati, P., Tripathi, L.P., et al., 2017. Integrating sequence and gene expression information predicts genome-wide DNA-binding proteins and suggests a cooperative mechanism. Nucleic Acids Res. 1–17. GKX1166.

Ahmad, S., Sarai, A., 2005. PSSM-based prediction of DNA binding sites in proteins. BMC Bioinform. 6, 33.

Al-Shahib, A., Breitling, R., Gilbert, D.R., 2007. Predicting protein function by machine learning on amino acid sequences – A critical evaluation. BMC Genom. 8, 78.

Andrabi, M., Mizuguchi, K., Sarai, A., Ahmad, S., 2009. Prediction of mono- and di-nucleotide-specific DNA-binding sites in proteins using neural networks. BMC Struct. Biol. 9, 30.

Bairoch, A., Apweiler, R., 2000. The SWISS-PROT protein sequence database and its supplement TrEMBL in 2000. Nucleic Acids Res. 28, 45–48.

Boutet, E., Lieberherr, D., Tognolli, M., Schneider, M., A, B., 2007. UniProtKB/Swiss-Prot. Methods Mol. Biol. 406, 89–112.

Chai, H., Zhang, J., Yang, G., Ma, Z., 2016. An evolution-based DNA-binding residue predictor using a dynamic query-driven learning scheme. Mol. Biosyst. 12, 3643–3650.

Fawcett, T., 2006. An introduction to ROC analysis. Pattern Recognit. Lett. 27, 861–874.

Fernandez, M., Kumagai, Y., Standley, D.M., et al., 2011. Prediction of dinucleotide-specific RNA-binding sites in proteins. BMC Bioinform. 12 (Suppl. 13), S5.

Glisovic, T., Bachorik, J.L., Yong, J., Dreyfuss, G., 2008. RNA-binding proteins and post-transcriptional gene regulation. FEBS Lett. 582, 1977–1986.

Hubbard, S.J., Thornton, J.M., 1993. NACCESS. Department of Biochemistry and Molecular Biology. University College London.

Hu, J., Li, Y., Zhang, M., et al., 2016. Predicting protein-DNA binding residues by weightedly combining sequence-based features and boosting multiple SVMs. IEEE/ACM Trans. Comput. Biol. Bioinform. 14 (6), 1389–1398.

Hwang, S., Gou, Z., Kuznetsov, I.B., 2007. DP-Bind: A web server for sequence-based prediction of DNA-binding residues in DNA-binding proteins. Bioinformatics 23, 634–636.

Joo, K., Lee, S.J., Lee, J., 2012. Sann: Solvent accessibility prediction of proteins by nearest neighbor method. Proteins, 80. . pp. 1791–1797.

Kabsch, W., Sander, C., 1983. Dictionary of protein secondary structure: Pattern recognition of hydrogen-bonded and geometrical features. Biopolymers 22, 2577–2637.

Kirsanov, D.D., Zanegina, O.N., Aksianov, E.A., et al., 2013. NPIDB: Nucleic acid-Protein Interaction DataBase. Nucleic Acids Res. 41, D517–D523.

Lancashire, L.J., Lemetre, C., Ball, G.R., 2009. An introduction to artificial neural networks in bioinformatics—application to complex microarray and mass spectrometry datasets in cancer studies. Briefings in bioinformatics 10, 315–329.

Lewis, B.A., Walia, R.R., Terribilini, M., et al., 2011. PRIDB: A protein–RNA interface database. Nucleic Acids Res. 29, D277–D282.

Li, S., Yamashita, K., Amada, K.M., Standley, D.M., 2014. Quantifying sequence and structural features of protein–RNA interactions. Nucleic Acids Res. 42, 10086–10098.

Lunde, B.M., Moore, C., Varani, G., 2007. RNA-binding proteins: Modular design for efficient function. Nat. Rev. Mol. Cell Biol. 8, 479–490.

Marceau, A.H., Felthousen, J.G., Goetsch, P.D., et al., 2016. Structural basis for LIN54 recognition of CHR elements in cell cycle-regulated promoters. Nat. Commun. 7, 12301.

Ma, X., Guo, J., Wu, J., et al., 2011. Prediction of RNA-binding residues in proteins from primary sequence using an enriched random forest model with a novel hybrid feature. Proteins 79, 1230–1239.

McGuffin, L.J., Bryson, K., Jones, D.T., 2000. The PSIPRED protein structure prediction server. Bioinformatics 16, 404–405.

Miao, Z., Westhof, E., 2015. Prediction of nucleic acid binding probability in proteins: A neighboring residue network based score. Nucleic Acids Res. 43, 5340–5351.

Pruitt, K.D., Tatusova, T., Maglott, D.R., 2007. NCBI reference sequences (RefSeq): A curated non-redundant sequence database of genomes, transcripts and proteins. Nucleic Acids Res. 35, D61–D65.

Ray, D., Kazan, H., Cook, K.B., et al., 2013. A compendium of RNA-binding motifs for decoding gene regulation. Nature 499, 172–177.

Rose, P.W., Prlic, A., Altunkaya, A., et al., 2017. The RCSB protein data bank: Integrative view of protein, gene and 3D structural information. Nucleic Acids Res. 45, D271–D281.

Rost, B., Sander, C., 1994. Conservation and prediction of solvent accessibility in protein families. Proteins Struct. Funct. Bioinform. 20, 216–226.

Singh, H., Chauhan, J.S., Gromiha, M.M., Raghava, G.P., 2012.ccPDB: Compilation and creation of data sets from Protein Data Bank. Nucleic Acids Res. 40, D486–D489.

Sokolova, M., Japkowicz, N., Szpakowicz, N., 2006. Beyond accuracy, F-score and ROC: A family of discriminant measures for performance evaluation. In: Proceedings of the Australasian Joint Conference on Artificial Intelligence, vol. 4304, pp. 1015–1021.

Sun, T., Zhou, B., Lai, L., Pei, J., 2017. Sequence-based prediction of protein protein interaction using a deep-learning algorithm. BMC Bioinform. 18, 277.

Touw, W.G., Baakman, C., Black, J., et al., 2015. A series of PDB-related databanks for everyday needs. Nucleic Acids Res. 43, D364–D368.

Tuvshinjargal, N., Lee, W., Park, B., Han, K., 2016. PRIdictor: Protein–RNA Interaction predictor. Biosystems 139, 17–22.

Walia, R.R., Caragea, C., Lewis, B.A., et al., 2012. Protein–RNA interface residue prediction using machine learning: An assessment of the state of the art. BMC Bioinform. 13, 89.

Walia, R.R., Xue, L.C., Wilkins, K., et al., 2014. RNABindRPlus: A predictor that combines machine learning and sequence homology-based methods to improve the reliability of predicted RNA-binding residues in proteins. PLOS ONE 9, e97725.

Wang, G., Dunbrack, R.L., 2003. PISCES: A protein sequence culling server. Bioinformatics 19, 1589–1591.

Wang, S., Peng, J., Ma, J., Xu, J., 2016. Protein secondary structure prediction using deep convolutional neural fields. Sci. Rep. 6, 18962.

Yang, L., Wang, C., Li, F., et al., 2017. The human RNA-binding protein and E3 ligase MEX-3C binds the MEX-3-recognition element (MRE) motif with high affinity. J. Biol. Chem. 292, 16221–16234.

Yan, J., Kurgan, L., 2017. DRNApred, fast sequence-based method that accurately predicts and discriminates DNA- and RNA-binding residues. Nucleic Acids Res. 45, e84.

Protein-Peptide Interactions in Regulatory Events

Upadhyayula S Raghavender, Birla Institute of Scientific Research (BISR), Jaipur, India
Ravindranath S Rathore, Central University of South Bihar, Patna, India

Introduction

Protein-Protein Interactions (PPI)

Eukaryotic cell is a complex collection of physical entities, i.e., biological molecules, which are in a constant flux of association and dissociation reactions. The milieu of cell provides the necessary and sufficient environment for cooperative interactions taking place between biological macromolecules (proteins, RNA, DNA, peptides). Majority of the physical interactions between the cellular components are context-dependent and are highly *specific*. In the case of proteins, the signals for binding events are encoded in their sequences. These signals, or interaction modules, diversify the functions of the proteins to performing activities like catalytic, regulatory, and binding a wide array of ligands. The multifarious functions of proteins in a cell is the reason for the diversity of interactions in a cell (Van Roey et al., 2014).

The eukaryotic cell is composed of many compartments within which a host of reactions and interactions are happening at exceptionally *fast rate* and with high *accuracy* and *fidelity*. The classical approach to understanding interactions is that of a structured protein interacting with a partner. Traditionally, protein-protein interactions (PPIs) are viewed as archetypal interactions between molecules with high affinity and stable domain structures. The assertion that stable, ordered and structured domains are necessary for describing the *"interactome"* has given way to recent observations that unstructured regions in a protein play a critical role in explaining the cellular events and dynamics of interactions. The regulatory events in a cell tend to opt, perhaps a large fraction, regions of protein without a well-defined stable conformation for the binding sites. These seminal observations have paved the way for a new field of interactome studies known as *Intrinsically Disordered Regions* (IDRs) in proteins (Tompa, 2012). A short stretch of amino acids in protein sequences, in particular IDRs, comprises of binding residues (*functional modules*). These linear interaction sites, or short peptides, have been designated as *short linear motifs* (SLiMs). Hence, the entire array of functions which can be performed by a protein are concentrated in SLiMs. With the availability of a suitable partner which can recognise these sites and bind to them, a sizeable fraction of the interactome can be understood quantitatively (Van Roey et al., 2014; Gouw et al., 2017).

Protein-protein interactions form the basis for many cellular processes. The protein interaction refers to specific physical contact(s) between two or more proteins, forming biologically active protein complex. There are two categories of contacts – *direct* PPI and *indirect* PPI. Indirect PPI are those wherein two interacting proteins may interact forming a complex via intervening partners. Disruption or deregulation of these complex interactions is the main cause of a significant number of diseases. Consequently, there is intense research interest in designing inhibitors that target specific protein-protein interactions. This places intricate protein-protein interactions at the heart of the development for novel protein-based drug leads often referred to as *biologics* (Caputo et al., 2008). The emergence of 'omic' technologies, namely genomics, transcriptomics and proteomics, has greatly accelerated our understanding of the protein-protein interaction networks leading to the discovery of a number of proteins and their interactions (Archakov et al., 2003).

Structural Intricacies of PPIs

The number of complex structures has exponentially grown in the Protein Data Bank in recent decades, which partly owes to various Structural Genomics initiatives. With the availability of a large number of structures of protein-protein complexes, the focus in the area has been shifted to understanding the molecular determinants of binding affinity and specificity of complex. The description of the interface in a protein-protein complex serves as a starting point for understanding the chemistry and physics at the interface. When complemented with the physico-chemical description of residues lining the interface, the study becomes quantitative providing deep insight into the interplay of strong and weak interactions during complex formation (Jones and Thornton, 1996; Bravo and Aloy, 2006).

PPI surfaces are relatively shallow and lack features as compared to protein-ligand or drug interactions. These interactions can be viewed as arising out of many cooperative weak interatomic interactions, in contrast to a few strong interactions dictating protein-ligand complex formation (Jones et al., 2000). PPI's are known to be highly regulated and depend on the environment in which they occur. In many cases, the complex formation occurs by post translational modification (like phosphorylation) which promotes recognition by conformational changes in the binding partners. SLiMs are inherently labile and serve as *regulatory motifs* in promoting a large set of protein interactions in surprisingly complex ways (Davey et al., 2015).

Computational Approaches

The existing high throughput experimental approaches such as two-hybrid, chip-based or TAP-MS to map protein interactions suffers from several limitations – Limited data set with high degree of false positives and negatives. X-ray crystallography, employed to elucidate atomic details of protein interactions, is often not feasible due to crystallization difficulties and complexities of interactions involved in case of membrane domains and multiple interacting partners. Many of the proteins are estimated to possess several interacting partners (Gogl *et al.*, 2013; Meller and Porollo, 2012). The computational methods have the potential to fill-in the gap in this scenario. Computation can be used to predict possible interactions and binding modes, to validate the experimental high-throughput screening data and to analyze the PPI networks from the data repositories (Zahiri *et al.*, 2013). Over 100 such PPI related repositories are available online (Orchard *et al.*, 2012), the prominent among them are – Biological General Repository for Interaction Datasets (BioGRID), Database of Interacting Proteins (DIP), Biomolecular INTeraction Network Database (BIND), Molecular Interaction Database (MINT), Human Protein Reference Database (HPRD), Search Tool for the Retrieval of Interacting Genes/Protein (STRING) and IntAct (Miryala *et al.*, 2017).

Protein-Peptide Interactions

Protein-peptide interactions play an important role in many regulatory processes of cell from co-activators to inhibitors and account for almost 40% of the protein-protein interactions. Peptides characteristically interact with specific protein domains such as SH2, SH3, MFC and PDZ domains. Thus development of peptide or peptidomimetic leads is an emerging area in biological therapeutics. Peptides 'as against small molecules' possess specific motifs hence they can mimic protein-binding domains and at the same time they are large enough to serve as competitive inhibitors for disrupting protein–protein interactions. With the objective of developing PPI inhibitors based on peptides or designed peptide derivatives to mimic the binding motif of one of the partners, one usually starts with a sequence similar to or harbouring the *recognition motif* (Stanfield and Wilson, 1995). In solution, the free form of peptides tend to possess a large array of conformations. But, in the presence of an interaction partner there is a drastic reduction in the conformational space sampled by the peptide and the complexation is promoted by the recognition motif with a concomitant lowering of the total entropy of the system (Jackrel *et al.*, 2009; Speltz *et al.*, 2015). It has been commented that PPI's are stabilised in the milieu of strong and weak interactions; but in the case of protein-peptide complexes the hydrogen bonds (particularly backbone-mediated) are pivotal and are key to complex formation (Zvelebil and Thornton, 1993). An attempt to correlate the geometrical parameters of the individual residues in designed peptides, in both free (deposited in Cambridge Structural Database) and bound (as in PDB), has revealed similarities in backbone conformations in the case of aliphatic residues from both the databases. This led to the generation of residue level backbone conformational libraries of peptide residues (canonical) in PDB (Raghavender, 2017).

Peptide-protein interactions have biological significance. They are important signaling components, acting as hormones and neurotransmitters (Brooks *et al.*, 2005; Petsalaki and Russell, 2008). The most famous and important example of a disease involving peptides derived from natural proteins is amyloid beta (Aβ), resulting from the hydrolysis of APP protein. Antimicrobial peptides are implied in innate immune system (Ganz, 2003). Further fusogenic peptides have been used as cargo to deliver drugs to target cells (Trabulo *et al.*, 2010). It has been claimed that this subclass of interactions are largely underrepresented in high-throughput experimental techniques used for studying protein-protein interactions (Lensink *et al.*, 2017). The transient nature of the interaction, dictated by the low affinity binding interfaces compounds the existing problems. Computational predictions of peptide binding to interaction partners have been assessed recently (Lensink *et al.*, 2017).

Theoretical Background

Polypeptide Conformation

G. N. Ramachandran is credited with the seminal contribution of describing the conformation of a polypeptide chain in 1960s (Ramachandran and Sasiskharan, 1968; Ramakrishnan, 2001). This resulted in what is now popularly known as **Ramachandran** or (ϕ,ψ) map. The basic idea is to get a 2-dimensional representation of the protein conformation, using backbone dihedral angles (ϕ,ψ). Surprisingly, the map was able to clearly separate regions of regular secondary structural features (α-helices and β-sheets) (Ramachandran *et al.*, 1963). Reverse turns such as α and β-turns, involved in the reversal of the polypeptide chain, could also be completely described using the backbone torsions (Venkatachalam, 1968; Nataraj *et al.*, 1995). The field of designed peptides gained momentum, with the application of conformationally constrained residues which were amenable to chemical synthesis (Balaram, 1992; Toniolo *et al.*, 2001). Aminoisobutyric acid (Aib) is a prototypical achiral amino acid which has been widely examined for the design of helices specifically 3_{10} helices. Proline, an imino acid, is known to occur frequently at the β-turn positions facilitating chain reversals. Hence, both L- and D-enantiomers of proline have been used to design synthetic β-turns as models of β-sheets (Mahalakshmi and Balaram, 2006).

The side chain conformations of residues (rotamers) were also observed to adopt specific conformations. This led to the development of rotamer libraries (Ponder and Richards, 1987) for modelling residue side chain conformations. It was also profitably used in sampling probable conformations in molecular modelling and simulations of proteins and in accurately modelling side chains into electron density maps of structures with not so high resolution (Dunbrack and Karplus, 1993; Dunbrack, 2002; Beglov *et al.*, 2012; Lovell *et al.*, 2000).

Many regulatory events in the eukaryotic cell are transient in nature, meaning they are short-lived as compared to rigid and stable protein complexes. In some such instances, either a short segment of a polypeptide chain or a fragment is involved in interacting with a protein. Initial attempts to elucidate the structural features of protein-peptide interactions revealed that extended chains (β-strands), β-turns and then by α-helix are the ways in which peptides fold and interact with their partners (Zvelebil and Thornton, 1993). The motifs in these segments were called 'recognition motifs' in the earlier days and are now appropriately called 'SLiMs'. In proteases, like HIV-1 protease, MHC-1, MHC-II, chaperones like PapD and Src homology domains (SH2 & SH3) the recognition motif is usually in an extended chain. Peptide and anti-peptide antibody complexes are frequently seen to bind a peptide with β-turn. Ca^{2+}-dependent calmodulin domain is seen to bind helical peptides. It has become clear that sequence conservation is not necessary for binding to a peptide-binding site, still structures of the bound peptides would have local conserved features (Stein and Aloy, 2008).

Statistical Mechanical Formulation of Molecular Association

A short review of the physio-chemical principles of binding are presented in this section. This should help reader get familiar with the methods used for binding energy estimation and computational docking currently in vogue. We begin with a simplistic formulation of molecular association and disassociation, borrowing from Kilburg and Gallicchio, (2017). Two physical entities A and B can associate by molecular interactions, in a reversible way and at equilibrium can be described by the equations:

$$A + B \overset{k_{on}}{\rightarrow} A \cdot B$$

$$A \cdot B \overset{k_{off}}{\rightarrow} A + B$$

The rate of forward and backward reactions are equal at equilibrium, hence *equilibrium constant* for binding K_b can be derived as:

$$K_b = \frac{1}{C^0} \frac{k_{on}}{k_{off}}$$

where C^0 is the standard state concentration set to 1 M. We can now get the standard *binding free energy* ΔG_b^0, which in principle is a thermodynamic measure of the *binding affinity*, as:

$$\Delta G_b^0 = -k_B T \ln K_b$$

where k_B is *Boltzmann's constant*. Such a simple formulation will be difficult to reconcile in a biological context, when the interacting species are in a constant flux of interconverting conformations. Hence, the need to resort to statistical mechanical approaches for modelling an "ensemble" of conformations. We skip the derivation and introduce the result of *configurational partition function* of the complex as:

$$Z_{N, A \cdot B} = \int_{bound} e^{-\beta U(x_A, x_B, \zeta_B, r_s)} dx_A dx_B d\zeta_B dr_s$$

where N is the number of molecules, r_s represents the degrees of freedom of solvent, $U(x)$ represents potential energy of solvent + solute system and ζ_B is any suitable structural parameter (e.g., distance between the center of mass of A and B). The above formulation is the backbone for present-day theoretical models on understanding protein-ligand/protein interactions.

The free energy calculation methods implemented in various programs fall into two distinct approaches. The first approach is based on pathways such as Free Energy Perturbation (FEP), Thermodynamic Integration (TI) and Slow Growth (SG). Such methods are very accurate but computationally intensive. The second set of approaches are less rigorous end-point (two-points) methods such as Linear interaction energy (LIE), Molecular Mechanics-Poisson Boltzmann Surface/Generalized Born Area (MM-PBSA/GBSA) and lambda (λ)-dynamics. They try to balance speed and accuracy to increase throughput to calculate free energy differences (Rathore *et al.*, 2013; Reddy *et al.*, 2014). An end-point method is effective as it ignores the intervening pathway intermediates when evaluating binding free energy, with the description being complete with just free protein, free peptide and protein-peptide states. The binding free energy is estimated in MM-GBSA formulation as:

$$\Delta G_{bind} = G_{A \cdot B} - G_A - G_B$$

with, $G = \langle E_{bond} \rangle + \langle E_{ele} \rangle + \langle E_{vdW} \rangle + \langle E_{pol} \rangle + \langle E_{np} \rangle - TS$

where the contributions come from interactions through covalent bonds (E_{bond}), electrostatic interactions (E_{ele}), van der Waals (E_{vdW}), polar (E_{pol}) and non-polar (E_{np}) forces to solvation free energy. These are typically modelled under implicit solvent representations.

Prediction & Modelling of Protein-Peptides Interactions

Protein-Peptide Docking

The interest towards the development of novel peptide or peptidomimetic has grown substantially in recent times. Peptides are highly flexible and they often interact weakly with their substrate, underlining their importance in signal transduction or regulation which often relies on transient processes. These obstacles make experimental structure determination often non-trivial and calls for complementary computational approaches like docking. Molecular docking is a preliminary step in lead identification and design. Although many well-established methods exist for protein-ligand and protein-protein rigid-body docking, they often fail to yield accurate results in cases that involve receptor flexibility and docking of large, flexible ligands like peptides (Audie and Swanson, 2012; Trellet *et al.*, 2013). Peptides in contrast to proteins are observed to adopt variable conformations. The excursions into conformational space can be curtailed by designing sequences which have conformationally constrained residues like Pro or non-standard aminoisobutyric acid (Aib) (Mahalakshmi and Balaram, 2006; Raghavender *et al.*, 2010). In a computational investigation involving peptide-protein docking, the peptide conformations are sampled either by running an explicit solvent molecular dynamics (MD) simulation or by a procedure involving implicit solvent simulations using Monte Carlo approaches (Raghavender and Sowdhamini, 2015). The latter is faster and yields results quickly, hence recommended for studies in general. The trajectories in a MD are clustered and low-energy representatives from top clusters are used for docking studies. Due to the lack of prior information on allowed conformations of peptide, it is suggested that all possible conformations be explored for studies.

Docking a peptide to a protein is relatively challenging as it involves considerably more number of degrees of freedom, as opposed to protein-ligand or protein-protein docking. The structure of the receptor protein must be known or one should have structural information of a closely related homolog (Kilburg and Gallicchio, 2016). Present protein-peptide docking procedures fall into two classes, namely:

(a) *Local Docking* – When there is information available of the binding site on the protein, predicting interactions is more accurately possible (Lavi *et al.*, 2013). In this case, a library of peptides are evaluated for best complex structure. HADDOCK program is suited for this type of investigation. It even allows the user to guide the docking by incorporating the biochemical and biophysical data into the docking protocol (Spiliotopoulos *et al.*, 2016). GalaxyPepDock is web based service which employs similarity-based docking. It builds model peptide conformations by identifying templates from the database of experimentally determined structures followed by energy-based optimization that allows for structural flexibility (Lee *et al.*, 2015). MedusaDock is another program which can effectively be used for induced-fit docking procedures(Ding and Dokholyan, 2013). The best pose selection in any of the above programs follows the authors own approach, hence there is a need to look at each pose carefully before proceeding further with analysis. Glide peptide docking module in Bioluminate (Schrödinger, 2017) systematically improve pose prediction accuracy of flexible peptides by enhancing characteristic Glide sampling using a series of hierarchical filters to search for accurate binding mode. The scoring of the poses is improved by post-processing with implicit solvation based MM-GBSA calculations (Tubert-Brohman *et al.*, 2013). Glide peptide docking method is accurate and several times faster than other programs. Rosetta FlexPepDock is a robust protocol for Protein-peptide docking (Raveh *et al.*, 2010) which tries to optimize the peptide backbone and rigid body orientation, using the Monte-Carlo with Minimization approach. Dyna method is new approach for docking peptides into flexible receptors. It follows a two step procedure: the Protein-Peptide conformational space is scanned first to approximately identify ligand poses followed by the pose-refinement by a new molecular dynamics-based method, optimized potential molecular dynamics (OPMD) using soft-core potentials for the protein-peptide interactions (Antes, 2010).

(b) *Global docking* – When there is little or no information available on the binding site, it needs to be searched for on protein surface. Such methods have limited accuracy for predicting the complex structures. However, there are recent examples of successful predictions of such methods (Yan *et al.*, 2016; Petsalaki *et al.*, 2009). In this scenario, one performs a docking with an ensemble of peptide conformations onto the surface of the target protein. Typically, one can complement it with some biochemical information on the plausibility of the binding site to be correlated with some interaction. Generally, one proceeds in a two-tiered way involving coarse-grained modelling of the receptor for filtering binding sites followed by atomic resolution docking and refinement. Programs like CABS-dock and PepATTRACT have been used recently in such studies (Blaszczyk *et al.*, 2016; De Vries *et al.*, 2017).

Predicting Hot-Spot Residues: Residue Scanning

The prediction of energetically important amino acid residues at the interface of protein-protein complexes is a step forward in biologics design. Such *hot-spot* residues (i.e., residues that significantly destabilize the PPI when mutated to Ala or specific residues possessing different chemical and structural character) have been investigated experimentally as well as computationally. Experimental site-directed mutagenesis is a powerful method for delineating important residues and key interactions at the protein-protein interfaces. A number of reports describe computational mutagenesis involving calculation of the effect of mutations on the binding free energy of protein-protein complexes using empirical energy models such as Robetta & FoldX (Kortemme *et al.*, 2004; Schymkowitz *et al.*, 2005). Other sophisticated methods of binding free energy calculation upon alanine mutation using implicit solvation models such as MM-PBSA/GBSA and Thermodynamic Integration have been proposed (Martins *et al.*, 2013; Beard *et al.*, 2013) even though they are computationally much more expensive. The MM-GBSA approach implemented in Bioluminate Residue scanning module (Schrödinger, 2017) employes the OPLS force field and the VSGB2.0 solvent model to calculate binding free energy differences between wild type and mutants. The individual or multiple residues are mutated followed by rotamer search algorithms implemented in Prime (Schrödinger, 2017). In an experimental data set comprising of 418 single residue mutations in 21 targets, the MM-GBSA based method has been demonstrated to perform well at picking hot-spots, and mutations within an accuracy of 1 kcal/mol (Beard *et al.*, 2013).

Case Studies

We present a few of the research investigations here which cover in part of the above concepts.

(i) Nuclear receptor (NR) box II peptide, with LxxLL motif (x is any amino acid), binds to oestrogen receptor α. One can see that the peptide forms an amphipathic α-helix and is lodged in a complementary groove on the receptor surface(Shiau *et al.*, 1998).

(ii)   PDZ domains which are protein interaction modules involved in signaling networks, bind the C-terminal regions of partners by adding a β-strand. This is known as *β-augmentation* (Remaut and Waksman, 2006).

(iii) SH3, WW and EVH1 domains, bind to linear motifs rich in proline residues and adopting polyproline II helix structures (Zarrinpar *et al.*, 2003).

(iv)   SH2, PTB and 14–3–3 domains are known to bind sites involved in post-translational modifications (Rittinger *et al.*, 1999).

(v)   MDM2-p53 interaction is known to be lethal. Mouse Double minute 2 (MDM2) binds to a short helix on p53. This interaction was mimicked by *cis*-imidazoline analogs, called Nutlins, which could completely inhibit the complex formation (Vassilev *et al.*, 2004).

Discussion

We elaborate on few of the important investigations discussed above in the following section.

(i)   *NR box II peptide + oestrogen receptor α (ERα)*. The transcription factor ERα is involved in the regulation of differentiation and maintenance of neural, skeletal, cardiovascular and reproductive tissues. Treatment of breast cancer, osteoporosis and cardiovascular disease employs compounds which modulate ERα activity. ERα binds a variety of ligands, and all the ligands bind at the C-terminus. In the structure of NR box II peptide bound to ERα, it can be seen that the peptide is helical, with approximately 1000 Å^2 hydrophobic surface area buried at the interface. The ligand binding domain (LBD) interacts primarily with the side chains of the peptide residues Ile-689, and Leu-690, Leu-693 and Leu-694. This interactions was found to be very potent and involving mostly non-polar interactions (van der Waals). Terminal capping interactions stabilize the lodged peptide, the γ-carboxylate of Glu-542 hydrogen bonds to the N-terminus of the peptide and Lys-362 (ε-amino group) forms hydrogen bonds with the C-terminus of the peptide helix (PDB code: 3ERD).

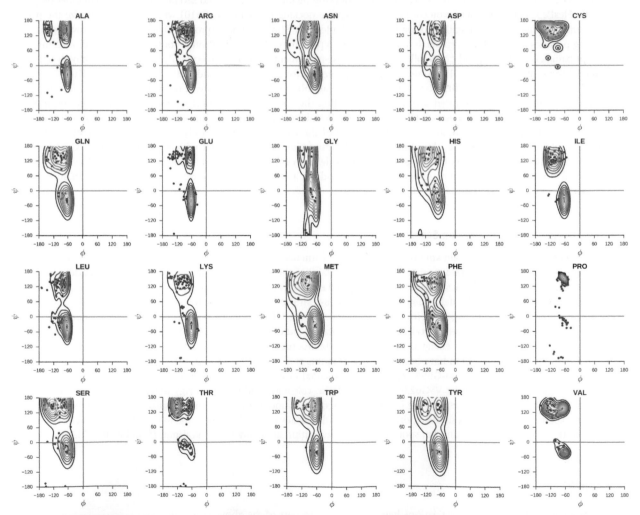

Fig. 1   Bivariate kernel density estimates (kde) of backbone torsion angles (φ, ψ) of peptide residues bound to protein partners in PDB. High resolution crystal structures, better than 1.5 Å, were used for the analysis. Only canonical residues have been investigated, with a view of utility in chemical synthesis of analogs. Cyclic peptides were excluded from the study.

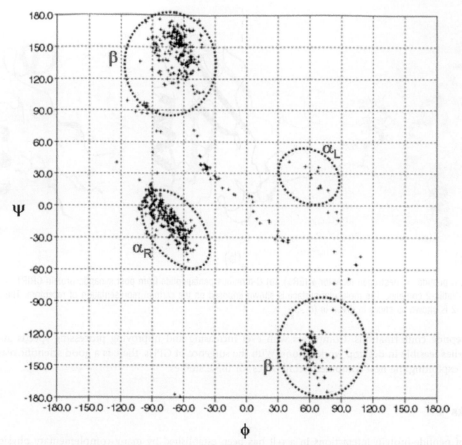

Fig. 2 Ramachandran Plot of the proline residues in CSD. The regions corresponding to helical (α_R-right-handed α_L-left-handed) and extended strands are marked in red circles. Cyclic peptides are also included in this plot for completeness, and they tend to be clustered at (0, 0). Reproduced from the Doctoral Thesis of Dr. U.S. Raghavender.

(ii) *C-terminus pentapeptide from post synaptic protein CRIPT + Synaptic protein PSD-95.* PDZ domains are known to be involved in important metabolic pathways. In the structure of synaptic protein PSD-95 in complex with a peptide derived from C-terminus of CRIPT, one observes that the peptide adopts a β-strand conformation and binds to the edge of the β-sheet from PSD-95. The protein-peptide complex formation in this case is augmented by the main chain interactions. The affinity of the interaction is directed by peptide backbone interactions leaving a wide scope for specificity, promoting the binding of shorter motifs at the binding site (PDB code: 1BE9).

(iii) *MDM2-Nutlin-2 complex.* MDM2 is a ubiquitin protein ligase and is known to bind to a short amphipathic α-helix on the p53 tumor suppressor and modulate its transcriptional activity and stability. The functions of p53 are impaired upon overexpression of MDM2 in human tumours. Hence, inhibition of MDM2-p53 interaction is a way forward for cancer therapy. The small molecule inhibitor, Nutlin-2, mimics the interactions of the p53 peptide to a high degree, with one bromophenyl moiety sitting deeply in the Trp pocket, the other bromophenyl group occupying the Leu pocket, and the ethyl ether side chain directed toward the Phe pocket. The imidazoline scaffold serves as a functional replacement of helical backbone of the peptide and is able to direct the projection of three groups into the pockets normally occupied by Phe. This is one of the very first studies in identifying small molecule compounds which involved disrupting a pathological protein-peptide interaction (PDB code: 1RV1).

Future Directions

First principle studies on protein-peptide interaction are presently out of reach from the perspective of both methods and the software programs implementing the theoretical approaches. A great step forward would be to comprehensively catalog, characterize, and associate Protein-peptide interactions with disease and other phenotypes. There is a good scope for development in all the areas of mechanistic description of protein-peptide interactions. In particular, sound theoretical approaches to accurately model the interaction incorporating both the chemical and physical information can be explored. Peptide design, protein-peptide docking and refinement of docked complexes have already been addressed computationally using many different approaches; still the search is ON for the best method which would be able to predict the correct protein-peptide interaction accounting for all the

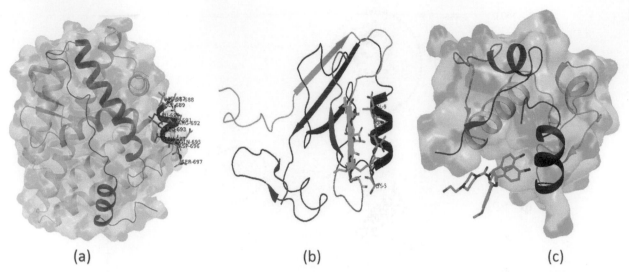

(a)   (b)   (c)

Fig. 3   (a) NR box II peptide + oestrogen receptor α (ERα). (b) C-terminus pentapeptide from post synaptic protein CRIPT + Synaptic protein PSD-95. (c) MDM2-Nutlin-2 complex. The molecular surface is shown imposed on the cartoon representation of receptors. The peptide residues are labelled. Nutulin-2 is shown as sticks in green in (c).

variabilities in peptide conformations. Computers with ever increasing and improving processing speeds and hardwares, are making these studies feasible in desktop workstations. With the surgence of GPUs, there is a good scientific reason to traverse to the new avenues exploiting the new computer architectures for these studies.

Closing Remarks

The prevalence of peptide-protein interactions in a cell has been established by many complementary physical, chemical and biochemical experiments. It is very clear that these are very abundant in a cell and are primarily involved in cellular regulation, thus offering enormous scope for protein theraputics. The existing experimental approaches to characterize PPI have high rates of false positives and computational methods serve an important role to predict and derive a mechanistic picture of these interactions. The limited accuracy of predictive methods calls for improving the existing computational methodologies. Additional and complementary physical and computational approaches can help remove ambiguity in predicting a true positive interaction, which can subsequently be validated using experimental techniques. The description of the entire interactome warrants accurate characterization and prediction of this important subclass of PPIs (**Figs. 1, 2, 3**).

Acknowledgement

Raghavender acknowledges SERB-DST for funding (File No: YSS/2015/1077/LS). Infrastructure support of BISR is acknowledged.

See also: Natural Language Processing Approaches in Bioinformatics

References

Antes, I., 2010. DynaDock: A new molecular dynamics-based algorithm for protein–Peptide docking including receptor flexibility. Proteins 78, 1084–1104.
Archakov, A.I., Govorun, V.M., Dubanov, A.V., *et al.*, 2003. Protein-protein interactions as a target for drugs in proteomics. Proteomics 3, 380–391.
Audie, J., Swanson, J., 2012. Recent work in the development and application of protein–Peptide docking. Future Med. Chem. 4, 1619–1644.
Balaram, P., 1992. Protein non-standard amino acids in peptide design and protein engineering. Curr. Opin. Struct. Biol. 2, 845–851.
Beard, H., Cholleti, A., Pearlman, D., Sherman, W., Loving, K.A., 2013. Applying physics-based scoring to calculate free energies of binding for single amino acid mutations in protein-protein complexes. PLOS ONE 8, e82849.
Beglov, D., Hall, D.R., Brenke, R., *et al.*, 2012. Minimal ensembles of side chain conformers for modeling protein-protein interactions. Proteins 80, 591–601.
Blaszczyk, M., Kurcinski, M., Kouza, M., *et al.*, 2016. Modeling of protein-peptide interactions using the CABS-dock web server for binding site search and flexible docking. Methods 93, 72–83.
Bravo, J., Aloy, P., 2006. Target selection for complex structural genomics. Curr. Opin. Struct. Biol. 16, 385–392.
Brooks, H., Lebleu, B., Vives, E., 2005. Tat peptide-mediated cellular delivery: Back to basics. Adv. Drug Deliv. Rev. 57, 559–577.
Caputo, G.A., Litvinov, R.I., Li, W., *et al.*, 2008. Computationally designed peptide inhibitors of protein-protein interactions in membranes. Biochemistry 47, 8600–8606.

Davey, N.E., Cyert, M.S., Moses, A.M., 2015. Short linear motifs – *Ex nihilo* evolution of protein regulation. Cell Commun. Signal. 13, 43.

De Vries, S.J., Rey, J., Schindler, C.E.M., Zacharias, M., Tuffery, P., 2017. The pepATTRACT web server for blind, large-scale peptide-protein docking. Nucleic Acids Res. 45, W361–W364.

Ding, F., Dokholyan, N.V., 2013. Incorporating backbone flexibility in MedusaDock improves ligand-binding pose prediction in the CSAR2011 docking benchmark. J. Chem. Inf. Model. 53, 1871–1879.

Dunbrack Jr., R.L., 2002. Rotamer libraries in the 21st century. Curr. Opin. Struct. Biol. 12, 431–440.

Dunbrack Jr., R.L., Karplus, M., 1993. Backbone-dependent rotamer library for proteins. Application to side-chain prediction. J. Mol. Biol. 230, 543–574.

Ganz, T., 2003. Defensins: Antimicrobial peptides of innate immunity. Nat. Rev. Immunol. 3, 710–720.

Gogl, G., Toro, I., Remenyi, A., 2013. Protein-peptide complex crystallization: A case study on the ERK2 mitogen-activated protein kinase. Acta Crystallogr. D Biol. Crystallogr. 69, 486–489.

Gouw, M., Samano-Sanchez, H., Van Roey, K., *et al.*, 2017. Exploring Short Linear Motifs Using the ELM Database and Tools. Curr. Protoc. Bioinform. 58, 8.22.1–8.22.35.

Jackrel, M.E., Valverde, R., Regan, L., 2009. Redesign of a protein-peptide interaction: Characterization and applications. Protein Sci. 18, 762–774.

Jones, S., Marin, A., Thornton, J.M., 2000. Protein domain interfaces: Characterization and comparison with oligomeric protein interfaces. Protein Eng. 13, 77–82.

Jones, S., Thornton, J.M., 1996. Principles of protein-protein interactions. Proc. Natl. Acad. Sci. USA 93, 13–20.

Kilburg, D., Gallicchio, E., 2016. Recent advances in computational models for the study of protein-peptide interactions. Adv. Protein Chem. Struct. Biol. 105, 27–57.

Kortemme, T., Kim, D.E., Baker, D., 2004. Computational alanine scanning of protein-protein interfaces. Sci. STKE 2004, pl2.

Lavi, A., Ngan, C.H., Movshovitz-Attias, D., *et al.*, 2013. Detection of peptide-binding sites on protein surfaces: The first step toward the modeling and targeting of peptide-mediated interactions. Proteins 81, 2096–2105.

Lee, H., Heo, L., Lee, M.S., Seok, C., 2015. GalaxyPepDock: A protein-peptide docking tool based on interaction similarity and energy optimization. Nucleic Acids Res. 43, W431–W435.

Lensink, M.F., Velankar, S., Wodak, S.J., 2017. Modeling protein-protein and protein-peptide complexes: CAPRI 6th edition. Proteins 85, 359–377.

Lovell, S.C., Word, J.M., Richardson, J.S., Richardson, D.C., 2000. The penultimate rotamer library. Proteins: Struct. Funct. Genet. 40, 389–408.

Mahalakshmi, R., Balaram, P., 2006. Non-protein amino acids in the design of secondary structure scaffolds. Methods. Mol. Biol. 340, 71–94.

Martins, Sílvia A., Perez, Marta A.S., Moreira, Irina S., *et al.*, 2013. Computational alanine scanning mutagenesis: MM-PBSA vs TI. J. Chem. Theory Comput. 9, 1311–1319.

Meller, J., Porollo, A., 2012. Computational methods for prediction of protein-protein interaction sites. In: Proceedings of the Protein-Protein Interactions – Computational and Experimental Tools edited by Weibo Cai and Hao Hong, ISBN 978-953-51-0397-4.

Miryala, K., AnandAnbarasu, A., Ramaiah, S., 2017. Gene, in press. Discerning molecular interactions: A comprehensive review on biomolecular interaction databases and network analysis tools. doi: 10.1016/j.gene.2017.11.028.

Nataraj, D.V., Srinivasan, N., Sowdhamini, R., Ramakrishnan, C., 1995. Alpha turns in protein structure. Curr. Sci. 69, 435–447.

Orchard, S., Kerrien, S., Abbani, S., *et al.*, 2012. Protein interaction data curation: The International Molecular Exchange (IMEx) consortium. Nat. Methods 9, 345–350.

Petsalaki, E., Russell, R.B., 2008. Peptide-mediated interactions in biological systems: New discoveries and applications. Curr. Opin. Biotechnol. 19, 344–350.

Petsalaki, E., Stark, A., Garcia-Urdiales, E., Russell, R.B., 2009. Accurate prediction of peptide binding sites on protein surfaces. PLOS Comput. Biol. 5, e1000335.

Ponder, J.W., Richards, F.M., 1987. Tertiary templates for proteins. Use of packing criteria in the enumeration of allowed sequences for different structural classes. J. Mol. Biol. 193, 775–791.

Raghavender, U.S., 2017. Analysis of residue conformations in peptides in Cambridge structural database and protein-peptide structural complexes. Chem. Biol. Drug Des. 89, 428–442.

Raghavender, U.S., Aravinda, S., Rai, R., Shamala, N., Balaram, P., 2010. Peptide hairpin nucleation with the obligatory Type I' beta-turn Aib-DPro segment. Org. Biomol. Chem. 8, 3133–3135.

Raghavender, U.S., Sowdhamini, R., 2015. Mechanistic basis of peptide-protein interaction in AtPep1-PEPR1 complex in Arabidopsis thaliana. Protein Pept. Lett. 22, 618–627.

Raveh, B., London, N., Schueler-Furman, O., 2010. Sub-angstrom modeling of complexes between flexible peptides and globular proteins. Proteins: Struct. Funct. Bioinform. 78, 2029–2040.

Ramachandran, G.N., Ramakrishnan, C., Sasisekharan, V., 1963. Stereochemistry of polypeptide chain configurations. J. Mol. Biol. 7, 95–99.

Ramachandran, G.N., Sasiskharan, V., 1968. Conformation of polypeptides and proteins. Adv. Protein Chem. 23, 283–437.

Ramakrishnan, C., 2001. Resonance, pp. 48–56.

Remaut, H., Waksman, G., 2006. Protein-protein interaction through beta-strand addition. Trends Biochem. Sci. 31, 436–444.

Rathore, R.S., Sumakanth, M., Reddy, M.S., *et al.*, 2013. Advances in binding free energies calculations: QM/MM-based free energy perturbation method for drug design. Curr. Pharm. Des. 19, 4674–4686.

Reddy, M.R., Reddy, C.R., Rathore, R.S., *et al.*, 2014. Free energy calculations to estimate ligand-binding affinities in structure-based drug design. Curr. Pharm. Des. 20, 3323–3337.

Rittinger, K., Budman, J., Xu, J., *et al.*, 1999. Structural analysis of 14-3-3 phosphopeptide complexes identifies a dual role for the nuclear export signal of 14-3-3 in ligand binding. Mol. Cell 4, 153–166.

Schrödinger, L.L.C., 2017. Small molecule drug discovery & biologics suite. New York, NY.

Schymkowitz, J., Borg, J., Stricher, F., *et al.*, 2005. The FoldX web server: An online force field. Nucleic Acids Res. 33 (Web Server issue), W382–W388.

Shiau, A.K., Barstad, D., Loria, P.M., *et al.*, 1998. The structural basis of estrogen receptor/coactivator recognition and the antagonism of this interaction by tamoxifen. Cell 95, 927–937.

Speltz, E.B., Nathan, A., Regan, L., 2015. Design of protein-peptide interaction modules for assembling supramolecular structures in vivo and in vitro. ACS Chem. Biol. 10, 2108–2115.

Spiliotopoulos, D., Kastritis, P.L., Melquiond, A.S., *et al.*, 2016. dMM-PBSA: A new HADDOCK scoring function for protein-peptide docking. Front. Mol. Biosci. 3, 46.

Stanfield, R.L., Wilson, I.A., 1995. Protein-peptide interactions. Curr. Opin. Struct. Biol. 5, 103–113.

Stein, A., Aloy, P., 2008. Contextual specificity in peptide-mediated protein interactions. PLOS ONE 3, e2524.

Tompa, P., 2012. Intrinsically disordered proteins: A 10-year recap. Trends Biochem. Sci. 37, 509–516.

Toniolo, C., Crisma, M., Formaggio, F., Peggion, C., 2001. Control of peptide conformation by the Thorpe-Ingold effect (C alpha-tetrasubstitution). Biopolymers 60, 396–419.

Trabulo, S., Cardoso, A.L., Mano, M., Pedroso de Lima, M.C., 2010. Cell-penetrating peptides – Mechanisms of cellular uptake and generation of delivery systems. Pharmaceuticals (Basel) 3, 961–993.

Trellet, M., Melquiond, S.J.A., Bonvin, A.M.J.J., 2013. A unified conformational selection and induced fit approach to protein-peptide docking. PLOS ONE 8, e58769.

Tubert-Brohman, I., Sherman, W., Repasky, M., Beuming, T., 2013. Improved docking of polypeptides with glide. J. Chem. Inform. Model. 53, 1689–1699.

Van Roey, K., Uyar, B., Weatheritt, R.J., *et al.*, 2014. Short linear motifs: Ubiquitous and functionally diverse protein interaction modules directing cell regulation. Chem. Rev. 114, 6733–6778.

Vassilev, L.T., Vu, B.T., Graves, B., *et al.*, 2004. In vivo activation of the p53 pathway by small-molecule antagonists of MDM2. Science 303, 844–848.

Venkatachalam, C.M., 1968. Stereochemical criteria for polypeptides and proteins. V. Conformation of a system of three linked peptide units. Biopolymers 6, 1425–1436.

Yan, C., Xu, X., Zou, X., 2016. Fully blind docking at the atomic level for protein-peptide complex structure prediction. Structure 24, 1842–1853.

Zahiri, J., Bozorgmehr, J.H., Masoudi-Nejad, A., 2013. Computational prediction of protein – Protein interaction networks: Algorithms and resources. Curr. Genom. 14, 397–414.

Zarrinpar, A., Bhattacharyya, R.P., Lim, W.A., 2003. The structure and function of proline recognition domains. Sci. STKE RE8.

Zvelebil, M.J., Thornton, J.M., 1993. Peptide-protein interactions: An overview. Q. Rev. Biophys. 26, 333–363.

Relevant Websites

http://foldxsuite.crg.eu/
    FoldX server.
http://galaxy.seoklab.org/cgi-bin/submit.cgi?type=PEPDOCK
    GalaxyPepDock.
http://bioserv.rpbs.univ-paris-diderot.fr/services/pepATTRACT/
    pepATTRACT.
https://www.ccdc.cam.ac.uk/
    The Cambridge Crystallographic Data Centre (CCDC).
http://www.rcsb.org/
    The Protein Data Bank.

Biographical Sketch

Dr. U.S. Raghavender did his Masters in Physics (specialization in Condensed Matter Physics) from the University of Hyderabad and obtained his PhD in Biocrystallography of Designed Peptides from the Indian Institute of Science (IISc, Bangalore) in 2010. He did his post-doctoral studies in Stanford Research International – Center for Advanced Drug Research (USA), National Center for Biological Sciences (NCBS-TIFR, Bangalore, India) and The Hebrew University of Jerusalem (Israel) in the area of computational studies involving protein-peptide interactions. He has expertise in peptide design, conformational analysis and computational studies of peptide mediated interactions. His research interests include applying computational approaches to studying transient protein-protein and protein-peptide interactions. His interests also span in studying genomes and transcriptomes of medicinally important plants. He is a recipient of award of Young Scientist Scheme of Science and Engineering Research Board (Department of Science & Technology, Government of India).

Dr. R.S. Rathore obtained M. Phil. In 1991 from Devi Ahilya University, Indore and PhD in 1999 from Indian Institute of Science, Bangalore, India, in Structural Biology in the area of X-ray crystallography and peptide *de novo* design. He further pursued postdoctoral work on protein crystallography and peptide design at the University of Texas Medical Branch at Galveston, USA. He is currently working as a Professor in the School of Earth, Biological and Environmental Sciences, Central University of South Bihar, Gaya, India. Rathore earlier worked in University of Hyderabad, India and Schrödinger Inc. (USA). His main interests are protein modelling and design and Free Energy Perturbation method for lead optimizations. He has published 95 articles in peer reviewed journals.

Homologous Protein Detection

Xuefeng Cui and Yaosen Min, Tsinghua University, Beijing, China

Introduction

Proteins carry a wide variety of functions within organisms. For example, antibody proteins can act as virus fighters to neutralize the target function causing a disease; enzyme proteins can act as catalysis to accelerate a chemical reaction by lowering its activation energy; hemoglobin proteins can transport oxygen via arterial blood; fibrous proteins can make up structural components, such as skin, hair, and nails. This is why it is very important to study how proteins function in organisms.

If we could understand how proteins function, we should be able to modify existing proteins or even to design new proteins. The newly designed proteins could help us to fight against cold virus or even Ebola virus, to further accelerate or even to slow down a chemical reaction within organisms. The ultimate goal of such protein designs is to benefit human lives, such as no one would get cold any more, or everyone could drink sea water directly. Unfortunately, we still understand very little about how proteins function, and biologists are still trying hard to study how proteins function in organisms.

It is widely accepted that protein functions are determined by protein structures (Crick, 1958). If we could find proteins with similar structures and similar functions, one could focus on the similarities as hints. Such hints suggest that the similar part of the complete protein structure tends to be the functioning part of the protein. This approach should significantly reduce the search space and hence speed up the study on protein functions. Initially, this work was done manually by expert. However, since biologists have experimentally determined more than 100,000 protein structures (Berman *et al.*, 2000), it is extremely labor extensive to exam the similarities between each pair of proteins manually.

This motivates the computational problem of homologous protein detection that automatically find proteins sharing a common ancestor during the course of evolution. Such homologous proteins tend to share conserved protein sequences, structures and functions. Thus, these proteins should be ideal cases for biologists to study how proteins function. Moreover, computers are much cheaper and faster comparing to human labors. Therefore, the homologous protein detection becomes an irreplaceable step towards understanding how proteins function.

Background

Formally, a protein complex consists of one or more chains of amino acids. Each chain is also called a polypeptide because the amino acids are connected by peptide bonds. For sake of simplicity, a protein in this article is referred to a single polypeptide. Then, a protein can be represented by a sequence of amino acids connected by peptide bonds, or a number of atoms in three-dimensional space connected by peptide or covalent bonds. Detailed explanations of related terminologies are provided as followings.

Amino acid: Amino acids are small organic molecules containing amine ($-NH_2$) and carboxyl ($-COOH$) functional groups, along with a side chain (i.e., the R group), which is used to identify the amino acid as shown in **Fig. 1**. Moreover, the carbon atom connected to the side chain is referred as the C_α atom, which is marked as a star in the figure. In total, there are 20 kinds of common amino acids identified by 20 kinds of side chains, and each kind of amino acids can be represented by a single character.

Polypeptide: Two or more amino acids form a polypeptide via dehydration reactions, and the polypeptide could be identified by its peptide bonds, which are amide groups as shown in **Fig. 2**. Each polypeptide has an N-terminus (i.e., the amine end) and a C-terminus (i.e., the carboxyl end). Usually, the amino acids that have been incorporated into polypeptides are also called "residues", and the residues are counted from the N-terminus to the C-terminus.

Primary structure: A protein is a polypeptide containing more than 50 residues. Recall that a polypeptide is a chain of residues, and each residue can be represented by a single character. Then, the primary structure or simply the sequence of a protein can be represented by a sequence of characters, where each character represents the type of the corresponding residue.

Secondary structure: The secondary structure of a protein indicates local structure patterns formed by hydrogen bonds between residues. The two main types of protein secondary structures are α-helices and β-sheets. The cartoon in **Fig. 3** (drawn using PyMOL, Delano, 2002) has been widely used to show the trace of residues forming an α-helix on the left and a β-sheet on the right. It can be seen that the α-helix has a right-handed helix pattern, and the β-sheet has a sheet pattern formed by parallel or anti-parallel β-strands.

Tertiary structure: The tertiary structure or simply the structure of a protein refers to the three-dimensional structure of the polypeptide. **Fig. 4** shows an example protein containing mainly α-helices that are connected by loop regions. A simplified representation of a protein structure consists of the three-dimensional coordinates of representative atoms. Typically, the C_α atom can be used as the representative atom for each residue because it approximately defines the three-dimensional location of the residue. Hence, the protein structure can be represented by a sequence of C_α coordinates in three-dimensional space.

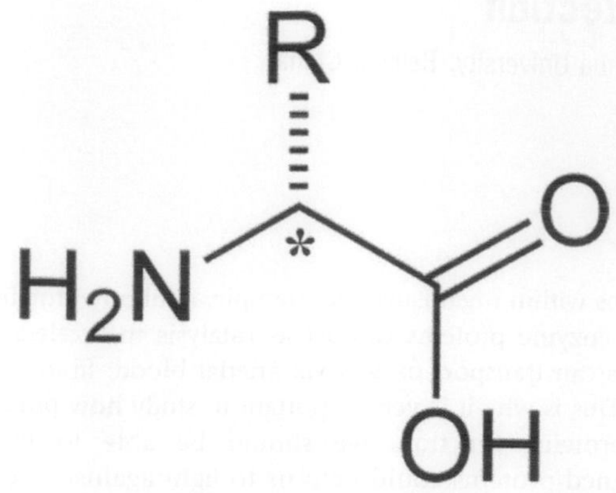

Fig. 1 An amino acid containing a C_α atom (star), an amine group (-NH₂), a carboxyl group (-COOH) and a side chain (R).

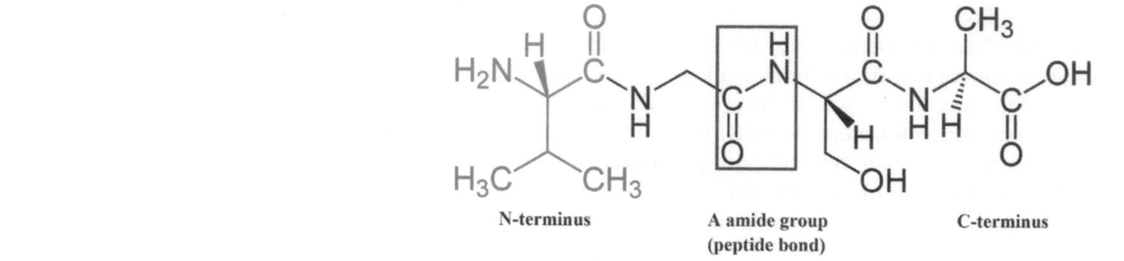

Fig. 2 A polypeptide with five residues.

Fig. 3 Secondary structures of proteins: An α-helix (left) and a β-sheet (right).

Quaternary structure: The quaternary structure of a protein complex refers to the overall three-dimensional structure of a protein complex consisting of two or more polypeptide molecules and possibly other molecules, such as ligand or RNA molecules. Since all the molecules are interacting with each other, they are called a protein complex. **Fig. 5** shows one example quaternary structure, but quaternary structures are beyond the scope of this article.

Homologous Protein Detection

In biology, homologous proteins are the ones sharing a common ancestor. Since we do not know the exact evolution histories of proteins, homologous proteins are computationally defined as proteins sharing significant similarities. For example, assuming that each residue is randomly selected from the 20 kinds of residues, the probability to see two protein sequences sharing N common residues is 20^{-N}. If N is a big number, such as 100, the probability becomes very small (i.e., $20^{-100} = 7.9 \times 10^{-131}$). Thus, such similarities are highly unlikely to happen by chance, and such observations should be strong evidences for homologous proteins. Therefore, such proteins are presumed to be homologous proteins in computational biology.

There are mainly two kinds of evidences commonly used to find homologous proteins: protein sequences and protein structures. The computational problem to find sequence similarities between a pair of sequences is called the sequence alignment problem, which is actually a string matching problem. Given two strings, the goal is to find character matchings between the two strings that maximizes a scoring function. Typically, a match could have a score of $+1$, a mismatch could have a score of -1, and an in-del (i.e., an insertion or a deletion) could also have a score of -1. Then, it is possible to use a dynamic programming algorithm (Needleman and Wunsch, 1970; Smith and Waterman, 1981) to find the optimal solution that maximizes the scoring function.

Fig. 4 The tertiary structure of a protein.

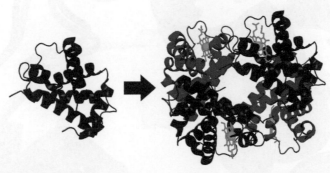

Fig. 5 The quaternary structure of a protein complex: A single chain (left) making up a complex (right).

The problem described above is a simple version of the protein sequence alignment problem (Henikoff and Henikoff, 1992; Altschul *et al.*, 1990; Ma *et al.*, 2002; Remmert *et al.*, 2012). In practice, a biologist might be interested in different things, and hence there are different algorithms designed for different requirements: finding global similarities or finding local similarities, targeting high accuracy or targeting high speed, and so on. Moreover, different scoring functions have also been designed: assuming all aligned residue pairs are independent, assuming the aligned residues pairs are position-specific, assuming the aligned residues pairs are pairwisely dependent, and so on.

Finding homologous proteins with structure similarities is much more complicated but more meaningful. Recall that protein functions are determined by protein structures. Sequence similarities work well in practice because proteins with highly similar sequences tend to have highly similar structures (e.g., **Fig. 6**). Moreover, it is computationally much faster to find sequence similarities than structure similarities. However, there are many homologous proteins sharing little sequence similarities but still sharing high structure similarities (e.g., **Fig. 7**). Such homologous proteins are called remote homologous proteins because they are conceptually remote as suggested by sequence similarities.

The computational problem to find structure similarities between a pair of protein structures is called the structure alignment problem (Kolodny *et al.*, 2005; Hasegawa and Holm, 2009). It can be divided into two sub-problems: the residue matching problem and the superposition problem. The residue matching problem is similar to the sequence alignment problem. The only difference is on the scoring function, which is now based on the distances between the aligned residue pairs in the three-dimensional space. The superposition problem is to find a rotation and a translation to rigidly transform one protein structure to the other one so that the aligned residue pairs are located closely each other.

The protein structure alignment problem is computationally expensive because its two sub-problems have a chicken-egg relationship: solving the residue matching problem requires the structures to be rigidly transformed first, while solving the superposition problem requires the residues to be aligned first. If we know the answer of one problem, it is computationally efficient (i.e., these exists algorithms running in polynomial time) to solve the other problem. However, if we would like to solve both problems at the same time, the problem becomes NP-hard (Goldman *et al.*, 1999; Li and Ng, 2011). Therefore, many heuristic algorithms are designed based on the idea of sampling local similarities first and then producing global similarities by

```
Seq 1     XGDVEKGKKIFVQKCAQCHTVEKGGKHKTGPNLHGLFGRKTGQAPGFTYTDANKNKGITWK  61
Match      GDVEKGKKIF  KC QCHTVEKGGKHKTGPNLHGLFGRKTGQAPG  YT ANKNKGI W
Seq 2     -GDVEKGKKIFIMKCSQCHTVEKGGKHKTGPNLHGLFGRKTGQAPGYSYTAANKNKGIIWG  60

Seq 1     EETLMEYLENPKKYIPGTKMIFAGIKKKTEREDLIAYLKKATNE  105
Match     E TLMEYLENPKKYIPGTKMIF GIKKK ER DLIAYLKKATNE
Seq 2     EDTLMEYLENPKKYIPGTKMIFVGIKKKEERADLIAYLKKATNE  104
```

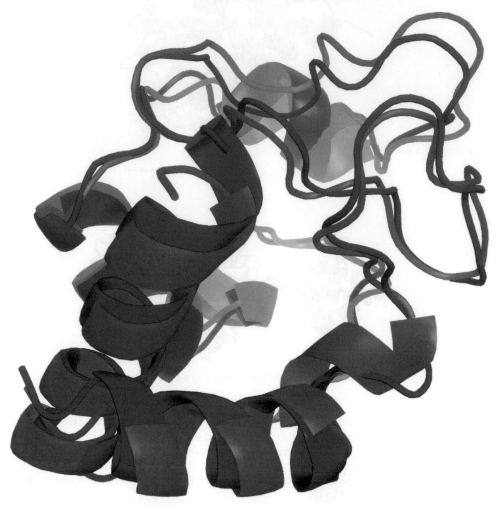

Fig. 6 Two close homologous proteins with similar sequences (top) and similar structures (bottom).

enlarging or combining local similarities (Shindyalov and Bourne, 1998; Krissinel and Henrick, 2004; Zhang and Skolnick, 2005; Cui *et al.*, 2013). Unfortunately, such heuristic algorithms can only find local optimal solutions.

Like the sequence alignment problem, different structure alignment algorithms have been designed to satisfy different interests of biologists: using global structures or focusing on interaction interfaces, targeting high accuracy or targeting high speed, using only structure information or fusing other available information (e.g., secondary structure information), and so on. Some algorithms also try to avoid solving the superposition problem, and to solve the residue matching problem directly (Holm and Sander, 1993; Holm and Rosenström, 2010). The main idea here is to use pairwise distances instead of three-dimensional coordinates to represent protein structures. The trick of such algorithms is that the pairwise distances do not change after any rigid transformations. However, the residue matching problem for the new presentation is still NP-hard, and simulated annealing algorithms have been used to solve the problem with local optimal solutions.

There is a highly related problem called the protein threading problem (Roy *et al.*, 2010; Källberg *et al.*, 2012; Söding *et al.*, 2005), which tries to find similarities between a protein without structure information (i.e., with primarily sequence information) and a protein with structure information. The motivation is the fact that there are significantly more proteins with known sequences than proteins with known structures. The main challenge here is how to compare the cross-modal information. The classical approach is transferring the sequence and the structure space into other spaces, such as the secondary structure space, the

```
Seq 1   VLSAADKSNVKACWGKIGSHAGEYGAEALERTFCSFPTTKTYFPHFDLSHGSAQVKA---  57
Match   VLS    V   WK      G    R   SPT      F       AKA
Seq 2   VLSEGEWQLVLHVWAKVEADVAGHGQDIHIRLYKSHPETLEKHDRFKHLKTEAEMKASED  60

Seq 1   ---HGQKVADALTQAVAHMDDLPTAMSALSDLHAYKLRVDPVNFKFLSHCLLVTLACHHP  114
Match      HG  V  AL           L    HA K       FS    L    HP
Seq 2   LKKHGVTVLTALGAILKKKGHHEAELKPLAQSHATKHKIPIKYLEFISEAIIHVLHSRHP  120

Seq 1   AEFTPAVHASLDKFFSAVSTVLTSKYR  141
Match    F        K          KY
Seq 2   GDFGADAQGAMNKALELFRKDIAAKYK  147
```

Fig. 7 Two remote homologous proteins with dissimilar sequences (top) and similar structures (bottom).

solvent accessibility space, and so on. Then, similarities can be found in the sequence and the transformed spaces. Recently, cross-modal learning algorithms (Lhota et al., 2015; Cui et al., 2016) have also been used to avoid such space transformations, and to solve the problem in two or more modals directly with improved accuracy.

Other than protein sequences and protein structures, many evidences have also been used to find homologous proteins. For example, if two proteins interact with the same group of proteins, they could also be presumed to be homologous proteins. However, such evidences carry less information comparing to the structure evidences because finding correlations between structures and functions is the key to understand how proteins function. Based on such protein-structure correlations, biologists can first hypothesize how proteins function, and then design biology experiments or molecular dynamic simulations to validate the hypothesis (Wüthrich and Wagner, 1978; Bennett et al., 1984). Although protein-protein interaction evidences cannot directly help to understand how proteins function, they could perform better than sequence or structure information for applications, such as the protein function prediction (Radivojac et al., 2013).

Application: Drug Repositioning

Drug design is both a time consuming and expensive task. The complete drug design process contains several stages: the early drug discovery stage, the pre-clinical research stage, the three clinical trial stages, the application stage and the post-approval study stage. Each stage could take between two and eight years, and the total time required for the complete process is typically between 15 and 25 years. Unfortunately, many patients cannot live that long waiting for the drug release. On the other hand, many patients cannot afford new drugs because of the high drug price due to the high cost of drug design. Taking America in 2013 for example, the total amount of money spent on drug design is approximately 50 billion US dollars, while there are only approximately 25 drugs released. On average, the cost to design a new drug is approximately two billion US dollars. Therefore, it is highly desirable to save both time and money to design new drugs.

It is difficult to save time and the money to design new drugs for several reasons. One reason for the long time is that finding a new drug candidate in the early drug discovery stage is labor intensive. This is actually where computers could help; thus, many algorithms have been designed for this purpose. Even with the help of modern computers and classical algorithms, finding a new drug candidate is still very difficult because of the infinite number of possible candidates. One reason for the high cost is that more than 90% of the drug candidates will fail the clinical stages. For example, it is very difficult to predict if a drug candidate has toxicities or other unacceptable side effects. Such issues can only be discovered by biology experiments or even clinical trials. Since most drug candidates failed the clinical trials, all the money spend in earlier stages will not produce any outcome.

Recently, a key observation opens a new door to solve the drug design problem. Traditionally, each drug was proposed to treat only one disease. However, recent experiments show that each drug could interact with six different proteins, on average, that exists in the human organism. Other than the target protein that is responsible for the disease, most interacting proteins are responsible for side effects or even toxicities. However, there are happy accidents such that the released drug could also interact with a protein that is responsible for another disease. That means, there exists drugs proposing to treat one disease could also treat another disease.

Finding such unknown relationships between drugs and diseases could significantly save time for drug design. Recall that finding a new drug candidate is difficult because of the infinite search space. Scanning the complete drug database for drug candidates reduces the infinite search space to a much smaller and finite search space. As a result, it could take only a couple of days for modern computers to finish the task. Once succeeded, it could save more than eight years of time by skipping the early drug discovery stage, the pre-clinical research stage, and the first clinical stage of drug design. Consequently, this could reduce the drug design time by a factor of approximately two.

Finding such unknown relationships between drugs and diseases could also save a lot of money for drug design. Recall that the high cost of drug design is mainly due to the high failure rate. However, new drug candidates are selected from the released drugs that has previously passed all clinical trials. Then, such drug candidates are highly likely to pass the clinical trials again. Previously, the main reason of the failure rate is because of the unacceptable side effects and toxicities. Now, the main reason becomes the advances in the clinical trials. This should instantly change the high failure rate to a high success rate. As a result, this could reduce the money required to design a new drug by a factor of at least ten.

In computational biology, the problem of finding such unknown relationships between drugs and diseases is called the drug repositioning problem (Ashburn and Thor, 2004; Chong and Sullivan, 2007). One approach to solve the problem is to apply structure alignment algorithms on the interaction interface structures (Gao and Skolnick, 2010; Cui *et al.*, 2015a,b; Naveed *et al.*, 2015). The idea is that if two interaction interfaces have highly similar structures, they tend to interact with the same group of drugs. For example, two novel target proteins, the peroxisome proliferator-activated receptor gamma and the oncogene B-cell lymphoma 2, have been discovered using this method. Both target proteins were first computationally predicted by structure alignment methods, and then experimentally verified by biological methods.

The drug repositioning approach is becoming more and more important for pharmaceutical companies as more and more drugs have been proposed using the approach. For example, Requip was initially proposed as a treatment of Parkinsonian, and then repositioned as a treatment of Restless Legs Syndrome; gabapentin was initially designed as an anti-epileptics drug, and then repositioned as a neuropathic pain reliever drug; and so on. Therefore, the success of drug repositioning has saved not only decades of time, but also tens of billions of US dollars for pharmaceutical companies. In the coming years, more computational drug repositioning methods will be proposed by computational biologists, and more repositioned drugs will be released by pharmaceutical companies. Consequently, more patients would be benefited from these repositioned drugs.

Application: Structure Determination and Prediction

Since protein structures are irreplaceable for understanding protein functions, several experimental methods have been designed to determine protein structures. Due to the importance of the problem, three Nobel Prizes have been awarded to protein structure determination methods: X-ray crystallography (Garman and Schneider, 1997), nuclear magnetic resonance (NMR) spectroscopy (Wüthrich, 1990) and cryo-electron microscopy (cryo-EM, Küohlbrandt, 2014; Callaway, 2015) in 1915, 1991 and 2017, respectively.

Current protein structure determination methods share a common high-level procedure. First, protein samples are purified and pre-processed. Then, experimental data are measured using the protein structure determination device. For example, an X-ray crystallography device produces scatter plots of the differentiation effects caused by the protein crystal; an NMR spectroscopy device produces atom-atom distances between close atoms of the protein structure; and a cryo-EM device produces two-dimensional projections of the three-dimensional protein structures. Finally, these experimental data are analyzed to build protein structure models (i.e., the three-dimensional coordinates of all atoms). The last step is done computationally as a data science problem to find protein structure models that are consistent with the observed experimental data.

Ideally, the experimental data contain small errors and the true protein structure model could be easily unveiled. For example, the scatter plots of X-ray crystallography could be used to reconstruct the electron density map containing all atoms of the protein structure. Such an electron density map could be imagined as a three-dimensional photo of the protein structure, where each atom is represented by a ball and each bond is represented by two overlapping balls. Thus, the protein structure model can be computed from the electron density map. Unfortunately, only a very small number of X-ray crystallography experiments have produced such ideal-quality protein structure models.

Generally, experimental data are not sufficient to build protein structure models directly; thus, additional knowledge-bases have to be used. For example, the bond lengths and the bond angles (between two connected bonds sharing a common atom) should have very small variances (Evans, 2007; Jaskolski et al., 2007). Moreover, the bond torsion angles (between two bond surfaces defined by three connected bonds) should obey a specific distribution (Laskowski et al., 1993; Davis et al., 2007). Such constraint and restraint knowledge can be used to reduce the model search space to protein-like structures. The goal is to build a protein structure model that is consistent with both the knowledge-bases and the experimental data. Approximately, 30% of the X-ray crystallography experiments have produced such high-quality protein structure models (Berman et al., 2000).

For the remaining 70% of the X-ray crystallography experiments, homology modelling methods are used to produce the protein structure model. The main problem here is the quality of the experimental data. Actually, homology modelling methods are even more popular when processing cryo-EM data because of their low data quality (Lawson et al., 2010). The idea of homology modelling methods is first identifying a homologous protein with a similar structure, and then refining the homologous structure to better fit the experimental data. Here, the key problem is to find a good homologous protein as the template structure. This can be done by employing sequence alignment algorithms, threading algorithms and recently cross-modal learning algorithms. These methods are highly related to the protein structure prediction methods described in the following two paragraphs.

Currently, multiple protein structure determination methods are frequently used because each method has its own advantages and limitations. Specifically, an X-ray crystallography device is able to produce protein structures with the highest qualities but it requires the proteins to be crystalized first, which is difficult or even impossible for large proteins; an NMR spectroscopy device is able to produce dynamic protein structures but the produced structure might contain a lot of errors; a cryo-EM device is able to produce large protein complex structures but the qualities are limited. Moreover, neither method is capable of experimentally determining all protein structures.

This motivates the protein structure prediction problem, and homology modelling methods again play key roles to solve the problem (Moult et al., 2017; Haas et al., 2017). Specifically, given the sequence of a target protein and the knowledge-base of all known protein structures, the first step is to identify a homologous protein structure from the knowledge-base. Then, the homologous protein structure is used as a template to initialize a decoy structure. The final predicted structure is produced by refining the decoy structure to optimize a potential energy function. A typical potential energy function involves the bond forces, the electrostatic forces and the van der Waals forces, and it is usually time consuming to evaluate (Brooks et al., 1983; Webb and Sali, 2014). Since homology modelling methods significantly reduce the model search space, the number of times to evaluate the potential energy function is significantly reduced (Roy et al., 2010; Källberg et al., 2012; Söding et al., 2005; Cui et al., 2016). Therefore, homology modelling methods usually perform much faster than Ab Initio methods.

Protein structure determination and prediction problems are among the most wanted solutions in biology, and breakthrough technologies have been developed recently to advance the existing solutions. The central dogma of molecular biology tells us that the RNA polymerase is responsible for the transcription function, the spliceosome is responsible for the splicing function, and the ribosome is responsible for the translation function. Two Novel Prizes have been awarded to solving the RNA polymerase structure and the ribosome structure in 2006 and 2009, respectively. Since 2012, cryo-EM opens a new gate to determine protein structures, and it has been used to solve many key protein structures, including the polymerase structure in 2015, playing key functions in organisms. In the future, computational methods will play more and more important roles in structure determination technologies and structure biology.

Discussions

In this article, we have covered the fundamentals of finding homologous proteins and its applications. It has been shown that it is important to find homologous proteins because they carry key information on studying how proteins function. Indeed, homologous protein detection is highly likely the first step in almost all protein function researches. Therefore, finding homologous proteins is a fundamental problem in protein bioinformatics.

Although many researchers have been working on this topic, there are still a lot of open problems waiting to be solved. For example, existing methods work well for homologous proteins within the same family or the same super-family. The main reason is that such homologous proteins tend to have global structure similarities, and this reduces the difficulty of the problem. However, for homologous proteins within the same fold, conserved high-level structure patterns can still be observed by human experts. Due to the lack of global structure similarities, it is more challenging for computational methods to distinguish true homologous proteins from the false ones. Thus, different computational methods tend to have different results, and the results might disagree with each other. Actually, there is no theoretical guarantee on finding such homologous proteins for any computational methods; thus, homologous protein detection in the fold level remains open.

This article also shows that computational methods are playing critical roles in protein structural biology. Actually, this is not only true in protein structural biology, but also true in life science. Indeed, recent advances in life science is driven by mathematical, statistical and computational methods. It is not difficult to see that the situation will remain the same in the future, and more interdisciplinary talents are needed to accomplish our goals.

See also: Identification of Homologs. Natural Language Processing Approaches in Bioinformatics

---

References

Altschul, S.F., Gish, W., Miller, W., Myers, E.W., Lipman, D.J., 1990. Basic local alignment search tool. Journal of Molecular Biology 215 (3), 403–410.

Ashburn, T.T., Thor, K.B., 2004. Drug repositioning: Identifying and developing new uses for existing drugs. Nature Reviews Drug Discovery 3 (8), 673–683.

Bennett, W.S., Huber, R., Engel, J., 1984. Structural and functional aspects of domain motions in protein. Critical Reviews in Biochemistry and Molecular Biology 15 (4), 291–384.

Berman, H.M., Westbrook, J., Feng, Z., *et al.*, 2000. The Protein Data Bank. Nucleic Acids Research 28, 235–242.

Brooks, B.R., Bruccoleri, R.E., Olafson, B.D., *et al.*, 1983. CHARMM: A program for macromolecular energy, minimization, and dynamics calculations. Journal of Computational Chemistry 4 (2), 187–217.

Callaway, E., 2015. The revolution will not be crystallized. Nature 525 (7568), 172.

Chong, C.R., Sullivan, D.J., 2007. New uses for old drugs. Nature 448 (7154), 645–646.

Crick, F.H.C., 1958. On protein synthesis. The Symposia of the Society for Experimental Biology 12, 138–163.

Cui, X., Kuwahara, H., Li, S.C., Gao, X. 2015b. Compare local pocket and global protein structure models by small structure patterns. In: Proceedings of the 6th ACM Conference on Bioinformatics, Computational Biology and Health Informatics, ACM, pp. 355–365.

Cui, X., Li, S.C., Bu, D., Li, M., 2013. Towards reliable automatic protein structure alignment. In: Proceedings of the International Workshop on Algorithms in Bioinformatics, WABI, pp. 18–32.

Cui, X., Lu, Z., Wang, S., Jing-Yan Wang, J., Gao, X., 2016. CMsearch: Simultaneous exploration of protein sequence space and structure space improves not only protein homology detection but also protein structure prediction. Bioinformatics 32 (12), i332–i340.

Cui, X., Naveed, H., Gao, X., 2015a. Finding optimal interaction interface alignments between biological complexes. Bioinformatics 31 (12), i133–i141.

Davis, I.W., Leaver-Fay, A., Chen, V.B., *et al.*, 2007. MolProbity: All-atom contacts and structure validation for proteins and nucleic acids. Nucleic Acids Research 35 (Web Server issue), W375–W383.

Delano, W.L., 2002. The PyMOL molecular graphics system. Proteins Structure Function and Bioinformatics 30, 442–454.

Evans, P.R., 2007. An introduction to stereochemical restraints. Acta Crystallographica Section D 63 (1), 58–61.

Gao, M., Skolnick, J., 2010. iAlign: A method for the structural comparison of protein-protein interfaces. Bioinformatics 26 (18), 2259–2265.

Garman, E.F., Schneider, T.R., 1997. Macromolecular cryocrystallography. Journal of Applied Crystallography 30 (3), 211–237.

Goldman, D., Istrail, S., Papadimitriou, C.H., 1999. Algorithmic aspects of protein structure similarity. In: Proceedings of the IEEE 40th Annual Symposium on Foundations of Computer Science, pp. 512–521.

Haas, J., Barbato, A., Behringer, D., *et al.*, 2017. Continuous automated model evaluation (cameo) complementing the critical assessment of structure prediction in casp12. Proteins: Structure, Function, and Bioinformatics 86, 387–398.

Hasegawa, H., Holm, L., 2009. Advances and pitfalls of protein structural alignment. Current Opinion in Structural Biology 19 (3), 341–348.

Henikoff, S., Henikoff, J.G., 1992. Amino acid substitution matrices from protein blocks. Proceedings of the National Academy of Sciences of the United States of America 89 (22), 10915–10919.

Holm, L., Rosenström, P., 2010. Dali server: Conservation mapping in 3D. Nucleic Acids Research 38 (Suppl_2), W545–W549.

Holm, L., Sander, C., 1993. Protein structure comparison by alignment of distance matrices. Journal of Molecular Biology 233 (1), 123–138.

Jaskolski, M., Gilski, M., Dauter, Z., Wlodawer, A., 2007. Stereochemical restraints revisited: How accurate are refinement targets and how much should protein structures be allowed to deviate from them? Acta Crystallographica Section D 63 (5), 611–620.

Källberg, M., Wang, H., Wang, S., *et al.*, 2012. Template-based protein structure modeling using the raptorx web server. Nature Protocols 7 (8), 1511–1522.

Kolodny, R., Koehl, P., Levitt, M., 2005. Comprehensive evaluation of protein structure alignment methods: Scoring by geometric measures. Journal of Molecular Biology 346 (4), 1173–1188.

Krissinel, E., Henrick, K., 2004. Secondary-structure matching (SSM), a new tool for fast protein structure alignment in three dimensions. Acta Crystallographica Section D: Biological Crystallography 60 (12), 2256–2268.

Küohlbrandt, W., 2014. Microscopy: Cryo-EM enters a new era. eLife 3, e03678.

Laskowski, R.A., MacArthur, M.W., Moss, D.S., Thornton, J.M., 1993. PROCHECK: A program to check the stereochemical quality of protein structures. Journal of Applied Crystallography 26 (2), 283–291.

Lawson, C.L., Baker, M.L., Best, C., *et al.*, 2010. EMDataBank.org: Unified data resource for CryoEM. Nucleic Acids Research 39 (Suppl. 1), D456–D464.

Lhota, J., Hauptman, R., Hart, T., Ng, C., Xie, L., 2015. A new method to improve network topological similarity search: Applied to fold recognition. Bioinformatics 31 (13), 2106–2114.

Li, S.C., Ng, Y.K., 2011. On protein structure alignment under distance constraint. Theoretical Computer Science 412 (32), 4187–4199.

Ma, B., Tromp, J., Li, M., 2002. PatternHunter: Faster and more sensitive homology search. Bioinformatics 18 (3), 440–445.

Moult, J., Fidelis, K., Kryshtafovych, A., Schwede, T., Tramontano, A., 2017. Critical assessment of methods of protein structure prediction (CASP)round XII. Proteins: Structure, Function, and Bioinformatics 86, 7–15.

Naveed, H., Hameed, U.S., Harrus, D., *et al.*, 2015. An integrated structure-and system-based framework to identify new targets of metabolites and known drugs. Bioinformatics 31 (24), 3922–3929.

Needleman, S.B., Wunsch, C.D., 1970. A general method applicable to the search for similarities in the amino acid sequence of two proteins. Journal of Molecular Biology 48 (3), 443–453.

Radivojac, P., Clark, W.T., Oron, T.R., *et al.*, 2013. A large-scale evaluation of computational protein function prediction. Nature Methods 10 (3), 221–227.

Remmert, M., Biegert, A., Hauser, A., Söding, J., 2012. HHblits: Lightning-fast iterative protein sequence searching by HMM-HMM alignment. Nature Methods 9 (2), 173–175.

Roy, A., Kucukural, A., Zhang, Y., 2010. I-TASSER: A unified platform for automated protein structure and function prediction. Nature Protocols 5 (4), 725–738.

Shindyalov, I.N., Bourne, P.E., 1998. Protein structure alignment by incremental combinatorial extension (CE) of the optimal path. Protein Engineering 11 (9), 739–747.

Smith, T.F., Waterman, M.S., 1981. Identification of common molecular subsequences. Journal of Molecular Biology 147 (1), 195–197.

Söding, J., Biegert, A., Lupas, A.N., 2005. The HHpred interactive server for protein homology detection and structure prediction. Nucleic Acids Research 33 (suppl_2), W244–W248.

Webb, B., Sali, A., 2014. Protein structure modeling with modeller. Protein Structure Prediction. 1–15.

Wüthrich, K., 1990. Protein structure determination in solution by nmr spectroscopy. Journal of Biological Chemistry 265 (36), 22059–22062.

Wüthrich, K., Wagner, G., 1978. Internal motion in globular proteins. Trends in Biochemical Sciences 3 (4), 227–230.

Zhang, Y., Skolnick, J., 2005. TM-align: A protein structure alignment algorithm based on the TM-score. Nucleic Acids Research 33 (7), 2302–2309.

Mutation Effects on 3D-Structural Reorganization Using HIV-1 Protease as a Case Study

Biswa R Meher, Berhampur University, Berhampur, India
Megha Vaishnavi, Central University of Jharkhand, Ranchi, India
Venkata SK Mattaparthi, Tezpur University, Tezpur, Assam, India
Seema Patel, San Diego State University, San Diego, CA, United States
Sandeep Kaushik, European Institute of Excellence on Tissue Engineering and Regenerative Medicine, Guimaraes, Portugal

Introduction

AIDS and HIV

Acquired immunodeficiency syndrome (AIDS) spread by the human immunodeficiency virus (HIV) has become an epidemic worldwide (Sanou et al., 2012). In 2016, it is assessed that about 36.7 million people were living with HIV, 19.5 million people were living with HIV on antiretroviral therapy, and a huge 1.8 million people were newly infected with HIV, and the infection is spreading at a shocking proportion. UNAIDS projections indicate that an additional 50 million people will be freshly infected in the coming decade, if the world doesn't get through to develop a potent therapy/medication (drugs or vaccine). However, remarkable progress against AIDS over the past 15 years has stimulated a global commitment to end the epidemic by 2030 (see "Relevant Websites section").

The lethal virus attacks the human immune system targeting the helper T-cells (specifically CD4$^+$ T cells), macrophages, and dendritic cells (Cunningham et al., 2010) reducing the human immunity (Hatziioannou and Evans, 2012). Regardless of vigorous public health efforts and laborious research efforts, AIDS remains a fatal syndrome. Nevertheless, antiretroviral therapy has given a chance to tackle AIDS in part, but due to the clever HIV the goal for complete destruction of the epidemic remains distant. Mutation-induced drug resistance has abolished the clinical effectiveness of most of the FDA-approved drugs administered. So, there is a great demand for developing and designing a potent and less vulnerable drug for antiretroviral therapy. As shown in **Fig. 1**, HIV is a globular enveloped retrovirus, enclosing dual copies of single-stranded, positive-sense RNA (Ganser-Pornillos et al., 2012). HIV infection starts with the attachment of the matured virus to the host cells containing CD4 + receptors and coreceptors CCR5 or CXCR4 with their envelope glycoproteins gp41 and gp120 (Tran et al., 2012). Upon attachment, the host cell membrane and the viral envelope dissolves and the inner genomic content (RNAs) of the virus enters to the host cell. The RNA is then reversibly transcribes to viral DNA by the reverse transcriptase (Le Grice, 2012), which is followed by transcription, translation to form large polypeptide chain (Gag and Gag-pol). The large polypeptide chain is eventually cleaved by the proteolytic events by HIV-pr to form small structural and functional proteins of the virus. Subsequently, with the process of budding and assembly (Bukrinskaya, 2007), the synthesized proteins and part of host cellular membrane form the new virions for next phase of infections to the new CD4 + cells.

HIV-1-Protease (HIV-Pr)

HIV-pr is an essential enzyme of HIV replication, and is a vital target for drug design strategies to fight AIDS. It cleaves the Gag and Gag-Pol polyproteins to generate the mature infectious virions capable of CD4 + cells infections (Fun et al., 2012). Deactivating the enzyme's function creates immature virions without having the infectious supremacy. Keeping that in mind, several drugs has

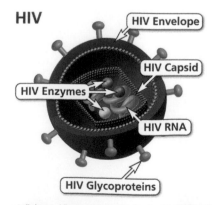

Fig. 1 A schematic structure of a Human Immunodeficiency Virus type 1(HIV-1). Credit: National Institute of Health (NIH).

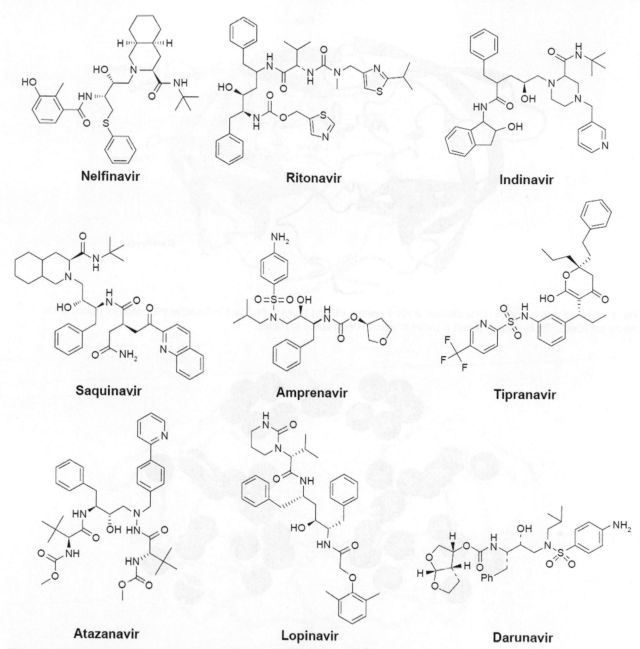

Fig. 2 2D structures of HIV-1 protease inhibitors that are approved by FDA to treat AIDS. Adapted from a research article Arodola, O.A., Soliman, M.E.S., 2015. "Could the FDA-approved anti-HIV PR inhibitors be promising anticancer agents? An answer from enhanced docking approach and molecular dynamics analyses." Drug Design, Development and Therapy 9, 6055–6065.

been designed, developed, and finally approved by FDA against AIDS. To date, at least nine FDA-approved protease inhibitors have been rolled out (**Fig. 2**), but none of them is effective after prolonged treatment time due to mutation-assisted drug resistance.

HIV-pr is a homodimeric aspartyl protease with C2 symmetric in the free form (Brik and Wong, 2003), containing 99 amino acids in both of its chain-A and B. HIV-pr residues are numbered as 1–99 for chain A and 1'–99' for chain B. Flap (residues 43–58 and 43' – 58'), flap elbow (residues 35–42 and 35' – 42'), fulcrum (residues 11–22 and 11' – 22'), cantilever (residues 59–75 and 59' – 75'), and the active ligand binding site organize different regions of the enzyme (**Fig. 3**). The active site of the protein is formed by dimerization of the two monomers and is crowned by two identical flexible glycine rich flaps. The volume of the active site and size is controlled by dynamics of the flaps (Piana *et al.*, 2002a,b). As a member of the aspartic protease family, the protease contains a catalytic triad (Asp25-Thr26-Gly27) in both the chains keeping functional aspartate residues at the dimer interface. The Asp residues are essential both catalytically and structurally while the Thr and Gly residues functions are still unknown at this time and are buried in the active site (Mager, 2001).

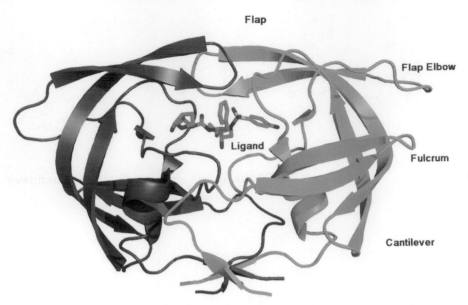

Fig. 3 Schematic representation of the structure of HIV-1 protease (HIV-pr) bound to the ligand in the active site. Important regions of the protein are labeled. The homodimer protein is shown in violet and cyan ribbon structures.

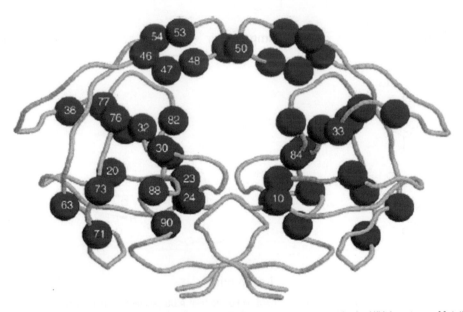

Fig. 4 The structural distribution of the most common mutations associated with drug resistance in the HIV-1 protease. Mutations can occur anywhere in the protease structure. Mutations within the binding cavity are very conservative and operate by distorting the shape of the cavity. Conformationally constrained inhibitors have difficulties in adapting to the altered geometry and lose significant binding affinity. Adapted from Overcoming HIV-1 resistance to protease inhibitors. Drug Discovery Today. Disease Mechanisms I Infectious diseases, vol. 3, No. 2, 2006.

Mutations and Drug Resistance of HIV-Protease Inhibitors

Nevertheless, the HIV-pr-based therapeutic tactics have accomplished reasonable victory, but there are still some hurdles of serious side effects due to mutation-induced drug resistance. Currently, at least more than 50 mutations at near about 30 different codon positions of HIV-pr have been acknowledged. Lists of mutations that occur on the HIV-pr backbone are shown in **Fig. 4**. A molecular level understanding of drug resistance requires the knowledge of both direct and indirect effects of mutation (Johnson et al., 2010). The mutant strains are increased in numbers by the drugs' abuse. Taking of numerous drugs has put selective pressure on the HIV leading to mutations and subsequent evolution of resistant variants (Chen and Lee, 2006). The mutations in HIV-pr are classified as those present near the active site (primary) and those appearing away from the active site (secondary). Both the mutations affect the ligand/drug binding directly and indirectly by direct or indirect effects (Meher and Wang, 2012; Bandyopadhyay and Meher, 2006). There have been several studies (both experimental and computer simulation) indicating the importance of different mutations for the drug resistance in HIV-pr. Molecular dynamics (MD) simulation based approaches has been utilized by researchers worldwide to understand the HIV-pr 3D-structure dynamics and the drug resistance behavior (Piana *et al.*, 2002a, 2002b; Meher and Wang, 2012; Bandyopadhyay and Meher, 2006; Collins *et al.*, 1995; Hornak *et al.*, 2006; Meagher and Carlson, 2005; Ode *et al.*, 2006; Perryman *et al.*, 2004; Scott and Schiffer, 2000; Toth and Borics, 2006).

HIV-pr 3D-Structure and its Dynamics

HIV-pr 3D-structural dynamics is mainly from the contribution of its flap and flap elbow dynamics, which have the maximum movements for accession of ligands or substrates in its active site region. To date, researchers have analyzed the dynamics of both unliganded and liganded forms of the HIV-pr. In all of the liganded forms, the flaps are pulled in toward the bottom of the active site, leading to a flap curling-in event. In the unliganded enzyme, flaps are shifted away from the active site (Hornak *et al.*, 2006) making the flaps curl out. The contribution of residues in the active site region and flaps to the stability is more distinct in the liganded form than in the unliganded form (Kurt *et al.*, 2003). However, in HIV-pr the anticorrelation movements of the flap-active site distances and fulcrum-flap elbow distances is more notable (Perryman *et al.*, 2004).

Flap Movement and Dynamics

The flexibility of the flap tips (Gly48-Gly52 and Gly48'-Gly52') is known as flap dynamics. It opens and closes the flaps determining the cavity size. The conformational change in the flaps is correlated with structural reorganization of residues in the active site (Torbeev *et al.*, 2011). The mutations in flap region result in adjustment of the nonbonding interactions (van der Waals and electrostatic interactions) between the drugs and protein, subsequently helping drug resistance and rendering the drugs ineffective (Cai *et al.*, 2012). Thus numerous computational studies have made an effort to understand flap dynamics behavior. The effects of mutations on the 3D-conformational dynamics and reorganization of HIV-pr have been considered using MD simulations.

Mutation Effects on HIV-pr 3D-Conformation

JE-2147 (Yoshimura *et al.*, 1999) is an experimental peptidomimetic HIV-pr inhibitor developed by Pfizer (**Fig. 5**). It was measured to be more effective than other prevailing HIV-pr inhibitors, which is potent against a wide range of HIV-1, HIV-2 strains. JE-2147 retains exclusive resistance profile (Kar and Knecht, 2012a) with two major mutations I84V and I47V. Nevertheless, I84V is common for other related ligands, I47V appears to be very particular for JE-2147 (Bandyopadhyay and Meher, 2006). The influence of I47V mutation is explored with MD simulation. Simulation outcomes showed greater flexibility of the side-chain of mutant Val47 than that of WT Ile47 in chain B of HIV-pr (Bandyopadhyay and Meher, 2006). Structural investigation exposed that the existence of a flexible P2' moiety is significant for the effectiveness of JE-2147 concerning wild-type (WT) and mutant viruses. These data propose that the use of flexible mechanisms may open a new opportunity for designing protease inhibitors with greater efficacy.

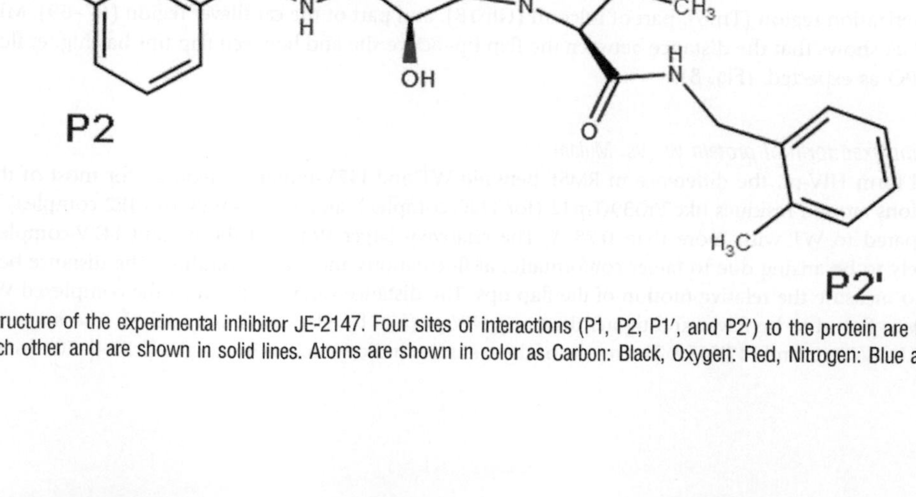

Fig. 5 Molecular structure of the experimental inhibitor JE-2147. Four sites of interactions (P1, P2, P1', and P2') to the protein are labeled. Atoms are shown bonded to each other and are shown in solid lines. Atoms are shown in color as Carbon: Black, Oxygen: Red, Nitrogen: Blue and Sulfur: Gray.

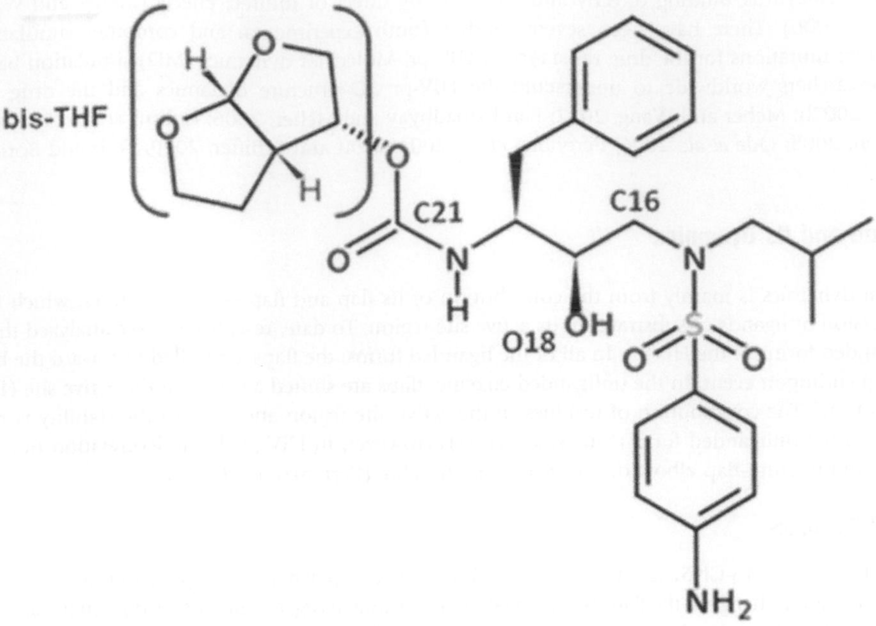

Fig. 6 Configuration of the inhibitor TMC114, with the moiety bis-THF enclosed in square bracket. Atoms playing critical role in the interactions between the inhibitor and the enzyme HIV-pr have been denoted in bold letters. Reprinted from Meher, B.R., Wang, Y., 2012. Interaction of I50V mutant and I50L/A71V double mutant HIV-protease with inhibitor TMC114 (darunavir): Molecular dynamics simulation and binding free energy studies. Journal of Physical Chemistry B 116, 1884–1900. With permission from J. Phys. Chem. B and publisher American Chemical Society (ACS).

TMC114, a nonpeptidic compound ended by the bis-tetrahydrofuran (bis-THF) moiety shown in **Fig. 6**, is an enormously effective protease inhibitor (PI) to deal with the drug resistant HIV strains. With the presence of the terminal bis-THF moiety, it slightly differs from its chemical analog, amprenavir. Several studies have shed light on the drug resistance behavior of HIV-pr mutants towards TMC114 (Meher and Wang, 2012, 2015; Kar and Knecht, 2012a, 2012b; Kovalevsky et al., 2006b; Tie et al., 2007; Chen et al., 2010; Vaishnavi et al., 2017).

I47V mutation effect on JE-2147 and TMC114 binding

Vaishnavi et al. (2017) have investigated the binding of inhibitor TMC114 and JE-2147 to WT, and I47V mutant HIV-pr with all-atom MD simulations as well as MM-PBSA (molecular mechanics with Poisson–Boltzmann and surface area solvation) calculation. In I47V mutant apo HIV-pr, flap–flap distance was larger than WT or TMC114 and JE2 complexed mutant form (**Fig. 7**). The I47V-mutant complex HIV-pr has less curled flap tips and flexibility compared to WT and the apo mutant I47V. The mutant I47V decreases the binding affinity of I47V-HIV-pr to both the inhibitors (TMC114 and JE2), resulting in a drug resistance; due to an increased volume of the active site. (**Fig. 9**) However, the drug resistance of TMC114 to I47V mutant is heavier than JE-2147. The decrease of the binding affinity for the TMC114 complexed mutant I47V-HIV-pr is resultant of the the decreased electrostatic energy as well as van der Waals energy.

Comparing the apo form of protein WT vs. Mutant

The difference in RMSF (root mean square fluctuations) between the mutant and WT HIV-pr for each residue shows that the maximum changes in RMSF occurs between WT and mutant HIV-pr for the residues in the flap elbows of the two chains (35–42, 40′–42′), the dimerization region (Trp6), part of fulcrum (Gln18), and part of the cantilever region (67–69). MD simulation data from Vaishnavi et al. shows that the distance between the flap tip–active site and between flap tips has higher fluctuations for WT-APO and I47V-APO as expected. (**Fig. 8**).

Comparing the complexed form of protein WT vs. Mutant

In the complexed form HIV-pr, the difference in RMSF between WT and I47V-mutant is reduced for most of the residues. It was observed that regions around residues like Pro39-Trp42 (for TMC complex), and Trpr6′–Arg8′ (for JE2 complex) shows remarkable fluctuations compared to WT with more than 0.75 Å. The relatively larger RMSF of the mutant I47V-complex to its apo-form counterpart is likely to be arising due to larger conformational fluctuations and weaker binding. The distance between Ile50-Ile50′ was determined to measure the relative motion of the flap tips. The distance variation between the complexed WT, I47V-TMC and I47V-JE2 HIV-pr was found to be fewer and tighter than apo HIV-pr (**Fig. 6**). Flap dynamics analysis also suggests larger active site volume in case of I47V-TMC and I47V-JE2. The results of these studies indicate that although the Ile50-Ile50′ distance was similar in

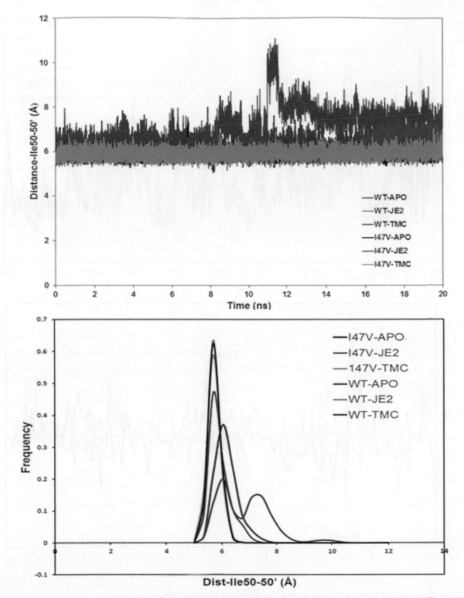

Fig. 7 Time-series (above) and frequency distribution (below) plots for the flap tip–flap tip distances for the HIV-pr WT vs I47V mutant complexes and apo-type.

the complexed HIV-pr there still exist differences in the Asp25′-Ile50′ distance, indicating the unique behavior of the two chains of a homodimeric enzyme like HIV-pr.

Molecular mechanism of drug resistance

In the I47V-mutant HIV-pr, the substitution of isoleucine with valine leads to the removal a of methyl group, which is likely to be decreasing the interaction with the central phenyl of TMC114 through C-H...π. Also, it is likely to be shortening the hydrophobic side chain and increasing the size of the active site, resulting in a reduced binding affinity to TMC114 and JE-2147. This change results in a decrease of van der Waals energy between Val47 and TMC114 comparative to the WT. However, for Val47 (47′) the change shows a significant decrease in van der Waals energy, which could possibly be due to the lessening of C-H...O interactions between the Val47 side chains and the P2′ position of JE-2147 and Val47 side chains and bis-THF (bis-tetrahydrofuran) moiety. The calculated binding free energies of complexes WT-JE2, I47V-JE2, WT-TMC, and I47V-TMC are −31.03, −29.76, −34.43, and −30.73 kcal/mol, respectively, indicating that the binding free energy of WT is higher than the mutant I47V. The binding affinities (ΔG) of I47V-JE2 and I47V-TMC complexes decrease by 1.27 and 3.70 kcal/mol from there WT counterpart, suggesting drug resistance for both the mutant. Residues like Val47′ in I47V-JE2 complex directly lowers the ΔG along with other residues like Gly49 and Val82′ (**Fig. 9**).

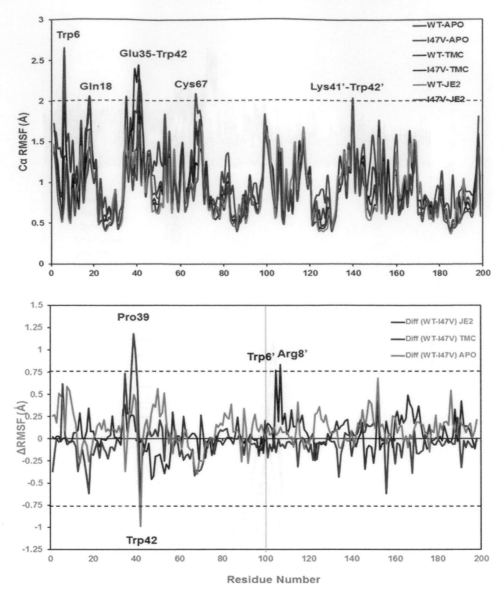

Fig. 8 Cα RMSF plot for the HIV-pr WT vs. I47V (above) and the difference is shown (below).

I50V and I50L/A71V mutations effect on TMC114 binding

The single mutation I50V and the double mutation (I50L/A71V) are recognized as two important residue point mutations in HIV-pr which affect protease inhibitors efficacy. Though both the mutations are located at critical region of HIV-pr structure, and their effect on other protease inhibitors have been studied previously, the effect of I50L/A71V mutation on TMC114 binding and the mechanism for drug resistance is still elusive. Meher and Wang (2012) explored the binding of TMC114 (**Fig. 6**) to WT, single (I50V) along with the double mutant HIV-pr with all-atom MD simulations and MM-PBSA calculation. The analysis of the apo and complexed HIV-pr indicates that the flap curling and opening events in double mutant I50L/A71V are more stable than WT or I50V. Further, the flap-flap and flap-active site distances also appears to be smaller in I50L/A71V when compared to that of WT or I50V (**Fig. 10**), resulting in a compact active site with smaller volume. I50V mutant reduces the binding affinity to inhibitor TMC114, causing drug resistance; while the I50L/A71V double mutant escalates the binding affinity (**Fig. 11**). It is remarkable to observe that the I50L/A71V escalates the binding affinity possibly by the stronger binding and better adaptability of the inhibitor TMC114 in its active site.

Comparing the apo form of protein WT vs. Mutant

Difference in B-factors or isotropic temperature factors could offer direct perceptions into the structural variations of HIV-pr in its WT and mutant forms. Each residue difference in B-factors amongst the mutant and WT HIV-pr is highest in the dimer interface region (6, 8 and 6′, 8′), flap elbow-A (35, 37, 39–41), and flap-A (49–52). Analysis of the WT and mutant simulations

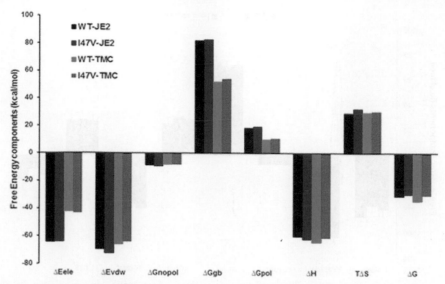

Fig. 9 Energy components (kcal/mol) for the binding of TMC114 and JE-2147 to the WT and I47V mutant: ΔE_{ele}: Electrostatic energy in the gas phase; ΔE_{vdw}: Van der Waals energy; ΔG_{nopol}: Nonpolar solvation energy; ΔG_{gb}: Polar solvation energy; ΔG_{pol}: $\Delta E_{ele} + \Delta G_{gb}$; $T\Delta S$: Total entropy contribution; $\Delta G_{total} = \Delta E_{ele} + \Delta E_{vdw} + \Delta E_{int} + \Delta G_{pb}$; $\Delta G = \Delta G_{total} - T\Delta S$.

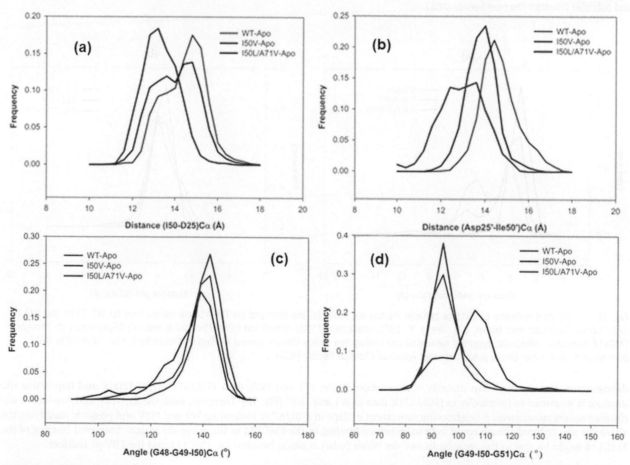

Fig. 10 Variability of histograms for the (a) Ile50–Asp25 distance; (b) Ile50' –Asp25' distance; (c) Gly48-Gly49-Ile50 TriCa angle; and (d) Gly49-Ile50-Gly51 TriCa angle for WT, I50V and I50L/A71V mutants' HIV-pr simulation of the apo-type. Reprinted from Meher, B.R., Wang, Y., 2012. Interaction of I50V mutant and I50L/A71V double mutant HIV-protease with inhibitor TMC114 (darunavir): Molecular dynamics simulation and binding free energy studies. Journal of Physical Chemistry B 116, 1884–1900. With permission from J. Phys. Chem. B and publisher American Chemical Society (ACS).

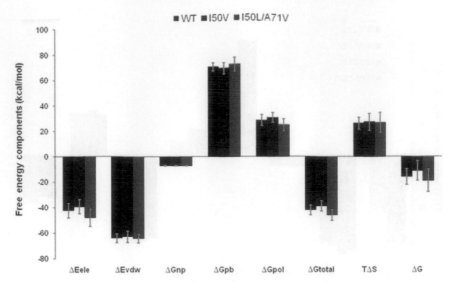

Fig. 11   Energy components (kcal/mol) for the binding of TMC114 to the WT, I50V and I50L/A71V: ΔE_{ele}: Electrostatic energy in the gas phase; ΔE_{vdw}: Van der Waals energy; ΔG_{np}: Nonpolar solvation energy; ΔG_{pb}: Polar solvation energy; ΔG_{pol}: $\Delta E_{ele} + \Delta G_{pb}$; T$\Delta$S: Total entropy contribution; $\Delta G_{total} = \Delta E_{ele} + \Delta E_{vdw} + \Delta E_{int} + \Delta G_{pb}$; $\Delta G = \Delta G_{total}$ - TΔS. Error bars in green solid line indicates the difference. Reprinted from Meher, B.R., Wang, Y., 2012. Interaction of I50V mutant and I50L/A71V double mutant HIV-protease with inhibitor TMC114 (darunavir): Molecular dynamics simulation and binding free energy studies. Journal of Physical Chemistry B 116, 1884–1900. With permission from J. Phys. Chem. B and publisher American Chemical Society (ACS).

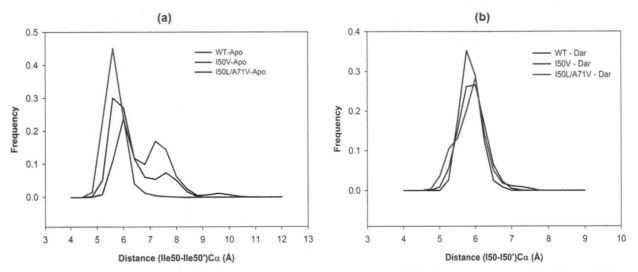

Fig. 12   Histogram distribution of distance between the flap tips in the (a) apo form and (b) TMC114 complexed form for WT, I50V, and I50L/A71V HIV-pr. Reprinted from Meher, B.R., Wang, Y., 2012. Interaction of I50V mutant and I50L/A71V double mutant HIV-protease with inhibitor TMC114 (darunavir): Molecular dynamics simulation and binding free energy studies. Journal of Physical Chemistry B 116, 1884–1900. With permission from J. Phys. Chem. B and publisher American Chemical Society (ACS).

demonstrates that the flap–flap distance changes more in the WT and I50V than I50L/A71V (**Fig. 12(a)**), and flap–active site distance is measured to be smaller in I50L/A71V than in WT and I50V (**Fig. 10**). Therefore, both the flap–flap and flap–active site distance results recommend a neighboring movement of flaps in I50L/A71V comparing WT and I50V and possibly modifying the active site size reduced, which could help in improved binding of the TMC114 to the active site region. Improved binding of the TMC114 might be due to the increase in van der Waals (vdw) contacts between the TMC114 and the HIV-pr residues.

Comparing the complexed form of protein WT vs. Mutant

All the complexes (WT vs mutants) show similar fashion of dynamic features from the B-factor perspectives albeit a few exceptions. B-factor difference between the TMC114 complexed and apo HIV-pr for WT and mutant shows that the B-factor is reduced for most of the residues, specifically noticeable in the flap tip and flap elbow regions. It was observed that four regions around

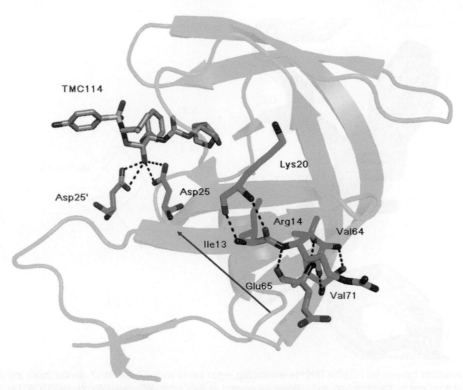

Fig. 13 Graphical representation of H-bond propagation in the double mutant I50L/A71V and Asp25(25')-TMC114 flip-flop interaction. Red color arrow shows the path of propagation.

17 (17'), 41 (41'), 53 (53'), and 70 (70') exert the highest dynamic fluctuations. The slightly reduced B-factor of the I50L/A71V-complex may be described by the comparatively less conformational variations and stronger binding. The reduced flexibility in the inhibitor-binding site directs to the reduction in K_m, resulting in an increase in the affinity of the enzymes for the inhibitor and stronger binding (Zoldak et al., 2004). In order to understand the flap dynamics behavior, the Ile50-Ile50' distance was studied. The difference among the complexed WT, I50V, and I50L/A71V HIV-pr was observed to be fewer and thinner than that of the apo HIV-pr (**Fig. 12(b)**). The utmost distinct motion for the HIV-pr complex was found to be the side-chain mobility of catalytic Asp25 about the inhibitor TMC114. It shows a flip-flop interaction of the Asp25 OD1/OD2 atoms with the O18 of TMC114 may be originated by the change in H-bonding pattern of the double mutant induced from A71V mutation (**Fig. 13**).

Molecular mechanism of drug resistance

In the I50L/A71V double mutant, the substitution of isoleucine to leucine, places the methyl group in an altered position, though structure of the side chain is not altered substantially. However, the replacement from alanine to valine adds two methyl groups to the backbone carbon in place of single methyl, which renders side chain bulkier. It is noted that, the change from Ala71 to Val71 in the cantilever region of the HIV-pr has not affected H-bond pattern; however, the H-bond between the residues Arg14' and Glu65' has been reduced (Meher and Wang, 2012). So, it is confirmed that the mutation A71V have no direct influence on the active site conformation and binding affinity. The mutation has allosteric effect on the binding affinity with change in the mobility of active site residues (**Fig. 13**). The resultant alteration in the conformation of the enzyme may affect its binding affinity to the inhibitor TMC114 to the protease.

In the I50V mutant HIV-pr, the replacement of isoleucine with valine leads to the loss of a methyl group. It lowers the contact with the central phenyl of TMC114, which leads to the decrement in the van der Waals energy between Val50 and TMC114. On the contrary, for Val50' the change displays a substantial decline in van der Waals energy (by 0.54 kcal/mol), which may be due to the falling of C-H...O interactions between the Val50' side chains and the O22 of TMC114. **Fig. 14** confirms that the distance of C...O22 (3.4 Å) for I50V-HIV-pr is longer than that for WT and I50L/A71V-HIV-pr (4.1 and 3.6 Å, respectively), which is likely to be the reason for the less binding affinity and drug resistance.

V32I and M46L mutations effect on TMC114 binding

Meher and Wang (2015) investigated the binding of inhibitor TMC114 (**Fig. 5**) to WT, V32I mutant, and M46L mutant HIV-pr with all-atom MD simulations as well as MM-PBSA calculation. The analysis describes the resistance profile of both the mutants (V32I and M46L) with their 1T (single TMC114 bound alone to the active site region) and 2T (bound to the flap and active site region simultaneously) forms. The average flap–flap distance and flap tip–active site distances are longer for the M46L-2T HIV-pr complex as compare to the WT-1T and V32I-2T complexes suggesting an increased flexibility in M46L-2T, feasibly making the

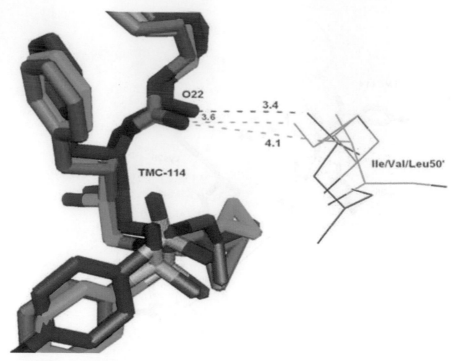

Fig. 14 C-H...O interactions between the inhibitor TMC114 and the flap region amino acids (Gly49, Gly40', Ile/Val/Leu50, and Ile/Val/Leu50'). TMC114 in stick form is colored by the atom type, and residues are denoted as lines (green-WT; cyan-I50V; purple-I50L/A71V). Reprinted from Meher, B.R., Wang, Y., 2012. Interaction of I50V mutant and I50L/A71V double mutant HIV-protease with inhibitor TMC114 (darunavir): Molecular dynamics simulation and binding free energy studies. Journal of Physical Chemistry B 116, 1884–1900. With permission from J. Phys. Chem. B and publisher American Chemical Society (ACS).

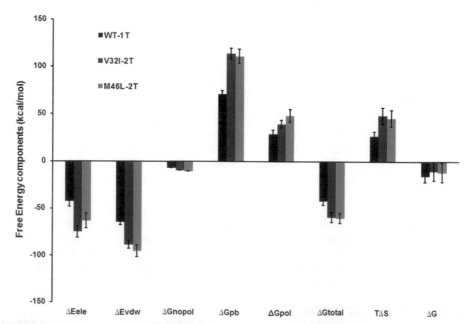

Fig. 15 Energy components (kcal/mol) for the binding of TMC114 to the WT-1T, V32I-2T, and M46L-2T: Eele, electrostatic energy in the gas phase; Evdw, van der Waals energy; Gnp, nonpolar solvation energy; Gpb, polar solvation energy; Gpol=Gele+Gpb; TS, total entropy contribution; H=Eele+Evdw+Gnp+Gpb; $\Delta G = \Delta H - T\Delta S$. The error bars refer to standard deviations (Std.). Reprinted from Meher, B.R., Wang, Y., 2015. Exploring the drug resistance of V32I and M46L mutant HIV-1 protease to inhibitor TMC114: Flap dynamics and binding mechanism. Journal of Molecular Graphics and Modelling 56, 60–73. With permission from J. Mol. Graph. Mod. and publisher Elsevier.

active site capacity larger. From the binding free energies of all the complexes, it was gathered that both the 1T and 2T forms of the protease HIV-pr mutants show resistance to the inhibitor TMC114. Also, it came forth that the binding of the TMC114 on the flap region has inconspicuous impact on the binding affinity (**Fig. 15**).

Comparing the complexed form of protein WT vs. Mutant

The difference of RMSF (root mean square fluctuations) for the whole protein in its complexed form shows that the two mutations (V32I and M46L) cause more conformational changes of the HIV-pr near the flap elbows, fulcrum (Trp6, Ile15-Gly16 and Glu35-Lys41 & Trp6′, Glu35′ and Arg57′), and cantilever regions (Pro63-His69 and Ala67′), than the WT counterpart. To explore the relative motion of the flap tips, flap tip–flap tip distance was examined, where, the variation between the double bound and single bound V32I-2T and M46L-2T/HIV-pr was found to be different, the former being broader (**Fig. 16**). Further studies on flap dynamics studies revealed that there is a floppy flaps movement in M46L-2T in comparison to WT-1T and V32I-2T/HIV-pr structures. Flap RMSD analysis indicates that the binding of TMC114 on the flap –B of the mutant structures has only subtle effect on the flap dynamics.

Molecular mechanism of drug resistance

V32I mutation can lead to drug resistance by affecting the interactions between the amino acid side chains and the inhibitor. In the V32I-mutant HIV-pr, the substitution of valine with isoleucine leads to a gain of methyl group. It increases the interaction with the central phenyl of TMC114, and possibly increases the steric hindrance (unfavorable interactions), resulting in a reduced binding affinity to TMC114. This change results in an increase in total entropy contribution (TΔS) by about 3.42 kcal/mol for V32I-1T and 20.89 kcal/mol for V32I-1T as compared to the WT-1T/TMC114 HIV-pr complex (Meher and Wang, 2015). M46L mutation does not impact the inhibitor binding the active site region, but the atoms of Met46 residue may be forming H-bonds

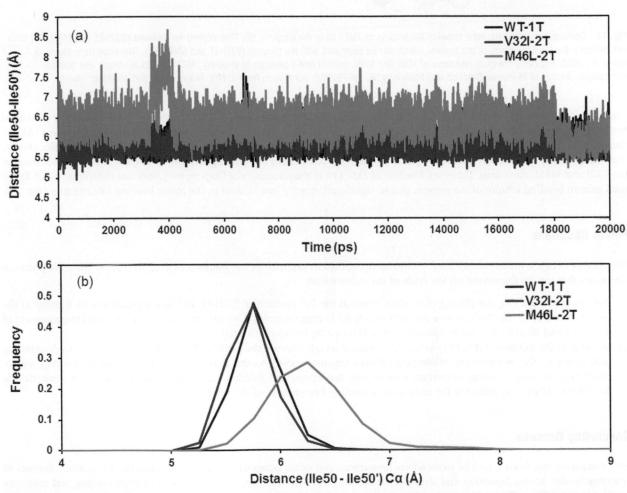

Fig. 16 (a) Time-series plot and (b) frequency distribution plot for the distance between the flap tip (Ile50-Ile50) C atoms for the double bound TMC114 to HIV-1-pr mutants and single bound to WT. Reprinted from Meher, B.R., Wang, Y., 2015. Exploring the drug resistance of V32I and M46L mutant HIV-1 protease to inhibitor TMC114: Flap dynamics and binding mechanism. Journal of Molecular Graphics and Modelling 56, 60–73. With permission from J. Mol. Graph. Mod. and publisher Elsevier.

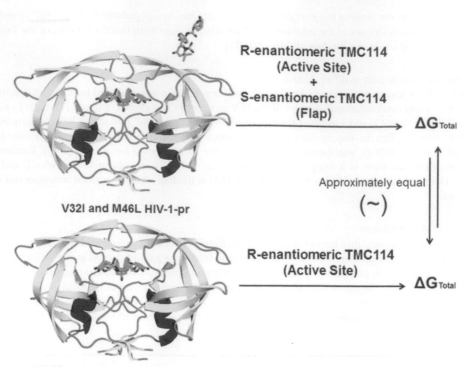

Fig. 17 Comparative schematic view showing the binding of TMC114 in the allosteric site (flap region) for mutants (V32I-2T and M46L-2T) does not influence the binding affinity of the system, which can be compared with the mutants (V32I-1T and M46L-1T). Reprinted from Meher, B.R., Wang, Y., 2015. Exploring the drug resistance of V32I and M46L mutant HIV-1 protease to inhibitor TMC114: Flap dynamics and binding mechanism. Journal of Molecular Graphics and Modelling 56, 60–73. With permission from J. Mol. Graph. Mod. and publisher Elsevier.

with substrate analogs (Tie *et al.*, 2005). Hence, M46L mutation can have effect on binding affinity indirectly via the weakened hydrophobic interactions (Kovalevsky *et al.*, 2006a). This alteration results in an increase in total entropy contribution ($T\Delta S$) by about 2.64 kcal/mol for M46L-1T and 16.83 kcal/mol for V32I-1T as compared to the WT-1T/TMC114 HIV-pr complex (Meher and Wang, 2015). Therefore, the entropy penalty ultimately compresses the binding affinities and elicit the drug resistance for the V32I and M46L mutations. However, binding of TMC114 in the allosteric site (flap region) does not contribute much in the total gain in binding affinity of the system, due to significant entropy loss leading to the lower binding free energies (**Fig. 17**).

Future Directions

The synergy between mutation and conformational dynamics has exposed the mechanisms of drug resistance. There are potential directions that can be discovered on the basis of the current work.

1) Information regarding the placing of a larger group at the P2′ position of JE-2147 and also replacement of a group at the position of O18 in the TMC114 structure will be helpful in drug designing. One can proceed for the structural improvement of TMC114 and JE-2147 in vitro and in silico as well based on the combinatorial chemistry.
2) Binding of the inhibitor (TMC114) in the flap region does not improve the binding affinity of the system. This understanding will promote the development of drugs/inhibitors targeting mostly to the active site region and not to the flap region. However, targeting to other important regions like flap elbow and fulcrum may help in development of allosteric site inhibitors, which may promote the total gain in binding free energies of the system.

Concluding Remarks

MD simulation has been a tool of tremendous importance and offers generous understandings into the mechanistic features of macromolecular 3D-conformation and dynamics at atomic level. It illuminates the mechanisms of drug binding and resistance profile towards HIV-pr. The study steered to the outcome that 3D-conformational dynamics of HIV-pr is affected by the change in 3D-data coordinates in the protein crystal structure due to mutations that have an important role on HIV-pr conformation and dynamics. Conclusively, the understanding of the molecular basis of drug resistance is a difficult job. However, the result of this study as well as other prior revisions on HIV-pr may offer insightful knowledge with which to design favorable and potent drugs/inhibitors.

Acknowledgement

The authors enthusiastically acknowledge Albany State University, Georgia, USA, SERC at Indian Institute of Science (IISc), Bangalore, India, and Pittsburgh Supercomputing Center (PSC), Pittsburgh, USA for provision of computing facility to accomplish this study. The authors also thankfully acknowledge IISc and Central University of Jharkhand (CUJ) for provision of Library facilities. BRM thanks DBT-BUILDER programme (BT/PR-9028/INF/22/193/2013) at CUJ for financial assistance to carry out some of the work depicted here.

See also: Biomolecular Structures: Prediction, Identification and Analyses. Natural Language Processing Approaches in Bioinformatics

References

Bandyopadhyay, P., Meher, B.R., 2006. Drug resistance of HIV-1 protease against JE-2147: I47V mutation investigated by molecular dynamics simulation. Chemical Biology & Drug Design 67, 155–161.

Brik, A., Wong, C.-H., 2003. HIV-1 protease: Mechanism and drug discovery. Organic and Biomolecular Chemistry 1, 5–14.

Bukrinskaya, A., 2007. HIV-1 matrix protein: A mysterious regulator of the viral life cycle. Virus Research 124, 1–11.

Cai, Y., Yilmaz, N.K., Myint, W., Ishima, R., Schiffer, C.A., 2012. Differential flap dynamics in Wild-type and a drug resistant variant of HIV-1 protease revealed by molecular dynamics and NMR relaxation. Journal of Chemical Theory and Computation 8, 3452–3462.

Chen, L., Lee, C., 2006. Distinguishing HIV-1 drug resistance, accessory, and viral fitness mutations using conditional selection pressure analysis of treated versus untreated patient samples. Biology Direct 1, 14.

Chen, J., Zhang, S., Liu, X., Zhang, Q., 2010. Insights into drug resistance of mutations D30N and I50V to HIV-1 protease inhibitor TMC-114: Free energy calculation and molecular dynamic simulation. Journal of Molecular Modeling 16, 459–468.

Collins, J.R., Burt, S.K., Erickson, J.W., 1995. Flap opening in HIV-1 protease simulated by 'activated' molecular dynamics. Nature Structural Biology 2, 334–338.

Cunningham, A.L., Donaghy, H., Harman, A.N., Kim, M., Turville, S.G., 2010. Manipulation of dendritic cell function by viruses. Current Opinion in Microbiology. 13, 524–529.

Fun, A., Wensing, A.M., Verheyen, J., Nijhuis, M., 2012. Human Immunodeficiency Virus Gag and protease: Partners in resistance. Retrovirology 9, 63.

Ganser-Pornillos, B.K., Yeager, M., Pornillos, O., 2012. Assembly and architecture of HIV. Advances in Experimental Medicine and Biology 726, 441–465.

Le Grice, S.F., 2012. Human immunodeficiency virus reverse transcriptase: 25 years of research, drug discovery, and promise. Journal of Biological Chemistry 287, 40850–40857.

Hatziioannou, T., Evans, D.T., 2012. Animal models for HIV/AIDS research. Nature Reviews Microbiology 10, 852–867.

Hornak, V., Okur, A., Rizzo, R.C., Simmerling, C., 2006. HIV-1 protease flaps spontaneously open and reclose in molecular dynamics simulations. Proceedings of the National Academy of Sciences of the United States of America 103, 915–920.

Johnson, V.A., Brun-Veziner, F., Clotet, B., et al., 2010. Update of the drug resistance mutations in HIV-1: December 2010. Topics in HIV Medicine 18, 156–163.

Kar, P., Knecht, V., 2012a. Origin of decrease in potency of darunavir and two related antiviral inhibitors against HIV-2 compared to HIV-1 protease. Journal of Physical Chemistry B 116, 2605–2614.

Kar, P., Knecht, V., 2012b. Energetic basis for drug resistance of HIV-1 protease mutants against amprenavir. Journal of Computer-Aided Molecular Design 26, 215–232.

Kovalevsky, A.Y., Liu, F., Leshchenko, S., et al., 2006a. Ultra-high resolution crystal structure of HIV-1 protease mutant reveals two binding sites for clinical inhibitor TMC114. Journal of Molecular Biology 363, 161–173.

Kovalevsky, A.Y., Tie, Y., Liu, F., et al., 2006b. Effectiveness of non-peptide clinical inhibitor TMC-114 on HIV-1 protease with highly drug resistant mutations D30N, I50V, and L90M. Journal of Medicinal Chemistry 49, 1379–1387.

Kurt, N., Scott, W.R., Schiffer, C.A., Haliloglu, T., 2003. Cooperative fluctuations of unliganded and substrate-bound HIV-1 protease: A structure-based analysis on a variety of conformations from crystallography and molecular dynamics simulations. Proteins 51, 409–422.

Mager, P.P., 2001. The active site of HIV-1 protease. Medicinal Research Reviews 21, 348–353.

Meagher, K.L., Carlson, H.A., 2005. Solvation influences flap collapse in HIV-1 protease. Proteins: Structure, Function, and Bioinformatics 58, 119–125.

Meher, B.R., Wang, Y., 2012. Interaction of I50V mutant and I50L/A71V double mutant HIV-protease with inhibitor TMC114 (darunavir): Molecular dynamics simulation and binding free energy studies. Journal of Physical Chemistry B 116, 1884–1900.

Meher, B.R., Wang, Y., 2015. Exploring the drug resistance of V32I and M46L mutant HIV-1 protease to inhibitor TMC114: Flap dynamics and binding mechanism. Journal of Molecular Graphics and Modelling 56, 60–73.

Ode, H., Neya, S., Hata, M., Sugiura, W., Hoshino, T., 2006. Computational simulations of HIV-1 proteases multi-drug resistance due to non-active site mutation L90M. Journal of the American Chemical Society 128, 7887–7895.

Perryman, A.L., Lin, J.-H., McCammon, J.A., 2004. HIV-1 protease molecular dynamics of a wild-type and of the V82F/I84V mutant: Possible contributions to drug resistance and a potential new target site for drugs. Protein Science 13, 1108–1123.

Piana, S., Carloni, P., Parinello, M., 2002a. Role of conformational fluctuations in the enzymatic reaction of HIV-1 protease. Journal of Molecular Biology 319, 567–583.

Piana, S., Carloni, P., Rothlisberger, U., 2002b. Drug resistance in HIV-1 protease: Flexibility assisted mechanism of compensatory mutations. Protein Science 11, 2393–2402.

Sanou, M.P., De Groot, A.S., Murphey-Corb, M., Levy, J.A., Yamamoto, J.K., 2012. HIV-1 Vaccine Trials: Evolving concepts and designs. Open AIDS Journal 6, 274–288.

Scott, W.R., Schiffer, C.A., 2000. Curling of flap tips in HIV-1 protease as a mechanism for substrate entry and tolerance of drug resistance. Structure 8, 1259–1265.

Tie, Y., Boross, P.I., Wang, Y.F., et al., 2005. Molecular basis for substrate recognition and drug resistance from 1.1 to 1.6 angstroms resolution crystal structures of HIV-1 protease mutants with substrate analogs. The FEBS Journal 272, 5265–5277.

Tie, Y., Kovalevsky, A.Y., Boross, P., et al., 2007. Atomic resolution crystal structures of HIV-1 protease and mutants V82A and I84V with saquinavir. Proteins 67, 232–242.

Torbeev, V.Y., Raghuraman, H., Hamelberg, D., et al., 2011. Protein conformational dynamics in the mechanism of HIV-1 protease catalysis. Proceedings of the National Academy of Sciences USA 108, 20982–20987.

Toth, G., Borics, A., 2006. Flap opening mechanism of HIV-1 protease. Journal of Molecular Graphics & Modelling 24, 465–474.

Tran, E.E., Borgnia, M.J., Kuybeda, O., et al., 2012. Structural mechanism of trimeric HIV-1 envelope glycoprotein activation. PLOS Pathogens 8, 1002797.

Vaishnavi, M., Kumari, S., Misra, A.N., Meher, B.R., 2017. Nature of I47V mutation to inhibitors (JE-2147 and TMC114) binding on HIV-1 protease: Flap dynamics and binding strategies. In: Proceedings of the International Conference on Frontiers in Chemical Sciences (ICFCS-2017), 16–18th March 2017 at Central University of Jharkhand, Ranchi, India.

Yoshimura, K., Kato, R., Yusa, K., et al., 1999. JE-2147: A dipeptide protease inhibitor (PI) that potently inhibits multi-PI-resistant HIV-1. Proceedings of the National Academy of Sciences USA 96, 8675–8680.

Zoldak, G., Sprinzl, M., Sedla, E., 2004. Modulation of activity of NADH oxidase from *Thermus thermophilus* through change in flexibility in the enzyme active site induced by Hofmeister series anions. European Journal of Biochemistry 271, 48–57.

Relevant Website

www.unaids.org
UNAIDS.

Biographical Sketch

Dr. Biswa Ranjan Meher is an Assistant Professor at the Computational Biology and Bioinformatics Laboratory, Department of Botany, Berhampur University, Berhampur, Odisha, India. He received his PhD in Biotechnology from Indian Institute of Technology, Guwahati, India. He worked as a Post-Doctoral Researcher at different US universities like the University of Kansas (KU), Kansas; Albany State University (ASU), Georgia; and University of Richmond (UR), Virginia. He also worked as a DS Kothari Post-Doctoral Fellow (DSKPDF) in the Department of Biochemistry at the Indian Institute of Science, Bangalore, India from 2014 to 2016. Before joining his current position, he also served as an Assistant Professor in the DBT-BUILDER Programme at the Centre for Life Sciences, Central University of Jharkhand, Ranchi, India from 2016 to 2017. He has published his research work in reputed international journals like *Journal of Physical Chemistry B, Journal of Biomolecular Structure and Dynamics, PLoS One, Chemical Biology and Drug Design, Journal of Molecular Graphics and Modeling,* and others. His current research interests include nanomedicine development and applications, molecular modeling and simulations of biomolecules, understanding the protein conformations through structure network analysis, and application of computational tools to solve biological problems.

Dr. Venkata Satish Kumar Mattaparthi received his PhD in Biotechnology from Indian Institute of Technology Guwahati, Assam, India in 2010. From 2010 to 2012, he was with the Centre for Condensed Matter Theory (CCMT), Department of Physics, Indian Institute of Science Bangalore, India. He is currently working as Assistant Professor in the Department of Molecular Biology and Biotechnology, School of Sciences, Tezpur University, Assam, India. His research interests include understanding the functioning of intrinsically disordered proteins (IDPs), pathways of protein aggregation mechanism in neurodegenerative diseases like Alzheimer, Parkinson, etc., and also the features of protein–RNA interactions using computational techniques. He has published his research in reputed international journals like *Journal of Biomolecular Structure and Dynamics, PLoS One, Journal of Physical Chemistry B, Biophysical Journal, Journal of Bioinformatics and Computational Biology,* and others.

Dr. Seema Patel, MSc, MS, PhD, is a graduate of Indian Institute of Technology Guwahati, India and San Diego State University, USA. She has worked in industrial microbiology and then on in silico clinical microbiology. She has served as Assistant Professor in Lovely Professional University, India and as Research Assistant in San Diego State University. She has been in the biomedical research field since 2007, and has written or edited eight books, and published more than 100 papers on microbiology, food science, bioinformatics, enzymology, immunology, endocrine disruption, and correlated topics.

Megha Vaishnavi, has worked as a Junior Research Fellow at the Computational Biology and Bioinformatics Laboratory at the Centre for Life Sciences, Central University of Jharkhand with the DBT-BUILDER Programme under the guidance of Dr. Biswa Ranjan Meher. She is a Post-Graduate in Microbiology from Central University of Rajasthan and graduate in Biotechnology from IPS Academy Indore, Devi Ahilya Vishva Vidyalaya (DAVV). Her research interest includes molecular modelling and simulations of therapeutically significant biomolecules and structure-based drug design.

Dr. Sandeep Kaushik is a passionate computational biologist with a wide exposure of computational approaches. Presently, he is carrying out his research as an Assistant Researcher (equivalent to Assistant Professor) at 3B's Research Group, University of Minho, Portugal. He has a PhD in Bioinformatics from National Institute of Immunology, New Delhi, India. He has a wide exposure on analysis of scientific data ranging from transcriptomic data on mycobacterial and human samples to genomic data from wheat. His research experience and expertise entails molecular dynamics simulations, RNA-sequencing data analysis using Bioconductor (R language based package), de novo genome assembly using various software like AbySS, automated protein prediction and annotation, database mining, agent-based modeling, and simulations. He has a cumulative experience of more than 10 years of programming using PERL, R language, and NetLogo. He has published his research in reputed international journals like *Molecular Cell*, *Biomaterials*, *Biophysical Journal*, and others. Currently, his research interest involves in silico modeling of disease conditions like breast cancer, using an agent-based modeling and simulations approach.

Structural Genomics

Shuhaila Mat-Sharani, Doris HX Quay, Chyan L Ng, and Mohd Firdaus-Raih, Universiti Kebangsaan Malaysia, Selangor, Malaysia

Introduction

Computational means of assigning function have been crucial for the annotation of the numerous genomes that are being sequenced. Without a computational function annotation system, much of the genome sequences generated would remain isolated voluminous non-sensical digital outputs. The primary means of assigning a function to a new open reading frame (ORF) or coding sequence (CDS) has been sequence alignment.

The function of a known protein sequence can be transferred to its homolog once the sequence similarity is considered adequate to infer shared function. The basis of such a function inference is the fact that the function of proteins are dependent on their three-dimensional (3D) structures. The work of Anfinsen (1972) has demonstrated that the information needed for a protein to fold into its functional 3D structure is contained within the sequence of amino acids that make up the polypeptide. The entropic (disordered) state of the different amino acids in a newly synthesized polypeptide chain drives it to fold into the 3D structure. Chothia and Lesk (1986) had determined that sequence similarity at 30% is enough for a protein to share similar folding and retain a similar function. This has thus been used as a cutoff point for many sequence alignments when assigning function from similarity.

Nevertheless, there remain vast numbers of sequences that have uncharacterized function. For many genome annotations, predicted ORFs with no characterized homologs have been assigned the label 'hypothetical protein'. Solving the structure of a hypothetical protein can be enough to identify any folding similarities to structures already available in the Protein Data Bank (PDB) (Dey et al., 2018; Laskowski et al., 2018) and thus point to potentially similar functions. The PDB is the central repository for structural coordinates of biological macromolecules that have been made publicly accessible. Visual examination and computational analysis of a protein's structure may yield clues regarding its function. If function characterization could be potentially achieved by acquiring the structures of the many proteins with yet to be determined functions, then a systematic high throughput means of acquiring such structures would ultimately accelerate such efforts.

Developments and progress in macromolecular structure determination methods, especially in X-ray crystallography, and lately in cryo-electron microscopy, have resulted in more than 130,000 structures being deposited in the PDB. The bulk of this number (approximately 90% in November 2017) were determined using X-ray crystallography. The availability of numerous genome sequences and the progress made in structural biology have therefore led to large scale projects with the specific objectives of determining the 3D structures for proteins encoded in these genomes, such an approach has been termed as structural genomics. For many of these projects, emphasis was placed on the hypothetical proteins that had no known sequence homologs with characterized functions. One of the earliest test case for structural genomics was the MJ0577 hypothetical protein structure of the hyperthermophile *Methanococcus jannaschii* that was solved to a high resolution (Zarembinski et al., 1998). The structure of MJ0577 was found to contain an ATP molecule, which directed the function search of the protein that was later confirmed as an ATPase (Zarembinski et al., 1998).

In this article, we review and discuss computational strategies currently in use for structural genomics, specifically for structures solved by X-ray diffraction of protein crystals. While the protein production and crystallography remain as molecular biology and chemistry problems, the selection of targets to be fed into a structural genomics pipeline and the analyses of the resulting structures are computational biology problems.

Background

Defining Structural Genomics

There are currently different definitions available for the term structural genomics. Several often used definitions are: (i) an effort to describe 3D structure of every protein encoded in a genome via experimental approaches or computational modelling or a combination of both; and (ii) knowledge on the structural organization of the genome thus allowing for all the genes in a genome to be located and characterized. This article will touch on the former, but will only proceed in depth for a subset, which is the solution of structures via experimental means. The second will not be discussed under this topic. In a way, the definitions have overlaps and all are arguably correct; however, these differences and similarities will not be discussed in depth here.

The Extent and Realities of Structural Genomics in Practice

Methods used for determining the 3D structures of proteins have improved tremendously over the past decade. The bulk of the PDB is composed of structures solved through X-ray crystallography with the remainder consisting of coordinates acquired through nuclear magnetic resonance (NMR) spectroscopy and cryo-electronmicroscopy (Cryo-EM). The X-ray crystallography technique is the most common method used in structural genomics because it can be applied to a wide range of protein sizes and types, including membrane proteins.

An increase in the computational capacity to process the theoretical folding of protein sequences into their 3D structures means that the generation of 3D structures for every protein in a genome is moving closer towards reality. Nevertheless, such capability is not expected in the foreseeable future. However, even for a wholly computational structural genomics approach, it may not be necessary to compute all the CDS in a target genome because for some proteins, an experimentally solved structure may already exist (Baugh *et al.*, 2013).

Similarly, it may not be necessary to experimentally determine the structure for every CDS in a genome because they are already available in the PDB, either for the same organism from another work, or as a homolog from another source. The constraints for an experimental structural genomics approach is grounded in the reality of costs and other limitations that include but are not limited to: the ability to clone, express, purify and crystallize the protein; followed by a requirement for the crystal to diffract and the data to be processable. This process of molecular biology by attrition can result from an initial starting point being thousands of CDS ending with perhaps solved structures that number in the hundreds or even less (Franklin *et al.*, 2015).

The structural genomics process gradually reduces the initial number of target genes acquired from the genome sequence via a systematic process up to the point of coordinate data acquisition for the encoded proteins. As such, this process can be made into a pipeline (**Fig. 1**) that begins by taking in all the predicted CDS from the genome sequence and proceeding with steps that can then be defined specifically to fit a project's requirements and objectives. For example, for many groups, a logical first step is to identify CDS that code for possibly insoluble proteins; in practice, this is done by identifying membrane proteins (**Fig. 1**). The next step may be to filter the CDS for those that have very similar examples already available in the PDB. The cut-off for similarity can vary depending on the interests and requirements of the project.

The filtering process can also be intervened from the start to begin with a smaller subset; for example, only CDS that have been annotated as hypothetical proteins can be selected for input into the structural genomics pipeline. Other examples would be to target for a selection that may be of existing focus in a research group – for example, potential drug targets (Franklin *et al.*, 2015; Fedorov *et al.*, 2007). Nevertheless, it must be noted that even for sequences that were initially targets in a structural genomics pipeline, but do not end up as crystallographic structures, may actually have varying degrees of useful functional characterization as a result of having passed through the pipeline (Ahmad *et al.*, 2015; Yusof *et al.*, 2016; Hashim *et al.*, 2013; Ramli *et al.*, 2013).

Although we do not discuss structures solved by NMR and cryo-EM, switching the experimental method that the pipeline feeds from protein crystallography to either NMR, cryo-EM or a combination of all three methods can also be carried out. Thus structural genomics in the present context can be an integration of all available methods to acquire 3D structure data. Similar to the case of filtering the ORFs for the purpose of crystallography, the pipeline can be redirected to identify targets for these other methods – such as identification of smaller molecular weight proteins that would be amenable to structure solution by NMR.

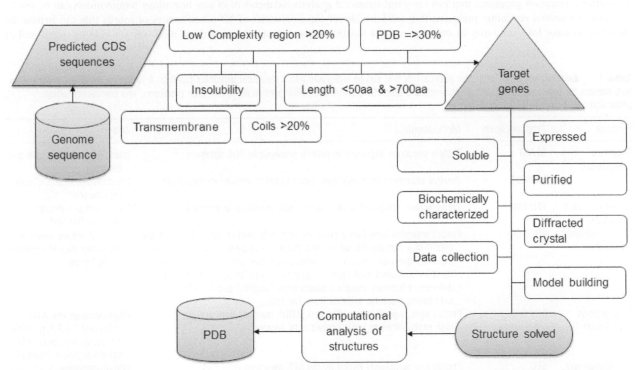

Fig. 1 The overall structural genomics process begins with computational filteration to get target genes and proceeds to solved structures via experimental means. The general filteration begins by removing genes that have transmembrane regions, are insoluble, have more than 20% of low complexity regions and coils. This is followed by removing predicted CDS with lengths less than 50 or more than 700 amino acids and have more than 30% sequence identity with entries in the PDB database.

Systems and/or Applications

A pipeline to process a genome sequence for the purpose of structural genomics can be assembled using proven tools (**Table 1**). Due to the potential volume of sequences that will be analysed, a local or fit for purpose installation of the programs required would be ideal. This would thus prevent the pipelines engineered for such projects from overloading publicly available servers at the expense of other users. Nevertheless, when such a practice is not possible, care and due consideration of other users of the service should exercised when scheduling input submissions. As discussed previously (Section "The Extent and Realities of Structural Genomics in Practice"), the starting point of the pipeline would vary depending on the requirements and capacity of the project.

A filter for insoluble proteins, which would be a logical feature and starting point for many projects, would obviously be unsuitable if the project were to actually include the solution of membrane proteins among its objectives. In order to perhaps maximize the return of the project in terms of finding novel folds or characterizing indescribed functions for hypothetical proteins, some projects would opt to further restrict the targets to sequences that are unrepresented in the PDB. This is usually done by employing a 30% sequence identity cutoff or dipping as low as 25% identity (Nair *et al.*, 2009).

For perhaps many projects, these two initial steps of screening for membrane and membrane associated proteins would be adequate to proceed on to the process of elimination from the pipeline by experimental attrition. However, It is also possible to specifically filter for a subset of sequences that contain either N-terminal or C-terminal associated membrane insertions. This is done by identifying whether the first and last thirty residues could potentially be membrane embedded by plotting hydrophobicity plots or predicting transmembrane helices for these sections of the sequence for every CDS in the genome (Marsden *et al.*, 2007). Once identified, these sequences are then cloned and expressed without the predicted transmembrane anchor. Although this does not guarantee solubility, this does increase the initial set of targets while at the same time allowing for the structures of membrane anchored proteins to be solved.

At this stage, the project can then proceed to the non-computational steps highlighted as in **Fig. 1**. A computational component can then be integrated again at the point where the structure data is available in PDB format. This second phase of the computational analysis will include structural similarity comparisons and in depth structural analysis. It is common practice to identify fold similarities for a solved structure once the final structure file has been acquired. Here we will discuss aspects of computational analysis on the structure but will exclude discussion of in depth visual scrutiny of the structure using molecular graphics.

In most cases, a fold similarity search, such as by the DALI program (Holm and Laakso, 2016) is sufficient to identify other structural homologs. There are however hypothetical proteins that have no similarity to known folds or are matched to structures of proteins with uncharacterized functions (Nadzirin and Firdaus-Raih, 2012). In such cases, the lack of fold similarity will not allow for association with any known structural features than can in turn provide clues as to possible function to be made. In such a situation, computer programs that can carry out structural analysis independent of any homology requirements can be used.

There are several computer programs that work by identifying similarities of 3D substructures or motifs that can bypass the necessity to have fold similarity in order to make a functional association. Many of these methods are able to search and/or

Table 1   Selected programs and their applications that can be integrated into a structural genomics pipeline. A listing of the seven programs or web servers for sequence alignment, transmembrane prediction, protein solubility prediction, coils region prediction, low complexity region prediction and a protein structure database

Function	Program/server	Method/content	URL
Sequence alignment	BLAST	Protein sequence alignment to protein sequence in PDB database.	https://blast.ncbi.nlm.nih.gov/Blast.cgi
	MUSCLE	Iterative alignment of protein sequences to get conserved residue/motif.	https://www.ebi.ac.uk/Tools/msa/muscle/
Transmembrane prediction	TMHMM	Predicts TMs using HMMs (edit this) – just providing an example.	http://www.cbs.dtu.dk/services/TMHMM/
Protein solubility prediction	PROSOII	Predict solubility based on a classifier by two-layered structure in which the output of a primary Parzen window model for sequence similarity and a logistic regression classifier of amino acid k-mer composition serve as input for a second level logistic regression classifier to exploiting subtle differences between soluble proteins from TargetDB and the PDB and notoriously insoluble proteins from TargetDB.	http://mbiljj45.bio.med.uni-muenchen.de:8888/prosoII/prosoII.seam
Coils regions prediction	COILS/Coiled-coil prediction	Predict coils regions using MTK and MTIDK matrices both assign high probabilities to known coiled coils segment.	https://embnet.vital-it.ch/software/COILS_form.html/ https://npsa-prabi.ibcp.fr/cgi-bin/primanal_lupas.pl
Low complexity region prediction	SEG	Predict low complexity region by the SEG algorithm represent compositionally biased regions based only on residue composition and taking into account the improbability of appearance of such sequences.	http://mendel.imp.ac.at/METHODS/seg.server.html
Protein structure database	Protein Data Bank (PDB)	A crystallographic database for the three-dimensional structural data of large biological molecules, such as proteins and nucleic acids.	https://www.rcsb.org/pdb/

compare directly a query arrangement (Debret *et al.*, 2009; Nadzirin *et al.*, 2012, 2013) against a database or take a query structure and compare it against a database of motifs (Nadzirin *et al.*, 2012). There are also services that allow for annotation of specific sites such as binding sites (Konc and Janezic, 2017).

Analysis and Assessment

The need to experimentally determine a structure can be made based on several factors. In situations where detailed information of the differences for atomic level interactions are required, such as for drug development applications, an experimentally solved structure is necessary. It is therefore not uncommon for structural genomics projects to target not only CDS that have less than 30% sequence identity to examples in the PDB but also proteins that are deemed as important where mechanistic details at the atomic level can still be different even though the proteins are homologous. However, for applications where the investigator would like to select residues for site directed mutagenesis as part of a larger characterization effort, then high quality predicted models may suffice (Bhattacharya *et al.*, 2007).

We provide an example where the sequence for an arginase acquired from the genome of *G. antarctica* (Firdaus-Raih *et al.*, 2018), a psychrophilic yeast, was predicted and compared to the structure that was solved by molecular replacement of the X-ray diffraction data (PDBID: 5ynl). The sequence identity between the *G. antarctica* arginase and the reference used for molecular replacement, a human arginase (PDBID: 4hze), is 45%. In this particular case, the decision was made to solve the structure of the arginase despite the sequence identity being higher than the 30% cutoff point used for most of the other targets in the project. It was deemed necessary to acquire a structure that could provide atomic level details of the function as they may be specific to yeasts, psychrophiles or simply unique to *G. antarctica*.

To make a comparison of the differences that could arise from a computationally predicted model, we compared the solved structure to one that was predicted using SWISS-MODEL (Biasini *et al.*, 2014). As expected, the prediction was able to generate the correct fold with discernible disagreements between the two structures only in the loop regions with the compared structures having an RMSD value of 1.06 Å. When the computed model was compared to the template, the differences were much lower at an RMSD of 0.31 Å. It is clear that the model is biased towards the template than the experimentally determined structure (**Fig. 2**).

We then examined how much an effect the modelling had on the side chain arrangements when the model was compared to the template and the experimental structure. For this comparison, eleven residues that have been reported to be involved in metal coordination and arginine binding were selected. As observed for the folding, it is clear that the predicted model is more biased to the reference used (**Fig. 3**). Nevertheless, with the exception of D194 and E288 – two of the putative arginine binding residues – the arrangement of side chains for the other nine residues were generally similar and could be seen as having acceptable overlaps. In E288, the side chains ended up in opposite directions despite the C-alpha position generally overlapping. For D194, the general position of the residues in the experimental structure and model were the same, but neither the side chain or the C-alpha position overlapped.

These limitations of protein structure prediction are well understood. Here, we demonstrate the fact that even when a homologous PDB structure is available at 45% sequence identity, an experimentally determined structure will still have valuable atomic level details that cannot be adequately transferred via comparative modelling. It is clear that despite the fold conservation, it is the intricate details that could be the factor in understanding mechanistic differences between homologous proteins. This in a way affects the target selection criteria for the structural genomics pipeline. As a result, manual intervention of the pipeline may allow for a more refined target list as opposed to a target list generated wholly based on pre-determined values and computed without expert curation.

(A)　　　　　　　　　　　　　　　　**(B)**

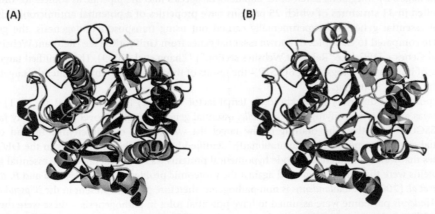

Fig. 2 Comparison of *G. antarctica* arginase structure generated from protein crystallography against a predicted model generated by SWISS-MODEL. The superposition of *G. antarctica* arginase structures between (A) predicted 3D model (dark blue) with X-ray crystal structure (gold) (RMSD: 1.06 Å/243 Cα) and (B) predicted 3D model (dark blue) with the template used for prediction (PDBID:4ity) (cyan) (RMSD: 0.31 Å/300 Cα). Superposition was done using CCP4MG.

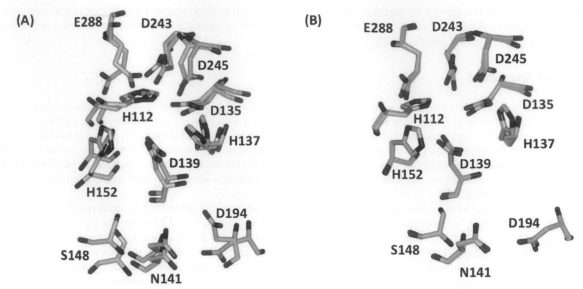

Fig. 3 Superposition of active site residues between (a) *G. antarctica* arginase structure solved by X-ray crystallography (gold) (PDB template used: 4hze) against the SWISS-MODEL predicted arginase (light blue) and (b) The SWISS-MODEL predicted arginase (light blue) against the template used for prediction (PDBID: 4ity). Active site residues are labeled based on the numbering of *G. antarctica* arginase crystal structure. The strictly conserved putative metal coordinating residues in *G. antarctica* arginase are H112, H137, D135, D139, D243 and D245 and several conserved putative arginine binding residues are D139, N141, S148, H152, D194 and E288.

Illustrative Examples and Case Studies

Burkholderia pseudomallei

Burkholderia pseudomallei is a pathogenic soil bacteria that causes the disease melioidosis. At the initial time of writing (circa November 2017), there were 237 PDB entries for *B. pseudomallei* in the PDB. Filtering those for structures that have less than 95% sequence identity retrieved 99 PDB entries. Due to the use of mutant structures as a means to characterize functional mechanisms, this reduced number is most likely the actual count for unique *B. pseudomallei* structures in the PDB. Of the 237 structures, 51% (121 entries) were deposited by the Seattle Structural Genomics Center for Infectious Disease (SSGCID) (Myler *et al.*, 2009). The number submitted by the SSGCID could be reduced to 63 entries when a sequence identity filter of 95% was used.

The SSGCID is a National Institute of Allergy and Infectious Diseases (NIAID) consortium applying structural genomics approaches for identifying potential drug targets (Stacy *et al.*, 2011). In the search for drugs against *B. pseudomallei*, the SSGCID embarked on a combined functional and structural genomics approach to identify essential proteins and solve their structures (Baugh *et al.*, 2013). This effort involved experimental identification of essential genes using transposon mutagenesis in *Burkholderia thailandensis*, a phylogenetically similar member of the *Burkholderia* genus. With 406 putative essential genes identified, an 'ortholog rescue' strategy was employed for difficult targets by integrating seven other Burkholderia species into the pipeline as sources for orthologous proteins.

These efforts resulted in 31 structures of which 25 proteins have properties of a potential antimicrobial drug target. Although the identification of essential genes was experimentally carried out using transposon mutagenesis, the genomes of the Burkholderia species were compared to examples of known essential genes from UniProtKB (see "Relevant Websites section") and the Database of Essential Genes – DEG (see "Relevant Websites section") (Zhang *et al.*, 2009). The identified targets were also used to identify the existence of human homologs using BLASTP – the results of this was used to further filter the target list to only proteins that did not have any human homologs.

The work that reported the discovery of Burkholderia lethal factor 1 (BLF-1) (Cruz-Migoni *et al.*, 2011) started on a similar footing. The project was aimed at identifying *B. pseudomallei* essential genes, as well as novel pathogenicity factors. Despite some similarities to the SSGCID initiative, the drafting of the target list was carried out differently. Instead of using transposon mutagenesis, potential essential genes were computationally identified based on their homologs in the DEG resource. An additional dataset of genes that were annotated to encode hypothetical proteins was also generated. The essential genes homologs and the hypothetical proteins were then cross-referenced against the proteomic profiles of *B. pseudomallei* and *B. thailandensis* reported by Wongtrakoongate *et al.* (2007). *B. thailandensis* is non-pathogenic, therefore proteins present in the *B. pseudomallei* proteome but absent in the *B. thailandensis* proteome were assumed to have potential roles in pathogenesis – these were then selected as targets for the pipeline. The BPSL1549 protein was found to be present in the 2D gel electrophoresis data of *B. pseudomallei* but absent in that of *B. thailandensis* thus leading to its selection for structure determination.

For decades, conclusive evidence for the pathogenicity and virulence factors of *B. pseudomallei* had eluded investigators (Stone, 2007). The BPSL1549 structure, which was renamed to BLF-1, had fold similarities to the catalytic domain of *Escherichia coli* cytotoxic necrotizing factor 1 (CNF-1) (Cruz-Migoni *et al.*, 2011). The solution of the BLF-1 structure led to the identification of its substrate, the eukaryotic translation eIF4A, hence characterizing the role of BLF-1 in the disruption of protein synthesis in its host.

Glaciozyma antarctica

Glaciozyma antarctica is an obligate psychrophilic yeast that is able to survive at temperatures below 20°C. From its genome annotation, a total of 7857 genes were predicted (Firdaus-Raih *et al.*, 2018). Target genes for structural genomics were then chosen by filtering out 1610 genes encoding transmembrane regions, 4874 proteins predicted to be insoluble, 198 proteins computed to have low complexity regions and 23 proteins where coils make up more than 20% of the total sequence. These filtering steps also selected genes that have lengths of between 50 and 700 amino acids and no similar examples in the PDB at a sequence identity of 30% or lower which produced 453 target genes with 53% of this number having been annotated as hypothetical proteins.

Several target genes from *G. antarctica* were further crystallized and six of the structures had been successfully solved at the time of writing with three having been deposited in the PDB (PDBIDs: 4xxf, 5yhp, 5ynl). A resource that tracks the progress of target CDS for structure solution is available as part of the GlacIER (*Glaciozyma antarctica* Integrated Exploration Resource) database (see "Relevant Websites section"). This is perhaps another aspect that a computational and informatics based approach can be integrated into structural genomics. In this case, a simple MySQL database was made accessible via a web interface that allowed members of the project as well as the public varying levels of access to the data. Users of the database can thus track the progress of the targets as they proceed through the pipeline. Undoubtedly, more complex enterprise level management of such pipelines are in use by larger structural genomics consortia that work on multiple target organisms, however, the GlacIER database demonstrates that a small group in extended collaboration with several other labs can also execute a structural genomics project.

Discussion and Future Directions

Although the bulk of the work done in structural genomics consists of experimental work to produce proteins and generate 3D structure coordinate data, it is clear that extensive sequence database searching needs to be carried out during the identification of targets for the pipeline. Computational approaches are once again called upon for analysis of the 3D structures once they become available. While most structural genomics pipelines that can be found in the literature adopt a similar structure to that presented in **Figs. 1** and **3**, this is expected to evolve as the resolutions of structures acquired using cryo-EM get higher.

It is not expected for cryo-EM to supplant protein crystallography in providing the bulk of the 3D structures in the PDB; however, future structural genomics projects may employ all three approaches in order to provide a wider coverage of the structures that can be acquired from an available genome sequence. These would thus require the target selection process to take into account the specific requirement for each method and no longer be highly dependent solely on protein solubility. Informatic approaches would be required to provide decision making tools to identify targets and estimate the requirement and/or necessity of solving specific homologous structures. The pipeline may also evolve further to include computational methods of structure determination.

Closing Remarks

The structural genomics pipeline and specific filters enable what can be an expensive endeavour to have a reduced workload and cost. This allows for smaller and less well funded groups outside of large structural genomics consortia to also practice structural genomics as discussed in the case studies examples.

Acknowledgement

MFR is funded by the Ministry of Science, Technology and Innovation grant 02-01-02-SF1278 and the Universiti Kebangsaan Malaysia grant GP-K011849.

See also: Biological Database Searching. Biomolecular Structures: Prediction, Identification and Analyses. Comparative Genomics Analysis. Identifying Functional Relationships Via the Annotation and Comparison of Three-Dimensional Amino Acid Arrangements in Protein Structures. Natural Language Processing Approaches in Bioinformatics. Next Generation Sequencing Data Analysis. Pipeline of High Throughput Sequencing. Sequence Analysis. Whole Genome Sequencing Analysis

References

Ahmad, L., Hung, T.L., Mat Akhir, N.A., *et al.*, 2015. Characterization of Burkholderia pseudomallei protein BPSL1375 validates the Putative hemolytic activity of the COG3176 N-Acyltransferase family. BMC Microbiol. 15, 270.

Anfinsen, C.B., 1972. The formation and stabilization of protein structure. Biochem. J. 128, 737–749.

Baugh, L., Gallagher, L.A., Patrapuvich, R., et al., 2013. Combining functional and structural genomics to sample the essential Burkholderia structome. PLOS ONE 8, e53851.

Bhattacharya, A., Tejero, R., Montelione, G.T., 2007. Evaluating protein structures determined by structural genomics consortia. Proteins 66, 778–795.

Biasini, M., Bienert, S., Waterhouse, A., et al., 2014. SWISS-MODEL: Modelling protein tertiary and quaternary structure using evolutionary information. Nucleic Acids Res. 42, W252–W258.

Chothia, C., Lesk, A.M., 1986. The relation between the divergence of sequence and structure in proteins. EMBO J. 5, 823–826.

Cruz-Migoni, A., Ruzheinikov, S.N., Sedelnikova, S.E., et al., 2011. Cloning, purification and crystallographic analysis of a hypothetical protein, BPSL1549, from Burkholderia pseudomallei. Acta. Crystallogr. Sect. F Struct. Biol. Cryst. Commun. 67, 1623–1626.

Debret, G., Martel, A., Cuniasse, P., 2009. RASMOT-3D PRO: A 3D motif search webserver. Nucleic Acids Res 37, W459–W464.

Dey, S., Ritchie, D.W., Levy, E.D., 2018. PDB-wide identification of biological assemblies from conserved quaternary structure geometry. Nat. Methods 15, 67–72.

Fedorov, O., Sundstrom, M., Marsden, B., Knapp, S., 2007. Insights for the development of specific kinase inhibitors by targeted structural genomics. Drug Discov. Today 12, 365–372.

Firdaus-Raih, M., Hashim, N.H.F., Bharudin, I., et al., 2018. The Glaciozyma antarctica genome reveals an array of systems that provide sustained responses towards temperature variations in a persistently cold habitat. PLOS ONE 13, e0189947.

Franklin, M.C., Cheung, J., Rudolph, M.J., et al., 2015. Structural genomics for drug design against the pathogen Coxiella burnetii. Proteins 83, 2124–2136.

Hashim, N.H., Bharudin, I., Nguong, D.L., et al., 2013. Characterization of Afp1, an antifreeze protein from the psychrophilic yeast Glaciozyma antarctica PI12. Extremophiles 17, 63–73.

Holm, L., Laakso, L.M., 2016. Dali server update. Nucleic Acids Res. 44, W351–W355.

Konc, J., Janezic, D., 2017. ProBiS tools (algorithm, database, and web servers) for predicting and modeling of biologically interesting proteins. Prog. Biophys. Mol. Biol. 128, 24–32.

Laskowski, R.A., Jablonska, J., Pravda, L., Varekova, R.S., Thornton, J.M., 2018. PDBsum: Structural summaries of PDB entries. Protein Sci. 27, 129–134.

Marsden, R.L., Lewis, T.A., Orengo, C.A., 2007. Towards a comprehensive structural coverage of completed genomes: A structural genomics viewpoint. BMC Bioinform. 8, 86.

Myler, P.J., Stacy, R., Stewart, L., et al., 2009. The seattle structural genomics center for infectious disease (SSGCID). Infect. Disord. Drug Targets 9, 493–506.

Nadzirin, N., Firdaus-Raih, M., 2012. Proteins of unknown function in the protein data bank (pdb): An inventory of true uncharacterized proteins and computational tools for their analysis. Int. J. Mol. Sci. 13, 12761–12772.

Nadzirin, N., Gardiner, E.J., Willett, P., Artymiuk, P.J., Firdaus-Raih, M., 2012. SPRITE and ASSAM: Web servers for side chain 3D-motif searching in protein structures. Nucleic Acids Res. 40, W380–W386.

Nadzirin, N., Willett, P., Artymiuk, P.J., Firdaus-Raih, M., 2013. IMAAAGINE: A webserver for searching hypothetical 3D amino acid side chain arrangements in the Protein Data Bank. Nucleic Acids Res. 41, W432–W440.

Nair, R., Liu, J., Soong, T.-T., et al., 2009. Structural genomics is the largest contributor of novel structural leverage. J. Struct. Funct. Genom. 10, 181–191.

Ramli, A.N., Azhar, M.A., Shamsir, M.S., et al., 2013. Sequence and structural investigation of a novel psychrophilic alpha-amylase from Glaciozyma antarctica PI12 for cold-adaptation analysis. J. Mol. Model. 19, 3369–3383.

Stacy, R., Begley, D.W., Phan, I., et al., 2011. Structural genomics of infectious disease drug targets: The SSGCID. Acta. Crystallogr. Sect. F Struct. Biol. Cryst. Commun. 67, 979–984.

Stone, R., 2007. Infectious disease. Racing to defuse a bacterial time bomb. Science 317, 1022–1024.

Wongtrakoongate, P., Mongkoldhumrongkul, N., Chaijan, S., Kamchonwongpaisan, S., Tungpradabkul, S., 2007. Comparative proteomic profiles and the potential markers between Burkholderia pseudomallei and Burkholderia thailandensis. Mol. Cell. Probes 21, 81–91.

Yusof, N.A., Hashim, N.H., Beddoe, T., et al., 2016. Thermotolerance and molecular chaperone function of an SGT1-like protein from the psychrophilic yeast, Glaciozyma antarctica. Cell Stress Chaperones 21, 707–715.

Zarembinski, T.I., Hung, L.-W., Mueller-Dieckmann, H.-J., et al., 1998. Structure-based assignment of the biochemical function of a hypothetical protein: A test case of structural genomics. Proc. Natl. Acad. Sci. USA 95, 15189–15193.

Zhang, Y., Lin, Z.A., Pan, J.J., et al., 2009. Concurrent control study of different radiotherapy for primary nasopharyngeal carcinoma: Intensity-modulated radiotherapy versus conventional radiotherapy. Ai Zheng 28, 1143–1148.

Relevant Websites

http://mfrlab.org/glacier/
GlacIER: Glaciozyma antarctica Integrated Exploration Resource.
http://www.uniprot.org
The UniProt knowledgebase.
http://tubic.tju.edu.cn/deg/
Tianjin University BioInformatics Centre.

Structure-Based Design of Peptide Inhibitors for Protein Arginine Deiminase Type IV (PAD4)

Teo Chian Ying, International Medical University, Bukit Jalil, Kuala Lumpur, Malaysia
Zalikha Ibrahim, International Islamic University Malaysia, Kuantan, Malaysia
Mohd Basyaruddin Abd Rahman, Universiti Putra Malaysia, Serdang, Selangor, Malaysia
Bimo A Tejo, UCSI University, Cheras, Kuala Lumpur, Malaysia

Introduction

Rheumatoid arthritis (RA) is a chronic inflammatory disease that is characterized by symmetrical pain in one or more joints (Landre-Beauvais, 2001). The symptoms usually start with stiffness in the morning, followed by joint tenderness and swelling. The number of affected joints varies, but most of the disease development involves five or more joints, including both small and big joints. Since its identification, RA has been the cause of joint inflammations in 0.5%–1% of the world's population (Gabriel, 2001).

The number of people diagnosed with RA in year 2008 has been estimated to be nearly 1.3 million in the United States (Helmick et al., 2008). The affected patients have a low health-related quality of life due to physical damages induced by the disease (Salaffi et al., 2009). This caused difficulties for the patients to perform their routine activities, and for some, it resulted in losing their jobs. With the assumption that human life span increases every year, it is expected that the frequency of correctly diagnosed patients with RA will increase in the future.

RA is regarded as an autoimmune disease (Davidson and Diamond, 2001). The word 'autoimmune' is a combination of two separate words that is auto and immune. Auto refers to self, while immune means the immune system. Therefore, autoimmune disease can be easily understood as a disease that is triggered by the abnormal response of the immune system against one's substance or tissue that is naturally presented in the body. In the case of RA, the target is the joint and the tissues that surround it. The onset of RA is caused by the stimulation of the immune system that is triggered by foreign substrates that mimic the joint cells (Davidson and Diamond, 2001). As a defensive mechanism, the immune components start to attack the invaders and coincidentally, the joint cells too. This in turn, causes the swelling of the synovial membrane, leading to joint inflammation.

Over the past 30 years, several classes of drugs have been introduced to treat RA. Routinely, these drugs are prescribed after the first tissue is damaged. The main aim is to minimize RA joint inflammations, but the drugs do not treating the underlying causes. At present, three classes of drugs are commercially available, namely corticosteroids, non-steroidal anti-inflammatory drugs (NSAID) and disease-modifying anti-rheumatic drugs (DMARD). Depending on the disease severity, an appropriate drug is prescribed and the patient status is reviewed from time to time. Among all three drugs classes, DMARD is the most commonly prescribed medication for RA patients. An example of a drug from this class is methotrexate (MTX) (Aletaha et al., 2010). Although it is effective in relieving RA symptoms, the mechanism of action of MTX in treating RA remains unclear. A major drawback of MTX is that it can cause the development of multiple side effects on the central nervous, hepatic, pulmonary, hematologic and gastrointestinal systems especially in long-term usage (Smolen et al., 2005). This drug also has a toxicity issue, which is why MTX was discontinued in certain, more susceptible RA patients (Smolen et al., 2010).

RA is not be a fatal disease, however, severe and unmanageable conditions may arise that gradually disrupts overall human function, and thus, the quality of life (Salaffi et al., 2009). Long-standing RA patients have an increased risk of suffering multiple health problems. Therefore, it is crucial to diagnose RA at an earlier stage of the disease; so that treatment can be administered sooner and the major damage of joint tissues can be prevented. Recent interest has been focused on citrullinated peptides, which is a true RA antigen (Schellekens et al., 1998, 2000). Detection of autoantibodies against this type of antigen is more specific and sensitive than the current RA serological marker, Rheumatoid Factor (RF). This makes the antibodies correspond to the citrullinated peptides, name Anti-Citrullinated Peptide Antibody (ACPA) a suitable clinical marker to be developed (Wegner et al., 2009).

Citrulline can be produced from an arginine residue in a peptide/protein (van Venrooij and Pruijn, 2000). Since the overall conversion involves the replacement of an imine group to a carbonyl group, the chemical reaction is often referred to as deimination (**Fig. 1**). The reaction is catalyzed by an enzyme called Protein Arginine Deiminase (PAD). In normal physiology, citrullinated peptides are present in proteins such as myelin sheath and histone (Jones et al., 2009). In the case of RA, irregular expressions of citrullinated peptides (and hence, ACPA) have been reported (Hoet and van Venrooij, 1992; Hoet et al., 1991; Vincent et al., 1999). Traces of the peptides and the enzyme catalyzing the reaction, PAD type 4 (PAD4) are found in the sera and joints of the patients (Kinloch et al., 2008). This triggers the autoimmune response, resulting in joint inflammation. Therefore, suppression of the citrullination pathway has been hypothesized to be a strategic yet specific way to slow down the disease. An ideal approach is to modulate the protein that catalyzes the reaction, namely PAD4.

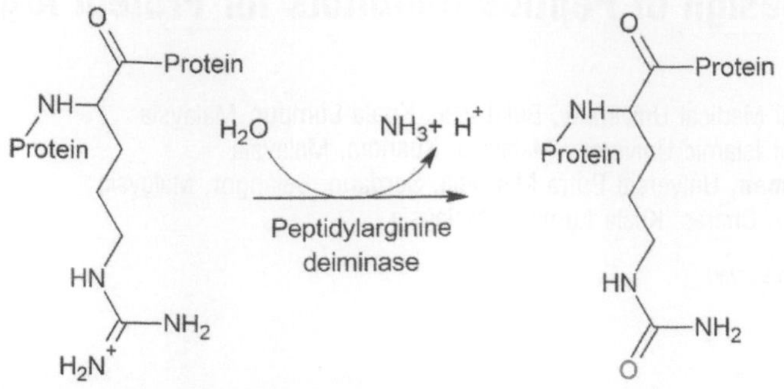

Fig. 1   Enzymatic conversion of peptidylarginine into peptidyl citrulline.

Related Autoantibodies in RA Diagnosis

RA is indeed a tricky disease to diagnose. This is because the clinical symptoms are visible only after the first tissue damage. Luckily, during the disease development, the immune cells of the RA patient excrete various types of autoantibodies that can be used as indicators. There are a numbers of excellent reviews regarding RA-related autoantibodies and their biochemistry (Boekel et al., 2002; Vossenaar, 2004).

Rheumatoid Factor (RF) is the first autoantibody found in RA patients. It was described in the late 1930s and is still used as one of the criteria for diagnosing RA (Aletaha et al., 2010; Arnett et al.,1988). It is reactive towards the tail (or known as Fc portion) of immunoglobulin G (IgG), which is an antibody that protects the human body from infections. This factor however, has also been found in many other diseases involving immune reactions and infections (Boekel et al., 2002). To a certain extent, this antibody has been found in 5% of healthy population, in which the percentage increases up to 30% in healthy elderly. It is interesting to note that not all RA patients would exhibit this formula. This results in the classification of 'seropositive' or 'seronegative' RA groups. The former are the ones who demonstrated physical symptoms with RF antibodies, the latter are those who manifested the symptoms with no evidence of elevated RF values (Arnett et al., 1988). Altogether, this indicates that the RF had low specificity and sensitivity; hence it can not be used as a single indicator in RA diagnosis.

In recent years, the emergence of autoantibodies towards citrullinated peptides has created a new path of research in rheumatology (van Venrooij and Pruijn, 2000). Historically, two autoantibodies namely the anti-perinuclear factor (APF) and the anti-keratin antibodies (AKA) are described to be specific for RA (Hoet and van Venrooij, 1992). Although the latter has lower specificity than the former, investigation on both antibodies shows that they are interrelated (Hoet et al., 1991; Vincent et al.,1999). They share the same antigen namely filaggrin in its matured form, which is citrulline-specific. Several years later, researchers find traces of other antibodies that also respond to citrulline-containing peptides, for example, anti-filaggrin in RA patients (Schellekens et al., 1998). This becomes a foundation for further studies on the use of citrulline-containing peptides for RA diagnosis. Reactivity investigation of diverse citrullinated peptides shows a remarkable pattern of APF and AKA responses. Of all tested peptides, antibody responses towards cyclic citrullinated peptides (CCP) are remarkable in RA patients with 98% specificity. Nowadays, enzymatic assay against CCP is used as a common procedure in RA diagnosis (Aletaha et al., 2010). The fact that the anti-citrullinated peptides antibodies (ACPA) can be detected before the first tissue damage makes them a reliable serological marker for early RA detection (Jansen et al., 2002).

Citrullination in the RA Cycle

While the anti-citrullinated peptide antibodies (ACPA) acts as a potential serological marker for RA, it has been hypothesized that the citrullination pathway may participate in the RA cycle (van Venrooij and Pruijn, 2008). The citrullination process converts the peptidyl-bound arginine residue into a peptidyl-bound citrulline residue, as a result of posttranslational modification. The upregulation of citrullinated peptides is said to break the immune tolerance, triggering the release of the CCP-related antibodies and consequently the onset of RA. This creates a new level of understanding and opened opportunities for studies of the disease process.

In a review by Klareskog and colleagues, they summarize several factors including environmental, citrullination and genetic variants that contributed primarily towards the rise of ACPA (Klareskog et al., 2011). The factors are interrelated, in which the disease could be triggered when multiple factors are present. Based on their early work, the research group discovered that the relation between smoking and RA could be seen via the presence of HLA-DR shared epitope (SE) genes in a particular person (Klareskog et al., 2006). The probability of stimulating the disease is 21-fold higher in the smokers with the genes, when compared to those with the absence of either factor. As the enzyme that catalyzes citrullination, PAD, is also involved in apoptosis, it becomes activated. This indirectly increases the ACPA.

On a different note, there is a review on oral citrullination by a Gram-negative bacterium called *Porphyromonas gingivalis* (Mangat et al., 2010). It is a major pathogen in periodontitis, an advanced gum disease that involves the inflammatory immune response. Given the fact that *P. gingivalis* is the only bacteria to date to express PAD in its cells, it is speculated that the PAD expressed by the bacteria may have been able to catalyze the citrullination of human peptidylarginine too. Once the tolerance is broken, the immune responses are invoked. The bacteria association with RA is also supported by the level of antibodies to *P. gingivalis* in RA patient when compared to a healthy sample, indicating that the bacteria may have indeed plays a role in the disease development (Mikuls *et al.*, 2009).

Protein Arginine Deiminase IV (PAD4)

PAD4 belongs to the family of guanidinium modifying superfamily (GMSF). As the name suggests, these are proteins that are responsible in converting the guanidinium side chain into other functional groups. Together with PAD4, there are also PAD1, PAD2, PAD3 and PAD6 in the PAD family. As a matter of fact, it was thought that human PAD5 was a novel PAD. However, detailed investigations on the sequence and expression shows that the human PAD5 is analogous to the mouse PAD4. Therefore, it is renamed as PAD4, leaving a vacancy on the fifth type (Vossenaar *et al.*, 2003). PAD4 has several specific roles in normal body. It is involved in the formation of neutrophil extracellular traps (NET). The foundations of this NET are neutrophils, which are among the first responders during the occurrence of a bacterial infection. By the stimulation from PAD4, the neutrophils are combined to form a more complex NET system. This is proven by the disruption of NET when PAD4 is inhibited (Lewis *et al.*, 2015). Apart from that, PAD4 is also a corepressor of the p53 protein. This p53 is a tumor suppressor, which can initiate apoptosis of damaged deoxyribonucleic acid (DNA). By corepressing p53, PAD4 might induce the growth of the tumor, evidenced by the trace of PAD4 in patients with malignant tumors (Chang *et al.*, 2009). Other reviews on PAD4 and its roles can be found below (Fuhrmann *et al.*, 2015; Jones *et al.*, 2009).

PAD4 Structure

PAD4 contains 663 amino acids, with a molecular weight of 74 kDa. The first 294 amino acids are arranged in two immunoglobulin-like (I g) structures, making the N-terminal domain (Arita *et al.*, 2004). These subdomains are proposed to assist substrate selection and protein-protein interaction. Inside the subdomain 1, there is a nuclear localization signal (NLS) (56-PPAKKKST-63) that is arranged in a loop. This loop region is highly flexible as it exposed to solvent, which is explained by the high temperature factor in the crystallographic data. Based on the records, PAD4 is the only PAD with this NLS region. The peptide sequence acts as a tag that will interact with the nuclear transport receptors embedded in the nucleus envelope, for import into the cell nucleus.

The remaining sequence, is folded into a α/β propeller and forms the C-terminal domain. This domain ports all the active residues that are needed for the citrullination catalysis. The key residues are D350, H471, D473 and C645. PAD4 is only active in the presence of calcium and naturally exists as a homodimeric protein in solution. The dimer is reported to be in a head-to-tail fashion; that is between the N-terminal subdomain 1 of one monomer and catalytic domain of the other monomer. **Fig. 2** illustrates the dimer structure of PAD4.

Calcium Dependency

It is common for proteins to have metal binding sites. A protein may contain one or more metal ions, which are unique in terms of their role and coordination. The basic functions of metals in proteins can be classified into five categories (Holm *et al.*, 1996): (1) For structural stability of the secondary or ternary protein structure, (2) for storage, (3) for electron transfer, (4) oxygen binding and lastly (5) for catalytic reaction. Data from crystallographic studies reveals that PAD4 had five unique calcium binding sites; three (Ca3–5) are in the N-terminal domain and another two (Ca1 and Ca2) are in the catalytic domain (Arita *et al.*, 2004). The recent 1.8 Å resolution structures of calcium-free and calcium-bound PAD4 (PDB ID: 1WD8 and 1WD9) reveals an interesting role of Ca1 and Ca2 towards the enzyme. The residues on the surface of PAD4 catalytic pocket is exposed to solvent in the calcium free PAD4. Upon the binding of the calcium, the residues are more structured. Further analysis of the electrostatic surface potential also indicates changes from the highly acidic to the more basic surface, where it is more favourable for peptidyl-arginine to bind. In addition, the geometry of the active site in the substrate-free, calcium bound PAD4 is found to be similar to that of the substrate bound PAD4, signifying that the formation of the active site is not dependent on substrate binding (**Fig. 3**). Overall, it is deduced that the catalytic pocket shape is highly dependent on these catalytic ions.

Liu and colleagues (Liu *et al.*, 2013) recently reported the role of calcium ions in the PAD4 N-terminal domain. Based on the kinetic studies, it is observed that the binding network of Ca3 and Ca4 is vital for full enzyme activation. Mutation of the residues that are coordinated with Ca3 and Ca4 namely D155, D157, and D179 diminishes the enzyme catalytic ability significantly. In contrast, the mutants with respect to the Ca5 binding show an indistinct effect on the catalytic efficiency, indicating that the enzyme has less dependency on the Ca5 binding.

Metal dependency of PAD4 has also been tested in a work reported by Kearney and co-workers (Kearney *et al.*, 2005). They concluded that only calcium can efficiently activate the PAD4 catalytic activity. Additionally, some of the metals even have the

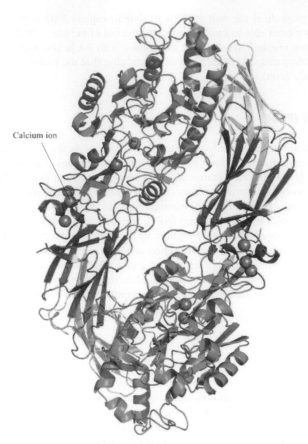

Fig. 2 PAD4 dimer structure in head-to-tail fashion. Subdomain 1 is colored in yellow, subdomain 2 is in orange, and the catalytic domain is in deep teal.

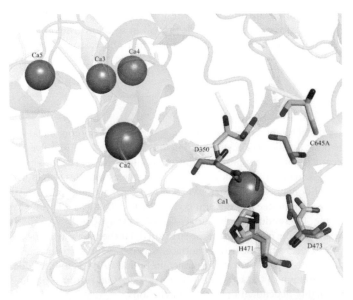

Fig. 3 Superimposition of deep-teal colored calcium-unbound PAD4 (PDB ID: 1WD8) onto lemon color calcium-bound PAD4 (1WD9). Some parts of the proteins were set in higher transparency for visualization purpose.

ability to inhibit the protein and could possibly be a PAD4 deactivator. Metals that display strong PAD4 inhibition properties are manganese, samarium and zinc. These findings prove the importance of calcium in PAD4 activation. Interestingly, although the calcium ions are needed for citrullination catalysis, they do not affect the formation of the PAD4 dimer (Arita *et al.*, 2004; Liu *et al.*, 2011).

Substrate Recognition

The PAD4 active site has a U-tunnel shape, with two door entrances (**Fig. 4**). The "front door" is the entrance where the actual substrate conversion takes place (Arita *et al.*, 2004, 2006). The "back door" on the other hand, is thought to provide access for solvent to enter and subsequently complete the hydrolysis (Linsky and Fast, 2010). The shape of tunnel is narrow, allowing only small molecules to enter and interact with the active residues. Similar two-door pockets have also been found in other guanidinium-modifying hydrolases, such as arginine deiminase (ADI) and dimethylarginine dimethylaminohydrolase (DDAH) (Linsky and Fast, 2010). An inspection on the structure of PAD4 complexed with benzoyl-arginine amide (BAA) substrate (**Fig. 5**) reveals several key residues that are important for substrate recognition. BAA is small substrate that mimics peptidylarginine and has been used widely as a positive control in any PAD4 related experiments. The guanidinium nitrogen atom of BAA is found to form double hydrogen bonds with the carbonyl side chain of D473 and D350. This secures the position of the guanidinium group for nucleophilic attack by C645. The opposite part of BAA is fastened by double and single hydrogen bonds from the R374 side chain and R639 backbone respectively. Another important residue is W347, which holds the part in between the substrate's ends. The effect is best described as providing large hydrophobic effects to the substrates. Consistent with this interaction analysis, mutations of the above residues distract protein-ligand interactions significantly.

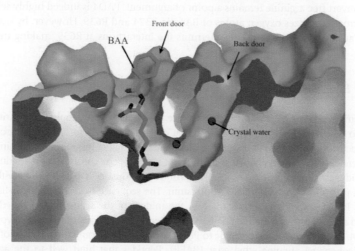

Fig. 4 Two-door pocket of PAD4 rendered using the crystal structure of PAD4 in bound with BAA (PDB ID: 1WDA). Some parts of protein are removed to ease visualization.

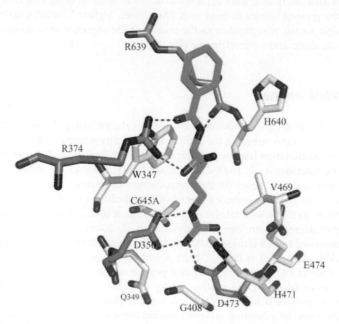

Fig. 5 Key residues in the PAD4-BAA interaction. Hydrogen bonds within 3.35 Å are presented in purple, when non-bonded contacts within the range of 2.90–3.90 are rendered in white.

Table 1   *Sequences of designed peptides.* The residues are presented in 1 letter amino acid code. C-terminal of each peptide was amidated

Peptide	Sequence
Pep1	MSPLRPQNY-NH$_2$
Pep2	QLSLRTVSL-NH$_2$
Pep3	PVVLRLKCG-NH$_2$
Pep4	ISGKRSAPG-NH$_2$
Pep5	KKSIRDTPA-NH$_2$
Pep6	SSTPRSKGQ-NH$_2$
Pep7	KNCFRMTDQ-NH$_2$
Pep8	LWQWRKSL-NH$_2$

The ability of PAD4 to convert free arginine remains a point of argument. PAD4 is indeed highly selective towards its substrates (Arita *et al.*, 2004). The enzyme recognizes oxygen atoms of BAA via R374 and R639. However, by using free arginine, the oxygen atom recognition by R374 cannot be established. This interrupts the interactions at R639, making free arginine a poor substrate.

Design of Peptide-Based PAD4 Inhibitors

There are several natural substrate of PAD4 such as histone, α-enolase, vimentin and nucleophosmin (Arita *et al.*, 2004; Hagiwara *et al.*, 2002; Suzuki *et al.*, 2007). To determine the peptide sequence that can bind strongly to PAD4, our group designed several peptides based on the sequence of nucleophosmin (Teo *et al.*, 2017). There are eight target residues i.e., arginine in the sequence of nucleophosmin so eight peptides were designed and named as Pep1 to Pep8. Pep1 to Pep7 consist of nine residues with four flanking residues before and after the target residue, arginine (region -4 to $+4$). While Pep8 consists of eight residues with only three flanking residues after arginine because it is near to the C-terminal of nucleophosmin. The sequence of each peptide is listed in **Table 1**.

The target amino acid of PAD4, arginine was positioned in the middle of the sequence and based on the sequence of nucleophosmin, four or three amino acids before and after arginine were chosen as the flanking residues that would aid in binding to residues around the active site of PAD4. The binding of each peptide to PAD4 was studied by comparing the rate of citrullination of each peptide to PAD4 small substrate, N-α-benzoyl arginine ethyl ester (BAEE). Peptides that bind well to the active site of PAD4 would be favourable in citrullination process and therefore more citrulline would be produced. To increase the affinity of the peptides in binding with PAD4, the best peptide was chosen for modification where the sequence was shortened from nine residues to 7, 5, and 3 residues.

The binding of the peptides after shortening were again is compared to BAEE in order to identify the best sequence for PAD4 binding. The peptide having the greatest affinity to bind with PAD4 (with highest % relative activity) was selected for peptide-based inhibitor design. The target amino acid, arginine in the middle of the sequence was substituted with two amino acids: an amino acid with free amino side chain and L-2-furylalanine (**Fig. 6**).

Activity of Peptide-Based PAD4 Inhibitors

The relative activity of PAD4 with the designed peptides as substrate is shown in **Fig. 7**. Each peptide shows different substrate efficiency for citrullination by PAD4 demonstrating the influence of primary sequence of a peptide flanking an arginine. The influence of flanking residues in citrullination has also been reported in previous studies (Arita *et al.*, 2006; Hagiwara *et al.*, 2005; Nakayama-Hamada *et al.*, 2005; Takahara *et al.*, 1985; Tarcsa *et al.*, 1996). However the amino acids could not be classified as favourable or unfavourable simply based on their physicochemical features. The influence of a residue on the citrullination by PAD4 is dependent on the overall sequence in which it is embedded (Stensland *et al.*, 2009).

Pep5 shows the highest activity to PAD4 with relative activity of 38%. It contains an aspartic acid at $+1$ position of arginine residue which results in a higher degree of citrullination (Stensland *et al.*, 2009). To improve the substrate efficiency for citrullination by PAD4, Pep5 was shortened from 9 residues to 7, 5 and 3 residues with the position of arginine remained at the middle of the peptides. The new peptides are named as Pep5_7, Pep5_5 and Pep5_3, respectively.

Fig. 8 shows the relative activity of PAD4 when the modified peptide served as substrate. When two amino acids are removed from each terminal in the sequence (Pep5_7), the relative activity of PAD4 increases drastically from less than 40% to nearly 100%. But when the number of residues is further reduced to five and three residues, the relative activity of PAD4 decreases. Pep5_5 and Pep5_3 may be too short in exhibiting sufficient interaction with PAD4 thus affected the substrate efficiency of the peptides on citrullination by the enzyme. This is in agreement with previous study where when long peptide was truncated, the peptides would be more unfavourable for citrullination (Stensland *et al.*, 2009).

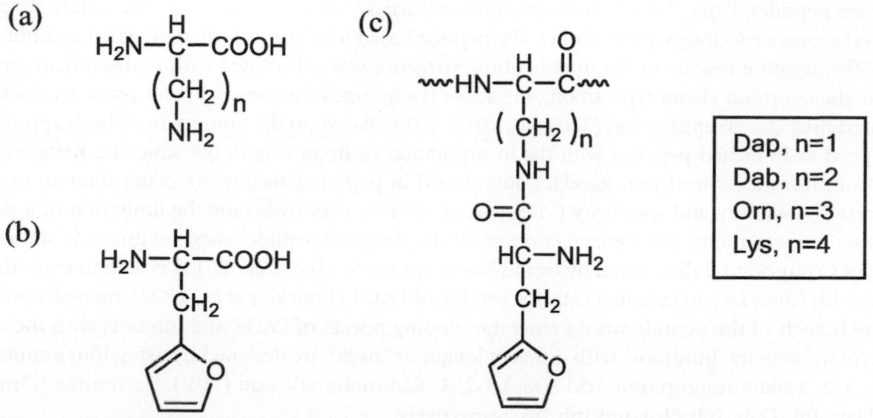

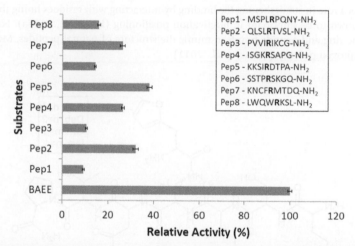

(a)

H₂N—C—COOH
(with H above central C, (CH₂)ₙ below, NH₂ at bottom)

(b)

H₂N—C—COOH
(CH₂ group, furan ring below)

(c)

~~~HN—C—C~~~
(with H above, O double bond right, (CH₂)ₙ below, NH, O=C, HC—NH₂, CH₂, furan ring)

Dap, n=1
Dab, n=2
Orn, n=3
Lys, n=4

Fig. 6 *Chemical structures of amino acids substituted arginine in peptide-based inhibitors.* (a) Amino acids with different side chain length ended with a free amino group, L-2,3-diaminopropionic acid (Dap), L-2,4-diaminobutyric acid (Dab), L-orthinine (Orn), and L-lysine (Lys). (b) L-2-furylalanine (Fal). (c) Branched peptide was formed by coupling free amino group of (a) with carboxylic group of (b).

Pep1 - MSPLRPQNY-NH₂
Pep2 - QLSLRTVSL-NH₂
Pep3 - PVVIRIKCG-NH₂
Pep4 - ISGKRSAPG-NH₂
Pep5 - KKSIRDTPA-NH₂
Pep6 - SSTPRSKGQ-NH₂
Pep7 - KNCFRMTDQ-NH₂
Pep8 - LWQWRKSL-NH₂

Substrates: Pep8, Pep7, Pep6, Pep5, Pep4, Pep3, Pep2, Pep1, BAEE

Relative Activity (%): 0, 20, 40, 60, 80, 100, 120

Fig. 7 *Screening of peptide substrates of PAD4.* Eight designed peptides are utilized as substrates of PAD4 and the relative activity of PAD4 is calculated based on BAEE. Sequences of the peptides are shown in 1 letter amino acid code. The target arginine residue of PAD4 is shown in bold. C-termini of each peptide is amidated.

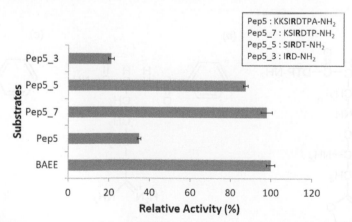

Pep5 : KKSIRDTPA-NH₂
Pep5_7 : KSIRDTP-NH₂
Pep5_5 : SIRDT-NH₂
Pep5_3 : IRD-NH₂

Substrates: Pep5_3, Pep5_5, Pep5_7, Pep5, BAEE

Relative Activity (%): 0, 20, 40, 60, 80, 100, 120

Fig. 8 *Screening of shortened Pep5 as substrate of PAD4.* Pep5 was shortened from 9 residues to 7, 5 and 3 residues and the modified peptides were utilized as substrate for PAD4. Sequences of the peptides are shown in 1 letter amino acid code. The target arginine residue of PAD4 is shown in bold. C-terminal of each peptide was amidated.

Among the designed peptides, Pep5_7 shows the highest relative activity on citrullination by PAD4 indicating that it has the most appropriate length and sequence to interact with PAD4. The peptide-based inhibitors are then designed according to the sequence of Pep5_7 (see **Fig. 8**). The arginine residue in the middle of the sequence was substituted with non-standard amino acid containing furan ring which was the common chemotype among the active compounds discovered by our previous works utilising structure-based and ligand-based drug design approaches (Teo *et al.*, 2012, 2013) Based on the findings from both approaches, peptide-based inhibitors were designed as branched peptides with the incorporation of furan ring in the structure. Branched peptide and peptidomimetic yielded from introduction of non-standard amino acid in peptide structure are better than an unmodified peptide in terms of biological activity, stability and specificity (Vlieghe *et al.*, 2010). They overcome the limitation of a peptide in acting as a drug with having better bioavailability. The general structure of the designed peptide-based inhibitors is shown in **Fig. 9**.

As the furan ring of Compound 5 discovered by ligand-based approach (Teo *et al.*, 2013) is able to enter the binding pocket of PAD4 and interacted with C645 i.e., an essential catalytic residue of PAD4 (Knuckley *et al.*, 2007) via hydrophobic interaction, our hypothesis is that the branch of the peptide would enter the binding pocket of PAD4 and interacts with the amino acids that are essential for the enzymatic activity. Inhibitors with different length of "neck" are designed by using four amino acids with different side chain length i.e., L-2, 3-diaminopropionic acid (Dap), L-2, 4-diaminobutyric acid (Dab), L-orthinine (Orn), and L-lysine (Lys) and named as Inh Dap, Inh Dab, Inh Orn and Inh Lys, respectively.

Most of the synthetic substrates and reported inhibitors of PAD4 (Jones *et al.*, 2012; Luo *et al.*, 2006a,b; Causey *et al.*, 2011) also having the "backbone", "neck" and "warhead" parts in the structures (**Fig. 10**). Such design is inspired by the structure of a small synthetic substrate of PAD4, benzoyl-L-arginine amide (BAA). The fluoroacetamidine acts as the warhead to the active site of PAD4 in F-amidine. Luo *et al.* (2006a) then modified the warhead by changing fluoroacetamidine to chloroacetamidine. They discovered that chloroacetamidine is more potent than fluoroacetamidine in inhibiting PAD4. The second portion, which is the neck, consists of an alkyl skeleton and plays a role in strengthening the binding by interacting with residues lining the pocket. The length of side chain i.e., the "neck" was shown to be important in inactivation positioning (Luo *et al.*, 2006a). For their backbones, they are basically consist of a benzene ring and peptide bonds to mimic the structure of natural peptides. Modification of the backbone results in inhibitors with improved potency (Causey *et al.*, 2011).

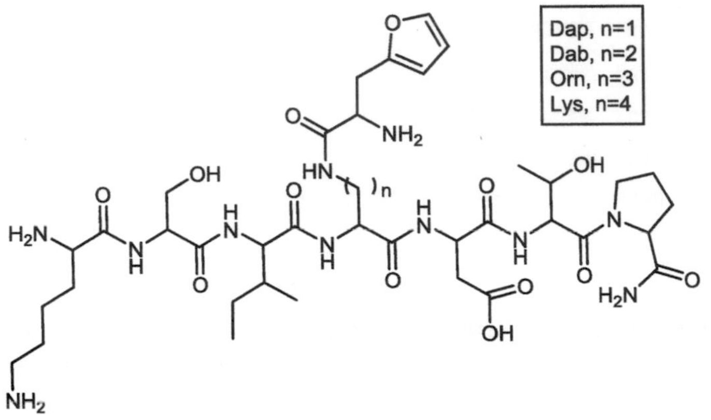

Fig. 9 *General structure of designed peptide-based inhibitors.* The target residue, arginine was substituted with non-standard amino acid containing furan ring with different side chain length. C-termini of peptide-based inhibitors were amidated.

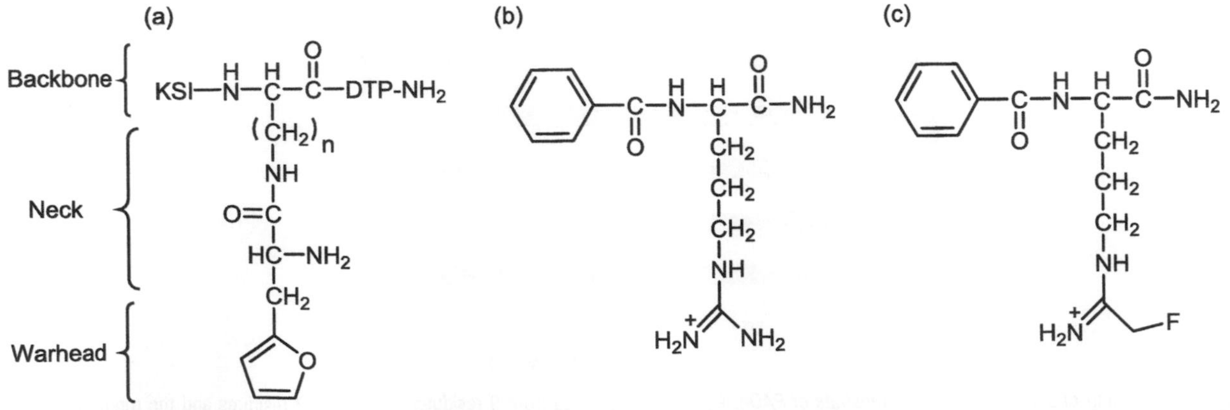

Fig. 10 *The chemical structures of (a) designed peptide-based inhibitors, (b) BAA, and (c) F-amidine.* All the structures are generally consisted of backbone, neck and warhead. Standard residues are shown in 1 letter amino acid code.

Table 2   *IC$_{50}$ values of the designed peptide-based inhibitors. IC$_{50}$ values were calculated using GraphPad Prism 5.1*

Inhibitors	IC$_{50}$ ± SD (μM)
Inh Dap	243.2 ± 2.4
Inh Dab	315.5 ± 6.2
Inh Orn	> 2 mM
Inh Lys	277.3 ± 2.7

Inhibitory Activity of Peptide-Based Inhibitors

The inhibitory activity of the designed peptide-based inhibitors is investigated by calculating the IC$_{50}$ value. Most of the inhibitors inhibit PAD4 significantly by reducing PAD4 activity to less than 50% at 2 mM except Inh Orn. The IC$_{50}$ values of the peptide-based inhibitors are shown in **Table 2**. Among the inhibitors, Inh Dap is the most active inhibitor followed by Inh Lys and Inh Dab.

There is no direct relationship between the "neck" lengths of the inhibitor with the inhibitor potency. Luo *et al.* (2006a) have also studied the relationship between the "neck" lengths with the inhibitory ability of the amidine-based inhibitors. The length of the "neck" of the amidine inhibitors is varied by manipulating the methylene group from two to four units. Similar to peptide-based inhibitors, the inhibition potency is not directly related to the "neck" length of the compound where they found that amidines with three methylene units are more potent compared to that of two or four units. However this indicates that suitable "neck" length is crucial for proper position of the warhead in interacting with the active site of PAD4.

Inh Dap inhibits PAD4 the most among the inhibitors could be due to the suitable "neck" length. The relatively low IC$_{50}$ values of peptide-based inhibitors compared to compounds discovered by structure-based and ligand-based virtual screening (Teo *et al.*, 2012, 2013) indicates that the incorporation of peptide with furan ring could be a better PAD4 inhibitor against PAD4 compare to conventional small molecule inhibitor.

Molecular Docking Analysis of Inh Dap

Molecular docking of Inh Dap against PAD4 is performed to investigate the interactions between the peptide with PAD4. The conformation of Inh Dap with the lowest energy calculated using NMR restrained MD simulations is selected for docking purpose. The binding affinity of Inh Dap to PAD4 is − 5.4 kcal/mol, suggesting that the peptide has favourable interaction with PAD4. There are three hydrogen bonds formed between the inhibitor and the residues on the binding site of PAD4. The first one is established between the backbone carbonyl group of Thr6 and the side chain hydroxyl group of Ser468. The second is formed between the side chain carboxylic acid of Asp5 and the side chain amine of R374, while the third one is observed between the side chain amine of Dfa4 and the side chain carboxylic acid of D350. The binding of Inh Dap is mostly favoured by hydrophobic interactions between Dfa4 side chain that contains the furan ring and residues such as R639, W347, C645, H471, H640, E474, and D473. Other parts of Inh Dap such as Asp5 and Thr6 also make hydrophobic contacts with E575, R441, G403, V469, and G641 (**Fig. 11**).

It is interesting to highlight that the furan ring enters the deep binding pocket of PAD4 and made contacts with the residues that involved in the catalytic mechanism of PAD4, which are H471, D473, D350 and C645 (Kearney *et al.*, 2005). Similar interaction is also observed in the docked complex of PAD4-ligand discovered via ligand-based virtual screening (Teo *et al.*, 2013). Moreover, it is also worth to note that the presence of a hydrogen bond between Asp5 of Inh Dap with R374 of PAD4. As mentioned before, R374 is an important amino acid in the substrate recognition for PAD4 (Arita *et al.*, 2006). We anticipate that the contacts made between Inh Dap with C645 and R374 give the major contribution in inhibiting the PAD4 activity.

CD spectroscopy and NMR studies showing that Inh Dap is in unordered structure. A bent conformation is induced on Inh Dap upon binding to PAD4 (see **Fig. 12**). Previous studies reported that it is important for the peptide around the target residue to have a highly disordered conformation as PAD4 recognizes an unstructured peptide at the molecular surface near the binding site cleft and induces a bent conformation on the peptide (Arita *et al.*, 2006; Takahara *et al.*, 1985; Tarcsa *et al.*, 1996). The induction of the bent conformation is due to the hydrogen bonding between Inh Dap and Arg374 (Arita *et al.*, 2006). The bent shape allows the furan ring to enter the deep binding pocket of PAD4. The binding of furan ring in the active site cleft of PAD4 again confirms the importance of this structural fragment in the structure of PAD4 inhibitors.

Concluding Remarks

We show a systematic approach in designing a peptide inhibitor for PAD4. The unique architecture of PAD4 binding pocket requires the inhibitor to be able to penetrate deeply into the binding pocket while anchoring itself on the outer surface of the

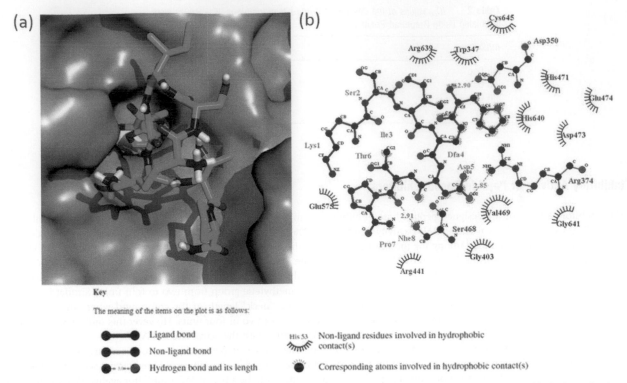

Fig. 11 *Binding conformation of Inh Dap inside the PAD4 binding pocket.* (a) Inh Dap is seen occupying the binding pocket with the furan ring is located in proximity with C645 (yellow). Some of the protein parts were removed to ease visualization (Schrodinger, 2002). (b) Hydrogen bonds and hydrophobic interactions of Inh Dap with residues in the binding pocket of PAD4. The 2-dimensional binding diagram was created using Ligplot+ version 1.4.5 (Laskowski and Swindells, 2011).

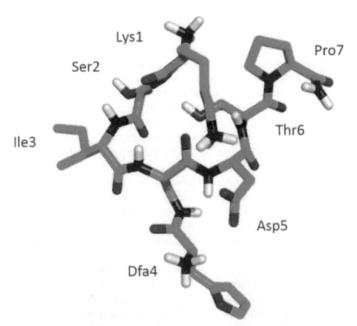

Fig. 12 *Conformation of Inh Dap after binding to PAD4.* A bent conformation was induced on Inh Dap upon its binding at the binding site of PAD4.

pocket. The screening of small molecules is carried out to choose the best "warhead" to attack the catalytic residues inside the binding pocket. The "warhead" is then attached to the carefully designed peptide with optimum neck and anchor lengths to ensure the peptide strongly binds to the neighboring residues while the "warhead" is attacking the catalytic residues. This approach in designing peptide inhibitor can be applied to similar cases where the catalytic residues are located far inside the binding pocket.

See also: Biomolecular Structures: Prediction, Identification and Analyses. Comparative Epigenomics. Computational Protein Engineering Approaches for Effective Design of New Molecules. Identifying Functional Relationships Via the Annotation and Comparison of Three-Dimensional Amino Acid Arrangements in Protein Structures. Molecular Dynamics Simulations in Drug Discovery. Natural Language Processing Approaches in Bioinformatics. Protein Design. Structure-Based Drug Design Workflow

References

Aletaha, D., Neogi, T., Silman, A.J., *et al.*, 2010. 2010 Rheumatoid arthritis classification criteria: An American College of Rheumatology/European league against rheumatism collaborative initiative. Arthritis Rheum. 62 (9), 2569–2581.

Arita, K., Hashimoto, H., Shimizu, T., *et al.*, 2004. Structural basis for Ca^{2+})-induced activation of human PAD4. Nat. Struct. Mol. Biol. 11 (8), 777–783.

Arita, K., Shimizu, T., Hashimoto, H., *et al.*, 2006. Structural basis for histone N-terminal recognition by human peptidylarginine deiminase 4. Proc. Natl. Acad. Sci. USA 103 (14), 5291–5296.

Arnett, F.C., Edworthy, S.M., Bloch, D.A., *et al.*, 1988. The American Rheumatism Association 1987 revised criteria for the classification of rheumatoid arthritis. Arthritis Rheum. 31 (3), 315–324.

van Boekel, M.A., Vossenaar, E.R., van den Hoogen, F.H., van Venrooij, W.J., 2002. Autoantibody systems in rheumatoid arthritis: Specificity, sensitivity and diagnostic value. Arthritis Res. 4 (2), 87–93.

Causey, C.P., Jones, J.E., Slack, J.L., *et al.*, 2011. The development of N-α-(2-carboxyl)benzoyl-N(5)-(2-fluoro-1-iminoethyl)-l-ornithine amide (o-F-amidine) and N-α-(2-carboxyl)benzoyl-N(5)-(2-chloro-1-iminoethyl)-l-ornithine amide (o-Cl-amidine) as second generation protein arginine deiminase (PAD) inhibit. J. Med. Chem. 54 (19), 6919–6935.

Chang, X., Han, J., Pang, L., *et al.*, 2009. Increased PADI4 expression in blood and tissues of patients with malignant tumors. BMC Cancer 9 (1), 40.

Davidson, A., Diamond, B., 2001. Autoimmune diseases. N. Engl. J. Hum. Genet. 345 (5), 340–350.

Fuhrmann, J., Clancy, K.W., Thompson, P.R., 2015. Chemical biology of protein arginine modifications in epigenetic regulation. Chem. Rev. 115 (11), 5413–5461.

Gabriel, S., 2001. The epidemiology of rheumatoid arthritis. Rheum. Dis. Clin. N. Am. 27 (2), 269–281.

Hagiwara, T., Hidaka, Y., Yamada, M., 2005. Deimination of histone H2A and H4 at arginine 3 in HL-60 granulocytes. Biochemistry 44 (15), 5827–5834.

Hagiwara, T., Nakashima, K., Hirano, H., Senshu, T., Yamada, M., 2002. Deimination of arginine residues in nucleophosmin/B23 and histones in HL-60 granulocytes. Biochem. Biophys. Res. Commun. 290 (3), 979–983.

Helmick, C.G., Felson, D.T., Lawrence, R.C., *et al.*, 2008. Estimates of the prevalence of arthritis and other rheumatic conditions in the United States. Part I. Arthritis Rheum. 58 (1), 15–25.

Hoet, R.M., Boerbooms, A.M., Arends, M., Ruiter, D.J., van Venrooij, W.J., 1991. Antiperinuclear factor, a marker autoantibody for rheumatoid arthritis: Colocalisation of the perinuclear factor and profilaggrin. Ann. Rheum. Dis. 50 (9), 611–618.

Hoet, R.M., van Venrooij, W.J., 1992. The Antiperinuclear Factor (APF) and Antikeratin Antibodies (AKA) in rheumatoid arthritis. In: Smolen, J.S., Kalden, J.R., Maini, R.N. (Eds.), Rheumatoid Arthritis. Berlin, Heidelberg: Springer Berlin Heidelberg, pp. 299–318.

Holm, R.H., Kennepohl, P., Solomon, E.I., 1996. Structural and functional aspects of metal sites in biology. Chem. Rev. 96 (7), 2239–2314.

Jansen, A.L.M.A., van der Horst-Bruinsma, I., van Schaardenburg, D., *et al.*, 2002. Rheumatoid factor and antibodies to cyclic citrullinated Peptide differentiate rheumatoid arthritis from undifferentiated polyarthritis in patients with early arthritis. J. Rheumatol. 29 (10), 2074–2076.

Jones, J.E., Causey, C.P., Knuckley, B., Slack-Noyes, J.L., Thompson, P.R., 2009. Protein arginine deiminase 4 (PAD4): Current understanding and future therapeutic potential. Curr. Opin. Drug Discov. Dev. 12 (5), 616–627.

Jones, J.E., Slack, J.L., Fang, P., *et al.*, 2012. Synthesis and screening of a haloacetamidine containing library to identify PAD4 selective inhibitors. ACS Chem. Biol. 7 (1), 160–165.

Kearney, P.L., Bhatia, M., Jones, N.G., *et al.*, 2005. Kinetic characterization of protein arginine deiminase 4: A transcriptional corepressor implicated in the onset and progression of rheumatoid arthritis. Biochemistry 44 (31), 10570–10582.

Kinloch, A., Lundberg, K., Wait, R., *et al.*, 2008. Synovial fluid is a site of citrullination of autoantigens in inflammatory arthritis. Arthritis Rheum. 58 (8), 2287–2295.

Klareskog, L., Malmström, V., Lundberg, K., Padyukov, L., Alfredsson, L., 2011. Smoking, citrullination and genetic variability in the immunopathogenesis of rheumatoid arthritis. Semin. Immunol. 23 (2), 92–98.

Klareskog, L., Stolt, P., Lundberg, K., *et al.*, 2006. A new model for an etiology of rheumatoid arthritis: Smoking may trigger HLA-DR (shared epitope)-restricted immune reactions to autoantigens modified by citrullination. Arthritis Rheum. 54 (1), 38–46.

Knuckley, B., Bhatia, M., Thompson, P.R., 2007. Protein arginine deiminase 4: Evidence for a reverse protonation mechanism. Biochemistry 46 (22), 6578–6587.

Landre-Beauvais, A.J., 2001. The first description of rheumatoid arthritis. Unabridged text of the doctoral dissertation presented in 1800. Joint Bone Spine: Revue Du Rhumatisme 68 (2), 130–143.

Laskowski, R.A., Swindells, M.B., 2011. LigPlot + : Multiple ligand–protein interaction diagrams for drug discovery. J. Chem. Inform. Model. 51 (10), 2778–2786.

Lewis, H.D., Liddle, J., Coote, J.E., *et al.*, 2015. Inhibition of PAD4 activity is sufficient to disrupt mouse and human NET formation. Nat. Chem Biol. 11 (3), 189–191.

Linsky, T., Fast, W., 2010. Mechanistic similarity and diversity among the guanidine-modifying members of the pentein superfamily. Biochim. Biophys. Acta 1804 (10), 1943–1953.

Liu, Y.L., Chiang, Y.H., Liu, G.Y., Hung, H.C., 2011. Functional role of dimerization of human peptidylarginine deiminase 4 (PAD4). PLOS ONE 6 (6), e21314.

Liu, Y.L., Tsai, I.C., Chang, C.W., *et al.*, 2013. Functional roles of the non-catalytic calcium-binding sites in the N-terminal domain of human peptidylarginine deiminase 4. PLOS ONE 8 (1), e51660.

Luo, Y., Arita, K., Bhatia, M., *et al.*, 2006a. Inhibitors and inactivators of protein arginine deiminase 4: Functional and structural characterization. Biochemistry 45 (39), 11727–11736.

Luo, Y., Knuckley, B., Lee, Y.H., Stallcup, M.R., Thompson, P.R., 2006b. A fluoroacetamidine-based inactivator of protein arginine deiminase 4: Design, synthesis, and in vitro and in vivo evaluation. J. Am. Chem. Soc. 128 (4), 1092–1093.

Mangat, P., Wegner, N., Venables, P.J., Potempa, J., 2010. Bacterial and human peptidylarginine deiminases: Targets for inhibiting the autoimmune response in rheumatoid arthritis? Arthritis Res. Ther. 12 (3), 201–209.

Mikuls, T.R., Payne, J.B., Reinhardt, R.A., *et al.*, 2009. Antibody responses to Porphyromonas gingivalis (P. gingivalis) in subjects with rheumatoid arthritis and periodontitis. Int. Immunopharmacol. 9 (1), 38–42.

Nakayama-Hamada, M., Suzuki, A., Kubota, K., *et al.*, 2005. Comparison of enzymatic properties between hPADI2 and hPADI4. Biochem. Biophys. Res. Commun. 327 (1), 192–200.

Salaffi, F., Carotti, M., Gasparini, S., Intorcia, M., Grassi, W., 2009. The health-related quality of life in rheumatoid arthritis, ankylosing spondylitis, and psoriatic arthritis: A comparison with a selected sample of healthy people. Health Qual. Life Outcomes 7 (1), 25.

Schellekens, G.A., de Jong, B.A., van den Hoogen, F.H., van de Putte, L.B., van Venrooij, W.J., 1998. Citrulline is an essential constituent of antigenic determinants recognized by rheumatoid arthritis-specific autoantibodies. J. Clin. Investig. 101 (1), 273–281.

Schellekens, G.A., Visser, H., de Jong, B.A., et al., 2000. The diagnostic properties of rheumatoid arthritis antibodies recognizing a cyclic citrullinated peptide. Arthritis Rheum. 43 (1), 155–163.

Schrodinger, L., 2002. The PyMOL Molecular Graphics System, Version 1.4.1.

Smolen, J.S., Aletaha, D., Machold, K.P., et al., 2005. Therapeutic strategies in early rheumatoid arthritis. Best Pract. Res. Clin. Rheum. 19 (1), 163–177.

Smolen, J.S., Landewé, R., Breedveld, F.C., et al., 2010. EULAR recommendations for the management of rheumatoid arthritis with synthetic and biological disease-modifying antirheumatic drugs. Ann. Rheum. Dis. 69 (6), 964–975.

Stensland, M.E., Pollmann, S., Molberg, O., Sollid, L.M., Fleckenstein, B., 2009. Primary sequence, together with other factors, influence peptide deimination by peptidylarginine deiminase-4. Biol. Chem. 390 (2), 99–107.

Suzuki, A., Yamada, R., Yamamoto, K., 2007. Citrullination by peptidylarginine deiminase in rheumatoid arthritis. Ann. N.Y. Acad. Sci. 1108, 323–339.

Takahara, H., Okamoto, H., Sugawara, K., 1985. Specific modification of the functional arginine residue in soybean trypsin inhibitor (Kunitz) by peptidylarginine deiminase. J. Biol. Chem. 260 (14), 8378–8383.

Tarcsa, E., Marekov, L.N., Mei, G., et al., 1996. Protein unfolding by peptidylarginine deiminase. Substrate specificity and structural relationships of the natural substrates trichohyalin and filaggrin. J. Biol. Chem. 271 (48), 30709–30716.

Teo, C.Y., Abdul Rahman, M.B., Chor, A.L.T., et al., 2013. Ligand-Based virtual screening for the discovery of inhibitors for Protein Arginine Deiminase Type 4 (PAD4). J. Postgenom. Drug Biomarker Dev. 3 (1), 1–5.

Teo, C.Y., Shave, S., Chor, A.L.T., et al., 2012. Discovery of a new class of inhibitors for the protein arginine deiminase type 4 (PAD4) by structure-based virtual screening. BMC Bioinform. 13 (Suppl. 17), S4.

Teo, C.Y., Tejo, B.A., Leow, A.T.C., Salleh, A.B., Abdul Rahman, M.B., 2017. Novel furan-containing peptide-based inhibitors of protein arginine deiminase type IV (PAD4). Chem. Biol. Drug Des. 90 (6), 1134–1146.

Wegner, N., Lundberg, K., Kinloch, A., et al., 2009. Autoimmunity to specific citrullinated proteins gives the first clues to the etiology of rheumatoid arthritis. Immunol. Rev. 233, 1–21.

van Venrooij, W.J., Pruijn, G.J.M., 2000. Citrullination : A small change for a protein with great consequences for rheumatoid arthritis. Arthritis Res. 2, 249–251.

van Venrooij, W.J., Pruijn, G.J.M., 2008. An important step towards completing the rheumatoid arthritis cycle. Arthritis Res. Ther. 10 (5), 117.

Vincent, C., de Keyser, F., Masson-Bessière, C., et al., 1999. Anti-perinuclear factor compared with the so called "antikeratin" antibodies and antibodies to human epidermis filaggrin, in the diagnosis of arthritides. Ann. Rheum. Dis. 58 (1), 42–48.

Vlieghe, P., Lisowski, V., Martinez, J., Khrestchatisky, M., 2010. Synthetic therapeutic peptides: Science and market. Drug Discov. Today 15 (1–2), 40–56.

Vossenaar, E.R., Zendman, A.J.W., Van, Venrooij., et al., 2003. PAD, a growing family of citrullinating enzymes: Genes, features and involvement in disease. BioEssays 25 (11), 1106–1118.

Vossenaar, E., 2004. Anti-CCP antibodies, a highly specific marker for (early) rheumatoid arthritis. Clin. Appl. Immunol. 4 (4), 239–262.

Small Molecule Drug Design

Vartika Tomar, University of Delhi, Delhi, India
Mohit Mazumder, Jawaharlal Nehru University, Delhi, India and University of Saskatchewan, Saskatoon, SK, Canada
Ramesh Chandra, University of Delhi, Delhi, India
Jian Yang and Meena K Sakharkar, University of Saskatchewan, Saskatoon, SK, Canada

Introduction

For the balanced and proper functioning of all the life sustaining processes, nature has provided our body with all the necessary chemical components or precursors, enzymes and neurotransmitters. Despite this, due to several factors, some exogenous and some endogenous, some machineries or bioprocesses fail to function. The exogenous factors responsible for disrupting the normal bodily function may vary from parasitic invasion to some chemical entities. The endogenous factors include over or under-production of few chemicals, faulty functioning of organs or any genetic or congenital factor leading to disorders like neuro-degenerative disorders like Alzheimer's or Parkinson's disease resulting from the imbalance of acetylcholine and dopamine in the central nervous system (Moore *et al.*, 2005). Hence, to restore the normal functioning, external aids called 'Drugs' or 'Medicines' are required and the process of designing/discovery of drugs is called drug discovery. During this process, combinations of computational, translational, experimental and clinical models are employed to identify new potential therapeutic entities. In early days, most of the drugs were discovered either by the identification of the active ingredients from traditional remedies or by serendipitous discovery. Despite having knowledge of biological systems and advanced biotechnology, drug discovery and its development is still an expensive, time consuming, laborious, complicated and inefficient process with a high attrition rate of new therapeutic discovery. Hence, designing a drug or a molecule with desired properties and function is an important industrial challenge.

What is a Drug?

Drugs are biological or chemical entities of synthetic or natural origin, which modulate the functions of the body without causing any new action on the body. They can be a single compound or a mixture of different compounds. Drugs function by interacting and modifying specific 'targets' in our bodies to create a molecular interaction signature that can be exploited for rapid therapeutic repurposing and discovery. They interact and bind with the targets that are complementary to them in shape and charge and work either by stimulating or blocking activity of their targets. For example, the analgesic effect of drug Aspirin is due to inhibition of prostaglandin biosynthesis by acetylation of cyclo-oxygenase.

What is a Small-Molecule Drug?

According to National Cancer Institute, a small molecule drug is any organic compound or substance capable of entering cells with an ease due to its low molecular weight (below 900 Daltons). Once it enters the cells, it can affect other molecules, such as proteins, and may cause death of cancer cells. This is different from drugs, such as monoclonal antibodies, which are not able to enter the cells easily because of their large molecular weight. Therefore, most of the targeted therapies are small-molecule drugs or small molecule inhibitors.

Advantages of a Small-Molecule Drug

1. Small-molecule drugs are mostly administered orally which gives them an edge over larger drugs that require invasive procedures like injections.

The simple structures and smaller sizes of the small-molecule drugs facilitate more generic competition in comparison to complex biologic drugs. Owing to small molecular weight (i.e., less than 900 Daltons), they have easy penetration into cell membranes or target organs, thereby giving an intra-cellular targeting advantage over extracellularly oriented, specific biological proteins. Since small molecule drugs can be processed into easily ingestible tablets or capsule, they can be orally administered. This increases the treatment regime, upregulates patient satisfaction and adherence and improves efficacy. Furthermore, these small molecule drugs have short half-life but longer shelf lives, which is of substantial therapeutic benefit especially in cases of rapid metabolism. Also, they require easy and less vigorous manufacturing processes as compared to complex biological drugs.

Characteristics of a Drug

A drug becomes active when it binds to its biological target, usually receptors. Receptors are protein having active sites for ligand binding. Hence, a good ligand can be designed, if the structure of such receptors and their active sites can be identified accurately. Before designing a drug, it is important to know what features we are looking for, in an "ideal drug candidate. The drug

    (i)   Must be safe and effective.
    (ii) Should be well absorbed orally and have good bioavailability.
    (iii) Should be metabolically stable and have a long half-life.
    (iv) Nontoxic with minimal or no side effects.
    (v) Should have selective distribution to target tissues.

Drug Discovery

Drug discovery plays an important role to the society and for any pharmaceutical industry in 'improving the therapeutic value and safety of agents' by launching newer and safe drugs in the market. Unfortunately, the process of discovery and development of drug is a long and complicated process. It involves the identification, synthesis, characterization, screening and assays of potential candidates for therapeutic efficacy. Drug discovery and development process includes preclinical studies on cell-based and animal models followed by clinical trials on humans, and finally moving towards the step of obtaining regulatory approval to market the drug. Usually it takes at least 14–16 years of research with a cost of 800 million US dollars for a compound to get developed into a drug. After establishment of the pre-clinical data and confirmation of its action and toxicity, the compound is approved for clinical studies which takes 1–2 years before it is released into the market. After release, several post-market surveillance and pharma-covigilance practices are maintained to identify adverse reactions or incompatibilities when used in combination therapies (Congreve et al., 2005). **Fig. 1** depicts entire drug discovery process with their tentative timelines.

Approaches for Drug Discovery/Designing

The traditional approach involves blind screening of chemical molecules obtained either from nature or synthesized in laboratories causing long design cycles and higher production cost. In modern drug discovery the identification of hits by screening, medicinal chemistry and optimization of these hits for enhances selectivity, metabolic stability and efficacy/potency, affinity and oral bioavailability. Enhanced electivity contributes towards reduction of potential side effects and metabolic stability increases half-life making the drug more stable. Drug discovery process can be made cost-effective and faster by using computer-aided drug design discovery process which involves structure-based drug design using in silico approach which plays a significant role in all stages of drug development. Since only a potential molecule is selected, this prevents late stage clinical failures thereby reducing the cost significantly. **Table 1** lists some inhibitors developed with computational chemistry and rational drug design strategies. Better understanding of the quantitative relationship of structure and biological activity reduces the development time of the drug to 6–8 years from 10 to 16 years. This supports the reasons to develop computer-aided molecular design (CAMD), towards automation of molecular design (Blaney, 1990; Bugg et al., 1993). **Fig. 2** outlines the steps involved in the drug development process.

Various Approaches Involved in Drug Designing

Virtual screening

Virtual screening is a computational method used for identifying lead compounds using a vast and diverse chemical compound library as a reference. This computational method is an important tool for discovering lead compounds as it is faster, more cost-efficient, and less resource intensive in comparison to experimental methods such as high-throughput screening (Walters et al., 1998; Shoichet, 2004; Kitchen et al., 2004; Schneider and Bohm, 2002). Virtual screening process consists of two steps: docking and scoring. AutoDock (Morris et al., 1998; Huey et al., 2007) performs ligand conformational searches for identifying potential bound conformations, and X-Score (Wang et al., 2002) is used in re-evaluating the binding affinity of the predicted structures. Novel lead compounds in many investigations have been successful identified using the freely available Autodock and X-score.

Docking and scoring

Docking is a computational way of predicting the most preferred orientation of one small molecule bound to a target, resulting into a stable complex. It consists of several steps. The first step is the application of docking algorithms that pose small molecules within the active site of the target. Through docking we aim to predict the stable drug interactions by inspecting and modelling drug molecular interactions between drug- and target receptor molecules. Various molecular docking tools are available, including AutoDock, FRED, eHITS, and FTDock, etc. (Maithri et al., 2016). Scoring function is used for computing non-bonded interaction terms between the receptor and ligand atoms. Scoring functions approximate the receptor–ligand interaction energy using multivariate regression of multiple parameters such as the number of hydrogen bonds, lipophilicity, ionic interactions, entropy penalties, etc. Scoring functions are specifically designed to complement these docking algorithms as they evaluate the interactions between compounds and potential targets, thereby predicting their biological activity.

High-throughput screening (HTS)

In this technique, a large number of biological modulators and effectors are screened and assayed against selected and specific targets. The principles and methods of HTS can be exploited for screening of proteins, peptides, genomics and combinatorial

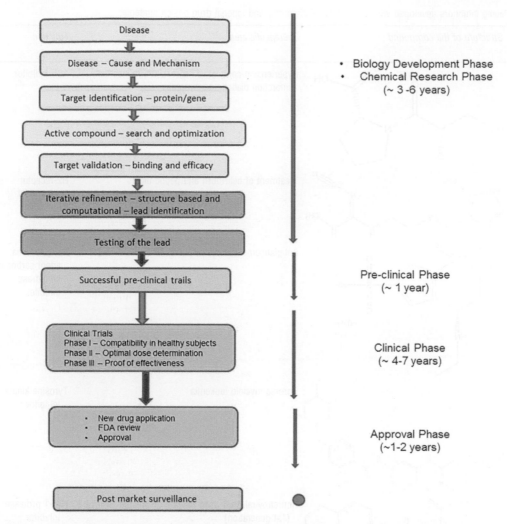

Fig. 1 Different phases of drug discovery process. Adapted and modified from Lombardino, J.G., Lowe, J.A., 2004. The role of the medicinal chemist in drug discovery—then and now. Nature Reviews Drug Discovery 3, 853–862.

chemistry libraries. HTS is a high-tech way to hasten the drug discovery process, allowing quick and efficient screening of large compound libraries at a rate of a few thousand compounds per day or per week. (Martis *et al.*, 2011).

Homology modelling

Computational methods can be used to predict the 3D structure of target proteins when experimental structures are not present. Since proteins with similar sequence have similar structures, comparative modelling is used to predict target structures based on a template with similar sequences. Homology modelling is a specific kind of comparative modelling in which the same evolutionary origin is shared by template and target proteins. Some computer programmes and web servers which are commonly used for automated homology modelling process are PSI-PRED and MODELER (Buchan *et al.*, 2010; Martí-Renom *et al.*, 2000).

Molecular dynamic simulations

Owing to the dynamic nature of biomolecules, a single static structure cannot be applied to predict putative binding sites. An assembly of target conformations starting from a single structure are obtained by applying classic molecular dynamic (MD) simulations. In MD methods principles of Newtonian mechanics are employed to calculate trajectory of conformations of a protein as a function of time. The problem with classic MD method is that it gets trapped in local energy minima. To overcome this problem, various advanced MD algorithms such as conformational folding simulations (Grubmüller, 1995), targeted–MD (Schlitter *et al.*, 1994), replica exchange MD (Sugita and Okamoto, 1999) and temperature accelerated MD simulations (Abrams and Vanden-Eijnden, 2010) have been employed for traversing multiple minima energy surface of proteins.

Monte Carlo simulation

The Monte Carlo simulation is based on the concept of statistical mechanics. Monte Carlo introduces a randomness in the system that allows hopping over the energy barriers thereby preventing the system from getting stuck in the local energy minima

Table 1   Selected inhibitors developed with computational chemistry and rational drug design strategies

Compound name	Structure of the compound	Therapeutic area	Function	Approval
Captopril		Hypertension congestive heart failure myocardial infarction diabetic nephropathy	ACE inhibitor	1975
Cimetidine		Treatment of heartburn and peptic ulcers	H2-receptor antagonist	1978
Dorzolamide		Antiglaucoma agent	Antiglaucoma agent carbonic anhydrase inhibitor	1989
Imatinib		Chronic myeloid leukemia	Tyrosine kinase inhibitor	1990
Saquinavir		Antiretroviral drug used to treat or prevent HIV/AIDS (1st generation)	HIV-1 protease inhibitor	1995
Oseltamivir		Antiviral (to treat influenza A and influenza B)	Influenza neuraminidase inhibitor	1996

(Continued)

Table 1 Continued

Compound name	Structure of the compound	Therapeutic area	Function	Approval
Indinavir		Antiretroviral drug used to treat HIV/AIDS (1st generation)	HIV protease inhibitor	1996
Ritonavir		Antiretroviral drug used to treat HIV/AIDS (1st generation)	HIV protease inhibitor	1996
Zanamivir		Antiviral (to treat influenza A and influenza B)	Neuraminidase inhibitor	1999
Nelfinavir		Antiretroviral drug used to treat HIV/AIDS (1st generation)	HIV protease inhibitor	1999

(*Continued*)

Table 1   Continued

Compound name	Structure of the compound	Therapeutic area	Function	Approval
Lopinavir		Antiretroviral drug used to treat HIV/AIDS against strains that are resistant to other protease inhibitors (1st generation)	Peptidomimetic HIV protease inhibitor	2000
Fosamprenavir		Antiretroviral prodrug used to treat HIV/AIDS (phosphorester that is rapidly and extensively metabolized to amprenavir) (1st generation)	HIV protease inhibitor	2003
Gefitinib		NSCLC	EGFR kinase inhibitor	2003
Atazanavir		Antiretroviral drug used to treat HIV/AIDS (2nd generation)	HIV protease inhibitor	2004

(*Continued*)

Table 1   Continued

Compound name	Structure of the compound	Therapeutic area	Function	Approval
Tipranavir		Antiretroviral drug used to treat HIV/AIDS (tipranavir is active against strains that are resistant to other protease inhibitors) (2nd generation)	Nonpeptidic HIV-1 protease inhibitor	2005
Erlotinib		NSCLC pancreatic cancer	EGFR kinase inhibitor	2005
Sorafenib		Renal cancer Liver cancer thyroid cancer	VEGFR kinase inhibitor	2005
Darunavir		Antiretroviral drug used to treat HIV/AIDS (2nd generation)	Nonpeptidic HIV-1 protease inhibitor	2006
Lapatinib		ERBB2-positive breast cancer	EGFR/ERBB2 inhibitor	2007
Abiraterone acetate		Metastatic castration-resistant prostate cancer or hormone-refractory prostate cancer	Androgen synthesis inhibitor	2011

(Continued)

Table 1   Continued

Compound name	Structure of the compound	Therapeutic area	Function	Approval
Crizotinib	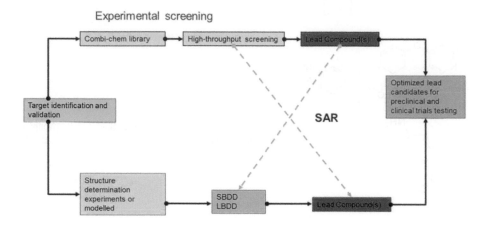	NSCLC	ALK inhibitor	2011

100ACE, angiotensin-converting enzyme; HIV, human immunodeficiency virus; AIDS, acquired immunodeficiency syndrome; EGFR, epidermal growth factor receptor; NSCLC, non-small cell lung cancer; VEGFR, vascular epidermal growth factor receptor; ERBB2, erb-b2 receptor tyrosine kinase 2 (also known as NEU, NGL, HER2, TKR1, CD340, HER-2, MLN 19, HER-2/neu); ALK, anaplastic lymphoma kinase.

Adapted and modified from Prada-Graciaa, D., Huerta-Yépezb, S., Moreno-Vargasb, L.M., 2016. Application of computational methods for anticancer drug discovery, design, and optimization. Boletin Medico Del Hospital Infantil De Mexico 73 (6), 411–423.

Fig. 2   Outline of the steps involved in drug development process. Adapted and modified from Kuhn, P., Wilson, K., Patch, M.G., Stevens, R.C., 2002. The genesis of high-throughput structure-based drug discovery using protein crystallography. Current Opinion in Chemical Biology 6 (5), 704–710.

(Allen and Tildesley, 1989). In protein dynamics, Monte Carlo simulation run is a sequence of random steps in conformation space inside a box where the step is decided on the basis of changes in the values of energy function during a simulation.

Metropolis criterion (MCM) simulations

Since MCM requires only energy function for evaluation and not the derivate of energy function unlike traditional MD which drives a system towards local energy minimum, conformational space is sampled faster with MCM than molecular dynamics. For flexible docking applications such as MCDOCK, MCM simulations have been adopted (Liu and Wang, 1999).

Rational drug design

Rational drug designing is based on the principle of logical reasoning before designing any therapeutic agents. For example, to prepare a competitive inhibitor relative to any specific target, the predicted structure should ensure that the designed molecule exhibits endogenous properties. The active site should be closely examined to get idea regarding the interacting amino acid residues, so that the nature and type of substituents and the favourable position in the molecule can be predicted, resulting in better binding.

Genetic algorithms

Genetic algorithms recombine parent conformations to child conformations which provides for molecular flexibility. The best scoring or "fittest" combinations are kept for another round of recombination during this evolutionary simulation process. Best possible set of solutions are evolved in the process retain favourable features from one generation to the next. Rational drug design does not involve exhaustive searches that involve impractical large combinatorial problems. The investigation of such problems is greatly aided by genetic algorithms; a class of algorithms mimicking some of the major characteristics of Darwinian evolution. In order to design small organic molecule with satisfying quantitative structure-activity relationship based rules (fitness), a specific algorithm called an LEA (Ligand by Evolutionary Algorithm) has been conceived. The fitness consists of a sum of constraints that act as range properties. The LEA takes an initial set of fragments and repeatedly improves them by means of mutation and crossover operators which are related to those involved in the Darwinian model of evolution (Dougueta et al., 2000).

Molecular fingerprint and similarity searches

Molecular fingerprinting is a way of representing molecules which can be exploited to identify and compare structurally similar molecules or to cluster them on the basis of structural similarity. This method is based on fewer hypotheses and is less computationally taxing than QSAR or pharmacophore mapping models and is more quantitative in nature since it relies entirely on chemical structure and omits compounds with known biological activity. Moreover, fingerprint-based methods equally consider all parts of the molecule instead of focusing on only those parts of the molecule which are thought to be most important for activity. Hence, this method is less prone to error overfitting and requires smaller datasets to begin with. Fingerprint methods can also be used for searching databases for compounds that are similar in structure to a lead query, thereby providing an extended collection of compounds that can be tested for improved activity over the lead.

De Novo *ligand designing*

Constructing novel molecules from scratch is called de novo drug design. This approach is particularly challenging because the compound space to be searched can often become enormous. Defining a binding site for molecules in a target and determining what atoms or functional groups should be placed at certain loci at the binding site is one of the most critical and difficult steps of de novo drug design. (Klebe, 2000; Bohm and Stahl, 2000).

Case Studies

Discovery of tyrosine kinase inhibitors by docking into a molecular dynamics generated inactive kinase conformation

Type II inhibitors, which are the inactive DFG-out conformation of tyrosine kinases show good binding and selective profiles with several small molecules over other kinase targets. An explicit solvent molecular dynamics (MD) simulation of the complex of the catalytic domain of a tyrosine kinase receptor, ephrin type-A receptor 3 (EphA3), and manual docking of type II inhibitors was performed to obtain a set of DFG-out structures by Zhao et al. (2012). A single snapshot from the MD trajectory(for virtual screening) was selected using the automatic docking of four previously reported type II inhibitors (**Fig. 3**). Since a glycine-rich loop (Gloop), can adopt various conformations, it tightly encompasses the small type I head group of compound 1 and collapses into the ATP binding site. As a result, the bigger type I head groups of compounds 2–4 clashes with the G-loop in the ATP binding site. In addition, the entry of the piperazine group of compound 4 is blocked by the side chain of Tyr742 (**Fig. 4**). High-throughput docking of a pharmacophore-tailored library of 175,000 molecules results in about 4 million poses, which can be further filtered and sorted by van der Waals efficiency and force-field-based energy function. Remarkably, about 20% of the compounds with predicted binding energy smaller than -10 kcalmol^{-1} are known to be type II inhibitors and besides, a series of 5-(piperazine-1-yl)isoquinoline derivatives was identified as a novel class of low-micromolar inhibitors of both EphA3 and dephosphorylated Abelson tyrosine kinase (Abl1). A similar affinity to the gatekeeper mutant T315I of Abl1 is suggested by the in silico binding mode of the new inhibitors and competition binding assay studies. Additional evidence for the type II binding mode was obtained by two 300 ns MD simulations of the complex between N-(3-chloro-4-(difluoromethoxy)-phenyl)-2-(4-(8-nitroisoquinolin-5-yl) piperazin-1-yl)acetamide and EphA3 provided additional evidence of the type II binding mode.

Most type II inhibitors can be mapped well into three major hydrophobic interactions: ATP front site, ATP back site, and the allosteric site (**Fig. 5**).

Computer-Aided Drug Design (CADD)

CADD helps scientists in minimizing the synthetic and biological testing efforts by focussing only on the most promising compounds. Besides explaining the molecular basis of therapeutic activity, it also predicts possible derivatives that would improve activity. CADDD entails (Kapetanovic, 2008):

(1) Drug discovery and development processes being streamlined by the use of computing power.
(2) Identification and optimization of new drugs using leverage of chemical and biological information about targets and/or ligands.
(3) In silico designing of filters for the elimination of undesirable compounds with properties like poor activity and/or poor absorption, distribution, metabolism, excretion and toxicity, ADMET which facilitate selection of the most promising candidates.

Advantages of CADD

The main advantages of drug discovery through CADD are:

(i) For experimental testing, smaller set of compounds are selected from large compound libraries.

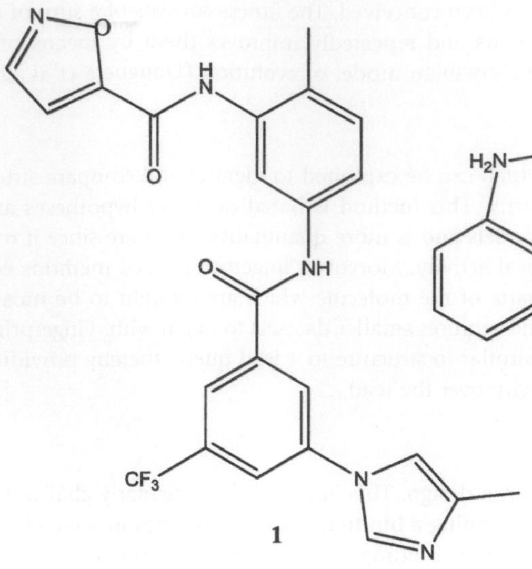

1

240 nm, -10.2Kcal mol^{-1}

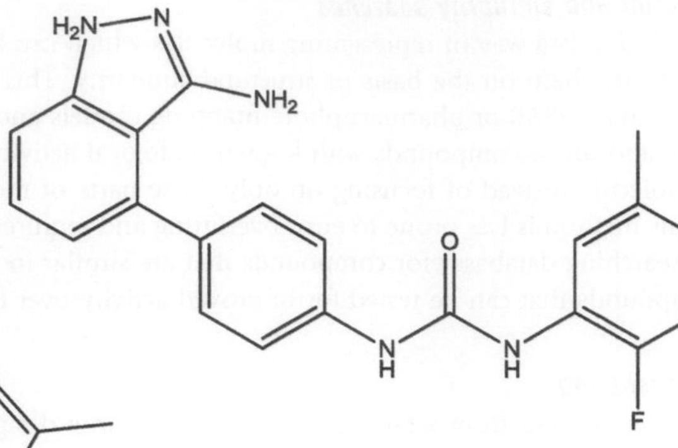

2

3500 nm, -10.2Kcal mol^{-1}

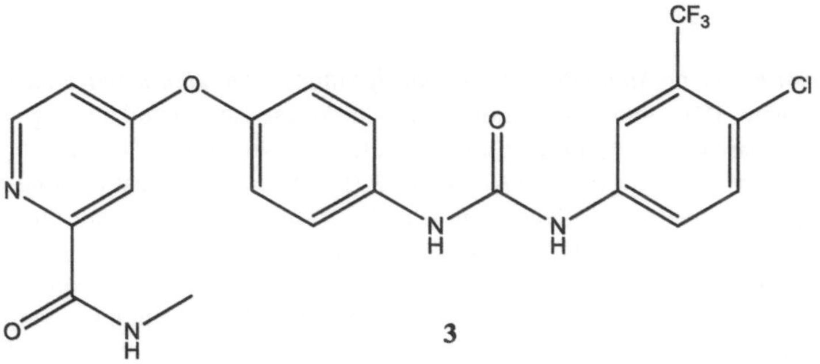

3

1900 nm, -10.3 Kcal mol^{-1}

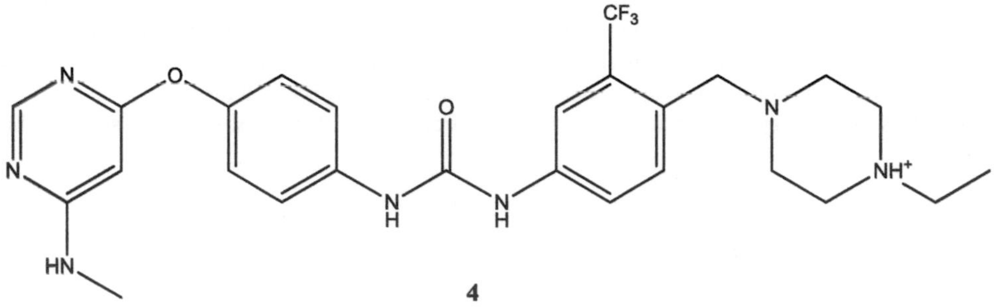

4

800 nm, -9.8 Kcal mol^{-1}

Fig. 3 Known type II inhibitors of EphA3. The values next to the compound number are the experimentally measured dissociation constant against phosphorylated EphA3 and the predicted binding free energy. These values were calculated by using the MD-IF structure and a scoring function with continuum solvation and hydrogen bonding penalty.

(ii) Drug metabolism and pharmacokinetics (DMPK) properties like absorption, distribution, metabolism, excretion and the potential for toxicity (ADMET) are increased by optimization of lead compounds.

(iii) Designing of novel compounds can be achieved either by "growing" starting molecules one functional group at a time or by piecing together fragments into novel chemotypes (Veselovsky and Ivanov, 2003).

(iv) Traditional experimentation which requires animal and human models can be replaced by CADD, saving both time and cost (Mallipeddi et al., 2014).

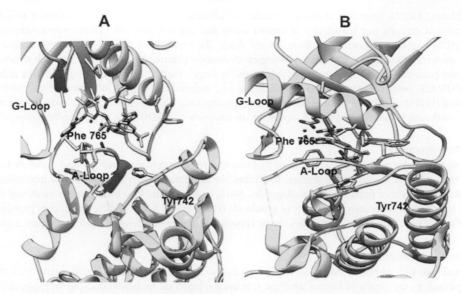

Fig. 4   Comparison of A) the crystal structure (PDB: 3DZQ) of the complex of EphA3 with inhibitor 1 and B) the binding mode obtained by docking compound 4 into the MD-IF structure. For the differences in orientations of Tyr 742 and Phe 765, and in the G-loop. Adapted and modified from Zhao, H., Huang, D., Caflisch, A., 2012. Discovery of tyrosine kinase inhibitors by docking into an inactive kinase conformation generated by molecular dynamics. ChemMedChem 7 (11), 1983–1990.

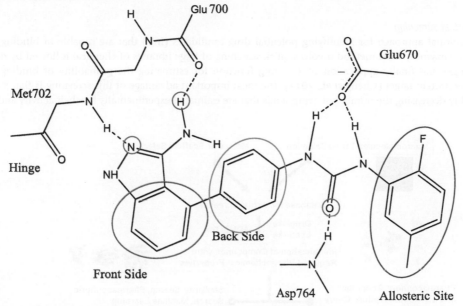

Fig. 5   Key interactions pharmacophore mapping of type II kinase inhibitors illustrated by compound 2 and EphA3. Dashed lines are hydrogen bonds. Pharmacophore elements used to filter the ZINC library: two acceptors (dashed circles), one donor (solid circle), and three hydrophobic rings (ovals). Because of the flexibility and solvent exposure of the Glu 670 side chain, the hydrogen bond to Glu 670 was not used as a pharmacophore.

(v)   Reduces the chances of drug resistance and thus would lead to production of lead compounds which would target the causative factor.

(vi)   CADD also leads to the construction of high quality datasets and libraries that can be optimized for high molecular diversity or similarity (Ou-Yang et al., 2012).

Types of CADD

The choice of CADD approaches to be employed is determined by the availability of the experimentally determined 3D structures of target proteins. Structure-based CADD uses our knowledge of the target protein structure to calculate interaction energies, whereas in ligand-based CADD, chemical similarity searches or construction of predictive, quantitative structure-activity relationship (QSAR) models exploits our knowledge of known active and inactive molecules.(Kalyaanamoorthy and Chen, 2011). Structure based CADD combines information from several fields, for example, X-ray crystallography and/or NMR, synthetic organic chemistry, molecular modelling, QSAR, and biological evaluation (Marrone *et al.*, 1997). Through structure based CADD, we aim to design compounds with strong binding affinity with the target, thereby exhibiting properties like reduced free energy, improved DMPK/ADMET properties and target specification i.e., reduced off-target (Jorgensen *et al.*, 2010). Virtual high-throughput screening (vHTS) also known as screening of virtual compound libraries is one of the most common applications of CADD Kalyaanamoorthy and Chen, 2011). **Fig. 6** represents an overview of CADD drug designing/design pipeline.

Structure–based drug discovery

This method exploits knowledge of the three-dimensional structure of a receptor complexed with a lead molecule for optimization of the bound ligand or a series of congeneric molecules. It requires the understanding of receptor–ligand interactions. The structural information can be obtained either from X-ray crystallography, NMR, or from homology modelling. A medicinal chemist can use a model with a given structure for computing the activity of a molecule (Lewis, 2005). Some of these approaches provide accurate binding modes, while cater to fast searching of large databases. Some approaches of structure-based drug designing are explained below.

Structure-based virtual high-throughput screening

Structure-based virtual high-throughput screening (SB-vHTS) is an *in-silico* method which helps identify putative hits out of hundreds of thousands of compounds to the targets of known structure. It is usually based on molecular docking. In molecular docking, a small molecule is fitted into the active site of protein model and here, comparison of the 3D structure of small molecule with the putative binding pocket is carried out. In the traditional HTS, the general ability of a ligand to bind, inhibit or allosterically alter the proteins function is asserted experimentally, whereas in SB-vHTS selects the ligands that are predicted to bind to a specific binding site. To ensure the feasibility of screening of large compound libraries within a finite time, limited conformational sampling of proteins and ligands is used by SB-vHTS along with a simplified approximation of binding energy that can be computed rapidly (Becker *et al.*, 2006).

Structure-based virtual screening

This is a computational approach for identifying potential drug candidates (hits) that are capable of binding to a drug target (protein receptors, enzymes). This method involves quick searching of large libraries of chemical followed by docking of the hit into a protein target and finally application of a scoring function for estimating the probability of binding affinity of drug candidate with the protein target (Cheng *et al.*, 2012). The most important advantage of this screening is that it enhances the hit rate by considerably decreasing the number of compounds that are estimated experimentally for their activity and hence improves

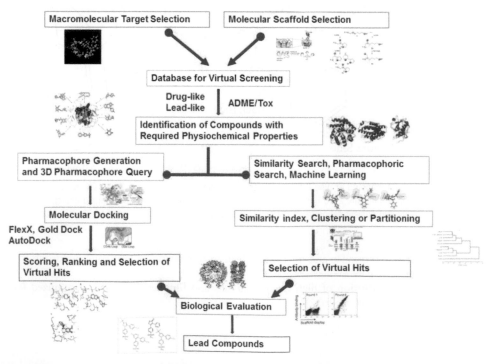

Fig. 6 An overview of CADD drug designing/design pipeline. Adapted and modified from Guido, R.V., Glaucius Oliva, G., Andricopulo, A.D., 2008. Virtual screening and its integration with modern drug design technologies. Current Medicinal Chemistry 15, 37–46.

the success rate of the *in vitro* experiments. This method has been applied extensively in pharmaceutical companies and academic groups for early-stage drug discovery.

Fragment-based lead discovery

This approach is based upon structure-activity relationships (SAR), obtained from NMR for identifying and optimizing the lead (Bienstock, 2011). High purity, weak potency but effective binding, good aqueous solubility, (molecular weight < 300, ClogP < 3, number of rotatable bonds, number of hydrogen bond donors and acceptors each should be < 3) are the criteria for selecting the chemical fragments (Congreve *et al.*, 2003). Later, these fragments are either expanded or combined for producing a lead with a higher affinity.

In silico structure-based lead optimization

After the desired hits are identified through virtual screening, this method speeds up the search for optimized lead by delineating the prediction about its pharmacological properties, thereby reducing the *in vitro* and *in vivo* experimental time.

ADMET modelling

This method, a common name for which is physiologically-based pharmacokinetic modelling is used in drug design and development, and in assessing of toxicity threat evaluation and specifically predicts absorption, distribution, metabolism, excretion and toxicology (ADMET) of drugs/compounds in humans. The ADMET parameters are based on the kinetics of the drug exposure to tissues and how the body will react to them, influencing the performance and pharmacological activity of the compound. Therefore, this method provides a key insight into the behaviour of a pharmaceutical compound within an organism. This approach aids in the selection of compounds during the very early phases of drug thereby playing a crucial role in drug discovery and development. This technique is cost- and time effective owing to a reduction in attrition of drugs during the pre-clinical / clinical phase trials at a later stage.

Ligand-based drug designing

The existing knowledge of active compounds against the target is used to predict new chemical entities that present similar behaviour in Ligand-based methods (Martin *et al.*, 2002). Given a single known active molecule, a pharmacophore model can be derived from a library of molecules to define the minimum necessary structural characteristics a molecule must possess in order to bind to the target of interest. A fingerprint-based similarity search is usually used to compare the active molecule to the library as here, the molecules are represented as bit strings which represent the presence or absence of predefined structural descriptors (Mishra and Siva-Prasad, 2011). In comparison, targeting structural information to determine whether a new compound is likely to bind and interact with a receptor is the method that structure-based methods rely on. No prior knowledge of active ligands is required in this method, which is a significant advantage (Kolb *et al.*, 2009). It is possible to design new ligands that can elicit a therapeutic effect from 3D structures. Therefore, the development of new drugs through the discovery and optimization of the initial lead compound are greatly impacted by structure-based approaches.

Ligand-based virtual screening (LBVS)

Ligand-based virtual screening is based on the "similarity principle" according to which similar molecules tend to exhibit similar biological properties. Scaffold hopping i.e., identification of iso-functional molecular structures with significantly different molecular backbones is the usual objective when using LBVS. "Scaffold hopping" is also known as "leapfrogging", "scaffold searching" and "leap hopping" (Kalliokoki, 2010). These methods are usually helpful in drug repurposing, wherein new targets and diseases are pursued for existing drug molecules.

Molecular descriptors

This is one of the simplest approaches in which the reference molecule/set of molecules are compared with a large library of compounds at a very low cost on the basis of physicochemical properties descriptors, such as molecular weight, volume, geometry, surface areas, atom types, dipole moment, polarizability, molar refractivity, octanol-water partition coefficient (log P), planar structures, electronegativity, or solvation properties that are obtained from experimental measurements or theoretical models. Molecules are represented by symbols for effective execution of the task (Prada-Graciaa *et al.*, 2016).

Quantitative structure-activity relationship models (QSAR)

The mathematical relation between structural attributes and target response for a set of chemicals are explained by Quantitative Structure-Activity Relationship models. Structural and/or property descriptors of compounds can also be correlated with their biological activities using QSAR (Bernard *et al.*, 2005). Through QSAR models we can correlate various features like rate constants, binding sites affinities of ligands, inhibition constants and other biological activities, either with certain structural features (Free Wilson analysis) or with atomic, molecular or group properties, such as lipophilicity, electronic, steric and polarizability, among congeneric series of compounds. (Kubinyi, 1995). Hence, the success of QSAR is dependent on the choice of descriptors and the ability to generate the appropriate mathematical relationship besides the quality of initial set of active/inactive compounds.

Pharmacophore modelling

More significant information can be drawn by employing various conformations of a range of ligands than just a single ligand structure. A pharmacophore model of the receptor site can be generated with a sufficiently broad range of ligands. Pharmacophore

Standard ligand(Gefitinib) for EGFR

Gefitinb Analog 2

Standard ligand (Tarceva) for EGFR

TARCEVA Analog 7

Fig. 7 Structures of Gefitinib and Tarceva and their analogs.

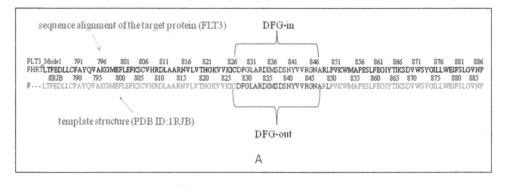

sequence alignment of the target protein (FLT3)   DFG-in

FLT3_Model   791   796   801   806   811   816   821   826   831   836   841   846   851   856   861   866   871   876   881   886
FHRTLTFEDLLCFAYQVAKGMEFLEFKSCVHRDLAARNVLVTHGKVVKICDFGLARDIMSDSNYVVRGNARLPVKWMAPESLFEGIYTIKSDVWSYGILLWEIFSLGVNP
1RJB   790   795   800   805   810   815   820   825   830   835   840   845   850   855   860   865   870   875   880   885
F---LTFEDLLCFAYQVAKGMEFLEFKSCVHRDLAARNVLVTHGKVVKICDFGLARDIMSDSNYVVRGNARLPVKWMAPESLFEGIYTIKSDVWSYGILLWEIFSLGVNP

template structure (PDB ID:1RJB)

DFG-out

A

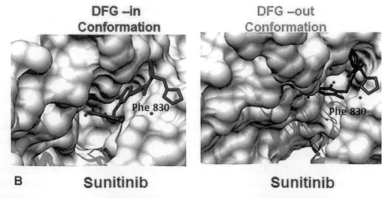

DFG –in Conformation   **DFG –out Conformation**

Phe 830   Phe 830

B   **Sunitinib**   **Sunitinib**

Fig. 8   (A) The sequence alignment of the target protein (FLT3) with the template structure in the DFG loop region. (B) Comparison of the DFG-in and DFG-out FLT3 structures. Adapted and modified from Ke, Y.Y., Singh, V.K., Coumar, M.S., *et al.*, 2015. Homology modeling of DFG-in FMS-like tyrosine kinase 3 (FLT3) and structure-based virtual screening for inhibitor identification. Scientific Reports 5, 11702. Doi: 10.1038/srep11702.

modelling of smaller, non-peptide molecules that might have improved stability and bioavailability over their peptide counterparts has resulted in successful outcomes so far (Nielsen *et al.*, 1999).

Case Studies

Computer aided drug designing (CADD) for EGFR protein controlling lung cancer

Epidermal growth factor receptor (EGFR), a receptor tyrosine kinase plays an important role in tumour cell survival. Phosphorylated EGFR upon activation causes phosphorylation of downstream proteins that lead to changes in cell proliferation, invasion, metastasis, and inhibition of apoptosis. Human EGFR was taken as a protein by Baskaran *et al.* (2012), and commercially available drugs (such as Gemzar, Gefitinib, Tarceva) were taken as ligands. The drugs were docked to this receptor and Gefitinib and Tarceva were chosen based on the energy values. To improve the binding efficiency and steric compatibility of these two drugs, modifications were made to the probable functional groups which were interacting with the receptor molecule. Analogs were prepared using ACD Chem Sketch in MOL format which were then converted to 3D structure using Weblab Viewer Lite, a 3D modelling program. It was then docked using Vega ZZ docking software. Gefitinib Analog 2(281) and Tarceva Analog 7 had significantly lower energy values and were found to be better than the conventional drugs available (**Fig. 7**).

Structure-based virtual screening (SBVS), for the identification of new chemotypes for FLT3 inhibition

FMS-like tyrosine kinase 3 (FLT3) is a type III tyrosine kinase receptor and is highly expressed in hematopoietic stem and progenitor cells. FLT3 binds to extracellular domain which activates cytoplasmic tyrosine kinase activity leading to activation of

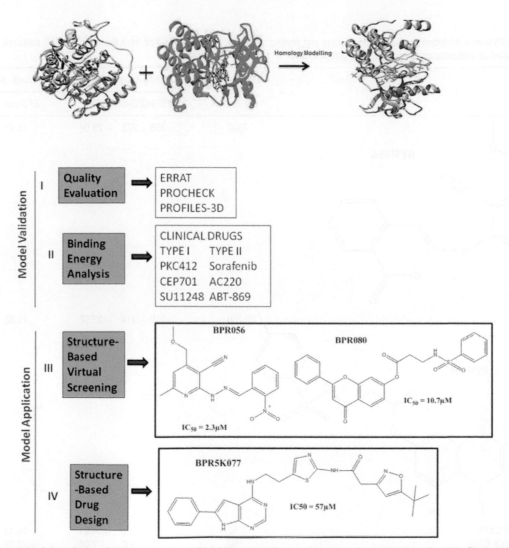

Fig. 9 Computer-aided drug design (CADD) strategy for FLT3 inhibitor identification. Adapted and modified from Ke, Y.Y., Singh, V.K., Coumar, M.S., *et al.*, 2015. Homology modeling of DFG-in FMS-like tyrosine kinase 3 (FLT3) and structure-based virtual screening for inhibitor identification. Scientific Reports 5, 11702. Doi: 10.1038/srep11702.

downstream cellular signalling which is essential for proliferation. Based on the position of the Phe residue of the DFG motif, the inhibitors are named Type I or Type II inhibitors. In a DFG-in conformation, the Phe residue is oriented outside the ATP binding site while in a DFG-out conformation; the Phe residue is oriented inside the ATP binding site. Inhibitors that bind to the DFG-in conformation are termed type-I inhibitors, and those that bind to the DFG-out conformation are referred to as type–II inhibitors. In **Fig. 8**, Ke *et al.* (2015), superimposed the FLT3-modeled (DFG-in) structure on the 1RJB (DFG-out) template structure to depict the structural differences between the DFG-in and DFG-out conformations. Since type-I inhibitors bind strongly to FLT3-ITD-mutated kinase, they are proven to be more effective against treatment of acute myeloid leukemia.

Homology modelling (HM) of the DFG-in FLT3 structure identifies known DFG-in (SU11248, CEP-701, and PKC-412) and DFG-out (Sorafenib, ABT-869 and AC220) FLT3 inhibitors using docking studies (citation of the study). SBVS of an HTS library of 125,000 compounds was done with the modeled structure. Out of the 97 top scoring compounds, two hits (BPR056, IC50 = 2.3 and BPR080, IC50 = 10.7 μM) were identified. Based on molecular dynamics simulation and density functional theory calculations BPR056 (MW: 325.32; cLogP: 2.48) was identified to interact with FLT3 in a stable manner and was studied to be chemically optimizable to realize a drug-like lead in the future. The overall CADD strategy used in this study is shown in **Fig. 9**.

This superimposition reveals that the activation loop in the DFG-in structure flipped away from the active site which leads to the placement of the Phe830 group away from this site. In the DFG-out structure, the activation loop overturned towards the active site, resulting in the placement of Phe830 in the active site. The different arrangements of the activation loop, particularly in regards to the placement of the Phe830 group, have profound implications for the binding of different types of inhibitors to FLT3 kinase.

More than 40% inhibition at a 10 μM concentration was observed for BPR056 and BPR080, out of 97 screened compounds (**Table 2**).

In order to design better FLT3 inhibitors it is important to understand the binding modes of these two high scoring poses in the modeled structure. Both the molecules were observed to bind at the ATP binding site by forming Hydrogen bonds with the

Table 2   FLT3 kinase inhibition profiles, docking score and binding energies of the hits identified from the in-house HTS database. PKC412 and sorafenib are used as reference compounds for the comparison

Compound	FLT3 IC$_{50}$ (nM)	Docking score		Predicted binding energy (kcal/mol)	
		DFG-in	DFG-out	DFG-in	DFG-out
BPR056	2300	− 355	− 276	− 23.04	16.41
BPR080	10,700	− 350	− 314	− 22.92	19.82
Midostaurin (PKC412)	37	− 269	− 165	− 34.21	19.13
Sorafenib (BAY43-9006)	102	− 183	− 300	− 7.06	− 12.32

Adapted and modified from Ke, Y.Y., Singh, V.K., Coumar, M.S., *et al.*, 2015. Homology modeling of DFG-in FMS-like tyrosine kinase 3 (FLT3) and structure-based virtual screening for inhibitor identification. Scientific Reports 5, 11702. Doi: 10.1038/srep11702.

hinge-region Cys694 residue. A hinge-region H-bond interaction between an inhibitor and kinase is an essential component in inhibitory activity and are common in several inhibitor–kinase complex structures.

DFG and FLT3 inhibitor complex was subjected to 20 ns using the Gromacs MD suite. The root mean square deviation showed that the both cases found to be at equilibrium from initial position and remained stable after 10 ns. In addition RMSF values of complex were also determined and it showed that the major differences occurs between the both complexes occurred in the loop region and more fluctuations in the FLT3-BPR080 interacting complex (Ke *et al.*, 2015). Detailed docking, DFT calculations and 20-ns MD simulations of the new hits in the DFG-in FLT3-modeled structure suggest that the interaction between BPR056 (MW: 325.32; cLogP: 2.48) and FLT3 is stable and could, in the future, be chemically optimized to realize a drug-like lead.

Fragment-based drug design to target the EphA4 kinase domain
The first approved drug that was developed via fragment-based approach is Vemurafenib (4, **Fig. 10**), a kinase inhibitor of the B-Raf V600E oncogenic mutant. High content screening (HCS), a type of phenotypical screening, followed by X-ray crystallography yielded an unselective 7-Azaindole fragment (Figure 12) as hit fragment, which was optimized via 2 into the selective B-Raf inhibitor PLX472077 (3) to end up with Vemurafenib (PLX4032, 4) (Bollag *et al.*, 2010).

Limitations of CADD

Despite the emergence of the numerous above-mentioned pioneering approaches, drug design and development is still an inherently risky business where the input costs are high and the success rate is low. Generally, only one in 1000 lead compounds reaches phase 1 clinical trials and only one in five drugs make it from phase 1 trials into the marketplace (Wishart, 2006). Some procedures concerning Computer Aided Drug Designing are time consuming, especially while looking for a proper lead component (Jorgensen, 2004). The current molecular docking algorithms do not estimate the absolute energy associated with the intermolecular interaction with satisfactory accuracy as most of the available scoring functions are classical approximations of events ruled by quantum mechanics. Further, there is lack of accurate experimental data that restricts further advancement of CADD (Bharath *et al.*, 2011). Hence, new experimental or computational tools and scientific approaches to identify correlations between the nature and structure-based properties of the drug and of its safety and efficacy in the human body (pharmacovigilance-based) are in vital need of improvement so

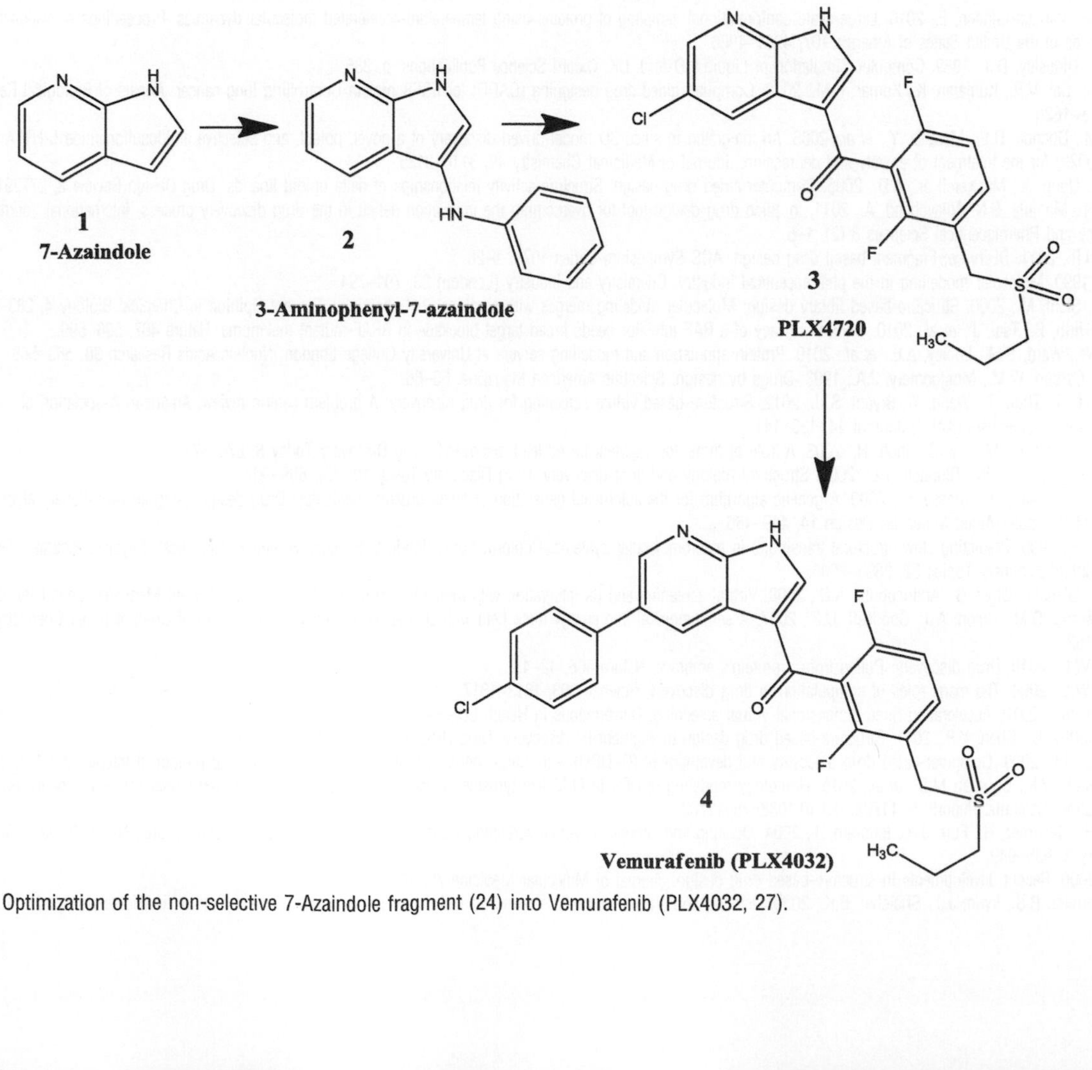

Fig. 10 Optimization of the non-selective 7-Azaindole fragment (24) into Vemurafenib (PLX4032, 27).

potentially problematic drug leads could be identified at the early stages in their development. This will improve the public health and provide a safe, effective and rational use of medicines and their development.

Conclusion & Future Perspectives

CADD has now become an indispensable tool in the long process of drug discovery and development. It also provides options for understanding chemical systems in different ways, yielding information that is not easy to obtain in laboratory analysis, with considerably less cost and effort than experiments. Initially, CADD had a rocky perception in the field of drug development, and perhaps some over-hyping of its promises, as is present in the initial stages of almost any new technology or development. Today, one can say that the discipline of computational medicinal chemistry has begun to mature and is a routinely used component of modern drug discovery process. Mastering different kinds of CADD approaches and their software and utilizing all computational resources that are valuable for drug design are certainly essential for becoming a successful computational medicinal chemist in today's world. In addition, having skills in one or more programming languages, such as Python or JAVA will help smooth routine drug-design work. SBVs and LBVs are also very likely to become routine in drug-discovery projects if they are not considered to have already done so. The use of more accurate methods like MD and QM, continue to grow. In conclusion, CADD is beneficial for pharmaceutical development in the areas of prediction of 3D structures, design of compounds, prediction of druggability, in silico ADMET prediction however, it must be realised that computational predictions need to be integrated with experimental approaches for successful drug discovery and development.

> *See also*: Biomolecular Structures: Prediction, Identification and Analyses. Comparative Epigenomics. Computational Protein Engineering Approaches for Effective Design of New Molecules. Molecular Dynamics Simulations in Drug Discovery. Natural Language Processing Approaches in Bioinformatics. Structure-Based Design of Peptide Inhibitors for Protein Arginine Deiminase Type IV (PAD4). Structure-Based Drug Design Workflow. Study of The Variability of The Native Protein Structure

References

Abrams, C.F., Vanden-Eijnden, E., 2010. Large-scale conformational sampling of proteins using temperature-accelerated molecular dynamics. Proceedings of National Academy of Sciences of the United States of America 107, 4961–4966.

Allen, M.P., Tildesley, D.J., 1989. Computer Simulation of Liquids. Oxford, UK: Oxford Science Publications, p. 385.

Baskaran, C., Bai, V.R., Kumaran, K., Kumar, K.M., 2012. Computer aided drug designing (CADD) for EGFR protein Controlling lung cancer. Annals of Biological Research 3 (4), 1815–1820.

Becker, O.M., Dhanoa, D.S., Marantz, Y., et al., 2006. An integrated in silico 3D model-driven discovery of a novel, potent, and selective amidosulfonamide 5-HT1A agonist (PRX-00023) for the treatment of anxiety and depression. Journal of Medicinal Chemistry 49, 3116–3135.

Bernard, D., Coop, A., MacKerell Jr., A.D., 2005. Computer-aided drug design: Structure-activity relationships of delta opioid ligands. Drug Design Review 2, 277291.

Bharath, E.N., Manjula, S.N., Vijaychand, A., 2011. In silico drug design tool for overcoming the innovation deficit in the drug discovery process. International Journal of Pharmacy and Pharmaceutical Sciences 3 (2), 1–5.

Bienstock, J.R., 2011. Overview: Fragment-based drug design. ACS Symposium Series 1076, 1–26.

Blaney, F., 1990. Molecular modelling in the pharmaceutical industry. Chemistry and Industry (London) 23, 791–794.

Bohm, H.J., Stahl, M., 2000. Structure-based library design: Molecular modeling merges with combinatorial chemistry. Current Opinion in Chemical Biology 4, 283–286.

Bollag, G., Hirth, P., Tsai, J., et al., 2010. Clinical efficacy of a RAF inhibitor needs broad target blockade in BRAF-mutant melanoma. Nature 467, 596–599.

Buchan, D.W., Ward, S.M., Lobley, A.E., et al., 2010. Protein annotation and modelling servers at University College London. Nucleic Acids Research 38, 563–568.

Bugg, C.E., Carson, W.M., Montgomery, J.A., 1993. Drugs by design. Scientific American Magazine. 60–66.

Cheng, T., Li, Q., Zhou, Z., Wang, Y., Bryant, S.H., 2012. Structure-based virtual screening for drug discovery: A problem-centric review. American Association of Pharmaceutical Scientists (AAPS) Journal 14, 133–141.

Congreve, M., Carr, R., Murray, C., Jhoti, H., 2003. A 'rule of three' for fragment based lead discovery? Drug Discovery Today 8, 876–877.

Congreve, M., Murray, C.W., Blundell, T.L., 2005. Structural biology and drug discovery. Drug Discovery Today 10 (13), 895–907.

Dougueta, D., Thoreaua, E., Grassy, G., 2000. A genetic algorithm for the automated generation of small organic molecules: Drug design using an evolutionary algorithm. Journal of Computer-Aided Molecular Design 14, 449–466.

Grubmüller, H., 1995. Predicting slow structural transitions in macromolecular systems: Conformational flooding. Physical Review E. Statistical, Physics, Plasmas, Fluids and Related Interdisciplinary Topics 52, 2893–2906.

Guido, R.V., Glaucius Oliva, G., Andricopulo, A.D., 2008. Virtual screening and its integration with modern drug design technologies. Current Medicinal Chemistry 15, 37–46.

Huey, R., Morris, G.M., Olson, A.J., Goodsell, D.S., 2007. A semiempirical free energy force field with charge-based desolvation. Journal of Computational Chemistry 28, 1145–1152.

Jorgensen, W.L., 2010. Drug discovery: Pulled from a protein's embrace. Nature 466, 42–43.

Jorgensen, W.L., 2004. The many roles of computation in drug discovery. Science 303, 1813–1817.

Kalliokoki, Tumo., 2010. Accelerating three dimensional virtual screening. Dissertations In Health Sciences.

Kalyaanamoorthy, S., Chen, Y.P., 2011. Structure-based drug design to augment hit discovery. Drug Discovery Today 16, 831–839.

Kapetanovic, I.M., 2008. Computer-aided drug discovery and development (CADDD) – In silico-chemical biological approach. Chemico-Biological Interactions 171, 165–176.

Ke, Y.Y., Singh, V.K., Coumar, M.S., et al., 2015. Homology modeling of DFG-in FMS-like tyrosine kinase 3 (FLT3) and structure-based virtual screening for inhibitor identification. Scientific Reports 5, 11702. doi:10.1038/srep11702.

Kitchen, D.B., Decornez, H., Furr, J.R., Bajorath, J., 2004. Docking and scoring in virtual screening for drug discovery: Methods and applications. Nature Reviews Drug Discovery 3, 935–949.

Klebe, G., 2000. Recent developments in structure-based drug design. Journal of Molecular Medicine 78, 269–281.

Kolb, P., Ferreira, R.S., Irwin, J.J., Shoichet, B.K., 2009. Docking and chemoinformatic screens for new ligands and targets. Current Opinion in Biotechnology 20, 429–436.

Kubinyi, H., 1995. in Burger's Medicinal Chemistry. Wolff, M.E. (Ed.), vol. 1. John Wiley & Sons, pp. 497–571.

Kuhn, P., Wilson, K., Patch, M.G., Stevens, R.C., 2002. The genesis of high-throughput structure-based drug discovery using protein crystallography. Current Opinion in Chemical Biology 6 (5), 704–710.

Lewis, R.A., 2005. A general method for exploiting QSAR models in lead optimization. Journal of Medicinal Chemistry 48 (5), 1638–1648.

Liu, M., Wang, S.M., 1999. MCDOCK: A Monte Carlo simulation approach to the molecular docking problem. Journal of Computer-Aided Molecular Design 13, 435–451.

Lombardino, J.G., Lowe, J.A., 2004. The role of the medicinal chemist in drug discovery — then and now. Nature Reviews Drug Discovery 3, 853–862.

Maithri, G., Manasa, B., Vani, S.S., Narendra, A., Harshita, T., 2016. Computational drug design and molecular dynamic studies – A review. International Journal of Biomedical Data Mining. 1–7.

Mallipeddi, P.L., Kumar, G., White, S.W., Webb, T.R., 2014. Recent advances in computer-aided drug design as applied to anti-influenza drug discovery. Current Topics in Medicinal Chemistry 14, 1875–1889.

Marrone, T.J., Briggs, J.M., McCammon, J.A., 1997. Structure-based drug design: Computational advances. Annual Review of Pharmacology and Toxicology 37, 71–90.

Martin, Y.C., Kofron, J.L., Linda, M., Traphagen, L.M., 2002. Do Structurally Similar Molecules Have Similar Biological Activity? Journal of Medicinal Chemistry 45, 4350–4358.

Martí-Renom, M.A., Stuart, A.C., Fiser, A., et al., 2000. Comparative protein structure modeling of genes and genomes. Annual Review of Biophysics and Biomolecular Structure 29, 291–325.

Martis, E.A., Radhakrishnan, R., Badve, R.R., 2011. High-throughput screening: The hits and leads of drug discovery – An overview. Journal of Applied Pharmaceutical Science 1 (1), 2–10.

Mishra, V., Siva-Prasad, CV., 2011. Ligand based virtual screening to find novel inhibitors against plant toxin Ricin by using the ZINC database. Bioinformation 7, 46–51.

Moore, D.J., West, A.B., Dawson, V.L., Dawson, T.M., 2005. Molecular pathophysiology of Parkinson's disease. Annual Review of Neuroscience 28, 57–87.

Morris, G.M., Goodsell, D.S., Halliday, R.S., et al., 1998. Automated docking using a Lamarckian genetic algorithm and an empirical binding free energy function. Journal of Computational Chemistry 19, 1639–1662.

Nielsen, K.J., Adarns, D., Thomas, L., et al., 1999. Structure-activity relationships of omega-conotoxins MVIIA, MVIIC and 14 loop splice hybrids at N and P/Q-type calcium channels. Journal of Molecular Biology 289 (5), 1405–1421.

Ou-Yang, S.S., Lu, J.Y., Kong, X.Q., et al., 2012. Computational drug discovery. Acta Pharmacologica Sinica 33, 1131–1140.

Prada-Graciaa, D., Huerta-Yépezb, S., Moreno-Vargasb, L.M., 2016. Application of computational methods for anticancer drug discovery, design, and optimization. Boletin Medico Del Hospital Infantil De Mexico 73 (6), 411–423.

Schlitter, J., Engels, M., Krüger, P., 1994. Targeted molecular dynamics: A new approach for searching pathways of conformational transitions. Journal of Molecular Graphics 12, 84–89.

Schneider, G., Bohm, H.J., 2002. Virtual screening and fast automated docking methods. Drug Discovery Today 7, 64–70.

Shoichet, B.K., 2004. Virtual screening of chemical libraries. Nature 432, 862–865.

Sugita, Y., Okamoto, Y., 1999. Replica-exchange molecular dynamics method for protein folding. Chemistry Physics Letters 314, 141–151.

Veselovsky, A.V., Ivanov, A.S., 2003. Strategy of computer-aided drug design. Current Drug Targets-Infectious Disorders 3, 33–40.

Walters, W.P., Stahl, M.T., Murcko, M.A., 1998. Virtual screening – An overview. Drug Discovery Today 3, 160–178.

Wang, R.X., Lai, L.H., Wang, S.M., 2002. Further development and validation of empirical scoring functions for structure based binding affinity prediction. Journal of Computer-Aided Molecular Design 16, 11–26.

Wishart, D.S., 2006. Metabolomics for drug discovery, development and monitoring. Business Briefing: Future Drug Discovery. 1–3.

Zhao, H., Huang, D., Caflisch, A., 2012. Discovery of tyrosine kinase inhibitors by docking into an inactive kinase conformation generated by molecular dynamics. ChemMedChem 7 (11), 1983–1990.

Further Reading

Arumugasamy, K., Tripathi, S.K., Singh, P., Singh, S.K., 2016. Protein-protein interaction for the de novo design of cyclin-dependent kinase peptide inhibitors. In: Orzáez, M., Sancho Medina, M., Pérez-Payá, E. (Eds.), Cyclin-Dependent Kinase (CDK) Inhibitors. Methods in Molecular Biology, vol. 1336. New York, NY: Humana Press.(ISBN: 978-1-4939-2926-9).

Baig, H.M., Ahmad, K., Roy, S., et al., 2016. Computer aided drug design: Success and limitations. Current Pharmaceutical Design 22 (5), 572–581.

Barril, X., 2017. Computer-aided drug design: Time to play with novel chemical matter. Expert Opinion on Drug Discovery 12 (10), 977–980.

Brooijmans, N., Kuntz, I.D., 2003. Molecular recognition and docking algorithms. Annual Review of Biophysics and Biomolecular Structure 32, 335–373.

Bursulaya, B.D., Totrov, M., Abagyan, R., Brooks 3rd, C.L., 2003. Comparative study of several algorithms for flexible ligand docking. Journal of Computer-Aided Molecular Design 17 (11), 755–763.

Friesner, R.A., Banks, J.L., Murphy, R.B., et al., 2004. Glide: A new approach for rapid, accurate docking and scoring. 1 Method and assessment of docking accuracy. Journal of Medicinal Chemistry 47 (7), 1739–1749.

Godwin, R.C., Melvin, R., Salsbury, F.R., 2015. Molecular dynamics simulations and computer-aided drug discovery. In: Zhang, W. (Ed.), Computer-Aided Drug Discovery. Methods in Pharmacology and Toxicology. New York, NY: Humana Press. ISBN: 978-1-4939-3521-5.

Liao, C., Sitzmann, M., Pugliese, A., Nicklaus, M.C., 2011. Software and resources for computational medicinal chemistry. Future Medicinal Chemistry 3 (8), 1057–1085.

Muegge, I., Bergner, A., Kriegl, J.M., 2017. Computer-aided drug design at Boehringer Ingelheim. Journal of Computer-Aided Molecular Design 31 (3), 275–285.

Talele, T.T., Khedkar, S.A., Rigby, A.C., 2010. Successful applications of computer aided drug discovery: Moving drugs from concept to the clinic. Current Topics in Medicinal Chemistry 10 (1), 127–141.

Wathieu, H., Issa, N.T., Stephen, W.B., Dakshanamurthy, S., 2016. Harnessing polypharmacology with computer-aided drug design and systems biology. Current Pharmaceutical Design 22 (21), 3097–3108.

Wong, Y.H., Chiu, C.C., Lin, C.L., et al., 2016. A new era for cancer target therapies: Applying systems biology and computer-aided drug design to cancer therapies. Current Pharmaceutical Biotechnology 17 (14), 1246–1267.

Yoshifumi, F., Tadaaki, M., Kiyotaka, M., et al., 2016. Miscellaneous topics in computer-aided drug design: Synthetic accessibility and GPU computing, and other topics. Current Pharmaceutical Design 22 (23), 3555–3568.

Relevant Websites

http://chem.sis.nlm.nih.gov/chemidplus
ChemIDplus.

www.ebi.ac.uk/Tools/sss/psiblast
    European Bioinformatics Institute. PSI-BLAST.
www.moldiscovery.com
    Molecular Discovery.
www.ncbi.nlm.nih.gov
    National Center for Biotechnology Information.
http://dtp.nci.nih.gov/webdata.html
    NCI discovery services.
http://cactus.nci.nih.gov/chemical/structure
    NCI/CADD Chemical Identifier Resolver.
http://195.178.207.233/PASS2008/en/index.html
    Prediction of activity spectra for substances.
www.pdb.org
    Protein Data Bank.
http://predictioncenter.org
    Protein Structure Prediction Center.
www.chemspider.com
    Royal Society of Chemistry. ChemSpider.
www.schrodinger.com
    Schrödinger Inc.
www.simulations-plus.com
    Simulations Plus, Inc.
http://thomsonreuters.com/products_services/science/science_products/a-z/world_drug_index/
    Thomson Reuters World Drug Index.
http://en.wikipedia.org/wiki/Molecular_dynamics#Major_software_for_MD_simulations
    Wikipedia. MD simulation program list.

In Silico Identification of Novel Inhibitors

Chong-Yew Lee, Ezatul E Kamarulzaman, Beow Keat Yap, Sy Bing Choi, and Habibah A Wahab, Universiti Sains Malaysia, Minden, Malaysia
Maywan Hariono, Sanata Dharma University, Sleman, Indonesia

Introduction

Computational docking simulation is no longer an unfamiliar step in drug discovery since the last few decades. As time and financial costs are crucial factors in drug discovery and development, it is important to constantly reform the drug discovery pipeline with novel technologies such as virtual screening or docking that can narrow down the candidates to the most promising lead compound for further testing. This *in silico* approach has been widely applied in the preliminary stage as well as to probe the insight into the molecular mechanism of the protein-ligand interaction in drug discovery life cycle. The past decade has witnessed tremendous growth in computational capabilities that enable computational docking to expedite the discovery of many potential inhibitors. Here, we review its potential application in the discovery of potential inhibitors to one of the deadly infectious diseases, namely the Dengue infection.

Background

Dengue is a growing global health concern with an estimated 390 million infections occurring each year (Bhatt *et al.*, 2013). It is caused by the Dengue virus (DENV), a flavivirus (*Flaviviridae*) that is transmitted by *Aedes aegypti* and *Aedes albopictus* mosquitoes. The infections are endemic in tropical and subtropical regions but are spreading to higher latitudes in recent times. To date, there are still no approved antivirals to stop dengue and currently, patients are only treated with supportive care to relieve fever, pain and dehydration. On the other hand, there have been a few vaccine candidates in advanced clinical pipeline. However, the development of an efficacious and safe vaccine for dengue is not without challenges as the virus has at least four serotypes. A major hurdle is the requirement for a working vaccine to be "tetravalent" that is immunogenically effective against all the four serotypes. If protection against one or more serotypes is insufficient, the "vaccinated" person may develop a more severe disease due to the mechanism called antibody-dependent enhancement (Halstead, 2014). Recent discovery of the fifth serotype of the DENV (Vasilakis *et al.*, 2013) further complicates the vaccine development effort.

Alternatively, the development of dengue antiviral small molecule seems viable as the structures of the proteins, the parts which make up the virus particle are largely well characterised (Kuhn *et al.*, 2002; Smit *et al.*, 2011). These DENV components are divided into "structural" proteins (capsid, envelope protein and M protein) that construct the virus and seven "non-structural" proteins (NS1, NS2A, NS2B, NS3, NS4A, NS4B and NS5) that play functional and enzymatic roles (**Fig. 1**). Knowledge and understanding of their structural features and roles in virus infection has grown tremendously. "Structural" proteins despite their names, have been shown to play active roles in the life cycle and propagation of the DENV. For example, the DENV envelope (E) protein, has been shown to play crucial roles in the attachment and entry of the virus into the host cells, the key steps in the infection (Rey, 2003; Modis *et al.*, 2004).

It is not surprising that anti-flaviviral discovery efforts in the recent decade (2006–2016) have focused on these viral proteins as targets for new small molecule inhibitors. In these target-oriented efforts, computational or *in silico* methods have played increasingly important roles in the discovery process. The availability of high resolution DENV proteins' crystal structures in the Protein Database (PDB) (Berman *et al.*, 2003) partly encourages this trend where docking technique, in particular, has been employed as a tool to virtually screen large libraries of compounds against the protein crystal structures. To a lesser extend, docking procedures have also been used to model the inhibitory activity of a promising lead and help rationalise its mechanism of action towards improving the ligand's potency.

This review aims to highlight recent (2006–2016) efforts in which *in silico* docking played important roles in the discovery of new DENV inhibitors. Whenever possible, we attempt to keep the review to projects where the docking results are followed through or validated with experimental data. We discuss the outcomes of these projects and evaluate their prospects, and finally identify least explored areas or targets which may hold promise for future *in silico* discovery of potential DENV inhibitors.

Case Studies

Elucidation of Potential Inhibitors on DENV Protein Targets

DENV structural proteins

The envelope (E) protein

The E protein of DENV (DENV E) is responsible for receptor recognition, attachment of the virus on the host cell and endocytosis into the cell. It also participates in the fusion of the viral membrane with the host membrane (Harrison, 2008). This protein comprises three domains (Domains I, II and III) (**Fig. 2**) that have been pursued as drug targets. However, the hydrophobic pocket

A

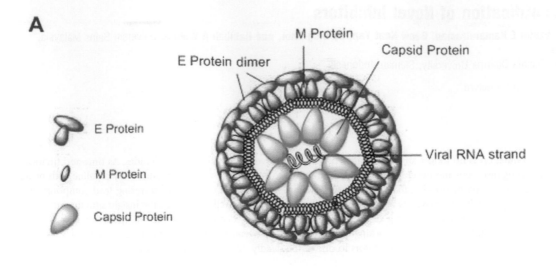

E Protein

M Protein

Capsid Protein

B

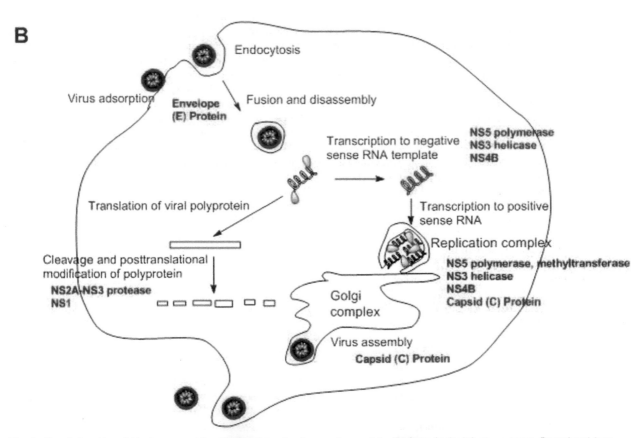

Fig. 1 Targeted and targetable dengue proteins. (A) Structure of a dengue virus particle. (B) Steps in the infection process. Reproduced from Behnam, M.A.M., Nitsche, C., Boldescu, V., Klein, C.D., 2016. The medicinal chemistry of dengue virus. J. Med. Chem. 59, 5622–5649.

between Domains I and II (Modis *et al.*, 2003) is the most amenable and widely used for virtual screening or docking. Also known as the n-octyl-*β-D*-glucoside (*β*-OG) pocket, this domain acts as a hinge point between the two domains and plays a role in the conformational rearrangement necessary for the fusion process.

Wang and co-workers was among the first groups to utilize the *β*-OG as a target for virtual screens (Wang *et al.*, 2009). Noting the conformational flexibility of the pocket from the two crystal structures published by Harrison and co-workers (Modis *et al.*, 2003, 2004), they incorporated soft van der Waals contact parameters into the docking parameters as a

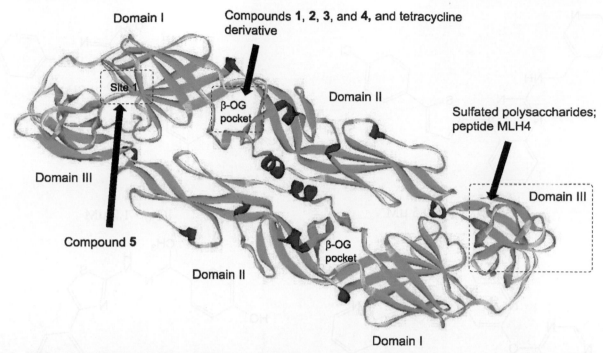

Fig. 2 Binding sites for identified DENV entry inhibitors on the crystal structure of DENV2 E protein dimer (PDB: 1OKE), shown in cartoon representation, coloured by secondary structure (helices in red and sheets in cyan).

compromise for the rigid protein requirement for docking. Compound (1) (Fig. 3) was the most potent compound as a result of this screen and verified by plaque reduction assay (EC_{50} = 0.068 to 0.496 µM in the four DENV serotypes). Redocking of (1) into the β-OG pocket using GOLD software, revealed a similar pose to that of the amphiphilic β-OG, with its hydrophobic portion (chloro-phenyl-thiophene) buried within the space occupied by the octyl tail of β-OG. The polar pyridinyl-methyl-quinazolinyl-amine part of the molecule bound near the entrance of the pocket and was exposed to solvent but the phenyl group of the quinazoline ring had a hydrophobic interaction with Leu198 and possibly Pro53 or Ala205 while the amine hydrogen interacted with Glu49 or Thr48. In the same year, a multi-tiered docking screen of the Maybridge chemical database on the β-OG pocket resulted in the identification of five hit compounds which were then subjected to biological evaluation (Kampmann et al., 2009). The most potent compound (2) (IC_{50} = 1.2 µM), interestingly showed similar binding pose as that reported by Wang et al. suggesting a common pharmacophore for β-OG pocket binders across diverse chemical structures. Indeed, on hindsight, the discovery of two tetracycline derivatives as verified hits (IC_{50} = 55–67 µM in a plaque reduction assay) against the β-OG pocket in an earlier in silico screen (Yang et al., 2007) suggested that this binding site was particularly distinct. Of the ten hits initially identified, these tetracycline derivatives were found to dock at the entrance of the pocket and extended into the pocket, particularly between the D and I segments along the stretch of residues 48–52. In contrast, other inactive compounds were docked deeper inside the β-OG pocket.

A recent in silico screen against the β-OG pocket (Leal et al., 2017) identified a quinazoline derivative (3) bearing some similarities to (1) as one of the hits. However, (3) showed a lower potency than (1) in a luciferase reporter assay of DENV (EC_{50} = 3.1 µM). Despite adopting a novel "hybrid" design using motifs from two previous in silico screen hits (Li et al., 2008; Zhou et al., 2008), Jayaprakash and co-workers discovered (4) (EC_{50} = 1.39 uM), the best hit which has several moieties of (2) (Jadav et al., 2015). Results as these, where similarly structured hits were discovered, may be due to overlaps in the ligands available in the databases used in these virtual screening campaigns as much as the fact that the docking models were fundamentally based on the binding mode of β-OG.

Taking advantage of the shifting features of the DENV E domains during the fusion process, Yennamalli and co-workers attempted to search for alternative sites similar to the β-OG pocket on the E protein in both pre-fusion (PDB ID: 1OKE) and post-fusion (PDB: 1OK8) forms of the protein using a cavity-detection algorithm termed "putative active sites with spheres" (Yennamalli et al., 2009). Two sites (named as Sites 1 and 2) were identified and were used in a large in silico docking screen of thirteen publicly and commercially available databases using a combination of GOLD, FlexX, and DOCK docking programs. After winnowing the hits against several criteria including drug-like features and chemical stability, seven compounds were biologically tested. The best compound (5), was able to reduce the plaque formation in infected Vero cells with an EC_{50} of 4 µM thus validating these novel sites of DENV E for virtual screening of new and potential DENV entry inhibitors.

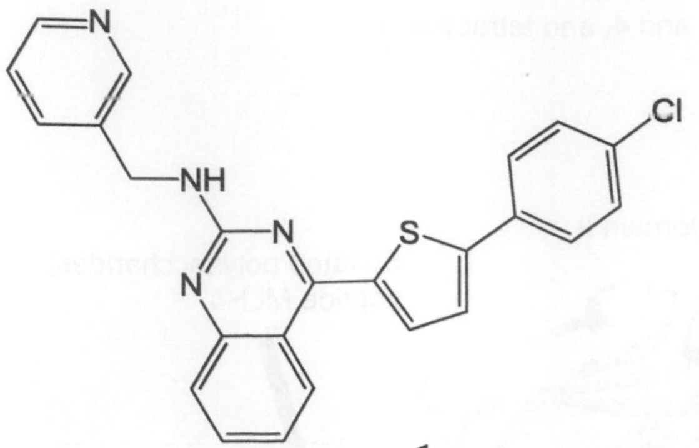

1
$EC_{50} = 0.1\text{-}0.5\ \mu M$

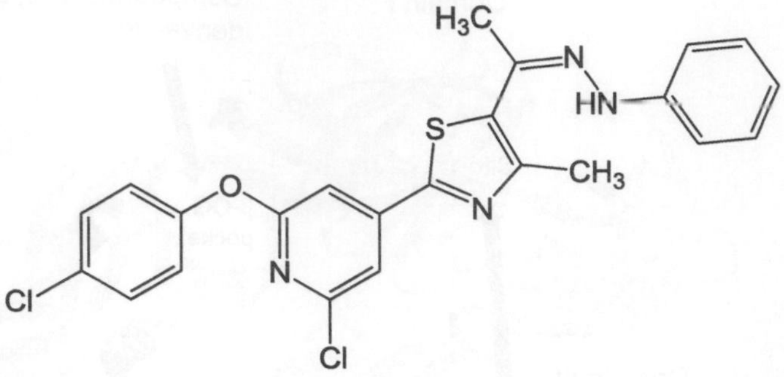

2
$IC_{50} = 1.2\ \mu M$

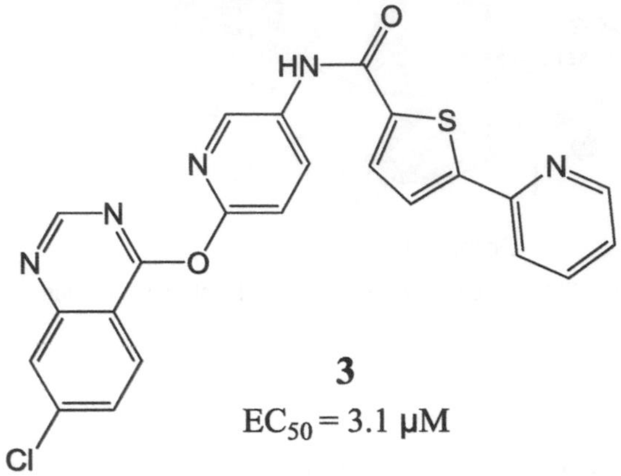

3
$EC_{50} = 3.1\ \mu M$

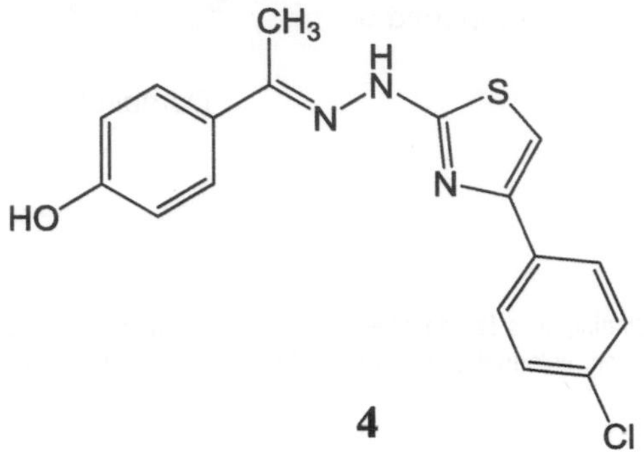

4
$EC_{50} = 1.4\ \mu M$

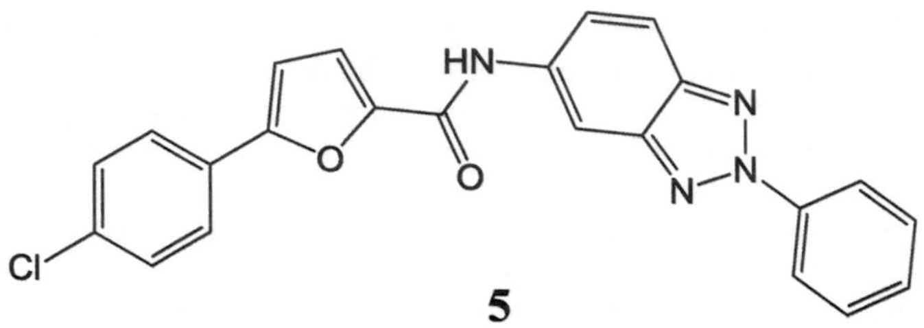

5
$EC_{50} = 4.0\ \mu M$

Fig. 3 DENV entry inhibitors identified from docking screens and verified experimentally.

The capsid (C) protein

The DENV Capsid (DENV C) is a 100 amino acid-length homodimeric protein with four α-helical regions and an intrinsically disordered NH terminal domain. A number of DENV C form a complex with the single-stranded viral RNA (nucleocapsid). They play a role in viral RNA recruitment during virus assembly and release of the genome during infection. Notably these RNA replication processes involve their interactions with the host intracellular lipid droplets and very low density lipoproteins (VLDL) (Byk and Gamarnik, 2016).

Research on the DENV C has just begun to shed light on its interaction mechanism with the host lipid entities (Martins et al., 2012; Faustino et al., 2015). Recent identification of key target ligands responsible for DENV C-lipid interactions such as apolipoprotein E and perilipin 3 (Faustino et al., 2014; Carvalho et al., 2012) has paved the way for the possibility of a structure-based discovery of DENV C binding inhibitors. However, there is presently no deposition of crystal structures of DENV C in the PDB except for a nuclear magnetic resonance (NMR) solution structure (PDB: 1R6R) (Ma et al., 2004; **Fig. 4**). As such, very limited docking studies against this protein have been reported to date. The best lead for initiating such endeavours so far lies in the only small molecule DENV C ligand ST-148 which was fortuitously discovered in a high-throughput screening of a library of over 200,000 compounds (Byrd et al., 2013). Docking analysis of ST-148 on the DENV C (PDB: 1R6R) suggested that the compound interacts with the protein thus enhanced its self-dimerization and this may have led to interference in the assembly and disassembly of the nucleocapsid necessary for RNA replication (Scaturro et al., 2014).

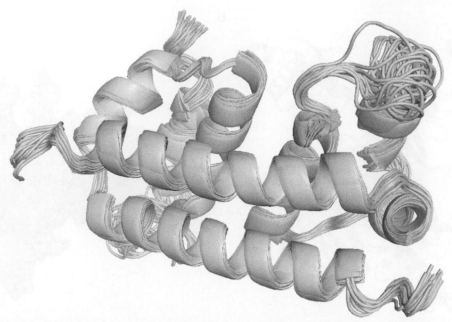

Fig. 4 NMR solution structure of DENV C Protein (PDB: 1R6R). Reproduced from Ma, L., Jones, C.T., Groesch, T.D., Kuhn, R.J., Post, C.B., 2004. Solution structure of dengue virus capsid protein reveals another fold. Proc. Natl. Acad. Sci. USA 101, 3414–3439. In cartoon representation.

DENV Non-Structural Proteins

NS1

NS1 is the first of seven non-structural proteins encoded for by the viral genome. It is a highly conserved 46 kDa non-structural glycoprotein of the DENV flavivirus, exists intracellularly, on cell surface and in secreted forms. NS1 plays an important role in viral particle production and viral RNA replication, presumably through post-translational N-glycosylation. NS1 contains two key N-glycosylation sites, located at Asn130 and Asn207, respectively, with Asn130 glycosylation site is more biologically important as Asn130 mutation has been shown to result in attenuation of dengue virus infection in both mammalian and mosquito cells (Tajima *et al.*, 2008).

To date, there is limited literature can be found with regards to *in silico* studies to discover novel NS1 inhibitors despite the fact that the crystal structure of DENV NS1 dimer has been solved (**Fig. 5**, PDB: 4O6B) (Akey *et al.*, 2014). The structure contains three domains: A small *β-roll* domain formed by two intertwined *β*-hairpins; a *Wing* domain, comprises an *α/β* subdomain and a discontinuous connector that sits against the *β-roll* and a *β-ladder* domain, formed by 18 antiparallel *β*-strands assembled in a continuous *β*-sheet that runs along the whole length of the dimer. Using this crystal structure, Qamar *et al.* (2014) attempted to identify potential inhibitors of Asn130 glycosylation site of NS1 by docking 2200 flavonoids from 405 medicinal plants using MOE docking program. Out of the top 100 flavonoids screened, six flavonoids showed significant interactions with Asn130, suggesting that flavonoids have potential to be DENV inhibitors, although further experimental evidence is required to support this observation.

Apart from the post-translational N-glycosylation, recent work found that NS1 also acts as an important modulator of cellular energy metabolism (Allonso *et al.*, 2015). Results from co-immunoprecipitation, cross-linking and ELISA assays have proposed that NS1 interacts with glyceraldehyde 3-phosphate dehydrogenase (GADPH), which results in the increase of glycolytic flux and ultimately the energy production, which is required for proper viral replication. *In silico* docking studies between the homology model of GADPH (PDB template: 1ZNQ) and the crystal structure of NS1 (PDB: 4O6B) using the web-based ClusPro server (Version 2.0; Kozakov *et al.*, 2017) revealed that the hydrophobic protrusion of NS1, located at the *β-roll* domain (Cys4, Val5, Leu13, Lys14, Cys15 of both monomers), interacts with the hydrophobic residues of GADPH located opposite its catalytic site. Interestingly, the NS1-GADPH binding interface is at a distant location from the N-glycosylation sites (**Fig. 5**), suggesting its potential as a novel target for the design and discovery of new drug candidate against the DENV viral replication.

NS2B–NS3 protease

NS3 is one of the most widely studied DENV proteins. It is a 69 kDa multifunctional protein which consists of 618 amino acids that carry two functional domains, the N-terminal trypsin-like serine protease domain and the C-terminus domain that contains the activities of a RNA helicase and a RNA-stimulated NTPase. The NS3 serine protease domain comprises 180 amino acid residues at its N-terminal with a catalytic triad formed by residues His51, Asp75 and Ser135 (Brinkworth *et al.*, 1999; Lescar *et al.*, 2008). The proteolytic activity of DENV NS3 protease (NS3pro) requires the NS2B protein, which is located in the polypeptide precursor

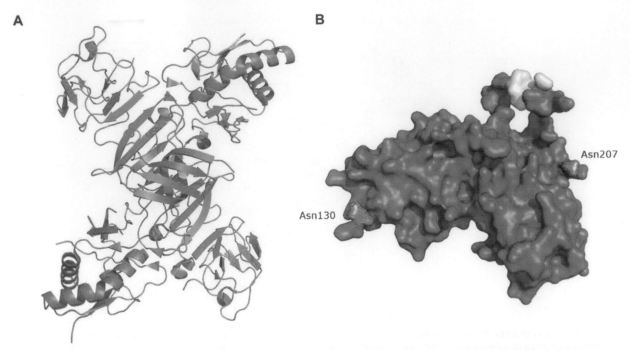

Fig. 5 (A)The crystal structure of DENV NS1 protein (PDB: 4O6B), in cartoon representation. (B) N-glycosylation sites (gold) and the GADPH binding site (cyan) of the DENV NS1 protein surface (blue). The separation between the N-glycosylation and GADPH binding sites suggest two possible targets for NS1 inhibitors as potential antiviral candidates.

upstream of the NS3pro domain, as a cofactor (Aleshin *et al.*, 2007). This structural activation probably resulted in conformational rearrangements of the catalytic triad and the subsite (S^5-$S^{5'}$) residues, which facilitates substrate binding and/or optimizes proton exchange during catalysis (Barbato *et al.*, 1999; Kim *et al.*, 1996). NS2B-NS3pro is responsible for the cleavage of DENV C and for cleavage at the NS2A/NS2B, NS2B/NS3, NS3/NS4A, NS4A/NS4B and NS4B/NS5 boundaries (Chambers *et al.*, 1993; Arias *et al.*, 1993; Yotmanee *et al.*, 2015). Therefore, blocking or inhibiting the activities of DENV NS2B-NS3pro has become an attractive target in anti-dengue drug discovery.

To date, there are thirteen 3D structures of NS3pro from the four dengue serotypes deposited in the Protein Data Bank (PDB). In general, the crystal structures of NS3pro in complex with the cofactor NS2B for the four serotypes demonstrated that the NS3pro domain adopts chymotrypsin-like structure consisting two β-barrels of which each barrel contains six β-strands. The β-barrel conformation typically is compact with short or absent loop structures. The active site is located in between the cleft of the two β-barrels. It is relatively shallow, contourless and composed of a catalytic triad containing His51, Asp75 and Ser135 (Yildiz *et al.*, 2013; Noble *et al.*, 2012; Luo *et al.*, 2008, 2010; Erbel *et al.*, 2006; Chandramouli *et al.*, 2010).

The initial structure-activity relationship of NS2B-NS3pro can be inferred from well-established cleavage sites of DENV polyprotein by NS2B-NS3pro. The cleavage sites preferable by this enzyme usually occur after two basic amino acid residues (Lys-Arg, Arg-Arg or Arg-Lys) or occasionally after Gln-Arg at the P1 and P2 positions (**Fig. 6**) and are usually followed by a short side-chain amino acids, most commonly Gly, Ser or Ala at P1' (Chambers *et al.*, 1990). A functional substrate profiling of the P1–P5 and P1'–P5' regions of the proteases from the four DENV serotypes showed that the enzyme shared very similar substrate specificities across the serotypes (Khumthong *et al.*, 2002; Chanprapaph *et al.*, 2005) with recent finding shows that the interaction between these substrates with the NS2B/NS3 protease is in the order of DENV C > intNS3 > NS2A/NS2B > NS4B/NS5 > NS3/NS4A > NS2B/NS3 (Yotmanee *et al.*, 2015) which is in agreement with experimental values.

Two tetrapeptides, Bz-Nle-Lys-Arg-Arg and Bz-Nle-Lys-Thr-Arg have been shown to have high affinities for NS2B-NS3pro (K_i=12.42 and 33.9 µM, respectively) (Yin *et al.*, 2006). A stepwise removal of the octapeptide down to tetrapeptide i.e., WYCW-NH$_2$ resulted in protease inhibition in low micromolar activities (K_i=4.2, 4.8, 24.4 and 11.2 µM for DENV1-4, respectively (Prusis *et al.*, 2013). The docked pose of the tetrapeptide on DENV3 is shown in **Fig. 7**. Tripeptide with a varied N-terminal cap groups and P2 Lys' side chain modification have also been shown to have micromolar activities against DENV2 NS2B-NS3pro. It was suggested that P2Arg play the specificity shift towards the protease while an extended P2 Lys failed to block the protease activity, suggesting a size-constrained S2 pocket (Schüller *et al.*, 2011).

Over the past ten years, there have been many efforts to search for small molecules anti-dengue through the mean of *in silico* approaches that target NS2B/NS3-protease. Many compounds either small molecules from natural products or synthetic chemicals have been discovered as potential inhibitors for the enzyme. Two cyclohexyl chalcone derivatives, 4-hydroxypanduratin A (**Fig. 8**: 6) and panduratin A (**Fig. 8**: 7) isolated from *Boesenbergia rotunda* (L.) Mansf. Kulturpfl. have shown good competitive inhibitory activity with K_i values of 21, and 25 µM, respectively (Tan *et al.*, 2006). The discovery has prompted the docking studies

A

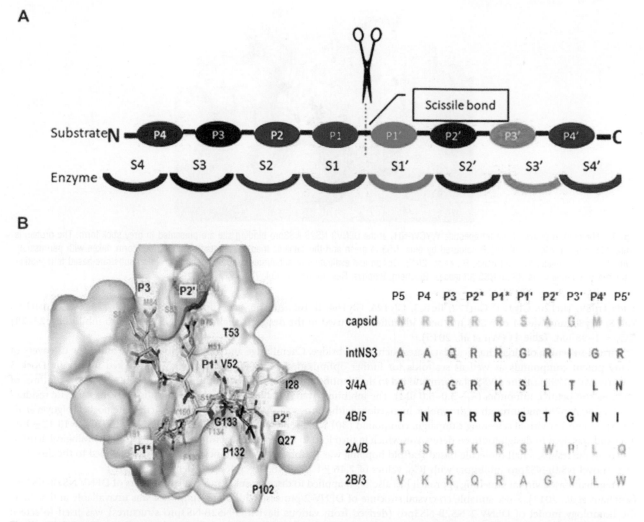

	P5	P4	P3	P2*	P1*	P1'	P2'	P3'	P4'	P5'
capsid	N	R	R	R	R	S	A	G	M	I
intNS3	A	A	Q	R	R	G	R	I	G	R
3/4A	A	A	G	R	K	S	L	T	L	N
4B/5	T	N	T	R	R	G	T	G	N	I
2A/B	T	S	K	K	R	S	W	P	L	Q
2B/3	V	K	K	Q	R	A	G	V	L	W

Fig. 6 (A) Schechter and Berger's Nomenclature of the peptide substrate. The substrate is cleaved between positions P1-P1'. Reproduced from Schechter, I., Berger, A., 1967. On the size of the active site in proteases. I. Papain. Biochem. Biophys. Res. Commun. 27, 157–162. (B) Models of DENV polypeptide substrates, Capsid, intNS3, NS3/NS4A, NS4B/NS5, NS2A/NS2B, NS2B/NS3 (stick model) superposed on the surface of DENV2 NS2B/NS3pro and their sequences from P5 – P5'. Reproduced from Yotmanee, P., Rungrotmongkol, T., Wichapong, K., et al., 2015. Binding specificity of polypeptide substrates in NS2B/NS3pro serine protease of dengue virus type 2: A molecular dynamics Study. J. Mol. Gr. Modell. 60, 24–33.

of these compounds which led to the synthesis of ethyl 3-(4-(hydroxymethyl)-2-methoxy-5-nitrophenoxy)propanoate (**Fig. 8**: 8) which also have strong inhibition (K_i=59 μM) (Kee et al., 2007). Docking noncompetitive inhibitors (**Fig. 8**: 9–14), which were previously isolated (Tan et al., 2006) using AutoDock3 (Morris et al., 1998) showed that these noncompetitive ligands bound to the allosteric sites, particularly at the backbone carbonyl of Lys74 (which is bonded to Asp75, one of the catalytic triad residues) of DENV2 NS2B-NS3pro, the results of which, are in accordance with the experimental study (Chandramouli et al., 2010). Based on these results, three series of panduratin A derivatives (i.e., of 246DA (**15**), 2446DA (**16**) and 20H46DA (**17**)) were designed by adding various substituents at the positions 1–5 of the benzyl ring A for both 4-hydroxypanduratin A and panduratin A. A docking calculation of these substituted benzyl compounds with NS2B/NS3pro showed favourable binding energies which are close to the computed energy of the parent compounds (Frimayanti et al., 2011).

Noncompetitive inhibition of NS2B-NS3pro especially that involved binding at the allosteric sites continues to generate interests in many researches. Previously, the 3F10 antibody was found to disrupt the interaction of NS2B with NS3 in vitro, which suggest the possibility of NS2B-NS3pro allosteric inhibition (Phong et al., 2011). Docking analysis of the noncompetitive inhibitors screened from 13,341 small compounds, with the backbone structures of chalcone, flavanone, and flavone, available in the ZINC database, showed four compounds (**Fig. 9**: 18–21) (the most potent, compound (**Fig. 9**: 18) with K_i=69.9 μM) formed hydrogen bonding interactions with the amino acid residues Glu88, Gly124, and Asn167, as well as π-cation interactions with Lys74. This site is located behind the active site (Ser135, Asp175, and His51) (Heh et al., 2013). Allosteric region near Ala125 has also been proposed as a target for the binding of noncompetitive NS2B-NS3pro inhibitors. Ala125 sits between the 120s and 150s loops, which have been shown to be very flexible (Yildiz et al., 2013). Other allosteric sites including that formed by the amino

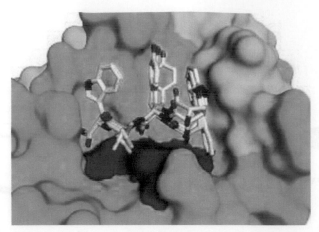

Fig. 7 The docked poses of the tetrapeptide WYCW-NH2 at the DENV3 NS2B-NS3pro binding site are presented in grey stick form. The protein is presented in surface form with NS2B coloured by blue, NS3 in green and the catalytic triad are spotted in red surface form. taken with permission from Prusis, P., Junaid, M., Petrovska, R., *et al.*, 2013. Design and evaluation of substrate-based octapeptide and non substrate-based tetrapeptide inhibitors of dengue virus NS2B–NS3 proteases. Biochem. Biophys. Res. Commun. 434, 767–772.

acids Trp89, Thr120, Gly121, Glu122, Ile123, Gly124, Gly164, Ile165, Ala166, and Gln167 of NS3 and Lys73, Lys74, Asn152, Val78, Gly82, and Met84 of NS2B has been identified and used in the design of eight potent NS2B-NS3pro inhibitors (**22–29**) (IC_{50}=1–98 µM, **Table 1**) (Wu *et al.*, 2015).

Virtual screening of large chemical databases such as Maybridge, ChemBridge and ZINC databases have aided the discovery of many potent compounds as well as scaffolds for further optimisation. 300,000 compounds were docked using AutoDock 3 (Morris *et al.*, 1998) on the GVSS platform and led to the identification of seven novel inhibitors ($IC_{50} \sim 4.0$–90 µM) with three of them as competitive inhibitors ($K_i \sim 3.0$–5.0 µM). The inhibitors were stabilised by forming H-bonds with the catalytic residues (His51 and Asp75) and through hydrophobic interactions with various amino acids in the NS3pro active site pocket (Nguyet *et al.*, 2013). In another virtual screening campaign, compound (**30**) was found to be active against NS2B-NS3pro (IC_{50}=13.12±1.03 µM) and was used to design fourteen derivatives which in turn lead to the discovery of four new inhibitors with biological activity. Based on the results, small molecule-based scaffold hopping was performed to design new compounds which led to the discovery of 17 novel NS2B-NS3pro inhibitors with IC_{50} values of 7.46±1.15 to 48.59±3.46 µM (Deng *et al.*, 2012).

Fragment-based virtual screening approach has also been applied to discover small molecule inhibitors of DENV NS2B-NS3pro (Knehans *et al.*, 2011). Since suitable co-crystal structure of DENV-2 protease with bound inhibitor was unavailable at that time, the homology model of DENV-2 NS2B-NS3pro (derived from various flavivirus NS2B-NS3pro structures) was used to screen 150,000 molecular fragments collected from ZINC database using AutoDock Vina (Knehans *et al.*, 2011; Trott and Olson, 2010) focusing on the interactions with the S1 and S2 pockets of NS2B-NS3pro. High scored fragments were then linked to generate new bioactive molecule where docking analysis showed that this compound interacted with S1 pocket (Asp129) *via* hydrogen bonding and electrostatic interaction. 23 compounds were tested experimentally that led to the identification of two inhibitors, compounds (**31**) and (**32**) (IC_{50}=7.7 µM and 37.9 µM, respectively).

There are many other docking studies as well as virtual screenings using docking which have been performed and able to give insight into the binding of potential NS2B-NS3pro. However, they are not validated experimentally, making it difficult to assess the successful of their *in silico* prediction. Such examples include Qamar *et al.* (2014) who had carried out a docking analysis with DENV NS2B-NS3 protease using a library of 940 phytochemicals. In their study, they found *Garcinia* phytochemicals to be their best hits, including gossypol, mangostenone C, garcidepsidone A, and dimethyl- calabaxanthone bound deeply inside the active site of DENV NS2B/NS3 protease among all tested phytochemicals and had interactions with catalytic triad (His51, Asp75, Ser135). In another study, a molecular docking analysis (using Molegro Molecular Docker (Thomsen and Christensen, 2006)) of 2194 plant-derived secondary metabolites with dengue virus protein targets carried out by Powers and Setzer (2016), showed that 24 compounds docked strongly to dengue virus NS2B-NS3 protease ($E_{dock} < -130$ kJ/mol) (Powers and Setzer, 2016). The lowest-energy docking poses of the chalcone ligands balsacone A, balsacone B, and balsacone C, bound into both the binding site of Lys-Arg as well as the catalytic site occupied by the co-crystallized inhibitor M9P. Although all these findings have not been validated experimentally, they did provide some insights into the development of DENV NS2B-NS3pro inhibitors.

NS3 helicase

Besides having the protease activity, the C-terminal fragment of NS3 behaves as an ATP-dependent RNA helicase and unwinds the double-stranded RNA genome during virus replication (Utama *et al.*, 2000). The helicase activity (Gorbalenya *et al.*, 1989; Li *et al.*, 1999) is vital in virus replication as it separates dsRNA during viral replication. The crystal structure of DENV-2 helicase catalytic domain revealed a three-lobed flattened topology with a large number of loops. It has a distinct structural feature with a long tunnel runs across the centre of one face of the protein (Xu *et al.*, 2005; Behnam *et al.*, 2016; Swarbrick *et al.*, 2017).

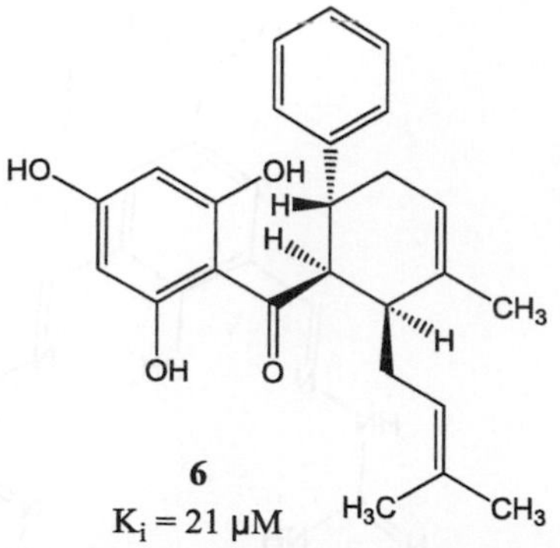

6
$K_i = 21\ \mu M$

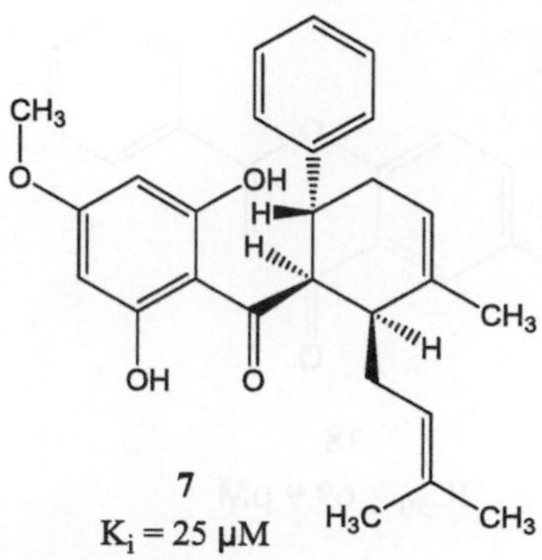

7
$K_i = 25\ \mu M$

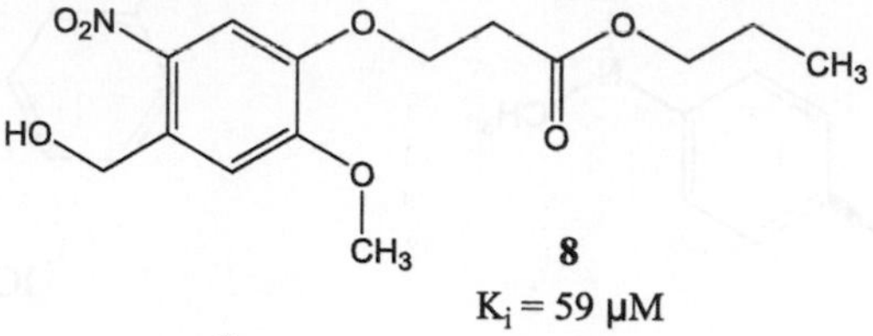

8
$K_i = 59\ \mu M$

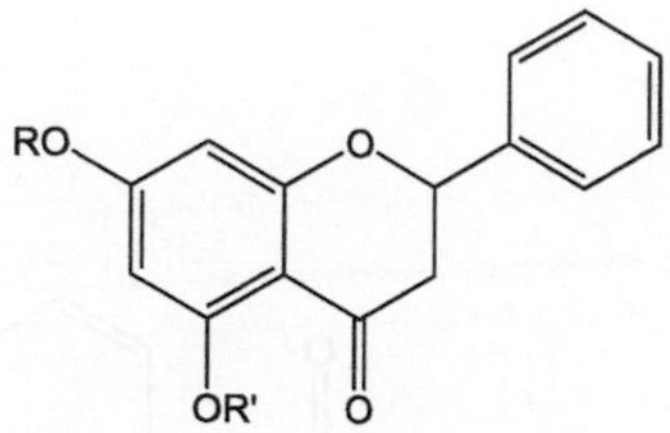

R = OMe, R'= OH ; Pinostrobin **(9)**
R = OH, R'= OH ; Pinocembrin **(10)**
R = OH, R' = OMe ; Alpinetin **(11)**

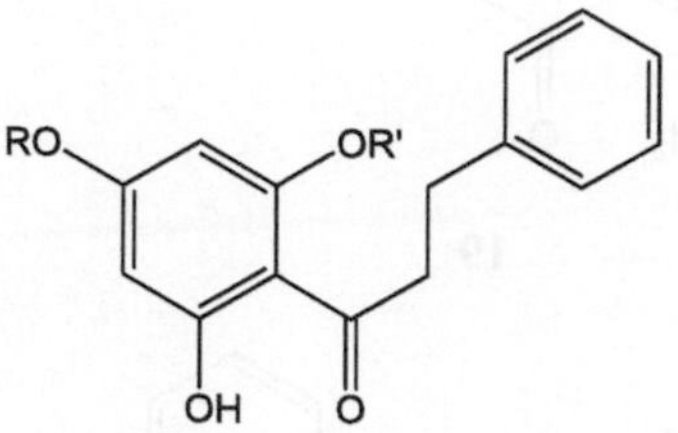

R = OMe, R'= OH ; Pinostrobin chalcone **(12)**
R = OH, R'= OH ; Pinocembrin chalcone **(13)**
R = OH, R' = OMe ; Cardamonin **(14)**

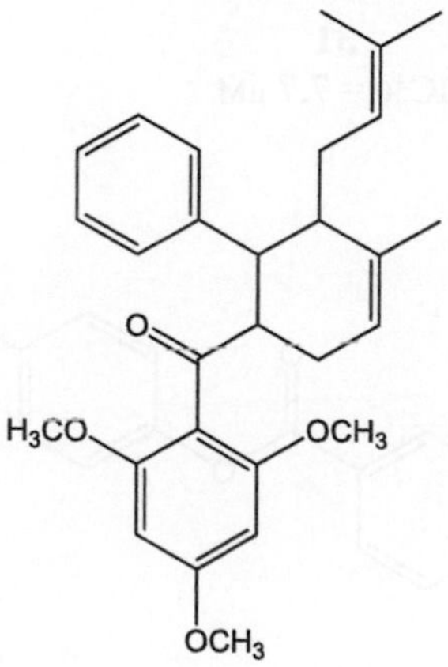

15
$K_i = 19.8\ \mu M$

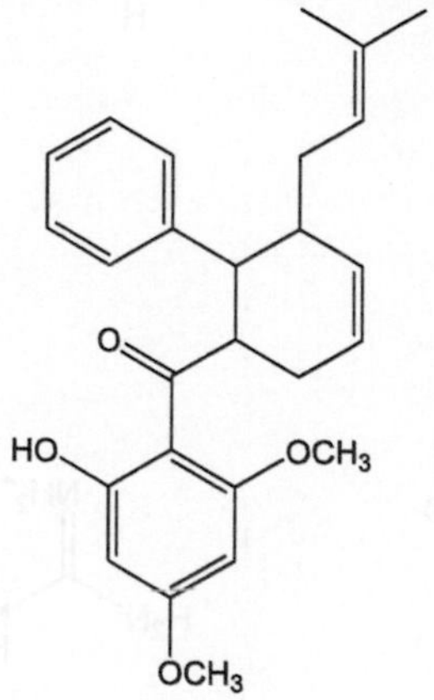

16
$K_i = 39.7\ \mu M$

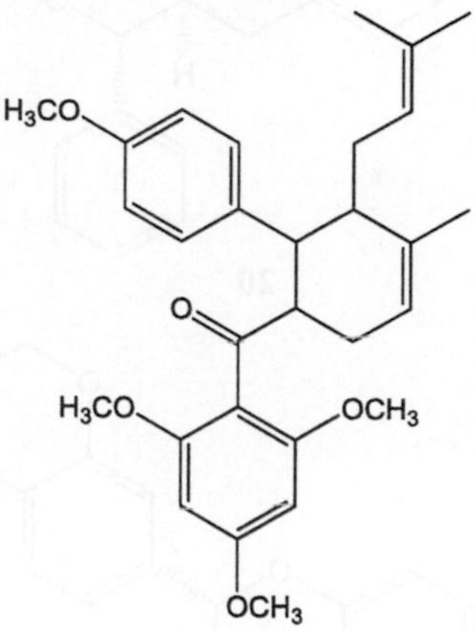

17
$K_i = 24.4\ \mu M$

Fig. 8 Structures of the competitive (4-hydroxypanduratin A (6), panduratin A (7)) and noncompetitive inhibitors (9–14) isolated from *Boesenbergia rotunda* (L.) Mansf. Kulturpfl. (Ethyl 3-(4-(hydroxymethyl)-2- methoxy-5-nitrophenoxy) propanoate (8), and panduratin A derivatives (15–17) are synthetic competitive inhibitors).

Therefore, due to its role in virus replication, NS3 helicase has also been considered as a target with high potential to develop dengue antiviral agents. There is limited information available on molecular docking involving this target. Recently, Halim and co-worker highlighted both structure and ligand-based approach in search of potential NS3 inhibitor from ZINC database (Halim *et al.*, 2017). A pharmacophore model generated using 16 compounds from literatures (Basavannacharya and Vasudevan, 2014; Sweeney *et al.*, 2015; Mastrangelo *et al.*, 2012) was used to filter 1,201,474 compounds from the ZINC database. Molecular docking using FRED docking program was then conducted on those compounds which fit the pharmacophore model. 25

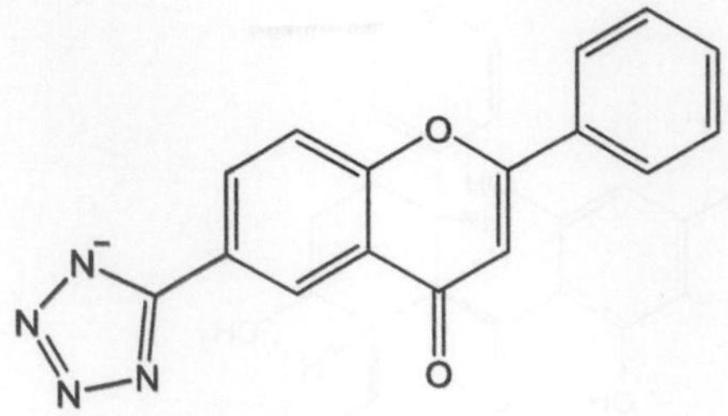

18

$IC_{50} = 69.9$ μM

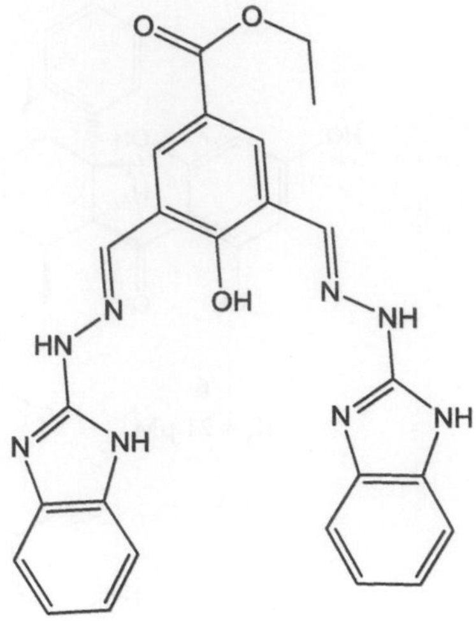

19

20

21

30

$IC_{50} = 13.1$ μM

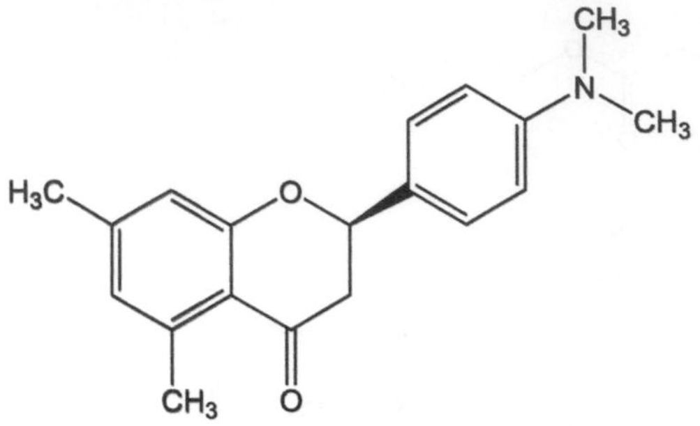

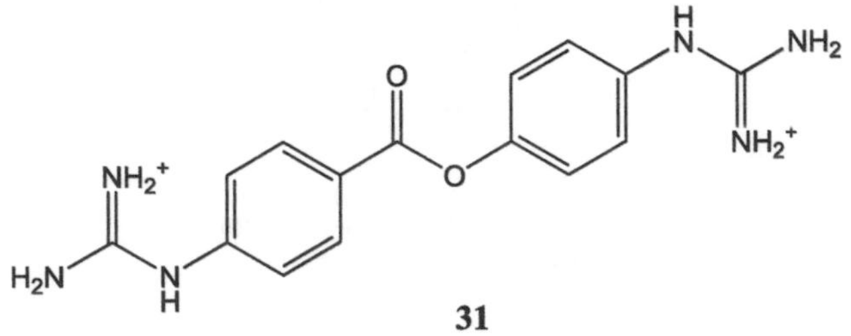

31

$IC_{50} = 7.7$ μM

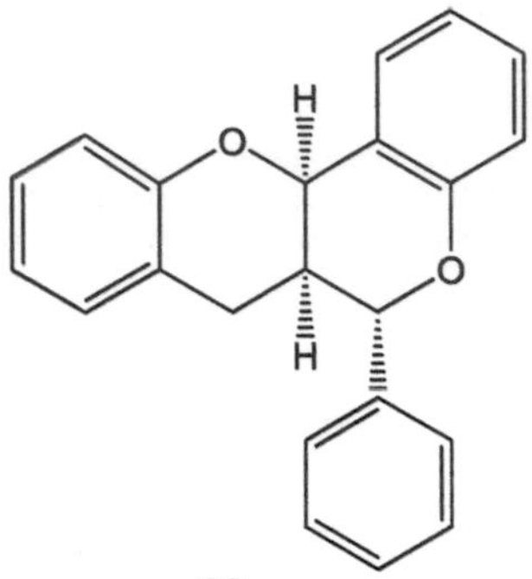

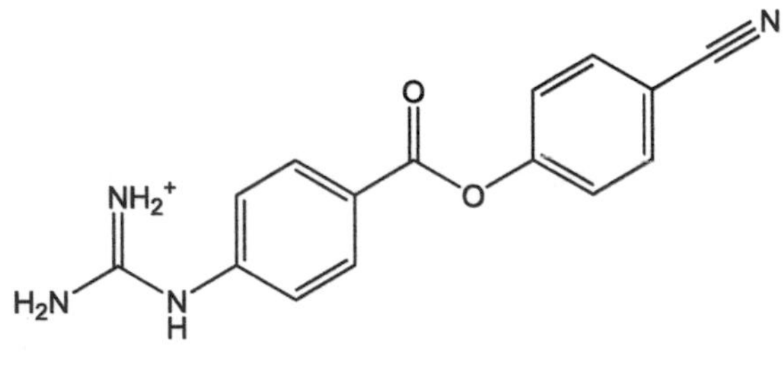

32

$IC_{50} = 37.9$ μM

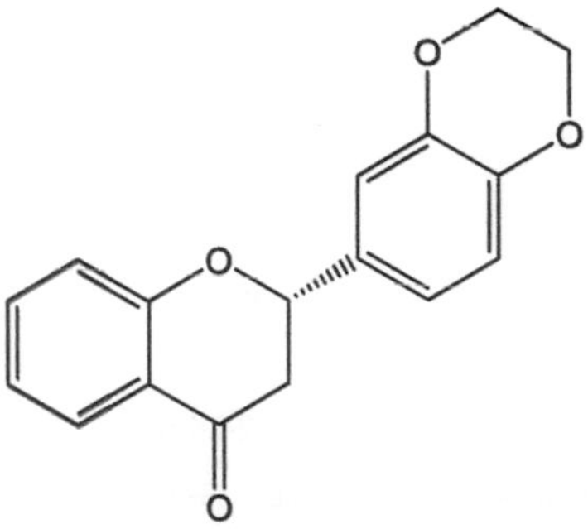

Fig. 9 Inhibitors of NS2B-NS3pro identified from small molecule-based virtual screening (18–21: noncompetitive inhibitors; (30): competitive inhibitor) and fragment-based virtual screening (31–32).

compounds with drug-like properties were selected and postulated as potent inhibitors for NS3 helicase. This postulation however, is not validated experimentally.

Since the crystal structure of this enzyme is only recently available, Milani and co-worker had initiated an investigation of DENV NS3 helicase using a built 3D model based on other flavivirus (Milani *et al.*, 2009). *In silico* screening was conducted against virtual Library of Pharmacologically Active Compounds (LOPAC) which included 1280 commercially available compounds from

Table 1   Structures and activities of potent NS2B/NS3pro Inhibitors

Compound	Chemical structure	Result for compound[a]:				
		DENV-2 (IC$_{50}$ [μM])[b]	DENV-3 (IC$_{50}$ [μM])[b]	Toxicity (IC$_{50}$ [μM])[c]	EC$_{50}$ [μM][d]	IC$_{50}$ [μM][e]
22		98 ± 4	31.8 ± 4.5	30	3.5 ± 0.3	15.6 ± 3.4
23		34 ± 5	31.8 ± 4.5	<1	ND[f]	ND
24		22 ± 1	21 ± 4	1	0.1 ± 0.0	0.2 ± 0.0
25		26 ± 1	ND	3	0.3 ± 0.1	0.7 ± 0.1
26		66 ± 3	12.3 ± 2.2	10	0.9 ± 0.1	2.3 ± 0.7
27		4.2 ± 0.44	0.99 ± 0.1	10	0.8 ± 0.2	3.2 ± 1.2

(Continued)

Table 1   Continued

Compound	Chemical structure	Result for compound[a]:				
		DENV-2 (IC$_{50}$ [μM])[b]	DENV-3 (IC$_{50}$ [μM])[b]	Toxicity (IC$_{50}$ [μM])[c]	FC$_{50}$ [μM][d]	IC$_{50}$ [μM][e]
28		10% inhibit-ion at 50 μM	NI[g]	30	2.5±0.1	9.3±2.5
29		3.6±0.11	9.1±1.02	3	>3	>3

[a]Values are indicated as means ± standard deviations from 3 independent experiments performed in triplicate.
[b]Inhibition of isolated proteases determined by fluorometric enzyme assays with an AMC-derived substrate.
[c]Concentration at which no influence on cellular metabolism was observed.
[d]Antiviral activity, inhibition of viral replication.
[e]Biochemical inhibition of PR in cell culture.
[f]ND, not done.
[g]NI, no inhibition at 50 μM.
Note: Adapted from Wu, H., Bock, S., Snitko, M., et al., 2015. Novel dengue virus NS2B/NS3 protease inhibitors. Antimicrob. Agents Chemother. 59, 1100–1109.

Sigma Aldrich (see "Relevant Website section") using Autodock 4. Three best compounds were selected namely paromomycin sulphate, ouabain and ivermectin displaying ΔG values between − 11.5 and − 9.5 kcal/mol. These compounds were found to interact with Arg409 and Tyr410. These compounds were then further tested experimentally using numerous *in vitro* approach from enzymatic to cell-based assay to rule out all non-specific inhibition of NS3 helicase. They proved that ivermectin behaves like uncompetitive helicase inhibitor which only binds to protein/RNA and blocks the enzymatic activity. However, the results from cell-based assay is not able to exclude the possibility that ivermectin exerts its antiviral activity on DENV *via* other mechanism (Mastrangelo *et al.*, 2012).

NS4

NS4A and NS4B are integral membrane proteins which play multiple roles in viral replication and virus-host interaction (Zou *et al.*, 2015). To date, only one *in silico*-based drug discovery campaign on NS4B was performed. Although Paul and co-workers proposed that three of the seven docked bioactive phytochemical compounds on the NS4B protein models of DENV1-4, i.e., (-)-catechin, epicatechin and DL-catechin, have the potential to be developed into effective anti-dengue drugs on DENV-1,2 and 4, however, it is unclear how the authors came to this conclusion as the predicted binding energies of these compounds were modest (< − 6 kcal/mol) and they were not validated experimentally (Paul *et al.*, 2016).

NS5

NS5 is the largest and most conserved protein in the dengue genome. It contains two functional domains, i.e., the RNA methyltransferase (MTase) domain at its *N*-terminus and the RNA-dependent RNA-polymerase (RdRp) domain at its *C*-terminus. MTase is highly important for mRNA stability, protein synthesis and viral replication as it is involved in the last two steps of mRNA capping process, i.e., transferring a methyl group from S-adenosyl-L-methionine (SAM) onto the N7 position of guanine-N7 methyltransferase (cap guanine) and to the 2′O position of the first nucleotide following the cap guanine (nucleoside-2′-methyltransferase), generating S-adenosyl-L-homocysteine (SAH) as the by-product. On the other hand, RdRp domain is involved in the generation of both minus and plus RNA strands, thus its role in viral RNA replication. Recently, Ahmad Jamil and co-workers have proposed based on their protein-protein docking results with HADDOCK that NS5 may also interact with the host protein SIAH2 which would then binds to STAT2 protein and results in the ubiquitination of the host proteins involved in IFN-mediated antiviral effect (Aslam *et al.*, 2015). This, however, remains to be confirmed by wet-lab experiments.

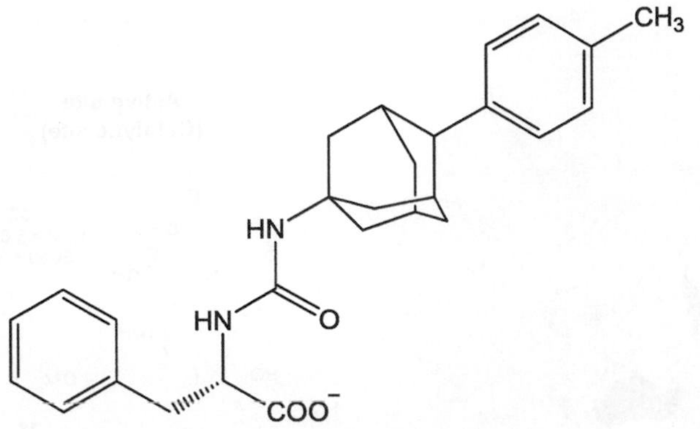

33
$IC_{50} = 60\ \mu M$ (SAM)

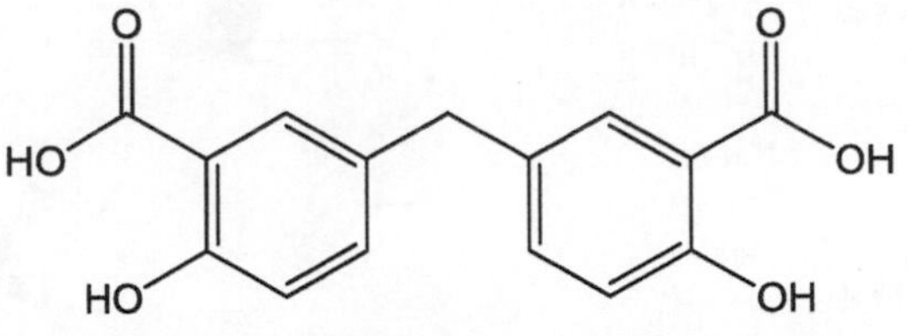

35
$IC_{50} = 9.5\ \mu M$ (SAM)

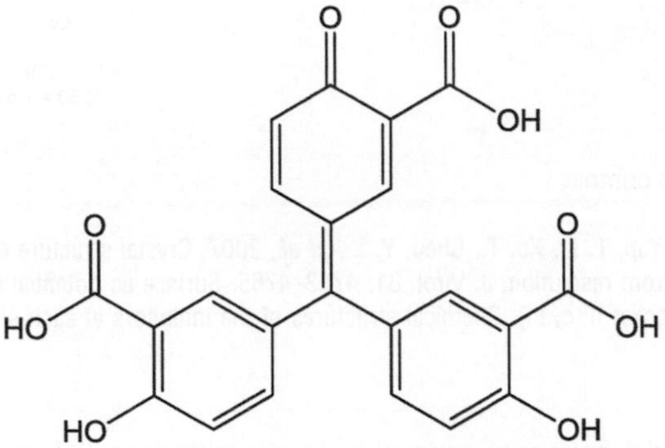

34
$IC_{50} = 2.3\ \mu M$ (RNA)
$= 127\ \mu M$ (SAM)

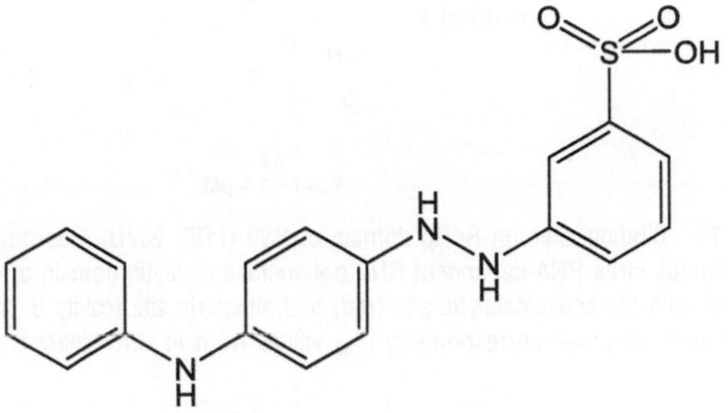

36
$IC_{50} = 7.1$ mM (RNA)

Fig. 10 Chemical structures of the inhibitors of NS5 (MTase domain) with their corresponding IC_{50} values from *in vitro* bioassays.

In the past decade, various research groups have attempted to find inhibitors of MTase, targeting either the S-adenosylmethionine (AdoMet/SAM) or the RNA cap site (GTP site), using a combination of computational and experimental techniques. Luzhkov *et al.* (2007) performed a high-throughput based virtual screening from 2.1 million commercially available compounds using 2D similarity searching, pharmacophore filtering based on the structure of SAH, and docked onto the SAM site of the NS5MTaseDV (dengue virus mRNA cap (nucleoside-2′O)-methyltransferase) with GOLD docking software (Luzhkov *et al.*, 2007). The 15 top-ranked compounds were then tested with bioassay test on recombinant MTase in competition with the RNA substrate. A novel inhibitor scaffold, (**33**) with IC_{50} value of 60 μM was identified from this approach (**Fig. 10**). Interestingly, investigation into the docked complex between (**33**) and the SAM site of MTase revealed that (**33**) did not form important polar interactions with Asp79, Trp87, Gly106, Glu111 and Asp131 at the binding site as SAH. Rather, the efficient binding of (**33**) is due to its good complementary fit to the target site. Similarly, Milani *et al.* successfully identified a non-specific inhibitor, ATA, (**34**) with IC_{50}=2.3 μM (RNA cap site); 127 μM (SAM site) from *in vitro* assay of the top three ranked *in silico* docked compounds from 1280 commercially available compounds in the LOPAC library with AutoDock4 . Another successful example is by Podvinec *et al.* (2009) who performed a multistage docking of more than 5 million commercially available compounds against the two binding sites of MTase with Glide, followed by experimental verification of 263 best compounds with MTase enzyme inhibition assay (Podvinec *et al.*, 2010). Four inhibitors with IC_{50} of < 10 μM in *in vitro* assay were successfully identified from this work, although only 2 of the four compounds were found later to be genuine, non-aggregating, low micromolar inhibitors (compounds (**35**) and (**36**), **Fig. 10**).

Recently, Benmansour *et al.* (2016) attempted to use *in silico* docking to guide fragment linking of 3 of the 7 fragment hits bound close to SAM binding site (IC_{50} values range between 180 μM – 9 mM) identified from a 500 fragments library *via* thermal shift assay, fragment-based x-ray crystallography screening, and enzymatic assays (Benmansour *et al.*, 2017). Analogues with different linkers at different positions of the two fragment hits were designed using the Link Multiple Fragment Tools of MOE and docked with and without 3D-pharmacophore constraint using MOE Docking tool and Glide, respectively. As only amide and urea-

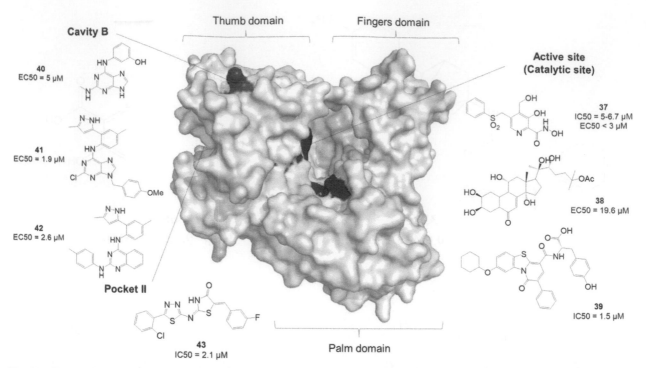

Fig. 11 Binding sites on RdRp domain of NS5 (PDB: 2J7U). Reproduced from Yap, T. L., Xu, T., Chen, Y. L., *et al.*, 2007. Crystal structure of the dengue virus RNA-dependent RNA polymerase catalytic domain at 1.85-angstrom resolution. J. Virol. 81, 4753–4765. Surface as potential drug targets with the active/catalytic site (red) and allosteric site (cavity B, magenta; pocket II, cyan). Chemical structures of the inhibitors at each site are shown with their corresponding IC_{50} values from *in vitro* bioassays.

based linker were able to maintain the correct orientation of the initial fragments, various analogues with these linkers were synthesized and tested. Ultimately, this led to a novel series of non-nucleoside inhibitors (N-phenyl-[(phenylcarbamoyl) amino] benzene-1-sulfonamide and phenyl [(phenylcarbamoyl) amino]benzene-1-sulfonate derivatives) with a 10–100-fold stronger inhibition of 2′-OMTase activity compared to the initial fragments ($IC_{50}=91$–452 μM). Their activities in the virus inhibition assay, however, remain uninspiring, presumably due to intrinsic low activity *ex vivo* or their poor ability to cross membrane. Other potential inhibitors of MTase that have been reported include cyclic peptides CTWYC and [Tyr123] human Prepro Endothelin (110 – 130) (SAM site), cyclic peptides CYEFC and human urotensin II (RNA-cap site) (Tambunan *et al.*, 2014; Idrus *et al.*, 2012), phytochemical compounds (isoborreverine, diplacone, styracifolin B, neosilyhermin A, and 8β-[4-hydroxy-5-(5-hydro-xytigloyloxy)tigloyl]-santamarin), SAH analogues (e.g., SAH-M331, SAH-M2696, SAH-M1356) (Tambunan *et al.*, 2017; Singh *et al.*, 2016)and ribavirin analogues (Sivakumar and Sivaraman, 2011). These ligands, however, were identified solely by *in silico* docking and molecular dynamics simulations, and thus further validation by *in vitro* assays is warranted.

While MTase domain remains the mainstream target for the inhibition of NS5 protein for the past decade, RdRp domain is becoming more popular in recent years. According to Yap *et al.* (2007), RdRp domain can be divided into three key subdomains, i.e., fingers, thumb and palm domains, stabilised by the NLS region, with loops L1, L2 and L3, linker α21-α22 and the priming loop encircling the catalytic active site (GTP site) and shaping the template tunnel (**Fig. 11**).

To date, most inhibitors of the RdRp domain of NS5 focus on either the active catalytic site or the allosteric sites in the thumbs domain. To illustrate, a highly specific, pyridoxine-derived small molecule inhibitor, (**37**) (DMB220) ($IC_{50}=5$–6.7 μM in enzymatic assay, $EC_{50} <3$ μM in antiviral cell-based assay) was designed as an active-site metal ion chelator to chelate divalent metal ions in the catalytic site of DENV RdRp. Docking studies with AutoDock Vina suggest that it interacts with active site residue Asp533, Asp663 and Asp664, with its sulfoxide oxygen and hydroxyl groups on the pyrimidine ring coordinates with both Mg ions at the active site (Xu *et al.*, 2015). Similarly, Cheng *et al.* (2016) reported a new and potent, highly selective antiviral compound, (**38**) (zoanthone A, $EC_{50}=19.6$ μM, $CC_{50}/EC_{50}=36.7$), isolated from ethanolic extract of plant *Zoanthus spp* (Cheng *et al.*, 2016). (**38**) formed three hydrogen bonds between C-6=O and charged NH residue of Arg729, OH-2 and backbone NH of Trp795, as well as OH-20 and NH at imidazole side chain of His798 of the NS5 RdRp tunnel, suggesting that the carbonyl group at C-6 and hydroxyl group at C-2 in ecdysone skeleton is essential for their bioactivities, in agreement with the SAR results of the ecdysone analogues performed. On the other hand, Milani and co-workers found that the top two (out of the 203) docked compounds on the protein active site of DENV-3 RdRp (Tarantino *et al.*, 2016) (PDB 2J7U) (Yap *et al.*, 2007) with AutoDock 4.2, the pyridobenzothiazole compound, HeE1-2Tyr, (**39**), was found to be able to inhibit Dengue RdRps' activity (IC_{50} DENV3 RdRp= 1.5 μM) and showed antiviral activity in cell culture against all four DENV serotypes (IC_{50} 6.8–15 μM). Other potential inhibitors of RdRp domain targeting the active site include plant-derived secondary metabolites (i.e., dimethylisoborreverine, drummondin

D, flinderole B, and pungiolide A), quercetin derivatives (i.e., quercetin 3-(6"-(*E*)-p-coumaroylsophoroside)-7-rhamnoside) and fragment-derived inhibitor (i.e., [2-(4-carbamoylpiperidin-1-yl)-2-oxoethyl]8-(1,3-benzothiazol-2-yl)naphthalene-1-carboxylate) (Yap *et al.*, 2007; Powers and Setzer, 2016; Anusuya *et al.*, 2016; Anusuya and Gromiha, 2016).

Apart from targeting the active site, various groups have also come up with inhibitors targeting the allosteric sites of NS5 RdRp. For example, Vincetti *et al.* (2015) performed virtual screening on the cavity B of DENV-2 NS5 RdRp (Leu328, Lys330, Trp859, Ile863) from a library of about 3000 known tyrosine protein kinase, Src active scaffolds (ChEMBL, BindingDB databases) and 10,000 virtual synthetically accessible compounds designed in house using the SmiLib v2.0 with both Glide and AutoDock Vina and found that purine derivatives were able to inhibit DEN-2 replication in virus cell-based assay (EC_{50}: 5–20 µM) while (**40**) also inhibit NS3-NS5 interaction (33% inhibition at 50 µM concentration), presumably due to the hydrophobic contacts and cation-pi interactions between purine and the side chain of Lys330. Similar observation was made by Venkatesham *et al.* (2017) for their purine lead compound, (**41**) and quinazoline lead compound, (**42**) with EC_{50} of 1.9 µM and 2.6 µM, respectively, although the reported binding modes varied slightly from Vincetti's, presumably due to difference in type of docking programme used. In a separate study, the most potent 4-thiazolidinone analogue, (**43**) was found to bind to pocket-II of the thumb domain *via* hydrophobic interactions with Ala776, Met809, Cys780, Ser785, Trp833, Thr880 and Tyr882, hydrogen bond interaction with backbone of Pro884, and electrostatic interaction with amide side chain of Asn777 of DENV-2 NS5 model, as predicted by molecular docking and confirmed by the fluorescence quenching assay (Manvar *et al.*, 2016). On the other hand, 39 non-nucleotide compounds, consisting of natural compounds and NITD1/2/29 analogues, were predicted *in silico* to bind strongly to a binding site at the RNA template tunnel (e.g., Arg737, Thr413, Met343 in DENV-3) (Galiano *et al.*, 2016).

Discussion and Future Direction

Progress in structural biology has successfully elucidated the structures of various proteins of dengue which certainly has contributed to vast efforts in computer-aided drug discovery of many potential anti-viral dengue inhibitors in the last ten years. Many studies have focused on the DENV E protein due to the fact that multiple of this protein cover most of the surface area of the viral particle. Furthermore, the knowledge of its conformational changes as well as well-defined crystal structures in the fusion event have created several binding site targets for potential DENV entry inhibitors such as β-OG pocket (the hydrophobic pocket), stem region and the domain III (Modis *et al.*, 2003, 2004).

DENV E protein has a key role in viral entry to the cells. It provides attachment through receptor interaction and subsequent endosomal fusion. Inhibiting the entry of the dengue virus to the cell thereby avoiding the infection is an attractive way to develop potent and specific dengue antivirals. These molecules would exert their effects without having to enter the cells, thus not subjected to strict structural and chemical constraints and may potentially limits the immune system hyperactivation that could lead to severe dengue (De La Guardia and Lleonart, 2014).

Perhaps a different approach to target the DENV E is through preventing it from establishing contacts with other proteins of the virus or the host cell for viral adsorption (Perera-Lecoin *et al.*, 2013). The discovery of some large molecular weight polysaccharides such as curdlan sulphate (Ichiyama *et al.*, 2013) and 3-O-sulfated GlcA (Hidari *et al.*, 2012) that were able to inhibit virus entry pointed to this possibility. Docking simulations with the active compounds predicted their binding to sites in which DENV E interacts with the host receptor such as the glycosaminoglycan receptors. A similar approach using a peptide that mimics the ectodomain of the DENV M protein (Panya *et al.*, 2014) also suggested the ability of the peptide inhibitor MLH40 to disrupt protein-protein interaction as predicted by their docking experiment. To date, no small molecules (m.w. < 500), were reported as hit compounds targeting these protein-protein "contact" sites of the E protein and thus, there is an immense opportunity to venture on finding small molecules targeting these receptor binding sites on DENV E.

Most of the entry inhibitors are peptidic compounds. Similarly, this class of compounds has also been considered as DENV protease inhibitors. Although the peptidic or peptidomimetic compounds are able prevent fusion to take place or inhibit DENV protease in low micromolar concentration, they do not possess drug-like structure. Thus, they will be likely to encounter physicochemical stability as well as pharmacokinetic problems during further stage of drug development. It is thus not surprising that, currently, no peptide inhibitor has been clinically used as a dengue antiviral agent. However, the knowledge of how these peptide inhibitors bind to DENV drug targets can be applied to derive a model with certain pharmacophoric features which in turn can be used in designing small molecule inhibitors (Gao *et al.*, 2010; Steuer *et al.*, 2011).

Other proteins such as C, NS2B-NS3 protease, NS3helicase, NS4 and NS5 are also feasible targets to look into in the screening for antiviral inhibitors. However, lack of crystal structure has hampered the discovery of potential binders to the capsid (C). High resolution crystal structures with well-defined binding sites are very much preferable in conducting molecular docking studies, the fact of which is true to the case of DENV NS2B-NS3 protease which has no doubt been the most favourite target for discovery of DENV antiviral agent as reviewed above.

NS2B-NS3pro is a chymotrypsin-like protease that has a catalytic triad formed by His51-Asp75-Ser135, which is essential for its substrate cleavage activity. In addition to the catalytic triad, Gly151 and Gly153 are also important residues as they participate in the formation of the oxyanion hole (along with Ser135) to stabilize the tetrahedral intermediate. This active site of the protease is flat and it would require a substantial conformational change in NS2B to enable the inhibitor to bind, thus, represent a major obstacle for the inhibitor to bind (Aguilera-Pesantes *et al.*, 2017). However, this limitation has not stalled the progress in searching for potential inhibitors as many researchers have also considered the inhibitors that target allosteric binding sites. In fact, a review by Leonel *et al.* (2018) showed that about 3,384,268 molecules including nitro, catechol, halogenated and quarternary compounds have been evaluated for the NS2B-NS3pro inhibition activity. However, none of them has entered clinical studies presumably that their toxicity, pharmacokinetic and pharmacodynamic (*absorption, distribution, metabolism, and excretion* and toxicity: ADMET) properties have yet to be characterised.

Most of the earlier researchers attempted to discover peptidic inhibitors targeting the active site, based on their understanding of cleavage activities of DENV polyprotein by NS2B-NS3pro. The cleavage sites preferable by this enzyme usually occur after two basic amino acid residues (Lys-Arg, Arg-Arg or Arg-Lys) or occasionally after Gln-Arg at the P1 and P2 positions. However, the host serine protease such as furin also recognises the two basic amino acid residues at P1 and P2 positions, thus, the selectivity and toxicity of the potential inhibitors might represent significant issues during the development stage. This limitation thus must be taken into account during the development of DENV NS2-NS3pro inhibitors. Considering other targets for DENV virus, which do not have any resemblance with the host proteins such as that displayed by DENV NS5 RNA-dependent RNA polymerase (RdRp) would be a good alternative as inferred from previous knowledge of antiviral agents that are now in clinical trials. This enzyme plays a critical role in viral replication by forming part of a multimeric complex. As there is no equivalent to flavivirus RdRp in the human host cells, DENV NS5 inhibitors are most likely to have little or no toxicity issues.

However, this fact is not true to the DENV NS5 inhibitors under current development. Although a lot of researches are ongoing in the search for inhibitors of NS5, in particular the RdRp protein, none of these potential drug leads has actually reaches clinical trial. To illustrate, the nucleoside analogue, NITD008, which showed significant reduction in DENV 1–4 replication in *in vitro* studies, appeared to be highly toxic in mice (Yin *et al.*, 2009). Similarly, various non-nucleoside inhibitors were also found to be either toxic in animal model or having poor inhibition potency (El Sahili and Lescar, 2017). The present drug for Hepatitis C virus (HCV), e.g., balapiravir, which are supposed to bind to RdRp protein of dengue (as both dengue and HCV shares similar architecture of RdRp), is found to be ineffective against the dengue RdRp protein (Nguyen *et al.*, 2013). These suggest that the search of novel inhibitors of RdRp that are potent and less toxic is highly essential. As this protein is highly druggable, with many potential druggable sites, including the active site and various allosteric sites, and with multiple crystal structures available, RdRp NS5 still definitely is an attractive target for *in silico*-guided design and discovery of novel dengue antiviral agents.

The review has highlighted many case studies which yield many potent compounds that could be developed further as dengue antiviral agents. However, it is worth noted that docking alone might not be sufficient to create molecules with high potential as dengue antiviral agent. One should elucidate further the pharmacophoric features of the active compounds or thorough mechanism of action by molecular dynamics simulation or a hybrid quantum/molecular mechanics (QM/MM) method before proceeding to lead optimisation. Multi-step *in silico* approach is valuable for optimisation of hit compounds discovered by virtual screening or molecular docking. Pharmacophore modelling, 3D quantitative structure-activity relationship (QSAR), fragment and scaffold hopping could be used further to optimise the hits reported in the literature for inhibitors with better activity. As demonstrated by Deng *et al.* (2012), small molecule-based scaffold hopping was able to optimise compound *30* (**Fig. 9**) identified from virtual screening using docking (verified active against NS2B-NS3pro with IC$_{50}$ = 13.12 ± 1.03 μM) towards to the discovery of 17 novel NS2B-NS3pro inhibitors with IC$_{50}$ values of 7.46 ± 1.15 to 48.59 ± 3.46 μM. In addition, the other future direction that should be considered is the evaluation of ADMET of these already discovered potential inhibitors. *In silico* approaches for ADMET have reached maturity and can be utilised, albeit, must be eventually validated by *in vitro* or *in vivo* experiments.

Taking novel compounds either new peptidic or small molecules from research to clinic is a daunting task and take a long time and resources. Drug repurposing has been considered by many researchers as it can significantly reduce the cost and development time as these off-patent, already marketed drugs, have demonstrated *safety* in humans and thus negates the need for Phase I clinical trials (Oprea *et al.*, 2011). Many researchers have conducted virtual screening as the starting point for drug repurposing for dengue inhibitors. Using *in silico* docking to explore the single-strand RNA access site within WNV helicase, ivermectin, a broad spectrum antiparasitic drug, was identified as potential inhibitor of NS3 helicase (Milani *et al.*, 2009). Ivermectin displayed uncompetitive inhibition of flaviviral helicase unwinding activity in biochemical assays in the upper nanomolar range for WNV and DENV but did not affect the ATPase activity of the NS$_3$ helicase domain. In cell culture, ivermectin caused virus titer reduction with an EC$_{50}$ of 0.7 μM for DENV and 4 μM for WNV (Mastrangelo *et al.*, 2012). Clinical trial involving ivermectin sponsored by Mahidol University and The Thailand government (clinical trial identifier: NCT02045069) is underway although the results on the clinical safety and efficacy have yet to be published as far as we are aware. Ivermectin is a natural product isolated from bacteria. The structure is rather big (m.w. = 875.10 g/mol), therefore might pose problem during absorption. Structure optimisation using either structure-based or ligand-based design could be further carried out to yield analogues with more desirable properties. Moreover, ivermectin is commercially used as a topical preparation for parasite, and thus its administration by oral route deserves to be studied more carefully. Ivermectin is just one example of potential drug for anti-dengue discovered *via* drug repurposing. Perhaps, more rigorous *in silico* drug repurposing would be able to discover other already marketed or off-patent drugs as clinical dengue antiviral agents.

Concluding Remark

Over the last decade, significant number of researches had been reported using computational docking approach in dengue drug discovery. As discussed earlier, either at the preliminary stage *via* high-throughput screening to confine the search from huge number of compound databases or to further predict the potential interaction from the selected hit, molecular docking no doubt aids in identifying potential hits. Nevertheless, it is also important to note that the integration of other computational approaches such dynamics study, QM/MM and QSAR will serve to enhance the chances of the elucidation of credible potential hits.

Acknowledgement

Authors acknowledge grant no 1001/PKIMIA/855006 that fund the work related to dengue in Universiti Sains Malaysia.

See also: Biomolecular Structures: Prediction, Identification and Analyses. Comparative Epigenomics. Computational Protein Engineering Approaches for Effective Design of New Molecules. Natural Language Processing Approaches in Bioinformatics. Structure-Based Design of Peptide Inhibitors for Protein Arginine Deiminase Type IV (PAD4). Structure-Based Drug Design Workflow. Study of The Variability of The Native Protein Structure

---

References

Aguilera-Pesantes, D., Robayo, L.E., Mendez, P.E., *et al.*, 2017. Discovering key residues of dengue virus NS2b-NS3-protease: New binding sites for antiviral inhibitors design. Biochem. Biophys. Res. Commun. 492, 631–642.

Akey, D.L., Brown, W.C., Dutta, S., *et al.*, 2014. Flavivirus NS1 structures reveal surfaces for associations with membranes and the immune system. Science 343, 881–885.

Aleshin, A., Shiryaev, S., Strongin, A., Liddington, R., 2007. Structural evidence for regulation and specificity of flaviviral proteases and evolution of the Flaviviridae fold. Protein Sci. 16, 795–806.

Allonso, D., Andrade, I.S., Conde, J.N., *et al.*, 2015. Dengue virus NS1 protein modulates cellular energy metabolism by increasing glyceraldehyde-3-phosphate dehydrogenase activity. J. Virol. 89, 11871–11883.

Anusuya, S., Gromiha, M.M., 2016. Quercetin derivatives as non-nucleoside inhibitors for dengue polymerase: Molecular docking, molecular dynamics simulation, and binding free energy calculation. J. Biomol. Struct. Dyn. 1–15.

Anusuya, S., Velmurugan, D., Gromiha, M.M., 2016. Identification of dengue viral RNA-dependent RNA polymerase inhibitor using computational fragment-based approaches and molecular dynamics study. J. Biomol. Struct. Dyn. 34, 1512–1532.

Arias, C., Preugschat, F., Strauss, J., 1993. Dengue 2 virus NS2B and NS3 form a stable complex that can cleave NS3 within the helicase domain. Virology 193, 888–899.

Aslam, B., Ahmad, J., Ali, A., *et al.*, 2015. Structural modeling and analysis of dengue-mediated inhibition of interferon signaling pathway. Genet. Mol. Res. 14, 4215–4237.

Barbato, G., Cicero, D.O., Nardi, M.C., *et al.*, 1999. The solution structure of the N-terminal proteinase domain of the hepatitis C virus (HCV) NS3 protein provides new insights into its activation and catalytic mechanism. J. Mol. Biol. 289, 371–384.

Basavannacharya, C., Vasudevan, S.G., 2014. Suramin inhibits helicase activity of NS3 protein of dengue virus in a fluorescence-based high throughput assay format. Biochem. Biophys. Res. Commun. 453, 539–544.

Behnam, M.A.M., Nitsche, C., Boldescu, V., Klein, C.D., 2016. The medicinal chemistry of dengue virus. J. Med. Chem. 59, 5622–5649.

Benmansour, F., Trist, I., Coutard, B., *et al.*, 2017. Discovery of novel dengue virus NS5 methyltransferase non-nucleoside inhibitors by fragment-based drug design. Eur. J. Med. Chem. 125, 865–880.

Berman, H., Henrick, K., Nakamura, H., 2003. Announcing the worldwide Protein Data Bank. Nat. Struct. Biol. 10, 980.

Bhatt, S., Gething, P.W., Brady, O.J., *et al.*, 2013. The global distribution and burden of dengue. Nature 496, 504–507.

Brinkworth, R.I., Fairlie, D.P., Leung, D., Young, P.R., 1999. Homology model of the dengue 2 virus NS3 protease: Putative interactions with both substrate and NS2B cofactor. J. Gen. Virol. 80 (Pt 5), 1167–1177.

Byk, L.A., Gamarnik, A.V., 2016. Properties and functions of the dengue virus capsid protein. Annu. Rev. Virol. 3, 263–281.

Byrd, C.M., Dai, D., Grosenbach, D.W., *et al.*, 2013. A novel inhibitor of dengue virus replication that targets the capsid protein. Antimicrob. Agents Chemother. 57, 15–25.

Carvalho, F.A., Carneiro, F.A., Martins, I.C., *et al.*, 2012. Dengue virus capsid protein binding to hepatic lipid droplets (LD) is potassium ion dependent and is mediated by LD surface proteins. J. Virol. 86, 2096–2108.

Chambers, T., Nestorowicz, A., Amberg, S., Rice, C., 1993. Mutagenesis of the yellow fever virus NS2B protein: Effects on proteolytic processing, NS2B-NS3complex formation, and viral replication. J. Virol. 67, 6797–6807.

Chambers, T.J., Weir, R.C., Grakoui, A., *et al.*, 1990. Evidence that the N-terminal domain of nonstructural protein NS3 from yellow fever virus is a serine protease responsible for site-specific cleavages in the viral polyprotein. Proc. Natl. Acad. Sci. USA 87, 8898–8902.

Chandramouli, S., Joseph, J.S., Daudenarde, S., *et al.*, 2010. Serotype-specific structural differences in the protease-cofactor complexes of the dengue virus family. J. Virol. 84, 3059–3067.

Chanprapaph, S., Saparpakorn, P., Sangma, C., *et al.*, 2005. Competitive inhibition of the dengue virus NS3 serine protease by synthetic peptides representing polyprotein cleavage sites. Biochem. Biophys. Res. Commun. 330, 1237–1246.

Cheng, Y.B., Lee, J.C., Lo, I.W., *et al.*, 2016. Ecdysones from Zoanthus spp. with inhibitory activity against dengue virus 2. Bioorg. Med. Chem. Lett. 26, 2344–2348.

Deng, J., Li, N., Liu, H., *et al.*, 2012. Discovery of novel small molecule inhibitors of dengue viral NS2B-NS3 protease using virtual screening and scaffold hopping. J. Med. Chem. 55, 6278–6293.

Erbel, P., Schiering, N., D'arcy, A., *et al.*, 2006. Structural basis for the activation of flaviviral NS3 proteases from dengue and West Nile virus. Nat. Struct. Mol. Biol. 13, 372–373.

Faustino, A.F., Carvalho, F.A., Martins, I.C., *et al.*, 2014. Dengue virus capsid protein interacts specifically with very low-density lipoproteins. Nanomedicine 10, 247–255.

Faustino, A.F., Guerra, G.M., Huber, R.G., *et al.*, 2015. Understanding dengue virus capsid protein disordered N-Terminus and pep14-23-based inhibition. ACS Chem. Biol. 10, 517–526.

Frimayanti, N., Chee, C.F., Zain, S.M., Rahman, N.A., 2011. Design of new competitive dengue NS2B/NS3 protease inhibitors-a computational approach. Int. J. Mol. Sci. 12, 1089–1100.

Galiano, V., Garcia-Valtanen, P., Micol, V., Encinar, J.A., 2016. Looking for inhibitors of the dengue virus NS5 RNA-dependent RNA-polymerase using a molecular docking approach. Drug Des. Dev. Ther. 10, 3163–3181.

Gao, Y., Cui, T., Lam, Y., 2010. Synthesis and disulfide bond connectivity – Activity studies of a kalata B1-inspired cyclopeptide against dengue NS2B–NS3 protease. Bioorg. Med. Chem. 18, 1331–1336.

Gorbalenya, A.E., Donchenko, A.P., Koonin, E.V., Blinov, V.M., 1989. N-terminal domains of putative helicases of flavi- and pestiviruses may be serine proteases. Nucleic Acids Res. 17, 3889–3897.

De La Guardia, C., Lleonart, R., 2014. Progress in the identification of dengue virus entry/fusion inhibitors. BioMed. Res. Int. 2014, 13.

Halim, S.A., Khan, S., Khan, A., et al., 2017. Targeting dengue virus NS-3 helicase by ligand based pharmacophore modeling and structure based virtual screening. Front. Chem. 5, 88.

Halstead, S.B., 2014. Dengue antibody-dependent enhancement: Knowns and unknowns. Microbiol. Spectr. 2.

Harrison, S.C., 2008. Viral membrane fusion. Nat. Struct. Mol. Biol. 15, 690–698.

Heh, C.H., Othman, R., Buckle, M.J., et al., 2013. Rational discovery of dengue type 2 non-competitive inhibitors. Chem. Biol. Drug Des. 82, 1–11.

Hidari, K.I., Ikeda, K., Watanabe, I., et al., 2012. 3-O-sulfated glucuronide derivative as a potential anti-dengue virus agent. Biochem Biophys Res Commun 424, 573–578.

Ichiyama, K., Gopala Reddy, S.B., Zhang, L.F., et al., 2013. Sulfated polysaccharide, curdlan sulfate, efficiently prevents entry/fusion and restricts antibody-dependent enhancement of dengue virus infection in vitro: A possible candidate for clinical application. PLOS Negl. Trop. Dis. 7, e2188.

Idrus, S., Tambunan, U.S., Zubaidi, A.A., 2012. Designing cyclopentapeptide inhibitor as potential antiviral drug for dengue virus ns5 methyltransferase. Bioinformation 8, 348–352.

Jadav, S.S., Kaptein, S., Timiri, A., et al., 2015. Design, synthesis, optimization and antiviral activity of a class of hybrid dengue virus E protein inhibitors. Bioorg. Med. Chem. Lett. 25, 1747–1752.

Kampmann, T., Yennamalli, R., Campbell, P., et al., 2009. In silico screening of small molecule libraries using the dengue virus envelope E protein has identified compounds with antiviral activity against multiple flaviviruses. Antivir. Res. 84, 234–241.

Kee, L.Y., Kiat, T.S., Wahab, H.A., Yusof, R., Rahman, N.A., 2007. Nonsubstrate based inhibitors of Dengue virus serine protease: A molecular docking approach to study binding interactions between protease and inhibitors. Asia Pac. J. Mol. Biol. Biotechnol. 15, 53–59.

Khumthong, R., Angsuthanasombat, C., Panyim, S., Katzenmeier, G., 2002. In vitro determination of dengue virus type 2 NS2B-NS3 protease activity with fluorescent peptide substrates. J. Biochem. Mol. Biol. 35, 206–212.

Kim, J.L., Morgenstern, K.A., Lin, C., et al., 1996. Crystal structure of the hepatitis C virus NS3 protease domain complexed with a synthetic NS4A cofactor peptide. Cell 87, 343–355.

Knehans, T., Schuller, A., Doan, D.N., et al., 2011. Structure-guided fragment-based in silico drug design of dengue protease inhibitors. J. Comput. Aided Mol. Des. 25, 263–274.

Kozakov, D., Hall, D.R., Xia, B., et al., 2017. The ClusPro web server for protein-protein docking. Nat. Protoc. 12 (2), 255–278.

Kuhn, R.J., Zhang, W., Rossmann, M.G., et al., 2002. Structure of dengue virus: Implications for flavivirus organization, maturation, and fusion. Cell 108, 717–725.

Leal, E.S., Aucar, M.G., Gebhard, L.G., et al., 2017. Discovery of novel dengue virus entry inhibitors via a structure-based approach. Bioorg. Med. Chem. Lett. 27, 3851–3855.

Leonel, C.A., Lima, W.G., Dos Santos, M., et al., 2018. Pharmacophoric characteristics of dengue virus NS2B/NS3pro inhibitors: A systematic review of the most promising compounds. Arch. Virol. 163, 575–586.

Lescar, J., Luo, D., Xu, T., et al., 2008. Towards the design of antiviral inhibitors against flaviviruses: The case for the multifunctional NS3 protein from Dengue virus as a target. Antivir. Res. 80, 94–101.

Li, H., Clum, S., You, S., Ebner, K.E., Padmanabhan, R., 1999. The serine protease and RNA-stimulated nucleoside triphosphatase and RNA helicase functional domains of dengue virus type 2 NS3 converge within a region of 20 amino acids. J. Virol. 73, 3108–3116.

Li, Z., Khaliq, M., Zhou, Z., et al., 2008. Design, synthesis, and biological evaluation of antiviral agents targeting flavivirus envelope proteins. J. Med. Chem. 51, 4660–4671.

Luo, D., Wei, N., Doan, D.N., et al., 2010. Flexibility between the protease and helicase domains of the dengue virus NS3 protein conferred by the linker region and its functional implications. J. Biol. Chem. 285, 18817–18827.

Luo, D., Xu, T., Hunke, C., et al., 2008. Crystal structure of the NS3 protease-helicase from dengue virus. J. Virol. 82, 173–183.

Luzhkov, V.B., Selisko, B., Nordqvist, A., et al., 2007. Virtual screening and bioassay study of novel inhibitors for dengue virus mRNA cap (nucleoside-2'O)-methyltransferase. Bioorg. Med. Chem. 15, 7795–7802.

Manvar, D., Kucukguzel, I., Erensoy, G., et al., 2016. Discovery of conjugated thiazolidinone-thiadiazole scaffold as anti-dengue virus polymerase inhibitors. Biochem. Biophys. Res. Commun. 469, 743–747.

Martins, I.C., Gomes-Neto, F., Faustino, A.F., et al., 2012. The disordered N-terminal region of dengue virus capsid protein contains a lipid-droplet-binding motif. Biochem. J. 444, 405–415.

Mastrangelo, E., Pezzullo, M., De Burghgraeve, T., et al., 2012. Ivermectin is a potent inhibitor of flavivirus replication specifically targeting NS3 helicase activity: New prospects for an old drug. J. Antimicrob. Chemother. 67, 1884–1894.

Ma, L., Jones, C.T., Groesch, T.D., Kuhn, R.J., Post, C.B., 2004. Solution structure of dengue virus capsid protein reveals another fold. Proc. Natl. Acad. Sci. USA 101, 3414–3419.

Milani, M., Mastrangelo, E., Bollati, M., et al., 2009. Flaviviral methyltransferase/RNA interaction: Structural basis for enzyme inhibition. Antivir. Res. 83, 28–34.

Modis, Y., Ogata, S., Clements, D., Harrison, S.C., 2003. A ligand-binding pocket in the dengue virus envelope glycoprotein. Proc. Natl. Acad. Sci. USA 100, 6986–6991.

Modis, Y., Ogata, S., Clements, D., Harrison, S.C., 2004. Structure of the dengue virus envelope protein after membrane fusion. Nature 427, 313–319.

Morris, G.M., Goodsell, D.S., Halliday, R.S., et al., 1998. Automated docking using a Lamarckian genetic algorithm and an empirical binding free energy function. J. Comput. Chem. 19, 1639–1662.

Nguyen, N.M., Tran, C.N., Phung, L.K., et al., 2013. A randomized, double-blind placebo controlled trial of balapiravir, a polymerase inhibitor, in adult dengue patients. J. Infect. Dis. 207, 1442–1450.

Nguyet, M.N., Duong, T.H., Trung, V.T., et al., 2013. Host and viral features of human dengue cases shape the population of infected and infectious Aedes aegypti mosquitoes. Proc. Natl. Acad. Sci. USA 110, 9072–9077.

Noble, C.G., Seh, C.C., Chao, A.T., Shi, P.Y., 2012. Ligand-bound structures of the dengue virus protease reveal the active conformation. J. Virol. 86, 438–446.

Oprea, T.I., Bauman, J.E., Bologa, C.G., et al., 2011. Drug repurposing from an academic perspective. Drug Discov. Today Ther. Strat. 8, 61–69.

Panya, A., Bangphoomi, K., Choowongkomon, K., Yenchitsomanus, P.T., 2014. Peptide inhibitors against dengue virus infection. Chem. Biol. Drug Des. 84, 148–157.

Paul, A., Vibhuti, A., Raj, S., 2016. Molecular docking NS4B of DENV 1–4 with known bioactive phyto-chemicals. Bioinformation 12, 140–148.

Perera-Lecoin, M., Meertens, L., Carnec, X., Amara, A., 2013. Flavivirus entry receptors: An update. Viruses 6, 69–88.

Phong, W.Y., Moreland, N.J., Lim, S.P., et al., 2011. Dengue protease activity: The structural integrity and interaction of NS2B with NS3 protease and its potential as a drug target. Biosci. Rep. 31, 399–409.

Podvinec, M., Lim, S.P., Schmidt, T., et al., 2010. Novel inhibitors of dengue virus methyltransferase: Discovery by in vitro-driven virtual screening on a desktop computer grid. J. Med. Chem. 53, 1483–1495.

Powers, C.N., Setzer, W.N., 2016. An in-silico investigation of phytochemicals as antiviral agents against dengue fever. Comb. Chem. High Throughput Screen. 19, 516–536.

Prusis, P., Junaid, M., Petrovska, R., et al., 2013. Design and evaluation of substrate-based octapeptide and non substrate-based tetrapeptide inhibitors of dengue virus NS2B–NS3 proteases. Biochem. Biophys. Res. Commun. 434, 767–772.

Qamar, M.T., Mumtaz, A., Naseem, R., et al., 2014. Molecular docking based screening of plant flavonoids as Dengue NS1 inhibitors. Bioinformation 10, 460–465.

Rey, F.A., 2003. Dengue virus envelope glycoprotein structure: New insight into its interactions during viral entry. Proc. Natl. Acad. Sci. USA 100, 6899–6901.

El Sahili, A., Lescar, J., 2017. Dengue virus non-structural protein 5. Viruses 9.

Scaturro, P., Trist, I.M., Paul, D., et al., 2014. Characterization of the mode of action of a potent dengue virus capsid inhibitor. J. Virol. 88, 11540–11555.

Schüller, A., Yin, Z., Chia, C.B., et al., 2011. Tripeptide inhibitors of dengue and West Nile virus NS2B–NS3 protease. Antivir. Res. 92, 96–101.

Singh, J., Kumar, M., Mansuri, R., Sahoo, G.C., Deep, A., 2016. Inhibitor designing, virtual screening, and docking studies for methyltransferase: A potential target against dengue virus. J. Pharm. Bioallied Sci. 8, 188–194.

Sivakumar, D., Sivaraman, T., 2011. In silico designing and screening of lead compounds to NS5-methyltransferase of dengue viruses. Med Chem 7, 655–662.

Smit, J.M., Moesker, B., Rodenhuis-Zybert, I., Wilschut, J., 2011. Flavivirus cell entry and membrane fusion. Viruses 3, 160–171.

Steuer, C., Gege, C., Fischl, W., et al., 2011. Synthesis and biological evaluation of α-ketoamides as inhibitors of the Dengue virus protease with antiviral activity in cell-culture. Bioorg. Med. Chem. 19, 4067–4074.

Swarbrick, C.M.D., Basavannacharya, C., Chan, K.W.K., et al., 2017. NS3 helicase from dengue virus specifically recognizes viral RNA sequence to ensure optimal replication. Nucleic Acids Res. 45, 12904–12920.

Sweeney, N.L., Hanson, A.M., Mukherjee, S., et al., 2015. Benzothiazole and pyrrolone flavivirus inhibitors targeting the viral helicase. ACS Infect. Dis. 1, 140–148.

Tajima, S., Takasaki, T., Kurane, I., 2008. Characterization of Asn130-to-Ala mutant of dengue type 1 virus NS1 protein. Virus Genes 36, 323–329.

Tambunan, U.S.F., Nasution, M.A.F., Azhima, F., et al., 2017. Modification of S-Adenosyl-l-Homocysteine as inhibitor of nonstructural protein 5 methyltransferase dengue virus through molecular docking and molecular dynamics simulation. Drug Target Insights 11.1177392817701726.

Tambunan, U.S., Zahroh, H., Utomo, B.B., Parikesit, A.A., 2014. Screening of commercial cyclic peptide as inhibitor NS5 methyltransferase of dengue virus through molecular docking and molecular dynamics simulation. Bioinformation 10, 23–27.

Tan, S.K., Pippen, R., Yusof, R., et al., 2006. Inhibitory activity of cyclohexenyl chalcone derivatives and flavonoids of fingerroot, Boesenbergia rotunda (L.), towards dengue-2 virus NS3 protease. Bioorg. Med. Chem. Lett. 16, 3337–3340.

Tarantino, D., Cannalire, R., Mastrangelo, E., et al., 2016. Targeting flavivirus RNA dependent RNA polymerase through a pyridobenzothiazole inhibitor. Antivir. Res. 134, 226–235.

Thomsen, R., Christensen, M.H., 2006. MolDock: A new technique for high-accuracy molecular docking. J. Med. Chem. 49, 3315–3321.

Trott, O., Olson, A.J., 2010. AutoDock Vina: Improving the speed and accuracy of docking with a new scoring function, efficient optimization, and multithreading. J. Comput. Chem. 31, 455–461.

Utama, A., Shimizu, H., Morikawa, S., et al., 2000. Identification and characterization of the RNA helicase activity of Japanese encephalitis virus NS3 protein. FEBS Lett. 465, 74–78.

Vasilakis, N., Ooi, M., Rabaa, M., et al., 2013. The daemon in the forest-emergence of a new dengue serotype in SouthEast Asia. In: Proceedings of the International Conference on Dengue and Dengue Haemorrhagic Fever, Bangkok, Thailand.

Venkatesham, A., Saudi, M., Kaptein, S., et al., 2017. Aminopurine and aminoquinazoline scaffolds for development of potential dengue virus inhibitors. Eur. J. Med. Chem. 126, 101–109.

Vincetti, P., Caporuscio, F., Kaptein, S., et al., 2015. Discovery of multitarget antivirals acting on both the dengue Virus NS5-NS3 interaction and the host Src/Fyn kinases. J. Med. Chem. 58, 4964–4975.

Wang, Q.Y., Patel, S.J., Vangrevelinghe, E., et al., 2009. A small-molecule dengue virus entry inhibitor. Antimicrob. Agents Chemother. 53, 1823–1831.

Wu, H., Bock, S., Snitko, M., et al., 2015. Novel dengue virus NS2B/NS3 protease inhibitors. Antimicrob. Agents Chemother. 59, 1100–1109.

Xu, H.T., Colby-Germinario, S.P., Hassounah, S., et al., 2015. Identification of a pyridoxine-derived small-molecule inhibitor targeting dengue virus RNA-dependent RNA polymerase. Antimicrob. Agents Chemother. 60, 600–608.

Xu, T., Sampath, A., Chao, A., et al., 2005. Structure of the dengue virus helicase/nucleoside triphosphatase Catalytic domain at a resolution of 2.4 √Ö. J. Virol. 79, 10278–10288.

Yang, J.-M., Chen, Y.-F., Tu, Y.-Y., Yen, K.-R., Yang, Y.-L., 2007. Combinatorial computational approaches to identify tetracycline derivatives as flavivirus inhibitors. PLOS ONE 2, e428.

Yap, T.L., Xu, T., Chen, Y.L., et al., 2007. Crystal structure of the dengue virus RNA-dependent RNA polymerase catalytic domain at 1.85-angstrom resolution. J. Virol. 81, 4753–4765.

Yennamalli, R., Subbarao, N., Kampmann, T., et al., 2009. Identification of novel target sites and an inhibitor of the dengue virus E protein. J. Comput. Aided Mol. Des. 23, 333–341.

Yildiz, M., Ghosh, S., Bell, J.A., Sherman, W., Hardy, J.A., 2013. Allosteric inhibition of the NS2B-NS3 protease from dengue virus. ACS Chem. Biol. 8, 2744–2752.

Yin, Z., Chen, Y.L., Schul, W., et al., 2009. An adenosine nucleoside inhibitor of dengue virus. Proc. Natl. Acad. Sci. USA 106, 20435–20439.

Yin, Z., Patel, S.J., Wang, W.L., et al., 2006. Peptide inhibitors of dengue virus NS3 protease. Part 2: SAR study of tetrapeptide aldehyde inhibitors. Bioorg. Med. Chem. Lett. 16, 40–43.

Yotmanee, P., Rungrotmongkol, T., Wichapong, K., et al., 2015. Binding specificity of polypeptide substrates in NS2B/NS3pro serine protease of dengue virus type 2: A molecular dynamics study. J. Mol. Gr. Model. 60, 24–33.

Zhou, Z., Khaliq, M., Suk, J.E., et al., 2008. Antiviral compounds discovered by virtual screening of small-molecule libraries against dengue virus E protein. ACS Chem. Biol. 3, 765–775.

Zou, J., Xie, X., Wang, Q.Y., et al., 2015. Characterization of dengue virus NS4A and NS4B protein interaction. J. Virol. 89, 3455–3470.

Relevant Website

www.sigmaaldrich.com
Sigma-Aldrich.

Drug Repurposing and Multi-Target Therapies

Ammu P Kumar and Suryani Lukman, Khalifa University of Science and Technology, Abu Dhabi, United Arab Emirates
Minh N Nguyen, Agency for Science, Technology and Research, Singapore

Drug Repurposing: Polypharmacology, Benefits and Drawbacks

Drug repurposing is based on polypharmacology, a field of study related to design, discovery, synthesis, and use of pharmaceutical agents (drugs, small molecules, antibodies, stabilized peptides, natural products, etc.) that act on multiple targets (genes or gene products) or disease pathways. Complex diseases (such as neurodegenerative diseases and cancers) involve networks of multiple genes, hence necessitate multi-pharmacophores as a part of their therapeutic and system biology-based approaches. By specifically regulating multiple targets, more effective drugs can be developed through polypharmacology (Anighoro et al., 2014). In need of treatment for critical illnesses and neglected diseases, efforts to match old drugs, that are already known to be safe and/or approved by US Food and Drug Administration (FDA) for diseases are in ongoing demand.

Since pharmaceutical agents can interact with multiple targets, unintended interactions between drugs and off-targets could result in toxicities or side effects. Side effects arising from a particular drug have been serendipitously used to usher a new use, such as treating other conditions and diseases. For example, sildenafil, commercially known as Viagra, is a blockbuster drug used to treat male erectile dysfunction; Viagra's clinical effects on treating erectile dysfunction were observed when it was studied for treating hypertension (Reaume, 2011).

Drug repurposing can reduce healthcare costs, given how laborious, time-consuming, and costly *de novo* drug discovery projects have been. Drug-candidate molecules that have been shown as being safe, yet insufficiently effective for the intended target (Oprea et al., 2011), can be considered for other targets, hence possibly reducing the costs of clinical trial. The increasing amount and availability of public and open source databases, knowledge, algorithms, and servers, have encouraged more participants of drug repurposing projects.

Drug discovery efforts have resulted in discovery of new modes of actions for approved drugs. For example, Fasudil is a Rho-kinase inhibitor and vasodilator, which was repurposed to improve memory and treat several neurodegenerative disorders (Iorio et al., 2010), such as Alzheimer's disease. In addition, orphan, rare, and neglected diseases with limited fundings have benefited from drug discovery efforts. For example, closantel, a veterinary anthelmintic, was repurposed to inhibit the chitin metabolism of the filarial nematode *Onchocerca volvulus*, that causes a neglected tropical disease Onchocerciasis (river blindness) (Gloeckner et al., 2010). Drug repurposing has also been achieved through combining approved drugs (multidrug cocktails) in novel ways to synergistically treat diseases, including HIV infection, cancer, and *Mycobacterium tuberculosis* infection (Borisy et al., 2003).

While drug repurposing brings numerous benefits, there are associated drawbacks of such an effort. Our understandings of the pathways and mechanisms of many complex diseases remain incomplete (Reddy and Zhang, 2013), yet efforts for drug repurposing often require analyzing complete data. Public databases have increasingly provided enormous information that can facilitate drug repurposing, yet they are non-synchronized (Wiegers et al., 2009). According to Oprea et al. (2011), there is no systematic mechanism to obtain fundings to support drug repurposing projects hitherto, in comparison to *de novo* drug discovery projects. To address this challenge, drug discovery project leaders have sought limited fundings from private and/or non-for-profit organizations, such as the Bill & Melinda Gates Foundation, Howard Hughes Medical Institute, and Simons Foundation.

Databases and Computational Resources for Drug Repurposing

The process of a new drug development is costly and time-consuming, and therefore drug repurposing has emerged as a time-efficient and cost-effective strategy to discover new indications for already approved drugs (Fu et al., 2013). A number of available and searchable drug databases has been designed and developed for supporting drug repurposing studies such as PROMISCUOUS (von Eichborn et al., 2011), DRAR-CPI (Luo et al., 2011), e-Drug3D (Pihan et al., 2012), PharmDB (Lee et al., 2012), PharmDB-K (Lee et al., 2015), DrugPredict (Simon et al., 2012), DrugMap Central (Fu et al., 2013), DrugBank (Law et al., 2014), RE:fine drugs (Moosavinasab et al., 2016), Mantra 2.0 (Carrella et al., 2014), repoDB (Brown and Patel, 2017), RepurposeDB (Shameer et al., 2017), SIDER (Kuhn et al., 2016), SWEETLEAD (Novick et al., 2013), DeSigN (Lee et al., 2017), and Connectivity Map (Cmap) (Lamb, 2006).

PROMISCUOUS database (see "Revelant Websites section") contains comprehensive data of drug-target interaction, drug side effect, and protein-protein interaction data. PROMISCUOUS has been proven to be useful for drug repurposing by connecting structural similarity of drugs and their side effects to protein – protein interactions. In addition, the integrated network visualization tools of PROMISCUOUS allow researchers to explore and understand the analysis of the interplay between drugs and targets, as well as identify candidates for drug repurposing.

DRAR-CPI server (see "Revelant Websites section") uses the database of 254 active form from 166 drugs with known adverse drug reaction (ADR) and 385 pockets from 353 human protein targets for predicting drug repurposing potential via chemical-protein interactome (CPI). When users submit a drug molecule, the DRAR-CPI server computes the binding energies of this drug with all 385 protein pockets in the database using the DOCK program (Ewing *et al.*, 2001), and then generates its CPI profile. Based on this CPI profile, the server identifies the association scores between the drug and all 166 drugs in the database, and predicts off-target proteins that possibly interact with it. Recently, the DRAR-CPI has been upgraded to DPDR-CPI server (see "Revelant Websites section") with the larger database of 2515 drugs and 611 human protein targets (Luo *et al.*, 2016). The AutoDock Vina program (Trott and Olson, 2009) is used in the new server for docking of drug molecules with human protein targets to generate CPI profiles.

The e-Drug3D (see "Revelant Websites section") provides the annotated database of 3D structures from FDA approved drugs as well as commercial sub-structures (fragments) of drugs. This database of 3D structures of drug can be used for virtual screening applications, such as fragment-based drug design and drug repurposing. DrugPredict collects and identifies effect profiles and 3D structures of small molecule drugs (Simon *et al.*, 2012). Using docking calculations, DrugPredict determines interactions of each drug and non-target protein binding sites, which are used for new drug effect predictions. DrugMap Central collects multi-level drug data from various established databases, including drug targets, chemical structures, target-related signaling pathways, FDA and clinical trial information (Fu *et al.*, 2013). DrugMap Central provides online query tool and visualization-based search to support researchers for drug repurposing studies.

PharmDB is an integrated database of drug development, disease indications, associated proteins, and their known interactions (Lee *et al.*, 2012). The Shared Neighborhood Scoring algorithm is developed for PharmDB to identify new indications of known drugs, which can be used for predicting drug repurposing potential. Another database, PharmDB-K offers comprehensive information relating to Traditional Korean Medicine (TKM), associated drugs (compound), disease indication, and protein relationships (Lee *et al.*, 2015). In PharmDB-K, information is organized as a network with five kinds of nodes: TKMs, drugs, diseases, proteins, and side effects. The website also integrates diverse tools to explore TKM-disease, TKM-drug, drug-disease, drug-drug, drug-protein, drug-side effect, disease-protein, and protein-protein relationships by analyzing the network.

RE:fine drugs contains information on 916 drugs, 567 genes and 1770 diseases (Moosavinasab *et al.*, 2016). The database is constructed based on the Transitive Property of Equality between drug-gene and gene-disease pairs of information extracted from previously published datasets (Moosavinasab *et al.*, 2016). Users can explore the database using drug/gene/disease information and identify drug-disease candidates for repurposing. The results can also be sorted based on P-value, odds ratio, literature support, clinical trials, disease name and/or drug name.

Mantra 2.0 maintains information on drugs as a network, with drugs as nodes and edges highlighting communities of drugs sharing similar mode of action (Carrella *et al.*, 2014; Iorio *et al.*, 2010). The network is constructed by exploiting similarities in gene expression profiles following drug treatment (Carrella *et al.*, 2014). Mantra allows users to provide gene expression profiles before and after drug treatment in one or multiple cell types as input. These gene expression profiles are transformed into a drug node and integrated in the drug network, which allows users to inspect its mode of action and repurposing opportunities.

The databases such as repoDB, RepurposeDB, SIDER, SWEETLEAD and DrugBank also have various information on repurposed/approved drugs (see **Table 1**) that can be used as references for drug repurposing experiments. The repoDB also has information on failed drugs (Brown and Patel, 2017). Information on failed drugs can be useful as there are many drugs that are abandoned after clinical trials due the lack of efficacy for their primary indications, and which possess the same benefits of approved drugs (Novick *et al.*, 2013). SWEETLEAD (Novick *et al.*, 2013) is a highly curated database of chemical structures for the globally approved drugs. It is developed with the objective of providing well curated, high quality information of the known approved drugs for drug repurposing experiments. DrugBank is also known for its expertly curated data on drugs and is the referential drug data source for many well-known databases (Law *et al.*, 2014), such as PDB (Rose *et al.*, 2013), PubChem (NCBI Resource Coordinators, 2013), UniProt (UniProt Consortium, 2013), among others. DrugBank has detailed information on drugs (i.e., chemical, pharmacological and pharmaceutical) and drug targets (i.e., sequence, structure, and pathway) (Law *et al.*, 2014). The latest version of DrugBank (version 5.0.9) has information on 10,505 drugs.

Resources such DeSigN and Cmap have large collections of drug-induced signatures and they integrate computational tools that facilitate drug repositioning based on genomic screening (see Virtual Screening)(Lee *et al.*, 2017; Lamb, 2006). The details of the databases discussed here are detailed in **Table 1**.

Computational Tools for Drug Repurposing

Currently, there are two major structure-based categories for drug repurposing by using (i) ligands/compounds similarity and (ii) binding pocket similarity. Computational methods using 1D or 2D representations for compound structures are commonly used in ligand-based virtual screening because chemical molecules are typically represented by 1D fingerprints or 2D molecular formula (Schwartz *et al.*, 2013; Helguera *et al.*, 2008; Hong *et al.*, 2008). However, the 3D structural information of compounds and target proteins as well as their atomic interactions in the 3D space are not captured by 1D and 2D methods. Furthermore, although the 1D and 2D representations of chemical molecules are not similar, these molecules could share biological activities if their 3D shape are similar. Binding affinity between compounds and target proteins is governed by atomic interactions in the 3D space. Therefore, 3D methods have potential to overcome the limitations of 1D and 2D methods and enhance performance for ligand-based virtual screening. In the past, there have been efforts with some degree of success in developing computational methods to identify similarities between the 3D structures of compounds (Schuffenhauer *et al.*, 2000; Kombo *et al.*, 2013; Shin *et al.*, 2015). Recently, we have applied our CLICK algorithm (Nguyen and Madhusudhan, 2011), whose main strength emerges from its unique ability to carry out topology independent comparisons, for comparing 3D structures of compounds.

Table 1   Databases for drug repurposing[a]

Databases	Key features	Website
PROMISCOUS von Eichborn *et al.* (2011)	• Contains information on 25,000 drugs (including withdrawn and experimental drugs), their side effects and targets. • Users can explore the database based on drugs, their targets, side effects or, metabolic and signaling pathways.	http://bioinformatics.charite.de/promiscuous
DPDR-CPI Luo *et al.* (2016)	• Contains information on 2515 drugs. • Predicts off-targets and potential indications for the small molecule input from the user.	https://cpi.bio-x.cn/dpdr/
e-Drug3D Pihan *et al.* (2012)	• Contains ready to screen SD files of drugs and commercial drug fragments. • Contains information on 1852 molecular structures.	http://chemoinfo.ipmc.cnrs.fr/MOLDB/
DrugPredict Simon *et al.* (2012)	• Contains information on 100,000 small molecule compounds including 1200 approved drugs. • Users can explore the database based on drugs/any desired effects.	http://www.drugpredict.com/
PharmDB Lee *et al.* (2012)	• Contains information on 11,792 drugs, 38,057 proteins and 6607 diseases and their relationship.	http://www.i-pharm.org/
PharmDB-K Lee *et al.* (2015)	• Provides information on Traditional Korean Medicine (TKM). • Contains information on 262 TKMs, 7815 drugs, 3721 diseases, 32,373 proteins, and 1887 side effects.	http://pharmdb-k.org/
RE:fine drugs Moosavinasab *et al.* (2016)	• Contains information on 916 drugs, their target genes and associated diseases. • Users can explore the database based on drug, indication or gene symbol.	http://drug-repurposing.nationwidechildrens.org
Mantra 2.0 Carrella *et al.* (2014)	• Provides the users insights on mode of action of drugs by comparing drug-induced signatures. • Contains information on 1309 small molecules.	http://mantra.tigem.it./
repoDB Brown and Patel (2017)	• Contains information on 1571 drugs (including approved and failed drugs), their indications and clinical trial status. • Users can explore the database based on drug/disease information.	http://apps.chiragjpgroup.org/repoDB/
RepurposeDB Shameer *et al.* (2017)	• Contains information on 253 repurposed drugs and their indications. • Users can explore the database based on drug/disease information, side effects, drug targets or pathways. • Facilitates chemical similarity search for new compounds and sequence similarity search for new protein-drugs against RepurposeDB. • Allows drug repurposing investigators to report their results to the community.	http://repurposedb.dudleylab.org/
SIDER Kuhn *et al.* (2016)	• Contains information on 1430 drugs and their side effects. • Users can explore the database based on drugs/side effect information.	http://sideeffects.embl.de/
SWEETLEAD Novick *et al.* (2013)	• Contains accurate chemical structures of 4442 compounds (including approved drugs and non-toxic chemicals). • The database can be downloaded and used for virtual screening/drug repurposing campaigns.	https://simtk.org/home/sweetlead
DrugBank 5.0.9 Law *et al.* (2014)	• Contains information on 10,505 drugs (including 1733 approved small molecule drugs, 870 approved biotech drugs, 105 nutraceuticals and over 5025 experimental drugs). • Provides detailed information on drugs (i.e., chemical, pharmacological and pharmaceutical) and drug targets (i.e., sequence, structure, and pathway) information.	https://www.drugbank.ca/
DeSigN Lee *et al.* (2017)	• Contains information on cancer-associated gene expression profiles from 140 drugs. • Allows drug repositioning based on genomic screening.	http://design.cancerresearch.my/
Cmap Lamb (2006)	• Contains gene expression profiles from 5000 small molecule compounds. • Allows drug repositioning based on genomic screening.	https://www.broadinstitute.org/connectivity-map-cmap

[a]Some relevant databases for drug repurposing, their key features and websites are listed as of 9th November 2017. The table lists only databases having active websites.

It is well understood that drugs bind to their protein targets because of complementarity in shapes of ligands fitting into their binding pocket. However, the shape of a particular binding pocket on a target is possibly found in some other proteins, given the diversity of protein shapes in a cell. This will inevitably lead to the binding of the drug to other proteins (off-target proteins) possessing structurally similar binding pockets (John Fox *et al.*, 2016). Hence, the discovery of the off-target proteins of a drug can lead to further use of this drug for additional targets in disease treatment. Clearly, the discovery of the off-target proteins will rely on an accurate determination of similarity of binding pocket. A major effort towards developing tools to search for such similarities has been focused on local structural alignment approaches (Shulman-Peleg *et al.*, 2007; Konc and Janežič, 2010). One such effort is the CLICK method (Nguyen *et al.*, 2011) that performs 3D structural superposition on pairs of structures based on similarity of local structural packing, and thus is capable of aligning structures with dissimilar conformations or even molecular types (Nguyen and Verma, 2015; Nguyen *et al.*, 2017b). These unique properties make CLICK particularly ideal for comparing the similarity of binding pocket (Lukman *et al.*, 2017; Nguyen *et al.*, 2017a).

In addition, investigation of complex interactions between drugs and diseases is crucial for new drug-disease association discovery and drug repurposing (Yang *et al.*, 2014). However, it is difficult to identify the comprehensive interactions of drugs and diseases because of the polypharmacological profiles of drugs (Reddy and Zhang, 2013) and complex diseases induced by genes' collective abnormalities (Wu *et al.*, 2013). Disease-based computational methods have been developed to identify the interactions between drugs and diseases by using shared molecular pathology, associative indication transfer, and side effect similarity (Dudley *et al.*, 2011a,b). Recently, computational methods using pathway-based Bayesian inference (Pratanwanich and Lió, 2014), network propagation (Huang *et al.*, 2013), and network-based inference (Cheng *et al.*, 2012a,b) have been applied for investigating drug-disease interactions. In these methods, the network of drug – Target – Pathway – Gene – Disease is constructed from multi-level interactions of drugs and diseases integrated from known databases. Next step, the interaction scores of drugs and diseases are computed by evaluating effects of drugs on multiple targets and pathways (Yang *et al.*, 2014). The new potential repurposing of the existing drug is then determined from the network of drug targets and disease-related genes (Pratanwanich and Lió, 2014).

Virtual Screenings: Genomic Screenings, High-Throughput Screenings

Virtual screening can be defined as a set of computer methods that analyse compounds in large databases in order to identify a smaller number of them for biological testing (Sotriffer, 2011).Virtual high-throughput screening (vHTS) and genomic screening are two virtual screening techniques that can be employed for drug repurposing. vHTS is the computational analogue of *in vitro* high-throughput screening (HTS). vHTS involves screening of large compound libraries to identify compounds/ligands that can bind to the biological target of interest with high affinity (Shoichet, 2004). Using vHTS, large collections of known compounds can be screened to identify their applicability to treat a new disease.

There are many public databases that can be employed for vHTS (Cheng *et al.*, 2012a,b). For example, ZINC (zinc.docking.org) is a public database that contains over twenty million commercially available compounds in biologically relevant representations, that can be downloaded in ready-to-dock formats (Irwin *et al.*, 2012). It is also possible to download the database in fractions based on physical properties, purchasability, and vendors, among other attributes. In a previous study, we have employed vHTS of 'Drugs Now' subset (a subset of 10,639,555 compounds having drug-like properties such as adequate chemical stability, metabolic stability, minimal toxic effects and oral bioavailability Lipinski, 2000) from the ZINC database, for the identification of inhibitors of aberrant proteins, such as (1) Ras proteins that are implicated in diverse cancers and developmental diseases (Grant *et al.*, 2011), (2) protein tyrosine phosphatase 1B that is associated with diabetes, obesity, cancers, and neurodegenerative disorders (Kumar *et al.*, 2018). In these examples, the inhibitors act allosterically. Indeed, drug repurposing efforts will generally be more beneficial if the drug binding sites are allosteric rather than orthosteric (Nussinov and Tsai, 2012).

vHTS can be classified as structure-based and ligand-based approaches (**Fig. 1**). Structure-based screening is employed when the three-dimensional structure of a disease-associated target is known. When the target structure is unknown and its prediction is challenging, ligand-based screening is employed. The objective of both these approaches is the same, i.e., to select a smaller subset of compounds from larger libraries and rank them using some scoring criteria, to be further used for experimental testing of their biological activity.

Structure-based screening involves molecular docking of candidate ligands from the library into a protein (target) followed by applying a scoring function (Liang *et al.*, 2009; Deng *et al.*, 2004; Amari *et al.*, 2006) to estimate the likelihood that the ligand will bind to the protein (Kroemer, 2007; Wang *et al.*, 2000). Since the computational cost of the docking is directly proportional to the number of compounds, pre-filtering of large libraries is highly desirable (Radusky *et al.*, 2017). Candidate compounds from the libraries can be filtered based on their drug-like properties (Lipinski, 2000; Lipinski *et al.*, 2001). Target-specific filters can also be used for creating focused libraries (Gozalbes *et al.*, 2008; Sage *et al.*, 2011). For example, more recently Radusky*et al.* developed 'LigQ' server (see "Revelant Websites section") that can assist in various steps of virtual screening (Radusky *et al.*, 2017). The webserver can be employed in initial stages of virtual screening to identify potential binders for targets from large databases. Enriching compound libraries in these ways can greatly reduce the computational cost of subsequent docking. The target and ligand structures also need to be prepared before docking by assigning proper tautomeric, stereoisomeric, and protonation states, among others (Rapp *et al.*, 2009; ten Brink and Exner, 2010). After pre-processing of target and compound library, docking is performed.

Many docking programs are available to computationally model the ligand – Target interaction. Some examples of docking programs in vHTS are listed in **Table 2**. These docking programs generally involve a search algorithm that searches the conformational space to find docking poses and a scoring function to predict the affinity of the ligand with the target in that pose (Sliwoski *et al.*, 2014). The candidate ligands that are selected through docking are then post-processed by examining their binding scores, interactions, and binding pose, among others, based on which a smaller number of compounds are selected for experimental testing (Lionta *et al.*, 2014). Numerous success stories have been reported in drug repurposing through the use of structure-based screening (Palos *et al.*, 2017; Lukman *et al.*, 2017; Bi *et al.*, 2017; Sahoo *et al.*, 2016). For example, Chan *et al.* (2011) identified an FDA approved drug methylene blue from a database of over 3000 compounds using structure-based screening to

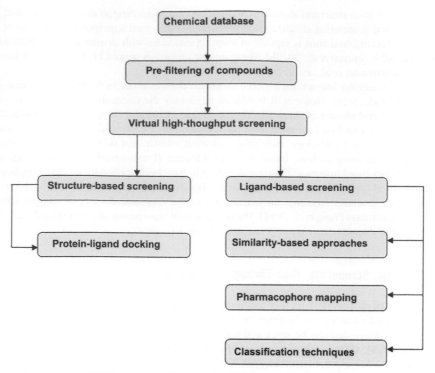

Fig. 1 Virtual high-throughput screening (vHTS) and its classifications. In vHTS, large compound databases are screened to identify candidate ligands for experimental testing. Pre-filtering of compounds in the databases is usually done before screening. vHTS can be classified as structure-based screening and ligand-based screening. Structure-based screening involves protein-ligand docking. Ligand-based screening can be classified as similarity-based approaches, pharmacophore mapping and classification techniques.

Table 2   Some docking programs employed in virtual high-throughput screening[a]

Program	Free for academic license ?	Website
AutoDock Forli *et al.* (2016), Morris *et al.* (2008)	Yes	http://autodock.scripps.edu/
FlexX Rarey *et al.* (1996)	No	https://omictools.com/flexx-tool
Surflex Jain (2003)	No	http://www.jainlab.org/downloads.html
GOLD Jones *et al.* (1997)	No	https://www.ccdc.cam.ac.uk/solutions/ csd-discovery/components/gold/
ICM Abagyan *et al.* (1994), Neves *et al.* (2012)	No	http://www.molsoft.com/docking.html
Glide Friesner *et al.* (2004)	No	https://www.schrodinger.com/
Lead Finder Stroganov *et al.* (2008)	No	http://moltech.ru/
MOE-Dock Sun (2016), Corbeil *et al.* (2012)	No	https://www.chemcomp.com/ MOE-Structure_Based_Design.htm
iGEMDOCK	Yes	http://gemdock.life.nctu.edu.tw/dock/igemdock.php
AutoDock Vina Trott and Olson (2009)	Yes	http://vina.scripps.edu/
rDock Ruiz-Carmona *et al.* (2014)	Yes	http://rdock.sourceforge.net/
UCSF Dock Allen *et al.* (2015)	Yes	http://dock.compbio.ucsf.edu/

[a]Some examples of docking programs and their websites are listed.

Note: Modified from Cheng, T., Li, Q., Zhou, Z., Wang, Y., Bryant, S.H., 2012. Structure-based virtual screening for drug discovery: A problem-centric review. AAPS J. 14, 133–141. Available from: https://doi.org/10.1208/s12248-012-9322-0.

stabilize the c-myc Pu27 G-quadruplex DNA that are putatively present in the promoter regions of oncogenes from the human genome Chan *et al.* (2011). Li *et al.* repositioned two organohalogen drugs to inhibit B-Raf protein kinase which is mutated in a broad range of human cancers by developing a docking program that takes into account halogen bond interactions Li *et al.* (2016).

Ligand-based screening makes use of the knowledge of ligands that binds to the target of interest for screening, based on the notion that ligands interacting with the same target show same structural or physicochemical properties. Ligand-based screening can be classified as molecular similarity-based approaches, pharmacophore mapping and compound classification techniques (Acharya *et al.*, 2011). Molecular similarity-based approaches usually employ 2D/3D chemical similarity analysis of the active ligand structure against a library of molecules (Bajorath, 2011; Bologa *et al.*, 2006; Lindert *et al.*, 2013) to identify chemically similar compounds. Molecular descriptors such as fingerprints derived from molecular graphs (2D) or conformers (3D)

(Cereto-Massagué *et al.*, 2015), topological indices (Fukunishi and Nakamura, 2009), molecular fields (Cheeseright *et al.*, 2006), and others, can be used for the similarity search of ligands. As a measure of comparison, similarity between molecular descriptors of two structures is quantified using a similarity coefficient. Most frequently, Tanimoto coefficient is used, which is defined as $N_{ab}/N_a + N_b - N_{ab}$, where N_a and N_b are the number of features in the fingerprint of compounds "a" and "b", respectively and N_{ab} is the number of features in fingerprints of both the compounds.

Pharmacophore mapping relies on the knowledge of molecular features (such as hydrogen bonds, charged interactions, hydrophobic and aromatic contacts) that are necessary for molecular recognition of a ligand by a target. By using the knowledge about the structurally diverse ligands that bind to a target, a model of target/pharmacophore can be built and can be employed for rapid screening of large databases (Sukumar and Das, 2011; Sun, 2008; Lin, 2000; Patel *et al.*, 2002; Pan *et al.*, 2013; Goodford, 1985). The quality of fitting the ligand into the pharmacophore query is more commonly expressed by the root mean square deviation (RMSD) between the features of the query and atoms of the molecule (Langer and Hoffmann, 2006).

Compound classification techniques include clustering techniques (such as PCA), partitioning techniques (such as recursive partitioning), and machine learning approaches (such as support vector machines, decision trees, k-nearest neighbours, naïve Bayesian methods, and artificial neural networks). The goal of this approach is to predict the activity of the compound based on models derived from the training set as well as the ranking of the database compounds based on the probability of their activity (Melville *et al.*, 2009; Bajorath, 2001).

As in structure-based screening, pre-filtering of compound libraries in accordance with the goals and constraints of the study is also beneficial in ligand-based screening (Yan *et al.*, 2016; Glaab, 2016). Many recent works have reported the usage of ligand-based screening for drug repurposing (Paz *et al.*, 2017; Keiser *et al.*, 2009; Vasudevan *et al.*, 2012; Crisan *et al.*, 2017). For example, Crisan *et al.* (2017) employed pharmacophore model for virtual screening and identification of known drugs that could inhibit glycogen synthase kinase-3 (GSK-3) which is involved in diseases such as psychiatric and neurological diseases, inflammatory diseases, and cancer. Anighoro *et al.* (2015) employed 2D ligand-based similarity analysis of ChEMBL database (see "Revelant Websites section") combined with support vector machine models and analysis of 3D structural information of ligand-target complexes, and identified a promising set of target combinations and associated ligands within the Hsp90 interactome, which contains several targets of key importance in cancer Anighoro *et al.* (2015).

A limitation of vHTS is that, it cannot identify the full spectrum of targets that a small molecule may be hitting, as a result of which drugs can elicit undesirable off-target effects. To overcome this drawback, vHTS can be integrated with deep molecular characterization and network analysis (Leung *et al.*, 2013). Network models allow integration of data from various information sources, capturing both quantitative and qualitative relationships between entities and the presence or absence of an interaction (Paolini *et al.*, 2006). For example connecting drugs by side effect similarity can provide insights into the drug's side effects and may also allow prediction of novel off-targets (Campillos *et al.*, 2008).

Often, structure-based screening requires thorough knowledge of the 3D structures of targets and their mechanisms at atomistic levels. Methods to resolve the 3D structures, such as X-ray crystallography and nuclear magnetic resonance method, are time- and cost-consuming. Atomistic-level of target mechanisms, observed through molecular dynamics simulations (Lukman *et al.*, 2012), can be very critical for drug repurposing. When we do not know the underlying mechanism associated with a disease, genomic screening methods are particularly useful. In such cases candidate ligands can be predicted using the molecular signature (i.e., significantly up and down regulated genes) of the disease that is generated through the analysis of differences in genomic patterns from disease affected and unaffected individuals. The corresponding signature of differential gene expression can be compared with differential gene expression signature induced by drugs, (i.e., changes brought about in the genomic patterns after exposure to a drug). If both the disease-associated and drug-induced signatures are sufficiently negatively correlated (i.e., the effects induced by drugs are opposite to the effects associated with the disease), then the drug may be able to revert the disease-associated signature and hence it can be considered as candidate for repurposing (Sirota *et al.*, 2011). Another approach employed in genomic screening is to look for drugs that can induce similar effects in gene expressions, by comparing the drug-induced signatures. It can be hypothesized that two drugs that can induce the same changes share similar mode of action/therapeutic application (Iorio *et al.*, 2010). Candidate ligands are thus identified in genomic screening by their direct or inverse correlation to the query signature (**Fig. 2**).

Publicly available databases such as Cmap (see "Revelant Websites section") (Lamb, 2006, 2007) and LINCS (see "Revelant Websites section") (Duan *et al.*, 2014) have thousands of gene signatures representing a diverse range of FDA approved drugs. The data from these databases can be integrated with functional genomics databases like NCBI-GEO (see "Revelant Websites section") (Edgar *et al.*, 2002) and ArrayExpress (see "Revelant Websites section") (Brazma *et al.*, 2003) for drug repositioning studies using genomic screening. Many previous studies have shown the benefits of employing Cmap data in drug repositioning (Iorio *et al.*, 2009, 2010 Napolitano *et al.*, 2013; Silberberg *et al.*, 2012; Parkkinen and Kaski, 2014; Yu *et al.*, 2015; Jadamba and Shin, 2016). For example, Dudley *et al.* employed Cmap data for repurposing topiramate, an anticonvulsant drug for treating inflammatory bowel disease (IBD) (Dudley *et al.*, 2011a,b). They employed gene expression data from NCBI-GEO and created a gene expression signature for IBD using the Significance Analysis of Microarrays (SAM) software (see "Revelant Websites section") (Tusher *et al.*, 2001). Then they systematically compared the signature to drug-induced signatures obtained from the Cmap. Drugs that are anti-correlated to the disease were selected based on their therapeutic scores that were computed based on a randomization algorithm.

Although genomic screening methods are advantageous in studying genome-wide patterns of how drugs are changing biological systems, there are still some limitations. Some portion of the genes that show significant expression differences in the drug-induced signatures, may be produced by drug side effects (Jadamba and Shin, 2016). Furthermore, the differential gene expression induced by drugs represents only a small subset of biological pathway (Jadamba and Shin, 2016). So as suggested in vHTS, the integration of

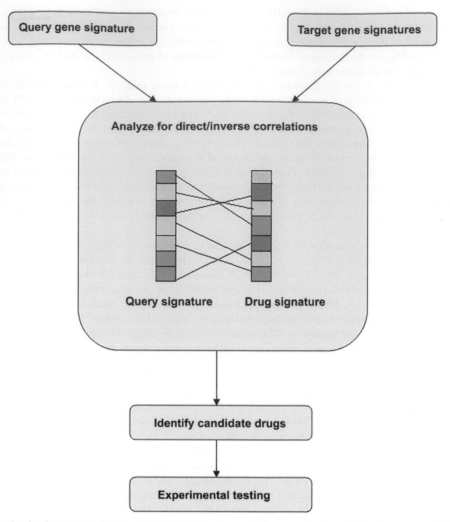

Fig. 2 Genomic screening for drug repurposing. In genomic screening approach, the query signature (either disease-associated or drug-induced signature) is compared with target signatures (drug-induced signatures) and their inverse or direct correlations are analyzed based on which the candidate ligands are chosen for experimental testing.

network models with genomic screening methods can provide better understanding of the drug-disease relationship. For example, more recently, Mulas *et al.* (2017) employed a network-based differential analysis of gene expression profiles to identify modes of actions of drugs. The proposed method is able to identify pathways significantly associated with the drug-induced signatures.

There are also many reports in literature of the combined use of the above-mentioned methods for drug repurposing studies. For example, Han *et al.* (2017) have recently identified a known drug that could inhibit Human enterovirus 71 (EV71) that can cause hand, foot and mouth disease. They have constructed EV71 protein interaction network and identified drugs that can target the interacting proteins. They used Cmap for the evaluation of drug influences on the genomic signatures of targets. Similarly, genomic screening methods can also be employed following vHTS for evaluating the candidate drugs. Phatak *et al.* have employed a multi-modal approach to repurpose existing drugs against ACK1, a cancer target significantly over expressed in breast and prostate cancers during their progression (Phatak and Zhang, 2013). They used structure-based screening followed by a pharmacophore-guided method to select a set of drugs as potential ACK1 inhibitors. To compensate for the limitations of the docking methods employed in their study, they employed different metrics based on chemical similarity, genomic similarity and drug-target bipartite graph to evaluate if complementary results can be obtained.

Since each screening method described above has its own field of applicability, drawbacks and limitations, integration of multiple methods described above may be beneficial for drug repurposing.

Challenges and Possible Solutions

Despite the potential benefits of drug repurposing, the pharmaceutical industry is less interested to find new uses of old drugs. One of the major barriers that hinders the development of repurposed drugs is lack of data exclusivity (Kato *et al.*, 2015). The period of data exclusivity for repurposed drugs is often insufficient for the pharmaceutical industries for making a reasonable profit (Shineman et al., 2014; Gaudry, 2011). Moreover, commercial returns for a newly formulated product depends on the coverage and reimbursement provided for it by a payer such as a third party private or government insurer (Shineman et al., 2014). When a generic drug is repurposed for a new indication through a new formulation, the payer is unlikely to provide the coverage unless they accept its clinical benefit over the generic drug (Shineman et al., 2014). All these reasons withhold the pharmaceutical industry from investing in drug repurposing.

To tackle these problems, non-profit organizations and governments can collaborate and take the initiatives to accelerate drug repurposing. The government can take actions to extend the period of data exclusivity for repurposed drugs (Shineman et al., 2014). Additionally, the government can offer meaningful incentives to the pharmaceutical companies for drug repurposing (Kato et al., 2015). Governments and non-profit organizations should work together to create awareness at the organizational and individual level to establish the notion that patient-relevant outcomes should ultimately drive the definition of value for drugs (Shineman et al., 2014). Moreover, research done at the academic institutions can also be motivational for the pharmaceutical industries to repurpose old drugs. Such research can be funded and an infrastructure can be created to co-ordinate the research interests of academic institutions and the pharmaceutical companies (Beachy et al., 2014).

Additionally, the interactions between drugs and their respective target(s) are influenced by the target's structure which is not static, but dynamic (Lukman et al., 2014). Considering the intrinsic dynamics of the target structure, i.e., the structure of proteins where drugs can bind to and regulate them, efforts to identify existing and novel binding sites from multiple structures of the same and/or related protein structures, for example through homology modeling, molecular dynamics simulations, and clustering approaches (Sim et al., 2013), have been undertaken for several targets. Examples of the targets are Bromo and Extra terminal (BET) proteins (Lukman et al., 2015a), insulin receptor (Lukman et al., 2015b), and insulin-degrading enzyme (Lukman, 2016). Identification of binding sites are critical for docking and ensemble docking (Lionta et al., 2014) of known drugs that was previously unknown for affecting a particular target of interest, yet have minimal toxicity.

Acknowledgements

We thank Al Jalila Foundation (AJF201507) for support. M.N. Nguyen would like to thank A*STAR Joint Council Office (JCO) Career Development Award [15302FG145] for support.

See also: Biomolecular Structures: Prediction, Identification and Analyses. Comparative Epigenomics. Molecular Dynamics Simulations in Drug Discovery. Natural Language Processing Approaches in Bioinformatics. Population Analysis of Pharmacogenetic Polymorphisms. Structure-Based Drug Design Workflow. Study of The Variability of The Native Protein Structure

References

Abagyan, R., Totrov, M., Kuznetsov, D., 1994. ICM? A new method for protein modeling and design: Applications to docking and structure prediction from the distorted native conformation. J. Comput. Chem. 15, 488–506. https://doi.org/10.1002/jcc.540150503.

Acharya, C., Coop, A., Polli, J.E., MacKerell, A.D., 2011. Recent advances in ligand-based drug design: Relevance and utility of the conformationally sampled pharmacophore approach. Curr. Comput. Aided-Drug Des. 7, 10–22. Available at: https://doi.org/10.2174/157340911793743547.

Allen, W.J., Balius, T.E., Mukherjee, S., et al., 2015. DOCK 6: Impact of new features and current docking performance. J. Comput. Chem. 36, 1132–1156. https://doi.org/10.1002/jcc.23905.

Amari, S., Aizawa, M., Zhang, J., et al., 2006. VISCANA: Visualized cluster analysis of protein — Ligand interaction based on the ab initio fragment molecular orbital method for virtual ligand screening. J. Chem. Inf. Model 46, 221–230. Available at: https://doi.org/10.1021/ci050262q.

Anighoro, A., Bajorath, J., Rastelli, G., 2014. Polypharmacology: Challenges and opportunities in drug discovery: Miniperspective. J. Med. Chem. 57, 7874–7887. Available at: https://doi.org/10.1021/jm5006463.

Anighoro, A., Stumpfe, D., Heikamp, K., et al., 2015. Computational polypharmacology analysis of the heat shock protein 90 interactome. J. Chem. Inf. Model 55, 676–686. Available at: 10.1021/ci5006959.

Bajorath, J., 2001. Selected concepts and investigations in compound classification, molecular descriptor analysis, and virtual screening. J. Chem. Inf. Comput. Sci. 41, 233–245. Available at: https://doi.org/10.1021/jm5006463.

Bajorath, J., 2011. Chemoinformatics and Computational Chemical Biology. New York: Humana Press.

Beachy, S.H., Johnson, S.G., Olson, S., Berger, A.C., Institute of Medicine(U.S.), 2014. Drug Repurposing and Repositioning: Workshop Summary. Washington, D.C.: The National Academies Press.

Bi, Y., Might, M., Vankayalapati, H., Kuberan, B., 2017. Repurposing of proton pump inhibitors as first identified small molecule inhibitors of endo -β- N -acetylglucosaminidase (ENGase) for the treatment of NGLY1 deficiency, a rare genetic disease. Bioorg. Med. Chem. Lett. 27, 2962–2966. Available at: https://doi.org/10.1016/j.bmcl.2017.05.010.

Bologa, C.G., Revankar, C.M., Young, S.M., et al., 2006. Virtual and biomolecular screening converge on a selective agonist for GPR30. Nat. Chem. Biol. 2, 207–212. Available at: https://doi.org/10.1038/nchembio775.

Borisy, A.A., Elliott, P.J., Hurst, N.W., et al., 2003. Systematic discovery of multicomponent therapeutics. Proc. Natl. Acad. Sci. USA 100, 7977–7982. Available at: https://doi.org/10.1073/pnas.1337088100.

Brazma, A., Parkinson, H., Sarkans, U., et al., 2003. ArrayExpress — A public repository for microarray gene expression data at the EBI. Nucleic Acids Res. 31, 68–71.

Brown, A.S., Patel, C.J., 2017. A standard database for drug repositioning. Sci. Data 4, 170029. Available at: https://doi.org/10.1038/sdata.2017.29.

Campillos, M., Kuhn, M., Gavin, A.-C., Jensen, L.J., Bork, P., 2008. Drug target identification using side-effect similarity. Science 321, 263–266. Available at: https://doi.org/10.1126/science.1158140.

Carrella, D., Napolitano, F., Rispoli, R., et al., 2014. Mantra 2.0: An online collaborative resource for drug mode of action and repurposing by network analysis. Bioinform. Oxf. Engl. 30, 1787–1788. Available at: https://doi.org/10.1093/bioinformatics/btu058.

Cereto-Massagué, A., Ojeda, M.J., Valls, C., et al., 2015. Molecular fingerprint similarity search in virtual screening. Methods 71, 58–63. Available at: https://doi.org/10.1016/j.ymeth.2014.08.005.

Chan, D.S.-H., Yang, H., Kwan, M.H.-I., et al., 2011. Structure-based optimization of FDA-approved drug methylene blue as a c-myc G-quadruplex DNA stabilizer. Biochimie 93, 1055–1064. Available at: https://doi.org/10.1016/j.biochi.2011.02.013.

Cheeseright, T., Mackey, M., Rose, S., Vinter, A., 2006. Molecular field extrema as descriptors of biological activity: Definition and validation. J. Chem. Inf. Model. 46, 665–676. Available at: https://doi.org/10.1021/ci050357s.

Cheng, F., Liu, C., Jiang, J., et al., 2012a. Prediction of drug-target interactions and drug repositioning via network-based inference. PLOS Comput. Biol. 8, e1002503. Available at: https://doi.org/10.1371/journal.pcbi.1002503.

Cheng, T., Li, Q., Zhou, Z., Wang, Y., Bryant, S.H., 2012b. Structure-based virtual screening for drug discovery: a problem-centric review. AAPS J. 14, 133–141. Available at: https://doi.org/s12248/s12248-012-9322-0.

Corbeil, C.R., Williams, C.I., Labute, P., 2012. Variability in docking success rates due to dataset preparation. J. Comput. Aided Mol. Des. 26, 775–786. https://doi.org/10.1007/s10822-012-9570-1.

Crisan, L., Avram, S., Pacureanu, L., 2017. Pharmacophore-based screening and drug repurposing exemplified on glycogen synthase kinase-3 inhibitors. Mol. Divers. 21, 385–405. Available at: https://doi.org/10.1007/s11030-016-9724-5.

Deng, Z., Chuaqui, C., Singh, J., 2004. Structural Interaction Fingerprint (SIFt): A novel method for analyzing three-dimensional protein — Ligand binding interactions. J. Med. Chem. 47, 337–344. Available at: https://doi.org/10.1021/jm030331x.

Duan, Q., Flynn, C., Niepel, M., et al., 2014. LINCS canvas browser: Interactive web app to query, browse and interrogate LINCS L1000 gene expression signatures. Nucleic Acids Res. 42, W449–W460. Available at: https://doi.org/10.1093/nar/gku476.

Dudley, J.T., Deshpande, T., Butte, A.J., 2011a. Exploiting drug-disease relationships for computational drug repositioning. Brief. Bioinform. 12, 303–311. Available at: https://doi.org/10.1093/bib/bbr013.

Dudley, J.T., Sirota, M., Shenoy, M., et al., 2011b. Computational repositioning of the anticonvulsant topiramate for inflammatory bowel disease. Sci. Transl. Med. 3, 96ra76. Available at: https://doi.org/10.1126/scitranslmed.3002648.

Edgar, R., Domrachev, M., Lash, A.E., 2002. Gene expression omnibus: NCBI gene expression and hybridization array data repository. Nucleic Acids Res. 30, 207–210.

Ewing, T.J.A., Makino, S., Skillman, A.G., Kuntz, I.D., 2001. DOCK 4.0: Search strategies for automated molecular docking of flexible molecule databases. J. Comput. Aided Mol. Des. 15, 411–428. Available at: https://doi.org/10.1023/A:1011115820450.

Forli, S., Huey, R., Pique, M.E., et al., 2016. Computational protein-ligand docking and virtual drug screening with the AutoDock suite. Nat. Protoc. 11, 905–919. https://doi.org/10.1038/nprot.2016.051.

Friesner, R.A., Banks, J.L., Murphy, R.B., et al., 2004. Glide: A New Approach for Rapid, Accurate Docking and Scoring. 1. Method and Assessment of Docking Accuracy. J. Med. Chem., 47. . pp. 1739–1749. https://doi.org/10.1021/jm0306430.

Fu, C., Jin, G., Gao, J., et al., 2013. DrugMap central: An on-line query and visualization tool to facilitate drug repositioning studies. Bioinformatics 29, 1834–1836. Available at: https://doi.org/10.1093/bioinformatics/btt279.

Fukunishi, Y., Nakamura, H., 2009. A similarity search using molecular topological graphs. J. Biomed. Biotechnol. 2009, 1–8. Available at: https://doi.org/10.1155/2009/231780.

Gaudry, K.S., 2011. Evergreening: A common practice to protect new drugs. Nat. Biotechnol. 29, 876–878. Available at: https://doi.org/10.1038/nbt.1993.

Glaab, E., 2016. Building a virtual ligand screening pipeline using free software: A survey. Brief. Bioinform. 17, 352–366. Available at: https://doi.org/10.1093/bib/bbv037.

Gloeckner, C., Garner, A.L., Mersha, F., et al., 2010. Repositioning of an existing drug for the neglected tropical disease Onchocerciasis. Proc. Natl. Acad. Sci. 107, 3424–3429. Available at: https://doi.org/10.1073/pnas.0915125107.

Goodford, P.J., 1985. A computational procedure for determining energetically favorable binding sites on biologically important macromolecules. J. Med. Chem. 28, 849–857.

Gozalbes, R., Simon, L., Froloff, N., et al., 2008. Development and experimental validation of a docking strategy for the generation of kinase-targeted libraries. J. Med. Chem. 51, 3124–3132. Available at: https://doi.org/10.1021/jm701367r.

Grant, B.J., Lukman, S., Hocker, H.J., et al., 2011. Novel allosteric sites on Ras for lead generation. PLOS ONE 6, e25711. Available at: https://doi.org/10.1371/journal.pone.0025711.

Han, L., Li, K., Jin, C., et al., 2017. Human enterovirus 71 protein interaction network prompts antiviral drug repositioning. Sci. Rep. 7, 43143. Available at: https://doi.org/10.1038/srep43143.

Helguera, A., Combes, R., Gonzalez, M., Cordeiro, M.N., 2008. Applications of 2D descriptors in drug design: A DRAGON Tale. Curr. Top. Med. Chem. 8, 1628–1655. Available at: https://doi.org/10.2174/156802608786786598.

Hong, H., Xie, Q., Ge, W., et al., 2008. Mold [2], molecular descriptors from 2D structures for chemoinformatics and toxicoinformatics. J. Chem. Inf. Model 48, 1337–1344. Available at: https://doi.org/10.1021/ci800038f.

Huang, Y.-F., Yeh, H.-Y., Soo, V.-W., 2013. Inferring drug-disease associations from integration of chemical, genomic and phenotype data using network propagation. BMC Med. Genom. 6, S4. Available at: https://doi.org/10.1186/1755-8794-6-S3-S4.

Iorio, F., Bosotti, R., Scacheri, E., et al., 2010. Discovery of drug mode of action and drug repositioning from transcriptional responses. Proc. Natl. Acad. Sci. 107, 14621–14626. Available at: https://doi.org/10.1073/pnas.1000138107.

Iorio, F., Tagliaferri, R., di Bernardo, D., 2009. Identifying network of drug mode of action by gene expression profiling. J. Comput. Biol. 16, 241–251. Available at: https://doi.org/10.1089/cmb.2008.10TT.

Irwin, J.J., Sterling, T., Mysinger, M.M., Bolstad, E.S., Coleman, R.G., 2012. ZINC: A free tool to discover chemistry for biology. J. Chem. Inf. Model 52, 1757–1768. Available at: https://doi.org/10.1021/ci3001277.

Jadamba, E., Shin, M., 2016. A systematic framework for drug repositioning from integrated omics and drug phenotype profiles using pathway-drug network. BioMed Res. Int. 2016.Available at: https://doi.org/10.1155/2016/7147039.

Jain, A.N., 2003. Surflex: Fully Automatic Flexible Molecular Docking Using a Molecular Similarity-Based Search Engine. J. Med. Chem. 46, 499–511. https://doi.org/10.1021/jm020406h.

John Fox, S., Li, J., Sing Tan, Y., et al., 2016. The multifaceted roles of molecular dynamics simulations in drug discovery. Curr. Pharm. Des. 22, 3585–3600. Available at: https://doi.org/10.2174/1381612822666160425120507.

Jones, G., Willett, P., Glen, R.C., Leach, A.R., Taylor, R., 1997. Development and validation of a genetic algorithm for flexible docking 1 1Edited by F. E. Cohen. J. Mol. Biol. 267, 727–748. https://doi.org/10.1006/jmbi.1996.0897.

Kato, S., Moulder, S.L., Ueno, N.T., et al., 2015. Challenges and perspective of drug repurposing strategies in early phase clinical trials. Oncoscience 2, 576–580.

Keiser, M.J., Setola, V., Irwin, J.J., et al., 2009. Predicting new molecular targets for known drugs. Nature 462, 175–181. Available at: https://doi.org/10.1038/nature08506.

Kombo, D.C., Tallapragada, K., Jain, R., et al., 2013. 3D molecular descriptors important for clinical success. J. Chem. Inf. Model 53, 327–342. Available at: https://doi.org/10.1021/ci300445e.

Konc, J., Janežič, D., 2010. ProBiS algorithm for detection of structurally similar protein binding sites by local structural alignment. Bioinformatics 26, 1160–1168. Available at: https://doi.org/10.1093/bioinformatics/btq100.

Kroemer, R.T., 2007. Structure-based drug design: Docking and scoring. Curr. Protein Pept. Sci. 8, 312–328.

Kuhn, M., Letunic, I., Jensen, L.J., Bork, P., 2016. The SIDER database of drugs and side effects. Nucleic Acids Res. 44, D1075–D1079. Available at: https://doi.org/10.1093/nar/gkv1075.

Kumar, A.P., Nguyen, M.N., Verma, C., Lukman, S., 2018. Structural analysis of protein tyrosine phosphatase 1B reveals potentially druggable allosteric binding sites. Proteins Struct. Funct. Bioinform. 86, 301–321. Available at: https://doi.org/10.1002/prot.25440.

Lamb, J., 2006. The Connectivity map: Using gene-expression signatures to connect small molecules, genes, and disease. Science 313, 1929–1935. Available at: https://doi.org/10.1126/science.1132939.

Lamb, J., 2007. The Connectivity map: A new tool for biomedical research. Nat. Rev. Cancer 7, 54–60. Available at: https://doi.org/10.1038/nrc2044.

Langer, T., Hoffmann, R.D., 2006. Pharmacophores and Pharmacophore Searches. Weinheim; Chichester: Wiley-VCH; John Wiley, distributor.

Law, V., Knox, C., Djoumbou, Y., et al., 2014. DrugBank 4.0: Shedding new light on drug metabolism. Nucleic Acids Res. 42, D1091–D1097. Available at: https://doi.org/10.1093/nar/gkt1068.

Lee, B.K.B., Tiong, K.H., Chang, J.K., et al., 2017. DeSigN: Connecting gene expression with therapeutics for drug repurposing and development. BMC Genom. 18. Available at: https://doi.org/10.1186/s12864-016-3260-7.

Lee, H., Bae, T., Lee, J.-H., et al., 2012. Rational drug repositioning guided by an integrated pharmacological network of protein, disease and drug. BMC Syst. Biol. 6, 80. Available at: https://doi.org/10.1186/1752-0509-6-80.

Lee, J.-H., Park, K.M., Han, D.-J., et al., 2015. PharmDB-K: Integrated bio-pharmacological network database for traditional Korean medicine. PLOS ONE 10, e0142624. Available at: https://doi.org/10.1371/journal.pone.0142624.

Leung, E.L., Cao, Z.-W., Jiang, Z.-H., Zhou, H., Liu, L., 2013. Network-based drug discovery by integrating systems biology and computational technologies. Brief. Bioinform. 14, 491–505. Available at: https://doi.org/10.1093/bib/bbs043.

Liang, S., Meroueh, S.O., Wang, G., Qiu, C., Zhou, Y., 2009. Consensus scoring for enriching near-native structures from protein-protein docking decoys. Proteins Struct. Funct. Bioinform. 75, 397–403. Available at: https://doi.org/10.1002/prot.22252.

Lindert, S., Zhu, W., Liu, Y.-L., et al., 2013. Farnesyl Diphosphate Synthase inhibitors from in silico screening. Chem. Biol. Drug Des. 81, 742–748. Available at: https://doi.org/10.1111/cbdd.12121.

Lin, S.-K., 2000. Pharmacophore perception, development and use in drug design. In: Osman, F. (Ed.), Güner Molecules 5. , pp. 987–989. Available at: https://doi.org/10.3390/50700987.

Lionta, E., Spyrou, G., Vassilatis, D.K., Cournia, Z., 2014. Structure-based virtual screening for drug discovery: Principles, applications and recent advances. Curr. Top. Med. Chem. 14, 1923–1938. Available at: https://doi.org/10.2174/1568026614666140929124445.

Lipinski, C.A., 2000. Drug-like properties and the causes of poor solubility and poor permeability. J. Pharmacol. Toxicol. Methods 44, 235–249.

Lipinski, C.A., Lombardo, F., Dominy, B.W., Feeney, P.J., 2001. Experimental and computational approaches to estimate solubility and permeability in drug discovery and development settings. Adv. Drug Deliv. Rev. 46, 3–26.

Li, Y., Guo, B., Xu, Z., et al., 2016. Repositioning organohalogen drugs: A case study for identification of potent B-Raf V600E inhibitors via docking and bioassay. Sci. Rep. 6. Available at: https://doi.org/10.1038/srep31074.

Lukman, S., 2016. Novel druggable sites of insulin-degrading enzyme identified through applied structural bioinformatics analysis. In: Proceedings of the International Conference on Computational Science, Procedia Computer Science, ICCS 2016, 80, pp. 2292–2296. San Diego, California, USA. Available at: https://doi.org/10.1016/j.procs.2016.05.419.

Lukman, S., Aung, Z., Sim, K., 2015a. Multiple structural clustering of bromodomains of the Bromo and Extra Terminal (BET) proteins highlights subtle differences in their structural dynamics and acetylated leucine binding pocket. Procedia Comput. Sci. 51, 735–744. Available at: https://doi.org/10.1016/j.procs.2015.05.192.

Lukman, S., Nguyen, M.N., Sim, K., Teo, J.C.M., 2017. Discovery of Rab1 binding sites using an ensemble of clustering methods: Clustering for finding Rab1 binding sites. Proteins Struct. Funct. Bioinforma. 85, 859–871. Available at: https://doi.org/10.1002/prot.25254.

Lukman, S., Robinson, R.C., Wales, D., Verma, C.S., 2012. Conformational dynamics of capping protein and interaction partners: Simulation studies. Proteins 80, 1066–1077. Available at: https://doi.org/10.1002/prot.24008.

Lukman, S., Safar, H.A., Lee, S.M., Sim, K., 2015b. Harnessing structural data of insulin and insulin receptor for therapeutic designs. J. Endocrinol. Metab. 5, 273–283. Available at: https://doi.org/10.14740/jem302w.

Lukman, S., Verma, C.S., Fuentes, G., 2014. Exploiting protein intrinsic flexibility in drug design. In: Han, K., Zhang, X., Yang, M. (Eds.), Protein Conformational Dynamics. Springer International Publishing, Cham, pp. 245–269. Available at: https://doi.org/10.1007/978-3-319-02970-2_11.

Luo, H., Chen, J., Shi, L., et al., 2011. DRAR-CPI: A server for identifying drug repositioning potential and adverse drug reactions via the chemical – Protein interactome. Nucleic Acids Res. 39, W492–W498. Available at: https://doi.org/10.1093/nar/gkr299.

Luo, H., Zhang, P., Cao, X.H., et al., 2016. DPDR-CPI, a server that predicts drug positioning and drug repositioning via chemical-protein interactome. Sci. Rep. 6. Available at: https://doi.org/10.1038/srep35996.

Melville, J., Burke, E., Hirst, J., 2009. Machine learning in virtual screening. Comb. Chem. High Throughput Screen. 12, 332–343. Available at: https://doi.org/10.2174/138620709788167980.

Moosavinasab, S., Patterson, J., Strouse, R., et al., 2016. 'RE:fine drugs': An interactive dashboard to access drug repurposing opportunities. Database 2016, baw083. Available at: https://doi.org/10.1093/database/baw083.

Morris, G.M., Huey, R., Olson, A.J., 2008. Using AutoDock for ligand–receptor docking. Curr. Protoc. Bioinforma.. Chapter 8, Unit 8.14 https://doi.org/10.1002/0471250953.bi0814s24.

Mulas, F., Li, A., Sherr, D.H., Monti, S., 2017. Network-based analysis of transcriptional profiles from chemical perturbations experiments. BMC Bioinform. 18. Available at: https://doi.org/10.1186/s12859-017-1536-9.

Napolitano, F., Zhao, Y., Moreira, V.M., et al., 2013. Drug repositioning: A machine-learning approach through data integration. J. Cheminform. 5, 30. Available at: https://doi.org/10.1186/1758-2946-5-30.

NCBI Resource Coordinators, 2013. Database resources of the National Center for Biotechnology Information. Nucleic Acids Res. 41, D8–D20. Available at: https://doi.org/10.1093/nar/gks1189.

Neves, M.A.C., Totrov, M., Abagyan, R., 2012. Docking and scoring with ICM: the benchmarking results and strategies for improvement. J. Comput. Aided Mol. Des. 26, 675–686. https://doi.org/10.1007/s10822-012-9547-0.

Nguyen, M.N., Madhusudhan, M.S., 2011. Biological insights from topology independent comparison of protein 3D structures. Nucleic Acids Res. 39, e94. Available at: https://doi.org/10.1093/nar/gkr348.

Nguyen, M.N., Pradhan, M.R., Verma, C., Zhong, P., 2017a. The interfacial character of antibody paratopes: Analysis of antibody – Antigen structures. Bioinformatics 33, 2971–2976. Available at: https://doi.org/10.1093/bioinformatics/btx389.

Nguyen, M.N., Sim, A.Y.L., Wan, Y., Madhusudhan, M.S., Verma, C., 2017b. Topology independent comparison of RNA 3D structures using the CLICK algorithm. Nucleic Acids Res. 45, e5. Available at: https://doi.org/10.1093/nar/gkw819.

Nguyen, M.N., Tan, K.P., Madhusudhan, M.S., 2011. CLICK – Topology-independent comparison of biomolecular 3D structures. Nucleic Acids Res. 39, W24–W28. Available at: https://doi.org/10.1093/nar/gkr393.

Nguyen, M.N., Verma, C., 2015. Rclick: A web server for comparison of RNA 3D structures. Bioinformatics 31, 966–968. Available at: https://doi.org/10.1093/bioinformatics/btu752.

Novick, P.A., Ortiz, O.F., Poelman, J., Abdulhay, A.Y., Pande, V.S., 2013. SWEETLEAD: An in silico database of approved drugs, regulated chemicals, and herbal isolates for computer-aided drug discovery. PLOS ONE 8, e79568. Available at: https://doi.org/10.1371/journal.pone.0079568.

Nussinov, R., Tsai, C.-J., 2012. The different ways through which specificity works in orthosteric and allosteric drugs. Curr. Drug Metab. 18, 1311–1316. Available at: https://doi.org/10.2174/138920012799362855.

Oprea, T.I., Bauman, J.E., Bologa, C.G., et al., 2011. Drug repurposing from an academic perspective. Drug Discov. Today Ther. Strateg. 8, 61–69. https://doi.org/10.1016/j.ddstr.2011.10.002.

Palos, I., Lara-Ramirez, E.E., Lopez-Cedillo, J.C., et al., 2017. Repositioning FDA Drugs as Potential Cruzain Inhibitors from Trypanosoma cruzi: Virtual Screening, In Vitro and In Vivo Studies. Molecules 22, 1015. https://doi.org/10.3390/molecules22061015.

Pan, Y., Wang, Y., Bryant, S.H., 2013. Pharmacophore and 3D-QSAR characterization of 6-Arylquinazolin-4-amines as Cdc2-like Kinase 4 (Clk4) and dual specificity tyrosine-phosphorylation-regulated kinase 1A (Dyrk1A) inhibitors. J. Chem. Inf. Model 53, 938–947. Available at: https://doi.org/10.1021/ci300625c.

Paolini, G.V., Shapland, R.H.B., van Hoorn, W.P., Mason, J.S., Hopkins, A.L., 2006. Global mapping of pharmacological space. Nat. Biotechnol. 24, 805–815. Available at: https://doi.org/10.1038/nbt1228.

Parkkinen, J.A., Kaski, S., 2014. Probabilistic drug connectivity mapping. BMC Bioinform. 15, 113. Available at: https://doi.org/10.1186/1471-2105-15-113.

Patel, Y., Gillet, V.J., Bravi, G., Leach, A.R., 2002. A comparison of the pharmacophore identification programs: Catalyst, DISCO and GASP. J. Comput. Aided Mol. Des. 16, 653–681. Available at: https://doi.org/10.1023/A:1021954728347.

Paz, O.S., de Jesus Pinheiro, M., do Espirito Santo, R.F., Villarreal, C.F., Castilho, M.S., 2017. Nanomolar anti-sickling compounds identified by ligand-based pharmacophore approach. Eur. J. Med. Chem. 136, 487–496. Available at: https://doi.org/10.1016/j.ejmech.2017.05.035.

Phatak, S.S., Zhang, S., 2013. A novel multi-modal drug repurposing approach for identification of potent ack1 inhibitors. Pac. Symp. Biocomput.. 29–40.

Pihan, E., Colliandre, L., Guichou, J.-F., Douguet, D., 2012. e-Drug3D: 3D structure collections dedicated to drug repurposing and fragment-based drug design. Bioinformatics 28, 1540–1541. Available at: https://doi.org/10.1093/bioinformatics/bts186.

Pratanwanich, N., Lió, P., 2014. Pathway-based Bayesian inference of drug – Disease interactions. Mol. BioSyst. 10, 1538–1548. Available at: https://doi.org/10.1039/C4MB00014E.

Radusky, L., Ruiz-Carmona, S., Modenutti, C., et al., 2017. LigQ: A webserver to select and prepare ligands for virtual screening. J. Chem. Inf. Model. 57, 1741–1746. Available at: https://doi.org/10.1021/acs.jcim.7b00241.

Rapp, C.S., Schonbrun, C., Jacobson, M.P., Kalyanaraman, C., Huang, N., 2009. Automated site preparation in physics-based rescoring of receptor ligand complexes. Proteins Struct. Funct. Bioinform. 77, 52–61. Available at: https://doi.org/10.1002/prot.22415.

Rarey, M., Kramer, B., Lengauer, T., Klebe, G., 1996. A Fast Flexible Docking Method using an Incremental Construction Algorithm. J. Mol. Biol. 261, 470–489. https://doi.org/10.1006/jmbi.1996.0477.

Reaume, A.G., 2011. Drug repurposing through nonhypothesis driven phenotypic screening. Drug Discov. Today Ther. Strateg. 8, 85–88. Available at: https://doi.org/10.1016/j.ddstr.2011.09.007.

Reddy, A.S., Zhang, S., 2013. Polypharmacology: Drug discovery for the future. Expert Rev. Clin. Pharmacol. 6, 41–47. Available at: https://doi.org/10.1586/ecp.12.74.

Rose, P.W., Bi, C., Bluhm, W.F., et al., 2013. The RCSB protein data bank: New resources for research and education. Nucleic Acids Res. 41, D475–D482. Available at: https://doi.org/10.1093/nar/gks1200.

Ruiz-Carmona, S., Alvarez-Garcia, D., Foloppe, N., et al., 2014. rDock: A Fast, Versatile and Open Source Program for Docking Ligands to Proteins and Nucleic Acids. PLOS Comput. Biol. 10, e1003571. https://doi.org/10.1371/journal.pcbi.1003571.

Sage, C., Wang, R., Jones, G., 2011. G-protein coupled receptors virtual screening using genetic algorithm focused chemical space. J. Chem. Inf. Model 51, 1754–1761. Available at: https://doi.org/10.1021/ci200043z.

Sahoo, M., Jena, L., Daf, S., Kumar, S., 2016. Virtual screening for potential inhibitors of NS3 protein of zika virus. Genom. Inform. 14, 104. Available at: https://doi.org/10.5808/GI.2016.14.3.104.

Schuffenhauer, A., Gillet, V.J., Willett, P., 2000. Similarity searching in files of three-dimensional chemical structures: Analysis of the BIOSTER database using two-dimensional fingerprints and molecular field descriptors. J. Chem. Inf. Comput. Sci. 40, 295–307. Available at: https://doi.org/10.1021/ci990263g.

Schwartz, J., Awale, M., Reymond, J.-L., 2013. SMIfp (SMILES fingerprint) chemical space for virtual screening and visualization of large databases of organic molecules. J. Chem. Inf. Model 53, 1979–1989. Available at: https://doi.org/10.1021/ci400206h.

Shameer, K., Glicksberg, B.S., Hodos, R., et al., 2017. Systematic analyses of drugs and disease indications in RepurposeDB reveal pharmacological, biological and epidemiological factors influencing drug repositioning. Brief. Bioinform.. Available at: https://doi.org/10.1093/bib/bbw136.

Shineman, D.W., Alam, J., Anderson, M., et al., 2014. Overcoming obstacles to repurposing for neurodegenerative disease. Ann. Clin. Transl. Neurol. 1, 512–518. Available at: https://doi.org/10.1002/acn3.76.

Shin, W.-H., Zhu, X., Bures, M., Kihara, D., 2015. Three-dimensional compound comparison methods and their application in drug discovery. Molecules 20, 12841–12862. Available at: https://doi.org/10.3390/molecules200712841.

Shoichet, B.K., 2004. Virtual screening of chemical libraries. Nature 432, 862–865. Available at: https://doi.org/10.1038/nature03197.

Shulman-Peleg, A., Shatsky, M., Nussinov, R., Wolfson, H.J., 2007. Spatial chemical conservation of hot spot interactions in protein-protein complexes. BMC Biol. 5, 43. Available at: https://doi.org/10.1186/1741-7007-5-43.

Silberberg, Y., Gottlieb, A., Kupiec, M., Ruppin, E., Sharan, R., 2012. Large-scale elucidation of drug response pathways in humans. J. Comput. Biol. 19, 163–174. Available at: https://doi.org/10.1089/cmb.2011.0264.

Sim, K., Yap, G.-E., Hardoon, D.R., et al., 2013. Centroid-based actionable 3D subspace clustering. IEEE Trans. Knowl. Data Eng. 25, 1213–1226.

Simon, Z., Peragovics, Á., Vigh-Smeller, M., et al., 2012. Drug effect prediction by polypharmacology-based interaction profiling. J. Chem. Inf. Model 52, 134–145. Available at: https://doi.org/10.1021/ci2002022.

Sirota, M., Dudley, J.T., Kim, J., et al., 2011. Discovery and preclinical validation of drug indications using compendia of public gene expression data. Sci. Transl. Med. 3, 96ra77. Available at: https://doi.org/10.1126/scitranslmed.3001318.

Sliwoski, G., Kothiwale, S., Meiler, J., Lowe, E.W., 2014. Computational methods in drug discovery. Pharmacol. Rev. 66, 334–395. Available at: https://doi.org/10.1124/pr.112.007336.

Sotriffer, C., 2011. Virtual Screening: Principles, Challenges, and Practical Guidelines, Methods and Principles in Medicinal Chemistry. Weinheim, Germany: Wiley-VCH.

Stroganov, O.V., Novikov, F.N., Stroylov, V.S., Kulkov, V., Chilov, G.G., 2008. Lead finder: An approach to improve accuracy of protein-ligand docking, binding energy estimation, and virtual screening. J. Chem. Inf. Model. 48, 2371–2385. https://doi.org/10.1021/ci800166p.

Sukumar, N., Das, S., 2011. Current trends in virtual high throughput screening using ligand-based and structure-based methods. Comb. Chem. High Throughput Screen. 14, 872–888.

Sun, H., 2008. Pharmacophore-based virtual screening. Curr. Med. Chem. 15, 1018–1024.

Sun, H., 2016. A practical guide to rational drug design.

ten Brink, T., Exner, T.E., 2010. pK(a) based protonation states and microspecies for protein-ligand docking. J. Comput. Aided Mol. Des. 24, 935–942. Available at: https://doi.org/10.1007/s10822-010-9385-x.

Trott, O., Olson, A.J., 2009. AutoDock Vina: Improving the speed and accuracy of docking with a new scoring function, efficient optimization, and multithreading. J. Comput. Chem. 31 (2), 455–461. Available at: https://doi.org/10.1002/jcc.21334.

Tusher, V.G., Tibshirani, R., Chu, G., 2001. Significance analysis of microarrays applied to the ionizing radiation response. Proc. Natl. Acad. Sci. USA 98, 5116–5121. Available at: https://doi.org/10.1073/pnas.091062498.

UniProt Consortium, 2013. Update on activities at the Universal Protein Resource (UniProt) in 2013. Nucleic Acids Res. 41, D43–D47. Available at: https://doi.org/10.1093/nar/gks1068.

Vasudevan, S.R., Moore, J.B., Schymura, Y., Churchill, G.C., 2012. Shape-based reprofiling of FDA-approved drugs for the H_1 histamine receptor. J. Med. Chem. 55, 7054–7060. Available at: https://doi.org/10.1021/jm300671m.

von Eichborn, J., Murgueitio, M.S., Dunkel, M., et al., 2011. PROMISCUOUS: A database for network-based drug-repositioning. Nucleic Acids Res. 39, D1060–D1066. Available at: https://doi.org/10.1093/nar/gkq1037.

Wang, R., Gao, Y., Lai, L., 2000. LigBuilder: A multi-purpose program for structure-based drug design. J. Mol. Model. 6, 498–516. Available at: https://doi.org/10.1007/s008940060498.

Wiegers, T.C., Davis, A., Cohen, K.B., Hirschman, L., Mattingly, C.J., 2009. Text mining and manual curation of chemical-gene-disease networks for the Comparative Toxicogenomics Database (CTD). BMC Bioinform. 10, 326. Available at: https://doi.org/10.1186/1471-2105-10-326.

Wu, Z., Wang, Y., Chen, L., 2013. Network-based drug repositioning. Mol. Biosyst. 9, 1268. Available at: https://doi.org/10.1039/c3mb25382a.

Yang, J., Li, Z., Fan, X., Cheng, Y., 2014. Drug – Disease association and drug-repositioning predictions in complex diseases using causal inference – Probabilistic matrix factorization. J. Chem. Inf. Model. 54, 2562–2569. Available at: https://doi.org/10.1021/ci500340n.

Yan, X., Liao, C., Liu, Z., et al., 2016. Chemical structure similarity search for ligand-based virtual screening: Methods and computational resources. Curr. Drug Targets 17, 1580–1585. Available at: https://doi.org/10.2174/1389450116666151102095555.

Yu, J., Putcha, P., Silva, J.M., 2015. Recovering drug-induced apoptosis subnetwork from connectivity Map data. BioMed Res. Int. 2015, 708563. Available at: https://doi.org/10.1155/2015/708563.

Revelant Websites

https://www.ebi.ac.uk/arrayexpress/
    ArrayExpress.
https://www.ebi.ac.uk/chembl/
    ChEMBL.
https://www.broadinstitute.org/cmap/
    Connectivity Map.
http://chemoinfo.ipmc.cnrs.fr/e-drug3d.html
    e-LEA3D: ChemInformatic Tools and Databases.
http://www.ncbi.nlm.nih.gov/geo/
    Gene Expression Omnibus.
http://www.lincscloud.org/
    lincscloud.
http://ligq.qb.fcen.uba.ar/
    LigQ.
https://cpi.bio-x.cn/dpdr/
    Predict drug positioning and drug repositioning - DPDR-CPI.
https://cpi.bio-x.cn/drar/
    Predict drug repositioning and adverse drug reaction - DRAR-CPI.
http://bioinformatics.charite.de/promiscuous
    PROMISCUOUS.
http://www-stat.stanford.edu/~tibs/SAM
    SAM: Significance Analysis of Microarrays.

Transcriptome Analysis

Anuj Srivastava, Joshy George, and Radha KM Karuturi, The Jackson Laboratory, CT, United States

Introduction

Transcriptome is a collection of all RNA molecules in one cell or a population of cells. RNA has long been at the center of molecular biology and its importance had been established in a series of paradigm-shifting discoveries over the last 60–70 years. Prior to 1940s, it was considered that proteins carried out both genetic information and enzymatic catalytic function of cells. In the 1950s, Crick published the central dogma that showed RNA served as an intermediary molecule during the transfer of genetic information of proteins (Crick, 1958). For many years, after the establishment of the central dogma, it was believed that RNA molecules come in 3 flavors (rRNA, tRNA, and mRNA) and their primary function involved protein syntheses. Later in the 1980s, several other types of RNAs including uridine (U)-rich U RNAs were discovered; in the same time period, Cech and Altman, studying the splicing in *Tetrahymena thermophile* and bacterial RNase P complex, respectively, concluded that RNA had catalytic functions as ribozymes (Cech *et al.*, 1983). In the 1990s, Ambros and colleagues (Lee *et al.*, 1993) showed the first evidence of RNA mediated regulation (by microRNA or miRNA) in *Caenorhabditis elegans* development and thus establishing three primary roles of RNAs: (i) Being the genetic material (ii) act as ribozymes (iii) and regulate other macromolecular processes. Hence, both mRNAs or messenger RNAs (protein-coding RNAs) and non-coding RNAs or ncRNAs (do not code proteins) are of interest in a variety of studies. The ncRNAs of particular interest are miRNAs which are short ncRNAs that regulate the lifetime of mRNAs; and, lncRNAs or long non-coding RNAs which are ≥ 200 nucleotides long, regulate the gene expression and also take part in a broad range of cellular & developmental processes.

The type and quantity of genes transcribed is dependent on the cell-type and its environment, and is tightly regulated. Disruptions to this regulatory process is often the cause of several diseases. Being intermediary between DNA and proteome as well as being molecules of regulatory role, understanding the variations in the transcriptome of a cell in response to the changes in the function and environment of the cell is critical to understanding the regulatory mechanisms pertinent to the mechanistic understanding of the development and disease. Thus, the composition of transcriptome is often used as a proxy for cellular functional status.

Our understanding of the transcriptome has been largely enabled by the advancement in technology. In the late 90's, microarrays could be used to profile the transcriptome of a population of cells. This technology essentially was used to measure the average expression level for each gene across a large population of input cells. However, microarrays detect only known RNAs, so they can't be used for discovery. In addition, background hybridization interferes with detection of low-level expression and probe saturation causes variation in highly expressed genes undetected. Recent advances in sequencing technology have made it possible to quantify the transcriptome of a population of cells by sequencing (RNA-seq or bulk RNA-seq). The number of reads mapping to a gene is a measure of the transcriptional level of that gene. RNA-seq, while being more precise than array based methods, it also offers simultaneous transcript discovery and quantification. Bulk RNA-sequencing enabled us to compare the transcriptome across different samples and had significant input into our understanding of several disease processes including cancer. In 2009 (Tang *et al.*, 2009), a new method was proposed to profile transcriptome from an individual cell. This technology is now referred to as single-cell RNA-seq (scRNA-seq) and has improved our understanding of the heterogeneity present in the otherwise homogeneous tissues. scRNA-seq allows to study new biological questions in which cell-specific changes in transcriptome are important and these include, cell type identification, heterogeneity of cell responses, stochasticity of gene expression and inference of gene regulatory networks across the cells.

Thus, in this article, we describe the guidelines for experimental design, data quality control and computational methods that can be used to derive biological insights from bulk RNA-seq data for mRNA, miRNA, and lncRNA; and scRNA-seq data. The procedures described in this article have been applied in multitude of studies such as Chow *et al.* (2017); George *et al.* (2016); Ucar *et al.* (2017).

Experimental Design, Data Processing & Quality Assessment

Experimental design is very important, though often neglected, step of the project. A well-designed experiment will have sufficient power to address the biological question of interest. A good experimental design in RNA-seq experiment considers library types (single end/paired end), number of reads or sequencing depth and number of replicates per condition. If the goal of the experiment does not involve the novel isoform discovery then single end data should serve the purpose. If the project requires only quantification of gene expression, as suggested by the ENCODE (encyclopedia of DNA elements) study, ~ 36 million mapped reads would be sufficient to accurately quantify the abundance of 80% of genes (Sims *et al.*, 2014). It's also been noted that to detect the novel and rare isoforms, ~ 200 million paired-end reads will be required in human cells.

Adding control sequences: It's important to consider including exogenous reference transcripts ('spike-ins') (Chen *et al.*, 2015) that are useful both for quality control and for library-size normalization. The *External RNA control consortium (ERCC) spike-in*

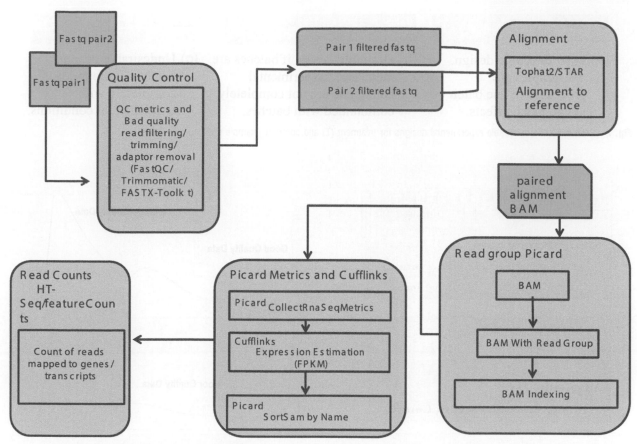

Fig. 1 Schematic for mRNA-seq quantification pipeline.

control mix consists of pre-formulated set of 96 polyadenylated transcripts with varying GC content and length can be used for this purpose.

Sample size estimation: Besides library preparation, estimation of the number of samples per condition is also important for a reliable identification of transcripts relevant to the study. Statistical power to detect differentially expressed genes (DEGs) varies with effect size, sequencing depth and the number of samples per condition. Analysis of data sets from several studies indicates the need for negative binomial distribution to account for the over-dispersion mainly caused by natural biological variation present in RNA-seq studies (Anders and Huber, 2010; Robinson and Oshlack, 2010). The complexity of this distribution makes it difficult to arrive at an analytical solution for power analysis and sample size estimation (Pham and Jimenez, 2012). Other issues that complicate the power estimation include multiple hypotheses correction, techniques used to estimate dispersion, and normalization methods used. Therefore, numerical methods such as Monte Carlo simulations have often been employed to analyze and estimate the sample size required for RNA-seq studies (Ching *et al.*, 2014). However, with fixed cost and limited resources for the experiment, reducing the number of reads per sample while increasing the number of samples will yield better results for DEG analysis. As a general rule, at least three samples per condition is recommended.

Batch Effect is defined as a non-biological source of the signal that is introduced into the data and that can confound with the biological signal. The batch effect is typically consistent across transcripts, exons or genes among samples in a batch and so may lead to gross errors in the calculation of statistical significance, estimation of effect sizes and other statistical measures. Several studies have noticed batch effects due to reagent batch and sequencing dates. Therefore, it is important to design RNA-seq experiments to minimize the effect of technical noise due to batch effects. However, batch effects cannot be completely eliminated due to the constraints of sample availability or other logistical limitations. In such situations, randomization of samples across library preparation batches and lanes is highly recommended to avoid technical factors completely confounding with the experimental conditions. For example, an experiment with all treatment samples are sequenced in one batch while the control samples are sequenced in another batch is difficult to analyze. A few examples of desirable and undesirable experimental designs are depicted in **Fig. 2**:

The processing of transcriptomic data (schematics are provided in **Figs. 1, 10** and **11**), RNA-seq data precisely, can be divided into 3 major steps.

(1) *Quality control (QC)*: Quality control (QC) is a critical step in both bulk and single-cell RNA-seq data analysis. For bulk RNA-seq, the QC steps include assessment of RNA quality and samples with inadequate quality will not be sequenced. Quality of raw sequencing data will be assessed based on the number of reads and the read quality scores. Examples for good and poor-

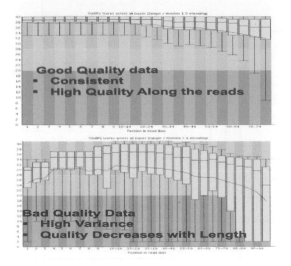

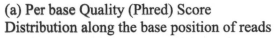

(a) Most desirable design. All samples are processed in one batch i.e. no batch effects.

(b) Desirable design if batches are inevitable. Experimental conditions are not completely confounded with batches.

(c) Undesirable design, batches confounded completely with experimental conditions.

Fig. 2   Desirable and undesirable experimental designs for treatment (T) and control(C) sample profiling.

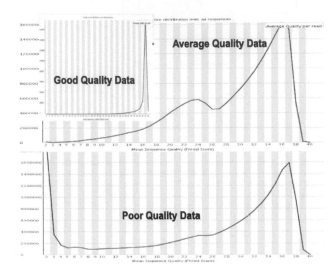

(a) Per base Quality (Phred) Score Distribution along the base position of reads

(b) Per Sequence Quality (Phred score) Distribution

Fig. 3   Quality assessment of RNA-seq libraries by checking.

quality data are shown in **Fig. 3**. Finally, the mapping quality score which is the probability that the read is misplaced after the alignment of the read, provides a measure of the overall quality of the data.

The raw read quality estimation involves determining per base quality and per sequence quality, identification of duplicates, GC content, and presence of adaptors/over-represented sequences (see **Fig. 4** for an example). FastQC (for Illumina: see "Relevant Websites section") and NGSQC (platform independent) (Dai *et al.*, 2010) are two popular tools, that provides the quick diagnostics of an NGS library. Removal of poor quality reads & bases, trimming of adaptors can be performed via FASTX-Toolkit (see "Relevant Websites section") and Trimmomatic (Bolger *et al.*, 2014).

In case of scRNA-seq data, distinguishing biological heterogeneity from technical artifacts makes it much more difficult to assess the quality. The limited amount of RNA available from a single cell makes it difficult to assess the quality of RNA prior to sequencing. Previous studies have used the expression levels of housekeeping genes. But this approach is not used anymore after the demonstration that they are highly variable and associated with cell-types (Oyolu *et al.*, 2012). Often the number of genes detected and the mapping rates are used as QC measures to remove low-quality cells prior to downstream analysis. The proportion of reads mapping to the mitochondrial genes is an indication of cells that are undergoing apoptosis and can be used to remove low-quality cells (Jiang *et al.*, 2016).

(2) *Mapping*: Reads from an RNA-seq experiment can be mapped to the genome or a known transcriptome. Mapping to the genome is performed if the goal of the experiment includes identification of novel isoforms. For a typical high-quality human sample library, >70% of mapping rate to human genome is expected. TopHat2 (Kim *et al.*, 2013) and STAR (Dobin *et al.*, 2013) are popular algorithms (spliced aware mapper i.e., accounting for splice junctions during mapping) for genome mapping. Whereas, the transcriptome based mapping can be performed by bowtie2/bwa (Langmead and Salzberg, 2012; Li and Durbin, 2010). Transcriptome based mapping yields lower percentage of reads mapped due to lack of sequences of unannotated transcripts. When a reference genome is not available (for non-model organisms) or is incomplete, then *de novo* transcriptome assembly should be performed. *Trinity* (Grabherr *et al.*, 2011), *Oases* (Schulz *et al.*, 2012) and *SOAP denovo-Trans* (Xie *et al.*, 2014) are some of the popular algorithms for transcriptome assembly. Longer reads or paired-end reads will aid in the *de novo* assembly. It is recommended to combine all the reads from multiple samples together and then do the combined assembly to generate the

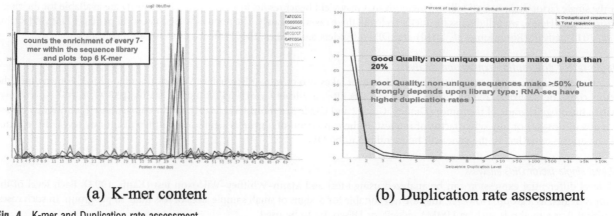

(a) K-mer content   (b) Duplication rate assessment

Fig. 4 K-mer and Duplication rate assessment.

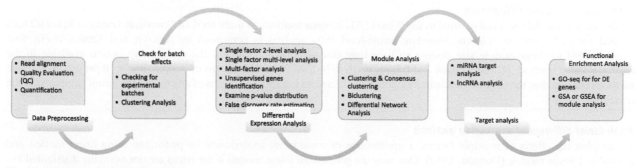

Fig. 5 Schematic of bulk sample analysis.

reference set of contigs. These reference contigs can be used for mapping, expression quantification, and comparison across different groups.

(3) *Quantification*: The important step in RNA-seq data analysis is to estimate gene and transcript abundance. *HTSeq* (Anders *et al.*, 2015) or *featureCounts* (Liao *et al.*, 2014) quantify the abundance by aggregating the number of mapped reads in each exon (determined by Gene Transfer Format [GTF] file), as desired. In addition to aggregating the raw counts, various per sample normalization methods have been developed that accounts for feature-length and library sizes. RPKM (reads per kilobase of exon model per million reads), FPKM (Fragment per kilobase of exon model per million reads) and TPM (Transcript Per Million) are common measures of expression provided by various analysis tools: cufflinks (Trapnell *et al.*, 2010), RSEM (Li and Dewey, 2011), eXpress (Roberts and Pachter, 2013) and Kallisto (Bray *et al.*, 2016). FPKM is used for paired-end read sequencing and RPKM for single-end reads. Whereas TPM, unlike RPKM, skips normalization for gene length after sequencing depth normalization. It makes the sum of all TPMs in all samples same and aid in the comparison of expression profiles among different samples. Transcript abundance is computed as average of normalized abundance of exons in the transcript.

Bulk Transcriptomic Analysis

Bulk sample analysis is a common feature of all experimental designs involving RNA-seq. Its primary aim is to identify genes and gene modules associated with biologically relevant structure in samples e.g., treated vs control samples, tumors of varying clinical attributes, samples of different cellular states, etc. The schematic in **Fig. 5** captures the core steps in bulk transcriptome analysis. Each step after the data preprocessing step is described below.

Differential Expression Analysis

A typical RNA-seq study may involve analysis of the impact of one or more factors relevant to the study on the transcriptome, the identification of DEGs. For example, several clinical conditions can affect genes' expression in a patient sample, multiple biological conditions such as cell cycle phase and gene knock-outs can affect the expression of genes in the associated pathways. A factor, representing a biological or a clinical condition, may be categorical with 2 or more levels, or real-valued.

From statistics point of view, the study designs can be classified into three categories: (1) Single factor, 2-level design, (2) single factor, multi-level design, and (3) multi-factor design. Though the analytical approaches used for multi-factor designs are applicable for the single factor designs, well-tailored methods that may yield better results in sensitivity and specificity are available for the single factor designs. Hence, we will discuss the methods for all three cases separately. The popularly used statistical packages LIMMA (Ritchie *et al.*, 2015), edgeR (Robinson *et al.*, 2010) and DEseq (Anders and Huber, 2010) offer options for all these cases.

Single factor differential expression analysis

In single factor differential expression analysis, the factor takes two or more discrete levels or continuous valued. For example, the factors could be oestrogen receptor (ER) status (ER+vs ER−, a 2-level factor), p53 mutation status (p53 + vs. p53 −, a 2-level factor), histological grade of the tumor (Grade1, Grade2 and Grade 3; a multi-level factor), treatment response (continuous valued in terms of dosage) or any other factor of interest. If the expression of a gene is significantly different for any level of the factor relative to the other levels, the gene will be identified to be DEG.

2-Level single factor DEG analysis

A 2-level differential expression can be analyzed using t-test and Mann–Whitney–Wilcoxon test (Kanji, 1993). Each level of the factor is treated as a group. However, they are not suitable for designs of small sample sizes of less than 10 per group. In such cases, empirical Bayes methods such as LIMMA, edgeR, or DEseq are to be used.

Multi-level single factor DEG analysis

While being applicable, it is not optimal to use 2-level DEG analysis methods to multi-level DEG analysis, owing to $K(K-1)/2$ tests needed for each gene for K-levels. Therefore, multi-level DEG analysis is performed by ANOVA and Kruskal-Wallis tests (Kanji, 1993) for large sample size designs such as large disease cohorts. However, the multi-group option available in the empirical Bayes methods (LIMMA, edgeR and DEseq) needs to be used for typical designs of sample sizes < 10 per group. All these methods test whether there are any statistically significant differences between the means of any one of the group compared to the remaining groups.

Multi-factor differential expression analysis

To decipher the effects of multiple factors, a multivariate or multi-factor analysis will be performed using linear models and generalized linear models (Dobson, 1990). One may use generalized linear models if the errors are not normally distributed but belong to one of the members of the exponential family of distributions. In this case, all samples are treated to belong to one group and the model accounts for the sample characteristics by their attributes. For example, Miller *et al.* (2005) used a linear model to identify p53 mutation specific changes among expression of nearly 30,000 genes using a cohort of >250 tumors. Expression of a gene is modeled as a combination of *tumor grade, ER status*, and *p53 mutation status*. The statistical significance of the estimated parameters of the linear model was evaluated using ANOVA procedure. The genes were ranked by the coefficient of the factor *p53 status* and the top genes were selected to have been affected by p53 mutation specifically.

Deconvolving batch effects

It is important to remove batch effects prior to downstream analysis of data using batch effect removal methods (Leek, 2014). The known batch effects can also be dealt by COMBAT (Johnson *et al.*, 2007) analysis or by incorporating the known batch factors as independent variables in multi-factor differential expression analysis. The unknown batch effects can be identified by whole transcriptome clustering of samples or Surrogate Variable Analysis (SVA) (Leek *et al.*, 2012). However, the observations have to be carefully interpreted for their biological relevance in the data before correcting for them. The more complicated situation is when the batch is completely confounded with that of the biological factor of interest (**Fig. 2(c)**). Though it is most undesirable, DEGs can be identified if the biological effect is significantly stronger than the batch effect on the gene expression measurements. In such a case, one can use iPLR (Li *et al.*, 2012), as was applied to identify DEGs in batch confounded analysis in this publication, for a better estimate of false discovery rate (FDR) of differential expression followed by effect size filtering.

False discovery rate (FDR) assessment

A critical step towards choosing the right set of differentially expressed genes is the assessment of false discovery rate. The popular differential expression analysis packages such as LIMMA and DEseq provide estimates of local and global FDR. However, the distribution of p-values needs to be examined, see **Fig. 6(A)** for ideal or theoretical distribution. However, it is common to see the distributions shown in **Fig. 6(B–D)**. FDR estimates can be improved by using *fdrtool* (Strimmer, 2008) or *ConReg-R* (Li *et al.*, 2011). Careful consideration of all aspects of FDR estimation lead to discovering the impact of mutation in PRPF8 on mRNA splicing in retinal tissue (Korir *et al.*, 2014).

Analysis for Module Identification

A Gene's function is dependent on how the other genes in the cell function. For example, transcription factors' expression affects the expression of their downstream genes, coordinated expression or repression of multiple genes is important to carry out functions such as DNA replication, proliferation and apoptosis. Such functional dependencies among genes need to be elicited in the biological conditions under investigation. Though biological systems are complex, they are amenable to systematic analysis to

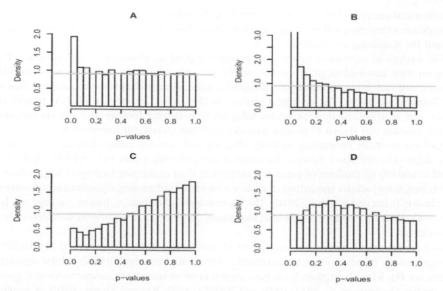

Fig. 6 (A) Desired or theoretical distribution of p-value, and (B–D) are typical distributions encountered in practice which need to be appropriately analyzed to get improved estimates of false discovery rates. The grey horizontal line shows the proportion of null hypotheses in the data, π_0. Reproduced from Li *et al.* (2011).

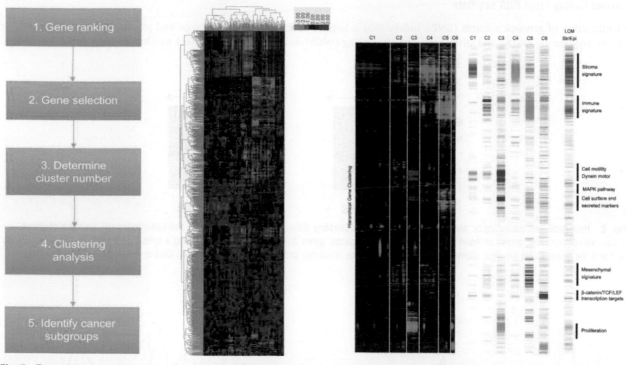

Fig. 7 Transcriptomic clustering procedure and an example of hierarchical clustering of expression data. Reproduced from Lawlor *et al.* (2012). And k-means based consensus clustering of ovarian cancer data for subtyping. Reproduced from Tothill *et al.* (2008).

elicit these functional dependencies by identifying gene sets or modules associated with biological conditions using 'module analysis' approaches: (1) Clustering, (2) biclustering, and (3) differential network analysis.

Clustering is an unsupervised analysis technique to discover hidden structure in the data such as, gene modules and heterogeneity among samples. Of the multitude of clustering techniques, hierarchical and K-means clustering are used extensively. The clustering analysis procedure for gene expression data and examples of clustering are shown in **Fig. 7**. The *multiClust* (Lawlor *et al.*, 2016) is an easy-2-use R-package to deal with all steps associated with clustering, including visualization. However, 'cluster' (Eisen *et al.*, 1998) software offers an easy to use graphical interface for clustering, though it doesn't offer important options for a variety of steps in clustering such as feature selection and distance metrics. The package "Treeview" (Eisen *et al.*, 1998) offers an easy to use graphical interface for interactive visualization of clustering results.

To eliminate spurious and unstable clustering of genes and samples, consensus clustering (CC) (Korir *et al.*, 2014) is employed. The central idea of consensus clustering is that the genes/samples that cluster together consistently for multiple bootstrap runs are the robust clusters and the remaining are spurious.

Clustering and CC analysis of expression data was successfully applied to identify subtypes in cancer. Cancers are typically classified depending on their tissue of origin. However, several genomic studies are providing more detailed molecular characterizations of tumors, and thus bring about the possibility of a more accurate classification based on their molecular profiling (Perou *et al.*, 2000; Tothill *et al.*, 2008). The molecular profiles, in *The Cancer Genome Atlas (TCGA)* project, revealed that cancer from the same tissue can be classified into molecular subtypes with distinct biology and clinical outcome. In many cases, molecular subtype information was shown to provide avenues for better therapeutic intervention.

Biclustering is based on mutually reinforcing modules of genes and samples, rather than all sample approach used in the clustering described above. The difference between biclustering and clustering (Chia and Karuturi, 2010) is depicted in **Fig. 8**. Biclustering was used to identify co-modules of genes and samples to elicit underlying biology in large cohorts of samples. *biclust* package (Kaiser and Leisch, 2008) allows researchers to explore a variety of biclustering algorithms which were shown to identify a different types of biclusters (Chia and Karuturi, 2010). The ChiaKaruturi() function in 'biclust' package can be used to unify the ranking of the biclusters output by multiple biclustering algorithms. Xie *et al.* (2018) provides overview of how biclustering was used in biological discovery.

Differential Network (co-expression) Analysis, in contrast to clustering and biclustering, is used to identify co-expressed gene modules in a supervised setting. In this case, we are interested in identifying gene modules that exhibit significant changes in their co-expression patterns, see **Fig. 9** for illustration. It has been shown to be an effective technique to identify gene modules and hub genes in numerous studies (Bostrom *et al.*, 2011; Gillis and Pavlidis, 2009; Ray and Zhang, 2010). A variety of algorithms are available to conduct univariate (2-level or multi-level) and multivariate differential co-expression analysis (Kostka and Spang, 2004; Li and Karuturi, 2010; Karuturi *et al.*, 2006; Liany *et al.*2017).

Variant Calling From RNA-seq Data

Identification of genomic variants (SNPs, Indels, SVs) is important to uncover the genotype and phenotype relationship. Whole exome sequencing (WES) and whole genome sequencing (WGS) are most commonly used to identify these genomic variants.

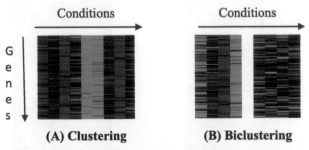

Fig. 8 Heatmaps (red for induction and green for repression) illustrating difference between clustering and biclustering (A) a cluster of genes, genes are co-expressed across all conditions; (B) a bicluster of genes, genes are co-expressed only among a subset of conditions (heatmap on the left) and the heatmap on the right shows no co-expression on the remaining conditions. Reproduced from Chia and Karuturi (2010).

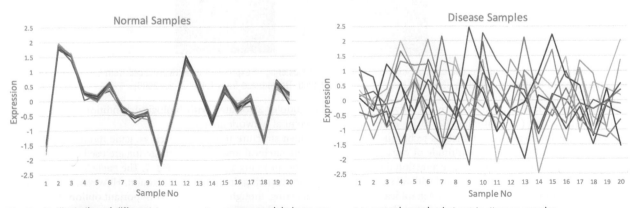

Fig. 9 An illustration of differential co-expression, a gene module is co-expressed in normal samples but not in disease samples.

Recently, calling genomic variants from RNA-seq data has become popular as it offers the variant information for samples without WES/WGS data, and with corresponding WES/WGS data, it offers secondary validation for the variant calls from within expressed transcripts. Piskol *et al.* (2013) have shown that ~40%–50% of the coding variants identified in WGS data and 70% of the variants in expressed genes can be identified from RNA-seq.

The primary challenge in RNA-seq based variant calling is the accurate placement of reads in the genome. Additional complexity in the mapping arises due to RNA splicing. Average human exon length is 150 bp and common sequence reads are (2 × 100) which leads to the generation of reads crossing the splice junctions. This can create a significant problem in downstream variant calling due to misalignments and thus pipeline used for variant calling needs to have high-quality splice junction databases along with additional filters to remove the false calls. A procedure for variant calling, including the recommended filters, is given in the schematic in **Fig. 10** (based on GATK best practices for RNA-seq variant calling and filter suggested in the Piskol *et al.* (2013)).

Analysis of Non-Coding RNAs (ncRNAs)

ncRNAs, such as miRNAs, exert their function by targeting mRNAs. Hence, it is important to understand the analysis of ncRNAs. We focus on the analysis of miRNAs and lncRNAs in this section. These procedures are used only when respective library preparation methods are used for sequencing.

miRNA-seq analysis

miRNAs belong to the family of small (~22 nucleotide long) ncRNAs and function as post-transcriptional regulators in plants and animals. miRNAs commonly function by binding to 3′UTR of target mRNAs and causing its cleavage or translation inhibition (Ambros, 2004; Lu *et al.*, 2008). Though, there is evidence that miRNAs may act as positive regulators in some cases (Vasudevan *et al.*, 2007). High conservation of miRNAs among evolutionarily divergent species suggests that these molecules are involved in essential biological processes (Pasquinelli *et al.*, 2000) such as cell growth, cell proliferations, embryonic development, apoptosis and tissue differentiation (Esquela-Kerscher and Slack, 2006).

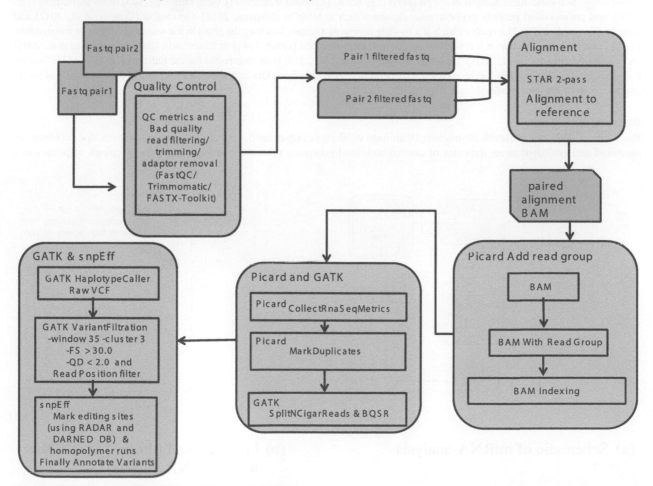

Fig. 10 Schematic of analysis of RNA-seq data for variant calling.

miRNA-seq data analysis scheme is shown in **Fig. 11(a)**. The first step in the analysis of miRNA-seq data is trimming of adaptor sequence and then examining the distribution of sequencing length to determine the quality of the library, peak at ~22 bp usually ensures high-quality library (**Fig. 11(b)**). Afterwards, depending on the goal of the experiment, sequences can be mapped to miRBase (a high-quality database of known miRNA species) or reference genome. Mapping to miRBase (Kozomara and Griffiths-Jones, 2014) will provide the quick estimation of the known miRNA species but mapping to the genome can detect novel miRNAs. Popular tools for miRNA analysis include miRdeep2 (Friedlander *et al.*, 2012), miRanalyzer (Hackenberg *et al.*, 2011) and miRspring (Humphreys and Suter, 2013). In Pullagura *et al.* (2018) we used these tools to investigate the requirement of the DICER cofactors TARBP2 and PRKRA in miRNA biogenesis.

lncRNA-seq analysis

Another class of ncRNAs is long ncRNAs (lncRNAs) with a length of more than 200 nucleotides (Kung *et al.*, 2013). Numerous lncRNAs are present throughout the genome. One-way to classify them is according to their genomic location (Kung *et al.*, 2013). According to the genomic location, lncRNAs can be classified as stand-alone lncRNAs (distinct transcription units located in sequence space not overlapping with protein-coding genes), Natural antisense transcripts, Pseudogenes ("remnant" of genes that have lost their coding potential due to mutations), Long intronic ncRNAs (Found within introns of annotated genes) and Divergent transcripts, promoter-associated transcripts, and enhancer RNAs (produced from the vicinity of transcription start sites or produced from the enhancer region). lncRNAs do perform various biological functions in a variety of developmental process and disease like cancer (Huarte, 2015). Typical bioinformatics workflow for the screening of lncRNAs has three steps: (i) Alignment to the genome of interest [Tophat2 and STAR]; (ii) reference guided (Cufflinks) or *ab initio* transcriptome assembly (Guttman *et al.*, 2010); and, (iii) coding potential estimation of assembled transcripts (Hu *et al.*, 2017). A comprehensive pipeline for lncRNA analysis is available online, see "Relevant Websites section".

Functional Analysis

The functional relevance analysis of the DEGs and gene modules is a critical step towards interpreting their function. It is typically carried out by conducting enrichment analysis of the pathways (e.g., KEGG (Kanehisa *et al.*, 2017)), Gene Ontology (GO) terms (Ashburner *et al.*, 2000), and pre-identified publicly available gene signatures such as MSigDB (Liberzon, 2014), GeneSigDB (Culhane *et al.*, 2012) and DSigDB (Yoo *et al.*, 2015). The central idea is if a module represents a certain function, the genes in the relevant pathway or the signature will be enriched in the module. It is typically tested using Fisher's exact test (Fisher, 1945) or KS test as in GSA (Subramanian *et al.*, 2005) and GSEA (Subramanian *et al.*, 2005). However, GO-seq (Young *et al.*, 2010) is recommended for the functional analysis of DEGs from RNA-seq data, GO-seq accounts for the gene length dependent bias in identifying DEGs (power to identify differential expression of longer genes is more in RNA-seq studies).

Diagnosis & prognosis

The National Institutes of Health Biomarkers Definitions Working Group defined a biomarker as a characteristic that is objectively measured and evaluated as an indicator of normal biological processes, pathogenic processes, or pharmacologic responses to a

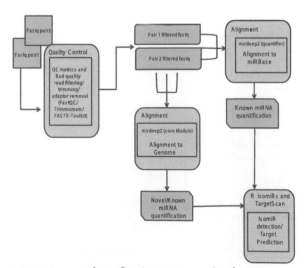

(a) Schematic of miRNA-analysis

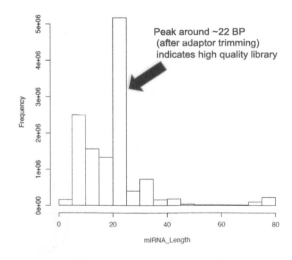

(b) Length based filtering of miRNAs from an RNA library

Fig. 11 Schematic of miRNA-seq data analysis procedure.

therapeutic intervention (Biomarkers Definitions Working, G, 2001). Gene expression signatures based biomarkers are used to diagnose disease (diagnostic biomarker) as well as to predict patient's prognosis (prognostic marker) or response to therapeutics (predictive marker) (Italiano, 2011).

In general, biomarkers are designed using systematic principles of classifier design. Based on the empirical study (Dudoit *et al.*, 2002) of gene expression based classifier design, simple classification algorithms like k-nearest neighbor (KNN) and diagonal linear discriminant analysis (DLDA) are recommended over more complicated classification algorithms like support vector machines (SVMs) for biomarker studies.

Single Cell Transcriptomic Analysis

Single cell transcriptome profiling is used to identify cell types, interactions among them and modeling stochasticity of gene expression in a sample, primarily using mRNA profiling. DEG analysis is fundamental to these objectives.

Differential Expression Analysis

The methods developed for identifying DEGs in bulk RNA-seq are suboptimal for scRNA-seq data due to higher noise contributed by both technical and biological factors specific to scRNA-seq data. The primary technical factors are low amount of transcriptome in a cell and hi-level of amplification required for sequencing which lead to amplification biases or dropout events i.e., the amplification or the capture is not successful for many mRNAs (Vallejos *et al.*, 2017). Biological variability is also higher in scRNA-seq data due to the stochastic nature of transcription (Raj *et al.*, 2006) and multimodality in gene expression (Shalek *et al.*, 2013) originating from the presence of multiple possible cell states within a cell population. All these together pose serious challenges for detection of DEGs.

Recently, several methods that explicitly model the technical and biological variability in scRNA-seq data have been developed to identify the DEGs in scRNA-seq data (Dal Molin *et al.*, 2017). Model-based Analysis of Single-cell Transcriptomics, MAST (Finak *et al.*, 2015), explicitly considers the dropouts using a bimodal distribution with expression strongly different from zero and proposes a generalized linear model to fit the data. Single-Cell Differential Expression (Kharchenko *et al.*, 2014), models the counts of each cell as a mixture of a zero-inflated Negative Binomial distribution and a dropout component and uses a Bayesian model to estimate the posterior probability that a gene is differentially expressed in one group with respect to another. Single-cell Differential Distributions, scDD (Korthauer *et al.*, 2016), is based on a multimodal Bayesian modeling framework for explicitly modeling the multimodal distributions of single cells and testing for differentially distributed genes associated with this multimodality.

Cell Type Identification

In a typical human body, there exists an estimated 40 trillion cells and is classified into approximately 200 cell-types based on morphology (Bianconi *et al.*, 2013). Advances in immunofluorescence and flow cytometry have enabled more refined classification based on the presence or absence of various surface markers (Pruszak *et al.*, 2007). However, the number of cell surface markers are limited to discern the plethora of cell types and these techniques are limited to easily dissociable tissues like blood (Roussel *et al.*, 2010). The development of scRNA-seq has changed the status quo and enabled the identification of novel cell-types based on the entire transcriptome of individual cells. scRNA-seq has been used to study different tissues and organs, both during development and at a fixed point in time (Rizvi *et al.*, 2017). Almost all the methods involve feature selection steps to remove noisy and irrelevant features, dimensionality reduction steps to avoid the "curse of dimensionality" and finally clustering steps to identify cell-types. The process of cell type identification and the recommended tools are outlined in **Fig. 12**. The most popular options currently available for each step are shown. These are not exhaustive lists and the most appropriate method in each step will depend on the data type and the technical platform used for generating the scRNA-seq data. SCEED package (Abrams *et al.*, 2018) helps in the experimental design and identifying optimal analysis procedure.

Cell:Cell Communication Analysis

Cell:Cell communication analysis is used to elicit cell communication networks facilitated by ligand-receptor interaction. *Single Cell-2-Cell Communicator (SC2CC)* [manuscript in preparation] helps identify cell:cell communication network using scRNA-seq data, in contrast to CCCExplorer (Choi *et al.*, 2015) which is used for sorted bulk RNA-seq data analysis. A preliminary version of *SC2CC* was used in Lawlor *et al.* (2017); **Fig. 13**. The primary features of *SC2CC* are: (1) *SC2CC* integrates cell type identification methodology described above into cell:cell communication analysis. (2) Selection of expressed ligands is based on both expression level and differential expression analysis. As scRNA-seq data enables identification of multiple cell types, *SC2CC* will identify differentially expressed ligands using multi-group analysis in *edgeR* and annotate a cell type with a ligand if the ligand's average expression in the cell type is more than the average expression in all cell types and it is significant by *edgeR* multi-group analysis. (3) *SC2CC* analyzes for both autocrine (cell communicates with itself) and paracrine (one cell communicates with another cell) signaling among all cell types. (4) *SC2CC* has augmented ligand-receptor pairs (1578, with 469 ligands and 342 receptors) database for the analysis. *SC2CC* identifies the receptor activation and assigns

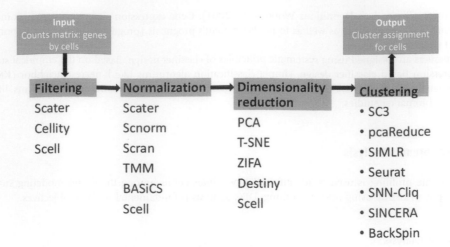

Fig. 12 Steps involved in cell-type identification from single-cell RNA-seq data.

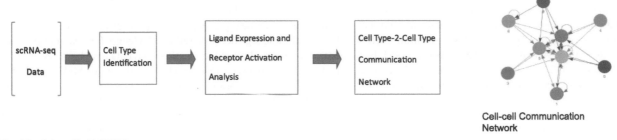

Fig. 13 Schematic of *SC2CC*.

autocrine/paracrine signaling using PAGODA (Fan *et al.*, 2016). The analysis of scRNA-seq data for cell:cell communication with *SC2CC* leads to a network of communication among different cell types, both autocrine and paracrine signaling.

Discussion

Transcriptomics data is a closer representation of abundance of regulatory molecules in the cell. In addition, the availability of easier-to-work and cost-effective technologies to generate transcriptomic data made it an integral part of most genomic studies, including disease genomics. Though mRNA, miRNA, and lncRNA are most commonly explored transcriptomic data, several other types of ncRNAs are being studied recently: circRNAs, piRNAs, and nasRNAs (Dong *et al.*, 2017; Kim *et al.*, 2009; Korneev and O'Shea, 2005; Weick and Miska, 2014). RNA specific library preparation methods have been employed to generate data for the type of RNA in consideration. Hence, several data processing steps need to be customized for the type of RNA analyzed. Multiple studies such as spermatogenesis require complex data processing of deeply sequenced data to effectively identify one type of ncRNA from the other type of ncRNAs (e.g., piRNAs from miRNAs) as they are of similar length and abundance. In addition to ncRNAs, fusion genes are another class of RNAs resulting from structural variations in the genome, especially in cancer transcriptomes. Several algorithms are available in the literature to identify fusion genes from RNA-seq data (Jia *et al.*, 2013; Kim and Salzberg, 2011). These methods analyze the junction reads (reads mapping to exons of different genes) and paired-end read mapping information (reads of the same paired-end read mapping to different genes). In addition, isoforms play a critical role in several biological systems, especially in the immune system. Though shotgun sequencing data (e.g., Illumina) has been used to identify isoforms, for better accuracy, it is being used in conjunction with long read sequencing technologies (PacBio and Oxford-nanopore) recently. These require specialized data processing steps (Weirather *et al.*, 2017).

Besides processing and analysis of primary RNA-seq data, a typical genomic study may require probing of transcriptomic data in different systems: model organisms, diseases, and populations. A variety of databases host plethora of transcriptomic data from a vast range of systems for researchers to query and examine the observations of the study in the context. Generic databases such as GEO and SRA, as well as specialized databases such as Oncomine (Rhodes *et al.*, 2004), CBio Portal (Cerami *et al.*, 2012; Gao *et al.*, 2013), and ImmGen (Heng *et al.*, 2008) facilitate such a contextual analysis and validation of the observations of the study. One of the major impediment to such a contextual analysis is the integration of data from multiple platforms as the transcriptomics data has been historically generated using a variety of platforms (e.g., microarrays: Affymetrix, Illumina, and Agilent; sequencing:

Illumina and PacBio, etc). Such an integrative analysis has to be carried out by considering platform specific normalization, and simple procedures such as z-scoring and housekeeping genes' based normalization have been proven to be useful.

In addition, most genomic studies include more than one type of transcriptomic data and genomic data (e.g., genomic variants data, epigenetic data, methylation data and TF-DNA interaction data). Typically, we are interested in studying the relationship and impact of a variety of genomic variants on the transcriptome. Each such analysis requires specialized integration strategies. For example, considerations of mapping single nucleotide or epigenetic variants in promoters to genes vary from that of enhancers or insulators due to their distance from genes; short-range structural variants may need to be interpreted differently from that of long-range structural variants. The strategies include mapping to the closest genes and conducting functional analysis of the mapped genes while accounting for non-uniform distribution of genes in the genome (McLean *et al.*, 2010; Zhou and Murthy Karuturi, 2012)

Taken together, transcriptomic data generation has been extremely impactful and the analysis is reasonably matured: from data processing, quality control, down-stream analysis and integrative analysis. Suitable experimental design, normalization and careful use of the plethora of databases will help elicit important biology of development and disease.

Author Contributions

George and Karuturi conceptualized and lead the writing of the chapter. All authors contributed equally to the chapter.

See also: Applications of Ribosomal RNA Sequence and Structure Analysis for Extracting Evolutionary and Functional Insights. Biological Database Searching. Characterizing and Functional Assignment of Noncoding RNAs. Codon Usage. Computational Pipelines and Workflows in Bioinformatics. Exome Sequencing Data Analysis. Functional Enrichment Analysis. Integrative Analysis of Multi-Omics Data. Natural Language Processing Approaches in Bioinformatics. Next Generation Sequencing Data Analysis. Pipeline of High Throughput Sequencing. Prediction of Coding and Non-Coding RNA. Sequence Analysis. Whole Genome Sequencing Analysis

---

References

Abrams, D., *et al.*, 2018. A computational method to aid the design and analysis of single cell RNA-seq experiments for cell type identification. Available at: https://doi.org/10.1101/247114.

Ambros, V., 2004. The functions of animal microRNAs. Nature 431 (7006), 350–355.

Anders, S., Huber, W., 2010. Differential expression analysis for sequence count data. Genome Biol. 11 (10), R106.

Anders, S., Pyl, P.T., Huber, W., 2015. HTSeq – A python framework to work with high-throughput sequencing data. Bioinformatics 31 (2), 166–169.

Ashburner, M., *et al.*, 2000. Gene ontology: Tool for the unification of biology. The Gene Ontology Consortium. Nat. Genet. 25 (1), 25–29.

Bianconi, E., *et al.*, 2013. An estimation of the number of cells in the human body. Ann. Hum. Biol. 40 (6), 463–471.

Biomarkers Definitions Working Group, G., 2001. Biomarkers and surrogate endpoints: Preferred definitions and conceptual framework. Clin. Pharmacol. Ther. 69 (3), 89–95.

Bolger, A.M., Lohse, M., Usadel, B., 2014. Trimmomatic: A flexible trimmer for Illumina sequence data. Bioinformatics 30 (15), 2114–2120.

Bostrom, P., *et al.*, 2011. MMP-1 expression has an independent prognostic value in breast cancer. BMC Cancer 11, 348.

Bray, N.L., *et al.*, 2016. Near-optimal probabilistic RNA-seq quantification. Nat. Biotechnol. 34 (5), 525–527.

Cech, T.R., *et al.*, 1983. Secondary structure of the Tetrahymena ribosomal RNA intervening sequence: Structural homology with fungal mitochondrial intervening sequences. Proc. Natl. Acad. Sci. USA 80 (13), 3903–3907.

Cerami, E., *et al.*, 2012. The cBio cancer genomics portal: An open platform for exploring multidimensional cancer genomics data. Cancer Discov. 2 (5), 401–404.

Chen, K., *et al.*, 2015. The overlooked fact: Fundamental need for spike-in control for virtually all genome-wide analyses. Mol. Cell. Biol. 36 (5), 662–667.

Chia, B.K., Karuturi, R.K.M., 2010. Differential co-expression framework to quantify goodness of biclusters and compare biclustering algorithms. Algorithms Mol. Biol. 5, 23.

Ching, T., Huang, S., Garmire, L.X., 2014. Power analysis and sample size estimation for RNA-seq differential expression. RNA 20 (11), 1684–1696.

Choi, H., *et al.*, 2015. Transcriptome analysis of individual stromal cell populations identifies stroma-tumor crosstalk in mouse lung cancer model. Cell Rep. 10 (7), 1187–1201.

Chow, K.H., *et al.*, 2017. S100A4 Is a biomarker and regulator of glioma stem cells that is critical for mesenchymal transition in glioblastoma. Cancer Res. 77 (19), 5360–5373.

Crick, F.H., 1958. On protein synthesis. Symp. Soc. Exp. Biol. 12, 138–163.

Culhane, A.C., *et al.*, 2012. GeneSigDB: A manually curated database and resource for analysis of gene expression signatures. Nucleic Acids Res. 40 (Database issue), D1060–D1066.

Dai, M., *et al.*, 2010. NGSQC: Cross-platform quality analysis pipeline for deep sequencing data. BMC Genom. 11 (Suppl 4), S7.

Dal Molin, A., Baruzzo, G., Di Camillo, B., 2017. Single-cell RNA-sequencing: Assessment of differential expression analysis methods. Front. Genet. 8, 62.

Dobin, A., *et al.*, 2013. STAR: Ultrafast universal RNA-seq aligner. Bioinformatics 29 (1), 15–21.

Dobson, A.J., 1990. An Introduction to Generalized Linear Models. London: Chapman and Hall.

Dong, Y., *et al.*, 2017. Circular RNAs in cancer: An emerging key player. J. Hematol. Oncol. 10 (1), 2.

Dudoit, S., Fridlyand, J., Speed, T.P., 2002. Comparison of discrimination methods for the classification of tumors using gene expression data. J. Am. Stat. Assoc. 97 (457), 77–87.

Eisen, M.B., *et al.*, 1998. Cluster analysis and display of genome-wide expression patterns. Proc. Natl. Acad. Sci. USA 95 (25), 14863–14868.

Esquela-Kerscher, A., Slack, F.J., 2006. Oncomirs – microRNAs with a role in cancer. Nat. Rev. Cancer 6 (4), 259–269.

Fan, J., *et al.*, 2016. Characterizing transcriptional heterogeneity through pathway and gene set overdispersion analysis. Nat. Methods 13 (3), 241–244.

Finak, G., et al., 2015. MAST: A flexible statistical framework for assessing transcriptional changes and characterizing heterogeneity in single-cell RNA sequencing data. Genome Biol. 16, 278.

Fisher, R.A., 1945. A new test for 2 × 2 tables. Nature 156, 388.

Friedlander, M.R., et al., 2012. miRDeep2 accurately identifies known and hundreds of novel microRNA genes in seven animal clades. Nucleic Acids Res. 40 (1), 37–52.

Gao, J., et al., 2013. Integrative analysis of complex cancer genomics and clinical profiles using the cBioPortal. Sci. Signal. 6 (269), p11.

George, J., et al., 2016. Leukaemia cell of origin identified by chromatin landscape of bulk tumour cells. Nat. Commun. 7, 12166.

Gillis, J., Pavlidis, P., 2009. A methodology for the analysis of differential coexpression across the human lifespan. BMC Bioinform. 10, 306.

Grabherr, M.G., et al., 2011. Full-length transcriptome assembly from RNA-seq data without a reference genome. Nat. Biotechnol. 29 (7), 644–652.

Guttman, M., et al., 2010. Ab initio reconstruction of cell type-specific transcriptomes in mouse reveals the conserved multi-exonic structure of lincRNAs. Nat. Biotechnol. 28 (5), 503–510.

Hackenberg, M., Rodriguez-Ezpeleta, N., Aransay, A.M., 2011. miRanalyzer: An update on the detection and analysis of microRNAs in high-throughput sequencing experiments. Nucleic Acids Res. 39 (Web Server issue), W132–W138.

Heng, T.S., Painter, M.W., 2008.The Immunological Genome Project: Networks of gene expression in immune cells. Nat. Immunol. 9 (10), 1091–1094.

Huarte, M., 2015. The emerging role of lncRNAs in cancer. Nat. Med. 21 (11), 1253–1261.

Humphreys, D.T., Suter, C.M., 2013. miRspring: A compact standalone research tool for analyzing miRNA-seq data. Nucleic Acids Res. 41 (15), e147.

Hu, L., et al., 2017. COME: A robust coding potential calculation tool for lncRNA identification and characterization based on multiple features. Nucleic Acids Res. 45 (1), e2.

Italiano, A., 2011. Prognostic or predictive? It's time to get back to definitions!. J. Clin. Oncol. 29 (35), 4718. (author reply 4718-9).

Jiang, P., Thomson, J.A., Stewart, R., 2016. Quality control of single-cell RNA-seq by SinQC. Bioinformatics 32 (16), 2514–2516.

Jia, W., et al., 2013. SOAPfuse: An algorithm for identifying fusion transcripts from paired-end RNA-seq data. Genome Biol. 14 (2), R12.

Johnson, W.E., Li, C., Rabinovic, A., 2007. Adjusting batch effects in microarray expression data using empirical Bayes methods. Biostatistics 8 (1), 118–127.

Kaiser, S., Leisch, F., 2008. Biclust – A toolbox for bicluster analysis in R. In: Proceedings of the Computational Statistics.

Kanehisa, M., et al., 2017. KEGG: New perspectives on genomes, pathways, diseases and drugs. Nucleic Acids Res. 45 (D1), D353–D361.

Kanji, G.K., 1993. 100 Statistical Tests. London: Sage Publications.

Karuturi, R.K.M., et al., 2006. Differential friendly neighbors algorithm for differential relationships based gene selection and classification using microarray data. In: Proceedings of the International Conference on Data Mining (DMIN).

Kharchenko, P.V., Silberstein, L., Scadden, D.T., 2014. Bayesian approach to single-cell differential expression analysis. Nat. Methods 11 (7), 740–742.

Kim, D., et al., 2013. TopHat2: Accurate alignment of transcriptomes in the presence of insertions, deletions and gene fusions. Genome Biol. 14 (4), R36.

Kim, V.N., Han, J., Siomi, M.C., 2009. Biogenesis of small RNAs in animals. Nat. Rev. Mol. Cell Biol. 10 (2), 126–139.

Kim, D., Salzberg, S.L., 2011. TopHat-fusion: An algorithm for discovery of novel fusion transcripts. Genome Biol. 12 (8), R72.

Korir, P.K., et al., 2014. A mutation in a splicing factor that causes retinitis pigmentosa has a transcriptome-wide effect on mRNA splicing. BMC Res. Notes 7, 401.

Korneev, S., O'Shea, M., 2005. Natural antisense RNAs in the nervous system. Rev. Neurosci. 16 (3), 213–222.

Korthauer, K.D., et al., 2016. A statistical approach for identifying differential distributions in single-cell RNA-seq experiments. Genome Biol. 17 (1), 222.

Kostka, D., Spang, R., 2004. Finding disease specific alterations in the co-expression of genes. Bioinformatics 20 (Suppl. 1), i194–i199.

Kozomara, A., Griffiths-Jones, S., 2014. miRBase: Annotating high confidence microRNAs using deep sequencing data. Nucleic Acids Res. 42 (Database issue), D68–D73.

Kung, J.T., Colognori, D., Lee, J.T., 2013. Long noncoding RNAs: Past, present, and future. Genetics 193 (3), 651–669.

Langmead, B., Salzberg, S.L., 2012. Fast gapped-read alignment with Bowtie 2. Nat. Methods 9 (4), 357–359.

Lawlor, N., et al., 2012. multiClust: An R-package for identifying biologically relevant clusters in Cancer Transcriptome profiles. Cancer Inform., Libertas Academica, 15, 103–114.

Lawlor, N., et al., 2017. Single-cell transcriptomes identify human islet cell signatures and reveal cell-type-specific expression changes in type 2 diabetes. Genome Res. 27 (2), 208–222.

Leek, J.T., 2014. svaseq: Removing batch effects and other unwanted noise from sequencing data. Nucleic Acids Res. 42 (21),

Leek, J.T., et al., 2012. The sva package for removing batch effects and other unwanted variation in high-throughput experiments. Bioinformatics 28 (6), 882–883.

Lee, R.C., Feinbaum, R.L., Ambros, V., 1993. The C. elegans heterochronic gene lin-4 encodes small RNAs with antisense complementarity to lin-14. Cell 75 (5), 843–854.

Liany, H., Rajapakse, J.C., Karuturi, R.K.M., 2017. MultiDCoX: Multi-factor analysis of differential co-expression. BMC Bioinform. 18 (Suppl. 16), 576. (bioRxiv).

Liao, Y., Smyth, G.K., Shi, W., 2014. featureCounts: An efficient general purpose program for assigning sequence reads to genomic features. Bioinformatics 30 (7), 923–930.

Liberzon, A., 2014. A description of the Molecular Signatures Database (MSigDB) Web site. Methods Mol. Biol. 1150, 153–160.

Li, J., Choi, K.P., Karuturi, R.K., 2012. Iterative piecewise linear regression to accurately assess statistical significance in batch confounded differential expression analysis. In: Proceedings of the International Symposium Bioinformatics Research and Applications (ISBRA), vol. 7292, pp. 153–164. Springer.

Li, B., Dewey, C.N., 2011. RSEM: Accurate transcript quantification from RNA-seq data with or without a reference genome. BMC Bioinform. 12, 323.

Li, H., Durbin, R., 2010. Fast and accurate long-read alignment with Burrows-Wheeler transform. Bioinformatics 26 (5), 589–595.

Li, J., et al., 2011. ConReg-R: Extrapolative recalibration of the empirical distribution of p-values to improve false discovery rate estimates. Biol. Direct 6, 27.

Li, H., Karuturi, R.K.M., 2010. Significance analysis and improved discovery of disease-specific differentially co-expressed gene sets in microarray data. Int. J. Data Min. Bioinform. 4 (6), 617–638.

Lu, M., et al., 2008. An analysis of human microRNA and disease associations. PLOS ONE 3 (10), e3420.

McLean, C.Y., et al., 2010. GREAT improves functional interpretation of cis-regulatory regions. Nat. Biotechnol. 28 (5), 495–501.

Miller, L.D., et al., 2005. An expression signature for p53 status in human breast cancer predicts mutation status, transcriptional effects, and patient survival. Proc. Natl. Acad. Sci. USA 102 (38), 13550–13555.

Oyolu, C., Zakharia, F., Baker, J., 2012. Distinguishing human cell types based on housekeeping gene signatures. Stem Cells 30 (3), 580–584.

Pasquinelli, A.E., et al., 2000. Conservation of the sequence and temporal expression of let-7 heterochronic regulatory RNA. Nature 408 (6808), 86–89.

Perou, C.M., et al., 2000. Molecular portraits of human breast tumours. Nature 406 (6797), 747–752.

Pham, T.V., Jimenez, C.R., 2012. An accurate paired sample test for count data. Bioinformatics 28 (18), i596–i602.

Piskol, R., Ramaswami, G., Li, J.B., 2013. Reliable identification of genomic variants from RNA-seq data. Am. J. Hum. Genet. 93 (4), 641–651.

Pruszak, J., et al., 2007. Markers and methods for cell sorting of human embryonic stem cell-derived neural cell populations. Stem Cells 25 (9), 2257–2268.

Pullagura, S.R.N., et al., 2018. Functional redundancy of DICER cofactors TARBP2 and PRKRA during murine embryogenesis does not involve miRNA biogenesis. Genetics 208 (4), 1513–1522.

Raj, A., et al., 2006. Stochastic mRNA synthesis in mammalian cells. PLOS Biol. 4 (10), e309.

Ray, M., Zhang, W., 2010. Analysis of Alzheimer's disease severity across brain regions by topological analysis of gene co-expression networks. BMC Syst. Biol. 4, 136.

Rhodes, D.R., et al., 2004. ONCOMINE: A cancer microarray database and integrated data-mining platform. Neoplasia 6 (1), 1–6.

Ritchie, M.E., et al., 2015. limma powers differential expression analyses for RNA-sequencing and microarray studies. Nucleic Acids Res. 43 (7), e47.

Rizvi, A.H., et al., 2017. Single-cell topological RNA-seq analysis reveals insights into cellular differentiation and development. Nat. Biotechnol. 35 (6), 551–560.

Roberts, A., Pachter, L., 2013. Streaming fragment assignment for real-time analysis of sequencing experiments. Nat. Methods 10 (1), 71–73.

Robinson, M.D., McCarthy, D.J., Smyth, G.K., 2010. edgeR: A Bioconductor package for differential expression analysis of digital gene expression data. Bioinformatics 26 (1), 139–140.

Robinson, M.D., Oshlack, A., 2010. A scaling normalization method for differential expression analysis of RNA-seq data. Genome Biol. 11 (3), R25.

Roussel, M., et al., 2010. Refining the white blood cell differential: The first flow cytometry routine application. Cytometry A 77 (6), 552–563.

Schulz, M.H., et al., 2012. Oases: Robust de novo RNA-seq assembly across the dynamic range of expression levels. Bioinformatics 28 (8), 1086–1092.

Shalek, A.K., et al., 2013. Single-cell transcriptomics reveals bimodality in expression and splicing in immune cells. Nature 498 (7453), 236–240.

Sims, D., et al., 2014. Sequencing depth and coverage: Key considerations in genomic analyses. Nat. Rev. Genet. 15 (2), 121–132.

Strimmer, K., 2008. fdrtool: A versatile R package for estimating local and tail area-based false discovery rates. Bioinformatics 24 (12), 1461–1462.

Subramanian, A., et al., 2005. Gene set enrichment analysis: A knowledge-based approach for interpreting genome-wide expression profiles. Proc. Natl. Acad. Sci. USA 102 (43), 15545–15550.

Tang, F., et al., 2009. mRNA-seq whole-transcriptome analysis of a single cell. Nat. Methods 6 (5), 377–382.

Tothill, R.W., et al., 2008. Novel molecular subtypes of serous and endometrioid ovarian cancer linked to clinical outcome. Clin. Cancer Res. 14 (16), 5198–5208.

Trapnell, C., et al., 2010. Transcript assembly and quantification by RNA-seq reveals unannotated transcripts and isoform switching during cell differentiation. Nat. Biotechnol. 28 (5), 511–515.

Ucar, D., et al., 2017. The chromatin accessibility signature of human immune aging stems from CD8(+) T cells. J. Exp. Med. 214 (10), 3123–3144.

Vallejos, C.A., et al., 2017. Normalizing single-cell RNA sequencing data: Challenges and opportunities. Nat. Methods 14 (6), 565–571.

Vasudevan, S., Tong, Y., Steitz, J.A., 2007. Switching from repression to activation: MicroRNAs can up-regulate translation. Science 318 (5858), 1931–1934.

Weick, E.M., Miska, E.A., 2014. piRNAs: From biogenesis to function. Development 141 (18), 3458–3471.

Weirather, J.L., et al., 2017. Comprehensive comparison of pacific biosciences and oxford nanopore technologies and their applications to transcriptome analysis. F1000Research 6, 100.

Xie, Y., et al., 2014. SOAPdenovo-Trans: De novo transcriptome assembly with short RNA-seq reads. Bioinformatics 30 (12), 1660–1666.

Xie, J., et al., 2018. It is time to apply biclustering: A comprehensive review of biclustering applications in biological and biomedical data. Brief. Bioinform.

Yoo, M., et al., 2015. DSigDB: Drug signatures database for gene set analysis. Bioinformatics 31 (18), 3069–3071.

Young, M.D., et al., 2010. Gene ontology analysis for RNA-seq: Accounting for selection bias. Genome Biol. 11 (2), R14.

Zhou, J., Li, H.R., Karuturi, R.K.M., 2012. RK Bias in genome scale functional analysis of transcription factors using binding site data. J. Phys. Chem. Biophys. S4 (S4:002),

Relevant Websites

https://www.bioinformatics.babraham.ac.uk/projects/fastqc/
Babraham Bioinformatics.
http://hannonlab.cshl.edu/fastx_toolkit/
FASTX-Toolkit.
https://github.com/NYU-BFX/lncRNA-screen
GitHub.

Regulation of Gene Expression

Y-h Taguchi, Chuo University, Tokyo, Japan

Introduction

The Importance of Regulation of Gene Expression

The regulation of gene expression (**Fig. 1**) is critical process because of the following reasons. All multicellular organisms start their development from the duplication of a single cell: a fertilized egg. Then cascade of duplication results in the formation of multicellular organism. Since no cells' fate (i.e., into which tissues or organs each cell will differentiate) can be predicted, each cell must keep all set of genes everytime it is duplicated. Consequently, all of differentiated cells must keep full set of genes. Thus, it is critically important for each cell to control which genes should be expressed. Loss of proper controls might result in diseases, not functional organs, and even death.

Because of its importance, bioinformatics is also aiming to target regulation of gene expression. Although gene expression is composed of two steps: transcription and translation, both of which are samely important, because of inbalanced development of measurement technology, regulation of transcription is more extensively investigated than that of translation. Although translation is also an important process, because of inferior measurement technology, bioinformatics of translation process is investigated much less. Therefore this article also mainly describes regulation of transcription processes.

Pre-Transcriptional Regulation

Regulation of transcription process is divided to two parts, pre- and post-transcription regulation, respectively. Among these two, the pre-transcription regulation is more popular topics.

Transcription Factor Binding Site

Especially, inference of transcription factor binding site (TFBS) is ever attracting researchers' interest. TF is the protein that binds to promoter region and initiates transcription. Because of its sequence specific nature of binding, TFBS is a easy target to attack using bioinformatics that has great benefits of sequence analysis. Suppose that you have a set of DNA sequences identified by using some technology to which a TF often binds (e.g., ChIP-Seq). Then, all you need to do is to identify enriched sequence (so called motif) among those collection of DNA fragments. If you are very successful, you can predict where each TF binds along DNA sequence by searching where the identified motifs are located.

Promoter Methylation

Although TFBS has ever been studied since TF is protein which can be studied even in pre-genomic era, recent popular topics are not always directly related to protein; it is called epigenetics which means gene expression alteration without DNA sequence

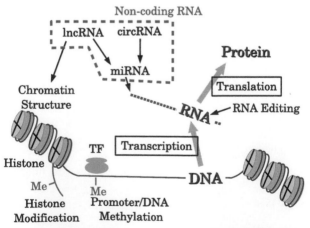

Fig. 1 Schematic that outlines regulation of gene expression. TF bindings, promoter/DNA methylation, histone modification, and chromatin structure affect regulation of gene expression during pre-transcriptional phase. On the other hand, various non-coding RNAs (miRNA, lncRNA and circRNA) and RNA editing affect it during post-transcription phases. Although there are numerous additional protein machineries that mediate these processes, all of them are omitted in order for simplicity. Although non-coding RNAs also must be transcribed from DNA, this process was also excluded from this illustration in order to avoid complicatedness.

modification. Epigenetics is composed of multiple functional elements. Most extensively studied epigenetic effect is promoter methylation. If promoter is methylated, since the binding of TF to the promoter is disturbed, transcription of corresponding mRNA is also disturbed. Since exhausted measurements of promoter methylation was ever established and its functional importance is cleared out, promoter methylation was the most frequently measured epigenetics.

From the technical point of views, methylation is measured by bisulfite treatment that transforms unmethylated cytosine to uracil while methylated cytosine is not. Thus, comparison between original DNA sequence and that treated by bisulfite can give us the information about which cytosine is methylated.

Histone Modification

The next popular epigenetic measurements is histone modification (Senda and Adachi, 2013). Histone is a protein around which DNA winds. Correct and tight winding between DNA and histone is critically important to store DNA which is extremely long polynucleotide into small space that cell nuclei occupies. From the point of views of regulation of gene expression, histone modification can contribute to store DNA in small space since histone modification can alter how tightly DNA winds around histone. When the density of histone along DNA is low, DNA sequence is bared and is easy to be transcribed. On the other hand, if DNA tightly winds around histone, it is not easy for DNA to be transcribed. Histone modification that means binding of small molecules to histone tails can alter affinity between DNA and histone, thus can affect the easiness of DNA to be transcribed. Fortunately, histone is protein, thus we can make use of the technology invented for the identification of TFBS. We can measure which histone modification is enriched in which place along DNA. In contrast to the methylation, histone modification has more than twenty variations dependent upon which small molecule binds and where in histone tail it binds to, some of which contribute to expression of genes while others of which interrupt the transcription. Thus, complicated competition between multiple histone modifications can contribute to regulation of gene expression in the multiple ways.

Chromatin Structure

The third popularly measured epigenetics is chromatin structure itself. Chromatin is a complex composed of DNA and histone. As mentioned in the above, although histone modification can alter chromatin structure, histone modification is not an only factor affecting chromatin structure. Thus, chromatin structure can be an independent factor that can affect regulation of gene expression. In contrast to the promoter methylation and histone modification, there are no de facto standard measurement methodology of chromatin structure. It is measured by wide range of technologies.

Post-Transcriptional Regulation

Although all of these above are pre-transcriptional regulation of gene expression, alternatively, some post-transcriptional regulation of gene expression is also often considered.

miRNA Regulation of Gene Expression

miRNA regulation of gene expression is ever the most popular mechanism of post-transcriptional regulation of gene expression. miRNA is non-coding RNA whose length is as long as about 22 nucleotide. Their seed region composed of eight nucleotide binds to complementary polynucleotide region within 3 prime untranslated region of mRNA with the help of protein machinery. miRNAs that bind to target mRNA either degradate mRNAs or interrupt translation of mRNAs. The number of miRNAs is as many as 2000 and their regulation of gene expression is highly context dependent. Thus, in spite of importance within the field of disease and developmental researches, their functionality is not yet fully understood. No effective measurements of miRNA regulation of gene expression are yet proposed. The inference of miRNA-mRNA interaction from bioinformatics is still under the development stage.

Others

Epitranscriptomics is another field of post-transcriptional regulation of gene expression and come to be collecting researchers' interest recently. Epitranscriptomics is mainly studying RNA editing that affects mRNA functions. Although it is obvious that epitranscriptomics plays critical roles in regulation of gene expression, the comprehensive investigations of these functions has just started (Xiong et al., 2017). Epitranscriptomics is composed of many kinds of modification of RNA; some examples are N^1-methyladenosine (m^1A) , pseudouridine (Ψ), 5-methylcytidine (m^5C), and N^6-methyladenosine (m^6A). They affect RNA in the various ways, e.g., affecting RNA structure, reducing mRNA stability, enhancing mRNA translation, and so on. At the moment, it is difficult to infer using bioinformatics the effect of epitranscriptomics toward regulation of gene expression.

Long non-coding RNA (lncRNA) is also an important factor that can regulate gene expression. LncRNA is defined as non-coding RNA longer than 200 nucleotide. It is known to contribute to modification of chromatin structure (Bhmdorfer and Wierzbicki, 2015) or to function as miRNA sponge (Wang et al., 2015a). At the moment, it is difficult to relate lncRNA to regulation of gene expression directly. Thus, investigation in bioinformatics along this line is also under the development stage.

Circular RNA (circRNA) (Szabo and Salzman, 2016) can also work as miRNA sponge (Wang *et al.*, 2015a). CircRNA is a different class of non-coding RNA which is expected to play critical roles in regulation of gene expression. Nevertheless, its functions remains not well known. As shown by name, circRNA forms circular structure that is distinct from other non-coding RNA. Although there are some proposed data bases (Chen *et al.*, 2016; Glažar *et al.*, 2014) for circRNA, main study of circRNA is at the moment still their identification. Although the investigation of their functions is waited, it is not yet fully understood.

RNA structure was also started to be considered as contributors to regulation of gene expression (Jacobs *et al.*, 2012). This means, even secondary and/or tertiary structures of mRNAs can contribute to gene expression in post-transcriptional manner. In the study of RNA structure, although theoretical inference of secondary structures of RNA has ever developed, the understanding of its relationship to biological function remains not well studied. The possible way by which RNA structure can contribute to post-transcriptional process is to affect splicing. Alternate splicing is important mechanism that generates multiple proteins (isoforms) based on a single DNA sequence. Since splicing is mediated by the interaction of proteins and mature mRNA, structure of mRNA can alter the binding affinity between proteins and mRNA and as a result affect the splicing. RNA structure can also affect translation since translation is also mediated by the binding between mRNA and proteins that perform translation.

As a consequence, we can have distribution along DNA of various factors that might affect regulation of gene expression in the phase of pre-transcription as well as various factors that might affect regulation of gene expression in the phase of post-transcription. The next task, which is also a main topics from the bioinformatics point of views, is how to relate these factors to regulation of gene expression.

Identification of Relationship Between Various Factors and Regulation of Gene Expression

In order to interpret the various factors that might affect regulation of gene expression, we need to relate various factors to gene body. The most frequently employed, but not biologically validated, way is to use transcription start site (TSS). If some factors enriched around TSS, these factors are assumed to regulate expression of the corresponding genes. Typically, 500 bp upstream and 2000 bp downstream around TSS is used, but this range can be altered. Then, some factors enriched around TSS are assumed to regulate differentially gene expression.

Although it is one to one correspondence, more sophisticated ways are popular in now a day. For example, inference of gene regulatory network (Macneil and Walhout, 2011) (GRN) is a useful strategy. GRN is network representation of regulation of gene expression. Multiple factors are connected with multiple genes. This structure itself expresses the complex regulatory relation between gene expression and multiple factors. There are multiple ways to construct GRN from gene expression profiles, e.g., correlation based and Bayesian based. As for correlation based GRN, correlation between elements (e.g., mRNA and miRNA expression) were employed to evaluate if elements are related. Pairs of elements associated with the correlation coefficients (or their absolute values) larger than the threshold values (or associated with significantly small *P*-values) are connected in GRN and others are not connected. In Bayesian approach, Bayesian network having the maximum posterior probability (or likelihood) was sought. In addition to this, additional external information (e.g., protein-protein interaction or miRNA-mRNA target information) are often considered. After that hub elements that have many connections with other elements are selected as critical elements that can play critical roles in regulation of gene expression.

Measurement Technologies

Microarray

Microarray is an old technology to measure mRNA expression. It is still used for the measurements of various factors that contribute to regulation of gen expression. Methylation arrays is also used for the measurement of DNA methylation. ChIP technology was originally invented for the usage together with microarray. It is yet used for histone modification and TFBS. miRNA and lncRNA expression is even measured using microarray specifically designed for the measurements of miRNA or lncRNA. The advantages of microarray technology is its easiness to use once they are suitably designed. On the other hand, the weakness of this technology is that it is not usable for organisms other than model organisms, e.g, mouse and fly, that are often used for genomic study.

Short Read

High-throughput sequencing (HTS) is a newly invented technology alternative to microarray. Although it is still relatively more expensive than microarray, it has several advantages even for the measurements of factors that affect regulation of gene expression. For example, HTS can be applied to non-model organism while microarray is restricted to model organism to which microarray has already been designed as mentioned above. Although RNA must be converted to DNA before HTS, since HTS can directly count the number of DNA/RNA fragments, HTS is believed to be also more quantitative than microarray. If HTS is binded to ChIP technology invented for ChIP-chip technology for microarray, ChIP-seq technology can be used for the measure histone modification and TFBS. If HTS is combined with bisulfite treatments, HTS can also be used for identification DNA methylation. The disadvantage of short read technology is that short read must be mapped to genome that is not always available. If genome sequence is missing, genome must be assembled independently prior to mapping short reads.

Long Read

Long read, which was invented by companies like nanopore (see Relevant Websites Section) or PacBiO (see Relevant Websites Section), is the next generation HTS. In contrast to short read technology whose length is limited to up to a few hundreds nucleotide, long read technology can measure read as long as a few thousand nucleotides. At the moment, although long read technology is rarely used for studying regulation of gene expression, it has potential to open a new era for the research of regulation of gene expression. For example, long read has a potential to identify multiple factors binding to DNA illustrated in **Fig. 1** simultaneously. This might enable us to study interplay between these factors more accurately. Alternatively, long read technology can detect isoforms (Byrne *et al.*, 2017) that short read technology can hardly identify since short fragments generated from distinct is forms are hardly distinguished by short read technology. Since there is a possibility that distinct isoforms are differently regulated by various factors, employment of long read technology might be critical in order to understand regulation of gene expression more precisely.

Applications

There are some applications aiming these above purposes. Especially, Bioconductor (Huber *et al.*, 2015) platform provides many ready made and useful packages.

GRN

For example, GeneNetworkBuilder (Ou *et al.*, 2017) package generates GRN from ChIP-chip/ChIP-seq and expression data. If your data set is time course, GRENITS (Morrissey, 2012) can be used. CoRegNet (Nicolle *et al.*, 2015) is another package that infers GRN from gene expression, TFBS and ChIP data set.

TFBS/Histone Modification

TFBSTools (Tan and Lenhard, 2016) is well made package that can analyze data for the identification of TFBS. Ringo (Toedling *et al.*, 2007) aims investigation of ChIP-chip microarray. BAC (Gottardo, 2007) uses a Bayesian hierarchical model to detect enriched regions from ChIP-chip experiments. Starr (Zacher *et al.*, 2009) aims simple tiling array analysis of Affymetrix ChIP-chip data. Rcade (Cairns, 2017) aims analysis of ChIP-seq and differential expression. geneXtendeR (Khomtchouk *et al.*, 2017) is designed to process histone Modification ChIP-seq aata. rMAT (Cheung *et al.*, 2017) is implementation from MAT program to normalize and analyze tiling arrays and ChIP-chip data. iChip (Mo, 2012) is Bayesian modeling of ChIP-chip data through hidden Ising models. Using these packages, researchers easily relate gene expression and TF binding and/or histone modifications

Chromatin State

There is a STAN (Zacher *et al.*, 2014) that infers chromatin state from histone modification as well as DNA methylation. DChIPRep (Chabbert *et al.*, 2016) also infers chromatin structure from Chip-seq data set.

DNA Methylation

As for DNA methylation, ChAMP (Tian *et al.*, 2017) provides us the method of processing methylation array. BPRMeth (Kapourani, 2017) is another package that can extract methylation profiles from HTS gene expression and row methylation profiles.

RNA Structure

RNAprobR (Kielpinski *et al.*, 2015) is a package that processes HTS data for the identification of RNA structure.

Gene Expression

In order to investigate regulation of gene expression, it is of course necessary to predict gene expression itself. However, it should have been discussed in other topics. Thus, this is not discussed here. Access other topics.

miRNA and lncRNA

Expression profiles of miRNA and lncRNA are easily obtained by HTS and microarray. Although treatment of miRNA/lncRNA array is similar to that of mRNA arrays, miRNA-seq does differ from RNA-seq aiming to measure mRNA expression (lncRNA-seq can be treated similarly to RNA-seq). The researcher must use tools designed specifically for miRNA profile. As for miRNA-seq, miRDeep2 (Friedlnder *et al.*, 2011) or miRDeep* (An *et al.*, 2012) are popular tools. Unfortunately, there are no de facto standard methods that relate miRNA expression to mRNA expression, although some tools are available (Wang *et al.*, 2015b) in Bioconductor. First of all, we need to know which mRNAs individual miRNAs target. Nevertheless, mRNA-miRNA interaction is highly context dependent. Even the most trustable experimentally validated miRNA-mRNA interaction database, miRTarBase (Chou *et al.*, 2015), is only valid for the diseases form which experimental results were collected. Thus, at the moment, although miRNA is believed to play critical roles in regulation of gene expression, it is practically difficult to relate miRNA expression to mRNA expression.

Illustrative Examples

In order to make easier to understand how one can process data sets, some illustrative examples are presented in the below. Since most of packages included in Bioconductor are accompanied with more examples, see documents attached with these packages for more examples.

Methylation Analysis Using ChAMP

Suppose R (R Core Team, 2017) is installed. In order to run with sample data sets, try **Fig. 2** in R. Then the list of genes associated with differential methylation regions should be in my DMR. In order to list genes, try **Fig. 3**. You can get a list of chromosomal regions, associated *P*-values, and genes having overlapping promoters. The sample data set is 450 k lung tumor data set and contains only 8 samples, 4 lung tumor samples and 4 control samples.

State Identification Using STAN

STAN enables us to identify chromosomal state with considering histone modification as well as methylation profiles. In order to run with sample data sets, try **Fig. 4** in R. In order to see results try **Fig. 5** Now, chromosomal regions are classified into ten classes with considering histone modification as well as methylation profiles. The sample data set contains ChIP-Seq experiments of seven histone modifications (H3K4me1, H3K4me3, H3K36me3, H3K27me3, H3K27ac and H3K9ac), as well as DNase-Seq and genomic input.

```
source("https://bioconductor.org/biocLite.R")
biocLite("ChAMP")
testDir=system.file("extdata",package="ChAMPdata")
myLoad <- champ.load(testDir,arraytype="450K")
champ.process(directory = testDir)
```

Fig. 2   Installation and execution of ChAMP.

```
head(myDMR$DMRcateDMR)
##       seqnames     start       end width strand no.cpgs      minfdr
## DMR_1     chr2 177021702 177030228  8527      *      48 3.243739e-69
## DMR_2     chr2 177012117 177017797  5681      *      33 1.137990e-59
## DMR_3    chr12 115134148 115136308  2161      *      51 3.571093e-108
## DMR_4    chr11  31820441  31828715  8275      *      40 3.087712e-43
## DMR_5    chr17  46655289  46658170  2882      *      27 1.565729e-85
## DMR_6     chr6  32115964  32118811  2848      *      50 5.055382e-123
##            Stouffer maxbetafc meanbetafc
## DMR_1 4.011352e-24 0.6962753  0.4383726
## DMR_2 6.555658e-20 0.6138975  0.4676655
## DMR_3 5.711951e-19 0.5372083  0.3601741
## DMR_4 1.206741e-18 0.5673115  0.4112588
## DMR_5 2.087453e-17 0.6859260  0.4812521
## DMR_6 7.216567e-16 0.5772168  0.2971849
##         overlapping.promoters
## DMR_1      HOXD3-001, HOXD3-004, RP11-387A1.5-001
## DMR_2      HOXD4-001, MIR10B-201, HOXD3-005
## DMR_3
## DMR_4      PAX6-016, PAX6-006, PAX6-014, PAX6-015, PAX6-007, PAX6-028, PAX6-025, PAX6-027, PAX6-029, PAX6-024, PAX6-026
## DMR_5      HOXB4-001, MIR10A-201, HOXB3-009, HOXB3-005, MIR10A-001
## DMR_6      PRRT1-002, PRRT1-201, PRRT1-007, PRRT1-006, PRRT1-003
```

Fig. 3   The results of ChAMP.

```
source("https://bioconductor.org/biocLite.R")
biocLite("STAN")
## Loading library and data
library(STAN)
data(trainRegions)
data(pilot.hg19)
## Model initialization
hmm_nb = initHMM(trainRegions[1:3], nStates=10, "NegativeBinomial")
## Model fitting
hmm_fitted_nb = fitHMM(trainRegions[1:3], hmm_nb, maxIters=10)
## Calculate state path
viterbi_nb = getViterbi(hmm_fitted_nb, trainRegions[1:3])
## Convert state path to GRanges object
viterbi_nb_gm12878 = viterbi2GRanges(viterbi_nb, pilot.hg19, 200)
```

Fig. 4 Installation and execution of STAN using sample data.

```
viterbi_poilog_gm12878
## GRanges object with 381 ranges and 1 metadata column:
## seqnames ranges strand | name
## <Rle> <IRanges> <Rle> | <character>
## [1] chr1 [151158001, 151159201] * | 6
## [2] chr1 [151159201, 151160801] * | 1
## [3] chr1 [151160801, 151161001] * | 2
## [4] chr1 [151161001, 151161601] * | 3
## [5] chr1 [151161601, 151162801] * | 4
## ... ... ... ... . ...
## [377] chr11 [2324601, 2326601] * | 10
## [378] chr11 [2326601, 2327601] * | 1
## [379] chr11 [2327601, 2328001] * | 2
## [380] chr11 [2328001, 2328201] * | 1
## [381] chr11 [2328201, 2349401] * | 10
## -------
## seqinfo: 3 sequences from an unspecified genome; no seqlengths
```

Fig. 5 The results of STAN.

Discussion

In the above, multiple factors that contribute to regulation of gene expression, technologies that measure these factors and bioinformatics tools to analyze these factors were discussed. Investigation of these factors are still on going and additional new factors that contribute to regulation of gene expression might appear. As more data accumulate and more technology develop, the manner of relating these factors to regulation of gene expression will become more complicated. Thus, the researchers aiming analysis of regulation of gene expression need to try to continuously collect updated knowledge. Even when simply more data become available, the conventional views listed in the above might be altered. The study of regulation of gene expression is on going and just started field. If there would be the revised version of this topics in the future, contents will be altered drastically.

Future Direction

Future direction of this topics is definitely the integration of multiple omics data set, i.e., trans omics analysis (Yugi *et al.*, 2016). As can be seen in the above multiple factors contribute to regulation of gene expression with interacting with one another. In spite of that, most of researches currently performed is mainly on regulation of gene expression with considering individual factors.

In spite of serious need along this direction, no established methods on trans omics analysis exist. Some promising direction includes network based (Yugi *et al.*, 2016), gene set enrichment analysis based (Zhang *et al.*, 2015), and tensor based (Taguchi, 2017) ones. Nevertheless, the best-fitted method for trans omics analysis is still continuously sought.

Concluding Remarks

In this article, various factors that might affect regulation of genes were discussed together with measurements technology and software that can process these measurements. Although it was not yet employed for the study of regulation of gene expression, single cell sequencing technology must be employed since regulation of gene expression differs form cell to cell. After the success of this direction, we might understand cellular function that manages regulation of gene expression more precisely.

See also: Codon Usage. Epigenetics: Analysis of Cytosine Modifications at Single Base Resolution. Exome Sequencing Data Analysis. Functional Enrichment Analysis. Integrative Analysis of Multi-Omics Data. Natural Language Processing Approaches in Bioinformatics. Next Generation Sequencing Data Analysis. Transcriptome Analysis. Whole Genome Sequencing Analysis

References

An, J., Lai, J., Lehman, M.L., Nelson, C.C., 2012. miRDeep*: An integrated application tool for miRNA identification from RNA sequencing data. Nucleic Acids Research 41, 727–737. doi:10.1093/nar/gks1187. Available at: https://doi.org/10.1093%2Fnar%2Fgks1187.

Bhmdorfer, G., Wierzbicki, A.T., 2015. Control of chromatin structure by long noncoding RNA. Trends in Cell Biology 25, 623–632. doi:10.1016/j.tcb.2015.07.002. Available at: https://doi.org/10.1016%2Fj.tcb.2015.07.002.

Byrne, A., Beaudin, A.E., Olsen, H.E., et al., 2017. Nanopore long-read RNAseq reveals widespread transcriptional variation among the surface receptors of individual b cells. Available at: https://doi.org/10.1101%2F126847.

Cairns, J., 2017. Rcade: A tool for integrating a count-based chip-seq analysis with differential expression summary data. Available at: https://www.bioconductor.org/packages/release/bioc/html/Rcade.html. R package version 1.18.0.

Chabbert, C.D., Steinmetz, L.M., Klaus, B., 2016. DChIPRep, an r/bioconductor package for differential enrichment analysis in chromatin studies. PeerJ 4, e1981. doi:10.7717/peerj.1981. Available at: https://www.bioconductor.org/packages/release/bioc/html/DChIPRep.html.

Chen, X., Han, P., Zhou, T., et al., 2016. circRNADb: A comprehensive database for human circular RNAs with protein-coding annotations. Scientific Reports 6. doi:10.1038/srep34985. Available at: https://doi.org/10.1038%2Fsrep34985.

Cheung, C., Droit, A., Gottardo, R., 2017. rMAT:R implementation from MAT program to normalize and analyze tiling arrays and ChIP-chip data. Available at: https://www.bioconductor.org/packages/release/bioc/html/rMAT.html. R package version 3.26.0, Available at: http://www.rglab.org.

Chou, C.H., Chang, N.W., Shrestha, S., et al., 2015. miRTarBase 2016: Updates to the experimentally validated miRNA-target interactions database. Nucleic Acids Research 44, D239–D247. doi:10.1093/nar/gkv1258. Available at: https://doi.org/10.1093%2Fnar%2Fgkv1258.

FriedInder, M.R., Mackowiak, S.D., Li, N., Chen, W., Rajewsky, N., 2011. miRDeep2 accurately identifies known and hundreds of novel microRNA genes in seven animal clades. Nucleic Acids Research 40, 37–52. doi:10.1093/nar/gkr688. Available at: https://doi.org/10.1093%2Fnar%2Fgkr688.

Glažar, P., Papavasileiou, P., Rajewsky, N., 2014. circB ase: A database for circular RNAs. RNA 20, 1666–1670. doi:10.1261/rna.043687.113. Available at: https://doi.org/10.1261%2Frna.043687.113.

Gottardo, R., 2007. BAC: Bayesian Analysis of Chip-Chip Experiment. Available at: https://www.bioconductor.org/packages/release/bioc/html/BAC.html. R package version 1.36.0.

Huber, W., Carey, V.J., Gentleman, R., et al., 2015. Orchestrating high-throughput genomic analysis with bioconductor. Nature Methods 12, 115–121. doi:10.1038/nmeth.3252. Available at: https://www.bioconductor.org/.

Jacobs, E., Mills, J.D., Janitz, M., 2012. The role of RNA structure in posttranscriptional regulation of gene expression. Journal of Genetics and Genomics 39, 535–543. doi:10.1016/j.jgg.2012.08.002. Available at: https://doi.org/10.1016%2Fj.jgg.2012.08.002.

Kapourani, C., 2017. BPRMeth: Model higher-order methylation profiles. Available at: https://www.bioconductor.org/packages/release/bioc/html/BPRMeth.html. R package version 1.2.0.

Khomtchouk, B.B., Van Booven, D., Wahlestedt, C., 2017. Genextender: Optimized functional° annotation of chip-seq data. bioRxiv. doi:10.1101/082347. Available at: https://www.bioconductor.org/packages/release/bioc/html/geneXtendeR.html.

Kielpinski, L.J., Sidiropoulos, N., Vinther, J., 2015. Reproducible analysis of sequencing-based RNA structure probing data with user-friendly tools. Methods in Enzymology. Elsevier. pp. 153–180. doi:10.1016/bs.mie.2015.01.014. Available at: https://www.bioconductor.org/packages/release/bioc/html/RNAprobR.html.

Macneil, L.T., Walhout, A.J., 2011. Gene regulatory networks and the role of robustness and stochasticity in the control of gene expression. Genome Res. 21, 645–657.

Mo, Q., 2012. iChip: Bayesian Modeling of ChIP-chip Data Through Hidden Ising Models. Available at: https://www.bioconductor.org/packages/release/bioc/html/iChip.html. R package version 1.30.0.

Morrissey, E., 2012. GRENITS: Gene Regulatory Network Inference Using Time Series. Available at: https://www.bioconductor.org/packages/release/bioc/html/GRENITS.html. R package version 1.28.1.

Nicolle, R., Radvanyi, F., Elati, M., 2015. CoReg-Net: Reconstruction and integrated analysis of co-regulatory networks. Bioinformatics 31, 3066–3068. doi:10.1093/bioinformatics/btv305. Available at: https://www.bioconductor.org/packages/release/bioc/html/CoRegNet.html.

Ou, J., Liu, H., Tissenbaum, H.A., Zhu, L.J., 2017. GeneNetworkBuilder: Build Regulatory Network From ChIP-chip/ChIP-seq and Expression Data. Available at: https://www.bioconductor.org/packages/release/bioc/html/GeneNetworkBuilder.html. R package version 1.18.1.

R Core Team, 2017. R: A Language and Environment for Statistical Computing. R Foundation for Statistical Computing. Vienna, Austria. Available at: https://www.R-project.org/.

Senda, T., Adachi, N., 2013. Post-translational modifications, histone. Encyclopedia of Systems Biology. New York: Springer, p. 896. doi:10.1007/978-1-4419-9863-7_100627. Available at: https://doi.org/10.1007%2F978-1-4419-9863-7_100627.

Szabo, L., Salzman, J., 2016. Detecting circular RNAs: Bioinformatic and experimental challenges. Nature Reviews Genetics 17, 679–692. doi:10.1038/nrg.2016.114. Available at: https://doi.org/10.1038%2Fnrg.2016.114.

Taguchi, Y.H., 2017. Tensor decomposition-based unsupervised feature extraction applied to matrix products for multi-view data processing. PLOS ONE 12, e0183933. doi:10.1371/journal.pone.0183933. Available at: https://doi.org/10.1371%2Fjournal.pone.0183933.

Tan, G., Lenhard, B., 2016. TFBSTools: Anr/bioconductor package for transcription factor binding site analysis. Bioinformatics 32, 1555–1556. doi:10.1093/bioinformatics/btw024. Available at: https://www.bioconductor.org/packages/release/bioc/html/TFBSTools.html.

Tian, Y., Morris, T.J., Webster, A.P., et al., 2017. ChAMP: Updated methylation analysis pipeline for illumina BeadChips. Bioinformatics. doi:10.1093/bioinformatics/btx513. Available at: https://www.bioconductor.org/packages/release/bioc/html/ChAMP.html.

Toedling, J., Skylar, O., Krueger, T., et al., 2007. Ringo an R/Bioconductor package for analyzing ChIP-chip readouts. BMC Bioinformatics 8, 443. doi:10.1186/1471-2105-8-443. Available at: https://www.bioconductor.org/packages/release/bioc/html/Ringo.html.

Wang, P., Zhi, H., Zhang, Y., et al., 2015a. miRSponge: A manually curated database for experimentally supported miRNA sponges and ceRNAs. Databas67e5 2015, bav098. doi:10.1093/database/bav098. Available at: https://doi.org/10.1093%2Fdatabase%2Fbav098.

Wang, T., Lu, T., Lee, C., et al., 2015b. anamiRan integrated analysis package of miRNA and mRNA expression. Available at: https://www.bioconductor.orgg/packages/release/bioc/html/anamiR.html. R package version 1.4.2.

Xiong, X., Yi, C., Peng, J., 2017. Epitranscriptomics: Toward a better understanding of RNA modifications. Genomics, Proteomics & Bioinformatics 15, 147–153. doi:101016/j.gpb.2017.03.003. Available at: https://doi.org/10.1016%2Fj.gpb.2017.03.003.

Yugi, K., Kubota, H., Hatano, A., Kuroda, S., 2016. Trans-omics: How to reconstruct biochemical networks across multiple 'omic' layers. Trends in Biotechnology 34, 276–290. doi:10.1016/j.tibtech.2015.12.013. Available at: https://doi.org/10.1016%2Fj.tibtech.2015.12.013.

Zacher, B., Lidschreiber, M., Cramer, P., Gag-neur, J., Tresch, A., 2014. Annotation of genomics data using bidirectional hidden markov models unveils variations in pol II transcription cycle. Molecular Systems Biology 10, 768. doi:10.15252/msb.20145654. Available at: https://www.bioconductor.org/packages/release/bioc/html/STAN.html.

Zacher, B., Soeding, J., Kuan, P., Siebert, M., Tresch, A., 2009. Starr: Simple tiling array analysis of Affymetrix ChIP-chip data. Available at: https://www.bioconductor.org/packages/release/bioc/html/Starr.html. R package version 1.32.0.

Zhang, F., Xiao, X., Hao, J., et al., 2015. CPAS: A trans-omics pathway analysis tool for jointly analyzing DNA copy number variations and mRNA expression profiles data. Journal of Biomedical Informatics 53, 363–366. doi:10.1016/j.jbi.2014.12.012. Available at: https://doi.org/10.1016%2Fj.jbi.2014.12.012.

Further Reading

Bioinformatics, Methods in Molecular Biology 1526/1527. In: Keith, J.M. (Ed.), Springer Protocols, Volume I: Data, Sequence Analysis, and Evolution, Volume II: Structure, Function, and Applications, second ed. New York: Humana Press/Springer. ISBN: 978-1-4939–6620-2/978-1-4939–6611-0.

Bioinformatics in MicroRNA Research. In: Huang, J., Borchert, G.M., Dou, D., et al. (Eds.), Methods in Molecura Biology 1617. New York: Springer Protocols, Humena Press/Springer.ISBN: kl978-1-4939-7044-5.

Cho, W.C.S. (Ed.), 2011. MicroRNAs in Cancer Translational Research. New York: Springer. ISBN: 978-94-007-0297-4.

Computational Methods for Next Generation Sequencing Data Analysis. In: Măndoiu, I.I., Zelikovsky, A. (Eds.), Wiley Series on Bioinformatics: Computational Techniques and Engneering. Hoboken: Wiley. ISBN: 978-1-118–16948-3.

Epigenetic Contributions in Autoimmune Disease. In: Ballestar, E. (Ed.), Advances in Experimental Medicine and Biology. New York: Springer. ISBN: 978-1-4419-8215-5.

Epigenetic Alterations in Oncogenesis. In: Karpf, A.R. (Ed.), Advances in Experimental Medicine and Biology 754. New York: Springer.ISBN 978-1-4419–9966-5.

Khalil, A.M., Coller, J. (Eds.), 2013. Molecular Biology of Long Non-Coding RNAs. New York: Springer. ISBN: 978-1-4614-8620-6.

Mallick, B., Ghosh, Z. (Eds.), 2012. Regulatory RNAs, Basics, Methods and Applications. New York: Springer. ISBN: 978-3-642-22516-1.

RNA Bioinformatics, Methods in Molecular Biology. In: Picardi, E. (Ed.), Springer Protocols 1269. New York: Springer.ISBN: 978-1-4939-2290-1.

Statistical Analysis of Next Generation Sequencing Data. In: Datta, S., Nettleton, D. (Eds.), Frontiers in Probability and the Statistical Sciences. New York: Springer. ISBN 978-3-319–07211-1.

Wu, W. (Ed.), MicroRNA and Cancer, MicroRNA and Cancer, Methods Humana Press/Springer, New York, 2011, ISBN 978-1-60761-862-1.

Yousef, M., Allmer, J. (Eds.) miRNomics, Methods in Molecular Biology 1107, Springer Protocols, Humana Press/Springer, New York, 2014, ISBN 978-1-62703-747-1.

Relevant Websites

http://www.genecards.org
   GeneCards.
http://www.mirbase.org
   miRBase.
https://nanoporetech.com/
   Nanopore.
https://www.ncbi.nlm.nih.gov/geo/
   NCBI.
https://www.ncbi.nlm.nih.gov/pubmed
   NCBI.
https://www.ncbi.nlm.nih.gov/sra
   NCBI.
http://www.pacb.com/
   Pacbio.

Biographical Sketch

Prof. Y-h. Taguchi is a physics professor at Department of Physics, Chuo University, Tokyo, Japan. He has obtained Dr. Sci. at 1988 for Statistical Physics, from Tokyo Institute of Technology, Japan. He has been an assistant Professor at Department of Physics, Tokyo Institute of Technology, 1988. Then, he has move to the present position as an associate professor at 1997. He has been a full professor since 2006. He has published more than 90 peer reviewed and conference proceedings papers including 28 single authored papers. His main present interests are feature extraction and feature selection using principal component analysis and tensor decomposition. His methods were applied to transcriptome and epigenetic profiles, which were further applied to in silco drug discovery as well as biomarker identification.

Comparative Transcriptomics Analysis

Y-h Taguchi, Chuo University, Tokyo, Japan

Introduction

Comparative Transcriptomics Analysis (CTA) is, as the name implies, the comparisons of the amount of transcripts between two distinct conditions. Typical distinct conditions are healthy controls vs disease patients, a pair of distinct tissues, distinct time points and even distinct species. The reason for this frequent execution of CTA is because almost all cells keep the full set of genes, although not all of the genes are expressed. Because of this sharing of the full set of genes between cells, CTA is a primary method to investigate the factors that make cells distinct from one another.

In contrast to the clearer purpose of CTA, performing CTA is much harder. This is primarily because the amount of transcripts is naturally a real number. Since real numbers cannot be exactly equal to one another by chance, we need some criterion when the amounts of two transcripts can be regarded to differ from each other. The most simplest solution of this problem is the introduction of some statistical models. Based upon the statistical models under the null hypothesis that the amounts of two transcripts are equal, we can identify transcripts associated with distinct values between two conditions by rejecting the null hypothesis. Thus, the point is how to assume the null hypothesis with which statistical models are assumed.

Dependent upon assumed statistical models, various strategies of CTA are possible. They are primarily divided to two categories dependent upon what kind of technology is used to measure the amount of transcript. The major two such technologies are microarray and high throughput sequencing (HTS), respectively. Although these two technologies measure biologically the same variables, i.e., the amount of transcripts, the outcomes differ from each other. In micoarray, the amounts of transcripts measured are inevitably real numbers, since microarray measures the amount of transcripts by the amount of light emission from nucleotide fragments that bind to complementary probes. On the other hands, the amount of transcript measured by HTS must be integer, since HTS counts the number of fragments cut out from mRNA. Since suitable statistical models for real numbers and integer differ, in the following, I separately discuss the basics and the applications of the two.

Statistical Models

Microarray

As described in the above, statistical models applied to the amount of transcripts measured by microarray must be that of real numbers. Most of popular statistical models assume that the amount of the transcript obeys t distribution, $t(n)$, where n is the number of samples in each class. When aiming to identify genes that have distinct mean μ between two classes, the null hypothesis that μ is equivalent between two classes is rejected with some P-value that is the threshold value, e.g., 0.05.

t-test is only applicable to two classes problem. Although t-test can be formally applied to multiple classes by dividing multiple classes to a set of pairwise comparison, it is erroneous because of the following reason. Suppose we have K multiple classes. Then, the number of pairwise comparisons is as many as $K(K-1)/2$. Thus, $P = 2/K(K-1)$ can be achieved by chance. If K is as large as ten, since $P = 2/K(K-1) \simeq 0.02$, usual threshold value $P = 0.05$ is clearly meaningless. If P-values are corrected, e.g., $P < 0.05 \times 2/K(K-1)$, the ability that t-test can detect genes associated with distinct amount of transcript between any pairs of multiple classes will drastically decrease.

In order to avoid these problems, for the CTAs associated with multiple classes, other strategies are employed. These other strategies include categorical regression (in other words, analysis of variance (ANOVA) (Upton and Cook, 2008)), χ^2 test, or any other extensions of them. Details of implementations differ from applications to applications, it will be discussed in the below in the applications section.

HTS

HTS is an alternate technology that can outperform microarray that has many limitations. Microarray must be designed prior to measurements. This means, non-model organisms are hard to be tested. In HTS, we do not need anything prior to the measurements, although genome sequence must be decided if it is not available prior to counting of the number of reads attributed to each gene. Genome sequence also can be decided by HTS.

HTS is roughly divided to two classes: genome sequencing and RNA-seq. In genome sequencing, fragmented genomic DNA are sequenced and whole genome is assembled from the reads sequence. On the other hand, RNA-seq tries to sequence reads taken from RNAs. For both cases, read can be single end or paired ends. For the latter, reads are generated from both ends of longer fragmented DNA or RNA. This strategy can increase the accuracy than the single end, because paired ends require additional constraint that paired end must be within the length of mRNA and fragmented DNA.

Assembling fragmented DNA to get whole genome sequence and transforming RNA-seq reads into transcript with consideration of splicing are the issues of statistical modeling. In other words, they are the tasks that decide the most probable genome sequence or mapping of RNA-seq reads to genome, based on the obtained read sequences. Since the measurement of the amount of transcript itself is out of scope of this article, refer to other articles for more details.

In contrast to the conventional HTS, where length of read sequences is limited to up to a few hundreds nucleotide, an alternative technology, long read sequencing (e.g., nanopore and PacBio, see Relevant Websites section), is recently gaining traction. In long read technology, each read can be as long as a few thousand nucleotides, which is long enough to measure whole genome of prokaryotes and individual whole transcript of eukaryotes. This has several advantages compared with short read technologies. For prokaryotes genome, it is obvious that long read technology allows to omit assembly in order to obtain whole genome sequences. For eukaryote transcripts, complicated splice junction identification process can be omitted. Thus, short read technology soon will be completely replaced with long read technologies.

Normalization

Prior to CTA, the amount of transcript must be normalized, since independent of the measurement technologies, maicroarray or HTS, the total amount of transcript is impossible to control during measurement. This process can be done either outside of CTA or as a part of CTA. In the former case, researchers can select their favorable methods while the latter employs the pre-defined strategy for normalization. In any case, dependent on the normalization strategy, the outcome of CTA varies and there are no de facto standard techniques for the normalization prior to CTA. This is an additional reason why CTA is difficult to perform, since incorrect normalization might result in the miss-identification of genes expressed distinctly between two conditions. Various applications aiming normalization prior to CTA will be introduced in applications section below.

Fold Change

Even if some genes can be identified as expressed differently between two conditions based on the criterion given by a statistical test, some genes might likely not biologically play critical roles. This is because the standard statistical tests often ignore the amount of transcripts itself. For example, in t-test, very small difference of μs between two classes can be judged as significant when estimated standard deviation in each class is much smaller that the estimated difference of μs between two classes. In extreme case, when the amounts of transcript in each class are completely same within each class, i.e., standard deviation is equal to zero, any tiny difference of μs between two classes can be regarded as significant, since $P=0$. Nevertheless, such a judgement is clearly meaningless from the biological point of views (Conversely, genes not associated with significant difference may biologically function. This often simply means inability of tests because of, e.g., not enough number of available samples).

In order to avoid these somewhat meaningless identifications of genes associated with distinct amount of transcript between distinct classes, fold change is often considered together with statistical tests. Fold change is often useful to screen genes associated with differential expression when statistical test cannot list any genes with significantly smaller P-values. Fold change is, as its name says, the ratio between the amount of transcripts in two classes. Then, genes associated with both significantly small P-values and large enough fold change (e.g., larger than two or less than a half) are regarded to be those associated with significant difference of amount of transcript between two classes. Although this strategy is known to work well empirically, there are no systematic ways that can decide how large or small fold change (larger than twice, larger than three times, smaller than one half, or smaller than one third) should be employed in order to get biologically reasonable answers.

Multiple Comparisons

Multiple comparison is another issue of CTA. Any statistical test can attribute to each gene, P-values that reject null hypothesis that two classes are equivalent in some sense. Nevertheless, since the number of genes is huge (c.a. 10^4), these P-values are misleading. If the number of genes is N, $P=1/N$ can happen by chance. This suggests that the frequently used criterion that $P<0.05$ is significant is useless.

At the moment, although there are no definite ways to address this problem, numerous trials were proposed. The simplest one is Bonferroni (Armstrong, 2014) where P is transformed to be NP. This apparently simple transformation has drawback that often misses the significant difference because of its too strict criterion. More robust way is to assume the uniform distribution for P-values. If null hypothesis is true, P-values must obey uniform distribution. Then, genes whose attributed P-values deviate from uniform distribution is regarded to be significant. The most frequently used criterion along this line is Benjamin-Hochberg (Benjamini and Hochberg, 1995). Empirically, the latter strategy was more often employed, since it can give us more biologically reasonable (interpretable) results empirically.

Batch Effect

Although it is somewhat related to normalization issue, batch effect can often heavily affect the outcomes of CTA. Batch effects generally means the uncontrollable external factors that can affect measured amount of transcript. Numerous factors can cause batch effects, e.g., days, time, institutes, persons, and so on. If batch effect is not removed effectively, CTA results in not the comparison between treated and control samples, but that among batches. Although there are many packages proposed for removing batch effects (Reese et al., 2013; Leck, 2014; Chen et al., 2011), there are no de facto standard methods that can remove batch effect well independent of the experimental situations. The best strategy that researchers can employ is to evaluate outcomes with considering biological significance of outcomes carefully. In principal, it is dangerous to mix gene expression profiles taken from different batches.

Enrichment Analysis

Although it is not directly related to CTA, biological interpretation of selected genes is often required and important. One of typical analysis for this purpose is enrichment analysis. In enrichment analysis, a set of genes is given, and various biological terms associated with the gene set with significantly small P-values computed by some statistical test, e.g., Fisher's exact test, are identified.

Here I list some of famous servers to be used for this purpose: DAVID (Huang et al., 2008), g:profiler (Reimand et al., 2016), TargetMine (Chen et al., 2016), Enricher (Kuleshov et al., 2016), IPA (QIAGEN, 2017) and MSigDB (Subramanian et al., 2005), although they have their own pros and cons.

qPCR

Other than two major technologies, microarray and HTS, quantitative polymerase chain reaction (qPCR) is also sometimes used to measure amount of transcript. In apite of the quantitative accuracy of qPCR compared with other two technologies, qPCR is used only less frequently. This is because qPCR has no ability to measure numerous transcripts simultaneously. For each transcript, experiments must be repeated independently. This is far from cost effective. In addition to this, qPCR often requires reference transcript that is not altered between treated and control samples. Since either identification of not altered transcript or artificial spike in of reference genes are additional time and cost consuming process, qPCR is mainly used for validating the limited number of transcripts among all transcripts measured by either microarray or HTS.

Single Cell Analysis

Although single cell analysis (SCA) (Yuan et al., 2017), which measures transcripts cell by cell, is a rising field, it is not developed enough to be included in this encyclopedia as an established field. First of all, because of technology currently developing, some transcripts are often missing. At the moment, there are no ways to judge if missing transcript is really missing (biologically) or not (technologically missing, i.e., failure of measurements). Thus, the purpose of SCA is often presently not identifying genes whose transcripts are expressed distinctly between treated and control samples, but clustering (grouping) cells based upon the measured transcripts. Since clustering cells is somewhat outside of CTA, SCA is not discussed here in details. Nonetheless, SCA is surely replacing conventional CTA in the future when the SCA technology is established.

Applications

There are numerous applications for CTA. In this article, those in Bioconductor (Huber et al., 2015) will be specifically introduced.

Normalization for Microarray

There are numerous methods to achieve normalization prior to CTA for microarray. There are generally two branches along this direction. The first one in the normalization based upon single microarray. This means that the amount of transcript is normalized with considering single measurement. One of the most frequent methodologies of single array based normalization is mas5, which is implemented as mas5 function, included in affy (Gautier et al., 2004) package. In single microarray based normalization, total amount of transcripts is assumed to be constant, independent of measurements. Another frequent strategy is normalization based upon multiple array. The most popular one along this direction is rma, which is implemented as rma function, also included in affy (Gautier et al., 2004) package. In multiple array based strategy, the amount of transcripts that share ranking among multiple arrays are assumed to take the same values. In actual, there are no ways by which we can judge the better one between these two. Generally speaking, multiple array based strategies are more popular since they are less affected by individual measurements. In principle, the choice of better strategy is highly context dependent. It must be evaluated based upon the biological outcomes.

Normalization for HTS

Although the amount of transcripts obtained by HTS technology is an integer, it has different difficulties than microarray normalization. Since the number of reads are that of RNA fragments, the number of reads mapped to individual genes is not proportional to the amount of transcripts. It is obvious that longer RNA has more fragments. This is a sharp contrast to microarray where the amount of transcripts measured is per gene base. Thus, there are two kinds of normalization strategy. One is to transform the number of reads mapped to each gene to that of per gene base. The most frequent definition of this line is RPKM (Reads per million mapped reads), which is defined as

$$\text{raw counts} \times \frac{10^6}{\text{all reads}} \times \frac{10^3}{\text{gene length}}$$

where raw counts is the number of reads mapped to each gene, all reads are total number of reads in each measurement. Although it looks reasonable, there is one drawback. When single gene expression drastically increases, because of all reads in denominator, all of other transcripts are regarded as being decreased, although it is clearly not reasonable.

Another strategy is raw reads, which is without any normalization. It might look strange, but raw reads as it is can be treated if suitable statistical models are proposed (see below).

CTA for Real Numbers

Since RPKM is a real number analogous to the amount of transcripts measured by microarray, we discuss these with that of microarray. As for CTA of real numbers, there are huge number of applications. Here I introduce two of them as the most frequently used ones. The first one is SAM (Significance Analysis of Microarrays) (Tusher *et al.*, 2001), which is implemented as sam function in siggenes package (Schwender, 2012). It can deal with both two classes and multiple classes, by employing modified t-test and χ^2 test accordingly. Another one is limma (Ritchie *et al.*, 2015), which is based upon linear model assuming Bayesian work frame. limma can also deal with both two classes and multiple classes. In actual, limma can be adapted to almost all situations, since it employs design matrix strategy by which user can designate any kinds of possible comparisons. sam and limma also can give users the adjusted P-values which considered multiple comparison criterion. Thus, researchers do not have to consider correction assuming multiple comparisons.

CTA for Integer Numbers

Since reads count by HTS is positive integers, we need null hypothesis fitted to this situation. Although Poisson distribution has long been employed, it has one "drawback";since Poisson distribution has only one parameter, it cannot be fitted to mean and variance simultaneously. In order to overcome this problem, negative binomial distribution is more often used. DESeq2 (Love *et al.*, 2014) is the most frequently used packages for this purpose. It also accepts raw reads as input and normalization is included in the data processing. It also gives us adjusted P-values so as not to consider multiple comparisons separately. It is also fitted to both two classes and multiple classes, since it employ design matrix strategy that limma employs.

In spite of frequent and successful usage of DEseq2 in CTA of HTS, the appearance of negative binomial distribution is not always guaranteed, since it lacks convergence theorem that normal distribution has. Because of this drawback, a non-parametric strategy is sometimes employed. NOISeq (Tarazona *et al.*, 2015) is one of the most frequently used non-parametric packages. NOISeq also implements data normalization, multiple comparison corrections, adapted to both two classes and multiple classes and so on.

CTA often results in distinct outcomes between DESeq2 and NOISeq. As in the microarray, there are not definite criteria that decide the best applications.

Conclusions

In summary, CTA is rather art than science. At the moment, there are no definite ways guaranteed to always work well regardless the situations considered. CTA must be done with much care in order to avoid getting results without any biological meanings. It is not an easy way, but must be tried.

See also: Characterizing and Functional Assignment of Noncoding RNAs. Codon Usage. Comparative Genomics Analysis. Exome Sequencing Data Analysis. Functional Enrichment Analysis. Integrative Analysis of Multi-Omics Data. Natural Language Processing Approaches in Bioinformatics. Next Generation Sequencing Data Analysis. Pipeline of High Throughput Sequencing. Regulation of Gene Expression. Sequence Analysis. Transcriptome Analysis. Whole Genome Sequencing Analysis

References

Armstrong, R.A., 2014. When to use the bonferroni correction. Ophthalmic and Physiological Optics 34, 502–508. doi:10.1111/opo.12131. Available at: https://doi.org/10.1111%2Fopo.12131.

Benjamini, Y., Hochberg, Y., 1995. Controlling the discovery rate: A practical and powerful approach to multiple testing. Journal of the Royal Statistical Society Series B (Methodological) 57, 289–300. doi:10.2307/2346101. Available at: https://doi.org/10.2307/2346101.

Chen, C., Grennan, K., Badner, J., *et al.*, 2011. Removing batch effects in analysis of expression microarray data: An evaluation of six batch adjustment methods. PLOS ONE 6, e17238. doi:10.1371/journal.pone.0017238. Available at: https://doi.org/10.1371%2Fjournal.pone.0017238.

Chen, Y.A., Tripathi, L.P., Mizuguchi, K., 2016. An integrative data analysis platform for gene set analysis and knowledge discovery in a data warehouse framework. In: Database 2016, baw009. doi:10.1093/database/baw009. Available at: https://doi.org/10.1093%2Fdatabase%2Fbaw009.

Gautier, L., Cope, L., Bolstad, B.M., Irizarry, R.A., 2004. affy-analysis of affymetrix GeneChip data at the probe level. Bioinformatics 20, 307–315. doi:10.1093/bioinformatics/btg405. Available at: https://doi.org/10.1093%2Fbioinformatics%2Fbtg405.

Huang, D.W., Sherman, B.T., Lempicki, R.A., 2008. Systematic and integrative analysis of large gene lists using DAVID bioinformatics resources. Nature Protocols 4, 44–57. doi:10.1038/nprot.2008.211. Available at: https://doi.org/10.1038%2Fnprot.2008.211.

Huber, W., Carey, V.J., Gentleman, R., *et al.*, 2015. Orchestrating high-throughput genomic analysis with bioconductor. Nature Methods 12, 115–121. doi:10.1038/nmeth.3252. Available at: https://www.bioconductor.org/.

Kuleshov, M.V., Jones, M.R., Rouillard, A.D., *et al.*, 2016. En-richr: A comprehensive gene set enrichment analysis web server 2016 update. Nucleic Acids Research 44, W90–W97. doi:10.1093/nar/gkw377. Available at: https://doi.org/10.1093%2Fnar%2Fgkw377.

Leek, J.T., 2014. svaseq: Removing batch effects and other unwanted noise from sequencing data. Nucleic Acids Research 42. doi:10.1093/nar/gku864. Available at: https://doi.org/10.1093%2Fnar%2Fgku864.

Love, M.I., Huber, W., Anders, S., 2014. Moderated estimation of fold change and dispersion for RNA-seq data with DESeq2. Genome Biology 15. doi:10.1186/s13059-014-0550-8. Available at: https://doi.org/10.1186%2Fs13059-014-0550-8.

QIAGEN, 2017. Ingenuity pathway analysis. Available at: https://wwwqiagenbioinformatics.com/products/ingenuity-pathway-analysis/.

Reese, S.E., Archer, K.J., Therneau, T.M., *et al.*, 2013. A new statistic for identifying batch effects in high-throughput genomic data that uses guided principal component analysis. Bioinformatics 29, 2877–2883. doi:10.1093/bioinformatics/btt480. Available at: https://doi.org/10.1093%2Fbioinformatics%2Fbtt480.

Reimand, J., Arak, T., Adler, P., *et al.*, 2016. g:profiler–A web server for functional interpretation of gene lists (2016 update). Nucleic Acids Research 44, W83–W89. doi:10.1093/nar/gkw199. Available at: https://doi.org/10.1093%2Fnar%2Fgkw199.

Ritchie, M.E., Phipson, B., Wu, D., *et al.*, 2015. limma powers differential expression analyses for RNA-sequencing and microarray studies. Nucleic Acids Research 43. doi:10.1093/nar/gkv007. Available at: https://doi.org/10.1093%2Fnar%2Fgkv007.

Schwender, H., 2012. siggenes: Multiple testing using SAM and Efron's empirical Bayes approaches. R package version 1.50.0. Available at: https://bioconductor.org/packages/release/bioc/html/siggenes.html.

Subramanian, A., Tamayo, P., Mootha, V.K., *et al.*, 2005. Gene set enrichment analysis: a knowledge-based approach for interpreting genome-wide expression profiles. Proceedings of the National Academy of Sciences 102, 15545–15550. doi:10.1073/pnas.0506580102. Available at: https://doi.org/10.1073%2Fpnas.0506580102.

Tarazona, S., Furió-Tarí, P., Turrà, D., *et al.*, 2015. Data quality aware analysis of differential expression in RNA-seq with NOISeq r/bioc package. Nucleic Acids Research. gkv711. doi:10.1093/nar/gkv711. Available at: https://doi.org/10.1093%2Fnar%2Fgkv711.

Tusher, V.G., Tibshirani, R., Chu, G., 2001. Significance analysis of microar-rays applied to the ionizing radiation response. Proceedings of the National Academy of Sciences 98, 5116–5121. doi:10.1073/pnas.091062498. Available at: https://doi.org/10.1073%2Fpnas.091062498.

Upton, G., Cook, I., 2008. A Dictionary of Statistics. Oxford University Press. Available at: https://doi.org/10.1093%2Facref%2F9780199541454.001.0001.

Yuan, G.C., Cai, L., Elowitz, M., *et al.*, 2017. Challenges and emerging directions in single-cell analysis. Genome Biology 18. doi:10.1186/s13059-017-1218-y. Available at: https://doi.org/10.1186%2Fs13059-017-1218-y.

Relevant Websites

https://nanoporetech.com/
   NANOPORE.
http://www.pacb.com/
   PACBIO.

Analyzing Transcriptome-Phenotype Correlations

Bryan T Li and Jin X Lim, Temasek Polytechnic, Singapore
Maurice HT Ling, Colossus Technologies LLP, Singapore

Introduction: Network Effects Between Transcriptome and Phenotype

Consider an electronic musician facing potentially thousands of knobs, switches, and myriad of various controls on his digital instruments and software. Although each dial, such as volume control, can be adjusted by the composer independently but it may be connected to one or more dials. For example, an incremental unit on Dial A may result in 0.1 unit increment to the setting on Dial B and 0.15 unit decrement to the setting on Dial C. Dial B and C may in turn affect other dials, which may then indirectly affect Dial A. The task of the musician is to manipulate the various controls to compose a techno piece.

In this analogy, each control represents a gene and the setting on that control represents the transcription level of that gene. The diversity of controls represents the thousands of genes in the genome. Given that the genome of each cell is identical in an organism (which several exceptions, such as immunoglobulin-producing cells), the musician represents the external stimuli to the cell and the relationships between the controls represent the complex network of signalling cross-talk where the expression of one gene may up-regulate or down-regulate other genes to varying degrees. Hence, how can the same set of controls (genome) result in different musical pieces (phenotype)?

It has been known that changes in the transcriptome may result in phenotypic changes (Sul *et al.*, 2009), some of which may result in diseased conditions; such as oncogenesis (Kang *et al.*, 2009), metabolic effects (Kyung *et al.*, 2017), or other diseases (Casamassimi *et al.*, 2017). However, the determination of phenotype from transcriptome may not be direct and can be affected by multiple levels of modulations (**Fig. 1**). For example, the effective concentration of the mRNA transcript may be affected by its antisense transcript expression (Zhao *et al.*, 2014b) and half-life (Belgrader *et al.*, 1994), various sequence features on the mRNA transcript may affect transcription efficiency leading to varying protein levels given the same amount of mRNA transcript (Evfratov *et al.*, 2017; Gamble *et al.*, 2016; Hockenberry *et al.*, 2017; Kumar *et al.*, 2014; Lahtvee *et al.*, 2017), and the effective abundance of each protein may be affected by varying half-life (Fishbain *et al.*, 2015).

Although phenotype prediction may be best carried out from proteome, the experimental techniques for large-scale proteomics studies are less developed compared to transcriptomics or genomics studies. A reason is that most transcriptome and genome techniques are based on polymerase chain reaction, which only exist for nucleic acids, and corresponding technique is absent in proteomics studies. Hence, a large volume of transcriptomics studies and data is present. Thus, there are substantial benefits to be able to predict phenotype from its transcriptome.

Determining the Transcriptome

The transcriptome is defined as the complete set of transcripts in a cell, and their quantity, for a specific developmental stage or physiological condition (Wang *et al.*, 2009). Transcripts are RNAs, the single-stranded nucleic acids, which possesses structural and

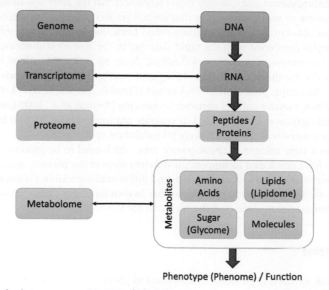

Fig. 1 Levels of omics and molecules between transcriptome and phenotype.

regulatory roles in many cellular processes. It is classified as protein-coding RNAs and nonprotein-coding RNAs (Eddy, 2001). Methods to comprehensively and systematically interrogate the expression of virtually all these RNA species have been developed over the past 20 years, from the initial expression sequencing tag (EST) based method (Boguski et al., 1994), to serial analysis of gene expression, SAGE (Velculescu et al., 1995) and cap analysis gene expression, CAGE (Shiraki et al., 2003), to the hybridization based gene microarray (Lashkari et al., 1997; Schena et al., 1995), and now the RNA-seq (Wang et al., 2009). The use of next generation sequencing (NGS) technology allows for a higher throughput and resolution level of transcriptome studies (Mardis, 2008).

EST Based Method. An expression sequencing tag (EST) is a short sub-sequence of a cDNA sequence. ESTs can be rapidly generated from either the 5′ or 3′ end of a cDNA clone in a high-throughput manner. In 1992, scientists at NCBI developed a new database, called dbEST, designed to serve as a collection point for ESTs. Data are submitted directly by laboratories and are not curated. Private EST databases such as SANBI (South Africa), MIPS (Munich), TIGEM (Italy) and DOTS (Pennsylvania) exist. Since ESTs represent portions of expressed genes, Sanger sequencing of EST is used in the early days of genome research (Boguski et al., 1994). ESTs can be used to design probes for DNA microarrays as well. However, it is impossible to achieve transcriptomic quantitative analysis using this method because of the limitation on throughput and high cost.

SAGE and CAGE. SAGE was invented by Dr. Victor Velculescu in 1995 to allow quantitative and simultaneous analysis of a large number of transcripts (Velculescu et al., 1995). The mRNA of an input sample is isolated, and cDNA is synthesized by means of biotinylated oligonucleotide primer. The cDNA is immobilized to streptavidin beads and type II restriction enzyme such as *NlaIII* is used to cleave cDNA to an average length of 256 bp with sticky ends. Captured cDNAs are ligated to linkers and then cleaved using tagging enzyme such as *BsmF1*. The ends were repaired using DNA polymerase to produce blunt end cDNA fragments. T4 DNA ligase is used to link two tags to form a 'ditag' with linker on either end. These linker-ditag-linker constructs are amplified by PCR, digested by the original anchoring enzyme, and then link together with other ditags to form cDNA concatemers. These concatemers are inserted into bacteria to create more copies, sequenced using high-throughput DNA sequencers and analyzed with computer programs. Over the years, variants of SAGE; such as, LongSAGE (Saha et al., 2002), RL-SAGE (Gowda et al., 2004) and SuperSAGE (Matsumura et al., 2005) have been developed.

While in SAGE, multiple 3′ cDNA ends were concatenated to be one close, CAGE concatenated the 5′ cDNA ends. The original CAGE method (Shiraki et al., 2003) was using biotinylated cap-trapper for capturing the 5′ ends, oligo-dT_{12-18} primers with superscript II RT in the presence of trehalose and sorbitol for synthesizing the cDNAs, the class II restriction enzyme Mmel for cleaving the tags, and the Sanger method (Sanger and Coulson, 1975; Sanger et al., 1977) for sequencing them. To better detect the non-polyadenylated RNAs, random reverse-transcription primers were introduced (Kodzius et al., 2006).

The output of SAGE and CAGE are a set of short nucleotide sequences known as tags with their observed counts. Using a reference genome, the mRNA from which the tag was extracted and its abundance could be obtained. Although protocols like *nAnTi-CAGE* (Murata et al., 2014) and updated *nanoCAGE* (Poulain et al., 2017) are published recently, due to the high cost of Sanger method for sequencing and the difficulty to map tags to the genome, CAGE and SAGE were most replaced by DNA microarray.

Microarray. The Microarray is based on nucleic acid hybridization. An array is constructed by immobilizing oligonucleotide probes on a solid support such as a silicon chip in an orderly manner. In the late 90's, DNA array technology progressed rapidly and three basic types of arrays production methods emerged during this frame: spotted arrays on glass (DeRisi et al., 1996), *in-situ* synthesized arrays (Fodor et al., 1991) and self-assembled arrays (Ferguson et al., 2000; Michael et al., 1998; Steemers et al., 2000; Walt, 2000). Fluorescence-labeled cDNA is incubated with the chip. Due to complementary binding of the cDNA to the probe, the abundance of cDNA, hence the RNA can be determined by measuring the fluorescence density. Several different types of microarrays; such as, splicing-specific microarray (Clark et al., 2002) and genome tiling array (Bertone et al., 2004); had been developed to cater for different needs.

The microarray is based on hybridization and can only detect sequences that the array was designed to detect. Genes that have not yet been annotated in a genome or non-coding RNAs that are not yet recognized as expressed cannot be detected and RNA molecules sharing high sequence similarity cannot be distinguished from one another using this method. The advent of next generation sequencing technologies combined with the rapid decrease in the cost of sequencing makes RNA-seq (Wang et al., 2009) the method of choice for measuring transcriptomes (Ledford, 2008; Su et al., 2014; Zhao et al., 2014a).

RNA-seq. RNA-seq refers to the combination of high-throughput next generation sequencing (NGS) with computational method to capture and quantify transcripts present in an RNA extract (Ozsolak and Milos, 2011). The RNA transcripts are isolated and reversely transcribed into cDNA. Massive parallel signature sequencing (Brenner et al., 2000), which consists of four rounds of restriction enzyme digestion and ligation reaction, is used to generate sequence tags of 25–500 bp. By analyzing these tags, the transcriptome can be studied qualitatively and quantitatively (Nagalakshmi et al., 2008).

The NGS technique generates a large volume of raw sequence data, which need to be processed to give meaning information. Numerous bioinformatics tools have developed to support the different steps of the process, and they can be classified under the following categories: quality control, alignment, quantification, and differential expression (Wang et al., 2009; Zhao et al., 2014a). Although it is the dominant transcriptomic technology, RNA-seq has its own limitations such as introducing bias during the cDNA library construction and RNA amplification stage, and the high cost for low input RNA-seq.

Making Sense of Transcriptome

After obtaining the transcriptome, we need to go from transcriptome to phenotype. This will be equivalent to making sense of the transcriptome data. For example, how changes in gene expressions lead to metabolic phenotypes? There are 2 main ways of looking at it: to map the data onto an existing database for visualization and functional analysis, or to compare the data with a baseline transcriptome data obtained earlier, such as comparing the genome-wide transcriptome profiling of cancerous tissue with the normal tissue to find out which subset of the transcriptome is up or down regulated. This can then be mapped onto metabolic pathways as differential gene expression is likely to result in differences in enzyme concentrations or to be analyzed by Gene Ontology, to gain insights into the molecular mechanism of cancer initiation and progression.

Transcriptome to Proteomics and Metabolomics. To integrate the transcriptomic data with proteomics and metabolomics is controversial due to the low squared Pearson's correlation coefficient (R^2) between mRNA and protein concentrations (de Sousa Abreu *et al.*, 2009). In bacteria, the correlation coefficient ranges from 0.20 to 0.47, in yeasts from 0.34 to 0.87, and in multi-cellular organisms from 0.09 to 0.46. The poor correlation suggests a significant role for post-transcriptional, translational and degradation regulation in the determination of protein concentrations (Vogel and Marcotte, 2012). Nevertheless, one may perform integrative analysis to understand genetic control of molecular dynamics and phenotypic diversity in a system-wide manner, such as or to probe protein splice variants in different tissues (Ning and Nesvizhskii, 2010), organisms (Bai *et al.*, 2014) and cells (Sheynkman *et al.*, 2013). A study (Low *et al.*, 2013) examining the liver transcriptome (using RNA sequencing) and proteome (using protein sequencing) from two rat strains (SHR and BN-Lx) found large number of RNA editing and splice variant, which demonstrates the power of integrating and interrogating various sources of omics data. Post-translational regulation can also be identified if certain peptides are present in the mass spectrometry analysis but are absent from the expressed genes of the RNA-seq dataset (Conesa *et al.*, 2016).

Integration of transcriptomics with metabolomics data has been used to identify pathways that are regulated at both the gene expression and the metabolite level, and many tools are capable of visualizing time-course data to see which pathways are active. This can be used to infer the changes of metabolic reaction rates (fluxes) across time or between different samples. This is commonly known as fluxomics (Niedenführ *et al.*, 2015; Winter and Krömer, 2013), which aims to study the differential movement of metabolites across metabolic network, leading to phenotypic observations. Large number of metabolites from prokaryotic and eukaryotic organism can be easily and precisely detected using mass spectrometry. MassTRIX uses a hypothesis-driven approach to annotate MS data within the genomic context of the organism under study, allowing user to interpret the metabolic state of the organism in the context of its potential and real enzymatic capacities (Suhre and Schmitt-Kopplin, 2008). Paintomics, on the other hand, takes complete transcriptomics and metabolomics datasets that are measured on different conditions for the same samples, together with lists of significant gene or metabolite changes, and paints this information on KEGG pathway maps (García-Alcalde *et al.*, 2011). To supports scientists during data analysis and interpretation phase, VANTED integrate experimental data into biological networks and providing a rich variety of simulation, analysis and visualization functionalities. It aims to achieve seven main tasks: network reconstruction, data visualization, integration of various data types, network simulation, data exploration, a manifold support of systems biology standards for visualization and data exchange (Rohn *et al.*, 2012). Sometimes more than one type of data is collected during the experiment and the Omics Integrator, which is improved from the initial SteinerNet, perform advanced integration of multiple types of high-throughput data as well as create condition-specific subnetworks of protein interactions that best connect the observed changes in various datasets. Unannotated molecular pathways might be detected as well (Tuncbag *et al.*, 2016).

Phenotypic Inference using GSEA. Gene Ontology (Ashburner *et al.*, 2000; Gene Ontology Consortium, 2001) is a set of defined hierarchical vocabulary aiming to describe genes and proteins, based on their molecular functions, biological processes, and cellular components. Molecular function is the biochemical activity (including specific binding to ligands or structures) of a gene product. Biological process refers to a biological objective to which the gene or gene product contributes. Cellular component refers to the cellular location where a gene product is active. Several genomes; such as, *Escherichia coli, Saccharomyces cerevisiae, Drosophila melanogaster, Mus musculus,* and *Homo sapiens;* had been annotated with Gene Ontology (GO). This allows us to use GO as a tool to analyse differential transcriptomic data (Fruzangohar *et al.*, 2017; Ho and Fraser, 2016; Kim *et al.*, 2016). Differential transcriptomes are result of statistical comparison between two transcriptomes (Trapnell *et al.*, 2013); for example, treated versus control, treatment A versus treatment B, and time point A versus time point B; and usually results in a list of differentially up-regulated genes and down-regulated genes. Recent examples of such studies are the study of gene expressions of seabuckthorn carpenter moth between room temperature and cold (Cui *et al.*, 2017), differential gene expression between the shoots and rhizomes of wild rice (*O. longistaminata*) subjected to cold stress (Zhang *et al.*, 2017), and differential gene expression between *Rhodnius montenegrensis* and *Rhodnius robustus* (de Carvalho *et al.*, 2017), potential vectors of Chagas disease. In all three studies, GO was used.

It is common to have lists of differentially expressed genes (both up-regulated and down-regulated) running into hundreds of genes. For example, a study of transcriptomic differences between thin and normal human endometrial tissue during the mid-luteal phase of the menstrual cycle (Maekawa *et al.*, 2017) showed 318 up-regulated genes and 322 down-regulated genes in the thin endometrium, compared to the control endometrium, as thin endometrium results in lower pregnancy rates due to implantation failures. The next issue facing the biologist is to make sense of these genes – which biological processes are up-regulated or down-regulated in thin endometrium compared to control?

This can be answered by Gene Set Enrichment Analysis (Subramanian *et al.*, 2005), or GSEA. The premise of GSEA is that; given that each gene within the genome is tagged with one or more GO terms; for each GO term, the number of genes in the up-regulated gene list can be analyzed to see whether the GO term occurs statistically more than random. The null hypothesis (random occurrence) is based on the proportion of genes in the genome or in a platform (such as, a microarray platform) that is tagged with a specific GO term. For example, if 10% of all human genes are tagged with "mitotic cell cycle" (GO:0000278), we will expect that 10% of the 318 up-regulated genes (or 32 genes) will tagged with "mitotic cell cycle" if null hypothesis is true. This implies that we expect 90% of the 318 up-regulated genes (or 286 genes) that are not tagged with "mitotic cell cycle". However, if there are 45 genes out of 318 up-regulated genes are tagged with "mitotic cell cycle" (278 genes not tagged with "mitotic cell cycle"), then is the function of mitosis occurring higher than random?

Using χ^2 test, we get a p-value of 0.02, suggesting that mitotic function occurs higher than random and implying that mitotic function is up-regulated in thin endometrium compared to normal endometrium. This can be done repeatedly with each of the more than 40 thousand GO terms and each GO term that occurs more than random is known as enriched term. The result of this series of analyses is to obtain a set of enriched GO terms, which represents the phenotypic differences between the 2 samples – in this case, phenotypes that are more prevalent in thin endometrium compared to normal endometrium. GSEA has been used in many studies to deduce the phenotype changes from one sample to the next (Elgendy *et al.*, 2016; He *et al.*, 2013; Heng *et al.*, 2011; Kong *et al.*, 2014; Li *et al.*, 2017; Ling, 2011; Ling and Poh, 2014; Mühleisen *et al.*, 2017; Too and Ling, 2012; Weidner *et al.*, 2017).

Gene Regulatory Network Inference. Scientist may want to elucidate gene regulatory network (GRN) from large scale experimental data. To select the network model and fit the available data into the network's structure parameter is a crucial step for constructing the network from expression data. These network models can be classified into two major categories: those use continuous variables and those use discrete variables in the modelling process.

For models with discrete variables, GenYsis (Garg *et al.*, 2008) utilises Boolean network model which assumes the gene is in either on (active or expressed) or off (inactive or unexpressed). Although it is easy to simulate, Boolean network model is not able to capture certain system behaviours that can be captured by continuous models (de Jong, 2002). To overcome this problem, the probabilistic Boolean network (Shmulevich *et al.*, 2002) was proposed, which introduced uncertainty at each network node in the form of regulatory functions with a predefined probability. Another popular model for discrete variables is the Bayesian network model, which specifies a set of conditional independence assumptions in addition to a set of conditional probabilities, to obtain a directed acyclic graph that explicitly establishes probabilistic relationships between network nodes. Although it is classified as a model for discrete variable, Bayesian network can also be used for continuous variables (Lee and Tzou, 2009). For continuous variable, one may also develop a model based on differential equation, such as the one uses stochastic modelling for parameter identification of genetic regulatory networks in prokaryotes (Cinquemani *et al.*, 2008).

The primary concern of biologists is how to translate the inferred network into hypotheses that can be tested with real-life experiments. It is important to utilize information from multiple sources to narrow down the search space after a GRN is constructed (Mobini *et al.*, 2009). Pathway databases; such as, KEGG (Okuda *et al.*, 2008), and DAVID (Dennis *et al.*, 2003); are used to match the inferred GRN to a module or subnetwork. The module or subnetwork is then used to search for genes with similar gene expression profiles.

The advances of the high-throughput next generation sequencing technology (NGS) and the development of various bioinformatics tools allowed researchers to fit theoretical models to experimental data on gene expression profile. A study (Gluck *et al.*, 2016) mapping mouse salivary gland transcriptome data onto gene regulatory networks not only confirms known modulators involved in salivary gland morphogenesis but also reveal novel transcription factors and signalling pathways unique to mouse salivary glands.

Concluding Remarks

One of the major reasons for using transcriptomic data as the source data to elucidate phenotype is the relative advancement in experimental techniques in the area of transcriptomics compared to proteomics and metabolomics. Hence, transcriptomic data acts as a convenient proxy to proteomic and metabolomics data. Earlier studies using only transcriptomic data had been promising (Curtis *et al.*, 2012). For example, a study (Urzúa *et al.*, 2010) found 60% of the biological variability observed in spontaneous ovarian tumor rates and reproductive parameters across four mouse strains (BalbC, C57BL6, FVB and SWR) can be attributed to transcriptomic differences measured using microarrays.

However, in recent years, there is an increase in the number of studies attempting to integrate various sources of omics data, including transcriptomics, to elucidate the molecular basis of phenotypes. For example, epigenomic, transcriptomic, and proteomic data had been integrated to explain dysfunction in human hepatocyte caused by valproic acid (Wolters *et al.*, 2018). Multi-omics approach had also been shown to improve survival prediction in patients with neuroblastoma (Francescatto *et al.*, 2018) and liver cancer (Chaudhary *et al.*, 2018). This has in turn triggered the development of algorithms to use multi-omics data (Mandal and Maji, 2018). Hence, it is foreseeable that with advances in high-throughput experimental techniques and improved computational algorithms, transcriptomics will be one of the data sources in a multi-omics pool to understand the why and how of phenotypes.

See also: Applications of Ribosomal RNA Sequence and Structure Analysis for Extracting Evolutionary and Functional Insights. Characterizing and Functional Assignment of Noncoding RNAs. Codon Usage. Comparative Transcriptomics Analysis. Exome Sequencing Data Analysis. Functional Enrichment Analysis. Integrative Analysis of Multi-Omics Data. Natural Language Processing Approaches in Bioinformatics. Next Generation Sequencing Data Analysis. Pipeline of High Throughput Sequencing. Regulation of Gene Expression. Transcriptome Analysis. Whole Genome Sequencing Analysis

---

References

Ashburner, M., Ball, C.A., Blake, J.A., *et al.*, 2000. Gene ontology: Tool for the unification of biology. The Gene Ontology Consortium. Nat. Genet. 25, 25–29.

Bai, Y., Hassler, J., Ziyar, A., *et al.*, 2014. Novel bioinformatics method for identification of genome-wide non-canonical spliced regions using RNA-Seq data. PLOS ONE 9, e100864.

Belgrader, P., Cheng, J., Zhou, X., Stephenson, L.S., Maquat, L.E., 1994. Mammalian nonsense codons can be cis effectors of nuclear mRNA half-life. Mol. Cell. Biol. 14, 8219–8228.

Bertone, P., Stolc, V., Royce, T.E., et al., 2004. Global identification of human transcribed sequences with genome tiling arrays. Science 306, 2242–2246.

Boguski, M.S., Tolstoshev, C.M., Bassett, D.E., 1994. Gene discovery in dbEST. Science 265, 1993–1994.

Brenner, S., Johnson, M., Bridgham, J., et al., 2000. Gene expression analysis by massively parallel signature sequencing (MPSS) on microbead arrays. Nat. Biotechnol. 18, 630–634.

de Carvalho, D.B., Congrains, C., Chahad-Ehlers, S., et al., 2017. Differential transcriptome analysis supports Rhodnius montenegrensis and Rhodnius robustus (Hemiptera, Reduviidae, Triatominae) as distinct species. PLOS ONE 12, e0174997.

Casamassimi, A., Federico, A., Rienzo, M., Esposito, S., Ciccodicola, A., 2017. Transcriptome profiling in human diseases: New advances and perspectives. Int. J. Mol. Sci. 18, 1652.

Chaudhary, K., Poirion, O.B., Lu, L., Garmire, L.X., 2018. Deep learning-based multi-omics integration robustly predicts survival in liver cancer. Clin. Cancer Res. 24, 1248–1259.

Cinquemani, E., Milias-Argeitis, A., Summers, S., Lygeros, J., 2008. Stochastic dynamics of genetic networks: Modelling and parameter identification. Bioinformatics 24, 2748–2754.

Clark, T.A., Sugnet, C.W., Ares, M., 2002. Genomewide analysis of mRNA processing in yeast using splicing-specific microarrays. Science 296, 907–910.

Conesa, A., Madrigal, P., Tarazona, S., et al., 2016. A survey of best practices for RNA-seq data analysis. Genome Biol. 17, 13.

Cui, M., Hu, P., Wang, T., Tao, J., Zong, S., 2017. Differential transcriptome analysis reveals genes related to cold tolerance in seabuckthorn carpenter moth, Eogystia hippophaecolus. PLOS ONE 12, e0187105.

Curtis, R.E., Yin, J., Kinnaird, P., Xing, E.P., 2012. Finding genome-transcriptome-phenome association with structured association mapping and visualization in GenAMap. Pac. Symp. Biocomput. 327–338.

Dennis Jr., G., Sherman, B.T., Hosack, D.A., et al., 2003. DAVID: Database for annotation, visualization, and integrated discovery. Genome Biol. 4, P3.

DeRisi, J., Penland, L., Brown, P.O., et al., 1996. Use of a cDNA microarray to analyse gene expression patterns in human cancer. Nat. Genet. 14, 457–460.

Eddy, S.R., 2001. Non-coding RNA genes and the modern RNA world. Nat. Rev. Genet. 2, 919–929.

Elgendy, R., Giantin, M., Castellani, F., et al., 2016. Transcriptomic signature of high dietary organic selenium supplementation in sheep: A nutrigenomic insight using a custom microarray platform and gene set enrichment analysis. J. Anim. Sci. 94, 3169–3184.

Evfratov, S.A., Osterman, I.A., Komarova, E.S., et al., 2017. Application of sorting and next generation sequencing to study 5'-UTR influence on translation efficiency in Escherichia coli. Nucleic Acids Res. 45, 3487–3502.

Ferguson, J.A., Steemers, F.J., Walt, D.R., 2000. High-density fiber-optic DNA random microsphere array. Anal. Chem. 72, 5618–5624.

Fishbain, S., Inobe, T., Israeli, E., et al., 2015. Sequence composition of disordered regions fine-tunes protein half-life. Nat. Struct. Mol. Biol. 22, 214–221.

Fodor, S.P., Read, J.L., Pirrung, M.C., et al., 1991. Light-directed, spatially addressable parallel chemical synthesis. Science 251, 767–773.

Francescatto, M., Chierici, M., Rezvan Dezfooli, S., et al., 2018. Multi-omics integration for neuroblastoma clinical endpoint prediction. Biol. Direct 13, 5.

Fruzangohar, M., Ebrahimie, E., Adelson, D.L., 2017. A novel hypothesis-unbiased method for Gene Ontology enrichment based on transcriptome data. PLOS ONE 12, e0170486.

Gamble, C.E., Brule, C.E., Dean, K.M., Fields, S., Grayhack, E.J., 2016. Adjacent codons act in concert to modulate translation efficiency in yeast. Cell 166, 679–690.

García-Alcalde, F., García-López, F., Dopazo, J., Conesa, A., 2011. Paintomics: A web based tool for the joint visualization of transcriptomics and metabolomics data. Bioinformatics 27, 137–139.

Garg, A., Di Cara, A., Xenarios, I., Mendoza, L., De Micheli, G., 2008. Synchronous versus asynchronous modeling of gene regulatory networks. Bioinformatics 24, 1917–1925.

Gene Ontology Consortium, 2001. Creating the gene ontology resource: Design and implementation. Genome Res. 11, 1425–1433.

Gluck, C., Min, S., Oyelakin, A., et al., 2016. RNA-seq based transcriptomic map reveals new insights into mouse salivary gland development and maturation. BMC Genom. 17, 923.

Gowda, M., Jantasuriyarat, C., Dean, R.A., Wang, G.-L., 2004. Robust-LongSAGE (RL-SAGE): A substantially improved LongSAGE method for gene discovery and transcriptome analysis. Plant Physiol. 134, 890–897.

He, W., Qi, B., Zhou, Q., et al., 2013. Key genes and pathways in thyroid cancer based on gene set enrichment analysis. Oncol. Rep. 30, 1391–1397.

Heng, S.S.J., Chan, O.Y.W., Keng, B.M.H., Ling, M.H.T., 2011. Glucan Biosynthesis Protein G (mdoG) is a suitable reference gene in Escherichia coli K-12. ISRN Microbiol. 2011.Article ID 469053.

Ho, M.-M., Fraser, D.A., 2016. Transcriptome data and gene ontology analysis in human macrophages ingesting modified lipoproteins in the presence or absence of complement protein C1q. Data Brief 9, 362–367.

Hockenberry, A.J., Pah, A.R., Jewett, M.C., Amaral, L.A.N., 2017. Leveraging genome-wide datasets to quantify the functional role of the anti-Shine-Dalgarno sequence in regulating translation efficiency. Open Biol. 7.

de Jong, H., 2002. Modeling and simulation of genetic regulatory systems: A literature review. J. Comput. Biol. 9, 67–103.

Kang, C.-J., Chen, Y.-J., Liao, C.-T., et al., 2009. Transcriptome profiling and network pathway analysis of genes associated with invasive phenotype in oral cancer. Cancer Lett. 284, 131–140.

Kim, H.-I., Kim, J.-H., Park, Y.-J., 2016. Transcriptome and Gene Ontology (GO) enrichment analysis reveals genes involved in biotin metabolism that affect L-lysine production in Corynebacterium glutamicum. Int. J. Mol. Sci. 17, 353.

Kodzius, R., Kojima, M., Nishiyori, H., et al., 2006. CAGE: Cap analysis of gene expression. Nat. Methods 3, 211.

Kong, B., Yang, T., Chen, L., et al., 2014. Protein-protein interaction network analysis and gene set enrichment analysis in epilepsy patients with brain cancer. J. Clin. Neurosci. 21, 316–319.

Kumar, S., van Raam, B.J., Salvesen, G.S., Cieplak, P., 2014. Caspase cleavage sites in the human proteome: CaspDB, a database of predicted substrates. PLOS ONE 9, e110539.

Kyung, D.S., Sung, H.R., Kim, Y.J., et al., 2017. Global transcriptome analysis identifies weight regain-induced activation of adaptive immune responses in white adipose tissue of mice. Int. J. Obes.

Lahtvee, P.-J., Sánchez, B.J., Smialowska, A., et al., 2017. Absolute quantification of protein and mRNA abundances demonstrate variability in gene-specific translation efficiency in yeast. Cell Syst. 4, 495–504. e5.

Lashkari, D.A., DeRisi, J.L., McCusker, J.H., et al., 1997. Yeast microarrays for genome wide parallel genetic and gene expression analysis. Proc. Natl. Acad. Sci. USA 94, 13057–13062.

Ledford, H., 2008. The death of microarrays? Nature 455, 847.

Lee, W.-P., Tzou, W.-S., 2009. Computational methods for discovering gene networks from expression data. Brief. Bioinform. 10, 408–423.

Li, W.-X., He, K., Tang, L., et al., 2017. Comprehensive tissue-specific gene set enrichment analysis and transcription factor analysis of breast cancer by integrating 14 gene expression datasets. Oncotarget 8, 6775–6786.

Ling, M.H., 2011. Bactome II: Analyzing gene list for gene ontology over-representation. The Python Papers Source Codes 3, 3.

Ling, M.H., Poh, C.L., 2014. A predictor for predicting Escherichia coli transcriptome and the effects of gene perturbations. BMC Bioinform. 15, 140.

Low, T.Y., van Heesch, S., van den Toorn, H., et al., 2013. Quantitative and qualitative proteome characteristics extracted from in-depth integrated genomics and proteomics analysis. Cell Rep. 5, 1469–1478.

Maekawa, R., Taketani, T., Mihara, Y., et al., 2017. Thin endometrium transcriptome analysis reveals a potential mechanism of implantation failure. Reprod. Med. Biol. 16, 206–227.

Mandal, A., Maji, P., 2018. FaRoC: Fast and robust supervised canonical correlation analysis for multimodal omics data. IEEE Trans. Cybern. 48, 1229–1241.

Mardis, E.R., 2008. Next-generation DNA sequencing methods. Annu. Rev. Genom. Hum. Genet. 9, 387–402.

Matsumura, H., Ito, A., Saitoh, H., et al., 2005. SuperSAGE. Cell. Microbiol. 7, 11–18.

Michael, K.L., Taylor, L.C., Schultz, S.L., Walt, D.R., 1998. Randomly ordered addressable high-density optical sensor arrays. Anal. Chem. 70, 1242–1248.

Mobini, R., Andersson, B.A., Erjefält, J., et al., 2009. A module-based analytical strategy to identify novel disease-associated genes shows an inhibitory role for interleukin 7 Receptor in allergic inflammation. BMC Syst. Biol. 3, 19.

Mühleisen, T.W., Reinbold, C.S., Forstner, A.J., et al., 2017. Gene set enrichment analysis and expression pattern exploration implicate an involvement of neurodevelopmental processes in bipolar disorder. J. Affect. Disord. 228, 20–25.

Murata, M., Nishiyori-Sueki, H., Kojima-Ishiyama, M., et al., 2014. Detecting expressed genes using CAGE. Methods Mol. Biol. 1164, 67–85.

Nagalakshmi, U., Wang, Z., Waern, K., et al., 2008. The transcriptional landscape of the yeast genome defined by RNA sequencing. Science 320, 1344–1349.

Niedenführ, S., Wiechert, W., Nöh, K., 2015. How to measure metabolic fluxes: A taxonomic guide for (13)C fluxomics. Curr. Opin. Biotechnol. 34, 82–90.

Ning, K., Nesvizhskii, A.I., 2010. The utility of mass spectrometry-based proteomic data for validation of novel alternative splice forms reconstructed from RNA-Seq data: A preliminary assessment. BMC Bioinform. 11 (Suppl. 11), S14.

Okuda, S., Yamada, T., Hamajima, M., et al., 2008. KEGG Atlas mapping for global analysis of metabolic pathways. Nucleic Acids Res. 36, W423–W426.

Ozsolak, F., Milos, P.M., 2011. RNA sequencing: Advances, challenges and opportunities. Nat. Rev. Genet. 12, 87–98.

Poulain, S., Kato, S., Arnaud, O., et al., 2017. NanoCAGE: A method for the analysis of coding and noncoding 5′-capped transcriptomes. Methods Mol. Biol. 1543, 57–109.

Rohn, H., Junker, A., Hartmann, A., et al., 2012. VANTED v2: A framework for systems biology applications. BMC Syst. Biol. 6, 139.

Saha, S., Sparks, A.B., Rago, C., et al., 2002. Using the transcriptome to annotate the genome. Nat. Biotechnol. 20, 508–512.

Sanger, F., Coulson, A.R., 1975. A rapid method for determining sequences in DNA by primed synthesis with DNA polymerase. J. Mol. Biol. 94, 441–448.

Sanger, F., Nicklen, S., Coulson, A.R., 1977. DNA sequencing with chain-terminating inhibitors. Proc. Natl. Acad. Sci. USA 74, 5463–5467.

Schena, M., Shalon, D., Davis, R.W., Brown, P.O., 1995. Quantitative monitoring of gene expression patterns with a complementary DNA microarray. Science 270, 467–470.

Sheynkman, G.M., Shortreed, M.R., Frey, B.L., Smith, L.M., 2013. Discovery and mass spectrometric analysis of novel splice-junction peptides using RNA-Seq. Mol. Cell Proteom. 12, 2341–2353.

Shiraki, T., Kondo, S., Katayama, S., et al., 2003. Cap analysis gene expression for high-throughput analysis of transcriptional starting point and identification of promoter usage. Proc. Natl. Acad. Sci. USA 100, 15776–15781.

Shmulevich, I., Dougherty, E.R., Kim, S., Zhang, W., 2002. Probabilistic Boolean networks: A rule-based uncertainty model for gene regulatory networks. Bioinformatics 18, 261–274.

de Sousa Abreu, R., Penalva, L.O., Marcotte, E.M., Vogel, C., 2009. Global signatures of protein and mRNA expression levels. Mol. Biosyst. 5, 1512–1526.

Steemers, F.J., Ferguson, J.A., Walt, D.R., 2000. Screening unlabeled DNA targets with randomly ordered fiber-optic gene arrays. Nat. Biotechnol. 18, 91.

Su, Z., Fang, H., Hong, H., et al., 2014. An investigation of biomarkers derived from legacy microarray data for their utility in the RNA-seq era. Genome Biol. 15, 523.

Subramanian, A., Tamayo, P., Mootha, V.K., et al., 2005. Gene set enrichment analysis: A knowledge-based approach for interpreting genome-wide expression profiles. Proc. Natl. Acad. Sci. USA 102, 15545–15550.

Suhre, K., Schmitt-Kopplin, P., 2008. MassTRIX: Mass translator into pathways. Nucleic Acids Res. 36, W481–W484.

Sul, J.-Y., Wu, C.K., Zeng, F., et al., 2009. Transcriptome transfer produces a predictable cellular phenotype. Proc. Natl. Acad. Sci. USA 106, 7624–7629.

Too, I.H.K., Ling, M.H.T., 2012. Signal peptidase complex subunit 1 and Hydroxyacyl-CoA Dehydrogenase Beta Subunit are suitable reference genes in human lungs. ISRN Bioinform. 2012.Article ID 790452.

Trapnell, C., Hendrickson, D.G., Sauvageau, M., et al., 2013. Differential analysis of gene regulation at transcript resolution with RNA-seq. Nat. Biotechnol. 31.10.1038/nbt.2450.

Tuncbag, N., Gosline, S.J.C., Kedaigle, A., et al., 2016. Network-based interpretation of diverse high-throughput datasets through the omics integrator software package. PLOS Comput. Biol. 12, e1004879.

Urzúa, U., Owens, G.A., Zhang, G.-M., et al., 2010. Tumor and reproductive traits are linked by RNA metabolism genes in the mouse ovary: A transcriptome-phenotype association analysis. BMC Genom. 11 (Suppl. 5), S1.

Velculescu, V.E., Zhang, L., Vogelstein, B., Kinzler, K.W., 1995. Serial analysis of gene expression. Science 270, 484–487.

Vogel, C., Marcotte, E.M., 2012. Insights into the regulation of protein abundance from proteomic and transcriptomic analyses. Nat. Rev. Genet. 13, 227–232.

Walt, D.R., 2000. Techview: Molecular biology. Bead-based fiber-optic arrays. Science 287, 451–452.

Wang, Z., Gerstein, M., Snyder, M., 2009. RNA-Seq: A revolutionary tool for transcriptomics. Nat. Rev. Genet. 10, 57–63.

Weidner, C., Steinfath, M., Wistorf, E., et al., 2017. A protocol for using gene set enrichment analysis to identify the appropriate animal model for translational research. J. Vis. Exp.

Winter, G., Krömer, J.O., 2013. Fluxomics – Connecting 'omics analysis and phenotypes. Environ. Microbiol. 15, 1901–1916.

Wolters, J.E.J., van Breda, S.G.J., Grossmann, J., et al., 2018. Integrated 'omics analysis reveals new drug-induced mitochondrial perturbations in human hepatocytes. Toxicol. Lett. 289, 1–13.

Zhang, T., Huang, L., Wang, Y., et al., 2017. Differential transcriptome profiling of chilling stress response between shoots and rhizomes of Oryza longistaminata using RNA sequencing. PLOS ONE 12, e0188625.

Zhao, S., Fung-Leung, W.-P., Bittner, A., Ngo, K., Liu, X., 2014a. Comparison of RNA-Seq and microarray in transcriptome profiling of activated T cells. PLOS ONE 9, e78644.

Zhao, T., Wu, Z., Wang, S., Chen, L., 2014b. Expression and function of natural antisense transcripts in mouse embryonic stem cells. Sci. China Life Sci. 57, 1183–1190.

Transcriptome During Cell Differentiation

Dwi A Pujianto, Universitas Indonesia, Jakarta, Indonesia

Introduction

The term development in animal is a very complex process in which a fertilized egg, the zygote, undergoes a series of gene-regulated changes to form a complete and adult organism. These changes involve not only cell proliferation but also specialization of the cells to become a certain cell type with a specific function. As the process begins, the single cell-zygote undergoes a series of cleavage to produce a morula (16–32 cells), blastula and gastrula in which three germ layers are formed. The three germ layers will differentiate into all organ systems in the mature organism. Development of an individual combines several different molecular mechanisms that can affect cell's number, morphology, behavior and function (Twyman, 2001). During development process there are changes as follow:

1. Cell proliferation: The number of cell increases as result of repeated cell division.
2. Cell growth: Increase in the production of molecules such as nucleotides, proteins, carbohydrates and lipids that cause an increase in cell's total volume.
3. Cell differentiation: Alteration of the cells from the stage of multipotent that can transform to any kind of cell to become more specific type with a specialized function.

All of these mechanisms are regulated by many genes and involves various gene regulatory proteins which determine time and location of the expression producing a specific protein in the embryo that directs cell behavior (Zasso *et al.*, 2018). Since multicellular organisms develop from a single cell (zigot), thus all cells contain the same genes. The question arises on how cells that contain the same genes behave differently? Therefore, for cell to behave differently during embryonic development, different set of genes are expressed in a certain type of cell. Moreover, especially in the eukaryotic cells, gene expression is much regulated by many transcription factors (Alberts *et al.*, 2015). Hence, development of an individual from zygote to adult is also governed by specific transcription factors (Kuo *et al.*, 1992). Simultaneous gene transcription analyses during development will reveal the key players in maintaining the multipotency and also key players responsible for cell differentiation to become specialized cell type with a specific function. In this article we will focus on gene expression profile during cell differentiation.

Cell Specialization During Development

After fertilization the zygote undergoes early cleavage producing blastomeres which are unspecialized. These blastomeres have characteristic to be totipotent, because they have capability to transform into all kinds of cells in the body, this includes amnion and chorion which are considered to be extra-embryonic membranes (**Fig. 1**). When the development occurs, cells undergo not only multiplication but also differentiation producing cells with a specialized function. After early cleavage of the zygote producing 2–4 blastomeres, the number of cell increases to form murbey-like structure called morula containing 16–32 blastomeres (Moore and Persaud, 2008). The blastomeres then differentiate into blastocyst with two different groups of cells. The first is the inner cell mass which will develop into embryo proper and amnion and the second population is the trophoblast which will develop into the chorion and part of the embryo called the placenta. The inner cell mass cells have characteristic of being pluripotent which mean these cells have potency to differentiate into any cell type in the developing embryo but they no longer have capacity to develop into extra-embryonic structure derived from the trophoblast.

Cells that have differentiated into inner cell mass subsequently develop into one of the three germ layers which is the characteristic of the gastrula. The three germ layers will differentiate into specific cell type that forms organ systems (**Fig. 1**). The internal layer endoderm is the future of internal organs such as respiratory and digestive organs. The middle layer mesoderm will differentiate into muscles, urogenital organs and connective tissues including blood cells and vessel. The external layer ectoderm gives rise to organs in the neural system, sense organs and outer epithelium of the body (Moore and Persaud, 2008). Cells in the three germ layers have characteristic of being multipotent. These cells have capacity to differentiate into many cell types but not all cell types in the embryo. Cells in the immune system and blood for instance, can differentiate into a progenitor cell with capacity to give rise only to few cells in the lineage such as lymphocytes which subsequently differentiate into lymphocyte B and T. This kind of cell is characterized to be oligopotent. Finally, some cells differentiate into precursor cells with capacity to transform only to one cell type. These cells are categorized as unipotent. The precursor cells such as hepatocytes, osteoblast and chondroblast usually have capacity to self-renewal or act as stem cell for terminally differentiated cells (Strachan and Read, 2004).

Gene Transcription During Cell Differentiation

Back to the previous question, how cells with the same genome behave differently and give rise to various cells with specific function? Obviously there are mechanisms to regulate gene expression during changes from cells with totipotent to multipotent

---

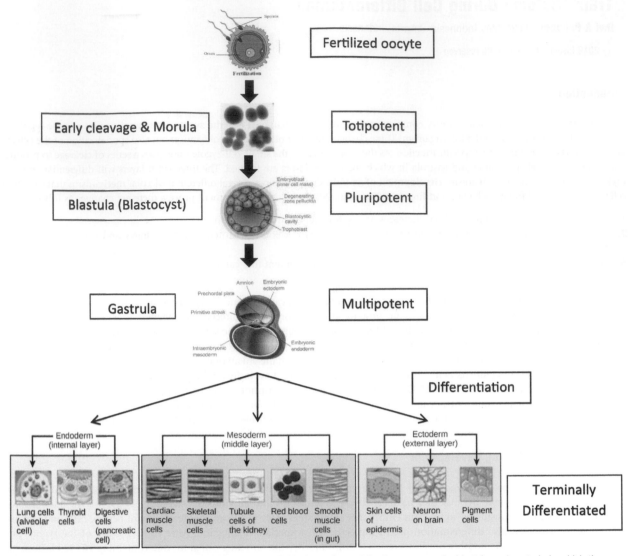

Fig. 1 Development of zigot (fertilized oocyte) to become an individual start from early cleavage, morula, blastula, and gastrula in which three germ layers are formed. The three germ layers undergo differentiation into various tissues and organs. Each stage of the development has its own potency whether totipotent, pluripotent or multipotent.

capacities to become specialized cell. Since development and differentiation involve cell proliferation, movement, interaction with other cells and specialization, the first important genes are the gene that encode for transmembrane molecules which is important for cell-cell adhesion and cell signaling (Alberts *et al.*, 2015; Sanchez-Arrones *et al.*, 2012). The second gene is the genes that encode for transcription factors which is important for regulating gene expression (Alberts *et al.*, 2015; Cave and Sockanathan, 2018). Regulation of gene expression during cell differentiation is also performed by epigenetic mechanisms involving chromatin modification and microRNA (Alvarez-Errico *et al.*, 2015; Huang *et al.*, 2014; Youngblood *et al.*, 2013). Differential gene expression among the cells undergoing differentiation is also dictated by signal molecules present in the environment. Signal molecules affect gene regulatory protein (transcription factor) binding to the gene promoter, thus some transcriptions are "ON" some others are "OFF" during differentiation. The presence of signal molecules also determine whether cell commit asymmetric or symmetric division to produce specialized cell (Alberts *et al.*, 2015). Some well characterized signal proteins among other things are TGFß superfamily, Wnt, Hedgehog and Notch. Gene expression profiling using cDNA microarray to analyze gene transcription (Transcriptome) during cell differentiation is a very challenging task to identify key players in the process.

Transcriptome of Cell Differentiation

The molecular mechanisms that can explain pluripotency and then differentiation from the inner cell mass of the blastocyst (embryonic stem cell, ESCs) are largely unknown. Embryonic stem cells are capable of self-renew because they have stem cell specific factors (Hochedlinger *et al.*, 2005; Hough *et al.*, 2006) and to initiate differentiation into any cell type of the three germ layers by activation of specific sets of genes by transcription factors that are required for each specific linenage (Szutorisz and Dillon, 2005). In addition to activation by specific transcription factors cell pluripotency and differentiation is also regulated by epigenetic mechanisms (Azuara *et al.*, 2006). Chromatin structure in the ESCs is characterized by specific features which is different with that of differentiated cells (Niwa, 2007). Chromatin in the ESCs is morphologically distinct from that of differentiated cells in which in the ESCs chromatin is looser so that more gene expressed in the ESCs compare to the differentiated cells (Aoto *et al.*, 2006). In the undifferentiated cells like ESCs chromatin indicate transcriptionally active state and express large regions of the genome, probably not in specific manner and at low levels (Meshorer and Misteli, 2006). Undifferentiated ESCs also express repetitive sequences, mobile elements, as well as lineage and tissue specific genes at low levels.

According to Efroni *et al.*, the properties of ESC chromatin such as global decondensation, looser binding of chromatin proteins and enrichment of active histone modification indicate transcriptionally active chromatin and it is hypothesized that undifferentiated cells (ESCs) are globally transcriptionally more active than differentiated cells. Efroni test this hypothesis, global transcription was measured by (3H) uridine incorporation and compared between undifferentiated ESCs and 7 day neuronal progenitor cells (NPCs) derived from ESCs by invitro differentiation. The results showed that total RNA and mRNA levels were almost two-fold higher in the ESCs compared to the differentiated NPCs (Efroni *et al.*, 2008). The increase in the transcriptional activity in the in the ESCs is caused by activity of the specific set of genes that reflect global activation of the genome in the ESCs. The phenomenon that higher transcription is found in the ESCs compare to the differentiated cells is evidenced in the experiment performed by Efroni which compared transcription of 12 lineage specific genes (**Fig. 2**).

Identification of Genes Involved in Cell Differentiation

At the blastocyst stage, the inner cell mass (ICM) will develop into three germ layers namely the ectoderm, mesoderm and endoderm. The ICM constitutes the embryonic stem cells that are capable of differentiating into any type of cells. This formation three germ layers is the characteristic of gastrulation and marks the beginning of differentiation into organs, for instance nervous system is derived from the ectoderm, skeletal muscle from the mesoderm and digestive system from the endoderm (Moore and Persaud, 2008). One of the clear examples of cell differentiation is the development of brain from the ectoderm layer. Brain development is one of the most complicated processes during embryogenesis. In the neuroectoderm differentiation, expression of pluripotent genes such as POU5F1, SOX2, NANOG decreases and the expression of neuroectoderm genes such as POU3F1, ZNF521, and also neural epithelial markers such as PAX6 and SOX1 increase and reach the peak at day 12 post fertilization (Li *et al.*, 2017) (**Fig. 3**).

Analyses gene expression profiling on the potency of human embryonic stem cell (hESC) to develop into neural system based on developmental period suggesting that stage 3, which is at day 8–10 of the invitro differentiation, is the critical windows for the transition from pluripotency to the neural epithelium. Moreover, several transcription factors are identified to be involved in this stage such as PAX6, SIX3, HESX1 and ID3. Deletion of either SIX3 or HESX1 causes abnormality in the development of hESC to become neural cells (Li *et al.*, 2017). Correlation analysis of the downstream target of these transcription factor found that SIX3 negatively correlated with pluripotent genes such as NANOG. This suggests that SIX3 gene promotes neural differentiation by regulating its downstream transcription factors.

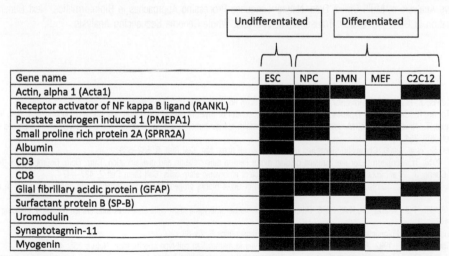

Fig. 2 Reduced global transcription in differentiated cells compared to undifferentiated cells (ESC). The differentiated cells are represented by ESC-derived neuronal progenitor cells (NPC), ESC-derived postmitotic neurons (PMN), mouse embryonic fibroblast (MEF), and immortalized mouse myoblast cell line (C2C12). Black filled boxes represent expressed genes whereas white boxes represent undetected gene expression. Modified from Efroni, S., Duttagupta, R., Cheng, J., *et al.*, 2008. Global transcription in pluripotent embryonic stem cells. Cell Stem Cell 2, 437–447.

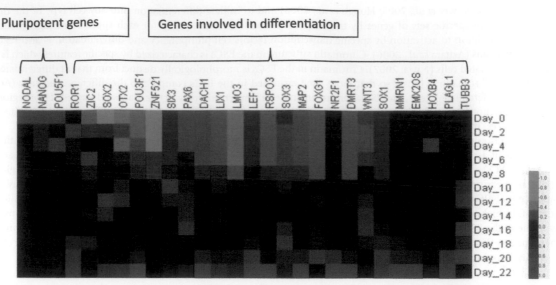

Fig. 3 Expression profile of pluripotent genes (NODAL, NANOG and POU5F1) and differentiation markers such as SOX2, OTX2, and POU3F1. At the beginning of embryogenesis at day 2–4 pluripotent genes are expressed (Indicates by red color), whereas during differentiation at day 6–22 expression of pluripotent genes decrease and differentiation genes are up-regulated. Red color indicates increase in the level of expression, green indicates expression decrease. Modified from Li, Y., Wang, R., Qiao, N., et al., 2017. Transcriptome analysis reveals determinant stages controlling human embryonic stem cell commitment to neuronal cells. J. Biol. Chem. 292, 19590–19604.

Conclusion

The development of multicellular organism starts with cell proliferation, growth and differentiation that produces specialized cells. At the pluripotent stage (stem cells) the chromatin packaging is looser so that there are more genes expressed at this stage although at low levels. When cells undergo differentiation, expression of pluripotent genes such as POU5F1, SOX2, NANOG decreases, whereas genes involved in differentiation such as POU3F1 and ZNF521 increase. At the critical windows for the transition from pluripotency to differentiated cells, there is a negative correlation between transcription factors and pluripotent genes such as NODAL, NANOG and POU5F1, but positive correlation with genes involved in differentiation such as SOX2, OTX2, and POU3F1.

See also: Applications of Ribosomal RNA Sequence and Structure Analysis for Extracting Evolutionary and Functional Insights. Characterizing and Functional Assignment of Noncoding RNAs. Codon Usage. Comparative Transcriptomics Analysis. Coupling Cell Division to Metabolic Pathways Through Transcription. Exome Sequencing Data Analysis. Functional Enrichment Analysis. Genome-Wide Scanning of Gene Expression. Integrative Analysis of Multi-Omics Data. Natural Language Processing Approaches in Bioinformatics. Next Generation Sequencing Data Analysis. Regulation of Gene Expression. Transcriptome Analysis. Whole Genome Sequencing Analysis

References

Alberts, B., Johnson, A., Lewis, J., et al., 2015. Molecular Biology of the Cell, sixth ed. New York: Garland Science.

Alvarez-Errico, D., Vento-Tormo, R., Sieweke, M., Ballestar, E., 2015. Epigenetic control of myeloid cell differentiation, identity and function. Nat. Rev. Immunol. 15, 7–17.

Aoto, T., Saitoh, N., Ichimura, T., Niwa, H., Nakao, M., 2006. Nuclear and chromatin reorganization in the MHC-Oct3/4 locus at developmental phases of embryonic stem cell differentiation. Dev. Biol. 298, 354–367.

Azuara, V., Perry, P., Sauer, S., et al., 2006. Chromatin signatures of pluripotent cell lines. Nat. Cell Biol. 8, 532–538.

Cave, C., Sockanathan, S., 2018. Transcription factor mechanisms guiding motor neuron differentiation and diversification. Curr. Opin. Neurobiol. 53, 1–7.

Efroni, S., Duttagupta, R., Cheng, J., et al., 2008. Global transcription in pluripotent embryonic stem cells. Cell Stem Cell 2, 437–447.

Hochedlinger, K., Yamada, Y., Beard, C., Jaenisch, R., 2005. Ectopic expression of Oct-4 blocks progenitor-cell differentiation and causes dysplasia in epithelial tissues. Cell 121, 465–477.

Hough, S.R., Clements, I., Welch, P.J., Wiederholt, K.A., 2006. Differentiation of mouse embryonic stem cells after RNA interference-mediated silencing of OCT4 and Nanog. Stem Cells 24, 1467–1475.

Huang, B., Jiang, C., Zhang, R., 2014. Epigenetics: The language of the cell? Epigenomics 6, 73–88.

Kuo, C.J., Conley, P.B., Chen, L., et al., 1992. A transcriptional hierarchy involved in mammalian cell-type specification. Nature 355, 457–461.

Li, Y., Wang, R., Qiao, N., et al., 2017. Transcriptome analysis reveals determinant stages controlling human embryonic stem cell commitment to neuronal cells. J. Biol. Chem. 292, 19590–19604.

Meshorer, E., Misteli, T., 2006. Chromatin in pluripotent embryonic stem cells and differentiation. Nat. Rev. Mol. Cell Biol. 7, 540–546.

Moore, K., Persaud, T., 2008. The Developing Human: Clinically Oriented Embryology. Philadelphia: Sauders.

Niwa, H., 2007. Open conformation chromatin and pluripotency. Genes Dev. 21, 2671–2676.

Sanchez-Arrones, L., Cardozo, M., Nieto-Lopez, F., Bovolenta, P., 2012. Cdon and Boc: Two transmembrane proteins implicated in cell-cell communication. Int. J. Biochem. Cell Biol. 44, 698–702.

Strachan, T., Read, A., 2004. Human Molecular Genetic, third ed. London and New York: Garland Science.

Szutorisz, H., Dillon, N., 2005. The epigenetic basis for embryonic stem cell pluripotency. Bioessays 27, 1286–1293.

Twyman, R., 2001. Signal transduction in development. In: Instant Notes in Developmental Biology. BIOS Scientific Publisher, Oxford.

Youngblood, B., Hale, J.S., Ahmed, R., 2013. T-cell memory differentiation: Insights from transcriptional signatures and epigenetics. Immunology 139, 277–284.

Zasso, J., Mastad, A., Cutarelli, A., Conti, L., 2018. Inducible alpha-synuclein expression affects human Neural Stem Cell behavior. Stem Cells Dev.

Characterization of Transcriptional Activities

Adison Wong, Singapore Institute of Technology, Singapore
Maurice HT Ling, Colossus Technologies LLP, Singapore, Singapore

Recent progress in DNA microarray and RNA sequencing have enabled large scale and high quality whole cell transcriptome analysis to be performed. When complemented with Gene Ontology, both technologies could rapidly isolate important genetic determinants for further validation by qPCR. Besides the measurement of transcription at the mRNA level, gene expressions can be quantified using reporter proteins; such as green fluorescent protein. The results of these studies are usually integrated into computational models to enable the prediction of gene expression at larger scale. The steps for doing this will be discussed in this review.

Experimental Techniques

In this section, three major experimental techniques for analyzing transcriptomic activities will be discussed, followed by a discussion on reporter proteins, which are instrumental for experimental validation of transcriptomic activity.

Reverse Transcription and qPCR. qPCR exploits the sensitivity and sequence specificity of PCR for gene expression analysis (**Fig. 1**) where transcriptional activities can be characterized as absolute transcripts abundance or relative quantitation between biological samples. qPCR had been used to validate results from high-throughput DNA microarray and RNA sequencing. An RNA stabilizing agent, RNAlater®, is often added prior to cell disruption to protect RNA integrity during mRNA extraction process. TRIzol®, a monophasic solution of phenol and guanidine isothiocyanate, is routinely used to extract total RNA. When chloroform is added to the samples homogenized in TRIzol®, RNA is preferentially extracted into the top aqueous phase. Isopropanol is added to precipitate RNA from aqueous phase. Purified RNA in sterile, diethylpyrocarbonate (DEPC)-treated water, comprising mainly of rRNAs and tRNAs and

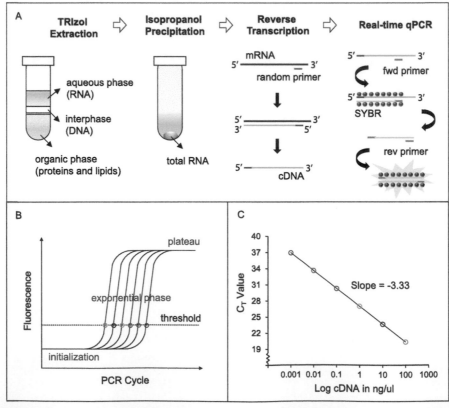

Fig. 1 qPCR analysis of targeted transcripts. (A) Sample preparation for qPCR. Total RNA is chemically extracted from biological sample and reverse transcribed into single-stranded cDNA molecules. Thereafter, the cDNA is used as templates for qPCR in real time thermocyclers. SYBR green bind to double-stranded cDNA during the extension process and fluorescence readings are recorded. (B) Sigmodal amplification of DNA during qPCR. A threshold is set above noise level in the exponential phase and used to determine the threshold cycle, Ct. (C) Relationship between cDNA concentration and Ct values under ideal condition, i.e., DNA exactly doubles with each PCR cycle. Hypothetical Ct values from (B) is reflected in (C) by colored circles.

about 1%–5% mRNA, is assayed for RNA integrity and quantity by spectrophotometer. Heuristically, the 260:280 nm ratio of the RNA preparation should be between 1.9 and 2.1 and that of 260:230 nm should be 2.0–2.2 as lower values may indicate the presence of contaminants. Distinct rRNA bands on agarose gel electrophoresis is indicative of good quality RNA. To generate cDNA templates for qPCR, the total RNA mRNA containing mRNA is reversed transcribed into single-stranded cDNA using random primers, dNTPs, buffer and reverse transcriptase. Depending on the expression level of the target gene, 1 ng–100 ng of total RNA may be required. Random 6–9mer primers are able to bind to any region in the RNA pool of most organisms. Other primers used for cDNA synthesis are oligo (dT)s which anneal to 3′-poly(A) tails, and sequence-specific primers to amplify targeted mRNA regions. Unlike random primers, oligo (dT)s are seldom used in prokaryotic cDNA synthesis as the poly(A) tails of prokaryotic mRNA are generally shorter (Sarkar, 1997). Although nonspecific primers may generate truncated cDNAs from internal mRNA sequence, gene expression results would not be much affected so long as qPCR primers are designed targeting the 5′-end of the mRNA. Sequence-specific primers for cDNA synthesis are commonly used for synthetic RNA standards or where analysis only involves a few gene targets.

In qPCR reaction, cDNA template, sequence-specific primers and nuclease-free water are added to qPCR master mix, comprising of DNA-binding dye (SYBR), dNTPs, magnesium and Taq polymerase, before importing into the qPCR thermocycler for gene expression measurement. qPCR could be performed in PCR tubes, 96-well or 384-well PCR plates. qPCR primers, typically 20–30 bp are designed to amplify approximately 60–150 bp of the sense strand of the target cDNA at the 5′-end. Amplicons above 150 bp usually suffers from poor PCR efficiency, resulting in gross underestimation on the number of transcripts. qPCR thermocycles are optically enabled to detect fluorescent signals. As qPCR cycle proceeds, double-stranded amplicons are generated, resulting in more PCR products for SYBR to bind which increases green fluorescence emission. Fluorescence intensity correlates directly with the amount of DNA amplicons, which is a proxy to the amount of cDNA template (mRNA transcripts). As a standard, gene expressions are calculated based on the threshold cycle (Ct) – the number of PCR cycles required for fluorescence to be at a critical value above background, which also indicates the start of PCR exponential phase. Ct values are inversely proportional to initial template amount. Variations in sampling procedures, RNA extraction, reverse transcription and qPCR reaction may significantly lead to bias and compounding error (Sanders et al., 2014). To mitigate such bias, gene expression results are normalized to internal reference genes. One common practice is using constitutive housekeeping genes as the normalization reference, which are assumed to have constant expression (mRNA levels), despite several studies showing otherwise (Bustin, 2000; Dundas and Ling, 2012; Thellin et al., 1999). To improve accuracy, target gene expression could be normalized to the geometric average internal control genes (Vandesompele et al., 2002),which should be validated with statistical software such as geNorm, NormFinder and BestKeeper (Andersen et al., 2004; Pfaffl et al., 2004; Vandesompele et al., 2002). The relative expression ratio of two samples could be determined using the generalized Pfaffl method as illustrated in Example 1 (Hellemans et al., 2007; Pfaffl, 2001). To determine the absolute amount of mRNA transcript, a standard curve of threshold cycle number plotted against varying amount of cDNA standard, Ct versus log [cDNA], could be developed by performing qPCR on synthesized cDNA standards with six or more serial dilutions. Importantly, the synthesized standard and target cDNA should be similar in PCR efficiency, amplicon length and primer binding efficiency, ensuring that the standard curve is applicable for the gene of interest. Known amounts of synthetic RNA standards could also be spiked into the extracted RNA to account for reverse transcription bias. Recommendations on experimental design, results reporting and selection of reference genes are described in MIQE guidelines (Bustin et al., 2009, 2010).

Example 1: Fold-expression Calculation. qPCR was performed to analyze how the gene expression of an efflux pump differed when cells were exposed to antibiotic. Results of the qPCR run is shown in **Table 1**. Here, three different housekeeping genes (Ref Gene A, B and C) were used as reference genes. "Treated" and "Control" represent the mRNA from cells with and without antibiotics treatment, respectively. For each gene, threshold cycles are the arithmetic mean of technical replicates.

The general formula for normalized relative quantities (NRQ) with multiple reference genes is,

$$NRQ = \frac{E_{GOI}^{\Delta Ct_{GOI}(control-treated)}}{\sqrt[f]{\prod_0^f E_{ref0}^{\Delta Ct_{ref0}(control-treated)}}}$$

We assumed 100% efficient amplification and amplicon exactly doubles with every exponential phase cycle. This gives an efficiency value of 2 for both the GOI and reference genes,

$$NRQ = \frac{2^{(34.00-28.50)}}{\sqrt[3]{0.59 \times 0.84 \times 0.5}} = \frac{45.25}{0.63} = 71.83$$

The $2^{\Delta Ct}$ value of GOI is 45.25. Similarly, the $2^{\Delta Ct}$ values of reference genes A, B and C are 0.59, 0.84 and 0.5, respectively; giving the geometric mean of 0.63. Hence, the efflux pump gene increased by $\sim$ 72-folds upon antibiotic exposure, implying gene up-regulation.

Table 1 qPCR analysis of gene encoding for efflux pump after exposure to antibiotics

	GOI	Ref Gene A	Ref Gene B	Ref Gene C
Efficiency	2	2	2	2
Treated	28.50	21.25	19.00	23.00
Control	34.00	20.50	18.75	22.00

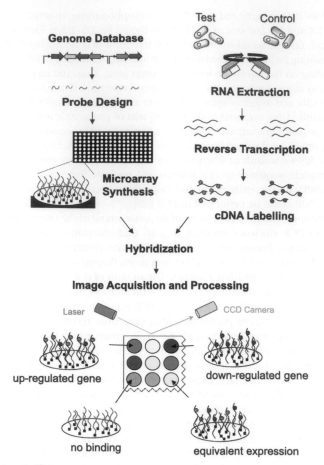

Fig. 2 Schematic of a DNA microarray workflow.

DNA Microarray. The DNA microarray is a structured 2D-array of short (25–80 bp), single-stranded picomoles of DNA molecules discretely spotted or synthesized on solid surfaces (**Fig. 2**). These DNA molecules, also known as oligo probes, are complementary to target gene sequences for hybridization between a fluorescent labeled target DNA and the immobilized probe upon contact. Experimentally, total RNA is isolated from both test and control biological samples, and assayed for microarray suitability using capillary electrophoresis and spectrophotometry. RNA quality ca be assayed by Agilent 2100 Bioanalyzer and a RNA integrity number (RIN) value of 7 or higher is considered suitable for microarray experiment. Depending on the microarray technology, cell type and nature of the study, 200 ng–20 μg of total RNA (~1 μg/μl) may be required (Kang and Chang, 2012; Ling *et al.*, 2013; Trevino *et al.*, 2007). In Affymetrix arrays, mRNA are used to generate labeled cDNAs in a one pot reverse transcription reaction. Comparatively, in Agilent arrays, mRNAs are retro-transcribed into T7 RNA promoter tailed cDNAs before converted into labeled cRNAs by the Eberwine reaction (Van Gelder *et al.*, 1990). In either workflows, the cDNA and cRNA molecules are labeled using fluorescent labeled nucleotides. Common fluorescent dyes used are the red Cy5 and the green Cy3. Following the generation of single-stranded cDNA (cRNA) molecules, equal amounts of test and control cDNAs (cRNAs) are pooled together and hybridized on the microarray slides where competitive hybridization occurs between the test and control cDNAs (cRNAs), each tagged to different fluorescent dye. The ratio of red and green intensities of each probe spot corresponds to the relative abundance of the target mRNA transcripts. These can be measured by fluorescent scanner equipped with excitation lasers and digital camera for imaging. Images are overlapped and processed to convert spot intensities into numerical values. Yellow spots are observed when transcripts from both samples are of comparable abundance. In general, genes are considered differentially expressed when test and control hybridizations exhibit at least two-fold differences. Microarray results are usually reported using MIAME guidelines by the Functional Genomics Data Society (Brazma *et al.*, 2001).

Example 2: Statistical Analysis of Microarray Results. Two-sample microarrays, also known as two-channel microarrays are used to determine differential gene expressions between two samples; such as, healthy tissues versus diseased tissues (as shown in **Fig. 2**). It is common for a gene to be represented more than once within a microarray for statistical calculations. In this example, we assume a hypothetical microarray of only five genes and each gene is represented by five probes. The summarized results are given in **Table 2**. The t-statistic of each gene and its p-value can be calculated, where n is the number of probes per gene.

$$t - statistic = \frac{|\overline{Healthy}_{Gene(i)} - \overline{Diseased}_{Gene(i)}|}{s_{Healthy}/\sqrt{n}}$$

Table 2   Microarray summarized values and statistics

Gene name	Healthy tissue signal		Diseased tissue signal		t-statistic	p-value	Significance
	Mean intensity	Standard deviation	Mean intensity	Standard deviation			
Gene A	14.09	1.703	14.82	0.023	1.242	0.2821	Not significant
Gene B	13.64	0.642	15.43	0.375	4.983	0.0076	Significant
Gene C	14.14	0.053	15.99	0.796	18.002	5.6E–05	Significant
Gene D	8.18	0.836	9.73	1.487	3.785	0.0194	Not significant
Gene E	12.72	1.102	13.39	1.227	1.413	0.2303	Not significant

The threshold (α) for determining statistical significance is taken as 0.05. From this point of view, Gene D is significantly upregulated in diseased tissue compared to healthy tissue (p-value = 0.0194). However, as there are multiple t-tests to be carried out (one test for each gene), the total threshold will increase – when 2 and 3 t-tests are carried out for an experiment, the threshold increases from 0.05 to 0.0975 ($1-0.95^2$) and 0.143 ($1-0.95^2$) respectively. Hence, there is a need to maintain the overall threshold at 0.05. Bonferroni correction is a simple method, which reduces the threshold to the quotient of 0.05 and the number of statistical tests required. Here, the Bonferroni corrected threshold is 0.01 (0.05/5) as there are 5 t-tests required. As a result, Gene D is not significantly upregulated in diseased tissue compared to healthy tissue.

RNA-Seq. In 1977, a method to decode extracted DNA sequences at single nucleotide level was developed by Nobel Prize chemist (Sanger *et al.*, 1977). This method, based on the selective incorporation of chain-terminating fluorescent dideoxy-nucleotide, was the core technology in the Human Genome Project (Schmutz *et al.*, 2004). Since then, a remarkable transformation is witnessed in the field of DNA sequencing with newly-developed chemistries and chip-based analytical platforms, giving rise to second and third generation sequencing technologies (Chen *et al.*, 2013; Heather and Chain, 2016; Schadt *et al.*, 2010; Voelkerding *et al.*, 2009). These led to higher throughput, sequencing depth and reliability, enabling applications beyond functional genomics, including the transcriptome analysis of prokaryotic and higher-order eukaryotic organisms, also known as RNA sequencing (RNA-Seq) (Croucher and Thomson, 2010; Mäder *et al.*, 2011; McGettigan, 2013). RNA-Seq measures transcript abundance by repeated, direct sequencing of reverse-transcribed cDNAs. Sequence data are mapped onto a reference genome and the number of mapped reads are normalized to quantify output expression as reads per kilobase of transcript per million mapped reads (RKPM) or transcripts per million (TPM) (Mortazavi *et al.*, 2008; Wagner *et al.*, 2012). Example 3 shows the different procedures to normalize raw transcripts output into RKPM or TPM. The normalization procedures are required because sequencing depth, i.e., the number of times a sample is read, and transcript length result in higher raw output readings on the detection platform. TPM provides a more straightforward breakdown of gene expression profile, although both normalization approaches are equally accepted by the scientific community (Wagner *et al.*, 2012).

Over the years, RNA-Seq has gradually displaced microarrays for transcriptomic analysis. Without the need to hybridize to transcript complementary probes, RNA-Seq provides significant advantages over microarrays. Firstly, microarray experimental design relied on the availability of known genome sequence for chip synthesis. When genome sequences are not available, the only way forward is by using chips originally intended for other closely related specie to capture cDNA. This approach may miss out on capturing the full transcriptome profile of the target due to sequence variability. In contrast, RNA-Seq could be performed for unknown samples in parallel with whole genome sequencing to access both functional genomics and transcriptome data. This greatly reduces experiment down time while also enables the identification of novel transcript isoforms (Trapnell *et al.*, 2010). A second advantage is the reliability of transcriptome data. RNA-Seq is not affected by the non-specific hybridization of cDNA to probes. Instead, multiple reads are performed on the same sample to ensure sequence reliability. This procedure allows transcription to be accurately mapped down to single nucleotide resolution, and could be particularly useful when characterizing transcriptomes with frequent repeats. As transcript abundance is measured by direct sequencing reads, RNA-Seq exhibits a larger dynamic range of detection, with better sensitivity at both low and high gene expression levels, whereas the upper detection limit of microarray is bounded by the optical sensitivity of microarray scanner under saturating condition (blinding effect). Despite the apparent advantages, there are a few considerations on the use of RNA-Seq, namely data management and storage, speed, and cost. RNA-Seq data are typically in the terabytes range while microarray data are in megabyte range. Hence, sequencing data is inherently more complicated to work with and would require a reliable suite of bioinformatics tools for data normalization and analysis (Trapnell *et al.*, 2012). However, a typical sequencing run takes between 2 and 14 days to complete while microarray experiment could be done within a day. Microarray consumables are currently substantially cheaper than RNA-Seq consumables. In the longer run, these concerns would likely be reconciled as new sequencing platforms with higher throughput, sequence accuracy and longer read lengths are developed. Ongoing efforts to correct experimental bias and consolidate best practices in RNA-Seq would eventually pave the way for dominance of this technology in high throughput transcriptomics study (Conesa *et al.*, 2016).

In the RNA-Seq workflow, total RNA is extracted and assayed for amount and quality on spectrophotometer and Agilent 2100 Bioanalyzer. RNA requirements for sequencing are more stringent than that for microarray; at least a RIN >8 for eukaryotic cells and >9.5 for prokaryotic cells should be satisfied. Illumina also recommends intact RNA in terms of the percentage of RNA fragments >200 nucleotides (DV_{200}) on Agilent 2100 Bioanalyzer. A few hundred nanograms total RNA with $DV_{200} > 30\%$ would be appropriate for downstream application. Before RNA-Seq library preparation, it is prudent to remove unwanted rRNA transcripts which competes with mRNA for sequencing capacity. For this purpose, terminator exonuclease (TEX), which degrades only rRNA substrates with 5′-monophosphate ends, could be added to the total RNA pool (Croucher *et al.*, 2009; Sharma *et al.*, 2010). Alternatively, commercial subtractive-hybridization kits could be used to deplete rRNAs. Oligonucleotide probes on magnetic beads support are used to capture rRNAs by hybridization, followed by subsequent ethanol extraction of mRNA from supernatant after beads pull down (Croucher *et al.*, 2009; O'Neil *et al.*, 2013; Petrova *et al.*, 2017; Stewart *et al.*, 2010; Westermann *et al.*, 2016). Depending on the sequencing equipment and the purpose of the study, different methods have been developed to prepare RNA-Seq cDNA libraries, which in turn determines if the directional information of transcriptional activities could be effectively captured (Croucher and Thomson, 2010). A common workflow involves fragmenting rRNA-depleted samples by ultra-sound sonication or nebulization into 200–400 bp fragments, followed by dephosphorylation on the 5′-end and ligation with sequencing adaptor on the 3′-end. Transcript 5′-ends before re-phosphorylated with T4 polynucleotide kinase and ligated with the second sequencing adaptor. Processed transcripts are reverse transcribed using 3′-adaptor as primer to generate first strand cDNA (Westermann *et al.*, 2016). Alternatively, rRNA-depleted samples could be 3′-polyadenylated with poly(A) polymerase and then treated with tobacco acid pyrophosphatase. This effectively converts 5′-triphosphate into monophosphate for 5′-adaptor ligation. Processed transcripts are reverse transcribed using oligo(dT)-adaptor primers to generate first strand cDNA (Westermann *et al.*, 2016). Adaptors are attached stepwise in specific orientation to preserve directional information. Besides mechanical fragmentation, transpososome could be used to fragment and incorporate modified adaptors onto doublestranded cDNA in a one pot reaction known as tagmentation (Adey *et al.*, 2010; Kia *et al.*, 2017). In this process, samples are reverse transcribed and amplified to generated double-stranded cDNA, using uracil instead of thymine for second strand synthesis. The resultant cDNA molecules are transposed with sequencing adaptors and treated with USER enzyme mix to deplete the second cDNA strand, retaining only tagged single stranded cDNA. This cDNA library is selectively amplified by Phusion polymerase (Phusion polymerase do not extent well on DNA templates with uracil residues) and purified (Gertz *et al.*, 2012).

The next step in RNA-Seq involves hybridizing cDNA libraries to solid surface, typically insoluble beads or glass slide, which contains oligonucleotides complementary to the adaptors. With sufficient dilution, each bead probabilistically capture only one cDNA molecule or sparsely distributed on the glass slide. Ion Torrent and SOLiD sequencing uses bead capture while Illumina uses glass slide in the form of a flow cell. Then, captured transcripts are clonally amplified by emulsion PCR into bead-bound libraries, or by isothermal bridge amplification into clusters of DNA clones. Finally,

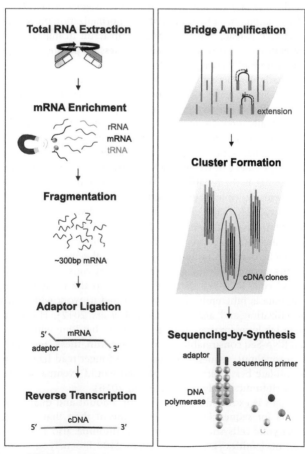

Fig. 3 Schematic of Illumina RNA-Seq workflow.

Table 3 Transcript abundance data from RNA-Seq

	Size (kb)	Mapped reads ($\times 10^6$)		
		Replicate I	Replicate II	Replicate III
Gene A	0.5	1.2	1.5	1.6
Gene B	1	3.0	3.2	2.9
Gene C	2	4.0	4.2	4.2
Gene D	3	2.0	1.8	2.2
Gene E	4	0.5	0.5	0.6

sequencing primers are added to initiate the actual sequencing process. Raw sequence reads are mapped to specific transcripts of the reference genome and normalized to provide accurate expression output data in RKPM or TPM. Currently, the Illumina sequencing-by-synthesis platform (SBS) is considered the most dominant next generation sequencing (NGS) technology (**Fig. 3**) (Greenleaf and Sidow, 2014). Other NGS platforms include (1) Ion Torrent that also works on the principle of SBS but detects H^+ proton instead of fluorescence during nucleotide addition, (2) ABI SOLiD that relies on ligation chemistry (synthesis-by-ligation), and (3) single molecule sequencing technologies from PacBio and Oxford Nanopore. For more information on the various NGS platforms, the reader is referred to comprehensive reviews published elsewhere (Heather and Chain, 2016; Mardis, 2017; Schadt et al., 2010).

Example 3: RKPM and TPM Calculation. An RNA-Seq experiment was performed to determine the transcript abundance in a cell culture with three technical replicates. For simplicity, it is assumed that the cell has expressed 5 different genes. Results of the sequencing run are presented in **Table 3** as raw transcript counts.

TPM is obtained after two normalization steps, first with gene size and then by sequencing depth. Sample calculation for Replicate I, Gene A with size of 0.5 kb.

$$normalized\ seq\ counts = \frac{seq\ counts}{gene\ size} = \frac{1.2}{0.5} = 2.40$$

		Size (kb)	Mapped reads ($\times 10^6$)		
			Replicate I	Replicate II	Replicate III
1st normalization by gene size	Gene A	0.5	2.40	3.00	3.20
	Gene B	1	3.00	3.20	3.30
	Gene C	2	2.00	2.10	2.10
	Gene D	3	0.67	0.60	0.73
	Gene E	4	0.13	0.13	0.15
	Total count		8.19	9.03	9.48

Total sequencing depth of Replicate I after 1st normalization is 8.19 million reads.

$$TPM = \frac{normalized\ seq\ counts}{total\ counts} = \frac{2.40}{8.19} = 0.29$$

		Size (kb)	Mapped reads in TPM		
			Replicate I	Replicate II	Replicate III
2nd normalization by sequencing depth	Gene A	0.5	0.29	0.33	0.34
	Gene B	1	0.37	0.35	0.35
	Gene C	2	0.24	0.23	0.22
	Gene D	3	0.08	0.07	0.08
	Gene E	4	0.02	0.01	0.02
	Total count		1.00	1.00	1.00

RKPM is obtained after two normalization steps in the reverse order of TPM, first with sequencing depth and then by gene size. Total sequencing depth of Replicate I before normalization is 10.7 million reads(*Total seq counts* = 1.2 + 3.0 + 4.0 + 2.0 + 0.5 = 10.7).

Sample calculation for Replicate I, Gene A (1st normalization by sequencing depth).

$$\frac{seq\ counts}{total\ counts} = \frac{1.2}{10.7} = 0.11$$

	Size (kb)	Mapped reads ($\times 10^6$)		
		Replicate I	Replicate II	Replicate III
1st normalization by sequencing depth	Gene A	0.5	0.11	0.13	0.13
	Gene B	1	0.28	0.29	0.28
	Gene C	2	0.37	0.38	0.35
	Gene D	3	0.19	0.16	0.18
	Gene E	4	0.05	0.04	0.05
	Total count		1.00	1.00	1.00

2nd normalization by gene size for the same gene, $RKPM = \frac{normalized\ seq\ counts}{gene\ size} = \frac{0.11}{0.5} = 0.22$

	Size (kb)	Mapped reads in RKPM		
		Replicate I	Replicate II	Replicate III
2nd normalization by gene size	Gene A	0.5	0.22	0.27	0.27
	Gene B	1	0.28	0.29	0.28
	Gene C	2	0.19	0.19	0.18
	Gene D	3	0.06	0.05	0.06
	Gene E	4	0.01	0.01	0.01
	Total count		0.75	0.81	0.80

Note that RKPM can be converted to TPM by dividing by the total RKPM values. Sample calculation for Replicate I, Gene A with RKPM value of 0.22, $TPM = \frac{RKPM}{\sum RKPM} = \frac{0.22}{0.75} = 0.29$.

Reporter Proteins. Reporter proteins are fluorescent proteins, or enzymes that can convert specific substrates into colorimetric or luminescent products. To quantify gene expression, genes that encode for reporter proteins are assembled downstream of DNA promoters and transformed into the biological host of choice. This approach has been adopted to characterize promoter strengths in diverse genetic context, including bacterial, yeast, plant, mammalian cells, and cell-free extracts (Auslander *et al.*, 2012; Canton *et al.*, 2008; Chappell *et al.*, 2013; Huang *et al.*, 2010; Redden and Alper, 2015; Reeve *et al.*, 2016; Schaumberg *et al.*, 2016; Wong *et al.*, 2015). The amount of reporter proteins generated during gene expression is assumed to be proportional to background-subtracted readings measured on optical instruments; such as, flow cytometry and fluorescent plate readers. Reporter proteins could also be purified and quantitated to obtain calibration plots. Direct quantification of gene expression by reporter proteins circumvent the need to isolate mRNA from cell cultures, a procedure that is often time consuming, labor intensive, costly and prone to human error. For this reason, the use of reporter proteins is preferred over qPCR for quantifying gene expression, especially for the large-scale validation of DNA promoters. Importantly, results from this approach reflects the combined effect of transcription, translation and post-translational activities, rather than mRNA transcription alone. Incorporating the results of reporter protein outputs into computational models could give estimate of the amount of transcript produced. This will require key modeling parameters, including the rates of mRNA degradation, protein maturation, protein degradation, and cell growth (Canton *et al.*, 2008; Milo *et al.*, 2010). Reporter proteins could also be used for functional analysis. For example, promoter sequences could be mutated and then assayed for changes in gene expression. When complemented with DNA sequencing, this procedure could rapidly identify core promoter regulatory regions and develop synthetic promoter libraries of varying strengths (Alper *et al.*, 2005; Hartner *et al.*, 2008; Rud *et al.*, 2006; Siegl *et al.*, 2013).

Due to the ease of use, fluorescent proteins are among the most commonly used reporter proteins in gene expression studies. The superfolder green fluorescent protein (sfGFP) in particular, is a variant of wild type GFP with unmatched performance in terms of folding kinetics, solubility and tolerance to high temperature and chemicals (Pédelacq *et al.*, 2006). A major limitation of GFP and its variants is the need for molecular oxygen as cofactor during fluorophore formation; thus, restricting its application to aerobic organisms. Flavin mononucleotide-based fluorescent proteins (FbFP) was developed for use in both aerobic and anaerobic condition but the low output fluorescence remains a technical hurdle to widespread adoption (Drepper *et al.*, 2007). For anaerobic organisms, non-fluorescent reporters such as light emitting luciferases and absorbance changing enzymes are still commonplace. Popular examples of enzyme-based reporter proteins include β-galactosidase, β-glucosidase and β-glucuronidase (Partow *et al.*, 2010; Siegl *et al.*, 2013). The recent development of Spinach2, an RNA aptamer that binds to 3,5-difluoro-4-hydroxybenzylidene-imidazolinone (fluorophore mimic of GFP), provides an exciting platform to study gene expression at the mRNA level *in vivo* (Strack *et al.*, 2013).

Bioinformatics Analysis/Applications

Bioinformatics can be applied to the study of transcriptional activities in two major ways – (1) the prediction of gene expression using sequence features (such as, response elements in promoters) or from the expression of other genes, and (2) constructing mathematical models for further analyses.

Predicting Gene Expressions. In prokaryotes, functionally related genes are often regulated by a common promoter and a set of enhancers, forming an operon. Hence, expression of genes within the same operon tends to be correlated (Sabatti *et al.*, 2002). This is supported by a study (De Hoon *et al.*, 2004) showing that genes within operons show higher correlation than genes across operons. Using expressional correlation, De Hoon *et al.* (2014) can predict whether the genes are from the same operon, with 79.9% accuracy. This concept of expressional correlation from genes within the same operon has been used to improve microarray analysis by noise reduction (Xiao *et al.*, 2006). However, the relative position of the genes within the operon may affect expression. A study on *Streptomyces coelicolor* operons found that the expression of genes decreases along the relative position on the operon by normalizing expression of all genes in the operon to that of the first gene in the operon (Laing *et al.*, 2006) but this expression decline is not statistically significant up to the 5th gene on the operon but this is not observed in *Escherichia coli* where the expression of all genes in the operon is constant regardless of position However, a study using synthetic operon found that gene expression increases linearly with the distance from the start of a gene to the end of the operon (Lim *et al.*, 2011). Nevertheless, these studies suggest that expression of genes within the same operon can be predicted by knowing the expression of one of the genes within the operon, subjected to species-specific variability as in the case of *S. coelicolor*.

In both prokaryotes and eukaryotes, several genes may be activated by the same transcription factor. Like the reason why genes within the same operon is likely to be expressionally correlated, a set of genes activated by the same set of transcription factors are also likely to be expressionally correlated. Binding of transcription factors to the promoter may affect chromatin accessibility (Lamparter *et al.*, 2017), leading to correlated expression patterns from genes affected by the same transcription factors (Mahdevar *et al.*, 2013). A study (Zhang and Li, 2017) examining more than 1000 human transcription factors found that transcription factor usage can be used to predict gene expression level (r^2 of up to 0.617). Genes with similar sequence features in the promoter sequence may also exhibit correlated expression profiles. For example, it has been shown that genes with dioxin-response element in their promoter demonstrate correlated expression (Kim *et al.*, 2006). Similar cases have also been discovered in other response elements; such as, immune response (Care *et al.*, 2015). It is plausible to conceive that several genes must be expressed in response to a given stimulus (Kim *et al.*, 2003), and the regulatory signaling of such stimulus may involve the same set of transcription factors or response elements.

This is supported by a previous study examining the functional aspects of genes with correlated expressions and found that genes with correlated expression demonstrate functional correspondence (Reverter *et al.*, 2005). Moreover, a study on transcriptomics (Ling *et al.*, 2008) also found large number of genes that are correlated. Hence, it may be possible to predict entire transcriptome from known expression of a handful of genes by constructing gene co-expression network. This concept is demonstrated by a study (Ling and Poh, 2014), which uses the expression values of 59 genes to predict the expression of the entire *E. coli* transcriptome. The correlation between predicted and actual expression value is 0.467, which is similar to the microarray intra-array variation. This suggests that intra-array variation accounts for a substantial portion of the transcriptome prediction error and further strengthen the potential of this approach with more reliable experimental data. Ling and Poh (2014) demonstrated the application of their predictive model using a case study – hydrogenase 2 maturation endopeptidase (hybD) can affect the efficiency of hydrogenase 2, a critical enzyme in hydrogen production during glucose (Maeda *et al.*, 2007) or glycerol fermentation (Trchounian *et al.*, 2013). The model predicted 87 genes significantly affected by the 56% knockdown of hybD, and was subjected to Gene Ontology Enrichment Analysis (Zheng and Wang, 2008). All 5 significant molecular functions enriched were of carbon/sugar transferase-typed activity, which corresponds to the expected activity as previously described (Maeda *et al.*, 2007; Trchounian *et al.*, 2013). Knowing that 56% knockdown of hybD significantly affects the expression of 87 genes, it is then possible to ask for the range of hybD expression variation that will not significantly affect any other genes; that is, the expression buffer of hybD. Using 10% stepwise changes of *hybD* from 100% knockout to 2x over-expression the number of affected genes is symmetrical and fits a quadratic model and solving the roots of the quadratic model, the expressional buffer of hybD in *E. coli* MG1655 is estimated to be 73.88% and 124.52% from its average expression (**Fig. 4**).

Two sequence features of the gene, GC content and codon usage, have been found to be useful in predicting gene expressions. In a study of more than four thousand human promoters across eight different cell lines (Landolin *et al.*, 2010), it was found that the GC content of promoters can be predictive of gene expression as promoters high in GC content (more than 50% GC) demonstrating constitutive expression and promoters with low GC content (less than 50% GC) more inclined towards cell-specific expression. This resulted in significant correlation ($r=0.43$) between promoter activity and reporter gene expression. Of the 789 genes expressed in all eight cell lines, 719 (91%) were genes with high GC promoters and only 70 (9%) were from genes with low GC promoters. Conversely, 378 of the 483 genes (78.3%) that were expressed in only one of the eight cell lines were from low GC promoters. This suggests that GC content of human promoters can be indicative of cell specificity.

However, the relative impact of GC content and codon usage on gene expression and transcript stability is a subject of debate. A study (Barahimipour *et al.*, 2015) attempted to resolve this by designing 4 yellow fluorescent protein (YFP) genes encoding the same amino acid sequence for expression in *Chlamydomonas reinhardtii* using differing GC content and codon usages. Using this, Barahimipour *et al.* (2015) found that codon usage plays a more important role in expression efficiency and transcript stability compared to GC content in *C. reinhardtii*. Expression efficiency is contributed by translational efficiency as the relative abundance between RNA and protein are highly correlated using RNA blot analysis, suggesting that expression efficiency is a result of transcriptional efficiency and the codon usage plays an important role in transcriptional efficiency. Moreover, this study also adds strength to the usefulness of transcriptomics analysis as a proxy for proteomics analysis as it depends on high correlation between transcript abundance and peptide abundance, given that it is experimentally easier to conduct transcriptomics studies (using experimental tools such as microarrays and RNA-seq) than proteomics studies (using experimental tools such as mass spectrometry).

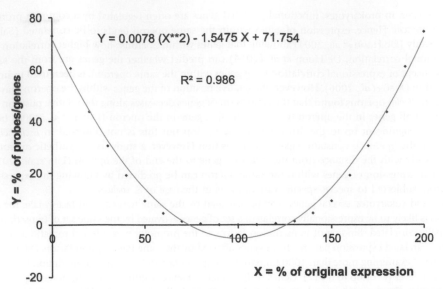

$$Y = 0.0078 (X^{**}2) - 1.5475 X + 71.754$$

$$R^2 = 0.986$$

Y = % of probes/genes

X = % of original expression

Fig. 4 Percentage of reachable genes affected by varying levels of hydrogenase 2 maturation endopeptidase (hybD) expressions.

There are several metrics to calculate codon usages bias. These include codon adaptation index (Sharp and Li, 1987), relative codon bias strength (Das *et al.*, 2012), relative codon adaptation (Fox and Erill, 2010), and modified relative codon bias strength (Sahoo and Das, 2014). Fox and Erill (2010) used relative codon usage bias to predict the expression levels of *E. coli* genes of more than 1000 bp, achieving a correlation of 0.489 between predicted and actual expression. Similarly, a study (Das *et al.*, 2017) found correlation between these metrics but modified relative codon bias strength was found to have the highest correlation with transcriptomics (r= − 0.31) and proteomics (r= − 0.44). Although the correlations are not high, these studies do suggest the potential of using codon usage bias to predict transcriptional activities.

Modeling and Simulation. The main reason for studying transcriptional activities of a cell is to use it as a proxy for peptide/protein abundance. This in turn allows for a door towards elucidating the genetic and biochemical basis of various conditions. For example, it is the fundamental step for analyzing differential gene expression between various conditions (such as, disease versus healthy, or different treatment conditions) or across various time points (Creecy and Conway, 2015; Du *et al.*, 2017; Herrera-Marcos *et al.*, 2017; Kato *et al.*, 2005; Lin *et al.*, 2016; Liu *et al.*, 2015), or to construct models to predict the phenotype given a transcriptomic change (transcriptome-phenotype correlation).

A biochemical reaction is commonly written as (where A, B, and C are the substrates; P, Q, and where A, B, and C are the substrates; P, Q, and R are the products are the products), with the following rate laws,

$$A \xrightarrow{Enzyme} P \text{ rate law } 1 = \frac{k_{cat}[Enzyme][A]}{K_m + [Enzyme][A]}$$

$$B + C \xrightarrow{Enzyme} Q + R \text{ rate law } 2 = \frac{k_{cat}[Enzyme][B][C]}{K_m + [Enzyme][B][C]}$$

Where k_{cat} and K_m are the turnover number (per unit time) and Michaelis-Menten constant (concentration) of the enzyme respectively, and $k_{cat}[Enzyme]$ corresponds to the V_{max} of the reaction (per unit time). When there is more than one substrate or product, the mechanism can take more complicated forms; such as ternary-complex mechanisms (Yang *et al.*, 2011) or ping-pong mechanisms (Nakamura *et al.*, 1994). However, these more complicated mechanisms will be unwieldy to be extended to enzymes using more than two substrates. In addition, these mechanisms will require a larger set of enzyme kinetics which is not easily obtainable. Hence, we propose to use an approximation where we consider the enzyme can only work when all the required substrates are present at the same location and with a random probability. Hence, the approximated rate law in generalized form can be written as

$$\frac{k_{cat}[enzyme]\left(\prod_{i=1}^{N}[substrate_i]\right)}{K_m + \left(\prod_{i=1}^{N}[substrate_i]\right)}$$

The concentration of enzymes, which can be directly represented by the transcriptional activity of the gene encoding the enzyme, play a crucial role in the rate laws. The concentrations of both substrate(s) and product(s) over time can be defined as ordinary differential equations (ODEs) as

$$\frac{d[A]}{dt} = - \text{ rate law } 1 \quad \frac{d[P]}{dt} = \text{rate law } 1$$

$$\frac{d[B]}{dt} = \frac{d[C]}{dt} = - rate \ law \ 2 \quad \frac{d[P]}{dt} = \frac{d[Q]}{dt} = rate \ law \ 2$$

As enzymes are the result of gene expression, the concentration of an enzyme can be modelled using ODEs developed in previous studies (Jayaraman *et al.*, 2016; Saeidi *et al.*, 2011). Briefly, expressed protein concentration from an inducible promoter can be modelled as

$$For \ constitutive \ expression : \frac{d[RNA]}{dt} = v_0 - \gamma_{RNA}[RNA]$$

$$For \ inducible \ expression : \frac{d[RNA]}{dt} = v_0 + \frac{v_{max} + [inducer]^n}{K_m + [inducer]^n} - \gamma_{RNA}[RNA]$$

$$For \ repressible \ expression : \frac{d[RNA]}{dt} = v_0 + \frac{v_{max}}{K_m + [repressor]^n} - \gamma_{RNA}[RNA]$$

$$\frac{d[Enzyme]}{dt} = \frac{d[protein]}{dt} = \beta[RNA] - \gamma_{protein}[protein]$$

Where v_0 and v_{max} are the baseline and maximum expression (concentration per second) of the promoter, K_m is the Michaelis-Menten constant (concentration), n is the Hill coefficient, β is the relative ribosome binding site (RBS) strength (Wang *et al.*, 2017), and γ_{RNA} and $\gamma_{protein}$ are the degradation rates (per unit time) of RNA and protein respectively.

Once created, models can be used as both a repository of knowledge and an *in silico* platform for hypothesis testing and analysis (Ling, 2016) for the purpose of advising the experimentalist on the parameters to optimize for the optimal yield (MacDonald *et al.*, 2011). This approach had been used in several studies. For example, an enzyme pathway kinetic model of mevalonate pathway had been constructed to study the crucial steps for the production of amorphadiene from mevalonate in *E. coli* (Weaver *et al.*, 2015). After model construction, global sensitivity analysis was carried out to determine which of the six enzymes are important and found that amorphadiene synthase expression and activity are most critical. Another study attempted to increase carotenoid production in maize also constructed an enzyme kinetic model (Comas *et al.*, 2016). While amorphadiene from mevalonate is a linear pathway (Weaver *et al.*, 2015), many carotenoids can be synthesized from phytoene in a branched pathway with many enzymes (Comas *et al.*, 2016). Therefore, it is not obvious which enzyme expression to target to increase the yield of specific carotenoids. By analyzing the model, four independent maize lines were engineered using insights from the model analysis and validated experimentally.

These studies suggest that modeling and simulation can provide important computational tools to advise experimentalists but the success of these tools depends on the quality of characterization data from previous experiments. The quality of experimental data can be improved using bioinformatics approaches to reduce noise (Xiao *et al.*, 2006). Hence, there is a reflective process between laboratory and experimental experimentation. It can then be expected that increased experimental data will improve current computational methods, and improved computational methods will better inform laboratory experiments. This trend is likely to stay in the foreseeable future.

See also: Analyzing Transcriptome-Phenotype Correlations. Applications of Ribosomal RNA Sequence and Structure Analysis for Extracting Evolutionary and Functional Insights. Characterizing and Functional Assignment of Noncoding RNAs. Codon Usage. Comparative Transcriptomics Analysis. Detecting and Annotating Rare Variants. Epigenetics: Analysis of Cytosine Modifications at Single Base Resolution. Exome Sequencing Data Analysis. Functional Enrichment Analysis. Genome-Wide Scanning of Gene Expression. Integrative Analysis of Multi-Omics Data. Natural Language Processing Approaches in Bioinformatics. Next Generation Sequencing Data Analysis. Pipeline of High Throughput Sequencing. Prediction of Coding and Non-Coding RNA. Regulation of Gene Expression. Transcriptome Analysis. Transcriptome During Cell Differentiation. Whole Genome Sequencing Analysis

References

Adey, A., Morrison, H.G., Asan, *et al.*, 2010. Rapid, low-input, low-bias construction of shotgun fragment libraries by high-density in vitro transposition. Genome Biol. 11, R119.

Alper, H., Fischer, C., Nevoigt, E., Stephanopoulos, G., 2005. Tuning genetic control through promoter engineering. Proc. Natl. Acad. Sci. USA 102, 12678–12683.

Andersen, C.L., Jensen, J.L., Orntoft, T.F., 2004. Normalization of real-time quantitative reverse transcription-PCR data: A model-based variance estimation approach to identify genes suited for normalization, applied to bladder and colon cancer data sets. Cancer Res. 64, 5245–5250.

Auslander, S., Auslander, D., Muller, M., Wieland, M., Fussenegger, M., 2012. Programmable single-cell mammalian biocomputers. Nature 487.

Barahimipour, R., Strenkert, D., Neupert, J., *et al.*, 2015. Dissecting the contributions of GC content and codon usage to gene expression in the model alga Chlamydomonas reinhardtii. Plant J. 84, 704–717.

Brazma, A., Hingamp, P., Quackenbush, J., *et al.*, 2001. Minimum information about a microarray experiment (MIAME)—toward standards for microarray data. Nat. Genet. 29, 365–371.

Bustin, S.A., 2000. Absolute quantification of mRNA using real-time reverse transcription polymerase chain reaction assays. J. Mol. Endocrinol. 25, 169–193.

Bustin, S.A., Beaulieu, J.-F., Huggett, J., *et al.*, 2010. MIQE précis: Practical implementation of minimum standard guidelines for fluorescence-based quantitative real-time PCR experiments. BMC Mol. Biol. 11, 74.

Bustin, S.A., Benes, V., Garson, J.A., et al., 2009. The MIQE guidelines: Minimum information for publication of quantitative real-time PCR experiments. Clin. Chem. 55, 611–622.

Canton, B., Labno, A., Endy, D., 2008. Refinement and standardization of synthetic biological parts and devices. Nat. Biotechnol. 26.

Care, M.A., Westhead, D.R., Tooze, R.M., 2015. Gene expression meta-analysis reveals immune response convergence on the IFNγ-STAT1-IRF1 axis and adaptive immune resistance mechanisms in lymphoma. Genome Med. 7, 96.

Chappell, J., Jensen, K., Freemont, P.S., 2013. Validation of an entirely in vitro approach for rapid prototyping of DNA regulatory elements for synthetic biology. Nucleic Acids Res. 41, 3471–3481.

Chen, F., Dong, M., Ge, M., et al., 2013. The history and advances of reversible terminators used in new generations of sequencing technology. Genom. Proteom. Bioinform. 11, 34–40.

Comas, J., Benfeitas, R., Vilaprinyo, E., et al., 2016. Identification of line-specific strategies for improving carotenoid production in synthetic maize through data-driven mathematical modeling. Plant J. 87, 455–471.

Conesa, A., Madrigal, P., Tarazona, S., et al., 2016. A survey of best practices for RNA-seq data analysis. Genome Biol. 17, 13.

Creecy, J.P., Conway, T., 2015. Quantitative bacterial transcriptomics with RNA-seq. Curr. Opin. Microbiol. 23, 133–140.

Croucher, N.J., Fookes, M.C., Perkins, T.T., et al., 2009. A simple method for directional transcriptome sequencing using Illumina technology. Nucleic Acids Res. 37, e148.

Croucher, N.J., Thomson, N.R., 2010. Studying bacterial transcriptomes using RNA-seq. Curr. Opin. Microbiol. 13, 619–624.

Das, S., Chottopadhyay, B., Sahoo, S., 2017. Comparative analysis of predicted gene expression among Crenarchaeal genomes. Genom. Inform. 15, 38–47.

Das, S., Roymondal, U., Chottopadhyay, B., Sahoo, S., 2012. Gene expression profile of the cynobacterium synechocystis genome. Gene 497, 344–352.

De Hoon, M.J.L., Imoto, S., Kobayashi, K., Ogasawara, N., Miyano, S., 2004. Predicting the operon structure of Bacillus subtilis using operon length, intergene distance, and gene expression information. Pac. Symp. Biocomput. 276–287.

Drepper, T., Eggert, T., Circolone, F., et al., 2007. Reporter proteins for in vivo fluorescence without oxygen. Nat. Biotechnol. 25, 443–445.

Dundas, J., Ling, M.H., 2012. Reference genes for measuring mRNA expression. Theory Biosci. 131, 1–9.

Du, Y., Zhao, B., Liu, Z., et al., 2017. Molecular subtyping of pancreatic cancer: Translating genomics and transcriptomics into the clinic. J. Cancer 8, 513–522.

Fox, J.M., Erill, I., 2010. Relative codon adaptation: A generic codon bias index for prediction of gene expression. DNA Res. 17, 185–196.

Gertz, J., Varley, K.E., Davis, N.S., et al., 2012. Transposase mediated construction of RNA-seq libraries. Genome Res. 22, 134–141.

Greenleaf, W.J., Sidow, A., 2014. The future of sequencing: Convergence of intelligent design and market Darwinism. Genome Biol. 15, 303.

Hartner, F.S., Ruth, C., Langenegger, D., et al., 2008. Promoter library designed for fine-tuned gene expression in Pichia pastoris. Nucleic Acids Res. 36, e76.

Heather, J.M., Chain, B., 2016. The sequence of sequencers: The history of sequencing DNA. Genomics 107, 1–8.

Hellemans, J., Mortier, G., De Paepe, A., Speleman, F., Vandesompele, J., 2007. qBase relative quantification framework and software for management and automated analysis of real-time quantitative PCR data. Genome Biol. 8, R19.

Herrera-Marcos, L.V., Lou-Bonafonte, J.M., Arnal, C., Navarro, M.A., Osada, J., 2017. Transcriptomics and the Mediterranean diet: A systematic review. Nutrients 9.

Huang, H.-H., Camsund, D., Lindblad, P., Heidorn, T., 2010. Design and characterization of molecular tools for a Synthetic Biology approach towards developing cyanobacterial biotechnology. Nucleic Acids Res. 38, 2577–2593.

Jayaraman, P., Devarajan, K., Chua, T.K., et al., 2016. Blue light-mediated transcriptional activation and repression of gene expression in bacteria. Nucleic Acids Res. 44, 6994–7005.

Kang, A., Chang, M.W., 2012. Identification and reconstitution of genetic regulatory networks for improved microbial tolerance to isooctane. Mol. Biosyst. 8, 1350–1358.

Kato, H., Saito, K., Kimura, T., 2005. A perspective on DNA microarray technology in food and nutritional science. Curr. Opin. Clin. Nutr. Metab. Care 8, 516–522.

Kia, A., Gloeckner, C., Osothprarop, T., et al., 2017. Improved genome sequencing using an engineered transposase. BMC Biotechnol. 17, 6.

Kim, B.-R., Hu, R., Keum, Y.-S., et al., 2003. Effects of glutathione on antioxidant response element-mediated gene expression and apoptosis elicited by sulforaphane. Cancer Res. 63, 7520.

Kim, W.K., In, Y.-J., Kim, J.-H., et al., 2006. Quantitative relationship of dioxin-responsive gene expression to dioxin response element in Hep3B and HepG2 human hepatocarcinoma cell lines. Toxicol. Lett. 165, 174–181.

Laing, E., Mersinias, V., Smith, C.P., Hubbard, S.J., 2006. Analysis of gene expression in operons of Streptomyces coelicolor. Genome Biol. 7, R46.

Lamparter, D., Marbach, D., Rueedi, R., Bergmann, S., Kutalik, Z., 2017. Genome-wide association between transcription factor expression and chromatin accessibility reveals regulators of chromatin accessibility. PLOS Comput. Biol. 13, e1005311.

Landolin, J.M., Johnson, D.S., Trinklein, N.D., et al., 2010. Sequence features that drive human promoter function and tissue specificity. Genome Res. 20, 890–898.

Lim, H.N., Lee, Y., Hussein, R., 2011. Fundamental relationship between operon organization and gene expression. Proc. Natl. Acad. Sci. USA 108, 10626–10631.

Ling, M., 2016. Of (biological) models and simulations. MOJ Proteom. Bioinform. 3, 00093.

Ling, H., Chen, B., Kang, A., Lee, J.-M., Chang, M.W., 2013. Transcriptome response to alkane biofuels in Saccharomyces cerevisiae: Identification of efflux pumps involved in alkane tolerance. Biotechnol. Biofuels 6, 95.

Ling, M.H., Lefevre, C., Nicholas, K.R., 2008. Filtering microarray correlations by statistical literature analysis yields potential hypotheses for lactation research. Python Pap. 3, 4.

Ling, M.H., Poh, C.L., 2014. A predictor for predicting Escherichia coli transcriptome and the effects of gene perturbations. BMC Bioinform. 15, 140.

Lin, M., Lachman, H.M., Zheng, D., 2016. Transcriptomics analysis of iPSC-derived neurons and modeling of neuropsychiatric disorders. Mol. Cell. Neurosci. 73, 32–42.

Liu, Y., Ai, N., Liao, J., Fan, X., 2015. Transcriptomics: A sword to cut the Gordian knot of traditional Chinese medicine. Biomark. Med. 9, 1201–1213.

MacDonald, J.T., Barnes, C., Kitney, R.I., Freemont, P.S., Stan, G.B., 2011. Computational design approaches and tools for synthetic biology. Integr. Biol. (Camb.) 3, 97–108.

Mäder, U., Nicolas, P., Richard, H., Bessières, P., Aymerich, S., 2011. Comprehensive identification and quantification of microbial transcriptomes by genome-wide unbiased methods. Curr. Opin. Biotechnol. 22, 32–41.

Maeda, T., Sanchez-Torres, V., Wood, T.K., 2007. Enhanced hydrogen production from glucose by metabolically engineered Escherichia coli. Appl. Microbiol. Biotechnol. 77, 879–890.

Mahdevar, G., Nowzari-Dalini, A., Sadeghi, M., 2013. Inferring gene correlation networks from transcription factor binding sites. Genes Genet. Syst. 88, 301–309.

Mardis, E.R., 2017. DNA sequencing technologies: 2006–2016. Nat. Protoc. 12, 213–218.

McGettigan, P.A., 2013. Transcriptomics in the RNA-seq era. Curr. Opin. Chem. Biol. 17, 4–11.

Milo, R., Jorgensen, P., Moran, U., Weber, G., Springer, M., 2010. BioNumbers – The database of key numbers in molecular and cell biology. Nucleic Acids Res. 38, D750–D753.

Mortazavi, A., Williams, B.A., McCue, K., Schaeffer, L., Wold, B., 2008. Mapping and quantifying mammalian transcriptomes by RNA-Seq. Nat. Methods 5, 621–628.

Nakamura, A., Haga, K., Yamane, K., 1994. The transglycosylation reaction of cyclodextrin glucanotransferase is operated by a Ping-Pong mechanism. FEBS Lett. 337, 66–70.

O'Neil, D., Glowatz, H., Schlumpberger, M., 2013. Ribosomal RNA depletion for efficient use of RNA-seq capacity. Curr. Protoc. Mol. Biol.. (Chapter 4, Unit 4.19).

Partow, S., Siewers, V., Bjørn, S., Nielsen, J., Maury, J., 2010. Characterization of different promoters for designing a new expression vector in Saccharomyces cerevisiae. Yeast 27, 955–964.

Pédelacq, J.-D., Cabantous, S., Tran, T., Terwilliger, T.C., Waldo, G.S., 2006. Engineering and characterization of a superfolder green fluorescent protein. Nat. Biotechnol. 24, 79–88.

Petrova, O.E., Garcia-Alcalde, F., Zampaloni, C., Sauer, K., 2017. Comparative evaluation of rRNA depletion procedures for the improved analysis of bacterial biofilm and mixed pathogen culture transcriptomes. Sci. Rep. 7, 41114.

Pfaffl, M.W., 2001. A new mathematical model for relative quantification in real-time RT-PCR. Nucleic Acids Res. 29, e45.

Pfaffl, M.W., Tichopad, A., Prgomet, C., Neuvians, T.P., 2004. Determination of stable housekeeping genes, differentially regulated target genes and sample integrity: BestKeeper–Excel-based tool using pair-wise correlations. Biotechnol. Lett. 26, 509–515.

Redden, H., Alper, H.S., 2015. The development and characterization of synthetic minimal yeast promoters. Nat. Commun. 6, 7810.

Reeve, B., Martinez-Klimova, E., de Jonghe, J., Leak, D.J., Ellis, T., 2016. The Geobacillus plasmid set: A modular toolkit for thermophile engineering. ACS Synth. Biol. 5, 1342–1347.

Reverter, A., Barris, W., Moreno-Sanchez, N., et al., 2005. Construction of gene interaction and regulatory networks in bovine skeletal muscle from expression data. Aust. J. Exp. Agric. 45, 821–829.

Rud, I., Jensen, P.R., Naterstad, K., Axelsson, L., 2006. A synthetic promoter library for constitutive gene expression in Lactobacillus plantarum. Microbiology (Reading) 152, 1011–1019.

Sabatti, C., Rohlin, L., Oh, M.-K., Liao, J.C., 2002. Co-expression pattern from DNA microarray experiments as a tool for operon prediction. Nucleic Acids Res. 30, 2886–2893.

Saeidi, N., Wong, C.K., Lo, T.-M., et al., 2011. Engineering microbes to sense and eradicate Pseudomonas aeruginosa, a human pathogen. Mol. Syst. Biol. 7, 521.

Sahoo, S., Das, S., 2014. Analyzing gene expression and codon usage bias in diverse genomes using a variety of models. Curr. Bioinform. 9, 102–112.

Sanders, R., Mason, D.J., Foy, C.A., Huggett, J.F., 2014. Considerations for accurate gene expression measurement by reverse transcription quantitative PCR when analysing clinical samples. Anal. Bioanal. Chem. 406, 6471–6483.

Sanger, F., Nicklen, S., Coulson, A.R., 1977. DNA sequencing with chain-terminating inhibitors. Proc. Natl. Acad. Sci. USA 74, 5463–5467.

Sarkar, N., 1997. Polyadenylation of mRNA in prokaryotes. Annu. Rev. Biochem. 66, 173–197.

Schadt, E.E., Turner, S., Kasarskis, A., 2010. A window into third-generation sequencing. Hum. Mol. Genet. 19, R227–R240.

Schaumberg, K.A., Antunes, M.S., Kassaw, T.K., et al., 2016. Quantitative characterization of genetic parts and circuits for plant synthetic biology. Nat. Methods 13, 94–100.

Schmutz, J., Wheeler, J., Grimwood, J., et al., 2004. Quality assessment of the human genome sequence. Nature 429, 365–368.

Sharma, C.M., Hoffmann, S., Darfeuille, F., et al., 2010. The primary transcriptome of the major human pathogen Helicobacter pylori. Nature 464, 250–255.

Sharp, P.M., Li, W.H., 1987. The codon Adaptation Index – A measure of directional synonymous codon usage bias, and its potential applications. Nucleic Acids Res. 15, 1281–1295.

Siegl, T., Tokovenko, B., Myronovskyi, M., Luzhetskyy, A., 2013. Design, construction and characterisation of a synthetic promoter library for fine-tuned gene expression in actinomycetes. Metab. Eng. 19, 98–106.

Vandesompele, J., De Preter, K., Pattyn, F., et al., 2002. Accurate normalization of real-time quantitative RT-PCR data by geometric averaging of multiple internal control genes. Genome Biol. 3.RESEARCH0034.

Stewart, F.J., Ottesen, E.A., DeLong, E.F., 2010. Development and quantitative analyses of a universal rRNA-subtraction protocol for microbial metatranscriptomics. ISME J. 4, 896–907.

Strack, R.L., Disney, M.D., Jaffrey, S.R., 2013. A superfolding Spinach2 reveals the dynamic nature of trinucleotide repeat-containing RNA. Nat. Methods 10, 1219–1224.

Thellin, O., Zorzi, W., Lakaye, B., et al., 1999. Housekeeping genes as internal standards: Use and limits. J. Biotechnol. 75, 291–295.

Trapnell, C., Roberts, A., Goff, L., et al., 2012. Differential gene and transcript expression analysis of RNA-seq experiments with TopHat and Cufflinks. Nat. Protoc. 7, 562–578.

Trapnell, C., Williams, B.A., Pertea, G., et al., 2010. Transcript assembly and quantification by RNA-Seq reveals unannotated transcripts and isoform switching during cell differentiation. Nat. Biotechnol. 28, 511–515.

Trchounian, K., Soboh, B., Sawers, R.G., Trchounian, A., 2013. Contribution of hydrogenase 2 to stationary phase H2 production by Escherichia coli during fermentation of glycerol. Cell Biochem. Biophys. 66, 103–108.

Trevino, V., Falciani, F., Barrera-Saldaña, H.A., 2007. DNA microarrays: A powerful genomic tool for biomedical and clinical research. Mol. Med. 13, 527–541.

Van Gelder, R.N., von Zastrow, M.E., Yool, A., et al., 1990. Amplified RNA synthesized from limited quantities of heterogeneous cDNA. Proc. Natl. Acad. Sci. USA 87, 1663–1667.

Voelkerding, K.V., Dames, S.A., Durtschi, J.D., 2009. Next-generation sequencing: From basic research to diagnostics. Clin. Chem. 55, 641–658.

Wagner, G.P., Kin, K., Lynch, V.J., 2012. Measurement of mRNA abundance using RNA-seq data: RPKM measure is inconsistent among samples. Theory Biosci. 131, 281–285.

Wang, H., Ling, M.H., Chua, T.K., Poh, C.L., 2017. Two cellular resource-based models linking growth and parts characteristics aids the study and optimisation of synthetic gene circuits. Eng. Biol. 1, 30–39.

Weaver, L.J., Sousa, M.M.L., Wang, G., et al., 2015. A kinetic-based approach to understanding heterologous mevalonate pathway function in E. coli. Biotechnol. Bioeng. 112, 111–119.

Westermann, A.J., Förstner, K.U., Amman, F., et al., 2016. Dual RNA-seq unveils noncoding RNA functions in host-pathogen interactions. Nature 529, 496–501.

Wong, A., Wang, H., Poh, C.L., Kitney, R.I., 2015. Layering genetic circuits to build a single cell, bacterial half adder. BMC Biol. 13, 40.

Xiao, G., Martinez-Vaz, B., Pan, W., Khodursky, A.B., 2006. Operon information improves gene expression estimation for cDNA microarrays. BMC Genom. 7, 87.

Yang, Y., Yamashita, T., Nakamaru-Ogiso, E., et al., 2011. Reaction mechanism of single subunit NADH-ubiquinone oxidoreductase (Ndi1) from Saccharomyces cerevisiae: Evidence for a ternary complex mechanism. J. Biol. Chem. 286, 9287–9297.

Zhang, L.-Q., Li, Q.-Z., 2017. Estimating the effects of transcription factors binding and histone modifications on gene expression levels in human cells. Oncotarget 8, 40090–40103.

Zheng, Q., Wang, X.-J., 2008. GOEAST: A web-based software toolkit for Gene Ontology enrichment analysis. Nucleic Acids Res. 36, W358–W363.

Survey of Antisense Transcription

Maurice HT Ling, Colossus Technologies, LLP, Singapore and University of Melbourne, Melbourne, VIC, Australia

Introduction

Antisense transcript refers to RNA transcripts that are complementary to the RNA transcript from a known gene. It has been shown that antisense transcription is widespread throughout eukaryotic genome with occurrence as high as 43% (Györffy et al., 2006). Terminologically speaking, the RNA transcript transcribed from a gene is then known as the sense transcript, which will be used as template for translation. In terms of nomenclature, a common way to name antisense transcript is to prefix or suffix "AS" to its sense transcript; for example, the antisense transcript if interleukin-1-alpha (IL-1α) is known as AS-IL-1α (Chan et al., 2015) whereas the antisense transcript of topomyosin I (TPM1) is known as TPM1-AS (Huang et al., 2017). The first of natural antisense transcripts discovered was found in the b2 gene region of coliphage lambda (Bovre and Szybalski, 1969). An early example of antisense transcript found (Mizuno et al., 1984) is complementary to the 5′-end of Outer Membrane Protein F (OmpF) RNA transcript. Upon hybridization, two consequences may occur. Firstly, the translation of sense transcript may be restricted as the abundance of single-stranded sense transcript decreases. In other cases, the splicing process may be interfered. For example, Zeb2 sense transcript hybridizes with its antisense transcript ad reduces the efficiency of ribosome-binding. This results in translational inefficiency, leading to effective down-regulation of the peptide (Beltran et al., 2008). Secondly, half-life of the sense transcript is likely to decrease as double-stranded RNA can be degraded by DICER (Fruscoloni et al., 2003), or short antisense transcript may be incorporated into RNA-induced silencing complex (RISC) to target the complementary sense transcript for degradation (Ibrahim et al., 2006).

In both cases, the abundance of resulting peptide/protein product can be modulated in the presence of antisense transcript. Moreover, it has also been suggested that sense and antisense transcripts may be independently regulated (Goyal et al., 2017); hence, adding another layer of translational regulation. It has also been shown that antisense transcripts may play a significant role in human oncogenesis (Balbin et al., 2015); thus, emphasizing antisense transcription as an important field of study.

However, antisense transcripts can be broadly divided into cis-antisense transcripts, where the antisense transcript originates from the same genomic locus as its sense counterpart, and trans-antisense transcript, where the antisense transcript originates from a different genomic locus as its sense counterpart. In this article, we will examine both cis- and trans-natural antisense transcription before exploring several known cases of natural antisense transcription and their effects.

Cis- and Trans-Antisense Transcription

The mRNA, which is used for translation, is transcribed from the antisense strand of the coding sequence of the DNA; hence, has the same sequence as the sense transcript. Cis-antisense transcript is then transcribed from the sense strand of the coding sequence; as a result, is complementary to the mRNA. Trans-antisense transcripts, on the other hand, refers to antisense transcripts that originate from a different gene locus but happen to share sequence similarity for RNA-RNA duplex formation. Compared to an estimated 20% occurrence in cis-antisense transcription (Ling et al., 2013), trans-antisense transcription occurs about 4% (Li et al., 2008).

There can be four possible orientations (**Fig. 1**) that can result in RNA-RNA hybrids between cis-antisense/sense transcript pairs (Wang et al., 2005). Of these four different orientations, head-to-head and tail-to-tail, also known as divergent and convergent respectively (Villegas and Zaphiropoulos, 2015), are common orientations (Lavorgna et al., 2004; Osato et al., 2007). Head-to-head orientation (**Fig. 1(A)**) is likely to result in occlusion of the ribosome-binding site (Osato et al., 2007) and this results in reduced efficiency of ribosomes to bind to the mRNA transcript to start translation. This in turn leads to reduced rate of peptide formation. However, it is also possible that head-to-head sense/antisense can lead to increased peptide levels in some cases. For example, antisense transcript of mouse ubiquitin carboxy-terminal hydrolase L1 (*Uchl1*) gene can activate polysomes for increased translation of Uchl1 under specific stress conditions (Carrieri et al., 2012), resulting in unilateral increase in peptide level without the corresponding increase in mRNA level. Tail-to-tail orientation (**Fig. 1(B)**) is commonly found in sense/antisense pairs with either similar polyadenylation tails (Gu et al., 2009; Zubko et al., 2011) or 3′ untranslated regions (Swaminathan and Beilharz, 2016). When tail-to-tail sense and antisense RNA are transcribed at the same time, this can result in collision and stalling of RNA polymerase at the 3′ end, which allows the free 5′ end of the antisense transcript to bind to nascent sense transcripts in the nucleus (Dang et al., 2016). In the cytoplasm, tail-to-tail sense/antisense duplex can also result in Dicer-2 processing, leading to silencing of both sense and antisense transcripts (Russo et al., 2016). Full overlap (**Fig. 1(C)**), known as embedded, occurs when the antisense transcript overlaps with the full length of the sense transcript, resulting in complete masking and protection of the sense transcript by RNase activity (Rosikiewicz and Makałowska, 2016). RNase masking occurs whenever RNA-RNA or RNA-DNA duplexes are formed; hence, can occur in all four orientations. For example, interferon-alpha 1 mRNA increases its stability after being partially masked by its natural antisense transcript (Kimura et al., 2013). Hence, it is plausible to consider that full overlapping antisense transcript may reduce RNase degradation to a greater level than partial overlaps (head-to-head, tail-to-tail, and internal).

 Encyclopedia of Bioinformatics and Computational Biology, Volume 3   doi:10.1016/B978-0-12-809633-8.20465-2

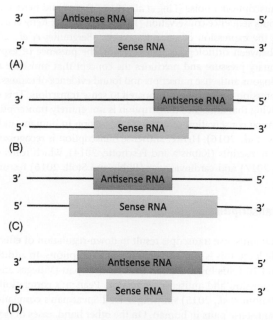

Fig. 1 Four possible orientations of cis-antisense/sense pairs. (A) 5′ to 5′ Overlap (Head-to-head), (B) 3′ to 3′ Overlap (Tail-to-tail), (C) Full Overlap, (D) Internal Overlap.

Detection of antisense transcripts. There are three main methods for detecting cis-antisense transcripts; namely, hybridization method (Collani and Barcaccia, 2012), antisense microarray method (Ge *et al.*, 2008), and RNA-seq identification method (Li *et al.*, 2013). Using the principle that double stranded DNA is protected against exonuclease degradation the same way that double stranded RNA is protected against RNase degradation, Collani and Barcaccia (2012) propose to reverse transcribe total RNA into cDNA for hybridization, before degradation of single strand cDNA by exonucleases. Undegraded hybridized cDNA molecules represents sense/antisense pairs, which can be identified by sequencing. Ge *et al.* (2008) removed a step from standard microarray protocol. This step elimination ensures that cDNA from antisense transcripts, instead of cDNA from sense transcripts, is complementary to the microarray probes; hence, able to use commercial microarrays to detect for antisense transcription. However, commercial microarrays is generally dependent on the sequencing status and quality of expressed sequence tags (ESTs) for a particular species. Hence, the availability of microarrays is limited to commonly studies species, which limits its use in antisense detection in new species. Next generation sequencing (NGS) is able to overcome this limitation by *ab initio* sequencing of entire RNA pool (which is commonly known as RNA-sequencing or RNA-seq), including antisense transcripts. This is the basis of NASTIseq (Li *et al.*, 2013), which uses strand-specific RNA sequencing (ssRNA-seq) of Arabidopsis and statistical modelling to identify thousands of potential cis-antisense transcripts. Furthermore, it has been well-acknowledge (Gluck *et al.*, 2016; Green *et al.*, 2017; Kukurba and Montgomery, 2015; Merrick *et al.*, 2013; Miller *et al.*, 2014; Zhai *et al.*, 2014) that RNA-seq provides higher sensitivity and resolution, and reduced biases, compared to microarray technology. Thus, RNA-seq is currently the preferred method for antisense detection (Oono *et al.*, 2017; Shao *et al.*, 2017) due to its increasing employment and gradual cost reduction.

Detection of cis-antisense transcripts differs from that of trans-antisense transcripts. For trans-antisense transcripts, an identification pipeline has been proposed (Li *et al.*, 2008). Briefly, trans-antisense/sense pairs can be detected by pair-wise sequence comparisons using either databases of known antisense transcripts; such as, NATsDB (Zhang *et al.*, 2007); or RNA-seq data sets; to identify high-quality potential sense/antisense pairs before *in silico* assessment of hybridization potential using DINAMelt (Markham and Zuker, 2005). Although NATsDB focuses on cis-antisense, it is also possible that these antisense transcripts may exhibit sufficient sequence similarity to act as antisense for sense transcripts of other gene loci; thus, making them trans-antisense transcripts as well. This is used in the detection of trans-antisense transcripts of soybeans (Zheng *et al.*, 2013). NATpipe (Yu *et al.*, 2016) is a computational tool to discover NATs from RNA-seq data by identifying potential pairs of complementary transcripts; thus, making it useful for identifying both cis- and trans-antisense transcripts. As an example, NATpipe was used to analyse RNA-seq data of *Dendrobium officinale*, a non-model plant species, and identified more than 600 thousand potential antisense transcript pairs; of which, 436 were identified as potential cis-antisense transcript pairs.

Due to the large numbers of computationally identified antisense transcripts over the years, several databases catering to antisense transcripts had been built. For example, antiCODE (see "Relevant Websites section") collated published antisense listings of more than 10 species, including mouse, human, and rice. PlantNATsDB (Chen *et al.*, 2012) (see "Relevant Websites section") had collated more than a million antisense transcripts from 70 plant species. It can be expected that existing antisense transcript databases will grow and antisense transcripts will be a feature in organism-specific databases.

Antisense is not transcriptional noise. Despite the prevalence of antisense transcription (Györffy *et al.*, 2006) and proposed biological functions (Werner, 2005; Werner and Sayer, 2009; Werner and Swan, 2010; Werner *et al.*, 2009), there were early concerns whether antisense transcription is a form of transcriptional noise (Ling *et al.*, 2013; Werner and Berdal, 2005) due to leaky transcription. It is known that evolutionary pressure favours sequence conservation (Hutter *et al.*, 2010; Keng *et al.*, 2014; Paulsen, 2011; Siafakas *et al.*, 2005) and several studies examining the expression of sense transcripts (Bergmiller *et al.*, 2012; Jordan *et al.*, 2005) found that expression conservation is a feature between orthologous genes. Hence, the presence of expression conservation in orthologous antisense transcripts suggests evolutionary pressure and precludes the concept that antisense transcription is solely transcriptional noise. Ling *et al.* (2013) studied orthologous antisense transcripts and found evidence of expression conservation among orthologous antisense transcripts despite lower expression conservation compared to sense transcripts. This suggests the presence of evolutionary pressure in antisense expression, implying that antisense transcription is not entirely transcriptional noise. This is corroborated by a study (Nielsen *et al.*, 2014) demonstrating conservation of antisense expression in humans and how antisense transcription may be regulated (Agarwal *et al.*, 2014; Uprety *et al.*, 2016). Hence, antisense transcription is recognized as a regulatory mechanism despite weaker regulation compared to sense transcripts (Kapusta and Feschotte, 2014), which leads to further studies in various medical fields; such as, skeletal (Huynh *et al.*, 2017) and cardiovascular (Rühle and Stoll, 2016) research.

Differing Effects of Antisense Transcription

Although it is generally considered that antisense transcripts result in down-regulation of effective level of the corresponding sense transcripts, leading to reduced peptide level; this is a heuristic with many exceptions. In addition, although the expression level of antisense transcript is generally around 10-folds lower than its sense counterpart (Villegas and Zaphiropoulos, 2015) and there is positive correlation between sense expression and antisense expression, Pearson's correlation averages at 0.44 (Ling *et al.*, 2013). This is supported by another study (Balbin *et al.*, 2015) showing overall Spearman's correlation of 0.28 and Pearson's correlation of 0.41 between head-to-head sense/antisense pairs in human. On the other hand, cases of negative correlation between sense and antisense expression has been found (Xu *et al.*, 2011). In this section, four cases are reviewed to exemplify varying and non-down-regulation impacts of antisense – (1) as-ssm1 increases the transcript level of ssm1 but has no impact on the protein level of ssm1 (Ostrowski and Saville, 2017), (2) TALAM1 (the antisense of MALAT1) increases the level of MALAT1 protein by increasing the maturation rate of MALAT1 transcript (Zong *et al.*, 2016), (3) Sox4 antisense transcripts have no effect on Sox4 mRNA or peptide level (Ling *et al.*, 2016), and (4) AS1DHRS1 silences DHRS4 gene cluster by chromatin modification (Li *et al.*, 2012). Taken together, this suggests that down-regulation of peptide levels is not the sole impact of antisense transcript. Rather, the effects of antisense transcript on the eventual peptide/protein level can be complex and should be considered on a case-by-case basis.

Ustilago maydis is a fungus that infects the corn, *Zea mays*, resulting in a fungal disease called smut. *U. maydis* mitochondrial seryl-tRNA synthetase (ssm1) is a crucial enzyme for mitochondrial function and is encoded by 2448 bases. The antisense of ssm1, as-ssm1, is a tail-to-tail antisense transcript of 2057 bases (Ostrowski and Saville, 2017). The 5′ end of as-ssm1 extends 20 bases into the 3′-UTR of ssm1 transcript. Hence, as-ssm1 overlaps the entire 3′ end of ssm1 transcript except 411 bases of its 5′ end (83.2% overlap). Using quantitative PCR, it was found that the formation of ssm1/as-ssm1 double stranded RNA duplex protects ssm1 transcript from S1 nuclease degradation but this protection does not extend to the non-duplexed 411 bases at the 5′ end of ssm1. Hence, the steady-state concentration of ssm1 is significantly increased as a result of as-ssm1 protection, leading to significant differences in growth rate and virulence of *U. maydis*. However, the protein abundance of ssm1 is not significantly different in the presence of as-ssm1 using standardized Bradford Assay. This suggests that the impact of as-ssm1 is not entirely on the level of ssm1 protein but may act as a preservation role to extend the half-life of ssm1 RNA transcript, leading to rapid translation of ssm1 transcript without undergoing transcription.

Maturation of metastasis-associated lung adenocarcinoma transcript 1 (MALAT1) RNA requires 3′ cleavage, resulting in a non-polyadenylated transcript. The antisense transcript of MALAT1 is known as TALAM1 (Zong *et al.*, 2016), which hybridize to MALAT1 at the 3′ end. In human genome, hMALAT1 is 8708 bases and hTALAM1 overlaps from 1551th base to the 3′ end of hMALAT1 with 963 bases of the 5′ end of hTALAM1 extending from the 3′ end of hMALAT1. Although the expression of MALAT1 is correlated to the expression of TALAM1 across different cell types, quantitative PCR shows that the TALAM1 transcripts in HeLa cells is about 290-times less abundant than MALAT1 transcripts. Using actinomycin D chase experiment, TALAM1 half-life drops from about 8 hours to about 3 hours in MALAT1-depleted cells (depleted using phosphorothioate internucleosidic linkage-modified DNA antisense oligonucleotides) compared to control cells. This suggests that MALAT1 confers protection to its antisense transcript despite a protection ratio of only 0.34% due to the relative abundance between MALAT1 and TALAM1. The reverse is also true – TALAM1-depleted cells shows significant reduction in the abundance of mature 3′ non-polyadenylated MALAT1 RNA transcript while the abundance of nascent 3′ polyadenylated MALAT1 RNA transcript is significantly increased. This suggests that MALAT1/TALAM1 sense/antisense pairs are co-reliant to maintain half-life and TALAM1 has an important role in processing and maturation of MALAT1 transcripts.

Sry-related high mobility group box 4 (Sox4) is a 47 kDa transcription factor, which binds to WWCAAW sequence, and is involved in DNA binding/bending, protein interactions and nuclear import/export. More than 20 antisense transcripts of varying lengths and from different transcription start sites have been found for Sox4 in E15.5 mouse cerebral cortex using 5′ RACE-Southern hybridization (Ling *et al.*, 2016). All of them are cytoplasmically co-localized using fluorescent *in situ* hybridization (FISH), suggesting that these antisense transcripts are exported out of the nucleus; hence, potentially active. However, over-expression of Sox4 antisense transcripts did not result in significant differences in the mRNA and peptide level of Sox4, which contradicted FISH results. It is known that RNA-RNA duplex, which can result from sense/antisense hybridization, may serve as template for processing into small RNA molecules and function via RNA interference (RNAi) machinery. A small RNA molecule, Sox4_sir3, has been found to originate from sense/antisense duplex and found to play a role in embryonic brain development. This suggests that the effects of antisense transcripts may go beyond duplex formation.

Short-chain dehydrogenase/reductase family member 4 (DHRS4) on human chromosome 14q11.2 encodes the NADPH dependent retinol dehydrogenase/reductase (NRDR), which is important in metabolism and detoxification of carbonyl compounds. The antisense transcript of DHRS4, AS1DHRS4, is a head-to-head spliced antisense transcript overlapping with exon 1 of DHRS4 (Li et al., 2012). DHRS4 mRNA level and NRDR protein level increase after using antisense oligonucleotides to AS1DHRS4 to reduce effective transcript abundance of AS1DHRS4, suggesting that AS1DHRS4 abundance is inversely proportional to the abundance DHRS4 mRNA, which implies that AS1DHRS4 transcript reduces the effective level of DHRS4 transcript. In addition, AS1DHRS4 duplexing with DHRS4 transcript results in histone modification and DNA methylation as revealed by ChIP assays. These led to the reduction of transcriptional activity of DHRS4 gene.

The above cases demonstrate the variety of means in which antisense transcript can affect the abundance and half-life of the sense transcript which may or may not lead to significant changes in the abundance of resulting peptide/protein. The reverse can also be true – antisense transcript may affect the abundance of resulting peptide/protein without significant changes to the abundance of the sense transcript. Hence, suggesting a separation between transcription and translation. More importantly, these cases illustrate that antisense transcript can function at various levels. At the first order level, antisense transcript forms RNA-RNA duplex with its sense transcript but this does not lead to a uniform reduction of effective sense transcript. At higher order, antisense expression may lead to a range of other effects; such as, RNA interference and changes at the epigenetic level; which must be considered on a case-by-case basis.

Collectively, this illustrates the myriad of roles played by antisense transcripts. It is clear the roles played by antisense goes beyond initial expectations – reducing the abundance of sense transcripts. Even in this role, the methods used by each sense-antisense system is likely to differ significantly. Therefore, presenting antisense as an important area for on-going study. It is highly plausible that antisense transcription may be a field of study in its own rights as antisense is currently being explored for therapeutic purposes (Chery, 2016; Zarouchlioti et al., 2018).

See also: Analyzing Transcriptome-Phenotype Correlations. Applications of Ribosomal RNA Sequence and Structure Analysis for Extracting Evolutionary and Functional Insights. Characterization of Transcriptional Activities. Characterizing and Functional Assignment of Noncoding RNAs. Comparative Transcriptomics Analysis. Exome Sequencing Data Analysis. Functional Enrichment Analysis. Genome-Wide Scanning of Gene Expression. Integrative Analysis of Multi-Omics Data. Natural Language Processing Approaches in Bioinformatics. Next Generation Sequencing Data Analysis. Regulation of Gene Expression. Transcriptome Analysis. Transcriptome During Cell Differentiation. Whole Genome Sequencing Analysis

---

References

Agarwal, T., Roy, S., Kumar, S., Chakraborty, T.K., Maiti, S., 2014. In the sense of transcription regulation by G-quadruplexes: Asymmetric effects in sense and antisense strands. Biochemistry 53, 3711–3718.

Balbin, O.A., Malik, R., Dhanasekaran, S.M., et al., 2015. The landscape of antisense gene expression in human cancers. Genome Res. 25, 1068–1079.

Beltran, M., Puig, I., Peña, C., et al., 2008. A natural antisense transcript regulates Zeb2/Sip1 gene expression during Snail1-induced epithelial-mesenchymal transition. Genes Dev. 22, 756–769.

Bergmiller, T., Ackermann, M., Silander, O.K., 2012. Patterns of evolutionary conservation of essential genes correlate with their compensability. PLOS Genet. 8, e1002803.

Bovre, K., Szybalski, W., 1969. Patterns of convergent and overlapping transcription within the b2 region of coliphage lambda. Virology 38, 614–626.

Carrieri, C., Cimatti, L., Biagioli, M., et al., 2012. Long non-coding antisense RNA controls Uchl1 translation through an embedded SINEB2 repeat. Nature 491, 454–457.

Chan, J., Atianand, M., Jiang, Z., et al., 2015. Cutting edge: A natural antisense transcript, AS-IL1α, controls inducible transcription of the proinflammatory cytokine IL-1α. J. Immunol. 195, 1359–1363.

Chen, D., Yuan, C., Zhang, J., et al., 2012. PlantNATsDB: A comprehensive database of plant natural antisense transcripts. Nucleic Acids Res. 40, D1187–D1193.

Chery, J., 2016. RNA therapeutics: RNAi and antisense mechanisms and clinical applications. Postdoc. J. 4, 35–50.

Collani, S., Barcaccia, G., 2012. Development of a rapid and inexpensive method to reveal natural antisense transcripts. Plant Methods 8, 37.

Dang, Y., Cheng, J., Sun, X., Zhou, Z., Liu, Y., 2016. Antisense transcription licenses nascent transcripts to mediate transcriptional gene silencing. Genes Dev. 30, 2417–2432.

Fruscoloni, P., Zamboni, M., Baldi, M.I., Tocchini-Valentini, G.P., 2003. Exonucleolytic degradation of double-stranded RNA by an activity in Xenopus laevis germinal vesicles. Proc. Natl. Acad. Sci. USA 100, 1639–1644.

Ge, X., Rubinstein, W.S., Jung, Y.C., Wu, Q., 2008. Genome-wide analysis of antisense transcription with Affymetrix exon array. BMC Genom. 9, 27.

Gluck, C., Min, S., Oyelakin, A., et al., 2016. RNA-seq based transcriptomic map reveals new insights into mouse salivary gland development and maturation. BMC Genom. 17, 923.

Goyal, A., Fiškin, E., Gutschner, T., et al., 2017. A cautionary tale of sense-antisense gene pairs: Independent regulation despite inverse correlation of expression. Nucleic Acids Res..

Green, R., Wilkins, C., Ferris, M.T., Gale, M., 2017. RNA-seq in the collaborative cross. Methods Mol. Biol. 1488, 251–263.

Gu, R., Zhang, Z., DeCerbo, J.N., Carmichael, G.G., 2009. Gene regulation by sense-antisense overlap of polyadenylation signals. RNA 15, 1154–1163.

Györffy, A., Tulassay, Z., Surowiak, P., Györffy, B., 2006. Computational analysis reveals 43% antisense transcription in 1182 transcripts in mouse muscle. DNA Seq. 17, 422–430.

Huang, G.-W., Zhang, Y.-L., Liao, L.-D., Li, E.-M., Xu, L.-Y., 2017. Natural antisense transcript TPM1-AS regulates the alternative splicing of tropomyosin I through an interaction with RNA-binding motif protein 4. Int. J. Biochem. Cell Biol. 90, 59–67.

Hutter, B., Bieg, M., Helms, V., Paulsen, M., 2010. Imprinted genes show unique patterns of sequence conservation. BMC Genom. 11, 649.

Huynh, N.P.T., Anderson, B.A., Guilak, F., McAlinden, A., 2017. Emerging roles for long noncoding RNAs in skeletal biology and disease. Connect. Tissue Res. 58, 116–141.

Ibrahim, F., Rohr, J., Jeong, W.-J., Hesson, J., Cerutti, H., 2006. Untemplated oligoadenylation promotes degradation of RISC-cleaved transcripts. Science 314, 1893.

Jordan, I.K., Marino-Ramirez, L., Koonin, E.V., 2005. Evolutionary significance of gene expression divergence. Gene 345, 119–126.

Kapusta, A., Feschotte, C., 2014. Volatile evolution of long noncoding RNA repertoires: Mechanisms and biological implications. Trends Genet. 30, 439–452.

Keng, B.M., Chan, O.Y., Ling, M.H., 2014. Codon usage bias is evolutionarily conserved. Asia Pac. J. Life Sci. 7, 233–242.

Kimura, T., Jiang, S., Nishizawa, M., et al., 2013. Stabilization of human interferon-α1 mRNA by its antisense RNA. Cell. Mol. Life Sci. 70, 1451–1467.

Kukurba, K.R., Montgomery, S.B., 2015. RNA Sequencing and Analysis. Cold Spring Harb. Protoc. 2015, 951–969.

Lavorgna, G., Dahary, D., Lehner, B., et al., 2004. In search of antisense. Trends Biochem. Sci. 29, 88–94.

Li, J.T., Zhang, Y., Kong, L., Liu, Q.R., Wei, L., 2008. Trans-natural antisense transcripts including noncoding RNAs in 10 species: Implications for expression regulation. Nucleic Acids Res. 36, 4833–4844.

Li, Q., Su, Z., Xu, X., et al., 2012. AS1DHRS4, a head-to-head natural antisense transcript, silences the DHRS4 gene cluster in cis and trans. Proc. Natl. Acad. Sci. USA 109, 14110–14115.

Li, S., Liberman, L.M., Mukherjee, N., Benfey, P.N., Ohler, U., 2013. Integrated detection of natural antisense transcripts using strand-specific RNA sequencing data. Genome Res. 23, 1730–1739.

Ling, K.-H., Brautigan, P.J., Moore, S., et al., 2016. Derivation of an endogenous small RNA from double-stranded Sox4 sense and natural antisense transcripts in the mouse brain. Genomics 107, 88–99.

Ling, M.H.T., Ban, Y., Wen, H., Wang, S.M., Ge, S.X., 2013. Conserved expression of natural antisense transcripts in mammals. BMC Genom. 14, 243.

Markham, N.R., Zuker, M., 2005. DINAMelt web server for nucleic acid melting prediction. Nucleic Acids Res. 33, W577–W581.

Merrick, B.A., Phadke, D.P., Auerbach, S.S., et al., 2013. RNA-Seq profiling reveals novel hepatic gene expression pattern in aflatoxin B1 treated rats. PLOS ONE 8, e61768.

Miller, J.A., Menon, V., Goldy, J., et al., 2014. Improving reliability and absolute quantification of human brain microarray data by filtering and scaling probes using RNA-Seq. BMC Genom. 15, 154.

Mizuno, T., Chou, M.Y., Inouye, M., 1984. A unique mechanism regulating gene expression: Translational inhibition by a complementary RNA transcript (micRNA). Proc. Natl. Acad. Sci. USA 81, 1966–1970.

Nielsen, M.M., Tehler, D., Vang, S., et al., 2014. Identification of expressed and conserved human noncoding RNAs. RNA 20, 236–251.

Oono, Y., Yazawa, T., Kanamori, H., et al., 2017. Genome-wide analysis of rice cis-natural antisense transcription under cadmium exposure using strand-specific RNA-Seq. BMC Genom. 18, 761.

Osato, N., Suzuki, Y., Ikeo, K., Gojobori, T., 2007. Transcriptional interferences in cis natural antisense transcripts of humans and mice. Genetics 176, 1299–1306.

Ostrowski, L.A., Saville, B.J., 2017. Natural antisense transcripts are linked to the modulation of mitochondrial function and teliospore dormancy in Ustilago maydis. Mol. Microbiol. 103, 745–763.

Paulsen, M., 2011. Unique patterns of evolutionary conservation of imprinted genes. Clin. Epigenet. 2, 405–410.

Rosikiewicz, W., Makałowska, I., 2016. Biological functions of natural antisense transcripts. Acta Biochim. Pol. 63, 665–673.

Rühle, F., Stoll, M., 2016. Long non-coding RNA databases in cardiovascular research. Genom. Proteom. Bioinform. 14, 191–199.

Russo, J., Harrington, A.W., Steiniger, M., 2016. Antisense transcription of retrotransposons in Drosophila: An origin of endogenous small interfering RNA precursors. Genetics 202, 107–121.

Shao, J., Chen, H., Yang, D., et al., 2017. Genome-wide identification and characterization of natural antisense transcripts by strand-specific RNA sequencing in Ganoderma lucidum. Sci. Rep. 7, 5711.

Siafakas, N., Papaventsis, D., Levidiotou-Stefanou, S., Vamvakopoulos, N.C., Markoulatos, P., 2005. Classification and structure of echovirus 5′-UTR sequences. Virus Genes 31, 293–306.

Swaminathan, A., Beilharz, T.H., 2016. Epitope-tagged yeast strains reveal promoter driven changes to 3′-end formation and convergent antisense-transcription from common 3′ UTRs. Nucleic Acids Res. 44, 377–386.

Uprety, B., Kaja, A., Ferdoush, J., Sen, R., Bhaumik, S.R., 2016. Regulation of antisense transcription by NuA4 histone acetyltransferase and other chromatin regulatory factors. Mol. Cell. Biol. 36, 992–1006.

Villegas, V.E., Zaphiropoulos, P.G., 2015. Neighboring gene regulation by antisense long non-coding RNAs. Int. J. Mol. Sci. 16, 3251–3266.

Wang, X.-J., Gaasterland, T., Chua, N.-H., 2005. Genome-wide prediction and identification of cis-natural antisense transcripts in Arabidopsis thaliana. Genome Biol. 6, R30.

Werner, A., 2005. Natural antisense transcripts. RNA Biol. 2, 53–62.

Werner, A., Berdal, A., 2005. Natural antisense transcripts: Sound or silence? Physiol. Genom. 23, 125–131.

Werner, A., Sayer, J.A., 2009. Naturally occurring antisense RNA: Function and mechanisms of action. Curr. Opin. Nephrol. Hypertension 18, 343–349.

Werner, A., Swan, D., 2010. What are natural antisense transcripts good for? Biochem. Soc. Trans. 38, 1144–1149.

Werner, A., Carlile, M., Swan, D., 2009. What do natural antisense transcripts regulate? RNA Biol. 6, 43–48.

Xu, Z., Wei, W., Gagneur, J., et al., 2011. Antisense expression increases gene expression variability and locus interdependency. Mol. Syst. Biol. 7, 468. n/a.

Yu, D., Meng, Y., Zuo, Z., Xue, J., Wang, H., 2016. NATpipe: An integrative pipeline for systematical discovery of natural antisense transcripts (NATs) and phase-distributed nat-siRNAs from de novo assembled transcriptomes. Sci. Rep. 6, 21666.

Zarouchlioti, C., Sanchez-Pintado, B., Hafford Tear, N.J., et al., 2018. Antisense therapy for a common corneal dystrophy ameliorates TCF4 repeat expansion-mediated toxicity. Am. J. Hum. Genet. 102, 528–539.

Zhai, W., Yao, X.-., Xu, Y.-., et al., 2014. Transcriptome profiling of prostate tumor and matched normal samples by RNA-Seq. Eur. Rev. Med. Pharmacol. Sci. 18, 1354–1360.

Zhang, Y., Li, J., Kong, L., et al., 2007. NATsDB: Natural antisense transcripts database. Nucleic Acids Res. 35, D156–D161.

Zheng, H., Qiyan, J., Zhiyong, N., Hui, Z., 2013. Prediction and identification of natural antisense transcripts and their small RNAs in soybean (Glycine max). BMC Genom. 14, 280.

Zong, X., Nakagawa, S., Freier, S.M., et al., 2016. Natural antisense RNA promotes 3′ end processing and maturation of MALAT1 lncRNA. Nucleic Acids Res. 44, 2898–2908.

Zubko, E., Kunova, A., Meyer, P., 2011. Sense and antisense transcripts of convergent gene pairs in Arabidopsis thaliana can share a common polyadenylation region. PLOS ONE 6, e16769.

Relevant Websites

http://www.bioinfo.org.cn/anticode/index.htm
    antiCODE.
http://bis.zju.edu.cn/pnatdb/
    Plant Natural Antisense Transcripts DataBase.

Statistical and Probabilistic Approaches to Predict Protein Abundance

Rubbiya A Ali and Ahmed M Mehdi, University of Queensland, Brisbane, QLD, Australia
Ali Naqi, Queensland University of Technology, Brisbane, QLD, Australia
Sarah Ali, Hamdard Institute of Engineering and Technology, Islamabad, Pakistan
Mashal Fatima, Bahauddin Zakariya University, Multan, Pakistan
Musarat Ishaq, St. Vincent's Institute of Medical Research, Melbourne, VIC, Australia

Introduction

Proteins are complex molecules with many vital roles in a cell such as signal reception, amplification and transduction. They also help to control gene expression, produce and transport molecules (Ford *et al.*, 2001; Yilmaz and Grotewold, 2010). The proper functioning of these processes is critically dependent on the protein abundance that is highly regulated in prokaryotes and eukaryotes. The proteins are involved in regulating the cellular homeostasis and other metabolic mechanisms. Therefore, to study an organism, it's crucial to understand the homeostasis and the balance between DNA, RNA and proteins. Any mutation in DNA/RNA or protein results in the disruption of the total cellular homeostasis and could lead to a disease (Leu *et al.*, 2011). Measuring the protein abundance to understand the dynamics between mRNA and protein levels has been investigated by several researchers. Here, we review experimental and predictive approaches to understand these dynamics.

Experimental Technologies for Measuring Protein Abundance

The expressions of proteins assist in regulating all the biochemical mechanism including signalling, transportation, degradation, genomic replication and translation of genomic data. The protein abundance and depletion is dealt with delicacy as it could disrupt the whole cellular biochemical dogma within cells (Steen and Pandey, 2002). Interestingly in yeast, 27% of total protein is expressed in the nucleus (Kumar *et al.*, 2002), indicating the importance of nuclear proteins abundance in replication, maintenance and repair of the genome. Furthermore, several diseases have been associated with proteins that are translocated in the nucleus. Therefore, it is crucial to correctly quantify protein to determine a disease or a type of disease for therapeutic purposes (Powers and Palecek, 2012). Several protein quantification techniques (such as immunohistochemistry, flow cytometry and ELISA) are in current use for the diagnosis of several diseases (Ferrier *et al.*, 1999; Yaziji *et al.*, 2008; Fromm *et al.*, 2009). Furthermore, techniques such as mass spectrometry (MS) (Vlahou *et al.*, 2003), proximity assays (Blokzijl *et al.*, 2010) and protein microarray (Ingvarsson *et al.*, 2008) are the emerging techniques for the protein quantification with more thorough output and more accurate quantification of multiple proteins at an instance. By so far, these protein quantification techniques have helped to recognize multiple markers for several diseases. However experimentally determining protein abundance is not as cost-effective as measuring mRNA concentration.

Researchers have measured protein abundance data using different technologies. For example, Ghaemmaghami *et al.*, (2003) created a *S. cerevisiae* library by tagging each ORF with high-affinity epitope and by using immunodetection to calculate the absolute measurements of protein abundance. Newman *et al.* (2006) identified GF-tagged strained at single-cell resolution using high throughput flow cytometric experiment. Newman and colleagues measured protein abundance levels both in rich and minimal medium conditions to investigate the impact of medium in measuring protein abundance. Lee and colleagues studied the association between mRNA expression and protein abundance. The authors measured protein abundance by combining mass spectrometry with isobaric tagging (Lee *et al.*, 2011).

Determinants of Protein Abundance

Several scientists have described using mRNA concentration to predict protein abundance and activity, assuming that mRNA expression values are the main basis of protein abundances predictions (Tuller *et al.*, 2007; Zur and Tuller, 2012; Mehdi *et al.*, 2014). The mRNA expression data can be used to develop accurate models of protein abundance (Greenbaum *et al.*, 2003). Experimentally measuring protein abundance is highly complex and expensive. The mRNA expression is usually studied utilising several techniques among them is Microarray and RNAseq techniques (Zhu *et al.*, 2008). The RNA expression is intern designed by the RNA polymerases through DNA. The ribosomal proteins then translate this mRNA and translated into protein (Roeder, 1996). The new studies have shown that the RNA expression is sometimes unable to represent the actual protein expression levels within cells (Koussounadis *et al.*, 2015). Therefore, it is always complicated to identify protein expression through RNA expression. Furthermore, other factors also contribute to protein expression such as the half-life of mRNA and protein molecules, protein specificity towards cell cycle (Belle *et al.*, 2006). Other important determinants of protein abundance are relative tRNA abundance (Shah and Gilchrist, 2010), evolutionary rates (Tuller *et al.*, 2007; Zur and Tuller, 2012), folding energy and RNA binding proteins (Mehdi *et al.*, 2014).

Linear Regression Methods to Predict Protein Abundance

A number of different researchers use univariate approach to measure the correlation between predicted and actual protein abundance values (Yu et al., 2007; Lahtvee et al., 2017; Zur and Tuller, 2012). Tuller et al. (2007) developed two linear models that predict protein abundance and translational efficiency. These models are based on the mRNA expression values, relative tRNA abundance and evolutionary rate. For any transcript/mRNA/protein/ORF represented as 'x', the two predicted protein abundance models are given below;

$$\text{Tuller} - 1: \quad \log PA(x) = 3.97 + 0.4 * \log mRNA(x) + 10.34 * tAI(x) - 3.35 * ER(x) \qquad (1)$$

$$\text{Tuller} - 2: \quad \log PA(x) = 3.47 + 0.63 * \log mRNA(x) + 10.89 * tAI(x) - 2.923 * ER(x) \qquad (2)$$

Tuller and colleagues have shown that by comparing actual protein abundance with predicted protein abundance the above models achieve spearman rank correlation coefficients of 0.63 an 0.76 respectively.

Probabilistic Approaches to Predict Protein Abundance

Very few scientists have used non-linear approaches to predict protein abundance. For example, Tuller et al. (2007) used support vector machines to develop protein abundance predictor, however the accuracy of their model was lower than linear models. The non-linear regression performed by Lahtvee et al. (2017) explained proteins abundance with maximum of 61% of its variance.

Recently a Bayesian networks approach was shown to surpass accuracy of all available predictors of protein abundance (Mehdi et al., 2014). Bayesian networks are belief networks that contain set of random variables. These variables have casual relationships with other variables that are represented as directed acyclic graphs. Mehdi et al. (2014) developed a probabilistic Bayesian networks models that integrate random variables from four different sources. The four data sources include mRNA values, protein abundance, mRNA sequence and mRNA/protein interaction data. Thus, their model combines different random variables measured with different technologies. The model is shown in **Fig. 1** (reproduced from the work of Mehdi and colleagues) where PA(x) is a random variable that predicts the abundance of proteins (see "Relevant Websites section" to access the model). The variable 'x' represents ORF/gene/protein/molecule.

Zur and Tuller (2012) have previously shown that mRNA expressions, folding energy and tRNA adaptation index (tAI) correlates with protein abundance. In the Bayesian networks model, the authors first integrate mRNA expression variable with protein abundance variable and mRNA folding energy variable by assuming that increase in folding of a mRNA molecule will increase its expression and/or translation (Zur and Tuller, 2012). The model links RBP(x) with mRNA(x) representing the interaction of RNA binding proteins with mRNA molecule that modulates protein abundance. Here RBP(x) is a discrete valued node representing no interaction with mRNA (RBP(x)=1), maximum of two interactions (RBP(x)=2), maximum of four interactions and minimum of three interactions (RBP(x)=3) and above four interactions between mRNA and RBP (RBP(x)=4). **Fig. 2(A)** represents the probability of interaction of mRNA with RBP learned by the model. For example, 5.4% of mRNA molecules do not interact with any RBPs. 35.1% of mRNA interacts with maximum of two RBPs, 42.4% of mRNA interacts with maximum of 3 or 4 RBPs and 17.1% of mRNA molecules interact with at least 5 RBPs. We further note (**Fig. 2(A)**) that mRNAs that do not interact with RBPs possess low expression ($\mu = -0.15$) as compared to those who interact with RBPs ($\mu = -0.08, -0.04$ and -0.07).

To further represent the effect of mRNA and protein degradation on protein translation, the model links mHL(x) and pHL(x) indirectly with protein abundance node PA(x). **Fig. 2(B)** represent the parameters learnt by nodes mRNA and protein half-life; mHL(x) and pHL(x) respectively. The model learns parameters with separate Gaussian distributions for each random variable. The smaller half-life (node L3=False) node gets smaller standard deviation. By looking into the regression weights (β) in **Table 1**, we note that shorter half-life of proteins result in high mRNA folding energy and codon usage and low protein abundance (see row 2 of **Table 1**).

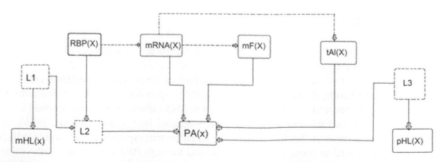

Fig. 1   Bayesian networks model predicts the protein abundance. Reproduced from Mehdi, A.M., Patrick, R., Bailey, T.L., Boden, M., 2014. Predicting the dynamics of protein abundance. Molecular and Cellular Proteomics 13 (5), 1330–1340. Each feature in the model is represented as a node. Latent nodes are represented with dotted lines. The casual relationships between parents and child nodes are shown with arrows.

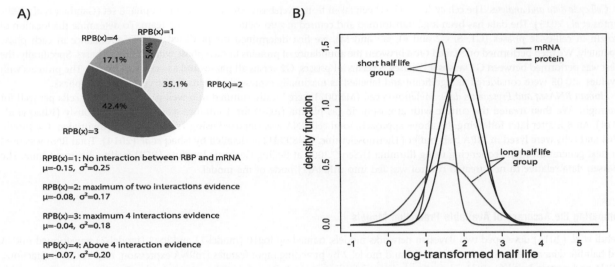

Fig. 2 Parameters learnt in Bayesian networks model. (A) Pie chart represents the probability distribution (in percentage) for RBPs to interact with mRNA. (B) Parameters of log transformed mRNA (red) and protein (black) half-life values are shown in terms of Gaussian distributions.

Table 1 Parameters learnt for PA(x) node in Bayesian networks model

Latent 2	Latent 3	μ_{PA}, σ_{PA}^2	β_{mRNA}	β_{mF}	β_{tAI}
F	F	-5.5, 0.63	-0.19	0.08	14.5
T	F	-27.5, 85.9	-1.3	0.29	62.3
F	T	-0.78, 0.04	0.12	0.02	2.6
T	T	-2.5, 0.07	0.32	0.03	7.7

Predicting Protein Abundance of Nuclear Proteins: A Case Study

This review now presents a case study by using four previously developed models to derive a correlation between RNA expression and protein abundance within the cell. Specifically, we present how to predict the abundance for the proteins typical involve in cell differentiation. Because multiple diseases including various cancers are associated with cell cycle related proteins (Otto and Sicinski, 2017), therefore, our case study will explore to what extent the nuclear proteins can be quantified in each phase of cell cycle. We also investigate how best a yeast-trained model can predict protein abundance in a human cancer cell line.

Data Resources to Develop Models

Experimental protein abundance data: In this case study, we used four experimental protein abundance datasets labelled as S1, S2, S3 and S4 (see "Relevant Websites section" to data access). The data source S1 is taken from the studies of Ghaemmaghami et al. (2003). The data sources S2 and S3 are taken from the study of Newman et al. (2006). The data source S4 is taken from the study of Lee et al. (2011).

Nuclear protein localization: Huh et al. (2003), classified proteins into 22 distinct localization in S. cerevisiae. 1434 of these were found to be either localized into nucleus or nucleolus. We downloaded the list of these open reading frames (ORFs) from Yeast GFP fusion localization database (see "Relevant Websites section") to define nuclear proteins.

mRNA expression data: The mRNA expression values of two large-scale datasets from the study of Ingolia and colleagues and Wang and colleagues have been averaged as described by Mehdi and colleagues are used in the case study (Wang et al., 2002; Ingolia et al., 2009). The final mRNA expression data was log-transformed prior to be used in the prediction model.

tRNA adaptation index: The tRNA adaptation index values that has been previously constructed by Mehdi and colleagues has been used in the case study (Mehdi et al., 2014).

Half-life values of transcript and protein: The half-life values (for both transcript and protein) were taken from the study of Shalem and colleagues and Belle and colleagues are used (Belle et al., 2006; Shalem et al., 2008). These half-life values were log-transformed before applying to the available models (where required).

mRNA folding energy and interaction data: The mRNA folding energy values were constructed by using the averaged PARS (parallel analysis of RNA structure) values available through the study of Kertesz et al. (2010). The mRNA-RNA binding proteins interaction data was taken from the research of Hogan et al. (2008).

Cell cycle data and analyses: The cell cycle data has been taken from Cyclebase, referred to Pramila-alpha38 set (Gauthier *et al.*, 2008; Santos *et al.*, 2015). The data has been log2 transformed and centred at zero values by Cyclebase team. To determine the location of protein in cell-cycle phases (G1, S, G2 and M, G2 and M), we first determined the predicted protein abundance in each phase separately. We then performed one-tailed t-test between the abundance of proteins in each phase with all other phases. Specifically, the t-test was performed between G1 versus all phases, S versus all phases, G2 versus all phases and M versus all phases. The proteins with p-values <0.05 were considered as significant and labelled as maximally expressed proteins in the corresponding phase.

Human RNAseq and Proteomics data: Melanoma cell (Mel007) were locally cultured in 6-well plates at 5×10^5 cells per well for overnight. We then treated the culture with atmospheric gas plasma (AGP) for 3 minutes as described previously (Ishaq *et al.*, 2014). An 8 h after later following the above approach, total cell RNA was extracted using Trizole reagent (Invitrogen, C#15596-026) and cells were lysed in RIPA lysis buffer (Thermoscientific, C#89901) as detailed by Ishaq *et al.* (2014). Total RNA was used for next generation RNA sequencing using Illumina HiSeq™2000 at Beijing Genomic Institute (BGI) facility, Beijing, China. The RNAseq data relative to non-treated control was fed into mRNA(x) node of the model.

Comparing the Accuracy of Available Prediction Models

Mehdi *et al.* (2014) developed two Bayesian networks models, trained on log10 (model-1) and log2 (model-2) transformed mRNA and half-life data respectively. We ran model-1 and model-2 by providing input features (mRNA expression, mRNA-RBP interactions, mRNA and protein half-life, tRNA adaptation index and folding energy). One of the advantages of using Bayesian networks model is its capability to deal with missing values. Therefore, there were many instances where the proteins have more than one missing values while predicting their abundance, therefore the nodes corresponding to missing values were unspecified. To find the correlation between predicted and actual protein abundance of nuclear proteins, we determined the Pearson and Spearman rank correlation coefficients. These correlation coefficients have been used to study protein abundance in several previous studies (Tuller *et al.*, 2007; Zur and Tuller, 2012). In practice, the Pearson correlation assumes a linear relationship between predicted and actual protein abundance. Spearman rank correlation is the non-parametric way of finding the Pearson correlation and is more useful where the strength of direction of two variables (predicted and actual protein abundance) is required. Spearman rank correlation determines if there is a monotonic relationship between predicted and actual protein abundance.

We used both models (model-1 and model-2) to determine the abundance of nuclear proteins. To determine the accuracy of the model, we used four protein abundance sources S1-S4, as described in Data Resources section to correlate with the predicted protein abundance. The correlation values (Spearman rank, Pearson) along with p-values are shown in **Table 2**.

The scatter plots in **Fig. 3(A–D)** shows the predicted protein abundance values (using model-1) and four experimental protein abundance datasets (S1-S4) along with Pearson correlation values. The scatter plot in **Fig. 3(E–H)** shows the correlation between predicted protein abundance (model-2) and actual protein abundance remain similar to that of model-1. Correlation using both methods are highly significant (*p-val* $<<0.0001$) and comparable. Thus, we displayed Pearson correlation in the **Fig. 3**. **Table 2** shows that highest correlation was found for protein abundance sources S2 and S3 (Pearson correlation, $r>0.7$). Sources S2 and S3 are generated under rich and minimal medium growth conditions respectively, thus representing that nuclear protein abundances are not affected by change in the medium. Sources S1 and S4 also showed high correlations ($r=0.62$ and 0.64 for data source S1 and 0.58 and 0.59 for data source S4) however lower than S2 and S3.

We also compared our predictions with the two models (Tuller-1 and Tuller-2) of Tuller *et al.* (2007) and the results are shown in **Table 2**. We found that the correlation values of protein abundance models of Tuller and colleagues are slightly higher than the

Table 2   Pearson and Spearman rank correlation values of predicted and actual protein abundance

Data source	Model	Pearson correlation	p-values	Spearman rank correlation	p-values
S1	Model-1	0.62	2.2×10^{-135}	0.62	2.2×10^{-134}
S2		0.71	5.8×10^{-124}	0.68	4.5×10^{-109}
S3		0.72	5.1×10^{-120}	0.66	3.7×10^{-95}
S4		0.59	2.5×10^{-69}	0.70	1.1×10^{-105}
S1	Model-2	0.64	6.9×10^{-146}	0.64	6.2×10^{-145}
S2		0.72	6.2×10^{-129}	0.69	2.7×10^{-113}
S3		0.72	3.3×10^{-123}	0.67	4.9×10^{-98}
S4		0.59	5.4×10^{-70}	0.69	2.3×10^{-104}
S1	Tuller-1	0.68	1.3×10^{-103}	0.68	2.7×10^{-102}
S2		0.74	2.2×10^{-83}	0.72	6.0×10^{-77}
S3		0.73	4.4×10^{-76}	0.70	1.6×10^{-65}
S4		0.64	1.7×10^{-50}	0.68	0.0×10^{00}
S1	Tuller-2	0.68	8.7×10^{-105}	0.68	1.4×10^{-102}
S2		0.75	6.6×10^{-86}	0.73	1.5×10^{-78}
S3		0.73	1.0×10^{-75}	0.69	6.8×10^{-65}
S4		0.64	1.3×10^{-50}	0.68	0.0×10^{00}

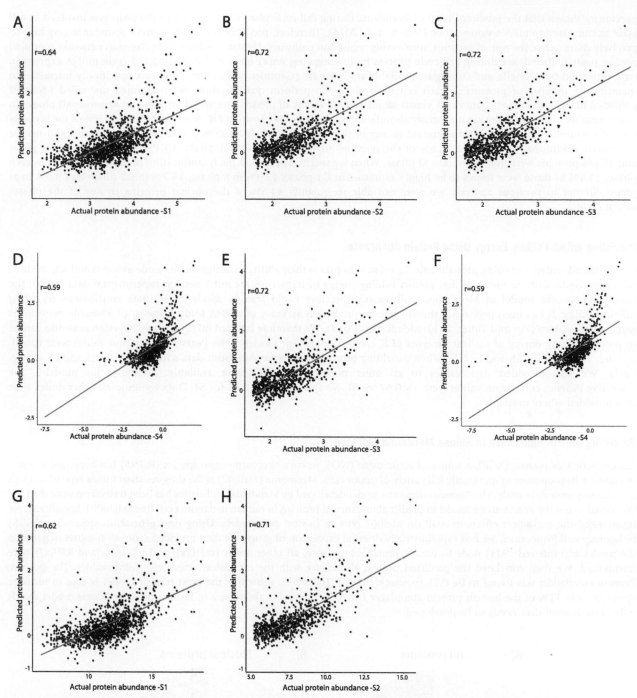

Fig. 3 Correlation of actual and predicted protein abundance using model-1 (A–D) and model-2 (E–H). Pearson correlation coefficient and linear fit is also shown.

models of Mehdi and colleagues. Highest Pearson correlation, $r = 0.74$ (Tuller-1) and $r = 0.75$ (Tuller-2) were found by correlating their protein abundance with S2 data source. Because the models of Tuller and colleagues are not capable to run on data with missing values, their model operated only on 703 (out of 1434) ORFs to determine the protein abundance thus we believe that the models of Mehdi *et al.*, are quite useful to predict protein abundance in practice and accuracy of prediction is not significantly compromised.

Predicting Abundance of Nuclear Proteins in Cell-Cycle Phases

The models of Mehdi and colleagues are capable of operating under condition variant stages such as cell cycle process. Perturbations in cell cycle can result in cellular death leading to various diseases including cancer. It has been previously shown that the predicted protein abundance during cell cycle phases better explains the processes involved in cell cycle as compared to mRNA values alone (Mehdi *et al.*, 2014). Therefore, predicting cell-cycle protein abundance may help to precisely characterize the role of proteins, uncovering regulation pathways. Here we evaluated the Bayesian networks model to predict protein abundance during cell-cycle process by investigating PA(x) node and providing cell-cycle mRNA expression data generated by Permella and colleagues available at Cyclebase (Gauthier *et al.*, 2008). We were specifically interested to quantify the number of proteins in each cell cycle phase. To perform quantification, we performed one-tailed t-tests of predicted protein abundance data in G1 versus all phases, G2 versus all phases, S versus all phases and M versus all phases to count number of proteins that are maximally abundant in each phase. As shown in **Fig. 4**, we found that 41.8% of the proteins were not found to be significantly abundant in any of the phases and their location inside cell-cycle phases could not be uncovered. Additionally, we found 16.6% of the proteins are associated with G1 phase, 15.4% S-phase, 15.5% G2 phase and 10.6% proteins were quantified into M phase. When we specifically looked the quantification of nuclear proteins in each phase, 13.4% of those were found to be highly expressed in G1 phase, 17.9% in S phase, 14.7% in G2 phase and 9.5% in M phase. Similar to previous analysis, we were not able to quantify 44.5% of the nuclear proteins in any of the phases of cell cycle.

Predicting mRNA Folding Energy Using Protein Abundance

One of the advantages of using probabilistic Bayesian networks is their ability to designate any node as input and any node as an output node. Current methods that predict folding energy of transcripts are not based on experimental data (except the Bayesian networks model of Mehdi and colleagues), therefore could lead in making inaccurate conclusions regarding mRNA folding. It has been previously shown that the prediction accuracy of mRNA folding energy of available methods is worse than random (Zur and Tuller, 2012; Mehdi *et al.*, 2014). We therefore inferred mF(x) node of Bayesian networks model to predict folding energy of nuclear proteins of *S. cerevisiae* data. For model-1, the Pearson correlation values were found; $r=0.62$, $r=0.57$, $r=0.58$ and $r=0.55$ when providing protein abundance data from data sources S1, S2, S3 and S4 respectively. We also provided data values to all other nodes of model where available. Similarly, for model-2, the respective Pearson correlation values were; $r=0.67$ for S1, S2 and S3 and $r=0.65$ for S4. Data values to all other nodes were also provided where available.

Predicting Protein Abundance in Human Melanoma Cell Line

Atmospheric Gas plasma (AGP), a source of nitric oxide (NO), reactive oxygen/nitrogen species (RONS) has been under investigation for its properties to specifically kill variety of tumor cells. Melanoma (Mel007) is the drug-resistant tumor type which lack genome sequence data study. The Bayesian networks model developed by Mehdi and colleagues has been trained on yeast data set. We aimed to test the yeast trained model to predict abundance of proteins in human melanoma cell line (Mel007). Specifically, we investigated the anticancer effects of AGP on Mel007 cells in in-vitro cell models. Using next generation sequencing (NGS) technology and Proteomics, we first experimentally detected expression of genes. We then provided expression values of genes to the model and inferred PA(x) node to predict protein abundance, all other nodes (mHL(x), pHL(x), tAI(x)and RBP(x)) were unspecified. We then correlated the predicted protein abundance with the expression actual expression values. The positive Pearson correlation was found to be 0.11 (*p-value* < <0.01). The results show that the yeast trained model is able to measure approximately 11% of the human protein abundance correctly. To predict abundance of human proteins, a new model that is trained on human data needs to be developed.

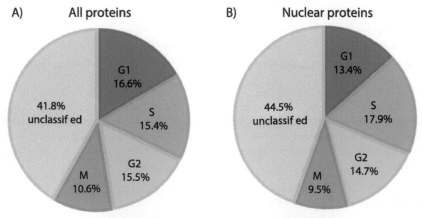

Fig. 4 Quantification of proteins in all phase of cell cycle. (A) Percentage of proteins in each phase is shown for all data. (B) Quantification for nuclear proteins in each cell-cycle shown.

Conclusions

While a number of different features have been shown to be associated with protein abundance, the available methods use very few of them. The models of Tuller and colleagues use mRNA expression, relative tRNA abundance and evolutionary rates. The models of Mehdi and colleagues use mRNA expression, relative tRNA abundance, mRNA folding energy, RBP and mRNA interactions, half-life values of transcripts and proteins. The reason for using fewer variables amongst the all determinants of protein abundance could possible because of (i) availability of an insufficient data to use them in developing models, (ii) the association between these variables and protein abundance further require experimental validations.

In this review, we presented a case study by using probabilistic Bayesian networks models developed by Mehdi and colleagues and linear regression models developed by Tuller and colleagues. The models of Mehdi and colleagues link transcriptional information with protein translation and predicts protein abundance. Their models help to understand how the transcript expressions are linked with its folding and interaction with RBPs, codon usage, half-life of ORFs and protein abundance. We have particularly shown how best their models predict abundance of nuclear proteins in *S. cerevisiae* and human melanoma cell line (Mel007).

We note that the models of Tuller and colleagues use additional information of evolutionary rate. Additionally, the inability to operate on missing value data makes them less important. The quantification of proteins in each phase of cell cycle can be performed using predicted protein abundance. We have also reviewed how the available prediction models can be used to predict mRNA folding energy. For example, when correlating predicted and experimental mRNA folding energy by using models of Mehdi and colleagues, we found a maximum Pearson correlation of only 0.67, challenging further research in this area.

See also: Analyzing Transcriptome-Phenotype Correlations. Characterization of Transcriptional Activities. Comparative Transcriptomics Analysis. Genome-Wide Scanning of Gene Expression. Introduction to Biostatistics. Natural Language Processing Approaches in Bioinformatics. Regulation of Gene Expression. Survey of Antisense Transcription. Transcriptome Analysis. Transcriptome During Cell Differentiation

References

Belle, A., Tanay, A., Bitincka, L., Shamir, R., O'Shea, E.K., 2006. Quantification of protein half-lives in the budding yeast proteome. Proc. Natl. Acad. Sci. USA 103 (35), 13004–13009.

Blokzijl, A., Friedman, M., Ponten, F., Landegren, U., 2010. Profiling protein expression and interactions: Proximity ligation as a tool for personalized medicine. J. Intern. Med. 268 (3), 232–245.

Ferrier, C.M., de Witte, H.H., Straatman, H., et al., 1999. Comparison of immunohistochemistry with immunoassay (ELISA) for the detection of components of the plasminogen activation system in human tumour tissue. Br. J. Cancer 79 (9–10), 1534–1541.

Ford, K.G., Souberbielle, B.E., Darling, D., Farzaneh, F., 2001. Protein transduction: An alternative to genetic intervention? Gene Ther. 8 (1), 1–4.

Fromm, J.R., Thomas, A., Wood, B.L., 2009. Flow cytometry can diagnose classical hodgkin lymphoma in lymph nodes with high sensitivity and specificity. Am. J. Clin. Pathol. 131 (3), 322–332.

Gauthier, N.P., Larsen, M.E., Wernersson, R., et al., 2008. Cyclebase.org – A comprehensive multi-organism online database of cell-cycle experiments. Nucleic Acids Res. 36 (Database issue), D854–D859.

Ghaemmaghami, S., Huh, W.K., Bower, K., et al., 2003. Global analysis of protein expression in yeast. Nature 425 (6959), 737–741.

Greenbaum, D., Colangelo, C., Williams, K., Gerstein, M., 2003. Comparing protein abundance and mRNA expression levels on a genomic scale. Genome Biol. 4 (9), 117.

Ilogan, D.J., Riordan, D.P., Gerber, A.P., Herschlag, D., Brown, P.O., 2008. Diverse RNA-binding proteins interact with functionally related sets of RNAs, suggesting an extensive regulatory system. PLOS Biol. 6 (10), e255.

Huh, W.K., Falvo, J.V., Gerke, L.C., et al., 2003. Global analysis of protein localization in budding yeast. Nature 425 (6959), 686–691.

Ingolia, N.T., Ghaemmaghami, S., Newman, J.R., Weissman, J.S., 2009. Genome-wide analysis in vivo of translation with nucleotide resolution using ribosome profiling. Science 324 (5924), 218–223.

Ingvarsson, J., Wingren, C., Carlsson, A., et al., 2008. Detection of pancreatic cancer using antibody microarray-based serum protein profiling. Proteomics 8 (11), 2211–2219.

Ishaq, M., Evans, M.D., Ostrikov, K.K., 2014. Atmospheric pressure gas plasma-induced colorectal cancer cell death is mediated by Nox2-ASK1 apoptosis pathways and oxidative stress is mitigated by Srx-Nrf2 anti-oxidant system. Biochim. Biophys. Acta 1843 (12), 2827–2837.

Ishaq, M., Kumar, S., Varinli, H., 2014. Atmospheric gas plasma-induced ROS production activates TNF-ASK1 pathway for the induction of melanoma cancer cell apoptosis. Mol. Biol. Cell 25 (9), 1523–1531.

Kertesz, M., Wan, Y., Mazor, E., et al., 2010. Genome-wide measurement of RNA secondary structure in yeast. Nature 467 (7311), 103–107.

Koussounadis, A., Langdon, S.P., Um, I.H., Harrison, D.J., Smith, V.A., 2015. Relationship between differentially expressed mRNA and mRNA-protein correlations in a xenograft model system. Sci. Rep. 5, 10775.

Kumar, A., Agarwal, S., Heyman, J.A., et al., 2002. Subcellular localization of the yeast proteome. Genes Dev. 16 (6), 707–719.

Lahtvee, P.J., Sanchez, B.J., Smialowska, A., et al., 2017. Absolute quantification of protein and mRNA abundances demonstrate variability in gene-specific translation efficiency in yeast. Cell Syst. 4 (5), 495–504. e495.

Lee, M.V., Topper, S.E., Hubler, S.L., et al., 2011. A dynamic model of proteome changes reveals new roles for transcript alteration in yeast. Mol. Syst. Biol. 7, 514.

Leu, K., Obermayer, B., Rajamani, S., Gerland, U., Chen, I.A., 2011. The prebiotic evolutionary advantage of transferring genetic information from RNA to DNA. Nucleic Acids Res. 39 (18), 8135–8147.

Mehdi, A.M., Patrick, R., Bailey, T.L., Boden, M., 2014. Predicting the dynamics of protein abundance. Mol. Cell Proteom. 13 (5), 1330–1340.

Newman, J.R., Ghaemmaghami, S., Ihmels, J., et al., 2006. Single-cell proteomic analysis of S. cerevisiae reveals the architecture of biological noise. Nature 441 (7095), 840–846.

Otto, T., Sicinski, P., 2017. Cell cycle proteins as promising targets in cancer therapy. Nat. Rev. Cancer 17 (2), 93–115.

Powers, A.D., Palecek, S.P., 2012. Protein analytical assays for diagnosing, monitoring, and choosing treatment for cancer patients. J. Healthc. Eng. 3 (4), 503–534.

Roeder, R.G., 1996. Nuclear RNA polymerases: Role of general initiation factors and cofactors in eukaryotic transcription. Methods Enzymol. 273, 165–171.

Santos, A., Wernersson, R., Jensen, L.J., 2015. Cyclebase 3.0: A multi-organism database on cell-cycle regulation and phenotypes. Nucleic Acids Res. 43 (Database issue), D1140–D1144.

Shah, P., Gilchrist, M.A., 2010. Effect of correlated tRNA abundances on translation errors and evolution of codon usage bias. PLOS Genet. 6 (9), e1001128.

Shalem, O., Dahan, O., Levo, M., et al., 2008. Transient transcriptional responses to stress are generated by opposing effects of mRNA production and degradation. Mol. Syst. Biol. 4, 223.

Steen, H., Pandey, A., 2002. Proteomics goes quantitative: Measuring protein abundance. Trends Biotechnol. 20 (9), 361–364.

Tuller, T., Kupiec, M., Ruppin, E., 2007. Determinants of protein abundance and translation efficiency in S. cerevisiae. PLOS Comput. Biol. 3 (12), e248.

Vlahou, A., Laronga, C., Wilson, L., et al., 2003. A novel approach toward development of a rapid blood test for breast cancer. Clin. Breast Cancer 4 (3), 203–209.

Wang, Y., Liu, C.L., Storey, J.D., et al., 2002. Precision and functional specificity in mRNA decay. Proc. Natl. Acad. Sci. USA 99 (9), 5860–5865.

Yaziji, H., Taylor, C.R., Goldstein, N.S., et al., 2008. Consensus recommendations on estrogen receptor testing in breast cancer by immunohistochemistry. Appl. Immunohistochem. Mol. Morphol. 16 (6), 513–520.

Yilmaz, A., Grotewold, E., 2010. Components and mechanisms of regulation of gene expression. Methods Mol. Biol. 674, 23–32.

Yu, E.Z., Burba, A.E., Gerstein, M., 2007. PARE: A tool for comparing protein abundance and mRNA expression data. BMC Bioinform. 8, 309.

Zhu, J., Zhang, B., Smith, E.N., et al., 2008. Integrating large-scale functional genomic data to dissect the complexity of yeast regulatory networks. Nat. Genet. 40 (7), 854–861.

Zur, H., Tuller, T., 2012. Strong association between mRNA folding strength and protein abundance in S. cerevisiae. EMBO Rep. 13 (3), 272–277.

Relevant Websites

https://cloudstor.aarnet.edu.au/plus/s/2R07zzIguoR8lrn
    Data Resources and Bayesian Network models used in case study.
https://yeastgfp.yeastgenome.org
    Yeast GFP Fusion Localization Database.

Identification of Proteins From Proteomic Analysis

Zainab Noor, Abidali Mohamedali, and Shoba Ranganathan, Macquarie University, Sydney, NSW, Australia

Introduction

The identification of proteins in a biological system is one of the cornerstones of the study of biological systems. Proteins are biopolymers (polypeptides) transcribed from DNA, made up of a set of 20 amino acids and are the functional elements in a biological system. The combinations of these amino acids in a sequence gives rise to each proteins' unique shape, structure and hence function. In addition, in higher pro- and eu-karyotes, these polypeptides can be modified post-translationally (PTMs) to form even more complex structures and functions (Ngounou Wetie *et al.*, 2014). Indeed, most PTM's have given rise to their own fields of study such as glycomics (sugar polymers on polypeptides), phosphoproteomics (phosphate molecules attached to amino acids), among others. Proteins can be identified in one of two ways: i) through their structure and shape – usually performed by tagged antibodies (Kingsmore, 2006) or ii) by sequencing the protein- usually done by mass spectrometry (MS). Often, proteins identified by MS are validated using an antibody approach to ensure the accuracy of identification especially in critical applications such as biomarker discovery (Lindskog, 2015; Marx, 2013). After the discovery of human genome profile, both, antibody and MS-based techniques have been utilized to create the map of the human proteome, e.g. Human Protein Atlas (Uhlen *et al.*, 2015) and Human Proteome Map (Kim *et al.*, 2014), respectively. This article will focus on protein identification by mass spectrometry.

Mass Spectrometry Strategies

There are two different strategies for the identification of proteins using MS, 'Bottom-up' proteomics or 'Top-down' proteomics. In the bottom-up method, proteins are digested into smaller sized peptides prior to ionization and mass analysis and consequently reassembled *in silico* to infer identity. This strategy is highly advantageous in case of complex samples of abundant proteins that require efficient and sensitive separation. In the top-down method, proteins are subjected to ionization and fragmentation in the intact form without digestion and passed through mass analysers often in tandem. This method determines the complete characterization of protein isoforms and post-translational modifications for small to medium-sized proteins. Both of these strategies can be employed for protein identification depending upon the size and nature of target protein.

Mass Spectrometry-Based Protein Identification

Protein characterization and identification by MS can be performed using various approaches (see **Fig. 1**). More commonly, data is acquired in 'Data Dependent Acquisition (DDA)' mode, which is also known as shotgun or discovery proteomics, to identify which proteins/peptides are present in the sample. In this approach, after passing through the first mass analyzer (MS1), only the fixed number of most abundant ions are selected and get fragmented into product ions and analysed in the second analyzer (MS2) (see **Fig. 2**). A further two approaches, mainly used for quantification and identification of less abundant proteins, are 'Targeted Proteomics (MRM- Multiple Reaction Monitoring or SRM- Selected Reaction Monitoring and PRM- Parallel Reaction Monitoring)' and 'Data Independent Acquisition (DIA)' to perform targeted examination where proteins of interest, identified in discovery mode, are analysed for their abundance (relative or absolute) in a particular sample (see **Fig. 2**). The basic working mechanism of these techniques is illustrated in **Fig. 2**.

The identification of proteins in the last two decades has taken a significant leap and use of MS is exponentially increasing the understanding of things as diverse as truffles (Islam *et al.*, 2013) to the discovery of biomarkers in disease (Domon and Aebersold, 2006). This article focuses on the brief understanding of MS data generation, and detailed overview of MS data analysis procedures and, the tools and methods that can be applied at each step.

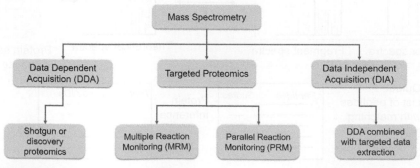

Fig. 1 Commonly used approaches in mass spectrometry (MS).

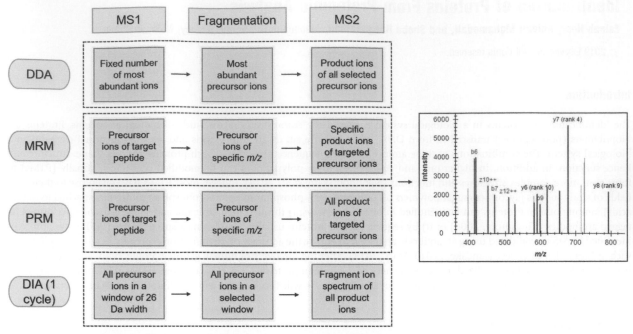

Fig. 2 Working mechanisms of MS-based approaches for protein identification and quantification.

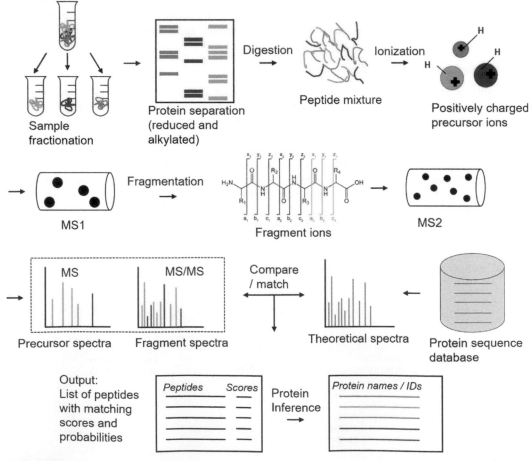

Fig. 3 Workflow of MS-based protein identification.

Sample Preparation

The MS procedure starts with the sample collection and purification of proteins. Complex mixtures are often fractionated or separated using some form of chromatography (Gel electrophoresis, ion exchange etc.). The cysteine residues are then alkylated and reduced (resulting in the oxidation of methionine residues as well as carbamylation of lysine residues) (Herbert *et al.*, 2003), which results in the formation linear polypeptides.

The complex mixture of polypeptides undergoes the process of digestion more often using trypsin that cleaves the proteins at lysine or arginine residues (Huynh *et al.*, 2009) (see **Fig. 3**). Digestion using trypsin alone may have certain limitations and has been found to be less efficient for membrane proteins and post-translational modification (PTM) sites. To overcome this problem, proteases, such as chymotrypsin, LysC, LysN, AspN, GluC and ArgC (Giansanti *et al.*, 2016), have been analysed in parallel with trypsin and are shown to be effective in the MS analysis of large-size proteins (Low *et al.*, 2013; Benevento *et al.*, 2014; Gauci *et al.*, 2009). Similarly, *in silico* proteolytic digestion is also performed using computational tools with the same enzyme as used in the sample preparation to generate the theoretical spectral profile of the protein. Software programs such as PeptideMass (Wilkins *et al.*, 1999), PeptideCutter (Wilkins *et al.*, 1999) and Proteogest (Cagney *et al.*, 2003) perform *in silico* cleavage of polypeptides using a range of enzymes or chemical reagents to produce search or match databases.

Subsequently, the digested peptide mixture undergoes separation using chromatography and enters into the ionization source of the mass spectrometer (MS) where they are charged. The charged peptide ions traverse into the mass analyzer for separation, according to their mass to charge (*m/z*) ratios, in a vacuum environment, under the influence of electric/magnetic field (see **Fig. 3**). Not all digested peptides are able to 'fly', if they are too big, for instance.

Fragmentation

In a single-analyzer system (MS1), the separated ions generate the spectra of precursor ions when they hit a detector. In multi-analyzer systems (tandem or MS/MS), precursor ions undergo fragmentation (usually using some form of inert gas (collision induced ionization, CID)) and are converted into smaller charged fragments or product ions. The precursor ions fragment in various ways (see **Fig. 3**) to form unique daughter ions, dependent on the fragmentation method, e.g. b-y ions by Collision Induced Dissociation (CID) and c-z ions by Electron Capture Dissociation (ECD) and Electron Transfer Dissociation (ETD). The daughter or product ions are then analysed again in the mass analyzer to generate spectra (MS2) (see **Fig. 3**). For sequencing and

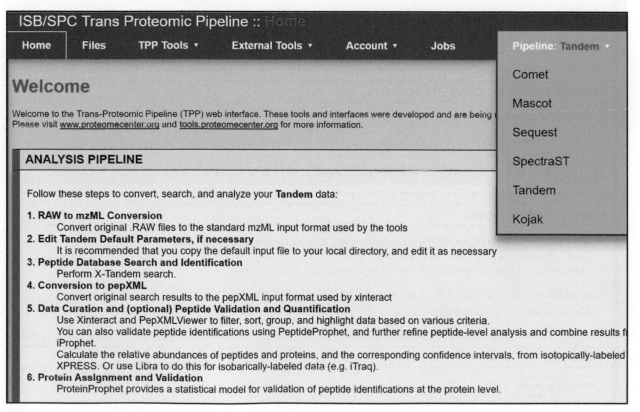

Fig. 4 Trans-proteomic pipeline software interface for proteomic identification and analysis.

identification, the precursor ions can be subjected to peptide mass finger printing (PMF) (Thiede *et al.*, 2005) or if MS2 data is also used (which is more accurate), the sequence of the precursor ions can be determined and searched against a database (described below) (see **Fig. 3**). It is also called as fragment ion spectra, produced in the raw form (details of this process can be found in a review article (Aebersold and Mann, 2003)).

Data Analysis

MS data acquisition and data analysis are performed utilising several computational tools, designed explicitly for MS-based protein identification. In this article, a sample data has been acquired through public repository to demonstrate different phases of protein identification using Trans-Proteomic pipeline (TPP) by Institute of Systems Biology (ISB) (Deutsch *et al.*, 2015). This will provide an overview of data analysis, required parameters at every stage and output of results. Additionally, The OpenMS Proteomics Pipeline (TOPP) by OpenMS (Kohlbacher *et al.*, 2007) and Central Proteomics Facilities Pipeline (CPFP) (Trudgian and Mirzaei, 2012) also maintains a compilation of bioinformatics analysis tools for MS-based proteomics. With the same parameters and guidelines, data can be analysed through standalone versions of all identification programs as well.

Sample Data Set

The raw sample data was obtained from 'fission yeast' (*Schizosaccharomyces pombe*) proteome study where ~3500 proteins (71%) of the predicted genes of yeast have been analysed using MS (Gunaratne *et al.*, 2013). The experiment was performed on nano-HPLC instrument coupled to the high-resolution Orbitrap mass spectrometer and is considered to be the largest protein dataset presented for fission yeast (Gunaratne *et al.*, 2013). The dataset is available at Peptide Atlas with the accession ID 'PAe003810'.

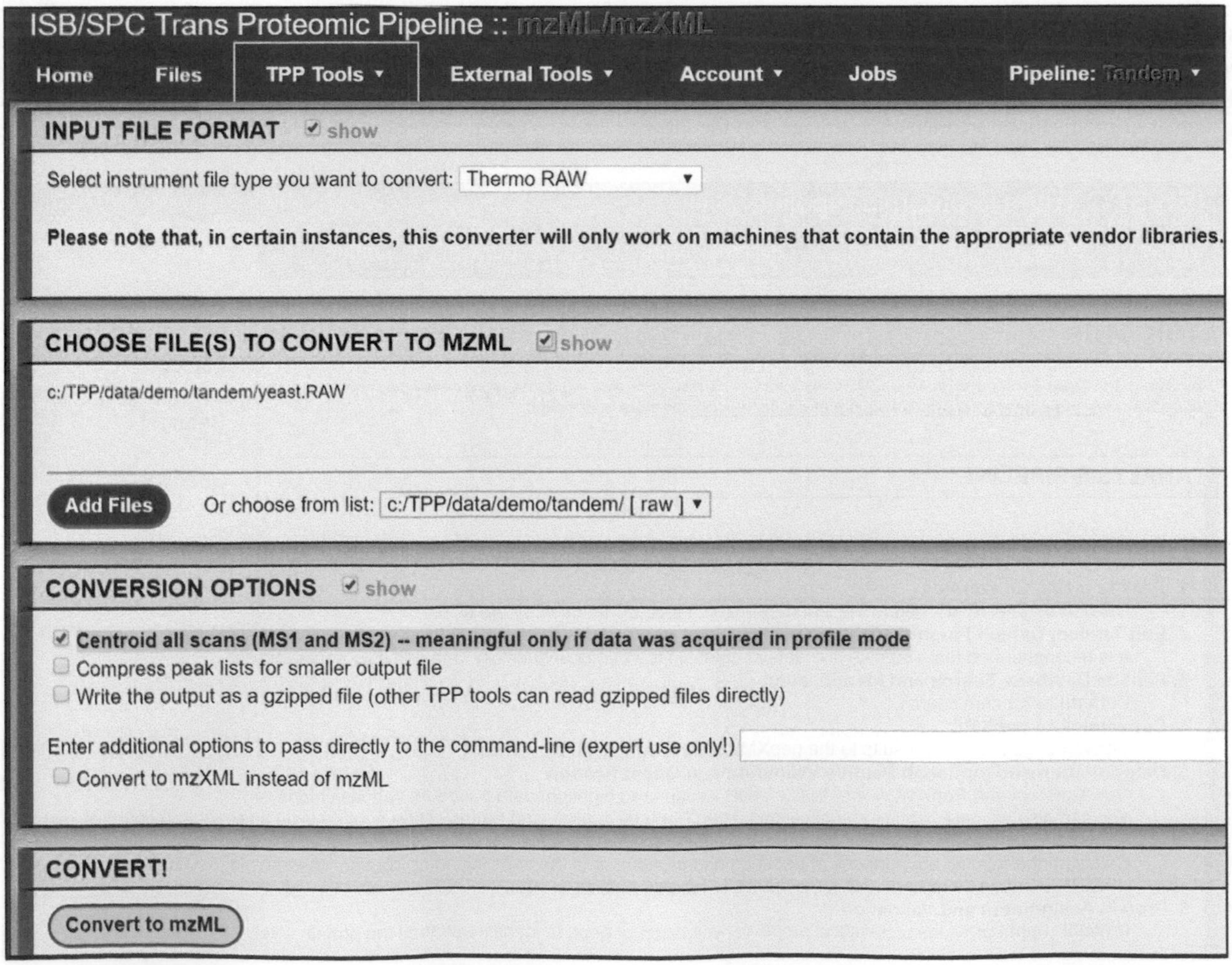

Fig. 5 Trans-proteomic pipeline data conversion module (Msconvert) and its parameters.

Computation Tools

TPP has multiple pipelines for, (i) identification through protein databases, such as Comet (Eng *et al.*, 2013), Sequest (Eng *et al.*, 2008), Tandem (Craig and Beavis, 2003) pipelines, and (ii) by means of spectral libraries, such as SpectraST (Lam *et al.*, 2007) pipeline (see **Fig. 4**). Searching through spectral libraries can also be performed through Bibliospec (Frewen and Maccoss, 2007) for comparison purposes. The sample input data (raw files), parameter files and output files can be accessed through PeptideAtlas (see Relevant Websites section) and TPP web interface can be accessed through the provided link (see Relevant Websites section).

Step 1: Data Conversion

The data which we acquire from mass spectrometry machines is in the raw form. Generally, the formats include *.wiff, *.dat, *.yep/*.baf, and *.raw from AB/Agilent, Agilent, Bruker and Thermo/Waters vendors, respectively. These data files are converted into standard data openXML formats such as mzXML, mzDATA and mzML. This can be performed through software, Mascot Distiller by ProteoWizard (Koenig *et al.*, 2008), Msconvert by ProteoWizard (Kessner *et al.*, 2008) and ReADW by Xcalibur (see Relevant Websites section). Conversion through any of these programs sets up the parameters for centroiding the MS scans, which are acquired in profile mode, also known as peak picking. Centroiding the data reduces the data points and lowers the sizes of files. In this example, data was available in raw format (*yeast.raw*) and was simply converted into mzML (*yeast.mzML*) format through Msconvert, under Tandem module of TPP, with centroiding (see **Fig. 5**).

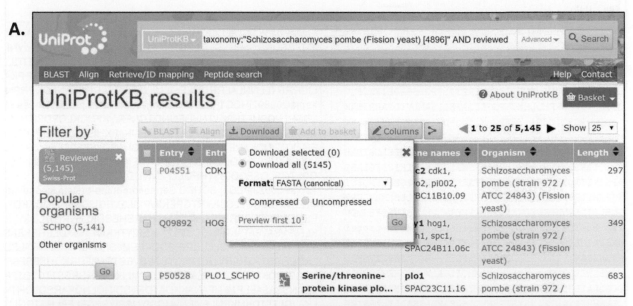

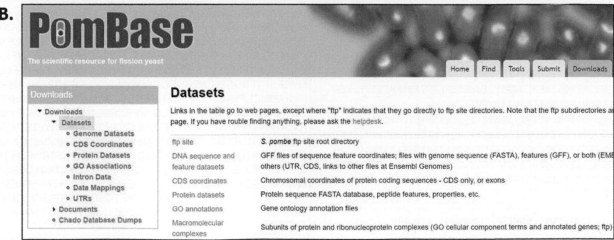

Fig. 6 Database FASTA file generation from (A) UniProt and (B) PomBase.

Step 2: Spectrum Identification

Spectrum identifications can be performed using one of three approaches, namely a database search, a spectral library search or a de-novo or hybrid search, each requiring their own properties and parameters. Identification through sequence databases entails searching against a broad list of potential proteins, which can be created or gathered from UniProt/SwissProt databases. Whereas a spectral library contains precursor mass/charge values, often obtained in one lab but is a prerequisite for identification through spectral matching.

Database search

For the fission yeast sample data, a database search is executed by Tandem, Sequest (the most common and freely available search engines) or Comet pipelines and respective search modules in TPP. The input files for the programs are:
  i. Mass spectrometry data files in mzML format, *yeast.mzML* (created in the previous step).
 ii. Tandem parameters file, *tandem.params* (available online and may be modified).
iii. Sequence database file, *yeast.fasta* (including decoys).

Tandem parameter file (*tandem.params*) contains information related to:

1. Search scoring scheme (*k-score*).
2. File locations (path to the input/output files).

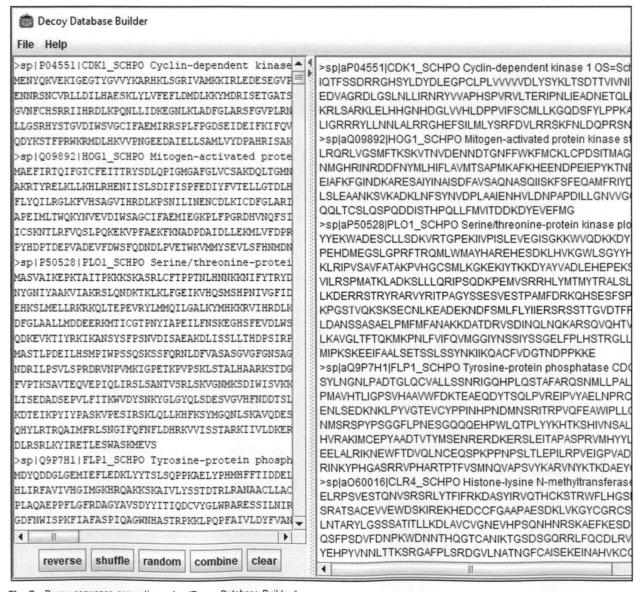

Fig. 7 Decoy sequence generation using "Decoy Database Builder."

3. Sequence database or taxonomy (name of the database file).
4. Precursor mass tolerance dependent on instrument used (default= − 2.0 to 4.0 Da).
5. Structural and isotopic modifications (according to sample run on the MS e.g. carbamidomethyl in Cysteine and/or oxidation in Methionine).
6. Peptide digestion through trypsin (fully-tryptic or semi-tryptic peptides).
7. Missed cleavages (default=2).

Parameter files for other database search software (*sequest.params* and *comet.params*) contain similar information with very few modifications and are available with the TPP, TOPP or CPFP identification pipeline.packages.

Sequence database files, usually in FASTA format (*yeast.fasta*), can be created by downloading the list of protein sequences (usually related to the target species) from UniProt (see Relevant Websites section). In this example, a single FASTA file comprising of more than 10,000 protein sequences has been formed with all the 'reviewed' proteins found against organism 'fission yeast' in UniProt and PomBase (protein sequence resource of fission yeast) (see Relevant Websites section) repositories (see **Fig. 6**). The FASTA file should also contain decoy protein sequences in order to perform statistical evaluation of peptide-spectrum match (PSM) (at a later stage) using target-decoy approach. To generate decoy sequences, several methods are available such as shifting the precursor *m/z* ratio values of *in silico* generated spectra and, randomly shuffling and reversing the database sequences (Elias and Gygi, 2010) (see **Fig. 7**). Different freely accessible programs and scripts have been developed to accomplish this task and are listed below:

1. DecoyPYrat by Sanger Institute generates a set of decoy sequences through reversing the database sequences (Wright and Choudhary, 2016). It is a python-based script 'decoyPYrate.py', can be downloaded (see Relevant Websites section) and run on Python ver. 3 or above (see Relevant Websites section).

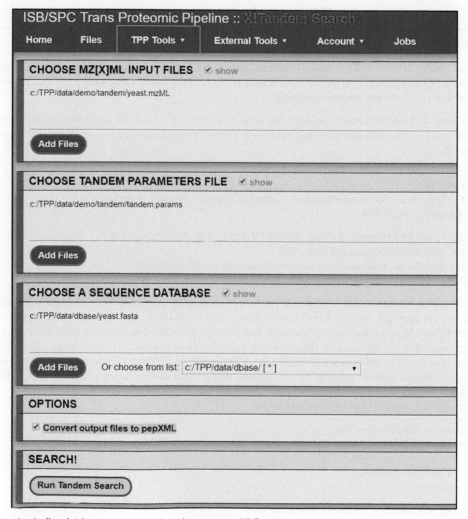

Fig. 8   Trans-proteomic pipeline database search module and parameters (X! Tandem).

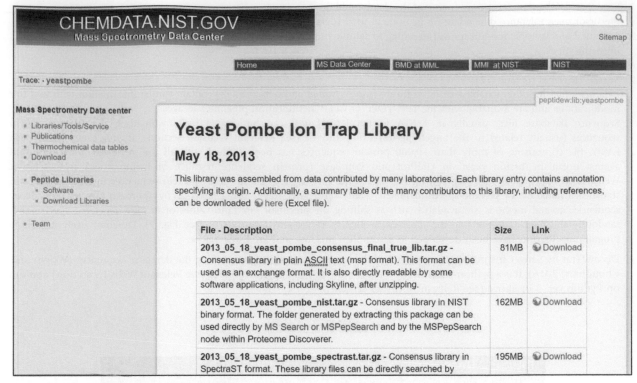

Fig. 9   Yeast spectral library from the NIST database.

2. Decoy Database Builder (DecoyDBB), a module of PeakQuant Suite, build the decoy databases by reversing, reshuffling and random generation of target protein sequences (Reidegeld *et al.*, 2008). A stand-alone version of this java-based program is available at the link (see Relevant Websites section).

X! Tandem, Sequest and Comet perform *in silico* digestion of proteins in FASTA file according to the provided parameters, generate the theoretical spectra (with precursor *m/z* values), followed by matching it to the observed spectra and calculates the search scores (see **Fig. 8**).

Spectral libraries search

Investigation of MS spectra by inquiring previously identified spectral libraries is performed by employing SpectraST search module with the following input files:

i. Mass spectrometry data files in mzML format, *yeast.mzML* (created in the previous step)
ii. Spectral libraries, *yeast.splib* (downloaded from NIST)
iii. SpectraST parameters file, *spectrast.params* (available online and can be modified)
iv. Sequence database file, *yeast.fasta* (including decoys)

Spectral libraries can be downloaded from different public repositories. These repositories contained highly-organized data for a number of species, for example, PeptideAtlas (Desiere *et al.*, 2006), SRMAtlas (Kusebauch *et al.*, 2016), ProteomeXchange (Vizcaino *et al.*, 2014), and National Institute of Standards and Technology (NIST) (see Relevant Websites section), among others. The spectral library against *S. prombe*, used in this review, is the NIST 'Yeast Pombe Ion Trap Library'. This consensus library is created using spectra generated in different scientific laboratories (Pointner *et al.*, 2012; Gunaratne *et al.*, 2013), and is available at the link (see Relevant Websites section) (see **Fig. 9**). The different data formats of spectral libraries are *.blib, *.clib, *.msp, *.sptxt, and *.splib. SpectraST usually works with libraries in the *.splib format.

SpectraST parameter file contains information related to:

1. File locations (path to input/output files)
2. Precursor *m/z* tolerance (default=3.0)
3. Structural and isotopic modifications
4. Accept/ignore the abnormal spectra
5. Peak selection options

SpectraST (see **Fig. 10**) matches the peaks in experimental and library spectra and calculates the dot product or *dotp* score (similarity measure). Values of *dotp* range from 0 to 1, where 0 means poor similarity and 1 means a perfect match.

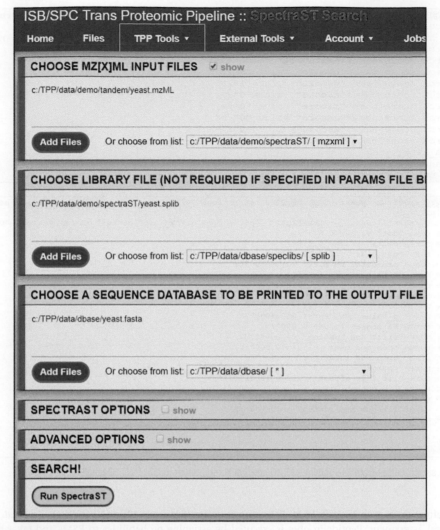

Fig. 10   Trans-proteomic pipeline spectraST search module and parameters.

Search output

The output result of both the database and spectral library search includes a *yeast.log* and a *yeast.pepXML* files, which contains the following information (see **Fig. 11**):

1. Query spectra
2. Retention time values
3. Identified peptides and their ranks
4. Search scores
5. Dot product scores (similarity significance)
6. Sensitivity and error scores

De Novo *and hybrid search approaches*

Besides database and spectral matching, *de novo* sequencing, i.e. explicit translation of spectral peaks into the sequence, and hybrid approach, i.e. a combination of database search and *de novo*, are also available but are not commonly used, only utilized in specific cases. PepNovo by Centre for Computational Mass Spectrometry (CCMS) (Frank *et al.*, 2007) and Sequit by Proteome Factory (Demine and Walden, 2004) are highly efficient and compatible tools for *de novo* sequencing. These approaches have been discussed elsewhere (Islam *et al.*, 2017b). Guten Tag by Yates Laboratory (Tabb *et al.*, 2003) and Spectral Networks by CCMS (Bandeira, 2011) are competent tools for identification of peptides through a hybrid approach.

Step 3: Peptide-Spectrum Match Statistical Validation

Peptide-spectrum match (PSM) validation is performed through PeptideProphet (Ma *et al.*, 2012), iProphet (Shteynberg *et al.*, 2011) and PTMProphet (Shteynberg *et al.*, 2012) modules of TPP which estimates the false discovery rates (FDRs) for PSMs.

A.
```
<spectrum_query spectrum="yeast.00031.00031.3" start_scan="31" end_scan="31" precursor_neutral
<search_result>
    <search_hit hit_rank="1" peptide="RFAFRHLYNTEK" peptide_prev_aa="R" peptide_next_aa="F" pro
        <search_score name="hyperscore" value="366"/>
        <search_score name="nextscore" value="355"/>
        <search_score name="bscore" value="0"/>
        <search_score name="yscore" value="1"/>
        <search_score name="cscore" value="0"/>
        <search_score name="zscore" value="0"/>
        <search_score name="ascore" value="0"/>
        <search_score name="xscore" value="0"/>
        <search_score name="expect" value="3.7"/>
    </search_hit>
</search_result>
</spectrum_query>
```

B.
```
<spectrum_query spectrum="yeast.02301.02301.2" start_scan="02301" end_scan="02301" precursor_neutral_mass="1146
<search_result>
<search_hit hit_rank="1" peptide="LVNHFIQEF" peptide_prev_aa="R" peptide_next_aa="K" protein="UniRef100_O59855"
<search_score name="dot" value="0.877"/>
<search_score name="delta" value="0.578"/>
<search_score name="dot_bias" value="0.000"/>
<search_score name="precursor_mz_diff" value="0.706"/>
<search_score name="hits_num" value="661"/>
<search_score name="hits_mean" value="0.096"/>
<search_score name="hits_stdev" value="0.062"/>
<search_score name="fval" value="0.790"/>
<search_score name="p_value" value="-1.000e+000"/>
<search_score name="KS_score" value="0.000"/>
<search_score name="first_non_homolog" value="2"/>
<search_score name="open_mod_mass" value="0.000"/>
<search_score name="open_mod_locations" value=""/>
<search_score name="charge" value="2"/>
<search_score name="lib_file_offset" value="168221077"/>
<search_score name="lib_probability" value="0.9910"/>
<search_score name="lib_status" value="Normal"/>
<search_score name="lib_num_replicates" value="3"/>
<search_score name="lib_remark" value="_NONE_"/>
</search_hit>
</search_result>
</spectrum_query>
```

Fig. 11   (A) Database search output from X! Tandem and (B) spectral library search output from SpectraST.

Additionally, standalone tools such as Scaffold by Proteome Software (Searle, 2010) and MAYU (Reiter *et al.*, 2009) can also be used for the statistical assessment. PeptideProphet is executed by assigning probabilities to PSMs and takes *yeast.pepXML* search output files as input. It takes into account the entire search score profile from pepXML files against correct and incorrect peptides and generates a 'correct match' probability for each result. On the TPP web interface, the program can be found in the 'Analyze Peptides' section of TPP tools (see **Fig. 12**) and run either in default mode or with other advanced options available for PeptideProphet such as considering pI information, phosphorylation or other PTMs information, and spectra RT values, among others. To filter out the correct identified peptides, significance level or 'PeptideProphet probability' is set to 0.05 (i.e. the probability of a peptide to be selected as correct by chance is less than 0.05) and minimum length of peptide is set to seven (7).

The output files generated by running PeptideProphet, on both Tandem and SpectraST files, are usually saved with the name *interact.pepXML*. These files comprise of statistical evaluation values for each of the peptides along with the peptide sequences and protein names from the protein sequence database file (*yeast.fasta*). The list of all the validated peptides can be viewed in TPP interface in tabular form where it can be sorted in a number of ways such as by probability, dot product values, protein names and *m/z* values (see **Fig. 13**). The peptides with the probability score close to 1 are most likely to be correct.

The program iProphet or interProphet performs the statistical refinement of the PeptideProphet results. It takes the *interact. pepXML* files as input and generates *interact.ipro.pepXML* files with the refined probability score (see **Fig. 13**), also called as 'iprob' and can be analysed in a similar way as PeptideProphet results. The files, *interact.pepXML* and *interact.ipro.pepXML*, can also be viewed in other text format programs for a detailed overview.

Step 4: Protein Inference and Validation

In order to correctly infer the protein identity using the identified peptides, which were actually present in the sample, is a highly extensive task. The presence of a single peptide sequence in multiple proteins complicates the process and needs a comprehensive statistical assessment. Most commonly programs used to accomplish this task are DTASelect (Tabb *et al.*, 2002), DBParser by Mascot Distiller (Yang *et al.*, 2004), Scaffold by Proteome Software (Searle, 2010) and ProteinProphet (Nesvizhskii *et al.*, 2003) by TPP. In

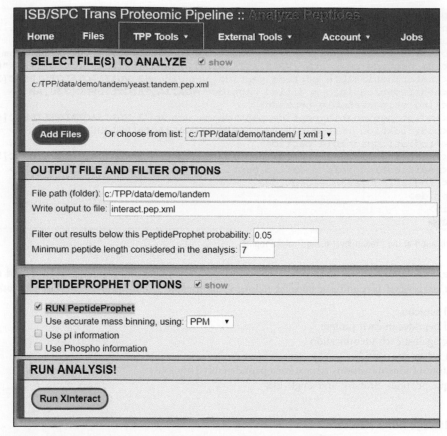

Fig. 12 Statistical validation of identified peptides using trans-proteomic pipeline "analyze peptides" module.

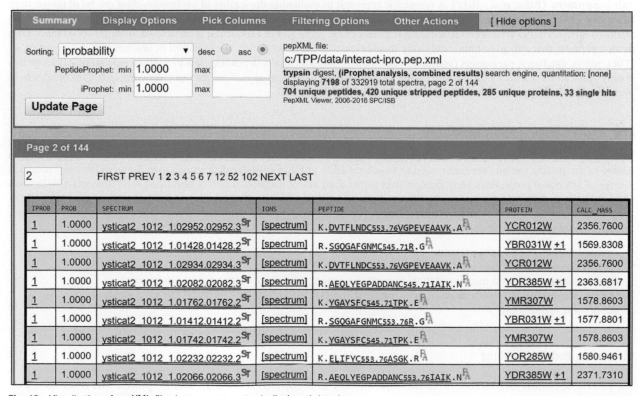

Fig. 13 Visualization of pepXML files in trans-proteomic pipeline's web interface.

```
<protein_group group_number="369" probability="0.9954">
    <protein protein_name="YML123C" n_indistinguishable_proteins="1" probability="0.9954"
        <parameter name="prot_length" value="588"/>
        <annotation protein_description="PHO84 SGDID:S000004592, Chr XIII from 25801-24038
        <peptide peptide_sequence="VGAIIAQTALGTLIDHNCAR" initial_probability="0.9990" nsp_
            <indistinguishable_peptide peptide_sequence="3_VGAIIAQTALGTLIDHNC[330]AR" char
            <modification_info modified_peptide="VGAIIAQTALGTLIDHNC[330]AR"/>
            </indistinguishable_peptide>
            <indistinguishable_peptide peptide_sequence="3_VGAIIAQTALGTLIDHNC[546]AR" char
            <modification_info modified_peptide="VGAIIAQTALGTLIDHNC[546]AR"/>
            </indistinguishable_peptide>
            <indistinguishable_peptide peptide_sequence="3_VGAIIAQTALGTLIDHNC[554]AR" char
            <modification_info modified_peptide="VGAIIAQTALGTLIDHNC[554]AR"/>
            </indistinguishable_peptide>
        </peptide>
    </protein>
</protein_group>
```

Fig. 14   Statistical validation at the protein level using ProteinProphet.

the current example, ProteinProphet was used which utilizes the statistical values and peptide/protein related data from *interact. pepXML* and *interact.ipro.pepXML* files and generates the following information in a file called as *interact.ipro.protXML* (see **Fig. 14**):

1. List of identified proteins
2. List of identified peptides in each protein
3. Probability score against each identification
4. Calculated mass values for peptides
5. Number and nature of ions/transitions against each peptide entry (b/y ions)
6. Number of unique peptides, proteins and single hits

Step 5: Validation through HUPO Metrics

The Human Proteome Organisation (HUPO), recognising the need to standardise the parameters and conditions to allow for accurate validation of protein identifications, proposed a set of matrices that would increase confidence in MS results, primarily for 'missing proteins' (Baker *et al.*, 2017). A systematic approach to evaluating the quality of proteomics data can be obtained from Islam *et al.* (2017a) which encompasses the most recent communally accepted metrics (Omenn *et al.*, 2016) (see Relevant Websites section). Briefly, HUPO recommends applying a threshold of ≤1% global FDR at the protein level, having two or more non-nested peptides that are ≥ 9 amino acids long in addition to other checks, such as calibration of instruments and reporting all FDR's, scores, databases, parameters (instrument and search) used and finally depositing data in a public repository. Although this is only applicable for missing proteins, applying such metrics in all protein identifications can greatly improve the confidence in proteins identified.

Step 6: Data Storage in Public Repositories

In order to eliminate the computational expense and data redundancy, all the mass spectrometer raw data and annotated files related to the specific sample, are encouraged to be submitted to publicly available data repositories. Some of the most common sources of MS-based proteomics identification data (other than above-mentioned library resources) are PRoteomics IDEntifications (PRIDE) by EBI (Vizcaino *et al.*, 2016), Computational Proteomics Analysis System (CPAS) (Rauch *et al.*, 2006), Open Proteomics Database (OPD) by Marcotte Lab (Prince *et al.*, 2004) and PeptideAtlas (Desiere *et al.*, 2006). The general conditions and requirements for data submission are as follows:

1. Targeted species and sample proteome.
2. Identify the type of MS data produced (MS or MS/MS).
3. Experiment protocols and instrumentation (growth, extraction, separation, digestion and informatics).
4. Usually, all the data files such as raw, mzML, pepXML, protXML etc.
5. Publication manuscript.

Discussion and Conclusions

The process of protein identification from mass spectrometry as is observed above is an iterative process that relies heavily on computation and statistical models and prediction. This introduces a significant number of variables and thresholds and depending on the parameters and computational algorithm or search database used (or chosen), can result in variable outcomes (Ramos-Fernandez et al., 2008). In addition, the starting material, the proteins themselves, are often highly heterogeneous both in structure and sequence with the same protein having multiple forms in form of splice variants, PTM's, single amino acid variations (SAAV's), and mutations, among others. Other compounding factors such as the resolution of different MS instruments, resolution and nature of sample preparation techniques and separation methodologies, the abundance of proteins, the ability of peptides to 'fly', and others, all play a role in the successful identification of a protein (Baldwin, 2004).

Despite the above, the probability-based statistical approach used in the identification of proteins in mass spectrometry over the last two decades has made significant improvements with more robust, reproducible and reliable computational methodologies allowing for greater confidence in data. Furthermore, improvements in quality and resolution of MS instrumentation also has had a significant impact in the identification of a large number of proteins accurately. Lastly, a communal recognition of the variability of data has led to initiatives such as that of HUPO to attempt to standardise and streamline the reporting of protein identifications and develop communally acceptable metrics for positive identification, though to date, no identification standards exist for PE1 (proteins with protein-level evidence). It is for this reason, that aside from orthogonal validation, the validation of MS data requires comprehensive and transparent reporting of all parameters and methodologies used (Martens and Hermjakob, 2007).

Further Analysis after Protein Identification

Upon accurate identification and validation of MS data, the list of identified proteins can be further processed through a series of post-data analysis computational and informatics pipelines to allow annotation (Islam et al., 2014), quantification, expression or network analysis, gene ontology analysis, among others. One of the primary ways to look at detailed annotation is to copy the protein ID from the output table (step 4) and search against UniProtKB database – one of the biggest protein databases. UniProtKB has accumulated, for every protein, the information related to its function, taxonomy, modifications, interactions, families and domains, among others. It also contains cross-references to additional databases such as GO for gene annotation, IntAct, STRING and MINT for molecular interactions, RCSB PDB for 3D structures against target protein sequence, SMART, Pfam and PROSITE for family and domains, Ensembl database for phylogenetics and KEGG for network analysis. The detailed post-data analysis methodologies and tools are beyond the scope of this article but have been discussed elsewhere (Bessarabova et al., 2012; Schmidt et al., 2014). Often the information from a post-MS data analysis is used to inform and select candidates for further orthogonal validation of the identification.

Orthogonal Validation of Identity

The most efficient and commonly acceptable way to confirm the identity of a protein is to use orthogonal techniques, especially in sensitive areas such as biomarker discovery (Rifai et al., 2006). The most common form of orthogonal validation is that of affinity-based identification such as western blotting, ELISA or protein/peptide arrays whereas more robust or stringent applications may indeed use functional (biochemical or biological) assays (Rabilloud and Lescuyer, 2014) to validate identifications, functional annotations and identities. As a discovery and hypothesis generating tool, MS-based identification in proteomics of multiple proteins remains the most efficient and accurate as long as accepted and standardised informatics methodologies are applied.

See also: Clinical Proteomics. Natural Language Processing Approaches in Bioinformatics. Sequence Analysis. Sequence Composition

References

Aebersold, R., Mann, M., 2003. Mass spectrometry-based proteomics. Nature 422, 198–207.
Baker, M.S., Ahn, S.B., Mohamedali, A., et al., 2017. Accelerating the search for the missing proteins in the human proteome. Nat Commun 8, 14271.
Baldwin, M.A., 2004. Protein identification by mass spectrometry: Issues to be considered. Mol. Cell Proteomics 3, 1–9.
Bandeira, N., 2011. Protein identification by spectral networks analysis. Methods Mol. Biol. 694, 151–168.
Benevento, M., Di Palma, S., Snijder, J., et al., 2014. Adenovirus composition, proteolysis, and disassembly studied by in-depth qualitative and quantitative proteomics. J. Biol. Chem. 289, 11421–11430.
Bessarabova, M., Ishkin, A., Jebailey, L., Nikolskaya, T., Nikolsky, Y., 2012. Knowledge-based analysis of proteomics data. BMC Bioinformatics 13 (Suppl 16), S13.
Cagney, G., Amiri, S., Premawaradena, T., Lindo, M., Emili, A., 2003. In silico proteome analysis to facilitate proteomics experiments using mass spectrometry. Proteome Sci. 1, 5.
Craig, R., Beavis, R.C., 2003. A method for reducing the time required to match protein sequences with tandem mass spectra. Rapid Commun. Mass Spectrom. 17, 2310–2316.
Demine, R., Walden, P., 2004. Sequit: Software for de novo peptide sequencing by matrix-assisted laser desorption/ionization post-source decay mass spectrometry. Rapid Commun. Mass Spectrom. 18, 907–913.
Desiere, F., Deutsch, E.W., King, N.L., et al., 2006. The PeptideAtlas project. Nucleic Acids Res. 34, D655–D658.
Deutsch, E.W., Mendoza, L., Shteynberg, D., et al., 2015. Trans-Proteomic Pipeline, a standardized data processing pipeline for large-scale reproducible proteomics informatics. Proteomics Clin. Appl. 9, 745–754.
Domon, B., Aebersold, R., 2006. Mass spectrometry and protein analysis. Science 312, 212–217.
Elias, J.E., Gygi, S.R., 2010. Target-decoy search strategy for mass spectrometry-based proteomics. Proteome Bioinformatics 604, 55–71.

Eng, J.K., Fischer, B., Grossmann, J., Maccoss, M.J., 2008. A fast SEQUEST cross correlation algorithm. J. Proteome Res. 7, 4598–4602.

Eng, J.K., Jahan, T.A., Hoopmann, M.R., 2013. Comet: An open-source MS/MS sequence database search tool. Proteomics 13, 22–24.

Frank, A.M., Savitski, M.M., Nielsen, M.L., Zubarev, R.A., Pevzner, P.A., 2007. De novo peptide sequencing and identification with precision mass spectrometry. J. Proteome Res. 6, 114–123.

Frewen, B., Maccoss, M.J., 2007. Using BiblioSpec for creating and searching tandem MS peptide libraries. Curr. Protocols Bioinformatics. 13.7 1–13.7, 12.

Gauci, S., Helbig, A.O., Slijper, M., et al., 2009. Lys-N and trypsin cover complementary parts of the phosphoproteome in a refined SCX-based approach. Anal. Chem. 81, 4493–4501.

Giansanti, P., Tsiatsiani, L., Low, T.Y., Heck, A.J., 2016. Six alternative proteases for mass spectrometry-based proteomics beyond trypsin. Nat. Protoc 11, 993–1006.

Gunaratne, J., Schmidt, A., Quandt, A., et al., 2013. Extensive mass spectrometry-based analysis of the fission yeast proteome: The Schizosaccharomyces pombe PeptideAtlas. Mol. Cell. Proteomics 12, 1741–1751.

Herbert, B., Hopwood, F., Oxley, D., et al., 2003. beta-elimination: An unexpected artefact in proteome analysis. Proteomics 3, 826–831.

Huynh, M.L., Russell, P., Walsh, B., 2009. Tryptic digestion of in-gel proteins for mass spectrometry analysis. Methods Mol Biol 519, 507–513.

Islam, M.T., Garg, G., Hancock, W.S., et al., 2014. Protannotator: A semiautomated pipeline for chromosome-wise functional annotation of the "missing" human proteome. J Proteome Res 13, 76–83.

Islam, M.T., Mohamedali, A., Ahn, S.B., et al., 2017a. A Systematic Bioinformatics Approach to Identify High Quality Mass Spectrometry Data and Functionally Annotate Proteins and Proteomes. Methods Mol. Biol. 1549, 163–176.

Islam, M.T., Mohamedali, A., Fernandes, C.S., Baker, M.S., Ranganathan, S., 2017b. De Novo peptide sequencing: Deep mining of high-resolution mass spectrometry data. Methods Mol. Biol. 1549, 119–134.

Islam, M.T., Mohamedali, A., Garg, G., et al., 2013. Unlocking the puzzling biology of the black perigord truffle tuber melanosporum. J. Proteome Res. 12, 5349–5356.

Kessner, D., Chambers, M., Burke, R., Agus, D., Mallick, P., 2008. ProteoWizard: Open source software for rapid proteomics tools development. Bioinformatics 24, 2534–2536.

Kim, M.S., Pinto, S.M., Getnet, D., et al., 2014. A draft map of the human proteome. Nature 509, 575.

Kingsmore, S.F., 2006. Multiplexed protein measurement: Technologies and applications of protein and antibody arrays. Nat. Rev. Drug Discovery 5, 310–320.

Koenig, T., Menze, B.H., Kirchner, M., et al., 2008. Robust prediction of the MASCOT score for an improved quality assessment in mass spectrometric proteomics. J. Proteome Res. 7, 3708–3717.

Kohlbacher, O., Reinert, K., Gropl, C., et al., 2007. TOPP – the OpenMS proteomics pipeline. Bioinformatics 23, E191–E197.

Kusebauch, U., Campbell, D.S., Deutsch, E.W., et al., 2016. Human SRMAtlas: A resource of targeted assays to quantify the complete human proteome. Cell 166, 766–778.

Lam, H., Deutsch, E.W., Eddes, J.S., et al., 2007. Development and validation of a spectral library searching method for peptide identification from MS/MS. Proteomics 7, 655–667.

Lindskog, C., 2015. The potential clinical impact of the tissue-based map of the human proteome. Expert Rev. Proteomics 12, 213–215.

Low, T.Y., Van Heesch, S., Van Den Toorn, H., et al., 2013. Quantitative and qualitative proteome characteristics extracted from in-depth integrated genomics and proteomics analysis. Cell Rep. 5, 1469–1478.

Ma, K., Vitek, O., Nesvizhskii, A.I., 2012. A statistical model-building perspective to identification of MS/MS spectra with PeptideProphet. BMC Bioinformatics 13 (Suppl 16), S1.

Martens, L., Hermjakob, H., 2007. Proteomics data validation: Why all must provide data. Mol. Biosyst. 3, 518–522.

Marx, V., 2013. Finding the right antibody for the job. Nat. Methods 10, 703–707.

Nesvizhskii, A.I., Keller, A., Kolker, E., Aebersold, R., 2003. A statistical model for identifying proteins by tandem mass spectrometry. Anal. Chem. 75, 4646–4658.

Ngounou Wetie, A.G., Woods, A.G., Darie, C.C., 2014. Mass spectrometric analysis of post-translational modifications (PTMs) and protein-protein interactions (PPIs). Adv. Exp. Med. Biol. 806, 205–235.

Omenn, G.S., Lane, L., Lundberg, E.K., et al., 2016. Metrics for the Human Proteome Project 2016: Progress on identifying and characterizing the human proteome, including post-translational modifications. J. Proteome Res. 15, 3951–3960.

Pointner, J., Persson, J., Prasad, P., et al., 2012. CHD1 remodelers regulate nucleosome spacing in vitro and align nucleosomal arrays over gene coding regions in S. pombe. EMBO J. 31, 4388–4403.

Prince, J.T., Carlson, M.W., Wang, R., Lu, P., Marcotte, E.M., 2004. The need for a public proteomics repository. Nat. Biotechnol. 22, 471–472.

Rabilloud, T., Lescuyer, P., 2014. The proteomic to biology inference, a frequently overlooked concern in the interpretation of proteomic data: A plea for functional validation. Proteomics 14, 157–161.

Ramos-Fernandez, A., Paradela, A., Navajas, R., Albar, J.P., 2008. Generalized method for probability-based peptide and protein identification from tandem mass spectrometry data and sequence database searching. Mol. Cell Proteomics 7, 1/48–1754.

Rauch, A., Bellew, M., Eng, J., et al., 2006. Computational proteomics analysis system (CPAS): An extensible, open-source analytic system for evaluating and publishing proteomic data and high throughput biological experiments. J. Proteome Res. 5, 112–121.

Reidegeld, K.A., Eisenacher, M., Kohl, M., et al., 2008. An easy-to-use Decoy Database Builder software tool, implementing different decoy strategies for false discovery rate calculation in automated MS/MS protein identifications. Proteomics 8, 1129–1137.

Reiter, L., Claassen, M., Schrimpf, S.P., et al., 2009. Protein identification false discovery rates for very large proteomics data sets generated by tandem mass spectrometry. Mol. Cellular Proteomics 8, 2405–2417.

Rifai, N., Gillette, M.A., Carr, S.A., 2006. Protein biomarker discovery and validation: The long and uncertain path to clinical utility. Nat. Biotechnol. 24, 971–983.

Schmidt, A., Forne, I., Imhof, A., 2014. Bioinformatic analysis of proteomics data. BMC Syst. Biol. 8 (Suppl 2), S3.

Searle, B.C., 2010. Scaffold: A bioinformatic tool for validating MS/MS-based proteomic studies. Proteomics 10, 1265–1269.

Shteynberg, D., Deutsch, E., Mendoza, L., et al., 2012. PTMProphet: TPP software for validation of modified site locations on post-translationally modified peptides. In: Proceedings of the 60th ASMS Conference on Mass Spectrometry, Vancouver, BC, Canada, pp. 20–24.

Shteynberg, D., Deutsch, E.W., Lam, H., et al., 2011. iProphet: Multi-level integrative analysis of shotgun proteomic data improves peptide and protein identification rates and error estimates. Mol Cell Proteomics 10.[M111 007690].

Tabb, D.L., Mcdonald, W.H., Yates, J.R., 2002. DTASelect and Contrast: Tools for assembling and comparing protein identifications from shotgun proteomics. J. Proteome Res. 1, 21–26.

Tabb, D.L., Saraf, A., Yates 3RD, J.R., 2003. GutenTag: High-throughput sequence tagging via an empirically derived fragmentation model. Anal Chem 75, 6415–6421.

Thiede, B., Hohenwarter, W., Krah, A., et al., 2005. Peptide mass fingerprinting. Methods 35, 237–247.

Trudgian, D.C., Mirzaei, H., 2012. Cloud CPFP: A shotgun proteomics data analysis pipeline using cloud and high performance computing. Journal of Proteome Research 11, 6282–6290.

Uhlen, M., Fagerberg, L., Hallstrom, B.M., et al., 2015. Tissue-based map of the human proteome. Science. 347.

Vizcaino, J.A., Csordas, A., Del-Toro, N., et al., 2016. 2016 update of the PRIDE database and its related tools. Nucleic Acids Res. 44, D447–D456.

Vizcaino, J.A., Deutsch, E.W., Wang, R., et al., 2014. ProteomeXchange provides globally coordinated proteomics data submission and dissemination. Nat. Biotechnol. 32, 223–226.

Wilkins, M.R., Gasteiger, E., Bairoch, A., et al., 1999. Protein identification and analysis tools in the ExPASy server. Methods Mol. Biol. 112, 531–552.

Wright, J.C., Choudhary, J.S., 2016. DecoyPyrat: Fast non-redundant hybrid decoy sequence generation for large scale proteomics. J. Proteomics Bioinform. 9, 176–180.
Yang, X., Dondeti, V., Dezube, R., et al., 2004. DBParser: Web-based software for shotgun proteomic data analyses. J. Proteome Res. 3, 1002–1008.

Further Reading

Kumar, C., Mann, M., 2009. Bioinformatics analysis of mass spectrometry-based proteomics data sets. FEBS Lett. 583 (11), 1703–1712.
Martins-De-Souza, D., 2014. Shotgun Proteomics. Methods Mol. Biol. 1156.
Matthiesen, R. (Ed.), 2007. Mass Spectrometry Data Analysis in Proteomics 1. Totowa, NJ: Humana Press.
Schmidt, A., Forne, I., Imhof, A., 2014. Bioinformatic analysis of proteomics data. BMC Syst. Biol. 8 (2), S3.
Smith, R., Mathis, A.D., Ventura, D., Prince, J.T., 2014. Proteomics, lipidomics, metabolomics: A mass spectrometry tutorial from a computer scientist's point of view. BMC Bioinformatics 15 (7), S9.
Veenstra, T.D., Yates, J.R., 2006. Proteomics for Biological Discovery. John Wiley & Sons.
Wu, C.H., Chen, C. (Eds.), 2011. Bioinformatics for Comparative Proteomics. Humana Press.

Relevant Websites

http://chemdata.nist.gov/dokuwiki/doku.php?id=peptidew:lib:yeastpombe
    CHEMDATA.NIST.GOV.
http://ftp.sanger.ac.uk/pub/resources/software/decoypyrat/
    DecoyPYrate.py.
https://hupo.org/Guidelines
    HUPO.
http://www.nist.gov
    National Institute of Standards and Technology.
http://ftp.peptideatlas.org/pub/PeptideAtlas/Repository/PAe003810
    PeptideAtlas.
https://www.pombase.org/
    PomBase.
https://www.python.org/
    Python.
https://www.ruhr-uni-bochum.de/mpc/software/DecoyBuilder/index.html.en
    RUB.
https://sourceforge.net/projects/sashimi/files/latest/download?source=files
    SOURCEFORGE.
https://www.thermofisher.com/au/en/home.html
    TheromoFisher.
http://www.uniprot.org/
    UniProt.

Biographical Sketch

Zainab is a PhD student in the department of Chemistry and Biomolecular sciences (Bioinformatics group) at Macquarie University. She has been working in the area of protein structure and function analysis during her bachelors and masters' studies. Previously, she worked on identifying novel potent drug-like compounds against histone deacetylases proteins by employing in silico drug designing techniques. Currently, she is involved in programming-based mass spectrometry data analysis of data generated through data-dependent acquisition (DDA) and data-independent acquisition (DIA) approaches related to colorectal cancer. More specifically, she is dealing with the customization of DDA based spectral libraries to be used in DIA data analysis for biomarker discovery.

Abidali is a Lecturer at Macquarie University in the Faculty of Science and Engineering. He completed his PhD in 2010 studying, using proteomics, the effects of single mutations in mouse model on brain development in the autism spectrum disorder, Rett syndrome. He then returned to Macquarie University undertaking a post-doc to study the biology of metastasis in colorectal cancer using proteomics and to determine novel therapeutic targets and develop novel technologies to examine the plasma proteome.

Shoba Ranganathan holds a Chair in Bioinformatics at Macquarie University since 2004. She has held research and academic positions in India, USA, Singapore and Australia, as well as a consultancy in industry. Shoba's research addresses several key areas of bioinformatics to understand biological systems using computational approaches. Her group has achieved both experience and expertise in different aspects of computational biology, ranging from metabolites and small molecules to biochemical networks, pathway analysis and computational systems biology. She has authored as well as edited several books, as well as contributed several articles to Springer's Encyclopedia of Systems Biology. She is currently the Editor-in-Chief of Elsevier's Encyclopedia of Bioinformatics and Computational Biology, as well as the Bioinformatics Section Editor for Elsevier's Reference Module in Life Sciences.

Quantification of Proteins From Proteomic Analysis

Zainab Noor, Subash Adhikari, Shoba Ranganathan, and Abidali Mohamedali, Macquarie University, Sydney, NSW, Australia

Protein Quantification – Introduction

All living biological entities rely on an intricate balance of metabolic activity, bio-molecules and non-organic molecules to maintain life. Inherent to this balance is the ability to respond rapidly to changes from within or without. Although the breadth of this response can be vast from activating enzymes to opening channels to allow ions to leave or enter, its temporal nature can be varied leading to permanent changes due to chronic signals or transient changes due to acute signals and every variation in between. One of the most fundamental changes that occur in cells is the variation in the abundance of proteins (Vogel and Marcotte, 2012) in response to external or internal stimuli. Indeed, it is well understood that although transient and rapid alterations in cells is often due to modification of the activity of proteins, sustained stimuli lead to sizeable changes in the proteome (the protein complement) of an organism due to changes in transcriptional and translational activity; therefore, protein abundance. This fact has been the source of understanding how biological systems respond to change which has led to the development of markers of change that have revolutionized medicine. An illustration is the discovery of Early pregnancy factor (EPF) as an indicator of early pregnancy (Fan and Zheng, 1997) has revolutionized early maternity practice.

Although it has been known that multiple proteins change expression in relation to stimuli (or treatment), most studies were able to measure and quantitate only a small number of proteins at a time using immunological methodologies (such as, ELISA and Western blotting). Upon the advent of mass spectrometry, researchers began to investigate how this new method could not only identify but also quantitate multiple proteins. The rapid expansion of the technologies and the development of novel label-based quantification and methodologies of label-free quantification using spectral counting led to significant advances in the field. By early 2007, it was possible to quantitate thousands of proteins in a single experiment. These methodologies had significant drawbacks especially around experiment design, technical variability, reproducibility and reliability (Bantscheff *et al.*, 2007). A more recent and powerful technique, loosely based on targeted quantification (multiple reaction monitoring), using a Data Independent Acquisition (DIA) mode on a mass spectrometer has made quantification far more reliable and robust. **Fig. 1** summarises the most common methodologies used to quantitate proteins. This book article will discuss in brief detail some of the most common proteomic methodologies of protein quantification, with a particular emphasis on DIA quantification. Using an example, the article will guide a reader through setting up their own data analysis workflow and to apply statistical and experimental validation techniques to accurately quantify thousands of proteins from a biological sample.

Label-Based Quantification

The basic principle of label-based protein quantification technique is labelling or tagging of peptides/proteins with stable heavy isotopes (13C, 15N, 18O and 2H) and comparing the unlabelled 'light' form of the sample with labelled 'heavy' variant in mass spectrometry. In a given mass spectrum, a mass shift of 3–4 Da occurs in a heavy isoform where the ratio of peak intensities of both isoforms depict the ratio of abundances (Lindemann *et al.*, 2017). This method has been employed in studying modified proteins, membrane proteins, quantifying disturbances or perturbations in a system due to changes in proteins and effects of drugs or inhibitory compounds on protein expression. Label-based quantification is limited by the number of labels that can be applied at the same time (multiplexing) such that up to 12 samples can currently be studied simultaneously (King *et al.*, 2017).

Label-Free Quantification

Label free quantitative proteomics is an extensively used semi-quantitative approach capable of multiplexing multiple MS runs into a single experiment. This approach has wide application in high throughput applications with large individual variation and large sample size, such as in clinical proteomics. Label free quantification in such case can yield more analytical depth and higher dynamic range for quantification (Distler *et al.*, 2016).

Label free quantification is based on comparison of precursor ion intensities between MS runs, measured in terms of peak area or peak intensity after feature alignment according to retention time, *m/z*, charge states etc. A reproducible LC-MS system is an absolute requirement for efficient feature alignment (Norbeck *et al.*, 2005). Label free quantification requires resource intensive computational capability for feature detection and alignment (Mueller *et al.*, 2008), but unlike label-based quantification, the only limit to number of samples that can be analyzed is computational.

Regardless of platform and method adopted, label free quantification relies on extracted ion chromatogram (XIC) intensity-based quantitation or spectral counting-based quantitation. It has been observed that ion concentration correlates with ESI signal intensity; that is, higher peptide concentration in sample yields higher area under integrated chromatogram of a MS spectra. Relative area under curve/chromatogram (peak area) or peak intensity between samples can be used for relative quantitation of peptides/proteins across samples (Neilson *et al.*, 2011).

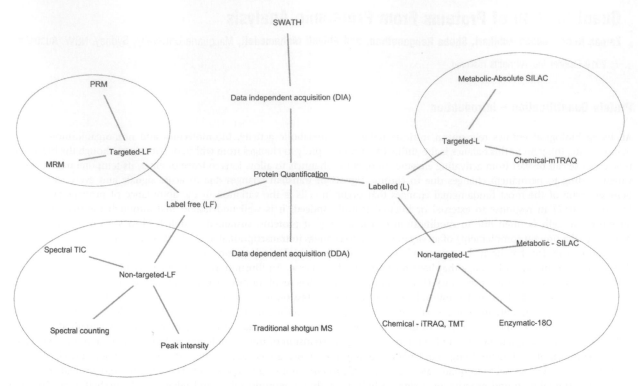

Fig. 1 Multiple approaches exist for MS based protein quantification. Labelling quantifies protein on basis of difference in signal intensities between heavy and light labelled peptides from different samples combined into a single run. Label free quantification is performed by measuring relative signal intensities between multiple sample runs. Quantifications are accomplished on DDA and DIA mode, depending on targeted and comprehensive data analysis.

Spectral counting-based quantification relies on assumption that number of tandem mass spectra are proportional to abundance of a protein, that more spectra are observed with increasing peptide concentration in the sample (Washburn *et al.*, 2001). Normalization factors relating to length and physiological properties of a peptide and its ability to be fragmented are taken into consideration (Ahrne *et al.*, 2013). One challenge with combining XIC-based quantitation with DDA-based identification is finding a balance between MS (quantitation) and MS² (identification) cycling. Devoting more scanning time to peptide identification decreases the number of data points available for MS quantitation, which limits the resolution, and hence accuracy of XIC-based quantitation.

Relative Quantification

Relative quantification is the measure of change in protein expression patterns as a function of biological function, expressed in terms of ratios between different biological states. Relative quantification is measured by either of labelled-based or label-free quantification, depending upon scope of the experiment. A number of labelled-based relative quantification strategies have been developed which are characterized by their mode of action. They are broadly classified into three categories (i) metabolic labelling, biological incorporation of isotopes or labels in a cell culture; (ii) chemical labelling, integration of heavy isotopes into the proteins using isotopic reagents or isobaric tags and (iii) enzymatic labelling, labelling with heavy isotope of oxygen during hydrolysis of protein through trypsin or other proteases. Similarly, various label-free approach could be adopted for relative quantification.

Absolute Quantification

Absolute quantification is the process of measuring the exact amount of a protein in a proteome. Proteins of interest (sample proteins) are spiked with known concentrations of labelled standard peptides bearing identical sequence and physicochemical properties as sample peptides. Quantification is performed by comparing the intensities of the sample and standard peptides/proteins, where unknown quantities of sample proteins can be deduced by means of known concentrations of standard proteins. Several peptide or protein-based approaches have been designed for absolute quantification including absolute SILAC, protein standard absolute quantification (PSAQ), full-length expressed stable isotope-labelled quantification (FLEXIQuant) and quantification Concatemers (QconCAT). Similarly, in the label-free context, MRM assays use the same approach described to accurately quantify selected peptide transitions and hence infer absolute protein abundance.

Quantification Through Data Independent Acquisition (DIA)

During the last decade, most of the MS-based proteomics studies were based on a discovery-based shotgun proteomics method, run in data-dependent acquisition (DDA) mode. Although, this helps to maximize amount of information obtained from an experiment, it has certain inherent limitations such as scan speed (Wenner and Lynn, 2004), selection of ion for further fragmentation, poor reproducibility, narrow dynamic range etc. (Law and Lim, 2013). Due to biases towards certain most intense fragments, DDA method has limitation of not being able to detect low abundant ion fragments. Targeted MS-based proteomics was developed to overcome these limitations of DDA mode. Targeted MS approach on Data independent mode (DIA) is dependent on a known reference spectrum, where identification could be performed from selected few fragment ion, rather than all possible fragment in DDA mode (Gillette and Carr, 2013). Success of data independent quantification relies on proper selection of distinct precursor ion-transitions (Tang et al., 2014). Hence, DDA mode is employed to filter top performing precursor-ions as inclusion list for DIA mode, so the MS instrument could select those specific fragments to aid in identification of low abundant ions/spectra.

Sequential Window Acquisition of all THeoretical fragment ion spectra coupled to Tandem Mass Spectrometry (SWATH-MS) is a novel identification/quantification methodology that operates in DIA mode in a label-free context. SWATH-MS, currently takes into account the peptides of mass/charge (m/z) range from 400 to 1200 and generates fragment ion spectra of all the precursor peptides falling within the window width of 25 Da in each cycle. A prerequisite assay library of peptides/proteins of interest, created in shotgun or discovery mode is required to identify and translate the detailed fragment ion spectral data which is produced in DIA mode and extracted through targeted data extraction approach (Vidova and Spacil, 2017). While performing the data analysis, a number of parameters are usually taken into consideration to perform efficient and high-confidence data analysis. These parameters are, precursor and product ion mass/charge values, retention times, generated spectra and relative intensities. Scores are calculated against peak groups and statistical validation is performed (see **Fig. 2**).

In this article, label-free relative quantification analysis using computational tools have been discussed and demonstrated on DIA data. Quantification data setup and pre-requisite steps to extract the useful information and measurements from experimental data have been illustrated in detail. Moreover, statistical analysis has been carried out on quantified experimental data to analyze proteome expression.

Data Analysis Software

The data independent acquisition strategy has led to the development of a number of specialized software and packages which implement high-speed accurate DIA analysis, from chromatogram extraction to quantification. Currently, in addition to the generalized data analysis packages, mass spectrometry vendors also encompass built-in software responsible for not only

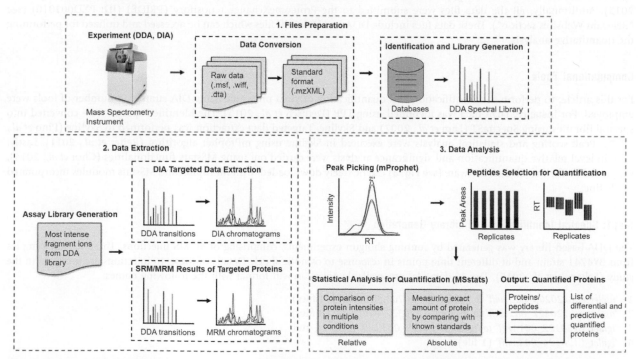

Fig. 2 Workflow of mass spectrometry based protein quantification. Data generated either in DIA or DDA (for the library) mode from a TOF or Orbitrap instrument are first converted to suitable standards followed by library generation from DDA data. Peaks are then extracted and picked for quantification. Finally, statistical analysis is performed to identify a list of differentially quantified proteins.

Table 1 Commonly used DIA (Data Independent Acquisition) data analysis software packages

Software	Enterprise	Specifications	Versions	Download link
PeakView	AB Sciex	• Commercial • Windows-based • Bio Tool Kit	V 1.1 (2010–2011) V 2.2 (2014)	https://sciex.com/products/ software/peakview-software
OpenSWATH (Rost *et al.*, 2014)	OpenMS	• Free – Open Source • Windows, Linux, Mac-based • Compatible with AB Sciex, Thermo and Water DIA data	V 2.2.0 (2017) V 2.1.0 (2016)	https://github.com/OpenMS/ OpenMS/releases
Skyline (Pino *et al.*, 2017)	MacCoss lab	• Free • Windows-based • Panorama repository	12 versions V 3.3 (2017)	https://skyline.ms/project/ home/software/Skyline/ begin.view
Spectronaut (Bruderer *et al.*, 2017)	Biognosys	• Commercial • Windows-based • Quantification of 1000 proteins from a single run	5 versions V 10.0 – Orion (latest)	https://biognosys.com/shop/ spectronaut
DIA-Umpire (Tsou *et al.*, 2015)	Alexey Nesvizshskii lab	• Free – Open Source • Untargeted, library-free peptide identification from DIA data	V 1.4 (2015) V 2.0 (2016) V 2.1 (2016)	http://diaumpire.sourceforge. net/

monitoring the MS experiment but also performing all the downstream data analysis. Some of the widely used software for DIA data analysis are presented in **Table 1**.

Sample Dataset

The sample data was collected for the detection and quantification studies of yeast (*Saccharomyces cerevisiae*) proteome (Selevsek *et al.*, 2015). In this study, changes in yeast proteome expression have been analyzed in the presence of osmotic stress, progressively at different times. As stated above, DIA data analysis requires initial DDA runs to generate the library of assays. It is preferred to run the shotgun injections on the same instrument type as the final DIA data, however, the library assays can be transferred to different instrument platforms if similar fragmentation and chromatography techniques are adopted. In the current example, shotgun and DIA runs were performed on a 5600 TripleTof mass spectrometer (ABSciex) with NanoLC-2Dplus HPLC system. The instrument setup, parameters, collision energy and window settings are available in the study (Selevsek *et al.*, 2015). Additionally, all the data files were submitted to the ProteomeXchange repository (PRIDE) (ID: PXD001010) (see "Relevant Websites section"). These data files include DDA and DIA .wiff files which can be accessed and utilized for performing the quantitative analysis.

Computational Tools

For this article, to perform the identification and quantification of yeast proteome using DIA strategy, a number of tools were employed. For instance, DDA data was identified using TPP (Deutsch *et al.*, 2015). The identified spectra were converted into spectral libraries using SpectraST (Lam *et al.*, 2007) and Skyline. Targeted data extraction was performed in Skyline (Pino *et al.*, 2017). Peak scoring and statistical analysis were executed in Skyline using mProphet algorithm (Reiter *et al.*, 2011). Lastly, protein level relative quantification and significance analysis were carried out using MSstats functionalities (Choi *et al.*, 2014), supported in Skyline. Skyline software (see **Fig. 3**) can be freely downloaded, with mProphet and MSstats modules incorporated in Skyline.

Step1: Spectral Identification and Library Generation

The DDA-based library was generated by running shotgun experiments, comprising of 46 MS injections. These include samples from BY4741 strain and at different time points in response to osmotic shock. Details of these 46 injections are provided in the study (Selevsek *et al.*, 2015). The 46 data files are available online in wiff format with the following names:

1. '*nselevse_L120203_006.wiff*' to '*nselevse_L120203_029.wiff*' (24 files);
2. '*nselevse_L120327_001.wiff*' to '*nselevse_L120327_018.wiff*' (18 files);
3. '*igillet_L120122_001.wiff*' to '*igillet_L120122_003.wiff*' (3 files), and
4. '*igillet_L120124_003.wiff*' (1 file).

The generated spectra were identified using TPP tools against Saccharomyces Genome Database (SGD) (Cherry *et al.*, 2012). The search results were statistically sorted according to probability at 1% FDR. The identified spectra from all the samples were then compiled to generate '*iProphet_Combined.pepXML*' file and used to build a consensus spectral library.

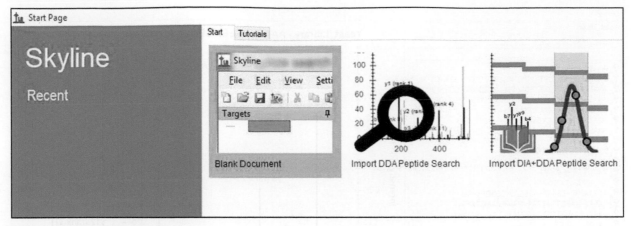

Fig. 3   Skyline software start-up page.

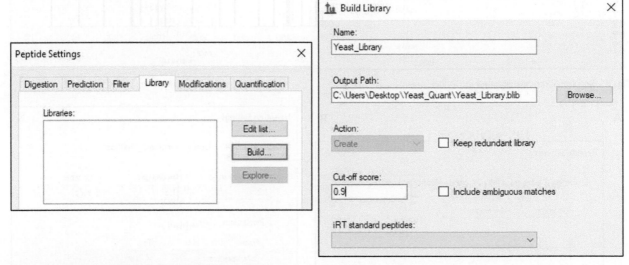

Fig. 4   Library settings in Skyline for generation of spectral library.

Building a spectral library requires the following files:

- pepXML file (search engine result)
- mzXML files (spectral data)

The pepXML file is available at ProteomeXchange repository (ID: PXD001010) whereas mzXML spectra files can be acquired by converting 46 DDA wiff files to XML format using Msconvert tool (Kessner *et al.*, 2008). These converted mzXML data files are necessary to extract the chromatograms from the spectral library during DIA targeted data extraction.

Spectral library using Skyline

Skyline has a 'Build Library' module in 'Peptide Settings' to generate the spectral library (see **Fig. 4**). It requires library name as '*Yeast_Library.blib*', output path and PeptideProphet cut-off score as '*0.9*' (false discovery rate of below 1%). Retention times, mass to charge values and relative intensity values for each spectrum are also stored in the spectral library, which can be visualized in the Skyline (see **Fig. 5**).

Step 2: Fragment Ion Library or Assay Library

Fragment ion library or assay library is a subset of the spectral library. It contains the most intense particular precursor and product ions (MS/MS transitions) from the spectral library or a targeted proteins list. These assays contribute in DIA targeted data extraction of peptides and proteins of interest. These characteristics have to be determined prior to importing the DIA data into the Skyline. For this purpose, Skyline provides various peptide and transition settings with 'Filter', 'Library' and 'Modifications' modules. 'Modification' allows one to include and exclude different types of structural and isotopic modifications. In addition to the default options, new

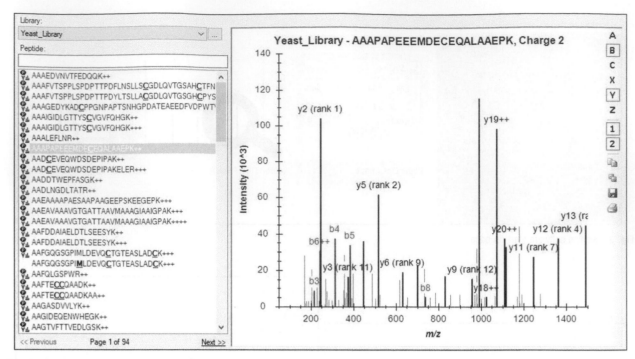

Fig. 5 Spectral library visualization in Skyline.

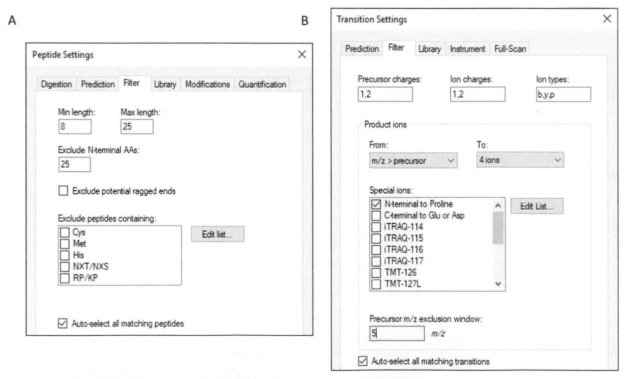

Fig. 6 Filter settings for transition selection in Skyline. (A) Peptide settings. (B) Transition settings.

modifications can also be added to the Skyline. In 'Filter' module, peptides length, precursor/product ion charges and types, and a number of ions can be determined (see **Fig. 6**). Subsequently, through 'Library' settings, ion match tolerance values (match between DIA and DDA data) and library to be added in the analysis can be set. It also provides options for selecting most intense transitions from the library, which also fulfils the 'Filter' settings (see **Fig. 7**). For the current data set, following criteria were set (see **Figs. 6** and **7**):

- Peptide length=min 8 and max 25
- Structural modifications=no oxidation on methionine

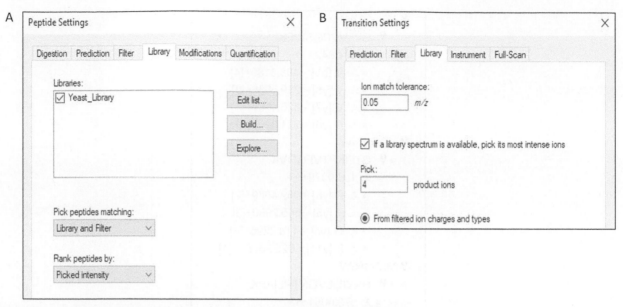

Fig. 7 Library settings for transition selection in Skyline. (A) Peptide settings. (B) Transition settings.

- Ion Intensities=highly intense in spectral library
- Ion Charges (precursor and product ions)=single (1) and double (2)
- Ion types=b, y and p (precursor) ions
- Precursor m/z exclusion window=5 m/z
- Match tolerance=0.05 m/z
- Number of selected transitions=top four

Using 'precursor m/z exclusion window' option, spectra in a mass window around precursor m/z value can be excluded to minimize the noise and extract the refined transitions. In the 'Library' and 'Filter' settings, further transition options are also given such as, 'auto-select all matching transitions', 'pick most intense transitions from library spectrum' and 'pick peptides matching both the library and filter settings'. After setting up the environment for transitions selection, a list of targeted proteins is loaded into the Skyline to generate the fragment or assay library.

Step 3: Targeted Proteins

In contrast to MRM data analysis, where proteins of interest are already determined prior to performing the experiment, in DIA, the list of targeted proteins or peptides are loaded after the experiment has been performed. This allows the extraction and analysis of DIA data that is only related to proteins of interest from the whole data independent run, which usually analyses all the peptides within the range of 400–1200 m/z (depending upon the instrument settings). The targeted proteins/ peptides list can be provided in different ways in Skyline, such as, selected externally and imported into the skyline using 'Import Fasta' module, and/or adding all those proteins/peptides which are available in the spectral library. It can also be added by simply inserting the proteins and peptide sequences in 'Targets' module. In this study, peptides which were identified and stored in the spectral library, and external protein data i.e. *'Yeast.fasta'* were added to the target list. The proteins present in the fasta file also undergo *in silico* tryptic digestion in Skyline. While the protein data is provided, all those transitions which matched the transition settings (in step 2) were added to the target list along with their abundances and retention time values, as shown in **Fig. 8**.

Step 4: DIA Data Extraction Environment

Before importing and extracting the DIA data from experimental runs, Skyline needs to set up the DIA environment. In this, all the instrument and isolation settings for MS1 and MS/MS filtering are configured in 'Transition Settings' under 'Full-Scan' module. The full-scan features include:

- Precursor mass analyzer
- Product mass analyzer
- Resolving powers of analyzers

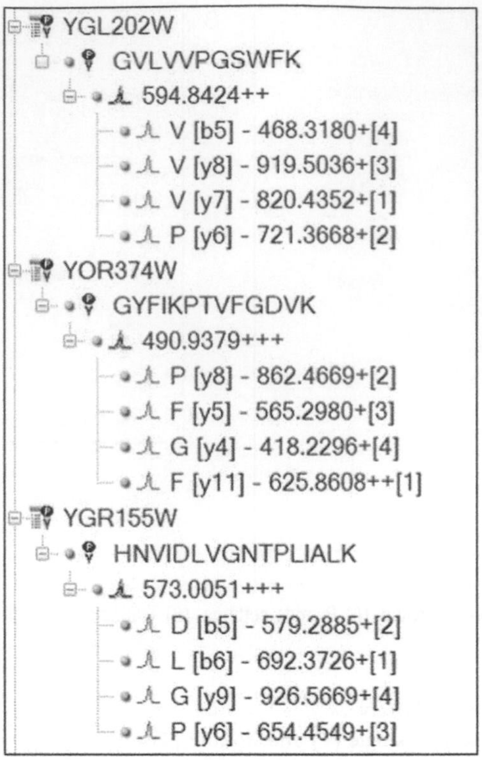

Fig. 8   Visualization of targeted transitions list in Skyline.

- Acquisition method
- Isolation Scheme (pattern of precursor isolation windows in DIA acquisition)
- Retention time filtering

A DIA isolation scheme defines the pattern for each acquisition window (m/z range) through the entire mass range by the specific instrument. Skyline provides default isolation schemes with a variety of patterns, for example, SWATH (15 m/z), SWATH (25 m/z) etc. A customized pattern can also be designed and added according to the particular instrument used for data acquisition experiment. To set up a user-specific isolation scheme, following parameters are required:

- Mass range = 400 to 1200 m/z
- Window (isolation) width = 25 m/z
- Number of windows = 32
- Total cycle time = 3.3 s
- Accumulation time (time spent on single transition) = 10 ms

For the current data set, these values are filled up according to the 5600 TripleTof mass spectrometer used for yeast proteome quantification, provided in the study (Selevsek *et al.*, 2015). After specifying the settings, Skyline displays the isolation windows in tabular and graphical form.

Retention time filtering defines the time range over which each chromatogram is extracted from DIA data against a single targeted transition. The chromatogram can be extracted over the entire gradient, however, it may result in the noisy and distorted peaks with a minimum understanding of correct chromatogram peak. For precise data extraction and identification, retention time value for each peptide in the experiment is required. Skyline provides couple of options limiting the RT range, such as, (i) using RT values of peptides found in the spectral library, (through DDA runs), (ii) predicting these values using SSRCalc hydrophobicity algorithm (Spicer *et al.*, 2007) and (iii) calculating RT values using standard RT peptides through empirical measurements (also called as normalized RTs or iRTs). Details of the SSRCalc and normalized RTs is available in the Skyline tutorial.

Subsequently, assigning the values to the other parameters in 'Full-Scan' module, set up the DIA and DDA environment in Skyline for data extraction and analysis (see **Fig. 9**).

- Precursor mass analyzer = TOF
- Product mass analyzer = TOF
- Resolving powers of analyzers = 30,000
- Acquisition method = DIA

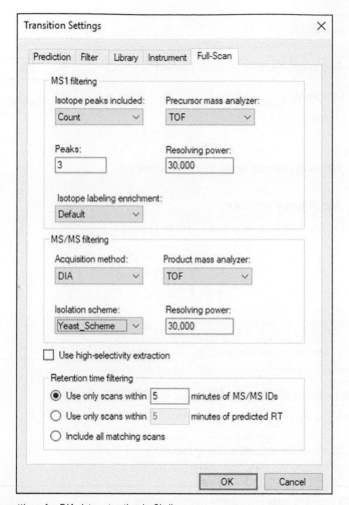

Fig. 9 MS1 and MS/MS filtering settings for DIA data extraction in Skyline.

- Isolation Scheme (pattern of precursor isolation windows in DIA acquisition)=Yeast_Scheme (user-defined)
- Retention time filtering=scans within 5 min of MS/MS IDs

This retention time filtering value will extract the chromatograms from DIA spectra within 5 min range of the peptide-spectrum match for each targeted peptide from the DDA run in a spectral library.

Step 5: DIA Targeted Data Extraction

Following setting up the environment in Skyline, data files from SWATH-MS runs for yeast biological replicates can be imported. In this study, changes in the *S. cerevisiae* proteome were quantified over 6-time points i.e. 0 min (T0), 15 min (T1), 30 min (T2), 60 min (T3), 90 min (T4) and 120 min (T5), as a result of osmolarity stress. Samples were collected, digested and analyzed using SWATH-MS in triplicates at each time point. The 18 data files are available on ProteomeXchange database (see "Relevant Websites section") in wiff format with following names:

1. 'L120412_001_SW.wiff' to 'L120412_003_SW.wiff' (T0) (3 files);
2. 'L120412_004_SW.wiff' to 'L120412_006_SW.wiff' (T1) (3 files);
3. 'L120412_007_SW.wiff' to 'L120412_009_SW.wiff' (T2) (3 files);
4. 'L120412_010_SW.wiff' to 'L120412_012_SW.wiff' (T3) (3 files);
5. 'L120412_013_SW.wiff' to 'L120412_015_SW.wiff' (T4) (3 files); and
6. 'L120412_016_SW.wiff' to 'L120412_018_SW.wiff' (T5) (3 files).

These files can be imported directly into Skyline (compatible with different file formats) using 'Import Results' option in 'File' menu. 'Import Results' provides multiple preferences including (i) add single-injection replicates in files, (ii) add multi-injection replicates in directories, (iii) add one new replicate for different types of results (see **Fig. 10**). As the SWATH runs were added to the Skyline for analysis, it extracted the chromatograms against peptides available in the 'Targets' list while taking into account the retention time filtering parameter. This is also called as 'Targeted Data Extraction'.

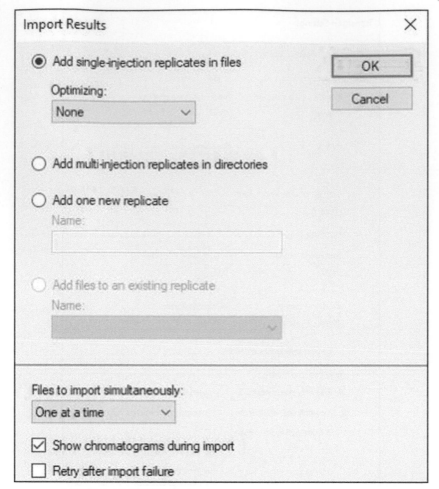

Fig. 10 Import results module for importing mass spectrometry results in Skyline.

Peak picking and scoring

The extracted chromatograms then undergo the process of identifying the correct peak for each targeted peptide, which correlates best with the spectrum in the spectral library. Although this is done automatically, peaks can also be picked manually. For each match, matching scores are allocated, also called as 'dot products'. In order to select the best peak, in addition to its conventional heuristic method, Skyline has also incorporated mProphet algorithm (Reiter *et al.*, 2011) scoring strategy for measuring the similarity between chromatogram and library peaks to choose the best match. The mProphet algorithm takes into account various parameters for scoring purposes, such as:

- Co-elution
- Mass accuracy
- Peak shape
- Ion intensity
- Relative product ion abundance correlation
- Predicted retention time

Additionally, Skyline is equipped with the facility of training and customizing the mProphet peak picking and scoring model for peak determination. This can be executed by generating decoy peptides and calculating FDRs for peaks selection. Details of manual peak-spectrum matching are available in further readings.

Step 6: DIA Data Exploration and Analysis

After importing the DIA data and performing peak selection, chromatograms for 18 biological replicates can be visualized, simultaneously. This can be done by arranging result files systematically into three groups in tabular form using 'Arrange Graphs' module of the Skyline in 'View' menu. Each group indicates the data for all six time points in each replicate. Chromatograms for the first replicate at time T0 to T5 are displayed in **Fig. 11**. In each graph, best peaks are displayed within the black dotted lines

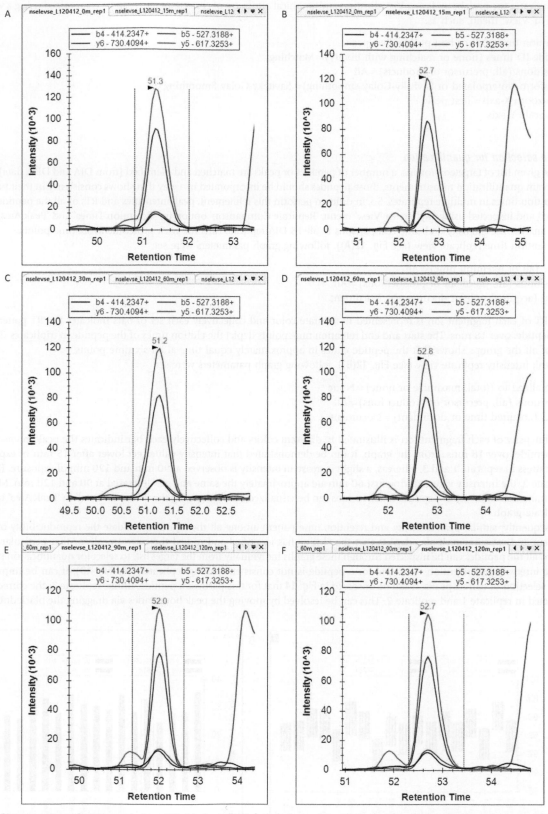

Fig. 11 Chromatograms of yeast peptide from DIA data in replicate 1 at six time points. (A) 0 min (T0). (B) 15 min (T1). (C) 30 min (T2). (D) 60 min (T3). (E) 90 min (T4). (F) 120 min (T5).

which indicates the peak boundaries. Visualization and graphical attributes of chromatograms can be customized using a variety of options in 'View' menu, such as:

- Retention times (all or best peak)=Best peak
- Peptide ID times (none or matching with library)=Matching
- Transitions (all, precursor or products)=All
- Transform (interpolated or Savitsky-Golay smoothing)=Savitzky-Golay Smoothing
- Auto-zoom X-axis=Best peak
- Auto-scale Y-axis

Peptides selection for quantification

From the given list of targeted proteins, a number of peptides or peaks are matched and identified (from DIA and DDA data). For the downstream quantification measurements, those peptides should be incorporated in a way that shows consistency in their peak areas and retention times in multiple replicates. So, in order to perform this refinement, peak intensities and RTs of all the peptides can be compared and inspected using Skyline. In 'View' menu, 'Replicate Comparison' option for 'Retention Times' and 'Peak Areas' can be used to analyze the intensity and time comparisons in all 18 DIA replicate runs for yeast proteome at six time points.

In retention time replicate view (see **Fig. 12(A)**), following graph parameters were set:

- Value (all or retention time)=All
- Transitions (all, precursor or product ions)=All
- Order (acquired time or document)=Document

The RT of each fragment ion is represented in separate color and collectively each set of bars indicates the RT pattern of the whole peptide, over 18 runs. The start and end retention time points depict the elution times of the peptide in triplicates. The same height of all the groups shows that the peptide elutes in approximately equal time at all six time points.

In peak intensity replicate view (see **Fig. 12(B)**), following graph parameters were set:

- Normalized to (total, maximize or none)=None
- Transitions (all, precursor or product ions)=All
- Order (acquired time or document)=Document

The intensity of each fragment ion is illustrated in different colors and collectively each bar indicates the peak intensity of the whole peptide, over 18 runs. From the graph, it can be demonstrated that intensity values get lower after 15 min of exposure to osmotic stress in replicate 1 and 3, whereas, a slight increase in intensity is observed at 90 min and 120 min of exposure. However, in replicate 2, the intensity values during first 60 min are approximately the same and get decreased at 90 and 120 min. Moreover, relative transition intensity of peptides in all 18 runs can be visualized by normalizing the values to 'Total' in 'Peak Area' option in the replicate graph.

Consequently, similar peak intensity and retention time pattern among all the replicates validate the reproducibility of the MS instrument and experiment. It also depicts that the Skyline has identified and picked the correct peak for that particular peptide. Similarly, all the peptides can be inspected through these graphs individually from the target list, to select for quantification purposes.

If the intensity and retention time data for a peptide is not consistent among replicates (see **Fig. 13**), it can be improved by manual selection of correct peaks. It can be observed in **Fig. 14** that for this particular peptide, unlike replicate 3, the correct peak is not selected in replicate 1 and replicate 2. This can be resolved by moving the peak boundaries via dragging the black dotted lines

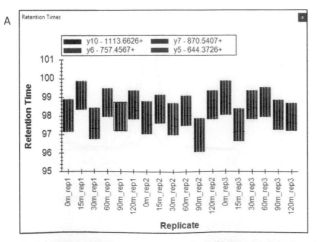
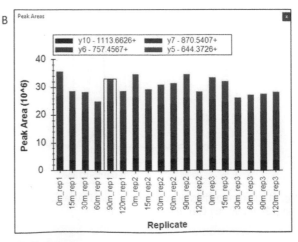

Fig. 12 Consistent replicate comparison graphs in Skyline. (A) Retention times (B) Peak areas.

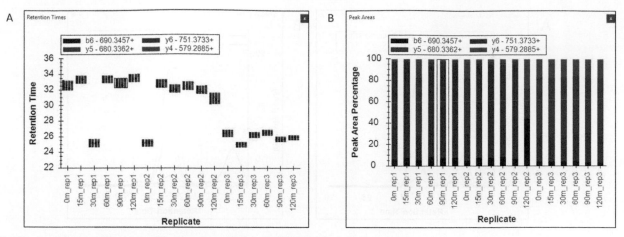

Fig. 13 Inconsistent replicate comparison graphs in Skyline. (A) Retention times (B) Peak areas.

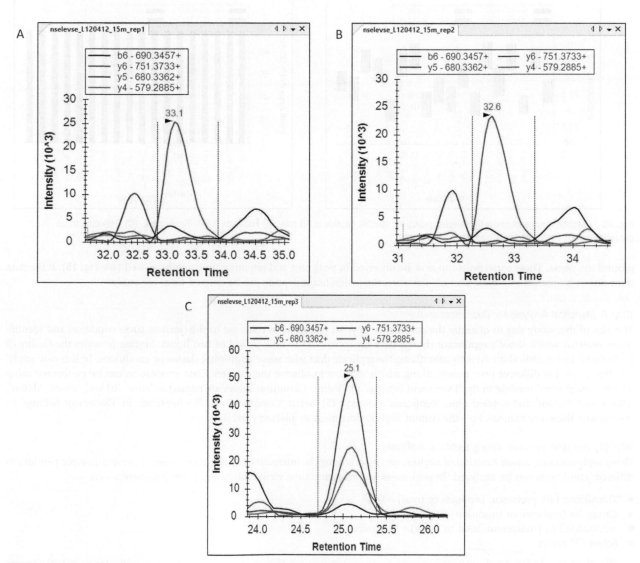

Fig. 14 Chromatograms of selected peaks at 15 min in Skyline. Incorrect peaks are selected in (A) Replicate 1 and (B) Replicate 2. (C) Peak in Replicate 3 is correctly identified.

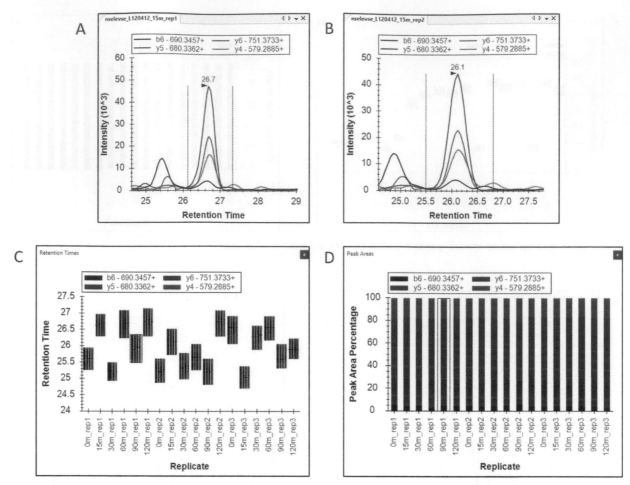

Fig. 15 Chromatograms of correctly selected peaks for specific peptide at 15 min. (A) Replicate 1. (B) Replicate 2. (C) Retention times consistency. (D) Peak areas consistency.

around the peaks. These corrections can now be observed in peak area and retention time graphs as well (see **Fig. 15**). If the data does not show consistency even after adjustments, the insignificant peptide can be deleted from the study.

Step 7: Statistical Analysis for Quantification

The aim of this study was to quantify the abundance of yeast proteome in response to the osmotic stress condition and identify those proteins which show a significant change over the course of the time period of two hours. Skyline provides the facility of performing this statistical analysis by annotating the replicate data with some additional classes or conditions. In this case study, conditions are the different time points, along which we have to observe the changes. Data annotation can be performed using 'Define Annotation' module in the 'Document Settings' in Skyline. Condition values are named as 'a0m', 'b15m', 'c30m', 'd60m', 'e90m' and 'f120m' and applied onto 'Replicates' (see **Fig. 16**). Select 'Condition' and 'BioReplicate' in 'Document Settings' to incorporate these annotations into the current Skyline document to analyze yeast data.

Intensity and time variation among technical replicates

Using replicate comparison function of Skyline, variation among the intensities and retention times of the quantotypic peptides in different conditions can be analyzed. In peak areas and retention time views, following graph parameters were set:

- Transitions (all, precursor, products or total)=Total
- Group by (replicate or condition)=Condition
- Normalized to (maximum, total or none)=Maximize
- Select CV values

Graphs shown in **Fig. 17** illustrate the variation among different conditions or time points for this particular peptide belonging to protein 'YGR240C', in all replicates. All the peptides can be analyzed by iterating over the entire set of targeted proteins. It can be deduced from the graph (see **Fig. 17**) that intensity of this specific peptide greatly varies among all replicates at 90 min after the exposure to osmotic stress environment and the least variation is observed at 0 min and 120 min.

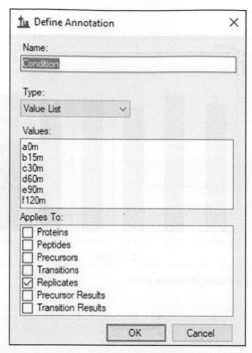

Fig. 16 Annotation module for defining new annotations for replicate data in Skyline.

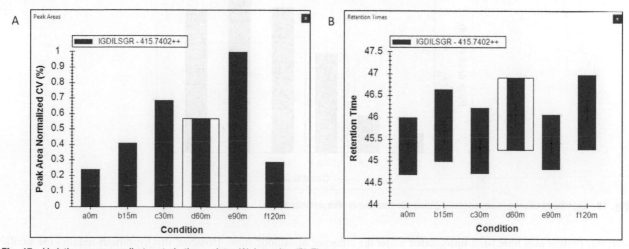

Fig. 17 Variation among replicates at six time points. (A) Intensity. (B) Time.

Average peptide abundance among conditions

To study the average peptide abundance or difference in peptide expression among different conditions, following graph parameters were set in peak areas replicate comparison view:

- Transitions (all, precursor, products or total)=Total
- Group by (replicate or condition)=Condition
- Normalized to (maximum, total or none)=Total
- Deselect CV values

The graph in **Fig. 18** presents the average mean of peptide abundances in triplicates among all conditions. The red bars in the graph represent the mean average values and black lines on the bars represent the standard deviation, which measures the amount of dispersion in the intensity values. A high standard deviation at 90 min depicts the high variation in data values at this time in all replicates.

Overlapping mean values for this specific peptide at six time points, shown in the **Figs. 17** and **18**, do not contribute greatly to the differential abundance analysis, and therefore, demonstrate that protein 'YGR240C' exhibits no significant response to osmotic stress. Contrary to this, peptide response from protein 'YMR169C', shown in **Fig. 19**, is highly predictive and presents a supposition

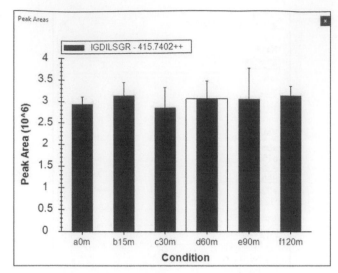

Fig. 18 Average peptide abundances among replicates at six time points.

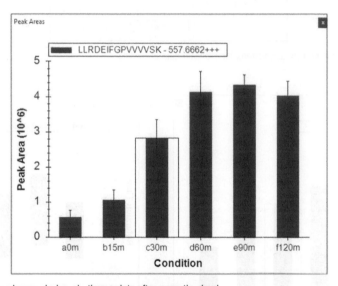

Fig. 19 Significant change in abundances during six time points after osmotic shock.

that this protein may have been upregulated under the influence of osmotic stress. However, this hypothesis requires the similar behaviour from more than one peptide to validate the up or down-regulation of the corresponding protein.

Group comparison among conditions

Differential abundance analysis between time points can also be performed through pairwise group comparison investigation i.e. measure the change in abundance between time points:

- 0 min (T0) to 15 min (T1)
- 0 min (T0) to 30 min (T2)
- 0 min (T0) to 60 min (T3)
- 0 min (T0) to 90 min (T4)
- 0 min (T0) to 120 min (T1)

In Skyline, 'Group Comparison' module in 'Document Settings' provides the facility of adding as many comparisons as required. In 'Edit Group Comparison' form, for the first comparison, following parameters were set:

- Name=T0 v. T1
- Control group annotation=Condition
- Control group value=a0m

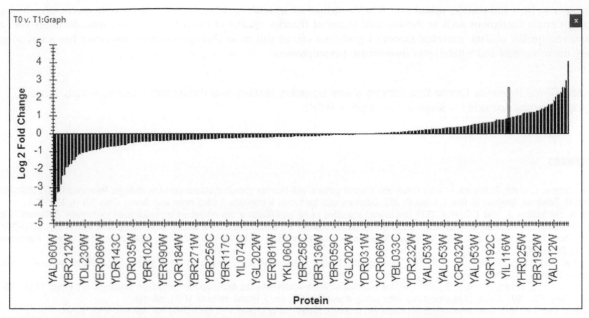

Fig. 20   Log2 fold change in abundances of proteins during the time period between 0 min (T0) and 15 min (T1).

- Value to compare against = b15m
- Identity annotation = BioReplicate
- Normalization method = Equalize medians
- Confidence level = 95%
- Scope = Peptide or Protein for peptide or protein level analysis, respectively

To inspect the abundances of proteins within the time frame of first 15 min, the graph can be visualized in 'View' and 'Group Comparison' menu of Skyline. The graph shown in **Fig. 20** illustrates the overall fold change, either increase or decrease or no effect, in yeast proteins. By employing the same method on all other comparison groups, protein expressions during different time periods can be analyzed.

Data Visualization

Different quantification strategies provide a measure of change in proteome between different biological conditions/samples. Elucidation of biological relevancy of these quantifications requires additional analysis. Perseus is widely adopted for analysis post-database search, for visualization and statistical analysis. There are various tools available for pathway enrichment and analysis, Gene ontology (GO) enrichment could be performed by Panther (Mi *et al.*, 2016), protein-protein interaction information could be obtained from STRING (Szklarczyk *et al.*, 2015), IntAct (Orchard *et al.*, 2014), Human Protein Reference Database (HPRD) (Keshava Prasad *et al.*, 2009) and Biological General Repository for Interaction Datasets (BioGRID) (Stark *et al.*, 2011) amongst others.

Perseus (Tyanova *et al.*, 2016) is a freely available software that performs shotgun proteomics analysis of biological relevance from processed raw files. In addition, can perform various visualization, clustering, principal component analysis (PCA) and statistical tests on quantitative and time series data, details of which are available on Perseus documentation.

Conclusion

Mass spectrometry based quantitative proteomics has rapidly changed the landscape of proteomics research spurred on by rapid technological advances and more importantly huge strides ahead in computational analysis and informatics. It has to be noted though, that the major limitation of quantitative studies is the thresholds and stringencies set by the users. Although there is yet to be standards developed for quantitative proteomics (Mohamedali *et al.*, 2017), it behoves researchers and users to be wary of and thoroughly statistically analyze all mass spectrometry data keeping strict stringency to eliminate false positives. The example used in this article illustrates that the procedure for the analysis for protein quantification by proteomics is relatively straightforward with freely available tools. It has to be emphasised though, that users have a good understanding of the theoretical underpinnings of Mass Spectrometry and informatics to ensure that the results obtained from their studies are robust and reproducible.

Furthermore, upon the identification of differentially expressed proteins between samples after a rigorous experimental and analytical approach, orthogonal techniques to validate potential candidates using targeted techniques such as MRM's and ELISA are almost a compulsory part of the reliability of MS quantification (Vidova and Spacil, 2017). The use therefore, of large scale quantitative proteomics using a label-free DIA approach has been a mainstay of the discovery part of proteomic studies and indeed has proven to be a formidable, robust and reliable method of quantifying large numbers of proteins in complex biological samples. Certain limitations such as the size and nature of libraries, quality of sample preparation, reproducibility on varied instruments, quality of data, statistical threshold guidelines etc. all still mean that quantitative proteomics has a way to go to achieve the robustness and reliability of quantitative transcriptomics.

See also: Clinical Proteomics. Genome-Wide Scanning of Gene Expression. Identification of Proteins from Proteomic Analysis. Natural Language Processing Approaches in Bioinformatics. Sequence Analysis

References

Ahrne, E., Molzahn, L., Glatter, T., Schmidt, A., 2013. Critical assessment of proteome-wide label-free absolute abundance estimation strategies. Proteomics 13 (17), 2567–2578.

Bantscheff, M., Schirle, M., Sweetman, G., Rick, J., Kuster, B., 2007. Quantitative mass spectrometry in proteomics: A critical review. Anal. Bioanal. Chem. 389 (4), 1017–1031.

Bruderer, R., Sondermann, J., Tsou, C.C., et al., 2017. New targeted approaches for the quantification of data-independent acquisition mass spectrometry. Proteomics 17 (9),

Cherry, J.M., Hong, E.L., Amundsen, C., et al., 2012. Saccharomyces genome database: The genomics resource of budding yeast. Nucleic Acids Res. 40 (D1), D700–D705.

Choi, M., Chang, C.Y., Clough, T., et al., 2014. MSstats: An R package for statistical analysis of quantitative mass spectrometry-based proteomic experiments. Bioinformatics 30 (17), 2524–2526.

Deutsch, E.W., Mendoza, L., Shteynberg, D., et al., 2015. Trans-Proteomic Pipeline, a standardized data processing pipeline for large-scale reproducible proteomics informatics. Proteomics Clin. Appl. 9 (7–8), 745–754.

Distler, U., Kuharev, J., Navarro, P., Tenzer, S., 2016. Label-free quantification in ion mobility-enhanced data-independent acquisition proteomics. Nat. Protoc. 11 (4), 795–812.

Fan, X.G., Zheng, Z.Q., 1997. A study of early pregnancy factor activity in preimplantation. Am. J. Reprod. Immunol. 37 (5), 359–364.

Gillette, M.A., Carr, S.A., 2013. Quantitative analysis of peptides and proteins in biomedicine by targeted mass spectrometry. Nat. Methods 10 (1), 28–34.

Keshava Prasad, T.S., Goel, R., Kandasamy, K., et al., 2009. Human protein reference database – 2009 update. Nucleic Acids Res. 37 (Database issue), D767–D772.

Kessner, D., Chambers, M., Burke, R., Agusand, D., Mallick, P., 2008. ProteoWizard: Open source software for rapid proteomics tools development. Bioinformatics 24 (21), 2534–2536.

King, C.D., Dudenhoeffer, J.D., Gu, L., Evans, A.R., Robinson, R.A.S., 2017. Enhanced sample multiplexing of tissues using combined precursor isotopic labeling and isobaric tagging (cPILOT). J. Vis. Exp. 123).

Lam, H., Deutsch, E.W., Eddes, J.S., et al., 2007. Development and validation of a spectral library searching method for peptide identification from MS/MS. Proteomics 7 (5), 655–667.

Law, K.P., Lim, Y.P., 2013. Recent advances in mass spectrometry: Data independent analysis and hyper reaction monitoring. Expert Rev. Proteomics 10 (6), 551–566.

Lindemann, C., Thomanek, N., Hundt, F., et al., 2017. Strategies in relative and absolute quantitative mass spectrometry based proteomics. Biol. Chem. 398 (5–6), 687–699.

Mi, H., Poudel, S., Muruganujan, A., Casagrande, J.T., Thomas, P.D., 2016. PANTHER version 10: Expanded protein families and functions, and analysis tools. Nucleic Acids Res. 44 (D1), D336–D342.

Mohamedali, A., Ahn, S.B., Sreenivasan, V.K.A., Ranganathan, S., Baker, M.S., 2017. Human Prestin: A candidate PE1 protein lacking stringent mass spectrometric evidence? J. Proteome Res. 16 (12), 4531–4535.

Mueller, L.N., Brusniak, M.Y., Mani, D.R., Aebersold, R., 2008. An assessment of software solutions for the analysis of mass spectrometry based quantitative proteomics data. J. Proteome Res. 7 (1), 51–61.

Neilson, K.A., Ali, N.A., Muralidharan, S., et al., 2011. Less label, more free: Approaches in label-free quantitative mass spectrometry. Proteomics 11 (4), 535–553.

Norbeck, A.D., Monroe, M.E., Adkins, J.N., et al., 2005. The utility of accurate mass and LC elution time information in the analysis of complex proteomes. J. Am. Soc. Mass Spectrom. 16 (8), 1239–1249.

Orchard, S., Ammari, M., Aranda, B., et al., 2014. The MIntAct project – IntAct as a common curation platform for 11 molecular interaction databases. Nucleic Acids Res. 42 (Database issue), D358–D363.

Pino, L.K., Searle, B.C., Bollinger, J.G., et al., 2017. The Skyline ecosystem: Informatics for quantitative mass spectrometry proteomics. Mass Spectrom. Rev.

Reiter, L., Rinner, O., Picotti, P., et al., 2011. mProphet: Automated data processing and statistical validation for large-scale SRM experiments. Nat. Methods 8 (5), 430–435.

Rost, H.L., Rosenberger, G., Navarro, P., et al., 2014. OpenSWATH enables automated, targeted analysis of data-independent acquisition MS data. Nat. Biotechnol. 32 (3), 219–223.

Selevsek, N., Chang, C.Y., Gillet, L.C., et al., 2015. Reproducible and consistent quantification of the Saccharomyces cerevisiae proteome by SWATH-mass spectrometry. Mol. Cell. Proteomics 14 (3), 739–749.

Spicer, V., Yamchuk, A., Cortens, J., et al., 2007. Sequence-specific retention calculator. A family of peptide retention time prediction algorithms in reversed-phase HPLC: Applicability to various chromatographic conditions and columns. Anal. Chem. 79 (22), 8762–8768.

Stark, C., Breitkreutz, B.J., Chatr-Aryamontri, A., et al., 2011. The BioGRID interaction database: 2011 update. Nucleic Acids Res. 39 (Database issue), D698–D704.

Szklarczyk, D., Franceschini, A., Wyder, S., et al., 2015. STRING v10: Protein-protein interaction networks, integrated over the tree of life. Nucleic Acids Res. 43 (Database issue), D447–D452.

Tang, H., Fang, H., Yin, E., et al., 2014. Multiplexed parallel reaction monitoring targeting histone modifications on the QExactive mass spectrometer. Anal. Chem. 86 (11), 5526–5534.

Tsou, C.C., Avtonomov, D., Larsen, B., et al., 2015. DIA-Umpire: Comprehensive computational framework for data-independent acquisition proteomics. Nat. Methods 12 (3), 258–264.

Tyanova, S., Temu, T., Sinitcyn, P., et al., 2016. The Perseus computational platform for comprehensive analysis of (prote)omics data. Nat. Methods 13 (9), 731–740.

Vidova, V., Spacil, Z., 2017. A review on mass spectrometry-based quantitative proteomics: Targeted and data independent acquisition. Anal. Chim. Acta 964, 7–23.

Vogel, C., Marcotte, E.M., 2012. Insights into the regulation of protein abundance from proteomic and transcriptomic analyses. Nat. Rev. Genet. 13 (4), 227–232.

Washburn, M.P., Wolters, D., Yates 3rd, J.R., 2001. Large-scale analysis of the yeast proteome by multidimensional protein identification technology. Nat. Biotechnol. 19 (3), 242–247.

Wenner, B.R., Lynn, B.C., 2004. Factors that affect ion trap data-dependent MS/MS in proteomics. J. Am. Soc. Mass Spectrom. 15 (2), 150–157.

Further Readings

Anand, S., Samuel, M., Ang, C.S., Keerthikumar, S., Mathivanan, S., 2017. Label-based and label-free strategies for protein quantitation. Proteome Bioinform. 31–43.

Anderle, M., Roy, S., Lin, H., Becker, C., Joho, K., 2004. Quantifying reproducibility for differential proteomics: Noise analysis for protein liquid chromatography-mass spectrometry of human serum. Bioinformatics 20 (18), 3575–3582.

Bantscheff, M., Lemeer, S., Savitski, M.M., Kuster, B., 2012. Quantitative mass spectrometry in proteomics: Critical review update from 2007 to the present. Anal. Bioanal. Chem. 404 (4), 939–965.

Chen, Y., Wang, F., Xu, F., Yang, T., 2016. Mass spectrometry-based protein quantification. In: Mirzaei, H., Carrasco, M. (Eds.), Modern Proteomics–Sample Preparation, Analysis and Practical Applications. Springer International Publishing, pp. 255–279.

Clough, T., Thaminy, S., Ragg, S., Aebersold, R., Vitek, O., 2012. Statistical protein quantification and significance analysis in label-free LC-MS experiments with complex designs. BMC Bioinform. 13 (16), S6.

Karpievitch, Y., Stanley, J., Taverner, T., et al., 2009. A statistical framework for protein quantitation in bottom-up MS-based proteomics. Bioinformatics 25 (16), 2028–2034.

Lill, J., 2003. Proteomic tools for quantitation by mass spectrometry. Mass Spectrom. Rev. 22 (3), 182–194.

Pan, S., Aebersold, R., Chen, R., et al., 2008. Mass spectrometry based targeted protein quantification: Methods and applications. J. Proteome Res. 8 (2), 787–797.

Wang, M., You, J., Bemis, K.G., Tegeler, T.J., Brown, D.P., 2008. Label-free mass spectrometry-based protein quantification technologies in proteomic analysis. Brief. Funct. Genom. Proteom. 7 (5), 329–339.

Wilm, M., 2009. Quantitative proteomics in biological research. Proteomics 9 (20), 4590–4605.

Relevant Websites

http://www.coxdocs.org/doku.php?id=maxquant:start
  MaxQuant.
http://www.openms.de/tutorials/
  OpenSWATH.
http://www.coxdocs.org/doku.php?id=perseus:start
  Perseus.
http://www.ebi.ac.uk/pride/archive/projects/PXD001010
  PRIDE Archive - PXD001010.
https://skyline.ms/wiki/home/software/Skyline/page.view?name=tutorials
  Skyline.

Biographical Sketch

Zainab is a PhD student in the department of Chemistry and Biomolecular sciences (Bioinformatics group) at Macquarie University. She has been working in the area of protein structure and function analysis during her bachelors and masters' studies. Previously, she worked on identifying novel potent drug-like compounds against histone deacetylases proteins by employing in silico drug designing techniques. Currently, she is involved in programming-based mass spectrometry data analysis of data generated through data-dependent acquisition (DDA) and data-independent acquisition (DIA) approaches related to colorectal cancer. More specifically, she is dealing with the customization of DDA based spectral libraries to be used in DIA data analysis for biomarker discovery.

Subash is a PhD student in Cancer proteomics. His main interest is on mass spectrometry based quantitative proteomics. He is currently working on peptide antagonist against specific membrane protein-protein interaction that are known to drive epithelial cancer metastasis.

Shoba Ranganathan holds a Chair in Bioinformatics at Macquarie University since 2004. She has held research and academic positions in India, USA, Singapore and Australia as well as a consultancy in industry. Shoba's research addresses several key areas of bioinformatics to understand biological systems using computational approaches. Her group has achieved both experience and expertise in different aspects of computational biology, ranging from metabolites and small molecules to biochemical networks, pathway analysis and computational systems biology. She has authored as well as edited several books as well as contributed several articles to Springer's Encyclopedia of Systems Biology. She is currently the Editor-in-Chief of Elsevier's Encyclopedia of Bioinformatics and Computational Biology as well as the Bioinformatics Section Editor for Elsevier's Reference Module in Life Sciences.

Abidali is a Lecturer at Macquarie University in the Faculty of Science and Engineering. He completed his PhD in 2010 studying, using proteomics, the effects of single mutations in mouse model on brain development in the autism spectrum disorder, Rett syndrome. He then returned to Macquarie University undertaking a post-doc to study the biology of metastasis in colorectal cancer using quantitative proteomics and to determine novel therapeutic targets and develop novel technologies to examine the plasma proteome.

Utilising IPG-IEF to Identify Differentially-Expressed Proteins

David I Cantor, Macquarie University, Sydney, NSW, Australia
Harish R Cheruku, Preston, VIC, Australia

Abbreviations

2D-DIGE	Two-dimensional differential in-gel electrophoresis	MRM	Multiple reaction monitoring
		MS	Mass spectrometry
CRC	Colorectal cancer	pI	Isoelectric point
HiRIEF	High-resolution isoelectric focusing	SDS-PAGE	Sodium dodecyl sulfate polyacrylamide gel electrophoresis
HPLC	High performance liquid chromatography	SILAC	Stable isotope labelling with amino acids in cell culture
IPG-IEF	Immobilized pH gradient isoelectric focussing	SRM	Single reaction monitoring
iTRAQ	Isobaric tag for relative and absolute quantitation	SWATH	Sequential window acquisition of all theoretical mass spectra
MALDI	Matrix assisted laser desorption/ionisation	TMT	Tandem mass tags
MARS	Multiple affinity removal system	TOF	Time of Flight

Introduction

Living cells and tissues exist in a state of constant flux, responding to, and acting upon, a complex matrix of biochemical signals and genetic programming in order to maintain and perpetuate life. As such, cells and tissues can be considered fluidic in terms of stimulus and response rather than remaining static. Though DNA encodes the foundational 'blueprint' for life, it is the shifting creation or destruction of its downstream effectors (RNAs, proteins and their modifications) that carry out the functionality of the ~ 20,300 protein-coding genes. The study of these shifts in the protein population as a result of disease, cancer, lifestyle, aging or response to treatment is known as proteomic analysis (or proteomics); which refers to the systematic identification and quantitation of the complete complement of proteins (the proteome) within a biological system at a specific point in time (see Relevant Websites section). Therefore, by establishing specific time points or suitable models of comparison, proteomic analysis can be applied to investigations of biological fluids, cells, tissues, organs or organisms as a means to assess the shifts in protein expression that accompany disease states such as cancer or as a means to identify specific markers of disease (biomarkers).

Thus, proteomics is a method for identifying the change in protein populations that correlate with the presence or progression of a disease. Though it can be applied to the tissue and whole-organism level for microbiota, its strength lies in its capacity to identify cellular behaviour, making it a well-adopted method to explore the cellular biology of cancer. One of the most studied yet still poorly understood diseases, cancer originates from a single malignantly-transformed cell in a multi-staged process that confers a growth advantage compared to the surrounding healthy cells (see Relevant Websites section) (Uhlen *et al.*, 2015). The transformation of a 'healthy' somatic cell into a cancerous lesion is not the result of a single mutation but rather the interplay between large numbers of genes with diverse normal functions. More than 500 genes have been implicated in the transformational process. Whilst these genes and their protein products are necessary for normal growth, survival and function, dysregulation of their expression is what drives or enables a cell to escape healthy cell programming and become cancerous. Dysregulation of normal expression can occur as either a result of overexpression, reduced expression (downregulation) or the expression of a defect protein, each of which can contribute to unregulated tumour growth. To grasp the scale of global morbidity, cancer killed 8.2 million people in 2012 as a result of unregulated cell growth that led to eventual metastasis, multiple organ failure and death (Ferlay *et al.*, 2015). A given cancer can be classified as one of several diseases based upon the organ of origin (i.e., where the primary cancer developed), tumour morphology or molecular features. Along with stage at the time of diagnosis, each of these factors form important determinants for the clinical outcome and choice of treatment for the patient.

Proteomic profiling is one of the several means to characterise a cancerous cell or tissue, providing information on the protein population within that sample and revealing a valuable insight into the biology of a given tumour. Proteomic profiling also facilitates detailed comparison between tumours and their corresponding tissue of origin, providing researchers and clinicians with the differential expression of biologically-relevant proteins between individual tumours or between different types of cancer. Proteomic profiling can also be employed to examine differential protein expression between regions of a given tumour, or of tumour cells at different cancer stages. The key task of these investigations is to identify proteins that are functionally relevant to the progression of the disease, such as markers of cancer stage, aggression and indicators of response to therapy. However, one of the primary difficulties faced by these studies is that these biologically-relevant proteins are found in very low abundance (or copy-number) relative to the vast numbers of somatic 'house-keeping' proteins. More specifically, the dynamic range of protein

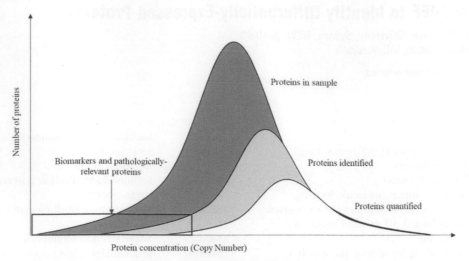

Fig. 1 Schematic representation of proteins identified and quantified within the observable proteome. Cellular proteins span a wide range of copy numbers, with only a fraction of the total being able to be identified, of which only a small percentage can be quantified using currently available molecular biology and mass spectrometry techniques. Biomarkers and pathologically important proteins are often found in very low abundance which makes it challenging to identify and quantify them. Figure modified from Bantscheff, M., Schirle, M., Sweetman, G., Rick, J., Kuster, B., 2007. Quantitative mass spectrometry in proteomics: A critical review. Anal Bioanal Chem 389, 1017–1031.

populations in a sample can span several orders of magnitude. The issue of dynamic range between proteins of interest and the somatic population is a constant challenge to the analysis of a range of specimen types such as cell lysates, tissue lysates or plasma. For example, clinical tissue sections contain highly abundant blood-derived proteins that originate from the tissue-embedded network of blood/lymph capillaries and interstitial fluid (Prieto *et al.*, 2014), whilst in biofluids such as plasma, the 22 most-abundant proteins constitute 99% of the total plasma protein mass (**Fig. 1**) (Prieto *et al.*, 2014; Bantscheff *et al.*, 2007).

As a result, investigations require the use of effective separation techniques to delve deeper into the proteome to identify proteins and peptides that are relevant to a given disease state. The field of proteomics has developed an extensive toolbox of methods that can be applied to such a problem, employing mass spectrometry (MS) as the principal technique for the identification of proteins (and their associated pathways) that are differentially-expressed as a result of carcinogenesis, progression or metastasis. MS enables researchers and clinicians to identify the specific mass and charge state of amino acid sequences which can be matched *in silico* to a peptide sequence and thus identify the parent protein from which the peptide was derived. This process is known as peptide-to-spectra matching. However, the complexity of biological samples can result in the masking of proteins of interest amongst the much more abundant house-keeping proteins. Therefore, reducing sample complexity or enriching for a protein subpopulation of interest is a critical component of the proteomic workflow, which can be achieved by methods such as mass-, charge- or hydrophobicity-based fractionation, subcellular or affinity-based fractionation (**Table 1**). These methods can be employed either individually or in combination at both the peptide and protein levels.

Once sample complexity has been reduced, multiple proteomic strategies may be used to identify the complement of proteins within. A hierarchical structure of the some commonly used workflows by biomedical researchers is illustrated in **Fig. 2**. These techniques and workflows are chosen on the basis of the experimental design and include methods such as: label-free and labelled proteomics, gel-based and gel-free proteomics. Each method possesses respective strengths and weaknesses which must be factored into a proposed experimental design.

One method that enables researchers to reduce sample complexity without relying upon mass-based separation is immobilised pH gradient isoelectric focussing (IPG-IEF), which enables separation based on isoelectric point (pI). This method addresses a problem with direct injection of a sample onto an LC-MS/MS system, which is that a single-dimension separation by reversed-phase LC and does not afford a sufficient peak capacity to successfully process all of the tens of thousands of peptide species that are present within an unfractionated tryptic digest of a complex biological sample. More specifically, IPG-IEF employs an immobilised pH gradient within an acrylamide matrix by integrating acrylamide buffer molecules during gel casting. As a result, when placed under a current, the peptides or proteins that are loaded onto the gel strip will migrate along the one-dimensional gel until they reach their respective isoelectric points, where they will cease to migrate. Once the run is complete, the gel strip can be fractionated by excising sections of the gel, eluting the peptides into solution followed by further separation by the front-end liquid chromatography prior to in-line MS (Pergande and Cologna, 2017; Liu *et al.*, 2016).

As mentioned previously, MS is most often applied for analysis of proteins in a single cell or an organism. Once sample complexity has been reduced using the protein/peptide separation techniques outlined in **Table 1**, low abundance proteins peptides/proteins can be identified by label-free or labelled proteomic approaches. The respective advantages and disadvantages of these methods are outlined in **Table 2**.

These respective strengths and weaknesses must be considered as current proteomic methods still only identify a small percentage of the total proteome (as shown in **Fig. 1**) (Bantscheff *et al.*, 2007). Furthermore, proteomic investigations must also

Table 1 A comparison of protein/peptide fractionation or enrichment methods that are commonly employed in proteomic workflows in order to reduce sample complexity

Fractionation/ enrichment procedure	Principle	Strengths	Weaknesses	Comments	Ref (s)
Gel-based fractionation methods					
1D SDS-PAGE	Separation based on protein charge and mass (i.e. protein size)	1. Applicable to a wide variety of samples 2. Simple to run 3. Fast turnaround	1. Requires fairly large amount of sample 2. High inter-gel variability 3. Multiplexing is not possible 4. Requires multiple runs for quantitation 5. Difficult to identify low-abundance and small proteins unless the sample has been enriched for those proteins 6. Proteins with similar masses cannot be resolved due to masking 7. Incomplete digestion may introduce error	This techniques is very widespread and used for many applications such as comparing the protein composition of different samples, analysis of the number and size of polypeptide subunits, western blotting coupled to immunodetection	Tiwari and Tiwari (2014), Abdallah et al. (2012)
IPG-IEF	Separation based on isoelectric point (pI) of peptides and/or proteins	1. High-resolution and high-capacity method for peptide separation 2. Full control of a well-defined pH range 3. Flexibility of choosing the desired pH gradient 4. Buffering capacity 5. Reproducible separation for technical replicates	1. Oil from IPG-IEF fractionation must be removed prior to MS 2. Additional sample-handling steps 3. Cathodic drift of proteins with alkaline pIs 4. Poor resolution under non-denaturing conditions	Separation by net charge at different pH values is not affected by protein molecular weight	Moreda-Pineiro et al. (2014) Abdallah et al. (2012); Manadas et al. (2010), Essader et al. (2005)
2D SDS-PAGE or 2D-DIGE	Separation based on pI (first dimension separation) and then by protein size (second dimension separation)	1. Simplistic to run 2. Robust 3. Can be multiplexed using Cy-dyes	1. Requires large sample amounts 2. Low throughput 3. High inter-gel variability 4. Co-migration of multiple proteins in a single spot renders comparative quantification rather inaccurate 5. Poor representation of low abundant proteins 6. Has issues separating highly acidic/basic proteins, or proteins with extreme size or hydrophobicity		Tiwari and Tiwari (2014), Abdallah et al. (2012)

(Continued)

Table 1 Continued

Fractionation/ enrichment procedure	Principle	Strengths	Weaknesses	Comments	Ref (s)
Salts/detergent based enrichment methods					
Sodium Carbonate	High alkalinity of sodium carbonate solution (pH 11) solubilises and strips loosely associated proteins from cell membranes	1. Simple procedure 2. Inexpensive reagents 3. Avoid labelling 4. Extended proteomic coverage 5. Highly abundant cytosolic proteins (e.g., ribosomal proteins, elongation factors) are easily separated	1. Require large amount of samples 2. Only enriches loosely bound membrane proteins which sometimes is not ideal 3. Involves centrifugation at $120,000 \times g$, which many not be suitable for all membrane types		Cantor *et al.* (2013), Molloy (2008)
Triton X-114 Phase partitioning	Triton X-114 is used to solubilise the membrane proteins which are then separated (at 20°C) from hydrophilic proteins	1. Simple workflow 2. Hydrophobic and hydrophilic proteins are enriched 3. Ideal for analysis of membrane proteins 4. Inexpensive	1. More difficult sample preparation procedure 2. Require large amount of samples 3. Sample loss at each step 4. Requires detergent removal which would otherwise interfere with MS analysis	This method was first introduced by Bordier in 1981. It has now established itself as one of the most powerful tools for preparing membrane proteins for analysis	Mathias *et al.* (2011), Pryde (1998); Bordier (1981)
Chromatographic fractionation methods					
Ion Exchange chromatography Anion exchange chromatography (AX) Cation exchange chromatography (CX)	AX: Positive groups have affinity for negatively charged peptides at basic pH CX: Negative groups attract positively charged peptides at acidic pH	1. Robust 2. Less labour intensive	1. Limited resolution	Strong cation exchange (SCX) is the most commonly used fractionation technique for proteomics. It has also been extensively used to study post-translational modifications	Chan and Issaq (2013), Mohammed and Heck (2011) Manadas *et al.* (2010), Essader *et al.* (2005)
Reverse phase chromatography	Separation is based on the analyte partition coefficient between the polar mobile phase and the hydrophobic (nonpolar) stationary phase	1. Can provide extremely high resolution separations 2. Reverse phase columns are relatively cheap and commercially available 3. Easy to use	1. Very sensitive to polarity, changes in temperature and pH 2. These can have profound effects on the results		Abdallah *et al.* (2012)

Method	Principle	Advantages	Disadvantages	Proteins removed	References
OFFGEL electrophoresis	Separation is based on pI of peptides/proteins	1. Improved pI resolutions 2. Sample is recovered in liquid phase 3. Low influence of offgel reagents on further separation techniques 4. High reproducibility 5. Multiple samples can be fractionated in parallel using IEF (currently 16)	1. Requires high amount of sample 2. Possible loss of sample 3. Long separation-times (few hours to 2–4 days) 4. Moderate number of protein identifications 5. Cathodic drift of proteins with alkaline pIs 6. Poor resolution under non-denaturing conditions		Moreda-Pineiro et al. (2014), Manadas et al. (2010) http://www.agilent.com

Depletion columns for enrichment

Method	Principle	Advantages	Disadvantages	Proteins removed	References
Multiple Affinity Removal System (MARS)-14	Antibody based protein capture	1. Removes 14 high-abundance proteins from human plasma samples 2. Enhances the ability to identify low abundance proteins	1. Variable depletion efficiency between proteins 2. Concomitant loss of non-targeted proteins 3. High cost 4. Can only be used with serum/plasma	14 proteins: Albumin, IgG, antitrypsin, IgA, transferrin, haptoglobin, fibrinogen, alpha2-macroglobulin, alpha1-acidglycoprotein, IgM, apolipoprotein AI, apolipoprotein AII, complement C3, transthyretin.	Ahn and Khan (2014), Tu et al. (2010) Pernemalm et al. (2008) http://www.agilent.com
ProteoPrep20 Plasma Immunodepletion Kit	Antibody based protein capture	1. Removes the 20 most-abundant proteins which allows for 50-fold increased protein loads 2. Increase the ability to visualize low abundance proteins and biomarkers 3. Convenient spin column format	1. Can only be used with biological fluids such as serum/plasma 2. Variable depletion efficiency 3. Concomitant loss of non-targeted proteins 4. High cost	20 proteins: Albumin, IgG, transferrin, fibrinogen, IgA, $\alpha 2$- macroglobulin, IgM, $\alpha 1$-antitrypsin, complement C3, haptoglobulin, apolipoprotein A1, A3 and B; $\alpha 1$- acid glycoprotein, ceruloplasmin, complement C4, C1q; IgD, prealbumin, and plasminogen	Liu et al. (2011), Cellar et al. (2009), Sigdel and Sarwal (2008) http://www.sigmaaldrich.com
HiTrap Albumin and IgG Depletion columns	Media containing recombinant Protein G fragments and recombinant protein binding human serum albumin (HAS)	1. Columns can be prepacked for either serum or plasma 2. Rapid and easy processing 3. Large sample volumes (~150 µl) 4. Can be used online with an LC system or be used manually with a syringe 5. High depletion capacity, >95% HSA and 90% IgG	1. High cost 2. Loss of low-abundance species that strongly bind to abundant proteins 3. Can only be used with biological fluids such as serum/plasma		de Morais-Zani et al. (2011) http://www.gelifesciences.com

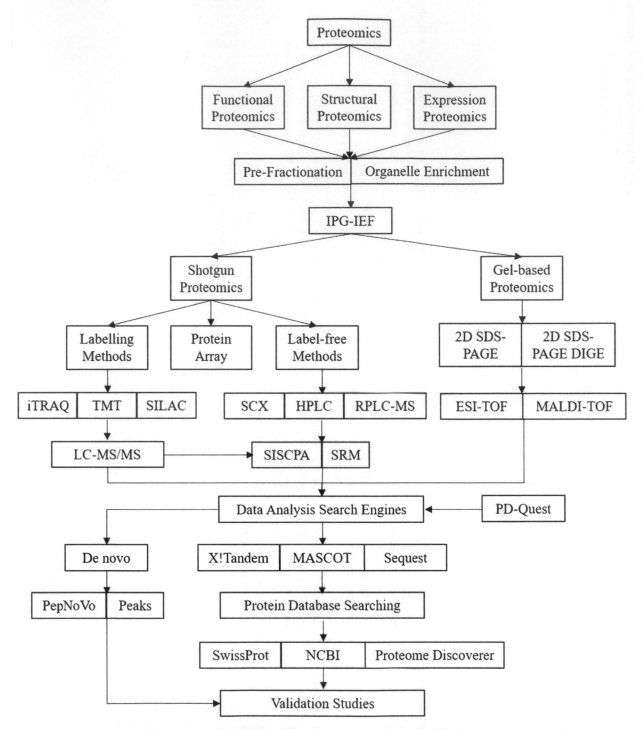

Fig. 2 An overview of mass spectrometry-based proteomic workflows that are commonly employed by biomedical researchers. Figure adapted from Chandramouli, K., Qian, P.Y., 2009. Proteomics: Challenges, techniques and possibilities to overcome biological sample complexity. Hum Genomics Proteomics 2009. doi:10.4061/2009/239204.

account for the required use of combination/s of separation techniques in order to reduce sample complexity, especially during technical stages which may introduce experimental variation and downstream quantitative error (**Fig. 3**).

Stand-alone MS is not inherently quantitative due to ion loss and the sources of variation outlined in **Fig. 3**. As a result, labelling methods such as TMT, iTRAQ or SILAC, or multiple reaction monitoring (MRM) are often employed to enable researchers to accurately quantitate protein expression between samples or in reference to standards (Chan *et al.*, 2016). The key challenge encountered in MS-based biomarker discovery studies is the need for the greatest proteomic coverage that can be reliably and reproducibly achieved in order to identify and quantify the low abundance proteins whose altered expression may indicate or mediate disease (Chan *et al.*, 2016).

Table 2   Relative strengths and weaknesses of labelled and label-free proteomic strategies

	Advantages	*Disadvantages*
Label-free proteomic approach	• Requires less amounts of sample • Higher proteomic coverage • Avoid labelling • Reagents are inexpensive • Applicable to wide variety of samples • Applicable to a wider variety of sample preparation workflows	• Multiplexing is not possible in one experiment • Semi-quantitative, requiring multiple runs for quantitation • Not suitable for low abundance proteins unless the sample has been enriched for those proteins • Incomplete digestion may introduce error • Technical variation must be tightly controlled
Labelled proteomic approach	• Faster MS analysis, requiring fewer runs. • Applicable to wide variety of samples • Allows multiplexing (3–10 samples) in a single in MS run, reducing technical variation between MS gradients. • Allows better quantitation through the use of standards • Minimises background by identifying tagged peptides only • Covalent labelling can be achieved using iTRAQ and TMT • Metabolic labelling can be performed using SILAC	• Requires greater amounts of sample • Incomplete/partial labelling can introduce quantitative error • Loss of the label causes peptide loss • Reagents are expensive, therefore limiting the number of experiments that can be performed using a single sample

Sources: Reproduced from Tiwari, V., Tiwari, M., 2014. Quantitative proteomics to study carbapenem resistance in *Acinetobacter baumannii*. Front Microbiol 5, 512; Abdallah, C., Dumas-Gaudot, E., Renaut, J., Sergeant, K., 2012. Gel-based and gel-free quantitative proteomics approaches at a glance. Int J Plant Genomics 2012, 494572.

As a result, additional dimensions of sample separation are beneficial to biomarker discovery studies as they increase resolution and sensitivity of the shotgun proteomic workflow, whilst facilitating the application of a pI filter to reduce false positive or false negative PSMs (Cargile *et al.*, 2005). This article will explore the use of the gel-based and gel-free methods to identify differentially-expressed proteins, outlining their respective strengths and utility for vastly different proteomic applications, from the detection of performance enhancing drugs to elucidating the molecular biology of leading cancer subtypes.

Application of IPG-IEF

IPG-IEF is a robust protein/peptide fractionation technique that provides reproducible high resolution separation, (Moreda-Pineiro *et al.*, 2014; Abdallah *et al.*, 2012) and is therefore an attractive method to employ in biomarker studies where it is crucial to overcome the issue of sample heterogeneity. As a method of separation, IPG-IEF and its related methodologies have been a widely employed approach to fractionate protein mixtures prior to MS (Pergande and Cologna, 2017; Cargile *et al.*, 2005). One of the earliest incarnations of this approach was two-dimensional electrophoresis (2DE), in which IPG-IEF was applied as the first dimension of separation. The strength of 2DE over one-dimensional gels was the ability to separate and identify different proteoforms present within the sample. This additional dimension enabled early efforts to investigate, characterise and identify post-translational modifications (PTMs), the strengths of which have been reviewed by Westermeier (2014).

However, early 2DE efforts were hamstrung by the inherent variations in gel composition and electrophoretic conditions, resulting in potentially significant gel-to-gel variation. Despite this issue, when employed in isolation, one of the greatest powers of 2DE and related IEF techniques was their complementarity with mass spectrometry. When used together, two-dimensional separation was able to reduce proteome complexity with sufficient resolution to facilitate the analysis of single proteoforms in greater depth compared to a standard shotgun approach (Pergande and Cologna, 2017). Furthermore, it is now common practice to perform 2DE with multiple Cy-dye labelled samples, thereby separating multiplexed protein samples under identical electrophoretic conditions and enabling researchers to visualise differential protein expression based on the size and location of protein spots. These gel spots are then easily excised and processed for MS analysis by either LC-MS or MALDI-TOF for *m/z*-based identification (Pergande and Cologna, 2017).

Additionally, the recent development of high-resolution isoelectric focusing (HiRIEF) by Branca *et al.* (2014) has allowed far deeper proteome coverage and the discovery of new protein-coding loci (Branca *et al.*, 2014). Using this specialised method, Branca *et al.*, were able to identify 77,985 human peptides, 39,941 of which had not been present in the human subset of the 2012 release of Peptide Atlas, corresponding to an increase of ∼52% (Branca *et al.*, 2014). HiRIEF employs a series of ultra-narrow IPG gradients within the acidic pH 3.7–5.0 range (i.e., 3.70–4.05, 4.00–4.25, 4.20–4.45 and 4.39–4.99) which were then fractionated into 72 fractions for analysis by LC-MS/MS (Branca *et al.*, 2014). This method concentrated on the separation of acidic peptides as it enabled the identification of one third of the human tryptic peptidome. Furthermore, fractionation can be performed with minimal redundancy whilst remaining relatively robust in terms of resolution, the reduction in sample complexity and overall

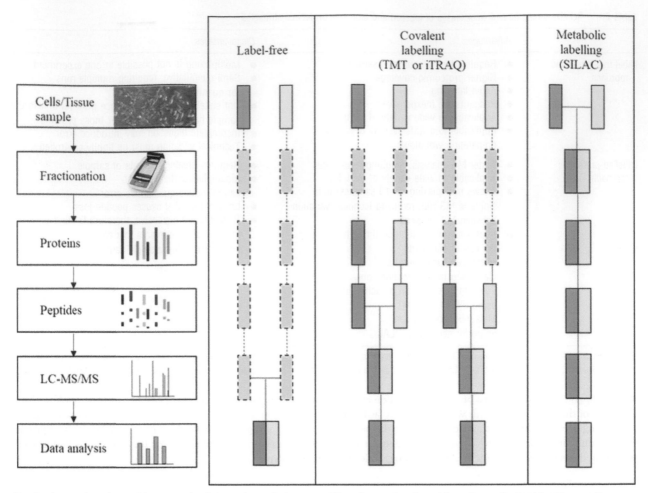

Fig. 3 An overview of potential sources of variation and quantitative error within various proteomic workflows. Boxes displayed in green or yellow represent separate experimental conditions along a vertical workflow, with horizontal lines indicating stages where samples/data are combined. Paler boxes with dashed lines indicate technical stages that are susceptible to experimental variation. Covalent chemical labelling can be performed at either the protein or peptide level depending upon experimental workflow. Figure modified and adapted from Bantscheff, M., Schirle, M., Sweetman, G., Rick, J., Kuster, B., 2007. Quantitative mass spectrometry in proteomics: A critical review. Anal Bioanal Chem 389, 1017–1031.

reproducibility (Branca *et al.*, 2014). HiRIEF has more recently been applied to analyse sequential phosphorylation by protein kinases through the combined use of fluorescent peptide substrates with microfluidic isoelectric focusing and monitoring of protein folding dynamics (Pergande and Cologna, 2017).

IPG-IEF has been applied to investigate a great number of biological questions, some of which have been summarised in **Table 3**. These studies employed IPG-IEF and/or related methodologies in order to investigate and array of disease models, or to identify and/or elucidate the role of specific proteins as potential markers of disease. Here, we provide two case studies to highlight the application of IPG-IEF in biomedical research. In the first case study, IPG-IEF was used in combination with MARS depletion and iTRAQ to identify markers of the use of Human Growth Hormone in athletes as a performance enhancing drug; whilst in the second case study, IPG-IEF was paired with sample enrichment techniques to facilitate the identification of low-abundance and technically challenging proteins by LC-MS.

Case Studies

Case Study I

The first Case Study that we wish to explore is the recently published work by Tan *et al.* (2017). This study demonstrates the application of proteomic technologies to identify markers of substance abuse, specifically the administration of human growth hormone (GH) as a performance enhancing drug in competitive sports (Tan *et al.*, 2017). The World Anti-Doping Agency currently adopts two approaches for the detection of GH abuse in elite sports; the GH isoform test and GH biomarker test (Tan *et al.*, 2017). The GH biomarker tests measures the concentration of two human GH-sensitive markers which are present in serum; insulin-like

Table 3 A selection of IPG-IEF-based investigations that have been undertaken in the past 5 years

Author	Year	Disease/cancer type/ application	IPG-IEF utilisation	Key findings/notes	References
Tan SH *et al.*	2017	Testing of human growth hormone intake	MARS-7 depleted plasma samples were subjected to 2D-DIGE and selected spots were identified using MALDI-TOF MS	1. 52 Spots from two phases were excised for MS analysis 2. 20 Proteins were identified from both phases 3. Five proteins AHSG, APOL1, KNG1, VDBP and VN were differentially expressed 4. Further cross validation using iTRAQ and Western blotting showed AHSG and APOL1 could be potential growth hormone responsive markers in athletes	Tan *et al.* (2017)
Panizza E *et al.*	2017	Identification of low abundance phospho-proteins using HeLa cells	Phospho-peptide enriched samples labelled with TMT tags were subjected to high-resolution isoelectric focusing (HiRIEF) and examined by LC-MS/MS analysis	1. This is a novel workflow for identification of low abundance phospho-proteins 2. Identified a total of 22,712 phosphorylation sites 3. 19,075 (14,965 Serine, 2916 threonine and 1203 tyrosine) phosphorylation sites were localized with high confidence 4. 1264 Novel sites (previously unreported) were identified	Panizza *et al.* (2017)
Wang DL *et al.*	2017	Breast cancer	Serum samples enriched for low abundant proteins were subjected to 2D-DIGE[a] and the separated proteins were transferred to the protein elution plate (PEP) and hexokinase (HK) activity was measured. Followed by measurement of protease activity using FITC-labelled casein as the protease substrate	1. Several potential functional protein biomarkers were identified from breast cancer patient sera 2. The workflow used showcases functional proteomics technology	Wang *et al.* (2017)
Sun Z *et al.*	2016	Lung cancer	2D-DIGE was employed following which the samples were transferred to the PEP and HK activity was measured. Fractions with high HK activity were analysed by LC-MS/MS	1. Many time-dependent hexokinase activity fractions were detected from both the normal and lung cancer sera 2. Multiple fractions showed a 10-fold difference between normal serum and lung cancer sera 3. Hexokinase regulation can provide a potential panel of biomarkers for lung cancer	Sun *et al.* (2016)

(Continued)

Table 3 Continued

Author	Year	Disease/cancer type/ application	IPG-IEF utilisation	Key findings/notes	References
Liu S *et al.*	2016	Cervical cancer	iTRAQ-labelled peptides were fractionated by IPG-IEF followed by MS analysis	1. MS analysis identified 3300 proteins of which 137 and 193 were found to be up-regulated down-regulated respectively. 2. LYN was significantly overexpressed in higher in cervical cancer tissues 3. LYN knockdown and overexpression studies showed that it could inhibit or promote migration, invasion and cell proliferation in vitro and in vivo	Liu *et al.* (2016)
Hsu TY *et al.*	2016	Edwards Syndrome (Trisomy 18) Pregnancies	Samples labelled with Cy Dye were subjected to 2D-DIGE. Spots with a fold change of more than ± 1.5 were selected for MS/MS analysis by MALDI-TOF/TOF	1. 12 Spots were chosen for MS/MS analysis 2. 5 Spots were successfully identified, of which APOA1 was up-regulated and four proteins, IGFBP − 1, VDBP, TTR, and A1AT were down-regulated 3. Further validation of these results is required using a larger sample size	Hsu *et al.* (2016)
Nakamura S *et al.*	2015	Tumour samples from gastric, pancreatic, colon, ovarian, renal, breast, lung, hepatocellular, oesophageal, prostate and thyroid cancers	Samples were subjected to 2D-DIGE, following which MS/MS analysis of selected spots was carried out by using MALDI-TOF/TOF Proteomic studies were performed using a FLAG-LIX1L-expressing HEK − 293 (HEK − 293FLG-LIX1L) cell line	1. Oncogenic activity of LIX1L and associated proteins was carried out using proteomic analysis 2. LIX1L was found to be associated with C-p89 and C-p80 kDa protein complexes when the cytoplasmic fraction was not treated with RNAase 3. Among the complexes, high immunoreactivity was observed for RIOK1, NCL and PABPC4 4. MS analysis of the nuclear fraction identified DHX9, NCL and HNRNPL to be differentially-expressed 5. Along with several other experiments LIX1L was suggested to be a putative RNA-binding proteins with implications in for therapeutic approaches for targeting LIX1L in LIX1L-expressing cancer cells	Nakamura *et al.* (2015)

Wu JY et al.	2014	Gastric cancer	Cy Dye labelled samples were subjected to 2D-DIGE followed by MALDI-TOF MS analysis	1. 15 proteins spots were examined. 10 proteins were excluded under the suspicion of PTMs as they were found in different locations 2. Five proteins, GRP78, GSTP1, APOAI, A1AT and GKN1 were confirmed and further validated by Western blotting and IHC as putative markers of gastric cancer	Wu et al. (2014)
Mundt F et al.	2014	Malignant mesothelioma	iTRAQ-labelled samples were subjected to HiRIEF. 72 fractions were collected and subjected to LC-MS/MS analysis	1. 1371 proteins were identified in the screened pleural effusions from patients with malignant mesothelioma ($n=6$), lung adenocarcinoma ($n=6$), or benign mesotheliosis ($n=7$) 2. Seven candidates from the proteomic data (AKR1B10, APOC1, LGALS1, MYO7B, SOD2, TNC, and THBS1) were validated by ELISA in a larger group of patients with mesothelioma ($n=37$) or metastatic carcinomas ($n=25$) 3. Galectin 1, aldo-keto reductase 1B10, and apolipoprotein C-I were all identified as potential prognostic biomarkers for malignant mesothelioma	Mundt et al. (2014)
Cantor D et al.	2013	Colorectal cancers	A membrane-enriched protein sample from SW480 cells overexpressing integrin β6 was separated by IPG-IEF and the resulting fractions were examined by LC-MS/MS	1. 708 proteins were found to have significant change in expression 2. 54 proteins previously proposed as cancer biomarkers were identified 3. β6 expression enhanced cell invasion and proteins involved in cancer-related pathways such as ILK and RAN	Cantor et al. (2013)

[a]2D-DIGE: First-dimension separation is done using isoelectric focussing (IEF) which is facilitated by immobilized pH gradient (IPG) strips. The second dimension separation performed using a gel.

Note. Observe the variety of applications and ability to be incorporated to different biological investigations, from identifying expression changes in various disease models to phospho-peptide enrichment and identification. Please note that Table 3 only identifies a brief selection of studies in order to demonstrate the utility of workflows incorporating IPG-IEF.

growth factor-I (IGF-I) and N-terminal pro-peptide of type III collagen (P-III-NP) (Tan *et al.*, 2017). However, these tests are insufficiently specific to indict or exonerate an athlete as having been administered GH as they do not ameliorate the variability imparted by factors such as age, gender, sport, ethnicity and dosage concentration. Furthermore, the GH isoform test remains unable to detect the administration of purified, pituitary-derived GH, which is commercially-available. As a result, there was an unmet need to accurately identify the exogenous administration of GH to athletes (Tan *et al.*, 2017). In their study, Tan *et al.* (2017) aimed to identify novel markers of GH administration in athlete plasma samples by an unbiased proteomic screening approach. This approach employed gel-based and gel-free proteomic methods which were undertaken in parallel. A simplified outline of this workflow is shown in **Fig. 4**.

Tan *et al.* employed a simple antibody-based sample enrichment step by utilising a MARS Human 7 (MARS-7) depletion column to remove seven high-abundance plasma proteins (albumin, IgG, IgA, transferrin, haptoglobin, antitrypsin, and fibrinogen) which respectively equated to approximately 40–50% of total plasma protein (by weight) (Tan *et al.*, 2017). Following the removal of these abundant constituents, the flowthrough from MARS-7 immunodepletion was then analysed in an unbiased fashion by employing a parallel analysis of each sample by 2D-DIGE and iTRAQ-based LC-MS analysis (Tan *et al.*, 2017).

In order to minimise technical variability between the experiments, Tan *et al.* carried out the study in two independent phases, wherein the 112 individual plasma samples were separated into two equal groups of 56 (Tan *et al.*, 2017). In an effort to further

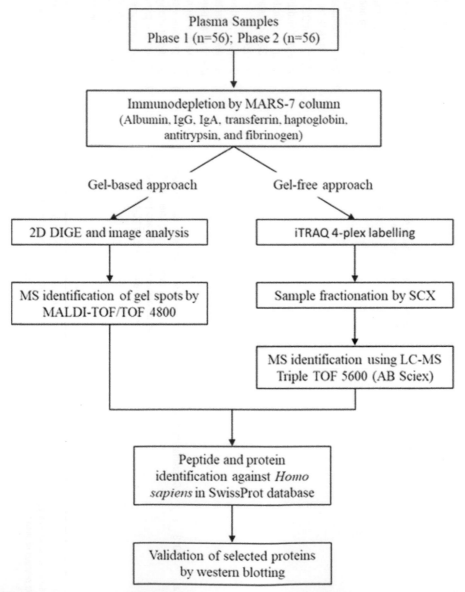

Fig. 4 Schematic overview of the proteomic workflow employed by Tan *et al.* The plasma samples were immunodepleted using a MARS-7 column with the flowthrough analysed in parallel by 2D-DIGE and iTRAQ LC-MS/MS. This was followed by peptide and protein identification, with subsequent validation performed upon of selected proteins. Reproduced from Tan, S.H., Lee, A., Pascovici, D., *et al.*, 2017. Plasma biomarker proteins for detection of human growth hormone administration in athletes. Sci Rep 7 (1), 10039.

reduce variation, Tan *et al.* created a pooled reference sample which was then incorporated into each DIGE gel to facilitate gel alignment and matching. By adopting these two simple approaches, Tan *et al.* estimated the coefficient of variation (CV) between 28 gels in this first phase of the study to be only 8% (Tan *et al.*, 2017), which was considered acceptable given the extent of sample handling involved in performing a DIGE experiment.

Following image analysis of DIGE gels, 195 proteins were found to be differentially expressed. Stringent selection criteria (Tan *et al.*, 2017) were then imposed upon on the candidate spots, leading to the selection of 54 spots for further analysis. Of these, only 52 spots were excised for identification by MALDI-MS/MS analysis. It is important to note that the remaining two spots were not visible when the gels were re-stained, resulting in their omission from MALDI-MS/MS analysis. This highlights one of the disadvantages of employing a gel-based approach, as some proteins may not bind to the dye used to visualise and excise protein spots for MS analysis. Of the 52 spots analysed by MS, 39 differentially-expressed proteins were identified, of which 20 were differentially expressed from both Phases. Among the identified proteins, APOL1, AHSG, KGN1, VDBP, and VN were also shown to be differentially expressed in the recombinant GH (rGH)-treated group from both analysis Phases. Subsequent analysis later showed that KNG1 and VN exhibited variable expression patterns between Phases 1 and 2, resulting in their exclusion from further evaluation (Tan *et al.*, 2017). Tan *et al.* reported that these varying expression patterns for KNG1 and VN could be a result of individual variability.

In this study, Tan *et al.* employed 2D-DIGE, an IPG-IEF methodology, to investigate the effects of rGH administration to athletes. 2D-DIGE is a robust and fairly simplistic method to evaluate protein samples, providing an in-depth view of the proteome whilst identifying differentially-expressed proteins (Tiwari and Tiwari, 2014; Abdallah *et al.*, 2012). To negate the issue of dynamic range, Tan *et al.* performed 2D-DIGE on plasma samples whose complexity had been reduced by pre-treatment on a MARS-7 immunodepletion column (Tan *et al.*, 2017). However, while immunodepletion columns are excellent in reducing sample complexity, they possess significant disadvantages such as those outlined in **Table 1**, which must be carefully considered. Encouragingly, Tan *et al.* demonstrated excellent reproducibility from the immunodepletion process, estimating that ~40%–50% of the total plasma proteins (by weight) had been successfully removed with a coefficient of variation of 3.5% (Tan *et al.*, 2017). This low coefficient of variation supports the experimental system and that conditions were tightly controlled during preliminary depletion of the plasma samples.

In addition to immunodepletion, the application of 2D-DIGE in this study further reduced sample complexity by providing two additional layers of separation (i.e., pI and mass) prior to identification of selected gel spots by MALDI-MS/MS. These separations reduced sample complexity by multiple folds, however it did not negate the co-migration of multiple proteins in a single spot (Tiwari and Tiwari, 2014; Abdallah *et al.*, 2012) or the inherent weaknesses of 2D-DIGE that were observed in this study. For example, AHSG and KNG1 proteins were concurrently identified from spot 1921 (Phase 1), and AHSG and VN proteins were identified from spot 1021 (Phase 2). Despite this observation, the results from the DIGE study identified several differentially-expressed proteins which outweighed the observation of co-migration in few gel-spots (Tan *et al.*, 2017).

In addition to 2D DIGE, Tan *et al.* employed iTRAQ LC-MS/MS, an independent approach, using pooled samples. Unlike 2D-DIGE which considers proteoforms as independent gel spots, iTRAQ protein quantitation is inferred from the detected tryptic peptides (Tan *et al.*, 2017). Using this approach, Tan *et al.* identified 385 proteins (Tan *et al.*, 2017). Upon imposing filtering restrictions of a$\geq \pm 1.2$ fold change (p≤ 0.05), ≥ 2 peptides match and 95% confidence, 7 unique proteins were found to be differentially expressed between the rGH-treated and placebo-treated (Group A) samples, whilst 10 unique proteins were found to be differentially-expressed between within the rGH-treated baseline against other time-points (Group B). Six proteins (APOL1, IGFBP-ALS, AFM, IGFBP 3, LUM, and ECM1) were found to be consistently different between Group A and Group B. Surprisingly, only APOL1 was similarly observed in the results of the 2D-DIGE analysis.

These 6 proteins that were identified by iTRAQ and the 3 proteins (APOL1, AHSG and VDBP) that were identified by 2-D DIGE were then proposed as rGH-dependent biomarkers of GH administration. Further statistical analysis showed that two proteins, APOL1 and AHSG, were found to be consistently GH-responsive within the 2D-DIGE studies and that this trend was also observed for APOL1 from the iTRAQ study (Tan *et al.*, 2017). However, AHSG did not show significant difference between rGH-treated and placebo-treated samples in iTRAQ analysis (Tan *et al.*, 2017). To confirm these expression changes, APOL1 and AHSG were evaluated by Western blotting which supported the proteomic results observed (Tan *et al.*, 2017). Unfortunately, AFM, IGFBP3, IGFBP-ALS, LUM and ECM1 proteins, which showed significant differential expression, were not evaluated by Western blotting (Tan *et al.*, 2017). Validation of these observations would be of value for clinical practices and should be evaluated by independent studies.

In summary, Tan *et al.* employed an unbiased proteomic approach to identify eight rGH-dependent plasma proteins. Two of these differentially expressed proteins (APOL1 and AHSG) had not been previously demonstrated to be GH-responsive and indicated potential clinical utility. These putative biomarkers were then validated by Western blotting to confirm both their identities and their expression patterns in the rGH- and placebo-treated subject cohorts (Tan *et al.*, 2017). We believe that independent studies on the remaining putative GH-responsive biomarkers would be of great value for clinical practices by providing an alternate method for detecting the administration of GH to athletes as a performance-enhancing drug.

Case Study II

In the second Case Study, we wish to demonstrate how IPG-IEF can be utilised to profile the technically-challenging membrane fraction of whole cell lysate, enriching low-abundance hydrophobic proteins for detection by LC-MS/MS. In our previously

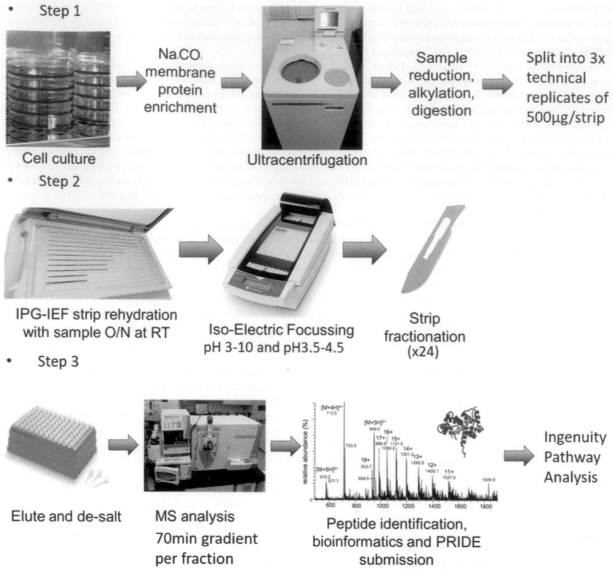

- Step 1

Cell culture → NaCO₃ membrane protein enrichment → Ultracentrifugation → Sample reduction, alkylation, digestion → Split into 3x technical replicates of 500µg/strip

- Step 2

IPG-IEF strip rehydration with sample O/N at RT → Iso-Electric Focussing pH 3-10 and pH3.5-4.5 → Strip fractionation (x24)

- Step 3

Elute and de-salt → MS analysis 70min gradient per fraction → Peptide identification, bioinformatics and PRIDE submission → Ingenuity Pathway Analysis

Fig. 5 Schematic overview of the proteomic workflow employed in the study (Cantor *et al.*, 2013). There are three main steps to the workflow presented. The first involved the culturing of at least 10^8 cells per cell line and strip range, followed by cell lysis, membrane protein enrichment, ultracentrifugation to precipitate the membrane-enriched fraction, sample reduction, alkylation and finally methanol-assisted tryptic digestion. The second step consisted of rehydrating the IPG-IEF strips with the peptide sample, followed by iso-electric focussing, before strip fractionation and elution. The third step of the workflow involved the elution of digested peptides out of the gel strip followed by sample clean-up, MS analysis, peptide identification and bioinformatics analysis.

published work, Cantor *et al.* (2013) generated a proteomic profile of CRC cell lines in order to determine the effect/s of induced expression of a suspected driver of CRC aggression (Cantor *et al.*, 2013). This was achieved by enriching CRC cell lysates for membrane-associated proteins by performing a 0.1 M sodium carbonate wash followed by ultracentrifugation, and has been displayed in a workflow schematic in **Fig. 5** (Cantor *et al.*, 2013).

This simplified enrichment method was employed as integral- or peripheral membrane proteins are often under represented within proteomic studies due to a combination of low relative abundance and reduced aqueous solubility; yet it is the cell membrane which contains the greatest potential for drug targeting or biomarker identification as the plasma membrane contains the interface between the cell and the extracellular space (Yin and Flynn, 2016). Furthermore, integral membrane proteins have been suggested to constitute greater than 60% of current therapeutic targets (Yin and Flynn, 2016). Following reduction, alkylation and methanol-assisted tryptic digestion, the membrane-enriched lysate samples were focussed on linear IPG-IEF strips with pH ranges of 3–10 and 3.5–4.5, respectively, fractionated and desalted to remove MS-incompatible salts (Cantor *et al.*, 2013). Membrane-enriched peptides were then analysed by LC-MS/MS followed by the calculation of normalised spectral abundance factors (NSAF) to test for statistical significance.

Comparing the two cell lines found that 492 proteins were significantly up- or downregulated (p < 0.05) in the pH 3–10 dataset, whilst 263 proteins were significantly different in the pH 3.5–4.5 dataset (Cantor *et al.*, 2013). Interestingly, of these 263 additional proteins, 216 were unique to the pH3.5–4.5 strip range, illustrating that delving deeper into the acidic peptide population was able to bolster the number of proteins identified by 43%, identifying proteins that may have been masked in the broader pH3–10 range (Cantor *et al.*, 2013). In total, 708 proteins were significantly up- or downregulated between the two cell lines, potentially indicating a proteomic signature of inducing the expression of a key cancer-associated protein, the $\alpha v\beta 6$ integrin (Cantor *et al.*, 2013). Pairing sodium carbonate-based membrane protein enrichment with IPG-IEF resulted in the identification of 115 membrane proteins whose expression was significantly different in the pH3–10 dataset, potentially representing actionable biomarkers (Cantor *et al.*, 2013). Once again, the use of the narrower pH range of 3.5–4.5 afforded a deeper insight into the membrane proteome, identifying 186 membrane-associated proteins whose expression was significantly different between the two cell lines (Cantor *et al.*, 2013). This is likely due to fact that while membrane proteins are hydrophobic in nature, they invariably contain hydrophilic peptide sequences that interact with the aqueous environment.

IPG-IEF was a valuable component of this study, providing an inexpensive yet effective insight into the membrane proteome of CRC cell lines in order to identify significant shifts in protein expression that may promote CRC aggression and metastasis. Membrane proteomics has historically been regarded as being inherently difficult due to the nature of the highly hydrophobic sub-population and their relatively low abundance within the cell (Helbig *et al.*, 2010), however, IPG-IEF helped overcome some of these intrinsic challenges. Firstly, adopting IPG-IEF helped reduce sample complexity by providing an additional dimension of sample preparation by separating peptides based on pI prior to separation by reversed phase high performance liquid chromatography prior to in-line MS. By fractionating the sample into 24 pI-based fractions, each 70 min LC-MS/MS gradient was able to observe and fractionate a greater number of peptides than would have been possible for the unfractionated digest. Though this did not remove high-abundance proteins from the sample, low-abundance peptides from proteins of interest (i.e. the urokinase-type plasminogen activator receptor and the αv and $\beta 6$ subunits of the $\alpha v\beta 6$ integrin) were able to be identified by MS for the first time within our research group. Though protein depletion methods such as MARS-14 or immunoaffinity columns are also able to reduce sample complexity, there remains a risk of variable depletion efficiency between proteins (Tu *et al.*, 2010; Pernemalm *et al.*, 2008) and the concomitant loss of non-targeted proteins (Bellei *et al.*, 2011; Zolotarjova *et al.*, 2008). Both of these consequences must be tightly controlled in biomarker discovery studies and require the purchase of expensive consumables to be performed.

The workflow employed in this study was also able to overcome the challenges of membrane protein solubility without resorting to the use of detergents or other MS-incompatible solvents, which would require additional sample clean-up procedures. This in particular was a result of employing methanol-assisted tryptic digestion, wherein proteins were digested in a 60:40 mixture of LC-MS-grade methanol to reduced and alkylated protein preparation (Chick *et al.*, 2008). The use of methanol increases the mobility of integral membrane proteins, increasing tryptic access to cleavage sites that may be shielded by associated proteins or by their proximity to the plasma membrane itself. Methanol is easily removed during routine vacuum drying and provides an inexpensive alternative to detergents such as CHAPS or Triton X-114 which must be carefully removed prior to LC-MS/MS lest they damage the column prior to in-line MS and impede successful liquid chromatography. Though it can be performed without much technical difficulty, it must be mentioned that this label-free workflow was labour intensive, requiring a great deal of sample handling and the generation of considerable amounts of starting material (10–20 mg of lysate protein per cell line and strip range) in order to account for sample loss at each stage of the process. In summary, IPG-IEF proved to be a successful method from the extensive toolbox of proteomic methods and techniques, effectively delving into this particular niche of the CRC proteome.

Discussion

Identifying differentially-expressed proteins is a key requirement to elucidate the molecular processes of cells, tissues or organs, whether they are healthy, responding to hormone treatment or afflicted with diseases such as cancer. The importance of identifying differentially expressed proteins is that it can reveal the associated protein networks that are disturbed or significantly altered between biological conditions. This is particularly important when disturbances can be observed in protein networks responsible for cellular signalling activity or the governance of cellular behaviours such as growth, migration and death. Understanding these disturbed protein networks in cancer specimens can even yield clinically-relevant information such as the potential loss of avenues for therapeutic intervention.

For example, the expression or absence of the estrogen, progesterone and Her-2 receptors are used to classify breast cancers and guide treatment options. The absence of these three oncoproteins in a breast cancer specimen denotes a particularly heterogenous form of breast cancer ('triple-negative') that is characterised by poor clinical outcomes for patients and a lack of targeted treatment options for clinicians (Lawrence *et al.*, 2015). Therefore, there is little purpose in employing treatments that target the Her-2 receptor in order to antagonise triple-negative breast cancers which already lack the expression of the oncoprotein. However, proteomic analysis of the cancer tissue may reveal the molecular features of a tumour specimen and potentially indicate the presence of compensatory signalling pathway activity, such as that observed by Lawrence *et al.* in the Akt1/2 pathway, which may then serve as a personalised option for treatment (Lawrence *et al.*, 2015). Strategies such as those employed by Lawrence *et al.* (2015), have successfully sought to quantify signalling proteins, biological pathways and biomarkers by mass spectrometry. However, despite their extensive study, Lawrence *et al.* employed a very simple sample preparation workflow involving lysis, brief centrifugation, reduction and alkylation followed by digestion with Lys-C or trypsin, desalting and stepped high-pH RP-HPLC prior to LC-MS/MS. Though understandable to adopt a simple shotgun proteomic workflow given the extensive amount of work performed in their study, Lawrence *et al.* were still only able to identify 12,775 distinct proteins encoded by 11,466 out of the estimated 20,537 genes ($\sim 56\%$) with a protein false discovery rate of < 1%. Thus, despite significant advances from identifying ~ 3000 proteins per sample from our study in 2013 to ~ 9000 for each of the twenty samples in 2015 (Lawrence *et al.*, 2015), there remains a great need to increase proteomic coverage in order to identify the technically-challenging or low-abundance biomarkers that remain undetected.

Therefore, linking sequential protein separation methodologies such as IPG-IEF with RP-HPLC fractionation or Hi-Res IPG-IEF stands to greatly increase proteomic coverage (Griffel, 1970). However, this consequently increases sample processing time and may introduce additional layers of handling-based technical variation; both of which are not ideal for biomarker studies. In spite of this, there is no current workflow which can sufficiently overcome all the various challenges of the human proteome. Despite the need to manage the strengths and weaknesses of respective workflows, MS-based methods stand to become increasingly quantitative, meeting the sensitivity and speed to measure proteomes at depths that are comparable to gene expression studies (Lawrence *et al.*, 2015; Kim *et al.*, 2014; Wilhelm *et al.*, 2014). Paired with specific sample preparation and fractionation methods, MS-based investigations are providing an increasingly favoured platform for biomarker discovery compared to the more traditional antibody-based methods. One of the key strengths of MS-based studies is the specificity of the analyte being detected; whilst antibodies recognise a three dimensional epitope that is susceptible to denaturation or proteolysis, MS provides a much more robust *m/z* value, corresponding to the specific mass and charge state for each ionised peptide detected. Though a protein may be degraded by uncontrolled proteolysis, the *m/z* value of a digested peptide will remain unique to that amino acid sequence, whilst remaining unaffected by denaturation of the secondary/tertiary protein structure; a factor that could prevent the formation of the antibody/antigen complex. Though MS-based methods excel at identifying the amino acid sequence of a peptide, they are less capable of identifying the extensive array of post-translational modifications (PTMs) that can occur during protein maturation. These variable structures and less predictable fragmentation patterns are much more difficult to identify from spectra. On the other hand, antibodies can be raised against phosphorylated or glycosylated forms of proteins and detected much more easily and efficiently. MS-based methods are also highly dependent upon the properties of the instrumentation. For example, quadrupole mass spectrometers exhibit greater mass ranges and resolution than ion trap instruments. Time-of-flight-based instruments demonstrate greater mass ranges again and are much faster; however, this comes at the cost of lower resolution and difficulty in adapting to electrospray ionisation. As a result, MS platforms must be carefully chosen in order to ensure that they possess the required capabilities for analysis.

Future Directions

Antibody-based methods have been routinely used in the previous decades of biomolecular research as they offered the ability to be signal-amplifying, detecting small quantities amongst a complex and heterogeneous background which early MS-based approaches had difficulty penetrating. It has only been in recent years with the adoption of efficient sample fractionation methodologies and the continual development of increasingly sensitive and selective MS instruments that MS-based methods have begun to surpass those requiring the use of antibodies.

In this article, we have explored IPG-IEF and its related techniques as a means to identify differentially-expressed proteins that would enable researchers to peer deeper into the observable proteome, shedding further insight into the molecular biology of cells and tissues. Once a distinct set of proteins have been observed to consistently reflect a pathological condition such as disease or cancer, it then will become necessary to validate these potential biomarkers by highly-selective MS methods such as SRM, MRM or sequential window acquisition of all theoretical mass spectra (SWATH) to ensure that the relative shift in protein expression can reproducibly indicate the presence of disease. As data-independent acquisition (DIA) methods such as SWATH begin to supersede most traditional proteomic technologies in the study of whole proteomes, it is important to recognise that it is a costly exercise to generate spectral libraries in order to perform full DIA-based analysis on a patient by patient basis, both in terms of financial cost and the time required.

Despite their weaknesses, MS-based methods are becoming increasingly economical once the capital equipment (i.e., mass spectrometer) has been purchased, with day to day running costs being relatively inexpensive as opposed to the necessity to purchase antibodies and specialised reagents for methods such as ELISA. Furthermore the use of MS-based proteomic workflows counters a key weakness of antibody-based methods which depend upon the availability of specific antibodies (either as a single or pair) which possess sufficient specificity for the analyte. High specificity is a crucial requirement as poor specificity can result in reduced sensitivity, leading to false positive/negative results. This issue also extends to the fact that immunoassays are multi-staged processes that are susceptible to batch-to-batch variation of the antibody itself, with a greater potential for challenges to both intra- and inter-lab reproducibility compared to MS-based workflows. MS-based investigations also stand to facilitate the analysis of smaller sample volumes than methods such as ELISA, requiring smaller sample amounts whilst also enabling further characterisation of the antigen beyond mere abundance. This is afforded by providing sequence identification and potential analysis of protein isoforms and post-translational modifications, which cannot be supported by immunoassays. Whilst both platforms offer the opportunity to multiplex assays, immunoassays offer the simultaneous detection of 92 human proteins by utilising the Olink Proseek proximity extension assays whilst MS is capable of detecting 12,775 distinct protein species (Lawrence *et al.*, 2015; Mahboob *et al.*, 2015).

The continual development and refinement of tools and techniques are helping to reshape the field of proteomics from a role of investigative discovery in biomedical research to a first-response clinical tool (Cantor *et al.*, 2015). These developments support the use of MS as a primary technology in biomarker discovery as protein identifications must be robust, capable of identifying a specific peptide or single reaction monitoring (SRM) transition which may be inherently variable as a result of post-translational modifications or glycosylation. MS stands as an effective method to identify differentially-expressed proteins in a manner that is reproducible between patients and institutions, in order to establish proteins of interest as clinically-relevant biomarkers.

Closing Remarks

All diseases involve proteins and networks of proteins, be it directly or indirectly. As a result, the relative flux of protein populations can be employed as biological insights into disease. However, the key challenge that faces biomedical researchers is the difficulty of finding that one protein of interest amongst the billions of somatic house-keeping proteins that constitute >99% of the cellular proteome. By continuing to drill deeper, it is hoped that the field of proteomics can generate more extensively characterised interpretations of what is occurring both within and between cells. It is the hope that these shifts in expression may ultimately be utilised as a clinical tool, either as a routine diagnostic or surveillance method, indicating the development of a disease before the onset of symptoms and thereby affording clinicians the best chance for a favourable patient outcome.

Acknowledgement

The authors would like to greatly thank Dr. Abidali Mohamedali (Macquarie University, Australia) for proof-reading the manuscript prior to submission. This manuscript has been prepared by the authors in their own time, with each contributing to the text. The authors declare that they received neither financial nor material assistance for the preparation of this work.

Appendix 1: List of gene abbreviations used in the article

Abbreviation	Gene Name	Protein name	UniProtKB accession number
AFM	AFM	Afamin	P43652
AHSG	AHSG	Alpha-2-HS-glycoprotein	P02765
AKR1B10	AKR1B10	Aldo-keto reductase family 1 member B10	O60218
APOA1	APOA1	Apolipoprotein A1	P02647
APOC1	APOC1	Apolipoprotein C-I	P02654
APOL1	APOL1	Apolipoprotein L1	O14791
N-p150	DHX9	ATP-dependent RNA helicase A	Q08211
ECM1	ECM1	Extracellular matrix protein 1	Q16610
VDBP	GC	Vitamin D-binding protein	P02774
GKN1	GKN1	Gastrokine-1	Q9NS71
GSTP1	GSTP1	Glutathione S-transferase P	P09211
N-p68	HNRNPL	Heterogeneous nuclear ribonucleoprotein L	P14866
GRP78	HSPA5	78 kDa glucose-regulated protein	P11021
IGFBP-1	IGFBP1	Insulin-like growth factor-binding protein 1	P08833
IGFBP3	IGFBP3	Insulin-like growth factor-binding protein 3	P17936
IGFBP-ALS	IGFBPALS	Insulin-like growth factor-binding protein complex acid labile subunit	P35858
ILK	ILK	Integrin-linked protein kinase	Q13418
KGN1	KNG1	Kininogen-1	P01042
LGALS1	LGALS1	Galectin-1	P09382
LIX1L	LIX1L	LIX1-like protein	Q8IVB5
LUM	LUM	Lumican	P51884
LYN	LYN	Tyrosine-protein kinase Lyn	P07948
MYO7B	MYO7B	Myosin-VIIb	Q6PIF6
C-p90	NCL	Nucleolin	P19338
PABPC4	PABPC4	Polyadenylate-binding protein 4	Q13310
RAN	RAN	GTP-binding nuclear protein Ran	P62826
C-p89	RIOK1	Serine/threonine-protein kinase RIO1	Q9BRS2
A1AT	SERPINA1	Alpha-1-antitrypsin	P01009
SOD2	SOD2	Superoxide dismutase, mitochondrial	P04179
THBS1	THBS1	Thrombospondin-1	P07996
TNC	TNC	Tenascin-C	P24821
TTR	TTR	Transthyretin	P02766
VN	VTN	Vitronectin	P04004

See also: Analyzing Transcriptome-Phenotype Correlations. Characterization of Transcriptional Activities. Comparative Transcriptomics Analysis. Genome-Wide Scanning of Gene Expression. Natural Language Processing Approaches in Bioinformatics. Regulation of Gene Expression. Statistical and Probabilistic Approaches to Predict Protein Abundance. Survey of Antisense Transcription. Transcriptome Analysis. Transcriptome During Cell Differentiation

References

Abdallah, C., Dumas-Gaudot, E., Renaut, J., Sergeant, K., 2012. Gel-based and gel-free quantitative proteomics approaches at a glance. Int J Plant Genomics 2012, 494572.

Ahn, S.B., Khan, A., 2014. Detection and quantitation of twenty-seven cytokines, chemokines and growth factors pre- and post-high abundance protein depletion in human plasma. EuPA Open Proteomics 3, 78–84.

Bantscheff, M., Schirle, M., Sweetman, G., Rick, J., Kuster, B., 2007. Quantitative mass spectrometry in proteomics: A critical review. Anal Bioanal Chem 389, 1017–1031.

Bellei, E., Bergamini, S., Monari, E., et al., 2011. High-abundance proteins depletion for serum proteomic analysis: Concomitant removal of non-targeted proteins. Amino Acids 40, 145–156.

Bordier, C., 1981. Phase separation of integral membrane proteins in Triton X-114 solution. J Biol Chem 256, 1604–1607.

Branca, R.M., Orre, L.M., Johansson, H.J., et al., 2014. HiRIEF LC-MS enables deep proteome coverage and unbiased proteogenomics. Nat Methods 11, 59–62.

Cantor, D.I., Nice, E.C., Baker, M.S., 2015. Recent findings from the Human Proteome Project: Opening the mass spectrometry toolbox to advance cancer diagnosis, surveillance and treatment. Expert Rev Proteomics 12, 279–293.

Cantor, D., Slapetova, I., Kan, A., Mcquade, L.R., Baker, M.S., 2013. Overexpression of alphavbeta6 integrin alters the colorectal cancer cell proteome in favor of elevated proliferation and a switching in cellular adhesion that increases invasion. J Proteome Res 12, 2477–2490.

Cargile, B.J., Sevinsky, J.R., Essader, A.S., Stephenson Jr., J.L., Bundy, J.L., 2005. Immobilized pH gradient isoelectric focusing as a first-dimension separation in shotgun proteomics. J Biomol Tech 16, 181–189.

Cellar, N.A., Karnoup, A.S., Albers, D.R., Langhorst, M.L., Young, S.A., 2009. Immunodepletion of high abundance proteins coupled on-line with reversed-phase liquid chromatography: A two-dimensional LC sample enrichment and fractionation technique for mammalian proteomics. J Chromatogr B Analyt Technol Biomed Life Sci 877, 79–85.

Chan, K.C., Issaq, H.J., 2013. Fractionation of peptides by strong cation-exchange liquid chromatography. Methods Mol Biol 1002, 311–315.

Chan, P.P., Wasinger, V.C., Leong, R.W., 2016. Current application of proteomics in biomarker discovery for inflammatory bowel disease. World J Gastrointest Pathophysiol 7, 27–37.

Chick, J.M., Haynes, P.A., Bjellqvist, B., Baker, M.S., 2008. A combination of immobilised pH gradients improves membrane proteomics. J Proteome Res 7, 4974–4981.

Essader, A.S., Cargile, B.J., Bundy, J.L., Stephenson Jr., J.L., 2005. A comparison of immobilized pH gradient isoelectric focusing and strong-cation-exchange chromatography as a first dimension in shotgun proteomics. Proteomics 5, 24–34.

Ferlay, J., Soerjomataram, I., Dikshit, R., et al., 2015. Cancer incidence and mortality worldwide: Sources, methods and major patterns in GLOBOCAN 2012. Int J Cancer 136, E359–E386.

Griffel, B., 1970. Kidney in collagen diseases. Harefuah 78, 455–457.

Helbig, A.O., Heck, A.J., Slijper, M., 2010. Exploring the membrane proteome – Challenges and analytical strategies. J Proteomics 73, 868–878.

Hsu, T.Y., Lin, H., Hung, H.N., et al., 2016. Two-dimensional differential gel electrophoresis to identify protein biomarkers in amniotic fluid of Edwards syndrome (Trisomy 18) pregnancies. PLOS ONE 11, e0145908.

Kim, M.S., Pinto, S.M., Getnet, D., et al., 2014. A draft map of the human proteome. Nature 509, 575–581.

Lawrence, R.T., Perez, E.M., Hernandez, D., et al., 2015. The proteomic landscape of triple-negative breast cancer. Cell Rep 11, 630–644.

Liu, B., Qiu, F.H., Voss, C., et al., 2011. Evaluation of three high abundance protein depletion kits for umbilical cord serum proteomics. Proteome Sci 9, 24.

Liu, S., Hao, X., Ouyang, X., et al., 2016. Tyrosine kinase LYN is an oncotarget in human cervical cancer: A quantitative proteomic based study. Oncotarget 7, 75468–75481.

Mahboob, S., Ahn, S.B., Cheruku, H.R., et al., 2015. A novel multiplexed immunoassay identifies CEA, IL-8 and prolactin as prospective markers for Dukes' stages A-D colorectal cancers. Clin Proteomics 12, 10.

Manadas, B., Mendes, V.M., English, J., Dunn, M.J., 2010. Peptide fractionation in proteomics approaches. Expert Rev Proteomics 7, 655–663.

Mathias, R.A., Chen, Y.S., Kapp, E.A., et al., 2011. Triton X-114 phase separation in the isolation and purification of mouse liver microsomal membrane proteins. Methods 54, 396–406.

Mohammed, S., Heck Jr., A.,, 2011. Strong cation exchange (SCX) based analytical methods for the targeted analysis of protein post-translational modifications. Curr Opin Biotechnol 22, 9–16.

Molloy, M.P., 2008. Isolation of bacterial cell membranes proteins using carbonate extraction. Methods Mol Biol 424, 397–401.

Morais-Zani, D.E., Grego, K., Tanaka, A. S, K.F., Tanaka-Azevedo, A.M., 2011. Depletion of plasma albumin for proteomic analysis of *Bothrops jararaca* snake plasma. J Biomol Tech 22, 67–73.

Moreda-Pineiro, A., Garcia-Otero, N., Bermejo-Barrera, P., 2014. A review on preparative and semi-preparative offgel electrophoresis for multidimensional protein/peptide assessment. Anal Chim Acta 836, 1–17.

Mundt, F., Johansson, H.J., Forshed, J., et al., 2014. Proteome screening of pleural effusions identifies galectin 1 as a diagnostic biomarker and highlights several prognostic biomarkers for malignant mesothelioma. Mol Cell Proteomics 13, 701–715.

Nakamura, S., Kahyo, T., Tao, H., et al., 2015. Novel roles for LIX1L in promoting cancer cell proliferation through ROS1-mediated LIX1L phosphorylation. Sci Rep 5, 13474.

Panizza, E., Branca, R.M.M., Oliviusson, P., Orre, L.M., Lehtio, J., 2017. Isoelectric point-based fractionation by HiRIEF coupled to LC-MS allows for in-depth quantitative analysis of the phosphoproteome. Sci Rep 7, 4513.

Pergande, M.R., Cologna, S.M., 2017. Isoelectric point separations of peptides and proteins. Proteomes 5.

Pernemalm, M., Orre, L.M., Lengqvist, J., et al., 2008. Evaluation of three principally different intact protein prefractionation methods for plasma biomarker discovery. J Proteome Res 7, 2712–2722.

Prieto, D.A., Johann Jr., D.J.,., Wei, B.R., et al., 2014. Mass spectrometry in cancer biomarker research: A case for immunodepletion of abundant blood-derived proteins from clinical tissue specimens. Biomark Med 8, 269–286.

Pryde, J.G., 1998. Partitioning of proteins in Triton X-114. Methods Mol Biol 88, 23–33.

Sigdel, T.K., Sarwal, M.M., 2008. The proteogenomic path towards biomarker discovery. Pediatr Transplant 12, 737–747.

Sun, Z., Chen, X., Wang, G., et al., 2016. Identification of functional metabolic biomarkers from lung cancer patient serum using PEP technology. Biomark Res 4, 11.

Tan, S.H., Lee, A., Pascovici, D., et al., 2017. Plasma biomarker proteins for detection of human growth hormone administration in athletes. Sci Rep 7, 10039.

Tiwari, V., Tiwari, M., 2014. Quantitative proteomics to study carbapenem resistance in *Acinetobacter baumannii*. Front Microbiol 5, 512.

Tu, C., Rudnick, P.A., Martinez, M.Y., et al., 2010. Depletion of abundant plasma proteins and limitations of plasma proteomics. J Proteome Res 9, 4982–4991.

Uhlen, M., Fagerberg, L., Hallstrom, B.M., *et al.*, 2015. Proteomics. Tissue-based map of the human proteome. Science 347, 1260419.

Wang, D.L., Xiao, C., Fu, G., Wang, X., Li, L., 2017. Identification of potential serum biomarkers for breast cancer using a functional proteomics technology. Biomark Res 5, 11.

Westermeier, R., 2014. Looking at proteins from two dimensions: A review on five decades of 2D electrophoresis. Arch Physiol Biochem 120, 168–172.

Wilhelm, M., Schlegl, J., Hahne, H., *et al.*, 2014. Mass-spectrometry-based draft of the human proteome. Nature 509, 582–587.

Wu, J.Y., Cheng, C.C., Wang, J.Y., *et al.*, 2014. Discovery of tumor markers for gastric cancer by proteomics. PLOS ONE 9, e84158.

Yin, H., Flynn, A.D., 2016. Drugging membrane protein interactions. Annu Rev Biomed Eng 18, 51–76.

Zolotarjova, N., Mrozinski, P., Chen, H., Martosella, J., 2008. Combination of affinity depletion of abundant proteins and reversed-phase fractionation in proteomic analysis of human plasma/serum. J Chromatogr A 1189, 332–338.

Further Reading

Aebersold, R., Bader, G.D., Edwards, A.M., *et al.*, 2013. The biology/disease-driven human proteome project (B/D-HPP): Enabling protein research for the life sciences community. J Proteome Res 12, 23–27. doi:10.1021/pr301151m.

Amaya, M., Baer, A., Voss, K., *et al.*, 2014. Proteomic strategies for the discovery of novel diagnostic and therapeutic targets for infectious diseases. Pathog Dis 71, 177–189. doi:10.1111/2049-632X.12150.

Anjo, S.I., Santa, C., Manadas, B., 2015. Short GeLC-SWATH: A fast and reliable quantitative approach for proteomic screenings. Proteomics 15, 757–762. doi:10.1002/pmic.201400221.

Baker, M.S., Ahn, S.B., Mohamedali, A., *et al.*, 2017. Accelerating the search for the missing proteins in the human proteome. Nat Commun 8, 14271. doi:10.1038/ncomms14271.

Cao, J., Seegmiller, J., Hanson, N.Q., Zaun, C., Li, D., 2015. A microfluidic multiplex proteomic immunoassay device for translational research. Clin Proteomics 12, 28. doi:10.1186/s12014-015-9101-x.

Chick, J.M., Haynes, P.A., Molloy, M.P., *et al.*, 2008. Characterization of the rat liver membrane proteome using peptide immobilized pH gradient isoelectric focusing. J Proteome Res 7, 1036–1045. doi:10.1021/pr700611w.

Dayon, L., Sanchez, J.C., 2012. Relative protein quantification by MS/MS using the tandem mass tag technology. Methods Mol Biol 893, 115–127. doi:10.1007/978-1-61779-885-6_9.

Eravci, M., Sommer, C., Selbach, M., 2014. IPG strip-based peptide fractionation for shotgun proteomics. Methods Mol Biol 1156, 67–77. doi:10.1007/978-1-4939-0685-7_5.

Gao, Y., Wang, X., Sang, Z., *et al.*, 2017. Quantitative proteomics by SWATH-MS reveals sophisticated metabolic reprogramming in hepatocellular carcinoma tissues. Sci Rep 7, 45913. doi:10.1038/srep45913.

Lee, M.S., Ji, Q.C. (Eds.), 2017. Protein Analysis using Mass Spectrometry: Accelerating Protein Biotherapeutics from Lab to Patient. John Wiley & Sons, Inc. Available at: http://dx.doi.org/10.1002/9781119371779

Ponten, F., Schwenk, J.M., Asplund, A., Edqvist, P.H., 2011. The Human Protein Atlas as a proteomic resource for biomarker discovery. J Intern Med 270, 428–446. doi:10.1111/j.1365-2796.2011.02427.x.

Relevant Websites

https://www.proteinatlas.org
    Human Protein Atlas.
www.nature.com/subjects/proteomic-analysis
    Nature.com.
https://www.nextprot.org/
    NeXtprot.
http://www.srmatlas.org/
    SRM Atlas.
https://www.hupo.org
    The Human Proteome Organisation (HUPO).
http://www.missingproteins.org/protein/web/
    The Missing ProteinPedIa.

Biographical Sketch

David Cantor is a Scientific Officer with extensive experience in proteomic research. After being awarded a Bachelor of Medical Science (Hons) from Macquarie University in 2011, he undertook a PhD in Biomedical Sciences, investigating the role of the αvβ6 in integrin in colorectal cancer. During this project, he performed an array of proteomic and phenotypic studies in order to elucidate the molecular biology of this putative oncogene. After being awarded his PhD in 2017, he has been responsible for the preparation and analysis of various samples/specimens within the Australian Proteome Analysis Facility (APAF). He has trained multiple students in the performance of IPG-IEF and other proteomic workflows and has authored or co-authored several scientific publications in the field.

Harish Cheruku is a PhD graduate with extensive experience in proteomic research. After being awarded a Master of Biotechnology from Macquarie University in 2010, he worked as a Research Assistant and continued on to a PhD in Biomedical Sciences, investigating the biology of transforming growth factor-beta (TGFβ) in colorectal cancer. He utilised an extensive set of proteomic tools to elucidate the effects TGFβ in colorectal cancer during his PhD which was awarded in 2017. He has extensive experience in label-free and label-based proteomic workflows in addition to various cell and molecular biology techniques. He has authored or co-authored several scientific publications in the field.

Clinical Proteomics

Marwenie F Petalcorin, Queen Mary University of London, London, United Kingdom
Naeem Shafqat and Zen H Lu, Universiti Brunei Darussalam, Bandar Seri Begawan, Brunei Darussalam
Mark IR Petalcorin, PAPRSB Institute of Health Sciences, Universiti Brunei Darussalam, Bandar Seri Begawan, Brunei Darussalam

Introduction

Clinical proteomics is the study of the entire protein content measured in patient's samples at a specific state or condition. Its primary goal is to analyze global protein profile of a biological system (cells, tissues, fluids) at a specific time point and state to confirm diagnosis, monitor treatment, screen for diseases, and take prognostic medical decisions (He and Chiu, 2003; Kulasingam and Diamandis, 2008a,b). The term "clinical" comes from the Greek word "klinike," which means "bedside," and the term "proteomics" is derived from both "proteome" and "omics" referring to the large-scale study of proteins including modified structures, variants, and mutations collectively called "proteoforms" (Schmit *et al.*, 2017; Toby *et al.*, 2016; Patrie, 2016; Wasinger *et al.*, 1995; Wilkins *et al.*, 1996a,b; Trenchevska *et al.*, 2016; Thygesen *et al.*, 2018). There is currently a tremendous amount of discoveries and information on proteins derived by mass spectrometry (MS) that can be applied in the clinic and can eventually revolutionize medical sciences and treatment. Although the amount of clinical proteomic profiles generated by MS measurements is remarkably increasing during the past two decades as indicated by the increase in rate of publications (**Fig. 1**), there is still a current gap between the patient's proteome profile and the real time conversion of these protein data into a more meaningful format that can reliably be applied in the clinics (Geyer *et al.*, 2017; Carvalho *et al.*, 2015; Lisitsa *et al.*, 2014; Kelleher *et al.*, 2014).

Multiparametric Panel of Proteome Profiles

Traditional clinical biochemistry relies on laboratory investigation results based on only a few single individual protein biomarkers, such as alanine aminotransferase (in liver function test), albumin, and creatinine (in kidney function test) among many others, to diagnose, treat, and monitor diseases while clinical proteomics considers profiling, which is the detection of panels of multiple biomarkers that provide more sensitivities and specificities (Penn *et al.*, 2018; Geyer *et al.*, 2017). In an era of information deluge with increasing data storage capacity and faster computational capability, the current challenge is how to increase further the technological advancement in proteomics instrumentation and data processing. The multiparametric and global nature of proteomic profiles derived from a patient's sample requires translation into a more useful form that is clinically relevant and more suitable in making diagnostic and prognostic decisions over the health status of patients (Matthiesen and Carvalho, 2013; Matthiesen, 2013a,b). This means increasing the sensitivity and robustness of MS-based instruments coupled with good experimental design standardized sampling techniques and more powerful bioinformatics analysis. This is necessary to generate accurate multiple biomarker profile panels that truly reflect the entire complement of proteins at a given particular state and condition (Matthiesen and Carvalho, 2013; Matthiesen and Bunkenborg, 2013; Penn *et al.*, 2018).

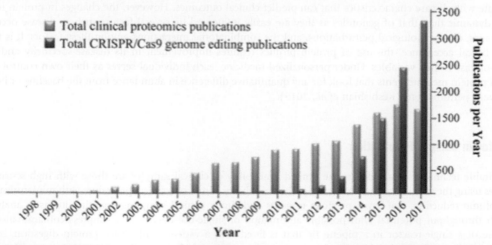

Fig. 1 Clinical proteomics and CRISPR/Cas9 literature review comparison. Total number of publications using MS-based clinical proteomics (blue) in comparison with the total number of publications in CRISPR/Cas9 (red), which is a technology that revolutionized genome editing recently and driving the medical field towards personalized treatments.

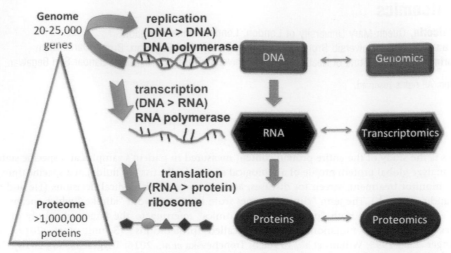

Fig. 2 Pathway from genome to proteome. Proteome is the entire complement of proteins including modifications produced by an organism or system. This set of proteins varies with time, physiological condition, and exposure to environment including stress that the cell or organism experience. Comparing between genome and proteome, genomics focuses on products of replicating the genetic code from DNA to another DNA mediated by DNA polymerase. Transcriptomics studies the products after transcribing DNA to RNA by the action of RNA polymerase. Proteomics, on the other hand, investigates the products of protein synthesis that uses the genetic code in RNA to produce proteins through ribosomal activity. The human genome is static over time with approximately 20,000 genes, which can be amplified by polymerase chain reaction (PCR), while the human proteome is dynamic that changes over time with more than 1,000,000 different proteins (according to the partial proteome map published in 2014) that determine functionalities of cells, tissues, and the human body.

Post-Translational Modifications in Proteoforms

Following the identification of about 20,500 genes after the completion of the human genome sequence in the year 2000, the "omics" era including genomics, transcriptomics, metabolomics, and proteomics began to receive a lot more attention (Van Karnebeek *et al.*, 2018; Piening *et al.*, 2018; Lacoste, 2018). The focus of scientific efforts has shifted from the human genome towards identifying the entire human proteome and measuring all the coded proteins and proteoforms (**Fig. 2**). Each gene gives rise to many proteins of various derivatives and alterations that cater to a particular specific functional role for homeostasis maintenance of the body's biological processes. These functional alterations are achieved by differential RNA splicing and post-translational modifications (PTM), such as phosphorylation, glycosylation, acetylation, proteolytic processing, and numerous other types of PTMs that can diversify protein structure, conformation, and functionalities to produce over a million types of proteins comprising the entire human proteome (Nickchi *et al.*, 2015; Sergeant *et al.*, 2017). Simultaneously analyzing multiple changes in PTMs by quantitative PTMomics is useful for biomarker discovery and disease mechanisms elucidation using low amounts of tissue or body fluids (Thygesen *et al.*, 2018). Diseases occur with deviation from the normal homeostatic metabolic processes resulting in specific and detectable changes in protein profiles. Thus, direct measurements of the global protein changes can be performed by MS to determine both the diseased and normal states of the human body. The protein patterns in a patient sample correlate with disease characteristics that can predict clinical outcomes. However, the changes in protein levels are more complex and dynamic than that of genomics as they are easily influenced by several factors such as disease occurrence, environmental changes, diet or biological perturbations, and the combinatorial interactions among these factors. It is for this reason that to gain clinical acceptance, the use of protein profiles requires improvement in its disease-specificity and sensitivity by reducing non-disease-related variables. Under personalized medicine, each individual serves as their own control across various time points of protein measurements that look for any quantitative difference in abundance from the baseline or before and after clinically relevant perturbations (Keshishian *et al.*, 2015).

Single Reactor in Sample Preparation

The most desirable techniques that address the limited availability of clinical samples are those with high sensitivity to detect protein profiles using the smallest amount of sample. The desirability of microanalytical procedure with miniaturization is defined by sample volume reduction that saves precious reagents and limits clinical sampling resulting in faster analysis time, and increased high throughput potential with possible automation of single-use devices that suppress contamination (Lion *et al.*, 2004). The use of a single-reactor in a pipette tip that is fitted with a variety of filters for protein digestion, separation, and purification (Kulak *et al.*, 2014) is less invasive showing improvement in the efficiency of sample preparation with minimal sample loss (Hughes *et al.*, 2014). To avoid protein alteration or contamination and to optimize protein digestion, a known concentration of samples is separated from reaction salts that impede readout and is stored at a specified temperature. Samples are labeled with

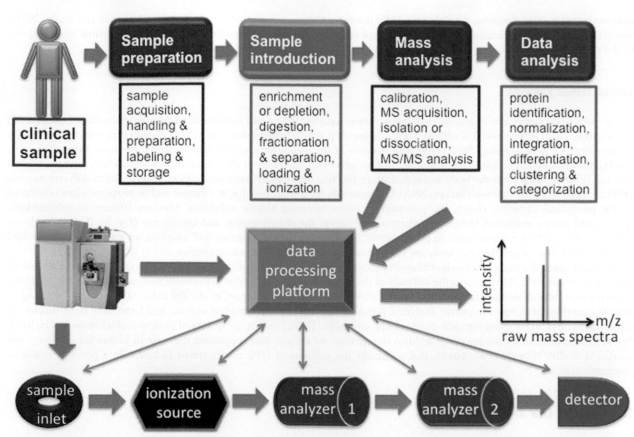

Fig. 3 *Mass spectrometry-based clinical proteomics workflow* from clinical sample acquisition and introduction to mass and data analysis. All mass analyzers use electromagnetic fields to manipulate gas-phase ions. Results are plotted as *spectra*, with mass-over-charge (*m/z*) on the X-axis and ion intensity on the Y-axis. The latter can be *absolute* (counts) or *relative*. The *ionization source* ensures that (a part) of the *sample* molecules are ionized and brought into the gas phase. The *detector* is an electron multiplier responsible for recording the presence of ions as signals that represent the abundance of the analyte. *Digitizers* (analog to digital converters, ADC) transform the continuous analog detector signal into a digital, discretized spectrum by data processing. The two *ion sources* are: (1) *MALDI* (matrix assisted laser desorption and ionization), which relies on matrix molecules alpha-cyano-hydroxycinnamic acid (CHCA), sinapinic acid (SA), 2,5-dihydroxybenzoic acid (DHB), and a pulsed nitrogen UV laser ($\upsilon = 337$ nm) and produce singly charged peptide ions; and (2) *ESI* (Electrospray ionization), which heats the needle to 40–100C to facilitate nebulization and evaporation, and produces multiple charged peptide ions (2^+, 3^+, 4^+). Mass analyzers include: (a) Time-of-flight (TOF) relates *m/z* to the velocity of the ion, and the speed to the travel time the field-free tube length; (b) ion trap (IT) operates by effectively trapping the ions in an oscillating electrical field achieving mass separation by ejecting only ions of a specific mass; (c) quadrupole (Q) uses a combined RF AC and DC current creating a high-pass mass filter between the first two rods and a low-pass mass filter between the other two rods permitting only a specific *m/z* interval; (d) *orbitrap* consists of an outer and inner coaxial electrode generating an electrostatic field in which the ions form an orbitally harmonic oscillation along the axis of the field where the frequency of the oscillation is inversely proportional to the m/z, and can again be calculated by Fourier transform. *Tandem mass spectrometry (MS/MS, MS²)* is accomplished by using two mass analyzers in series (tandem). The first mass analyzer performs the function of ion selector, by selectively allowing only ions of a given *m/z* to pass through while the second mass analyzer is situated after triggering fragmentation and is used in its normal capacity as a mass analyzer for the fragments.

stable isotopes for mass identification and data quantification with reference to the protein sequence databases and the peptide quantitative information (Bantscheff and Kuster, 2012; Bantscheff *et al.*, 2012). Various methods have emerged in handling different types of samples. The range of human protein abundance is from 0.01 to 10,000 ppm (Wang *et al.*, 2012) with high abundance proteins such as extracellular matrix (ECM) in tissues masking the low abundance cellular proteins resulting in a narrow proteome coverage (Mann *et al.*, 2013). For instance, differences of protein levels in normal and tumor tissues are measured and used to select against cancer cells that proliferate disproportionately and to identify drug targets or weak points in a cancer cell (Soldes *et al.*, 1999a,b; Seow *et al.*, 2001; Celis *et al.*, 1999a,b,c, 2002; Celis and Gromov, 1999; Meehan *et al.*, 2002; Franzen *et al.*, 1997; Bini *et al.*, 1997).

In sample handling (**Fig. 3**), storage conditions affect the serum peptidome MS profiles suggesting the importance of standardized blood sampling and storage for biobanks and interlaboratory multistudies using serum samples. Variations in proteome profiles can be avoided by standardizing sample collection considering the time between venipuncture and serum preparation that affects peptidome patterns (Tsuchida *et al.*, 2018). Targeted in situ peptide fractionation in shotgun proteomics aims to reduce the complexity of peptide mixtures. This is achieved by selective enrichment of those digested peptides that possess specific features enabling them to bind into functionalized filter material in pipette tips. The nonbinding nontargeted peptides flow through as unbound fraction after digestion. A good example for this is the CS-trap sample preparation method (Zougman and Banks, 2015), which uses the quartz depth filter surface functionalized with the pyridyl-dithiol group thereby allowing reversible in situ capture of the peptides with cysteines in the suspension trap-based digest (Zougman and Banks, 2015).

Human Tissue Samples

Protein analysis is carried out in two types of human tissue samples, frozen and formalin-fixed paraffin-embedded tissues (FFPE) (Wisniewski, 2013; Wisniewski et al., 2013). Cancer diagnosis is generally dependent upon the FFPE with properly preserved tissue morphology and good staining. FFPE works with majority of the tissues for easy maintenance and long-term storage (Fox et al., 1985). However protein profiles vary in samples that are processed differently at the preanalytical phase such as the time interval between tissue removal from the body and stabilization affecting data quality. Moreover, tissues collected from different patients exhibit variation in protein levels (Becker, 2015). Differences in protein profiles due to a disease and its progression are influenced by the procedural variables. Hence, the preanalytical phase involving sample collection, handling (transport, stabilization), storage, and analyte extraction need standardization to increase the sample quality and consistency (Fig. 3). Performing histological examination on samples prior to protein extraction to verify the cell structure and adopting an internationally standard step-by-step process of preanalytical assay are important for a systematized workflow (Becker, 2015) (Fig. 3).

Assessing tissues for cancer studies is challenging because they are comprised of cell populations that are a mixture of neoplastic and nonneoplastic cells. To overcome the difficulty of detecting indistinct signals due to the noise from surrounding cells, the laser capture tissue microdissection and cell sorting are now extensively used (Cecconi et al., 2011a,b). Microanalysis handling of minute quantities of samples improves analytical performance with reduced sampling volume and faster time to obtain results (Lion et al., 2004). In handling formalin-fixed paraffin-embedded (FFPE) tissues, the quality of protein profiles measured by label-free MS is less affected by the length of archival storage time for tissues, thus supporting their use in biomarker discovery and validation studies (Craven et al., 2013). This will make the millions of FFPE tissues stored in biobanks a practical source of proteomic samples.

Enrichment of Low Abundance Proteins

Biological fluids contain a wide range of protein levels having the high-abundant proteins obscuring the detection of low-abundant proteins. The approach to mitigate this challenge is to remove the overabundant proteins thereby reducing the dynamic range of protein levels in the sample. Antibody-based affinity is used for selective removal of unwanted highly abundance specific proteins by binding the unwanted proteins to recover the flow-through consisting of low abundance proteins. Multiple affinity removal system is used in biological fluid proteomics to deplete abundant proteins by bundling to the carrier proteins thereby enriching detection of low abundance deep proteome (Krief et al., 2012; Darde et al., 2007). To address this, the affinity bound fraction is analyzed doubling the number of samples entering the downstream process (Giorgianni and Beranova-Giorgianni, 2016). Another method of reducing the level of high-abundant proteins is through the use of dynamic range compression that uses combinatorial ligand libraries in capturing and preferentially enriching low-abundant proteins (Righetti and Boschetti, 2008). This approach allows equalization of all proteins where high-abundant proteins are decreased and low-abundant proteins are boosted (Giorgianni and Beranova-Giorgianni, 2016). Another alternative technique is by using biochemical fractionation where peptides or proteins are divided into several fractions thereby reducing complexity in each fraction (Keshishian et al., 2015). Sampling of body fluids for discovery and development of new biomarkers is in a form of serum/plasma, urine, cerebrospinal fluid, saliva, or bronchoalveolar lavage fluid. Prior to processing, the nonprotein elements are removed including the impurities such as cell debris, salts, lipids, and other minute molecular components. Fluids containing very low protein level undergo initial centrifugation to remove particles and contaminants followed by concentration of protein analytes and cleaning by either ultrafiltration with membrane filters or by protein precipitation with acetone or trichloroacetic acid.

Clinical Sample Processing: Electrospray Ionization and Matrix-Assisted Laser Desorption/Ionization

Proteomics by MS has two major approaches, comprehensive and targeted proteomics, which generally follow a workflow that includes sample preparation, protein extraction, protein digestion, peptide separation, mass analysis, and protein identification, validation, and biochemical characterization (Fig. 3). Comprehensive proteomics aims to identify all proteins in a sample using search algorithms like Mascot, Andromeda, SEQUEST, and so on (see Table 1). Targeted proteomics is used to program mass spectrometers into analyzing the preselected set of peptides produced by cleaving target proteins with Trypsin, LysC, or other proteases (Tsiatsiani and Heck, 2015).

Various samples, such as, cells, tissues, or body fluids, have been used in proteomics to characterize the entire protein content (Aebersold and Mann, 2016; Aebersold et al., 2016). These samples are analyzed to diagnose particular diseases using an array of potential protein biomarkers measured that can indicate the incidence of outcome or disease (Ruhaak et al., 2016). A promising biomarker molecule must exhibit precision, sensitivity, and reproducibility (Chahrour et al., 2015) as accurately quantified by

Table 1   List of bioinformatics tools useful for clinical proteomics

Bioinformatics tools	Website/Source	Description
A-Score	https://www.ncbi.nlm.nih.gov/pubmed/16964243	A probability-based score that measures the probability of correct phosphorylation site localization based on the presence and intensity of site-determining ions in MS/MS spectra (Beausoleil et al., 2006).
Andromeda	https://omictools.com/andromeda-tool	A peptide search engine based on probabilistic scoring with performance similar to Mascot that handles data with arbitrarily high fragment mass accuracy, assigns and scores complex patterns of PTM, and accommodates extremely large databases (Cox et al., 2011).
APOSTL	https://github.com/bornea/APOSTL	Automated Processing of SAINT Templated Layouts (APOSTL) is a freely available Galaxy-integrated software suite and analysis pipeline for reproducible, interactive analysis of affinity proteomics (AP-MS) data using Galaxy workflows, which are intuitive for the user to move from raw data to publication-quality figures within a single interface.
Bio-TDS	http://biotds.org/)	Bio-TDS (Bioscience Query Tool Discovery Systems assists researchers in retrieving the most applicable analytic tools by allowing them to formulate their questions as free text using a flexible retrieval system that affords users from multiple bioscience domains (e.g., genomic, proteomic, bioimaging) the ability to query over 12,000 analytic tool descriptions integrated from well-established, community repositories.
CPAS	https://www.ncbi.nlm.nih.gov/pubmed/16396501	The open-source Computational Proteomics Analysis System contains an entire data analysis and management pipeline for liquid chromatography tandem mass spectrometry (LC-MS/MS) proteomics, including experiment annotation, protein database searching and sequence management, and mining LC-MS/MS peptide and protein identifications featuring general experiment annotation component, installation software, and data security management useful for collaborative projects across geographical locations and for proteomics laboratories without substantial computational support (Rauch et al., 2006).
DBToolkit	http://genesis.UGent.be/dbtoolkit/	DBToolkit allows the processing of protein sequence databases to peptide-centric sequence databases to enhance optimized search spaces for efficient identification of peptide fragmentation spectra obtained by mass spectrometry and for solving a range of other typical tasks in processing sequence databases (Martens et al., 2005).
ExPASy	https://www.expasy.org/	SIB Bioinformatics Resource Portal that provides access to scientific databases and software tools in proteomics, genomics, phylogeny, systems biology, population genetics, transcriptomics (expasy.org).
gpmdb	http://gpmdb.thegpm.org	The Global Proteome Machine Database provides the information obtained by GPM servers to aid in validating peptide MS/MS spectra and protein coverage patterns, integrated into the GPM server pages allowing users to quickly compare their experimental results with the best results previously observed by other users of the machine (thegpm.org).
IDPicker	http://proteowizard.sourceforge.net/idpicker/	IDPicker views and filters peptide-spectrum-matches by reading and combining results from many different proteomic identification tools, including database search engines and spectral library matches.
InsPecT	https://bioinfo.ird.fr/index.php/resources/49-uncategorised/111-inspect	INsPECT (INtracellular ParasitE CounTer) is a free and open source software dedicated to automate quantification of Leishmania intracellular parasites based on fluorescent DNA images.
IntAct	https://www.ebi.ac.uk/intact/	IntAct provides a freely available, open source database system and analysis tools for molecular interaction data derived from literature curation or direct user submissions (ebi.ac.uk).
InterPro	https://www.ebi.ac.uk/interpro/	InterPro provides functional analysis of proteins by families, predicted domains and important sites with searchable resource for protein signatures from powerful integrated database and diagnostic tool (ebi.ac.uk).
itracker	https://www.ncbi.nlm.nih.gov/pmc/articles/PMC1276793/	i-Tracker software extracts reporter ion peak ratios from noncentroided tandem MS peak lists in a format easily linked to the results of protein identification tools such as Mascot and Sequest.
jPOSTrepo	https://repository.jpostdb.org/)	An international standard data repository for proteomes with a high-speed file uploading, flexible file management, and easy-to-use interfaces containing various proteomic datasets and is available for researchers worldwide.
MASCOT	http://www.matrixscience.com	A powerful search engine that integrates all of the proven methods of searching using the mass spectrometry data to identify proteins from primary sequence databases and serves as a benchmark for identification, characterization and quantitation of proteins. (matrixscience.com)
MaxQuant	http://www.biochem.mpg.de/5111795/maxquant	A quantitative proteomics software package that analyzes large-scale mass-spectrometric data sets using a set of algorithms that includes peak detection and scoring of peptides for mass calibration, database searching, protein identification, quantitation of identified proteins, and provision of summary statistics.
ModifiComb	https://www.ncbi.nlm.nih.gov/pubmed/16439352	Maps hundred types of PTM at a time including novel and unexpected PTMs.

(Continued)

Table 1   Continued

Bioinformatics tools	Website/Source	Description
MSAmanda	http://ms.imp.ac.at/?goto=msamanda	A scoring algorithm for high mass accuracy generally applicable to HCD, ETD, and CID fragmentation type data that provides free of charge both as stand alone version for integration into custom workflows and as a plugin for the Proteome Discoverer platform (Dorfer *et al.*, 2014).
msCompare	https://trac.nbic.nl/mscompare),	A modular framework that allows the arbitrary combination of different feature detection/quantification and alignment/matching algorithms with a novel scoring method to evaluate their overall performance and to assess the performance of workflows built from modules of publicly available data processing packages such as SuperHirn, OpenMS, and MZmine.
mzIdentML	http://www.psidev.info/mzidentml.	Proteomics Standards Initiative mzIdentML open data standard captures the outputs of peptide and protein identification software supporting scores associated with localization of modifications on peptides, statistics performed at the level of peptides, identification of cross-linked peptides, and support for proteogenomics approaches.
neXtProt	https://www.nextprot.org)	The neXtProt human protein knowledgebase focuses on proteomics and genetic variation data for over 85% of the human proteins, as well as new tools tailored to the proteomics community including over 8000 phenotypic observations for over 4000 variations in a number of genes involved in hereditary cancers and channelopathies.
OMSSA	http://proteomicsresource.washington.edu/protocols06/omssa.php	A free search engine for analyzing and identifying peptides from tandem mass spectrometry (ms/ms) peptide spectra using the OMSSA algorithm that scores peptide hits using a probability-based method comparing experimental fragments with those calculated from libraries of known protein sequences (proteomicresource.washington.edu).
Panther Classification System	http://pantherdb.org	The PANTHER (**P**rotein **AN**alysis **TH**rough **E**volutionary **R**elationships) Classification System classifies proteins (and their genes) to facilitate high throughput analysis. The PANTHER Classifications are the result of human curation as well as sophisticated bioinformatics algorithms (pantherdb.org).
PaxDb	https://pax-db.org/about	A meta-resource of whole-organism and tissue-resolved data covering 85,000 proteins in 12 model organisms that integrates information on absolute protein abundance levels with emphasis on deep coverage, consistent postprocessing, and comparability across different organisms.
PDBe	http://www.ebi.ac.uk/pdbe/	(Protein Database Europe) European resource that provides the collection, organization and dissemination of data on macromolecular structures (ebi.ac.uk).
PEAKS	https://academic.oup.com/bioinformatics/article/23/2/243/204806	Analyzes any group of sequences that share a known reference element, such as the transcription start site, the initiation codon, a known TFBS or any other predefined site to detect any other motifs that show a significant clustering at a particular distance from the reference element, or sequence positions that show matches to motifs from a user-selected library.
PepNovo	http://proteomics.ucsd.edu/software-tools/531-2/	A high throughput de novo peptide sequencing analysis for tandem mass spectrometry (MS/MS) data that produces models of peptide fragmentation events by using a probabilistic network and a likelihood ratio hypothesis test to detect if peaks are produced under the fragmentation model or under a probabilistic model.
Peptide fragment fingerprinting	http://prowl.rockefeller.edu/prowl/pepfrag.html	PepFrag identifies proteins from a collection of sequences that matches a single tandem mass spectrum (expasy.org).
Peptide sequence database	http://pepbank.mgh.harvard.edu	Database of peptides based on sequence text mining and public peptide data sources that stores only peptides with 20 amino acids or shorter and with available sequences (pepbank.mgh.harvard.edu).
PeptideAtlas	http://www.peptideatlas.org	It is a multiorganism, publicly accessible compendium of peptides identified in a large set of tandem mass spectrometry experiments that provides output files collected from human, mouse, yeast, and several other organisms, searchable using the latest search engines and protein sequences containing the raw data, search results, and full builds (peptideatlas.org).
Peptidome (NCBI Peptide Data Resources)	http://www.ncbi.nlm.nih.gov/peptidome.	A public resource that archives and freely distributes tandem MS peptide and protein identification data generated by the scientific community, promotes sharing and dissemination of experimental data at a level of detail that is useful to both the specialized community and to the general biological community (ncbi.cnim.nih.gov).
Perseus	http://www.biochem.mpg.de/5111810/perseus	A software package for shotgun proteomics data analyses that extracts biologically meaningful information from processed raw files and performs bioinformatic analyses of the output of MaxQuant thereby completing the proteomics analysis pipeline (coxdocx.org).
Phenyx	http://www.ionsource.com/functional_reviews/Phenyx/phenyx-web.htm	Phenyx is a new sequence search engine based on the true probabilistic and flexible scoring system OLAV that uses mass spectrometry data to identify proteins and provide an automated second round search function.
PRIDE	https://www.ebi.ac.uk/pride/archive/	PRIDE database is a centralized, standards compliant, public data repository for proteomics data including protein and peptide identifications, PTM, supporting spectral evidence that provides a single point to submit MS-based proteomics data to public domain repositories (ebi.ac.uk).

Table 1 Continued

Bioinformatics tools	Website/Source	Description
ProDom	http://prodom.prabi.fr/prodom/current/html/home.php	ProDom is a comprehensive set of protein domain families automatically generated from the UniProt Knowledge Databases, constructed automatically by clustering homologous segments consisting of domain family entries that provides a multiple sequence alignment of homologous domains and a family consensus sequence (prodom.prabi.fr).
ProSite	https://prosite.expasy.org	Provides documentation entries describing protein domains, families and functional sites as well as associated patterns and profiles to identify them (prosite.expasy.org).
ProteinProphet	http://proteinprophet.sourceforge.net	ProteinProphet™ automatically validates protein identification made on the basis of peptides assigned to MS/MS spectra by database search programs such as SEQUEST.
ProteomicsDB	https://www.ProteomicsDB.org	A protein-centric in-memory database for the exploration of large collections of quantitative mass spectrometry-based proteomics data to enable the interactive exploration of the first draft of the human proteome.
Proteowizard	http://proteowizard.sourceforge.net	The ProteoWizard Library and Tools are a set of modular and extensible open source, cross-platform tools and software libraries that facilitate proteomics data analysis and enable rapid tool creation by providing a robust, pluggable development framework, which simplifies and unifies data file access, and performs standard chemistry and LCMS dataset computations.
PTM Score	http://www.bioinfor.com/peaks-ptm/	Identifies and characterizes PTMs of proteins such as phosphorylation, ubiquitination, acetylation, and methylation that play critical roles in diverse biological processes such as signaling and regulatory processes, protein activity and degradation, regulation of gene expression essential for a comprehensive understanding of cellular biology and human diseases with a wide range of applications.
R	https://www.r-project.org	R is a free, software environment for statistical analysis, with many useful features that promote and facilitate reproducible research (r-project.org).
ROTS	https://www.bioconductor.org/packages/ROTS).	The reproducibility-optimized test statistic adjusts a modified t-statistic according to the inherent properties of the data and provides a ranking of the features based on their statistical evidence for differential expression between two groups applicable in transcriptomics and proteomics.
SEQUEST	https://omictools.com/sequest-tool	SEQUEST provides fragmentation patterns in tandem mass spectra to detect AAS from protein and nucleotide database, correlates the spectrum and allows searches with the experimental data via the prediction of fragment ions of an AAS and offers to users the ability to correlate exactly uninterpreted tandem mass spectra to sequences in the database (omictools.com).
Skyline	http://proteome.gs.washington.edu/software/skyline	An open source and freely available windows client application for targeted proteomics method creation and quantitative data analysis that simplifies the development of mass spectrometer methods and the analysis of data from targeted proteomics experiments performed using SRM.
SMART	http://smart.embl-heidelberg.de	SMART (Simple Modular Architecture Research Tool) allows the identification and annotation of genetically mobile domains and the analysis of domain architectures (embl-hidelberg.de).
Spectrum Mill	https://www.agilent.com/en/products/software-informatics/masshunter-suite/masshunter-for-life-science-research/spectrum-mill	Spectrum Mill for MassHunter Workstation quickly identifies proteins and peptides through fast database searches with automatic or manual match validation and unique algorithms that minimize false positives, offers de novo spectral interpretation for proteins not found in databases, identifies relative abundance differences of two-fold or greater without complicated isotope labeling, and summarizes results in formats that provide maximum insight and convenience.
SWISS-PROT	https://web.expasy.org/docs/swiss-prot_guideline.html	Curated protein sequence database that provides a high level of annotation, minimal level of redundancy and high level of integration with other databases (Bairoch et al., 2004).
TOPP	http://ftp.mi.fu-berlin.de/pub/OpenMS/release-documentation/html/index.html	TOPP (The OpenMS Proteomics Pipeline) provides a set of computational tools combined into easy analysis pipelines for nonexperts of proteomics workflows with useful utilities file format conversion, peak picking, and supports known applications (e.g., Mascot) to generate new algorithmic techniques for data reduction and data analysis.
TPP	http://tools.proteomecenter.org/wiki/index.php?title=Software:TPP	The Trans-Proteomic Pipeline is a collection of integrated tools for MS/MS proteomics developed at the SPC.
UniProt (universal Protein Resource)	http://www.uniprot.org	A comprehensive resource for protein sequence and annotation data that provides the scientific community with a comprehensive, high quality and freely accessible resource of protein sequence and functional information (Bairoch et al., 2005) (uniprot.org).
X!Tandem	http://www.thegpm.org/TANDEM	X! Tandem open source is software that can match tandem mass spectra with peptide sequences in protein identification.
ZBIT Bioinformatics Toolbox	https://webservices.cs.uni-tuebingen.de/.	The Center for Bioinformatics Tuebingen (ZBIT) Bioinformatics Toolbox provides web-based access to a collection of bioinformatics tools developed for systems biology, protein sequence annotation, and expression data analysis (Romer et al., 2016).

proteomic technologies. Electrospray ionization (ESI) and matrix-assisted laser desorption/ionization (MALDI) are the two main technologies for sample processing in MS that focus on quantitative proteomics analysis. ESI processes neutral compounds to generate ions that are detected as mass/charge (*m/z*) ratio of each peptide, which is recorded by a computer and shown as a mass spectrum (Ho *et al.*, 2003). MALDI on the other hand uses a laser beam to light up a solid sample into an ionized form that travels through the mass spectrometer, detected and translated into the mass/charge (*m/z*) measurements (Andersson *et al.*, 2010; Duncan *et al.*, 2016). Variability of outcome in protein measurements depends on sample handling whereby protein denaturation, incomplete digestions, desalting, and depletion failures, which cause loss of pertinent data, need to be avoided (Buchler *et al.*, 2016). Both the molecular labeling method used to tag samples for quantification and the resolution capacity of MS also influence results, and thus need consideration early on in the experimental design prior to measurements (Tsuchida *et al.*, 2018). Quantification of targeted proteomics depends on selected or multiple reaction monitoring, which requires complex statistical analysis, and validation of the result is laborious. Several groups endeavor to improve the validation by developing the Sequential Windowed Acquisition of All Theoretical Fragment Ion Mass Spectra in combination with a nontargeted acquisition or combining different ion sources without any interference in a single mass spectrometer (Kostyukevich and Nikolaev, 2018).

Bottom-Up and Top-Down Proteomics

Proteomics is divided into two types of analysis based on whether the measurements are made on broken-to-pieces proteins (bottom-up proteomics) and intact proteins (top-down proteomics). Although top-down proteomics is advantageous for examining protein modifications, it is not as well-established as the bottom-up approach, facing more technical challenges as intact proteins are more complicated to handle with their poor solubility than peptides. Bottom-up or shotgun proteomics is easier to fractionate in liquid chromatography and easier to analyze in tandem mass spectrometer (LC-MS/MS) due to their smaller size and easier transfer to MS through ESI. Using proteases, proteins are first converted to small pieces of peptides, into which measurements are performed. Proteins are digested with trypsin that cleaves after every lysine and arginine residues resulting in truncated peptides of around 6–25 amino acids, although other proteases are also used. MS is then applied to measure the mass-to-charge ratio of each peptide in mixtures of thousands of peptides to determine the amino acid sequence. There are four stages of the process, consisting of sample preparation, separation of peptides, MS, and bioinformatics analysis of the data (**Fig. 3**). The critical factor in this approach is the sample preparation that requires protein fractionation or depletion methodologies to isolate low-abundant proteins. Peptide matches also need examination and manual validation for a series of consecutive sequence-specific b-type and y-type ions. Moreover, the correct peptide sequence and accurate quantification of proteins are achieved by using a newer generation of mass spectrometers with higher resolution. In targeted LC-MS/MS, a set of phenotypic/signature peptides containing the target protein sequences are selected using bioinformatics tools such as UniProt Database, Expasy, PeptideAtlas, and so on (**Table 1**). The selected peptides are then synthesized as labeled internal standards (absolute quantification AQUA (Gerber *et al.*, 2007, 2003), QconCAT (Beynon *et al.*, 2014), PSAQ (Dupuis *et al.*, 2008)), chromatographed, eluted by ESI to MS, detected, and measured in available platform of LC-MS/MS (**Fig. 3**). Targeted MS/MS instruments include quadrupole-Orbitraps and quadrupole time-of-flight with high resolution of 140–240,000 and 100,000, and with mass accuracy of 2 ppm and 2–5 ppm, respectively.

Top-down proteomics identifies intact proteins containing PTMs including the truncated proteoforms translated from reference ORFs or alternative open reading frames (altORFs) increasing the size of the actual proteome. Top-down proteomics can provide the whole sequence information of the proteoforms useful in analyzing various structural modifications due to variations in genes, RNA, and proteins (**Fig. 2**). Top-down mass spectral database searches that align millions of spectra against thousands of protein sequences in high throughput proteome level analyses have been made available recently (Leduc *et al.*, 2018; Kou *et al.*, 2018). In MALDI-imaging or MALDI-IMS, proteins including their molecular arrangement in samples are analyzed. It can scan a broad range of protein from a tissue section at defined geometrical coordinates producing an ion-density map. A fresh-frozen tissue section is used resembling the real tissue where the relative abundance of the selected ion is displayed on a color-intensity scale at each coordinate location (pixel) (Seeley *et al.*, 2008). MALDI-IMS has limited mass range that detects only small proteins thus needing further enhancement. MALDI-TOF-MS provides a rapid technique to identify microorganisms useful in pathogenic bacteria taxonomy, clinical microbiology, and food safety (Fagerquist, 2017).

An important step in proteomics is validation that is needed in translating research into the clinic. Confirmation by Western blotting excludes false-positive results. The functional significance of the molecules involved is verified by *in vitro* or *in vivo* assays, which demonstrate inhibition or activation of the pathway followed by analysis of its biological effects. *In situ* validation uses antibodies to detect isoforms such as phosphorylated proteins at specific locations. Several antibodies are used to validate the various components of a pathway (Cecconi *et al.*, 2011b).

Personalized Proteomics and Precision Medicine

Currently drug prescription for patients is based on general information about what generally works. If the medication is not working then the patient is switched to another medicine based on trial and error, which sometimes results in adverse drug responses making patients suffer from side effects of unnecessary or inappropriate use of medications. This approach to treatment is now changing with the progress made in personalized medicine. P4 medicine (preventive, predictive, personalized, and participatory) tailors medical treatment to the individual characteristics, needs, and preferences of a patient during all stages of care, including prevention, diagnosis, treatment, and follow-up (Tian et al., 2012; Van Karnebeek et al., 2018). The patient's treatment is catered upon their individual genetic makeup, entire genetic profile, and personalized proteomics data (Duarte and Spencer, 2016). Proteomics studies open the door for the clinicians to understand diseases at protein levels. A collection of protein data in combination with the DNA information provides insights into the development of therapies. Proteomics connects the gap between diagnostics and therapeutics by facilitating detection of protein biomarkers (Jain, 2016). Pharmaceutical industries use clinical proteomics to determine relevant drug targets, which are typically proteins that play many important roles in the metabolic pathways (Snyder et al., 2014). The FDA and other agencies also request protein profiles in new drug development, attracting high interest for both for the healthcare sector, as well as the pharmaceutical and biotech industry (Szasz et al., 2017; Marko-Varga and Labaer, 2017).

To illustrate the potential of proteomic analysis, a study was conducted in bladder cancer using different proteomic platforms. In bladder cancer cases, the degree of tumor spread into the bladder wall is classified into three different categories, namely non-muscle invasive, muscle invasive, and metastatic disease (Babjuk et al., 2017). The monitoring device is invasive cystoscopy, which uses a thin camera to look inside the bladder of patients. However, having proteomics profiling of urine and tissues decreases the dependency on invasive cystoscopy improving bladder cancer patient management. In this example, the negative result avoids the unnecessary cystoscopy invasion while the positive result points to a more thorough examination. Tissue molecular profiling further revealed that bladder cancer is a highly heterogeneous disease with genetic alterations found in the adjoining tissues in bladder cancer patients (Thomsen et al., 2017). Detailed assessment of molecular alterations indicates the direct site of disease initiation and progression thus is beneficial in identifying potential therapeutic targets and prediction of treatment response. Urine proteome profiling enables diagnosis, monitoring, and stratification by looking at the gradual change of the amount of urinary peptides as the cancer advances (Latosinska et al., 2017a,b).

Several studies have utilized proteomics to identify biomarkers. For example, endogenous peptide of pleiotrophin was identified as a new biomarker of Alzheimer's disease (Blennow and Zetterberg, 2015). A group of Japanese researchers have also identified leucine-rich alpha-2 glycoprotein as a potential biomarker to diagnose Kawasaki disease based on proteomics analysis (Kimura et al., 2017). High throughput verification of hundreds of biomarker candidate proteins to detect early stage colorectal cancer was done using targeted proteomics resulting in identification of the annexin family of proteins as promising colorectal cancer biomarker candidates (Shiromizu et al., 2017). With the improvement and enhancements made in the proteomic technologies, workflows, computational tools, instruments, and availability of data obtained from other "omics" analysis, personalized medicine is now becoming possible although there are still limitations that need to be mitigated. Proteomics data are useful in designing a treatment plan distinct to the condition the individual experiences.

Proteoform Bioinformatics

The Human Proteome Project (HPP) (see "Relevant Websites section") was created through the coordinated efforts of many research laboratories around the world with the goal of mapping the entire human proteome (Omenn et al., 2017). It has two main goals: The comprehensive and systematic analysis of the human proteome map and the creation of analytical tools to measure proteins relevant in health and disease (Segura et al., 2017). In 2014, two independent groups published the first draft of human proteome using many different tissues by MS, thereby, putting proteomics into the spotlight and laying a foundation for development of diagnostic, prognostic, therapeutic, and preventive medical applications. The advances in biology using technologies that produce high throughput data have fueled the development of systems biology. ProteomicsDB (see "Relevant Websites section") enables interactive use of the human proteome and its large quantitative MS database (Schmidt et al., 2018). Powerful bioinformatics tools are much needed to enable new applications of proteomics data in precision medicine and in the clinics. JS-MS is a stand-alone cross-platform that enables 3-D visualization for MS data processing and evaluation (Rosen et al., 2017).

The SWISS-PROT is an annotated protein sequence database created by A. Bairoch on 21 July 1986 that integrates with other databases at that time including EMBL Nucleotide Sequence Database, PDB (Protein Data Bank), PIR (Protein Identification Resource), HIV (the human retroviruses and AIDS Database), OMIM (the online version of the book *Mendelian Inheritance in Man*), PROSITE (the Dictionary of Protein Sites and Patterns), and REBASE (the database of type 2 restriction enzymes) (Bairoch and Boeckmann, 1991). The first software developed for 2DE image analysis in 1979 was ELSIE, which was followed by a vast array of current proteomics tools such as ExPASsy, IntAct, InterPro, Matrix Science, OMSSA, Panther Classification System, PDBe (Protein Database Europe), PeptideAtlas, Peptidome (NCBI Peptide Data Resources), PRIDE, ProDom, ProSite, thegpmdb, SEQUEST, UniProt (universal Protein Resource), R, and SMART among many others (see **Table 1**). The neXtProt is a protein knowledgebase (see "Relevant Websites section") that focuses on proteomics and genetic variation data for over 85% of the human proteins, includes new proteomics tools and over 8000 phenotypic observations for over 4000 variations in genes involved in hereditary cancers and channelopathies, and provides an API access and a SPARQL endpoint for technical applications (Gaudet et al., 2017).

Clinical proteomics involves a complex process that starts with sample extraction and processing, followed by protein and peptide fractionation, MS measurement, and finally protein identification and quantification (**Fig. 3**) (Mallick and Kuster, 2010).

The synergy of the high throughput MS-based proteomics data along with the network-based computational analysis has facilitated the investigation of the cellular networks associated with certain disease important to basic and clinical research (Schmidt *et al.*, 2014). Bioinformatics has provided the tools and methods necessary for processing genetic information from patients integrating the clinical, environmental and genetic data. It has played a vital role in generating, storing, and curating protein sequence databases, developing relevant software for the proteomics data analysis, integrating protein interaction networks, and consolidating data from other "omics" to produce a meaningful biological information (Felgueiras *et al.*, 2018; Uppal *et al.*, 2018).

Several steps are involved in bioinformatics, namely: (1) Collecting statistics from biological data, (2) building a computational model, (3) solving a computational modeling problem, and (4) testing and evaluating computational algorithm (Can, 2014). A successful analysis outcome is obtained by integrating proteomics data with other "omics" data using data-driven integration and network analysis tool such as xMWAS, for example (Uppal *et al.*, 2018). Various repositories have also been created such as PeptideAtlas (Desiere *et al.*, 2006; Deutsch *et al.*, 2005; Schwenk *et al.*, 2017), GPMDB (Craig *et al.*, 2006), PRoteomics IDEntifications (PRIDE) (see "Relevant Websites section") (Martens *et al.*, 2005; Vizcaino *et al.*, 2016a,b), UniProt (The Uniprot Consortium, 2018), and neXtProt (Gaudet *et al.*, 2017) among many others that store proteomics experimental information. These repositories were designed to be made publicly available and can be directly used or reused in producing novel findings, which would generate new knowledge (Jarnuczak and Vizcaino, 2017; Vizcaino *et al.*, 2017; Okuda *et al.*, 2017; Chen *et al.*, 2017; Keerthikumar and Mathivanan, 2017). These data can be used for investigation and mining to extract relevant, usable, and quality information for clinical application (Islam *et al.*, 2017). To assess the key steps of MS data analysis process, database search engines, and methods in quality control (QC), protein assembly and data integration, the entrapment sequence method has been used as the standard (Feng *et al.*, 2017).

The HPP provides MS and antibody-based data on all human proteins from various physiological and pathological conditions (Omenn *et al.*, 2017). For 15 years, the Proteomics Standards Initiative of the Human Proteome Organization (HUPO) has provided guidelines for sharing data sets to the public establishing open community standards and software tools for proteomics such as PSI-MI, XML, MITAB, mzML, mzIdentML, mzQuantML, mzTab, and the MIAPE (Minimum Information About a Proteomics Experiment) (Deutsch *et al.*, 2017). One of its key aspects is the use of standardized and well-defined terminology to complete the values in the data files (Mayer *et al.*, 2014). Moreover, two novel standard data formats (proBed and proBAM) for proteogenomics were recently developed with functionalities in file generation, file conversion, and data analysis (Menschaert *et al.*, 2018) improving the integration of genomics and proteomics information and the evaluation of peptide spectrum matches (PSM). An easy-to-use tool proBAMconvert (see "Relevant Websites section") allows conversion of mzIdentML, mzTab, and pepXML file formats to proBAM/probed or output at PSM and peptide levels using a command line and graphical user interface (Olexiouk and Menschaert, 2017). Furthermore, several ongoing analytical designs are nearly completed including formats for a spectral library standard, a universal spectrum identifier, the qcML quality control, and the Protein Expression Interface web services Application Programming Interface in synergy with ProteomeXchange Consortium, HPP, and other "omics" community (Deutsch *et al.*, 2017). Additional initiatives such as multiorganism proteome (iMOP) (Tholey *et al.*, 2017), the Human Cancer Proteome Project (Cancer-HPP) (Jimenez *et al.*, 2018), the Human Eye Proteome Project (EyeOme) (Ahmad *et al.*, 2018), Chromosome-Centric Human Proteome Project (C-HPP) (Meyfour *et al.*, 2018), Human Immuno-Peptidome Project (Caron *et al.*, 2017), fecal proteome (Jin *et al.*, 2017) among many others are examples that support HPP in proteome research aimed at improving the human health using multiparameter diagnostics applicable for personalized medicine.

The Human Protein Atlas provides protein localization and expression data in human tissues and cells (Thul and Lindskog, 2018). It has a collection of antibodies to map the entire human proteome by immunohistochemistry and immunocytochemistry generating more than 10 million images of protein expression patterns at a single-cell level (see "Relevant Websites section") (Thul and Lindskog, 2018). These resources can be freely accessed allowing scientists and clinicians to explore the human proteome. Public data sharing used to be problematic but is now becoming feasible encouraged by the scientific journals and funding agencies as part of good scientific practice (Spidlen and Brinkman, 2018) and enhanced by the availability of user-friendly online resources and tools (Perez-Riverol *et al.*, 2016a,b). To bypass difficulty of data sharing due to variable types of data formats, the PSI of the HUPO has lead the development of standard file formats and controlled vocabularies (Vizcaino *et al.*, 2017; Bittremieux *et al.*, 2017). A popular format is mzML, which stores raw MS data and processed peak list spectra (Martens *et al.*, 2011). The freely available pymzML (see "Relevant Websites section") has optimized source code and data retrieval algorithms, provided faster random access to compressed files and quicker numerical calculations, suitable for large file sizes having a versatile scripting language (Kosters *et al.*, 2018). Another format is mzIdentML for peptide and protein identifications obtained from MS data that allows various software tools to communicate with each other (Vizcaino *et al.*, 2017). Moreover, the mzQuantML data standard format records detailed quantitative information (Walzer *et al.*, 2013) from a variety of popular discovery based workflows such as SILAC or dimethyl or MS2 tag based TMT or iTRAQ. This format is now able to store results from targeted techniques such as selected/parallel reaction monitoring (SRM). The ProteoWizard's msConvert and msConvertGUI softwares are useful in converting data from vendor-specific propriety binary files generated by diverse mass spectrometers to open-format files (Adusumilli and Mallick, 2017). Recently a simpler text-based format called msTab was produced that stores both identification and quantification information (Griss *et al.*, 2014). It follows a tabular design making it simpler to load into a spreadsheet. MzTab is now supported as part of popular analysis tools such as PRIDE, MassIVE, and jPOST. The PRIDE Inspector Toolsuite is a freely available modular set of open-source cross-platform libraries for handling and visualizing different experimental output files including spectra (mzML, mzXML), peptide and protein identification data (mzIdentML, PRIDE XML, mzTab), and quantification data (mzTab, PRIDE XML) (see "Relevant Websites section") (Perez-Riverol *et al.*, 2016b).

With open-access data, QC of proteomics has been given more importance and attention recently. Relevant software tools for performing QC are now available, which assess the consistency of the data submission in a form of correspondence between the mass spectra and identification results, detecting clear annotation errors, ensuring acceptable level of technical and biological metadata. Users of Pride Inspector, a freely available tool to browse MS proteomic data are also encouraged to flag any potential errors detected.

Bioinformatics plays a key role in various aspects of proteomics analysis including peptide-spectra matching (PSM) based on the new data-independent acquisition paradigm, resolving missing proteins, dealing with biological and technical heterogeneity in data and statistical feature selection. Further work is still required to enhance the proteomic analysis, performance, and reproducibility so that it can be applied in clinical medicine. More powerful bioinformatics tools with greater accuracy and resolution, faster protein identification algorithms, reduced false positives, and automated data validation capabilities that allow the consolidation of results from multiple studies will enable deeper understanding of the full proteome map of tissues or cells. Linking various omics is important to achieve proper interpretation of complex biological systems.

Conclusion

Examining the proteome is likened to getting a "snapshot" of the total protein environment at any given time point to have various insight into what is happening in the cell and how the cells are working. Interaction among proteins is a dynamic process that changes quickly over time but can be captured in proteome analysis to predict the underlying causes of diseases. The capability of time course proteomics data as a monitoring process is confirmed in several experiments such as the analysis of dynamic responses to ER stress in HeLa cell proteome (Cheng *et al.*, 2016), the discovery of different features of human metabolism in long-term space travel simulation experiments (Binder *et al.*, 2014), and the measurements of proteome dynamics in pathological cardiac hypertrophy model (Lau *et al.*, 2018) among many others. The proteome map illustrates beneficial information about the patients' well being and the effectiveness of any drug administration for treatment. Through proteomics, molecules that affect drug target identification such as proteoforms and all modified proteins are characterized to develop more effective novel drugs with fewer side effects (Kuhlmann *et al.*, 2018; Daher and De Groot, 2018). Quantitative analysis of these proteoforms has been anticipated to deliver the next generation of multiparametric biomarkers applicable in personalized medicine (Mueller *et al.*, 2018). But approval of these biomarkers in the clinic requires a tremendous amount of work involving standardized collection of samples from patients towards simplifying the grand scale of the collected protein information into something that can easily be interpreted as useful by health care professionals (Schmit *et al.*, 2017; Nedelkov, 2017). Although faced with a lot of challenges, it is just a matter of time before the application of proteomics in personalized medicine by proteome profiling of an individual's condition is achieved in a clinical setting. The use of bioinformatics in clinical proteomic research has not been exploited extensively as most have favored the wet lab based activities (Akhter and Shehu, 2018). However, big proteomics data generated would certainly bring benefits to the clinical environment particularly in the understanding of the molecular origins of pathologies and drug mechanisms (Trindade *et al.*, 2018).

See also: Disease Biomarker Discovery. Drug Repurposing and Multi-Target Therapies. Experimental Platforms for Extracting Biological Data: Mass Spectrometry, Microarray, Next Generation Sequencing. Identification and Extraction of Biomarker Information. Natural Language Processing Approaches in Bioinformatics. Sequence Analysis

---

References

Adusumilli, R., Mallick, P., 2017. Data conversion with ProteoWizard msConvert. Methods in Molecular Biology 1550, 339–368.

Aebersold, R., Bensimon, A., Collins, B.C., Ludwig, C., Sabido, E., 2016. Applications and developments in targeted proteomics: From SRM to DIA/SWATH. Proteomics 16, 2065–2067.

Aebersold, R., Mann, M., 2016. Mass-spectrometric exploration of proteome structure and function. Nature 537, 347–355.

Ahmad, M.T., Zhang, P., Dufresne, C., Ferrucci, L., Semba, R.D., 2018. The human eye proteome project: Updates on an emerging proteome. Proteomics 18 (5–6), e1700394.

Akhter, N., Shehu, A., 2018. From extraction of local structures of protein energy landscapes to improved decoy selection in template-free protein structure prediction. Molecules 23.

Andersson, M., Andren, P., Caprioli, R.M., 2010. MALDI imaging and profiling mass spectrometry in neuroproteomics. In: Alzate, O. (Ed.), Neuroproteomics. FSL: Boca Raton.

Babjuk, M., Bohle, A., Burger, M., *et al.*, 2017. EAU guidelines on non-muscle-invasive urothelial carcinoma of the bladder: Update 2016. European Urology 71, 447–461.

Bairoch, A., Apweiler, R., Wu, C.H., *et al.*, 2005. The Universal Protein Resource (UniProt). Nucleic Acids Research 33, D154–D159.

Bairoch, A., Boeckmann, B., Ferro, S., Gasteiger, E., 2004. Swiss-Prot: Juggling between evolution and stability. Briefing in Bioinformatics 5, 39–55.

Bairoch, A., Boeckmann, B., 1991. The SWISS-PROT protein sequence data bank. Nucleic Acids Research 19 (Suppl.), 2247–2249.

Bantscheff, M., Kuster, B., 2012. Quantitative mass spectrometry in proteomics. Analytical and Bioanalytical Chemistry 404, 937–938.

Bantscheff, M., Lemeer, S., Savitski, M.M., Kuster, B., 2012. Quantitative mass spectrometry in proteomics: Critical review update from 2007 to the present. Analytical and Bioanalytical Chemistry 404, 939–965.

Beausoleil, S.A., Villen, J., Gerber, S.A., Rush, J., Gygi, S.P., 2006. A probability-based approach for high-throughput protein phosphorylation analysis and site localization. Nature Biotechnology 24, 1285–1292.

Becker, K.F., 2015. Using tissue samples for proteomic studies-critical considerations. Proteomics Clinical Applied 9, 257–267.

Beynon, R.J., Armstrong, S.D., Gomez-Baena, G., *et al.*, 2014. The complexity of protein semiochemistry in mammals. Biochemical Society Transactions 42, 837–845.

Binder, H., Wirth, H., Arakelyan, A., et al., 2014. Time-course human urine proteomics in space-flight simulation experiments. BMC Genomics 15 (Suppl. 12), S2.

Bini, L., Magi, B., Marzocchi, B., et al., 1997. Protein expression profiles in human breast ductal carcinoma and histologically normal tissue. Electrophoresis 18, 2832–2841.

Bittremieux, W., Walzer, M., Tenzer, S., et al., 2017. The human proteome organization-proteomics standards initiative quality control working group: Making quality control more accessible for biological mass spectrometry. Analytical Chemistry 89, 4474–4479.

Blennow, K., Zetterberg, H., 2015. Understanding biomarkers of neurodegeneration: Ultrasensitive detection techniques pave the way for mechanistic understanding. Nature Medicine 21, 217–219.

Buchler, R., Wendler, S., Muckova, P., Grosskreutz, J., Rhode, H., 2016. The intricacy of biomarker complexity-the identification of a genuine proteomic biomarker is more complicated than believed. Proteomics Clinical Applications 10, 1073–1076.

Can, T., 2014. Introduction to bioinformatics. Methods in Molecular Biology 1107, 51–71.

Caron, E., Aebersold, R., Banaei-Esfahani, A., Chong, C., Bassani-Sternberg, M., 2017. A case for a Human Immuno-Peptidome Project Consortium. Immunity 47, 203–208.

Carvalho, A.S., Penque, D., Matthiesen, R., 2015. Bottom up proteomics data analysis strategies to explore protein modifications and genomic variants. Proteomics 15, 1789–1792.

Cecconi, D., Lonardoni, F., Favretto, D., et al., 2011a. Changes in amniotic fluid and umbilical cord serum proteomic profiles of foetuses with intrauterine growth retardation. Electrophoresis 32, 3630–3637.

Cecconi, D., Palmieri, M., Donadelli, M., 2011b. Proteomics in pancreatic cancer research. Proteomics 11, 816–828.

Celis, J.E., Celis, P., Ostergaard, M., et al., 1999a. Proteomics and immunohistochemistry define some of the steps involved in the squamous differentiation of the bladder transitional epithelium: A novel strategy for identifying metaplastic lesions. Cancer Research 59, 3003–3009.

Celis, J.E., Celis, P., Palsdottir, H., et al., 2002. Proteomic strategies to reveal tumor heterogeneity among urothelial papillomas. Molecular and Cellular Proteomics 1, 269–279.

Celis, J.E., Gromov, P., 1999. 2D protein electrophoresis: Can it be perfected? Current Opinion in Biotechnology 10, 16–21.

Celis, J.E., Ostergaard, M., Rasmussen, H.H., et al., 1999b. A comprehensive protein resource for the study of bladder cancer: http://biobase.dk/cgi-bin/celis. Electrophoresis 20, 300–309.

Celis, J.E., Wolf, H., Ostergaard, M., 1999c. Proteomic strategies in bladder cancer. IUBMB Life 48, 19–23.

Chahrour, O., Cobice, D., Malone, J., 2015. Stable isotope labelling methods in mass spectrometry-based quantitative proteomics. Journal of Pharmaceutical and Biomedical Analysis 113, 2–20.

Chen, C., Huang, H., Wu, C.H., 2017. Protein bioinformatics databases and resources. Methods in Molecular Biology 1558, 3–39.

Cheng, Z., Rendleman, J., Vogel, C., 2016. Time-course proteomics dataset monitoring HeLa cells subjected to DTT induced endoplasmic reticulum stress. Data in Brief 8, 1168–1172.

Cox, J., Neuhauser, N., Michalski, A., et al., 2011. Andromeda: A peptide search engine integrated into the MaxQuant environment. Journal of Proteome Research 10, 1794–1805.

Craig, R., Cortens, J.C., Fenyo, D., Beavis, R.C., 2006. Using annotated peptide mass spectrum libraries for protein identification. Journal of Proteome Research 5, 1843–1849.

Craven, R.A., Cairns, D.A., Zougman, A., et al., 2013. Proteomic analysis of formalin-fixed paraffin-embedded renal tissue samples by label-free MS: Assessment of overall technical variability and the impact of block age. Proteomics Clinical Applications 7, 273–282.

Daher, A., De Groot, J., 2018. Rapid identification and validation of novel targeted approaches for Glioblastoma: A combined ex vivo-in vivo pharmaco-omic model. Experimental Neurology 299, 281–288.

Darde, V.M., Barderas, M.G., Vivanco, F., 2007. Depletion of high-abundance proteins in plasma by immunoaffinity subtraction for two-dimensional difference gel electrophoresis analysis. Methods in Molecular Biology 357, 351–364.

Desiere, F., Deutsch, E.W., King, N.L., et al., 2006. The PeptideAtlas project. Nucleic Acids Research 34, D655–D658.

Deutsch, E.W., Eng, J.K., Zhang, H., et al., 2005. Human Plasma PeptideAtlas. Proteomics 5, 3497–3500.

Deutsch, E.W., Orchard, S., Binz, P.A., et al., 2017. Proteomics standards initiative: Fifteen years of progress and future work. Journal of Proteome Research 16, 4288–4298.

Dorfer, V., Pichler, P., Stranzl, T., et al., 2014. MS Amanda, a universal identification algorithm optimized for high accuracy tandem mass spectra. Journal of Proteome Research 13, 3679–3684.

Duarte, T.T., Spencer, C.T., 2016. Personalized proteomics: The future of precision medicine. Proteomes 4.

Duncan, M.W., Nedelkov, D., Walsh, R., Hattan, S.J., 2016. Applications of MALDI mass spectrometry in clinical chemistry. Clinical Chemistry 62, 134–143.

Dupuis, A., Hennekinne, J.A., Garin, J., Brun, V., 2008. Protein Standard Absolute Quantification (PSAQ) for improved investigation of staphylococcal food poisoning outbreaks. Proteomics 8, 4633–4636.

Fagerquist, C.K., 2017. Unlocking the proteomic information encoded in MALDI-TOF-MS data used for microbial identification and characterization. Expert Review of Proteomics 14, 97–107.

Felgueiras, J., Silva, J.V., Fardilha, M., 2018. Adding biological meaning to human protein-protein interactions identified by yeast two-hybrid screenings: A guide through bioinformatics tools. Journal of Proteomics 171, 127–140.

Feng, X.D., Li, L.W., Zhang, J.H., et al., 2017. Using the entrapment sequence method as a standard to evaluate key steps of proteomics data analysis process. BMC Genomics 18, 143.

Fox, C.H., Johnson, F.B., Whiting, J., Roller, P.P., 1985. Formaldehyde fixation. Journal of Histochemistry and Cytochemistry 33, 845–853.

Franzen, B., Linder, S., Alaiya, A.A., et al., 1997. Analysis of polypeptide expression in benign and malignant human breast lesions. Electrophoresis 18, 582–587.

Gaudet, P., Michel, P.A., Zahn-Zabal, M., et al., 2017. The neXtProt knowledgebase on human proteins: 2017 update. Nucleic Acids Research 45, D177–D182.

Gerber, S.A., Kettenbach, A.N., Rush, J., Gygi, S.P., 2007. The absolute quantification strategy: Application to phosphorylation profiling of human separase serine 1126. Methods in Molecular Biology 359, 71–86.

Gerber, S.A., Rush, J., Stemman, O., Kirschner, M.W., Gygi, S.P., 2003. Absolute quantification of proteins and phosphoproteins from cell lysates by tandem MS. Proceedings of the National Academy of Sciences of the United States of America 100, 6940–6945.

Geyer, P.E., Holdt, L.M., Teupser, D., Mann, M., 2017. Revisiting biomarker discovery by plasma proteomics. Molecular Systems Biology 13, 942.

Giorgianni, F., Beranova-Giorgianni, S., 2016. Phosphoproteome discovery in human biological fluids. Proteomes 4.

Griss, J., Jones, A.R., Sachsenberg, T., et al., 2014. The mzTab data exchange format: Communicating mass-spectrometry-based proteomics and metabolomics experimental results to a wider audience. Molecular and Cellular Proteomics 13, 2765–2775.

He, Q.Y., Chiu, J.F., 2003. Proteomics in biomarker discovery and drug development. Journal of Cellular Biochemistry 89, 868–886.

Ho, C.S., Lam, C.W., Chan, M.H., et al., 2003. Electrospray ionisation mass spectrometry: Principles and clinical applications. Clinical Biochemist Reviews 24, 3–12.

Hughes, C.S., Foehr, S., Garfield, D.A., et al., 2014. Ultrasensitive proteome analysis using paramagnetic bead technology. Molecular Systems Biology 10, 757.

Islam, M.T., Mohamedali, A., Ahn, S.B., et al., 2017. A systematic bioinformatics approach to identify high quality mass spectrometry data and functionally annotate proteins and proteomes. Methods in Molecular Biology 1549, 163–176.

Jain, K.K., 2016. Role of proteomics in the development of personalized medicine. In: Advances in Protein Chemistry and Structural Biology 102, pp. 41–52.

Jarnuczak, A.F., Vizcaino, J.A., 2017. Using the PRIDE database and ProteomeXchange for submitting and accessing public proteomics datasets. Current Protocols in Bioinformatics 59, 13.31.11–13.31.12.

Jimenez, C.R., Zhang, H., Kinsinger, C.R., Nice, E.C., 2018. The cancer proteomic landscape and the HUPO Cancer Proteome Project. Clinical Proteomics 15, 4.

Jin, P., Wang, K., Huang, C., Nice, E.C., 2017. Mining the fecal proteome: From biomarkers to personalised medicine. Expert Review of Proteomics 14, 445–459.

Keerthikumar, S., Mathivanan, S., 2017. Proteomic data storage and sharing. Methods in Molecular Biology 1549, 5–15.

Kelleher, N.L., Thomas, P.M., Ntai, I., Compton, P.D., Leduc, R.D., 2014. Deep and quantitative top-down proteomics in clinical and translational research. Expert Review of Proteomics 11, 649–651.

Keshishian, H., Burgess, M.W., Gillette, M.A., et al., 2015. Multiplexed, quantitative workflow for sensitive biomarker discovery in plasma yields novel candidates for early Myocardial Injury. Molecular and Cellular Proteomics 14, 2375–2393.

Kimura, Y., Yanagimachi, M., Ino, Y., et al., 2017. Identification of candidate diagnostic serum biomarkers for Kawasaki disease using proteomic analysis. Scientific Reports 7, 43732.

Kosters, M., Leufken, J., Schulze, S., et al., 2018. pymzML v2.0: Introducing a highly compressed and seekable gzip format. Bioinformatics.

Kostyukevich, Y.I., Nikolaev, E.N., 2018. Ion source multiplexing on a single mass spectrometer. Analytical Chemistry 90 (5), 3576–3583.

Kou, Q., Wu, S., Liu, X., 2018. Systematic evaluation of protein sequence filtering algorithms for proteoform identification using top-down mass spectrometry. Proteomics 18 (3–4)

Krief, G., Deutsch, O., Zaks, B., et al., 2012. Comparison of diverse affinity based high-abundance protein depletion strategies for improved bio-marker discovery in oral fluids. Journal of Proteomics. 75, 4165–4175.

Kuhlmann, L., Cummins, E., Samudio, I., Kislinger, T., 2018. Cell-surface proteomics for the identification of novel therapeutic targets in cancer. Expert Review of Proteomics. 1–17.

Kulak, N.A., Pichler, G., Paron, I., Nagaraj, N., Mann, M., 2014. Minimal, encapsulated proteomic-sample processing applied to copy-number estimation in eukaryotic cells. Nature Methods 11, 319–324.

Kulasingam, V., Diamandis, E.P., 2008a. Strategies for discovering novel cancer biomarkers through utilization of emerging technologies. Nature Clinical Practice Oncology 5, 588–599.

Kulasingam, V., Diamandis, E.P., 2008b. Tissue culture-based breast cancer biomarker discovery platform. International Journal of Cancer 123, 2007–2012.

Lacoste, J., 2018. Research in rare disease: From genomics to proteomics. Assay and Drug Development Technologies 16, 12–14.

Latosinska, A., Frantzi, M., Vlahou, A., Merseburger, A.S., Mischak, H., 2017b. Clinical proteomics for precision medicine: The bladder cancer case. Proteomics Clinical Applications 12 (2),

Latosinska, A., Mokou, M., Makridakis, M., et al., 2017a. Proteomics analysis of bladder cancer invasion: Targeting EIF3D for therapeutic intervention. Oncotarget 8, 69435–69455.

Lau, E., Cao, Q., Lam, M.P.Y., et al., 2018. Integrated omics dissection of proteome dynamics during cardiac remodeling. Nature Communication 9, 120.

Leduc, R.D., Schwammle, V., Shortreed, M.R., et al., 2018. ProForma: A standard proteoform notation. Journal of Proteome Research 17 (3), 1321–1325.

Lion, N., Reymond, F., Girault, H.H., Rossier, J.S., 2004. Why the move to microfluidics for protein analysis? Current Opinion in Biotechnology 15, 31–37.

Lisitsa, A., Moshkovskii, S., Chernobrovkin, A., Ponomarenko, E., Archakov, A., 2014. Profiling proteoforms: Promising follow-up of proteomics for biomarker discovery. Expert Review of Proteomics 11, 121–129.

Mallick, P., Kuster, B., 2010. Proteomics: A pragmatic perspective. Nature Biotechnology 28, 695–709.

Mann, M., Kulak, N.A., Nagaraj, N., Cox, J., 2013. The coming age of complete, accurate, and ubiquitous proteomes. Molecular Cell 49, 583–590.

Marko-Varga, G., Labaer, J., 2017. The Immune system and the proteome. Journal of Proteome Research 16, 1.

Martens, L., Chambers, M., Sturm, M., et al., 2011. mzML – A community standard for mass spectrometry data. Molecular and Cellular Proteomics 10.R110 000133.

Martens, L., Hermjakob, H., Jones, P., et al., 2005. PRIDE: The proteomics identifications database. Proteomics 5, 3537–3545.

Martens, L., Vandekerckhove, J., Gevaert, K., 2005. DBToolkit: Processing protein databases for peptide-centric proteomics. Bioinformatics 21, 3584–3585.

Matthiesen, R., 2013a. Algorithms for database-dependent search of MS/MS data. Methods in Molecular Biology 1007, 119–138.

Matthiesen, R., 2013b. LC-MS spectra processing. Methods in Molecular Biology 1007, 47–63.

Matthiesen, R., Bunkenborg, J., 2013. Introduction to mass spectrometry-based proteomics. Methods in Molecular Biology 1007, 1–45.

Matthiesen, R., Carvalho, A.S., 2013. Methods and algorithms for quantitative proteomics by mass spectrometry. Methods in Molecular Biology 1007, 183–217.

Mayer, G., Jones, A.R., Binz, P.A., et al., 2014. Controlled vocabularies and ontologies in proteomics: Overview, principles and practice. Biochimica et Biophysica Acta 1844, 98–107.

Meehan, K.L., Holland, J.W., Dawkins, H.J., 2002. Proteomic analysis of normal and malignant prostate tissue to identify novel proteins lost in cancer. Prostate 50, 54–63.

Menschaert, G., Wang, X., Jones, A.R., et al., 2018. The proBAM and proBed standard formats: Enabling a seamless integration of genomics and proteomics data. Genome Biology 19, 12.

Meyfour, A., Pahlavan, S., Sobhanian, H., Salekdeh, G.H., 2018. 17(th) Chromosome-Centric Human Proteome Project (C-HPP) symposium in Tehran. Proteomics 18 (7), e1800012.

Mueller, C., Haymond, A., Davis, J.B., Williams, A., Espina, V., 2018. Protein biomarkers for subtyping breast cancer and implications for future research. Expert Review of Proteomics 15, 131–152.

Nedelkov, D., 2017. Human proteoforms as new targets for clinical mass spectrometry protein tests. Expert Review of Proteomics 14, 691–699.

Nickchi, P., Jafari, M., Kalantari, S., 2015. PEIMAN 1.0: Post-translational modification Enrichment, Integration and Matching ANalysis. Database (Oxford) 2015, bav037.

Okuda, S., Watanabe, Y., Moriya, Y., et al., 2017. jPOSTrepo: An international standard data repository for proteomes. Nucleic Acids Research 45, D1107–D1111.

Olexiouk, V., Menschaert, G., 2017. proBAMconvert: A conversion tool for proBAM/proBed. Journal of Proteome Research 16, 2639–2644.

Omenn, G.S., Lane, L., Lundberg, E.K., Overall, C.M., Deutsch, E.W., 2017. Progress on the HUPO draft human proteome: 2017 metrics of the human proteome project. Journal of Proteome Research 16, 4281–4287.

Patrie, S.M., 2016. Top-down mass spectrometry: Proteomics to proteoforms. Advances in Experimental Medicine and Biology 919, 171–200.

Penn, A.M., Bibok, M.B., Saly, V.K., et al., 2018. Verification of a proteomic biomarker panel to diagnose minor stroke and transient ischaemic attack: Phase 1 of SpecTRA, a large scale translational study. Biomarkers. 1–48.

Perez-Riverol, Y., Gatto, L., Wang, R., et al., 2016a. Ten simple rules for taking advantage of Git and GitHub. PLOS Computational Biology 12, e1004947.

Perez-Riverol, Y., Xu, Q.W., Wang, R., et al., 2016b. PRIDE inspector toolsuite: Moving toward a universal visualization tool for proteomics data standard formats and quality assessment of proteomeXchange datasets. Molecular and Cellular Proteomics 15, 305–317.

Piening, B.D., Zhou, W., Contrepois, K., et al., 2018. Integrative personal omics profiles during periods of weight gain and loss. Cell Systems 6 (2), 157–170.

Rauch, A., Bellew, M., Eng, J., et al., 2006. Computational Proteomics Analysis System (CPAS): An extensible, open-source analytic system for evaluating and publishing proteomic data and high throughput biological experiments. Journal of Proteome Research 5, 112–121.

Righetti, P.G., Boschetti, E., 2008. The ProteoMiner and the FortyNiners: Searching for gold nuggets in the proteomic arena. Mass Spectrometry Reviews 27, 596–608.

Romer, M., Eichner, J., Drager, A., et al., 2016. ZBIT Bioinformatics Toolbox: A web-platform for systems biology and expression data analysis. PLOS ONE 11, e0149263.

Rosen, J., Handy, K., Gillan, A., Smith, R., 2017. JS-MS: A cross-platform, modular javascript viewer for mass spectrometry signals. BMC Bioinformatics 18, 469.

Ruhaak, L.R., Van Der Burgt, Y.E., Cobbaert, C.M., 2016. Prospective applications of ultrahigh resolution proteomics in clinical mass spectrometry. Expert Review of Proteomics 13, 1063–1071.

Schmidt, M.S., King, C.L., Thomsen, E.K., et al., 2014. Liquid chromatography-mass spectrometry analysis of diethylcarbamazine in human plasma for clinical pharmacokinetic studies. Journal of Pharmaceutical and Biomedical Analysis 98, 307–310.

Schmidt, T., Samaras, P., Frejno, M., et al., 2018. ProteomicsDB. Nucleic Acids Research 46, D1271–D1281.

Schmit, P.O., Vialaret, J., Wessels, H., *et al.*, 2018. Towards a routine application of Top-Down approaches for label-free discovery workflows. Journal of Proteomics 175, 12–26.

Schwenk, J.M., Omenn, G.S., Sun, Z., *et al.*, 2017. The Human Plasma Proteome Draft of 2017: Building on the Human Plasma PeptideAtlas from mass spectrometry and complementary assays. Journal of Proteome Research 16, 4299–4310.

Seeley, E.H., Oppenheimer, S.R., Mi, D., Chaurand, P., Caprioli, R.M., 2008. Enhancement of protein sensitivity for MALDI imaging mass spectrometry after chemical treatment of tissue sections. Journal of the American Society for Mass Spectrometry 19, 1069–1077.

Segura, V., Garin-Muga, A., Guruceaga, E., Corrales, F.J., 2017. Progress and pitfalls in finding the 'missing proteins' from the human proteome map. Expert Review of Proteomics 14, 9–14.

Seow, T.K., Korke, R., Liang, R.C., *et al.*, 2001. Proteomic investigation of metabolic shift in mammalian cell culture. Biotechnology Progress 17, 1137–1144.

Sergeant, K., Printz, B., Gutsch, A., *et al.*, 2017. Didehydrophenylalanine, an abundant modification in the beta subunit of plant polygalacturonases. PLOS ONE 12, e0171990.

Shiromizu, T., Kume, H., Ishida, M., *et al.*, 2017. Quantitation of putative colorectal cancer biomarker candidates in serum extracellular vesicles by targeted proteomics. Scientific Reports 7, 12782.

Snyder, M., Mias, G., Stanberry, L., Kolker, E., 2014. Metadata checklist for the integrated personal OMICS study: Proteomics and metabolomics experiments. OMICS 18, 81–85.

Soldes, O.S., Kuick, R.D., Thompson 2nd, I.A., *et al.*, 1999b. Differential expression of Hsp27 in normal oesophagus, Barrett's metaplasia and oesophageal adenocarcinomas. British Journal of Cancer 79, 595–603.

Soldes, O.S., Younger, J.G., Hirschl, R.B., 1999a. Predictors of malignancy in childhood peripheral lymphadenopathy. Journal of Pediatric Surgery 34, 1447–1452.

Spidlen, J., Brinkman, R.R., 2018. Use FlowRepository to share your clinical data upon study publication. Cytometry Part B: Clinical Cytometry 94, 196–198.

Szasz, A.M., Gyorffy, B., Marko-Varga, G., 2017. Cancer heterogeneity determined by functional proteomics. Seminars in Cell and Developmental Biology 64, 132–142.

2018.UniProt: The universal protein knowledgebase. Nucleic Acids Research.

Tholey, A., Taylor, N.L., Heazlewood, J.L., Bendixen, E., 2017. We are not alone: The iMOP initiative and its roles in a biology- and disease-driven human proteome project. Journal of Proteome Research 16, 4273–4280.

Thomsen, M.B.H., Nordentoft, I., Lamy, P., *et al.*, 2017. Comprehensive multiregional analysis of molecular heterogeneity in bladder cancer. Scientific Reports 7, 11702.

Thul, P.J., Lindskog, C., 2018. The human protein atlas: A spatial map of the human proteome. Protein Science 27, 233–244.

Thygesen, C., Boll, I., Finsen, B., Modzel, M., Larsen, M.R., 2018. Characterizing disease-associated changes in post-translational modifications by mass spectrometry. Expert Review of Proteomics. 1–14.

Tian, Q., Price, N.D., Hood, L., 2012. Systems cancer medicine: Towards realization of predictive, preventive, personalized and participatory (P4) medicine. Journal of Internal Medicine 271, 111–121.

Toby, T.K., Fornelli, L., Kelleher, N.L., 2016. Progress in Top-Down Proteomics and the Analysis of Proteoforms. Annual Review of Analytical Chemistry (Palo Alto Calif) 9, 499–519.

Trenchevska, O., Nelson, R.W., Nedelkov, D., 2016. Mass Spectrometric Immunoassays in Characterization of Clinically Significant Proteoforms. Proteomes 4.

Trindade, F., Ferreira, R., Magalhaes, B., *et al.*, 2018. How to use and integrate bioinformatics tools to compare proteomic data from distinct conditions? A tutorial using the pathological similarities between Aortic Valve Stenosis and Coronary Artery Disease as a case-study. Journal of Proteomics 171, 37–52.

Tsiatsiani, L., Heck, A.J., 2015. Proteomics beyond trypsin. The FEBS Journal 282, 2612–2626.

Tsuchida, S., Satoh, M., Umemura, H., *et al.*, 2018. Assessment by matrix-assisted laser desorption/ionization time-of-flight mass spectrometry of the effects of preanalytical variables on serum peptidome profiles following long-term sample storage. Proteomics Clinical Applications 12 (13), e1700047.

Uppal, K., Ma, C., Go, Y.M., Jones, D.P., Wren, J., 2018. xMWAS: A data-driven integration and differential network analysis tool. Bioinformatics 34, 701–702.

Van Karnebeek, C.D.M., Wortmann, S.B., Tarailo-Graovac, M., *et al.*, 2018. The role of the clinician in the multi-omics era: Are you ready? Journal of Inherited Metabolic Disease.

Vizcaino, J.A., Csordas, A., Del-Toro, N., *et al.*, 2016a. 2016 update of the PRIDE database and its related tools. Nucleic Acids Research 44, 11033.

Vizcaino, J.A., Csordas, A., Del-Toro, N., *et al.*, 2016b. 2016 update of the PRIDE database and its related tools. Nucleic Acids Research 44, D447–D456.

Vizcaino, J.A., Mayer, G., Perkins, S., *et al.*, 2017. The mzIdentML Data Standard Version 1.2, Supporting Advances in Proteome Informatics. Molecular and Cellular Proteomics 16, 1275–1285.

Walzer, M., Qi, D., Mayer, G., *et al.*, 2013. The mzQuantML data standard for mass spectrometry-based quantitative studies in proteomics. Molecular and Cellular Proteomics 12, 2332–2340.

Wang, M., Weiss, M., Simonovic, M., *et al.*, 2012. PaxDb, a database of protein abundance averages across all three domains of life. Molecular and Cellular Proteomics 11, 492–500.

Wasinger, V.C., Cordwell, S.J., Cerpa-Poljak, A., *et al.*, 1995. Progress with gene-product mapping of the Mollicutes: Mycoplasma genitalium. Electrophoresis 16, 1090–1094.

Wilkins, M.R., Sanchez, J.C., Gooley, A.A., *et al.*, 1996b. Progress with proteome projects: Why all proteins expressed by a genome should be identified and how to do it. Biotechnology & Genetic Engineering Reviews 13, 19–50.

Wilkins, M.R., Sanchez, J.C., Williams, K.L., Hochstrasser, D.F., 1996a. Current challenges and future applications for protein maps and post-translational vector maps in proteome projects. Electrophoresis 17, 830–838.

Wisniewski, J.R., 2013. Proteomic sample preparation from formalin fixed and paraffin embedded tissue. Journal of Visualized Experiments. 79.

Wisniewski, J.R., Dus, K., Mann, M., 2013. Proteomic workflow for analysis of archival formalin-fixed and paraffin-embedded clinical samples to a depth of 10,000 proteins. Proteomics Clinical Applications 7, 225–233.

Zougman, A., Banks, R.E., 2015. C-STrap sample preparation method – In-situ cysteinyl peptide capture for bottom-up proteomics analysis in the STrap format. PLOS ONE 10, e0138775.

Relevant Websites

https://hupo.org/human-proteome-project
　HUPO.
https://www.nextprot.org
　neXtProt.
http://www.ebi.ac.uk/pride/archive/
　PRIDE.
http://github.com/PRIDE-Toolsuite/
　PRIDE-Toolsuite.
http://probam.biobix.be
　proBAM.

https://www.ProteomicsDB.org
    ProteomicsDB.
https://pymzml.github.io
    pymzML.
www.proteinatlas.org
    THE HUMAN PROTEIN ATLAS.

Molecular Mechanisms Responsible for Drug Resistance

Molecular Mechanisms Responsible for Drug Resistance

Mun Fai Loke and Aimi Hanafi, University of Malaya, Kuala Lumpur, Malaysia

Introduction

In general, drug resistance is the reduction in effectiveness of a medication or drug to cure a disease or condition. More commonly, antimicrobial resistance (also known as drug resistance) is the ability of microbes, such as bacteria, viruses, parasites, or fungi, to survive in the presence of a chemical drug that that was previously effective in killing it or inhibiting its growth. The concept of drug resistance was first considered when bacteria became resistant to certain antibiotics, but since then similar mechanisms have been found to occur in other diseases; among many are cancer cells developing resistance to chemotherapy drugs and human immunodeficiency virus (HIV) becoming resistance to antiretroviral drugs.

The first true antibiotic, penicillin, was discovered by Alexander Fleming, Professor of Bacteriology at the St. Mary's Hospital in London in 1928. However, as early as 1908, Paul Ehrlich, the father of modern chemotherapy, had already observed the existence of stably inherited drug resistance in *Trypanosoma* (Ehrlich, 1909). Thus, antimicrobial resistance is not a new concept. Antimicrobial resistance was recognized even before the dawn of the antibiotic era. By the 1950s, the medical community was already aware of the problem of antimicrobial resistance. Notably, methicillin was first clinically used in 1959 and only 2 years later, scientists had already identified the first case of methicillin-resistant *Staphylococcus aureus* (Jevons, 1961). This demonstrated the short evolution cycle in the development of antimicrobial resistance in bacteria and other microorganisms.

Less than a century since the discovery of the first antibiotic, antimicrobial resistance has become one of the biggest threats to global health and human development. Many common pathogens are becoming resistant to the antibiotics resulting in longer illnesses and higher mortality. Concurrently, not enough new antimicrobial drugs are being developed to replace increasingly ineffective ones. In September 2016, a historical meeting of world leaders at the United Nations (UN) General Assembly was held to address the seriousness and scope of the situation and commit to fighting antimicrobial resistance together. Notably, this was only the fourth time in UN history that a health topic is discussed at the General Assembly (HIV, noncommunicable diseases, and Ebola were the others).

Definitions

Following the definition by Brauner *et al.* (2016), "resistance" describes the inheritable ability of microorganisms to grow at high concentrations of an antimicrobial agent by acquiring resistance mutations and is quantified by the minimum inhibitory concentration (MIC) of the particular agent. The genes that are involved in these mechanisms are collectively termed the resistome. However, microorganisms can also survive extensive antimicrobial treatments without acquiring resistance mutations. The terms "tolerance" and "persistence" distinguish these modes of survival from "resistance," but the definitions of these different terms, and their distinction from one another, have remained somewhat ambiguous. "Tolerance" is more generally used to describe the ability of microorganisms to survive transient exposure to high concentrations of an antimicrobial agent without a change in the MIC, which is often achieved by slowing down an essential microbial process, such as growth or metabolism. Tolerance may be acquired through a genetic mutation or conferred by environmental conditions. Dormancy may be viewed as an extreme case of slow growth and low metabolism, and dormancy that leads to tolerance may also be termed "drug indifference." For example, *Bacillus anthracis* and *Clostridium difficile* can form highly resistant endospores under unfavorable conditions. In contrast to resistance and tolerance, which are attributes of the whole bacterial populations, "persistence" is the ability of a subpopulation of a clonal bacterial population to survive exposure to high concentrations of an antimicrobial agent. Persistence is typically observed when the majority of the bacterial population is rapidly killed while a subpopulation persists for a much longer period of time, despite the population being clonal.

The joint initiative by the European Centre for Disease Prevention and Control and the Centers for Disease Control and Prevention defined multiple drug resistance (MDR) as antimicrobial resistance shown by a microorganism to at least one antimicrobial agent in three or more drug categories. Recognizing different degrees of MDR, the terms "extensively drug resistant (XDR)" and "pandrug-resistant (PDR)" have also been introduced (Magiorakos *et al.*, 2012). XDR is defined as nonsusceptibility to at least one antimicrobial agent in all but two or fewer drug categories (i.e., bacterial isolates remain susceptible to only one or two categories) and PDR refers to nonsusceptibility to all antimicrobial agents in all drug categories.

Molecular Mechanisms of Antimicrobial Resistance

The genetic characterization of antibiotic-resistant bacterial strains has uncovered many molecular mechanisms of resistance. The five fundamental mechanisms of antibiotic-resistance are (1) enzymatic activity that directly inactivate or degrade the antibiotic, (2) alteration of bacterial proteins that are targets of antibiotics, (3) reduction in membrane permeability to antibiotics, (4) activation of efflux pumps that pump out antibiotics, and (5) activation of resistant bacterial metabolic pathways. Key candidate genes involved in the mechanisms of antibiotic-resistance are described in **Table 1**.

Bacteria can destroy or modify antibiotics, thus resisting their action. Inactivation of antibiotics by hydrolysis is a major mechanism of antibiotic-resistance. Antibiotics can also be inactivated by transfer of chemical group. The addition of chemical groups to vulnerable sites on the antibiotic molecule by bacterial enzymes prevents the antibiotic from binding to its target protein as a result of steric hindrance. Various different chemical groups can be transferred, including acyl, phosphate, nucleotidyl, and ribitoyl groups, and the enzymes that are responsible form a large and diverse family of antibiotic-resistance enzymes.

Modification of the bacterial protein target is also an effective means of antibiotic resistance. Most antibiotics bind to the specific protein targets with high affinity, thus preventing the normal activity of the proteins. Changes to the protein structure that prevent efficient antibiotic binding, but still enable the protein to perform its normal function, can confer resistance to antibiotics.

Most antibiotics are targeted at intracellular processes, and must be able to penetrate the bacterial cell envelope to be effective. Compared to Gram-positive bacteria, Gram-negative bacteria are intrinsically less permeable to many antibiotics because of their outer membrane, which forms a permeability barrier. There are essentially two pathways by which antibiotics can penetrate the outer membrane: A lipid-mediated pathway for hydrophobic antibiotics, and general diffusion porins for hydrophilic antibiotics. The lipid and protein compositions of the outer membrane have a strong impact on the sensitivity of bacteria to many types of antibiotics, and drug resistance involving modifications of these macromolecules is common. The two major porin-based mechanisms for antibiotic-resistance are (1) reduction of porins or replacement of one or two major porins by another, and (2) altered function due to specific mutations reducing permeability.

Bacterial efflux pumps have physiological functions and their expression is tightly regulated in response to environmental and physiological triggers. Genes encoding for efflux pump proteins can be found on chromosomes or plasmids. Bacterial efflux pumps can be classified into five families based on their composition, number of transmembrane spanning regions, energy sources, and substrates. The five families are (1) resistance-nodulation-division (RND) family, (2) major facilitator superfamily (MFS), (3) ATP (adenosine triphosphate)-binding cassette (ABC) superfamily, (4) drug/metabolite transporter superfamily, and (5) multidrug and toxic compound extrusion family. The RND superfamily is only found in Gram-negative bacteria. On the other hand, efflux systems of the other four families are widely found in both Gram-positive and -negative bacteria. Bacterial efflux pumps actively transport many antibiotics out of the bacterial cell and are major contributors to the intrinsic resistance of bacteria. RND and MFS family pumps are associated extensively with clinically significant antibiotic resistance. When overexpressed, efflux pumps can also confer high levels of drug resistance to many clinically useful antibiotics. Some efflux pumps have narrow substrate specificity but many transport a wide range of structurally dissimilar substrates and are known as multidrug resistance efflux pumps. Our knowledge of MDR determinants are continuously propelled by the growing availability of the X-ray crystal structures of efflux pumps. These guide the development of novel efflux pump inhibitors that can potentially help in our war

Table 1   Key candidate genes involved in the mechanisms of antibiotic resistance

Mode of action	Class of antibiotics	Candidate genes	Mechanisms of resistance
Inhibition of protein synthesis	Macrolides	Erythromycin ribosome methylation genes (erm)	Posttranscriptional modifications of the 23SrRNA
		Macrolide efflux genes (mef) macA-macB genes	Active drug efflux
		23SrRNA gene	Mutations of the 50S ribosomal subunit target
	Chloramphenicol	Chloramphenicol acetyltransferase gene (cat)	Elaboration of chloramphenicol acetyltransferase that inactivates chloramphenicol
		23SrRNA gene	Mutations of the 50S ribosomal subunit target
	Aminoglycosides	Acriflavine resistance genes (acr)	Probable aminoglycoside efflux pump
		Aminoglycoside N(6')-acetyltransferase genes (aacA)	Aminoglycoside-modifying enzyme
		16SrRNA gene	Mutations of the 30S ribosomal subunit target
	Tetracyclines	Tetracycline resistance gene (Tet)	Active drug efflux
Interference with cell wall production	β-Lactam antibiotics	β-lactamase structural genes (bla)	Inactivate the antibiotics by hydrolyzing the β-lactam ring
	Methicillin & other β-lactamase-resistant penicillins	mecA gene	Alternative low-affinity penicillin-binding protein PBP2a
Interrupting nucleic acid synthesis	Fluoroquinolones	DNA gyrase (gyr), DNA topoisomerase IV (par)	Mutations in target enzyme
	Rifampicin	DNA-dependent RNA polymerase B (rpoB)	Mutations in target enzyme
Blocking of DNA replication	Trimethoprim	dfr gene	Mutations of the target dihydrofolate reductase (DHFR)
		folA gene	Mutations of the structural gene for DHFR
	Sulfonamide (structural analogs of p-aminobenzoic acid)	Dihydropteroate synthase gene (dhps)	Mutations of the target dihydropteroate synthase
		Sulfonamide resistance genes (sul)	Resistant sulfonamide-resistant dihydropteroate synthase
		folP gene	Mutations of the structural gene for DHPS

against antimicrobial resistance. In addition, preventing the overexpression of efflux genes by targeting to their transcription regulators is also an alternative emerging strategy to combat antimicrobial resistance.

Bacteria acquire resistant gene mutation and/or horizontal gene transfer via transformation, transduction, or conjugation. Antibiotic-resistance can be either plasmid-mediated or maintained on the bacterial chromosome. Many times, microorganisms employ several mechanisms in order to attain drug resistance.

Drug resistance among pathogenic fungal species, including *Candida*, *Aspergillus*, and *Cryptococcus*, generally involve similar mechanisms as antibiotic-resistance in bacteria. Reduced drug accumulation in fungal cells involve overexpression of efflux pumps as well as pH- and ATP-independent facilitated diffusion mechanisms. Efflux pumps in fungi mainly belong to the ABC superfamily and the MFS family. In addition, mutations in drug target genes may result in structural change of the fungal protein targets, thereby reducing the affinity of the inhibitors to their specific target. For example, mutations in *ERG11* (in *Candida albicans* and *Cryptococcus neoformans*) or *cyp51* (in *Aspergillus fumigatus*) that code for the ergosterol biosynthetic enzyme, lanosterol demethylase, change the structure of the enzyme, and decrease its affinity to specific antifungal drugs (Gonçalves *et al.*, 2016). Inhibition of ergosterol biosysnthesis prevents the biosynthesis of ergosterol, which is a unique fungal cell membrane component, therefore the evoking the resistance mechanism. Another mechanism employed in resistant fungal strains is the overexpression of the drug target. Antifungal resistance can also be activated through stress response pathway regulation. For example, Hsp90 is a molecular chaperone that stabilizes the regulators in cellular stress responses. In response to drug inhibition, Hsp90 and other components of the pathway, including calcineurin and the Pkc1 signaling, are overexpressed (Robbins *et al.*, 2017).

Besides antimicrobial resistance, drug resistance also emerges in treatments of noninfectious human diseases. Drug resistance in cancer cells can also be observed. Besides playing a role in antimicrobial resistance, efflux pumps in cancer cells also act to reduce the accumulation of chemotherapeutic drugs in cancer cells. This often involves efflux pump proteins belonging to the ABC superfamily, which includes P-glycoprotein (P-gp), multidrug resistance protein 1, breast cancer resistance protein, and lung resistance-related protein. Anticancer drugs can also be inactivated by the enzymatic activity of glutathione S-transferase, which catalyzes the conjugation of glutathione to a xenobiotic compound by forming a thioether bond. Alterations in drug targets can also occur in drug-resistant cancer cells. Unlike normal cells, resistant tumor cells in breast cancer that lack estrogen receptors no longer depend on estrogen for growth. This leads to resistance to endocrine therapy. Decreased level of membrane permeability to chemotherapeutic drugs is demonstrated in the presence of lower levels of cholesterols and differences in lipid composition in cancer cells compared to normal cells.

In addition to the general mechanisms mentioned, cancer cells have also developed specific drug resistance mechanisms. Changes in the cell cycle may affect the balance between cell cycle arrest and apoptosis and disturbance to cell cycle checkpoints could lead to drug resistance. The activation of DNA damage checkpoint components allows the survival of cells after a drug treatment. Drug-resistant cancer cells may also evade apoptosis by enabling cell proliferation. Tumor suppressors in normal cells, such as p53, and phosphatase and tensin homolog deleted on chromosome 10, are defective in cancer cells, thereby disabling DNA damage repairs and cell cycle arrests. In addition to the defect in tumor suppressors, the overexpression of oncogenes, such as *Bcl-2* genes, may also inhibit apoptosis (Kartal-Yandim *et al.*, 2016).

The molecular mechanisms in antiviral resistance differ at different stages of viral infections. Mutations in genes coding for replication of viral DNA can decrease the affinity and binding of DNA polymerase to inhibitors, decrease the viral replication capacity, and affect hydrophobic interactions between nucleotides. Furthermore, antiviral drug resistance may also be caused by mutations in viral thymidine kinase encoding genes and lead to the decrease in phosphorylation of nucleoside analogs. It is because the phosphotransferase is used in antiviral therapies to produce competitive inhibitors for viral DNA polymerase. Mutations can also occur around active sites to prevent integrase and protease inhibitors from binding. Virus can also use different host cell coreceptors or the same coreceptors with changes in tropism, which may be the result of multiple mutations, to bypass the effects of inhibitors (Shafer *et al.*, 2011).

Bioinformatics in Combating Antimicrobial Resistance

Mutations introduce diversity into genomes, leading to selective changes and driving evolution. In particular, nonsynonymous single-nucleotide polymorphisms within the protein coding regions of the genome have been strongly associated with occurrence of drug resistance. Next-generation sequencing technologies have made the sequencing of whole-microbial genomes and metagenomes more affordable and have increased the feasibility of applying rapid whole-microbial genome sequencing in clinical microbiology laboratories. Furthermore, the number of microbial genomes and metagenomes deposited in the NCBI GenBank database has increased exponentially as more and more genomes are sequenced in a short time span. However, the barrier to the routine implementation of whole-genome sequencing is the lack of automated, user-friendly bioinformatics tools that interpret the sequence data and provide clinically meaningful information by scientists and clinicians. Several general databases are available to aid in rapidly identifying existing, putative, new, or emerging antibiotics resistance genes and mutations in chromosomic target genes that are associated with resistance. These include Antibiotic Resistance Genes Online (see "Relevant Website section"), the microbial database of protein toxins, virulence factors, and antibiotic-resistance genes for biodefense applications (see "Relevant Website section"), the Antibiotic Resistance Genes Database (see "Relevant Website section"), Resfinder database (see "Relevant Website section"), the Comprehensive Antibiotic Resistance Database (see "Relevant Website section"), the Antibiotic Resistance Gene-ANNOTation database (see "Relevant Website section"), the Resfams (see "Relevant Website section") and the MEGARes database (see "Relevant Website section"). In response to increasing concern over antimicrobial resistance, the team at Pathosystems Resource

Integration Center (PATRIC) has also developed new tools to facilitate researchers' understanding of the genetic basis of drug resistance (Antonopoulos *et al.*, 2017). The team used antimicrobial resistance phenotype data of more than 15,000 genomes in the PATRIC database to build machine learning-based classifiers that can predict the antimicrobial resistance phenotypes and the genomic regions associated with drug resistance that can be used for comparative analysis. Drug resistance databases for specific organisms, such as HIV and *Mycobacterium tuberculosis*, have also been developed. However, most research on bacterial antibiotic-resistance did not take into consideration gene–gene interactions and multiple genetic mutations in the emergence of transmissible drug resistance. Recently, a group of researchers from Huazhong Agricultural University (Wuhan, China) identified gene pairs associated with *Mycobacterium tuberculosis* drug resistance using GBOOST, a software package for identifying gene–gene interactions in genome-wide association studies (Cui *et al.*, 2016). GBOOST was used to detect SNP–SNP interactions on risk of drug resistance and a chi-square test method to examine the interaction effect between two SNPs and phenotypes. This method is also useful for providing a deeper insight into the mechanisms underlying drug resistance in other bacteria.

Cancer therapies are limited by the development of drug resistance, and mutations in drug targets are one of the main driving factors for the developing resistance to chemotherapeutic drugs. CancerDR is a cancer drug resistance database that will be useful for identification of genetic alterations in genes encoding drug targets, and in turn the residues responsible for drug resistance.

Systematic experimental evaluation of all genomic mutations and characterizing mutation effects of all mutations in a system of interest is impractically time-consuming and not cost-effective, even more so considering the range of different mechanisms in which mutations can affect protein function and interactions. Thus, this has created interest in the development of computational tools to understand the molecular consequences of mutations to aid and guide rational experimentation. These tools can also be employed to prioritize mutations for further experimental investigation, identification, and anticipation of resistant variants and resistance hotspots. Such knowledge can then be applied to the design of drugs less prone to resistance, as well as to drive the development of public health policies and aid in establishing more appropriate and personalized treatments. Computational methods, particularly homology modeling of the 3-dimensional structure of proteins, have been developed to understand the effects of coding mutations to protein function and interactions.

Currently, high-throughput screening (HTS) is widely used to screen large natural and artificial compound libraries against specific protein targets in drug discovery. However, this method can be costly and time-consuming even with the use of robotics. Computer-assisted or virtual screening (VS) can help to overcome some of the disadvantages of a full HTS when used to complement the HTS process in drug discovery. In the latter, VS is used to shortlist potential active compounds from large libraries, thus reducing the size of the library prior to the more costly and time-consuming HTS experiments. Unlike HTS experiments, VS simulations do not require the physical synthesis of compounds. However, VS still requires experimental information, such as protein structure for structure-based approach or binding properties of known active compounds for ligand-based approach. Molecular docking methodology is widely used in VS simulations in large part due to the efficiency of these calculations. In contrast to laboratory testing, molecular docking typically requires only a few minutes of computing time on a single core per ligand; thus, 10,000 to 100,000 compounds can be virtually screened on a small- to medium-sized cluster in a day. While molecular docking forms the basis for structure-based VS, the ligand-based approach is built upon the similarity principle in which similar compounds are assumed to cause similar biological effects. With this approach large ligand libraries can then be screened for compounds with similar chemical properties to the known actives, resulting in the identification of novel potentially active compounds. However, computer-assisted drug screening should still be a verified experimentally and VS is perhaps best used as an aid to HTS for prefiltering larger libraries to select subsets of compounds (focused library) to increase productivity in drug discovery.

Conclusion

The application of bioinformatics tools make it possible to practice precision medicine – the right medicine at the right dose for the right patient at the right time – in combating the drug resistance crisis by changing the way therapeutic drugs are developed and used to treat both infectious and noninfectious diseases, such as cancers.

See also: Comparative Epigenomics. Molecular Dynamics Simulations in Drug Discovery. Natural Language Processing Approaches in Bioinformatics. Structure-Based Drug Design Workflow

References

Antonopoulos, D.A., Assaf, R., Aziz, R.K., *et al.*, 2017. PATRIC as a unique resource for studying antimicrobial resistance. Briefings in Bioinformatics 2017, 1–9.
Brauner, A., Fridman, O., Gefen, O., Balaban, N.Q., 2016. Distinguishing between resistance, tolerance and persistence to antibiotic treatment. Nature Reviews Microbiology 14 (5), 320–330.
Cui, Z.J., Yang, Q.Y., Zhang, H.Y., Zhu, Q., Zhang, Q.Y., 2016. Bioinformatics identification of drug resistance-associated gene pairs in *Mycobacterium tuberculosis*. International Journal of Molecular Sciences 27 (9), E1417.
Ehrlich, P., 1909. Ueber Moderne Chemotherapie. Leipzig: Akademische Verlagsgesellschaft m.b.H., pp. 167–202.
Gonçalves, S.S., Souza, A.C.R., Chowdhary, A., Meis, J.F., Colombo, A.L., 2016. Epidemiology and molecular mechanisms of antifungal resistance in *Candida* and *Aspergillus*. Mycoses 59 (4), 198–219.
Jevons, M.P., 1961. "Celbenin" – Resistant Staphylococci. British Medical Journal 1, 124.
Kartal-Yandim, M., Adan-Gokbulut, A., Baran, Y., 2016. Molecular mechanisms of drug resistance and its reversal in cancer. Critical Reviews in Biotechnology 36 (4), 716–726.

Magiorakos, A.P., Srinivasan, A., Carey, R.B., *et al.*, 2012. Multidrug-resistant, extensively drug-resistant and pandrug-resistant bacteria: An international expert proposal for interim standard definitions for acquired resistance. Clinical Microbiology and Infection 18 (3), 268–281.

Robbins, N., Caplan, T., Cowen, L.E., 2017. Molecular evolution of antifungal drug resistance. Annual Review of Microbiology 71 (1).

Shafer, R.W., Najera, I., Chou, S., 2011. Mechanisms of resistance to antiviral agents. In: Versalovic, J., Carroll, K.C., Funke, G., *et al.* (Eds.), Manual of Clinical Microbiology, tenth ed. American Society of Microbiology, pp. 1710–1728.

Further Reading

Alliance for the Prudent Use of Antibiotics (APUA) Fact Sheets on Antibiotic Resistance. Available at: http://emerald.tufts.edu/med/apua/consumers/fact_sheets.shtml.

Centers for Disease Control and Prevention. Available at: https://www.cdc.gov/drugresistance/index.html.

"The Race Against Drug Resistance": A Report of the Center for Global Development's Drug Resistance Working Group (CGD). Available at: https://www.cgdev.org/publication/race-against-drug-resistance.

World Health Organization Fact Sheets on Antibiotic resistance and Antimicrobial resistance. Available at: http://www.who.int/mediacentre/factsheets/en/.

Relevant Websites

http://www.mediterranee-infection.com/article.php?laref=282&titer=arg-annot
    Antibiotic Resistance Gene-ANNOTation (ARG-ANNOT) database.
https://ardb.cbcb.umd.edu/
    Antibiotic Resistance Genes Database (ARDB).
http://www.argodb.org/
    Antibiotic Resistance Genes Online (ARGO).
http://crdd.osdd.net/raghava/cancerdr/
    CancerDR.
https://card.mcmaster.ca/
    Comprehensive Antibiotic Resistance Database (CARD).
https://megares.meglab.org
    MEGARes.
http://mvirdb.llnl.gov/
    Microbial database of protein toxins, virulence factors, and antibiotic resistance genes for bio-defence applications (MvirDB).
http://umr5558-bibiserv.univ-lyon1.fr/mubii/mubii-select.cgi
    MUBII-TB-DB database.
https://patricbrc.org/view/DataType/AntibioticResistance
    Pathosystems Resource Integration Center Antimicrobial Resistance (AMR).
http://www.dantaslab.org/resfams/
    Resfams.
https://cge.cbs.dtu.dk/services/ResFinder/
    Resfinder database.
https://hivdb.stanford.edu/
    Stanford H.I.V. Drug Resistance Database (HIVDB).
https://tbdreamdb.ki.se/Info/Default.aspx
    Tuberculosis Drug Resistance Mutation Database (TBDReamDB).
https://extranet.who.int/hivdrug-surveillance/
    W.H.O. HIV drug resistance database (Database assess is restricted to designated ministry of health/ART programme users only).

Biographical Sketch

Mun Fai Loke obtained his PhD from the Department of Microbiology, Yong Loo Lin School of Medicine, National University of Singapore and his MBA from the University of Southern Queensland. He was a Senior Lecturer at the Department of Medical Microbiology, Faculty of Medicine, University of Malaya and a researcher with KK Women's and Children's Hospital. His main research interests are *Helicobacter pylori*, human gastrointestinal diseases, and rare genetic disorders.

Aimi Hanafi graduated with a master's degree from the Faculty of Medicine and Health Science, Universiti Putra Malaysia. Currently, she is a PhD student at the Department of Medical Microbiology, Faculty of Medicine, University of Malaya. Her PhD work focuses on the studying of antibiotic resistance mechanism and compensation in the human gastric pathogen, *Helicobacter pylori*.

Network-Based Analysis of Host-Pathogen Interactions

Lokesh P Tripathi, Yi-An Chen, and **Kenji Mizuguchi,** National Institutes of Biomedical Innovation, Health and Nutrition, Osaka, Japan
Eiji Morita, Hirosaki University, Hirosaki, Japan

Introduction

Infectious diseases are defined as disorders caused by pathogenic microorganisms, such as bacteria, viruses, parasites or fungi that can be spread directly or indirectly (vector-borne) from one individual to another. Despite the rapid advances in treating infectious diseases over the last century, infectious diseases - such as pneumonia, flu, tuberculosis, HIV/AIDS, malaria etc. – continue to result in millions of deaths worldwide. As per the World Health Organization (WHO) and Center for Infectious Disease Research (CIDR) estimates, the mortality rates of many infectious diseases may have actually worsened over the past few decades; the infectious diseases therefore, remain a pressing concern for the public healthcare systems. The societal burden of such diseases have been further exacerbated by the emergence of new and more virulent strains of drug resistant pathogens; these events have, therefore, led to more and more research efforts to understand disease pathogenesis and to identify new candidate targets for more effective therapeutic intervention against infectious diseases. However, the strategies by which pathogens evade the host immune system and manipulate key host cellular processes for their survival remain to be fully elucidated and are, therefore, an impediment to the development of more effective therapeutics. Understanding the behaviour of the pathogen as it colonises its host and the emergent host behaviour when it comes into contact with the pathogen are, therefore, of prime interest for the researchers investigating the pathogenesis of infectious diseases.

Host-pathogen protein-protein interactions (PHIs) perform vital roles in the pathogenesis of infectious diseases. In the PHIs, the proteins encoded by the pathogenic genome invade the host cellular networks to subvert the host immune responses and to co-opt the host cellular machinery to colonise the host and spread the infection (Bhavsar *et al.*, 2007; **Fig. 1**). In response, host cells have evolved mechanisms to sense and clear out the pathogenic infection. This host-pathogen interplay can be highly competitive and often antagonistic in nature as the pathogens competitively disrupt the native PPIs and establish new ones with the host cellular factors. Therefore, the underlying organisational and functional structures of the PHI networks can be markedly different from those of the native host interactome (Franzosa and Xia, 2011). To understand the biology of pathogen infection, it is necessary to obtain a detailed understanding of how pathogenic proteins function inside the host cell, their interactions with the host cellular machinery and how these interactions impact cellular signalling pathways. Therefore, there is a pressing need for an integrative analysis of PHIs (Fels *et al.*, 2017; Ma-Lauer *et al.*, 2012).

The availability of complete genome sequences of many pathogens and their hosts, together with the rapid proliferation of omics technologies and the development of new experimental technologies that were more amenable to PPI mapping on a larger

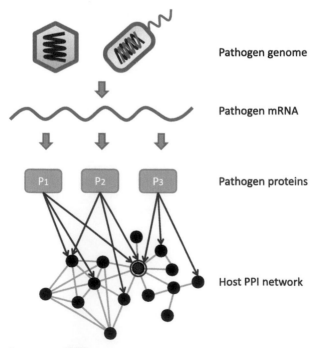

Fig. 1 A schematic of host-pathogen interactions (PHIs).

scale, have made it easier to generate large scale PHI data for many different host-pathogen systems at different organisational levels. Systems-based approaches seek to integrate experimental data with bioinformatics tools for data analysis and modelling to generate new hypotheses and prioritise further experimental investigation; such approaches have emerged as ideal approaches to investigate the biology of PHIs, generate new hypotheses and prioritise targets for clinical therapies (Durmus et al., 2015).

Significant amount of progress has been made in genome-wide mapping of PHIs for different pathogens (de Chassey et al., 2008; Tripathi et al., 2010; Uetz et al., 2006; Brito and Pinney, 2017; Calderwood et al., 2007; Friedel and Haas, 2011; de Chassey et al., 2013a) and also there have been attempts to integrate interaction networks and 3D structural data to extract the general principles of PHIs (Franzosa and Xia, 2011). These studies have provided valuable insights into mechanisms of pathogenicity of different pathogens. Among the various pathogens, the maximum research effort has gone into systematic mapping of virus-human host interactions on a genome wide scale (Lum and Cristea, 2016); the low complexity of the viral genomes makes it relatively easier to map PHIs involving viral pathogens compared with PHIs involving pathogenic bacteria, fungi or eukaryotes.

In this review, we will discuss PHIs largely from the perspective of the viral pathogens of human diseases. We first discuss how experimentally defined PHI data have been utilised for understanding the infection and survival mechanisms of pathogens in their hosts. Next, we briefly outline the computational methods for large-scale PHI prediction and how they can help in highlighting useful PHIs and in knowledge discovery. Finally, we discuss the applications and likely future directions of PHI data analysis.

Experimental Methods to Determine PHIs on a Large Scale

Different experimental methods have been applied to identify cellular proteins interacting with pathogen proteins. These methods differ widely in their approach; they have their advantages and shortcomings and often provide coverage of the different aspects of PHIs. Yeast two-hybrid (Y2H) system and co-affinity purification are among the most frequently used and traditional technologies to experimentally characterise PHIs; these methodologies can be easily scaled to survey PHIs on a proteome-wide scale and it is, therefore, not surprising that they together have contributed over 90% of the publicly available PHI data (Guirimand et al., 2015). In addition, protein arrays and protein-complementation assays are also being increasingly employed.

Y2H is an *in vivo* system based on the fact that a certain transcription factor (TF) can be divided into two separate domains, an activating domain (AD) and the DNA binding domain (DBD), and these two domains can still function together to drive transcription when they co-locate in close proximity. In Y2H, both the DBD and the AD are fused to two separate proteins, called the *bait* and *prey*. If the bait and prey proteins interact with each other, the DBD recognises a specific DNA sequence in a promoter region and the AD is recruited within the proximity; the reconstituted TF stimulates transcription by enabling the RNA polymerase II to transcribe the downstream reporter gene (Fields and Song, 1989). Hence, the bait and prey proteins form a bridge between the DBD and AD. The yeast strain is usually deficient in the components of the pathways for histidine biosynthesis. Therefore, by using HIS3 gene, which encodes for the protein Imidazoleglycerol-phosphate dehydratase that catalyses the sixth step in histidine biosynthesis, as a reporter for the transcriptional activation, *bait* and *prey* protein interactions are easily detected by monitoring yeast growth on culture dishes with a solid medium lacking histidine. Researchers can also construct a cDNA library instead of the prey-fused protein coding regions, and perform the screening of the binding partners from the cDNA library. Sometimes, whole cDNA library screening process is automated, thereby, permitting high- throughput analysis (Buckholz et al., 1999).

Y2H system has many advantages. It does not require any specialised equipment, and it is cost-effective. PPIs can be easily detected by monitoring the transformed yeast growth. Moreover, Y2H screening is highly sensitive. Therefore, this system is suitable for detecting weak and transient interactions, which are often the most interesting in PHI-induced signalling cascades. Third, the interaction reflects *in vivo* status. Yeast is a eukaryote; therefore, it supports the correct folding of eukaryotic proteins, including post-translational modifications (PTMs). These advantages therefore, easily facilitate the characterisation of phy-siologically relevant PPIs; thus, Y2H has become the method of choice to characterise PHIs in many host-pathogen systems (Durmus et al., 2015; de Chassey et al., 2008; Uetz et al., 2006; Tripathi et al., 2013; Nicod et al., 2017; Dolan et al., 2013; Shapira et al., 2009).

However, Y2H suffers from notable deficiencies. Since the assay is highly sensitive, the self-activation of transcription and reporter gene expression by *bait* protein in the absence of *prey* protein may commonly occur; thus, leading to the identification of false positive PPIs. Y2H may also fail to detect many physiologically relevant PPIs since the yeast cell environment is different from that of a mammalian cell. Therefore, some important post-translational aspects such as protein sub-cellular localisation and/or post-translational modifications (PTMs), which are often required for certain PPIs, may not be reflected within yeast. Y2H is also at a slight disadvantage when characterising PPIs involving extracellular proteins or membrane proteins, since the two-hybrid system requires the fusion proteins to be translocated to the yeast nucleus. Moreover, Y2H is optimised for binary protein interactions and some PPIs require correct folding as subunits of a large protein complex. To overcome such limitations, different variations of Y2H, such as the mammalian cell based two-hybrid assay (Luo et al., 1997), the membrane anchored two-hybrid assay (Snider et al., 2010), and the three-hybrid assay (Maruta et al., 2016) have been developed. For example, the Y2H membrane protein system, which identifies PPIs involving integral membrane proteins and membrane-associated proteins in an *in vivo* setting at the cellular membrane, was used to identify novel host protein interactions for hepatitis C virus (HCV) Core and NS4B proteins (Tripathi et al., 2010), nearly all of which were not characterised by previously by the high throughput screens for HCV-host interactions using the conventional Y2H approach (de Chassey et al., 2008).

Affinity purification–mass spectrometry (AP-MS) is another method to identify PPIs on a large scale; the method involves biochemical purification of protein complexes from cells, followed by the mass spectrometric identification of the components of the purified protein complexes (Dunham *et al.*, 2012). Immuno-precipitation using specific antibodies is a classical method to purify target proteins from the cells under native conditions. Affinity purification system is also available to purify ectopically expressed proteins. After the purification of an endogenous protein or an ectopically expressed affinity-tagged target protein, the co-purified proteins that are associated with the target proteins are identified by mass-spectrometry analysis, resulting in the mapping of the PPIs of the target protein. This method is widely used to characterise protein complexes of target proteins due to the simplicity and sensitivity of the mass-spectrometry analysis. For instance, flaviviruses, a group of positive-strand RNA viruses generally induce intracellular membrane rearrangement and form an organelle like structure, called the "replication organelle" that facilitates efficient genomic replication. Replication organelle appears in close proximity to the endoplasmic reticulum and also serves as a shell that protects the viruses against various cellular stress responses and therefore, it allows for a persistent viral replication in the cytoplasm. In a specific study, the replication organelle was biochemically purified from JEV (Japanese encephalitis virus, a member of the flaviviridae) infected cells and subject to extensive mass-spectrometry analyses that identified many host factors, including ESCRT subunits, and ER membrane shaping proteins, innate immunity factors as the constituents of the replication organelle. Subsequent analysis by Y2H revealed binary interactions between some of these factors and viral non-structural proteins and the follow up siRNA depletion experiments further confirmed their essential roles in viral propagation (Tabata *et al.*, 2016). In another study, Jäger *et al.* (2011) employed AP-MS coupled with a quantitative scoring system to identify 497 high-confidence HIV-human PPIs.

To overcome non-specific detection of co-purified proteins, several two-step tandem affinity protein purification systems have been developed (Burckstummer *et al.*, 2006). This approach allows the preparation of a substantially pure target protein complex and reduces the background signals. The quantitative mass-spectrometry analysis also has been used to identify the contaminants (Trinkle-Mulcahy *et al.*, 2008). However, the method does not always capture the direct interactions between a target protein and its binding partners and reflects only steady-state interactions, and therefore, possibly missing weak and transient interactions.

Eventually, a combination of different methods will provide a more comprehensive map of protein interaction dynamics, since each method will likely lead to the exploration of a different aspect of PHI interactome.

PPI Network-Based Analysis of PHIs

Construction and analysis of PHI networks (PHINs) spanning extensive protein-protein interaction (PPI) maps between host and pathogen interactomes is a promising avenue to obtain a better understanding of the biological context of PHIs and to understand the pathogenesis of infectious diseases.

Network topology that is the connectivity of the proteins in a PPI network (PPIN) can often provide relevant insights into the biological functions of the proteins and their relative importance in a PPIN (Raman, 2010). Analyses of PHIN across different pathogen-host systems have revealed systematic trends in host-pathogen interaction networks. In specific studies that examined host-pathogen PPIs in the context of pathogenesis of infectious diseases, it was noted that viral and bacterial pathogens preferentially interacted with network 'hubs' and 'bottlenecks' in the human protein interactome (de Chassey *et al.*, 2008; Tripathi *et al.*, 2013; Dyer *et al.*, 2008). Network topological attributes can indeed guide the prioritisation and selection of candidates for experimental characterisation of pathogen-induced disorders (Tripathi *et al.*, 2012). For instance, Diamond *et al.* (2012) combined topological properties derived from a protein association network based on clinical data to evaluate the onset and acuteness of HCV-induced liver fibrosis and they identified a novel role of protein kinase A RII-α, which was judged to be a 'bottleneck' in the protein association network, to play a key role in HCV-induced liver injury (Diamond *et al.*, 2012).

Halehalli and Nagarajaram (2015) further established that in addition to targeting 'hubs' and 'bottlenecks', pathogenic proteins disproportionately form complexes with intrinsically disordered proteins and they proposed disorder associated conformational flexibility as one of the typical characteristics of VHIs (Halehalli and Nagarajaram, 2015).

PHIs Across Pathogenic Species

PHINs are also very useful in understanding the differences in strategies adopted by phylogenetically different pathogenic species to circumvent the host defence systems and modulate the host cellular machinery to survive in the intracellular environment and for their propagation during the infectious process. For instance, a comparison of PHI networks involving DNA and RNA viruses highlighted that while the DNA viruses simultaneously perturbed both the cellular and metabolic processes, RNA viruses preferentially targeted host factors associated with intracellular transport, translational machinery and sub-cellular localisation (Durmus and Ulgen, 2017). Among other examples, pathogenic bacteria also interact with host interactomes via different mechanisms and some of these mechanisms are remarkably different from those employed by pathogenic viruses (Nicod *et al.*, 2017). A key difference is that bacteria do not explicitly depend on the host cellular machinery for their own replication, since unlike viruses, bacteria have a living and a fully functional cellular machinery of their own. Therefore, a deeper understanding of the specifics of PHI networks involved in the infection by different classes of pathogenic organisms will facilitate a development of more specific and probably more effective therapeutics against infectious diseases.

Despite the rapid strides in the construction and analysis of PHINs, a more detailed and broad-based analysis is hampered by the limited amount of large-scale PHI data and the host PPI interactome data, especially in the case of animal model systems

(Murakami *et al.*, 2017) that are often used to investigate the pathogenesis of infectious human diseases. Therefore, it is necessary to deploy computational tools and approaches for literature mining and PHI prediction to maximise the availability of PHI and host PPI data and ensure the robustness of biological analyses leveraging PHINs (**Table 1**).

An example of such an approach would to leverage the principle of orthology in model organism research; this is based on the belief that the genetic makeup of the different cellular processes (such as PPIs) is inherently conserved across different organisms. Tripathi *et al.* (2012), for instance, analysed the biological significance of differential protein levels in transgenic mouse models of HCV infection. The differentially expressed mouse proteins were assimilated into an orthologous human protein interactome with the help of TargetMine data analysis platform (Chen *et al.*, 2011, 2016), to highlight the cellular pathways significantly impacted by HCV infection and to prioritise novel anti-HCV host factors. Follow-up cellular assays validated VTI1A, a vesicular transport associated factor, as a novel regulator of HCV propagation.

Extracting PHIs From Literature and Public Databases

PHIs are scattered across several published studies in the biomedical literature and many publicly available databases that catalogue different types of PHIs. For instance, virus–host interactions (VHIs) for a large number of viruses can be easily sourced from organism-specific resources such as Human Immunodeficiency Virus (HIV)-1 Human-Interaction Database (Fu *et al.*, 2009) or databases that are entirely dedicated to VHIs such as VirHostNet (Guirimand *et al.*, 2015), VirusMentha (Calderone *et al.*, 2015) and ViRBase (Li *et al.*, 2015). Likewise, PATRIC (Wattam *et al.*, 2014) is a resource that exclusively catalogues bacterial-host interactions. Additionally, there are comprehensive publicly available databases such as HPIDB (Ammari *et al.*, 2016), PHI-base (Urban *et al.*, 2017), PHIDIAS (Xiang *et al.*, 2007) and PHISTO (Durmus *et al.*, 2013) that offer a more generic repository of PHIs and occasionally tools to visualise and analyse PHI data. However, due to an ever increasing volume of the biomedical literature describing the pathogenesis of infectious diseases, the identification of specific PHIs and their roles in pathogenicity is a non-trivial task and therefore, it can be a while before many discoveries are reflected in the PHI databases. A vast amount of PHI data, thus, remains tucked away uncurated in a large number of published studies; therefore, the recent years have witnessed a rapid development of computational methods for biomedical literature mining, especially in the context of PHIs (see below).

Some studies have used publicly available computational tools that facilitate the retrieval and extraction of relevant information from the biomedical literature such as PubMed to gather abstracts containing the relevant host and pathogen keywords as well as interaction verbs (including "interact", "bind", "attach", "associate"). These steps were followed by a careful manual curation to extract pairwise PHIs to complement the experimentally determined PHIs (de Chassey *et al.*, 2008; Tripathi *et al.*, 2013). However, such methods are laborious, highly context-specific and difficult to employ on a larger scale and for extracting PHIs in general. To address the challenges of extracting PHIs from the literature, different methods using text mining have been employed to extract PHIs from the biomedical literature (Durmus *et al.*, 2015). These have included methods that focus on gathering and selecting literature abstracts that contain PHI-related information; Yin *et al.* (2010) were the first to report a machine learning-based automated text-mining system to identify research articles describing PHIs. Subsequently, Thieu *et al.* (2012) developed a hybrid procedure encompassing machine learning and language-based approaches to perform a more rigorous

Table 1   A selection of computational approaches for prediction and analysis of PHIs

S. No.	Method	Type of method	Pathogenic species	Reference
1.	Yin *et al.* – Document classification	Text-mining	All	Yin *et al.* (2010)
2.	Thieu *et al.* – Semantic analysis with machine learning and language processing	Text-mining	All	Thieu *et al.* (2012)
3.	Cui *et al.* – Protein sequence information	Machine learning using SVM classifier	Viruses	Cui *et al.* (2012)
4.	Dyer *et al.* – Protein domain profiles	Bayesian statistics	*Plasmodium falciparum*	Dyer *et al.* (2007)
5.	de Chassey *et al.* – Protein structure and interactome information	Structural homology and interaction redundancy	Viruses – Influenza virus N1 protein	de Chassey *et al.* (2013b)
6.	Coelho *et al.* – Ensemble approach using literature mining, sequence, functional overlap, orthology and domain interactions	Machine learning using naïve Bayes classifier	Oral microbiome	Coelho *et al.* (2014)
7.	Kshirsagar *et al.* – Transfer learning based on homology	Combinatorial supervised machine learning	Bacteria – *Salmonella, Yersinia*	Kshirsagar *et al.* (2012)
8.	Kshirsagar *et al.* – Combinatorial feature selection for model building	Multitask learning	Bacteria – *Y. pestis, F. tularensis, Salmonella, B. anthracis*	Kshirsagar *et al.* (2013)
9.	Zhou *et al.* – Protein sequence information and amino acid properties	Homology based PPI prediction	*M. tuberculosis*	Zhou *et al.* (2014)
10.	Han *et al.* – Interlog and protein domain-domain interaction	PPI network-based prediction	*Bacillus licheniformis*	Han *et al.* (2016)

semantic analysis of the biomedical literature to extract PHIs. The development of newer and more sophisticated methods that take into account the unique aspects of different PHIs (Karadeniz *et al.*, 2015) for PHI extraction from the biomedical literature will not only improve and the visibility and coverage of PHIs with the researchers and existing PHI repositories, but also complement PHIN-centric analyses to better understand the biology of pathogenesis.

In Silico Prediction of PHIs

Despite the increasing availability of experimentally defined PHIs, much of the available data provides only a partial coverage of all the probable PHIs and that too mostly for well-studied pathogens. The limited coverage of experimentally-determined PHIs is chiefly because these methods are resource-intensive and time consuming and thus, the construction of PHI interactomes using experimental methods is technically challenging. Therefore, it is of significant importance to develop new computational methods that can build inter-species PPI prediction models to prioritise the experimental scope and accelerate the discovery of PHIs (Nourani *et al.*, 2015; Halder *et al.*, 2017).

Many different approaches for *in silico* prediction of PHIs have been developed; they variously utilise protein sequence information (Cui *et al.*, 2012), protein domain profiles (Dyer *et al.*, 2007), protein structural properties and structural similarity (Franzosa and Xia, 2011; de Chassey *et al.*, 2013b) and principles of homology and "interologues" based on known PHIs (Coelho *et al.*, 2014) among others, using classical machine learning approaches. These "classical" methods work well enough where sufficient training data are available, but as often is the case with PHIs, there is a distinct scarcity of high-quality PHI data, especially for many less studied pathogens, and this problem contributes to a lack of sufficient PHI features for supervised machine learning (Kshirsagar *et al.*, 2012). More recently, methods that employ integrative genomics data and more sophisticated machine-learning frameworks, such as multitask learning that aims to simultaneously examine different related tasks (in this instance sufficiently related pathogenic diseases) and to extract common features and combine them into a predictive model, are becoming increasingly popular for predicting PHIs (Kshirsagar *et al.*, 2013).

However, the bulk of PHI prediction methods remain focused on species-specific PHIs. To name a few, Zhou *et al.* (2014) employed a homology-based approach to predict host-pathogen PPIs between human and a tuberculosis-causing bacterial pathogen *M. tuberculosis* and identified key properties of the host and pathogen proteins involved in these PPIs. Han *et al.* (2016) constructed a computationally predicted PPIN of *Bacillus licheniformis* and identified novel protein complexes and assigned functional annotations for previously uncharacterised proteins.

Conclusions

Studies on PHIs have observed common themes underlying the onset of various human diseases associated with pathogenic infection in humans, a better understanding of which may be helpful in optimising broad spectrum approaches to counteracting a wide range of pathogenic infections.

A deeper analysis and understanding of PHIs will considerably aid in the identification of new clinically relevant targets for optimising the therapeutic strategies to manipulate PHIs and thus, more effectively combat infectious diseases. Moreover, the genetic variability of pathogenic, especially viral genomes has facilitated the emergence of drug resistance against drugs that target pathogenic components. Therefore, antibacterials and antivirals that target less mutable host proteins that are critical to pathogenesis, preferably with minimal adverse side effects, may provide attractive alternatives to existing therapies. Additional studies on the evolution of PHIs along with the evolution of the pathogens and hosts themselves, should also contribute to developing better strategies for inhibiting PHIs for newer and better therapies.

See also: Algorithms for Graph and Network Analysis: Clustering and Search of Motifs in Graphs. Algorithms for Graph and Network Analysis: Graph Alignment. Algorithms for Graph and Network Analysis: Graph Indexes/Descriptors. Algorithms for Graph and Network Analysis: Traversing/Searching/Sampling Graphs. Genome Analysis – Identification of Genes Involved in Host-Pathogen Protein-Protein Interaction Networks. Host-Pathogen Interactions. Large Scale Ecological Modeling With Viruses: A Review. Mapping the Environmental Microbiome. Natural Language Processing Approaches in Bioinformatics. Networks in Biology. Protein–Protein Interaction Databases. Vaccine Target Discovery

---

References

Ammari, M.G., *et al.*, 2016. HPIDB 2.0: A curated database for host–pathogen interactions. Database 2016, baw103.
Bhavsar, A.P., Guttman, J.A., Finlay, B.B., 2007. Manipulation of host-cell pathways by bacterial pathogens. Nature 449 (7164), 827–834.
Brito, A.F., Pinney, J.W., 2017. Protein-protein interactions in virus-host systems. Front. Microbiol. 8, 1557.
Buckholz, R.G., *et al.*, 1999. Automation of yeast two-hybrid screening. J. Mol. Microbiol. Biotechnol. 1 (1), 135–140.
Burckstummer, T., *et al.*, 2006. An efficient tandem affinity purification procedure for interaction proteomics in mammalian cells. Nat. Methods 3 (12), 1013–1019.

Calderone, A., Licata, L., Cesareni, G., 2015. VirusMentha: A new resource for virus-host protein interactions. Nucleic Acids Res. 43 (Database issue), D588–D592.

Calderwood, M.A., et al., 2007. Epstein-Barr virus and virus human protein interaction maps. Proc. Natl. Acad. Sci. USA 104 (18), 7606–7611.

de Chassey, B., et al., 2008. Hepatitis C virus infection protein network. Mol. Syst. Biol. 4, 230.

de Chassey, B., et al., 2013a. The interactomes of influenza virus NS1 and NS2 proteins identify new host factors and provide insights for ADAR1 playing a supportive role in virus replication. PLOS Pathog. 9 (7), e1003440.

de Chassey, B., et al., 2013b. Structure homology and interaction redundancy for discovering virus-host protein interactions. EMBO Rep. 14 (10), 938–944.

Chen, Y.A., Tripathi, L.P., Mizuguchi, K., 2011. TargetMine, an integrated data warehouse for candidate gene prioritisation and target discovery. PLOS ONE 6 (3), e17844.

Chen, Y.A., Tripathi, L.P., Mizuguchi, K., 2016. An integrative data analysis platform for gene set analysis and knowledge discovery in a data warehouse framework. Database 2016.

Coelho, E.D., et al., 2014. Computational prediction of the human-microbial oral interactome. BMC Syst. Biol. 8, 24.

Cui, G., Fang, C., Han, K., 2012. Prediction of protein-protein interactions between viruses and human by an SVM model. BMC Bioinform. 13 (Suppl 7), S5.

Diamond, D.L., et al., 2012. Proteome and computational analyses reveal new insights into the mechanisms of hepatitis C virus-mediated liver disease posttransplantation. Hepatology 56 (1), 28–38.

Dolan, P.T., et al., 2013. Identification and comparative analysis of hepatitis C virus-host cell protein interactions. Mol. Biosyst. 9 (12), 3199–3209.

Dunham, W.H., Mullin, M., Gingras, A.C., 2012. Affinity-purification coupled to mass spectrometry: Basic principles and strategies. Proteomics 12 (10), 1576–1590.

Durmus, S., et al., 2015. A review on computational systems biology of pathogen-host interactions. Front. Microbiol. 6, 235.

Durmus, T.S., et al., 2013. PHISTO: Pathogen-host interaction search tool. Bioinformatics 29 (10), 1357–1358.

Durmus, S., Ulgen, K.O., 2017. Comparative interactomics for virus-human protein-protein interactions: DNA viruses versus RNA viruses. FEBS Open Bio 7 (1), 96–107.

Dyer, M.D., Murali, T.M., Sobral, B.W., 2007. Computational prediction of host-pathogen protein-protein interactions. Bioinformatics 23 (13), i159–i166.

Dyer, M.D., Murali, T.M., Sobral, B.W., 2008. The landscape of human proteins interacting with viruses and other pathogens. PLOS Pathog. 4 (2), e32.

Fels, U., Gevaert, K., Van Damme, P., 2017. Proteogenomics in aid of host-pathogen interaction studies: A bacterial perspective. Proteomes 5 (4), 26.

Fields, S., Song, O., 1989. A novel genetic system to detect protein-protein interactions. Nature 340 (6230), 245–246.

Franzosa, E.A., Xia, Y., 2011. Structural principles within the human-virus protein-protein interaction network. Proc. Natl. Acad. Sci. USA 108 (26), 10538–10543.

Friedel, C.C., Haas, J., 2011. Virus-host interactomes and global models of virus-infected cells. Trends Microbiol. 19 (10), 501–508.

Fu, W., et al., 2009. Human immunodeficiency virus type 1, human protein interaction database at NCBI. Nucleic Acids Res. 37 (Database issue), D417–D422.

Guirimand, T., Delmotte, S., Navratil, V., 2015. VirHostNet 2.0: Surfing on the web of virus/host molecular interactions data. Nucleic Acids Res. 43 (Database issue), D583–D587.

Halder, A.K., et al., 2017. Review of computational methods for virus-host protein interaction prediction: A case study on novel Ebola-human interactions. Brief. Funct. Genomics.

Halehalli, R.R., Nagarajaram, H.A., 2015. Molecular principles of human virus protein-protein interactions. Bioinformatics 31 (7), 1025–1033.

Han, Y.C., et al., 2016. Prediction and characterization of protein-protein interaction network in Bacillus licheniformis WX-02. Sci. Rep. 6, 19486.

Jager, S., et al., 2011. Global landscape of HIV-human protein complexes. Nature 481 (7381), 365–370.

Karadeniz, I., et al., 2015. Literature mining and ontology based analysis of Host-Brucella Gene-Gene Interaction Network. Front. Microbiol. 6, 1386.

Kshirsagar, M., Carbonell, J., Klein-Seetharaman, J., 2012. Techniques to cope with missing data in host-pathogen protein interaction prediction. Bioinformatics 28 (18), i466–i472.

Kshirsagar, M., Carbonell, J., Klein-Seetharaman, J., 2013. Multitask learning for host-pathogen protein interactions. Bioinformatics 29 (13), i217–i226.

Li, Y., et al., 2015. ViRBase: A resource for virus-host ncRNA-associated interactions. Nucleic Acids Res. 43 (Database issue), D578–D582.

Lum, K.K., Cristea, I.M., 2016. Proteomic approaches to uncovering virus-host protein interactions during the progression of viral infection. Expert Rev. Proteomics 13 (3), 325–340.

Luo, Y., et al., 1997. Mammalian two-hybrid system: A complementary approach to the yeast two-hybrid system. Biotechniques 22 (2), 350–352.

Ma-Lauer, Y., et al., 2012. Virus-host interactomes – Antiviral drug discovery. Curr. Opin. Virol. 2 (5), 614–621.

Maruta, N., Trusov, Y., Botella, J.R., 2016. Yeast three-hybrid system for the detection of protein-protein interactions. Methods Mol. Biol. 1363, 145–154.

Murakami, Y., et al., 2017. Network analysis and in silico prediction of protein-protein interactions with applications in drug discovery. Curr. Opin. Struct. Biol. 44, 134–142.

Nicod, C., Banaei-Esfahani, A., Collins, B.C., 2017. Elucidation of host-pathogen protein-protein interactions to uncover mechanisms of host cell rewiring. Curr. Opin. Microbiol. 39, 7–15.

Nourani, E., Khunjush, F., Durmus, S., 2015. Computational approaches for prediction of pathogen-host protein-protein interactions. Front. Microbiol. 6, 94.

Raman, K., 2010. Construction and analysis of protein-protein interaction networks. Autom. Exp. 2 (1), 2.

Shapira, S.D., et al., 2009. A physical and regulatory map of host-influenza interactions reveals pathways in H1N1 infection. Cell 139 (7), 1255–1267.

Snider, J., et al., 2010. Detecting interactions with membrane proteins using a membrane two-hybrid assay in yeast. Nat. Protoc. 5 (7), 1281–1293.

Tabata, K., et al., 2016. Unique requirement for ESCRT factors in flavivirus particle formation on the endoplasmic reticulum. Cell Rep. 16 (9), 2339–2347.

Thieu, T., et al., 2012. Literature mining of host-pathogen interactions: Comparing feature-based supervised learning and language-based approaches. Bioinformatics 28 (6), 867–875.

Trinkle-Mulcahy, L., et al., 2008. Identifying specific protein interaction partners using quantitative mass spectrometry and bead proteomes. J. Cell Biol. 183 (2), 223–239.

Tripathi, L.P., et al., 2010. Network based analysis of hepatitis C virus Core and NS4B protein interactions. Mol. Biosyst. 6 (12), 2539–2553.

Tripathi, L.P., et al., 2012. Proteomic analysis of hepatitis C virus (HCV) core protein transfection and host regulator PA28gamma knockout in HCV pathogenesis: A network-based study. J. Proteome Res. 11 (7), 3664–3679.

Tripathi, L.P., et al., 2013. Understanding the biological context of NS5A-host interactions in HCV infection: A network-based approach. J. Proteome Res. 12 (6), 2537–2551.

Uetz, P., et al., 2006. Herpesviral protein networks and their interaction with the human proteome. Science 311 (5758), 239–242.

Urban, M., et al., 2017. PHI-base: A new interface and further additions for the multi-species pathogen-host interactions database. Nucleic Acids Res. 45 (D1), D604–D610.

Wattam, A.R., et al., 2014. PATRIC, the bacterial bioinformatics database and analysis resource. Nucleic Acids Res. 42 (Database issue), D581–D591.

Xiang, Z., Tian, Y., He, Y., 2007. PHIDIAS: A pathogen-host interaction data integration and analysis system. Genome Biol. 8 (7), R150.

Yin, L., et al., 2010. Document classification for mining host pathogen protein-protein interactions. Artif. Intell. Med. 49 (3), 155–160.

Zhou, H., et al., 2014. Stringent homology-based prediction of H. sapiens-M. tuberculosis H37Rv protein-protein interactions. Biol. Direct 9, 5.

Phylogenetic Analysis: Early Evolution of Life

Himakshi Sarma, Sushmita Pradhan, and Venkata SK Mattaparthi, Tezpur University, Tezpur, India
Sandeep Kaushik, European Institute of Excellence on Tissue Engineering and Regenerative Medicine, Guimaraes, Portugal

Introduction

The earth formed about 4.5 billion years ago had no signs of life, until 1 billion years later, when Earth saw the emergence of life, the evidence of which can be found in fossils dating back to 3.5 billion years ago (Brasier *et al.*, 2006; Dalrymple, 2001; Dodd *et al.*, 2017; Mojzsis *et al.*, 1996; Schopf and Packer, 1987). Since then, life on earth has seen three major phases of evolution. The first was the appearance of prokaryotic organisms (single celled organism having undefined nucleus), then came eukaryotes (highly organized single cell with defined nucleus and chromosomes with an arranged DNA), and finally the evolution of multicellular organisms (combination of eukaryotic cells), which occurred mainly in the Precambrian period (Knoll, 2003, 2015; Schopf, 2001). Thus, evolution can be defined as a transition or adaptation of an organism, in response to the environmental conditions over the course of time. Evolution can be classified into three types: Chemical evolution (Oró, 1983), molecular evolution, and Darwinian evolution. Chemical evolution majorly denotes the prebiotic (before biology) formation of organic molecules in the period between the formation of the earth and the first appearance of a living cell. Molecular evolution refers to the changes in living systems that have occurred thereafter, eventually leading to the formation of unicellular and multicellular organisms. Darwinian evolution refers to the events after molecular evolution, which led to the speciation as seen today on Earth. **Fig. 1** provides a schematic representation of the evolutionary changes that took place (Pattabhi and Gautham, 2002).

Stages of Evolution

Chemical Evolution (Prebiotic Earth)

The current understanding of the conditions on prebiotic Earth and the idea of gradual chemical evolution of life, otherwise known as abiogeneisis (spontaneous generation), were put forth independently by Oparin and Haldane (see references in Fox, 1974).

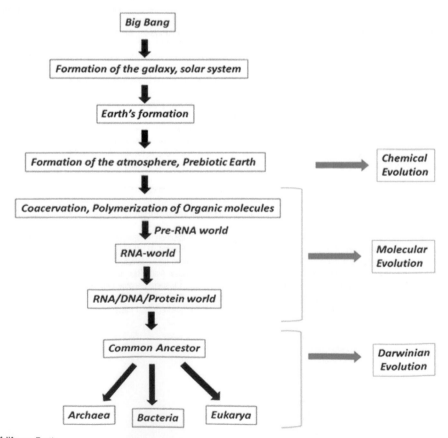

Fig. 1 Beginning of life on Earth.

Spontaneous generation

Oparin and Haldane were the first ones to revive the idea of abiogeneisis. Haldane, in particular, was fascinated with the experiments where organic molecules were formed from the mixture of H_2O, CO_2, and NH_2 in the presence of ultraviolet light. Haldane further suggested that the strong reducing conditions may have been present at that time, which paved the way for the atmosphere of the early earth. Haldane's article in 1929 recommended that the earth's prebiotic soup would have formed first, after which organic mixes of simple sugars and amino acids came into being (Haldane, 1929). Oparin, on the other hand, stated that the primordial soup consisting of organic molecules could be created in an anaerobic atmosphere in the presence of sunlight, wherein the coacervate droplets would be formed as a result of the complex reaction undergone by the organic molecules (Oparin, 1924). These coacervate droplets would then merge with the neighbor droplets, and reproduce by the fission process (Fox, 1974). Inspired by the strong arguments of Oparin and Haldane, Stanley Miller, along with his graduate advisor Harold Urey, tested Oparin–Haldane's early earth hypothesis in 1953 (Miller, 1953; Miller and Urey, 1959).

Miller–Urey experiment

The Miller–Urey experiment established the capability of the earth's primitive atmosphere in building life from inorganic materials. It proved that the conditions existing in the earth's primitive atmosphere were sufficient enough to form organic molecules like amino acids. Their experimental steps consisted of (1) assemblage of a reducing atmosphere rich in hydrogen, and devoid of gaseous oxygen; (2) reducing atmospheres of H_2 over water at ocean's brim; (3) maintenance of H_2 and H_2O mixture below $100°C$; and (4) trigger lightning in the form of sparks.

In order to prove the hypothesis, they placed the molecules that may have been present at the early stages of the earth's time, like methane (CH_4), hydrogen (H_2), and ammonia (NH_3) gases into a moist locale above a water-containing flask (mock ocean of water). To mimic the primordial lightning, they used electrical current for the setup. A few days later, they could observe organic compounds in the flask, some of which were amino acids, the precursor of proteins. Using chromatographic techniques, they were able to confirm the presence of amino acids (glycine, alanine, aspartic acid, glutamic acid, β-alanine), purine and pyrimidines, and other organic compounds such as urea, lactic acid, glycolic acid, succinic acid, and propionic acid. The Miller–Urey experiment was able to successfully validate the emergence of biological molecules from the nonbiological substances (Miller, 1953; Miller and Urey, 1959) **(Fig. 2)**.

Molecular Evolution (Complex Biological Molecules and Protocells)

Though Miller–Urey demonstrated the formation of simple biomolecules, the actual chemical evolution would depend upon the polymerization or condensation of these monomers into polymers (macromolecules like polypeptides, polysaccharides). For example, nucleic acid bases can be synthesized under prebiotic conditions (condensation of HCN and H_2O catalyzed by NH_3), while the sugars can be synthesized by the polymerization of formaldehyde (CH_2O) catalyzed by the divalent cations, alumina, or clay (Miller, 1953; Miller and Urey, 1959). But how these molecules organized themselves to form a cell was the next big question.

Sydney Fox and his team in the 1950s synthesized some peptidelike products by heating a dry mixture of amino acids at the temperature between 150 and $180°C$, which they termed as proteinoids, meaning a thermal protein. Unlike the default linear

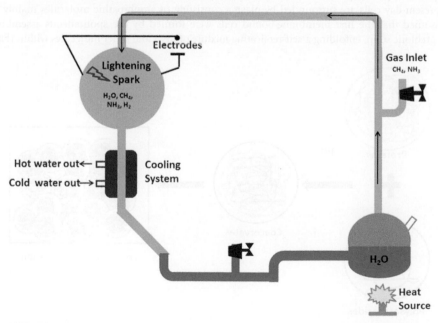

Fig. 2 Schematic representation of Miller–Urey's experiment.

proteins that are produced by the cell, proteinoids are highly branched polypeptides, exhibiting catalytic activity, and susceptibility to digestion by proteases, which are the properties shown only by the biological proteins (Fox *et al.*, 1959).

Origin of cells and organized structure

Macromolecules, due to their intermolecular forces, may have aggregated to form the membrane-enclosed droplets known as coacervates and microsphere, which exhibits features similar to that of a living system (selective permeability, and energy use). Coacervates (meaning "to assemble together or cluster") are an agglomeration of colloidal particles in a liquid phase that stays in the form of minuscule droplets (**Fig. 3**). Coacervates display a number of compelling features:

- exchange substance with the environment,
- increases in size,
- selective concentration of the compounds within them (De Jong and Kruyt, 1929).

Oparin had earlier proposed that coacervates may have been the intermediate stage between loose molecules and living systems. He observed that droplets survived longer when they carried out polymerization reactions. Microscopic membrane-bound spheres (termed microspheres), however, are formed when proteinoids are boiled in water and cooled off. These microspheres are uniform in size, stable, and double membrane-bound, resembling a typical cell, and can multiply by fission and budding. They also present the properties of osmosis, growth in size, and selective absorption of chemicals, which are usually associated with normal cells. This spontaneous self-congregation of macromolecules into coacervates and microspheres is indicative of the fact that the contingency of similar structures under those primitive atmospheres may have probably led to the development of more organized and defined membrane-bound structure containing molecules, called protocells. Later, protocells may have been subjected to natural selection, which acted as a driving force in the origination of much more dominant and favorable molecules, and structures (Oparin, 2003).

Membrane defined the first cell

This idea was first proposed by Haldane (1929), saying that "the cell consists of numerous half-living chemical molecules suspended in water and enclosed in an oily film. When the whole sea was a vast chemical laboratory the conditions for the formation of such films must have been relatively favourable....". Goldacre (1958) went on to suggest that the first cell membranes may be been formed as a result of the wave-action behavior of the lipid-like surfactants. Bangham *et al.* (1965) were the first group to prove that phospholipids readily formed lipid-bilayer vesicles, called liposomes. The development of an outer membrane must have been the path-defining events leading to the formation of the first cell. The need for containment is generally attained by the amphipathic property of any molecule, where the molecule is semihydrophobic and semihydrophilic. When such a molecule is placed in water, they assemble, arranging their hydrophobic halves as close to one another away from water, while keeping their hydrophilic halves exposed to water. These amphipathic molecules readily gather to form bilayers, creating closed vesicles. Several studies have shown the production of the phospholipids using simulated prebiotic conditions from mixtures of fatty acids, glycerol, and phosphate (Hargreaves *et al.*, 1977; Rao *et al.*, 1982).

Majorly all the present-day cells are surrounded by plasma consisting of amphipathic molecules mainly the phospholipids. Hence, it can be assumed that the first membrane-bound cells were formed by the spontaneous assembly of phospholipids molecules from the prebiotic soup, enfolding a self-replicating mixture of RNA and other molecules within (**Fig. 4**). However, it is

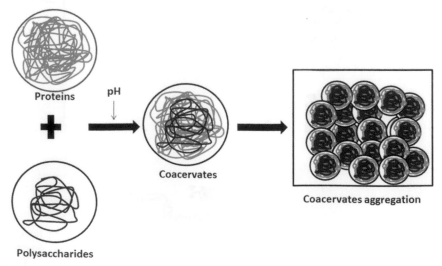

Proteins

pH

+

Coacervates

Coacervates aggregation

Polysaccharides

Fig. 3 Coacervation process.

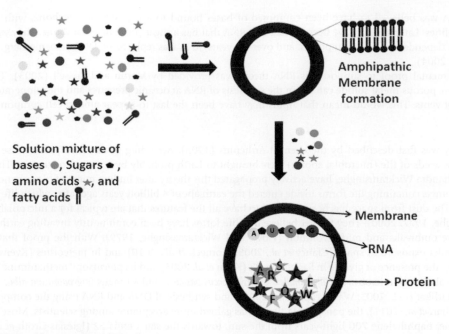

Fig. 4 Formation of the membrane enclosed first cell.

not clear as to when this happened. But, once the RNA molecules were enclosed inside a closed membrane, they may have begun to evolve into carriers of genetic instructions.

Current model for origin of life hypothesis

Many scientists have debated as to what came first – Was it RNA, proteins, or lipids? However, the hypotheses that have been proposed so far depend on the number of discoveries about the origin of molecular and cellular components of life; these are listed in the order of postulated emergence:

Clay hypothesis

The complexity of RNA makes it doubtful as to whether it can be produced nonbiologically or not. So scientists have suggested that some clays have properties to act as enhancers for the creation of the RNA world. This proposal saw very less support among the scientific community (Ferris, 1999). Researchers have demonstrated that clay (montmorillonite) has the ability to enhance the conversion of fatty acids to "bubbles," which can encapsulate RNA. These bubbles then merge with nearby lipids, and then multiply. This proves that primitive cells may have been formed via similar process (Hanczyc et al., 2003).

Lipid world

Many evolutionists believe that double-walled lipids may have set the initial basis of life on earth as these can readily form liposome structures, and reproduce (Garwood, 2012; Trevors and Psenner, 2001). Though they are devoid of any genetic information, but after passing through selection pressure points, RNA may have formed inside the liposome, thus giving way to the origin of life (Segré et al., 2001).

Iron–sulfur world

A series of experiments successfully demonstrated that using sulfides (iron sulfide and nickel sulfide) as catalysts, one can produce proteins, amino acids from inorganic materials (CO, H_2S). The steps required were maintained at 100°C, with moderate pressures. This suggested that some of the self-sustaining protein may have been produced in the vicinity of hydrothermal vents (Wächtershäuser, 2000).

RNA world

This is the most widely accepted model to explain the initiation of life on Earth. The discovery of ribozymes puts forth that earlier life forms may have been entirely based on RNA. They held the view that RNA may have acted as both template and enzyme (ribozyme), and thus replicated on its own, thereby setting the foundations of life on Earth. This theory was further supported when cofactors, which often carry RNA nucleotides with them, were placed in the argued scenario (Orgel and Crick, 1993; Shapiro, 2007).

Though ribozymes like enzymes were produced in in vitro conditions, some were still doubtful of their reality in the early Earth time frame. Many came up with suggestions that there may have been a pre-RNA world before the RNA world, where the earliest ribozymes may have been formed of PNA (peptide nucleic acid), a simpler form of RNA (Böhler et al., 1995; Nelson et al., 2000;

Orgel, 2000). PNA was believed to have been composed of bases bound to a peptide-like backbone, with spontaneous polymerization capabilities. Later, it may have been replaced by RNA that has a sugar-phosphate backbone. They would also have had no speciation, but depended on selection points, and over the years, RNA was replaced by DNA (Hoenigsberg, 2003; Joyce, 2002; Trevors and Abel, 2004).

Another experimental proof to support this RNA theory was provided by Martin and Russell (2003). They proposed that precipitates of some porous metal sulfide can aid in the synthesis of RNA at oceanic pressures and the temperature of about 100°C near hydrothermal vents. This would mean that lipids may have been the last to appear among cell components.

Panspermia

Panspermia theory was first described by the chemist Arrhenius (1903). According to this theory, life arose somewhere in the universe, and these seeds of life (microbial spores) were brought to Earth probably by a meteor or comets. The astronomer duo, Fred Hoyle and Chandra Wickramsinghe, have actively propagated this theory after finding traces of biopolymer in the space dust. They stated that comets containing life forms inside entered the earth about 4 billion years ago, after which life began on earth 4.5 billion years ago. The dust from space has been reported to have all the features that are typical for a microbial occurrence (Hoyle and Wickramasinghe, 1977, 2000). They further believe that life forms have been continuously invading earth from outside, and are causing disease outbreaks and microevolution (Hoyle and Wickramasinghe, 1979). With the proof that the microbes can survive the ultraviolet exposure in space (Clancy et al., 2005; Horneck et al., 2010) and in meteorites (Kvenvolden et al., 1970; McKay et al., 1996), the presence of glycine in Sagittarius B2 (Kuan et al. 2003) and its precursor, "methanimine" in Arp 220 (Salter et al., 2008), the isolation of microbes *Bacillus simplex*, *Staphylococcus pasteuri*, and a fungus *Engyodontium albus* via air sampling of the tropopause (Narlikar et al,. 2003; Wainwright et al., 2002), and synthesis of DNA and RNA using the compounds found inside a meteorite (Callahan et al., 2011), the panspermia theory has gained more acceptance among scientists. Most recent studies have detected anthracene, naphthalene 700 light-years from the sun, towards the star Cernis 52 (Iglesias-Groth et al., 2008, 2010).

Darwinian Evolution

Darwin was an English naturalist who provided the world with the evidence for the scientific theory of evolution. He defined evolution as "descent with modification," which states that all species have evolved over the time from a "common ancestor" through the process of natural selection. This theory of natural selection acting as a base point for evolution has been widely accepted by the scientific community, and now has become the basis of modern evolutionary theory.

Darwin's trip on the *Beagle* and his study on finches led him to theorize the three main principles of evolution in his book *The Origin of Species* (**Fig. 5**): (1) variation in characters exists among individuals in a given population, (2) these variations can be inherited by the next generation, (3) some forms of inherited traits prove to be advantageous for some individual in terms of survival and reproduction rates than the others (Darwin, 1859, 1871; Darwin and Wallace, 1858). Although Darwin developed his theory of evolution without basics on the molecular basis of life, but even at the molecular level, Darwin's principles can be observed. For example, when one molecule becomes divergent, giving many variations, such variations at the molecular level can

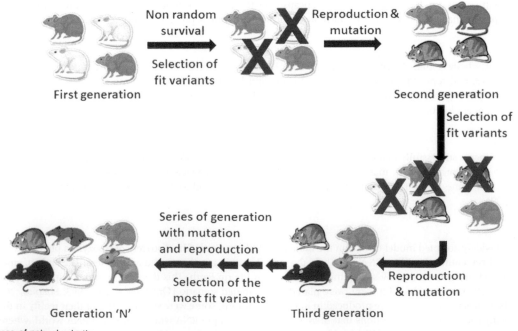

Fig. 5 Process of natural selection.

be induced by various kinds of mutations, genetic drift, etc. at the nucleotide level, which in turn can hamper the protein structure and its function (Hartwell *et al.*, 2014; Patthy, 2009). However, the diversification of the common ancestors to their new progenies are dependent not only upon the natural selection, but also on the mutational and genetic drift effects.

Homology and Development

Richard Owen introduced the term *homolog* in 1843, defining it as "the same organ in different animals under every variety of form and function." He next defined analogs as a "part or organ in one animal which has the same function as another part or organ in a different animal" (Owen, 1848). Though Darwin never used the term homology, Huxley's review of Darwin's book *The Origin of Species* invoked homology as evidence of evolution (Huxley, 1860).

Evolution is directly associated with homology, which is the eventual result of synapomorphies. *Homologs* can be either paralogs or orthologs (**Fig. 6**), where *paralogs* are homologous sequences separated by a gene duplication event, and *orthologs* are homologous sequences separated by a speciation event (when one species diverges into two) (Fitch, 1970; Panchen, 1994).

Speciation

Speciation is an evolutionary process that gives rise to two or more new and distinct biological species as a result of lineage-splitting from ancestral population. This manifests upon the insufficiency of gene flow between sister populations that directs each population to become irreversibly committed to entirely different evolutionary descent. The primal causes of speciation: Natural selection, genetic drift, and mutation.

Natural selection

Darwin popularized the idea of natural selection stating that speciation was the direct impact of the prolonged action of natural selection upon them. It is a process of diversification in survival and reproduction rate of individuals due to variation in their phenotypes. Here, the organisms in a given population that best adapt to the environment increase in frequency compared to less adapted ones over a number of generations (Darwin, 1859, 1871; Darwin and Wallace, 1858).

Genetic Drift

Genetic drift, often called the Sewall Wright effect, after the individual who set forth the idea of hereditary float, is the adjustment in the recurrence of a previous gene variant (allele) in a populace because of impact of random sampling (Barton and Charlesworth, 1984; Masel, 2011). Drift can cause allele fixation in a population.

Once an allele is fixed, genetic drift ceases; the allele frequency cannot be changed unless another allele is brought into the populace by means of mutation or gene flow. Although both genetic drift and natural selection affect evolution, genetic drift operates randomly, while natural selection functions in a direction that ensures survival and reproductive fitness of that particular organism (Kimura, 1968). One of the best examples of genetic drift is a genetic bottleneck (Charlesworth, 2009).

Genetic bottleneck

This is an evolutionary event where a population reduces drastically to a smaller size as a result of environmental factors, like earthquakes, floods, fires, disease, or droughts, or human activities, like genocide. This causes reduction in the genetic diversity of

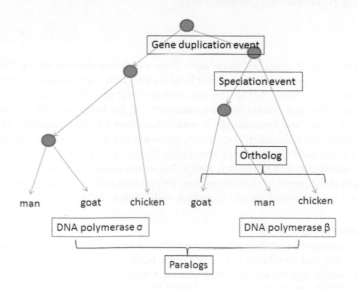

Fig. 6 Orthologs and paralogs.

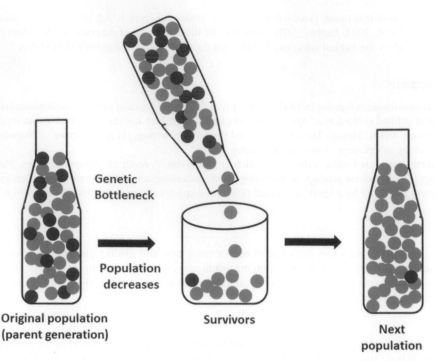

Fig. 7 Bottleneck effect.

the small population, compared to its parent population (**Fig. 7**). This leads to certain alleles getting overexpressed in the survival population, while other alleles may get underexpressed, or are absent altogether. As a direct aftermath of genetic drift, inbreeding and homogeneity increase in these populations, giving rise to the occurrence of deleterious mutations. For example, antigenic shift of the influenza virus (Webster, 1999), diversification of hyperthermophilic *Pyrococcus* due to genetic drift and natural selection (Escobar-Páramo *et al.*, 2005), etc.

Mutation

Neither selective pressure nor genetic drift can operate in the absence of mutation, which is responsible for the genetic variation (**Fig. 8**). The randomness of mutation is the prerequisite for Darwinian evolution where changes in the heritable feature in an organism occur randomly, without the interference from the organism's environment. Cairns observed that *E. coli* genes mutated in a such a directed way that it enabled the bacterial population to survive in the different environmental situations (Cairns *et al.*, 1988). Mutations of the ancestral genes can lead to specific adaptations in an individual, which may or may not be beneficial. For example, alcohol dehydrogenases in yeasts that help them to consume accumulated alcohol (Thomson *et al.*, 2005), and gain of pathogenicity in some bacteria (Groisman and Ochman, 1997).

Common Ancestor

Darwin was the first to propose that all living beings on earth share a common descent, saying "Therefore, I should infer from analogy that probably all the organic beings which have ever lived on this earth have descended from some one primordial form, into which life was first breathed" (Darwin, 1859). The common ancestor gave rise to the "last universal common ancestor" (LUCA), which is used to denote the most current common ancestor of all life forms on earth that share a common descent. The last known LUCA was morphologically and metabolically diverse, temperature adaptive, contained an RNA genome, and is said to have lived during the Paleoarchean era (Glansdorff *et al.*, 2008), signifying that it was probably similar to extremophiles. Scientists have recently identified 355 genes from the LUCA, by comparing the genomes from archaea, bacteria, and eukaryotes, which constitute the three domain classifications of life (Weiss, 2001). This would mean that even before speciation into three domains of life, LUCA already consisted of the means of conducting complex processes such as transcription and translation, and may have later acquired important genes via horizontal transfer (Gogarten and Deamer, 2016).

Diving deep into the evidences of early forms

It has been reported that the prokaryotes were the earliest forms of life on earth after LUCA. They possessed a single nucleus, DNA, RNA, some proteins and enzymes, had membrane-bound cell walls, but no cell organelles, except for the presence of ribosomes. They were believed to have lived in aquatic environments around 3 billion to 1.5 billion years ago (Penny and Poole, 1999). Below, we discuss the proof of their existence in early earth durations.

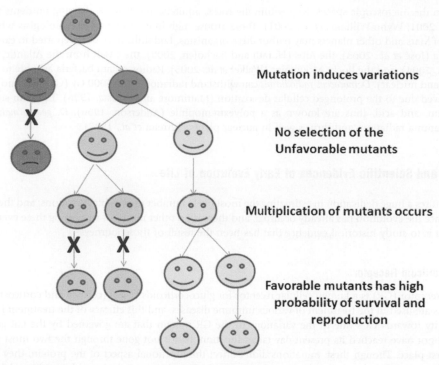

Mutation induces variations

No selection of the
Unfavorable mutants

Multiplication of mutants occurs

Favorable mutants has high
probability of survival and
reproduction

Fig. 8 Effect of mutation in evolution.

Extremophiles

Extremophiles are unicellular microbes (bacteria and archaea) that thrive in extreme environments. Many of these belong to archaea, which are considered to be an ancient bridge between bacteria and eukarya. They can be thermophilic, hyperthermophilic, acidophilic, and alkalophilics, etc. They have been considered to be the closest link to the organism that evolved on the earth (Rampelotto 2010; Rothschild and Mancinelli, 2001).

Thermophiles are heat-loving microbes that grow above 45°C, while hyperthermophiles live beyond 110°C, preferably in between 80 and 121°C. They have been found in hot springs, hydrothermal vents, and the deep subsurface, etc. (Rampelotto 2010; Rothschild and Mancinelli, 2001). Many scientists believe that life on earth started from the hydrothermal vents in the form of thermophiles and hyperthermophiles, due to their ability to resist a wide range of temperature and anaerobic conditions (Li and Kusky, 2007). Wächtershäuser, the iron–sulfur theorist, had identified LUCA inside a black smoker (hydrothermal vent) in the Atlantic Ocean (Huber and Wächtershäuser, 1998). *Pyrococcus fumaris*, one of the highly heat resistant bacteria, which is able to reproduce at 113°C, was also found near the walls of black smokers (Postgate, 1994). Some of the hyperthermophiles studied by Lin *et al.* (2006) were found to have lived in hydrothermal vents in South Africa for about million of years without photosynthesis. *Arqueobacteria*, found near the ancients black smoker chimneys in China are known to live in temperature of about 400°C, depending mainly upon chemosynthesis to produce H_2S (Martin and Russell, 2003). A thermoalkalophilic bacteria, *Thermus brockianus* isolated by Thompson *et al.* (2003) shows catalase activity over wide pH, and temperature range of 6–10 and 30–94°C, respectively. All these instances thus provide strong reinforcement that life may have been indeed originated from the deep ocean beds.

Acidophiles thrive at a low pH, while alkalophiles live in higher pH environments. Though most of the organisms are mesophilic in nature within the pH range of 5–9, acidophiles and alkalophiles have specific adaptations that help them survive an extreme pH range. Acidic environments can be observed in places having geochemical activities, which include the generation of H_2S near in hydrothermal vents, hot springs, coal mine debris, etc. (Rampelotto 2010; Rothschild and Mancinelli, 2001). Alkalophiles can be found in places rich in carbonates, like soda lakes in Egypt, the Rift Valley of Africa, and the western US. Halophiles prefer living in regions that have a high level of salinity, like the Great Salt Lake (US). Hoover *et al.* (2003) identified a novel species of obligate anaerobic, haloalkalophilic spirochete, *Spirocheta Americana*, that prefers living in salty alkaline sediments of California's Mono Lake; it can survive within a temperature range of 10–44°C, salt concentration of 2%–12% (w/v), and pH range 8–10.5.

Another type of extremophile is psychrophiles, which live in extreme cold environments, like the Arctic and Antarctica regions, due to the adaptation of their protein structures to the cold climate. The high amount of glycine in their structure help retain flexibility, while the low amount of charged and hydrophobic amino acids help reduce their inter/intra molecular interactions and allows the protein core to be smaller, in order to avoid freezing (Rampelotto 2010; Rothschild and Mancinelli, 2001). Christner *et al.* (2014) have found some archaean species in West Antarctic Ice Sheet that depended solely on NH_4^+ and CH_4 for survival, and have been doing so for millions of years in total absence of sunlight or wind. Cryptoendoliths, also known as endoliths, in particular, survive in the microscopic spaces deep within the rocks, aquifers, and fissures, deriving nutrients via chemosynthesis (Ehrenfreund *et al.*, 2001; Wynn-Williams *et al.*, 2001). These arouse high interest among astrobiologists who theorize that the endolithic regions of Mars and other planets may harbor these organisms. Endoliths have been reported to exist in the permafrost regions of Antarctica (José *et al.*, 2003), the Alps (Horath and Bachofen, 2009), the basalt from the Atlantic, Indian, and Pacific oceans (Lysnes *et al.*, 2004), and the Rocky Mountains (Walker *et al.*, 2005). Radioresistant bacteria are able to resist high levels of radiation (ionizing and nuclear). *Deinococcus radiodurans* can withstand radiation up to 5000 Gy (Gy), with no viability loss. Their radioresistance evolved due to the prolonged cellular desiccation (Mattimore and Battista, 1996). They can survive extreme cold, dehydration, vacuum, and acid, thus are known as a polyextremophile (Anderson, 1956). *D. geothermalis* can resist higher concentrations of gamma radiation, and thrives well in nuclear plants (Ferreira *et al.*, 1997).

Historical Proofs and Scientific Evidences of Early Evolution of Life

Evolution study requires a huge dedication in estimating the most likely number of possible mutations, and the probable elements that factor them. Since the evolution has already occurred, and there is no other means of witnessing these events, so the only way to understand them is to study historical evidence that has been the result of those journeys.

Evolution of Glucocorticoid Receptor

The glucocorticoid receptor (GR) is a known cellular receptor for glucocorticoids (GCs) (cortisol and corticosterone), which are a stress hormone. GCs are used in the treatment of various immune diseases, and this efficacy of the treatment is wholly dependent upon one's sensitivity towards GCs due to the variations in the GR protein that are governed by the GR gene. This particular protein, GR, would not have reached its present-day target function, had it not gone through the two most unlikely permissive mutations in the first place. Though these mutations didn't affect the functional aspect of the protein, they made sure that the protein gained tolerance towards later mutations, so that its sensitivity towards cortisol could be achieved (Carroll *et al.*, 2011; Harms and Thornton, 2014; Ortlund *et al.*, 2007).

Harms and Thornton (2010) were able to resurrect the ancestral gene of GR (precursor of modern-day GR and mineralocorticoid (MR) receptors), which existed 450 million years ago, before it evolved its capacity to specifically recognize cortisol. They were able to identify two historical mutations that led to the evolution of GR's specificity. These mutations altered few crucial residues to create novel intermolecular (protein-ligand) and intramolecular contacts. The permissive effect of the mutation helped stabilize the specific section of the receptor, without obstructing protein structure, which in turn allowed it to endure the later function-switching mutations, thus defining the GR's sensitivity towards GC's reaction. Scientists have explored many other alternate theories, but none of them could explain the evolution of GR's sensitivity towards cortisol, except this one.

Evolution of Biological Carbon Fixation

The early ancestors of cyanobacteria are believed to be the ones to start the carbon fixation. When they first evolved their process of photosynthesis, water (H_2O) was used as the electron donor source in the etc pathway for the generation of ATP molecules, as a result of which the autotrophy came into being. However, this ability of cyanobacteria to use water as an electron source created the radical oxygenation of the atmosphere/environment, thereby leading to the large amount of CO_2 consumption (Brasier *et al.*, 2006; Kopp *et al.*, 2005; Tomitani *et al.*, 2006).

There are six known CO_2 fixation pathways that have functional overlaps, but their evolutionary journey and diversification from the parent pathway was not understood well before. It was Braakman and Smith (2012) whose study shed light into this complex diversification. They mapped the evolutionary journey of biological carbon fixation using the metabolic and parsimony-built phylogenetic data analysis, which traced all the modern pathways to a single parent pathway. It was remarked that this diversification was one of the earliest divergences in the tree of life that occurred solely due to the physicochemical changes (energy optimization and oxygen toxicity) in that particular environment. The root of the parsimony-generated phylogenetic tree was observed to be the combination two subnetwork pathway (reductive citric acid cycle and the Wood–Ljungdahl pathway) coalescing into a single network. These trees combine into a single connected network, one being the reductive citric acid cycle and the other being the Wood–Ljungdahl pathway, which is a linear folate-based pathway of the CO_2 reduction pathway. Though these selection pressures cannot be observed in the modern pathways, these were responsible for the primitive diversification of the ancestral carbon fixation.

The Origins of Fermentation, Evolution of Alcohol Dehydrogenases

Alcohol dehydrogeneases (Adh) are crucial to the fermentation process, which converts pyruvate to ethanol forming acetaldehyde in between. Yeast was the first organism to have evolved this enzyme, wherein they convert sugars into alcohol using Adh1, and then later consume the accumulated alcohol using Adh2 enzyme, a homolog of Adh1 differing by 24 amino acids. However, research shows that the primitive form of Adh had the ability to only produce alcohol, and not consume them

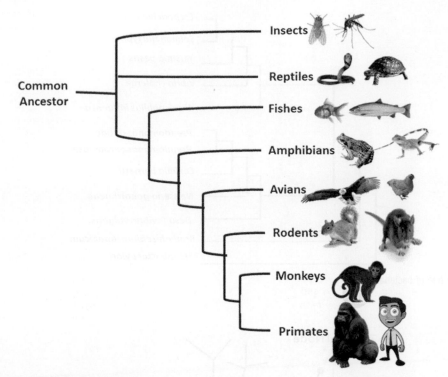

Fig. 9 Phylogenetic tree of contemporary organisms.

(Danielsson and Jörnvall, 1992; Gutheil *et al.*, 1992; Persson *et al.*, 2008). Thomson *et al.* (2005) used paleobiochemistry techniques to isolate AdhA, the last common ancestor of both Adh (Adh1 and Adh2) to identify the reason behind this variation. They found that the Adh$_A$ was optimized to only produce alcohol from sugars and recycle the NADH generated from glycolysis. Excess production of alcohol helped yeasts eliminate their competitors, but as the earth evolved, the Cretaceous age brought upon the existence of fleshy fruits. Since fruits contain high amount of alcohols, especially rotting fruits, silent nucleotide dating proposed that yeasts needed a way to metabolize these exogenous alcohols, hence duplicated of Adh into Adh1 and Adh2.

Adaptations of Aromatases in Pigs

Aromatases are cytochrome P450-dependent enzymes that catalyze the conversion of an androgenic steroid (such as testosterone) to an estrogenic steroid (such as estradiol). The protein existed much before the emergence of fish and tetrapods (Callard *et al.*, 1984). Researchers have reported many aromatase genes to date. Teleost fish have two aromatase genes (Callard and Tchoudakova, 1997; Chang *et al.*, 1997), while cattle possess both a functional gene and a pseudogene (Fürbaß and Vanselow, 1995; Hinshelwood *et al.*, 1993). The majority of mammals have only one aromatase gene that codes for the aromatase enzyme through alternative splicing (Boerboom *et al.*, 1997; Delarue *et al.*, 1996, 1998; Harada, 1988; Hickey *et al.*, 1990; Terashima *et al.*, 1991; Simpson *et al.*, 1997).

However, pigs (*Sus scrofa*) have been reported to have three different mRNAs for aromatases (Callard and Tchoudakova, 1997; Choi *et al.*, 1996, 1997a,b; Corbin *et al.*, 1995; Conley *et al.*, 1997). Evidence suggests that these three aromatase gene variants were the result of gene duplication events, which occurred recently in the geologic time scale (Corbin *et al.*, 2004; Graddy *et al.*, 2000). The speculations identifying the functional aspects of these paralogs depend upon the order in which the gene duplication took place. For example, the recent events may have helped domestication of the pigs.

Adaptations of the Elongation Factors

The physical environment to which an ancestral organism may have been exposed can be speculated by resurrecting the protein of that particular organism in in vitro conditions, and then study its properties (Adey *et al.*, 1994; Chandrasekharan *et al.*, 1996; Chang *et al.*, 2002; Golding and Dean, 1998; Jermann *et al.*, 1995; Malcolm *et al.*, 1990; Miyazaki *et al.*, 2001). Researchers have been able to revive the protein sequences for Tu family (EF-Tu), the elongation factors that existed in ancient bacteria, and estimated their properties with respect to temperature. The ancient EF-Tu proteins were observed to be functional at the optimal temperature of 55–65°C, which indicates that they were thermophillic in nature, and not hyperthermophilic or mesophilic. This result can be thoroughly corroborated from the dispersion of thermophiles in the bacterial ancestries (Hugenholtz *et al.*, 1998), the G + C content of ancient rRNAs (Galtier *et al.*, 1999), and the geographical record of the molecular clocks (Cavalier-Smith, 2002).

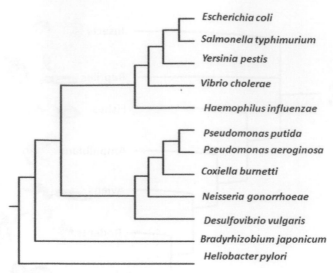

Fig. 10 Phylogenetic tree of bacteria.

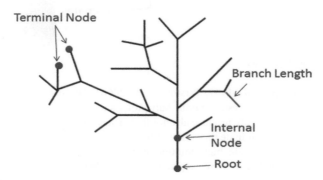

Fig. 11 Elements of a typical phylogram.

Researchers have made use of paleobiochemistry techniques and phylogenetic analysis between many such microorganisms to investigate more about their ancestors.

Tracing the Evolutionary Steps Using Phylogeny

Phylogeny can be described as the relationship between all the organisms on Earth that have descended from a common ancestor, whether they are extinct or extant. Phylogenetics is the science of studying the evolutionary relatedness among biological groups and a phylogenetic tree is used to graphically represent this evolutionary relation related to the species of interest (**Figs. 9–11**).

More specialized phylogenetic methods have been developed now to meet specific needs, such as species and molecular phylogenetic tests, biogeographic hypotheses, testing, for evaluating amino acids of extinct or extant proteins, establish disease epidemiology and evolution, and even in forensic studies (Linder and Warnow, 2005).

Conclusion

The evolution traces the journey of life on Earth from water to land and air, from an ill-defined membrane-bound cell to modern day multicellular, complex organism over the vast layers of time and generations. With each step of evolution, distinct characters emerged following speciation; some retained their previous features, some developed new sets of traits making contemporary humans curious to understand these changes.

In this encyclopedic article, we have studied the different stages, theories, and evidences of evolution. We shed light on the forces responsible for the genetic variations and speciation. We have also discussed some of the specific adaptations undergone by some of the genes/characters and how these adaptations proved to be beneficial in shaping their survival. Last, but not the least, we have also vaguely touched upon the topic of phylogeny using which the phylogenetic relatedness of any organism can be traced.

Acknowledgement

Firstly, we would like to extend our sincere gratification to Central Library, Tezpur University for lending us their vast resource of study material in order to complete this article.

See also: Genetics and Population Analysis. Natural Language Processing Approaches in Bioinformatics

Reference

Adey, N.B., Tollefsbol, T.O., Sparks, A.B., Edgell, M.H., Hutchison, C.A., 1994. Molecular resurrection of an extinct ancestral promoter for mouse L1. Proceedings of the National Academy of Sciences of the United States of America 91 (4), 1569–1573.

Anderson, A.W., 1956. Studies on a radioresistant micrococcus. 1. Isolation, morphology, cultural characteristics, and resistance to γ radiation. Food Technology 10, 575–578.

Arrhenius, S., 1903. Die verbreitung des lebens im weltenraum. Die Umschau 7, 481–485.

Bangham, A.D., Standish, M.M., Watkins, J.C., 1965. Diffusion of univalent ions across the lamellae of swollen phospholipids. Journal of molecular biology 13 (1), 238–252.

Barton, N.H., Charlesworth, B., 1984. Genetic revolutions, founder effects, and speciation. Annual Review of Ecology and Systematics 15 (1), 133–164.

Boerboom, D., Kerban, A., Sirois, J., 1997. Molecular characterization of the equine cytochrome P450 aromatase cDNA and its regulation in preovulatory follicles. In: Biology of Reproduction, vol. 56. Madison, WI: Soc Study Reproduction, p. 479.

Böhler, C., Nielsen, P.E., Orgel, L.E., 1995. Template switching between PNA and RNA oligonucleotides. Nature 376 (6541), 578–581.

Braakman, R., Smith, E., 2012. The emergence and early evolution of biological carbon-fixation. PLOS Computational Biology 8 (4), e1002455.

Brasier, M., McLoughlin, N., Green, O., Wacey, D., 2006. A fresh look at the fossil evidence for early Archaean cellular life. Philosophical Transactions of the Royal Society B: Biological Sciences 361 (1470), 887–902.

Cairns, J., Overbaugh, J., Miller, S., 1988. The origin of mutants. Nature 335 (6186), 142–145.

Callahan, M.P., Smith, K.E., Cleaves, H.J., et al., 2011. Carbonaceous meteorites contain a wide range of extraterrestrial nucleobases. Proceedings of the National Academy of Sciences of the United States of America 108 (34), 13995–13998.

Callard, G.V., Pudney, J.A., Kendall, S.L., Reinboth, R., 1984. In vitro conversion of androgen to estrogen in amphioxus gonadal tissues. General and Comparative Endocrinology 56 (1), 53–58.

Callard, G.V., Tchoudakova, A., 1997. Evolutionary and functional significance of two CYP19 genes differentially expressed in brain and ovary of goldfish. The Journal of Steroid Biochemistry and Molecular Biology 61 (3–6), 387–392.

Carroll, S.M., Ortlund, E.A., Thornton, J.W., 2011. Mechanisms for the evolution of a derived function in the ancestral glucocorticoid receptor. PLOS Genetics 7 (6), e1002117.

Cavalier-Smith, T., 2002. The neomuran origin of archaebacteria, the negibacterial root of the universal tree and bacterial megaclassification. International Journal of Systematic and Evolutionary Microbiology 52 (1), 7–76.

Chandrasekharan, U.M., Sanker, S., Glynias, M.J., Karnik, S.S., Husain, A., 1996. Angiotensin II-forming activity in a reconstructed ancestral chymase. Science 271 (5248), 502–505.

Chang, B.S., Jönsson, K., Kazmi, M.A., Donoghue, M.J., Sakmar, T.P., 2002. Recreating a functional ancestral archosaur visual pigment. Molecular Biology and Evolution 19 (9), 1483–1489.

Chang, X.T., Kobayashi, T., Kajiura, E.H., Nakamura, M., Nagahama, Y., 1997. Isolation and characterization of the cDNA encoding the tilapia (Oreochromis niloticus) cytochrome P450 aromatase (P450arom): Changes in P450arom mRNA, protein and enzyme activity in ovarian follicles during oogenesis. Journal of Molecular Endocrinology 18 (1), 57–66.

Charlesworth, B., 2009. Effective population size and patterns of molecular evolution and variation. Nature Reviews Genetics 10 (3), 195–205.

Choi, I., Collante, W.R., Simmen, R.C., Simmen, F.A., 1997a. A developmental switch in expression from blastocyst to endometrial/placental-type cytochrome P450 aromatase genes in the pig and horse. Biology of Reproduction 56 (3), 688–696.

Choi, I.N.H.O., Simmen, R.C., Simmen, F.A., 1996. Molecular cloning of cytochrome P450 aromatase complementary deoxyribonucleic acid from periimplantation porcine and equine blastocysts identifies multiple novel 5′-untranslated exons expressed in embryos, endometrium, and placenta. Endocrinology 137 (4), 1457–1467.

Choi, I., Troyer, D.L., Cornwell, D.L., et al., 1997b. Closely related genes encode developmental and tissue isoforms of porcine cytochrome P450 aromatase. DNA and Cell Biology 16 (6), 769–777.

Christner, B.C., Priscu, J.C., Achberger, A.M., et al., 2014. A microbial ecosystem beneath the West Antarctic ice sheet. Nature 512 (7514), 310–313.

Clancy, P., Brack, A., Horneck, G., 2005. Looking for Life, Searching the Solar System. Cambridge University Press.

Conley, A., Corbin, J., Smith, T., et al., 1997. Porcine aromatases: Studies on tissue-specific, functionally distinct isozymes from a single gene? The Journal of Steroid Biochemistry and Molecular Biology 61 (3–6), 407–413.

Corbin, C.J., Khalil, M.W., Conley, A.J., 1995. Functional ovarian and placental isoforms of porcine aromatase. Molecular and Cellular Endocrinology 113 (1), 29–37.

Corbin, C.J., Mapes, S.M., Marcos, J., et al., 2004. Paralogues of porcine aromatase cytochrome P450: A novel hydroxylase activity is associated with the survival of a duplicated gene. Endocrinology 145 (5), 2157–2164.

Dalrymple, G.B., 2001. The age of the Earth in the twentieth century: A problem (mostly) solved. Geological Society, London, Special Publications 190 (1), 205–221.

Danielsson, O., Jörnvall, H., 1992. " Enzymogenesis": Classical liver alcohol dehydrogenase origin from the glutathione-dependent formaldehyde dehydrogenase line. Proceedings of the National Academy of Sciences of the United States of America 89 (19), 9247–9251.

Darwin, C., Wallace, A., 1858. On the tendency of species to form varieties; and on the perpetuation of varieties and species by natural means of selection. Zoological Journal of the Linnean Society 3 (9), 45–62.

Darwin, C., 1871. The Descent of Man and Selection in Relation to Sex. London: John Murray.

Darwin, C., 1859. The Origin of Species by Means of Natural Selection. Modern Library.

Delarue, B., Breard, E., Mittre, H., Leymarie, P., 1998. Expression of two aromatase cDNAs in various rabbit tissues. The Journal of Steroid Biochemistry and Molecular Biology 64 (1–2), 113–119.

Delarue, B., Mittre, H., Féral, C., Benhaim, A., Leymarie, P., 1996. Rapid sequencing of rabbit aromatase cDNA using RACE PCR. Comptes rendus de l'Academie des sciences. Serie III, Sciences De La Vie 319 (8), 663–670.

Dodd, M.S., Papineau, D., Grenne, T., et al., 2017. Evidence for early life in Earth's oldest hydrothermal vent precipitates. Nature 543 (7643), 60–64.

Ehrenfreund, P., Bernstein, M.P., Dworkin, J.P., Sandford, S.A., Allamandola, L.J., 2001. The photostability of amino acids in space. The Astrophysical Journal Letters 550 (1), L95–L99.

Escobar-Páramo, P., Ghosh, S., DiRuggiero, J., 2005. Evidence for genetic drift in the diversification of a geographically isolated population of the hyperthermophilic archaeon Pyrococcus. Molecular Biology and Evolution 22 (11), 2297–2303.

Ferreira, A.C., Nobre, M.F., Rainey, F.A., *et al.*, 1997. Deinococcus geothermalis sp. nov. and Deinococcus murrayi sp. nov., two extremely radiation-resistant and slightly thermophilic species from hot springs. International Journal of Systematic and Evolutionary Microbiology 47 (4), 939–947.

Ferris, J.P., 1999. Prebiotic synthesis on minerals: Bridging the prebiotic and RNA worlds. The Biological Bulletin 196 (3), 311–314.

Fitch, W.M., 1970. Distinguishing homologous from analogous proteins. Systematic Zoology 19 (2), 99–113.

Fox, S.W., 1974. Coacervate droplets, proteinoid microspheres, and the genetic apparatus. In: The Origin of Life and Evolutionary Biochemistry. Boston, MA: Springer, pp. 119–132.

Fox, S.W., Harada, K., Kendrick, J., 1959. Production of spherules from synthetic proteinoid and hot water. Science 129 (3357), 1221–1223.

Fürbaβ, R., Vanselow, J., 1995. An aromatase pseudogene is transcribed in the bovine placenta. Gene 154 (2), 287–291.

Galtier, N., Tourasse, N., Gouy, M., 1999. A nonhyperthermophilic common ancestor to extant life forms. Science 283 (5399), 220–221.

Garwood, R., 2012. Patterns in Palaeontology: The first 3 billion years of evolution. Palaeontology [Online] 2.

Glansdorff, N., Xu, Y., Labedan, B., 2008. The last universal common ancestor: Emergence, constitution and genetic legacy of an elusive forerunner. Biology Direct 3 (1), 29.

Gogarten, J.P., Deamer, D., 2016. Is LUCA a thermophilic progenote? Nature Microbiology 1 (12), 16229.

Goldacre, R.J., 1958. Surface films, their collapse on compression, the shapes and sizes of cells, and the origin of life. Surface Phenomena in Chemistry and Biology 10.

Golding, G.B., Dean, A.M., 1998. The structural basis of molecular adaptation. Molecular Biology and Evolution 15 (4), 355–369.

Graddy, L.G., Kowalski, A.A., Simmen, 2000. Multiple isoforms of porcine aromatase are encoded by three distinct genes. The Journal of steroid biochemistry and molecular biology 73 (1–2), 49–57.

Groisman, E.A., Ochman, H., 1997. How Salmonella became a pathogen. Trends in Microbiology 5 (9), 343–349.

Gutheil, W.G., Holmquist, B., Vallee, B.L., 1992. Purification, characterization, and partial sequence of the glutathione-dependent formaldehyde dehydrogenase from Escherichia coli: A class III alcohol dehydrogenase. Biochemistry 31 (2), 475–481.

Haldane, J.B.S., 1929. The origin of life, rationalist annual (reprinted in Haldane, JBS, science and life, with an introduction by Maynard Smith, J (1968).

Hanczyc, M.M., Fujikawa, S.M., Szostak, J.W., 2003. Experimental models of primitive cellular compartments: Encapsulation, growth, and division. Science 302 (5645), 618–622.

Harada, N., 1988. Cloning of a complete cDNA encoding human aromatase: Immunochemical identification and sequence analysis. Biochemical and Biophysical Research Communications 156 (2), 725–732.

Hargreaves, W.R., Mulvihill, S.J., Deamer, D.W., 1977. Synthesis of phospholipids and membranes in prebiotic conditions. Nature 266 (5597), 78–80.

Harms, M.J., Thornton, J.W., 2010. Analyzing protein structure and function using ancestral gene reconstruction. Current Opinion in Structural Biology 20 (3), 360–366.

Harms, M.J., Thornton, J.W., 2014. Historical contingency and its biophysical basis in glucocorticoid receptor evolution. Nature 512 (7513), 203–207.

Hartwell, L., Goldberg, M.L., Fischer, J.A., Hood, L., Aquadro, C.F., 2014. Genetics: From Genes to Genomes. McGraw-Hill Science/Engineering/Math.

Hickey, G.J., Krasnow, J.S., Beattie, W.G., Richards, J.S., 1990. Aromatase cytochrome P450 in rat ovarian granulosa cells before and after luteinization: Adenosine 3′, 5′-monophosphate-dependent and independent regulation. Cloning and sequencing of rat aromatase cDNA and 5′ genomic DNA. Molecular Endocrinology 4 (1), 3–12.

Hinshelwood, M.M., Corbin, C.J., Tsang, P.C., Simpson, E.R., 1993. Isolation and characterization of a complementary deoxyribonucleic acid insert encoding bovine aromatase cytochrome P450. Endocrinology 133 (5), 1971–1977.

Hoenigsberg, H., 2003. Evolution without speciation but with selection: LUCA, the Last Universal Common Ancestor in Gilbert's RNA world. Genetics and Molecular Research Journal 2 (4), 366–375.

Hoover, R.B., Pikuta, E.V., Bej, A.K., *et al.*, 2003. Spirochaeta americana sp. nov., a new haloalkaliphilic, obligately anaerobic spirochaete isolated from soda Mono Lake in California. International Journal of Systematic and Evolutionary Microbiology 53 (3), 815–821.

Horath, T., Bachofen, R., 2009. Molecular characterization of an endolithic microbial community in dolomite rock in the central Alps (Switzerland). Microbial Ecology 58 (2), 290–306.

Horneck, G., Klaus, D.M., Mancinelli, R.L., 2010. Space microbiology. Microbiology and Molecular Biology Reviews 74 (1), 121–156.

Hoyle, F., Wickramasinghe, C., 1979. Diseases from Space. London: JM Dent, p. 196.

Hoyle, F., Wickramasinghe, N.C., 1977. Polysaccharides and infrared spectra of galactic sources. Nature 268 (5621), 610–612.

Hoyle, F., Wickramasinghe, N.C., 2000. On the nature of interstellar grains. In: Astronomical Origins of Life. Dordrecht: Springer, pp. 249–262.

Huber, C., Wächtershäuser, G., 1998. Peptides by activation of amino acids with CO on (Ni, Fe) S surfaces: Implications for the origin of life. Science 281 (5377), 670–672.

Hugenholtz, P., Goebel, B.M., Pace, N.R., 1998. Impact of culture-independent studies on the emerging phylogenetic view of bacterial diversity. Journal of Bacteriology 180 (18), 4765–4774.

Huxley, T.H.H., 1860. The origin of species. Westminst. Rev. 17, 541–570.

Iglesias-Groth, S., Manchado, A., García-Hernández, D.A., Hernández, J.G., Lambert, D.L., 2008. Evidence for the naphthalene cation in a region of the interstellar medium with anomalous microwave emission. The Astrophysical Journal Letters 685 (1), L55–L58.

Iglesias-Groth, S., Manchado, A., Rebolo, R., *et al.*, 2010. A search for interstellar anthracene towards the Perseus anomalous microwave emission region. Monthly Notices of the Royal Astronomical Society 407 (4), 2157–2165.

Jermann, T.M., Opitz, J.G., Stackhouse, J., Benner, S.A., 1995. Reconstructing the evolutionary history of the artiodactyl ribonuclease superfamily. Nature 374 (6517), 57–59.

De Jong, H.B., Kruyt, H.R., 1929. Coacervation. In: Proceedings of the Royal Academy of Sciences at Amsterdam, 32, pp. 849–856.

José, R., Goebel, B.M., Friedmann, E.I., Pace, N.R., 2003. Microbial diversity of cryptoendolithic communities from the McMurdo Dry Valleys, Antarctica. Applied and Environmental Microbiology 69 (7), 3858–3867.

Joyce, G.F., 2002. The antiquity of RNA-based evolution. Nature 418 (6894), 214–221.

Kimura, M., 1968. Evolutionary rate at the molecular level. Nature 217 (5129), 624–626.

Knoll, A.H., 2003. Life on a Young Planet: The First Three Billion Years of Evolution on Earth. Princeton University Press.

Knoll, A.H., 2015. Life on a Young Planet: The First Three Billion Years of Evolution on Earth. Princeton University Press.

Kopp, R.E., Kirschvink, J.L., Hilburn, I.A., Nash, C.Z., 2005. The Paleoproterozoic snowball Earth: A climate disaster triggered by the evolution of oxygenic photosynthesis. Proceedings of the National Academy of Sciences of the United States of America 102 (32), 11131–11136.

Kuan, Y.J., Charnley, S.B., Huang, H.C., Tseng, W.L., Kisiel, Z., 2003. Interstellar glycine. The Astrophysical Journal 593 (2), 848–867.

Kvenvolden, K., Lawless, J., Pering, K., *et al.*, 1970. Evidence for extraterrestrial amino-acids and hydrocarbons in the Murchison meteorite. Nature 228 (5275), 923–926.

Linder, C.R., Warnow, T., 2005. Chapter 19: An overview of phylogeny reconstruction. In: Aluru, S. (Ed.), Handbook of Computational Molecular Biology. CRC Press.

Lin, L.H., Wang, P.L., Rumble, D., *et al.*, 2006. Long-term sustainability of a high-energy, low-diversity crustal biome. Science 314 (5798), 479–482.

Li, J., Kusky, T.M., 2007. World's largest known Precambrian fossil black smoker chimneys and associated microbial vent communities, North China: Implications for early life. Gondwana Research 12 (1–2), 84–100.

Lysnes, K., Torsvik, T., Thorseth, I.H., Pedersen, R.B., 2004. Microbial populations in ocean floor basalt: Results from ODP Leg 187. In: Pedersen, R.B., Christie, D.M., Miller, D.J. (Eds.), Proceedings of the Ocean Drilling Program, Scientific Results, vol. 187. College Station, TX: Ocean Drilling Program, pp. 1–27.

Malcolm, B.A., Wilson, K.P., Matthews, B.W., Kirsch, J.F., Wilson, A.C., 1990. Ancestral lysozymes reconstructed, neutrality tested, and thermostability linked to hydrocarbon packing. Nature 345 (6270), 86–89.

Martin, W., Russell, M.J., 2003. On the origins of cells: A hypothesis for the evolutionary transitions from abiotic geochemistry to chemoautotrophic prokaryotes, and from prokaryotes to nucleated cells. Philosophical Transactions of the Royal Society B: Biological Sciences 358 (1429), 59–85.

Masel, J., 2011. Genetic drift. Current Biology 21 (20), R837–R838.

Mattimore, V., Battista, J.R., 1996. Radioresistance of Deinococcus radiodurans: Functions necessary to survive ionizing radiation are also necessary to survive prolonged desiccation. Journal of Bacteriology 178 (3), 633–637.

McKay, D.S., Gibson, E.K., Thomas-Keprta, K.L., *et al.*, 1996. Search for past life on Mars: Possible relic biogenic activity in Martian meteorite ALH84001. Science 273 (5277), 924–930.

Miller, S.L., Urey, H.C., 1959. Organic compound synthesis on the primitive earth. Science 130 (3370), 245–251.

Miller, S.L., 1953. A production of amino acids under possible primitive earth conditions. Science 117 (3046), 528–529.

Miyazaki, J., Nakaya, S., Suzuki, T., *et al.*, 2001. Ancestral residues stabilizing 3-isopropylmalate dehydrogenase of an extreme thermophile: Experimental evidence supporting the thermophilic common ancestor hypothesis. The Journal of Biochemistry 129 (5), 777–782.

Mojzsis, S.J., Arrhenius, G., McKeegan, K.D., *et al.*, 1996. Evidence for life on Earth before 3800 million years ago. Nature 384 (6604), 55–59.

Narlikar, J.V., Lloyd, D., Wickramasinghe, N.C., *et al.*, 2003. A balloon experiment to detect microorganisms in the outer space. Astrophysics and Space Science 285 (2), 555–562.

Nelson, K.E., Levy, M., Miller, S.L., 2000. Peptide nucleic acids rather than RNA may have been the first genetic molecule. Proceedings of the National Academy of Sciences of the United States of America 97 (8), 3868–3871.

Oparin, A., 1924. Proiskhozhdenie Zhizni Izd. Moskowakii, Rabochii, Moscow, The Origin of Life(1938). New York: The MacMillan Company.

Oparin, A.I., 2003. The origin of life. Courier Corporation.

Orgel, L., 2000. A simpler nucleic acid. Science 290 (5495), 1306–1307.

Orgel, L.E., Crick, F.H., 1993. Anticipating an RNA world. Some past speculations on the origin of life: Where are they today? The FASEB Journal 7 (1), 238–239.

Oró, J., 1983. Chemical evolution and the origin of life. Advances in Space Research 3 (9), 77–94.

Ortlund, E.A., Bridgham, J.T., Redinbo, M.R., Thornton, J.W., 2007. Crystal structure of an ancient protein: Evolution by conformational epistasis. Science 317 (5844), 1544–1548.

Owen, R., 1848. On the Archetype and Homologies of the Vertebrate Skeleton. Van Voorst.

Panchen, A.L., 1994. Richard Owen and The Concept of Homology. Homology: The Hierarchical Basis of Comparative Biology. 1994. San Diego, CA: Academic Press, pp. 21–62.

Pattabhi, V., Gautham, N., 2002. Origin and evolution of life. Biophysics. 232–241.

Patthy, L., 2009. Protein Evolution. John Wiley & Sons.

Penny, D., Poole, A., 1999. The nature of the last universal common ancestor. Current Opinion in Genetics & Development 9 (6), 672–677.

Persson, B., Hedlund, J., Jörnvall, H., 2008. Medium-and short-chain dehydrogenase/reductase gene and protein families. Cellular and Molecular Life Sciences 65 (24), 3879–3894.

Postgate, J.R., 1994. The Outer Reaches of Life. Cambridge University Press.

Rampelotto, P.H., 2010. Resistance of microorganisms to extreme environmental conditions and its contribution to astrobiology. Sustainability 2 (6), 1602–1623.

Rao, M., Eichberg, J., Oró, J., 1982. Synthesis of phosphatidylcholine under possible primitive Earth conditions. Journal of Molecular Evolution 18 (3), 196–202.

Rothschild, L.J., Mancinelli, R.L., 2001. Life in extreme environments. Nature 409 (6823), 1092–1101.

Salter, C.J., Ghosh, T., Catinella, B., *et al.*, 2008. The arecibo ARP 220 spectral census. I. Discovery of the pre-biotic molecule methanimine and new cm-wavelength transitions of other molecules. The Astronomical Journal 136 (1), 299–389.

Schopf, J.W., Packer, B.M., 1987. Early Archean (3.3-billion to 3.5-billion-year-old) microfossils from Warrawoona Group, Australia. Science 237 (4810), 70–73.

Schopf, J.W., 2001. Cradle of Life: The Discovery of Earth's Earliest Fossils. Princeton University Press.

Segré, D., Ben-Eli, D., Deamer, D.W., Lancet, D., 2001. The lipid world. Origins of Life and Evolution of the Biosphere 31 (1–2), 119–145.

Shapiro, R., 2007. A simpler origin for life. Scientific American 296 (6), 46–53.

Simpson, E.R., Michael, M.D., Agarwal, V.R., *et al.*, 1997. Cytochromes P450 11: Expression of the CYP19 (aromatase) gene: An unusual case of alternative promoter usage. The FASEB Journal 11 (1), 29–36.

Terashima, M., Toda, K., Kawamoto, T., *et al.*, 1991. Isolation of a full-length cDNA encoding mouse aromatase P450. Archives of Biochemistry and Biophysics 285 (2), 231–237.

Thompson, V.S., Schaller, K.D., Apel, W.A., 2003. Purification and characterization of a novel thermo-alkali-stable catalase from Thermus brockianus. Biotechnology Progress 19 (4), 1292–1299.

Thomson, J.M., Gaucher, E.A., Burgan, M.F., *et al.*, 2005. Resurrecting ancestral alcohol dehydrogenases from yeast. Nature Genetics 37 (6), 630–635.

Tomitani, A., Knoll, A.H., Cavanaugh, C.M., Ohno, T., 2006. The evolutionary diversification of cyanobacteria: Molecular–phylogenetic and paleontological perspectives. Proceedings of the National Academy of Sciences of the United States of America 103 (14), 5442–5447.

Trevors, J.T., Abel, D.L., 2004. Chance and necessity do not explain the origin of life. Cell Biology International 28 (11), 729–739.

Trevors, J.T., Psenner, R., 2001. From self-assembly of life to present-day bacteria: A possible role for nanocells. FEMS Microbiology Reviews 25 (5), 573–582.

Wächtershäuser, G., 2000. Life as we don't know it. Science 289 (5483), 1307–1308.

Wainwright, M., Wickramasinghe, N.C., Narlikar, J.V., Rajaratnam, P., 2002. Microorganisms cultured from stratospheric air samples obtained at 41 km. FEMS Microbiology Letters 218 (1), 161–165.

Walker, J.J., Spear, J.R., Pace, N.R., 2005. Geobiology of a microbial endolithic community in the Yellowstone geothermal environment. Nature 434 (7036), 1011–1014.

Webster, R.G., 1999. Antigenic variation in influenza viruses. In: Domingo, E., Webster, R., Holland, J. (Eds.), Origin and Evolution of Viruses. Elsevier, pp. 377–390.

Weiss, R.A., 2001. Polio vaccines exonerated. Nature 410 (6832), 1035–1036.

Wynn-Williams, D.A., Newton, E.M., Edwards, H.G.M., 2001. The role of habitat structure for biomolecule integrity and microbial survival under extreme environmental stress in Antarctica (and Mars?): Ecology and technology. Exo-/Astro-Biology 496, 225–237.

Biographical Sketch

Himakshi Sarma is a PhD scholar at Molecular Modelling and Simulation Laboratory, Department of Molecular Biology and Biotechnology, Tezpur University, Assam, India. She has done her Post Graduation in Biotechnology from NEHU, shillong, Meghalaya, in the year 2014. She is expertise on molecular dynamics (MD) simulation of biomolecules, molecular docking, virtual screening, drug designing and in silico alanine scanning mutagenesis (ASM). She is presently working on in silico modeling of Lemur tyrosine kinase (LMTK3), which is a protein kinase implicated in breast cancer progression and metastasis, using modeling and simulation approach.

Sushmita Pradhan is a PhD research scholar at the Molecular Modelling and Simulation Laboratory, Department of Molecular Biology and Biotechnology, Tezpur University, Tezpur, Assam since 2016. She completed her Masters in Microbiology from Bangalore University in the year 2015. She has strong hands on analyzing the biomolecules using on molecular dynamics (MD) simulation, molecular docking, free energy analysis, mutational approaches, etc. She is currently working on Xeroderma pigmentosum A (XPA) protein, functions as the scaffold protein in nucleotide excision repair (NER).

Sandeep Kaushik is a passionate computational biologist with a wide exposure of computational approaches. Presently, he is carrying out his research as an Assistant Researcher (equivalent to Assistant Professor) at 3B's Research Group, University of Minho, Portugal. He has a PhD in Bioinformatics from National Institute of Immunology, New Delhi, India. He has a wide exposure on analysis of scientific data ranging from transcriptomic data on mycobacterial and human samples to genomic data from wheat. His research experience and expertise entails molecular dynamics simulations, RNA-sequencing data analysis using Bioconductor (R language based package), de novo genome assembly using various software like AbySS, automated protein prediction and annotation, database mining, agent-based modeling, and simulations. He has a cumulative experience of more than 10 years of programming using PERL, R language, and NetLogo. He has published his research in reputed international journals like *Molecular Cell*, *Biomaterials*, *Biophysical Journal*, and others. Currently, his research interest involves in silico modeling of disease conditions like breast cancer, using agent-based modeling and simulations approach.

M. V. Satish Kumar received a PhD in Biotechnology from Indian Institute of Technology Guwahati, Assam, India in 2010. From 2010 to 2012, he was with the Centre for Condensed Matter Theory (CCMT), Department of Physics, Indian Institute of Science Bangalore, India. He is currently working as Assistant Professor in the Department of Molecular Biology and Biotechnology, School of Sciences, Tezpur University, Assam, India. His research interests include understanding the functioning of intrinsically disordered proteins (IDPs), pathways of protein aggregation mechanism in neurodegenerative diseases like Alzheimer, Parkinson, etc., and also the features of protein–RNA interactions using computational techniques.

Inference of Horizontal Gene Transfer: Gaining Insights Into Evolution via Lateral Acquisition of Genetic Material

Suhaila Sulaiman, Nur S Yusoff, Ng S Mun, Haslina Makmur, and Mohd Firdaus-Raih, Universiti Kebangsaan Malaysia, Bangi, Malaysia

Introduction

Horizontal gene transfer (HGT) is defined as the movement of genetic materials between distantly related organisms (Crisp *et al.*, 2015). HGT is also referred to as lateral gene transfer. It was first reported in 1928 by Frederick Griffith, who demonstrated the uptake of foreign DNA through transformation in bacteria (Griffith, 1928). HGT has been shown to take place in both prokaryotes and eukaryotes although its mechanisms are more extensively studied for prokaryotes (Huang, 2013; Zhaxybayeva and Doolittle, 2011). Popa and Dagan (2011) reported that almost 75% of total genes in a microbial genome are the results of HGT events. In microbes, HGT may occur via three classical mechanisms: (i) Transformation (the uptake of nucleic acids), (ii) transduction (virus-mediated gene transfer) or (iii) conjugation (plasmid-mediated gene transfer).

Detection of HGT requires the separation of vertical and horizontal arrangements in a genome of interest. Vertical transfer involves a time-consuming transfer of genetic material from parents to progenies. On the other hand, horizontal transfer usually happens between individuals that are not in parent-progenies relationships; thus, it influences the genome diversity and evolution of a species. A process named amelioration usually occurs that ensures the horizontally acquired gene is beneficial to the new host. Thus, the acquired regions will be less apparent from their original hosts and amended according to new host genome (Lawrence and Ochman, 1997). Normally the acquired gene will ameliorate due to spontaneous mutations, ecological adaptation and interactions with environment (Gyles and Boerlin, 2014). This process makes the detection between closest relatives laborious, due to the similarities in genetic content and phylogeny (Adato *et al.*, 2015).

HGT often contributes to new functions and phenotypic variations such as adaptations to changing environments (Gyles and Boerlin, 2014; Yue *et al.*, 2012) or variations in pathogenicity and antibiotic resistance (Juhas, 2015; McElroy *et al.*, 2014). Cases of HGT in eukaryotes are reportedly associated with many modifying traits (Keeling and Palmer, 2008). Besides parasitic plants, HGT encompasses a huge range of autotrophic lineages (Keeling and Palmer, 2008; Sanchez-Puerta, 2014), bryophytes (Yue *et al.*, 2012), ferns (Davis *et al.*, 2005), basal angiosperms (Bergthorsson *et al.*, 2004) and grasses (Christin *et al.*, 2012). It is hypothesized that the number of horizontally transferred genes correlates with increasing heterotrophic dependence (Yang *et al.*, 2016).

Three approaches are widely implemented in HGT detection based on best pair-wise alignment (BLAST) matches, sequence composition, or phylogenetic analysis (Zhaxybayeva, 2009). The composition of the sequence is one of the earliest ways to detect the HGT event and is done by assessing the bias of synonymous codons in the recipient genome (Lawrence and Ochman, 1997). Besides assessing the discrepancy of genome composition, analyzing phylogenetic relationships is also a commonly used practice to identify horizontally transferred genes; where gene phylogenies that diverge from the organism's own known lineage is an indication of the presence of HGT events (Keeling and Palmer, 2008).

In this article, we review and compare several approaches for HGT detection in bacteria and parasitic plant systems. Due to the diverse complexity of genome composition, determining a pipeline for HGT detection remains challenging.

Background

HGT Events

HGT is the transfer of genetic information from one organism to another where the transferred material can be between related organisms within the same kingdom or even between different kingdoms.

Intra-kingdom (prokaryote to prokaryote; eukaryote to eukaryote)

HGT is more common in prokaryotes due to its asexual reproduction and simpler cell organization. Other than gaining drug resistance, HGT rescues prokaryotes from irreversible deleterious mutations (Muller's ratchet) to maintain the genomic information (Takeuchi *et al.*, 2014). Mechanisms on how HGT occur in prokaryotes are clearer compared to in eukaryotes because the passing of genetic information in eukaryotes is mainly via vertical gene transfer. HGT events that occur between eukaryotes are more complex and can be of different combinations: between unicellular eukaryotes, between multicellular eukaryotes, between unicellular and multicellular eukaryotes, and within the eukaryote that is between the organellar genome and the nuclear genome (Blanchard and Lynch, 2000; Keeling and Palmer, 2008; Richardson and Palmer, 2007).

Inter-kingdom (prokaryote to eukaryote; eukaryote to prokaryote)

Inter-kingdom HGT is highly interesting because it occurs between distant organisms. The most common direction of inter-kingdom HGT is the transfer of genetic material from prokaryotes to eukaryotes. The fact that there are larger populations of prokaryotes compared to eukaryotes in nature tend to make eukaryotes the gene recipients instead of the donor (Keeling and Palmer, 2008). Normally, eukaryotes gain prokaryotic genes mainly for adaptive evolution (Husnik and McCutcheon, 2017; Lacroix and Citovsky, 2016). Eukaryote-to-prokaryote transfer events are rare; however, the receipt of eukaryotic genes by prokaryotes has been reported as a means environmental adaptation (Sieber *et al.*, 2017) and for the general improvement of functions in prokaryotic systems (Koonin *et al.*, 2001).

HGT Detection

The surrogate and comparative methods are commonly used to study HGT (Ravenhall *et al.*, 2015) and is also applicable in eukaryotes (Jaron *et al.*, 2014). The surrogate or parametric method investigates the nucleotide base composition of the DNA sequence of interest (Jaron *et al.*, 2014). This method is extremely useful before the advent of next-generation sequencing technologies, and is able to depend only on the genome of interest to infer HGT events (Ravenhall *et al.*, 2015). In contrast, the comparative approach requires prior knowledge of a genome, which utilises phylogenetic identification for input genes or local alignment comparisons against a reference sequence database (Jaron *et al.*, 2014). All-against-all BLASTP searches are carried out to identify sequences with high similarities. Genes with BLAST hits to organisms distant from its close relatives and having relevance to the host are considered as horizontally derived ones. Over the years, many methods have been developed to detect HGT at the genome level. It is believed that by combining predictions from parametric and comparative methods, a more complete set of putative horizontally acquired genes can be retrieved (Ravenhall *et al.*, 2015).

Computational Analysis of HGT Genes

Traditionally, attention was given to a single genome of interest to study HGT events. As a result, only a handful of HGT events were identified due to the limitation of available data. With genome sequencing becoming more common and less cost prohibitive, the acquisition of genome sequences need no longer be limited to a single representative strain or individual as a species representative. This allows for the full complement of genes in a taxonomy to be represented by a pan-genome (Tettelin *et al.*, 2005).

However, in some cases where there is no genome sequence available, transcriptome data exploration is an alternative approach to discover the HGTs. This is applicable especially for larger organisms such as eukaryotes (plants and fungi) that are more costly to sequence the genomes compared to smaller genomes like bacteria and viruses. Here, we discuss the identification of HGT genes in bacterial genomes via pan-genome analysis (**Fig. 1**) and in plants via transcriptome profiling. A list of the computational tools that are discussed in this article is presented in **Table 1**.

Pan-Genome Informatics

Annotated genome sequences for organisms of interest are required to study HGT events via pan-genome analysis. Many approaches are taken to first annotate the genome sequences, and these may depend on several factors including computational capacities, genome size, type of organism and project strategic planning. For instance, The National Center for Biotechnology Information (NCBI) uses the Prokaryotic Genome Annotation Pipeline (PGAP) and the Eukaryotic Genome Annotation Pipeline (EGAP) for annotating prokaryote and eukaryote genomes, respectively. They are supported by the high performance computing cluster that enable the implementation of both pipelines containing many integrated analysis tools. On the other hand, other researchers with less capacity of computational resources show different implementation of genome annotation based on their customised approaches (Firdaus-Raih *et al.*, 2018; Noor *et al.*, 2014).

Although various genome annotation methods are in use, the mutual goal is still to derive as much information from the genome sequence as possible. The availability of annotated complete genomes enable the pan-genome analysis for an organism; this allows for the sets of core and variable genes from the organism's gene pool to be determined. The core genes refers to genes that are present in all organisms in the taxonomy and normally consist of housekeeping genes that are responsible for main phenotypic traits (Tettelin *et al.*, 2005). In contrast, the variable genes, also known as dispensable genes, are those that are present in some of the organisms (two or more strains) and typically involve functions such as virulence mechanisms, ecological adaptation and survival in different environments (Jeong *et al.*, 2017; Medini *et al.*, 2005).

Compiling the pan-genome can be done using several tools including EDGAR (Blom *et al.*, 2009), PGAT (Brittnacher *et al.*, 2011), PanGP (Zhao *et al.*, 2012) and Panseq (Xiao *et al.*, 2015) (**Table 1**). The resulting orthologous clusters can then be used to identify genes that are possibly involved in HGT events. On top of the catalogue of entire genes in the organism, more analysis can be performed to enrich the information, thus consolidation of these data will converge into a holistic understanding of the entire organism.

Atypical sequence signatures

Deviation of a gene's sequence composition signature, such as GC content, from the mean can be indicative of its origins from a foreign genome (Garcia-Vallvé *et al.*, 2000). Thus, the prediction of HGT gene candidates can be inferred with lower or higher GC content than the mean of the genome's GC content (Liu *et al.*, 2009). Many tools were developed to analyze the GC content of genes and genomes, such as EMBOSS geecee which calculates the percentage of GC (Rice *et al.*, 2000), GC-Profile which analyses

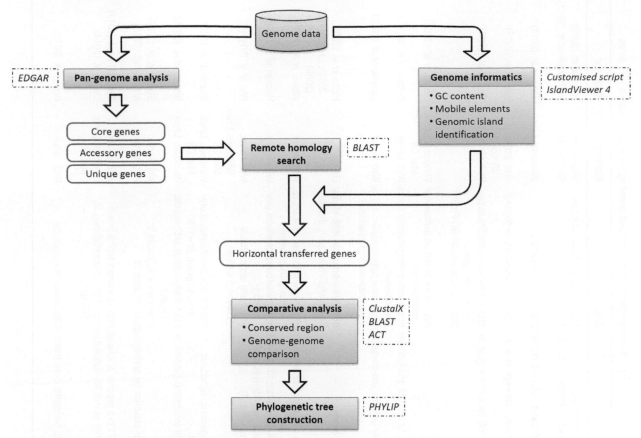

Fig. 1 Approaches in analysis of HGT using pan-genome data. The availability of genome data allows for a series of investigations via pan-genome analysis that can lead to the identification of horizontally transferred genes within the organism.

GC content by segmenting the genome (Gao and Zhang, 2006), and Artemis which allows for visualization of both the GC percentage and its deviation (Carver *et al.*, 2008).

Identification of genomic islands (GIs)

Genomic islands (GIs) refer to discrete DNA segments that establish horizontally transferred genes in a population (Jaron *et al.*, 2014). This region may integrate into the chromosome of the host; excised and transferred to a new host by transformation, conjugation or transduction. Proteins encoded within this region possibly present new functions in the recipient organism (Casacuberta and González, 2013). The prediction of GIs in prokaryotes can be better carried out than in eukaryotes due to the complexity of eukaryotic genomes. Many tools were developed to predict the occurrence of GIs in prokaryotic genomes such as GIPSy (Soares *et al.*, 2015), Zisland Explorer (Wei *et al.*, 2017) and IslandViewer 4 (Bertelli *et al.*, 2017). A good practice in predicting GIs is by consolidating the prediction outcomes from different tools by taking into account the different approaches that each tool implements to solve the problem.

In the most widely used software, IslandViewer 4, the prediction of GIs can be carried out using pre-computed genomes (complete bacterial and archaeal genomes from NCBI) or by uploading a genome sequence in EMBL or GENBANK format. This software incorporates four high precision prediction methods: IslandPick (Langille *et al.*, 2008), IslandPath-DIMOB (Hsiao *et al.*, 2003, 2005; Langille *et al.*, 2008), SIGI-HMM (Waack *et al.*, 2006), and Islander (Hudson *et al.*, 2015). The implementation of multiple prediction tools is important to ensure precise results and to reduce false positives in the predictions.

Predicting accurate GI boundaries is essential to obtain precise GI regions in the genome. This can be achieved by using IslandPick via comparative genomics approach if a reference genome is available (Langille *et al.*, 2008). Otherwise, Islander is recommended as it is capable of precisely discovering direct repeats that flank the acquired region (Hudson *et al.*, 2015). On the other hand, IslandPath-DIMOB and SIGI-HMM seem to have lower precision when predicting GI boundaries and tend to return fragmented horizontally transferred regions. Nevertheless, in the case of finding GIs via gene-based nucleotide bias approaches, both tools are favoured to generally anticipate more dispersed segments gained by HGT (Hsiao *et al.*, 2003, 2005; Waack *et al.*, 2006).

Identification of mobile elements

Mobile elements are DNA segments that can move within the genome or out to other organisms and while moving, it will bring along the donor genes to pass on to the recipient genome (Rankin *et al.*, 2011). Such an ability make these mobile elements a key

Table 1 List of tools applicable for the analysis of horizontal gene transfer events. Different computational tools for different platforms (web-based and operating systems) to analyze HGT genes

Category	Programs	Approach	URL	Platform	Reference
(a) Pan-genome analysis	EDGAR	A software framework for the comparative analysis of prokaryotic genomes.	http://edgar.computational.bio/	Web server	Blom et al. (2009)
	PGAT	A web-based database that compared multistrain microbial organisms' gene content and SNPs and impact of SNPs to encoded proteins.	http://nwrce.org/pgat	Web server	Brittnacher et al. (2011)
	PanGP	Integrates two sampling algorithms TR (totally random) and DG (distance guide) to perform pan-genome analysis in large scale bacterial genomes.	http://pangp.big.ac.cn/	Windows, Linux	Zhao et al. (2014)
	Panseq	Determine core and accessory region in genomes, SNPs within shared core regions and calculate loci in sets of accessory loci or core SNPs.	https://lfz.corefacility.ca/panseq/	Web server, Windows, Linux	Xiao et al. (2015)
(b) Identification of atypical sequence signatures	geecee	A tool from the EMBOSS package to calculate fraction of GC per 100 bp within a gene or genome.	http://www.bioinformatics.nl/cgi-bin/emboss/geecee	Web server, Linux	Rice et al. (2000)
	GC-Profile Web server	GC profile analysis by segmenting the genome. Gao and Zhang (2006)	http://tubic.tju.edu.cn/GC-Profile/		
	Artemis	GC content (%) and its 2.5 SD cutoff from graph menu.	http://www.sanger.ac.uk/science/tools/artemis	Windows, Linux, Mac OS	Carver et al. (2008)
(c) Identification of GIs	IslandViewer 4	Integrate four GIs prediction tools: IslandPick, IslandPath-DIMOD, SIGI-HMM and Islander.	http://www.pathogenomics.sfu.ca/islandviewer/	Web server	Bertelli et al. (2017)
	IslandPick	Identify GIs by using distance function, unique region only to query genome and conserved regions across genomes.	http://www.pathogenomics.sfu.ca/islandviewer2/run_islandpick.php	Web server	Langille et al. (2008)
	IslandPath-DIMOB	Identify GIs by require dinucleotide bias and presence of mobility genes.	http://www.brinkman.mbb.sfu.ca/~mlangill/islandpath_dimob/	Linux	Hsiao et al. (2003, 2005), Langille et al. (2008)
	SIGI-HMM	It predicts GIs and putative donor of foreign genes based on codon usage analysis of gene or genome and HMM approach.	http://www.brinkman.mbb.sfu.ca/~mlangill/sigi-hmm/	Web server	Waack et al. (2006)
	Islander	A database that mapped GIs that were integrated into tDNAs, flanked by intact tDNAs and displaced tDNAs fragments, and contain integrase gene of tyrosine recombinase family.	http://bioinformatics.sandia.gov/islander/	Web server	Hudson et al. (2015)
	Zisland explorer	Predict GIs based on segmental cumulative GC profile (from GC-profile tool).	http://cefg.uestc.edu.cn/Zisland_Explorer/	Web server, Windows, Linux, Mac OS	Wei et al. (2017)
(d) Identification of ME	GIPSy	Predict types of GIs: PAIs, MIs, RIs and SIs. It predicts by using genomic signatures deviation, tRNA genes, presence of MEs, and conserved regions.	https://www.bioinformatics.org/groups/?group_id=1180	Windows, Linux, Mac OS	Soares et al. (2015)
	ISQuest	Identify and annotate mobile genetic elements in raw read, partially assembled genome or fully assembled genome. It uses Blast to identify the MGEs.	https://sourceforge.net/projects/isquest/	Windows, Linux	Biswas et al. (2015)
	ISFinder	A bacterial insertion sequences database.	https://www-is.biotoul.fr	Web server	Siguier et al. (2006)
	PHASTER	Identify and annotate phage sequences within bacterial genomes or plasmids by performing database comparison.	https://phaster.ca	Web server	Arndt et al. (2016)
(e) HGT detection	Alienness	Parse BLAST results against public libraries to identify candidate HGT in a genome of interest.	http://alienness.sophia.inra.fr	Web server	Rancurel et al. (2017)
	HGTector	Analyze BLAST hit distribution patterns based on sequence homology search hit distribution statistics. All-against-all BLASTP search	https://github.com/DittmarLab/HGTector	Windows, Linux, Mac OS	Zhu et al. (2014)
	T-REX	Reconstruct phylogenetic trees, reticulate networks and to infer the horizontal gene transfer events.	http://www.trex.uqam.ca/	Web server	Boc et al. (2012)

factor in evolution. Mobile elements include plasmid, bacteria-infecting viruses (bacteriophages), transposons, and insertion sequences. Examples of prediction tools for mobile elements are PHASTER for phages (Arndt *et al.*, 2016), ISFinder for identifying bacterial insertion sequences (Siguier *et al.*, 2006) and ISQuest for finding insertion sequences and transposons (Biswas *et al.*, 2015).

Identification of HGT Events Using Transcriptome Data

Since *de novo* whole genome assembly of a plant genome is complicated by the presence of repeat sequences, assessing HGT at the transcriptome level provides a direct approach to reveal the expression status of the genes. In host-parasite systems, a gene is considered horizontally acquired if it is phylogenetically placed nearer to its host rather than to its closest relatives. HGT detection using software is made possible for plants with the development of various tools, such as T-rex (Boc *et al.*, 2012), Alienness (Rancurel *et al.*, 2017) and HGTector (Zhu *et al.*, 2014). Nevertheless, some of these tools require specific files and preparation steps to conduct the HGT search. For instance, two newick trees generated for species and gene of interest are required as the input files. As with Alienness, a BLAST file of a whole proteome of interest is required to blast against any NCBI protein library. This tool calculates an Alien Index (AI) for early query protein and an AI > 0 indicates a possible HGT. HGTector takes one or more protein sets as input. In principle, this tool formulates a grouping scenario, calculates the three weights of each gene, defines certain cutoffs and then identifies the genes that exhibit atypical distribution.

In a case study that involves a parasitic plant (Section HGT in Plants), two web servers, OrthoVenn (see "Relevant Websites section") (Wang *et al.*, 2015) and eggNOG-mapper of the EggNOG v 4.5 (see "Relevant Websites section") (Huerta-Cepas *et al.*, 2016), were used to cluster orthologous genes across *Rafflesia* (parasite) and *Tetrastigma* (host) predicted proteomes. Homologous sequences were retrieved for each candidate HGT genes and were aligned using the multiple sequence alignment tool MUSCLE (Edgar, 2004) embedded in MEGA7 (Kumar *et al.*, 2016), which was later used to perform phylogenetic analysis through maximum likelihood searching.

Illustrative Case Studies

HGT in Bacteria

Here, we describe some cases of genes that were possibly transferred by HGT in a Gram-negative bacteria, *Burkholderia pseudomallei*, that in addition to being a versatile pathogen is notable for its highly plastic genome (Tumapa *et al.*, 2008). This flexibility is thought to be partly due to the HGT effect which turns this pathogenic soil bacteria into a highly adaptable organism that can live in a wide range of hosts (Currie, 2003) and has even been shown to actively respond and survive in very low nutrient environments (Mohd-Padil *et al.*, 2017). The pan-genome data of 48 complete *B. pseudomallei* genomes resulted in a total of 10,698 orthologous groups (OG) that encompassed 39% (4220 OGs) core genes and 61% (6478 OGs) accessory genes. Two observations of HGT are highlighted here; conserved hypothetical genes of *B. pseudomallei* and unique genes that were found in a specific *B. pseudomallei* strain.

Core hypothetical proteins in B. pseudomallei

In *B. pseudomallei* pan-genome data, 171 core genes encoding for hypothetical proteins (HPs) that were conserved in 48 complete *B. pseudomallei* genomes obtained from NCBI (**Table 2**). Further remote homology searching using BLAST (Altschul *et al.*, 1990) of these core HPs against a non redundant database revealed a range of conservation level in the sequences, from phylum down to species (**Fig. 2**).

Case 1: Hypothetical genes conserved in Burkholderiaceae family and two non-proteobacteria species
Up to December 2017, four hypothetical proteins – BPSL3171, BPSL3235, BPSS0337 and BPSS1590 (using the nomenclature for K96243) – are conserved in the Burkholderiaceae family and remote organisms from non proteobacteria phylum namely *Mumia flava* and *Streptomyces pluripotens*. Both bacteria were isolated from mangrove soil in Kuantan and Tanjung Lumpur of Pahang state, Malaysia, respectively (Lee *et al.*, 2014a,b). They are members of actinobacteria phylum that are highly adapted to various ecological environments and might be inhabitants of soil or aquatic environments, plant symbionts, plant pathogens or gastrointestinal commensal (Barka *et al.*, 2016). Mangrove soil is a highly dynamic ecosystem that is believed to force the soil bacterial populations to undergo rapid niche-specific adaptation. One mechanism for such adaptation is by acquiring beneficial genes from other bacteria in the same niche. Limited information is known about the *M. flava* genome as it is a novel actinobacterial strain (Lee *et al.*, 2014a), while *S. pluripotens* showed the presence of a wide-range of bacteriocins against pathogens such as *Staphylococcus aureus*, *Salmonella typhi* and *Aeromonas hydrophila* (Lee *et al.*, 2014b).

In terms of GC content, all four genes showed deviation from its chromosome GC average. Both BPSL3171 and BPSL3235 have lower GC content than K96243's large chromosome (67.7%), denoted by 51.46% and 55.84%, respectively. On another note, in the smaller second chromosome with GC percentage of 68.5%, the GC content in BPSS0337 is lower (62.59%), while it is higher in BPSS1590 (75.32%). This deviation is an informative indicator of horizontal gene transfer events that might have occurred at those positions.

Table 2   List of 48 *B. pseudomallei* strains used in the pan-genome study. A list of complete *B. pseudomallei* genomes that were sequenced up to October 2017

Country	Strain	Assembly ID	Size (Mb)	GC%
Australia	668	GCA_000015905.1	7.04	68.27
Australia	MSHR146	GCA_000521645.1	7.313	68.02
Australia	MSHR1655	GCA_000756165.1	7.028	67.99
Australia	MSHR2543	GCA_000959225.1	7.447	67.9
Australia	MSHR305	GCA_000439695.1	7.428	67.89
Australia	MSHR491	GCA_000959205.1	7.356	67.98
Australia	MSHR511	GCA_000520895.1	7.316	68.02
Australia	MSHR520	GCA_000583835.1	7.451	67.89
Australia	MSHR5848	GCA_000755965.1	7.29	68.08
Australia	MSHR5855	GCA_000756065.1	7.298	68.02
Australia	MSHR5858	GCA_000755945.1	7.072	68.28
Australia	MSHR62	GCA_000770395.1	7.225	68.17
Australia	MSHR668	GCA_000959305.1	7.043	68.27
Australia	MSHR840	GCA_000959185.1	7.13	68.09
Australia	NAU20B	GCA_000511915.1	7.314	68.02
Australia	NCTC_13179	GCA_000494855.1	7.337	67.99
Australia	NAU35A-3	GCA_000764575.1	7.204	68.08
Australia	NCTC 13,178	GCA_000511895.1	7.391	67.94
Australia	TSV 48	GCA_000770495.1	7.338	68.02
China	BPC006	GCA_000294635.1	7.155	68.22
Ecuador	7894	GCA_000959265.1	7.382	67.92
Malaysia	982	GCA_001277975.1	7.185	68.21
Malaysia	D286	In-house	7.102	68.25
Malaysia	H10	In-house	7.287	68.15
Malaysia	M1	GCA_001695715.1	7.318	67.98
Malaysia	MS	GCA_001695735.1	7.314	67.98
Malaysia	PMC2000	In-house	7.187	68.2
Malaysia	R15	In-house	7.179	68.25
Papua New Guinea	A79A	GCA_000770535.1	7.272	68.04
Papua New Guinea	B03	GCA_000770455.1	7.265	68.04
Papua New Guinea	K42	GCA_000770515.1	7.297	67.98
Taiwan	vgh07	GCA_000954175.1	7.046	68.2
Taiwan	vgh16R	GCA_001277875.1	7.267	68.08
Taiwan	vgh16W	GCA_001277895.1	7.267	68.08
Thailand	576	GCA_000756185.1	7.267	68.03
Thailand	3921	GCA_000953095.1	7.162	68.15
Thailand	1026b	GCA_000260515.1	7.231	68.16
Thailand	1106a	GCA_000756145.1	7.086	68.26
Thailand	1710b	GCA_000012785.1	7.308	67.99
Thailand	406e	GCA_000959145.1	7.272	68.07
Thailand	HBPUB10134a	GCA_000755925.1	7.218	68.12
Thailand	HBPUB10303a	GCA_000755905.1	7.178	68.18
Thailand	K96243	GCA_000011545.1	7.25	68.05
Thailand	Mahidol-1106a	GCA_000756125.1	7.085	68.26
Thailand	PHLS 112	GCA_000757015.2	7.202	68.18
USA	Bp1651	GCA_001318245.1	7.26	68.1
USA	PB08298010	GCA_000959345.1	7.376	67.95
Vietnam	Pasteur 52,237	GCA_000757035.2	7.325	68

Two domains of unknown function (DUFs), DUF1835 and DUF 3658, that have orthologs in both *M. flava* and *S. pluripotens* could also be found in the sequence encoding for BPSL3235. The latter domain can be found in bacteria and retains two highly conserved residues (Aspartic Acid and Arginine) that may play important functional roles. The gene is located in the same operon with that containing *bpsl3236*, a tetracycline (TetR) family transcriptional regulator that controls the level of susceptibility towards tetracycline antibiotics, a commonly used antibiotics against bacteria (Aleksandrov *et al.*, 2008; Grkovic *et al.*, 2002). There are also inverted repeats (palindrome) motifs found within 500 bp upstream and downstream of the *bpsl3235* gene together with additional motif of Rho-independent transcription terminator TERM 1195 located on the upstream region. According to Ooi *et al.* (2013), *bpsl3235* was found to be expressed in several conditions including during antibiotic treatment, osmotic stress, temperature stress, UV irradiation, oxidative stress and aerobic state.

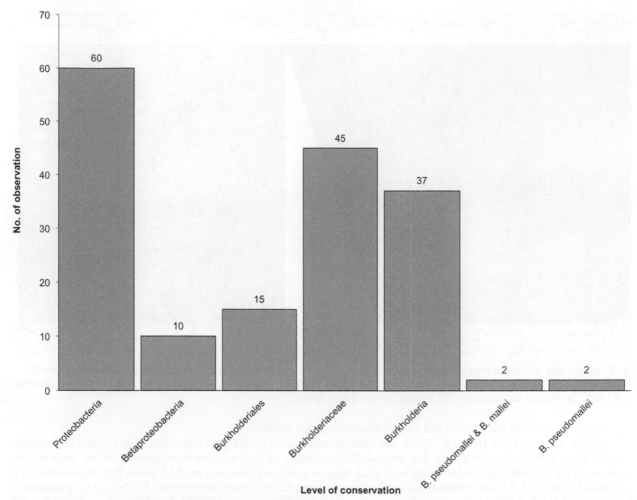

Fig. 2 Number of cases for different conservation levels in *B. pseudomallei* core hypothetical proteins. Various distribution of conservation from phylum to species can be seen in core HPs of *B. pseudomallei*.

The other three hypothetical proteins, BPSL3171, BPSS0337 and BPSS1590 have similarities with *M. flava* only. Inverted repeats (palindrome) motifs are found at 500 bp downstream of each gene while the *bpsl3171* gene is located in the operon together with sequences encoding two other hypothetical proteins (BPSL3172 and BPSL3173). Both *bpsl3171* and *bpss1590* are flanked respectively by secretion system protein genes and type III secretion system gene together with type IV pilus protein. Whereas *bpss0337* is flanked by an insertion element gene and an araC family transcriptional regulator. Interestingly, *bpsl3171* is only expressed during anaerobic condition and *in vivo* infection (Ooi *et al.*, 2013) thus indicating that the gene may have important roles for *B. pseudomallei* survival and pathogenicity. In contrast, expression of BPSS0337 and BPSS1590 were detected in most conditions except *in vivo* infection conditions.

However, none of the genes discussed are predicted to be part of genomic islands. Since not all horizontally transferred genes must be located in a genomic island, this observation alludes to the possibility that these genes may have been transferred and have undergone amelioration, hence providing a possible explanation as to why some tools can no longer distinguish these regions as being foreign. In context, it can be assumed that these genes may have been horizontally transferred between *Burkholderia* and two non proteobacteria due to their presence in the same niche although the origin species of these genes remains unknown or have yet to be isolated and sequenced.

Unique genes in B. pseudomallei

In this discussion, a unique gene or singleton refers to a strain-specific gene that is found in the *B. pseudomallei* pan-genome (Tettelin *et al.*, 2005). In total, 13% (1352 OGs) of the accessory genes in *B. pseudomallei* are categorized as singletons. Such genes could also be of uncharacterized function, however due consideration should be given when annotating such singletons in a pan-genome dataset because homologs may actually exist in strains that do not yet have available genome sequences. It is recommended that these annotations are cross-checked against the vast non-redundant database in GenBank and also periodically revisited as the number of genomes in the pan-genome dataset increases.

Fig. 3 An ACT view showing an insertion of a region (8514 bp) in the first *B. pseudomallei* chromosome that absent in reference genome of K96243 strain. The highlighted region in yellow consists of D286.1_0401 and D286.1_0402 genes that may have arised due to HGT events in the D286 strain. The region is not observed in the reference genome (upper section).

Case 1: Unique genes in B. pseudomallei *that are also found in other soil bacteria*

In *B. pseudomallei* strain D286 (Lee *et al.*, 2007), two adjacent unique genes encoding 393 residues (D286.1_0401) of a sequence with no other available homologs and 408 residues (D286.1_0402) of DNA-cytosine methyltransferase, are strain-specific. Extension of the genomic regions containing both genes suggests that a sequence with 8514 bp in the first chromosome of *B. pseudomallei* is observed in D286 strain while it is absent in reference genome of strain K96243 (**Fig. 3**). The low GC percentage of this region (53.01%), a relatively large deviation from the mean GC of its genome (67.87%) disturbs the genomic stability. The deviation gives an insight into gene acquisition of the strain although D286.1_0401 is predicted to be part of a genomic island albeit with low confidence and the extended discussed region has no predicted mobile elements.

The homology search using D286.1_0401 as a query yielded detectable similarities to five distant organisms from different phylums including proteobacteria (*Novosphingobium barchaimii* and *Pelobacter seleniigenes*) (Nasaringarao and Häggblom, 2007; Niharika *et al.*, 2013), acidobacteria (*Granulicella pectinivorans* and *Acidobacteria bacterium*) (Pankratov and Dedysh, 2010) and Terrabacteria group (*Brevibacterium* sp. 239c). Interestingly, all of them share the mutual characteristics of being physiologically diverse and capable of living in a wide range of environments, especially soil, although this is common of many bacteria. On the other hand, its adjacent gene of D286.1_0402, has a vast similarity to many other organisms including *G. pectinivorans*, *A. bacterium* and *Eubacterium plexicaudatum* (Pankratov and Dedysh, 2010; Wilkins *et al.*, 1974).

Case 2: Unique genes in B. pseudomallei *detected as part of a genomic island*

Based on available pan-genome data, four unique genes in the D286 strain were identified to reside within a 53,131 bp length GI region predicted by IslandViewer 4. The four genes are annotated as hypothetical gene (D286.1_3048), HNH endonuclease family protein, (D286.1_3063), ATPase (D286.1_3064) and hypothetical protein encoding gene, (D286.1_3071). The HNH endonuclease family protein, (D286.1_3063) and ATPase (D286.1_3064) share similarity with diverse remote genomes but no similarities to any from *Burkholderia* sp. while D286.1_3048 is similar but also appear to have orthologs in three *Burkholderia* sp.. The sequence encoded by D286.1_3071 shows similarity with only one hypothetical protein from *B. vietnamiensis*. Compared to the mean GC of its genome (67.87%), this region carries a lower GC percentage of 59.66%, indicating that foreign gene influx may have occurred at that position. This is supported by the finding of the presence of tRNA genes that is well known to be associated to GI that were obtained from foreign organisms (Tuller, 2011).

Around 20% of genes in the GI encode for hypothetical proteins. Our results show that this island also consists of a phage-related integrase gene next to the tRNA gene, proposing that this GI may possibly have been generated by a phage or plasmid with integrative functions (Odenbreit and Haas, 2002; Semsey *et al.*, 2002). In addition to the phage integrase family protein gene, another group of genes that were also present were those for components of the Type VI secretion system (T6SS) that is well known as a virulence factor for pathogenic bacteria and as a mechanism for protein transport across the cell envelope in proteobacteria

(Pukatzki *et al.*, 2006). Furthermore, there are also phage-related genes present, such as those encoding phage virion morphogenesis protein, phage tail protein and phage capsid protein. A part of the GI seems to be similar with other *B. pseudomallei* strains, however part of the region is missing in the reference genome of the K96243 strain. Thus, from the pan-genome data, we can obtain some indicators that these unique genes might be an effect of a HGT event.

HGT in Plants

Lateral gene transfer in parasitic flowering plants is known to occur via genomic DNA (Xi *et al.*, 2012), or via mRNA intermediates (Kim *et al.*, 2014). Therefore, HGT involving plants is studied using both genome (Yue *et al.*, 2012) and transcriptome (Kim *et al.*, 2014; Xi *et al.*, 2012; Zhang *et al.*, 2014, 2013) data whenever possible. Nuclear HGTs are less common among multicellular eukaryotes such as animals, fungi and plants (Richardson and Palmer, 2007) compared to organellar genes. However, a total of 47 horizontally acquired nuclear genes were identified from *R. cantleyi* using a combination of BLAST and phylogenomic approaches (Xi *et al.*, 2012). Using the same approach, an approximation of 24%–41% of the mitochondrial gene sequences were identified to be horizontally acquired from their host (Xi *et al.*, 2013).

Clustering of orthologous groups across two or more distant species results in a list of horizontally acquired candidate genes. Through reciprocal proteome clustering between *Rafflesia* and *Tetrastigma*, 59 orthologous clusters and 67 candidate orthologs were identified from OrthoVenn and eggNOG-mapper respectively to be *Tetrastigma*-related and these genes were subjected to phylogenetic analysis. Thirteen genes were identified to be transferred through HGT. Interestingly, only rhamnose synthase was similarly identified by the two approaches used in this case study and the analysis conducted by Xi *et al.* (2012). The remaining 12 genes were found to span across cell wall formation, degradation, defense mechanism, stress response, amino acid biosynthesis and glycolysis. Additionally, 24 *Rafflesia* genes were not grouped together, either with its closest relatives nor with *Tetrastigma*. Of these genes, six were reported to be horizontally transferred by Xi *et al.* (2012). The discrepancy could be attributed to the polyphyletic status or unresolved ambiguity exerted by the evolving elements.

Discussion and Future Directions

Several methods have been developed to improve the accuracy in addition to reducing the computational time to search for HGTs. Compared to the different approaches employed by Xi *et al.* (2012), the methods described here identifies much lower numbers of HGTs, possibly due to stringent parameters applied for orthologous clustering during the early search. This may rule out the set of genes that have lost the signatures of their donor as a result of evolution. In contrast, the classification of homologous sequences into the respective species presents a higher number of candidates for HGT identification in an organism of interest.

Choosing an appropriate method for HGT detection is not straightforward. It depends on the nature of the study, species of interest, computational resources and time. With the development of bioinformatic tools and pipelines, HGT detection can now be performed on large-scale data sets, covering both prokaryotes and eukaryotes. Care should be taken in order to avoid false positives that could lead to a pool of unresolved artifacts. For instance, despite the application of BLAST-based detection in some studies (Yoshida *et al.*, 2010; Zhang *et al.*, 2014, 2017), comprehensive follow up work is required to eliminate high false positives, such as misidentification of contaminant sequences, deficient taxon sampling, intriguing gene birth and death processes, improper rooting and frame-shift errors that must also be accounted for (Yang *et al.*, 2016). Similarly, incomplete lineage sorting during phylogeny construction can lead to inaccurate HGT identification (Than *et al.*, 2007).

To date, there is no true one-stop solution for the identification of genes that were potentially horizontally transferred. However, the results of tools used for sequence analysis and phylogenetics can be used and the relevant context provided to allow for inference of HGT events. As more genomes become available, it would perhaps be timely for a fit for purpose tool or pipeline to be developed for inferring HGT events despite such tools requiring significant capacity and resource allocations.

Acknowledgement

MFR is funded by the Universiti Kebangsaan Malaysia grant DIP-2017–013.

See also: Genetics and Population Analysis. Natural Language Processing Approaches in Bioinformatics. Phylogenetic analysis: Early evolution of life. Sequence Analysis

References

Adato, O., Ninyo, N., Gophna, U., Snir, S., 2015. Detecting horizontal gene transfer between closely related taxa. PLOS Comput. Biol. 11, e1004408.
Aleksandrov, A., Schuldt, L., Hinrichs, W., Simonson, T., 2008. Tet repressor induction by tetracycline: A molecular dynamics, continuum electrostatics, and crystallographic study. J. Mol. Biol. 378, 896–910. Available at: https://doi.org/10.1016/j.jmb.2008.03.022.

Altschul, S.F., Gish, W., Miller, W., Myers, E.W., Lipman, D.J., 1990. Basic local alignment search tool. J. Mol. Biol. 215, 403–410. Available at: https://doi.org/10.1016/S0022-2836(05)80360-2.

Arndt, D., Grant, J.R., Marcu, A., et al., 2016. PHASTER: A better, faster version of the PHAST phage search tool. Nucleic Acids Res. 44 (W1), W16–W21. Available at: https://doi.org/10.1093/nar/gkw387.

Barka, E.A., Vatsa, P., Sanchez, L., et al., 2016. Taxonomy, physiology, and natural products of actinobacteria. Microbiol. Mol. Biol. Rev. 80, 1–43. Available at: https://doi.org/10.1128/MMBR.00019-15.

Bergthorsson, U., Richardson, A.O., Young, G.J., Goertzen, L.R., Palmer, J.D., 2004. Massive horizontal transfer of mitochondrial genes from diverse land plant donors to the basal angiosperm Amborella. Proc. Natl. Acad. Sci. USA 101, 17747 LP–17717752.

Bertelli, C., Laird, M.R., Williams, K.P., et al., 2017. IslandViewer 4: Expanded prediction of genomic islands for larger-scale datasets. Nucleic Acids Res. 45, W30–W35.

Biswas, A., Gauthier, D.T., Ranjan, D., Zubair, M., 2015. ISQuest: Finding insertion sequences in prokaryotic sequence fragment data. Bioinformatics 31, 3406–3412. Available at: https://doi.org/10.1093/bioinformatics/btv388.

Blanchard, J.L., Lynch, M., 2000. Organellar genes: Why do they end up in the nucleus? Trends Genet. 16, 315–320.

Blom, J., Albaum, S.P., Doppmeier, D., et al., 2009. EDGAR: A software framework for the comparative analysis of prokaryotic genomes. BMC Bioinform. 10, 154. Available at: https://doi.org/10.1186/1471-2105-10-154.

Boc, A., Diallo, A.B., Makarenkov, V., 2012. T-REX: A web server for inferring, validating and visualizing phylogenetic trees and networks. Nucleic Acids Res. 40, W573–W579. Available at: https://doi.org/10.1093/nar/gks485.

Brittnacher, M.J., Fong, C., Hayden, H.S., et al., 2011. PGAT: A multistrain analysis resource for microbial genomes. Bioinformatics 27, 2429–2430. Available at: https://doi.org/10.1093/bioinformatics/btr418.

Carver, T., Berriman, M., Tivey, A., et al., 2008. Artemis and ACT: Viewing, annotating and comparing sequences stored in a relational database. Bioinformatics 24, 2672–2676. Available at: https://doi.org/10.1093/bioinformatics/btn529.

Casacuberta, E., González, J., 2013. The impact of transposable elements in environmental adaptation. Mol. Ecol. 22, 1.5.0.3.–1517. Available at: https://doi.org/10.1111/mec.12170.

Christin, P.-A., Wallace, M.J., Clayton, H., et al., 2012. Multiple photosynthetic transitions, polyploidy, and lateral gene transfer in the grass subtribe Neurachninae. J. Exp. Bot. 63, 6297–6308. Available at: https://doi.org/10.1093/jxb/ers282.

Crisp, A., Boschetti, C., Perry, M., Tunnacliffe, A., Micklem, G., 2015. Expression of multiple horizontally acquired genes is a hallmark of both vertebrate and invertebrate genomes. Genome Biol. 16, 50. Available at: https://doi.org/10.1186/s13059-015-0607-3.

Currie, B.J., 2003. Melioidosis: An important cause of pneumonia in residents of and travellers returned from endemic regions. Eur. Respir. J. 22, 542 LP–542550.

Davis, C.C., Anderson, W.R., Wurdack, K.J., 2005. Gene transfer from a parasitic flowering plant to a fern. Proc. R. Soc. B Biol. Sci. 272, 2237–2242. Available at: https://doi.org/10.1098/rspb.2005.3226.

Edgar, R.C., 2004. MUSCLE: Multiple sequence alignment with high accuracy and high throughput. Nucleic Acids Res. 32, 1792–1797. Available at: https://doi.org/10.1093/nar/gkh340.

Firdaus-Raih, M., Hashim, N.H.F., Bharudin, I., et al., 2018. The Glaciozyma antarctica genome reveals an array of systems that provide sustained responses towards temperature variations in a persistently cold habitat. PLOS ONE 13, e0189947.

Gao, F., Zhang, C.-T., 2006. GC-Profile: A web-based tool for visualizing and analyzing the variation of GC content in genomic sequences. Nucleic Acids Res. 34 (Web Server Issue), W686–W691. Available at: https://doi.org/10.1093/nar/gkl040.

Garcia-Vallvé, S., Romeu, A., Palau, J., 2000. Horizontal gene transfer in bacterial and archaeal complete genomes. Genome Res. 10 (11), 1719–1725. Available at: https://doi.org/10.1101/gr.130000.

Griffith, F., 1928. The significance of pneumococcal types. J. Hyg. (Lond.) 27, 113–159.

Grkovic, S., Brown, M.H., Skurray, R.A., 2002. Regulation of bacterial drug export systems. Microbiol. Mol. Biol. Rev. 66, 671–701. Available at: https://doi.org/10.1128/MMBR.66.4.671.

Gyles, C., Boerlin, P., 2014. Horizontally transferred genetic elements and their role in pathogenesis of bacterial disease. Vet. Pathol. 51, 328–340. Available at: https://doi.org/10.1177/0300985813511131.

Hsiao, W.W.L., Ung, K., Aeschliman, D., et al., 2005. Evidence of a large novel gene pool associated with prokaryotic genomic islands. PLOS Genet. 1, e62. Available at: https://doi.org/10.1371/journal.pgen.0010062.

Hsiao, W., Wan, I., Jones, S.J., Brinkman, F.S.L., 2003. IslandPath: Aiding detection of genomic islands in prokaryotes. Bioinformatics 19, 418–420.

Huang, J., 2013. Horizontal gene transfer in eukaryotes: The weak-link model. Bioessays 35, 868–875. Available at: https://doi.org/10.1002/bies.201300007.

Hudson, C.M., Lau, B.Y., Williams, K.P., 2015. Islander: A database of precisely mapped genomic islands in tRNA and tmRNA genes. Nucleic Acids Res. 43, D48–D53.

Huerta-Cepas, J., Szklarczyk, D., Forslund, K., et al., 2016. eggNOG 4.5: A hierarchical orthology framework with improved functional annotations for eukaryotic, prokaryotic and viral sequences. Nucleic Acids Res. 44, D286–D293. Available at: https://doi.org/10.1093/nar/gkv1248.

Husnik, F., McCutcheon, J.P., 2017. Functional horizontal gene transfer from bacteria to eukaryotes. Nat. Rev. Microbiol. 16, 67.

Jaron, K.S., Moravec, J.C., Martínková, N., 2014. SigHunt: Horizontal gene transfer finder optimized for eukaryotic genomes. Bioinformatics 30, 1081–1086.

Jeong, D.-W., Heo, S., Ryu, S., Blom, J., Lee, J.-H., 2017. Genomic insights into the virulence and salt tolerance of Staphylococcus equorum. Sci. Rep. 7, 5383. Available at: https://doi.org/10.1038/s41598-017-05918-5.

Juhas, M., 2015. Type IV secretion systems and genomic islands-mediated horizontal gene transfer in Pseudomonas and Haemophilus. Microbiol. Res. 170, 10–17. Available at: https://doi.org/10.1016/j.micres.2014.06.007.

Keeling, P.J., Palmer, J.D., 2008. Horizontal gene transfer in eukaryotic evolution. Nat. Rev. Genet. 9, 605–618. Available at: https://doi.org/10.1038/nrg2386.

Kim, G., LeBlanc, M.L., Wafula, E.K., dePamphilis, C.W., Westwood, J.H., 2014. Plant science. Genomic-scale exchange of mRNA between a parasitic plant and its hosts. Science 345, 808–811. Available at: https://doi.org/10.1126/science.1253122.

Koonin, Eugene V., Makarova, Kira S., Aravind, L., 2001. Horizontal gene transfer in prokaryotes: Quantification and classification. Annu. Rev. Microbiol. 55, 709–742. Available at: https://doi.org/10.1146/annurev.micro.55.1.709.

Kumar, S., Stecher, G., Tamura, K., 2016. MEGA7: Molecular Evolutionary Genetics Analysis version 7.0 for bigger datasets. Mol. Biol. Evol. 33, 1870–1874. Available at: https://doi.org/10.1093/molbev/msw054.

Lacroix, B., Citovsky, V., 2016. Transfer of DNA from bacteria to eukaryotes. MBio 7 (4), Available at: https://doi.org/10.1128/mBio.00863-16.

Langille, M.G.I., Hsiao, W.W.L., Brinkman, F.S.L., 2008. Evaluation of genomic island predictors using a comparative genomics approach. BMC Bioinform. 9, 329. Available at: https://doi.org/10.1186/1471-2105-9-329.

Lawrence, J.G., Ochman, H., 1997. Amelioration of bacterial genomes: Rates of change and exchange. J. Mol. Evol. 44. Available at: https://doi.org/10.1007/PL00006158.

Lee, S.-H., Chong, C.-E., Lim, B.-S., et al., 2007. Burkholderia pseudomallei animal and human isolates from Malaysia exhibit different phenotypic characteristics. Diagn. Microbiol. Infect. Dis. 58, 263–270. Available at: https://doi.org/10.1016/j.diagmicrobio.2007.01.002.

Lee, L.H., Zainal, N., Azman, A.S., et al., 2014a. Mumia flava gen. nov., sp. nov., an actinobacterium of the family Nocardioidaceae. Int. J. Syst. Evol. Microbiol. 64, 1461–1467. Available at: https://doi.org/10.1099/ijs.0.058701-0.

Lee, L.H., Zainal, N., Azman, A.S., et al., 2014b. Streptomyces pluripotens sp. nov., A bacteriocin-producing streptomycete that inhibits meticillin-resistant Staphylococcus aureus. Int. J. Syst. Evol. Microbiol. 64, 3297–3306. Available at: https://doi.org/10.1099/ijs.0.065045-0.

Liu, M., Siezen, R.J., Nauta, A., 2009. *In silico* prediction of horizontal gene transfer events in Lactobacillus bulgaricus and Streptococcus thermophilus reveals protocooperation in yogurt manufacturing. Appl. Environ. Microbiol. 75, 4120–4129. Available at: https://doi.org/10.1128/AEM.02898-08.

McElroy, K., Thomas, T., Luciani, F., 2014. Deep sequencing of evolving pathogen populations: Applications, errors, and bioinformatic solutions. Microb. Inform. Exp. 4, 1. Available at: https://doi.org/10.1186/2042-5783-4-1.

Medini, D., Donati, C., Tettelin, H., Masignani, V., Rappuoli, R., 2005. The microbial pan-genome. Curr. Opin. Genet. Dev. 15, 589–594. Available at: https://doi.org/10.1016/j.gde.2005.09.006.

Mohd-Padil, H., Damiri, N., Sulaiman, S., *et al.*, 2017. Identification of sRNA mediated responses to nutrient depletion in *Burkholderia pseudomallei*. Sci. Rep. 7, 17173. Available at: https://doi.org/10.1038/s41598-017-17356-4.

Nasaringarao, P., Häggblom, M.M., 2007. *Pelobacter seleniigenes* sp. nov., a selenaterespiring bacterium. Int. J. Syst. Evol. Microbiol. 57, 1937–1942. Available at: https://doi.org/10.1099/ijs.0.64980-0.

Niharika, N., Moskalikova, H., Kaur, J., *et al.*, 2013. *Novosphingobium barchaimii* sp. nov., isolated from hexachlorocyclohexane-contaminated soil. Int. J. Syst. Evol. Microbiol. 63, 667–672. Available at: https://doi.org/10.1099/ijs.0.039826-0.

Noor, Y.M., Samsulrizal, N.H., Jema'on, N.A., *et al.*, 2014. A comparative genomic analysis of the alkalitolerant soil bacterium Bacillus lehensis G1. Gene 545, 253–261. Available at: https://doi.org/10.1016/j.gene.2014.05.012.

Odenbreit, S., Haas, R., 2002. Helicobacter pylori: impact of gene transfer and the role of the cag pathogenicity island for host adaptation and virulence. Current topics in microbiology and immunology 264, 1–22.

Ooi, W.F., Ong, C., Nandi, T., *et al.*, 2013. The condition-dependent transcriptional landscape of Burkholderia pseudomallei. PLOS Genet. 9. Available at: https://doi.org/10.1371/journal.pgen.1003795.

Pankratov, T.A., Dedysh, S.N., 2010. *Granulicella paludicola* gen. nov., sp. nov., *Granulicella pectinivorans* sp. nov., *Granulicella aggregans* sp. nov. and *Granulicella rosea* sp. nov., acidophilic, polymer-degrading acidobacteria from Sphagnum peat bogs. Int. J. Syst. Evol. Microbiol. 60, 2951–2959. Available at: https://doi.org/10.1099/ijs.0.021824-0.

Popa, O., Dagan, T., 2011. Trends and barriers to lateral gene transfer in prokaryotes. Curr. Opin. Microbiol. 14 (5), 615–623. Available at: https://doi.org/10.1016/j.mib.2011.07.027.

Pukatzki, S., Ma, A.T., Sturtevant, D., *et al.*, 2006. Identification of a conserved bacterial protein secretion system in Vibrio cholerae using the *Dictyostelium* host model system. Proc. Natl. Acad. Sci. USA 103, 1528–1533. Available at: https://doi.org/10.1073/pnas.0510322103.

Rancurel, C., Legrand, L., Danchin, E.G.J., 2017. Alienness: Rapid detection of candidate horizontal gene transfers across the tree of life. Genes (Basel) 8, E248.

Rankin, D.J., Rocha, E.P.C., Brown, S.P., 2011. What traits are carried on mobile genetic elements, and why? Heredity (Edinb) 106 (1), 1–10. Available at: https://doi.org/10.1038/hdy.2010.24.

Ravenhall, M., Skunca, N., Lassalle, F., Dessimoz, C., 2015. Inferring horizontal gene transfer. PLOS Comput. Biol. 11, e1004095. Available at: https://doi.org/10.1371/journal.pcbi.1004095.

Rice, P., Longden, I., Bleasby, A., 2000. EMBOSS: The European Molecular Biology Open Software Suite. Trends Genet. 16, 276–277.

Richardson, A.O., Palmer, J.D., 2007. Horizontal gene transfer in plants. J. Exp. Bot. 58, 1–9. Available at: https://doi.org/10.1093/jxb/erl148.

Sanchez-Puerta, M.V., 2014. Involvement of plastid, mitochondrial and nuclear genomes in plant-to-plant horizontal gene transfer. Acta Soc. Bot. Pol. 83, 317–323. Available at: https://doi.org/10.5586/asbp.2014.041.

Semsey, S., Blaha, B., Köles, K., Orosz, L., Papp, P.P., 2002. Site-specific integrative elements of rhizobiophage 16-3 can integrate into proline tRNA (CGG) genes in different bacterial genera. J. Bacteriol. 184, 177–182. Available at: https://doi.org/10.1128/JB.184.1.177-182.2002.

Sieber, K.B., Bromley, R.E., Hotopp, J.C.D., 2017. Lateral gene transfer between prokaryotes and eukaryotes. Exp. Cell Res. 358, 421–426. Available at: https://doi.org/10.1016/j.yexcr.2017.02.009.

Siguier, P., Perochon, J., Lestrade, L., Mahillon, J., Chandler, M., 2006. ISfinder: The reference centre for bacterial insertion sequences. Nucleic Acids Res. 34 (Database Issue), D32–D36. Available at: https://doi.org/10.1093/nar/gkj014.

Soares, S.C., Geyik, H., Ramos, R.T.J., *et al.*, 2016. GIPSy: Genomic island prediction software. J. Biotechnol. 232, 2–11. Available at: https://doi.org/10.1016/j.jbiotec.2015.09.008.

Takeuchi, N., Kaneko, K., Koonin, E.V., 2014. Horizontal gene transfer can rescue prokaryotes from Muller's Ratchet: Benefit of DNA from dead cells and population subdivision. G3 GenesIGenomesIGenetics 4 (2), 325–339. Available at: https://doi.org/10.1534/g3.113.009845.

Tettelin, H., Masignani, V., Cieslewicz, M.J., *et al.*, 2005. Genome analysis of multiple pathogenic isolates of *Streptococcus agalactiae*: Implications for the microbial "pan-genome". Proc. Natl. Acad. Sci. USA 102, 13950–13955. Available at: https://doi.org/10.1073/pnas.0506758102.

Than, C., Ruths, D., Innan, H., Nakhleh, L., 2007. Confounding factors in HGT detection: Statistical error, coalescent effects, and multiple solutions. J. Comput. Biol. 14, 517–535. Available at: https://doi.org/10.1089/cmb.2007.A010.

Tuller, T., 2011. Codon bias, tRNA pools and horizontal gene transfer. Mob. Genet. Elements 1, 75–77. Available at: https://doi.org/10.4161/mge.1.1.15400.

Tumapa, S., Holden, M.T.G., Vesaratchavest, M., *et al.*, 2008. *Burkholderia pseudomallei* genome plasticity associated with genomic island variation. BMC Genom. 9, 190. Available at: https://doi.org/10.1186/1471-2164-9-190.

Waack, S., Keller, O., Asper, R., *et al.*, 2006. Score-based prediction of genomic islands in prokaryotic genomes using hidden Markov models. BMC Bioinform. 7, 142. Available at: https://doi.org/10.1186/1471-2105-7-142.

Wang, Y., Coleman-Derr, D., Chen, G., Gu, Y.Q., 2015. OrthoVenn: A web server for genome wide comparison and annotation of orthologous clusters across multiple species. Nucleic Acids Res. 43, W78–W84. Available at: https://doi.org/10.1093/nar/gkv487.

Wei, W., Gao, F., Du, M.-Z., *et al.*, 2017. Zisland Explorer: Detect genomic islands by combining homogeneity and heterogeneity properties. Brief. Bioinform. 18, 357–366. Available at: https://doi.org/10.1093/bib/bbw019.

Wilkins, T.D., Fulghum, R.S., Wilkins, J.H., 1974. *Eubacterium plexicaudatum* sp. nov., an anaerobic bacterium with a subpolar tuft of flagella, isolated from a mouse cecum. Int. J. Syst. Bacteriol. 24, 408–411. Available at: https://doi.org/10.1099/00207713-24-4-408.

Xi, Z., Bradley, R.K., Wurdack, K.J., *et al.*, 2012. Horizontal transfer of expressed genes in a parasitic flowering plant. BMC Genom. 13, 227. Available at: https://doi.org/10.1186/1471-2164-13-227.

Xi, Z., Wang, Y., Bradley, R.K., *et al.*, 2013. Massive mitochondrial gene transfer in a parasitic flowering plant clade. PLOS Genet. 9, e1003265. Available at: https://doi.org/10.1371/journal.pgen.1003265.

Xiao, J., Zhang, Z., Wu, J., Yu, J., 2015. A brief review of software tools for pangenomics. Genom. Proteom. Bioinform. 13, 73–76. Available at: https://doi.org/https://doi.org/10.1016/j.gpb.2015.01.007.

Yang, Z., Zhang, Y., Wafula, E.K., *et al.*, 2016. Horizontal gene transfer is more frequent with increased heterotrophy and contributes to parasite adaptation. Proc. Natl. Acad. Sci. USA 113, E7010–E7019. Available at: https://doi.org/10.1073/pnas.1608765113.

Yoshida, S., Maruyama, S., Nozaki, H., Shirasu, K., 2010. Horizontal gene transfer by the parasitic plant *Striga hermonthica*. Science 328, 1128 LP–1121128. (80-.).

Yue, J., Hu, X., Sun, H., Yang, Y., Huang, J., 2012. Widespread impact of horizontal gene transfer on plant colonization of land. Nat. Commun. 3, 1152.

Zhang, Y., Fernandez-Aparicio, M., Wafula, E.K., *et al.*, 2013. Evolution of a horizontally acquired legume gene, albumin 1, in the parasitic plant *Phelipanche aegyptiaca* and related species. BMC Evol. Biol. 13, 48. Available at: https://doi.org/10.1186/1471-2148-13-48.

Zhang, X., Liu, X., Liang, Y., *et al.*, 2017. Adaptive evolution of extreme acidophile *Sulfobacillus thermosulfidooxidans* potentially driven by horizontal gene transfer and gene loss. Appl. Environ. Microbiol. 83. Available at: https://doi.org/10.1128/AEM.03098-16.

Zhang, D., Qi, J., Yue, J., et al., 2014. Root parasitic plant *Orobanche aegyptiaca* and shoot parasitic plant *Cuscuta australis* obtained Brassicaceae-specific strictosidine synthase-like genes by horizontal gene transfer. BMC Plant Biol. 14, 19. Available at: https://doi.org/10.1186/1471-2229-14-19.

Zhao, Y., Wu, J., Yang, J., et al., 2012. PGAP: Pan-genomes analysis pipeline. Bioinformatics 28, 416–418. Available at: https://doi.org/10.1093/bioinformatics/btr655.

Zhao, Y., Jia, X., Yang, J., et al., 2014. PanGP: A tool for quickly analyzing bacterial pan-genome profile. Bioinformatics 30, 1297–1299. Available at: https://doi.org/10.1093/bioinformatics/btu017.

Zhaxybayeva, O., 2009. Detection and quantitative assessment of horizontal gene transfer. In: Gogarten, M.B., Gogarten, J.P., Olendzenski, L.C. (Eds.), Horizontal Gene Transfer: Genomes in Flux. Totowa, NJ: Humana Press, pp. 195–213. Available at: https://doi.org/10.1007/978-1-60327-853-9_11.

Zhaxybayeva, O., Doolittle, W.F., 2011. Lateral gene transfer. Curr. Biol. 21, R242–R246. Available at: https://doi.org/https://doi.org/10.1016/j.cub.2011.01.045.

Zhu, Q., Kosoy, M., Dittmar, K., 2014. HGTector: An automated method facilitating genome-wide discovery of putative horizontal gene transfers. BMC Genom. 15, 717. Available at: https://doi.org/10.1186/1471-2164-15-717.

Relevant Websites

http://eggnog-mapper.embl.de
  EggNOG.
http://www.bioinfogenome.net/OrthoVenn/
  OrthoVenn.

Gene Duplication and Speciation

Tiratha R Singh and Ankush Bansal, Jaypee University of Information Technology, Solan, India

Background

Significant progress has been made in the past few decades in understanding Darwin's theory of the origin of species. Different genomic methods have helped to understand the genetic variations and gene flow that makes new species (Magadum *et al.*, 2013; Shapiro *et al.*, 2016). Although new methods have not changed the previous speculations about how species formed, they have quickened the pace of information gathering (Reams and Roth, 2015). Compiling studies on hereditary investigations would be useful to answer queries of the upcoming generations on the relative occurrence and significance of various procedures that occur during speciation (Liu *et al.*, 2016).

Many 20th century biologists viewed genes as traits of species, exquisitely tuned to current utility. This resulted in the assumption that each species should possess different genes. Gene duplication was recognized, but was implicitly assumed to have occurred recently (Rose and Oakley, 2007). Many biologists now assume that most genes have their origins in gene duplication events, which happen throughout evolutionary history. As a result, many genes form families that have persisted for hundreds of millions of years.

Gene duplication events and results of such events play a crucial role in determination of the function of novel genes. There have been various models and theories that have emerged to support the concept of gene copies (Liu *et al.*, 2016; Singh *et al.*, 2009). However, a clear picture of gene duplication events is still not clear and needs more information to come to any conclusion. Different prediction software and tools based models such as hidden Markov models give insight to evolutionary functional properties and dynamics (Singh and Pardasani, 2009). Hence, understanding the gene duplication events and speciation is an essential step towards understanding and identifying the major mechanisms that are involved in the evolution (Seehausen *et al.*, 2014).

Gene Duplication

The evolutionary understanding of gene duplication events was first performed by Haldane and John (1932), who suggested that a redundant duplicate(s) of a gene may acquire divergent mutations and eventually emerge as a new gene. A gene duplication event was first noted by Bridges (1936) in the Bar locus in *Drosophila*. A substantial increase in the number of copies of a DNA segment can be brought by various types of gene duplication (White, 1977; Raj Singh, 2008). There are various studies where gene duplication and deletion events are being systematically observed (Ma *et al.*, 2014; Schacherer *et al.*, 2004; Simillion *et al.*, 2002; Stephens, 1951). Many types of duplications are recognized: First, partial gene duplication; second, complete gene duplication; third, partial chromosomal duplication; fourth, complete chromosomal duplication; fifth, genome duplication (Innan and Kondrashov, 2010; Conant and Wolfe, 2008; Panchy *et al.*, 2016). The first four are treated as regional duplicates as they do not alter the haploid set of chromosomes. The main reason for gene duplication includes uneven crossing over (Iñiguez and Hernández, 2017; Levasseur and Pontarotti, 2011; Qian and Zhang, 2014). Uneven crossing over in two nonaligned sequences gives a duplicated region on one chromosome along with deletion on second on the basis of the size of the nonaligned region. DNA sequence duplication in tandem results in a progressive increase in uneven crossing over, which ultimately increases the number of duplicate copies (Mendivil Ramos and Ferrier, 2012).

Partial Gene Duplication

Tandem duplication events in DNA sequences may provide information about genetic evolution events in terms of the complete gene while tandem duplication in a small region, or maybe in part of gene, ultimately results in mutations and is the cause of various diseases (Hu and Worton, 1992; Hu *et al.*, 1988). The duplication arrangement can be understood by taking the inference from molecular information lying in the sequence (Toll-Riera *et al.*, 2011). For instance, structure level changes induced by changes in nucleotide and amino acid sequence level influences the protein evolution. Toll-Riera *et al.* (2011) have demonstrated this by considering a large dataset of human and mouse orthologs protein and later mapping with PDB structures. Evidence from literature suggests that duplication may arise from either homologous (Alu-Alu) recombination or nonhomologous recombination, the latter possibly mediated by topoisomerases. For the dystrophin gene, in which most duplications have been identified, these recombination events are intrachromosomal, which suggests that unequal sister chromatid exchange is the major mechanism (Toll-Riera *et al.*, 2011).

Domain Duplication and Gene Elongation

A domain is a well-defined region within a protein that either performs a specific function within a protein, such as substrate binding, or constitutes a stable, independently folding, compact structural unit within the protein that can be distinguished from all the other parts" (Li and Makova, 2001). Theoretically, several possible relationships may be envisioned between the structural domains and the arrangements of the exons in the gene, e.g., in many globular proteins, a more or less exact correspondence exists between exons of gene and the structural domains of the protein product. Alternate splicing is one of the main reasons for exon shuffling in a duplication event as there are always chances for repetition of a similar exon set again. In a considerable number of cases, several adjacent models were found to be encoded by the same exon (Li and Makova, 2001).

The vertebrate hemoglobin α and β chains, consist of four domains, whereas their genes consist of only three exons, the second of which encodes two adjacent domains. In *Caenorhabditis elegans*, a globin-encoding gene, during the evolution of a globin gene family from a four exon ancestral gene, several lineages lost some or all of their three introns, thereby, generating panoply of exon–intron permutations (Vogel *et al.*, 2005). In the majority of cases, a domain duplication at the protein level indicates that an exon duplication has occurred at the DNA level. Moreover, many proteins of present day organisms show internal repeats often correspond to functional or structural domains within the proteins. A survey of modern genes in eukaryotes shows that the internal duplications have occurred frequently in evolution. This gene duplication is one of the most important steps in the evolution of complex genes from the simple ones (Vogel *et al.*, 2005).

Theoretically, elongation of genes can also occur by other means; for example, a mutation change converting a stop codon into a sense codon can also elongate the gene, which could be a part of recoding event (Singh and Pardasani, 2009). Similarly, either insertion of a foreign DNA segment into an exon or the occurrence of a mutation obliterating a splicing site will achieve same result. These types of molecular changes most probably disrupt the function of the elongated gene. In the vast majority of cases, such molecular changes have been found to be associated with pathological manifestations. By contrast, duplication of a structural domain is less likely to be problematic. Indeed, such a duplication can sometimes even enhance the function of the protein produced for example by increasing the number of active sites (a quantitative change), thus enabling the gene to perform its function more rapidly and efficiently or by having a synergistic effect yielding a new function (a qualitative change) (Nacher *et al.*, 2010).

Emergence of novel function can be derived from partial gene as divergence in the sequence may lead to different functions. Complete gene duplication produces two identical paralogous copies (Nacher *et al.*, 2010). Duplicated genes can be divided into two types – Variant and invariant repeats. Invariant repeats are identical or nearly identical in sequence to one another. Variant repeats are copies of a gene that, although similar to each other, differ in their sequences to a lesser or greater extent. All the genes that belong to a certain group of repeated sequences in a genome are referred to as a gene or a multigene family. Functional and nonfunctional members of a gene family may reside in close proximity to one another on the same chromosome or they may be located on different chromosomes. A member of a gene family that is located alone at a different genomic location than the other members of the family is called an orphan. The term *superfamily* was coined by Dayhoff in order to distinguish closely related proteins from distantly related ones (Dayhoff and Schwartz, 1978). Proteins that exhibit at least 50% similarity to each other at the amino acid level are considered as members of a superfamily, for example, α and β globins are classified into two separate families and together with myoglobin they form the globin superfamily (Li and Makova, 2001). An important feature associated with gene duplication is that as long as two or more copies of a gene exist in proximity to each other, the process of gene duplication can be greatly accelerated in this region, and numerous copies may be produced. There may be two reasons for the general positive correlation between genome size and number of copies of RNA specifying genes. Either a large genome requires large quantities of RNA, or the number of RNA-specifying genes is simply a passive consequence of genome enlargement by duplication. Highly repetitive genes, like rRNA genes, are generally very similar to each other (Li and Makova, 2001).

One factor responsible for homogeneity may be purifying selection. In addition to invariant repeats, the genomes of higher organisms contain numerous multigene families whose members have diverged to various extents such as genes coding for isozymes, such as lactate dehydrogenase, aldolase, creatine kinase, carbonic anhydrase, and pyruvate kinase. Isozymes are enzymes that catalyze the same biochemical reaction but may differ from one another in tissue specificity, developmental regulation, electrophoretic mobility, or biochemical properties. Isozymes are encoded by different loci, usually duplicated genes, as opposed to allozymes, which are distinct forms of the same enzyme encoded by different alleles at a single locus (Li and Makova, 2001; Vogel *et al.*, 2005).

Exon Shuffling

There are three types of exon shuffling: (1) Exon duplication, (2) exon insertion, and (3) exon deletion. Exon duplication refers to the duplication of one or more exons in a gene and so is a type of internal duplication (Patthy, 1999). Exon insertion is the process by which structural or functional domains are exchanged between proteins or inserted into a protein. Exon deletion results in the removal of a segment of amino acids from the protein. All types of shuffling have occurred in the evolutionary process of creating new genes (Kolkman and Stemmer, 2001; Patthy, 1999). Exon shuffling could be represented through various phases as shown in **Fig. 1**.

Mosaic or Chimeric Proteins

A mosaic or chimeric protein is a protein encoded by a gene that contains regions that are also found in other genes (Nicolson, 2015; Singer and Nicolson, 1972). The existence of such proteins indicates that exon shuffling has occurred during the evolutionary history of their genes. The first described mosaic protein was tissue plasminogen activator (Iñiguez and Hernández, 2017). For an exon to be inserted, deleted, or duplicated without causing a frameshift in the reading frame, certain phase limitations of the exonic structure of the gene must be respected. Mosaic proteins can be made when two adjacent genes are transcribed together and are therefore made into the same protein.

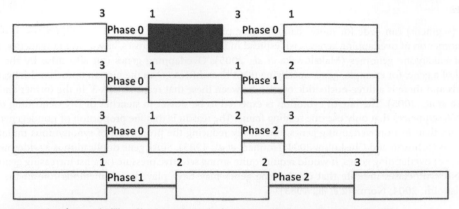

Fig. 1 Schematic representationof exon shuffling. Numbers above the box represents the position of nucleotide.

To understand this, we need to consider introns in terms of their possible positions relative to the coding regions (Nicolson, 2014). Introns residing between coding regions are classified into three types according to the way in which the coding region is interrupted (Jeon, 2004). An intron is of phase 0 if it lies between two codons, of phase 1 if it lies between the first and second nucleotide of a codon, and of phase 2 if it lies between the second and third nucleotides of a codon. Exons are grouped into classes according to the phases of their flanking introns. Here are four middle exons, said to be (0–0), (0–1), (0–2), and (1–2) exons. An exon that is flanked by introns of the same phase at both ends is called a symmetrical exon, otherwise it is asymmetrical. The first exon (middle) is a symmetrical exon, represented by black box. The length of a symmetrical exon is always a multiple of three nucleotides. Only symmetrical exons can be duplicated in tandem or deleted without affecting the reading frame.

Duplication or deletion of asymmetrical exons would disrupt the reading frame downstream. Similarly, only symmetrical exons can be inserted into introns, but with the restriction of, a 0–0 exon can only be inserted in phase-0-introns, a 1–1 exon is inserted into phase 1 introns, and 2–2 exons into phase-2 introns for avoiding frameshifts. All the exons coding for the modules of mosaic proteins are symmetrical. Since nonrandom intron phase usage is a necessary consequence of exon duplication or insertion, this property may be used as a diagnostic feature of gene assembly through exon shuffling. In terms of splicing, introns are classified into two categories, self-splicing and spliceosomal (Wang *et al.*, 2013). The vast majority of introns in eukaryotic nuclear genes are spliceosomal. Self-splicing introns play a vital role in their own removal, some regions of the introns are involved in self-complimentary interactions important for forming the 3-D structure possessing splicing activity. Exon shuffling probably did not play a role in the formation of genes in the early stages of evolution. Exon shuffling came to full bloom with the evolution of spliceosomal introns, which do not play a role in their self excision. These introns contain mainly nonessential parts and therefore could accommodate quantities of "foreign" DNA (Wang *et al.*, 2013).

Exonization and Pseudoexonization

Exonization is the process through which an intronic sequence becomes an exon. An exon created by exonization must abide by the same rules of exon insertion (Schmitz and Brosius, 2011). The opposite process is called pseudoexonization. It occurs when nonfunctionalization affects a single exon rather than the entire gene. The result is the creation of a pseudoexon, and the most obvious consequence of such a process is gene abridgement (as opposed to gene elongation). Pseudoexons are often created by the nonfunctionalization of internal gene duplications, for example, the aggrecan gene in rat contains 18 repeated exons and one pseudoexon. Some complex biological functions that require several enzymes may be specified by genes encoding different combinations of protein modules. In some species we may find single-module proteins, while in others we may find different combinations of multimodular proteins, for example, genes in a multistep process in the synthesis of fatty acids from Acetyl Co-A require seven enzymatic activities and an acyl–carrier protein. In fungi, these activities are distributed between two nonidentical polypeptides encoded by two unlinked intronless genes, FAS1 and FAS2. FAS1 encodes two and FAS2 encodes five enzymatic activities. In most bacteria, however, these functions are carried on by discrete monofunctional proteins (Schweizer and Hofmann, 2004).

In animals, key functions associated with fatty acid metabolism are controlled with a single polypeptide chain called fatty acid synthase. The fatty acid synthase gene in fungi and mammals are most probably mosaic proteins that have assembled from single-domain proteins like the ones found in bacteria (Stower, 2013). The fact that arrangement of domains is different in fungi from that in mammals indicates not only that the two lineages evolved multimodularity independently, but also that different strategies may be employed in the assembly of genes encoding multimodular proteins.

Nested and Overlapping Genes and Their Association With Speciation

In addition to gene duplication and exon shuffling, many other mechanisms for producing new genes or polypeptides are available. Few such entities are overlapping genes, pseudogenes, and nested genes.

Overlapping Genes

A DNA fragment (segment) can code for more than one gene product by using different reading frames or different initiation codons. This phenomenon of overlapping genes is widespread in DNA and RNA viruses, as well as in organelles, and bacteria, also known in nuclear eukaryotic genomes (Makalowska et al., 2005). Overlapping genes can also arise by the use of the complementary strand of a gene; for example, genes specifying tRNA^{ILE} andtRNA^{GLN} in the human mitochondrial genome are located on different strands and there is a three-nucleotide overlap between these that reads 5'-CTA-3' in the former and 5'-TAG-3' in the latter (Makalowska et al., 2005). The rate of evolution is expected to be slower in stenches of DNA encoding overlapping genes than in similar DNA sequences that only use one reading frame. The reason is that the proportion of nondegenerate sites is higher in overlapping genes than in nonoverlapping genes, thus vastly reducing the proportion of synonymous mutations out of total number of mutations (Johnson and Chisholm, 2004; Normark et al., 1983). Since gene duplication is a widespread phenomenon for the maintenance of overlapping genes, it would require quite strong selective pressure (against increasing genome size). Studies on aminoacyl tRNA synthetases indicate that overlapping genes may have played a momentous role in the evolution of life (Johnson and Chisholm, 2004; Normark et al., 1983).

Alternate Splicing

Alternative splicing of a primary RNA transcript results in the production of different mRNAs from the same DNA segment, which in turn may be translated into different polypeptides (Baralle and Giudice, 2017). There are two types of exons: Constitutive, that is, exons that are included within all the mRNAs transcribed from a gene, and facultative,that is, exons that are sometimes spliced in and sometimes spliced out (Kornblihtt et al., 2013). There are different types of alternative splicing; the most trivial form is the intron retention (Lee and Rio, 2015). However, more commonly, intron retention results in the premature termination of translation due to frameshifts. Sometimes, alternative splicing involves the use of alternative internal donor or acceptor sites, that is, excisions of introns of different lengths with complementary variation in the size of neighboring exons. Such use of competing splice sites was found in several transcription units of adenoviruses, as well as in eukaryotic cells such as the transformer gene in *Drosophila melanogaster* (Lee and Rio, 2015). Some cases of alternative splicing involved the use of mutually exclusive exons, that is, two exons are never spliced out together, nor are both retained in the same mRNA for example, M1 and M2 from a single gene by mutually exclusive use of exons 9 and 10. A special case of mutual exclusivity is the cassette exon (Roy et al., 2013). A cassette is either spliced in or spliced out in the alternative mRNA molecules. Alternative splicing has often been used as a means of developmental regulation (Wang et al., 2015). A very intriguing situation is seen in several genes involved in the process of sex determination in *D. melanogaster*. At least three genes, doublesex (dsx), Sexlethal (sxl), and transformer (tra), are spliced differently in males and females (Wang et al., 2015). There is rich literature available on alternate splicing and its distribution in almost all available lineages.

Intron-Encoded Proteins and Nested Genes

An intron may sometimes contain an ORF that encodes a protein or part of a protein that is completely different in function from the one encoded by the flanking exons (Kumar, 2009). In many cases, intron-encoded protein genes are located within type-I self-splicing introns. From a mechanistic point of view, an intron-encoded protein gene that is transcribed from the same strand as the neighboring exons may be regarded as special instance of alternative splicing (Lee and Chang, 2013; Yu et al., 2005). When an intron-encoded protein gene is transcribed from the opposite strand of the other gene, it is referred to as a nested gene. A case of nested genes was found in *Drosophila*, where a pupal cuticle protein gene is encoded on the positive strand of an intron within the gene encoding the purine pathway enzyme glycinamide ribotide-transformylase (Kaer et al., 2011).

Functional Convergence

Function of a protein is frequently determined by only a few of its amino acids; a protein performing one function may sometimes arise from a gene encoding a protein performing a markedly different function. If the new function is performed in other species by proteins of unrelated structure and descent, functional convergence may occur. The myoglobin of abalone *Sulculus* consists of 377 amino acids, which are 2.5 times larger than myoglobins belonging to the globin superfamily (Suzuki et al., 1996). Functional convergence provides a robust parameter associated with the existence of a functional protein for a family or superfamily. This convergence is reflected in various levels of organisms at the family and superfamily level based upon rate of selection pressure.

RNA Editing

RNA editing is a molecular process by which protein-coding gene change its message. One of the most common types of RNA editing is C-to-U conversion. This conversion may occur partially or completely in some tissues but not in others, leading to differential gene expression. Occasionally, it can produce a new protein with a different function from the unedited transcript, foe example, apolipoprotein B gene, one of the lipid carriers in the blood (Cooper, 1999). There are two types – Apo B-100 and apo B-48. Despite differences in length, amino acid sequences of the gigantic protein apo B-100 (4536 amino acid) with that of apo B-48 (2152 amino acid), the result of alignment for the alignable part is 100% identity. It was found that apo B-48 is translated from a very long mRNA that is identical to that of apo B-100 with the execution of an in-frame stop codon resulting from the RNA editing of codon 2153 from CAA (Gln) to UAA (stop). Thus, by using RNA editing, two quite different proteins are produced from the same gene (Cooper, 1999). (**Figs. 2,3,4,5**).

Gene Sharing

Gene sharing means that a gene acquires and maintains a second function without divergent duplication and without loss of the primary function. Gene sharing may, however, require a change in the regulation system of tissue specificity or developmental timing (Cvekl and Zheng, 2009; Patthy, 2007). In literature, the term "multifunctional protein" is frequently used instead of "gene sharing." Gene sharing was first discovered in crystallins, which are the major water-soluble proteins in the

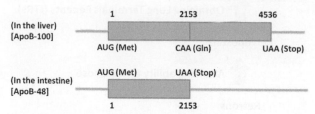

Fig. 2 Mechanism of RNA editing may leads to truncation.

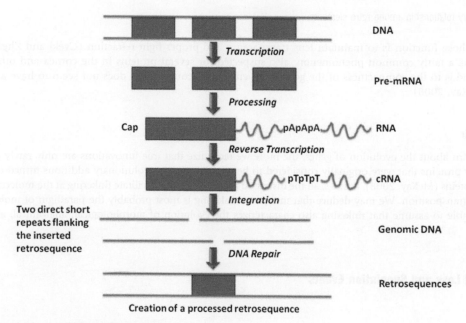

Fig. 3 Molecular mechanism explaining molecular repair.

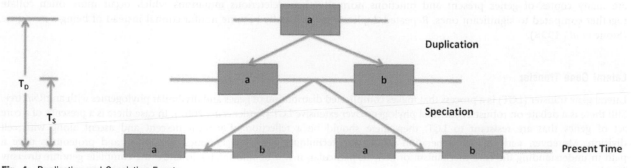

Fig. 4 Duplication and Speciation Events.

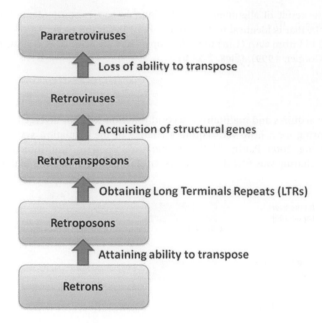

Possible evolutionary relationship among retroelements

Fig. 5 Evolutionary relationship among retro elements.

eye lens, and whose function is to maintain lens transparency and proper light refraction (Cvekl and Zheng, 2009). Gene sharing might be a fairly common phenomenon, also suspected for several proteins in the cornea and other tissues. Gene sharing clearly adds to the compactness of the genome, even though compactness does not seem to have a high priority in eukaryotes (McKay, 2008).

Molecular Repair

The more we learn about the evolution of genes, the more we recognize that true innovations are only rarely produced during evolution. Many proteins that were originally considered to be relatively recent evolutionary additions turned out to be derived from ancient proteins (McKay, 2008). Besides, all the discussed mechanisms that facilitate tinkering at the molecular level are gene conversion and transposition. We may deduce that molecular tinkering is most probably the paradigm of molecular evolution, and it is reasonable to assume that tinkering also characterizes the evolution of morphological, anatomical, and physiological traits as well.

Gene Gain and Loss and Speciation Events

Gene Loss

More than 7000 diseases and disorders were documented in research papers and literature sources, which state that mutations have a crucial role in destroying and gaining function at the gene level (McKusick, 2007). A number of such mutations either get deleted at a very fast rate from population or sustained at very low frequency due to genetic drift. If there are many copies of genes present and functions normally then deleterious mutations which occur more often collate together compared to significant ones. Repeated duplicate genes usually become nonfunctional instead of being a new gene (Stone *et al.*, 1998).

Lateral Gene Transfer

Lateral gene transfer (LGT) is a process that makes complicated distribution of genes and dissimilar phylogenies with an rRNA tree. Still there is a debate on robust organismal phylogeny over extensive LGT (Kettler *et al.*, 2007). In case there is a presence of a core set of genes that are resistant to LGT, then there should be a reflection of vertical descent and ascent along with cell division. Moreover, various next generation sequencing techniques like metagenomics, genomics, and proteomics pave a path in understanding the core mechanism of LGT. In particular, it will be informative to know the complete genome diversity (Kettler *et al.*, 2007).

Dating Gene Duplication and other Computations

Dating Gene Duplications

Two genes are said to be paralogous if they are derived from a duplication event, but orthologous if they are derived from a speciation event.

Here, genes a and b were derived from the duplication of an ancestral gene and are paralogous, while gene a from species 1 and gene a from species 2 are orthologous, as are genes b from species 1 and gene b from species 2 (Chen *et al.*, 2000). We can estimate the date of duplication, T_D, from sequence data if we know the rate of substitution in genes a and b. The rate of substitution can be estimated from the number of substitutions between the orthologous genes in conjunction with knowledge of the time of divergences T_S, between species 1 and 2. For gene a, let K_a be the number of substitutions per site between the two species. Then the rate of substitution in gene a, γ_a is estimated by:

$$\gamma a = \frac{Ka}{2TS} \tag{1}$$

The rate of substitution in gene b, γ_b can also be obtained in a similar way. The average substitution rate for the two genes:

$$\gamma = \frac{\gamma a + \gamma b}{2} \tag{2}$$

To estimate T_D, we need to know the number of substitutions per site between gene a and b (Kab). This number can be estimated from four pairwise comparisons: (1) Gene a from species 1 and gene b from species 2, (2) (Robinson-Rechavi *et al.*, 2004). Gene a from species 2 and gene b from species 1. (3) Gene a and gene b from species 1. (4) Gene a and b from species 2. From these four estimates, we can compute the average value for K ab from which we can estimate T_D as:

$$TD = \frac{Kab}{2\gamma} \tag{3}$$

In case of protein coding genes, by using the number of synonymous and nonsynonymous substitutions separately, we can obtain two independently estimates of T_D. The average of these two may be used as the final estimate of T_D. Sometimes problems are due to concerted T_D estimation. Another method for dating gene duplication events is to consider the phylogenetic distribution of genes in conjunction with paleontological data pertinent to the divergence date of the species in question (Zhou *et al.*, 2010).

Unprocessed Pseudogenes

The silencing of a gene due to deletion in a nucleotide and causing deleterious mutation ultimately results in production of pseudogene. Such pseudogenes do not undergo RNA processing. Unprocessed pseudogenes may be the result of derivation from nonfunctionality of a duplicate functional gene. There is much less chance that functional genes come into existence without duplication. Unprocessed pseudogenes may result in various diseases and disorders like frameshift mutation, nonmature stop codon, and misorientation of sliced transcripts or regulatory elements; therefore, it is easy to identify a change in sequence in terms of mutations resulting directly in gene silencing (Tutar, 2012). It is possible in some cases to identify the mutation responsible for nonfunctionalization of a gene through a phylogenetic analysis, for example, human pseudogene $\psi\eta$ in the b-globin family contains numerous defects, each of which could have been sufficient to silence it (Pink *et al.*, 2011). The b-globin clusters in chimpanzee and gorilla were found to contain the same number of genes and pseudogenes as in humans, indicating that the pseudogenes were created and silenced before these three species diverged from one another.

Interestingly, mutations that cause nonfunctionalization are only rarely missense mutations, most probably because such mutations result in the production of defective proteins that may be incorporated into final biological products and thus may have deleterious effects. Because unprocessed pseudogenes are usually created by duplication, they usually found in the neighborhood of the homologous functional genes from which they have been derived.

Unitary Pseudogenes

The pseudogene has no functional correlation with the human genome, called unitary pseudogene. Guinea pigs and humans suffer from scurvy unless they consume L-ascorbic acid in their diet, because they lack a protein called L-gulono-y-lactone oxidase, an enzyme that catalyzes the terminal step in L-ascorbic acid synthesis (Pink *et al.*, 2011). In humans, L-gulono-y-lactone oxidase is a pseudogene that contains molecular defects as the deletion of at least two exons (out of 12), deletions and insertion of nucleotides in the reading frame, and obliterations of intron–exon boundaries (Pink *et al.*, 2011). It has been assumed that the guinea pig and human ancestors managed to survive on a naturally ascorbic acid-rich diet; hence, the loss of this enzyme did not reflect a disadvantage.

Case Studies

There are several case studies where bioinformatics has been implemented successfully to connect molecular evolution events with their functional consequences. Genomics studies paved the path to understand variation at the genomic level through phylogenetic approaches (Pradhan *et al.*, 2017; Wang *et al.*, 2018). Further network reconstruction approaches using co-expression network modules also helps to trace the gene duplication events (Feng *et al.*, 2016; Malviya *et al.*, 2016). For instance, phylogenetic investigation of human FGFR-bearing paralogons favors piecemeal duplication theory of vertebrate genome evolution (Ajmal *et al.*, 2014). All given studies indicate that duplication and speciation events are very much diverse in nature and take many years to evolve and confirm to contribute to significant changes.

Tools and Methods

S.No.	Tool or method	Description	References
1.	Control-FREEC | CNV detection: HTS analysis	A tool for detection of copy-number changes and allelic imbalances (including LOH) using deep-sequencing data. Control-FREEC automatically computes, normalizes, segments copy number and beta allele frequency profiles, then calls copy number alterations and LOH. The control (matched normal) sample is optional. The program can also use mappability data (files created by GEM).	Boeva *et al.* (2012, 2011)
2.	mrCaNaVaR | micro-read Copy number variant regions	A copy number caller that analyzes the whole-genome next-generation sequence mapping read depth to discover large segmental duplications and deletions. mrCaNaVaR also has the capability of predicting absolute copy numbers of genomic intervals.	Alkan *et al.* (2009)
3.	forestSV | Structural variant detection: HTS analysis	Integrates prior knowledge about the characteristics of SVs. forestSV is a statistical learning approach, based on Random Forests, that leads to improved discovery in high throughput sequencing (HTS) data. This application offers high sensitivity and specificity coupled with the flexibility of a data-driven approach. It is particularly well suited to the detection of rare variants because it is not reliant on finding variant support in multiple individuals.	Michaelson and Sebat (2012)
4.	CTDGFinder | Duplication detection: HTS analysis	Formalizes and automates the identification of clusters of tandemly duplicated genes (CTDGs) by examining the physical distribution of individual members of families of duplicated genes across chromosomes. Application of CTDGFinder accurately identified CTDGs for many well-known gene clusters (e.g., Hox and beta-globin gene clusters) in the human, mouse, and 20 other mammalian genomes. Examination of human genes showing tissue-specific enhancement of their expression by CTDGFinder identified members of several well-known gene clusters (e.g., cytochrome P450s and olfactory receptors) and revealed that they were unequally distributed across tissues. By formalizing and automating CTDG identification, CTDGFinder will facilitate understanding of CTDG evolutionary dynamics, their functional implications, and how they are associated with phenotypic diversity.	Ortiz and Rokas (2017)
5.	cn.MOPS | Copy number estimation by a Mixture Of PoissonS	A data processing pipeline for copy number variations and aberrations (CNVs and CNAs) from next generation sequencing (NGS) data. The package supplies functions to convert BAM files into read count matrices or genomic ranges objects, which are the input objects for cn.MOPS. It models the depths of coverage across samples at each genomic position. Therefore, it does not suffer from read count biases along chromosomes. Using a Bayesian approach, cn.MOPS decomposes read variations across samples into integer copy numbers and noise by its mixture components and Poisson distributions, respectively.	Klambauer *et al.* (2012)
6.	RDXplorer | CNV detection: HTS analysis	A computational tool for copy number variants (CNV) detection in whole human genome sequence data using read depth (RD) coverage. CNV detection is based on the event-wise testing (EWT) algorithm. The read depth coverage is estimated in nonoverlapping intervals (100 bp Windows) across an individual genome based on the pileup generated by SAMTools.	Yoon *et al.* (2009)
7.	cnvHiTSeq | CNV detection: HTS analysis	A set of Java-based command-line tools for detecting copy number variants (CNVs) using next-generation sequencing data.	Bellos *et al.* (2012)

Source: *This data is referred from OMICSTOOLS resource. There are various other tools which may be referred at https://omictools.com/duplication-detection-category.

Conclusion

Gene duplication and speciation are two prominent mechanisms for finding clues for evolution. Phylogenetic analysis helps researchers to understand the ancestral association of species or sequence of their interest. Gene duplication events, exon shuffling, and speciation have a potent role in the process of evolution and to study convergence and divergence from ancestral data. This article provides descriptive information about basic concepts of phylogeny that may help students and researchers to become aware of terminologies used in gene duplication and speciation analysis. It is presented in a way where basic to advanced level information is being compiled on the diverse topics and it is estimated that this information will serve as comprehensive information to students, faculty members, and researchers working in this area. It reflects how bioinformatics can shape a computational pipeline for the analysis of biological data in an evolutionary scenario and will help the evolutionary biologists also to implement bioinformatics at some level for further exploration of basic principles.

See also: Genetics and Population Analysis. Inference of Horizontal Gene Transfer: Gaining Insights Into Evolution via Lateral Acquisition of Genetic Material. Natural Language Processing Approaches in Bioinformatics. Phylogenetic analysis: Early evolution of life. Sequence Analysis. Sequence Composition

---

References

Ajmal, W., Khan, H., Abbasi, A.A., 2014. Phylogenetic investigation of human FGFR-bearing paralogons favors piecemeal duplication theory of vertebrate genome evolution. Molecular Phylogenetics and Evolution 81, 49–60. Available at: https://doi.org/10.1016/j.ympev.2014.09.009.

Alkan, C., Kidd, J.M., Marques-Bonet, T., *et al.*, 2009. Personalized copy number and segmental duplication maps using next-generation sequencing. Nature Genetics 41, 1061–1067. Available at: https://doi.org/10.1038/ng.437.

Baralle, F.E., Giudice, J., 2017. Alternative splicing as a regulator of development and tissue identity. Nature Reviews Molecular Cell Biology 18, 437–451. Available at: https://doi.org/10.1038/nrm.2017.27.

Bellos, E., Johnson, M.R., M. Coin, L.J., 2012. cnvHiTSeq: Integrative models for high-resolution copy number variation detection and genotyping using population sequencing data. Genome Biology 13, R120. Available at: https://doi.org/10.1186/gb-2012-13-12-r120.

Boeva, V., Popova, T., Bleakley, K., *et al.*, 2012. Control-FREEC: A tool for assessing copy number and allelic content using next-generation sequencing data. Bioinformatics (Oxford, England) 28, 423–425. Available at: https://doi.org/10.1093/bioinformatics/btr670.

Boeva, V., Zinovyev, A., Bleakley, K., *et al.*, 2011. Control-free calling of copy number alterations in deep-sequencing data using GC-content normalization. Bioinformatics (Oxford, England) 27, 268–269. Available at: https://doi.org/10.1093/bioinformatics/btq635.

Bridges, C.B., 1936. The bar "gene" a duplication. Science 83, 210–211. Available at: https://doi.org/10.1126/science.83.2148.210.

Chen, K., Durand, D., Farach-Colton, M., 2000. NOTUNG: A program for dating gene duplications and optimizing gene family trees. Journal of Computational Biology 7, 429–447. https://doi.org/10.1089/106652700750050871.

Conant, G.C., Wolfe, K.H., 2008. Turning a hobby into a job: How duplicated genes find new functions. Nature Reviews Genetics 9, nrg2482. Available at: https://doi.org/10.1038/nrg2482.

Cooper, D.N., 1999. Human Gene Evolution. Elsevier.

Cvekl, A., Zheng, D., 2009. Gene sharing and evolution. Human Genomics 4, 66–67. Available at: https://doi.org/10.1186/1479-7364-4-1-66.

Dayhoff, M.O., Schwartz, R.M., 1978. Chapter 22: A model of evolutionary change in proteins, in: In Atlas of Protein Sequence and Structure.

Feng, K., Liu, F., Zou, J., *et al.*, 2016. Genome-wide identification, evolution, and co-expression network analysis of mitogen-activated protein kinase kinase kinases in *Brachypodium Distachyon*. Frontiers in Plant Science. 7, 1400. Available at: https://doi.org/10.3389/fpls.2016.01400.

Haldane, J.B.S., John, B.S., 1932. The Causes of Evolution. London: Longmans, Green.

Hu, X.Y., Burghes, A.H., Ray, P.N., *et al.*, 1988. Partial gene duplication in Duchenne and Becker muscular dystrophies. Journal of Medical Genetics 25, 369–376.

Hu, X., Worton, R.G., 1992. Partial gene duplication as a cause of human disease. Human Mutation 1, 3–12. Available at: https://doi.org/10.1002/humu.1380010103.

Iñiguez, L.P., Hernández, G., 2017. The evolutionary relationship between alternative splicing and gene duplication. Frontiers in Genetics 8.Available at: https://doi.org/10.3389/fgene.2017.00014.

Innan, H., Kondrashov, F., 2010. The evolution of gene duplications: Classifying and distinguishing between models. Nature Reviews Genetics 11, nrg2689. Available at: https://doi.org/10.1038/nrg2689.

Jeon, K.W., 2004. International Review of Cytology: A Survey of Cell Biology. Academic Press.

Johnson, Z.I., Chisholm, S.W., 2004. Properties of overlapping genes are conserved across microbial genomes. Genome Research 14, 2268–2272. Available at: https://doi.org/10.1101/gr.2433104.

Kaer, K., Branovets, J., Hallikma, A., Nigumann, P., Speek, M., 2011. Intronic L1 retrotransposons and nested genes cause transcriptional interference by inducing intron retention, exonization and cryptic polyadenylation. PLOS ONE 6, e26099. Available at: https://doi.org/10.1371/journal.pone.0026099.

Kettler, G.C., Martiny, A.C., Huang, K., *et al.*, 2007. Patterns and Implications of gene gain and loss in the evolution of prochlorococcus. PLOS Genetics 3, e231. Available at: https://doi.org/10.1371/journal.pgen.0030231.

Klambauer, G., Schwarzbauer, K., Mayr, A., *et al.*, 2012. cn.MOPS: Mixture of Poissons for discovering copy number variations in next-generation sequencing data with a low false discovery rate. Nucleic Acids Research 40, e69. Available at: https://doi.org/10.1093/nar/gks003.

Kolkman, J.A., Stemmer, W.P.C., 2001. Directed evolution of proteins by exon shuffling. Nature Biotechnology 19.Available at: https://doi.org/10.1038/88084.

Kornblihtt, A.R., Schor, I.E., Alló, M., *et al.*, 2013. Alternative splicing: A pivotal step between eukaryotic transcription and translation. Nature Reviews Molecular Cell Biology 14, 153–165. Available at: https://doi.org/10.1038/nrm3525.

Kumar, A., 2009. An overview of nested genes in Eukaryotic genomes. Eukaryotic Cell 8, 1321–1329. Available at: https://doi.org/10.1128/EC.00143-09.

Lee, Y.C.G., Chang, H.-H., 2013. The evolution and functional significance of nested gene structures in Drosophila melanogaster. Genome Biology and Evolution 5, 1978–1985. Available at: https://doi.org/10.1093/gbe/evt149.

Lee, Y., Rio, D.C., 2015. Mechanisms and regulation of alternative pre-mRNA splicing. Annual Review of Biochemistry 84, 291–323. Available at: https://doi.org/10.1146/annurev-biochem-060614-034316.

Levasseur, A., Pontarotti, P., 2011. The role of duplications in the evolution of genomes highlights the need for evolutionary-based approaches in comparative genomics. Biology Direct 6, 11. Available at: https://doi.org/10.1186/1745-6150-6-11.

Liu, Z., Tavares, R., Forsythe, E.S., *et al.*, 2016. Evolutionary interplay between sister cytochrome P450 genes shapes plasticity in plant metabolism. Nature Communications 7. Available at: https://doi.org/10.1038/ncomms13026.

Li, W.-H., Makova, K.D., 2001. Domain Duplication and Gene Elongation. ELS. John Wiley & Sons, Ltd. Available at: https://doi.org/10.1038/npg.els.0005097.

Malviya, N., Jaiswal, P., Yadav, D., 2016. Genome- wide characterization of Nuclear Factor Y (NF-Y) gene family of sorghum [Sorghum bicolor (L.) Moench]: a bioinformatics approach. Physiol. Mol. Biol. Plants 22, 33–49. Available at: https://doi.org/10.1007/s12298-016-0349-z.

Magadum, S., Banerjee, U., Murugan, P., Gangapur, D., Ravikesavan, R., 2013. Gene duplication as a major force in evolution. Journal of Genetics 92, 155–161.

Makalowska, I., Lin, C.-F., Makalowski, W., 2005. Overlapping genes in vertebrate genomes. Computational Biology and Chemistry 29, 1–12. Available at: https://doi.org/10.1016/j.compbiolchem.2004.12.006.

Ma, Q., Reeves, J.H., Liberles, D.A., et al., 2014. A phylogenetic model for understanding the effect of gene duplication on cancer progression. Nucleic Acids Research 42, 2870–2878. Available at: https://doi.org/10.1093/nar/gkt1320.

McKay, S.A.B., 2008. Gene sharing and evolution: The diversity of protein functions. By Joram Piatigorsky. The Quarterly Review of Biology 83, 99. Available at: https://doi.org/10.1086/586921.

McKusick, V.A., 2007. Mendelian inheritance in man and its online version, OMIM. American Journal of Human Genetics 80, 588–604.

Mendivil Ramos, O., Ferrier, D.E.K., 2012. Mechanisms of gene duplication and translocation and progress towards understanding their relative contributions to animal genome evolution [WWW Document]. International Journal of Evolutionary Biology. Available at: https://doi.org/10.1155/2012/846421.

Michaelson, J.J., Sebat, J., 2012. forestSV: Structural variant discovery through statistical learning. Nature Methods 9, 819–821. Available at: https://doi.org/10.1038/nmeth.2085.

Nacher, J.C., Hayashida, M., Akutsu, T., 2010. The role of internal duplication in the evolution of multi-domain proteins. Biosystems 101, 127–135. Available at: https://doi.org/10.1016/j.biosystems.2010.05.005.

Nicolson, G.L., 2015. Cell membrane fluid-mosaic structure and cancer metastasis. Cancer Research 75, 1169–1176. Available at: https://doi.org/10.1158/0008-5472.CAN-14-3216.

Nicolson, G.L., 2014. The Fluid – Mosaic Model of Membrane Structure: Still relevant to understanding the structure, function and dynamics of biological membranes after more than 40 years. Biochimica et Biophysica Acta (BBA) - Biomembranes 1838, 1451–1466. Available at: https://doi.org/10.1016/j.bbamem.2013.10.019.

Normark, S., Bergstrom, S., Edlund, T., et al., 1983. Overlapping Genes. Annual Review of Genetics 17, 499–525. Available at: https://doi.org/10.1146/annurev.ge.17.120183.002435.

Ortiz, J.F., Rokas, A., 2017. CTDGFinder: A novel homology-based algorithm for identifying closely spaced clusters of tandemly duplicated genes. Molecular Biology and Evolution 34, 215–229. Available at: https://doi.org/10.1093/molbev/msw227.

Panchy, N., Lehti-Shiu, M., Shiu, S.-H., 2016. Evolution of gene duplication in plants1[OPEN]. Plant Physiology 171, 2294–2316. Available at: https://doi.org/10.1104/pp.16.00523.

Patthy, L., 2007. A general theory of gene sharing. Nature Genetics 39, ng0607–ng0701. Available at: https://doi.org/10.1038/ng0607-701.

Patthy, L., 1999. Genome evolution and the evolution of exon-shuffling – A review. Gene 238, 103–114.

Pink, R.C., Wicks, K., Caley, D.P., et al., 2011. Pseudogenes: Pseudo-functional or key regulators in health and disease? RNA 17, 792–798. Available at: https://doi.org/10.1261/rna.2658311.

Pradhan, S., Kant, C., Verma, S., Bhatia, S., 2017. Genome-wide analysis of the CCCH zinc finger family identifies tissue specific and stress responsive candidates in chickpea (Cicer arietinum L.). PLOS ONE. 12. Available at: https://doi.org/10.1371/journal.pone.0180469.

Qian, W., Zhang, J., 2014. Genomic evidence for adaptation by gene duplication. Genome Research 24, 1356–1362. Available at: https://doi.org/10.1101/gr.172098.114.

Raj Singh, T., 2008. Mitochondrial gene rearrangements: New paradigm in the evolutionary biology and systematics. Bioinformation 3, 95–97.

Reams, A.B., Roth, J.R., 2015. Mechanisms of gene duplication and amplification. Cold Spring Harbor Perspectives in Biology. 7. Available at: https://doi.org/10.1101/cshperspect.a016592.

Robinson-Rechavi, M., Boussau, B., Laudet, V., 2004. Phylogenetic dating and characterization of gene duplications in vertebrates: The cartilaginous fish reference. Molecular Biology and Evolution 21, 580–586. Available at: https://doi.org/10.1093/molbev/msh046.

Rose, M.R., Oakley, T.H., 2007. The new biology: Beyond the modern synthesis. Biology Direct 2, 30. Available at: https://doi.org/10.1186/1745-6150-2-30.

Roy, B., Haupt, L.M., Griffiths, L.R., 2013. Review: Alternative Splicing (AS) of genes as an approach for generating protein complexity. Current Genomics 14, 182–194. Available at: https://doi.org/10.2174/1389202911314030004.

Schacherer, J., Tourrette, Y., Souciet, J.-L., Potier, S., de Montigny, J., 2004. Recovery of a function involving gene duplication by retroposition in saccharomyces cerevisiae. Genome Research 14, 1291–1297. Available at: https://doi.org/10.1101/gr.2363004.

Schmitz, J., Brosius, J., 2011. Exonization of transposed elements: A challenge and opportunity for evolution. Biochimie 93, 1928–1934. Available at: https://doi.org/10.1016/j.biochi.2011.07.014.

Schweizer, E., Hofmann, J., 2004. Microbial Type I Fatty Acid Synthases (FAS): Major players in a network of cellular FAS systems. Microbiology and Molecular Biology Reviews, 68. pp. 501–517. Available at: https://doi.org/10.1128/MMBR.68.3.501-517.2004.

Seehausen, O., Butlin, R.K., Keller, I., et al., 2014. Genomics and the origin of species. Nature Reviews Genetics 15, nrg3644. Available at: https://doi.org/10.1038/nrg3644.

Shapiro, B.J., Leducq, J.-B., Mallet, J., 2016. What is speciation? PLOS Genetics 12, e1005860. Available at: https://doi.org/10.1371/journal.pgen.1005860.

Simillion, C., Vandepoele, K., Montagu, M.C.E.V., Zabeau, M., Peer, Y.V. de, 2002. The hidden duplication past of Arabidopsis thaliana. Proceedings of the National Academy of Sciences 99, 13627–13632. Available at: https://doi.org/10.1073/pnas.212522399.

Singer, S.J., Nicolson, G.L., 1972. The fluid mosaic model of the structure of cell membranes. Science 175, 720–731.

Singh, T.R., Pardasani, K.R., 2009. Ambush hypothesis revisited: Evidences for phylogenetic trends. Computational Biology and Chemistry 33, 239–244. Available at: https://doi.org/10.1016/j.compbiolchem.2009.04.002.

Singh, T.R., Tsagkogeorga, G., Delsuc, F., et al., 2009. Tunicate mitogenomics and phylogenetics: Peculiarities of the Herdmania momus mitochondrial genome and support for the new chordate phylogeny. BMC Genomics 10, 534. Available at: https://doi.org/10.1186/1471-2164-10-534.

Stephens, S.G., 1951. Possible significance of duplication in evolution. In: Demerec, M. (Ed.), Advances in Genetics. Academic Press, pp. 247–265. Available at: https://doi.org/10.1016/S0065-2660(08)60237-0.

Stone, D.L., Agarwala, R., Schäffer, A.A., et al., 1998. Genetic and physical mapping of the McKusick-Kaufman syndrome. Human Molecular Genetics 7, 475–481. Available at: https://doi.org/10.1093/hmg/7.3.475.

Stower, H., 2013. Alternative splicing: Regulating Alu element "exonization". Nature Reviews Genetics 14, nrg3428. Available at: https://doi.org/10.1038/nrg3428.

Suzuki, T., Yuasa, H., Imai, K., 1996. Convergent evolution. The gene structure of Sulculus 41 kDa myoglobin is homologous with that of human indoleamine dioxygenase. Biochimica et Biophysica Acta 1308, 41–48.

Toll-Riera, M., Laurie, S., Radó-Trilla, N., Alba, M.M., 2011. Partial Gene Duplication and the Formation of Novel Genes. IntechOpen. Available at: https://doi.org/10.5772/21846.

Tutar, Y., 2012. Pseudogenes [WWW Document]. International Journal of Genomics 2012, 4. Available at: https://doi.org/10.1155/2012/424526.

Vogel, C., Teichmann, S.A., Pereira-Leal, J., 2005. The relationship between domain duplication and recombination. Journal of Molecular Biology 346, 355–365. Available at: https://doi.org/10.1016/j.jmb.2004.11.050.

Wang, Y., Liu, J., Huang, B., et al., 2015. Mechanism of alternative splicing and its regulation (Review). Biomedical Reports 3, 152–158.

Wang, T.-T., Si, F.-L., He, Z.-B., Chen, B., 2018. Genome-wide identification, characterization and classification of ionotropic glutamate receptor genes (iGluRs) in the malaria vector Anopheles sinensis (Diptera: Culicidae). Parasites & Vectors 11 (1), 34. Available at: https://doi.org/10.1186/s13071-017-2610-x.

Wang, X., Wheeler, D., Avery, A., et al., 2013. Function and evolution of DNA methylation in nasonia vitripennis. PLOS Genetics 9, e1003872. Available at: https://doi.org/10.1371/journal.pgen.1003872.

White, M.J.D., 1977. Animal Cytology and Evolution. CUP Archive.

Yoon, S., Xuan, Z., Makarov, V., Ye, K., Sebat, J., 2009. Sensitive and accurate detection of copy number variants using read depth of coverage. Genome Research 19, 1586–1592. Available at: https://doi.org/10.1101/gr.092981.109.

Yu, P., Ma, D., Xu, M., 2005. Nested genes in the human genome. Genomics 86, 414–422. Available at: https://doi.org/10.1016/j.ygeno.2005.06.008.

Zhou, X., Lin, Z., Ma, H., 2010. Phylogenetic detection of numerous gene duplications shared by animals, fungi and plants. Genome Biology 11, R38. Available at: https://doi.org/10.1186/gb-2010-11-4-r38.

Epidemiology: A Review

Vijayaraghava S Sundararajan, Ministry of Environmental Agency, Singapore; Bioclues.org, Hyderabad, India and Bioclues.org, Hyderabad, India

Introduction

Those living in the tropics and subtropical regions are at higher risk of dengue fever and dengue hemorrhagic fever and epidemics occur unexpectedly and can cause a great concern to the healthcare authorities. Climate, demography and ecology, urbanization are vital reasons in dengue transmission and epidemiology.

Dengue virus, an arbovirus that is transmitted by Aedes mosquitos in the tropics and subtropics of the world, causes an estimated 390 million infections per year, resulting in 96 million clinically symptomatic cases (Bhatt *et al.*, 2013a). DENV has four serotypes (DENV-1, DENV-2, DENV-3, and DENV-4) that each circulate worldwide. Spatial propagation of long-distance spread over large geographical distances is difficult to measure directly, but epidemiological coupling of locations revealed by synchrony in population-level disease patterns has been used successfully to infer mechanisms of spread (Grenfell *et al.*, 2001; Viboud *et al.*, 2006; Rohani *et al.*, 1999).

Dengue virus is transmitted mainly by Aedes aegypti and Aedes albopictus mosquitoes (Rosen *et al.*, 1983). World Health Organization has estimated that there are 50–100 million dengue infections per year (Rigau-Pérez *et al.*, 1998) and a recent study estimates that this figure to 390 million, of which ~96 million are symptomatic (Bhatt *et al.*, 2013b). Dengue infection in humans is mostly self-limiting although antiviral drugs are under development (Lim *et al.*, 2013; Rathore *et al.*, 2011). Some dengue cases may require hospital admission, and the more severe manifestations of dengue may lead to death (Murphy and Whitehead, 2011) and case fatality rates of dengue fever and severe dengue vary from 0%–5% to 3%–5% (Halstead, 1999).

DENV is a positive sense single stranded RNA virus of the genus *Flavivirus*, genome of approximately 11.8 kb encodes for a single polypeptide arranged in three structural (Capsid-pre-Membrane-Envelope) and seven non-structural (NS) proteins (NS1-NS2A-NS2B-NS3-NS4A-NS4B-NS5). The exposure to a particular serotype of DENV elicits type-specific life-long immunity (Simmons *et al.*, 2012) and display high mutation rates as a result of the error-prone RNA polymerase activity during genome replication (Steinhauer *et al.*, 1992). Genetic recombination further facilitates their opportunity for genetic novelty (Behura and Severson, 2013) and results in genetically diverse virus populations consisting of multiple genotypes of monophyletic nature. RNA virus populations often appear to exist as ensembles of mutant spectra that collectively behave as "quasi-species" (Domingo *et al.*, 2012) and serotype is composed of highly heterogeneous genotypes that demonstrates geographical-wide pattern spread (Holmes and Twiddy, 2003).

Dengue fever replaced malaria as the most important mosquito-borne disease in Singapore in the mid-1960s and attention is on vector source reduction through surveillance, enforcement, community engagement, careful urban planning and operational research. Aedes house index was successfully reduced to 50% in 1960s and further to a less than 5% by the late 1970s and dengue incidence reduced (Chan *et al.*, 1977; Goh, 1997, 1995; Chan *et al.*, 1971). However, dengue fever started to resurge in the country in 1980s, in a typical 5–6 year epidemic cycle and epidemics escalated within each cycle during the last decade even though house index was below 1% (Koh *et al.*, 2008; Lee *et al.*, 2010; Ler *et al.*, 2011). The geo-expansion of *A. aegypti* and resurgence is due to an increase in human population density, low herd immunity resulting from long periods of low transmission, local transportation that facilitates virus dissemination, virus importations and the (Ang *et al.*, 2015; Yew *et al.*, 2009; Goh and Yamazaki, 1987; Low *et al.*, 2015).

Research Studies

The entomological surveillance show caused an increase in both larval and adult *Aedes aegypti* (main source of vector transmission) population during the epidemic season. The ground conditions are conducive to sustain virus transmission on a longer period causing uncontrollable epidemic of dengue.

Region-Wide Synchrony and Traveling Waves of Dengue Across Eight Countries in Southeast Asia (Panhuis *et al.*, 2015)

The spatial and temporal dynamics of dengue transmission are poorly understood, limiting disease control efforts. A study with a large-scale dataset and analysed continental-scale patterns of dengue in Southeast Asia, travel pattern of dengue was studied and reported.

Dengue Transmission: Strong synchrony over the region for dengue cycles is reported. Statistically significant multiannual cycles changed over time, the highest in 1993–2004. In comparison, the average power of annual cycles was more constant over time but reduced in 1997–2001. The regional median for annual cycles was consistent over time, ranging between 0.50 and 0.64. The average synchrony decreased as the distance between province pairs increased up to ~1000 km. Synchrony of multiannual cycles peaked at 0.55 [95% confidence interval (95% CI)=0.45–0.67] compared with annual cycles.

Climate: The dengue cycles in 1997–2001 coincided with high temperatures across most latitude; but not with an anomaly in precipitation. High temperatures in these years were related to the strongest El Niño episode of the past century (Slingo and Annamalai, 2000; Webster and Palmer, 1997). We measured a strong wavelet coherency (>0.8) between multiannual dengue cycles and the Oceanic Niño Index (ONI) during 1993–2002 and during 2009–2010 for almost all provinces.

Travel Waves: Epidemic timings between provinces were measured and found, positive θ indicated that a province was timed earlier (leading ahead) vs. the other, and a negative θ indicated that a province was timed later (lagging behind). Provinces with outgoing traveling waves were located in west Thailand and the Bangkok area, central Laos (Savannakhét and Khammouan), and southern Philippines (Bohol).

Data and methods: Monthly dengue surveillance data and corresponding population (U.S. Census Bureau, 2014) and climate data (Fan and van den Dool, 2008; Becker *et al.*, 2013; Center for International Earth Science Information Network CIESIN, Columbia University, Centro Internacional de Agricultura Tropical (CIAT), 2005) at the provincial level (GADM, 2013) were available for 273 provinces in Thailand, Cambodia, Laos, Vietnam, Malaysia, Singapore, the Philippines, and Taiwan. Province names were standardized based on the administrative levels. Wavelet analysis which is well suited to characterize epidemiological time series is used isolate cycles with multiannual and annual periodicities. Synchrony between provinces was derived as the pairwise Pearson correlation coefficient with timing and amplitude of signals. Wavelet Coherency uses wave transforms of two time series to indicate their localized phase relationship in a time–frequency spectrum. Phase angles for annual and multiannual cycles as indicators of epidemic timing were computed. Traveling waves for a province is computed as a statistically significant positive linear association between θ and geographical distances between that province and the other provinces. Sensitivity analysis is conducted on the effect of the value for the wavelet parameters ω_0 and δj on synchrony.

The multi-country collaborative study improved insight that may lead to improved prediction of dengue transmission patterns and more effective disease surveillance and control efforts.

Three-Month Real-Time Dengue Forecast Models: An Early Warning System for Outbreak Alerts and Policy Decision Support in Singapore (Shi *et al.*, 2016)

Statistical models are built through machine learning methods in deriving potential recurrent infectious dengue outbreaks. In this study models are built with data that are available at the time of forecast, to forecast weeks or months, to get predictive performance, and be able to process new data rapidly. Weekly covariates were used to match the frequency of reported dengue data (Ministry of Health), time horizon used for all variables was January 2001 to December 2012.

Case data is downloaded as the weekly number of cases (natural log–transformed, $+1$) from Ministry of Health, Singapore. *Population data* (mid-year) is retrieved from Singapore Department of Statistics for residents and foreign non-residents (natural log–transformed). Weekly mean temperature (T) in degrees Celsius, maximum hourly temperature, number of hours of high temperature (>27.8°C) each week, and weekly relative humidity (RH) were obtained from *Meteorological* Services, Singapore. *Vector surveillance* weekly breeding percentage (BP) is an in-house index developed by NEA that provides an estimate of the proportion of *Ae. aegypti*, the primary vector of dengue in Singapore is calculated for the study. *Trend and seasonality data* with climatic factors (dengue is affected by other factors such as changes to vector control and circulating serotypes) and non-climatic factors (disease dynamics, dengue incidence into terms for trend and for annual seasonality) are derived.

The Least Absolute Shrinkage and Selection Operator (LASSO) is a technique that has inspired much interest in the statistical methodology community on "small n large p" problems (Tibshirani, 1996). This framework use logistic regression selecting parameters to be included in the model rather than optimizing the (log) likelihood $L(y|\beta, x)$ for dependent variable y, independent variables x and coefficients β, as in standard regression. Covariates were considered at lags of up to 20 weeks based on the findings (Hii *et al.*, 2012a,b), but in contrast to their approach, we allowed the effect of a single factor (such as temperature) to have multiple lags in influencing future dengue cases.

Result: 12-week forecasts including 95% prediction intervals for various time points over the period 2001–2002 are reported. Also the forecasts at various time points in Singapore's record-breaking 2013 epidemic, in which 22,170 cases were reported, are presented.

Epidemiology studies are challenging as local weather conditions within a region differs significantly. Integrating weather data into predictive models may not be always feasible as long term data not available.

Intra-Epidemic Evolutionary Dynamics of a Dengue Virus Type 1 Population Reveal Mutant Spectra That Correlate With Disease Transmission (Hapuarachchi *et al.*, 2016a)

Environmental Health Institute (EHI) received blood samples obtained from dengue suspected patients through an island wide network of hospitals and general practitioners during November 2012 to May 2014 for the DENV infection confirmed by SD Bioline Dengue Duo kit. All NS1 positive samples were subjected to serotyping. All consented DENV positive samples were used for genome sequencing as part of the existing virus surveillance programme.

Data: Virus strains were isolated from acute-phase sera (Koo *et al.*, 2013) and a maximum of three passages was done for each sample based on the original virus load. Viral RNA was extracted from sera using the QIAGEN viral RNA mini kit. The complementary DNA (cDNA) was synthesized using extracted RNA (Koo *et al.*, 2013). DENV serotypes were determined by using a real-time PCR assay (Koo *et al.*, 2013; Lai *et al.*, 2007). Whole genome and envelope (*E*) gene sequences were generated directly from patient sera, whereas whole genome sequencing was performed on strains isolated from respective patient sera. Raw nucleotide sequences were assembled using the Laser gene package. Contiguous sequences were aligned in Bio-Edit (Hall, 1999).

Methods: The whole-polyprotein based maximum clade credibility tree was constructed using the Bayesian Markov Chain Monte Carlo (MCMC) method implemented in the BEAST (Drummond *et al.*, 2012). Based on jModelTest (Darriba *et al.*, 2012), the general time reversible model with gamma distribution and invariant sites (GTR + G + I) were used together with an uncorrelated log-normal relaxed molecular clock model. The dataset included 38 whole polyprotein sequences generated in this study and 44 DENV-1 sequences retrieved from GenBank database. Of 83 whole genomes generated, only 38 sequences representative of each variant were included in the phylogenetic analyses to minimize overcrowding.

Protein Data Bank (PDB) structures 3J2P (Zhang *et al.*, 2013) which illustrates the M and E-protein heterotetramer, 2JLV (Luo *et al.*, 2008) which represents the NS3 protein (serine protease as well as RNA helicase and RTPase/NTPase) and 4C11 showing the NS5 protein were downloaded from the Research Collaborator for Structural Bioinformatics (RCSB) protein data bank and visualized using YASARA (Krieger *et al.*, 2002). Changes to protein stability were estimated using Fold-X (Schymkowitz *et al.*, 2005).

Statistical analysis: The correlation between the diversity of epidemic lineage and transmission intensity, are compared with the number of DENV-1 genotype III variants against the total number of DENV-1 cases and total number of reported cases on a monthly basis (November 2012 to May 2014). The strength of correlation was quantified using Pearson's correlation coefficient in 'R' package.

Results: DENV-1 genotype III strains of the epidemic lineage were first detected locally in November 2012. The genetic distinction of the epidemic lineage from the locally circulating DENV-1 strains indicated that its emergence in Singapore was likely to be due to an introduction. The resulting mutant diversity intensified during periods of high transmission, implying a relationship between the force of *in-situ* evolution and transmission intensity during the epidemic. Tracking genetic diversity through time is a useful tool to infer DENV transmission dynamics and to complement surveillance data in a risk assessment and cross-sectional surveys and longitudinal virus surveillance efforts with limited sample sizes tend to underestimate the true diversity of viral populations.

Epidemic Resurgence of Dengue Fever in Singapore in 2013–2014: A Virological and Entomological Perspective (Hapuarachchi *et al.*, 2016b)

Case burden of the dengue epidemic in 2013 and 2014 was unprecedented, recording 1.7 times more cases than those reported during the last DENV-1 epidemic during 2004–05. The epidemic is due to demographic, social, virological, entomological, immunological, climatic and ecological factors that contribute to DENV transmission.

Epidemic: The control of vector-borne dengue in Singapore is carried out by National Environmental Agency which manages the day-to-day vector control and Clinical management and surveillance is overseen by Ministry of Health (Ng and Vythilingum, 2011). NEA and MOH jointly perform the below activities to manage the epidemic crisis at Singapore:

1. Enhanced case surveillance measures to increase the diagnostic coverage at the very early phase of the epidemic. MOH initiates high clinical suspicion of dengue among febrile cases and existing network of general practitioners was encouraged to utilize a subsidized laboratory testing service provided by EHI, one of the public health laboratories under NEA, Singapore.

2. Projection of case numbers to facilitate stockpiling of diagnostic reagents in advance to tackle a sudden endemic of dengue. Statistical models are used on weekly case numbers (Shi *et al.*, 2016) arrangements were made to extend EHI diagnostic services during weekends and to stockpile diagnostic reagents several months ahead of the peak of the epidemic. The close communication between MOH and NEA on the weekly case projection also allowed hospitals to plan for increased demand on the healthcare system resulting from extra consultations and admissions.

3. Expansion of virus surveillance was extended to include samples from polyclinics, hospitals and private laboratories through a joint initiative between NEA and MOH. Even during non-epidemic periods, joint efforts are thrown to screen a small proportion of reported cases to have regular surveillances. Serotype analysis was achieved in 33% of reported cases and genotype coverage was doubled during 2013–14. Genetic fingerprinting of virus strains allowed monitoring of their spread between locations and facilitated targeted vector control in newly-introduced sites.

4. Early launch of the dengue campaign was a key success to promote community awareness on dengue. NEA launched "Do the Mozzie Wipe-out" drive at clustered housing estates b street banners and social media. A tri-colour coded banner (Green: no dengue; Yellow: cluster with less than 10 cases; Red: cluster with more than 10 cases) was introduced to make public to have an immediate knowledge on their sector. Dengue volunteers are trained to support community outreach through seminars, talks, roadshows and media.

5. Enhanced source reduction for mosquito breeding is achieved by increased premises inspections, entomological surveillance, enforcement activities, and daily checks on common ground areas, public areas and congregation areas for potential mosquito breeding spots. Chemical larviciding activities were carried out in housing estates, industrial premises and public places on a regular basis and whenever *Aedes* breeding was detected through inspections. The public was encouraged to use pellets containing *Bacillus thuringiensis* in places such as roof gutters. Fogging activities were conducted in major clusters during the peak periods of transmission to reduce adult *Aedes* population density especially when the intensity of transmission sustained

despite other source reduction efforts. Data on *Aedes* immatures collected through field inspections was used to gauge *Aedes* population density in a particular area.

6. Launch of gravitrap is a greater milestone in detecting and monitoring adult Aedes population and viral carriers in any area. The breeding data collected on a regular basis from sentinel locations and gravitrap and are matched with cluster locations.
7. Spatial risk map is drawn based on data pertaining to Aedes breeding, past dengue exposure, population density, and circulation virus strains and is used as a guide for resource allocation during epidemic.
8. Integrated vector management activities in Singapore are closely aligned with the whole-of-government's effort in establishing people, public and private (3P) partnership to develop innovative and sustainable initiatives to promote environmental ownership in the community. NEA leads an Inter-Agency Dengue Task Force (Koh *et al.*, 2008) comprising 27 stakeholders from the 3P sectors to coordinate nationwide dengue control efforts. The Inter-Agency Dengue Task Force assisted the epidemic control by ensuring the planning and implementation of operational activities of each agency to align with source reduction and vector control efforts carried out by NEA.

The integrated surveillance framework is supported by Improved operational response; Early warning of outbreaks based on virus surveillance; Understanding the distribution of vectors and their density fluctuations through entomological surveillance; Understanding the relationship between environmental parameters and outbreak risk.

Discussion

The spread and prevalence of dengue and dengue fever are better understood through region-wide synchrony, travelling waves, dengue forecast models, evolutionary studies, and epidemic resurgence.

In this short review, we have briefed studies that were conducted in and around Singapore. These countries (Thailand, Singapore, Malaysia) notice a huge human traffic cross bordering each and every day. The patterns from these studies caution authorities to monitor the spread across these countries in this region. An epidemiological study to understand the virus resurgence can't be successfully performed without inherent data from nearby countries and disease population data. A multi-level approach involving epidemiological, virological and entomological is required in a combined population across nations.

Acknowledgments

We thank Elsevier for giving an opportunity to write this article. We sincerely thank Dr Asif Khan for the invitation to write a book article.

> *See also*: Ecosystem Monitoring Through Predictive Modeling. Genetics and Population Analysis. Large Scale Ecological Modeling With Viruses: A Review. Mapping the Environmental Microbiome. Natural Language Processing Approaches in Bioinformatics. Sequence Analysis

References

Ang, L.W., Cutter, J., James, L., Goh, K.T., 2015. Sero-epidemiology of dengue virus infection in the adult population in tropical Singapore. Epidemiol. Infect. 143, 1585–1593.

Becker, A., *et al.*, 2013. A description of the global land-surface precipitation data products of the Global Precipitation Climatology Centre with sample applications including centennial (trend) analysis from 1901–present. Earth Syst. Sci. Data 5 (1), 71–99.

Behura, S.K., Severson, D.W., 2013. Nucleotide substitutions in dengue virus serotypes from Asian and American countries: Insights into intra codon recombination and purifying selection. BMC Microbiol. 13, 37.

Bhatt, S., *et al.*, 2013a. The global distribution and burden of dengue. Nature 496 (7446), 504–507.

Bhatt, S., Gething, P.W., Brady, O.J., *et al.*, 2013b. The global distribution and burden of dengue. Nature 496, 504–507.

Center for International Earth Science Information Network (CIESIN), Columbia University; Centro Internacional de Agricultura Tropical (CIAT), 2005. Gridded Population of the World Version 3 (GPWv3), NASA Socioeconomic Data and Applications Center (SEDAC), Palisades, NY.

Chan, K.L., Ng, S.K., Chew, L.M., 1977. The 1973 dengue haemorrhagic fever outbreak in Singapore and its control. Singap. Med. J. 18, 81–93.

Chan, Y.C., Ho, B.C., Chan, K.L., 1971. Aedes aegypti (L.) and Aedes albopictus (Skuse) in Singapore City. 5. Observations in relation to dengue haemorrhagic fever. Bull. World Health Organ. 44, 651–657.

Darriba, D., Taboada, G.L., Doallo, R., Posada, D., 2012. jModelTest 2: More models, new heuristics and parallel computing. Nat. Methods 9, 772.

Domingo, E., Sheldon, J., Perales, C., 2012. Viral quasi-species evolution. Microbiol. Mol. Biol. Rev. 76, 159–216.

Drummond, A.J., Suchard, M.A., Xie, D., Rambaut, A., 2012. Bayesian phylogenetics with BEAUti and the BEAST 1.7. Mol. Biol. Evol. 29, 1969–1973.

Fan, Y., van den Dool, H., 2008. A global monthly land surface air temperature analysis for 1948–present. J. Geophys. Res. 113 (D1), D01103.

GADM, 2013. Database of global administrative areas. gadm.org/home (accessed 21.07.15).

Goh, K.T., 1995. Changing epidemiology of dengue in Singapore. Lancet 346, 1098.

Goh, K.T., 1997. Dengue – A re-emerging infectious disease in Singapore. Ann. Acad. Med. Singap. 26, 664–670.

Goh, K.T., Yamazaki, S., 1987. Serological survey on dengue virus infection in Singapore. Trans. R. Soc. Trop. Med. Hyg. 81, 687–689.

Grenfell, B.T., Bjørnstad, O.N., Kappey, J., 2001. Travelling waves and spatial hierarchies in measles epidemics. Nature 414 (6865), 716–723.

Hall, T.A., 1999. BioEdit: A user-friendly biological sequence alignment editor and analysis program for Windows 95/98/NT. Nucleic Acid Symp. Ser. 41, 95–98.

Halstead, S.B., 1999. Is there an in apparent dengue explosion? Lancet 353, 1100–1101.

Hapuarachchi, H.C., Koo, C., Kek, R., *et al.*, 2016a. Intra-epidemic evolutionary dynamics of a Dengue virus type 1 population reveal mutant spectra that correlate with disease transmission. Sci. Rep. 6, 22592.

Hapuarachchi, H.C., Koo, C., Rajarethinam, J., *et al.*, 2016b. Epidemic resurgence of dengue fever in Singapore in 2013–2014: A virological and entomological perspective. BMC Infect. Dis. 16, 300.

Hii, Y.L., Rocklöv, J., Wall, S., *et al.*, 2012a. Optimal lead time for dengue forecast. PLOS Negl. Trop. Dis. 6, e1848.

Hii, Y.L., Zhu, H., Ng, N., Ng, L.C., Rocklöv, J., 2012b. Forecast of dengue incidence using temperature and rainfall. PLOS Negl. Trop. Dis. 6, e1908.

Holmes, E.C., Twiddy, S.S., 2003. The origin, emergence and evolutionary genetics of dengue virus. Infect. Genet. Evol. 3, 19–28.

Koh, B.K., Ng, L.C., Kita, Y., *et al.*, 2008. The 2005 dengue epidemic in Singapore: Epidemiology, prevention and control. Ann. Acad. Med. Singap. 37, 538–545.

Koo, C., *et al.*, 2013. Evolution and heterogeneity of multiple serotypes of Dengue virus in Pakistan, 2006-2011. Virol. J. 10, 275.

Krieger, E., Koraimann, G., Vriend, G., 2002. Increasing the precision of comparative models with YASARA NOVA – A self-parameterizing force field. Proteins 47, 393–402.

Lai, Y.L., *et al.*, 2007. Cost-effective real-time reverse transcriptase PCR (RT-PCR) to screen for Dengue virus followed by rapid single-tube multiplex RT-PCR for serotyping of the virus. J. Clin. Microbiol. 45, 935–941.

Lee, K.S., Lai, Y.L., Lo, S., *et al.*, 2010. Dengue virus surveillance for early warning, Singapore. Emerg. Infect. Dis. 16 (5), 847–849.

Ler, T.S., Ang, L.W., Yap, G.S., *et al.*, 2011. Epidemiological characteristics of the 2005 and 2007 dengue epidemics in Singapore – Similarities and distinctions. Western Pac. Surveill. Response J. 2, 24–29.

Lim, S.P., Wang, Q.Y., Noble, C.G., *et al.*, 2013. Ten years of dengue drug discovery: Progress and prospects. Antiviral Res. 100, 500–519.

Low, S.L., Lam, S., Wong, W.Y., *et al.*, 2015. Dengue seroprevalence of healthy adults in Singapore: Serosurvey among blood donors, 2009. Am. J. Trop. Med. Hyg. 93, 40–45.

Luo, D., *et al.*, 2008. Insights into RNA unwinding and ATP hydrolysis by the flavivirus NS3 protein. EMBO J. 27, 3209–3219.

Murphy, B.R., Whitehead, S.S., 2011. Immune response to dengue virus and prospects for a vaccine. Annu. Rev. Immunol. 29, 587–619.

Ng, L.C., Vythilingum, I. (Eds.), 2011. Vectors of Flaviviruses and Strategies for Control, in Molecular Virology and Control of Flaviviruses. Poole, United Kingdom: Caister Academic Press.

Panhuis, W.G., Choisy, M., Xiong, X., *et al.*, 2015. Region-wide synchrony and traveling waves of dengue across eight countries in Southeast Asia. Proc. Natl. Acad. Sci. USA 112 (42), 13069–13074.

Rathore, A.P.S., Paradkar, P.N., Watanabe, S., *et al.*, 2011. Celgosivir treatment misfolds dengue virus NS1 protein, induces cellular pro-survival genes and protects against lethal challenge mouse model. Antiviral Res. 92, 453–460.

Rigau-Pérez, J.G., Clark, G.G., Gubler, D.J., *et al.*, 1998. Dengue and dengue haemorrhagic fever. Lancet 352, 971–977.

Rohani, P., Earn, D.J., Grenfell, B.T., 1999. Opposite patterns of synchrony in sympatric disease metapopulations. Science 286 (5441), 968–971.

Rosen, L., Shroyer, D.A., Tesh, R.B., Freier, J.E., Lien, J.C., 1983. Transovarial transmission of dengue viruses by mosquitoes: Aedes albopictus and Aedes aegypti. Am. J. Trop. Med. Hyg. 32, 1108–1119.

Schymkowitz, J.W., *et al.*, 2005. Prediction of water and metal binding sites and their affinities by using the Fold-X force field. Proc. Natl. Acad. Sci. USA 102, 10147–10152.

Shi, Y., Liu, X., Kok, S.-Y., *et al.*, 2016. Three-month real-time dengue forecast models: An early warning system for outbreak alerts and policy decision support in Singapore. Environ. Health Perspect. 124 (9), 1369–1375.

Simmons, C.P., Farrar, J.J., Nguyen, V.V., Wills, B., 2012. Dengue. N. Engl. J. Med. 366, 1423–1432.

Slingo, J.M., Annamalai, H., 2000. 1997: The El Niño of the century and the response of the Indian summer monsoon. Mon. Weather Rev. 128 (6), 1778–1797.

Steinhauer, D.A., Domingo, E., Holland, J.J., 1992. Lack of evidence for proofreading mechanisms associated with an RNA virus polymerase. Gene 122, 281–288.

Tibshirani, R., 1996. Regression shrinkage and selection via the lasso. J. R. Stat. Soc. Ser. B Stat. Methodol. 58, 267–288.

U.S. Census Bureau, 2014. International database.

Viboud, C., *et al.*, 2006. Synchrony, waves, and spatial hierarchies in the spread of influenza. Science 312 (5772), 447–451.

Webster, P.J., Palmer, T.N., 1997. The past and the future of El Niño. Nature 390 (12), 562–564.

Yew, Y.W., Ye, T., Ang, L.W., *et al.*, 2009. Seroepidemiology of dengue virus infection among adults in Singapore. Ann. Acad. Med. Singap. 38, 667–675.

Zhang, X., *et al.*, 2013. Cryo-EM structure of the mature dengue virus at 3.5-A resolution. Nat. Struct. Mol. Biol. 20, 105–110.

Biographical Sketch

Dr. Vijayaraghava Seshadri Sundararajan is an advisor of Bioclues.org who is organizing international conferences/workshops.

Identification of Homologs

William R Pearson, University of Virginia School of Medicine, Charlottesville, VA, United States

Background/Fundamentals

Modern genome biology relies on the inference of homology from protein and DNA sequence similarity searching. As the number of sequenced genomes has grown from the dozens to the thousands and tens of thousands today, except for a small number of experimental model organisms, most functional annotations on newly sequenced genomes are transferred based on similarity searches. This section examines the philosophical and statistical basis for inferring homology from excess similarity.

The inference of homology – common evolutionary ancestry – is a conclusion about relationships based on biological events that often occurred from 0.5 to 3 billion years ago. For example, based on excess protein sequence similarity, about 40% of human enzymes have easily identified homologs in *E. coli* (**Fig. 1**). This observation of excess similarity implies that large fraction of human and *E. coli* proteins existed more than 3 billion years ago in the organism that was the last common ancestor of mammals and bacteria. And 40% is a very conservative estimate; it is likely that a much larger fraction of human enzymes have homologs in *E. coli*, but 40% are easily detected in a BLASTP search.

The ability to identify such distant homologs was unexpected. In the late 1960s, as the first protein sequences became available, one of the first uses of "homology" to denote excess similarity (Winter *et al.*, 1968) explicitly denied that the traditional evolutionary meaning of the word (common ancestry) was appropriate in the protein context, suggesting that excess similarity might be the result of very similar protein sequences emerging independently, analogous to the emergence of the ability to fly in insects and vertebrates. But this argument was short-lived, as early researchers came to understand that the space of possible protein sequences is astronomically large (McLachlan, 1971; Altschul *et al.*, 1994). Thus, faced with the two logical alternatives for excess similarity – common ancestry or independent origins – the more parsimonious explanation, in the presence of excess similarity, is common ancestry.

The "homology:excess similarity" relationship is also confused by the use of the term "homology" in place of "identity," as in the phrase "these sequences are 30% homologous." Because homology is a qualitative inference, two proteins are either homologous, or they are not homologs (Reeck *et al.*, 1987). Homology and identity are not interchangeable; homology is a *qualitative* statement about evolutionary ancestry, while identity is a *quantitative* statement about sequence similarity. While sequence identity can be a

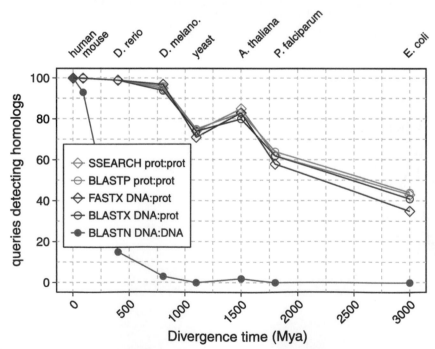

Fig. 1 Sensitivity of protein and DNA sequence comparison – One hundred human RefSeq proteins and their corresponding mRNA sequences from proteins with E.C. numbers (enzymes) were compared to proteomes and mRNA sequence sets from the indicated genomes. Plotted are the number of queries that had at least one homolog with enough excess similarity that the score would be expected in fewer than 1000 searches by chance ($E() < 0.001$) in searches against the indicated proteomes/RNA-sets using SSEARCH and BLASTP for protein:protein comparisons, FASTX and BLASTX for DNA:protein comparisons, and BLASTN for DNA:DNA comparisons. Divergence times from timetree.org.

reliable (though insensitive) measure of excess similarity, and identity is a useful indicator of evolutionary distance (homologous sequences that are 90% identical are much more closely related than sequences that are 30% identical), identity (or similarity) and homology are fundamentally different concepts. Amino-acid residues can be homologous (share a common evolutionary history) without being identical, and residues may be identical simply by chance (thus not sharing common ancestry).

Homology inference is often based on excess pair-wise sequence similarity found in a similarity search, using a program like BLASTP (Altschul *et al.*, 1990; Altschul *et al.*, 1997; Camacho *et al.*, 2009). Pair-wise sequence similarity is effective because modern sequence databases are comprehensive – complete proteomes are known for thousands of organisms. However, pair-wise sequence comparison is less sensitive than comparison based on excess structural similarity (Pearson and Sierk, 2005). Excess structural similarity is considered the "gold standard" for inferring homology, but the argument for homology from excess similarity is the same. If two structures share much more similarity than is expected by chance, the simplest explanation is that the excess similarity reflects common ancestry. Methods to improve sequence-based homology inference often rely on homology inferences based on excess structural similarity. While structure comparison is far more sensitive than pair-wise sequence comparison, only a fraction of protein sequences are homologous to proteins with known structures. Because there are so many complete proteomes, sequence comparison can be used to identify homologs for almost every protein in a newly sequenced genome.

Intermediate in sensitivity between pair-wise sequence comparison and pair-wise structure comparison are sequence based methods that use sequence models, using either Position-Specific Scoring Matrices (PSSMs, Altschul *et al.*, 1997; Schaffer *et al.*, 2001; Altschul and Koonin, 1998), or Hidden Markov Models (HMMs, Sonnhammer *et al.*, 1998; Finn *et al.*, 2011; Eddy, 2011). Model-based methods (PSSMs, HMMs) can be 5–10-fold more sensitive than pair-wise alignment (Pearson *et al.*, 2017) Model-based methods provide an automated approach to transitive similarity searching – if *A* shares significant similarity with *B*, and *B* with *C*, then *A* can be inferred to be homologous to *C* without sharing significant pair-wise similarity (Gerstein, 1998).

Application

The inference of homology from excess similarity requires both (1) algorithms to align sequences and produce similarity scores and (2) an accurate model of how much similarity is expected by chance. The first algorithm used to align protein sequences (Needleman and Wunsch, 1970) produced a *global* sequence alignment – sequences were aligned from end-to-end – and accommodated a variety of match/mismatch penalties, from simple identities to more sophisticated measures of amino-acid similarity. The Needleman-Wunsch algorithm used a penalty-*per*-gap strategy; a gap of one residue, or two, or five would all have the same cost.

Today, most similarity searching programs, including BLAST, calculate a local alignment score – one in which the alignment can begin and end anywhere in the sequences as long as it produces a maximum score. Local alignments can identify homologous domains in different sequence contexts, and work well with partial protein sequences produced by exons in genome assemblies. The first rigorous local alignment algorithm was described by Smith and Waterman (1981). Modern algorithms use a more efficient form described by Gotoh (1982), vectorized versions of the rigorous Smith-Waterman-Gotoh local alignment algorithm (Farrar, 2007) can speed searches 10–20-fold.

In addition to an algorithm to calculate alignment scores, homology inference requires an understanding of alignment score statistics. To recognize *excess* similarity, it is critical to understand how much similarity is expected by chance (between random or unrelated sequences), particularly in the context of a database search, where tens of thousands to tens of millions of sequences are compared. Early protein sequence analysts understood the importance of evaluating statistical significance using unrelated (typically shuffled) sequences (McLachlan, 1971), but without a statistical model of the distribution of unrelated scores, it was impossible to accurately estimate probabilities. The recognition that local similarity scores between random protein or DNA sequences are accurately described by the extreme-value distribution (Arratia *et al.*, 1986; Karlin and Altschul, 1990), even for gapped alignments (Mott and Tribe, 1999), allows excess similarity to be measured and thus homology to be identified routinely. These statistical foundations enabled the BLAST programs (Altschul *et al.*, 1990, 1997) to provide the first accurate statistical estimates for similarity scores. Today, all widely-used similarity search programs provide accurate statistical estimates (Brenner *et al.*, 1998; Pearson and Sierk, 2005).

The most widely used sequence comparison algorithm, BLAST (Altschul *et al.*, 1990, 1997; Camacho *et al.*, 2009), uses the Karlin and Altschul statistical model (Karlin and Altschul, 1990) to set heuristic thresholds for the inclusion of *k*-letter amino-acid "words" (typically $k=3$ for proteins) to dramatically accelerate sequence comparison by not examining alignments that are unlikely to reflect homology. Since homologous sequences are rarely more than 1.0% of a comprehensive sequence database (in the human proteome, only 6 of 6116 Pfam domain families are present in more than 1.0% of proteins, with the most abundant domains, protein kinases and Zn-fingers, appearing in 2% of proteins), focusing on sequences that could produce significant alignments can speed up similarity searches 100-fold.

Local sequence alignment scores between random sequences are well described by the extreme value distribution:

$$p(S_{raw}) \leq 1 - exp(Kmne^{-\lambda S_{raw}})$$
(1)

where S_{raw} is the calculated alignment score, m,n are the lengths of the two sequences being aligned, λ is a parameter that captures the "scaling" of the scoring matrix used to produce the alignment score, and K is a parameter that captures how the similarity scores of random sequence alignments increase with sequence length. For alignment scores with $p < 0.1$, this equation can be simplified to:

$$p(S_{raw}) \leq Kmne^{-\lambda S_{raw}} \tag{2}$$

which can also be expressed in terms of a "bit" score as

$$p(S_{bits}) \leq mn2^{-S_{bits}} \tag{3}$$

where $S_{bits} = (\lambda S_{raw} - ln(K))/ln(2)$

The "bit" score has the advantage that Eq. (3) can be used to calculate the probability of any S_{bit} score, regardless of the scoring matrix, and "bit" scores are available for most similarity searching programs (BLASTP, Camacho *et al.*, 2009; FASTA, (Pearson, 2016); and HMMER3, (Eddy, 2011)).

The $p(S)$ value calculated in Eqs. (1)–(3) reflects the probability of obtaining a score $\geq S$, in a *single* sequence alignment between two unrelated proteins. Because it assumes that only one alignment score has been calculated, $p(S)$ is not the appropriate measure of statistical significance in a similarity search of a protein or DNA database, where hundreds of thousands to tens of millions of sequences have been examined. To account for the thousands to millions of multiple tests (alignments) that were considered in a search, the p-value is converted to an expectation value using a Bonferroni correction:

$$E(S) \leq p(S)D \tag{4}$$

where D is the number of alignments performed. Equivalently:

$$E(S_{bit}) \leq Dmn2^{-S_{bit}} \tag{5}$$

or, for BLAST where the length of the database is: $N = Dn$

$$E(S_{bit}) \leq mN2^{-S_{bit}} \tag{6}$$

Because the Bonferroni correction (Eqs. (4)–(6)) changes the expectation value depending on the size of the database (the number of comparisons, or tests), the same similarity score can be statistically significant in some contexts (e.g., a single proteome with 20,000 sequences) but not in others (e.g., comprehensive protein databases with tens of millions of sequences). For example, alignment of human RefSeq protein NP_000444 (a sodium/iodide cotransporter, 643 amino acids) with *E. coli* NP_418491 (an acetate transporter, 549 amino acids) produces a local alignment score of 45 bits. If the *E. coli* sequence had been identified in a search of human proteins ($\sim 40,000$ sequences), the relationship would be statistically significant, with $E(S_{bits}=45,D=40,000) \leq 40,000 \times 643 \times 549 \times 2^{-45} = 4.2 \times 10^{-4}$. In contrast, the same alignment would not be significant if the *E. coli* protein had been compared to UniProt ($\sim 40,000,000$ sequences, $E() \leq 0.42$) or RefSeq ($\sim 80,000,000$ sequences, $E() \leq 0.84$).

This loss of statistical significance with increased database size can be disconcerting, because it suggests that two sequences can be homologous in searches of small proteome databases but not in searches of large comprehensive sequence sets. The discrepancy highlights the fundamental asymmetry when inferring homology using statistical significance; a *significant* similarity score *can* be used to *infer* homology, but a *non-significant* similarity score *cannot* be used to infer *non-homology*.

In this example, the alignment does reflect homology; both proteins contain a sodium:solute symporter family domain (PF00074, Finn *et al.*, 2016) but the alignment score (45 bits) is not large enough to guarantee statistical significance after the Bonferroni correction for large datasets. In databases with tens of millions of sequences, a score of 45 bits will often occur by chance.

The relationship between database size and homology inference is key to interpreting similarity search results. Homology inference is asymmetrical; sequences that share statistically significant similarity can be reliably inferred to be homologous, and non-homologous sequences should never share statistically significant similarity after the significance has been corrected for multiple testing, but sequences that do not share significant similarity are not always non-homologous.

The expectation value $E(D)$ reports the number of times (on average) that an alignment score would be expected by chance in a database of D unrelated sequences. Thus, an alignment with an $E()$-value of 0.001 would be expected to occur by chance once in 1000 searches of the database. $E() \leq 0.001$ is frequently used to infer homology in a single similarity search (but it *cannot* be used to infer non-homology). As the example shows, there may be more distantly related homologs with $E()$-values ~ 1 or even higher, mixed among alignments of unrelated sequences with $E() \sim 1$.

The relationship between bit scores and statistical significance (Eqs. (4)–(6)) can be used to calculate the minimum bit score that would be statistically significant in searches of databases with different numbers of sequences. For average length proteins (400 amino-acids), to achieve $E() \leq 0.001$, a score of:

$$0.001 \leq D \times 400 \times 400 \times 2^{-S_{bits}} \tag{7}$$

$$D \geq 0.001 / \left(400 \times 400 \times 2^{-S_{bits}}\right) \tag{8}$$

$$160,000 \times D/0.001 \leq 2^{S_{bits}} \tag{9}$$

the $-S_{bits}$ exponent is inverted

$$log_2(160,000,000 \times D) \leq S_{bits} \tag{10}$$

$$27.25 + log_2(D) \leq S_{bits} \tag{11}$$

For *E. coli*, $log_2(4000) = 12$ so a 40-bit score is significant ($E(S_{bit}=40, D=4000) < 0.001$); for human $log_2(40,000) \simeq 15$, so 43 bits are required. For large protein databases like UniProt ($log_2(40 \times 10^6) \simeq 25$), so ~ 50–55 bits are required for statistical significance.

Protein sequence similarity searching can routinely identify homologs – proteins sharing a common ancestor – that diverged >2 billion years ago, using a single protein query sequence. More sophisticated methods, such as PSI-BLAST (Altschul *et al.*, 1997) and HMMER3/jackhmmer (Eddy, 2011) are dramatically more sensitive. These approaches build an ancestral model of a protein family or domain that typically can identify 5–10 times as many homologs as a single sequence BLASTP search. For PSI-BLAST, this model is a Position Specific Scoring Matrix (PSSM) that captures the specific sequence changes possible at each residue across the length of the protein or domain. HMMER3/jackhmmer uses a more sophisticated approach to build a Hidden Markov Model (HMM) that captures both the substitution frequencies at each position across the model and the variation in gap-frequency at different locations. However, despite their much higher sensitivity compared with pairwise-sequence comparison, PSI-BLAST and HMMER3 can also fail to identify distant homologs that can be identified using structure comparison (Pearson and Sierk, 2005). Today, there is no sequence-based method that is as sensitive as structure comparison, though methods that use HMM-HMM comparison approach this ideal (Sadreyev *et al.*, 2003; Remmert *et al.*, 2012).

Case Studies

The discussion above has focused on the inference of homology from protein sequence comparison. Protein sequence comparison provides dramatically greater evolutionary look-back time than DNA sequence comparison for several reasons: (1) protein sequences change more slowly than DNA sequences, because many DNA changes are silent – they do not change the encoded amino acid; (2) protein sequence comparison can take advantage of an informative scoring matrix, e.g., the BLO-SUM62 matrix gives similar, but non-identical (e.g., arginine, lysine, histidine, or leucine, isoleucine, and valine) positive alignment scores, and gives amino-acids that are rarely substituted negative scores; (3) the amino-acid alphabet is larger (20 vs 4 residues), so chance alignments between protein sequences occur at much lower percent identity; (4) protein sequence databases are much smaller than DNA sequence databases, since 95% or more of metazoan genomes do not code for protein; and (5) while unrelated protein sequences are indistinguishable from random protein sequences, unrelated DNA sequences can have local composition and other biases that make it difficult to produce random DNA sequences that look like real, unrelated DNA sequences. As a result, while expectation values with $E() < 0.001$ will occur by chance once in 1000 searches for protein sequences (Pearson and Sierk, 2005), they occur much more often in DNA sequences, so $E() < 10^{-10}$ is often used as a threshold for inferring homology with DNA:DNA comparison.

The dramatic difference in sensitivity between protein and DNA comparison is illustrated in **Fig. 1**, which shows how the sensitivity of sequence similarity searches drops with evolutionary distance, using protein:protein, DNA:protein, and DNA:DNA comparisons. The figure illustrates that protein:protein (SSEARCH, BLASTP) and translated-DNA:protein (FASTX, BLASTX) can identify homologs in 99%–100% of the queries among the vertebrates (500 Mya), in more than 95% of the queries among metazoa (800 Mya), in more than 80% of queries between humans and plants (1500 Mya), and in ∼40% of queries between humans and *E. coli*. Moreover, there is relatively little loss in sensitivity with translated-DNA:protein vs protein:protein alignments. In contrast, while DNA:DNA searches (BLASTN) can find homologs for 93% of the queries between human and mouse (and this number is high because the DNA sequences encode protein; non-coding sensitivity would be much lower), comparison of human queries find homologs for only 15% of queries in fish, and less than 5% of queries between humans and *Drosophila*. Protein:protein and translated-DNA:protein comparisons allow homologs to be identified 10-times earlier in evolutionary time than DNA:DNA comparisons.

Discussion

The identification of biological homologs – genes, protein sequences, or protein structures that share a common ancestor – is based on the parsimonious principle that when sequences or structures share much more similarity than is expected by chance, the simplest explanation for the excess similarity is common ancestry, i.e., the sequences are similar because they are descendants (copies) of an ancient protein. Thus, the ability to recognize distant homologs depends both on a method to calculate a similarity score, e.g., BLASTP (Camacho *et al.*, 2009) or FASTA (Pearson, 2016), *and* an accurate model of the amount of similarity expected by chance. Today, because there are so many fully sequenced genomes and their corresponding proteomes, virtually every similarity search identifies hundreds if not thousands of homologs. But pair-wise similarity searches sometimes miss large numbers of homologs that can be detected by transitive similarity searches, model based methods (PSI-BLAST, HMMER3), and structure comparison. As a result, even the most sensitive sequence based similarity searches miss distant homologs. Despite its imperfections, homology inference from excess sequence similarity is the most powerful and reliable strategy for characterizing new protein and DNA sequences, and is most effective when comparisons use protein sequence databases.

See also: Gene Duplication and Speciation. Inference of Horizontal Gene Transfer: Gaining Insights Into Evolution via Lateral Acquisition of Genetic Material. Natural Language Processing Approaches In Bioinformatics. Phylogenetic analysis: Early evolution of life. Sequence Analysis

References

Altschul, S.F., Boguski, M.S., Gish, W., Wootton, J.C., 1994. Issues in searching molecular sequence databases. Nat. Genet. 6, 119–129.

Altschul, S.F., Gish, W., Miller, W., Myers, E.W., Lipman, D.J., 1990. A basic local alignment search tool. J. Mol. Biol. 215, 403–410.

Altschul, S.F., Koonin, E.V., 1998. Iterated profile searches with PSI-BLAST – A tool for discovery in protein databases. Trends Biochem. Sci. 23, 444–447.

Altschul, S.F., Madden, T.L., Schaffer, A.A., et al., 1997. Gapped BLAST and PSI-BLAST: A new generation of protein database search programs. Nucleic Acids Res. 25, 3389–3402.

Arratia, R., Gordon, L., Waterman, M.S., 1986. An extreme value theory for sequence matching. Ann. Stat. 14, 971–993.

Brenner, S.E., Chothia, C., Hubbard, T.J., 1998. Assessing sequence comparison methods with reliable structurally identified distant evolutionary relationships. Proc. Natl. Acad. Sci. USA 95, 6073–6078.

Camacho, C., Coulouris, G., Avagyan, V., et al., 2009. Blast +: Architecture and applications. BMC Bioinform. 10, 421.

Eddy, S.R., 2011. Accelerated profile HMM searches. PLOS Comput. Biol. 7 (10), e1002195.

Farrar, M., 2007. Striped Smith-Waterman speeds database searches six times over other SIMD implementations. Bioinformatics 23, 156–161.

Finn, R.D., Clements, J., Eddy, S.R., 2011. HMMER web server: Interactive sequence similarity searching. Nucleic Acids Res. 39, W29–W37.

Finn, R.D., Coggill, P., Eberhardt, R.Y., et al., 2016. The Pfam protein families database: Towards a more sustainable future. Nucleic Acids Res. 44 (D1), D279–D285.

Gerstein, M., 1998. Measurement of the effectiveness of transitive sequence comparison, through a third 'intermediate' sequence. Bioinformatics 14 (8), 707–714.

Gotoh, O., 1982. An improved algorithm for matching biological sequences. J. Mol. Biol. 162, 705–708.

Karlin, S., Altschul, S.F., 1990. Methods for assessing the statistical significance of molecular sequence features by using general scoring schemes. Proc. Natl. Acad. Sci. USA 87, 2264–2268.

McLachlan, A.D., 1971. Tests for comparing related amino-acid sequences: Cytochrome c and cytochrome c 551. J. Mol. Biol. 61, 409–424.

Mott, R., Tribe, R., 1999. Approximate statistics of gapped alignments. J. Comput. Biol. 6, 91–112.

Needleman, S.B., Wunsch, C.D., 1970. A general method applicable to the search for similarities in the amino acid sequence of two proteins. J. Mol. Biol. 48, 443–453.

Pearson, W.R., 2016. Finding protein and nucleotide similarities with FASTA. Curr. Protoc. Bioinformatics 53, 3.9.1–3.9.25.

Pearson, W.R., Li, W., Lopez, R., 2017. Query-seeded iterative sequence similarity searching improves selectivity 5–20-fold. Nucleic Acids Res. 45 (7), e46.

Pearson, W.R., Sierk, M.L., 2005. The limits of protein sequence comparison? Curr. Opin. Struct. Biol. 15, 254–260.

Reeck, G.R., de Haen, C., Teller, D.C., et al., 1987. Homology in proteins and nucleic acids: A terminology muddle and a way out of it. Cell 50, 667.

Remmert, M., Biegert, A., Hauser, A., Soeding, J., 2012. HHblits: Lightning-fast iterative protein sequence searching by HMM-HMM alignment. Nat. Methods 9 (2), 173–175.

Sadreyev, R.I., Baker, D., Grishin, N.V., 2003. Profile-profile comparisons by COMPASS predict intricate homologies between protein families. Protein Sci. 12, 2262–2272.

Schaffer, A.A., Aravind, L., Madden, T.L., et al., 2001. Improving the accuracy of PSI-BLAST protein database searches with composition-based statistics and other refinements. Nucleic Acids Res. 29, 2994–3005.

Smith, T.F., Waterman, M.S., 1981. Identification of common molecular subsequences. J. Mol. Biol. 147, 195–197.

Sonnhammer, E.L.L., Eddy, S.R., Birney, E., Bateman, A., Durbin, R., 1998. Pfam: Multiple sequence alignments and HMM-profiles of protein domains. Nucleic Acids Res. 26, 322–325.

Winter, W.P., Walsh, K.A., Neurath, H., 1968. Homology as applied to proteins. Science 162 (3861), 1433.

DNA Barcoding: Bioinformatics Workflows for Beginners

John-James Wilson, University of South Wales, Pontypridd, United Kingdom and Naresuan University, Phitsanulok, Thailand
Kong-Wah Sing, Kunming Institute of Zoology, Chinese Academy of Sciences, Yunnan, P.R. China
Narong Jaturas, Naresuan University, Phitsanulok, Thailand

Introduction

Just as species show differences in their morphology, ecology, and behavior, they also show differences in their DNA sequences (Wilson *et al.*, 2017). "DNA barcoding," used in a broad sense, refers to the use of short, standardized DNA sequences as markers for the recognition of species. When used more precisely, "DNA barcoding" refers to the technique of sequencing a short fragment of the DNA sequence of the mitochondrial cytochrome c oxidase subunit I (COI) gene, the animal "DNA barcode," from a taxonomically unknown specimen and performing comparisons with a library of DNA barcodes from taxonomically known specimens to establish a taxonomic identification.

DNA barcoding requires basic molecular biology methods (which pre-date the term DNA barcoding) to extract and amplify the DNA barcode sequence fragment from the unknown specimen (**Fig. 1**). Generally, this sample of amplified DNA is then passed to commercial companies for inexpensive Sanger sequencing, or, particularly in the case of mixed, bulk samples, for high-throughput (next generation) sequencing. These molecular biology methods are not covered in this article which focuses on bioinformatics workflows following the receipt of digital DNA sequences from a sequencer (**Fig. 1**). For a step-by-step guide to the molecular biology methods used for standard (animal) DNA barcoding see Wilson (2012) and for an approximation of costs in developing countries see Sing *et al.* (2016). Brandon-Mong *et al.* (2015) provide an example of a method (bulk extraction and bulk PCR) for use prior to high-throughput sequencing, i.e., DNA metabarcoding.

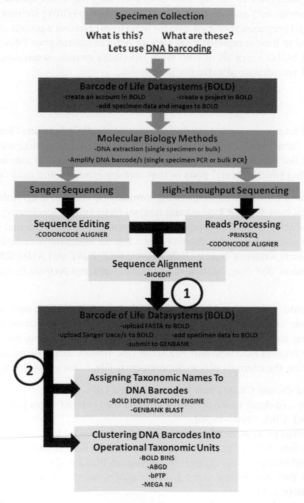

Fig. 1 The DNA barcoding workflow.

The ultimate aim of a DNA barcoding bioinformatics workflow is to (1) produce a "clean" or "reliable" digital representation of the DNA barcodes, and (2) use these DNA barcodes to obtain information about the taxonomy of the unknown specimen through algorithms enabling DNA sequence comparisons, in conjunction with DNA sequence libraries (**Fig. 1**).

Background/Fundamentals

It is important to realize that full exploitation of DNA barcodes for species recognition will only be possible after assembling a comprehensive library linking organisms (and Linnaean taxonomy) with their DNA barcodes (see Wilson *et al.*, 2017 for an assessment of DNA barcode library coverage for insects). With this in mind, in an effort to promote DNA barcoding research and DNA barcode library building (e.g., Wilson *et al.*, 2013), we have been organizing and facilitating DNA barcoding workshops in Southeast Asia, a mega diverse region with relatively low DNA barcode coverage in public libraries (Wilson *et al.*, 2016). We have created a website, DNA Barcoding Workshops (DBW), as a companion resource to our workshops and much of the material in this article derives for our experience running these workshops.

This article is intended as a guide for absolute beginners to DNA barcoding, and provides step-by-step instructions for basic bioinformatics workflows following receipt of DNA sequences from a DNA sequencing facility.

Application

Getting Started With DNA Barcoding: The Barcode of Life Datasystems

The Barcode of Life Datasystems (BOLD) (Ratnasingham and Hebert, 2013) is a cloud-based data storage and analysis platform developed and maintained by the Centre for Biodiversity Genomics (CBG) in Canada. It consists of four main modules, a data portal, an educational portal, a registry of Barcode Index Numbers (BINs) (putative species), and a data collection and analysis workbench. BOLD is the recommended place to manage your DNA barcoding research. Please see the BOLD Handbook available from the BOLD website (under "Resources") and the DNA Barcoding Workshop (DBW) website for step-by-step instructions for: (i) creating an account on BOLD; (ii) preparing specimen data for BOLD; (iii) creating a project on BOLD; and (iv) adding records and images to BOLD. You will need to have completed these steps in order to upload your DNA barcode sequences to BOLD and to use the BINs system. Note that BOLD keeps all of your work (specimen records, sequences, etc.) private, accessible only to yourself and your coworkers, until you choose to make the work public.

Editing Sanger Sequences

To learn more about the process of Sanger sequencing see the resources on the DNA Learning Centre website from the Cold Spring Harbor Laboratory. The outputs of Sanger sequencers are trace files (also known as chromatograms and electropherograms), digital representations of DNA sequences. For a number of reasons, a trace may not be "clean", it may be "messy", and the first step is to "edit" the sequence, a process during which "messy" parts of sequence are removed and only "reliable" sequence is retained.

a) Usually your sequences will come back from the sequencing company by email in a zip (folder) file. An example of a zip file containing 12 trace files (6 each trace files for forward and reverse) (6 unknown specimens), representing the kind of zip file you could receive from a sequencing company, is provided for download as Supplemental File 1.

b) Unpack (extract) the zip file to your desktop. This should create a regular folder on your desktop, which you can name *Traces*. There are two sets of files for each sequence (e.g., *NUMBEROFSAMPLE_F.ab1* and *NUMBEROFSAMPLE_F.txt*). The files you are interested in have an extension .ab1 (e.g., *NUMBEROFSAMPLE_F.ab1* and *NUMBEROFSAMPLE_R.ab1*). Delete the other files in the folder.

For sequence editing we recommend the program CODONCODE ALIGNER which is used at the Canadian Centre for DNA Barcoding (CCDB). Information on CODONCODE ALIGNER, including a free trial version, can be found at the Codoncode Corporation website. The following steps describe the process of Sanger sequence editing for multiple specimens whose DNA barcodes were amplified using the primers *LCO1490* and *HCO2198* (see Wilson, 2012; Brandon-Mong *et al.*, 2015). For practice you can go through these steps using the example files in Supplemental File 1. For other primer sets adapt accordingly.

a) Open CodonCode Aligner and choose *Create a new project* and press *OK*.

b) Go to *File > Import > Add Folder...* navigate to the desktop and select the folder of traces [which should be named *Traces* if you followed the suggestion above]. Click *Open > Import*.

c) To see the files you just imported press ► besides the *Unassembled Samples* folder.

d) The .ab1 files should be of the form *NUMBEROFSAMPLE_F.ab1* where the second part "F" refers to the direction, i.e. Forward.

e) Sort the files by quality by double-clicking on *Quality*. Any sequences that are of very poor quality (look for a big difference between the sequence length and the quality score; a higher quality score is better) can be deleted by highlighting the sequence and clicking *Edit > Move to Trash*.

f) Next we will group our sequences by direction for easy editing.

g) Make sure the *Unassembled Samples* folder is highlighted. Select the *Contig* menu and move the cursor over *Advanced Assembly*. From the options that appear select *Assemble in Groups*.

h) A new window will appear. Click the button *Define name parts...*

i) There are two name parts to our file names (see above). The first part of our file names refers to the number of the sample and for our purposes the option in the *Meaning* menu (first row) can be left as *Clone*. Since the sample number is followed by an underscore, choose *_ (underscore)* in the *Delimiter* menu next to *Clone* (if it is not already selected).

j) For the second row choose *Direction* in the *Meaning* menu. We can ignore the *Delimiter* menu for the *Direction* part because there is nothing following the direction in our file names.

k) Delete all additional name parts that may appear in the window (if any), and next click *Preview...* to check how CodonCode Aligner is interpreting the sample names.

l) Click *Close* to exit the preview. Click *OK* to return to the *Assemble in Groups* window.

m) We first want to assemble our samples according to direction. Choose *Direction* in the *Name part:* dropdown menu. Then click *Assemble*. You should now have two folders, one called **F** with the forward sequences and one called **R** with the reverse sequences. [Note: if you only sent your PCR products for sequencing in one direction, i.e., with one primer, then you will only have one folder.].

n) We will deal with the reverse sequences first. The first step is to reverse complement the sequences. Highlight the **R** folder, select *Edit > Reverse complement*.

o) Next we need to cut the primer from the sequence. Double click the **R** folder to open it. For the reverse sequences, you need to find the forward primer motif and delete it from the beginning of the consensus sequence at the bottom of the window. You will find the primer around 30 nucleotides from the end of the raw sequence. For example, you would need to delete the section of the sequence marked below in **bold** and everything to the left of it. Highlight it on the **consensus** sequence at the bottom of the window and press the Backspace key on the keyboard. ←AAAGAT**ATTGG**AACATTATATTTTATTTTT...

p) Next go to the opposite end of the consensus, the far right. Delete the consensus sequence from the point where the sequence gets messy. This will be apparent due to lots of green highlight. For example [it will not look exactly like this], delete the section marked in **bold** and everything to the right of it. Highlight it on the **consensus** sequence at the bottom of the window and press the Delete key on the keyboard. Close the window. ... TCTTTTTTTGACCCTGCTGGTGGAGGGTTTGG**TAGGAGGATG**→

q) Double click the **F** folder to open it. Go to the far right of the consensus sequence and find the reverse complement reverse primer motif at the very end. This should be around 650 bp on the raw sequence. For example, you would delete the section marked in **bold** and everything to the right of it. Highlight it on the **consensus** sequence at the bottom of the window and press the Delete key on the keyboard. ... CAACATTTATTT**TGATTTTTGG**→

r) Next go to the opposite end of the consensus, the far left, and delete the consensus sequence from the point where the sequences get messy. This will be apparent due to lots of green highlight. For example [it will not look exactly like this], you would delete the sequence in **bold** and everything to the left of it. Highlight the region on the consensus sequence at the bottom of the window and press the Backspace key on the keyboard. Close the window. ←ATGCT**TTTTTTTTKGG**TGTTTAATCAGGACTAATTGGAACTTC

s) Dissolve both the **F** and **R** folders by highlighting them and clicking the button marked with a red X.

t) Now we are going to combine the forward and reverse sequence from each specimen into a contig. Highlight the *Unassembled Samples* folder and open the *Contig* menu. Move the cursor over *Advanced Assembly*. From the options that appear select *Assemble in Groups*. This time choose *Clone* in the *Name part:* menu, then click *Assemble*. [Note: if you only sent your PCR products for sequencing in one direction (with one primer) then you will need to check each sequence individually rather than checking a consensus (contig).][Note: specimens which only sequenced successfully in one direction will have files which remain in the *Unassembled Samples* folder.]

u) The contigs are likely to be in reverse complement orientation. Highlight every folder (contig), select *Edit > Reverse complement*.

v) Open each folder (contig) in turn by double-clicking. Correct ambiguous positions (shown in red, in green highlight, and/or as N) and gaps ("—") in the consensus sequence by checking the original traces. This is done by double-clicking on the **consensus sequence** at the bottom of the window. Always check both trace files (forward and reverse) and compare them. [Note: the corrected consensus sequence should have **NO** gaps.].

w) Generally if traces conflict (i.e., different colored peaks appear in the same location on the forward and reverse chromatograms) you can decide which is more reliable based on sequence quality (e.g., less background noise, taller peaks).

x) Check the contigs first, then check the individual single sequences in the Unassembled Samples folder, if any.

y) To export the consensus sequences, highlight all the folders, go *File > Export > Consensus Sequences...*, choose *Current selection*. Open the *Options* and select *Include gaps in FASTA* but deselect all other options. Press *Export*. Save the file to the desktop as *sequences.fasta*.

z) If necessary, to export single direction sequences, go *File > Export > Samples...*, choose *Current selection*. Press *Export*. Save the file to the desktop as *sequences_single.fasta*.

Processing High-Throughput Sequencing Reads

The files output by an Illumina MiSeq high-throughput sequencer are in FASTQ format. FASTQ is similar to FASTA but contains additional data. Note that high-throughput sequencing reads are generally demultiplexed and adapter and primer-trimmed onboard the sequencer (e.g., onboard the MiSeq using the MiSeq Reporter software). Because the FASTQ outputs are large files, the sequencing company probably will not send the files by email but will email you a link to a website from where you can download the files, usually (like Sanger sequences), packed into a zip file. Two FASTQ files (Paired-end files) are output from each sequencing run, which you can think of as the *Forward* and *Reverse* sequences.

The following workflow describe steps taken for processing high-throughput reads for bulk arthropod samples whose DNA was amplified using the primers *mlCOIintF* and *HCO2198* (see Brandon-Mong *et al.*, 2015). A zip file containing some example FASTQ Paired-end files are available for download as Supplemental File 2. For practice you can go through these steps using these example files. For convenience, save the files in a folder (called *Reads*) on your Desktop.

It is important to note that the steps provided below are crude methods for processing a very small number of high-throughput sequencing reads. The field of DNA metabarcoding is a relatively new field and much work is being undertaken to develop methods to reduce the number of "spurious" reads generated and retained by bioinformatics pipelines for high-throughput sequencing reads (Brandon-Mong *et al.*, 2015) (see Future Directions below). For FASTQ files which are larger than the example provided as Supplemental File 2, CODONCODE ALIGNER is probably not a suitable program, and for beginners, it may be better to register and use applications provided on the GALAXY webserver. Considering that DNA metabarcoding is the focus of another article in this book, we do not provide additional details here.

a) Open the PRINSEQ webserver (Schmieder and Edwards, 2011), click *Use PRINSEQ* and click on *Upload Data*.
b) Your files are *FASTQ Paired-end* so choose that option.
c) Select the two FASTQ files you have saved on your Desktop (in the *Reads* folder).
d) Under *Please select the statistics you want to generate*. Choose *None* for all options then click *Continue*.
e) Wait while PRINSEQ processes your data.
f) Once it is finished click *Process Input Data*.
g) Choose the options from **Table 1**.
h) Choose to Output the data as FASTA, *Data passing all the filters (good)*.

Table 1   Parameters used for processing high-throughput sequencer reads

Program	Parameter	Option
PRINSEQ	Trim #nucleotides from 5′-end	25
	Trim #nucleotides from 3′-end	25
	Trim ends by quality scores	While Mean of scores is < (less then) 10 (5′-end) and 10 (3′-end_ using window size of 5 with step size 5
	Trim poly-A/T tails from 5′-end	That are equal to or longer than 5
	Trim poly-A/T tails from 3′-end	That are equal to or longer than 5
	Minimum sequence length in bp	200
	Maximum sequence length in bp	300
	Minimum mean quality score	32
	Minimum GC content in %	25
	Maximum GC content in %	35
	Maximum allowed rate of Ns in %	0
	Maximum number of allowed Ns	0
	Remove sequences with characters other than A, C, G, T or N	Yes
	Low-complexity threshold	80 (using Entropy)
	Dereplicate data	Remove exact sequence duplicates, Remove 5′ sequence duplicates, Remove 3′ sequence duplicates, Remove reverse complement exact sequence duplicates, Remove reverse complement 5′/3′ sequence duplicates
CODONCODE ALIGNER	Algorithm	Local alignments
	Min. percent identity	97.5
	Min overlap length	20
	Min score	20
	Max. unaligned end overlap	100.00
	Bandwidth (max. gap size)	30
	Word length	10
	Max successive failures	50
	Match score	1
	Mismatch penalty	−2
	Gap penalty	−2
	Additional first gap penalty	−3

i) Click *Generate Files*.

j) Use right click on the file you want (all of the FASTA files) to download and select "Save Link As" to save the file into a folder on your Desktop (which you could name *Filtered Reads*).

k) Next we will be using CODONCODE ALIGNER (see above). Go to *File > Import > Add Folder...* Import the sequences in the FASTA files in the *Filtered Reads* folder. Click *Rename Duplicates*.

l) Select all the sequences and click *Assemble*. Make sure the settings for *Assembly* found under *Edit > Preferences* are set to match those in **Table 1**.

m) Select all the contigs, including the *Unassembled Samples* folder and again, *Assemble*. Repeat until the number of contigs cannot be reduced any further.

n) Delete (*Move to Trash*) the sequences still remaining in the *Unassembled Samples* folder.

o) Export all the remaining contigs as consensus sequences (FASTA file), highlight all the folders, go *File > Export > Consensus Sequences...*, choose *Current selection*. Make sure none of the *Options* are selected.

Sequence Alignment

The alignment of DNA barcode sequences is a necessary step before two or more DNA barcode sequences can be compared with one another. Sequence alignment is the process of lining up nucleotides which are assumed to have the same common ancestor (i.e., thought to be homologous). BIOEDIT is the most commonly used program for small-scale sequence alignment, and is free for use by any and all interested parties. BIOEDIT can be downloaded from the program website but is no longer being regularly maintained.

a) Open your FASTA file (e.g., *sequences.fasta*) in BIOEDIT.

b) If necessary, you can then use *File > Import > Sequence alignment file* to add additional sequences (e.g., *sequences_single.fasta*) to the alignment.

c) Make sure *Mode:* is set to *Edit* using the dropdown menu.

d) Another dropdown menu will become visible to the right of the *Edit* dropdown. Make sure this is set to *Insert*.

e) Sequences that have ended up in the FASTA file in the wrong orientation (with standard primers, full length arthropod DNA barcodes should typically start AAC or TAC) may be corrected by highlighting the sequence name by clicking the cursor on it, clicking the *Sequences* menu at the top of the screen. Moving the cursor down the dropdown to *Nucleic Acid* and clicking *Reverse complement*.

f) Sequences all need to be the same length (typically 658 bp for full length DNA barcodes; 300 bp for metabarcodes) and aligned to each other (before proceeding for further analysis or before uploading to BOLD and GenBank). This can be done by typing additional *N(s)* at the beginning and end of the sequences in the *Edit* mode. Be sure to check across the whole of the alignment of the sequences that you have added the correct number of *N(s)*.

g) In **Fig. 2** featuring a 50-bp barcode for simplification, *JKN001-17* is of full length. *JKN002-17* needs 6 *Ns* adding to the left side of the sequence to become aligned, while *JKN003-17* needs 4 *Ns* adding to the right side of the sequence to be 50 bps long. *JKN005-17_F* needs to be reverse complemented to be in the same orientation as the other sequences.

h) Sanger sequences which were not part of a consensus (i.e., when one direction failed but the single sequence is of sufficient length and quality for submission to BOLD) may appear in the FASTA still tagged with the direction. This needs to be deleted, e.g., the sequence named *JKN005-17_F* should be renamed as *JKN005-17*.

i) If you are having trouble with the alignment, a good quality (i.e., 658[0n]) sequence can be downloaded from BOLD and imported into your alignment file as a guide, e.g., *MHAHC824-05* (**Fig. 2**). Be sure to delete this sequence before saving the file.

j) Save the file (*File > Save*) (e.g., save as *sequences_aligned.fasta*).

Following these steps you can upload your FASTA file (i.e., *sequences_aligned.fasta*) (and Sanger sequence trace files) to your project on BOLD. Step-by-step instruction can be found on the DBW website. Once sequences are registered in BOLD, they can also be submitted to GenBank using the *Submit to GenBank* option under the *Publication* tab on the BOLD project console.

Assigning Taxonomic Names to DNA Barcodes

For the assignment of taxonomic names to DNA barcodes (and by extension, checking sequences for contamination) we find it is best to use online tools to ensure you are searching the most recent DNA barcode library available (the DNA barcode library is constantly growing; Wilson *et al.*, 2017). For checking DNA barcodes for contamination and/or establishing a taxonomic identity, we would commonly "blast" our DNA barcodes against the BOLD and GenBank libraries. By statistically assessing how well library and query (unknown) DNA barcodes match, we can infer homology and transfer information (such as putative species membership) to the unknown specimen.

When there are no species-level matches in the libraries, some Linnaean taxonomic information may still be retrievable. Wilson *et al.* (2011) performed an investigation of the possibilities of assigning DNA barcodes to higher taxonomic groups (genus, family) when no species matches (i.e., with >98% similarity) are available in the library. Based on those results we suggest using a strict tree-based approach. BOLD can provide a Neighbor-Joining tree containing the query DNA barcode and the top matches by clicking *Tree Based Identification* on the *Specimen Identification Request* page (see below).

Contig

```
JKN001-17_F    AACTNTATATTTTATTTTTGGAATTTGACCAGGAATAGTAGGAACCTCTT  (Forward)
JKN001-17_R    AACTTTATATTTTATTTTTGGAATTTGACCAGGAATAGTAGGAACCTCTN  (Reverse)
JKN001-17      AACTTTATATTTTATTTTTGGAATTTGACCAGGAATAGTAGGAACCTCTT  (Consensus)
```

[A contig is two or more sequences grouped together in the same folder, usually one Forward and one Reverse, to produce a Consensus. Note: **N** = A, T, C, or G]

Unaligned FASTA (BIOEDIT) (*sequences.fasta*)

```
JKN001-17      AACTTTATATTTTATTTTTGGAATTTGACCAGGAATAGTAGGAACCTCTT
JKN002-17      ATATTTTATTTTTGGAATTTGAGCTGGATTAATTGGAACTTCAT
JKN003-17      AACTCTATATTTTATTTTTGGAATTTGACCAGGATTACTAGGAACT
JKN004-17      TCTATATTTTATTTTTGGAATTTGACCAGGTTTAGTTGGAACTTCAT
JKN005-17_F    ATGATGTTCCTAACATACCTGCTCAAATACCAAAAATAAAATATAAAGTT
MHAHC82-05     AACTTTATATTTTATTTTTGGAATTTGACCAGGAATAGTAGGAACCTCTT
```

Aligned FASTA (BIOEDIT) (*sequences_aligned.fasta*)

```
JKN001-17      AACTTTATATTTTATTTTTGGAATTTGACCAGGAATAGTAGGAACCTCTT
JKN002-17      NNNNNNATATTTTATTTTTGGAATTTGAGCTGGATTAATTGGAACTTCAT
JKN003-17      AACTCTATATTTTATTTTTGGAATTTGACCAGGATTACTAGGAACTNNNN
JKN004-17      NNNTCTATATTTTATTTTTGGAATTTGACCAGGTTTAGTTGGAACTTCAT
JKN005-17      AACTTTATATTTTATTTTTGGAATTTGACCAGGTATGTTAGGAACATCAT
```

Aligned FASTA (MS WORD) (*sequences_aligned.fasta*)

```
>JKN001-17
AACTTTATATTTTATTTTTGGAATTTGACCAGGAATAGTAGGAACCTCTT
>JKN002-17
NNNNNNATATTTTATTTTTGGAATTTGAGCTGGATTAATTGGAACTTCAT
>JKN003-17
AACTCTATATTTTATTTTTGGAATTTGACCAGGATTACTAGGAACTNNNN
>JKN004-17
NNNTCTATATTTTATTTTTGGAATTTGACCAGGTTTAGTTGGAACTTCAT
>JKN005-17
AACTTTATATTTTATTTTTGGAATTTGACCAGGTATGTTAGGAACATCAT
```

Fig. 2 Examples of DNA sequences viewed in BIOEDIT and MS WORD.

BOLD identification engine

a) Open your aligned FASTA file (i.e., *sequences_aligned.fasta*) in MS WORD using right click *Open with*. *Select All* of the text and *Copy*.

b) Click *IDENTIFICATION* on the BOLD homepage, select *All Barcode Records On BOLD*, paste the text from your FASTA file (i.e., *sequences_aligned.fasta*) into the box *Enter sequences in fasta format:*.

c) BOLD was designed specifically for DNA barcoding, so the *Specimen Identification Request* page displays a list of library records and their similarity to the query (i.e., the DNA barcode of the unknown specimen). A self-explanatory *Identification Summary* is also provided. An example of a BOLD search result is shown in **Fig. 3(a)** where the sequence can be conclusively identified as *Amauthuxidia amythaon*.

GenBank BLAST

a) Click *Nucleotide BLAST* on the BLAST homepage, paste the text from your FASTA file into the box *Enter accession number(s), gi (s), or FASTA sequence(s)*, and make sure the *Database* selection is *Others*.

b) BLAST pre-dates DNA barcoding, and is used for a variety of purposes, so the output is a little more difficult to interpret. Like BOLD, a list of library records is displayed, generally with the closest matching library sequence (i.e., the highest % *Identity*) at the top. Four other statistics are supplied: *Max score* indicates the highest alignment score (bit-score) between the query DNA barcode and the library sequence segment (the higher the better, 1000 is very good); *Total score* and *Query coverage* are generally not applicable for protein-coding genes such as the animal DNA barcode; *E-value* is the most important statistic for DNA barcoding and indicates number of alignments expected by chance with a particular score or higher (the closer to 0 the better). An example of a BLAST search result is shown in **Fig. 3(b)** where the sequence can be conclusively identified as *Amauthuxidia amythaon*.

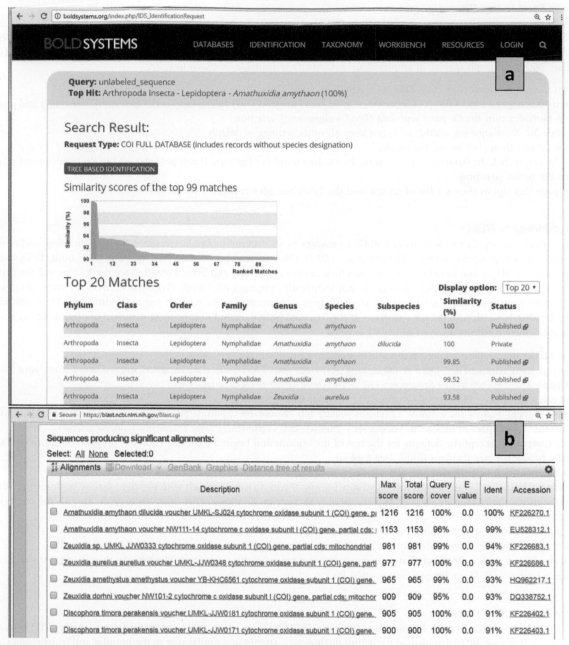

Fig. 3 Examples of the results of sequence identification requests using (a) BOLD identification engine and (b) GenBank BLAST.

Clustering DNA Barcodes Into Operational Taxonomic Units

Due to the incompleteness of DNA barcode reference libraries, and inconsistencies in the use of Linnaean names, besides assigning Linnaean taxonomy to DNA barcodes, it is also valuable and common practice to cluster DNA barcodes into Operational Taxonomic Units (OTU) (see Sukantamala *et al.*, 2017; Casas *et al.*, 2017). OTU are groupings of similar sequences which are objective, operational, "species"-level units (Ratnasingham and Hebert, 2013). Several methods are available for clustering DNA barcodes into OTU and we provide step-by-step instructions for the most commonly used and easily accessible programs in this article.

BOLD Barcode Index Number system

DNA barcodes of a minimal length (200 bp) and quality (maximum proportion of Ns) requirement are automatically clustered into OTU known as Barcode Index Numbers (BINs) upon upload to BOLD. Such clusters, produced by refine single linkage analysis across the entire BOLD library have been shown to closely correspond to species recognized through traditional taxonomic approaches (i.e., morphology). Consequently, the alphanumeric identifiers can act as surrogate taxonomic names in the absence of full Linnaean assignments (Wilson *et al.*, 2016).

Automatic Barcode Gap Discovery

Another popular tool to cluster DNA barcodes into OTU is Automatic Barcode Gap Discovery (ABGD) (Puillandre *et al.*, 2012). ABGD uses an automatic recursive procedure to converge on the best patterns for the dataset and clusters DNA barcodes into groups accordingly. The median number of ABDG groups can be used as the basis for OTU as this has produced good correspondence with traditional species in empirical studies. ABGD is available as a web interface.

a) From the ABGD homepage click *Take me to ABGD Web site.*
b) Open your aligned FASTA file (i.e., *sequences_aligned.fasta*) in MS WORD (using right click *Open with*), then copy and paste the DNA barcodes into the *Or paste your data (FASTA alignement) here* box.
c) Change the *X (relative gap width):* to 1, but keep all other settings as default.
d) Click *Go* and then click to see the results.
e) On the graph click the datapoint representing the median number of groups. If available choose the Recursive partition, rather than the Initial partition.
f) The page that opens shows a list of groups and the DNA barcodes contained within them.

Neighbor-Joining in MEGA

Molecular Evolutionary Genetics Analysis (MEGA) program is an extremely popular program for tree-building and is free to download from the program website (Tamura *et al.*, 2013). Once a Neighbor-Joining (NJ) tree has been built, DNA barcodes can be sorted to OTU ad hoc based on the tree branching pattern (topology) and branch lengths (see the NJ tree and discussion in Sukantamala *et al.*, 2017). Note that NJ trees are not technically "phylogenetic" trees. Phylogenetic trees are constructed on the basis of synapomorphies, whereas NJ trees are phenetic trees, constructed on the basis of sequence similarity. DNA barcoding is concerned with relationships amongst sequences at the "species" boundary and not the reconstruction of phylogeny, so generally NJ trees are sufficient for the analysis of DNA barcodes.

a) Start MEGA by double-clicking on the MEGA desktop icon.
b) You can then choose *File > Open A File/Session… > Select* your FASTA file (i.e., *sequences_aligned.fasta*) from your Desktop *> Open > Analyze > Nucleotide Sequences > OK > Yes > Invertebrate Mitochondrial > OK.*
c) You can then choose *Phylogeny > Construct/Test Neighbor-Joining Tree… > Yes.*
d) In the *Analysis Preferences* window *Options Summary* tab choose the options: *Substitutions Type: Nucleotide; Model/Method: p-distance; Substitutions to Include: d. Transitions + Transversions; Gaps/Missing Data Treatment: Pairwise deletion.*
e) Click *Compute* to accept the defaults for the rest of the options and begin the computations. A progress indicator will appear briefly before the tree displays in the *Tree Explorer.*
f) The tree can then be exported as a Newick (text) file (e.g., *tree.nwk*) *File > Export Current Tree (Newick).*
g) To select a branch, click on it with the left mouse button. If you click on a branch with the right mouse button, you will get a small options menu that will let you flip the branch and perform various other operations on it. To edit the taxon labels, double click on them.
h) Change the branch style by using *View > Tree/Branch Style.*
i) Select *View > Topology Only* to display the branching pattern (without actual branch lengths on the screen).
j) Edit your tree to create the image that you want to use in your publication or report. The tree can then be exported as an image *Image > Save as PDF file* or *Image > Save as PNG file.*

Bayesian Poisson Tree Processes

A Bayesian implementation of the Poisson Tree Processes (bPTP) (Zhang *et al.*, 2013) program for generating OTU is available through a web interface. bPTP can be used to delimit phylogenetic species in a similar way to the popular and widely used General Mixed Yule Coalescent (GMYC) approach (Pons *et al.*, 2006), but without the requirement for an ultrametric tree.

a) From the bPTP homepage, click the *Browse…* button to locate and upload your NJ tree (select the Newick file, e.g., *tree.nwk*, not the image file).
b) Leave all the settings as the defaults and enter your email address.
c) Click to refresh until the results appear. Two trees are displayed (a maximum likelihood solution and a Bayesian solution) but they are likely to be the same topology.
d) Click *Download delimitation results.* The page that opens shows a list of groups (species) and the DNA barcodes contained within them.

Illustrative Example(s) or Case Studies

We have used DNA barcoding in several biodiversity studies in Southeast Asia (Wilson *et al.*, 2016) covering a wide range of animal groups including butterflies (Jisming-See *et al.*, 2016), bats (Syaripuddin *et al.*, 2014), sandflies (Polseela *et al.*, 2016; Sukantamala *et al.*, 2017) and dragonflies (Casas *et al.*, 2017). Two illustrative examples are provided below.

Butterflies of Setiu Wetlands, Malaysia

As part of the Setiu Wetlands Scientific Expedition organized by WWF-Malaysia in 2016, we conducted a survey of butterflies at Lata Changkah, Terengganu, Malaysia. All sampled butterflies were brought back to the laboratory and subjected to standard molecular methods for DNA barcoding (Wilson, 2012; Jisming-See et al., 2016) and bioinformatics methods described above (see Sections Editing Sanger Sequences and Sequence Alignment). The DNA barcodes were submitted to BOLD where they are publicly available under the project code: SETIU. Species assignments were obtained on basis of >98% sequence similarity with records in BOLD (see Section BOLD identification engine), which was possible due to the existing DNA barcode reference library for the butterflies of Peninsular Malaysia (Wilson et al., 2013). However, a strict tree-based criterion (Wilson et al., 2011) was used to assign three DNA barcodes that did not share >98% similarity with any BOLD records to genera. Forty-nine species were recorded suggesting Lata Changkah can currently support rare butterflies (Sing and Wilson, 2017).

Sandflies of Northern Thailand

We collected sandflies using CDC light traps from five tourist caves in Northern Thailand. Specimens were brought back to the laboratory and subjected to standard molecular methods for DNA barcoding (Wilson, 2012; Jisming-See et al., 2016) and bioinformatics methods described above (see Sections Editing Sanger Sequences and Sequence Alignment). We combined our new DNA barcodes with selected publicly available DNA barcodes in BOLD, which included species reported from Thailand (includes records from Thailand, India, and Sri Lanka). The combined dataset (394 DNA barcodes) is publicly available in BOLD under the code: DS-SFNTH. Using a combination of methods (see Sections BOLD Barcode Index Number (BIN) system and Neighbor-Joining (NJ) in MEGA), the specimens were clustered into 34 OTU. Several of the taxa thought to be present in multiple caves, based on morphospecies sorting, split into cave-specific OTU which likely represented cryptic species. The resulting species checklist and DNA barcode library contributed to a growing set of records for sandflies which is useful for monitoring and vector control (Polseela et al., 2016; Sukantamala et al., 2017).

Discussion

DNA barcoding is being used by researchers across an increasing number of biological fields reflecting the fact that DNA sequence information can be cheap and easy to obtain and can enable assignment of taxonomic names to organisms without requiring researchers to be familiar with intricate morphological features. Likewise, molecular OTU can be suitable surrogates for partitioning diversity into interoperable units for biodiversity studies enabling researchers to obtain taxonomic data much faster than possible with traditional morphological approaches, making studies scalable across much larger taxonomic groups and wider geographical regions (Wilson et al., 2017). Yet, the prospect of DNA barcoding can be daunting for beginners (Wilson et al., 2016). Mastering a basic bioinformatics workflow is essential to ensure the quality and reliability of data and to generate meaningful results (Wilson and Sing, 2013).

Future Directions

High-throughput sequencers are replacing Sanger sequencers in most molecular applications. The development of the sub-discipline of DNA metabarcoding grew directly from the major advantages offered by high-throughput sequencing through circumventing the sorting and isolation of the thousands of individuals in bulk mixed samples of organisms (Brandon-Mong et al., 2015). However, the short read lengths and high error rates limited the use of high-throughput sequencers for conventional, individual specimen, DNA barcoding (Hebert et al., 2017), and in particular, for DNA barcode reference library construction (Liu et al., 2017). The continued reliance on Sanger sequencing has constrained reductions in the cost of DNA barcoding and led to uneven DNA barcoding efforts around the world (Liu et al., 2017). Recently developed approaches using the latest generation of high-throughput sequencing platforms (Pacific Biosciences SEQUEL and Illumina HiSeq 4000) have produced full length DNA barcodes of equivalent length and quality to those generated by Sanger sequencing, but with substantially reduced costs of 10-fold (Liu et al., 2017) to 40-fold (Hebert et al., 2017). Bioinformatics pipelines to complement these new approaches have developed concurrently. The mBRAVE webserver developed by the team behind BOLD, and with direct links to the BOLD reference libraries (Hebert et al., 2017) is an important development and likely represents a landmark shift in standard DNA barcoding protocols.

Closing Remarks

In this article, we provide beginners with step-by-step instructions for converting raw DNA sequences into clean DNA barcodes (sequence editing, sequence alignment), to commonly used tools for assigning taxonomic names to DNA barcodes, and to cluster DNA barcodes into OTU. As more researchers become comfortable with such bioinformatics workflows, and the DNA barcoding community continues to grow, essential questions for society: "What is this specimen on an agricultural shipment?", "Who eats whom in this whole food web?", and even "How many species are there?" become answerable (Adamowicz, 2015). It is promising that capacity for DNA barcoding is growing in the parts of the world where it is needed most, particularly among the younger generation of researchers who can easily connect with the barcoding analogy (Adamowicz, 2015; Wilson *et al.*, 2016).

Acknowledgements

Kong-Wah Sing is supported by the Chinese Academy of Sciences President's International Fellowship Initiative. We thank the BOLD team, especially Megan Milton, for their continuous support of our DNA barcoding workshops in Southeast Asia. We are grateful to CodonCode Corporation for supplying teaching licenses during our workshops. We thank previous sponsors and hosts of our DNA barcoding workshops: the Centre of Excellence in Fungal Research, the Department of Microbiology and Parasitology, and the Faculty of Medical Science at Naresuan University, Phitsanulok, Thailand; the Zoological and Ecological Research Network, and Museum of Zoology at the University of Malaya, Kuala Lumpur, Malaysia; the University of Nottingham Malaysia Campus, Selangor, Malaysia; Tunku Abdul Rahman University College, Kuala Lumpur, Malaysia; and the Asia-Pacific Network for Global Change Research. We also thank the scientists who have helped facilitate our workshops: Paul Hebert, Brandon Mong Guo Jie, Lee Ping Shin, Evan Chin, Kharunnisa Syaripuddin, Jedsada Sukantamala, Cheah Men How, Siti Azizah M Nor, Noor Adelyna M Akib, Mr Foo, Mr Chin, Elizabeth Clare.

Appendix A   Supplementary Information

Supplementary data associated with this article can be found in the online version at 10.1016/B978-0-12-809633-8.20468-8.

See also: Computational Pipelines and Workflows in Bioinformatics. Natural Language Processing Approaches in Bioinformatics

---

References

Adamowicz, S.J., 2015. International barcode of life: Evolution of a global research community. Genome 58, 151–162.

Brandon-Mong, G.J., Gan, H.M., Sing, K.W., et al., 2015. DNA metabarcoding of insects and allies: An evaluation of primers and pipelines. Bulletin of Entomological Research 105, 717–727.

Casas, P.A.S., Sing, K.W., Lee, P.S., et al., 2017. DNA barcodes for dragonflies and damselflies (Odonata) of Mindanao, Philippines. Mitochondrial DNA Part A, Online Early. doi:10.1080/24701394.2016.1267157.

Hebert, P.D.N., Braukmann, T.W.A., Prosser, S.W.J., et al., 2017. A sequel to sanger: Amplicon sequencing that scales. bioRxiv. 191619. Available at: https://doi.org/10.1101/191619.

Jisming- See, S.W., Sing, K.W., Wilson, J.J., 2016. DNA barcodes and citizen science provoke a diversity reappraisal for the "ring" butterflies of Peninsular Malaysia (Ypthima: satyrinae: Nymphalidae: lepidoptera). Genome 59, 879–888.

Liu, S., Yang, C., Zhou, C., Zhou, X., 2017. Filling reference gaps via assembling DNA barcodes using high-throughput sequencing-moving toward barcoding the world. Gigascience 6, 1–8.

Polseela, R., Jaturas, N., Thanwisai, A., Sing, K.W., Wilson, J.J., 2016. Towards monitoring the sandflies (Diptera: psychodidae) of Thailand: DNA barcoding the sandflies of Wihan Cave, Uttaradit. Mitochondrial DNA Part A 27, 3795–3801.

Pons, J., Barraclough, T.G., Gomez-Zurita, J., et al., 2006. Sequence-based species delimitation for the DNA taxonomy of undescribed insects. Systematic Biology 55, 595–609.

Puillandre, N., Lambert, A., Brouillet, S., Achaz, G., 2012. ABGD, Automatic barcode gap discovery for primary species delimitation. Molecular Ecology 21, 1864–1877.

Ratnasingham, S., Hebert, P.D.N., 2013. A DNA-based registry for all animal species: The Barcode Index Number (BIN) system. PLOS ONE 8, e66213.

Schmieder, R., Edwards, R., 2011. Quality control and preprocessing of metagenomic datasets. Bioinformatics 27, 863–864.

Sing, K.W., Syaripuddin, K., Wilson, J.J., 2016. How to rapidly accelerate biodiversity inventory in places where most of the species are unknown? Malayan Nature Journal 68, 131–134.

Sing, K.W., Wilson, J.J., 2017. Butterfly diversity at a recreation hotspot in Setiu Wetlands, Terengganu, Malaysia. Prosiding Seminar Ekspedisi Saintifik Tanah Bencah Setiu 2016. Selangor. WWF-Malaysia. pp. 86–96.

Sukantamala, J., Sing, K.W., Jaturas, N., Polseela, R., Wilson, J.J., 2017. Unexpected diversity of sandflies (Diptera: psychodidae) in tourist caves in Northern Thailand. Mitochondrial DNA Part A 28, 949–955.

Syaripuddin, K., Kumar, A., Sing, K.W., et al., 2014. Mercury accumulation in bats near hydroelectric reservoirs in Peninsular Malaysia. Ecotoxicology 23, 1164–1171.

Tamura, K., Stecher, G., Peterson, D., Filipski, A., Kumar, S., 2013. MEGA6: Molecular evolutionary genetics analysis Version 6.0. Molecular Biology and Evolution 30, 2725–2729.

Wilson, J.J., 2012. DNA barcodes for insects. In: Kress, W.J., Erikson, D.L. (Eds.), DNA Barcodes: Methods and Protocols. New York: Humana Press.

Wilson, J.J., Rougerie, R., Shonfeld, J., et al., 2011. When species matches are unavailable are DNA barcodes correctly assigned to higher taxa? An assessment using sphingid moths. BMC Ecology 11, 18.

Wilson, J.J., Sing, K.W., 2013. DNA barcoding can successfully identify Penaeus monodon, associate life cycle stages, and generate hypotheses of unrecognised diversity. Sains Malaysiana 42, 1827–1829.

Wilson, J.J., Sing, K.W., Floyd, R.M., Hebert, P.D.N., 2017. DNA barcodes and insect biodiversity. In: Foottit, R.G., Adler, P.H. (Eds.), Insect Biodiversity: Science and Society, second ed. Oxford: Blackwell Publishing Ltd, pp. 575–592.

Wilson, J.J., Sing, K.W., Lee, P.S., Wee, A.K.S., 2016. Application of DNA barcodes in wildlife conservation in Tropical East Asia. Conservation Biology 30, 982–989.

Wilson, J.J., Sing, K.W., Sofian-Azirun, M., 2013. Building a DNA barcode reference library for the true butterflies (Lepidoptera) of Peninsula Malaysia: What about the subspecies? PLOS ONE 8, e79969.

Zhang, J., Kapli, P., Pavlidis, P., Stamatakis, A., 2013. A general species delimitation method with applications to phylogenetic placements. Bioinformatics 29, 2869–2876.

Further Reading

Adamowicz, S.J., Chain, F.J.J., Clare, E.L., *et al.*, 2016. From barcodes to biomes: Special issues from the 6th international barcode of life conference. Genome 59, v–ix.

Kress, W.J., Erikson, D.L. (Eds.), 2012. DNA Barcodes: Methods and Protocols. New York: Humana Press.

Relevant Websites

http://wwwabi.snv.jussieu.fr/public/abgd/
    ABGD.
www.boldsystems.org
    Barcode of Life Datasystems (BOLD).
www.mbio.ncsu.edu/bioedit/bioedit.html
    BIOEDIT.
http://species.h-its.org/ptp/
    bPTP.
www.codoncode.com
    CODONCODE ALIGNER.
www.barcodingasia.weebly.com
    DNA Barcoding Workshops (DBW).
www.usegalaxy.org
    GALAXY.
https://blast.ncbi.nlm.nih.gov/Blast.cgi
    GenBank BLAST.
http://www.megasoftware.net/
    Molecular Evolutionary Genetics Analysis (MEGA).
www.prinseq.sourceforge.net
    PRINSEQ.

Text Mining Applications

Raul Rodriguez-Esteban, F. Hoffmann-La Roche Ltd., Basel, Switzerland

Glossary

Co-reference References in a text that allude to the same thing using different names. Examples of co-references can be pronouns or abbreviations.
Corpus Collection of documents.
Manual curation Review and evaluation of data or information by humans.

Natural language Language that has evolved organically and thus has not been formally designed. Most spoken human languages are natural languages.
Pharmacovigilance Tracking of potential adverse events associated to marketed drugs.

Introduction

Biomedical text mining (henceforth, text mining) is primarily an applied scientific discipline. An important focus of text mining research is to increase the efficiency and efficacy of everyday biomedical work requiring the analysis of textual information. Due to the pervasiveness of text in the biomedical realm, text mining has applications in numerous settings, such as medical facilities, pharmaceutical and academic research institutions, etc. In each of these settings, however, there is interest in different questions, which can only be answered through the information contained in particular types of textual sources. However, each type of question and textual source brings its own challenges that necessarily condition the text mining tools that are used to answer them. Thus, text mining applications can be broadly organized around both the types of questions and the sources of text that are utilized.

Sources of Text

There is considerable variation in the writing style used within different textual sources. Notable differences can be seen between text mining applications for clinical settings, which deal with medical records, and those geared toward scientific text from scientific articles or grants. Similarly, text mining applications for social media or patents occupy their own niches. The reason for this is that each of these textual sources follows grammatical and semantic rules that differentiate them. These differences cause performance degradation in text mining tools that are applied to types of text that are different from the ones they were originally designed for. For example, patents may contain complicated claim dependencies (i.e., patent claims that make reference to other claims within the patent) that do not fit the natural language patterns that appear in other types of text. Another example of unusual writing style comes from social media, which is often ungrammatical and built with its particular contextual cues. It is worthy, thus, to discuss some of the different sources of text used in text mining before delving into particular applications.

Before discussing types of textual sources it is important to briefly point out the role that availability plays. Cost and privacy issues can be significant hurdles to access valuable biomedical information, thereby affecting the development of text mining applications. Free, electronic and easily downloadable content can more easily enable the development of such applications. With that in mind some relevant types of text sources are:

- Scientific abstracts: the main freely available sources are Medline and Europe PubMed Central (Europe PMC).
- Scientific full text articles: a growing subset of Open Access full text articles is available from PMC and Europe PMC.
- Patents: US patents are provided in bulk for free by the United States Patent and Trademark Office (USPTO). Other patent authorities typically require a fee for bulk electronic access.
- Grants: the main sources are the National Institutes of Health (NIH) RePORTER in the United States and the European Bioinformatics Institute (EBI) Grist database in Europe.
- Clinical trial records: ClinicalTrials.gov, the World Health Organization (WHO), and International Clinical Trials Registry Platform (ICTRP) are extensive free repositories that can be downloaded in bulk.
- Medical records and clinical notes: due to privacy concerns only limited samples are freely available, such as the i2b2 corpus.
- Pharmacovigilance and safety: pharmacovigilance records are available from the US Food and Drug Administration (FDA) FAERS and European Molecular Biology Laboratory (EMBL) SIDER databases. US drug labels are available from FDA's DailyMed.
- Social media: multiple blogs, microblogs, and forums can be downloaded from their internet locations. However, most of these sources require customized downloading and processing.
- News: freely available RSS feeds from news services, news agencies and newspapers provide an easy way to access current news content. Access to archival news is more limited (Breiner and Rodriguez-Esteban, 2012).

Documents coming from each of these sources are split into different sections, each with its own properties. For example, the abstract of a scientific article has a different structure, style, and content than the full text (Martin *et al.*, 2004; Schuemie *et al.*, 2004; Cohen *et al.*, 2010). Moreover, within document sections one can find structures, such as tables and figures, which require specialized processing.

Building Blocks

Text mining applications are often driven by the capabilities of the algorithms that have been the focus of most research attention in text mining. Such algorithms have both enabled and limited the applications that are currently possible. Thus, we may call these algorithms the "building blocks" of text mining applications. Where adequate algorithms do not exist, or yield low performance, applications become unfeasible. Examples of applications that have had very limited success for lack of effective algorithms are synonym detection (Cohen *et al.*, 2005), co-reference resolution (Kim *et al.*, 2012), and question answering (QA) (Yang *et al.*, 2014). Thus, any discussion on text mining applications needs to make a reference to the possibilities that are enabled by the algorithms that have been successfully developed thus far.

Some of these building blocks are:

1. Named-entity recognition (NER). One of the most studied areas in text mining is NER. NER consists in identifying specific types of names and other entities written in text. NER in biomedicine is faced with a particular set of challenges because some types of names that are of interest in biomedicine have large, complex vocabularies and can be uncommon in other realms. Examples of these are the names of diseases, genes, chemicals, drugs, mutations, cell types, and species. The precise identification of such names enables the extraction of other, more complicated facts. Therefore, high-quality NER is a prerequisite for many other text mining algorithms. Identifying such names by solely using lists of synonyms (a.k.a. concept recognition) does not often deliver results of acceptable quality (see Section "Evaluation Metrics"). Thus, there has been significant amount of work in machine learning algorithms to improve NER.

2. Relation extraction. A step further from NER is finding relations between pairs of entities. Many descriptions of biological and chemical phenomena involve multiple entities, such as the descriptions of signaling pathways, biomarkers, mutation–disease links, and drug–drug interactions. Descriptions of such phenomena may be simplified into a set of relations between pairs of entities. For example, a signaling cascade may be described by a set of individual protein-binding interactions. While such type of representation might be too simple for some applications it can still be useful to highlight relevant facts that can then be further explored.

3. Event extraction. In order to tackle more complex biological phenomena that may not be described adequately with relations, text miners have come up with the task of "event" extraction. Within this task an event is considered rather generically as a molecular status or change of status described in text (Kim *et al.*, 2008). An example of molecular event could be a translocation or a change in gene expression. Events can be multifaceted and conditioned by temporal and contextual parameters, which complicate their identification and the extraction of their details. Thus, more complex extraction and representation approaches are necessary to capture them and their different types of dependencies. Not surprisingly, the more complex the events that need to be extracted the more challenging it is for text mining algorithms. Thus, NER and relation extraction algorithms have achieved higher performance than those algorithms specialized in event extraction.

4. Document classification and clustering. Assigning a document to a specific class (classification) or grouping documents according to their similarity (clustering) is useful for certain text mining applications, such as for organizing and exploring the scientific landscape around a certain topic. It is also particularly useful for the task of selecting documents that can then be further analyzed or mined. Thus, an initial classification or clustering can reduce the work or improve the quality involved in later processing steps. This can be considered a "filtering" of documents. For example, due to the cost associated to accessing the full text of scientific articles, documents can be filtered first by the content of their freely available abstracts before accessing them.

5. Document segmentation and zone detection. As mentioned, many documents are divided into certain standard sections. For example, scientific articles are often organized into introduction, methods, results and discussion (IMRaD). Concentrating the focus of an application on particular sections can improve the quality of the results. However, the content of a document may not be appropriately located in the correct sections (Agarwal and Yu, 2009). Thus, recognizing the different segments and discursive zones of a document can help in its analysis. For example, by identifying the zones of a patent that deal with experimental setups one may get a better idea of the results that are being reported in the patent (Rodriguez-Esteban and Bundschus, 2016).

6. Co-reference resolution. Generally, co-references (see Glossary) are challenging to mine, especially those that refer to something mentioned in another sentence in the text. On the other hand, a special case of co-reference that is easy to resolve is the abbreviation. Algorithms to map abbreviations to their definitions have been highly successful (Wren and Garner, 2002; Pustejovsky *et al.*, 2001), because abbreviations are often defined in the text in typical ways, where the abbreviation is followed by the definition in parentheses, for example, natural language processing (NLP).

Evaluation Metrics

It is important to consider the metrics used to rate the performance of text mining applications in order to be able to assess the quality of the results they provide. These metrics are similar to those used in information retrieval (IR). Two of the metrics are the counts of type I errors, known as false positives (FPs), and type II errors, known as false negatives (FNs). FPs represent items that are incorrectly included in the results, while FNs are items that are incorrectly missing from the results. Moreover, true positives (TPs) are items that appear correctly in the results and true negatives (TNs) items that, correctly, do not appear in the results. Because in IR the number of TNs is often hard to quantify, or even conceptualize, performance metrics are based on TPs, FPs, and FNs. Two typical metrics that derive from them are precision and recall:

$$precision = \frac{TP}{TP + FP}, \ recall = \frac{TP}{TP + FN}$$

Even though, precision and recall are widely used, finding a single metric has been always of interest because it makes comparisons easier across text mining applications. Thus, there are single metrics that have been devised to encapsulate the value of precision and recall, the most typical of them being the F-measure. The F-measure is the harmonic mean of precision and recall:

$$F = \frac{2*precision*recall}{precision + recall}$$

Even though, it is the most widely used single metric, the F-measure has flaws and several alternative measures have been proposed, such as area under the curve (AUC) and overhead (Rodriguez-Esteban, 2009, 2015).

Another aspect to consider is that the use of multiple text mining applications to solve a problem can lead to an overall reduced performance as errors are compounded. As can be seen in **Fig. 1**, setting several text mining applications in series produces a degradation of performance as FNs and FPs accumulate at every step. Thus, increases in complexity of a text mining application may lead to results of lower quality, which in the end hinders our ability to identify complex phenomena in text.

Applications

Biomedical questions that can be answered using textual information are the engines behind the development of text mining applications. Such questions are context dependent because they change according to the settings and the textual sources available. Some of the questions that can be addressed with text mining are:

1. Questions that can be answered with relations. Questions that can be answered by mining relations are common in multiple biomedical contexts. Therefore, extracting relations is a major focus of text mining, especially for molecular-level relationships. In particular, the relations that have drawn the most attention have been the so-called protein–protein interactions (PPIs), which involve any relations between pairs of proteins or genes, whether direct or indirect (thus, not just protein binding). PPIs are useful to build signaling pathways and describe other phenomena, such as gene–gene co-expression.

   Another application based on extracting relations is the identification of biomarkers. There are several types of biomarkers (e.g., mechanistic vs. descriptive biomarkers, efficacy biomarkers, safety biomarkers). They typically involve a subrogate measurement of a biological effect that cannot be measured directly or it is costly to do so. Such subrogate measurements can be extracted from relationships in text, for example, by identifying downstream proteins in a pathological pathway or by extracting protein–metabolite relations.

   In addition to extraction of PPIs, many other applications are based on identifying relations. Identifying drug–drug relations can be helpful in clinical settings to discern pernicious drug interactions. Gene–disease and mutation–disease relations can lead to the identification of pharmaceutical targets, especially in cases in which the relation is causal. A subset of causal gene–disease relations, for example, are called perturbations, which are gene modifications that have been shown experimentally to improve or worsen a disease phenotype (Rodriguez-Esteban et al., 2009). In the realm of pharmacovigilance, signal detection, which involves the flagging of potential drug-adverse event relations, is of great importance (Harpaz et al., 2014). Another area of interest relates to pharmacogenomics, which is concerned with gene–compound relations (Garten and Altman, 2009).

2. Biological processes beyond relations. A relation is often an overtly simplified representation of a biological phenomenon. Events, on the other hand, can encompass even fairly complex descriptions of biological processes. Example applications that are based on extracting such biological processes are gene regulation, gene transcription, gene-variant-disease relations, protein catabolism, and phosphorylation. Protein phosphorylation, for example, may involve the identification of a kinase,

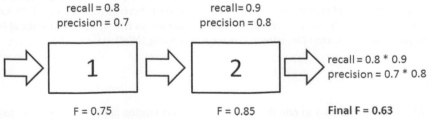

Fig. 1 Decreasing performance of serial text mining applications. When the input text needs to be processed by more than one text mining application the performance degrades.

a substrate and a phosphorylation site (Hu *et al.*, 2005). Gene regulation, on the other hand, may involve the identification of genes that are expressed in particular cell types or anatomic locations (Gerner *et al.*, 2010). Gene-variant-disease relations present the challenge of identifying the gene associated to a specific genetic variant such as a mutation (Lee *et al.*, 2016).

3. Biomedical QA (BioQA). QA entails the answering of a natural-language question by seeking an adequate fragment of text that can function as an answer or that provides a fact that answers the question. QA is typically composed of two parts: (1) understanding the question being posed and (2) finding the fragment of text that correctly answers the question. In the biomedical setting, QA (or BioQA) can be used toward addressing questions that appear in real time, for example, questions from medical practitioners in clinical settings. Despite its potential usefulness, BioQA applications have not yet shown a level of performance that enables their practical use in such settings.

4. Semi-automated curation. Many biological databases use text mining to filter documents or text snippets before they are evaluated by human curators and added to the database (Rodriguez-Esteban, 2015). This can significantly reduce the amount of curation effort that is spent while minimizing the number of relevant information that is missed through this filtering. The goal is to apply filters that have high recall and moderate precision. High recall ensures that there is a small number of FNs, while moderate precision leads to a reduction in the amount of items that need to be curated by avoiding potential FPs. Besides biological databases, text mining for semi-automated curation can be used for other tasks, such as for writing systematic reviews (O'Mara-Eves *et al.*, 2015). Graphical applications that enable semi-automated curation have been developed for many different curatorial settings (Rinaldi *et al.*, 2014).

5. Biological similarity. All the text written about a biological entity can be used as a fingerprint of said entity. Because such text covers the knowledge that we have about the entity it can be used to make a number of predictions and comparisons. For example, all the documents mentioning a protein can be used together to predict the protein's function (Verspoor, 2014), its subcellular localization (Shatkay *et al.*, 2007), or its structure (Koussounadis *et al.*, 2009). Another example is similarity across diseases, which can be computed by analyzing the documents that mention each disease.

6. Knowledge discovery. One can connect facts that have been extracted from different documents through the use of text mining. Because scientists are unable to follow all publications even in their own field they are prone to miss facts that could be relevant to their research. Thus, finding pairs or sets of related facts that are present in different publications ("connecting the dots") can lead to the discovery of knowledge that had not been evident to the individual scientists that contributed the facts. This way, for example, one may be able to explain the mechanism leading to certain adverse drug effects (Hristovski *et al.*, 2016) or anticipate future discoveries (Frijters *et al.*, 2010).

7. Pharmacovigilance. Identifying reports of potential adverse events associated to specific drugs can be very time consuming, requiring the work of multiple human curators. Moreover, social media is becoming an increasingly relevant source of adverse event reports. Thus, there is a need to filter all the documents potentially associated to drug-adverse events to focus solely on those that are more likely to be relevant. Such filtering needs to be done carefully to minimize the number of FNs.

8. Figure mining. Figures are integrated within many textual sources, such as patents and scientific articles. Thus, analyzing the content of figures requires mixing textual and image analysis. Applications of figure mining include figure classification (Rodriguez-Esteban and Iossifov, 2009) and linking an article's figures to text fragments within the article that explain the figure (Yu *et al.*, 2009).

9. Landscaping and tracking biomedical knowledge. Following and landscaping biomedical trends can be useful to identify emerging technologies, areas of high research impact (Cokol and Rodriguez-Esteban, 2008; Cokol *et al.*, 2007), scientific trends (Rodriguez-Esteban and Loging, 2013) and novel discoveries, such as new pharmaceutical targets. Landscaping is of particular interest in patent mining, where it can be used to detect technological areas with low level of patenting (white spots) or to craft research strategies.

10. Pharmacokinetics and systems biology modeling. Measurements and parameters that can be used for systems biology or pharmacokinetics modeling are difficult to identify using traditional search engines. Such numerical information can be better identified, for example, through rule-based approaches. Even more challenging is to associate these values to the relevant entity they describe. For example, to associate a protein concentration measurement to the protein that was measured.

11. Enrichment of genomic analyses. Typically, genomic data, coming from high-throughput experiments, such as genome-wide association study (GWAS), pharmacogenomics, microarray, and RNAseq, can produce long lists of genes that need to be prioritized or grouped to further analyze their function or to decide on follow-up experiments. Text mining can help manage such lists in a high-throughput manner by parsing the literature associated to each gene (Ailem *et al.*, 2016) and providing an overall picture, for example, of the pathways and functions most often associated to a group of genes of interest. Such text mining results can be complemented with data from biological databases to create an integrated approach.

Conclusions

There are multiple ways in which text mining applications can impact biomedical work. A few have been discussed here but more can be explored within the text mining literature. See the Further Reading section for additional information on this topic.

See also: Biological Database Searching. Data-Information-Concept Continuum From a Text Mining Perspective. Natural Language Processing Approaches in Bioinformatics. Text Mining Basics in Bioinformatics. Text Mining for Bioinformatics Using Biomedical Literature

References

Agarwal, S., Yu, H., 2009. Automatically classifying sentences in full-text biomedical articles into introduction, methods, results and discussion. Bioinformatics 25, 3174–3180.

Ailem, M., Role, F., Nadif, M., et al., 2016. Unsupervised text mining for assessing and augmenting GWAS results. Journal of Biomedical Informatics 60, 252–259.

Breiner, D.A., Rodriguez-Esteban, R., 2012. What's in the News? Web Scraping Technology as a Cost-Effective Solution for News Alerting. Pharma-Bio-Med, Lisbon, Portugal, September 2012.

Cohen, A.M., Hersh, W.R., Dubay, C., et al., 2005. Using co-occurrence network structure to extract synonymous gene and protein names from MEDLINE abstracts. BMC Bioinformatics 6, 103.

Cohen, K.B., Johnson, H.L., Verspoor, K., et al., 2010. The structural and content aspects of abstracts versus bodies of full text journal articles are different. BMC Bioinformatics 11, 492.

Cokol, M., Rodriguez-Esteban, R., 2008. Visualizing evolution and impact of biomedical fields. Journal of Biomedical Informatics 41, 1050–1052.

Cokol, M., Rodriguez-Esteban, R., Rzhetsky, A., 2007. A recipe for high impact. Genome Biology 8, 406.

Frijters, R., van Vugt, M., Smeets, R., et al., 2010. Literature mining for the discovery of hidden connections between drugs, genes and diseases. PLOS Computational Biology 6 (9), Available at: http://dx.doi.org/10.1371/journal.pcbi.1000943

Garten, Y., Altman, R.B., 2009. Pharmspresso: A text mining tool for extraction of pharmacogenomic concepts and relationships from full text. BMC Bioinformatics 10 (Suppl. 2), S6.

Gerner, M., Nenadic, G., Bergman, C.M., 2010. An exploration of mining gene expression mentions and their anatomical locations from biomedical text. In: Proceedings of the 2010 Workshop on Biomedical Natural Language Processing.

Harpaz, R., Callahan, A., Tamang, S., et al., 2014. Text mining for adverse drug events: The promise, challenges, and state of the art. Drug Safety 37, 777–790.

Hristovski, D., Kastrin, A., Dinevski, D., et al., 2016. Using literature-based discovery to explain adverse drug effects. Journal of Medical Systems 40, 185.

Hu, Z.Z., Narayanaswamy, M., Ravikumar, K.E., et al., 2005. Literature mining and database annotation of protein phosphorylation using a rule-based system. Bioinformatics 21, 2759–2765.

Kim, J.D., Nguyen, N., Wang, Y., et al., 2012. The genia event and protein coreference tasks of the BioNLP shared task 2011. BMC Bioinformatics 13 (Suppl. 11), S1.

Kim, J.D., Ohta, T., Tsujii, J., 2008. Corpus annotation for mining biomedical events from literature. BMC Bioinformatics 9, 10.

Koussounadis, A., Redfern, O.C., Jones, D.T., 2009. Improving classification in protein structure databases using text mining. BMC Bioinformatics 10, 129.

Lee, K., Lee, S., Park, S., et al., 2016. BRONCO: Biomedical entity Relation ONcology COrpus for extracting gene-variant-disease-drug relations. Database (Oxford). Available at: http://dx.doi.org/10.1093/database/baw043

Martin, E.P.G., Bremer, E.G., Guerin, M., DeSesa, C., Jouve, O., 2004. Analysis of protein/protein interactions through biomedical literature: Text mining of abstracts vs. text mining of full text articles. In: López, J.A., Benfenati, E., Dubitzky, W. (Eds.), Knowledge Exploration in Life Science Informatics. Lecture Notes in Computer Science. Berlin; Heidelberg: Springer, pp. 96–108.

O'Mara-Eves, A., Thomas, J., McNaught, J., et al., 2015. Using text mining for study identification in systematic reviews: A systematic review of current approaches. Systematic Reviews 4, 5.

Pustejovsky, J., Castaño, J., Cochran, B., et al., 2001. Automatic extraction of acronym-meaning pairs from MEDLINE databases. Studies in Health Technology and Informatics 84 (Pt. 1), 371–375.

Rinaldi, F., Clematide, S., Marques, H., et al., 2014. OntoGene web services for biomedical text mining. BMC Bioinformatics 15, S6.

Rodriguez-Esteban, R., 2009. Biomedical text mining and its applications. PLOS Computational Biology 5, e1000597.

Rodriguez-Esteban, R., 2015. Biocuration with insufficient resources and fixed timelines. Database (Oxford). Available at: http://dx.doi.org/10.1093/database/bav116

Rodriguez-Esteban, R., Bundschus, M., 2016. Text mining patents for biomedical knowledge. Drug Discovery Today 21, 997–1002.

Rodriguez-Esteban, R., Iossifov, I., 2009. Figure mining for biomedical research. Bioinformatics 25, 2082–2084.

Rodriguez-Esteban, R., Loging, W.T., 2013. Quantifying the complexity of medical research. Bioinformatics 29, 2918–2924.

Rodriguez-Esteban, R., Roberts, P.M., Crawford, M.E., 2009. Identifying and classifying biomedical perturbations in text. Nucleic Acids Research 37, 771–777.

Schuemie, M.J., Weeber, M., Schijvenaars, B.J., et al., 2004. Distribution of information in biomedical abstracts and full-text publications. Bioinformatics 20, 2597–2604.

Shatkay, H., Höglund, A., Brady, S., et al., 2007. SherLoc: High-accuracy prediction of protein subcellular localization by integrating text and protein sequence data. Bioinformatics 23, 1410–1417.

Verspoor, K.M., 2014. Roles for text mining in protein function prediction. Methods in Molecular Biology 1159, 95–108.

Wren, J.D., Garner, H.R., 2002. Heuristics for identification of acronym-definition patterns within text: Towards an automated construction of comprehensive acronym-definition dictionaries. Methods of Information in Medicine 41, 426–434.

Yang, Z., Li, Y., Cai, J., et al., 2014. QUADS: Question answering for decision support. In: Proceedings of the 37th international ACM SIGIR Conference on Research & Development in Information Retrieval (SIGIR'14), pp. 375–384.

Yu, H., Agarwal, S., Johnston, M., et al., 2009. Are figure legends sufficient? Evaluating the contribution of associated text to biomedical figure comprehension. Journal of Biomedical Discovery and Collaboration 4, 1.

Further Reading

Rebholz-Schuhmann, D., Oellrich, A., Hoehndorf, R., 2012. Text-mining solutions for biomedical research: Enabling integrative biology. Nature Reviews Genetics 13, 829–839.

Rodriguez-Esteban, R., 2009. Biomedical text mining and its applications. PLOS Computational Biology 5, e1000597.

Rodriguez-Esteban, R., 2016. Understanding human disease knowledge through text mining: What is text mining? In: Loging, W. (Ed.), Bioinformatics and Computational Biology in Drug Discovery and Development. Cambridge: Cambridge University Press.

Rodriguez-Esteban, R., 2016. Appendix. I. Additional knowledge-based analysis approaches. In: Loging, W. (Ed.), Bioinformatics and Computational Biology in Drug Discovery and Development. Cambridge: Cambridge University Press.

Rzhetsky, A., Seringhaus, M., Gerstein, M., 2008. Seeking a new biology through text mining. Cell 134, 9–13.

Relevant Websites

http://bionlp.org/
BioNLP.org.
https://www.i2b2.org/NLP/DataSets/Main.php
i2b2.

Index

A

Printed and bound by CPI Group (UK) Ltd, Croydon, CR0 4YY

03/10/2024

01040321-0016